TABLE OF INDICES AND POWER RESIDUES

For All Primes and Prime Powers Below 2000

INTRODUCTION BY

H. S. VANDIVER, *University of Texas*

DESIGNED BY

C. A. NICOL, *University of Oklahoma*

and JOHN L. SELFRIDGE, *University of Washington*

PROGRAMMED BY

LOWRY MCKEE, *University of Oklahoma*

A TABLE OF INDICES AND POWER RESIDUES

For All Primes and Prime Powers Below 2000

Computed by

THE UNIVERSITY OF OKLAHOMA MATHEMATICAL TABLES PROJECT

UNDER THE DIRECTION OF

RICHARD V. ANDREE, Chairman,

Department of Mathematics and Astronomy, University of Oklahoma

W· W· NORTON & COMPANY · INC · NEW YORK

Library of Congress Catalog Card No. 62–8624

Published simultaneously in the Dominion of Canada
by George J. McLeod Limited, Toronto

PRINTED IN THE UNITED STATES OF AMERICA

PREFACE

The motivation for producing this table is that much of number theory was and is deduced by considering examples. Most early workers in the subject were led to theorems by consideration of a large number of specific cases. Many of these number theorists constructed smaller versions of the present tables,[1] but an extensive table of indices was not available until the appearance in 1839 of the monumental *Canon Arithmeticus of C. G. J. Jacobi.* This table listed all indices and residues for each power of a prime less than one thousand. The Jacobi table remained in print until recently. It was extended to include composite moduli $2p^{\alpha} < 1000$ and also tables for the computation of the sum and difference of indices.[2] To conserve space in this more extensive table, the latter were not included, nor have we included moduli of the form 2^{α}. Major definitions and theorems used in computation are included in the *Introduction* and the remainder are readily available in text books of number theory.[3]

The indices and power residues were computed on the extended IBM 650–653 at the University of Oklahoma. Each prime and power of prime less than 2000 was used to compute power residues. The power residues were temporarily stored on a magnetic disk file, and were then used to determine indices, which were also placed on a magnetic disk. The indices and power residues were printed using an on-line 407. As each line was printed on paper, it was also written on magnetic tape for permanent storage.

[1] D. H. Lehmer, *Guide to Tables in the Theory of Numbers*, Washington, D.C., National Research Council, 1941.

[2] H. Brandt and W. Patz, *Canon Arithmeticus of C. G. J. Jacobi*, Akademie-Verlag, Berlin, 1956.

[3] e.g., W. J. Le Veque, *Topics in Number Theory*, Vol. 1, Addison-Wesley Pub. Co., 1956.

For checking purposes, the indices and power residues were summed separately. The totals were then compared with a total computed from formulas. Echo checking of the output pulse was used at each print cycle. The printed sheets were spot-checked for accuracy. Some time after computation, another partial print-out was made from the magnetic tapes and the second print-out compared with the first to detect possible misprinting. None was found.

This table is the first in a series being computed at the University of Oklahoma under the direction of Dr. Richard V. Andree. They were originally suggested by Dr. A. A. Albert of the University of Chicago. The problem analysis was done by Dr. C. Nicol of the University of Oklahoma and Dr. John L. Selfridge of the University of Washington with the encouragement of Dr. H. S. Vandiver of the University of Texas, who has written the introduction, and Dr. C. B. Tompkins of U.C.L.A. The actual coding, running, and the format design are the work of Mr. L. McKee of the University of Oklahoma.

Your suggestions for additional tables needed in specialized work will be most welcome. Address inquiries and suggestions to Richard V. Andree, Department of Mathematics, The University of Oklahoma, Norman, Oklahoma.

October, 1961
Norman, Oklahoma

INTRODUCTION by H. S. Vandiver

Aside, possibly, from the theorem that each integer greater than one factors uniquely into primes, there appears to be no elementary tool in number theory which is used so much in that subject as the concept of *primitive root* and the *related idea of indices,* with respect to a power of an odd prime. This is true not only in the elementary topics but also in the most advanced parts. For example, in abstract algebra the theory of group characters can be made to depend (in part at least) on the idea of primitive root. This explains why tables related to these topics have so far been very useful to investigators.

It is assumed that anyone using these tables will have some interest in the mathematical theories which are particularly related to them, as well as in the history of these theories, and also in the history of the tables previously published along this line. In addition to these items, an account of the applications which have been made of tables of this sort appears to be in order. We shall first discuss the history of the subject, and later we shall attempt to outline a connected theory of the topics closely associated with the theory of primitive roots, without proofs of the results stated. The advisability of setting up other tables, involving extensions of these topics, will also be considered.

Perhaps the first contribution to the theory which appears in mathematical history is as follows: In a letter to Frenicle de Bessy dated October 18, 1640, Fermat writes:[1]

[1] Oystein Ore, *Number Theory and Its History* (1st ed.; New York: McGraw-Hill Book Co., Inc., 1948), p. 272. In connection with the history treated in this introduction, we also made free use of Dickson's *History of the Theory of Numbers* and D. H. Lehmer's *Guide to Tables in the Theory of Numbers.*

"It seems to me after this that I should tell you the foundation on which I support the demonstrations of all which concerns geometric progressions, namely:

"Every prime number measures [divides] infallibly one of the powers minus unity in any progression, and the exponent of this power is a divisor of the given prime number minus one; and after one has found the first power which satisfies the condition, all those whose exponents are multiples of the first satisfy the condition." Fermat uses the example of the powers of three,

1,	2,	3,	4,	5,	6,
3,	9,	27,	81,	243,	729,

where the first line gives the exponents. He points out that $3^3 - 1$ is the first such expression that is divisible by 13 and that the exponent 3 divides $13 - 1 = 12$, so that $3^{12} - 1$ is divisible by 13."

Fermat continues: "And this proposition is generally true for all series and all prime numbers. I would send you the demonstration, if I did not fear it being too long."

Shortly after (1677), Leibniz [2] noted without proof that if we express a positive integer to any base b then $1/n$ gives rise to a purely periodic fraction, provided that n and b are prime to each other. In particular, if $1/n$ is expressed as a decimal fraction, the decimal is purely periodic when n is prime to 10. The theory of infinite periodic fractions depends almost entirely on the theory of primitive roots. Gauss,[3] in 1801, proved that if a is not divisible by the odd prime $p \neq 5$ the length of the period for a/p^n is the exponent e to which 10 belongs modulo p^n. These results constitute some of the first applications of the theory of primitive roots.

From Fermat's statement above,

$$a^d \equiv 1 \pmod{p}, \tag{1}$$

[2] Manuscript in Bibliothek Hannover, vol. III, 24; XII, 2, Blatt 4; also, III, 25, Blatt 1, seq., 10, January, 1687. Cf. D. Mahnke, *Bibliotheca Math.*, (3), 13 (1912–13), 45–48.

[3] *Disquisitiones Arith.*, 1801, Arts. 312–18. A part was reproduced by Wertheim, *Elemente der Zahlentheorie* (1887), 153–56.

with d a divisor of $p - 1$, and a prime to p, it follows that if $dk = p - 1$, then, raising each side of the congruence to the kth power, we have

$$a^{p-1} \equiv 1 \pmod{p}, \tag{2}$$

which is known as *Fermat's theorem.*

In 1760, Euler [4] generalized congruence (2). He proved that if m is any integer greater than 1 and if $\varphi(m)$ denotes the number of integers less than, and prime to, m, then

$$a^{\varphi(m)} \equiv 1 \pmod{m}, \tag{3}$$

for a prime to m.

We noted above that Fermat observed that if we use $p = 13$ that $3^3 - 1$ is divisible by 13, but $3^k - 1$ is not divisible by 13 for $0 < k < 3$. However, if we take powers of 2 with respect to the modulus 13, we find that $2^{12} - 1$ is divisible by 13, but $2^h - 1$ is not divisible for $0 < h < 12$. This is an example of what is called a *primitive root* of 13. In this connection, J. H. Lambert,[5] in 1769, stated without proof that there exists a primitive root g of any given prime p. That is, $g^e - 1$ is divisible by p for $e = p - 1$, but not for $0 < e < p - 1$. Lambert's statement was first proved completely by Gauss [6] in 1801. If we extend the notion of primitive roots for the case of the composite modulus, that is, e is a primitive root of m if and only if $e^{\varphi(m)} \equiv 1 \pmod{m}$, but $e^d \not\equiv 1 \pmod{m}$ for $0 < d < \varphi(m)$, then Gauss proved that primitive roots exist for m if and only if $m = 2, 4, p^n, 2p^n$ where now p is an odd prime.

From now on, we shall assume that any reader of this introduction is familiar with the elements of number theory and group theory, as well as the elementary theory of algebraic equations.

[4] *Novi Comm. Ac. Petrop.*, 8 (1760–61), 74; *Comm. Arith.*, 1, 274–86; 2, 524–26.

[5] *Nova Acta Eruditorum* (Leipzig: 1769), p. 127.

[6] *Disquisitiones Arith.*, 1801, Arts. 52–55, 92.

Using a known theorem limiting the number of roots of a conditional congruence in one unknown together with [7]

Theorem I. *A finite group G of order n and identity E, is cyclic if and only if for every d dividing n, the relation $X^d = E$ has at most d solutions X in G,* will yield proofs of the above statements.

Since the above discussion shows that we do not have primitive roots corresponding to all moduli, we may consider the problem of determining the order of the maximal cyclic group contained in the group of residue classes modulo m under multiplication, each class corresponding to integers prime to m,

$$C_{r_1}, C_{r_2} \ldots, C_{r_{\varphi(m)}} \tag{4}$$

where the r's are the $\varphi(m)$ positive integers less than, and prime to, m. Carmichael [8] defined a numerical function $\lambda(m)$ having the following properties:

$$\lambda(2^a) = \phi(2^a) \text{ if } a = 0, 1, 2;$$
$$\lambda(2^a) = \tfrac{1}{2}\phi(2^a) \text{ if } a > 2;$$
$$\lambda(p^a) = \phi(p^a) \text{ if } p \text{ is an odd prime;}$$
$$\lambda(2^a p_1^{a_1} p_2^{a_2} \ldots p_n^{a_n}) = M, \text{ with each } p \text{ an odd prime,}$$

where M is the least common multiple of $\lambda(2^a)$, $\lambda(p_1^{a_1})$, $\ldots$, $\lambda(p_n^{a_n})$.

Let

$$m = 2^a p_1^{a_1} p_2^{a_2} \ldots p_n^{a_n}.$$

It then follows that

$$a^{\lambda(m)} \equiv 1 \pmod{m}. \tag{5}$$

[7] Hans Zassenhaus, *The Theory of Groups* (New York: Chelsea Publishing Company, 1947, p. 74) gave the result: "A finite group must be cyclic if, for every natural number n it has at most n elements whose n-th power is E." Our Theorem I may be easily derived from this and was originally given as Theorem III by the writer in an article entitled "On a p-adic Representation of Rings and Abelian Groups," *Annals of Mathematics*, 48 (1947).

[8] R. D. Carmichael, "Note on a New Number Theory Function," *Bull. Amer. Math. Soc.*, 16 (1910), 232–38.

By the properties of the primitive roots of $p_i^{a_i}$, $i = 1, \ldots, n$, Carmichael shows that there exists what he calls a primitive λ-root of m, i. e., if $r^{\lambda(m)}$ is the lowest power ($\neq 0$) of r which is congruent to 1 modulo m, r is said to be a primitive λ-root modulo m. It follows from Rel. (5) that $\lambda(m)$ is the degree of a maximal cyclic subgroup of (4).

However, we cannot apply our tables directly as they stand when $m \neq p^n$ or $\neq 2p^n$. If one had occasion to do much calculation with primitive λ roots in general, it would be convenient to set up tables analogous to the present ones.

The theory of primitive roots with respect to powers of primes enables us to set up a basis for the Abelian group elements in (4). By these means, we can determine [9] integers $r, r_0, r_1, \ldots, r_k$ such that the incongruent integers modulo m are congruent in turn to $r^s r_0^{s_0} \ldots r_k^{s_k}$ where s ranges over the set 0, 1; s_0 ranges over the set $0, 1, \ldots, 2^{h_0} - 1$; r_i ranges over the set $0, 1, \ldots, \phi(q_i^{h_i}) - 1$; $i = 1, 2, 3, \ldots, k$ where the q's are odd primes and

$$m = 2^{h_0} q_1^{h_1} q_2^{h_2} \ldots q_k^{h_k}. \tag{6}$$

Here the r_i's, $i = 1, 2, \ldots, k$, have the property $r_i \equiv g_i \pmod{q_i^{h_i}}$ where g_i is a primitive root of $q_i^{h_i}$ for $i = 1, 2, \ldots, k$, and also $r_i \equiv 1 \pmod{m/q_i^{h_i}}$. The case for an even modulus is treated somewhat similarly.

So far we have discussed only residue classes modulo m, such as (4), where the class is defined by an integer prime to m. We can, however, consider the question of what happens when we take a class, modulo m, defined by an integer having a divisor > 1 in common with them, and raise it to successive powers. We shall first examine some special cases. When 30 is raised to successive powers, we obtain the set of incongruent integers modulo 360: 30, 180, 0. Similarly 12 generates the least residues: 12, 144, 288, 216, 72 modulo 360. This set contains the set: 144,

[9] Cf., for example, Leopold Kronecker, *Vorlesungen über Zahlentheorie* (Leipzig: B. G. Teubner, 1901), pp. 424–26.

288, 216, 72 which has the properties modulo 360: each one divides the others modulo 360; $a \cdot 216 = a \pmod{360}$ for each a of the subset; and 288 generates the subset. 5 generates a set of least residues modulo 360, which has the property: each divides the others modulo 360.

There does not seem to be much rhyme or reason to the special patterns we have obtained above, and, in fact, it appears quite difficult to explain the behavior in general of the residues, as discussed above in special cases, without a little of the theory of semi-groups. We begin by defining the finite cyclic semi-group: Consider

$$A, A^2, \ldots, A^k, \ldots, A^s. \tag{7}$$

Assume $s > 1$, and that the first $s - 1$ elements in (7) are distinct, but that

$$A^k = A^s, \qquad s > k > 0.$$

Now it is possible to show that the elements [10]

$$A^k, A^{k+1}, \ldots, A^{s-1}, \tag{8}$$

using Theorem I, form a cyclic group. In the cases where this cyclic group is isomorphic with the residue classes modulo p^n or $2p^n$ with p an odd prime, the present tables may be employed in case we need to go into detailed computations concerning semi-groups of the type (7).

The theory of the cyclic semi-group (7) was used by Milo W. Weaver [11] to determine the values of k and s in (7) when the cyclic semi-group consisted of the powers of a residue class C_r, (mod m), *where r is not confined to integers prime to m as in (4).*

Starting with the residue classes modulo p, a prime, we generalized in several different directions the ideas of primitive roots in what preceded. Here we em-

[10] F. C. Biesele, "An Introduction to the Theory of Semi-groups," unpublished M.A. thesis, University of Texas, June, 1933, pp. 9–11.

[11] Milo W. Weaver, "Cosets in a Semi-group," *Math. Mag.*, 25 (1952), 129–32.

ployed the residue classes modulo m which formed under addition and multiplication a finite ring in general. Instead of this type of generalization, however, we may note that the residue classes modulo p form a finite field under addition and multiplication. We may then examine what the generalization of the ideas of primitive root turns out to be when we consider the multiplicative semi-group of the field. In general, the finite field, denoted by $F[p^n]$, consists of p^n elements, and any non-zero element satisfies the equation $a^{p^n-1} = 1$ in $F[p^n]$. Under multiplication, the elements, aside from the zero element, form a cyclic group of order $(p^n - 1)$, as is known. This result is a direct generalization of the fact that the residue classes modulo p, aside from the zero class, form a cyclic group of order $p - 1$ under multiplication if primitive roots exist.

Any $F[p^n]$ is isomorphic to a Galois field, that is, the field obtained by the residue classes corresponding to the residues with respect to the (modd $f(x)$, p) where $f(x)$ is a polynomial with rational integer coefficients of degree n and irreducible modulo p. In view of this, we obtain a polynomial representation for the elements of any finite field, and in particular, we obtain a representation of a generator of the cyclic group of non-zero elements under multiplication, which we shall call a *primitive element* of the field. These primitive elements, expressed as polynomials, have been tabulated for various small values of p and n, but *it is very desirable that more extensive tables of this kind be set up with the use of rapid computing machines.*

We may note also that if k is an algebraic field, and we consider the ring of integers in k (call it R), then the residue classes modulo $\mathfrak{p}$, $\mathfrak{p}$ being a prime ideal in R, form a finite field under addition and multiplication. Therefore, under multiplication, the non-zero elements form a cyclic group, that is, primitive roots exist for a prime ideal $\mathfrak{p}$ in R.

Now consider the mth roots of unity by Theorem I. These roots form an Abelian group which is cyclic, since $x^d = 1$, with d a divisor of n, has no more than d complex solutions. A generator of this cyclic group is called a primitive nth root of unity. *In view of these cyclic properties, it is not surprising that there are many connections between the theory of primitive roots and the theory of roots of unity, and some of these we shall now discuss.*

Let l be an odd prime integer and ζ a primitive lth root of unity. Then the primitive roots are $\zeta, \zeta^2, \ldots, \zeta^{l-1}$. These quantities constitute the $n = l - 1$ roots of the equation

$$f(x) = \frac{x^l - 1}{x - 1} = x^{l-1} + x^{l-2} + \ldots + x + 1 = 0. \tag{9}$$

We now make use of the fact that the group of the non-zero residue classes modulo l is cyclic, and therefore the incongruent residues modulo l may be represented by

$$1, g, g^2, \ldots, g^{n-1},$$

where g is a primitive root of l. We then have an application to the Galois theory of equations, as the Galois group of Eq. (9) is cyclic and is generated by the substitution which carries ζ into ζ^g. Consequently, the primitive lth roots of unity may be written as

$$\zeta, \zeta^g, \zeta^{g^2}, \ldots, \zeta^{g^{n-1}}, \quad \text{where} \quad \zeta^{g^n} = \zeta. \tag{10}$$

Set

$$\zeta^{g^\gamma} = \zeta_\gamma.$$

We note that

$$\zeta^{g^{\gamma+kn}} = \zeta^{g^\gamma} \quad \text{or} \quad \zeta_\gamma = \zeta_{\gamma+kn}.$$

We put, if $ef = l - 1$,

$$\eta_\gamma = \zeta_\gamma + \zeta_{\gamma+e} + \zeta_{\gamma+2e} + \ldots + \zeta_{\gamma+(f-1)e},$$
$$(\gamma = 0, \ldots, e - 1).$$

These are the *cyclotomic periods* of Gauss. They form a basis for a subfield of the field generated by ζ. They have been employed in the theory of the algebraic solution of Eq. (9), and in the case where $l = 17$, this leads to the well-known ruler-and-compass construction of a regular polygon of 17 sides.[12]

The theory of cyclotomic fields associated with the *algebraic solution* of $x^n = 1$, called *cyclotomy* (*Kreisteilung*), is now an extensive topic, and the ideas of primitive roots and indices pervade most of it.[13]

We shall now consider the relation of primitive roots to the *theory of group characters*. We have already noted how convenient it turned out to be in cyclotomy and related topics to use these lth roots of unity in form (10) where ζ is a primitive root of $x^l = 1$ and g is a primitive root of the prime l, instead of writing these as

$$\zeta, \zeta^2, \zeta^3, \ldots, \zeta^{l-1}. \tag{11}$$

However, we may consider another way of writing these lth roots of unity. Define ind a with respect to g as

$$g^{\text{ind } a} \equiv a \pmod{l}; \; 0 < a < l.$$

We see that

$$\begin{aligned} \zeta^{\text{ind } a} \cdot \zeta^{\text{ind } b} &= \zeta^{\text{ind } a + \text{ind } b} \\ &= \zeta^{\text{ind } (ab)}. \end{aligned}$$

This principle of replacing a certain type of addition in exponents by a certain type of multiplication turns out to be very convenient for various purposes in a number of topics in mathematics. We may apply the above idea to any cyclic group G of order l, say, if E is the identity element of G,

$$A, A^2, \ldots, A^{l-1} = E,$$

[12] This result, and the related questions concerning Eq. (1) and the periods obtained therefrom, are discussed in more detail in B. L. Van der Waerden, *Modern Algebra*, vol. 1 (New York: Frederick Ungar Publishing Co., 1949), pp. 163–68.

[13] Cf. A. L. Whiteman, "Finite Fourier Series and Equations in Finite Fields," *Trans. Amer. Math. Soc.*, 74 (1953), 97–98, where an extensive bibliography is given. Perusal of these articles will provide a number of other references on cyclotomy which Whiteman did not have to use.

and consider

$$\zeta^{\text{ind }(1)}, \zeta^{\text{ind }(2)}, \ldots, \zeta^{\text{ind }(l-1)}. \tag{12}$$

Any element of this set in this form [14] is called a *group character* of G, also written as

$$\chi(a) = \zeta^{\text{ind }(a)},$$

and we have for each a one of these corresponding *to each primitive root* of l. The reader should compare the difference between the representations (10) and (12) of (11).

Of particular importance is the application of the theory of characters to the group G of residue classes (4). Then for $m > 1$ we use the value of m given in Eq. (6). We shall confine ourselves to a case where the present table may be used if necessary. Hence, we may write

$$m = p_1^{h_1} \ldots p_k^{h_k}$$

with the p's all odd distinct primes. It is well known [15] that the Abelian group (4) may be expressed as the product of cyclic groups of the orders

$$\phi(p_1^{h_1}), \phi(p_2^{h_2}), \ldots, \phi(p_k^{h_k}),$$

respectively. Call these groups G_i, $i = 1, 2, \ldots, k$. Let g_i be some primitive root of $p_i^{h_i}$ which is also such that $g_i \equiv 1 \pmod{m/p_i^{h_i}}$, then

$$g_i, g_i^2, \ldots, g_i^{j_i}, \tag{13}$$

where $j_i = \phi(p_i^{h_i})$, are incongruent modulo m, and if

$$g_i^s \equiv t \pmod{m},$$

we write $s = \text{ind}_i\, t$.

[14] The characters are not always written in this explicit form. Cf. H. S. Vandiver, "On a Generalization of a Jacobi Exponential Sum Associated with Cyclotomy," *Proc. Natl. Acad. Sci.*, 36 (1950), 146.

[15] Kronecker, *op. cit.*

Let

$$\theta_i = e^{2i\pi/p_i^{h_i}}.$$

Then the numbers

$$\theta_i^{b_{1_i}},\ \theta_i^{b_{2_i}},\ .\ .\ .\ ,\ \theta_i^{b_{j_i}}, \tag{14}$$

where $b_{d_i} = \text{ind } r_d^{(i)}$ and where the $r_d^{(i)}$'s range over the $\phi(p_i^{h_i})$ integers less than, and prime to $p_i^{h_i}$, are the characters of G_i, where G_i is the subgroup of G corresponding to $p_i^{h_i}$. We obtain the characters of G itself by multiplying in all ways the characters given in Set (14) for each value of i. Consequently, for r any integer prime to m we obtain each character by proper multiplication of the θ's given in Set (14) for each i. If we write $\chi(r)$ for the character of r, obviously we have the property with $\chi(r')$ being the character of r',

$$\chi(r)\ \chi(r') = \chi(rr')$$

by the properties of indices, which is the characteristic property of characters in general. The idea of characters modulo m has been employed in the famous L series,

$$L(s, \chi) = \sum_{n=1}^{\infty} \frac{\chi(n)}{n^s}.$$

In abstract algebra, the idea of characters has been extended in different ways which have little or nothing to do with primitive roots, the main idea being to preserve a relation analogous to our relation

$$\chi(a)\ \chi(b) = \chi(ab).$$

For example, a character of a group is sometimes defined by means of its matrix representation.

We shall now discuss the direct application of the present tables to problems in the elementary theory of congruences and their generalizations. Consider the congruence, if p is an odd prime,

$$x^n \equiv r \pmod{p^a}, \tag{15}$$

with $(r, p) = 1$, and g is a primitive root of p^a. Then we have

$$n \text{ ind } x \equiv \text{ind } r \pmod{\overline{p-1}},$$

and we may solve this linear congruence by using the tables, to find the incongruent values for x. If we have

$$x^n \equiv r \pmod{m},$$

we may obtain the solutions of it by considering the congruences obtained from the congruence numbered (15), when we replace it by each of the congruences obtained by substituting in it, in turn, each of the prime power factorizations of m for p^a.

The theory of primitive roots has been applied to generalizations of the last mentioned problem. Consider the congruence, *conditional in the* x's,

$$c_1 x_1^{a_1} + c_2 x_2^{a_2} + \ldots + c_s x_s^{a_s} + c_{s+1} \equiv 0 \pmod{p}, \tag{16}$$

where the c's are integers, p a prime, $c_1 \ldots c_s \not\equiv 0 \pmod{p}$; $s > 1$ for $c_{s+1} \not\equiv 0 \pmod{p}$; and $s > 2$ for $c_{s+1} \equiv 0 \pmod{p}$. For some investigations, it has been found convenient to replace Rel. (16), for $c_{s+1} \not\equiv 0 \pmod{p}$, by

$$1 + g^{j_1 + m_1 a_1} + \ldots + g^{j_s + m_s a_s} \equiv 0 \pmod{p}, \tag{17}$$

where g is a primitive root of p, and consider all the possible a's which satisfy this congruence. The problem of finding directly all these has not as yet been solved in all cases without trial, but for the trinomial cases, $s = 2$, there are many subsidiary questions, such as finding the number of solutions of Rel. (17), where the tables are quite useful. (For the extensive literature, consult note 14.)

We shall now consider the history of previously published tables of indices of the character of the present table, that is, where the tables include inverse tables of powers of the primitive root for each prime. Such a table gives, for each prime considered, the value of a in

$$g^k \equiv a \pmod{p^\alpha},$$

with $0 < a < p$, where g^α is a certain primitive root of p^α; also, the value of k in the above relation, with a given, $(a, p) = 1$, and in the set $0 < a < p^\alpha$, and $0 < k < \phi(p^\alpha)$. Ostrogradsky [16] published such tables in 1838 for $\alpha = 1$, $p < 200$. Following this, in 1839, Jacobi [17] published the monumental *Canon Arithmeticus*, which extends to $p^\alpha < 1000$. In spite of their age, copies of this latter set of tables were procurable in Germany until the second World War.

[16] M. Ostrogradsky, "Tables des racines primitives pour tous les nombres premiers au dessous de 200, avec les tables pour trouver l'indice d'un nombre donne, et pour trouver le nombre d'après l'indice," Akad. Nauk S.S.S.R., Leningrad, *Memoires . . . Sci. math., phys. et nat.*, (6) 1 (1838), 359–85.

[17] C. G. J. Jacobi, *Canon Arithmeticus, sive tabulae quibus exhibentur pro singulis numeris primis vol primorum potestatibus infra 1000 numeri ad datos indices et indices ad datos numeros pertinentes* (Berlin; 1839), xl + 248 pp.

TABLE OF INDICES AND POWER RESIDUES

For All Primes and Prime Powers Below 2000

P = 3

	INDICES 0	1	2	3	4	5	6	7	8	9		POWER RESIDUES 0	1	2	3	4	5	6	7	8	9
0		0	1								0	1	2								

P = 5

	INDICES 0	1	2	3	4	5	6	7	8	9		POWER RESIDUES 0	1	2	3	4	5	6	7	8	9
0		0	1	3	2						0	1	2	4	3						

P = 7

	INDICES 0	1	2	3	4	5	6	7	8	9		POWER RESIDUES 0	1	2	3	4	5	6	7	8	9
0		0	2	1	4	5	3				0	1	3	2	6	4	5				

P = 11

	INDICES 0	1	2	3	4	5	6	7	8	9		POWER RESIDUES 0	1	2	3	4	5	6	7	8	9
0		0	1	8	2	4	9	7	3	6	0	1	2	4	8	5	10	9	7	3	6
1	5	0									1										

P = 13

	INDICES 0	1	2	3	4	5	6	7	8	9		POWER RESIDUES 0	1	2	3	4	5	6	7	8	9
0		0	1	4	2	9	5	11	3	8	0	1	2	4	8	3	6	12	11	9	5
1	10	7	6								1	10	7								

P = 17

	INDICES 0	1	2	3	4	5	6	7	8	9		POWER RESIDUES 0	1	2	3	4	5	6	7	8	9
0		0	14	1	12	5	15	11	10	2	0	1	3	9	10	13	5	15	11	16	14
1	3	7	13	4	9	6	8				1	8	7	4	12	2	6				

P = 19

	INDICES 0	1	2	3	4	5	6	7	8	9		POWER RESIDUES 0	1	2	3	4	5	6	7	8	9
0		0	1	13	2	16	14	6	3	8	0	1	2	4	8	16	13	7	14	9	18
1	17	12	15	5	7	11	4	10	9		1	17	15	11	3	6	12	5	10		

P = 23

	INDICES 0	1	2	3	4	5	6	7	8	9		POWER RESIDUES 0	1	2	3	4	5	6	7	8	9
0		0	2	16	4	1	18	19	6	10	0	1	5	2	10	4	20	8	17	16	11
1	3	9	20	14	21	17	8	7	12	15	1	9	22	18	21	13	19	3	15	6	7
2	5	13	11								2	12	14								

P = 29

	INDICES 0	1	2	3	4	5	6	7	8	9		POWER RESIDUES 0	1	2	3	4	5	6	7	8	9
0		0	1	5	2	22	6	12	3	10	0	1	2	4	8	16	3	6	12	24	19
1	23	25	7	18	13	27	4	21	11	9	1	9	18	7	14	28	27	25	21	13	26
2	24	17	26	20	8	16	19	15	14		2	23	17	5	10	20	11	22	15		

P = 31

INDICES

	0	1	2	3	4	5	6	7	8	9
0		0	24	1	18	20	25	28	12	2
1	14	23	19	11	22	21	6	7	26	4
2	8	29	17	27	13	10	5	3	16	9
3	15	0								

POWER RESIDUES

	0	1	2	3	4	5	6	7	8	9
0	1	3	9	27	19	26	16	17	20	29
1	25	13	8	24	10	30	28	22	4	12
2	5	15	14	11	2	6	18	23	7	21
3										

P = 37

INDICES

	0	1	2	3	4	5	6	7	8	9
0		0	1	26	2	23	27	32	3	16
1	24	30	28	11	33	13	4	7	17	35
2	25	22	31	15	29	10	12	6	34	21
3	14	9	5	20	8	19	18			

POWER RESIDUES

	0	1	2	3	4	5	6	7	8	9
0	1	2	4	8	16	32	27	17	34	31
1	25	13	26	15	30	23	9	18	36	35
2	33	29	21	5	10	20	3	6	12	24
3	11	22	7	14	28	19				

P = 41

INDICES

	0	1	2	3	4	5	6	7	8	9
0		0	26	15	12	22	1	39	38	30
1	8	3	27	31	25	37	24	33	16	9
2	34	14	29	36	13	4	17	5	11	7
3	23	28	10	18	19	21	2	32	35	6
4	20	0								

POWER RESIDUES

	0	1	2	3	4	5	6	7	8	9
0	1	6	36	11	25	27	39	29	10	19
1	32	28	4	24	21	3	18	26	33	34
2	40	35	5	30	16	14	2	12	31	22
3	9	13	37	17	20	38	23	15	8	7
4										

P = 43

INDICES

	0	1	2	3	4	5	6	7	8	9
0		0	27	1	12	25	28	35	39	2
1	10	30	13	32	20	26	24	38	29	19
2	37	36	15	16	40	8	17	3	5	41
3	11	34	9	31	23	18	14	7	4	33
4	22	6	21							

POWER RESIDUES

	0	1	2	3	4	5	6	7	8	9
0	1	3	9	27	38	28	41	37	25	32
1	10	30	4	12	36	22	23	26	35	19
2	14	42	40	34	16	5	15	2	6	18
3	11	33	13	39	31	7	21	20	17	8
4	24	29								

P = 47

INDICES

	0	1	2	3	4	5	6	7	8	9
0		0	18	20	36	1	38	32	8	40
1	19	7	10	11	4	21	26	16	12	45
2	37	6	25	5	28	2	29	14	22	35
3	39	3	44	27	34	33	30	42	17	31
4	9	15	24	13	43	41	23			

POWER RESIDUES

	0	1	2	3	4	5	6	7	8	9
0	1	5	25	31	14	23	21	11	8	40
1	12	13	18	43	27	41	17	38	2	10
2	3	15	28	46	42	22	16	33	24	26
3	36	39	7	35	34	29	4	20	6	30
4	9	45	37	44	32	19				

P = 53

INDICES

	0	1	2	3	4	5	6	7	8	9
0		0	1	17	2	47	18	14	3	34
1	48	6	19	24	15	12	4	10	35	37
2	49	31	7	39	20	42	25	51	16	46
3	13	33	5	23	11	9	36	30	38	41
4	50	45	32	22	8	29	40	44	21	28
5	43	27	26							

POWER RESIDUES

	0	1	2	3	4	5	6	7	8	9
0	1	2	4	8	16	32	11	22	44	35
1	17	34	15	30	7	14	28	3	6	12
2	24	48	43	33	13	26	52	51	49	45
3	37	21	42	31	9	18	36	19	38	23
4	46	39	25	50	47	41	29	5	10	20
5	40	27								

P = 59

INDICES

	0	1	2	3	4	5	6	7	8	9
0		0	1	50	2	6	51	18	3	42
1	7	25	52	45	19	56	4	40	43	38
2	8	10	26	15	53	12	46	34	20	28
3	57	49	5	17	41	24	44	55	39	37
4	9	14	11	33	27	48	16	23	54	36
5	13	32	47	22	35	31	21	30	29	

POWER RESIDUES

	0	1	2	3	4	5	6	7	8	9
0	1	2	4	8	16	32	5	10	20	40
1	21	42	25	50	41	23	46	33	7	14
2	28	56	53	47	35	11	22	44	29	58
3	57	55	51	43	27	54	49	39	19	38
4	17	34	9	18	36	13	26	52	45	31
5	3	6	12	24	48	37	15	30		

P = 61

INDICES

	0	1	2	3	4	5	6	7	8	9
0		0	1	6	2	22	7	49	3	12
1	23	15	8	40	50	28	4	47	13	26
2	24	55	16	57	9	44	41	18	51	35
3	29	59	5	21	48	11	14	39	27	46
4	25	54	56	43	17	34	58	20	10	38
5	45	53	42	33	19	37	52	32	36	31
6	30	0								

POWER RESIDUES

	0	1	2	3	4	5	6	7	8	9
0	1	2	4	8	16	32	3	6	12	24
1	48	35	9	18	36	11	22	44	27	54
2	47	33	5	10	20	40	19	38	15	30
3	60	59	57	53	45	29	58	55	49	37
4	13	26	52	43	25	50	39	17	34	7
5	14	28	56	51	41	21	42	23	46	31
6										

P = 67

INDICES

	0	1	2	3	4	5	6	7	8	9
0		0	1	39	2	15	40	23	3	12
1	16	59	41	19	24	54	4	64	13	10
2	17	62	60	28	42	30	20	51	25	44
3	55	47	5	32	65	38	14	22	11	58
4	18	53	63	9	61	27	29	50	43	46
5	31	37	21	57	52	8	26	49	45	36
6	56	7	48	35	6	34	33			

POWER RESIDUES

	0	1	2	3	4	5	6	7	8	9
0	1	2	4	8	16	32	64	61	55	43
1	19	38	9	18	36	5	10	20	40	13
2	26	52	37	7	14	28	56	45	23	46
3	25	50	33	66	65	63	59	51	35	3
4	6	12	24	48	29	58	49	31	62	57
5	47	27	54	41	15	30	60	53	39	11
6	22	44	21	42	17	34				

P = 71

INDICES

	0	1	2	3	4	5	6	7	8	9
0		0	6	26	12	28	32	1	18	52
1	34	31	38	39	7	54	24	49	58	16
2	40	27	37	15	44	56	45	8	13	68
3	60	11	30	57	55	29	64	20	22	65
4	46	25	33	48	43	10	21	9	50	2
5	62	5	51	23	14	59	19	42	4	3
6	66	69	17	53	36	67	63	47	61	41
7	35	0								

POWER RESIDUES

	0	1	2	3	4	5	6	7	8	9
0	1	7	49	59	58	51	2	14	27	47
1	45	31	4	28	54	23	19	62	8	56
2	37	46	38	53	16	41	3	21	5	35
3	32	11	6	42	10	70	64	22	12	13
4	20	69	57	44	24	26	40	67	43	17
5	48	52	9	63	15	34	25	33	18	55
6	30	68	50	66	36	39	60	65	29	61
7										

P = 73

INDICES

	0	1	2	3	4	5	6	7	8	9
0		0	8	6	16	1	14	33	24	12
1	9	55	22	59	41	7	32	21	20	62
2	17	39	63	46	30	2	67	18	49	35
3	15	11	40	61	29	34	28	64	70	65
4	25	4	47	51	71	13	54	31	38	66
5	10	27	3	53	26	56	57	68	43	5
6	23	58	19	45	48	60	69	50	37	52
7	42	44	36							

POWER RESIDUES

	0	1	2	3	4	5	6	7	8	9
0	1	5	25	52	41	59	3	15	2	10
1	50	31	9	45	6	30	4	20	27	62
2	18	17	12	60	8	40	54	51	36	34
3	24	47	16	7	35	29	72	68	48	21
4	32	14	70	58	71	63	23	42	64	28
5	67	43	69	53	46	11	55	56	61	13
6	65	33	19	22	37	39	49	26	57	66
7	38	44								

P = 79

INDICES

	0	1	2	3	4	5	6	7	8	9
0		0	4	1	8	62	5	53	12	2
1	66	68	9	34	57	63	16	21	6	32
2	70	54	72	26	13	46	38	3	61	11
3	67	56	20	69	25	37	10	19	36	35
4	74	75	58	49	76	64	30	59	17	28
5	50	22	42	77	7	52	65	33	15	31
6	71	45	60	55	24	18	73	48	29	27
7	41	51	14	44	23	47	40	43	39	

POWER RESIDUES

	0	1	2	3	4	5	6	7	8	9
0	1	3	9	27	2	6	18	54	4	12
1	36	29	8	24	72	58	16	48	65	37
2	32	17	51	74	64	34	23	69	49	68
3	46	59	19	57	13	39	38	35	26	78
4	76	70	52	77	73	61	25	75	67	43
5	50	71	55	7	21	63	31	14	42	47
6	62	28	5	15	45	56	10	30	11	33
7	20	60	22	66	40	41	44	53		

P = 83

INDICES

	0	1	2	3	4	5	6	7	8	9
0		0	1	72	2	27	73	8	3	62
1	28	24	74	77	9	17	4	56	63	47
2	29	80	25	60	75	54	78	52	10	12
3	18	38	5	14	57	35	64	20	48	67
4	30	40	81	71	26	7	61	23	76	16
5	55	46	79	59	53	51	11	37	13	34
6	19	66	39	70	6	22	15	45	58	50
7	36	33	65	69	21	44	49	32	68	43
8	31	42	41							

POWER RESIDUES

	0	1	2	3	4	5	6	7	8	9
0	1	2	4	8	16	32	64	45	7	14
1	28	56	29	58	33	66	49	15	30	60
2	37	74	65	47	11	22	44	5	10	20
3	40	80	77	71	59	35	70	57	31	62
4	41	82	81	79	75	67	51	19	38	76
5	69	55	27	54	25	50	17	34	68	53
6	23	46	9	18	36	72	61	39	78	73
7	63	43	3	6	12	24	48	13	26	52
8	21	42								

P = 89

INDICES

	0	1	2	3	4	5	6	7	8	9
0		0	16	1	32	70	17	81	48	2
1	86	84	33	23	9	71	64	6	18	35
2	14	82	12	57	49	52	39	3	25	59
3	87	31	80	85	22	63	34	11	51	24
4	30	21	10	29	28	72	73	54	65	74
5	68	7	55	78	19	66	41	36	75	43
6	15	69	47	83	8	5	13	56	38	58
7	79	62	50	20	27	53	67	77	40	42
8	46	4	37	61	26	76	45	60	44	

POWER RESIDUES

	0	1	2	3	4	5	6	7	8	9
0	1	3	9	27	81	65	17	51	64	14
1	42	37	22	66	20	60	2	6	18	54
2	73	41	34	13	39	28	84	74	44	43
3	40	31	4	12	36	19	57	82	68	26
4	78	56	79	59	88	86	80	62	8	24
5	72	38	25	75	47	52	67	23	69	29
6	87	83	71	35	16	48	55	76	50	61
7	5	15	45	46	49	58	85	77	53	70
8	32	7	21	63	11	33	10	30		

P = 97

INDICES

	0	1	2	3	4	5	6	7	8	9
0		0	34	70	68	1	8	31	6	44
1	35	86	42	25	65	71	40	89	78	81
2	69	5	24	77	76	2	59	18	3	13
3	9	46	74	60	27	32	16	91	19	95
4	7	85	39	4	58	45	15	84	14	62
5	36	63	93	10	52	87	37	55	47	67
6	43	64	80	75	12	26	94	57	61	51
7	66	11	50	28	29	72	53	21	33	30
8	41	88	23	17	73	90	38	83	92	54
9	79	56	49	20	22	82	48			

POWER RESIDUES

	0	1	2	3	4	5	6	7	8	9
0	1	5	25	28	43	21	8	40	6	30
1	53	71	64	29	48	46	36	83	27	38
2	93	77	94	82	22	13	65	34	73	74
3	79	7	35	78	2	10	50	56	86	42
4	16	80	12	60	9	45	31	58	96	92
5	72	69	54	76	89	57	91	67	44	26
6	33	68	49	51	61	14	70	59	4	20
7	3	15	75	84	32	63	24	23	18	90
8	62	19	95	87	47	41	11	55	81	17
9	85	37	88	52	66	39				

P = 101

INDICES

	0	1	2	3	4	5	6	7	8	9
0		0	1	69	2	24	70	9	3	38
1	25	13	71	66	10	93	4	30	39	96
2	26	78	14	86	72	48	67	7	11	91
3	94	84	5	82	31	33	40	56	97	35
4	27	45	79	42	15	62	87	58	73	18
5	49	99	68	23	8	37	12	65	92	29
6	95	77	85	47	6	90	83	81	32	55
7	34	44	41	61	57	17	98	22	36	64
8	28	76	46	89	80	54	43	60	16	21
9	63	75	88	53	59	20	74	52	19	51
10	50	0								

POWER RESIDUES

	0	1	2	3	4	5	6	7	8	9
0	1	2	4	8	16	32	64	27	54	7
1	14	28	56	11	22	44	88	75	49	98
2	95	89	77	53	5	10	20	40	80	59
3	17	34	68	35	70	39	78	55	9	18
4	36	72	43	86	71	41	82	63	25	50
5	100	99	97	93	85	69	37	74	47	94
6	87	73	45	90	79	57	13	26	52	3
7	6	12	24	48	96	91	81	61	21	42
8	84	67	33	66	31	62	23	46	92	83
9	65	29	58	15	30	60	19	38	76	51
10										

P = 103

INDICES

	0	1	2	3	4	5	6	7	8	9
0		0	44	39	88	1	83	4	30	78
1	45	61	25	72	48	40	74	70	20	80
2	89	43	3	24	69	2	14	15	92	86
3	84	57	16	100	12	5	64	93	22	9
4	31	50	87	77	47	79	68	85	11	8
5	46	7	58	97	59	62	34	17	28	98
6	26	36	101	82	60	73	42	13	56	63
7	49	67	6	33	35	41	66	65	53	18
8	75	54	94	38	29	71	19	23	91	99
9	21	76	10	96	27	81	55	32	52	37
10	90	95	51							

POWER RESIDUES

	0	1	2	3	4	5	6	7	8	9
0	1	5	25	22	7	35	72	51	49	39
1	92	48	34	67	26	27	32	57	79	86
2	18	90	38	87	23	12	60	94	58	84
3	8	40	97	73	56	74	61	99	83	3
4	15	75	66	21	2	10	50	44	14	70
5	41	102	98	78	81	96	68	31	52	54
6	64	11	55	69	36	77	76	71	46	24
7	17	85	13	65	16	80	91	43	9	45
8	19	95	63	6	30	47	29	42	4	20
9	100	88	28	37	82	101	93	53	59	89
10	33	62								

P = 107

INDICES

	0	1	2	3	4	5	6	7	8	9
0		0	1	70	2	47	71	43	3	34
1	48	22	72	14	44	11	4	29	35	78
2	49	7	23	62	73	94	15	104	45	32
3	12	27	5	92	30	90	36	38	79	84
4	50	40	8	59	24	81	63	66	74	86
5	95	99	16	52	105	69	46	42	33	21
6	13	10	28	77	6	61	93	103	31	26
7	91	89	37	83	39	58	80	65	85	98
8	51	68	41	20	9	76	60	102	25	88
9	82	57	64	97	67	19	75	101	87	56
10	96	18	100	55	17	54	53			

POWER RESIDUES

	0	1	2	3	4	5	6	7	8	9
0	1	2	4	8	16	32	64	21	42	84
1	61	15	30	60	13	26	52	104	101	95
2	83	59	11	22	44	88	69	31	62	17
3	34	68	29	58	9	18	36	72	37	74
4	41	82	57	7	14	28	56	5	10	20
5	40	80	53	106	105	103	99	91	75	43
6	86	65	23	46	92	77	47	94	81	55
7	3	6	12	24	48	96	85	63	19	38
8	76	45	90	73	39	78	49	98	89	71
9	35	70	33	66	25	50	100	93	79	51
10	102	97	87	67	27	54				

P = 109

INDICES

	0	1	2	3	4	5	6	7	8	9
0		0	57	52	6	76	1	40	63	104
1	25	83	58	67	97	20	12	93	53	75
2	82	92	32	33	7	44	16	48	46	34
3	77	14	69	27	42	8	2	5	24	11
4	31	45	41	30	89	72	90	17	64	80
5	101	37	73	49	105	51	103	19	91	47
6	26	10	71	36	18	35	84	95	99	85
7	65	78	59	56	62	96	81	15	68	23
8	88	100	102	70	98	61	87	86	38	28
9	21	107	39	66	74	43	13	4	29	79
10	50	9	94	55	22	60	106	3	54	

POWER RESIDUES

	0	1	2	3	4	5	6	7	8	9
0	1	6	36	107	97	37	4	24	35	101
1	61	39	16	96	31	77	26	47	64	57
2	15	90	104	79	38	10	60	33	89	98
3	43	40	22	23	29	65	63	51	88	92
4	7	42	34	95	25	41	28	59	27	53
5	100	55	3	18	108	103	73	2	12	72
6	105	85	74	8	48	70	93	13	78	32
7	83	62	45	52	94	19	5	30	71	99
8	49	76	20	11	66	69	87	86	80	44
9	46	58	21	17	102	67	75	14	84	68
10	81	50	82	56	9	54	106	91		

P = 113

INDICES

	0	1	2	3	4	5	6	7	8	9
0		0	12	1	24	83	13	8	36	2
1	95	74	25	22	20	84	48	5	14	99
2	107	9	86	41	37	54	34	3	32	89
3	96	50	60	75	17	91	26	67	111	23
4	7	94	21	47	98	85	53	31	49	16
5	66	6	46	52	15	45	44	100	101	71
6	108	102	62	10	72	105	87	109	29	42
7	103	77	38	63	79	55	11	82	35	73
8	19	4	106	40	33	88	59	90	110	93
9	97	30	65	51	43	70	61	104	28	76
10	78	81	18	39	58	92	64	69	27	80
11	57	68	56							

POWER RESIDUES

	0	1	2	3	4	5	6	7	8	9
0	1	3	9	27	81	17	51	40	7	21
1	63	76	2	6	18	54	49	34	102	80
2	14	42	13	39	4	12	36	108	98	68
3	91	47	28	84	26	78	8	24	72	103
4	83	23	69	94	56	55	52	43	16	48
5	31	93	53	46	25	75	112	110	104	86
6	32	96	62	73	106	92	50	37	111	107
7	95	59	64	79	11	33	99	71	100	74
8	109	101	77	5	15	45	22	66	85	29
9	87	35	105	89	41	10	30	90	44	19
10	57	58	61	70	97	65	82	20	60	67
11	88	38								

P = 127

INDICES

	0	1	2	3	4	5	6	7	8	9
0		0	72	1	18	87	73	115	90	2
1	33	68	19	94	61	88	36	38	74	84
2	105	116	14	121	91	48	40	3	7	113
3	34	46	108	69	110	76	20	98	30	95
4	51	80	62	71	86	89	67	60	37	104
5	120	39	112	107	75	29	79	85	59	119
6	106	78	118	117	54	55	15	43	56	122
7	22	16	92	12	44	49	102	57	41	100
8	123	4	26	23	8	125	17	114	32	93
9	35	83	13	47	6	45	109	97	50	70
10	66	103	111	28	58	77	53	42	21	11
11	101	99	25	124	31	82	5	96	65	27
12	52	10	24	81	64	9	63			

POWER RESIDUES

	0	1	2	3	4	5	6	7	8	9
0	1	3	9	27	81	116	94	28	84	125
1	121	109	73	92	22	66	71	86	4	12
2	36	108	70	83	122	112	82	119	103	55
3	38	114	88	10	30	90	16	48	17	51
4	26	78	107	67	74	95	31	93	25	75
5	98	40	120	106	64	65	68	77	104	58
6	47	14	42	126	124	118	100	46	11	33
7	99	43	2	6	18	54	35	105	61	56
8	41	123	115	91	19	57	44	5	15	45
9	8	24	72	89	13	39	117	97	37	111
10	79	110	76	101	49	20	60	53	32	96
11	34	102	52	29	87	7	21	63	62	59
12	50	23	69	80	113	85				

P = 131

INDICES

	0	1	2	3	4	5	6	7	8	9
0		0	1	72	2	46	73	96	3	14
1	47	56	74	18	97	118	4	43	15	35
2	48	38	57	23	75	92	19	86	98	51
3	119	29	5	128	44	12	16	41	36	90
4	49	126	39	124	58	60	24	105	76	62
5	93	115	20	26	87	102	99	107	52	82
6	120	78	30	110	6	64	129	71	45	95
7	13	55	17	117	42	34	37	22	91	85
8	50	28	127	11	40	89	125	123	59	104
9	61	114	25	101	106	81	77	109	63	70
10	94	54	116	33	21	84	27	10	88	122
11	103	113	100	80	108	69	53	32	83	9
12	121	112	79	68	31	8	111	67	7	66
13	65	0								

POWER RESIDUES

	0	1	2	3	4	5	6	7	8	9
0	1	2	4	8	16	32	64	128	125	119
1	107	83	35	70	9	18	36	72	13	26
2	52	104	77	23	46	92	53	106	81	31
3	62	124	117	103	75	19	38	76	21	42
4	84	37	74	17	34	68	5	10	20	40
5	80	29	58	116	101	71	11	22	44	88
6	45	90	49	98	65	130	129	127	123	115
7	99	67	3	6	12	24	48	96	61	122
8	113	95	59	118	105	79	27	54	108	85
9	39	78	25	50	100	69	7	14	28	56
10	112	93	55	110	89	47	94	57	114	97
11	63	126	121	111	91	51	102	73	15	30
12	60	120	109	87	43	86	41	82	33	66
13										

P = 137

INDICES

	0	1	2	3	4	5	6	7	8	9
0		0	10	1	20	75	11	42	30	2
1	85	122	21	25	52	76	40	38	12	46
2	95	43	132	125	31	14	35	3	62	91
3	86	73	50	123	48	117	22	102	56	26
4	105	119	53	97	6	77	135	19	41	84
5	24	39	45	131	13	61	72	47	101	104
6	96	134	83	44	60	100	133	59	58	126
7	127	65	32	128	112	15	66	28	36	33
8	115	4	129	81	63	113	107	92	16	109
9	87	67	9	74	29	121	51	37	94	124
10	34	90	49	116	55	118	5	18	23	130
11	71	103	82	99	57	64	111	27	114	80
12	106	108	8	120	93	89	54	17	70	98
13	110	79	7	88	69	78	68			

POWER RESIDUES

	0	1	2	3	4	5	6	7	8	9
0	1	3	9	27	81	106	44	132	122	92
1	2	6	18	54	25	75	88	127	107	47
2	4	12	36	108	50	13	39	117	77	94
3	8	24	72	79	100	26	78	97	17	51
4	16	48	7	21	63	52	19	57	34	102
5	32	96	14	42	126	104	38	114	68	67
6	64	55	28	84	115	71	76	91	136	134
7	128	110	56	31	93	5	15	45	135	131
8	119	83	112	62	49	10	30	90	133	125
9	101	29	87	124	98	20	60	43	129	113
10	65	58	37	111	59	40	120	86	121	89
11	130	116	74	85	118	80	103	35	105	41
12	123	95	11	33	99	23	69	70	73	82
13	109	53	22	66	61	46				

P = 139

INDICES

	0	1	2	3	4	5	6	7	8	9
0		0	1	41	2	86	42	50	3	82
1	87	76	43	64	51	127	4	107	83	61
2	88	91	77	27	44	34	65	123	52	94
3	128	56	5	117	108	136	84	80	62	105
4	89	32	92	115	78	30	28	98	45	100
5	35	10	66	47	124	24	53	102	95	21
6	129	37	57	132	6	12	118	16	109	68
7	137	40	85	49	81	75	63	126	106	60
8	90	26	33	122	93	55	116	135	79	104
9	31	114	29	97	99	9	46	23	101	20
10	36	131	11	15	67	39	48	74	125	59
11	25	121	54	134	103	113	96	8	22	19
12	130	14	38	73	58	120	133	112	7	18
13	13	72	119	111	17	71	110	70	69	

POWER RESIDUES

	0	1	2	3	4	5	6	7	8	9
0	1	2	4	8	16	32	64	128	117	95
1	51	102	65	130	121	103	67	134	129	119
2	99	59	118	97	55	110	81	23	46	92
3	45	90	41	82	25	50	100	61	122	105
4	71	3	6	12	24	48	96	53	106	73
5	7	14	28	56	112	85	31	62	124	109
6	79	19	38	76	13	26	52	104	69	138
7	137	135	131	123	107	75	11	22	44	88
8	37	74	9	18	36	72	5	10	20	40
9	80	21	42	84	29	58	116	93	47	94
10	49	98	57	114	89	39	78	17	34	68
11	136	133	127	115	91	43	86	33	66	132
12	125	111	83	27	54	108	77	15	30	60
13	120	101	63	126	113	87	35	70		

P = 149

INDICES

	0	1	2	3	4	5	6	7	8	9
0		0	1	87	2	104	88	142	3	26
1	105	109	89	53	143	43	4	124	27	84
2	106	81	110	95	90	60	54	113	144	120
3	44	132	5	48	125	98	28	72	85	140
4	107	41	82	93	111	130	96	138	91	136
5	61	63	55	18	114	65	145	23	121	57
6	45	38	133	20	6	9	49	116	126	34
7	99	67	29	12	73	147	86	103	141	25
8	108	52	42	123	83	80	94	59	112	119
9	131	47	97	71	139	40	92	129	137	135
10	62	17	64	22	56	37	19	8	115	33
11	66	11	146	102	24	51	122	79	58	118
12	46	70	39	128	134	16	21	36	7	32
13	10	101	50	78	117	69	127	15	35	31
14	100	77	68	14	30	76	13	75	74	

POWER RESIDUES

	0	1	2	3	4	5	6	7	8	9
0	1	2	4	8	16	32	64	128	107	65
1	130	111	73	146	143	137	125	101	53	106
2	63	126	103	57	114	79	9	18	36	72
3	144	139	129	109	69	138	127	105	61	122
4	95	41	82	15	30	60	120	91	33	66
5	132	115	81	13	26	52	104	59	118	87
6	25	50	100	51	102	55	110	71	142	135
7	121	93	37	74	148	147	145	141	133	117
8	85	21	42	84	19	38	76	3	6	12
9	24	48	96	43	86	23	46	92	35	70
10	140	131	113	77	5	10	20	40	80	11
11	22	44	88	27	54	108	67	134	119	89
12	29	58	116	83	17	34	68	136	123	97
13	45	90	31	62	124	99	49	98	47	94
14	39	78	7	14	28	56	112	75		

P = 151

INDICES

	0	1	2	3	4	5	6	7	8	9
0		0	70	81	140	112	1	67	60	12
1	32	94	71	41	137	43	130	58	82	90
2	102	148	14	115	141	74	111	93	57	114
3	113	28	50	25	128	29	2	16	10	122
4	22	51	68	8	84	124	35	26	61	134
5	144	139	31	129	13	56	127	21	34	30
6	33	119	98	79	120	3	95	63	48	46
7	99	17	72	117	86	5	80	11	42	147
8	92	24	121	123	138	20	78	45	4	23
9	44	108	105	109	96	52	131	88	54	106
10	64	69	59	136	101	110	49	9	83	143
11	126	97	47	85	91	77	104	53	100	125
12	103	38	39	132	18	36	149	66	40	89
13	73	27	15	7	133	55	118	62	116	146
14	19	107	87	135	142	76	37	65	6	145
15	75	0								

POWER RESIDUES

	0	1	2	3	4	5	6	7	8	9
0	1	6	36	65	88	75	148	133	43	107
1	38	77	9	54	22	132	37	71	124	140
2	85	57	40	89	81	33	47	131	31	35
3	59	52	10	60	58	46	125	146	121	122
4	128	13	78	15	90	87	69	112	68	106
5	32	41	95	117	98	135	55	28	17	102
6	8	48	137	67	100	147	127	7	42	101
7	2	12	72	130	25	150	145	115	86	63
8	76	3	18	108	44	113	74	142	97	129
9	19	114	80	27	11	66	94	111	62	70
10	118	104	20	120	116	92	99	141	91	93
11	105	26	5	30	29	23	138	73	136	61
12	64	82	39	83	45	119	110	56	34	53
13	16	96	123	134	49	143	103	14	84	51
14	4	24	144	109	50	149	139	79	21	126
15										

P = 157

INDICES

	0	1	2	3	4	5	6	7	8	9
0		0	141	82	126	1	67	147	111	8
1	142	28	52	26	132	83	96	40	149	124
2	127	73	13	135	37	2	11	90	117	129
3	68	62	81	110	25	148	134	116	109	108
4	112	21	58	113	154	9	120	92	22	138
5	143	122	152	59	75	29	102	50	114	45
6	53	85	47	155	66	27	95	72	10	61
7	133	20	119	121	101	84	94	19	93	15
8	97	16	6	23	43	41	98	55	139	88
9	150	17	105	144	77	125	7	131	123	36
10	128	24	107	153	137	74	44	65	60	100
11	14	42	87	76	35	136	99	34	30	31
12	38	56	70	103	32	3	140	146	51	39
13	12	89	80	115	57	91	151	49	46	71
14	118	18	5	54	104	130	106	64	86	33
15	69	145	79	48	4	63	78			

POWER RESIDUES

	0	1	2	3	4	5	6	7	8	9
0	1	5	25	125	154	142	82	96	9	45
1	68	26	130	22	110	79	81	91	141	77
2	71	41	48	83	101	34	13	65	11	55
3	118	119	124	149	117	114	99	24	120	129
4	17	85	111	84	106	59	138	62	153	137
5	57	128	12	60	143	87	121	134	42	53
6	108	69	31	155	147	107	64	6	30	150
7	122	139	67	21	105	54	113	94	156	152
8	132	32	3	15	75	61	148	112	89	131
9	27	135	47	78	76	66	16	80	86	116
10	109	74	56	123	144	92	146	102	39	38
11	33	8	40	43	58	133	37	28	140	72
12	46	73	51	98	19	95	4	20	100	29
13	145	97	14	70	36	23	115	104	49	88
14	126	2	10	50	93	151	127	7	35	18
15	90	136	52	103	44	63				

P = 163

INDICES

	0	1	2	3	4	5	6	7	8	9
0		0	1	101	2	15	102	73	3	40
1	16	47	103	51	74	116	4	57	41	125
2	17	12	48	9	104	30	52	141	75	107
3	117	69	5	148	58	88	42	33	126	152
4	18	160	13	38	49	55	10	28	105	146
5	31	158	53	144	142	62	76	64	108	135
6	118	78	70	113	6	66	149	25	59	110
7	89	92	43	137	34	131	127	120	153	95
8	19	80	161	100	14	72	39	46	50	115
9	56	124	11	8	29	140	106	68	147	87
10	32	151	159	37	54	27	145	157	143	61
11	63	134	77	112	65	24	109	91	136	130
12	119	94	79	99	71	45	114	123	7	139
13	67	86	150	36	26	156	60	133	111	23
14	90	129	93	98	44	122	138	85	35	155
15	132	22	128	97	121	84	154	21	96	83
16	20	82	81							

POWER RESIDUES

	0	1	2	3	4	5	6	7	8	9
0	1	2	4	8	16	32	64	128	93	23
1	46	92	21	42	84	5	10	20	40	80
2	160	157	151	139	115	67	134	105	47	94
3	25	50	100	37	74	148	133	103	43	86
4	9	18	36	72	144	125	87	11	22	44
5	88	13	26	52	104	45	90	17	34	68
6	136	109	55	110	57	114	65	130	97	31
7	62	124	85	7	14	28	56	112	61	122
8	81	162	161	159	155	147	131	99	35	70
9	140	117	71	142	121	79	158	153	143	123
10	83	3	6	12	24	48	96	29	58	116
11	69	138	113	63	126	89	15	30	60	120
12	77	154	145	127	91	19	38	76	152	141
13	119	75	150	137	111	59	118	73	146	129
14	95	27	54	108	53	106	49	98	33	66
15	132	101	39	78	156	149	135	107	51	102
16	41	82								

P = 167

INDICES

	0	1	2	3	4	5	6	7	8	9
0		0	40	94	80	1	134	118	120	22
1	41	28	8	103	158	95	160	53	62	58
2	81	46	68	99	48	2	143	116	32	150
3	135	90	34	122	93	119	102	61	98	31
4	121	97	86	87	108	23	139	132	88	70
5	42	147	17	109	156	29	72	152	24	113
6	9	66	130	140	74	104	162	165	133	27
7	159	45	142	89	101	96	138	146	71	65
8	161	44	137	43	126	54	127	78	148	154
9	63	55	13	18	6	59	128	76	110	50
10	82	79	21	157	57	47	149	92	30	107
11	69	155	112	73	26	100	64	125	153	5
12	49	56	106	25	4	3	14	38	114	15
13	144	19	36	10	39	117	7	52	67	115
14	33	60	85	131	16	151	129	164	141	145
15	136	77	12	75	20	91	111	124	105	37
16	35	51	84	163	11	123	83			

POWER RESIDUES

	0	1	2	3	4	5	6	7	8	9
0	1	5	25	125	124	119	94	136	12	60
1	133	164	152	92	126	129	144	52	93	131
2	154	102	9	45	58	123	114	69	11	55
3	108	39	28	140	32	160	132	159	127	134
4	2	10	50	83	81	71	21	105	24	120
5	99	161	137	17	85	91	121	104	19	95
6	141	37	18	90	116	79	61	138	22	110
7	49	78	56	113	64	153	97	151	87	101
8	4	20	100	166	162	142	42	43	48	73
9	31	155	107	34	3	15	75	41	38	23
10	115	74	36	13	65	158	122	109	44	53
11	98	156	112	59	128	139	27	135	7	35
12	8	40	33	165	157	117	84	86	96	146
13	62	143	47	68	6	30	150	82	76	46
14	63	148	72	26	130	149	77	51	88	106
15	29	145	57	118	89	111	54	103	14	70
16	16	80	66	163	147	67				

P = 173

INDICES

	0	1	2	3	4	5	6	7	8	9
0		0	1	27	2	39	28	95	3	54
1	40	23	29	130	96	66	4	73	55	33
2	41	122	24	20	30	78	131	81	97	144
3	67	102	5	50	74	134	56	162	34	157
4	42	138	123	84	25	93	21	64	31	18
5	79	100	132	155	82	62	98	60	145	147
6	68	13	103	149	6	169	51	70	75	47
7	135	15	57	166	163	105	35	118	158	151
8	43	108	139	8	124	112	85	171	26	38
9	94	53	22	129	65	72	32	121	19	77
10	80	143	101	49	133	161	156	137	83	92
11	63	17	99	154	61	59	146	12	148	168
12	69	46	14	165	104	117	150	107	7	111
13	170	37	52	128	71	120	76	142	48	160
14	136	91	16	153	58	11	167	45	164	116
15	106	110	36	127	119	141	159	90	152	10
16	44	115	109	126	140	89	9	114	125	88
17	113	87	86							

POWER RESIDUES

	0	1	2	3	4	5	6	7	8	9
0	1	2	4	8	16	32	64	128	83	166
1	159	145	117	61	122	71	142	111	49	98
2	23	46	92	11	22	44	88	3	6	12
3	24	48	96	19	38	76	152	131	89	5
4	10	20	40	80	160	147	121	69	138	103
5	33	66	132	91	9	18	36	72	144	115
6	57	114	55	110	47	94	15	30	60	120
7	67	134	95	17	34	68	136	99	25	50
8	100	27	54	108	43	86	172	171	169	165
9	157	141	109	45	90	7	14	28	56	112
10	51	102	31	62	124	75	150	127	81	162
11	151	129	85	170	167	161	149	125	77	154
12	135	97	21	42	84	168	163	153	133	93
13	13	26	52	104	35	70	140	107	41	82
14	164	155	137	101	29	58	116	59	118	63
15	126	79	158	143	113	53	106	39	78	156
16	139	105	37	74	148	123	73	146	119	65
17	130	87								

P = 179

INDICES

	0	1	2	3	4	5	6	7	8	9
0		0	1	108	2	138	109	171	3	38
1	139	15	110	114	172	68	4	166	39	54
2	140	101	16	135	111	98	115	146	173	118
3	69	62	5	123	167	131	40	149	55	44
4	141	155	102	80	17	176	136	36	112	164
5	99	96	116	121	147	153	174	162	119	160
6	70	72	63	31	6	74	124	86	168	65
7	132	59	41	33	150	28	56	8	45	11
8	142	76	156	24	103	126	81	48	18	88
9	177	107	137	170	37	14	113	67	165	53
10	100	134	97	145	117	61	122	130	148	43
11	154	79	175	35	163	95	120	152	161	159
12	71	30	73	85	64	58	32	27	7	10
13	75	23	125	47	87	106	169	13	66	52
14	133	144	60	129	42	78	34	94	151	158
15	29	84	57	26	9	22	46	105	12	51
16	143	128	77	93	157	83	25	21	104	50
17	127	92	82	20	49	91	19	90	89	

POWER RESIDUES

	0	1	2	3	4	5	6	7	8	9
0	1	2	4	8	16	32	64	128	77	154
1	129	79	158	137	95	11	22	44	88	176
2	173	167	155	131	83	166	153	127	75	150
3	121	63	126	73	146	113	47	94	9	18
4	36	72	144	109	39	78	156	133	87	174
5	169	159	139	99	19	38	76	152	125	71
6	142	105	31	62	124	69	138	97	15	30
7	60	120	61	122	65	130	81	162	145	111
8	43	86	172	165	151	123	67	134	89	178
9	177	175	171	163	147	115	51	102	25	50
10	100	21	42	84	168	157	135	91	3	6
11	12	24	48	96	13	26	52	104	29	58
12	116	53	106	33	66	132	85	170	161	143
13	107	35	70	140	101	23	46	92	5	10
14	20	40	80	160	141	103	27	54	108	37
15	74	148	117	55	110	41	82	164	149	119
16	59	118	57	114	49	98	17	34	68	136
17	93	7	14	28	56	112	45	90		

P = 181

INDICES

	0	1	2	3	4	5	6	7	8	9
0		0	1	56	2	156	57	15	3	112
1	157	62	58	164	16	32	4	175	113	135
2	158	71	63	53	59	132	165	168	17	48
3	33	99	5	118	176	171	114	26	136	40
4	159	83	72	20	64	88	54	13	60	30
5	133	51	166	97	169	38	18	11	49	36
6	34	125	100	127	6	140	119	102	177	109
7	172	129	115	80	27	8	137	77	41	142
8	160	44	84	121	73	151	21	104	65	145
9	89	179	55	155	14	111	61	163	31	174
10	134	70	52	131	167	47	98	117	170	25
11	39	82	19	87	12	29	50	96	37	10
12	35	124	126	139	101	108	128	79	7	76
13	141	43	120	150	103	144	178	154	110	162
14	173	69	130	46	116	24	81	86	28	95
15	9	123	138	107	78	75	42	149	143	153
16	161	68	45	23	85	94	122	106	74	148
17	152	67	22	93	105	147	66	92	146	91
18	90	0								

POWER RESIDUES

	0	1	2	3	4	5	6	7	8	9
0	1	2	4	8	16	32	64	128	75	150
1	119	57	114	47	94	7	14	28	56	112
2	43	86	172	163	145	109	37	74	148	115
3	49	98	15	30	60	120	59	118	55	110
4	39	78	156	131	81	162	143	105	29	58
5	116	51	102	23	46	92	3	6	12	24
6	48	96	11	22	44	88	176	171	161	141
7	101	21	42	84	168	155	129	77	154	127
8	73	146	111	41	82	164	147	113	45	90
9	180	179	177	173	165	149	117	53	106	31
10	62	124	67	134	87	174	167	153	125	69
11	138	95	9	18	36	72	144	107	33	66
12	132	83	166	151	121	61	122	63	126	71
13	142	103	25	50	100	19	38	76	152	123
14	65	130	79	158	135	89	178	175	169	157
15	133	85	170	159	137	93	5	10	20	40
16	80	160	139	97	13	26	52	104	27	54
17	108	35	70	140	99	17	34	68	136	91
18										

P = 191

INDICES

	0	1	2	3	4	5	6	7	8	9
0		0	44	116	88	50	160	171	132	42
1	94	85	14	112	25	166	176	98	86	1
2	138	97	129	134	58	100	156	158	69	33
3	20	175	30	11	142	31	130	15	45	38
4	182	165	141	8	173	92	178	123	102	152
5	144	24	10	9	12	135	113	117	77	4
6	64	111	29	23	74	162	55	168	186	60
7	75	13	174	143	59	26	89	66	82	62
8	36	84	19	151	185	148	52	149	27	163
9	136	93	32	101	167	51	146	72	6	127
10	188	41	68	122	54	147	53	90	56	114
11	179	131	157	177	161	184	121	154	48	79
12	108	170	155	91	73	150	67	169	118	124
13	16	159	99	172	22	18	40	107	104	105
14	119	49	57	7	28	83	187	78	103	46
15	70	87	133	140	110	35	126	47	106	125
16	80	115	128	164	63	61	5	153	39	34
17	2	43	96	181	3	81	71	120	17	109
18	180	189	137	37	76	65	145	183	21	139
19	95	0								

POWER RESIDUES

	0	1	2	3	4	5	6	7	8	9
0	1	19	170	174	59	166	98	143	43	53
1	52	33	54	71	12	37	130	178	135	82
2	30	188	134	63	51	14	75	88	144	62
3	32	35	92	29	169	155	80	183	39	168
4	136	101	9	171	2	38	149	157	118	141
5	5	95	86	106	104	66	108	142	24	74
6	69	165	79	164	60	185	77	126	102	28
7	150	176	97	124	64	70	184	58	147	119
8	160	175	78	145	81	11	18	151	4	76
9	107	123	45	91	10	190	172	21	17	132
10	25	93	48	148	138	139	158	137	120	179
11	154	61	13	56	109	161	3	57	128	140
12	177	116	103	47	129	159	156	99	162	22
13	36	111	8	152	23	55	90	182	20	189
14	153	42	34	73	50	186	96	105	85	87
15	125	83	49	167	117	122	26	112	27	131
16	6	114	65	89	163	41	15	94	67	127
17	121	7	133	44	72	31	16	113	46	110
18	180	173	40	187	115	84	68	146	100	181
19										

P = 193

INDICES

	0	1	2	3	4	5	6	7	8	9
0		0	34	84	68	1	118	104	102	168
1	35	183	152	141	138	85	136	31	10	145
2	69	188	25	162	186	2	175	60	172	123
3	119	82	170	75	65	105	44	5	179	33
4	103	151	30	24	59	169	4	29	28	16
5	36	115	17	77	94	184	14	37	157	148
6	153	47	116	80	12	142	109	18	99	54
7	139	177	78	91	39	86	21	95	67	167
8	137	144	185	122	64	32	58	15	93	147
9	11	53	38	166	63	146	62	158	50	159
10	70	134	149	107	51	189	111	154	128	160
11	26	89	48	41	71	163	191	117	182	135
12	187	174	81	43	150	3	114	13	46	108
13	176	20	143	57	52	61	133	110	88	190
14	173	113	19	132	112	124	125	100	73	155
15	120	126	55	7	129	83	101	140	9	161
16	171	74	178	23	27	76	156	79	98	90
17	66	121	92	165	49	106	127	40	181	42
18	45	56	87	131	72	6	8	22	97	164
19	180	130	96							

POWER RESIDUES

	0	1	2	3	4	5	6	7	8	9
0	1	5	25	125	46	37	185	153	186	158
1	18	90	64	127	56	87	49	52	67	142
2	131	76	187	163	43	22	110	164	48	47
3	42	17	85	39	2	10	50	57	92	74
4	177	113	179	123	36	180	128	61	112	174
5	98	104	134	91	69	152	181	133	86	44
6	27	135	96	94	84	34	170	78	4	20
7	100	114	184	148	161	33	165	53	72	167
8	63	122	31	155	3	15	75	182	138	111
9	169	73	172	88	54	77	192	188	168	68
10	147	156	8	40	7	35	175	103	129	66
11	137	106	144	141	126	51	62	117	6	30
12	150	171	83	29	145	146	151	176	108	154
13	191	183	143	136	101	119	16	80	14	70
14	157	13	65	132	81	19	95	89	59	102
15	124	41	12	60	107	149	166	58	97	99
16	109	159	23	115	189	173	93	79	9	45
17	32	160	28	140	121	26	130	71	162	38
18	190	178	118	11	55	82	24	120	21	105
19	139	116								

P = 197

INDICES

	0	1	2	3	4	5	6	7	8	9
0		0	1	181	2	89	182	146	3	166
1	90	29	183	25	147	74	4	159	167	154
2	91	131	30	120	184	178	26	151	148	36
3	75	141	5	14	160	39	168	192	155	10
4	92	110	132	78	31	59	121	66	185	96
5	179	144	27	72	152	118	149	139	37	8
6	76	64	142	116	6	114	15	17	161	105
7	40	19	169	45	193	163	156	175	11	107
8	93	136	111	42	133	52	79	21	32	55
9	60	171	122	126	67	47	186	82	97	195
10	180	88	145	165	28	24	73	158	153	130
11	119	177	150	35	140	13	38	191	9	109
12	77	58	65	95	143	71	117	138	7	63
13	115	113	16	104	18	44	162	174	106	135
14	41	51	20	54	170	125	46	81	194	87
15	164	23	157	129	176	34	12	190	108	57
16	94	70	137	62	112	103	43	173	134	50
17	53	124	80	86	22	128	33	189	56	69
18	61	102	172	49	123	85	127	188	68	101
19	48	84	187	100	83	99	98			

POWER RESIDUES

	0	1	2	3	4	5	6	7	8	9
0	1	2	4	8	16	32	64	128	59	118
1	39	78	156	115	33	66	132	67	134	71
2	142	87	174	151	105	13	26	52	104	11
3	22	44	88	176	155	113	29	58	116	35
4	70	140	83	166	135	73	146	95	190	183
5	169	141	85	170	143	89	178	159	121	45
6	90	180	163	129	61	122	47	94	188	179
7	161	125	53	106	15	30	60	120	43	86
8	172	147	97	194	191	185	173	149	101	5
9	10	20	40	80	160	123	49	98	196	195
10	193	189	181	165	133	69	138	79	158	119
11	41	82	164	131	65	130	63	126	55	110
12	23	46	92	184	171	145	93	186	175	153
13	109	21	42	84	168	139	81	162	127	57
14	114	31	62	124	51	102	7	14	28	56
15	112	27	54	108	19	38	76	152	107	17
16	34	68	136	75	150	103	9	18	36	72
17	144	91	182	167	137	77	154	111	25	50
18	100	3	6	12	24	48	96	192	187	177
19	157	117	37	74	148	99				

P = 199

INDICES

	0	1	2	3	4	5	6	7	8	9
0		0	106	1	14	138	107	142	120	2
1	46	189	15	172	50	139	28	123	108	55
2	152	143	97	118	121	78	80	3	156	70
3	47	164	134	190	31	82	16	11	161	173
4	60	167	51	88	5	140	26	76	29	86
5	184	124	186	158	109	129	64	56	176	195
6	153	126	72	144	42	112	98	105	137	119
7	188	49	122	151	117	79	69	133	81	160
8	166	4	75	183	157	63	194	71	111	136
9	48	116	132	165	182	193	135	131	192	191
10	92	93	32	36	94	83	66	33	17	147
11	37	12	170	95	162	58	84	174	103	67
12	61	180	34	168	178	18	52	23	148	89
13	20	38	6	197	13	141	45	171	27	54
14	96	77	155	163	30	10	59	87	25	85
15	185	128	175	125	41	104	187	150	68	159
16	74	62	110	115	181	130	91	35	65	146
17	169	57	102	179	177	22	19	196	44	53
18	154	9	24	127	40	149	73	114	90	145
19	101	21	43	8	39	113	100	7	99	

POWER RESIDUES

	0	1	2	3	4	5	6	7	8	9
0	1	3	9	27	81	44	132	197	193	181
1	145	37	111	134	4	12	36	108	125	176
2	130	191	175	127	182	148	46	138	16	48
3	144	34	102	107	122	167	103	110	131	194
4	184	154	64	192	178	136	10	30	90	71
5	14	42	126	179	139	19	57	171	115	146
6	40	120	161	85	56	168	106	119	158	76
7	29	87	62	186	160	82	47	141	25	75
8	26	78	35	105	116	149	49	147	43	129
9	188	166	100	101	104	113	140	22	66	198
10	196	190	172	118	155	67	2	6	18	54
11	162	88	65	195	187	163	91	74	23	69
12	8	24	72	17	51	153	61	183	151	55
13	165	97	92	77	32	96	89	68	5	15
14	45	135	7	21	63	189	169	109	128	185
15	157	73	20	60	180	142	28	84	53	159
16	79	38	114	143	31	93	80	41	123	170
17	112	137	13	39	117	152	58	174	124	173
18	121	164	94	83	50	150	52	156	70	11
19	33	99	98	95	86	59	177	133		

P = 211

INDICES

	0	1	2	3	4	5	6	7	8	9
0		0	1	43	2	132	44	139	3	86
1	133	162	45	144	140	175	4	199	87	154
2	134	182	163	21	46	54	145	129	141	179
3	176	115	5	205	200	61	88	118	155	187
4	135	17	183	80	164	8	22	124	47	68
5	55	32	146	208	130	84	142	197	180	52
6	177	203	116	15	6	66	206	195	201	64
7	62	168	89	170	119	97	156	91	188	102
8	136	172	18	112	184	121	81	12	165	99
9	9	73	23	158	125	76	48	93	69	38
10	56	190	33	26	147	104	209	42	131	138
11	85	161	143	174	198	153	181	20	53	128
12	178	114	204	60	117	186	16	79	7	123
13	67	31	207	83	196	51	202	14	65	194
14	63	167	169	96	90	101	171	111	120	11
15	98	72	157	75	92	37	189	25	103	41
16	137	160	173	152	19	127	113	59	185	78
17	122	30	82	50	13	193	166	95	100	110
18	10	71	74	36	24	40	159	151	126	58
19	77	29	49	192	94	109	70	35	39	150
20	57	28	191	108	34	149	27	107	148	106
21	105	0								

POWER RESIDUES

	0	1	2	3	4	5	6	7	8	9
0	1	2	4	8	16	32	64	128	45	90
1	180	149	87	174	137	63	126	41	82	164
2	117	23	46	92	184	157	103	206	201	191
3	171	131	51	102	204	197	183	155	99	198
4	185	159	107	3	6	12	24	48	96	192
5	173	135	59	118	25	50	100	200	189	167
6	123	35	70	140	69	138	65	130	49	98
7	196	181	151	91	182	153	95	190	169	127
8	43	86	172	133	55	110	9	18	36	72
9	144	77	154	97	194	177	143	75	150	89
10	178	145	79	158	105	210	209	207	203	195
11	179	147	83	166	121	31	62	124	37	74
12	148	85	170	129	47	94	188	165	119	27
13	54	108	5	10	20	40	80	160	109	7
14	14	28	56	112	13	26	52	104	208	205
15	199	187	163	115	19	38	76	152	93	186
16	161	111	11	22	44	88	176	141	71	142
17	73	146	81	162	113	15	30	60	120	29
18	58	116	21	42	84	168	125	39	78	156
19	101	202	193	175	139	67	134	57	114	17
20	34	68	136	61	122	33	66	132	53	106
21										

P = 223

INDICES

	0	1	2	3	4	5	6	7	8	9
0		0	180	1	138	89	181	210	96	2
1	47	107	139	147	168	90	54	144	182	172
2	5	211	65	163	97	178	105	3	126	128
3	48	82	12	108	102	77	140	152	130	148
4	185	204	169	118	23	91	121	50	55	198
5	136	145	63	80	183	196	84	173	86	9
6	6	73	40	212	192	14	66	175	60	164
7	35	157	98	26	110	179	88	95	106	167
8	143	4	162	104	127	11	76	129	203	22
9	49	135	79	83	8	39	13	59	156	109
10	94	142	103	75	21	78	38	155	141	20
11	154	153	42	43	131	30	44	149	189	132
12	186	214	31	205	220	45	170	124	150	119
13	194	190	24	160	133	92	18	187	122	16
14	215	51	115	32	56	217	206	199	68	221
15	137	209	46	146	53	171	64	177	125	81
16	101	151	184	117	120	197	62	195	85	72
17	191	174	34	25	87	166	161	10	202	134
18	7	58	93	74	37	19	41	29	188	213
19	219	123	193	159	17	15	114	216	67	208
20	52	176	100	116	61	71	33	165	201	57
21	36	28	218	158	113	207	99	70	200	27
22	112	69	111							

POWER RESIDUES

	0	1	2	3	4	5	6	7	8	9
0	1	3	9	27	81	20	60	180	94	59
1	177	85	32	96	65	195	139	194	136	185
2	109	104	89	44	132	173	73	219	211	187
3	115	122	143	206	172	70	210	184	106	95
4	62	186	112	113	116	125	152	10	30	90
5	47	141	200	154	16	48	144	209	181	97
6	68	204	166	52	156	22	66	198	148	221
7	217	205	169	61	183	103	86	35	105	92
8	53	159	31	93	56	168	58	174	76	5
9	15	45	135	182	100	77	8	24	72	216
10	202	160	34	102	83	26	78	11	33	99
11	74	222	220	214	196	142	203	163	43	129
12	164	46	138	191	127	158	28	84	29	87
13	38	114	119	134	179	91	50	150	4	12
14	36	108	101	80	17	51	153	13	39	117
15	128	161	37	111	110	107	98	71	213	193
16	133	176	82	23	69	207	175	79	14	42
17	126	155	19	57	171	67	201	157	25	75
18	2	6	18	54	162	40	120	137	188	118
19	131	170	64	192	130	167	55	165	49	147
20	218	208	178	88	41	123	146	215	199	151
21	7	21	63	189	121	140	197	145	212	190
22	124	149								

P = 227

INDICES

	0	1	2	3	4	5	6	7	8	9
0		0	1	46	2	11	47	154	3	92
1	12	28	48	61	155	57	4	99	93	178
2	13	200	29	34	49	22	62	138	156	8
3	58	197	5	74	100	165	94	77	179	107
4	14	131	201	150	30	103	35	218	50	82
5	23	145	63	168	139	39	157	224	9	90
6	59	97	198	20	6	72	75	129	101	80
7	166	222	95	70	78	68	180	182	108	192
8	15	184	132	209	202	110	151	54	31	194
9	104	215	36	17	219	189	51	186	83	120
10	24	134	146	86	64	211	169	173	140	204
11	40	123	158	112	225	45	10	153	91	27
12	60	56	98	177	199	33	21	137	7	196
13	73	164	76	106	130	149	102	217	81	144
14	167	38	223	89	96	19	71	128	79	221
15	69	67	181	191	183	208	109	53	193	214
16	16	188	185	119	133	85	210	172	203	122
17	111	44	152	26	55	176	32	136	195	163
18	105	148	216	143	37	88	18	127	220	66
19	190	207	52	213	187	118	84	171	121	43
20	25	175	135	162	147	142	87	126	65	206
21	212	117	170	42	174	161	141	125	205	116
22	41	160	124	115	159	114	113			

POWER RESIDUES

	0	1	2	3	4	5	6	7	8	9
0	1	2	4	8	16	32	64	128	29	58
1	116	5	10	20	40	80	160	93	186	145
2	63	126	25	50	100	200	173	119	11	22
3	44	88	176	125	23	46	92	184	141	55
4	110	220	213	199	171	115	3	6	12	24
5	48	96	192	157	87	174	121	15	30	60
6	120	13	26	52	104	208	189	151	75	150
7	73	146	65	130	33	66	132	37	74	148
8	69	138	49	98	196	165	103	206	185	143
9	59	118	9	18	36	72	144	61	122	17
10	34	68	136	45	90	180	133	39	78	156
11	85	170	113	226	225	223	219	211	195	163
12	99	198	169	111	222	217	207	187	147	67
13	134	41	82	164	101	202	177	127	27	54
14	108	216	205	183	139	51	102	204	181	135
15	43	86	172	117	7	14	28	56	112	224
16	221	215	203	179	131	35	70	140	53	106
17	212	197	167	107	214	201	175	123	19	38
18	76	152	77	154	81	162	97	194	161	95
19	190	153	79	158	89	178	129	31	62	124
20	21	42	84	168	109	218	209	191	155	83
21	166	105	210	193	159	91	182	137	47	94
22	188	149	71	142	57	114				

P = 229

INDICES

	0	1	2	3	4	5	6	7	8	9
0		0	21	208	42	98	1	107	63	188
1	119	162	22	117	128	78	84	60	209	92
2	140	87	183	109	43	196	138	168	149	145
3	99	29	105	142	81	205	2	220	113	97
4	161	59	108	144	204	58	130	131	64	214
5	217	40	159	132	189	32	170	72	166	65
6	120	36	50	67	126	215	163	55	102	89
7	226	218	23	25	13	176	134	41	118	83
8	182	148	80	160	129	158	165	125	225	133
9	79	224	151	9	152	190	85	70	7	122
10	10	33	61	202	180	185	153	171	210	27
11	53	200	191	73	93	207	187	77	86	167
12	141	96	57	39	71	66	88	175	147	124
13	8	121	184	199	76	38	123	37	110	193
14	19	111	11	51	44	15	46	194	34	68
15	197	4	155	20	62	127	139	137	104	112
16	203	216	169	49	101	12	181	164	150	6
17	179	52	186	56	146	75	18	45	154	103
18	100	178	17	16	172	90	30	222	173	47
19	211	227	106	116	91	195	28	219	143	213
20	31	35	54	24	82	157	223	69	201	26
21	206	95	174	198	192	14	3	136	48	5
22	74	177	221	115	212	156	94	135	114	

POWER RESIDUES

	0	1	2	3	4	5	6	7	8	9
0	1	6	36	216	151	219	169	98	130	93
1	100	142	165	74	215	145	183	182	176	140
2	153	2	12	72	203	73	209	109	196	31
3	186	200	55	101	148	201	61	137	135	123
4	51	77	4	24	144	177	146	189	218	163
5	62	143	171	110	202	67	173	122	45	41
6	17	102	154	8	48	59	125	63	149	207
7	97	124	57	113	220	175	134	117	15	90
8	82	34	204	79	16	96	118	21	126	69
9	185	194	19	114	226	211	121	39	5	30
10	180	164	68	179	158	32	192	7	42	23
11	138	141	159	38	228	223	193	13	78	10
12	60	131	99	136	129	87	64	155	14	84
13	46	47	53	89	76	227	217	157	26	156
14	20	120	33	198	43	29	174	128	81	28
15	168	92	94	106	178	152	225	205	85	52
16	83	40	11	66	167	86	58	119	27	162
17	56	107	184	188	212	127	75	221	181	170
18	104	166	80	22	132	105	172	116	9	54
19	95	112	214	139	147	195	25	150	213	133
20	111	208	103	160	44	35	210	115	3	18
21	108	190	224	199	49	65	161	50	71	197
22	37	222	187	206	91	88	70	191		

P = 233

INDICES

	0	1	2	3	4	5	6	7	8	9
0		0	72	1	144	165	73	222	216	2
1	5	197	145	158	62	166	56	103	74	136
2	77	223	37	112	217	98	230	3	134	132
3	6	182	128	198	175	155	146	8	208	159
4	149	85	63	25	109	167	184	139	57	212
5	170	104	70	195	75	130	206	137	204	89
6	78	53	22	224	200	91	38	11	15	113
7	227	192	218	177	80	99	48	187	231	143
8	221	4	157	55	135	36	97	133	181	174
9	7	148	24	183	211	69	129	203	52	199
10	10	226	176	47	142	156	35	180	147	210
11	202	9	46	34	209	45	44	160	161	93
12	150	162	125	86	94	31	64	151	40	26
13	163	60	110	126	83	168	87	13	185	95
14	67	140	32	123	58	65	17	213	152	19
15	171	41	120	105	27	115	71	164	215	196
16	61	102	76	111	229	131	127	154	207	84
17	108	138	169	194	205	88	21	90	14	191
18	79	186	220	54	96	173	23	68	51	225
19	141	179	201	33	43	92	124	30	39	59
20	82	12	66	122	16	18	119	114	214	101
21	228	153	107	193	20	190	219	172	50	178
22	42	29	81	121	118	100	106	189	49	28
23	117	188	116							

POWER RESIDUES

	0	1	2	3	4	5	6	7	8	9
0	1	3	9	27	81	10	30	90	37	111
1	100	67	201	137	178	68	204	146	205	149
2	214	176	62	186	92	43	129	154	229	221
3	197	125	142	193	113	106	85	22	66	198
4	128	151	220	194	116	115	112	103	76	228
5	218	188	98	61	183	83	16	48	144	199
6	131	160	14	42	126	145	202	140	187	95
7	52	156	2	6	18	54	162	20	60	180
8	74	222	200	134	169	41	123	136	175	59
9	177	65	195	119	124	139	184	86	25	75
10	225	209	161	17	51	153	226	212	170	44
11	132	163	23	69	207	155	232	230	224	206
12	152	223	203	143	196	122	133	166	32	96
13	55	165	29	87	28	84	19	57	171	47
14	141	190	104	79	4	12	36	108	91	40
15	120	127	148	211	167	35	105	82	13	39
16	117	118	121	130	157	5	15	45	135	172
17	50	150	217	185	89	34	102	73	219	191
18	107	88	31	93	46	138	181	77	231	227
19	215	179	71	213	173	53	159	11	33	99
20	64	192	110	97	58	174	56	168	38	114
21	109	94	49	147	208	158	8	24	72	216
22	182	80	7	21	63	189	101	70	210	164
23	26	78								

P = 239

INDICES

	0	1	2	3	4	5	6	7	8	9
0		0	66	74	132	138	140	1	198	148
1	204	4	206	43	67	212	26	52	214	155
2	32	75	70	63	34	38	109	222	133	160
3	40	188	92	78	118	139	42	31	221	117
4	98	99	141	15	136	48	129	113	100	2
5	104	126	175	209	50	142	199	229	226	61
6	106	6	16	149	158	181	144	28	184	137
7	205	154	108	77	97	112	49	5	183	111
8	164	58	165	130	207	190	81	234	202	59
9	114	44	195	24	179	55	166	101	68	152
10	170	84	192	131	3	213	37	91	116	128
11	208	105	27	96	57	201	54	191	127	53
12	172	8	72	173	82	176	215	146	224	89
13	9	235	210	156	94	122	12	73	203	51
14	33	187	220	47	174	60	143	76	163	233
15	178	83	115	200	71	88	11	46	177	45
16	230	64	124	168	231	216	196	227	35	86
17	18	65	147	25	62	39	30	135	125	225
18	180	107	110	80	23	169	90	56	7	223
19	121	219	232	10	167	17	134	22	218	217
20	236	102	150	161	20	237	197	211	69	159
21	41	14	103	228	157	153	182	189	194	151
22	36	95	171	145	93	186	162	87	123	85
23	29	79	120	21	19	13	193	185	119	

POWER RESIDUES

	0	1	2	3	4	5	6	7	8	9
0	1	7	49	104	11	77	61	188	121	130
1	193	156	136	235	211	43	62	195	170	234
2	204	233	197	184	93	173	16	112	67	230
3	176	37	20	140	24	168	220	106	25	175
4	30	210	36	13	91	159	157	143	45	76
5	54	139	17	119	116	95	187	114	81	89
6	145	59	174	23	161	171	2	14	98	208
7	22	154	122	137	3	21	147	73	33	231
8	183	86	124	151	101	229	169	227	155	129
9	186	107	32	224	134	221	113	74	40	41
10	48	97	201	212	50	111	60	181	72	26
11	182	79	75	47	90	152	108	39	34	238
12	232	190	135	228	162	178	51	118	109	46
13	83	103	4	28	196	177	44	69	5	35
14	6	42	55	146	66	223	127	172	9	63
15	202	219	99	215	71	19	133	214	64	209
16	29	203	226	148	80	82	96	194	163	185
17	100	222	120	123	144	52	125	158	150	94
18	180	65	216	78	68	237	225	141	31	217
19	85	117	102	236	218	92	166	206	8	56
20	153	115	88	138	10	70	12	84	110	53
21	132	207	15	105	18	126	165	199	198	191
22	142	38	27	189	128	179	58	167	213	57
23	160	164	192	149	87	131	200	205		

P = 241

INDICES

	0	1	2	3	4	5	6	7	8	9
0		0	190	182	140	138	132	1	90	124
1	88	25	82	47	191	80	40	111	74	85
2	38	183	215	57	32	36	237	66	141	154
3	30	151	230	207	61	139	24	73	35	229
4	228	6	133	219	165	22	7	114	222	2
5	226	53	187	134	16	163	91	27	104	118
6	220	42	101	125	180	185	157	166	11	239
7	89	79	214	153	23	218	225	26	179	78
8	178	8	196	148	83	9	169	96	115	55
9	212	48	197	93	64	223	172	44	192	149
10	176	159	3	69	137	81	84	236	206	227
11	113	15	41	10	217	195	54	171	68	112
12	170	50	232	188	51	174	75	97	130	161
13	135	233	107	86	116	204	201	17	189	123
14	39	56	29	72	164	52	103	184	213	77
15	168	92	175	235	216	49	129	203	28	76
16	128	58	198	59	146	105	98	143	33	94
17	199	209	119	131	46	37	65	60	5	221
18	162	100	238	224	147	211	43	136	14	67
19	173	106	122	102	234	127	142	45	99	13
20	126	108	109	155	193	144	19	181	87	110
21	31	150	34	21	186	117	156	152	177	95
22	63	158	205	194	231	160	200	71	167	202
23	145	208	4	210	121	12	18	20	62	70
24	120	0								

POWER RESIDUES

	0	1	2	3	4	5	6	7	8	9
0	1	7	49	102	232	178	41	46	81	85
1	113	68	235	199	188	111	54	137	236	206
2	237	213	45	74	36	11	77	57	158	142
3	30	210	24	168	212	38	25	175	20	140
4	16	112	61	186	97	197	174	13	91	155
5	121	124	145	51	116	89	141	23	161	163
6	177	34	238	220	94	176	27	189	118	103
7	239	227	143	37	18	126	159	149	79	71
8	15	105	12	84	106	19	133	208	10	70
9	8	56	151	93	169	219	87	127	166	198
10	181	62	193	146	58	165	191	132	201	202
11	209	17	119	110	47	88	134	215	59	172
12	240	234	192	139	9	63	200	195	160	156
13	128	173	6	42	53	130	187	104	5	35
14	4	28	196	167	205	230	164	184	83	99
15	211	31	217	73	29	203	216	66	221	101
16	225	129	180	55	144	44	67	228	150	86
17	120	117	96	190	125	152	100	218	80	78
18	64	207	3	21	147	65	214	52	123	138
19	2	14	98	204	223	115	82	92	162	170
20	226	136	229	157	135	222	108	33	231	171
21	233	185	90	148	72	22	154	114	75	43
22	60	179	48	95	183	76	50	109	40	39
23	32	224	122	131	194	153	107	26	182	69
24										

P = 251

INDICES

	0	1	2	3	4	5	6	7	8	9
0		0	235	16	220	130	1	248	205	32
1	115	211	236	182	233	146	190	74	17	163
2	100	14	196	24	221	10	167	48	218	83
3	131	186	175	227	59	128	2	207	148	198
4	85	4	249	247	181	162	9	185	206	246
5	245	90	152	103	33	91	203	179	68	51
6	116	153	171	30	160	62	212	104	44	40
7	113	7	237	34	192	26	133	209	183	92
8	70	64	239	94	234	204	232	99	166	174
9	147	180	244	202	170	43	191	69	231	243
10	230	136	75	52	137	144	88	97	18	117
11	76	223	188	150	164	154	53	214	36	72
12	101	172	138	20	156	140	15	31	145	13
13	47	226	197	161	89	178	29	39	25	63
14	98	201	242	143	222	213	19	12	177	200
15	11	105	118	106	194	66	168	45	77	119
16	55	22	49	41	224	107	79	109	219	114
17	189	195	217	58	84	8	151	67	159	112
18	132	238	165	169	229	87	187	35	155	46
19	28	241	176	193	54	78	216	158	228	27
20	215	120	121	81	60	134	37	56	122	124
21	129	210	73	23	82	127	3	184	102	50
22	61	6	208	93	173	42	135	96	149	71
23	139	225	38	142	199	65	21	108	57	111
24	86	240	157	80	123	126	5	95	141	110
25	125	0								

POWER RESIDUES

	0	1	2	3	4	5	6	7	8	9
0	1	6	36	216	41	246	221	71	175	46
1	25	150	147	129	21	126	3	18	108	146
2	123	236	161	213	23	138	75	199	190	136
3	63	127	9	54	73	187	118	206	232	137
4	69	163	225	95	68	157	189	130	27	162
5	219	59	103	116	194	160	207	238	173	34
6	204	220	65	139	81	235	155	177	58	97
7	80	229	119	212	17	102	110	158	195	166
8	243	203	214	29	174	40	240	185	106	134
9	51	55	79	223	83	247	227	107	140	87
10	20	120	218	53	67	151	153	165	237	167
11	249	239	179	70	169	10	60	109	152	159
12	201	202	208	244	209	250	245	215	35	210
13	5	30	180	76	205	226	101	104	122	230
14	125	248	233	143	105	128	15	90	38	228
15	113	176	52	61	115	188	124	242	197	178
16	64	133	45	19	114	182	88	26	156	183
17	94	62	121	224	89	32	192	148	135	57
18	91	44	13	78	217	47	31	186	112	170
19	16	96	74	193	154	171	22	132	39	234
20	149	141	93	56	85	8	48	37	222	77
21	211	11	66	145	117	200	196	172	28	168
22	4	24	144	111	164	231	131	33	198	184
23	100	98	86	14	84	2	12	72	181	82
24	241	191	142	99	92	50	49	43	7	42
25										

P = 257

INDICES

	0	1	2	3	4	5	6	7	8	9
0		0	48	1	96	55	49	85	144	2
1	103	196	97	106	133	56	192	120	50	125
2	151	86	244	28	145	110	154	3	181	94
3	104	242	240	197	168	140	98	219	173	107
4	199	19	134	207	36	57	76	61	193	170
5	158	121	202	89	51	251	229	126	142	118
6	152	138	34	87	32	161	245	100	216	29
7	188	163	146	44	11	111	221	25	155	22
8	247	4	67	15	182	175	255	95	84	102
9	105	191	124	243	109	180	241	167	218	198
10	206	75	169	201	250	141	137	31	99	187
11	43	220	21	66	174	83	190	108	166	205
12	200	136	186	20	82	165	135	81	80	208
13	209	7	37	210	148	58	8	72	77	38
14	236	62	211	46	194	149	92	171	59	227
15	159	9	13	122	73	41	203	78	70	90
16	39	113	52	237	115	252	63	233	230	212
17	223	127	47	54	143	195	132	119	150	27
18	153	93	239	139	172	18	35	60	157	88
19	228	117	33	160	215	162	10	24	246	14
20	254	101	123	179	217	74	249	30	42	65
21	189	204	185	164	79	6	147	71	235	45
22	91	226	12	40	69	112	114	232	222	53
23	131	26	238	17	156	116	214	23	253	178
24	248	64	184	5	234	225	68	231	130	16
25	213	177	183	224	129	176	128			

POWER RESIDUES

	0	1	2	3	4	5	6	7	8	9
0	1	3	9	27	81	243	215	131	136	151
1	196	74	222	152	199	83	249	233	185	41
2	123	112	79	237	197	77	231	179	23	69
3	207	107	64	192	62	186	44	132	139	160
4	223	155	208	110	73	219	143	172	2	6
5	18	54	162	229	173	5	15	45	135	148
6	187	47	141	166	241	209	113	82	246	224
7	158	217	137	154	205	101	46	138	157	214
8	128	127	124	115	88	7	21	63	189	53
9	159	220	146	181	29	87	4	12	36	108
10	67	201	89	10	30	90	13	39	117	94
11	25	75	225	161	226	164	235	191	59	177
12	17	51	153	202	92	19	57	171	256	254
13	248	230	176	14	42	126	121	106	61	183
14	35	105	58	174	8	24	72	216	134	145
15	178	20	60	180	26	78	234	188	50	150
16	193	65	195	71	213	125	118	97	34	102
17	49	147	184	38	114	85	255	251	239	203
18	95	28	84	252	242	212	122	109	70	210
19	116	91	16	48	144	175	11	33	99	40
20	120	103	52	156	211	119	100	43	129	130
21	133	142	169	250	236	194	68	204	98	37
22	111	76	228	170	253	245	221	149	190	56
23	168	247	227	167	244	218	140	163	232	182
24	32	96	31	93	22	66	198	80	240	206
25	104	55	165	238	200	86				

P = 263

INDICES

	0	1	2	3	4	5	6	7	8	9
0		0	190	50	118	1	240	79	46	100
1	191	166	168	62	7	51	236	126	28	43
2	119	129	94	156	96	2	252	150	197	221
3	241	136	164	216	54	80	218	170	233	112
4	47	17	57	154	22	101	84	65	24	158
5	192	176	180	189	78	167	125	93	149	163
6	169	56	64	179	92	63	144	145	244	206
7	8	11	146	103	98	52	161	245	40	71
8	237	200	207	88	247	127	82	9	212	68
9	29	141	12	186	255	44	214	147	86	4
10	120	259	104	34	108	130	117	99	6	42
11	95	220	53	111	21	157	77	162	91	205
12	97	70	246	67	254	3	107	41	20	204
13	253	203	72	122	73	151	172	238	134	123
14	198	115	201	228	74	222	31	208	26	152
15	242	184	89	226	173	137	230	248	261	239
16	165	235	128	251	135	217	16	83	175	124
17	55	143	10	160	199	81	140	213	258	116
18	219	76	69	106	202	171	114	30	183	229
19	234	15	142	139	75	113	14	13	194	223
20	48	195	187	38	32	18	224	256	36	209
21	58	49	45	61	27	155	196	215	232	153
22	23	188	148	178	243	102	39	87	211	185
23	85	33	5	110	90	66	19	121	133	227
24	25	225	260	250	174	159	257	105	182	138
25	193	37	35	60	231	177	210	109	132	249
26	181	59	131							

POWER RESIDUES

	0	1	2	3	4	5	6	7	8	9
0	1	5	25	125	99	232	108	14	70	87
1	172	71	92	197	196	191	166	41	205	236
2	128	114	44	220	48	240	148	214	18	90
3	187	146	204	231	103	252	208	251	203	226
4	78	127	109	19	95	212	8	40	200	211
5	3	15	75	112	34	170	61	42	210	261
6	253	213	13	65	62	47	235	123	89	182
7	121	79	132	134	144	194	181	116	54	7
8	35	175	86	167	46	230	98	227	83	152
9	234	118	64	57	22	110	24	120	74	107
10	9	45	225	73	102	247	183	126	104	257
11	233	113	39	195	186	141	179	106	4	20
12	100	237	133	139	169	56	17	85	162	21
13	105	262	258	238	138	164	31	155	249	193
14	176	91	192	171	66	67	72	97	222	58
15	27	135	149	219	43	215	23	115	49	245
16	173	76	117	59	32	160	11	55	12	60
17	37	185	136	154	244	168	51	255	223	63
18	52	260	248	188	151	229	93	202	221	53
19	2	10	50	250	198	201	216	28	140	174
20	81	142	184	131	129	119	69	82	147	209
21	256	228	88	177	96	217	33	165	36	180
22	111	29	145	199	206	241	153	239	143	189
23	156	254	218	38	190	161	16	80	137	159
24	6	30	150	224	68	77	122	84	157	259
25	243	163	26	130	124	94	207	246	178	101
26	242	158								

P = 269

INDICES

	0	1	2	3	4	5	6	7	8	9
0		0	1	109	2	208	110	19	3	218
1	209	230	111	142	20	49	4	105	219	223
2	210	128	231	176	112	148	143	59	21	187
3	50	259	5	71	106	227	220	56	224	251
4	211	200	129	254	232	158	177	32	113	38
5	149	214	144	196	60	170	22	64	188	203
6	51	12	260	237	6	82	72	132	107	17
7	228	47	221	174	57	257	225	249	252	30
8	212	168	201	235	130	45	255	28	233	26
9	159	161	178	100	33	163	114	122	39	180
10	150	265	215	102	145	68	197	35	61	79
11	171	165	23	119	65	116	189	92	204	124
12	52	192	13	41	261	88	238	182	7	95
13	83	152	73	242	133	267	108	207	18	217
14	229	141	48	104	222	127	175	147	58	186
15	258	70	226	55	250	199	253	157	31	37
16	213	195	169	63	202	11	236	81	131	16
17	46	173	256	248	29	167	234	44	27	25
18	160	99	162	121	179	264	101	67	34	78
19	164	118	115	91	123	191	40	87	181	94
20	151	241	266	206	216	140	103	126	146	185
21	69	54	198	156	36	194	62	10	80	15
22	172	247	166	43	24	98	120	263	66	77
23	117	90	190	86	93	240	205	139	125	184
24	53	155	193	9	14	246	42	97	262	76
25	89	85	239	138	183	154	8	245	96	75
26	84	137	153	244	74	136	243	135	134	

POWER RESIDUES

	0	1	2	3	4	5	6	7	8	9
0	1	2	4	8	16	32	64	128	256	243
1	217	165	61	122	244	219	169	69	138	7
2	14	28	56	112	224	179	89	178	87	174
3	79	158	47	94	188	107	214	159	49	98
4	196	123	246	223	177	85	170	71	142	15
5	30	60	120	240	211	153	37	74	148	27
6	54	108	216	163	57	114	228	187	105	210
7	151	33	66	132	264	259	249	229	189	109
8	218	167	65	130	260	251	233	197	125	250
9	231	193	117	234	199	129	258	247	225	181
10	93	186	103	206	143	17	34	68	136	3
11	6	12	24	48	96	192	115	230	191	113
12	226	183	97	194	119	238	207	145	21	42
13	84	168	67	134	268	267	265	261	253	237
14	205	141	13	26	52	104	208	147	25	50
15	100	200	131	262	255	241	213	157	45	90
16	180	91	182	95	190	111	222	175	81	162
17	55	110	220	171	73	146	23	46	92	184
18	99	198	127	254	239	209	149	29	58	116
19	232	195	121	242	215	161	53	106	212	155
20	41	82	164	59	118	236	203	137	5	10
21	20	40	80	160	51	102	204	139	9	18
22	36	72	144	19	38	76	152	35	70	140
23	11	22	44	88	176	83	166	63	126	252
24	235	201	133	266	263	257	245	221	173	77
25	154	39	78	156	43	86	172	75	150	31
26	62	124	248	227	185	101	202	135		

P = 271

INDICES

	0	1	2	3	4	5	6	7	8	9
0		0	154	117	38	170	1	142	192	234
1	54	238	155	165	26	17	76	194	118	9
2	208	259	122	15	39	70	49	81	180	225
3	171	228	230	85	78	42	2	148	163	12
4	92	204	143	29	6	134	169	237	193	14
5	224	41	203	236	235	138	64	126	109	139
6	55	178	112	106	114	65	239	214	232	132
7	196	127	156	221	32	187	47	110	166	96
8	246	198	88	140	27	94	183	72	160	56
9	18	37	53	75	121	179	77	91	168	202
10	108	113	195	46	87	159	120	107	119	217
11	22	265	218	115	10	185	263	129	23	66
12	209	206	62	51	266	240	260	175	268	146
13	219	215	123	151	98	251	116	233	16	258
14	80	84	11	133	40	125	105	131	186	197
15	71	74	201	158	264	128	50	145	250	83
16	130	157	82	254	242	255	24	222	181	60
17	248	243	67	33	226	212	44	256	210	188
18	172	153	191	25	207	48	229	162	5	223
19	63	111	231	31	245	182	52	167	86	21
20	262	61	267	97	79	104	200	249	241	247
21	43	190	4	244	261	199	3	100	101	68
22	176	89	149	58	102	34	269	141	164	8
23	69	227	147	28	13	137	177	213	220	95
24	93	36	90	45	216	184	205	174	150	257
25	124	73	144	253	59	211	152	161	30	20
26	103	189	99	57	7	136	35	173	252	19
27	135	0								

POWER RESIDUES

	0	1	2	3	4	5	6	7	8	9
0	1	6	36	216	212	188	44	264	229	19
1	114	142	39	234	49	23	138	15	90	269
2	259	199	110	118	166	183	14	84	233	43
3	258	193	74	173	225	266	241	91	4	24
4	144	51	35	210	176	243	103	76	185	26
5	156	123	196	92	10	60	89	263	223	254
6	169	201	122	190	56	65	119	172	219	230
7	25	150	87	251	151	93	16	96	34	204
8	140	27	162	159	141	33	198	104	82	221
9	242	97	40	240	85	239	79	203	134	262
10	217	218	224	260	205	146	63	107	100	58
11	77	191	62	101	64	113	136	3	18	108
12	106	94	22	132	250	145	57	71	155	117
13	160	147	69	143	45	270	265	235	55	59
14	83	227	7	42	252	157	129	232	37	222
15	248	133	256	181	2	12	72	161	153	105
16	88	257	187	38	228	13	78	197	98	46
17	5	30	180	267	247	127	220	236	61	95
18	28	168	195	86	245	115	148	75	179	261
19	211	182	8	48	17	102	70	149	81	215
20	206	152	99	52	41	246	121	184	20	120
21	178	255	175	237	67	131	244	109	112	130
22	238	73	167	189	50	29	174	231	31	186
23	32	192	68	137	9	54	53	47	11	66
24	125	208	164	171	213	194	80	209	170	207
25	158	135	268	253	163	165	177	249	139	21
26	126	214	200	116	154	111	124	202	128	226
27										

P = 277

INDICES

	0	1	2	3	4	5	6	7	8	9
0		0	147	188	18	1	59	22	165	100
1	148	7	206	222	169	189	36	103	247	252
2	19	210	154	208	77	2	93	12	40	74
3	60	47	183	195	250	23	118	87	123	134
4	166	126	81	55	25	101	79	218	224	44
5	149	15	240	67	159	8	187	164	221	246
6	207	39	194	122	54	223	66	220	121	120
7	170	4	265	171	234	190	270	29	5	116
8	37	200	273	266	228	104	202	262	172	98
9	248	244	226	235	89	253	95	257	191	107
10	20	181	162	271	111	211	214	113	30	237
11	155	275	58	6	35	209	92	46	117	125
12	78	14	186	38	65	3	269	199	201	243
13	94	180	213	274	91	13	268	179	267	129
14	41	130	151	229	136	75	42	232	105	63
15	61	131	141	203	176	48	152	216	263	255
16	184	230	71	173	144	196	137	17	99	168
17	251	76	73	249	133	24	43	158	245	53
18	119	233	115	227	97	88	106	110	236	34
19	124	64	242	90	128	135	62	175	254	143
20	167	132	52	96	33	127	142	32	258	259
21	82	204	85	192	260	56	177	69	108	83
22	26	49	146	21	205	102	153	11	182	86
23	80	217	239	163	193	219	264	28	272	261
24	225	256	161	112	57	45	185	198	212	178
25	150	231	140	215	70	16	72	157	114	109
26	241	174	51	31	84	68	145	10	238	27
27	160	197	139	156	50	9	138			

POWER RESIDUES

	0	1	2	3	4	5	6	7	8	9
0	1	5	25	125	71	78	113	11	55	275
1	267	227	27	135	121	51	255	167	4	20
2	100	223	7	35	175	44	220	269	237	77
3	108	263	207	204	189	114	16	80	123	61
4	28	140	146	176	49	245	117	31	155	221
5	274	262	202	179	64	43	215	244	112	6
6	30	150	196	149	191	124	66	53	265	217
7	254	162	256	172	29	145	171	24	120	46
8	230	42	210	219	264	212	229	37	185	94
9	193	134	116	26	130	96	203	184	89	168
10	9	45	225	17	85	148	186	99	218	259
11	187	104	243	107	258	182	79	118	36	180
12	69	68	63	38	190	119	41	205	194	139
13	141	151	201	174	39	195	144	166	276	272
14	252	152	206	199	164	266	222	2	10	50
15	250	142	156	226	22	110	273	257	177	54
16	270	242	102	233	57	8	40	200	169	14
17	70	73	88	163	261	197	154	216	249	137
18	131	101	228	32	160	246	122	56	3	15
19	75	98	213	234	62	33	165	271	247	127
20	81	128	86	153	211	224	12	60	23	115
21	21	105	248	132	106	253	157	231	47	235
22	67	58	13	65	48	240	92	183	84	143
23	161	251	147	181	74	93	188	109	268	232
24	52	260	192	129	91	178	59	18	90	173
25	34	170	19	95	198	159	241	97	208	209
26	214	239	87	158	236	72	83	138	136	126
27	76	103	238	82	133	111				

P = 281

INDICES

	0	1	2	3	4	5	6	7	8	9
0		0	204	1	128	186	205	182	52	2
1	110	253	129	9	106	187	256	166	206	221
2	34	183	177	197	53	92	213	3	30	172
3	111	62	180	254	90	88	130	135	145	10
4	238	23	107	132	101	188	121	75	257	84
5	16	167	137	210	207	159	234	222	96	200
6	35	147	266	184	104	195	178	21	14	198
7	12	153	54	125	59	93	69	155	214	240
8	162	4	227	39	31	72	56	173	25	245
9	112	191	45	63	279	127	181	109	8	255
10	220	176	91	29	61	89	134	237	131	120
11	83	136	158	95	146	103	20	11	124	68
12	239	226	71	24	190	278	108	219	28	133
13	119	157	102	123	225	189	218	118	122	217
14	216	76	77	262	258	78	49	85	263	242
15	17	259	273	168	79	248	138	50	164	211
16	86	99	208	264	151	160	243	6	235	18
17	276	223	260	271	97	274	229	201	169	231
18	36	80	115	148	249	41	267	139	203	185
19	51	252	105	165	33	196	212	171	179	87
20	144	22	100	74	15	209	233	199	265	194
21	13	152	58	154	161	38	55	244	44	126
22	7	175	60	236	82	94	19	67	70	277
23	27	156	224	117	215	261	48	241	272	247
24	163	98	150	5	275	270	228	230	114	40
25	202	251	32	170	143	73	232	193	57	37
26	43	174	81	66	26	116	47	246	149	269
27	113	250	142	192	42	65	46	268	141	64
28	140	0								

POWER RESIDUES

	0	1	2	3	4	5	6	7	8	9
0	1	3	9	27	81	243	167	220	98	13
1	39	117	70	210	68	204	50	150	169	226
2	116	67	201	41	123	88	264	230	128	103
3	28	84	252	194	20	60	180	259	215	83
4	249	185	274	260	218	92	276	266	236	146
5	157	190	8	24	72	216	86	258	212	74
6	222	104	31	93	279	275	263	227	119	76
7	228	122	85	255	203	47	141	142	145	154
8	181	262	224	110	49	147	160	199	35	105
9	34	102	25	75	225	113	58	174	241	161
10	202	44	132	115	64	192	14	42	126	97
11	10	30	90	270	248	182	265	233	137	130
12	109	46	138	133	118	73	219	95	4	12
13	36	108	43	129	106	37	111	52	156	187
14	280	278	272	254	200	38	114	61	183	268
15	242	164	211	71	213	77	231	131	112	55
16	165	214	80	240	158	193	17	51	153	178
17	253	197	29	87	261	221	101	22	66	198
18	32	96	7	21	63	189	5	15	45	135
19	124	91	273	257	209	65	195	23	69	207
20	59	177	250	188	2	6	18	54	162	205
21	53	159	196	26	78	234	140	139	136	127
22	100	19	57	171	232	134	121	82	246	176
23	247	179	256	206	56	168	223	107	40	120
24	79	237	149	166	217	89	267	239	155	184
25	271	251	191	11	33	99	16	48	144	151
26	172	235	143	148	163	208	62	186	277	269
27	245	173	238	152	175	244	170	229	125	94
28										

P = 283

INDICES

	0	1	2	3	4	5	6	7	8	9
0		0	159	1	36	233	160	278	195	2
1	110	152	37	254	155	234	72	221	161	207
2	269	279	29	100	196	184	131	3	32	168
3	111	175	231	153	98	229	38	59	84	255
4	146	40	156	165	188	235	259	263	73	274
5	61	222	8	69	162	103	191	208	45	86
6	270	78	52	280	108	205	30	57	257	101
7	106	246	197	248	218	185	243	148	132	117
8	23	4	199	238	33	172	42	169	65	212
9	112	250	136	176	140	158	232	194	151	154
10	220	268	99	130	167	230	228	83	39	187
11	262	60	68	190	85	51	204	256	245	217
12	147	22	237	41	211	135	157	150	267	166
13	82	261	189	203	216	236	134	266	260	215
14	265	264	123	124	74	119	125	275	95	75
15	62	48	120	223	25	126	9	16	276	70
16	182	96	163	6	76	104	115	63	192	226
17	49	209	201	121	46	180	224	87	89	26
18	271	240	127	79	13	10	53	91	17	281
19	35	277	109	253	71	206	28	183	31	174
20	97	58	145	164	258	273	7	102	44	77
21	107	56	105	247	242	116	198	171	64	249
22	139	193	219	129	227	186	67	50	244	21
23	210	149	81	202	133	214	122	118	94	47
24	24	15	181	5	114	225	200	179	88	239
25	12	90	34	252	27	173	144	272	43	55
26	241	170	138	128	66	20	80	213	93	14
27	113	178	11	251	143	54	137	19	92	177
28	142	18	141							

POWER RESIDUES

	0	1	2	3	4	5	6	7	8	9
0	1	3	9	27	81	243	163	206	52	156
1	185	272	250	184	269	241	157	188	281	277
2	265	229	121	80	240	154	179	254	196	22
3	66	198	28	84	252	190	4	12	36	108
4	41	123	86	258	208	58	174	239	151	170
5	227	115	62	186	275	259	211	67	201	37
6	111	50	150	167	218	88	264	226	112	53
7	159	194	16	48	144	149	164	209	61	183
8	266	232	130	107	38	114	59	177	248	178
9	251	187	278	268	238	148	161	200	34	102
10	23	69	207	55	165	212	70	210	64	192
11	10	30	90	270	244	166	215	79	237	145
12	152	173	236	142	143	146	155	182	263	223
13	103	26	78	234	136	125	92	276	262	220
14	94	282	280	274	256	202	40	120	77	231
15	127	98	11	33	99	14	42	126	95	2
16	6	18	54	162	203	43	129	104	29	87
17	261	217	85	255	199	31	93	279	271	247
18	175	242	160	197	25	75	225	109	44	132
19	113	56	168	221	97	8	24	72	216	82
20	246	172	233	133	116	65	195	19	57	171
21	230	124	89	267	235	139	134	119	74	222
22	100	17	51	153	176	245	169	224	106	35
23	105	32	96	5	15	45	135	122	83	249
24	181	260	214	76	228	118	71	213	73	219
25	91	273	253	193	13	39	117	68	204	46
26	138	131	110	47	141	140	137	128	101	20
27	60	180	257	205	49	147	158	191	7	21
28	63	189								

P = 293

INDICES

	0	1	2	3	4	5	6	7	8	9
0		0	1	157	2	173	158	213	3	22
1	174	115	159	243	214	38	4	220	23	111
2	175	78	116	207	160	54	244	179	215	129
3	39	46	5	272	221	94	24	154	112	108
4	176	91	79	82	117	195	208	103	161	134
5	55	85	245	188	180	288	216	268	130	120
6	40	278	47	235	6	124	273	198	222	72
7	95	166	25	144	155	211	113	36	109	205
8	177	44	92	106	80	101	83	286	118	233
9	196	164	209	203	104	284	162	282	135	137
10	56	17	86	139	246	251	189	58	181	64
11	289	19	217	51	269	88	131	265	121	141
12	41	230	279	248	48	227	236	253	7	239
13	125	191	274	32	199	60	223	256	73	183
14	96	260	167	66	26	10	145	291	156	172
15	212	21	114	242	37	219	110	77	206	53
16	178	128	45	271	93	153	107	90	81	194
17	102	133	84	187	287	267	119	277	234	123
18	197	71	165	143	210	35	204	43	105	100
19	285	232	163	202	283	281	136	16	138	250
20	57	63	18	50	87	264	140	229	247	226
21	252	238	190	31	59	255	182	259	65	9
22	290	171	20	241	218	76	52	127	270	152
23	89	193	132	186	266	276	122	70	142	34
24	42	99	231	201	280	15	249	62	49	263
25	228	225	237	30	254	258	8	170	240	75
26	126	151	192	185	275	69	33	98	200	14
27	61	262	224	29	257	169	74	150	184	68
28	97	13	261	28	168	149	67	12	27	148
29	11	147	146							

POWER RESIDUES

	0	1	2	3	4	5	6	7	8	9
0	1	2	4	8	16	32	64	128	256	219
1	145	290	287	281	269	245	197	101	202	111
2	222	151	9	18	36	72	144	288	283	273
3	253	213	133	266	239	185	77	154	15	30
4	60	120	240	187	81	162	31	62	124	248
5	203	113	226	159	25	50	100	200	107	214
6	135	270	247	201	109	218	143	286	279	265
7	237	181	69	138	276	259	225	157	21	42
8	84	168	43	86	172	51	102	204	115	230
9	167	41	82	164	35	70	140	280	267	241
10	189	85	170	47	94	188	83	166	39	78
11	156	19	38	76	152	11	22	44	88	176
12	59	118	236	179	65	130	260	227	161	29
13	58	116	232	171	49	98	196	99	198	103
14	206	119	238	183	73	146	292	291	289	285
15	277	261	229	165	37	74	148	3	6	12
16	24	48	96	192	91	182	71	142	284	275
17	257	221	149	5	10	20	40	80	160	27
18	54	108	216	139	278	263	233	173	53	106
19	212	131	262	231	169	45	90	180	67	134
20	268	243	193	93	186	79	158	23	46	92
21	184	75	150	7	14	28	56	112	224	155
22	17	34	68	136	272	251	209	125	250	207
23	121	242	191	89	178	63	126	252	211	129
24	258	223	153	13	26	52	104	208	123	246
25	199	105	210	127	254	215	137	274	255	217
26	141	282	271	249	205	117	234	175	57	114
27	228	163	33	66	132	264	235	177	61	122
28	244	195	97	194	95	190	87	174	55	110
29	220	147								

P = 307

INDICES

	0	1	2	3	4	5	6	7	8	9
0		0	93	81	186	1	174	116	279	162
1	94	4	267	253	209	82	66	204	255	168
2	187	197	97	179	54	2	40	243	302	263
3	175	293	159	85	297	117	42	184	261	28
4	280	224	290	211	190	163	272	287	147	232
5	95	285	133	136	30	5	89	249	50	113
6	268	245	80	278	252	254	178	301	84	260
7	210	146	135	49	277	83	48	120	121	282
8	67	18	11	122	77	205	304	38	283	46
9	256	63	59	68	74	169	240	138	19	166
10	188	258	72	12	226	198	229	128	123	106
11	98	265	182	78	36	180	143	109	206	14
12	55	8	32	305	173	3	65	196	39	292
13	41	223	271	284	88	244	177	145	47	17
14	303	62	239	257	228	264	142	7	64	222
15	176	61	141	60	213	294	214	23	69	217
16	160	295	111	75	104	86	215	150	170	200
17	298	24	91	241	131	118	70	194	139	192
18	43	218	156	20	152	185	161	208	167	53
19	262	296	27	189	231	29	112	251	259	276
20	281	76	45	73	165	225	105	35	13	172
21	291	87	16	227	221	212	216	103	199	130
22	191	151	52	230	275	164	171	220	129	274
23	273	201	236	124	202	288	299	57	107	237
24	148	25	101	99	125	233	92	115	266	203
25	96	242	158	183	289	286	132	248	79	300
26	134	119	10	37	58	137	71	127	181	108
27	31	195	270	144	238	6	140	22	110	149
28	90	193	155	207	26	250	44	34	15	102
29	51	219	235	56	100	114	157	247	9	126
30	269	21	154	33	234	246	153			

POWER RESIDUES

	0	1	2	3	4	5	6	7	8	9
0	1	5	25	125	11	55	275	147	121	298
1	262	82	103	208	119	288	212	139	81	98
2	183	301	277	157	171	241	284	192	39	195
3	54	270	122	303	287	207	114	263	87	128
4	26	130	36	180	286	202	89	138	76	73
5	58	290	222	189	24	120	293	237	264	92
6	153	151	141	91	148	126	16	80	93	158
7	176	266	102	203	94	163	201	84	113	258
8	62	3	15	75	68	33	165	211	134	56
9	280	172	246	2	10	50	250	22	110	243
10	294	242	289	217	164	206	109	238	269	117
11	278	162	196	59	295	247	7	35	175	261
12	77	78	83	108	233	244	299	267	107	228
13	219	174	256	52	260	72	53	265	97	178
14	276	152	146	116	273	137	71	48	240	279
15	167	221	184	306	302	282	182	296	252	32
16	160	186	9	45	225	204	99	188	19	95
17	168	226	209	124	6	30	150	136	66	23
18	115	268	112	253	37	185	4	20	100	193
19	44	220	179	281	177	271	127	21	105	218
20	169	231	234	249	17	85	118	283	187	14
21	70	43	215	154	156	166	216	159	181	291
22	227	214	149	131	41	205	104	213	144	106
23	223	194	49	245	304	292	232	239	274	142
24	96	173	251	27	135	61	305	297	257	57
25	285	197	64	13	65	18	90	143	101	198
26	69	38	190	29	145	111	248	12	60	300
27	272	132	46	230	229	224	199	74	63	8
28	40	200	79	88	133	51	255	47	235	254
29	42	210	129	31	155	161	191	34	170	236
30	259	67	28	140	86	123				

P = 311

INDICES

	0	1	2	3	4	5	6	7	8	9
0		0	22	164	44	196	186	140	66	18
1	218	135	208	80	162	50	88	1	40	207
2	240	304	157	283	230	82	102	182	184	241
3	72	247	110	299	23	26	62	139	229	244
4	262	245	16	233	179	214	305	210	252	280
5	104	165	124	264	204	21	206	61	263	47
6	94	145	269	158	132	276	11	34	45	137
7	48	293	84	8	161	246	251	275	266	152
8	284	36	267	260	38	197	255	95	201	170
9	236	220	17	101	232	93	274	231	302	153
10	126	57	187	13	146	190	286	54	226	234
11	43	303	228	20	83	169	285	98	69	141
12	116	270	167	99	291	278	180	194	154	87
13	298	103	33	37	56	68	67	272	159	122
14	70	64	5	215	106	127	30	134	183	213
15	268	151	273	19	297	133	288	142	174	118
16	306	113	58	28	289	185	282	261	60	160
17	219	225	277	4	117	222	223	211	192	188
18	258	143	242	309	39	25	123	136	254	12
19	115	271	296	224	253	130	14	238	175	73
20	148	198	79	71	209	131	35	301	168	32
21	212	281	308	147	76	119	248	77	256	172
22	65	81	15	46	250	100	42	193	105	112
23	191	129	307	111	120	96	91	6	163	239
24	138	203	292	200	189	166	121	287	3	114
25	300	249	202	108	216	51	176	49	109	279
26	10	259	125	97	55	150	59	24	78	171
27	90	107	89	74	294	217	181	178	144	265
28	92	227	86	29	27	257	237	75	128	2
29	149	85	52	195	156	243	205	7	235	53
30	290	63	173	221	295	31	41	199	9	177
31	155	0								

POWER RESIDUES

	0	1	2	3	4	5	6	7	8	9
0	1	17	289	248	173	142	237	297	73	308
1	260	66	189	103	196	222	42	92	9	153
2	113	55	2	34	267	185	35	284	163	283
3	146	305	209	132	67	206	81	133	84	184
4	18	306	226	110	4	68	223	59	70	257
5	15	255	292	299	107	264	134	101	162	266
6	168	57	36	301	141	220	8	136	135	118
7	140	203	30	199	273	287	214	217	268	202
8	13	221	25	114	72	291	282	129	16	272
9	270	236	280	95	60	87	235	263	117	123
10	225	93	26	131	50	228	144	271	253	258
11	32	233	229	161	249	190	120	174	159	215
12	234	246	139	186	52	262	100	145	288	231
13	195	205	64	155	147	11	187	69	240	37
14	7	119	157	181	278	61	104	213	200	290
15	265	151	79	99	128	310	294	22	63	138
16	169	74	14	238	3	51	245	122	208	115
17	89	269	219	302	158	198	256	309	277	44
18	126	276	27	148	28	165	6	102	179	244
19	105	230	178	227	127	293	5	85	201	307
20	243	88	252	241	54	296	56	19	12	204
21	47	177	210	149	45	143	254	275	10	170
22	91	303	175	176	193	171	108	281	112	38
23	24	97	94	43	109	298	90	286	197	239
24	20	29	182	295	39	41	75	31	216	251
25	224	76	48	194	188	86	218	285	180	261
26	83	167	40	58	53	279	78	82	150	62
27	121	191	137	152	96	77	65	172	125	259
28	49	211	166	23	80	116	106	247	156	164
29	300	124	242	71	274	304	192	154	130	33
30	250	207	98	111	21	46	160	232	212	183
31										

P = 313

INDICES

	0	1	2	3	4	5	6	7	8	9
0		0	274	56	236	39	18	123	198	112
1	1	148	292	214	85	95	160	205	74	108
2	275	179	110	27	254	78	176	168	47	182
3	57	211	122	204	167	162	36	163	70	270
4	237	209	141	13	72	151	301	37	216	246
5	40	261	138	21	130	187	9	164	144	191
6	19	3	173	235	84	253	166	71	129	83
7	124	102	310	99	125	134	32	271	232	132
8	199	224	171	184	103	244	287	238	34	89
9	113	25	263	267	311	147	178	210	208	260
10	2	101	223	24	100	218	295	142	92	29
11	149	219	283	120	126	66	106	14	153	16
12	293	296	277	265	135	117	197	73	46	69
13	215	143	128	231	33	207	91	152	45	44
14	86	93	64	50	272	221	61	302	87	289
15	96	30	306	5	233	250	194	38	94	77
16	161	150	186	252	133	243	146	217	65	116
17	206	220	249	242	200	201	308	247	51	189
18	75	284	299	59	225	202	229	41	273	291
19	109	121	140	137	172	309	170	262	222	282
20	276	127	63	305	185	248	298	139	62	256
21	180	67	257	158	104	52	54	22	303	155
22	111	107	181	269	245	190	82	131	88	259
23	28	15	68	43	288	76	115	188	290	281
24	255	154	258	280	239	285	227	10	97	240
25	79	17	159	175	35	300	8	165	31	286
26	177	294	105	196	90	60	193	145	307	228
27	169	297	53	81	114	226	7	192	6	11
28	48	278	55	213	26	203	12	20	234	98
29	183	266	23	119	264	230	49	4	251	241
30	58	136	304	157	268	42	279	174	195	80
31	212	118	156							

POWER RESIDUES

	0	1	2	3	4	5	6	7	8	9
0	1	10	100	61	297	153	278	276	256	56
1	247	279	286	43	117	231	119	251	6	60
2	287	53	217	292	103	91	284	23	230	109
3	151	258	76	134	88	254	36	47	157	5
4	50	187	305	233	139	138	128	28	280	296
5	143	178	215	272	216	282	3	30	300	183
6	265	146	208	202	142	168	115	211	232	129
7	38	67	44	127	18	180	235	159	25	250
8	309	273	226	69	64	14	140	148	228	89
9	264	136	108	141	158	15	150	248	289	73
10	104	101	71	84	214	262	116	221	19	190
11	22	220	9	90	274	236	169	125	311	293
12	113	191	32	7	70	74	114	201	132	68
13	54	227	79	164	75	124	301	193	52	207
14	192	42	107	131	58	267	166	95	11	110
15	161	45	137	118	241	219	312	303	213	252
16	16	160	35	37	57	257	66	34	27	270
17	196	82	194	62	307	253	26	260	96	21
18	210	222	29	290	83	204	162	55	237	179
19	225	59	277	266	156	308	263	126	8	80
20	174	175	185	285	33	17	170	135	98	41
21	97	31	310	283	13	130	48	167	105	111
22	171	145	198	102	81	184	275	246	269	186
23	295	133	78	154	288	63	4	40	87	244
24	249	299	173	165	85	224	49	177	205	172
25	155	298	163	65	24	240	209	212	242	229
26	99	51	197	92	294	123	291	93	304	223
27	39	77	144	188	2	20	200	122	281	306
28	243	239	199	112	181	245	259	86	234	149
29	238	189	12	120	261	106	121	271	206	182
30	255	46	147	218	302	203	152	268	176	195
31	72	94								

P = 317

INDICES

	0	1	2	3	4	5	6	7	8	9
0		0	1	249	2	243	250	50	3	182
1	244	288	251	149	51	176	4	263	183	303
2	245	299	289	192	252	170	150	115	52	29
3	177	280	5	221	264	293	184	138	304	82
4	246	285	300	112	290	109	193	201	253	100
5	171	196	151	66	116	215	53	236	30	204
6	178	166	281	232	6	76	222	256	265	125
7	294	61	185	10	139	103	305	22	83	156
8	247	48	286	174	301	190	113	278	291	80
9	110	199	194	213	202	230	254	59	101	154
10	172	276	197	228	152	226	67	69	117	311
11	216	71	54	40	237	119	31	15	205	313
12	179	260	167	218	282	97	233	73	7	45
13	77	56	223	37	257	42	266	269	126	239
14	295	134	62	121	186	272	11	33	140	144
15	104	17	306	129	23	207	84	90	157	315
16	248	242	49	181	287	148	175	262	302	298
17	191	169	114	28	279	220	292	137	81	284
18	111	108	200	99	195	65	214	235	203	165
19	231	75	255	124	60	9	102	21	155	47
20	173	189	277	79	198	212	229	58	153	275
21	227	225	68	310	70	39	118	14	312	259
22	217	96	72	44	55	36	41	268	238	133
23	120	271	32	143	16	128	206	89	314	241
24	180	147	261	297	168	27	219	136	283	107
25	98	64	234	164	74	123	8	20	46	188
26	78	211	57	274	224	309	38	13	258	95
27	43	35	267	132	270	142	127	88	240	146
28	296	26	135	106	63	163	122	19	187	210
29	273	308	12	94	34	131	141	87	145	25
30	105	162	18	209	307	93	130	86	24	161
31	208	92	85	160	91	159	158			

POWER RESIDUES

	0	1	2	3	4	5	6	7	8	9
0	1	2	4	8	16	32	64	128	256	195
1	73	146	292	267	217	117	234	151	302	287
2	257	197	77	154	308	299	281	245	173	29
3	58	116	232	147	294	271	225	133	266	215
4	113	226	135	270	223	129	258	199	81	162
5	7	14	28	56	112	224	131	262	207	97
6	194	71	142	284	251	185	53	106	212	107
7	214	111	222	127	254	191	65	130	260	203
8	89	178	39	78	156	312	307	297	277	237
9	157	314	311	305	293	269	221	125	250	183
10	49	98	196	75	150	300	283	249	181	45
11	90	180	43	86	172	27	54	108	216	115
12	230	143	286	255	193	69	138	276	235	153
13	306	295	273	229	141	282	247	177	37	74
14	148	296	275	233	149	298	279	241	165	13
15	26	52	104	208	99	198	79	158	316	315
16	313	309	301	285	253	189	61	122	244	171
17	25	50	100	200	83	166	15	30	60	120
18	240	163	9	18	36	72	144	288	259	201
19	85	170	23	46	92	184	51	102	204	91
20	182	47	94	188	59	118	236	155	310	303
21	289	261	205	93	186	55	110	220	123	246
22	175	33	66	132	264	211	105	210	103	206
23	95	190	63	126	252	187	57	114	228	139
24	278	239	161	5	10	20	40	80	160	3
25	6	12	24	48	96	192	67	134	268	219
26	121	242	167	17	34	68	136	272	227	137
27	274	231	145	290	263	209	101	202	87	174
28	31	62	124	248	179	41	82	164	11	22
29	44	88	176	35	70	140	280	243	169	21
30	42	84	168	19	38	76	152	304	291	265
31	213	109	218	119	238	159				

P = 331

INDICES

	0	1	2	3	4	5	6	7	8	9
0		0	121	1	242	236	122	81	33	2
1	27	137	243	145	202	237	154	184	123	14
2	148	82	258	295	34	142	266	3	323	271
3	28	220	275	138	305	317	244	119	135	146
4	269	133	203	112	49	238	86	205	155	162
5	263	185	57	188	124	43	114	15	62	173
6	149	195	11	83	66	51	259	6	96	296
7	108	128	35	69	240	143	256	218	267	160
8	60	4	254	88	324	90	233	272	170	230
9	29	226	207	221	326	250	276	103	283	139
10	54	157	306	92	178	318	309	191	245	76
11	164	120	235	32	136	201	183	147	294	265
12	270	274	316	134	132	48	204	262	187	113
13	172	10	50	95	127	239	217	59	87	232
14	229	206	249	282	156	177	190	163	31	182
15	264	315	47	186	9	126	58	228	281	189
16	181	46	125	280	45	44	209	210	115	290
17	211	16	24	116	63	223	291	174	21	212
18	150	99	17	196	328	25	12	321	117	84
19	41	64	67	252	224	52	74	292	260	215
20	175	7	278	22	97	39	213	297	299	151
21	109	105	100	129	312	18	36	301	197	70
22	285	329	241	80	26	144	153	13	257	141
23	322	219	304	118	268	111	85	161	56	42
24	61	194	65	5	107	68	255	159	253	89
25	169	225	325	102	53	91	308	75	234	200
26	293	273	131	261	171	94	216	231	248	176
27	30	314	8	227	180	279	208	289	23	222
28	20	98	327	320	40	251	73	214	277	38
29	298	104	311	300	284	79	152	140	303	110
30	55	193	106	158	168	101	307	199	130	93
31	247	313	179	288	19	319	72	37	310	78
32	302	192	167	198	246	287	71	77	166	286
33	165	0								

POWER RESIDUES

	0	1	2	3	4	5	6	7	8	9
0	1	3	9	27	81	243	67	201	272	154
1	131	62	186	227	19	57	171	182	215	314
2	280	178	203	278	172	185	224	10	30	90
3	270	148	113	8	24	72	216	317	289	205
4	284	190	239	55	165	164	161	152	125	44
5	132	65	195	254	100	300	238	52	156	137
6	80	240	58	174	191	242	64	192	245	73
7	219	326	316	286	196	257	109	327	319	295
8	223	7	21	63	189	236	46	138	83	249
9	85	255	103	309	265	133	68	204	281	181
10	212	305	253	97	291	211	302	244	70	210
11	299	235	43	129	56	168	173	188	233	37
12	111	2	6	18	54	162	155	134	71	213
13	308	262	124	41	123	38	114	11	33	99
14	297	229	25	75	225	13	39	117	20	60
15	180	209	296	226	16	48	144	101	303	247
16	79	237	49	147	110	330	328	322	304	250
17	88	264	130	59	177	200	269	145	104	312
18	274	160	149	116	17	51	153	128	53	159
19	146	107	321	301	241	61	183	218	323	307
20	259	115	14	42	126	47	141	92	276	166
21	167	170	179	206	287	199	266	136	77	231
22	31	93	279	175	194	251	91	273	157	140
23	89	267	139	86	258	112	5	15	45	135
24	74	222	4	12	36	108	324	310	268	142
25	95	285	193	248	82	246	76	228	22	66
26	198	263	127	50	150	119	26	78	234	40
27	120	29	87	261	121	32	96	288	202	275
28	163	158	143	98	294	220	329	325	313	277
29	169	176	197	260	118	23	69	207	290	208
30	293	217	320	298	232	34	102	306	256	106
31	318	292	214	311	271	151	122	35	105	315
32	283	187	230	28	84	252	94	282	184	221
33										

P = 337

INDICES

	0	1	2	3	4	5	6	7	8	9
0		0	304	314	272	33	282	318	240	292
1	1	171	250	16	286	11	208	9	260	109
2	305	296	139	229	218	66	320	270	254	257
3	315	101	176	149	313	15	228	148	77	330
4	273	220	264	78	107	325	197	90	186	300
5	34	323	288	331	238	204	222	87	225	63
6	283	311	69	274	144	49	117	103	281	207
7	319	227	196	221	116	44	45	153	298	192
8	241	248	188	265	232	42	46	235	75	173
9	293	334	165	79	58	142	154	51	268	127
10	2	167	291	108	256	329	299	62	206	191
11	172	126	190	326	55	262	193	308	31	327
12	251	6	279	198	37	99	242	129	112	56
13	17	244	85	91	71	303	249	138	175	263
14	287	68	195	187	164	290	189	278	84	194
15	12	215	13	301	121	134	266	93	160	309
16	209	211	216	35	156	182	233	178	200	32
17	10	65	14	324	203	48	43	41	141	328
18	261	98	302	289	133	181	47	180	26	252
19	110	21	122	332	19	27	236	119	95	7
20	306	81	135	239	259	253	76	185	224	280
21	297	74	267	205	30	111	174	83	159	199
22	140	25	94	223	158	22	294	4	23	38
23	230	131	161	88	276	123	335	170	295	100
24	219	322	310	226	247	333	166	125	5	243
25	67	214	210	64	97	20	80	73	24	130
26	321	213	212	284	53	28	59	151	39	113
27	271	285	217	312	106	237	143	115	231	57
28	255	54	36	70	163	120	155	202	132	18
29	258	29	157	275	246	96	52	105	162	245
30	316	60	183	145	317	8	269	147	89	86
31	102	152	234	50	61	307	128	137	277	92
32	177	40	179	118	184	82	3	169	124	72
33	150	114	201	104	146	136	168			

POWER RESIDUES

	0	1	2	3	4	5	6	7	8	9
0	1	10	100	326	227	248	121	199	305	17
1	170	15	150	152	172	35	13	130	289	194
2	255	191	225	228	258	221	188	195	265	291
3	214	118	169	5	50	163	282	124	229	268
4	321	177	85	176	75	76	86	186	175	65
5	313	97	296	264	281	114	129	279	94	266
6	301	314	107	59	253	171	25	250	141	62
7	283	134	329	257	211	88	206	38	43	93
8	256	201	325	217	148	132	309	57	233	308
9	47	133	319	157	222	198	295	254	181	125
10	239	31	310	67	333	297	274	44	103	19
11	190	215	128	269	331	277	74	66	323	197
12	285	154	192	235	328	247	111	99	316	127
13	259	231	288	184	155	202	335	317	137	22
14	220	178	95	276	64	303	334	307	37	33
15	330	267	311	77	96	286	164	292	224	218
16	158	232	298	284	144	92	246	101	336	327
17	237	11	110	89	216	138	32	320	167	322
18	187	185	165	302	324	207	48	143	82	146
19	112	109	79	116	149	142	72	46	123	219
20	168	332	287	174	55	213	108	69	16	160
21	252	161	262	261	251	151	162	272	24	240
22	41	73	56	223	208	58	243	71	36	23
23	230	278	84	166	312	87	196	275	54	203
24	8	80	126	249	131	299	294	244	81	136
25	12	120	189	205	28	280	104	29	290	204
26	18	180	115	139	42	83	156	212	98	306
27	27	270	4	40	63	293	234	318	147	122
28	209	68	6	60	263	271	14	140	52	183
29	145	102	9	90	226	238	21	210	78	106
30	49	153	182	135	2	20	200	315	117	159
31	242	61	273	34	3	30	300	304	7	70
32	26	260	241	51	173	45	113	119	179	105
33	39	53	193	245	91	236				

P = 347

INDICES

	0	1	2	3	4	5	6	7	8	9
0		0	1	152	2	277	153	289	3	304
1	278	272	154	238	290	83	4	183	305	145
2	279	95	273	91	155	208	239	110	291	192
3	84	54	5	78	184	220	306	159	146	44
4	280	315	96	322	274	235	92	189	156	232
5	209	335	240	212	111	203	292	297	193	136
6	85	338	55	247	6	169	79	50	185	243
7	221	72	307	28	160	14	147	215	45	225
8	281	262	316	254	97	114	323	344	275	302
9	236	181	93	206	190	76	157	313	233	230
10	210	295	336	167	241	26	213	260	112	300
11	204	311	293	24	298	22	194	196	137	126
12	86	198	339	121	56	139	248	32	7	128
13	170	286	80	88	51	41	186	200	244	69
14	222	341	73	164	308	123	29	38	161	58
15	15	61	148	141	216	331	46	250	226	18
16	282	34	263	267	317	9	255	64	98	130
17	115	103	324	172	345	151	276	288	303	271
18	237	82	182	144	94	90	207	109	191	53
19	77	219	158	43	314	321	234	188	231	334
20	211	202	296	135	337	246	168	49	242	71
21	27	13	214	224	261	253	113	343	301	180
22	205	75	312	229	294	166	25	259	299	310
23	23	21	195	125	197	120	138	31	127	285
24	87	40	199	68	340	163	122	37	57	60
25	140	330	249	17	33	266	8	63	129	102
26	171	150	287	270	81	143	89	108	52	218
27	42	320	187	333	201	134	245	48	70	12
28	223	252	342	179	74	228	165	258	309	20
29	124	119	30	284	39	67	162	36	59	329
30	16	265	62	101	149	269	142	107	217	319
31	332	133	47	11	251	178	227	257	19	118
32	283	66	35	328	264	100	268	106	318	132
33	10	177	256	117	65	327	99	105	131	176
34	116	326	104	175	325	174	173			

POWER RESIDUES

	0	1	2	3	4	5	6	7	8	9
0	1	2	4	8	16	32	64	128	256	165
1	330	313	279	211	75	150	300	253	159	318
2	289	231	115	230	113	226	105	210	73	146
3	292	237	127	254	161	322	297	247	147	294
4	241	135	270	193	39	78	156	312	277	207
5	67	134	268	189	31	62	124	248	149	298
6	249	151	302	257	167	334	321	295	243	139
7	278	209	71	142	284	221	95	190	33	66
8	132	264	181	15	30	60	120	240	133	266
9	185	23	46	92	184	21	42	84	168	336
10	325	303	259	171	342	337	327	307	267	187
11	27	54	108	216	85	170	340	333	319	291
12	235	123	246	145	290	233	119	238	129	258
13	169	338	329	311	275	203	59	118	236	125
14	250	153	306	265	183	19	38	76	152	304
15	261	175	3	6	12	24	48	96	192	37
16	74	148	296	245	143	286	225	103	206	65
17	130	260	173	346	345	343	339	331	315	283
18	219	91	182	17	34	68	136	272	197	47
19	94	188	29	58	116	232	117	234	121	242
20	137	274	201	55	110	220	93	186	25	50
21	100	200	53	106	212	77	154	308	269	191
22	35	70	140	280	213	79	158	316	285	223
23	99	198	49	98	196	45	90	180	13	26
24	52	104	208	69	138	276	205	63	126	252
25	157	314	281	215	83	166	332	317	287	227
26	107	214	81	162	324	301	255	163	326	305
27	263	179	11	22	44	88	176	5	10	20
28	40	80	160	320	293	239	131	262	177	7
29	14	28	56	112	224	101	202	57	114	228
30	109	218	89	178	9	18	36	72	144	288
31	229	111	222	97	194	41	82	164	328	309
32	271	195	43	86	172	344	341	335	323	299
33	251	155	310	273	199	51	102	204	61	122
34	244	141	282	217	87	174				

P = 349

INDICES

	0	1	2	3	4	5	6	7	8	9
0		0	1	26	2	314	27	67	3	52
1	315	21	28	271	68	340	4	258	53	188
2	316	93	22	184	29	280	272	78	69	146
3	341	156	5	47	259	33	54	126	189	297
4	317	264	94	137	23	18	185	75	30	134
5	281	284	273	303	79	335	70	214	147	287
6	342	231	157	119	6	237	48	276	260	210
7	34	61	55	38	127	306	190	88	298	219
8	318	104	265	82	95	224	138	172	24	65
9	19	338	186	182	76	154	31	295	135	73
10	282	333	285	117	274	59	304	217	80	170
11	336	152	71	115	215	150	148	323	288	325
12	343	42	232	290	158	246	120	327	7	163
13	238	345	49	255	277	44	261	131	211	234
14	35	101	62	292	56	112	39	160	128	109
15	307	248	191	310	89	122	299	206	220	329
16	319	251	105	9	266	13	83	165	96	194
17	225	240	139	199	173	347	25	313	66	51
18	20	270	339	257	187	92	183	279	77	145
19	155	46	32	125	296	263	136	17	74	133
20	283	302	334	213	286	230	118	236	275	209
21	60	37	305	87	218	103	81	223	171	64
22	337	181	153	294	72	332	116	58	216	169
23	151	114	149	322	324	41	289	245	326	162
24	344	254	43	130	233	100	291	111	159	108
25	247	309	121	205	328	250	8	12	164	193
26	239	198	346	312	50	269	256	91	278	144
27	45	124	262	16	132	301	212	229	235	208
28	36	86	102	222	63	180	293	331	57	168
29	113	321	40	244	161	253	129	99	110	107
30	308	204	249	11	192	197	311	268	90	143
31	123	15	300	228	207	85	221	179	330	167
32	320	243	252	98	106	203	10	196	267	142
33	14	227	84	178	166	242	97	202	195	141
34	226	177	241	201	140	176	200	175	174	

POWER RESIDUES

	0	1	2	3	4	5	6	7	8	9
0	1	2	4	8	16	32	64	128	256	163
1	326	303	257	165	330	311	273	197	45	90
2	180	11	22	44	88	176	3	6	12	24
3	48	96	192	35	70	140	280	211	73	146
4	292	235	121	242	135	270	191	33	66	132
5	264	179	9	18	36	72	144	288	227	105
6	210	71	142	284	219	89	178	7	14	28
7	56	112	224	99	198	47	94	188	27	54
8	108	216	83	166	332	315	281	213	77	154
9	308	267	185	21	42	84	168	336	323	297
10	245	141	282	215	81	162	324	299	249	149
11	298	247	145	290	231	113	226	103	206	63
12	126	252	155	310	271	193	37	74	148	296
13	243	137	274	199	49	98	196	43	86	172
14	344	339	329	309	269	189	29	58	116	232
15	115	230	111	222	95	190	31	62	124	248
16	147	294	239	129	258	167	334	319	289	229
17	109	218	87	174	348	347	345	341	333	317
18	285	221	93	186	23	46	92	184	19	38
19	76	152	304	259	169	338	327	305	261	173
20	346	343	337	325	301	253	157	314	279	209
21	69	138	276	203	57	114	228	107	214	79
22	158	316	283	217	85	170	340	331	313	277
23	205	61	122	244	139	278	207	65	130	260
24	171	342	335	321	293	237	125	250	151	302
25	255	161	322	295	241	133	266	183	17	34
26	68	136	272	195	41	82	164	328	307	265
27	181	13	26	52	104	208	67	134	268	187
28	25	50	100	200	51	102	204	59	118	236
29	123	246	143	286	223	97	194	39	78	156
30	312	275	201	53	106	212	75	150	300	251
31	153	306	263	177	5	10	20	40	80	160
32	320	291	233	117	234	119	238	127	254	159
33	318	287	225	101	202	55	110	220	91	182
34	15	30	60	120	240	131	262	175		

P = 353

INDICES

	0	1	2	3	4	5	6	7	8	9
0		0	164	1	328	309	165	99	140	2
1	121	60	329	337	263	310	304	228	166	70
2	285	100	224	6	141	266	149	3	75	156
3	122	93	116	61	40	56	330	107	234	338
4	97	302	264	38	36	311	170	218	305	198
5	78	229	313	67	167	17	239	71	320	187
6	286	172	257	101	280	294	225	33	204	7
7	220	207	142	20	271	267	46	159	150	307
8	261	4	114	300	76	185	202	157	200	25
9	123	84	334	94	30	27	117	80	10	62
10	242	253	41	211	125	57	231	291	331	324
11	181	108	51	86	235	315	132	339	351	327
12	98	120	336	303	69	223	265	74	92	39
13	106	96	37	169	197	312	16	319	171	279
14	32	219	19	45	306	113	184	199	83	29
15	79	241	210	230	323	50	314	350	119	68
16	73	105	168	15	278	18	112	82	240	322
17	349	72	14	111	321	13	12	188	189	145
18	287	190	248	173	146	64	258	288	194	102
19	191	344	281	249	244	295	174	138	226	147
20	54	34	65	255	205	259	23	8	289	130
21	221	195	43	208	103	347	143	192	136	21
22	345	213	272	282	215	268	250	89	47	245
23	127	160	296	274	151	175	163	308	139	59
24	262	227	284	5	148	155	115	55	233	301
25	35	217	77	66	238	186	256	293	203	206
26	270	158	260	299	201	24	333	26	9	252
27	124	290	180	85	131	326	335	222	91	95
28	196	318	31	44	183	28	209	49	118	104
29	277	81	348	110	11	144	247	63	193	343
30	243	137	53	254	22	129	42	346	135	212
31	214	88	126	273	162	58	283	154	232	216
32	237	292	269	298	332	251	179	325	90	317
33	182	48	276	109	246	342	52	128	134	87
34	161	153	236	297	178	316	275	341	133	152
35	177	340	176							

POWER RESIDUES

	0	1	2	3	4	5	6	7	8	9
0	1	3	9	27	81	243	23	69	207	268
1	98	294	176	175	172	163	136	55	165	142
2	73	219	304	206	265	89	267	95	285	149
3	94	282	140	67	201	250	44	132	43	129
4	34	102	306	212	283	143	76	228	331	287
5	155	112	336	302	200	247	35	105	315	239
6	11	33	99	297	185	202	253	53	159	124
7	19	57	171	160	127	28	84	252	50	150
8	97	291	167	148	91	273	113	339	311	227
9	328	278	128	31	93	279	131	40	120	7
10	21	63	189	214	289	161	130	37	111	333
11	293	173	166	145	82	246	32	96	288	158
12	121	10	30	90	270	104	312	230	337	305
13	209	274	116	348	338	308	218	301	197	238
14	8	24	72	216	295	179	184	199	244	26
15	78	234	349	341	317	245	29	87	261	77
16	231	340	314	236	2	6	18	54	162	133
17	46	138	61	183	196	235	352	350	344	326
18	272	110	330	284	146	85	255	59	177	178
19	181	190	217	298	188	211	280	134	49	147
20	88	264	86	258	68	204	259	71	213	286
21	152	103	309	221	310	224	319	251	47	141
22	70	210	277	125	22	66	198	241	17	51
23	153	106	318	248	38	114	342	320	254	56
24	168	151	100	300	194	229	334	296	182	193
25	226	325	269	101	303	203	256	62	186	205
26	262	80	240	14	42	126	25	75	225	322
27	260	74	222	313	233	346	332	290	164	139
28	64	192	223	316	242	20	60	180	187	208
29	271	107	321	257	65	195	232	343	323	263
30	83	249	41	123	16	48	144	79	237	5
31	15	45	135	52	156	115	345	329	281	137
32	58	174	169	154	109	327	275	119	4	12
33	36	108	324	266	92	276	122	13	39	117
34	351	347	335	299	191	220	307	215	292	170
35	157	118								

P = 359

INDICES

	0	1	2	3	4	5	6	7	8	9
0		0	314	186	270	118	142	1	226	14
1	74	42	98	205	315	304	182	306	328	157
2	30	187	356	190	54	236	161	200	271	123
3	260	107	138	228	262	119	284	326	113	33
4	344	60	143	257	312	132	146	80	10	2
5	192	134	117	97	156	160	227	343	79	155
6	216	217	63	15	94	323	184	115	218	18
7	75	331	240	24	282	64	69	43	347	166
8	300	28	16	109	99	66	213	309	268	95
9	88	206	102	293	36	275	324	211	316	56
10	148	220	90	185	73	305	53	106	112	131
11	116	154	183	23	299	308	35	219	111	307
12	172	84	173	246	19	354	329	170	50	85
13	279	76	140	158	71	318	174	289	332	251
14	31	266	287	247	196	241	338	188	238	82
15	20	208	25	320	357	225	303	355	122	283
16	256	191	342	93	330	346	65	101	55	52
17	22	171	169	70	265	237	224	341	51	223
18	44	230	162	45	58	86	249	348	350	201
19	231	234	280	244	167	151	272	163	12	77
20	104	301	176	124	46	178	141	204	29	199
21	261	59	9	159	62	17	68	108	87	210
22	72	153	110	353	139	250	337	319	255	100
23	264	229	349	150	175	198	67	352	263	351
24	128	290	40	214	129	120	202	4	333	295
25	310	291	285	232	126	252	6	269	41	327
26	235	137	32	145	96	215	114	281	27	267
27	274	89	130	34	245	278	288	195	207	121
28	345	168	222	248	243	103	203	61	152	254
29	197	39	294	5	144	273	194	242	38	37
30	334	258	164	48	339	335	276	296	313	13
31	181	189	259	325	311	133	78	322	239	165
32	212	292	147	105	298	83	49	317	286	81
33	302	92	21	340	57	233	11	177	8	209
34	336	149	127	3	125	136	26	277	221	253
35	193	47	180	321	297	91	7	135	179	

POWER RESIDUES

	0	1	2	3	4	5	6	7	8	9
0	1	7	49	343	247	293	256	356	338	212
1	48	336	198	309	9	63	82	215	69	124
2	150	332	170	113	73	152	346	268	81	208
3	20	140	262	39	273	116	94	299	298	291
4	242	258	11	77	180	183	204	351	303	326
5	128	178	169	106	24	168	99	334	184	211
6	41	287	214	62	75	166	85	236	216	76
7	173	134	220	104	10	70	131	199	316	58
8	47	329	149	325	121	129	185	218	90	271
9	102	355	331	163	64	89	264	53	12	84
10	229	167	92	285	200	323	107	31	217	83
11	222	118	108	38	266	67	110	52	5	35
12	245	279	158	29	203	344	254	342	240	244
13	272	109	45	315	51	357	345	261	32	224
14	132	206	6	42	294	263	46	322	100	341
15	233	195	288	221	111	59	54	19	133	213
16	55	26	182	197	302	319	79	194	281	172
17	127	171	120	122	136	234	202	337	205	358
18	352	310	16	112	66	103	3	21	147	311
19	23	161	50	350	296	277	144	290	235	209
20	27	189	246	286	207	13	91	278	151	339
21	219	97	320	86	243	265	60	61	68	117
22	101	348	282	179	176	155	8	56	33	231
23	181	190	253	335	191	260	25	175	148	318
24	72	145	297	284	193	274	123	143	283	186
25	225	139	255	349	289	228	160	43	301	312
26	30	210	34	238	230	174	141	269	88	257
27	4	28	196	295	270	95	306	347	275	130
28	192	267	74	159	36	252	328	142	276	137
29	241	251	321	93	292	249	307	354	324	114
30	80	201	330	156	15	105	17	119	115	87
31	250	314	44	308	2	14	98	327	135	227
32	153	353	317	65	96	313	37	259	18	126
33	164	71	138	248	300	305	340	226	146	304
34	333	177	162	57	40	280	165	78	187	232
35	188	239	237	223	125	157	22	154		

P = 367

INDICES

	0	1	2	3	4	5	6	7	8	9
0		0	292	75	218	267	1	12	144	150
1	193	163	293	28	304	342	70	289	76	275
2	119	87	89	296	219	168	320	225	230	165
3	268	340	362	238	215	279	2	248	201	103
4	45	142	13	335	15	51	222	6	145	24
5	94	364	246	206	151	64	156	350	91	210
6	194	182	266	162	288	295	164	278	141	5
7	205	209	294	208	174	243	127	175	29	329
8	337	300	68	244	305	190	261	240	307	128
9	343	40	148	49	298	176	71	235	316	313
10	20	30	290	199	172	354	132	330	77	153
11	356	323	82	338	276	197	17	178	136	301
12	120	326	108	217	192	69	88	229	214	44
13	221	245	90	287	204	126	67	306	297	19
14	131	81	135	191	220	66	134	99	100	262
15	169	186	53	73	101	241	321	97	255	281
16	263	308	226	33	360	139	170	129	231	56
17	116	59	187	344	166	180	233	285	54	41
18	269	158	332	257	74	149	341	86	224	237
19	102	50	363	349	161	4	242	299	239	48
20	312	353	322	177	216	43	125	80	98	72
21	280	138	58	284	256	236	3	352	79	283
22	282	317	249	37	8	318	264	314	202	114
23	123	250	309	21	104	273	62	38	227	31
24	46	271	252	9	34	291	143	303	118	319
25	361	200	14	93	155	265	140	173	336	260
26	147	315	171	355	16	107	213	203	130	133
27	52	254	359	115	232	331	223	160	311	124
28	57	78	7	122	61	251	117	154	146	212
29	358	310	60	357	25	111	26	22	188	324
30	95	347	112	105	345	83	365	11	27	274
31	167	339	247	334	23	63	181	277	207	328
32	189	39	234	198	152	196	325	228	286	18
33	65	185	96	32	55	179	157	85	348	47
34	42	137	351	36	113	272	270	302	92	259
35	106	253	159	121	211	110	346	10	333	327
36	195	184	84	35	258	109	183			

POWER RESIDUES

	0	1	2	3	4	5	6	7	8	9
0	1	6	36	216	195	69	47	282	224	243
1	357	307	7	42	252	44	264	116	329	139
2	100	233	297	314	49	294	296	308	13	78
3	101	239	333	163	244	363	343	223	237	321
4	91	179	340	205	129	40	240	339	199	93
5	191	45	270	152	178	334	169	280	212	171
6	292	284	236	315	55	330	145	136	82	125
7	16	96	209	153	184	3	18	108	281	218
8	207	141	112	305	362	337	187	21	126	22
9	132	58	348	253	50	300	332	157	208	147
10	148	154	190	39	234	303	350	265	122	365
11	355	295	302	344	229	273	170	286	248	20
12	120	353	283	230	279	206	135	76	89	167
13	268	140	106	269	146	142	118	341	211	165
14	256	68	41	246	8	48	288	260	92	185
15	9	54	324	109	287	254	56	336	181	352
16	277	194	63	11	66	29	174	310	25	150
17	166	262	104	257	74	77	95	203	117	335
18	175	316	61	366	361	331	151	172	298	320
19	85	143	124	10	60	360	325	115	323	103
20	251	38	228	267	134	70	53	318	73	71
21	59	354	289	266	128	34	204	123	4	24
22	144	130	46	276	188	27	162	238	327	127
23	28	168	274	176	322	97	215	189	33	198
24	87	155	196	75	83	131	52	312	37	222
25	231	285	242	351	271	158	214	183	364	349
26	259	86	149	160	226	255	62	5	30	180
27	346	241	345	235	309	19	114	317	67	35
28	210	159	220	219	213	177	328	133	64	17
29	102	245	2	12	72	65	23	138	94	197
30	81	119	347	247	14	84	137	88	161	232
31	291	278	200	99	227	261	98	221	225	249
32	26	156	202	111	299	326	121	359	319	79
33	107	275	182	358	313	43	258	80	113	311
34	31	186	15	90	173	304	356	301	338	193
35	57	342	217	201	105	263	110	293	290	272
36	164	250	32	192	51	306				

P = 373

INDICES

	0	1	2	3	4	5	6	7	8	9
0		0	1	238	2	169	239	198	3	104
1	170	245	240	90	199	35	4	126	105	27
2	171	64	246	351	241	338	91	342	200	284
3	36	318	5	111	127	367	106	254	28	328
4	172	84	65	95	247	273	352	235	242	24
5	339	364	92	361	343	42	201	265	285	346
6	37	145	319	302	6	259	112	45	128	217
7	368	122	107	20	255	204	29	71	329	77
8	173	208	85	268	66	295	96	150	248	310
9	274	288	353	184	236	196	243	33	25	349
10	340	316	365	326	93	233	362	40	344	300
11	43	120	202	75	266	148	286	194	347	324
12	38	118	146	322	320	135	303	137	7	333
13	260	305	113	225	46	139	129	162	218	9
14	369	101	123	335	108	81	21	262	256	17
15	205	307	30	230	72	115	330	159	78	227
16	174	177	209	48	86	280	269	141	67	180
17	296	131	97	155	151	164	249	212	311	220
18	275	58	289	11	354	51	185	371	237	168
19	197	103	244	89	34	125	26	63	350	337
20	341	283	317	110	366	253	327	83	94	272
21	234	23	363	360	41	264	345	144	301	258
22	44	216	121	19	203	70	76	207	267	294
23	149	309	287	183	195	32	348	315	325	232
24	39	299	119	74	147	193	323	117	321	134
25	136	332	304	224	138	161	8	100	334	80
26	261	16	306	229	114	158	226	176	47	279
27	140	179	130	154	163	211	219	57	10	50
28	370	167	102	88	124	62	336	282	109	252
29	82	271	22	359	263	143	257	215	18	69
30	206	293	308	182	31	314	231	298	73	192
31	116	133	331	223	160	99	79	15	228	157
32	175	278	178	153	210	56	49	166	87	61
33	281	251	270	358	142	214	68	292	181	313
34	297	191	132	222	98	14	156	277	152	55
35	165	60	250	357	213	291	312	190	221	13
36	276	54	59	356	290	189	12	53	355	188
37	52	187	186							

POWER RESIDUES

	0	1	2	3	4	5	6	7	8	9
0	1	2	4	8	16	32	64	128	256	139
1	278	183	366	359	345	317	261	149	298	223
2	73	146	292	211	49	98	196	19	38	76
3	152	304	235	97	194	15	30	60	120	240
4	107	214	55	110	220	67	134	268	163	326
5	279	185	370	367	361	349	325	277	181	362
6	351	329	285	197	21	42	84	168	336	299
7	225	77	154	308	243	113	226	79	158	316
8	259	145	290	207	41	82	164	328	283	193
9	13	26	52	104	208	43	86	172	344	315
10	257	141	282	191	9	18	36	72	144	288
11	203	33	66	132	264	155	310	247	121	242
12	111	222	71	142	284	195	17	34	68	136
13	272	171	342	311	249	125	250	127	254	135
14	270	167	334	295	217	61	122	244	115	230
15	87	174	348	323	273	173	346	319	265	157
16	314	255	137	274	175	350	327	281	189	5
17	10	20	40	80	160	320	267	161	322	271
18	169	338	303	233	93	186	372	371	369	365
19	357	341	309	245	117	234	95	190	7	14
20	28	56	112	224	75	150	300	227	81	162
21	324	275	177	354	335	297	221	69	138	276
22	179	358	343	313	253	133	266	159	318	263
23	153	306	239	105	210	47	94	188	3	6
24	12	24	48	96	192	11	22	44	88	176
25	352	331	289	205	37	74	148	296	219	65
26	130	260	147	294	215	57	114	228	83	166
27	332	291	209	45	90	180	360	347	321	269
28	165	330	287	201	29	58	116	232	91	182
29	364	355	337	301	229	85	170	340	307	241
30	109	218	63	126	252	131	262	151	302	231
31	89	178	356	339	305	237	101	202	31	62
32	124	248	123	246	119	238	103	206	39	78
33	156	312	251	129	258	143	286	199	25	50
34	100	200	27	54	108	216	59	118	236	99
35	198	23	46	92	184	368	363	353	333	293
36	213	53	106	212	51	102	204	35	70	140
37	280	187								

P = 379

INDICES

	0	1	2	3	4	5	6	7	8	9
0		0	1	137	2	144	138	155	3	274
1	145	217	139	313	156	281	4	115	275	232
2	146	292	218	24	140	288	314	33	157	255
3	282	205	5	354	116	299	276	318	233	72
4	147	60	293	107	219	40	25	323	141	310
5	289	252	315	37	34	361	158	369	256	339
6	283	364	206	51	6	79	355	264	117	161
7	300	185	277	201	319	47	234	372	73	238
8	148	170	61	132	294	259	108	14	220	211
9	41	90	26	342	324	376	142	272	311	113
10	290	286	253	352	316	58	38	308	35	367
11	362	77	159	199	370	168	257	209	340	270
12	284	56	365	197	207	54	52	242	7	244
13	80	19	356	9	265	177	118	246	162	96
14	301	82	186	152	278	21	202	69	320	358
15	48	182	235	11	373	349	74	267	239	174
16	149	179	171	225	62	120	133	228	295	248
17	260	128	109	164	15	65	221	98	212	102
18	42	303	91	123	27	84	343	332	325	188
19	377	136	143	154	273	216	312	280	114	231
20	291	23	287	32	254	204	353	298	317	71
21	59	106	39	322	309	251	36	360	368	338
22	363	50	78	263	160	184	200	46	371	237
23	169	131	258	13	210	89	341	375	271	112
24	285	351	57	307	366	76	198	167	208	269
25	55	196	53	241	243	18	8	176	245	95
26	81	151	20	68	357	181	10	348	266	173
27	178	224	119	227	247	127	163	64	97	101
28	302	122	83	331	187	135	153	215	279	230
29	22	31	203	297	70	105	321	250	359	337
30	49	262	183	45	236	130	12	88	374	111
31	350	306	75	166	268	195	240	17	175	94
32	150	67	180	347	172	223	226	126	63	100
33	121	330	134	214	229	30	296	104	249	336
34	261	44	129	87	110	305	165	194	16	93
35	66	346	222	125	99	329	213	29	103	335
36	43	86	304	193	92	345	124	328	28	334
37	85	192	344	327	333	191	326	190	189	

POWER RESIDUES

	0	1	2	3	4	5	6	7	8	9
0	1	2	4	8	16	32	64	128	256	133
1	266	153	306	233	87	174	348	317	255	131
2	262	145	290	201	23	46	92	184	368	357
3	335	291	203	27	54	108	216	53	106	212
4	45	90	180	360	341	303	227	75	150	300
5	221	63	126	252	125	250	121	242	105	210
6	41	82	164	328	277	175	350	321	263	147
7	294	209	39	78	156	312	245	111	222	65
8	130	260	141	282	185	370	361	343	307	235
9	91	182	364	349	319	259	139	278	177	354
10	329	279	179	358	337	295	211	43	86	172
11	344	309	239	99	198	17	34	68	136	272
12	165	330	281	183	366	353	327	275	171	342
13	305	231	83	166	332	285	191	3	6	12
14	24	48	96	192	5	10	20	40	80	160
15	320	261	143	286	193	7	14	28	56	112
16	224	69	138	276	173	346	313	247	115	230
17	81	162	324	269	159	318	257	135	270	161
18	322	265	151	302	225	71	142	284	189	378
19	377	375	371	363	347	315	251	123	246	113
20	226	73	146	292	205	31	62	124	248	117
21	234	89	178	356	333	287	195	11	22	44
22	88	176	352	325	271	163	326	273	167	334
23	289	199	19	38	76	152	304	229	79	158
24	316	253	127	254	129	258	137	274	169	338
25	297	215	51	102	204	29	58	116	232	85
26	170	340	301	223	67	134	268	157	314	249
27	119	238	97	194	9	18	36	72	144	288
28	197	15	30	60	120	240	101	202	25	50
29	100	200	21	42	84	168	336	293	207	35
30	70	140	280	181	362	345	311	243	107	214
31	49	98	196	13	26	52	104	208	37	74
32	148	296	213	47	94	188	376	373	367	355
33	331	283	187	374	369	359	339	299	219	59
34	118	236	93	186	372	365	351	323	267	155
35	310	241	103	206	33	66	132	264	149	298
36	217	55	110	220	61	122	244	109	218	57
37	114	228	77	154	308	237	95	190		

P = 383

INDICES

	0	1	2	3	4	5	6	7	8	9
0		0	134	208	268	1	342	198	20	34
1	135	317	94	237	332	209	154	156	168	130
2	269	24	69	246	228	2	371	242	84	296
3	343	32	288	143	290	199	302	293	264	63
4	21	107	158	234	203	35	380	369	362	14
5	136	364	123	87	376	318	218	338	48	145
6	95	5	166	232	40	238	277	170	42	72
7	333	274	54	358	45	210	16	133	197	93
8	155	68	241	287	292	157	368	122	337	165
9	169	53	132	240	121	131	114	115	148	351
10	270	138	116	28	257	25	221	149	128	201
11	70	119	352	186	90	247	182	271	279	354
12	229	252	139	315	300	3	366	117	174	60
13	372	309	29	328	304	243	176	258	206	82
14	85	195	26	172	188	297	110	222	179	214
15	344	125	150	190	267	33	331	129	227	295
16	289	62	202	13	375	144	39	71	44	92
17	291	164	120	350	256	200	89	353	299	59
18	303	81	187	213	266	294	374	91	255	58
19	265	57	248	74	249	64	282	183	103	75
20	22	378	272	112	250	108	162	280	9	65
21	159	311	355	100	283	235	262	230	335	184
22	204	11	253	98	104	36	320	140	224	76
23	381	341	316	153	23	370	31	301	106	379
24	363	217	4	276	273	15	67	367	52	113
25	137	220	118	181	251	365	308	175	194	109
26	124	330	61	38	163	88	80	373	56	281
27	377	161	310	261	10	319	340	30	216	66
28	219	307	329	79	160	339	306	305	322	312
29	49	323	244	360	356	146	313	177	348	101
30	96	50	259	346	284	6	324	207	19	236
31	167	245	83	142	263	233	361	86	47	231
32	41	357	196	286	336	239	147	27	127	185
33	278	314	173	327	205	171	178	189	226	12
34	43	349	298	212	254	73	102	111	8	99
35	334	97	223	152	105	275	51	180	193	37
36	55	260	215	78	321	359	347	345	18	141
37	46	285	126	326	225	211	7	151	192	77
38	17	325	191							

POWER RESIDUES

	0	1	2	3	4	5	6	7	8	9
0	1	5	25	125	242	61	305	376	348	208
1	274	221	339	163	49	245	76	380	368	308
2	8	40	200	234	21	105	142	327	103	132
3	277	236	31	155	9	45	225	359	263	166
4	64	320	68	340	168	74	370	318	58	290
5	301	356	248	91	72	360	268	191	189	179
6	129	262	161	39	195	209	279	246	81	22
7	110	167	69	345	193	199	229	379	363	283
8	266	181	139	312	28	140	317	53	265	176
9	114	187	169	79	12	60	300	351	223	349
10	213	299	346	198	224	354	238	41	205	259
11	146	347	203	249	96	97	102	127	252	111
12	172	94	87	52	260	151	372	328	108	157
13	19	95	92	77	2	10	50	250	101	122
14	227	369	313	33	165	59	295	326	98	107
15	152	377	353	233	16	80	17	85	42	210
16	284	271	206	264	171	89	62	310	18	90
17	67	335	143	332	128	257	136	297	336	148
18	357	253	116	197	219	329	113	182	144	337
19	153	382	378	358	258	141	322	78	7	35
20	175	109	162	44	220	334	138	307	3	15
21	75	375	343	183	149	362	278	241	56	280
22	251	106	147	352	228	374	338	158	24	120
23	217	319	63	315	43	215	309	13	65	325
24	93	82	27	135	292	311	23	115	192	194
25	204	254	121	222	344	188	174	104	137	302
26	361	273	216	314	38	190	184	154	4	20
27	100	117	202	244	71	355	243	66	330	118
28	207	269	196	214	304	371	323	83	32	160
29	34	170	84	37	185	159	29	145	342	178
30	124	237	36	180	134	287	286	281	256	131
31	272	211	289	296	331	123	232	11	55	275
32	226	364	288	291	306	381	373	333	133	282
33	261	156	14	70	350	218	324	88	57	285
34	276	231	6	30	150	367	303	366	298	341
35	173	99	112	177	119	212	294	321	73	365
36	293	316	48	240	51	255	126	247	86	47
37	235	26	130	267	186	164	54	270	201	239
38	46	230								

P = 389

INDICES

	0	1	2	3	4	5	6	7	8	9
0		0	1	271	2	84	272	328	3	154
1	85	172	273	32	329	355	4	376	155	262
2	86	211	173	13	274	168	33	37	330	47
3	356	297	5	55	377	24	156	371	263	303
4	87	126	212	41	174	238	14	223	275	268
5	169	259	34	21	38	256	331	145	48	334
6	357	323	298	94	6	116	56	148	378	284
7	25	99	157	384	372	51	264	112	304	188
8	88	308	127	337	213	72	42	318	175	247
9	239	360	15	180	224	346	276	192	269	326
10	170	353	260	11	35	295	22	301	39	221
11	257	254	332	92	146	97	49	186	335	316
12	358	344	324	9	299	252	95	314	7	312
13	117	119	57	202	149	121	379	290	285	59
14	26	106	100	204	158	131	385	151	373	165
15	52	123	265	142	113	381	305	244	189	292
16	89	341	309	287	128	139	338	61	214	64
17	73	28	43	234	319	108	176	217	248	102
18	240	230	361	206	16	67	181	160	225	365
19	347	133	277	76	193	387	270	83	327	153
20	171	31	354	375	261	210	12	167	36	46
21	296	54	23	370	302	125	40	237	222	267
22	258	20	255	144	333	322	93	115	147	283
23	98	383	50	111	187	307	336	71	317	246
24	359	179	345	191	325	352	10	294	300	220
25	253	91	96	185	315	343	8	251	313	311
26	118	201	120	289	58	105	203	130	150	164
27	122	141	380	243	291	340	286	138	60	63
28	27	233	107	216	101	229	205	66	159	364
29	132	75	386	82	152	30	374	209	166	45
30	53	369	124	236	266	19	143	321	114	282
31	382	110	306	70	245	178	190	351	293	219
32	90	184	342	250	310	200	288	104	129	163
33	140	242	339	137	62	232	215	228	65	363
34	74	81	29	208	44	368	235	18	320	281
35	109	69	177	350	218	183	249	199	103	162
36	241	136	231	227	362	80	207	367	17	280
37	68	349	182	198	161	135	226	79	366	279
38	348	197	134	78	278	196	77	195	194	

POWER RESIDUES

	0	1	2	3	4	5	6	7	8	9
0	1	2	4	8	16	32	64	128	256	123
1	246	103	206	23	46	92	184	368	347	305
2	221	53	106	212	35	70	140	280	171	342
3	295	201	13	26	52	104	208	27	54	108
4	216	43	86	172	344	299	209	29	58	116
5	232	75	150	300	211	33	66	132	264	139
6	278	167	334	279	169	338	287	185	370	351
7	313	237	85	170	340	291	193	386	383	377
8	365	341	293	197	5	10	20	40	80	160
9	320	251	113	226	63	126	252	115	230	71
10	142	284	179	358	327	265	141	282	175	350
11	311	233	77	154	308	227	65	130	260	131
12	262	135	270	151	302	215	41	82	164	328
13	267	145	290	191	382	375	361	333	277	165
14	330	271	153	306	223	57	114	228	67	134
15	268	147	294	199	9	18	36	72	144	288
16	187	374	359	329	269	149	298	207	25	50
17	100	200	11	22	44	88	176	352	315	241
18	93	186	372	355	321	253	117	234	79	158
19	316	243	97	194	388	387	385	381	373	357
20	325	261	133	266	143	286	183	366	343	297
21	205	21	42	84	168	336	283	177	354	319
22	249	109	218	47	94	188	376	363	337	285
23	181	362	335	281	173	346	303	217	45	90
24	180	360	331	273	157	314	239	89	178	356
25	323	257	125	250	111	222	55	110	220	51
26	102	204	19	38	76	152	304	219	49	98
27	196	3	6	12	24	48	96	192	384	379
28	369	349	309	229	69	138	276	163	326	263
29	137	274	159	318	247	105	210	31	62	124
30	248	107	214	39	78	156	312	235	81	162
31	324	259	129	258	127	254	119	238	87	174
32	348	307	225	61	122	244	99	198	7	14
33	28	56	112	224	59	118	236	83	166	332
34	275	161	322	255	121	242	95	190	380	371
35	353	317	245	101	202	15	30	60	120	240
36	91	182	364	339	289	189	378	367	345	301
37	213	37	74	148	296	203	17	34	68	136
38	272	155	310	231	73	146	292	195		

P = 397

INDICES

	0	1	2	3	4	5	6	7	8	9
0		0	243	182	90	1	29	329	333	364
1	244	140	272	101	176	183	180	21	211	128
2	91	115	383	206	119	2	344	150	23	188
3	30	324	27	322	264	330	58	104	371	283
4	334	253	358	78	230	365	53	376	362	262
5	245	203	191	213	393	141	266	310	35	247
6	273	97	171	297	270	102	169	368	111	388
7	177	159	301	224	347	184	218	73	130	44
8	181	332	100	210	205	22	321	370	77	361
9	212	34	296	110	223	129	209	76	109	108
10	92	239	50	93	38	116	60	234	240	193
11	384	286	113	51	157	207	278	69	94	350
12	120	280	340	39	18	3	144	196	117	260
13	345	106	16	61	215	151	354	390	235	305
14	24	162	6	241	148	189	71	48	194	63
15	31	84	65	385	316	325	373	165	287	395
16	28	139	179	114	343	323	57	252	52	202
17	265	96	168	158	217	331	320	33	208	238
18	59	285	277	279	143	105	353	161	70	83
19	372	138	56	95	319	284	352	137	351	153
20	335	154	86	121	293	254	336	174	281	268
21	359	155	303	341	81	79	87	257	40	10
22	231	122	133	19	356	366	294	67	4	250
23	54	255	125	145	312	377	337	226	197	89
24	363	175	127	118	187	263	282	229	261	392
25	246	269	387	346	43	204	360	222	107	37
26	192	156	349	17	259	214	304	147	62	315
27	394	342	201	216	237	142	82	318	152	292
28	267	80	9	355	249	311	88	186	391	42
29	36	258	314	236	291	248	41	290	306	307
30	274	11	327	25	308	98	232	14	163	275
31	172	123	220	7	12	298	134	379	242	328
32	271	20	382	149	26	103	357	375	190	309
33	170	367	300	72	99	369	295	75	49	233
34	112	68	339	195	15	389	5	47	64	164
35	178	251	167	32	276	160	55	136	85	173
36	302	256	132	66	124	225	126	228	386	221
37	348	146	200	317	8	185	313	289	326	13
38	219	378	381	374	299	74	338	46	166	135
39	131	227	199	288	380	45	198			

POWER RESIDUES

	0	1	2	3	4	5	6	7	8	9
0	1	5	25	125	228	346	142	313	374	282
1	219	301	314	379	307	344	132	263	124	223
2	321	17	85	28	140	303	324	32	160	6
3	30	150	353	177	91	58	290	259	104	123
4	218	296	289	254	79	395	387	347	147	338
5	102	113	168	46	230	356	192	166	36	180
6	106	133	268	149	348	152	363	227	341	117
7	188	146	333	77	385	337	97	88	43	215
8	281	214	276	189	151	358	202	216	286	239
9	4	20	100	103	118	193	171	61	305	334
10	82	13	65	325	37	185	131	258	99	98
11	93	68	340	112	163	21	105	128	243	24
12	120	203	221	311	364	232	366	242	19	95
13	78	390	362	222	316	389	357	197	191	161
14	11	55	275	184	126	233	371	267	144	323
15	27	135	278	199	201	211	261	114	173	71
16	355	187	141	308	349	157	388	352	172	66
17	330	62	310	359	207	241	14	70	350	162
18	16	80	3	15	75	375	287	244	29	145
19	328	52	260	109	148	343	127	238	396	392
20	372	272	169	51	255	84	23	115	178	96
21	83	18	90	53	265	134	273	174	76	380
22	312	369	257	94	73	365	237	391	367	247
23	44	220	306	339	107	138	293	274	179	101
24	108	143	318	2	10	50	250	59	295	284
25	229	351	167	41	205	231	361	217	291	264
26	129	248	49	245	34	170	56	280	209	251
27	64	320	12	60	300	309	354	182	116	183
28	121	208	246	39	195	181	111	158	393	377
29	297	294	279	204	226	336	92	63	315	384
30	332	72	360	212	266	139	298	299	304	329
31	57	285	234	376	292	269	154	373	277	194
32	176	86	33	165	31	155	378	302	319	7
33	35	175	81	8	40	200	206	236	386	342
34	122	213	271	164	26	130	253	74	370	262
35	119	198	196	186	136	283	224	326	42	210
36	256	89	48	240	9	45	225	331	67	335
37	87	38	190	156	383	327	47	235	381	317
38	394	382	322	22	110	153	368	252	69	345
39	137	288	249	54	270	159				

P = 401

INDICES

	0	1	2	3	4	5	6	7	8	9
0		0	26	1	52	48	27	62	78	2
1	74	194	53	319	88	49	104	383	28	163
2	100	63	220	291	79	96	345	3	114	360
3	75	107	130	195	9	110	54	233	189	320
4	126	328	89	286	246	50	317	218	105	124
5	122	384	371	213	29	242	140	164	386	391
6	101	283	133	64	156	367	221	373	35	292
7	136	69	80	206	259	97	215	256	346	179
8	152	4	354	40	115	31	312	361	272	198
9	76	381	343	108	244	211	131	67	150	196
10	148	349	10	142	397	111	239	351	55	58
11	268	234	166	332	190	339	12	321	17	45
12	127	388	309	329	159	144	90	299	182	287
13	393	277	247	225	399	51	61	73	318	103
14	162	219	95	113	106	8	232	125	285	316
15	123	370	241	385	282	155	372	135	205	214
16	178	353	30	271	380	243	66	147	141	238
17	57	165	338	16	387	158	298	392	224	60
18	102	94	7	284	369	281	134	177	270	65
19	237	337	157	223	93	368	176	236	222	175
20	174	374	375	22	36	376	168	293	23	357
21	137	37	265	70	377	334	81	169	84	207
22	294	302	260	24	192	98	358	187	216	138
23	365	257	38	341	347	266	43	180	71	230
24	153	378	14	5	335	172	355	82	185	41
25	170	323	116	85	325	32	208	306	313	295
26	19	362	303	118	273	261	251	199	25	47
27	77	193	87	382	99	290	344	359	129	109
28	188	327	245	217	121	212	139	390	132	366
29	34	68	258	255	151	39	311	197	342	210
30	149	348	396	350	267	331	11	44	308	143
31	181	276	398	72	161	112	231	315	240	154
32	204	352	379	146	56	15	297	59	6	280
33	269	336	92	235	173	21	167	356	264	333
34	83	301	191	186	364	340	42	229	13	171
35	184	322	324	305	18	117	250	46	86	289
36	128	326	120	389	33	254	310	209	395	330
37	307	275	160	314	203	145	296	279	91	20
38	263	300	363	228	183	304	249	288	119	253
39	394	274	202	278	262	227	248	252	201	226
40	200	0								

POWER RESIDUES

	0	1	2	3	4	5	6	7	8	9
0	1	3	9	27	81	243	328	182	145	34
1	102	306	116	348	242	325	173	118	354	260
2	379	335	203	208	223	268	2	6	18	54
3	162	85	255	364	290	68	204	211	232	295
4	83	249	346	236	307	119	357	269	5	15
5	45	135	4	12	36	108	324	170	109	327
6	179	136	7	21	63	189	166	97	291	71
7	213	238	313	137	10	30	90	270	8	24
8	72	216	247	340	218	253	358	272	14	42
9	126	378	332	194	181	142	25	75	225	274
10	20	60	180	139	16	48	144	31	93	279
11	35	105	315	143	28	84	252	355	263	388
12	362	284	50	150	49	147	40	120	360	278
13	32	96	288	62	186	157	70	210	229	286
14	56	168	103	309	125	375	323	167	100	300
15	98	294	80	240	319	155	64	192	175	124
16	372	314	140	19	57	171	112	336	206	217
17	250	349	245	334	200	199	196	187	160	79
18	237	310	128	384	350	248	343	227	280	38
19	114	342	224	271	11	33	99	297	89	267
20	400	398	392	374	320	158	73	219	256	367
21	299	95	285	53	159	76	228	283	47	141
22	22	66	198	193	178	133	399	395	383	347
23	239	316	146	37	111	333	197	190	169	106
24	318	152	55	165	94	282	44	132	396	386
25	356	266	397	389	365	293	77	231	292	74
26	222	265	394	380	338	212	235	304	110	330
27	188	163	88	264	391	371	311	131	393	377
28	329	185	154	61	183	148	43	129	387	359
29	275	23	69	207	220	259	376	326	176	127
30	381	341	221	262	385	353	257	370	308	122
31	366	296	86	258	373	317	149	46	138	13
32	39	117	351	251	352	254	361	281	41	123
33	369	305	113	339	215	244	331	191	172	115
34	345	233	298	92	276	26	78	234	301	101
35	303	107	321	161	82	246	337	209	226	277
36	29	87	261	382	344	230	289	65	195	184
37	151	52	156	67	201	202	205	214	241	322
38	164	91	273	17	51	153	58	174	121	363
39	287	59	177	130	390	368	302	104	312	134
40										

P = 409

INDICES

	0	1	2	3	4	5	6	7	8	9
0		0	82	86	164	24	168	323	246	172
1	106	189	250	321	405	110	328	280	254	309
2	188	1	271	178	332	48	403	258	79	293
3	192	51	2	275	362	347	336	97	391	407
4	270	302	83	303	353	196	260	233	6	238
5	130	366	77	272	340	213	161	395	375	249
6	274	339	133	87	84	345	357	359	36	264
7	21	112	10	125	179	134	65	104	81	177
8	352	344	384	144	165	304	385	379	27	312
9	278	236	342	137	315	333	88	41	320	361
10	212	64	40	330	159	25	354	145	14	94
11	295	183	243	139	69	202	49	85	331	195
12	356	378	13	388	215	72	169	197	166	389
13	19	38	31	224	33	282	118	404	346	160
14	103	319	194	102	92	317	207	324	261	305
15	216	267	147	44	186	75	163	47	259	358
16	26	93	18	266	58	299	226	256	247	234
17	386	73	59	209	53	371	109	335	394	80
18	360	355	318	17	16	121	219	61	397	173
19	7	380	170	300	123	23	402	232	35	311
20	294	37	146	208	122	326	4	350	241	90
21	107	239	28	198	227	327	96	374	176	211
22	377	193	265	15	325	220	221	114	151	156
23	284	190	131	313	167	257	5	263	277	182
24	30	43	52	22	95	262	62	222	297	230
25	154	55	251	367	279	390	248	351	63	12
26	101	57	120	3	113	296	306	398	115	307
27	364	142	200	322	78	237	20	235	242	223
28	185	370	401	373	276	11	184	217	174	152
29	399	127	289	253	406	273	343	39	387	91
30	298	218	349	150	229	363	126	244	268	8
31	157	116	245	292	129	111	341	138	32	74
32	108	231	175	181	100	369	348	180	140	148
33	381	285	308	269	338	383	329	214	316	225
34	60	240	155	153	141	288	291	337	135	70
35	45	171	191	365	9	136	68	281	162	334
36	34	210	29	56	400	149	99	287	98	66
37	203	187	301	132	143	158	71	206	255	396
38	89	283	54	199	252	128	382	67	205	392
39	105	50	76	124	314	201	117	46	393	310
40	376	42	119	372	228	368	290	286	204	

POWER RESIDUES

	0	1	2	3	4	5	6	7	8	9
0	1	21	32	263	206	236	48	190	309	354
1	72	285	259	122	108	223	184	183	162	130
2	276	70	243	195	5	105	160	88	212	362
3	240	132	318	134	360	198	68	201	131	297
4	102	97	401	241	153	350	397	157	25	116
5	391	31	242	174	382	251	363	261	164	172
6	340	187	246	258	101	76	369	387	356	114
7	349	376	125	171	319	155	392	52	274	28
8	179	78	2	42	64	117	3	63	96	380
9	209	299	144	161	109	244	216	37	368	366
10	324	260	143	140	77	390	10	210	320	176
11	15	315	71	264	227	268	311	396	136	402
12	262	185	204	194	393	73	306	291	385	314
13	50	232	373	62	75	348	355	93	317	113
14	328	344	271	374	83	107	202	152	329	365
15	303	228	289	343	250	342	229	310	375	104
16	139	56	358	156	4	84	128	234	6	126
17	192	351	9	189	288	322	218	79	23	74
18	327	323	239	111	286	280	154	371	20	11
19	231	352	30	221	142	119	45	127	213	383
20	272	395	115	370	408	388	377	146	203	173
21	361	219	100	55	337	124	150	287	301	186
22	225	226	247	279	133	339	166	214	404	304
23	249	321	197	47	169	277	91	275	49	211
24	341	208	278	112	307	312	8	168	256	59
25	12	252	384	293	18	378	167	235	27	158
26	46	148	245	237	69	222	163	151	308	333
27	40	22	53	295	60	33	284	238	90	254
28	17	357	135	381	230	331	407	367	345	292
29	406	346	313	29	200	110	265	248	300	165
30	193	372	41	43	85	149	266	269	332	19
31	399	199	89	233	394	94	338	145	182	141
32	98	13	273	7	147	224	205	215	16	336
33	103	118	24	95	359	177	36	347	334	61
34	54	316	92	296	81	65	138	35	326	302
35	207	257	80	44	106	181	120	66	159	67
36	180	99	34	305	270	353	51	253	405	325
37	281	175	403	283	217	58	400	220	121	87
38	191	330	386	335	82	86	170	298	123	129
39	255	38	389	398	178	57	379	188	267	290
40	364	282	196	26	137	14	294	39		

P = 419

INDICES

	0	1	2	3	4	5	6	7	8	9
0		0	1	100	2	272	101	44	3	200
1	273	287	102	304	45	372	4	393	201	339
2	274	144	288	280	103	126	305	300	46	50
3	373	327	5	387	394	316	202	24	340	404
4	275	136	145	14	289	54	281	220	104	88
5	127	75	306	269	301	141	47	21	51	266
6	374	377	328	244	6	158	388	83	395	380
7	317	361	203	238	25	226	341	331	405	40
8	276	400	137	357	146	247	15	150	290	33
9	55	348	282	9	221	193	105	116	89	69
10	128	161	76	251	307	416	270	198	302	391
11	142	124	48	385	22	134	52	86	267	19
12	375	156	378	236	329	398	245	31	7	114
13	159	414	389	383	84	154	396	112	381	110
14	318	320	362	173	204	322	239	188	26	364
15	227	294	342	175	332	181	406	206	41	369
16	277	324	401	217	138	241	358	37	147	190
17	248	121	16	28	151	170	291	366	34	167
18	56	229	349	59	283	296	10	262	222	344
19	194	232	106	177	117	258	90	334	70	352
20	129	183	162	94	77	408	252	62	308	208
21	417	99	271	43	199	286	303	371	392	338
22	143	279	125	299	49	326	386	315	23	403
23	135	13	53	219	87	74	268	140	20	265
24	376	243	157	82	379	360	237	225	330	39
25	399	356	246	149	32	347	8	192	115	68
26	160	250	415	197	390	123	384	133	85	18
27	155	235	397	30	113	413	382	153	111	109
28	319	172	321	187	363	293	174	180	205	368
29	323	216	240	36	189	120	27	169	365	166
30	228	58	295	261	343	231	176	257	333	351
31	182	93	407	61	207	98	42	285	370	337
32	278	298	325	314	402	12	218	73	139	264
33	242	81	359	224	38	355	148	346	191	67
34	249	196	122	132	17	234	29	412	152	108
35	171	186	292	179	367	215	35	119	168	165
36	57	260	230	256	350	92	60	97	284	336
37	297	313	11	72	263	80	223	354	345	66
38	195	131	233	411	107	185	178	214	118	164
39	259	255	91	96	335	312	71	79	353	65
40	130	410	184	213	163	254	95	311	78	64
41	409	212	253	310	63	211	309	210	209	

POWER RESIDUES

	0	1	2	3	4	5	6	7	8	9
0	1	2	4	8	16	32	64	128	256	93
1	186	372	325	231	43	86	172	344	269	119
2	238	57	114	228	37	74	148	296	173	346
3	273	127	254	89	178	356	293	167	334	249
4	79	158	316	213	7	14	28	56	112	224
5	29	58	116	232	45	90	180	360	301	183
6	366	313	207	414	409	399	379	339	259	99
7	198	396	373	327	235	51	102	204	408	397
8	375	331	243	67	134	268	117	234	49	98
9	196	392	365	311	203	406	393	367	315	211
10	3	6	12	24	48	96	192	384	349	279
11	139	278	137	274	129	258	97	194	388	357
12	295	171	342	265	111	222	25	50	100	200
13	400	381	343	267	115	230	41	82	164	328
14	237	55	110	220	21	42	84	168	336	253
15	87	174	348	277	135	270	121	242	65	130
16	260	101	202	404	389	359	299	179	358	297
17	175	350	281	143	286	153	306	193	386	353
18	287	155	310	201	402	385	351	283	147	294
19	169	338	257	95	190	380	341	263	107	214
20	9	18	36	72	144	288	157	314	209	418
21	417	415	411	403	387	355	291	163	326	233
22	47	94	188	376	333	247	75	150	300	181
23	362	305	191	382	345	271	123	246	73	146
24	292	165	330	241	63	126	252	85	170	340
25	261	103	206	412	405	391	363	307	195	390
26	361	303	187	374	329	239	59	118	236	53
27	106	212	5	10	20	40	80	160	320	221
28	23	46	92	184	368	317	215	11	22	44
29	88	176	352	285	151	302	185	370	321	223
30	27	54	108	216	13	26	52	104	208	416
31	413	407	395	371	323	227	35	70	140	280
32	141	282	145	290	161	322	225	31	62	124
33	248	77	154	308	197	394	369	319	219	19
34	38	76	152	304	189	378	337	255	91	182
35	364	309	199	398	377	335	251	83	166	332
36	245	71	142	284	149	298	177	354	289	159
37	318	217	15	30	60	120	240	61	122	244
38	69	138	276	133	266	113	226	33	66	132
39	264	109	218	17	34	68	136	272	125	250
40	81	162	324	229	39	78	156	312	205	410
41	401	383	347	275	131	262	105	210		

P = 421

INDICES

	0	1	2	3	4	5	6	7	8	9
0		0	1	404	2	278	405	366	3	388
1	279	376	406	63	367	262	4	286	389	237
2	280	350	377	187	407	136	64	372	368	105
3	263	116	5	360	287	224	390	201	238	47
4	281	307	351	109	378	246	188	33	408	312
5	137	270	65	401	373	234	369	221	106	267
6	264	39	117	334	6	341	361	42	288	171
7	225	293	391	301	202	120	239	322	48	416
8	282	356	308	337	352	144	110	89	379	129
9	247	9	189	100	34	95	409	148	313	344
10	138	74	271	176	66	208	402	364	374	260
11	235	185	370	114	222	45	107	31	268	232
12	265	332	40	291	118	414	335	87	7	93
13	342	174	362	183	43	230	289	85	172	228
14	226	17	294	19	392	383	302	296	203	80
15	121	21	240	254	323	394	49	153	417	385
16	283	133	357	304	309	218	338	298	353	126
17	145	205	111	329	90	82	380	251	130	123
18	248	56	10	23	190	59	101	242	35	318
19	96	256	410	13	149	325	314	161	345	396
20	139	26	75	51	272	165	177	155	67	193
21	209	419	403	277	365	387	375	62	261	285
22	236	349	186	135	371	104	115	359	223	200
23	46	306	108	245	32	311	269	400	233	220
24	266	38	333	340	41	170	292	300	119	321
25	415	355	336	143	88	128	8	99	94	147
26	343	73	175	207	363	259	184	113	44	30
27	231	331	290	413	86	92	173	182	229	84
28	227	16	18	382	295	79	20	253	393	152
29	384	132	303	217	297	125	204	328	81	250
30	122	55	22	58	241	317	255	12	324	160
31	395	25	50	164	154	192	418	276	386	61
32	284	348	134	103	358	199	305	244	310	399
33	219	37	339	169	299	320	354	142	127	98
34	146	72	206	258	112	29	330	412	91	181
35	83	15	381	78	252	151	131	216	124	327
36	249	54	57	316	11	159	24	163	191	275
37	60	347	102	198	243	398	36	168	319	141
38	97	71	257	28	411	180	14	77	150	215
39	326	53	315	158	162	274	346	197	397	167
40	140	70	27	179	76	214	52	157	273	196
41	166	69	178	213	156	195	68	212	194	211
42	210	0								

POWER RESIDUES

	0	1	2	3	4	5	6	7	8	9
0	1	2	4	8	16	32	64	128	256	91
1	182	364	307	193	386	351	281	141	282	143
2	286	151	302	183	366	311	201	402	383	345
3	269	117	234	47	94	188	376	331	241	61
4	122	244	67	134	268	115	230	39	78	156
5	312	203	406	391	361	301	181	362	303	185
6	370	319	217	13	26	52	104	208	416	411
7	401	381	341	261	101	202	404	387	353	285
8	149	298	175	350	279	137	274	127	254	87
9	174	348	275	129	258	95	190	380	339	257
10	93	186	372	323	225	29	58	116	232	43
11	86	172	344	267	113	226	31	62	124	248
12	75	150	300	179	358	295	169	338	255	89
13	178	356	291	161	322	223	25	50	100	200
14	400	379	337	253	85	170	340	259	97	194
15	388	355	289	157	314	207	414	407	393	365
16	309	197	394	367	313	205	410	399	377	333
17	245	69	138	276	131	262	103	206	412	403
18	385	349	277	133	266	111	222	23	46	92
19	184	368	315	209	418	415	409	397	373	325
20	229	37	74	148	296	171	342	263	105	210
21	420	419	417	413	405	389	357	293	165	330
22	239	57	114	228	35	70	140	280	139	278
23	135	270	119	238	55	110	220	19	38	76
24	152	304	187	374	327	233	45	90	180	360
25	299	177	354	287	153	306	191	382	343	265
26	109	218	15	30	60	120	240	59	118	236
27	51	102	204	408	395	369	317	213	5	10
28	20	40	80	160	320	219	17	34	68	136
29	272	123	246	71	142	284	147	294	167	334
30	247	73	146	292	163	326	231	41	82	164
31	328	235	49	98	196	392	363	305	189	378
32	335	249	77	154	308	195	390	359	297	173
33	346	271	121	242	63	126	252	83	166	332
34	243	65	130	260	99	198	396	371	321	221
35	21	42	84	168	336	251	81	162	324	227
36	33	66	132	264	107	214	7	14	28	56
37	112	224	27	54	108	216	11	22	44	88
38	176	352	283	145	290	159	318	215	9	18
39	36	72	144	288	155	310	199	398	375	329
40	237	53	106	212	3	6	12	24	48	96
41	192	384	347	273	125	250	79	158	316	211
42										

P = 431

INDICES

	0	1	2	3	4	5	6	7	8	9
0		0	220	280	10	342	70	1	230	130
1	132	418	290	167	221	192	20	31	350	174
2	352	281	208	326	80	254	387	410	11	248
3	412	59	240	268	251	343	140	307	394	17
4	142	364	71	83	428	42	116	315	300	2
5	44	311	177	416	200	330	231	24	38	134
6	202	224	279	131	30	79	58	393	41	176
7	133	57	360	361	97	104	184	419	237	13
8	362	260	154	323	291	373	303	98	218	309
9	262	168	336	339	105	86	90	288	222	118
10	264	185	101	379	397	193	206	55	420	332
11	120	157	21	271	244	238	258	297	354	32
12	422	406	14	214	69	166	351	409	250	363
13	299	329	278	175	183	322	261	287	396	156
14	353	165	277	155	150	160	151	282	317	170
15	324	358	404	161	209	401	27	292	233	266
16	152	327	50	188	374	180	113	283	81	334
17	163	304	93	368	318	255	8	414	99	356
18	52	171	388	74	126	219	129	19	325	411
19	306	427	310	37	78	359	12	302	338	263
20	54	243	405	249	321	276	169	26	187	162
21	413	125	426	337	275	425	210	60	122	211
22	340	198	377	402	241	384	61	106	34	190
23	28	269	48	123	87	227	144	293	252	95
24	212	91	196	110	234	344	4	341	289	173
25	386	267	141	314	199	223	40	103	153	308
26	89	378	119	296	68	328	395	159	403	265
27	112	367	51	18	77	242	186	424	376	189
28	143	109	385	102	67	366	375	365	370	62
29	380	138	371	181	72	46	107	398	390	63
30	114	84	148	35	194	136	381	284	429	229
31	191	207	247	139	82	43	23	29	56	236
32	372	335	117	205	270	421	408	182	164	316
33	400	49	333	7	73	305	301	320	124	121
34	383	47	94	3	313	88	158	76	108	369
35	45	147	228	22	204	399	319	312	146	145
36	272	348	391	256	178	273	294	245	346	64
37	9	417	349	253	239	16	115	415	201	392
38	96	259	217	85	100	331	257	213	298	286
39	149	357	232	179	92	355	128	36	53	25
40	274	197	33	226	195	172	39	295	111	423
41	66	137	389	135	246	235	407	6	382	75
42	203	347	345	15	216	285	127	225	65	5
43	215	0								

POWER RESIDUES

	0	1	2	3	4	5	6	7	8	9
0	1	7	49	343	246	429	417	333	176	370
1	4	28	196	79	122	423	375	39	273	187
2	16	112	353	316	57	399	207	156	230	317
3	64	17	119	402	228	303	397	193	58	406
4	256	68	45	315	50	350	295	341	232	331
5	162	272	180	398	200	107	318	71	66	31
6	217	226	289	299	369	428	410	284	264	124
7	6	42	294	334	183	419	347	274	194	65
8	24	168	314	43	301	383	95	234	345	260
9	96	241	394	172	342	239	380	74	87	178
10	384	102	283	257	75	94	227	296	348	281
11	243	408	270	166	300	376	46	322	99	262
12	110	339	218	233	338	211	184	426	396	186
13	9	63	10	70	59	413	305	411	291	313
14	36	252	40	280	236	359	358	351	302	390
15	144	146	160	258	82	143	139	111	346	267
16	145	153	209	170	328	141	125	13	91	206
17	149	181	405	249	19	133	69	52	364	393
18	165	293	327	134	76	101	276	208	163	279
19	229	310	15	105	304	404	242	401	221	254
20	54	378	60	420	354	323	106	311	22	154
21	216	219	240	387	123	430	424	382	88	185
22	2	14	98	255	61	427	403	235	352	309
23	8	56	392	158	244	415	319	78	115	374
24	32	224	275	201	114	367	414	312	29	203
25	128	34	238	373	25	175	363	386	116	381
26	81	136	90	199	100	269	159	251	33	231
27	324	113	360	365	400	214	205	142	132	62
28	3	21	147	167	307	425	389	137	97	248
29	12	84	157	237	366	407	263	117	388	130
30	48	336	197	86	171	335	190	37	259	89
31	192	51	357	344	253	47	329	148	174	356
32	337	204	135	83	150	188	23	161	265	131
33	55	385	109	332	169	321	92	213	198	93
34	220	247	5	35	245	422	368	421	361	372
35	18	126	20	140	118	395	179	391	151	195
36	72	73	80	129	41	287	285	271	173	349
37	288	292	320	85	164	286	278	222	261	103
38	290	306	418	340	225	282	250	26	182	412
39	298	362	379	67	38	266	138	104	297	355
40	330	155	223	268	152	202	121	416	326	127
41	27	189	30	210	177	377	53	371	11	77
42	108	325	120	409	277	215	212	191	44	308
43										

P = 433

INDICES

	0	1	2	3	4	5	6	7	8	9
0		0	78	400	156	1	46	365	234	368
1	79	130	124	274	11	401	312	16	14	409
2	157	333	208	179	202	2	352	336	89	109
3	47	421	390	98	94	366	92	6	55	242
4	235	316	411	105	286	369	257	359	280	298
5	80	416	430	350	414	131	167	377	187	8
6	125	329	67	301	36	275	176	159	172	147
7	12	103	170	387	84	402	133	63	320	270
8	313	304	394	229	57	17	183	77	364	123
9	15	207	335	389	5	410	358	429	376	66
10	158	169	62	393	76	334	428	61	60	244
11	209	406	245	253	23	180	265	210	86	381
12	203	260	407	284	145	3	379	246	114	73
13	353	51	254	342	237	337	250	24	225	128
14	90	327	181	404	248	110	33	266	162	43
15	48	189	211	384	141	422	398	87	348	318
16	391	112	382	199	40	99	307	204	135	116
17	95	345	261	215	155	367	10	408	201	108
18	93	241	285	297	413	7	35	146	83	269
19	56	122	4	65	75	243	22	380	144	72
20	236	127	247	42	140	317	39	115	154	107
21	412	268	74	71	139	106	138	354	322	355
22	287	290	52	196	323	370	331	255	101	356
23	258	31	343	20	288	360	164	238	27	291
24	281	220	338	272	53	299	362	251	223	197
25	81	69	25	309	324	417	192	226	151	371
26	431	45	129	311	332	351	420	91	315	256
27	415	166	328	175	102	132	303	182	206	357
28	168	427	405	264	259	378	50	249	326	32
29	188	397	111	306	344	9	240	34	121	21
30	126	38	267	137	289	330	30	163	219	361
31	68	191	44	419	165	302	426	49	396	239
32	37	29	190	425	28	276	277	212	118	292
33	177	278	385	374	282	160	213	142	194	221
34	173	119	423	231	339	148	293	399	233	273
35	13	178	88	97	54	104	279	349	186	300
36	171	386	319	228	363	388	375	392	59	252
37	85	283	113	341	224	403	161	383	347	198
38	134	214	200	296	82	64	143	41	153	70
39	321	195	100	19	26	271	222	308	150	310
40	314	174	205	263	325	305	120	136	218	418
41	395	424	117	373	193	230	232	96	185	227
42	58	340	346	295	152	18	149	262	217	372
43	184	294	216							

POWER RESIDUES

	0	1	2	3	4	5	6	7	8	9
0	1	5	25	125	192	94	37	185	59	295
1	176	14	70	350	18	90	17	85	425	393
2	233	299	196	114	137	252	394	238	324	321
3	306	231	289	146	297	186	64	320	301	206
4	164	387	203	149	312	261	6	30	150	317
5	286	131	222	244	354	38	190	84	420	368
6	108	107	102	77	385	193	99	62	310	251
7	389	213	199	129	212	194	104	87	2	10
8	50	250	384	188	74	370	118	157	352	28
9	140	267	36	180	34	170	417	353	33	165
10	392	228	274	71	355	43	215	209	179	29
11	145	292	161	372	128	207	169	412	328	341
12	406	298	191	89	12	60	300	201	139	262
13	11	55	275	76	380	168	407	303	216	214
14	204	154	337	386	198	124	187	69	345	426
15	398	258	424	388	208	174	4	20	100	67
16	335	376	148	307	236	314	271	56	280	101
17	72	360	68	340	401	273	66	330	351	23
18	115	142	277	86	430	418	358	58	290	151
19	322	311	256	414	338	391	223	249	379	163
20	382	178	24	120	167	402	278	91	22	110
21	117	152	327	336	381	173	432	428	408	308
22	241	339	396	248	374	138	257	419	363	83
23	415	343	416	348	8	40	200	134	237	319
24	296	181	39	195	109	112	127	202	144	287
25	136	247	369	113	132	227	269	46	230	284
26	121	172	427	403	283	116	147	302	211	189
27	79	395	243	349	13	65	325	326	331	356
28	48	240	334	371	123	182	44	220	234	304
29	221	239	329	346	431	423	383	183	49	245
30	359	63	315	276	81	405	293	166	397	253
31	399	263	16	80	400	268	41	205	159	362
32	78	390	218	224	254	404	288	141	272	61
33	305	226	264	21	105	92	27	135	242	344
34	421	373	133	232	294	171	422	378	158	357
35	53	265	26	130	217	219	229	279	96	47
36	235	309	246	364	88	7	35	175	9	45
37	225	259	429	413	333	366	98	57	285	126
38	197	119	162	377	153	332	361	73	365	93
39	32	160	367	103	82	410	318	291	156	347
40	3	15	75	375	143	282	111	122	177	19
41	95	42	210	184	54	270	51	255	409	313
42	266	31	155	342	411	323	316	281	106	97
43	52	260								

P = 439

INDICES

	0	1	2	3	4	5	6	7	8	9
0		0	78	315	156	124	393	162	234	192
1	202	80	33	26	240	1	312	211	270	100
2	280	39	158	197	111	248	104	69	318	374
3	79	103	390	395	289	286	348	91	178	341
4	358	391	117	209	236	316	275	339	189	324
5	326	88	182	424	147	204	396	415	14	161
6	157	90	181	354	30	150	35	355	367	74
7	364	290	426	264	169	125	256	242	419	331
8	436	384	31	206	195	335	287	251	314	269
9	394	188	353	418	417	224	267	151	402	272
10	404	349	166	132	260	163	64	143	225	378
11	282	406	36	308	55	321	92	218	239	373
12	235	160	168	268	259	372	432	356	108	86
13	228	179	113	262	433	193	7	222	152	62
14	4	216	368	106	66	60	342	201	247	357
15	203	363	334	403	320	227	59	75	409	301
16	76	359	24	11	109	81	284	304	273	52
17	413	292	365	121	329	410	392	38	347	87
18	34	383	266	405	431	215	58	291	57	231
19	302	118	345	127	229	27	42	19	350	94
20	44	232	427	98	244	77	210	389	338	180
21	241	352	142	167	221	333	303	265	18	141
22	360	237	46	84	114	2	386	361	133	22
23	399	119	170	429	296	25	317	208	13	263
24	313	131	238	261	246	10	346	126	337	83
25	12	276	72	277	434	212	186	47	164	253
26	306	128	257	173	191	110	340	146	73	194
27	271	54	85	65	300	328	230	243	140	295
28	82	190	294	278	8	101	184	115	144	422
29	138	28	420	123	279	285	325	149	435	223
30	281	371	3	226	412	214	43	332	398	9
31	305	327	137	213	153	40	49	387	379	16
32	154	20	437	311	102	274	89	255	187	63
33	159	6	362	283	382	41	351	385	130	185
34	53	183	370	48	5	198	199	134	407	175
35	50	95	32	68	116	414	425	250	165	217
36	112	200	23	37	344	388	45	207	71	145
37	293	148	136	254	369	249	135	400	309	376
38	380	233	196	177	423	366	205	401	307	107
39	105	408	120	56	97	17	428	336	172	139
40	122	397	310	129	67	70	176	171	322	298
41	155	99	288	323	29	330	416	377	258	61
42	319	51	430	93	220	21	245	252	299	421
43	411	15	381	174	343	375	96	297	219	

POWER RESIDUES

	0	1	2	3	4	5	6	7	8	9
0	1	15	225	302	140	344	331	136	284	309
1	245	163	250	238	58	431	319	395	218	197
2	321	425	229	362	162	235	13	195	291	414
3	64	82	352	12	180	66	112	363	177	21
4	315	335	196	306	200	366	222	257	343	316
5	350	421	169	340	271	114	393	188	186	156
6	145	419	139	329	106	273	144	404	353	27
7	405	368	252	268	69	157	160	205	2	30
8	11	165	280	249	223	272	129	179	51	326
9	61	37	116	423	199	351	436	394	203	411
10	19	285	324	31	26	390	143	389	128	164
11	265	24	360	132	224	287	354	42	191	231
12	392	173	400	293	5	75	247	193	261	403
13	338	241	103	228	347	376	372	312	290	399
14	278	219	212	107	288	369	267	54	371	297
15	65	97	138	314	320	410	4	60	22	330
16	121	59	7	105	258	358	102	213	122	74
17	232	407	398	263	433	349	406	383	38	131
18	209	62	52	341	286	339	256	328	91	48
19	281	264	9	135	269	84	382	23	345	346
20	361	147	10	150	55	386	83	367	237	43
21	206	17	255	313	305	185	141	359	117	438
22	424	214	137	299	95	108	303	155	130	194
23	276	189	201	381	8	120	44	221	242	118
24	14	210	77	277	204	426	244	148	25	375
25	357	87	427	259	373	327	76	262	418	124
26	104	243	133	239	73	217	182	96	123	89
27	18	270	99	168	325	46	251	253	283	294
28	20	300	110	333	166	295	35	86	412	34
29	71	187	171	370	282	279	234	437	409	428
30	274	159	190	216	167	310	260	388	113	378
31	402	323	16	240	88	3	45	236	28	420
32	154	115	408	413	49	296	50	311	275	174
33	415	79	307	215	152	85	397	248	208	47
34	266	39	146	434	364	192	246	178	36	101
35	198	336	211	92	63	67	127	149	40	161
36	220	227	332	151	70	172	385	68	142	374
37	342	301	125	119	29	435	379	417	109	318
38	380	432	334	181	81	337	226	317	365	207
39	32	41	176	6	90	33	56	401	308	230
40	377	387	98	153	100	183	111	348	391	158
41	175	430	304	170	355	57	416	94	93	78
42	292	429	289	384	53	356	72	202	396	233
43	422	184	126	134	254	298	80	322		

P = 443

INDICES

	0	1	2	3	4	5	6	7	8	9
0		0	1	318	2	241	319	235	3	194
1	242	295	320	286	236	117	4	376	195	407
2	243	111	296	133	321	40	287	70	237	107
3	118	179	5	171	377	34	196	122	408	162
4	244	150	112	265	297	435	134	270	322	28
5	41	252	288	183	71	94	238	283	108	104
6	119	432	180	429	6	85	172	52	378	9
7	35	278	197	143	123	358	409	88	163	302
8	245	388	151	217	113	175	266	425	298	202
9	436	79	135	55	271	206	323	313	29	47
10	42	381	253	398	289	352	184	336	72	12
11	95	440	239	192	284	374	109	38	105	169
12	120	148	433	26	181	281	430	83	7	141
13	86	386	173	200	53	311	379	350	10	190
14	36	146	279	139	198	348	144	346	124	126
15	359	366	410	128	89	420	164	361	303	59
16	246	368	389	258	152	412	218	232	114	130
17	176	159	267	91	426	275	299	422	203	395
18	437	166	80	308	136	363	56	229	272	305
19	207	210	324	61	314	403	30	248	48	213
20	43	370	382	342	254	391	399	327	290	260
21	353	331	185	154	337	64	73	414	13	19
22	96	220	441	317	240	234	193	294	285	116
23	375	406	110	132	39	69	106	178	170	33
24	121	161	149	264	434	269	27	251	182	93
25	282	103	431	428	84	51	8	277	142	357
26	87	301	387	216	174	424	201	78	54	205
27	312	46	380	397	351	335	11	439	191	373
28	37	168	147	25	280	82	140	385	199	310
29	349	189	145	138	347	345	125	365	127	419
30	360	58	367	257	411	231	129	158	90	274
31	421	394	165	307	362	228	304	209	60	402
32	247	212	369	341	390	326	259	330	153	63
33	413	18	219	316	233	293	115	405	131	68
34	177	32	160	263	268	250	92	102	427	50
35	276	356	300	215	423	77	204	45	396	334
36	438	372	167	24	81	384	309	188	137	344
37	364	418	57	256	230	157	273	393	306	227
38	208	401	211	340	325	329	62	17	315	292
39	404	67	31	262	249	101	49	355	214	76
40	44	333	371	23	383	187	343	417	255	156
41	392	226	400	339	328	16	291	66	261	100
42	354	75	332	22	186	416	155	225	338	15
43	65	99	74	21	415	224	14	98	20	223
44	97	222	221							

POWER RESIDUES

	0	1	2	3	4	5	6	7	8	9
0	1	2	4	8	16	32	64	128	256	69
1	138	276	109	218	436	429	415	387	331	219
2	438	433	423	403	363	283	123	246	49	98
3	196	392	341	239	35	70	140	280	117	234
4	25	50	100	200	400	357	271	99	198	396
5	349	255	67	134	268	93	186	372	301	159
6	318	193	386	329	215	430	417	391	339	235
7	27	54	108	216	432	421	399	355	267	91
8	182	364	285	127	254	65	130	260	77	154
9	308	173	346	249	55	110	220	440	437	431
10	419	395	347	251	59	118	236	29	58	116
11	232	21	42	84	168	336	229	15	30	60
12	120	240	37	74	148	296	149	298	153	306
13	169	338	233	23	46	92	184	368	293	143
14	286	129	258	73	146	292	141	282	121	242
15	41	82	164	328	213	426	409	375	307	171
16	342	241	39	78	156	312	181	362	281	119
17	238	33	66	132	264	85	170	340	237	31
18	62	124	248	53	106	212	424	405	367	291
19	139	278	113	226	9	18	36	72	144	288
20	133	266	89	178	356	269	95	190	380	317
21	191	382	321	199	398	353	263	83	166	332
22	221	442	441	439	435	427	411	379	315	187
23	374	305	167	334	225	7	14	28	56	112
24	224	5	10	20	40	80	160	320	197	394
25	345	247	51	102	204	408	373	303	163	326
26	209	418	393	343	243	43	86	172	344	245
27	47	94	188	376	309	175	350	257	71	142
28	284	125	250	57	114	228	13	26	52	104
29	208	416	389	335	227	11	22	44	88	176
30	352	261	79	158	316	189	378	313	183	366
31	289	135	270	97	194	388	333	223	3	6
32	12	24	48	96	192	384	325	207	414	385
33	327	211	422	401	359	275	107	214	428	413
34	383	323	203	406	369	295	147	294	145	290
35	137	274	105	210	420	397	351	259	75	150
36	300	157	314	185	370	297	151	302	161	322
37	201	402	361	279	115	230	17	34	68	136
38	272	101	202	404	365	287	131	262	81	162
39	324	205	410	377	311	179	358	273	103	206
40	412	381	319	195	390	337	231	19	38	76
41	152	304	165	330	217	434	425	407	371	299
42	155	310	177	354	265	87	174	348	253	63
43	126	252	61	122	244	45	90	180	360	277
44	111	222								

P = 449

INDICES

	0	1	2	3	4	5	6	7	8	9
0		0	254	1	60	96	255	44	314	2
1	350	264	61	115	298	97	120	347	256	177
2	156	45	70	108	315	192	369	3	104	425
3	351	23	374	265	153	140	62	259	431	116
4	410	438	299	51	324	98	362	143	121	88
5	446	348	175	102	257	360	358	178	231	242
6	157	250	277	46	180	211	71	112	407	109
7	394	77	316	233	65	193	237	308	370	385
8	216	4	244	281	105	443	305	426	130	188
9	352	159	168	24	397	273	375	414	342	266
10	252	262	154	423	429	141	356	209	63	279
11	166	260	164	389	432	204	37	117	48	391
12	411	80	56	439	83	288	300	182	434	52
13	17	133	325	221	366	99	213	206	363	149
14	200	144	331	379	122	73	39	89	319	29
15	447	59	43	349	114	119	176	69	191	103
16	22	152	258	409	50	361	87	174	359	230
17	249	179	111	393	232	236	384	243	442	129
18	158	396	413	251	422	355	278	163	203	47
19	79	82	181	16	220	212	148	330	72	318
20	58	113	68	21	408	86	229	110	235	441
21	395	421	162	78	15	147	317	67	85	234
22	420	14	66	419	418	194	195	290	238	196
23	10	309	291	93	371	239	302	386	197	171
24	217	11	334	5	310	184	245	292	337	282
25	94	296	106	372	436	444	240	405	306	303
26	271	427	387	54	131	198	27	189	172	382
27	353	218	19	160	12	8	169	335	403	25
28	6	135	398	311	137	274	185	34	376	246
29	327	415	293	400	343	338	125	267	283	223
30	253	95	313	263	297	346	155	107	368	424
31	373	139	430	437	323	142	445	101	357	241
32	276	210	406	76	64	307	215	280	304	187
33	167	272	341	261	428	208	165	388	36	390
34	55	287	433	132	365	205	199	378	38	28
35	42	118	190	151	49	173	248	392	383	128
36	412	354	202	81	219	329	57	20	228	440
37	161	146	84	13	417	289	9	92	301	170
38	333	183	336	295	435	404	270	53	26	381
39	18	7	402	134	136	33	326	399	124	222
40	312	345	367	138	322	100	275	75	214	186
41	340	207	35	286	364	377	41	150	247	127
42	201	328	227	145	416	91	332	294	269	380
43	401	32	123	344	321	74	339	285	40	126
44	226	90	268	31	320	284	225	30	224	

POWER RESIDUES

	0	1	2	3	4	5	6	7	8	9
0	1	3	9	27	81	243	280	391	275	376
1	230	241	274	373	221	214	193	130	390	272
2	367	203	160	31	93	279	388	266	349	149
3	447	443	431	395	287	412	338	116	348	146
4	438	416	350	152	7	21	63	189	118	354
5	164	43	129	387	263	340	122	366	200	151
6	4	12	36	108	324	74	222	217	202	157
7	22	66	198	145	435	407	323	71	213	190
8	121	363	191	124	372	218	205	166	49	147
9	441	425	377	233	250	301	5	15	45	135
10	405	317	53	159	28	84	252	307	23	69
11	207	172	67	201	154	13	39	117	351	155
12	16	48	144	432	398	296	439	419	359	179
13	88	264	343	131	393	281	394	284	403	311
14	35	105	315	47	141	423	371	215	196	139
15	417	353	161	34	102	306	20	60	180	91
16	273	370	212	187	112	336	110	330	92	276
17	379	239	268	355	167	52	156	19	57	171
18	64	192	127	381	245	286	409	329	89	267
19	352	158	25	75	225	226	229	238	265	346
20	140	420	362	188	115	345	137	411	335	107
21	321	65	195	136	408	326	80	240	271	364
22	194	133	399	299	448	446	440	422	368	206
23	169	58	174	73	219	208	175	76	228	235
24	256	319	59	177	82	246	289	418	356	170
25	61	183	100	300	2	6	18	54	162	37
26	111	333	101	303	11	33	99	297	442	428
27	386	260	331	95	285	406	320	62	186	109
28	327	83	249	298	445	437	413	341	125	375
29	227	232	247	292	427	383	251	304	14	42
30	126	378	236	259	328	86	258	325	77	231
31	244	283	400	302	8	24	72	216	199	148
32	444	434	404	314	44	132	396	290	421	365
33	197	142	426	380	242	277	382	248	295	436
34	410	332	98	294	433	401	305	17	51	153
35	10	30	90	270	361	185	106	318	56	168
36	55	165	46	138	414	344	134	402	308	26
37	78	234	253	310	32	96	288	415	347	143
38	429	389	269	358	176	79	237	262	337	113
39	339	119	357	173	70	210	181	94	282	397
40	293	430	392	278	385	257	322	68	204	163
41	40	120	360	182	97	291	424	374	224	223
42	220	211	184	103	309	29	87	261	334	104
43	312	38	114	342	128	384	254	313	41	123
44	369	209	178	85	255	316	50	150		

P = 457

INDICES

	0	1	2	3	4	5	6	7	8	9
0		0	162	394	324	345	100	44	30	332
1	51	201	262	1	206	283	192	348	38	260
2	213	438	363	181	424	234	163	270	368	308
3	445	203	354	139	54	389	200	423	422	395
4	375	127	144	447	69	221	343	406	130	88
5	396	286	325	337	432	90	74	198	14	253
6	151	173	365	376	60	346	301	218	216	119
7	95	331	362	388	129	172	128	245	101	248
8	81	208	289	27	306	237	153	246	231	145
9	383	45	49	141	112	149	292	23	250	77
10	102	241	448	125	31	327	43	212	138	342
11	252	361	236	249	360	70	176	333	415	392
12	313	402	335	65	71	123	82	418	222	385
13	52	350	7	304	380	159	378	177	281	209
14	257	344	37	202	68	197	94	26	291	341
15	334	158	290	224	407	92	263	268	410	275
16	243	225	370	416	451	28	189	131	12	2
17	399	136	315	427	408	278	393	191	307	143
18	89	215	207	111	211	312	303	93	274	314
19	311	238	454	397	185	284	412	442	239	319
20	264	156	403	352	154	16	287	57	193	5
21	33	455	205	269	374	336	300	247	48	326
22	414	349	67	267	398	110	411	4	66	294
23	232	183	338	170	39	295	121	186	98	276
24	19	72	108	146	41	433	227	261	233	421
25	285	59	244	382	124	175	384	36	91	11
26	214	184	56	413	169	226	10	83	86	46
27	321	75	84	439	339	435	443	317	371	79
28	419	165	50	180	199	87	364	171	230	240
29	359	417	256	223	188	142	453	15	47	182
30	40	35	320	179	452	62	386	106	113	63
31	254	322	425	296	430	265	116	29	437	53
32	405	150	387	152	76	235	122	280	157	450
33	190	310	351	299	293	107	174	85	164	187
34	105	404	298	132	21	8	133	24	114	366
35	440	271	99	259	353	220	13	330	305	22
36	251	64	377	340	369	277	273	155	373	3
37	18	381	9	78	255	61	436	309	20	329
38	17	356	400	357	160	134	103	323	347	444
39	446	73	118	288	148	137	401	379	25	242
40	426	302	318	204	109	97	58	168	316	358
41	178	115	449	297	219	372	355	147	167	194
42	195	428	161	282	367	126	431	217	80	140
43	42	391	6	196	409	135	210	441	32	266
44	120	420	55	434	229	34	429	279	104	258
45	272	328	117	96	166	390	228			

POWER RESIDUES

	0	1	2	3	4	5	6	7	8	9
0	1	13	169	369	227	209	432	132	345	372
1	266	259	168	356	58	297	205	380	370	240
2	378	344	359	97	347	398	147	83	165	317
3	8	104	438	210	445	301	257	142	18	234
4	300	244	430	106	7	91	269	298	218	92
5	282	10	130	319	34	442	262	207	406	251
6	64	375	305	309	361	123	228	222	144	44
7	115	124	241	391	56	271	324	99	373	279
8	428	80	126	267	272	337	268	285	49	180
9	55	258	155	187	146	70	453	405	238	352
10	6	78	100	386	448	340	307	335	242	404
11	225	183	94	308	348	411	316	452	392	69
12	440	236	326	125	254	103	425	41	76	74
13	48	167	343	346	385	435	171	395	108	33
14	429	93	295	179	42	89	243	417	394	95
15	321	60	323	86	204	367	201	328	151	135
16	384	422	2	26	338	281	454	418	407	264
17	233	287	75	61	336	255	116	137	410	303
18	283	23	299	231	261	194	237	339	294	166
19	330	177	16	208	419	420	433	145	57	284
20	36	11	143	31	403	212	14	182	81	139
21	436	184	107	20	260	181	68	427	67	414
22	355	45	128	293	153	161	265	246	456	444
23	288	88	230	248	25	325	112	85	191	198
24	289	101	399	160	252	77	87	217	79	113
25	98	360	110	59	310	374	292	140	449	353
26	19	247	12	156	200	315	439	223	157	213
27	27	351	450	366	188	159	239	365	175	447
28	327	138	423	15	195	250	51	206	393	82
29	152	148	96	334	229	235	313	413	342	333
30	216	66	401	186	133	358	84	178	29	377
31	331	190	185	120	189	172	408	277	402	199
32	302	270	311	387	4	52	219	105	451	379
33	357	71	9	117	150	122	215	53	232	274
34	363	149	109	46	141	5	65	388	17	221
35	131	332	203	354	32	416	381	383	409	290
36	114	111	72	22	286	62	349	424	28	364
37	162	278	415	368	214	40	63	362	136	397
38	134	371	253	90	256	129	306	322	73	35
39	455	431	119	176	3	39	50	193	224	170
40	382	396	121	202	341	320	47	154	174	434
41	158	226	196	263	220	118	163	291	127	280
42	441	249	38	37	24	312	400	173	421	446
43	314	426	54	245	443	275	376	318	21	273
44	350	437	197	276	389	30	390	43	102	412
45	329	164	304	296	192	211				

P = 461

INDICES

	0	1	2	3	4	5	6	7	8	9
0		0	1	111	2	48	112	259	3	222
1	49	89	113	35	260	159	4	358	223	164
2	50	370	90	180	114	96	36	333	261	107
3	160	303	5	200	359	307	224	15	165	146
4	51	190	371	24	91	270	181	173	115	58
5	97	9	37	242	334	137	262	275	108	86
6	161	330	304	21	6	83	201	204	360	291
7	308	425	225	298	16	207	166	348	147	383
8	52	444	191	363	372	406	25	218	92	186
9	271	294	182	414	174	212	116	66	59	311
10	98	43	10	286	38	418	243	428	335	324
11	138	126	263	450	276	228	109	257	87	157
12	162	178	331	301	305	144	22	171	7	135
13	84	19	202	423	205	381	361	216	292	210
14	309	284	426	124	226	155	299	169	17	379
15	208	122	167	120	349	351	148	398	384	353
16	53	439	445	150	192	248	364	400	373	70
17	407	386	26	457	219	355	93	197	187	55
18	272	80	295	441	183	63	415	447	175	132
19	213	152	117	436	67	194	60	433	312	250
20	99	315	44	366	11	238	287	402	39	253
21	419	375	244	76	429	72	336	102	325	409
22	139	393	127	388	264	318	451	28	277	340
23	229	459	110	47	258	221	88	34	158	357
24	163	369	179	95	332	106	302	199	306	14
25	145	189	23	269	172	57	8	241	136	274
26	85	329	20	82	203	290	424	297	206	347
27	382	443	362	405	217	185	293	413	211	65
28	310	42	285	417	427	323	125	449	227	256
29	156	177	300	143	170	134	18	422	380	215
30	209	283	123	154	168	378	121	119	350	397
31	352	438	149	247	399	69	385	456	354	196
32	54	79	440	62	446	131	151	435	193	432
33	249	314	365	237	401	252	374	75	71	101
34	408	392	387	317	27	339	458	46	220	33
35	356	368	94	105	198	13	188	268	56	240
36	273	328	81	289	296	346	442	404	184	412
37	64	41	416	322	448	255	176	142	133	421
38	214	282	153	377	118	396	437	246	68	455
39	195	78	61	130	434	431	313	236	251	74
40	100	391	316	338	45	32	367	104	12	267
41	239	327	288	345	403	411	40	321	254	141
42	420	281	376	395	245	454	77	129	430	235
43	73	390	337	31	103	266	326	344	410	320
44	140	280	394	453	128	234	389	30	265	343
45	319	279	452	233	29	342	278	232	341	231
46	230	0								

POWER RESIDUES

	0	1	2	3	4	5	6	7	8	9
0	1	2	4	8	16	32	64	128	256	51
1	102	204	408	355	249	37	74	148	296	131
2	262	63	126	252	43	86	172	344	227	454
3	447	433	405	349	237	13	26	52	104	208
4	416	371	281	101	202	404	347	233	5	10
5	20	40	80	160	320	179	358	255	49	98
6	196	392	323	185	370	279	97	194	388	315
7	169	338	215	430	399	337	213	426	391	321
8	181	362	263	65	130	260	59	118	236	11
9	22	44	88	176	352	243	25	50	100	200
10	400	339	217	434	407	353	245	29	58	116
11	232	3	6	12	24	48	96	192	384	307
12	153	306	151	302	143	286	111	222	444	427
13	393	325	189	378	295	129	258	55	110	220
14	440	419	377	293	125	250	39	78	156	312
15	163	326	191	382	303	145	290	119	238	15
16	30	60	120	240	19	38	76	152	304	147
17	294	127	254	47	94	188	376	291	121	242
18	23	46	92	184	368	275	89	178	356	251
19	41	82	164	328	195	390	319	177	354	247
20	33	66	132	264	67	134	268	75	150	300
21	139	278	95	190	380	299	137	274	87	174
22	348	235	9	18	36	72	144	288	115	230
23	460	459	457	453	445	429	397	333	205	410
24	359	257	53	106	212	424	387	313	165	330
25	199	398	335	209	418	375	289	117	234	7
26	14	28	56	112	224	448	435	409	357	253
27	45	90	180	360	259	57	114	228	456	451
28	441	421	381	301	141	282	103	206	412	363
29	265	69	138	276	91	182	364	267	73	146
30	292	123	246	31	62	124	248	35	70	140
31	280	99	198	396	331	201	402	343	225	450
32	439	417	373	285	109	218	436	411	361	261
33	61	122	244	27	54	108	216	432	403	345
34	229	458	455	449	437	413	365	269	77	154
35	308	155	310	159	318	175	350	239	17	34
36	68	136	272	83	166	332	203	406	351	241
37	21	42	84	168	336	211	422	383	305	149
38	298	135	270	79	158	316	171	342	223	446
39	431	401	341	221	442	423	385	309	157	314
40	167	334	207	414	367	273	85	170	340	219
41	438	415	369	277	93	186	372	283	105	210
42	420	379	297	133	266	71	142	284	107	214
43	428	395	329	197	394	327	193	386	311	161
44	322	183	366	271	81	162	324	187	374	287
45	113	226	452	443	425	389	317	173	346	231
46										

P = 463

INDICES

	0	1	2	3	4	5	6	7	8	9
0		0	34	1	68	125	35	153	102	2
1	159	43	69	55	187	126	136	296	36	281
2	193	154	77	39	103	250	89	3	221	326
3	160	370	170	44	330	278	70	443	315	56
4	227	257	188	116	111	127	73	456	137	306
5	284	297	123	185	37	168	255	282	360	362
6	194	148	404	155	204	180	78	344	364	40
7	312	177	104	446	15	251	349	196	90	8
8	261	4	291	243	222	421	150	327	145	142
9	161	208	107	371	28	406	171	414	340	45
10	318	63	331	460	157	279	219	441	71	166
11	202	444	289	206	316	164	394	57	396	449
12	228	86	182	258	438	375	189	59	238	117
13	214	80	112	434	378	128	398	353	74	303
14	346	457	211	98	138	451	18	307	49	366
15	285	389	383	298	230	33	124	101	42	186
16	295	192	38	88	325	169	277	314	256	110
17	455	283	184	254	361	403	179	363	176	14
18	195	260	242	149	141	106	405	339	62	156
19	440	201	205	393	448	181	374	237	79	377
20	352	345	97	17	365	382	32	41	191	324
21	313	454	253	178	13	241	105	61	200	447
22	236	351	16	31	323	252	240	199	350	322
23	198	197	428	429	91	119	430	9	21	92
24	262	247	120	5	216	431	292	336	10	244
25	409	22	223	82	93	422	272	263	151	134
26	248	328	114	121	146	310	6	143	412	217
27	162	436	432	209	387	293	108	174	337	372
28	380	11	29	426	245	407	132	410	172	130
29	23	415	52	224	341	25	83	46	400	94
30	319	269	423	64	417	273	332	355	264	461
31	67	152	158	54	135	280	76	249	220	369
32	329	442	226	115	72	305	122	167	359	147
33	203	343	311	445	348	7	290	420	144	207
34	27	413	317	459	218	165	288	163	395	85
35	437	58	213	433	397	302	210	450	48	388
36	229	100	294	87	276	109	183	402	175	259
37	140	338	439	392	373	376	96	381	190	453
38	12	60	235	30	239	321	427	118	20	246
39	215	335	408	81	271	133	113	309	411	435
40	386	173	379	425	131	129	51	24	399	268
41	416	354	66	53	75	368	225	304	358	342
42	347	419	26	458	287	84	212	301	47	99
43	275	401	139	391	95	452	234	320	19	334
44	270	308	385	424	50	267	65	367	357	418
45	286	300	274	390	233	333	384	266	356	299
46	232	265	231							

POWER RESIDUES

	0	1	2	3	4	5	6	7	8	9
0	1	3	9	27	81	243	266	335	79	237
1	248	281	380	214	179	74	222	203	146	438
2	388	238	251	290	407	295	422	340	94	282
3	383	223	206	155	2	6	18	54	162	23
4	69	207	158	11	33	99	297	428	358	148
5	444	406	292	413	313	13	39	117	351	127
6	381	217	188	101	303	446	412	310	4	12
7	36	108	324	46	138	414	316	22	66	198
8	131	393	253	296	425	349	121	363	163	26
9	78	234	239	254	299	434	376	202	143	429
10	361	157	8	24	72	216	185	92	276	365
11	169	44	132	396	262	323	43	129	387	235
12	242	263	326	52	156	5	15	45	135	405
13	289	404	286	395	259	314	16	48	144	432
14	370	184	89	267	338	88	264	329	61	183
15	86	258	311	7	21	63	189	104	312	10
16	30	90	270	347	115	345	109	327	55	165
17	32	96	288	401	277	368	178	71	213	176
18	65	195	122	366	172	53	159	14	42	126
19	378	208	161	20	60	180	77	231	230	227
20	218	191	110	330	64	192	113	339	91	273
21	356	142	426	352	130	390	244	269	344	106
22	318	28	84	252	293	416	322	40	120	360
23	154	462	460	454	436	382	220	197	128	384
24	226	215	182	83	249	284	389	241	260	317
25	25	75	225	212	173	56	168	41	123	369
26	181	80	240	257	308	461	457	445	409	301
27	440	394	256	305	452	430	364	166	35	105
28	315	19	57	171	50	150	450	424	346	112
29	336	82	246	275	362	160	17	51	153	459
30	451	427	355	139	417	325	49	147	441	397
31	265	332	70	210	167	38	114	342	100	300
32	437	385	229	224	209	164	29	87	261	320
33	34	102	306	455	439	391	247	278	371	187
34	98	294	419	331	67	201	140	420	334	76
35	228	221	200	137	411	307	458	448	418	328
36	58	174	59	177	68	204	149	447	415	319
37	31	93	279	374	196	125	375	199	134	402
38	280	377	205	152	456	442	400	274	359	151
39	453	433	373	193	116	348	118	354	136	408
40	298	431	367	175	62	186	95	285	392	250
41	287	398	268	341	97	291	410	304	449	421
42	337	85	255	302	443	403	283	386	232	233
43	236	245	272	353	133	399	271	350	124	372
44	190	107	321	37	111	333	73	219	194	119
45	357	145	435	379	211	170	47	141	423	343
46	103	309								

P = 467

INDICES

	0	1	2	3	4	5	6	7	8	9
0		0	1	450	2	41	451	148	3	434
1	42	141	452	30	149	25	4	284	435	387
2	43	132	142	338	453	82	31	418	150	213
3	26	209	5	125	285	189	436	119	388	14
4	44	96	133	310	143	9	339	408	454	296
5	83	268	32	74	419	182	151	371	214	38
6	27	129	210	116	6	71	126	319	286	322
7	190	344	437	461	120	66	389	289	15	163
8	45	402	97	224	134	325	311	197	144	334
9	10	178	340	193	409	428	455	394	297	109
10	84	347	269	413	33	173	75	245	420	440
11	183	103	152	256	372	379	215	464	39	432
12	28	282	130	80	211	123	117	94	7	294
13	72	369	127	69	320	459	287	400	323	332
14	191	392	345	171	438	254	462	280	121	292
15	67	398	390	252	290	250	16	18	164	58
16	46	20	403	158	98	166	225	301	135	60
17	326	355	312	48	198	230	145	22	335	206
18	11	405	179	113	341	160	194	425	410	100
19	429	91	456	168	395	55	298	227	110	88
20	85	303	348	361	270	137	414	306	34	62
21	174	241	76	328	246	351	421	357	441	445
22	184	314	104	364	153	50	257	262	373	200
23	380	273	216	232	465	449	40	147	433	140
24	29	24	283	386	131	337	81	417	212	208
25	124	188	118	13	95	309	8	407	295	267
26	73	181	370	37	128	115	70	318	321	343
27	460	65	288	162	401	223	324	196	333	177
28	192	427	393	108	346	412	172	244	439	102
29	255	378	463	431	281	79	122	93	293	368
30	68	458	399	331	391	170	253	279	291	397
31	251	249	17	57	19	157	165	300	59	354
32	47	229	21	205	404	112	159	424	99	90
33	167	54	226	87	302	360	136	305	61	240
34	327	350	356	444	313	363	49	261	199	272
35	231	448	146	139	23	385	336	416	207	187
36	12	308	406	266	180	36	114	317	342	64
37	161	222	195	176	426	107	411	243	101	377
38	430	78	92	367	457	330	169	278	396	248
39	56	156	299	353	228	204	111	423	89	53
40	86	359	304	239	349	443	362	260	271	447
41	138	384	415	186	307	265	35	316	63	221
42	175	106	242	376	77	366	329	277	247	155
43	352	203	422	52	358	238	442	259	446	383
44	185	264	315	220	105	375	365	276	154	202
45	51	237	258	382	263	219	374	275	201	236
46	381	218	274	235	217	234	233			

POWER RESIDUES

	0	1	2	3	4	5	6	7	8	9
0	1	2	4	8	16	32	64	128	256	45
1	90	180	360	253	39	78	156	312	157	314
2	161	322	177	354	241	15	30	60	120	240
3	13	26	52	104	208	416	365	263	59	118
4	236	5	10	20	40	80	160	320	173	346
5	225	450	433	399	331	195	390	313	159	318
6	169	338	209	418	369	271	75	150	300	133
7	266	65	130	260	53	106	212	424	381	295
8	123	246	25	50	100	200	400	333	199	398
9	329	191	382	297	127	254	41	82	164	328
10	189	378	289	111	222	444	421	375	283	99
11	198	396	325	183	366	265	63	126	252	37
12	74	148	296	125	250	33	66	132	264	61
13	122	244	21	42	84	168	336	205	410	353
14	239	11	22	44	88	176	352	237	7	14
15	28	56	112	224	448	429	391	315	163	326
16	185	370	273	79	158	316	165	330	193	386
17	305	143	286	105	210	420	373	279	91	182
18	364	261	55	110	220	440	413	359	251	35
19	70	140	280	93	186	372	277	87	174	348
20	229	458	449	431	395	323	179	358	249	31
21	62	124	248	29	58	116	232	464	461	455
22	443	419	371	275	83	166	332	197	394	321
23	175	350	233	466	465	463	459	451	435	403
24	339	211	422	377	287	107	214	428	389	311
25	155	310	153	306	145	290	113	226	452	437
26	407	347	227	454	441	415	363	259	51	102
27	204	408	349	231	462	457	447	427	387	307
28	147	294	121	242	17	34	68	136	272	77
29	154	308	149	298	129	258	49	98	196	392
30	317	167	334	201	402	337	207	414	361	255
31	43	86	172	344	221	442	417	367	267	67
32	134	268	69	138	276	85	170	340	213	426
33	385	303	139	278	89	178	356	245	23	46
34	92	184	368	269	71	142	284	101	202	404
35	341	215	430	393	319	171	342	217	434	401
36	335	203	406	345	223	446	425	383	299	131
37	262	57	114	228	456	445	423	379	291	115
38	230	460	453	439	411	355	243	19	38	76
39	152	304	141	282	97	194	388	309	151	302
40	137	274	81	162	324	181	362	257	47	94
41	188	376	285	103	206	412	357	247	27	54
42	108	216	432	397	327	187	374	281	95	190
43	380	293	119	238	9	18	36	72	144	288
44	109	218	436	405	343	219	438	409	351	235
45	3	6	12	24	48	96	192	384	301	135
46	270	73	146	292	117	234				

P = 479

INDICES

	0	1	2	3	4	5	6	7	8	9
0		0	362	446	246	134	330	202	130	414
1	18	422	214	1	86	102	14	237	298	217
2	380	170	306	76	98	268	363	382	448	327
3	464	223	376	390	121	336	182	361	101	447
4	264	265	54	147	190	70	438	157	460	404
5	152	205	247	187	266	78	332	185	211	311
6	348	284	107	138	260	135	274	55	5	44
7	220	96	66	174	245	236	463	146	331	43
8	148	350	149	365	416	371	31	295	74	226
9	432	203	322	191	41	351	344	196	288	358
10	36	229	89	48	131	304	71	198	150	140
11	440	329	216	375	69	210	95	415	195	439
12	232	366	168	233	469	402	22	81	144	115
13	19	302	158	419	417	38	367	276	406	378
14	104	125	458	423	428	461	58	372	129	169
15	120	156	347	173	30	357	215	401	405	155
16	32	278	234	50	33	46	249	338	300	2
17	255	153	393	296	179	470	436	279	110	243
18	316	292	87	252	206	17	75	181	403	106
19	235	73	228	68	80	103	172	248	242	227
20	398	23	113	51	451	399	410	12	15	161
21	188	62	433	64	82	281	34	425	24	142
22	324	238	213	267	100	204	259	145	431	47
23	94	114	457	356	299	291	79	11	323	355
24	116	84	250	318	52	60	117	218	353	333
25	286	192	384	20	443	339	28	452	477	85
26	381	263	186	273	42	321	303	194	301	427
27	400	254	251	171	160	212	290	352	262	159
28	466	3	9	411	342	319	307	467	312	474
29	345	164	420	314	256	445	13	326	53	77
30	4	349	40	197	231	418	57	154	392	16
31	241	61	99	10	285	272	289	473	39	271
32	394	166	162	454	118	269	412	108	395	359
33	408	368	133	297	222	189	184	219	364	343
34	139	167	37	128	277	178	180	397	63	258
35	354	383	320	261	163	230	472	407	127	471
36	200	434	176	334	449	308	136	455	90	201
37	379	389	437	310	65	370	287	328	468	275
38	119	49	435	105	112	280	430	83	442	193
39	465	313	56	270	132	177	126	388	111	387
40	282	92	385	224	475	6	413	305	335	459
41	283	244	294	35	374	21	377	346	45	109
42	72	450	424	93	317	27	426	8	444	391
43	165	221	396	199	309	429	386	293	26	25
44	208	340	122	421	97	360	151	137	462	225
45	88	209	143	124	29	337	315	67	409	141
46	456	59	476	253	341	325	240	453	183	257
47	175	369	441	91	373	7	207	123	239	

POWER RESIDUES

	0	1	2	3	4	5	6	7	8	9
0	1	13	169	281	300	68	405	475	427	282
1	313	237	207	296	16	208	309	185	10	130
2	253	415	126	201	218	439	438	425	256	454
3	154	86	160	164	216	413	100	342	135	318
4	302	94	264	79	69	418	165	229	103	381
5	163	203	244	298	42	67	392	306	146	461
6	245	311	211	348	213	374	72	457	193	114
7	45	106	420	191	88	186	23	299	55	236
8	194	127	214	387	241	259	14	182	450	102
9	368	473	401	423	230	116	71	444	24	312
10	224	38	15	195	140	383	189	62	327	419
11	178	398	384	202	231	129	240	246	324	380
12	150	34	442	477	453	141	396	358	343	148
13	8	104	394	332	5	65	366	447	63	340
14	109	459	219	452	128	227	77	43	80	82
15	108	446	50	171	307	159	151	47	132	279
16	274	209	322	354	291	430	321	341	122	149
17	21	273	196	153	73	470	362	395	345	174
18	346	187	36	468	336	57	262	53	210	335
19	44	93	251	389	267	118	97	303	107	433
20	360	369	7	91	225	51	184	476	440	451
21	115	58	275	222	12	156	112	19	247	337
22	70	431	334	31	403	449	89	199	192	101
23	355	304	120	123	162	190	75	17	221	478
24	466	310	198	179	411	74	4	52	197	166
25	242	272	183	463	271	170	294	469	349	226
26	64	353	278	261	40	41	54	223	25	325
27	393	319	315	263	66	379	137	344	161	177
28	385	215	400	410	61	314	250	376	98	316
29	276	235	181	437	412	87	173	333	18	234
30	168	268	131	266	105	407	22	286	365	434
31	373	59	288	391	293	456	180	424	243	285
32	352	265	92	238	220	465	297	29	377	111
33	6	78	56	249	363	408	35	455	167	255
34	441	464	284	339	96	290	417	152	60	301
35	81	95	277	248	350	239	233	155	99	329
36	445	37	2	26	338	83	121	136	331	471
37	375	85	147	474	414	113	32	416	139	370
38	20	260	27	351	252	402	436	399	397	371
39	33	429	308	172	320	328	432	347	200	205
40	270	157	125	188	49	158	138	357	330	458
41	206	283	326	406	9	117	84	134	305	133
42	292	443	11	143	422	217	426	269	144	435
43	386	228	90	212	361	382	176	372	46	119
44	110	472	388	254	428	295	3	39	28	364
45	421	204	257	467	323	367	460	232	142	409
46	48	145	448	76	30	390	280	287	378	124
47	175	359	356	317	289	404	462	258		

P = 487

INDICES

	0	1	2	3	4	5	6	7	8	9
0		0	238	1	476	99	239	75	228	2
1	337	127	477	287	313	100	466	305	240	36
2	89	76	365	157	229	198	39	3	65	420
3	338	22	218	128	57	174	478	195	274	288
4	327	108	314	429	117	101	395	211	467	150
5	436	306	277	92	241	226	303	37	172	115
6	90	258	260	77	456	386	366	408	295	158
7	412	262	230	154	433	199	26	202	40	291
8	79	4	346	374	66	404	181	421	355	458
9	339	362	147	23	449	135	219	382	388	129
10	188	141	58	452	29	175	330	368	479	73
11	464	196	55	427	275	256	410	289	353	380
12	328	254	10	109	12	297	315	86	208	430
13	138	205	118	111	160	102	47	268	396	168
14	164	212	14	414	468	33	392	151	185	83
15	437	299	264	307	440	121	278	222	43	93
16	317	232	242	237	98	227	126	312	304	88
17	156	38	419	217	173	273	107	116	210	435
18	91	302	114	259	385	294	261	432	201	78
19	373	180	457	146	134	387	140	28	367	463
20	426	409	379	9	296	207	204	159	267	163
21	413	391	82	263	120	42	231	97	311	155
22	216	106	434	113	293	200	179	133	27	425
23	8	203	162	81	41	310	105	292	132	7
24	80	104	6	5	248	249	347	323	250	375
25	49	348	67	284	324	405	446	251	182	270
26	376	422	443	50	356	191	349	459	398	68
27	340	474	285	363	20	325	148	170	406	24
28	402	447	450	53	252	136	166	183	220	124
29	271	383	144	377	389	214	423	130	321	444
30	189	18	51	142	16	357	59	334	192	453
31	359	350	30	416	460	176	281	399	331	61
32	69	369	470	341	480	485	475	74	336	286
33	465	35	364	197	64	21	56	194	326	428
34	394	149	276	225	171	257	455	407	411	153
35	25	290	345	403	354	361	448	381	187	451
36	329	72	54	255	352	253	11	85	137	110
37	46	167	13	32	184	298	439	221	316	236
38	125	87	418	272	209	301	384	431	372	145
39	139	462	378	206	266	390	119	96	215	112
40	178	424	161	309	131	103	247	322	48	283
41	445	269	442	190	397	473	19	169	401	52
42	165	123	143	213	320	17	15	333	358	415
43	280	60	469	484	335	34	63	193	393	224
44	454	152	344	360	186	71	351	84	45	31
45	438	235	417	300	371	461	265	95	177	308
46	246	282	441	472	400	122	319	332	279	483
47	62	223	343	70	44	234	370	94	245	471
48	318	482	342	233	244	481	243			

POWER RESIDUES

	0	1	2	3	4	5	6	7	8	9
0	1	3	9	27	81	243	242	239	230	203
1	122	366	124	372	142	426	304	425	301	416
2	274	335	31	93	279	350	76	228	197	104
3	312	449	373	145	435	331	19	57	171	26
4	78	234	215	158	474	448	370	136	408	250
5	263	302	419	283	362	112	336	34	102	306
6	431	319	470	436	334	28	84	252	269	320
7	473	445	361	109	327	7	21	63	189	80
8	240	233	212	149	447	367	127	381	169	20
9	60	180	53	159	477	457	397	217	164	5
10	15	45	135	405	241	236	221	176	41	123
11	369	133	399	223	182	59	177	44	132	396
12	214	155	465	421	289	380	166	11	33	99
13	297	404	238	227	194	95	285	368	130	390
14	196	101	303	422	292	389	193	92	276	341
15	49	147	441	349	73	219	170	23	69	207
16	134	402	232	209	140	420	286	371	139	417
17	277	344	58	174	35	105	315	458	400	226
18	191	86	258	287	374	148	444	358	100	300
19	413	265	308	437	337	37	111	333	25	75
20	225	188	77	231	206	131	393	205	128	384
21	178	47	141	423	295	398	220	173	32	96
22	288	377	157	471	439	343	55	165	8	24
23	72	216	161	483	475	451	379	163	2	6
24	18	54	162	486	484	478	460	406	244	245
25	248	257	284	365	121	363	115	345	61	183
26	62	186	71	213	152	456	394	208	137	411
27	259	290	383	175	38	114	342	52	156	468
28	430	316	461	409	253	272	329	13	39	117
29	351	79	237	224	185	68	204	125	375	151
30	453	385	181	56	168	17	51	153	459	403
31	235	218	167	14	42	126	378	160	480	466
32	424	298	407	247	254	275	338	40	120	360
33	106	318	467	427	307	434	328	10	30	90
34	270	323	482	472	442	352	82	246	251	266
35	311	446	364	118	354	88	264	305	428	310
36	443	355	91	273	332	22	66	198	107	321
37	476	454	388	190	83	249	260	293	392	202
38	119	357	97	291	386	184	65	195	98	294
39	395	211	146	438	340	46	138	414	268	317
40	464	418	280	353	85	255	278	347	67	201
41	116	348	70	210	143	429	313	452	382	172
42	29	87	261	296	401	229	200	113	339	43
43	129	387	187	74	222	179	50	150	450	376
44	154	462	412	262	299	410	256	281	356	94
45	282	359	103	309	440	346	64	192	89	267
46	314	455	391	199	110	330	16	48	144	432
47	322	479	463	415	271	326	4	12	36	108
48	324	485	481	469	433	325				

P = 491

INDICES

	0	1	2	3	4	5	6	7	8	9
0		0	1	320	2	376	321	179	3	150
1	377	456	322	332	180	206	4	270	151	477
2	378	9	457	239	323	262	333	470	181	221
3	207	372	5	286	271	65	152	290	478	162
4	379	168	10	430	458	36	240	367	324	358
5	263	100	334	275	471	342	182	307	222	229
6	208	72	373	329	6	218	287	33	272	69
7	66	142	153	199	291	92	479	145	163	194
8	380	300	169	348	11	156	431	51	459	109
9	37	21	241	202	368	363	325	190	359	116
10	264	294	101	437	335	385	276	82	472	95
11	343	120	183	405	308	125	223	482	230	449
12	209	422	73	488	374	148	330	268	7	260
13	219	284	288	166	34	356	273	305	70	216
14	67	197	143	298	154	107	200	188	292	383
15	93	403	480	420	146	258	164	303	195	105
16	381	418	301	416	170	172	349	57	12	174
17	157	137	432	351	52	441	460	59	110	410
18	38	14	22	392	242	176	203	236	369	159
19	364	339	326	139	191	48	360	434	117	446
20	265	353	295	400	102	54	438	389	336	443
21	386	313	277	462	83	316	473	61	96	29
22	344	112	121	280	184	412	406	44	309	40
23	126	465	224	16	483	253	231	24	450	86
24	210	394	423	130	74	244	489	319	375	178
25	149	455	331	205	269	476	8	238	261	469
26	220	371	285	64	289	161	167	429	35	366
27	357	99	274	341	306	228	71	328	217	32
28	68	141	198	91	144	193	299	347	155	50
29	108	20	201	362	189	115	293	436	384	81
30	94	119	404	124	481	448	421	487	147	267
31	259	283	165	355	304	215	196	297	106	187
32	382	402	419	257	302	104	417	415	171	56
33	173	136	350	440	58	409	13	391	175	235
34	158	338	138	47	433	445	352	399	53	388
35	442	312	461	315	60	28	111	279	411	43
36	39	464	15	252	23	85	393	129	243	318
37	177	454	204	475	237	468	370	63	160	428
38	365	98	340	227	327	31	140	90	192	346
39	49	19	361	114	435	80	118	123	447	486
40	266	282	354	214	296	186	401	256	103	414
41	55	135	439	408	390	234	337	46	444	398
42	387	311	314	27	278	42	463	251	84	128
43	317	453	474	467	62	427	97	226	30	89
44	345	18	113	79	122	485	281	213	185	255
45	413	134	407	233	45	397	310	26	41	250
46	127	452	466	426	225	88	17	78	484	212
47	254	133	232	396	25	249	451	425	87	77
48	211	132	395	248	424	76	131	247	75	246
49	245	0								

POWER RESIDUES

	0	1	2	3	4	5	6	7	8	9
0	1	2	4	8	16	32	64	128	256	21
1	42	84	168	336	181	362	233	466	441	391
2	291	91	182	364	237	474	457	423	355	219
3	438	385	279	67	134	268	45	90	180	360
4	229	458	425	359	227	454	417	343	195	390
5	289	87	174	348	205	410	329	167	334	177
6	354	217	434	377	263	35	70	140	280	69
7	138	276	61	122	244	488	485	479	467	443
8	395	299	107	214	428	365	239	478	465	439
9	387	283	75	150	300	109	218	436	381	271
10	51	102	204	408	325	159	318	145	290	89
11	178	356	221	442	393	295	99	198	396	301
12	111	222	444	397	303	115	230	460	429	367
13	243	486	481	471	451	411	331	171	342	193
14	386	281	71	142	284	77	154	308	125	250
15	9	18	36	72	144	288	85	170	340	189
16	378	265	39	78	156	312	133	266	41	82
17	164	328	165	330	169	338	185	370	249	7
18	14	28	56	112	224	448	405	319	147	294
19	97	194	388	285	79	158	316	141	282	73
20	146	292	93	186	372	253	15	30	60	120
21	240	480	469	447	403	315	139	278	65	130
22	260	29	58	116	232	464	437	383	275	59
23	118	236	472	453	415	339	187	374	257	23
24	46	92	184	368	245	490	489	487	483	475
25	459	427	363	235	470	449	407	323	155	310
26	129	258	25	50	100	200	400	309	127	254
27	17	34	68	136	272	53	106	212	424	357
28	223	446	401	311	131	262	33	66	132	264
29	37	74	148	296	101	202	404	317	143	286
30	81	162	324	157	314	137	274	57	114	228
31	456	421	351	211	422	353	215	430	369	247
32	3	6	12	24	48	96	192	384	277	63
33	126	252	13	26	52	104	208	416	341	191
34	382	273	55	110	220	440	389	287	83	166
35	332	173	346	201	402	313	135	270	49	98
36	196	392	293	95	190	380	269	47	94	188
37	376	261	31	62	124	248	5	10	20	40
38	80	160	320	149	298	105	210	420	349	207
39	414	337	183	366	241	482	473	455	419	347
40	203	406	321	151	302	113	226	452	413	335
41	179	358	225	450	409	327	163	326	161	322
42	153	306	121	242	484	477	463	435	379	267
43	43	86	172	344	197	394	297	103	206	412
44	333	175	350	209	418	345	199	398	305	119
45	238	476	461	431	371	251	11	22	44	88
46	176	352	213	426	361	231	462	433	375	259
47	27	54	108	216	432	373	255	19	38	76
48	152	304	117	234	468	445	399	307	123	246
49										

P = 499

INDICES

	0	1	2	3	4	5	6	7	8	9
0		0	435	447	372	208	384	1	309	396
1	145	17	321	429	436	157	246	421	333	91
2	82	448	452	47	258	416	366	345	373	212
3	94	450	183	464	358	209	270	153	28	378
4	19	427	385	100	389	106	482	316	195	2
5	353	370	303	305	282	225	310	40	149	285
6	31	455	387	397	120	139	401	342	295	494
7	146	185	207	320	90	365	463	18	315	281
8	454	294	364	363	322	131	37	161	326	323
9	43	430	419	399	253	299	132	477	437	413
10	290	176	307	38	240	158	242	62	219	274
11	162	102	247	193	475	255	86	327	222	422
12	466	34	392	376	324	126	334	24	57	49
13	76	44	338	92	279	55	232	128	431	166
14	83	265	122	446	144	420	257	449	27	105
15	302	284	400	319	453	160	252	175	218	254
16	391	48	231	445	301	174	300	486	259	360
17	68	487	472	133	98	417	263	234	260	79
18	478	440	367	404	356	361	336	438	190	346
19	236	141	69	7	414	88	374	470	350	488
20	227	291	113	213	244	137	473	443	177	108
21	95	330	179	134	497	308	156	451	211	269
22	99	352	39	119	184	314	130	418	412	241
23	192	465	23	278	264	26	159	230	359	262
24	403	235	469	243	329	210	313	22	261	312
25	63	12	271	64	459	80	492	220	484	154
26	13	110	479	408	275	15	29	272	216	441
27	490	163	169	379	65	433	368	288	103	348
28	20	460	202	405	59	248	383	428	81	344
29	357	426	194	224	386	493	462	362	42	476
30	239	101	221	125	337	165	256	318	390	485
31	97	439	189	87	112	107	155	118	191	229
32	328	11	483	14	168	347	382	223	238	317
33	111	10	237	51	423	52	196	480	297	142
34	5	467	424	3	409	204	70	151	35	53
35	354	276	200	8	171	393	197	371	16	332
36	415	182	377	481	304	30	341	89	293	325
37	298	306	273	85	375	75	127	143	283	217
38	173	471	78	335	6	226	442	496	351	411
39	25	468	311	491	407	489	287	58	425	41
40	164	188	228	381	50	4	150	170	181	292
41	74	77	410	286	380	73	114	115	45	205
42	32	66	267	214	116	339	71	456	434	395
43	245	46	93	152	388	369	148	138	206	280
44	36	398	289	61	474	33	56	54	121	104
45	251	444	67	233	355	140	349	136	178	268
46	129	277	402	21	458	109	215	432	201	343
47	461	124	96	117	167	9	296	203	199	331
48	340	84	172	495	406	187	180	72	266	394
49	147	60	250	135	457	123	198	186	249	

POWER RESIDUES

	0	1	2	3	4	5	6	7	8	9
0	1	7	49	343	405	340	384	193	353	475
1	331	321	251	260	323	265	358	11	77	40
2	280	463	247	232	127	390	235	148	38	266
3	365	60	420	445	121	348	440	86	103	222
4	57	399	298	90	131	418	431	23	161	129
5	404	333	335	349	447	135	446	128	397	284
6	491	443	107	250	253	274	421	452	170	192
7	346	426	487	415	410	375	130	411	382	179
8	255	288	20	140	481	373	116	313	195	367
9	74	19	133	432	30	210	472	310	174	220
10	43	301	111	278	449	149	45	315	209	465
11	261	330	314	202	416	417	424	473	317	223
12	64	448	142	495	471	303	125	376	137	460
13	226	85	96	173	213	493	457	205	437	65
14	455	191	339	377	144	10	70	490	436	58
15	406	347	433	37	259	316	216	15	105	236
16	155	87	110	271	400	305	139	474	324	272
17	407	354	482	380	165	157	101	208	458	212
18	486	408	361	32	224	71	497	485	401	312
19	188	318	230	113	292	48	336	356	496	478
20	352	468	282	477	345	419	438	72	5	35
21	245	218	29	203	423	466	268	379	158	108
22	257	302	118	327	293	55	385	200	402	319
23	237	162	136	453	177	241	190	332	328	300
24	104	229	106	243	204	430	16	112	285	498
25	492	450	156	94	159	115	306	146	24	168
26	178	248	239	176	234	141	488	422	459	219
27	36	252	267	372	109	264	351	461	233	134
28	439	79	54	378	151	59	413	396	277	442
29	100	201	409	368	81	68	476	338	370	95
30	166	164	150	52	364	53	371	102	215	8
31	56	392	249	246	225	78	47	329	307	153
32	73	12	84	89	124	369	88	117	320	244
33	211	479	359	18	126	383	186	304	132	425
34	480	366	67	469	289	27	189	325	279	456
35	198	388	221	50	350	454	184	290	34	238
36	169	185	297	83	82	75	26	182	276	435
37	51	357	4	28	196	374	123	362	39	273
38	414	403	326	286	6	42	294	62	434	44
39	308	160	122	355	489	429	9	63	441	93
40	152	66	462	240	183	283	484	394	263	344
41	412	389	228	99	194	360	25	175	227	92
42	145	17	119	334	342	398	291	41	287	13
43	91	138	467	275	428	2	14	98	187	311
44	181	269	386	207	451	163	143	3	21	147
45	31	217	22	154	80	61	427	494	464	254
46	281	470	296	76	33	231	120	341	391	242
47	197	381	172	206	444	114	299	97	180	262
48	337	363	46	322	258	309	167	171	199	395
49	270	393	256	295	69	483	387	214		

P = 503

INDICES

	0	1	2	3	4	5	6	7	8	9
0		0	202	156	404	1	358	86	104	312
1	203	42	58	124	288	157	306	229	12	237
2	405	242	244	414	260	2	326	468	490	225
3	359	31	6	198	431	87	214	371	439	280
4	105	235	444	66	446	313	114	246	462	172
5	204	385	26	265	168	43	190	393	427	178
6	59	304	233	398	208	125	400	94	131	68
7	289	21	416	18	71	158	139	128	482	118
8	307	122	437	396	144	230	268	381	146	175
9	13	210	316	187	448	238	162	262	374	354
10	406	201	85	57	228	243	467	5	370	443
11	245	25	392	232	93	415	127	436	380	315
12	261	84	4	391	435	3	98	99	410	222
13	327	340	100	323	296	469	333	411	270	363
14	491	402	223	166	116	226	220	328	273	285
15	360	299	341	39	330	32	182	101	320	421
16	7	500	324	383	137	199	96	297	346	248
17	432	47	470	150	81	88	348	334	377	275
18	215	451	412	460	16	372	389	271	148	52
19	440	133	364	485	464	281	74	492	54	292
20	106	250	403	311	287	236	259	224	430	279
21	445	171	167	177	207	67	70	117	143	174
22	447	353	227	442	92	314	434	221	295	362
23	115	284	329	420	136	247	80	274	15	51
24	463	291	286	278	206	173	91	361	135	50
25	205	49	300	456	301	386	110	342	424	457
26	27	35	40	212	302	266	23	331	498	387
27	169	78	33	366	111	44	472	183	63	343
28	191	478	102	196	425	394	368	321	318	458
29	428	418	422	194	28	179	475	8	487	36
30	60	152	501	357	41	305	241	325	30	213
31	234	113	384	189	303	399	20	138	121	267
32	209	161	200	466	24	126	83	97	339	332
33	401	219	298	181	499	95	46	347	450	388
34	132	73	249	258	170	69	352	433	283	79
35	290	90	48	109	34	22	77	471	477	367
36	417	474	151	240	112	19	160	82	218	45
37	72	351	89	76	473	159	350	349	254	184
38	140	255	335	10	64	129	185	378	164	344
39	483	141	276	496	192	119	256	216	494	479
40	308	336	452	155	103	123	11	413	489	197
41	438	65	461	264	426	397	130	17	481	395
42	145	186	373	56	369	231	379	390	409	322
43	269	165	272	38	319	382	345	149	376	459
44	147	484	53	310	429	176	142	441	294	419
45	14	277	134	455	423	211	497	365	62	195
46	317	193	486	356	29	188	120	465	338	180
47	449	257	282	108	476	239	217	75	253	9
48	163	495	493	154	488	263	480	55	408	37
49	375	309	293	454	61	355	337	107	252	153

POWER RESIDUES

	0	1	2	3	4	5	6	7	8	9
0	1	5	25	125	122	107	32	160	297	479
1	383	406	18	90	450	238	184	417	73	365
2	316	71	355	266	324	111	52	260	294	464
3	308	31	155	272	354	261	299	489	433	153
4	262	304	11	55	275	369	336	171	352	251
5	249	239	189	442	198	487	423	103	12	60
6	300	494	458	278	384	411	43	215	69	345
7	216	74	370	341	196	477	373	356	271	349
8	236	174	367	326	121	102	7	35	175	372
9	351	246	224	114	67	335	166	327	126	127
10	132	157	282	404	8	40	200	497	473	353
11	256	274	364	311	46	230	144	217	79	395
12	466	318	81	405	13	65	325	116	77	385
13	416	68	340	191	452	248	234	164	317	76
14	380	391	446	218	84	420	88	440	188	437
15	173	362	301	499	483	403	3	15	75	375
16	366	321	96	480	388	431	143	212	54	270
17	344	211	49	245	219	89	445	213	59	295
18	469	333	156	277	379	386	421	93	465	313
19	56	280	394	461	293	459	283	409	33	165
20	322	101	2	10	50	250	244	214	64	320
21	91	455	263	309	36	180	397	476	368	331
22	146	227	129	142	207	29	145	222	104	17
23	85	425	113	62	310	41	205	19	95	475
24	363	306	21	105	22	110	47	235	169	342
25	201	502	498	478	378	381	396	471	343	206
26	24	120	97	485	413	53	265	319	86	430
27	138	187	432	148	237	179	392	451	243	209
28	39	195	472	348	231	149	242	204	14	70
29	350	241	199	492	448	228	134	167	332	151
30	252	254	264	314	61	305	16	80	400	491
31	443	203	9	45	225	119	92	460	288	434
32	158	287	429	133	162	307	26	130	147	232
33	154	267	329	136	177	382	401	496	468	328
34	131	152	257	279	389	436	168	337	176	377
35	376	371	346	221	99	495	463	303	6	30
36	150	247	229	139	192	457	273	359	286	424
37	108	37	185	422	98	490	438	178	387	426
38	118	87	435	163	312	51	255	269	339	186
39	427	123	112	57	285	419	83	415	63	315
40	66	330	141	202	4	20	100	500	488	428
41	128	137	182	407	23	115	72	360	291	449
42	233	159	292	454	258	284	414	58	290	444
43	208	34	170	347	226	124	117	82	410	38
44	190	447	223	109	42	210	44	220	94	470
45	338	181	402	501	493	453	253	259	289	439
46	183	412	48	240	194	467	323	106	27	135
47	172	357	276	374	361	296	474	358	281	399
48	486	418	78	390	441	193	462	298	484	408
49	28	140	197	482	398	481	393	456	268	334

P = 503

INDICES

	0	1	2	3	4	5	6	7	8	9
50	407	453	251							

POWER RESIDUES

	0	1	2	3	4	5	6	7	8	9
50	161	302								

P = 509

INDICES

	0	1	2	3	4	5	6	7	8	9
0		0	1	9	2	90	10	323	3	18
1	91	470	11	377	324	99	4	408	19	483
2	92	332	471	300	12	180	378	27	325	358
3	100	119	5	479	409	413	20	202	484	386
4	93	143	333	312	472	108	301	41	13	138
5	181	417	379	241	28	52	326	492	359	453
6	101	75	120	341	6	467	480	24	410	309
7	414	450	21	186	203	189	485	285	387	149
8	94	36	144	206	334	498	313	367	473	170
9	109	192	302	128	42	65	14	176	139	488
10	182	166	418	428	380	422	242	288	29	438
11	53	211	327	236	493	390	360	395	454	223
12	102	432	76	152	121	270	342	252	7	321
13	468	97	481	298	25	117	411	384	310	39
14	415	50	451	339	22	448	187	147	204	365
15	190	63	486	426	286	209	388	221	150	250
16	95	115	37	337	145	61	207	248	335	246
17	499	501	314	82	368	503	474	462	171	316
18	110	400	193	84	303	292	129	370	43	350
19	66	505	15	405	177	476	140	135	489	464
20	183	33	167	173	419	233	429	318	381	445
21	423	112	243	459	289	402	30	442	439	195
22	54	277	212	86	328	198	237	305	494	162
23	391	294	361	57	396	131	455	158	224	372
24	103	280	433	45	77	228	153	352	122	215
25	271	68	343	262	253	507	8	89	322	17
26	469	376	98	407	482	331	299	179	26	357
27	118	478	412	201	385	142	311	107	40	137
28	416	240	51	491	452	74	340	466	23	308
29	449	185	188	284	148	35	205	497	366	169
30	191	127	64	175	487	165	427	421	287	437
31	210	235	389	394	222	431	151	269	251	320
32	96	297	116	383	38	49	338	447	146	364
33	62	425	208	220	249	114	336	60	247	245
34	500	81	502	461	315	399	83	291	369	349
35	504	404	475	134	463	32	172	232	317	444
36	111	458	401	441	194	276	85	197	304	161
37	293	56	130	157	371	279	44	227	351	214
38	67	261	506	88	16	375	406	330	178	356
39	477	200	141	106	136	239	490	73	465	307
40	184	283	34	496	168	126	174	164	420	436
41	234	393	430	268	319	296	382	48	446	363
42	424	219	113	59	244	80	460	398	290	348
43	403	133	31	231	443	457	440	275	196	160
44	55	156	278	226	213	260	87	374	329	355
45	199	105	238	72	306	282	495	125	163	435
46	392	267	295	47	362	218	58	79	397	347
47	132	230	456	274	159	155	225	259	373	354
48	104	71	281	124	434	266	46	217	78	346
49	229	273	154	258	353	70	123	265	216	345

POWER RESIDUES

	0	1	2	3	4	5	6	7	8	9
0	1	2	4	8	16	32	64	128	256	3
1	6	12	24	48	96	192	384	259	9	18
2	36	72	144	288	67	134	268	27	54	108
3	216	432	355	201	402	295	81	162	324	139
4	278	47	94	188	376	243	486	463	417	325
5	141	282	55	110	220	440	371	233	466	423
6	337	165	330	151	302	95	190	380	251	502
7	495	481	453	397	285	61	122	244	488	467
8	425	341	173	346	183	366	223	446	383	257
9	5	10	20	40	80	160	320	131	262	15
10	30	60	120	240	480	451	393	277	45	90
11	180	360	211	422	335	161	322	135	270	31
12	62	124	248	496	483	457	405	301	93	186
13	372	235	470	431	353	197	394	279	49	98
14	196	392	275	41	82	164	328	147	294	79
15	158	316	123	246	492	475	441	373	237	474
16	439	369	229	458	407	305	101	202	404	299
17	89	178	356	203	406	303	97	194	388	267
18	25	50	100	200	400	291	73	146	292	75
19	150	300	91	182	364	219	438	367	225	450
20	391	273	37	74	148	296	83	166	332	155
21	310	111	222	444	379	249	498	487	465	421
22	333	157	314	119	238	476	443	377	245	490
23	471	433	357	205	410	311	113	226	452	395
24	281	53	106	212	424	339	169	338	167	334
25	159	318	127	254	508	507	505	501	493	477
26	445	381	253	506	503	497	485	461	413	317
27	125	250	500	491	473	437	365	221	442	375
28	241	482	455	401	293	77	154	308	107	214
29	428	347	185	370	231	462	415	321	133	266
30	23	46	92	184	368	227	454	399	289	69
31	138	276	43	86	172	344	179	358	207	414
32	319	129	258	7	14	28	56	112	224	448
33	387	265	21	42	84	168	336	163	326	143
34	286	63	126	252	504	499	489	469	429	349
35	189	378	247	494	479	449	389	269	29	58
36	116	232	464	419	329	149	298	87	174	348
37	187	374	239	478	447	385	261	13	26	52
38	104	208	416	323	137	274	39	78	156	312
39	115	230	460	411	313	117	234	468	427	345
40	181	362	215	430	351	193	386	263	17	34
41	68	136	272	35	70	140	280	51	102	204
42	408	307	105	210	420	331	153	306	103	206
43	412	315	121	242	484	459	409	309	109	218
44	436	363	217	434	359	209	418	327	145	290
45	71	142	284	59	118	236	472	435	361	213
46	426	343	177	354	199	398	287	65	130	260
47	11	22	44	88	176	352	195	390	271	33
48	66	132	264	19	38	76	152	304	99	198
49	396	283	57	114	228	456	403	297	85	170

P = 509

INDICES	0	1	2	3	4	5	6	7	8	9
50	272	257	69	264	344	256	263	255	254	

POWER RESIDUES	0	1	2	3	4	5	6	7	8	9
50	340	171	342	175	350	191	382	255		

P = 521

INDICES

	0	1	2	3	4	5	6	7	8	9
0		0	318	1	116	52	319	11	434	2
1	370	298	117	294	329	53	232	187	320	171
2	168	12	96	217	435	104	92	3	127	200
3	371	132	30	299	505	63	118	452	489	295
4	486	343	330	195	414	54	15	78	233	22
5	422	188	410	152	321	350	445	172	518	368
6	169	125	450	13	348	346	97	139	303	218
7	381	164	436	99	250	105	287	309	93	19
8	284	4	141	158	128	239	513	201	212	495
9	372	305	333	133	396	223	31	326	340	300
10	220	440	506	7	208	64	470	277	119	383
11	148	453	243	362	490	269	316	296	166	198
12	487	76	443	344	248	156	331	438	146	196
13	144	405	415	182	457	55	101	407	16	467
14	179	79	482	72	234	252	417	23	48	509
15	423	42	85	189	107	184	411	161	337	153
16	82	228	322	289	459	351	476	427	446	68
17	37	173	311	57	519	115	10	369	293	231
18	170	95	103	126	131	504	451	485	194	14
19	21	409	349	517	124	347	138	380	98	286
20	18	140	238	211	304	395	325	219	6	469
21	382	242	268	165	75	247	437	143	181	100
22	466	481	251	47	41	106	160	81	288	475
23	67	310	114	292	94	130	484	20	516	137
24	285	237	394	5	241	74	142	465	46	159
25	474	113	129	515	236	240	464	473	514	463
26	462	202	203	254	213	204	500	496	255	389
27	373	214	419	306	205	402	334	501	265	134
28	497	25	397	256	280	224	390	354	32	374
29	50	327	215	28	341	420	366	301	307	511
30	221	206	360	441	403	177	507	335	425	8
31	502	122	209	266	479	65	135	44	471	498
32	400	278	26	358	120	398	87	384	257	89
33	149	281	274	454	225	191	244	391	386	363
34	355	430	491	33	109	270	375	259	317	51
35	433	297	328	186	167	216	91	199	29	62
36	488	342	413	77	421	151	444	367	449	345
37	302	163	249	308	283	157	512	494	332	222
38	339	439	207	276	147	361	315	197	442	155
39	145	404	456	406	178	71	416	508	84	183
40	336	227	458	426	36	56	9	230	102	503
41	193	408	123	379	17	210	324	468	267	246
42	180	480	40	80	66	291	483	136	393	73
43	45	112	235	472	461	253	499	388	418	401
44	264	24	279	353	49	27	365	510	359	176
45	424	121	478	43	399	357	86	88	273	190
46	385	429	108	258	432	185	90	61	412	150
47	448	162	282	493	338	275	314	154	455	70
48	83	226	35	229	192	378	323	245	39	290
49	392	111	460	387	263	352	364	175	477	356

POWER RESIDUES

	0	1	2	3	4	5	6	7	8	9
0	1	3	9	27	81	243	208	103	309	406
1	176	7	21	63	189	46	138	414	200	79
2	237	190	49	147	441	281	322	445	293	358
3	32	96	288	343	508	482	404	170	510	488
4	422	224	151	453	317	430	248	223	148	444
5	290	349	5	15	45	135	405	173	519	515
6	503	467	359	35	105	315	424	230	169	507
7	479	395	143	429	245	214	121	363	47	141
8	423	227	160	480	398	152	456	326	457	329
9	466	356	26	78	234	181	22	66	198	73
10	219	136	408	182	25	75	225	154	462	344
11	511	491	431	251	232	175	4	12	36	108
12	324	451	311	412	194	61	183	28	84	252
13	235	184	31	93	279	316	427	239	196	67
14	201	82	246	217	130	390	128	384	110	330
15	469	365	53	159	477	389	125	375	83	249
16	226	157	471	371	71	213	118	354	20	60
17	180	19	57	171	513	497	449	305	394	140
18	420	218	133	399	155	465	353	17	51	153
19	459	335	484	410	188	43	129	387	119	357
20	29	87	261	262	265	274	301	382	104	312
21	415	203	88	264	271	292	355	23	69	207
22	100	300	379	95	285	334	481	401	161	483
23	407	179	16	48	144	432	254	241	202	85
24	255	244	211	112	336	487	419	215	124	372
25	74	222	145	435	263	268	283	328	463	347
26	520	518	512	494	440	278	313	418	212	115
27	345	514	500	458	332	475	383	107	321	442
28	284	331	472	374	80	240	199	76	228	163
29	489	425	233	178	13	39	117	351	11	33
30	99	297	370	68	204	91	273	298	373	77
31	231	172	516	506	476	386	116	348	2	6
32	18	54	162	486	416	206	97	291	352	14
33	42	126	378	92	276	307	400	158	474	380
34	98	294	361	41	123	369	65	195	64	192
35	55	165	495	443	287	340	499	455	323	448
36	302	385	113	339	496	446	296	367	59	177
37	10	30	90	270	289	346	517	509	485	413
38	197	70	210	109	327	460	338	493	437	269
39	286	337	490	428	242	205	94	282	325	454
40	320	439	275	304	391	131	393	137	411	191
41	52	156	468	362	44	132	396	146	438	272
42	295	364	50	150	450	308	403	167	501	461
43	341	502	464	350	8	24	72	216	127	381
44	101	303	388	122	366	56	168	504	470	368
45	62	186	37	111	333	478	392	134	402	164
46	492	434	260	259	256	247	220	139	417	209
47	106	318	433	257	250	229	166	498	452	314
48	421	221	142	426	236	187	40	120	360	38
49	114	342	505	473	377	89	267	280	319	436

P = 521

INDICES

	0	1	2	3	4	5	6	7	8	9
50	272	428	431	60	447	492	313	69	34	377
51	38	110	262	174	271	59	312	376	261	58
52	260	0								

POWER RESIDUES

	0	1	2	3	4	5	6	7	8	9
50	266	277	310	409	185	34	102	306	397	149
51	447	299	376	86	258	253	238	193	58	174
52										

P = 523

INDICES

	0	1	2	3	4	5	6	7	8	9
0		0	1	297	2	49	298	128	3	72
1	50	270	299	506	129	346	4	420	73	464
2	51	425	271	410	300	98	507	369	130	188
3	347	104	5	45	421	177	74	181	465	281
4	52	66	426	90	272	121	411	289	301	256
5	99	195	508	78	370	319	131	239	189	453
6	348	435	105	200	6	33	46	503	422	185
7	178	118	75	432	182	395	466	398	282	219
8	53	144	67	61	427	469	91	485	273	494
9	122	112	412	401	290	513	302	155	257	342
10	100	285	196	215	509	474	79	250	371	222
11	320	478	132	377	240	459	190	56	454	26
12	349	18	436	363	106	147	201	83	7	387
13	34	520	47	70	504	418	423	96	186	43
14	179	64	119	254	76	237	433	31	183	430
15	396	142	467	492	399	153	283	472	220	375
16	54	16	145	385	68	94	62	235	428	490
17	470	14	92	488	486	226	274	228	495	354
18	123	276	113	210	413	230	402	168	291	497
19	514	324	303	356	156	330	258	125	343	407
20	101	278	286	316	197	115	216	482	510	212
21	475	23	80	415	251	139	372	232	223	207
22	321	404	479	136	133	170	378	445	241	293
23	460	173	191	499	57	338	455	516	27	381
24	350	326	19	441	437	305	364	448	107	358
25	148	163	202	158	84	244	8	332	388	309
26	35	260	521	296	48	127	71	269	505	345
27	419	463	424	409	97	368	187	103	44	176
28	180	280	65	89	120	288	255	194	77	318
29	238	452	434	199	32	502	184	117	431	394
30	397	218	143	60	468	484	493	111	400	512
31	154	341	284	214	473	249	221	477	376	458
32	55	25	17	362	146	82	386	519	69	417
33	95	42	63	253	236	30	429	141	491	152
34	471	374	15	384	93	234	489	13	487	225
35	227	353	275	209	229	167	496	323	355	329
36	124	406	277	315	114	481	211	22	414	138
37	231	206	403	135	169	444	292	172	498	337
38	515	380	325	440	304	447	357	162	157	243
39	331	308	259	295	126	268	344	462	408	367
40	102	175	279	88	287	193	317	451	198	501
41	116	393	217	59	483	110	511	340	213	248
42	476	457	24	361	81	518	416	41	252	29
43	140	151	373	383	233	12	224	352	208	166
44	322	328	405	314	480	21	137	205	134	443
45	171	336	379	439	446	161	242	307	294	267
46	461	366	174	87	192	450	500	392	58	109
47	339	247	456	360	517	40	28	150	382	11
48	351	165	327	313	20	204	442	335	438	160
49	306	266	365	86	449	391	108	246	359	39

POWER RESIDUES

	0	1	2	3	4	5	6	7	8	9
0	1	2	4	8	16	32	64	128	256	512
1	501	479	435	347	171	342	161	322	121	242
2	484	445	367	211	422	321	119	238	476	429
3	335	147	294	65	130	260	520	517	511	499
4	475	427	331	139	278	33	66	132	264	5
5	10	20	40	80	160	320	117	234	468	413
6	303	83	166	332	141	282	41	82	164	328
7	133	266	9	18	36	72	144	288	53	106
8	212	424	325	127	254	508	493	463	403	283
9	43	86	172	344	165	330	137	274	25	50
10	100	200	400	277	31	62	124	248	496	469
11	415	307	91	182	364	205	410	297	71	142
12	284	45	90	180	360	197	394	265	7	14
13	28	56	112	224	448	373	223	446	369	215
14	430	337	151	302	81	162	324	125	250	500
15	477	431	339	155	310	97	194	388	253	506
16	489	455	387	251	502	481	439	355	187	374
17	225	450	377	231	462	401	279	35	70	140
18	280	37	74	148	296	69	138	276	29	58
19	116	232	464	405	287	51	102	204	408	293
20	63	126	252	504	485	447	371	219	438	353
21	183	366	209	418	313	103	206	412	301	79
22	158	316	109	218	436	349	175	350	177	354
23	185	370	217	434	345	167	334	145	290	57
24	114	228	456	389	255	510	497	471	419	315
25	107	214	428	333	143	286	49	98	196	392
26	261	522	521	519	515	507	491	459	395	267
27	11	22	44	88	176	352	181	362	201	402
28	281	39	78	156	312	101	202	404	285	47
29	94	188	376	229	458	393	263	3	6	12
30	24	48	96	192	384	245	490	457	391	259
31	518	513	503	483	443	363	203	406	289	55
32	110	220	440	357	191	382	241	482	441	359
33	195	390	257	514	505	487	451	379	235	470
34	417	311	99	198	396	269	15	30	60	120
35	240	480	437	351	179	358	193	386	249	498
36	473	423	323	123	246	492	461	399	275	27
37	54	108	216	432	341	159	318	113	226	452
38	381	239	478	433	343	163	326	129	258	516
39	509	495	467	411	299	75	150	300	77	154
40	308	93	186	372	221	442	361	199	398	273
41	23	46	92	184	368	213	426	329	135	270
42	17	34	68	136	272	21	42	84	168	336
43	149	298	73	146	292	61	122	244	488	453
44	383	243	486	449	375	227	454	385	247	494
45	465	407	291	59	118	236	472	421	319	115
46	230	460	397	271	19	38	76	152	304	85
47	170	340	157	314	105	210	420	317	111	222
48	444	365	207	414	305	87	174	348	173	346
49	169	338	153	306	89	178	356	189	378	233

P = 523

INDICES

	0	1	2	3	4	5	6	7	8	9
50	149	10	164	312	203	334	159	265	85	390
51	245	38	9	311	333	264	389	37	310	263
52	36	262	261							

POWER RESIDUES

	0	1	2	3	4	5	6	7	8	9
50	466	409	295	67	134	268	13	26	52	104
51	208	416	309	95	190	380	237	474	425	327
52	131	262								

P = 541

INDICES

	0	1	2	3	4	5	6	7	8	9
0		0	1	104	2	496	105	258	3	208
1	497	295	106	133	259	60	4	99	209	218
2	498	362	296	188	107	452	134	312	260	279
3	61	430	5	399	100	214	210	199	219	237
4	499	140	363	76	297	164	189	82	108	516
5	453	203	135	68	313	251	261	322	280	19
6	62	335	431	466	6	89	400	223	101	292
7	215	309	211	73	200	16	220	13	238	388
8	500	416	141	241	364	55	77	383	298	423
9	165	391	190	534	83	174	109	35	517	503
10	454	524	204	448	136	318	69	419	314	46
11	252	303	262	151	323	144	281	341	20	357
12	63	50	336	244	432	408	467	127	7	180
13	90	367	401	476	224	268	102	256	293	58
14	216	186	310	428	212	235	74	80	201	249
15	17	464	221	307	14	386	239	381	389	172
16	501	446	417	301	142	355	242	125	365	266
17	56	426	78	462	384	170	299	123	424	168
18	166	437	392	439	191	155	535	394	84	30
19	175	441	110	115	36	193	518	349	504	157
20	455	327	525	537	205	96	449	396	137	513
21	319	86	70	413	420	32	315	148	47	177
22	253	232	304	443	263	120	152	112	324	510
23	145	117	282	285	342	38	21	492	358	195
24	64	288	51	520	337	472	245	351	433	345
25	409	506	468	483	128	159	8	41	181	457
26	91	487	368	329	402	24	477	527	225	373
27	269	539	103	495	257	207	294	132	59	98
28	217	361	187	451	311	278	429	398	213	198
29	236	139	75	163	81	515	202	67	250	321
30	18	334	465	88	222	291	308	72	15	12
31	387	415	240	54	382	422	390	533	173	34
32	502	523	447	317	418	45	302	150	143	340
33	356	49	243	407	126	179	366	475	267	255
34	57	185	427	234	79	248	463	306	385	380
35	171	445	300	354	124	265	425	461	169	122
36	167	436	438	154	393	29	440	114	192	348
37	156	326	536	95	395	512	85	412	31	147
38	176	231	442	119	111	509	116	284	37	491
39	194	287	519	471	350	344	505	482	158	40
40	456	486	328	23	526	372	538	494	206	131
41	97	360	450	277	397	197	138	162	514	66
42	320	333	87	290	71	11	414	53	421	532
43	33	522	316	44	149	339	48	406	178	474
44	254	184	233	247	305	379	444	353	264	460
45	121	435	153	28	113	347	325	94	511	411
46	146	230	118	508	283	490	286	470	343	481
47	39	485	22	371	493	130	359	276	196	161
48	65	332	289	10	52	531	521	43	338	405
49	473	183	246	378	352	459	434	27	346	93

POWER RESIDUES

	0	1	2	3	4	5	6	7	8	9
0	1	2	4	8	16	32	64	128	256	512
1	483	425	309	77	154	308	75	150	300	59
2	118	236	472	403	265	530	519	497	453	365
3	189	378	215	430	319	97	194	388	235	470
4	399	257	514	487	433	325	109	218	436	331
5	121	242	484	427	313	85	170	340	139	278
6	15	30	60	120	240	480	419	297	53	106
7	212	424	307	73	146	292	43	86	172	344
8	147	294	47	94	188	376	211	422	303	65
9	130	260	520	499	457	373	205	410	279	17
10	34	68	136	272	3	6	12	24	48	96
11	192	384	227	454	367	193	386	231	462	383
12	225	450	359	177	354	167	334	127	254	508
13	475	409	277	13	26	52	104	208	416	291
14	41	82	164	328	115	230	460	379	217	434
15	327	113	226	452	363	185	370	199	398	255
16	510	479	417	293	45	90	180	360	179	358
17	175	350	159	318	95	190	380	219	438	335
18	129	258	516	491	441	341	141	282	23	46
19	92	184	368	195	390	239	478	415	289	37
20	74	148	296	51	102	204	408	275	9	18
21	36	72	144	288	35	70	140	280	19	38
22	76	152	304	67	134	268	536	531	521	501
23	461	381	221	442	343	145	290	39	78	156
24	312	83	166	332	123	246	492	443	345	149
25	298	55	110	220	440	339	137	274	7	14
26	28	56	112	224	448	355	169	338	135	270
27	540	539	537	533	525	509	477	413	285	29
28	58	116	232	464	387	233	466	391	241	482
29	423	305	69	138	276	11	22	44	88	176
30	352	163	326	111	222	444	347	153	306	71
31	142	284	27	54	108	216	432	323	105	210
32	420	299	57	114	228	456	371	201	402	263
33	526	511	481	421	301	61	122	244	488	435
34	329	117	234	468	395	249	498	455	369	197
35	394	247	494	447	353	165	330	119	238	476
36	411	281	21	42	84	168	336	131	262	524
37	507	473	405	269	538	535	529	517	493	445
38	349	157	314	87	174	348	155	310	79	158
39	316	91	182	364	187	374	207	414	287	33
40	66	132	264	528	515	489	437	333	125	250
41	500	459	377	213	426	311	81	162	324	107
42	214	428	315	89	178	356	171	342	143	286
43	31	62	124	248	496	451	361	181	362	183
44	366	191	382	223	446	351	161	322	103	206
45	412	283	25	50	100	200	400	259	518	495
46	449	357	173	346	151	302	63	126	252	504
47	467	393	245	490	439	337	133	266	532	523
48	505	469	397	253	506	471	401	261	522	503
49	465	389	237	474	407	273	5	10	20	40

P = 541

INDICES

	0	1	2	3	4	5	6	7	8	9
50	410	229	507	489	469	480	484	370	129	275
51	160	331	9	530	42	404	182	377	458	26
52	92	228	488	479	369	274	330	529	403	376
53	25	227	478	273	528	375	226	272	374	271
54	270	0								

POWER RESIDUES

	0	1	2	3	4	5	6	7	8	9
50	80	160	320	99	198	396	251	502	463	385
51	229	458	375	209	418	295	49	98	196	392
52	243	486	431	321	101	202	404	267	534	527
53	513	485	429	317	93	186	372	203	406	271
54										

P = 547

INDICES

	0	1	2	3	4	5	6	7	8	9
0		0	1	429	2	179	430	103	3	312
1	180	70	431	286	104	62	4	151	313	230
2	181	532	71	293	432	358	287	195	105	318
3	63	303	5	499	152	282	314	487	231	169
4	182	91	533	145	72	491	294	266	433	206
5	359	34	288	244	196	249	106	113	319	511
6	64	235	304	415	6	465	500	340	153	176
7	283	529	315	484	488	241	232	173	170	327
8	183	78	92	49	534	330	146	201	73	129
9	492	389	295	186	267	409	434	398	207	382
10	360	81	35	99	289	165	245	525	197	95
11	250	370	107	134	114	472	320	52	512	254
12	65	140	236	520	305	537	416	440	7	28
13	466	18	501	333	341	374	154	544	177	310
14	284	149	530	356	316	497	485	89	489	204
15	242	111	233	463	174	482	171	76	328	127
16	184	396	79	163	93	132	50	138	535	26
17	331	542	147	495	202	461	74	394	130	24
18	493	392	390	118	296	120	187	221	268	298
19	410	404	435	122	399	348	208	189	383	476
20	361	223	82	421	36	270	100	59	290	300
21	166	263	246	412	526	324	198	406	96	367
22	251	437	371	353	108	124	135	458	115	401
23	473	56	321	350	53	445	513	210	255	448
24	66	191	141	507	237	385	521	516	306	478
25	538	217	417	363	441	213	8	225	29	44
26	467	84	19	258	502	423	334	12	342	38
27	375	451	155	272	545	428	178	102	311	69
28	285	61	150	229	531	292	357	194	317	302
29	498	281	486	168	90	144	490	265	205	33
30	243	248	112	510	234	414	464	339	175	528
31	483	240	172	326	77	48	329	200	128	388
32	185	408	397	381	80	98	164	524	94	369
33	133	471	51	253	139	519	536	439	27	17
34	332	373	543	309	148	355	496	88	203	110
35	462	481	75	126	395	162	131	137	25	541
36	494	460	393	23	391	117	119	220	297	403
37	121	347	188	475	222	420	269	58	299	262
38	411	323	405	366	436	352	123	457	400	55
39	349	444	209	447	190	506	384	515	477	216
40	362	212	224	43	83	257	422	11	37	450
41	271	427	101	68	60	228	291	193	301	280
42	167	143	264	32	247	509	413	338	527	239
43	325	47	199	387	407	380	97	523	368	470
44	252	518	438	16	372	308	354	87	109	480
45	125	161	136	540	459	22	116	219	402	346
46	474	419	57	261	322	365	351	456	54	443
47	446	505	514	215	211	42	256	10	449	426
48	67	227	192	279	142	31	508	337	238	46
49	386	379	522	469	517	15	307	86	479	160

POWER RESIDUES

	0	1	2	3	4	5	6	7	8	9
0	1	2	4	8	16	32	64	128	256	512
1	477	407	267	534	521	495	443	339	131	262
2	524	501	455	363	179	358	169	338	129	258
3	516	485	423	299	51	102	204	408	269	538
4	529	511	475	403	259	518	489	431	315	83
5	166	332	117	234	468	389	231	462	377	207
6	414	281	15	30	60	120	240	480	413	279
7	11	22	44	88	176	352	157	314	81	162
8	324	101	202	404	261	522	497	447	347	147
9	294	41	82	164	328	109	218	436	325	103
10	206	412	277	7	14	28	56	112	224	448
11	349	151	302	57	114	228	456	365	183	366
12	185	370	193	386	225	450	353	159	318	89
13	178	356	165	330	113	226	452	357	167	334
14	121	242	484	421	295	43	86	172	344	141
15	282	17	34	68	136	272	544	541	535	523
16	499	451	355	163	326	105	210	420	293	39
17	78	156	312	77	154	308	69	138	276	5
18	10	20	40	80	160	320	93	186	372	197
19	394	241	482	417	287	27	54	108	216	432
20	317	87	174	348	149	298	49	98	196	392
21	237	474	401	255	510	473	399	251	502	457
22	367	187	374	201	402	257	514	481	415	283
23	19	38	76	152	304	61	122	244	488	429
24	311	75	150	300	53	106	212	424	301	55
25	110	220	440	333	119	238	476	405	263	526
26	505	463	379	211	422	297	47	94	188	376
27	205	410	273	546	545	543	539	531	515	483
28	419	291	35	70	140	280	13	26	52	104
29	208	416	285	23	46	92	184	368	189	378
30	209	418	289	31	62	124	248	496	445	343
31	139	278	9	18	36	72	144	288	29	58
32	116	232	464	381	215	430	313	79	158	316
33	85	170	340	133	266	532	517	487	427	307
34	67	134	268	536	525	503	459	371	195	390
35	233	466	385	223	446	345	143	286	25	50
36	100	200	400	253	506	465	383	219	438	329
37	111	222	444	341	135	270	540	533	519	491
38	435	323	99	198	396	245	490	433	319	91
39	182	364	181	362	177	354	161	322	97	194
40	388	229	458	369	191	382	217	434	321	95
41	190	380	213	426	305	63	126	252	504	461
42	375	203	406	265	530	513	479	411	275	3
43	6	12	24	48	96	192	384	221	442	337
44	127	254	508	469	391	235	470	393	239	478
45	409	271	542	537	527	507	467	387	227	454
46	361	175	350	153	306	65	130	260	520	493
47	439	331	115	230	460	373	199	398	249	498
48	449	351	155	310	73	146	292	37	74	148
49	296	45	90	180	360	173	346	145	290	33

P = 547

INDICES

	0	1	2	3	4	5	6	7	8	9
50	539	21	218	345	418	260	364	455	442	504
51	214	41	9	425	226	278	30	336	45	378
52	468	14	85	159	20	344	259	454	503	40
53	424	277	335	377	13	158	343	453	39	276
54	376	157	452	275	156	274	273			

POWER RESIDUES

	0	1	2	3	4	5	6	7	8	9
50	66	132	264	528	509	471	395	243	486	425
51	303	59	118	236	472	397	247	494	441	335
52	123	246	492	437	327	107	214	428	309	71
53	142	284	21	42	84	168	336	125	250	500
54	453	359	171	342	137	274				

P = 557

INDICES

	0	1	2	3	4	5	6	7	8	9
0		0	1	435	2	529	436	458	3	314
1	530	233	437	173	459	408	4	446	315	320
2	531	337	234	369	438	502	174	193	460	394
3	409	241	5	112	447	431	316	427	321	52
4	532	543	338	384	235	287	370	21	439	360
5	503	325	175	497	194	206	461	199	395	138
6	410	523	242	216	6	146	113	56	448	248
7	432	230	317	190	428	381	322	135	53	378
8	533	72	544	536	339	419	385	273	236	211
9	288	75	371	120	22	293	440	66	361	547
10	504	480	326	87	176	310	498	539	195	186
11	207	306	462	30	200	342	396	487	139	348
12	411	466	524	422	243	475	217	80	7	263
13	147	388	114	222	57	166	449	34	249	276
14	433	456	231	406	318	367	191	239	429	50
15	382	19	323	204	136	214	54	228	379	376
16	534	271	73	291	545	85	537	304	340	346
17	420	78	386	164	274	404	237	17	212	374
18	289	302	76	402	372	400	121	123	23	95
19	294	125	441	355	67	25	362	12	548	97
20	505	491	481	296	327	516	88	127	177	553
21	311	443	499	109	540	357	196	143	187	69
22	208	63	307	27	463	260	31	364	201	268
23	343	14	397	352	488	550	140	257	349	99
24	412	102	467	507	525	333	423	493	244	415
25	476	483	218	46	81	298	8	105	264	329
26	148	152	389	518	115	470	223	90	58	41
27	167	129	450	510	35	179	250	156	277	555
28	434	528	457	313	232	172	407	445	319	336
29	368	501	192	393	240	111	430	426	51	542
30	383	286	20	359	324	496	205	198	137	522
31	215	145	55	247	229	189	380	134	377	71
32	535	418	272	210	74	119	292	65	546	479
33	86	309	538	185	305	29	341	486	347	465
34	421	474	79	262	387	221	165	33	275	455
35	405	366	238	49	18	203	213	227	375	270
36	290	84	303	345	77	163	403	16	373	301
37	401	399	122	94	124	354	24	11	96	490
38	295	515	126	552	442	108	356	142	68	62
39	26	259	363	267	13	351	549	256	98	101
40	506	332	492	414	482	45	297	104	328	151
41	517	469	89	40	128	509	178	155	554	527
42	312	171	444	335	500	392	110	425	541	285
43	358	495	197	521	144	246	188	133	70	417
44	209	118	64	478	308	184	28	485	464	473
45	261	220	32	454	365	48	202	226	269	83
46	344	162	15	300	398	93	353	10	489	514
47	551	107	141	61	258	266	350	255	100	331
48	413	44	103	150	468	39	508	154	526	170
49	334	391	424	284	494	520	245	132	416	117

POWER RESIDUES

	0	1	2	3	4	5	6	7	8	9
0	1	2	4	8	16	32	64	128	256	512
1	467	377	197	394	231	462	367	177	354	151
2	302	47	94	188	376	195	390	223	446	335
3	113	226	452	347	137	274	548	539	521	485
4	413	269	538	519	481	405	253	506	455	353
5	149	298	39	78	156	312	67	134	268	536
6	515	473	389	221	442	327	97	194	388	219
7	438	319	81	162	324	91	182	364	171	342
8	127	254	508	459	361	165	330	103	206	412
9	267	534	511	465	373	189	378	199	398	239
10	478	399	241	482	407	257	514	471	385	213
11	426	295	33	66	132	264	528	499	441	325
12	93	186	372	187	374	191	382	207	414	271
13	542	527	497	437	317	77	154	308	59	118
14	236	472	387	217	434	311	65	130	260	520
15	483	409	261	522	487	417	277	554	551	545
16	533	509	461	365	173	346	135	270	540	523
17	489	421	285	13	26	52	104	208	416	275
18	550	543	529	501	445	333	109	218	436	315
19	73	146	292	27	54	108	216	432	307	57
20	114	228	456	355	153	306	55	110	220	440
21	323	89	178	356	155	310	63	126	252	504
22	451	345	133	266	532	507	457	357	157	314
23	71	142	284	11	22	44	88	176	352	147
24	294	31	62	124	248	496	435	313	69	138
25	276	552	547	537	517	477	397	237	474	391
26	225	450	343	129	258	516	475	393	229	458
27	359	161	322	87	174	348	139	278	556	555
28	553	549	541	525	493	429	301	45	90	180
29	360	163	326	95	190	380	203	406	255	510
30	463	369	181	362	167	334	111	222	444	331
31	105	210	420	283	9	18	36	72	144	288
32	19	38	76	152	304	51	102	204	408	259
33	518	479	401	245	490	423	289	21	42	84
34	168	336	115	230	460	363	169	338	119	238
35	476	395	233	466	375	193	386	215	430	303
36	49	98	196	392	227	454	351	145	290	23
37	46	92	184	368	179	358	159	318	79	158
38	316	75	150	300	43	86	172	344	131	262
39	524	491	425	293	29	58	116	232	464	371
40	185	370	183	366	175	350	143	286	15	30
41	60	120	240	480	403	249	498	439	321	85
42	170	340	123	246	492	427	297	37	74	148
43	296	35	70	140	280	3	6	12	24	48
44	96	192	384	211	422	287	17	34	68	136
45	272	544	531	505	453	349	141	282	7	14
46	28	56	112	224	448	339	121	242	484	411
47	265	530	503	449	341	125	250	500	443	329
48	101	202	404	251	502	447	337	117	234	468
49	379	201	402	247	494	431	305	53	106	212

P = 557

INDICES

	0	1	2	3	4	5	6	7	8	9
50	477	183	484	472	219	453	47	225	82	161
51	299	92	9	513	106	60	265	254	330	43
52	149	38	153	169	390	283	519	131	116	182
53	471	452	224	160	91	512	59	253	42	37
54	168	282	130	181	451	159	511	252	36	281
55	180	158	251	280	157	279	278			

POWER RESIDUES

	0	1	2	3	4	5	6	7	8	9
50	424	291	25	50	100	200	400	243	486	415
51	273	546	535	513	469	381	205	410	263	526
52	495	433	309	61	122	244	488	419	281	5
53	10	20	40	80	160	320	83	166	332	107
54	214	428	299	41	82	164	328	99	198	396
55	235	470	383	209	418	279				

P = 563

INDICES

	0	1	2	3	4	5	6	7	8	9
0		0	1	530	2	115	531	130	3	498
1	116	554	532	504	131	83	4	322	499	46
2	117	98	555	302	533	230	505	466	132	205
3	84	459	5	522	323	245	500	201	47	472
4	118	423	99	341	556	51	303	30	534	260
5	231	290	506	125	467	107	133	14	206	350
6	85	476	460	66	6	57	523	182	324	270
7	246	112	501	95	202	198	48	122	473	267
8	119	434	424	369	100	437	342	173	557	517
9	52	72	304	427	31	161	535	77	261	490
10	232	372	291	138	507	213	126	298	468	103
11	108	169	134	448	15	417	207	440	351	452
12	86	546	477	391	461	345	67	386	7	309
13	58	189	524	176	183	19	325	362	271	409
14	247	560	113	496	502	320	96	228	203	520
15	199	421	49	258	123	12	474	55	268	93
16	120	432	435	515	425	75	370	211	101	446
17	438	544	343	307	174	360	558	318	518	256
18	53	430	73	444	305	316	428	314	32	34
19	162	148	536	36	78	25	262	164	491	355
20	233	150	373	335	292	538	139	238	508	38
21	214	278	127	80	299	456	469	27	104	63
22	109	264	170	158	135	166	449	383	16	493
23	418	90	208	357	441	145	352	235	453	155
24	87	152	547	402	478	375	392	550	462	337
25	346	194	68	294	387	405	8	540	310	331
26	59	141	190	481	525	240	177	485	184	510
27	20	378	326	40	363	222	272	216	410	395
28	248	280	561	529	114	129	497	553	503	82
29	321	45	97	301	229	465	204	458	521	244
30	200	471	422	340	50	29	259	289	124	106
31	13	349	475	65	56	181	269	111	94	197
32	121	266	433	368	436	172	516	71	426	160
33	76	489	371	137	212	297	102	168	447	416
34	439	451	545	390	344	385	308	188	175	18
35	361	408	559	495	319	227	519	420	257	11
36	54	92	431	514	74	210	445	543	306	359
37	317	255	429	443	315	313	33	147	35	24
38	163	354	149	334	537	237	37	277	79	455
39	26	62	263	157	165	382	492	89	356	144
40	234	154	151	401	374	549	336	193	293	404
41	539	330	140	480	239	484	509	377	39	221
42	215	394	279	528	128	552	81	44	300	464
43	457	243	470	339	28	288	105	348	64	180
44	110	196	265	367	171	70	159	488	136	296
45	167	415	450	389	384	187	17	407	494	226
46	419	10	91	513	209	542	358	254	442	312
47	146	23	353	333	236	276	454	61	156	381
48	88	143	153	400	548	192	403	329	479	483
49	376	220	393	527	551	43	463	242	338	287

POWER RESIDUES

	0	1	2	3	4	5	6	7	8	9
0	1	2	4	8	16	32	64	128	256	512
1	461	359	155	310	57	114	228	456	349	135
2	270	540	517	471	379	195	390	217	434	305
3	47	94	188	376	189	378	193	386	209	418
4	273	546	529	495	427	291	19	38	76	152
5	304	45	90	180	360	157	314	65	130	260
6	520	477	391	219	438	313	63	126	252	504
7	445	327	91	182	364	165	330	97	194	388
8	213	426	289	15	30	60	120	240	480	397
9	231	462	361	159	318	73	146	292	21	42
10	84	168	336	109	218	436	309	55	110	220
11	440	317	71	142	284	5	10	20	40	80
12	160	320	77	154	308	53	106	212	424	285
13	7	14	28	56	112	224	448	333	103	206
14	412	261	522	481	399	235	470	377	191	382
15	201	402	241	482	401	239	478	393	223	446
16	329	95	190	380	197	394	225	450	337	111
17	222	444	325	87	174	348	133	266	532	501
18	439	315	67	134	268	536	509	455	347	131
19	262	524	485	407	251	502	441	319	75	150
20	300	37	74	148	296	29	58	116	232	464
21	365	167	334	105	210	420	277	554	545	527
22	491	419	275	550	537	511	459	355	147	294
23	25	50	100	200	400	237	474	385	207	414
24	265	530	497	431	299	35	70	140	280	560
25	557	551	539	515	467	371	179	358	153	306
26	49	98	196	392	221	442	321	79	158	316
27	69	138	276	552	541	519	475	387	211	422
28	281	562	561	559	555	547	531	499	435	307
29	51	102	204	408	253	506	449	335	107	214
30	428	293	23	46	92	184	368	173	346	129
31	258	516	469	375	187	374	185	370	177	354
32	145	290	17	34	68	136	272	544	525	487
33	411	259	518	473	383	203	406	249	498	433
34	303	43	86	172	344	125	250	500	437	311
35	59	118	236	472	381	199	398	233	466	369
36	175	350	137	274	548	533	503	443	323	83
37	166	332	101	202	404	245	490	417	271	542
38	521	479	395	227	454	345	127	254	508	453
39	343	123	246	492	421	279	558	553	543	523
40	483	403	243	486	409	255	510	457	351	139
41	278	556	549	535	507	451	339	115	230	460
42	357	151	302	41	82	164	328	93	186	372
43	181	362	161	322	81	162	324	85	170	340
44	117	234	468	373	183	366	169	338	113	226
45	452	341	119	238	476	389	215	430	297	31
46	62	124	248	496	429	295	27	54	108	216
47	432	301	39	78	156	312	61	122	244	488
48	413	263	526	489	415	267	534	505	447	331
49	99	198	396	229	458	353	143	286	9	18

P = 563

INDICES

	0	1	2	3	4	5	6	7	8	9
50	347	179	195	366	69	487	295	414	388	186
51	406	225	9	512	541	253	311	22	332	275
52	60	380	142	399	191	328	482	219	526	42
53	241	286	178	365	486	413	185	224	511	252
54	21	274	379	398	327	218	41	285	364	412
55	223	251	273	397	217	284	411	250	396	283
56	249	282	281							

POWER RESIDUES

	0	1	2	3	4	5	6	7	8	9
50	36	72	144	288	13	26	52	104	208	416
51	269	538	513	463	363	163	326	89	178	356
52	149	298	33	66	132	264	528	493	423	283
53	3	6	12	24	48	96	192	384	205	410
54	257	514	465	367	171	342	121	242	484	405
55	247	494	425	287	11	22	44	88	176	352
56	141	282								

P = 569

INDICES

	0	1	2	3	4	5	6	7	8	9
0		0	510	1	452	296	511	222	394	2
1	238	79	453	38	164	297	336	30	512	329
2	180	223	21	487	395	24	548	3	106	467
3	239	419	278	80	540	518	454	151	271	39
4	122	132	165	484	531	298	429	127	337	444
5	534	31	490	85	513	375	48	330	409	553
6	181	462	361	224	220	334	22	538	482	488
7	460	458	396	471	93	25	213	301	549	398
8	64	4	74	231	107	326	426	468	473	291
9	240	260	371	420	69	57	279	95	386	81
10	476	208	541	501	432	519	27	528	455	383
11	317	152	558	440	272	215	351	40	495	252
12	123	158	404	133	303	320	166	294	162	485
13	276	130	532	551	480	299	424	55	430	438
14	402	128	400	117	338	195	413	445	35	119
15	535	66	155	32	243	147	491	101	340	86
16	6	141	514	347	16	376	173	197	49	76
17	268	331	368	249	410	246	415	554	233	561
18	182	263	202	463	313	447	362	109	11	225
19	567	451	221	237	37	335	328	20	23	105
20	418	539	150	121	483	428	443	489	374	408
21	461	219	537	459	470	212	397	73	325	472
22	259	68	94	475	500	26	382	557	214	494
23	157	302	293	275	550	423	437	399	194	34
24	65	242	100	5	346	172	75	367	245	232
25	262	312	108	566	236	327	104	149	427	373
26	218	469	72	258	474	381	493	292	422	193
27	241	345	366	261	565	103	372	71	380	421
28	344	564	70	343	342	58	59	354	280	60
29	137	96	355	88	387	281	545	82	61	525
30	477	138	8	209	97	190	542	356	185	502
31	89	143	433	388	43	520	282	392	28	546
32	516	529	83	359	456	62	289	384	526	349
33	318	478	115	153	139	266	559	9	18	441
34	210	498	273	98	310	216	191	378	352	543
35	188	41	357	113	496	186	175	253	503	177
36	124	90	205	159	144	199	405	434	255	134
37	389	307	304	44	51	321	521	505	167	283
38	509	295	393	78	163	29	179	486	547	466
39	277	517	270	131	530	126	533	84	47	552
40	360	333	481	457	92	300	63	230	425	290
41	370	56	385	207	431	527	316	439	350	251
42	403	319	161	129	479	54	401	116	412	118
43	154	146	339	140	15	196	267	248	414	560
44	201	446	10	450	36	19	417	120	442	407
45	536	211	324	67	499	556	156	274	436	33
46	99	171	244	311	235	148	217	257	492	192
47	365	102	379	563	341	353	136	87	544	524
48	7	189	184	142	42	391	515	358	288	348
49	114	265	17	497	309	377	187	112	174	176

POWER RESIDUES

	0	1	2	3	4	5	6	7	8	9
0	1	3	9	27	81	243	160	480	302	337
1	442	188	564	554	524	434	164	492	338	445
2	197	22	66	198	25	75	225	106	318	385
3	17	51	153	459	239	148	444	194	13	39
4	117	351	484	314	373	550	512	398	56	168
5	504	374	553	521	425	137	411	95	285	286
6	289	298	325	406	80	240	151	453	221	94
7	282	277	262	217	82	246	169	507	383	11
8	33	99	297	322	397	53	159	477	293	310
9	361	514	404	74	222	97	291	304	343	460
10	242	157	471	275	256	199	28	84	252	187
11	561	545	497	353	490	332	427	143	429	149
12	447	203	40	120	360	511	395	47	141	423
13	131	393	41	123	369	538	476	290	301	334
14	433	161	483	311	364	523	431	155	465	257
15	202	37	111	333	430	152	456	230	121	363
16	520	422	128	384	14	42	126	378	565	557
17	533	461	245	166	498	356	499	359	508	386
18	20	60	180	540	482	308	355	496	350	481
19	305	346	469	269	238	145	435	167	501	365
20	526	440	182	546	500	362	517	413	101	303
21	340	451	215	76	228	115	345	466	260	211
22	64	192	7	21	63	189	567	563	551	515
23	407	83	249	178	534	464	254	193	10	30
24	90	270	241	154	462	248	175	525	437	173
25	519	419	119	357	502	368	535	467	263	220
26	91	273	250	181	543	491	335	436	170	510
27	392	38	114	342	457	233	130	390	32	96
28	288	295	316	379	568	566	560	542	488	326
29	409	89	267	232	127	381	5	15	45	135
30	405	77	231	124	372	547	503	371	544	494
31	344	463	251	184	552	518	416	110	330	421
32	125	375	556	530	452	218	85	255	196	19
33	57	171	513	401	65	195	16	48	144	432
34	158	474	284	283	280	271	244	163	489	329
35	418	116	348	475	287	292	307	352	487	323
36	400	62	186	558	536	470	272	247	172	516
37	410	92	276	259	208	55	165	495	347	472
38	278	265	226	109	327	412	98	294	313	370
39	541	485	317	382	8	24	72	216	79	237
40	142	426	140	420	122	366	529	449	209	58
41	174	522	428	146	438	176	528	446	200	31
42	93	279	268	235	136	408	86	258	205	46
43	138	414	104	312	367	532	458	236	139	417
44	113	339	448	206	49	147	441	185	555	527
45	443	191	4	12	36	108	324	403	71	213
46	70	210	61	183	549	509	389	29	87	261
47	214	73	219	88	264	223	100	300	331	424
48	134	402	68	204	43	129	387	23	69	207
49	52	156	468	266	229	118	354	493	341	454

P = 569

INDICES

	0	1	2	3	4	5	6	7	8	9
50	204	198	254	306	50	504	508	77	178	465
51	269	125	46	332	91	229	369	206	315	250
52	160	53	411	145	14	247	200	449	416	406
53	323	555	435	170	234	256	364	562	135	523
54	183	390	287	264	308	111	203	305	507	464
55	45	228	314	52	13	448	322	169	363	522
56	286	110	506	227	12	168	285	226	284	

POWER RESIDUES

	0	1	2	3	4	5	6	7	8	9
50	224	103	309	358	505	377	562	548	506	380
51	2	6	18	54	162	486	320	391	35	105
52	315	376	559	539	479	299	328	415	107	321
53	394	44	132	396	50	150	450	212	67	201
54	34	102	306	349	478	296	319	388	26	78
55	234	133	399	59	177	531	455	227	112	336
56	439	179	537	473	281	274	253	190		

P = 571

INDICES

	0	1	2	3	4	5	6	7	8	9
0		0	545	1	520	422	546	231	495	2
1	397	268	521	352	206	423	470	413	547	457
2	372	232	243	246	496	274	327	3	181	200
3	398	90	445	269	388	83	522	332	432	353
4	347	365	207	454	218	424	221	565	471	462
5	249	414	302	253	548	120	156	458	175	60
6	373	526	65	233	420	204	244	443	363	247
7	58	361	497	427	307	275	407	499	328	31
8	322	4	340	166	182	265	429	201	193	71
9	399	13	196	91	540	309	446	292	437	270
10	224	107	389	19	277	84	228	385	523	190
11	95	333	131	409	433	98	150	354	35	74
12	348	536	501	366	40	126	208	568	395	455
13	179	330	219	118	418	425	338	11	222	188
14	33	566	336	50	472	52	402	463	282	324
15	250	319	382	415	474	512	303	508	6	254
16	297	477	549	54	315	121	141	342	157	134
17	240	459	404	16	176	505	168	61	46	102
18	374	465	558	527	171	184	66	111	515	234
19	284	544	421	494	267	205	412	371	245	326
20	199	444	82	431	364	217	564	248	252	155
21	59	64	203	362	360	306	498	321	165	428
22	70	195	308	436	106	276	384	94	408	149
23	73	500	125	394	329	417	10	32	49	401
24	323	381	511	5	476	314	341	239	15	167
25	101	557	183	514	543	266	370	198	430	563
26	154	202	305	164	194	105	93	72	393	9
27	400	510	313	14	556	542	197	153	163	92
28	8	312	541	162	311	310	25	26	447	256
29	27	293	377	448	438	482	257	271	299	28
30	225	115	294	108	357	378	390	479	449	20
31	487	439	278	145	483	85	551	258	229	468
32	272	386	452	300	524	56	29	191	290	226
33	96	38	116	334	317	295	132	44	109	410
34	215	358	434	123	379	99	561	391	151	23
35	480	355	143	450	36	213	21	75	77	488
36	349	344	440	537	533	279	502	79	146	367
37	159	484	41	530	86	127	490	552	209	136
38	259	569	519	230	396	351	469	456	242	273
39	180	89	387	331	346	453	220	461	301	119
40	174	525	419	442	57	426	406	30	339	264
41	192	12	539	291	223	18	227	189	130	97
42	34	535	39	567	178	117	337	187	335	51
43	281	318	473	507	296	53	140	133	403	504
44	45	464	170	110	283	493	411	325	81	216
45	251	63	359	320	69	435	383	148	124	416
46	48	380	475	238	100	513	369	562	304	104
47	392	509	555	152	7	161	24	255	376	481
48	298	114	356	478	486	144	550	467	451	55
49	289	37	316	43	214	122	560	22	142	212

POWER RESIDUES

	0	1	2	3	4	5	6	7	8	9
0	1	3	9	27	81	243	158	474	280	269
1	236	137	411	91	273	248	173	519	415	103
2	309	356	497	349	476	286	287	290	299	326
3	407	79	237	140	420	118	354	491	331	422
4	124	372	545	493	337	440	178	534	460	238
5	143	429	145	435	163	489	325	404	70	210
6	59	177	531	451	211	62	186	558	532	454
7	220	89	267	230	119	357	500	358	503	367
8	530	448	202	35	105	315	374	551	511	391
9	31	93	279	266	227	110	330	419	115	345
10	464	250	179	537	469	265	224	101	303	338
11	443	187	561	541	481	301	332	425	133	399
12	55	165	495	343	458	232	125	375	554	520
13	418	112	336	437	169	507	379	566	556	526
14	436	166	498	352	485	313	368	533	457	229
15	116	348	473	277	260	209	56	168	504	370
16	539	475	283	278	263	218	83	249	176	528
17	442	184	552	514	400	58	174	522	424	130
18	390	28	84	252	185	555	523	427	139	417
19	109	327	410	88	264	221	92	276	257	200
20	29	87	261	212	65	195	14	42	126	378
21	563	547	499	355	494	340	449	205	44	132
22	396	46	138	414	100	300	329	416	106	318
23	383	7	21	63	189	567	559	535	463	247
24	170	510	388	22	66	198	23	69	207	50
25	150	450	208	53	159	477	289	296	317	380
26	569	565	553	517	409	85	255	194	11	33
27	99	297	320	389	25	75	225	104	312	365
28	524	430	148	444	190	570	568	562	544	490
29	328	413	97	291	302	335	434	160	480	298
30	323	398	52	156	468	262	215	74	222	95
31	285	284	281	272	245	164	492	334	431	151
32	453	217	80	240	149	447	199	26	78	234
33	131	393	37	111	333	428	142	426	136	408
34	82	246	167	501	361	512	394	40	120	360
35	509	385	13	39	117	351	482	304	341	452
36	214	71	213	68	204	41	123	369	536	466
37	256	197	20	60	180	540	478	292	305	344
38	461	241	152	456	226	107	321	392	34	102
39	306	347	470	268	233	128	384	10	30	90
40	270	239	146	438	172	516	406	76	228	113
41	339	446	196	17	51	153	459	235	134	402
42	64	192	5	15	45	135	405	73	219	86
43	258	203	38	114	342	455	223	98	294	311
44	362	515	403	67	201	32	96	288	293	308
45	353	488	322	395	43	129	387	19	57	171
46	513	397	49	147	441	181	543	487	319	386
47	16	48	144	432	154	462	244	161	483	307
48	350	479	295	314	371	542	484	310	359	506
49	376	557	529	445	193	8	24	72	216	77

P = 571

INDICES

	0	1	2	3	4	5	6	7	8	9
50	76	343	532	78	158	529	489	135	518	350
51	241	88	345	460	173	441	405	263	538	17
52	129	534	177	186	280	506	139	503	169	492
53	80	62	68	147	47	237	368	103	554	160
54	375	113	485	466	288	42	559	211	531	528
55	517	87	172	262	128	185	138	491	67	236
56	553	112	287	210	516	261	137	235	286	260
57	285	0								

POWER RESIDUES

	0	1	2	3	4	5	6	7	8	9
50	231	122	366	527	439	175	525	433	157	471
51	271	242	155	465	253	188	564	550	508	382
52	4	12	36	108	324	401	61	183	549	505
53	373	548	502	364	521	421	121	363	518	412
54	94	282	275	254	191	2	6	18	54	162
55	486	316	377	560	538	472	274	251	182	546
56	496	346	467	259	206	47	141	423	127	381
57										

P = 577

INDICES

	0	1	2	3	4	5	6	7	8	9
0		0	148	564	296	1	136	485	444	552
1	149	102	284	467	57	565	16	214	124	60
2	297	473	250	434	432	2	39	540	205	267
3	137	224	164	90	362	486	272	549	208	455
4	445	219	45	521	398	553	6	471	4	394
5	150	202	187	34	112	103	353	48	415	318
6	285	517	372	461	312	468	238	63	510	422
7	58	396	420	41	121	566	356	11	27	235
8	17	528	367	387	193	215	93	255	546	97
9	125	376	154	212	43	61	152	441	542	78
10	298	131	350	83	335	474	182	332	260	451
11	251	537	501	571	196	435	563	443	466	123
12	433	204	89	207	520	3	33	414	460	509
13	40	26	386	545	211	541	82	259	570	465
14	206	459	544	569	568	268	189	382	269	340
15	138	244	504	190	159	225	175	482	383	22
16	165	343	100	270	515	91	535	80	341	358
17	363	36	241	139	403	487	118	306	245	169
18	273	86	524	505	302	550	360	316	191	449
19	209	20	300	160	13	456	114	69	226	309
20	446	51	279	176	498	220	231	410	483	162
21	46	365	330	384	480	522	408	133	23	29
22	399	105	109	166	73	554	143	347	344	263
23	7	575	135	101	15	472	38	223	271	218
24	5	201	352	516	237	395	355	527	92	375
25	151	130	181	536	562	203	32	25	81	458
26	188	243	174	342	534	35	117	85	359	19
27	113	50	230	364	407	104	142	574	37	200
28	354	129	31	242	116	49	141	128	140	428
29	416	429	337	404	530	319	417	66	488	325
30	286	430	392	119	76	518	338	401	307	71
31	373	405	323	246	54	462	531	476	170	369
32	313	320	491	274	248	469	418	439	87	380
33	239	67	107	525	228	64	489	293	506	559
34	511	326	184	303	389	423	287	295	551	56
35	59	431	266	361	454	397	393	111	317	311
36	421	120	234	192	96	42	77	334	450	195
37	122	519	508	210	464	567	339	158	21	514
38	357	402	168	301	448	12	308	497	161	479
39	28	72	262	14	217	236	374	561	457	533
40	18	406	199	115	427	529	324	75	70	53
41	368	247	379	227	558	388	55	453	310	95
42	194	463	513	447	478	216	532	426	52	557
43	94	477	556	280	281	256	171	494	177	282
44	547	370	253	499	257	98	314	328	221	172
45	126	321	291	232	495	377	492	145	411	178
46	155	275	147	484	283	213	249	539	163	548
47	44	470	186	47	371	62	419	10	366	254
48	153	440	349	331	500	442	88	413	385	258
49	543	381	503	481	99	79	240	305	523	315

POWER RESIDUES

	0	1	2	3	4	5	6	7	8	9
0	1	5	25	125	48	240	46	230	573	557
1	477	77	385	194	393	234	16	80	400	269
2	191	378	159	218	513	257	131	78	390	219
3	518	282	256	126	53	265	171	278	236	26
4	130	73	365	94	470	42	210	473	57	285
5	271	201	428	409	314	416	349	14	70	350
6	19	95	475	67	335	521	297	331	501	197
7	408	309	391	224	543	407	304	366	99	495
8	167	258	136	103	515	267	181	328	486	122
9	33	165	248	86	430	419	364	89	445	494
10	162	233	11	55	275	221	528	332	506	222
11	533	357	54	270	196	403	284	266	176	303
12	361	74	370	119	18	90	450	519	287	281
13	251	101	505	217	508	232	6	30	150	173
14	288	286	276	226	553	457	554	462	2	10
15	50	250	96	480	92	460	569	537	377	154
16	193	388	209	468	32	160	223	538	382	179
17	318	436	449	514	262	156	203	438	459	564
18	512	252	106	530	342	556	472	52	260	146
19	153	188	363	84	420	369	114	570	542	402
20	279	241	51	255	121	28	140	123	38	190
21	373	134	93	465	17	85	425	394	239	41
22	205	448	509	237	31	155	198	413	334	516
23	272	206	453	534	362	79	395	244	66	330
24	496	172	283	261	151	178	313	411	324	466
25	22	110	550	442	479	87	435	444	489	137
26	108	540	392	229	568	532	352	29	145	148
27	163	238	36	180	323	461	574	562	502	202
28	433	434	439	464	12	60	300	346	576	572
29	552	452	529	337	531	347	4	20	100	500
30	192	383	184	343	561	497	177	308	386	199
31	418	359	64	320	446	499	187	358	59	295
32	321	451	524	312	406	299	341	551	447	504
33	212	483	107	535	367	104	520	292	306	376
34	149	168	263	161	228	563	507	227	558	482
35	102	510	242	56	280	246	76	380	169	268
36	186	353	34	170	273	211	478	82	410	319
37	441	474	62	310	396	249	91	455	544	412
38	329	491	147	158	213	488	132	83	415	344
39	566	522	302	356	49	245	71	355	44	220
40	523	307	381	174	293	311	401	274	216	503
41	207	458	559	487	127	58	290	296	326	476
42	72	360	69	345	571	547	427	404	289	291
43	301	351	24	120	23	115	575	567	527	327
44	481	97	485	117	8	40	200	423	384	189
45	368	109	545	417	354	39	195	398	259	141
46	128	63	315	421	374	139	118	13	65	325
47	471	47	235	21	105	525	317	431	424	389
48	214	493	157	208	463	7	35	175	298	336
49	526	322	456	549	437	454	539	387	204	443

P = 577

INDICES	0	1	2	3	4	5	6	7	8	9
50	299	68	278	409	329	132	108	346	134	222
51	351	526	180	24	173	84	229	573	30	127
52	336	65	391	400	322	475	490	438	106	292
53	183	294	265	110	233	333	507	157	167	496
54	261	560	198	74	378	452	512	425	555	493
55	252	327	290	144	146	538	185	9	348	412
56	502	304	277	345	179	572	390	437	264	156
57	197	424	289	8	276	436	288			

POWER RESIDUES	0	1	2	3	4	5	6	7	8	9
50	484	112	560	492	152	183	338	536	372	129
51	68	340	546	422	379	164	243	61	305	371
52	124	43	215	498	182	333	511	247	81	405
53	294	316	426	399	264	166	253	111	555	467
54	27	135	98	490	142	133	88	440	469	37
55	185	348	9	45	225	548	432	429	414	339
56	541	397	254	116	3	15	75	375	144	143
57	138	113	565	517	277	231				

P = 587

INDICES

	0	1	2	3	4	5	6	7	8	9
0		0	1	478	2	205	479	346	3	370
1	206	83	480	305	347	97	4	38	371	233
2	207	238	84	363	481	410	306	262	348	432
3	98	354	5	561	39	551	372	201	234	197
4	208	251	239	336	85	575	364	176	482	106
5	411	516	307	212	263	288	349	125	433	272
6	99	157	355	130	6	510	562	220	40	255
7	552	523	373	182	202	302	235	429	198	572
8	209	154	252	426	240	243	337	324	86	26
9	576	65	365	246	177	438	483	19	107	453
10	412	340	517	461	308	443	213	395	264	327
11	289	93	350	172	126	568	434	89	273	384
12	100	166	158	143	356	29	131	277	7	228
13	511	421	563	579	221	467	41	488	256	59
14	553	68	524	388	374	51	183	584	203	368
15	303	36	236	408	430	559	199	249	573	104
16	210	123	155	508	253	180	427	152	241	24
17	244	17	338	441	325	170	87	164	27	226
18	577	486	66	49	366	406	247	121	178	22
19	439	162	484	404	20	402	108	110	454	314
20	413	112	341	192	518	456	462	147	309	316
21	444	472	214	415	396	541	265	114	328	74
22	290	343	94	360	351	194	173	285	127	520
23	569	321	435	458	90	381	274	464	385	33
24	101	149	167	46	159	311	144	538	357	318
25	30	535	132	446	278	135	8	474	229	547
26	512	216	422	449	564	417	580	504	222	398
27	468	281	42	543	489	493	257	267	60	138
28	554	116	69	530	525	330	389	11	375	76
29	52	497	184	292	585	477	204	345	369	82
30	304	96	37	232	237	362	409	261	431	353
31	560	550	200	196	250	335	574	175	105	515
32	211	287	124	271	156	129	509	219	254	522
33	181	301	428	571	153	425	242	323	25	64
34	245	437	18	452	339	460	442	394	326	92
35	171	567	88	383	165	142	28	276	227	420
36	578	466	487	58	67	387	50	583	367	35
37	407	558	248	103	122	507	179	151	23	16
38	440	169	163	225	485	48	405	120	21	161
39	403	401	109	313	111	191	455	146	315	471
40	414	540	113	73	342	359	193	284	519	320
41	457	380	463	32	148	45	310	537	317	534
42	445	134	473	546	215	448	416	503	397	280
43	542	492	266	137	115	529	329	10	75	496
44	291	476	344	81	95	231	361	260	352	549
45	195	334	174	514	286	270	128	218	521	300
46	570	424	322	63	436	451	459	393	91	566
47	382	141	275	419	465	57	386	582	34	557
48	102	506	150	15	168	224	47	119	160	400
49	312	190	145	470	539	72	358	283	319	379

POWER RESIDUES

	0	1	2	3	4	5	6	7	8	9
0	1	2	4	8	16	32	64	128	256	512
1	437	287	574	561	535	483	379	171	342	97
2	194	388	189	378	169	338	89	178	356	125
3	250	500	413	239	478	369	151	302	17	34
4	68	136	272	544	501	415	243	486	385	183
5	366	145	290	580	573	559	531	475	363	139
6	278	556	525	463	339	91	182	364	141	282
7	564	541	495	403	219	438	289	578	569	551
8	515	443	299	11	22	44	88	176	352	117
9	234	468	349	111	222	444	301	15	30	60
10	120	240	480	373	159	318	49	98	196	392
11	197	394	201	402	217	434	281	562	537	487
12	387	187	374	161	322	57	114	228	456	325
13	63	126	252	504	421	255	510	433	279	558
14	529	471	355	123	246	492	397	207	414	241
15	482	377	167	334	81	162	324	61	122	244
16	488	389	191	382	177	354	121	242	484	381
17	175	350	113	226	452	317	47	94	188	376
18	165	330	73	146	292	584	581	575	563	539
19	491	395	203	406	225	450	313	39	78	156
20	312	37	74	148	296	5	10	20	40	80
21	160	320	53	106	212	424	261	522	457	327
22	67	134	268	536	485	383	179	358	129	258
23	516	445	303	19	38	76	152	304	21	42
24	84	168	336	85	170	340	93	186	372	157
25	314	41	82	164	328	69	138	276	552	517
26	447	307	27	54	108	216	432	277	554	521
27	455	323	59	118	236	472	357	127	254	508
28	429	271	542	497	407	227	454	321	55	110
29	220	440	293	586	585	583	579	571	555	523
30	459	331	75	150	300	13	26	52	104	208
31	416	245	490	393	199	398	209	418	249	498
32	409	231	462	337	87	174	348	109	218	436
33	285	570	553	519	451	315	43	86	172	344
34	101	202	404	221	442	297	7	14	28	56
35	112	224	448	309	31	62	124	248	496	405
36	223	446	305	23	46	92	184	368	149	298
37	9	18	36	72	144	288	576	565	543	499
38	411	235	470	353	119	238	476	365	143	286
39	572	557	527	467	347	107	214	428	269	538
40	489	391	195	390	193	386	185	370	153	306
41	25	50	100	200	400	213	426	265	530	473
42	359	131	262	524	461	335	83	166	332	77
43	154	308	29	58	116	232	464	341	95	190
44	380	173	346	105	210	420	253	506	425	263
45	526	465	343	99	198	396	205	410	233	466
46	345	103	206	412	237	474	361	135	270	540
47	493	399	211	422	257	514	441	295	3	6
48	12	24	48	96	192	384	181	362	137	274
49	548	509	431	275	550	513	439	291	582	577

P = 587

INDICES

	0	1	2	3	4	5	6	7	8	9
50	31	44	536	533	133	545	447	502	279	491
51	136	528	9	495	475	80	230	259	548	333
52	513	269	217	299	423	62	450	392	565	140
53	418	56	581	556	505	14	223	118	399	189
54	469	71	282	378	43	532	544	501	490	527
55	494	79	258	332	268	298	61	391	139	55
56	555	13	117	188	70	377	531	500	526	78
57	331	297	390	54	12	187	376	499	77	296
58	53	186	498	295	185	294	293			

POWER RESIDUES

	0	1	2	3	4	5	6	7	8	9
50	567	547	507	427	267	534	481	375	163	326
51	65	130	260	520	453	319	51	102	204	408
52	229	458	329	71	142	284	568	549	511	435
53	283	566	545	503	419	251	502	417	247	494
54	401	215	430	273	546	505	423	259	518	449
55	311	35	70	140	280	560	533	479	371	155
56	310	33	66	132	264	528	469	351	115	230
57	460	333	79	158	316	45	90	180	360	133
58	266	532	477	367	147	294				

P = 593

INDICES

	0	1	2	3	4	5	6	7	8	9
0		0	428	1	264	535	429	579	100	2
1	371	161	265	451	415	536	528	498	430	172
2	207	580	589	248	101	478	287	3	251	540
3	372	388	364	162	334	522	266	360	8	452
4	43	53	416	179	425	537	84	571	529	566
5	314	499	123	506	431	104	87	173	376	518
6	208	127	224	581	200	394	590	369	170	249
7	358	82	102	198	196	479	436	148	288	352
8	471	4	481	574	252	441	15	541	261	385
9	373	438	512	389	407	115	365	28	402	163
10	150	22	335	49	551	523	342	137	267	290
11	532	361	515	12	9	191	212	453	354	485
12	44	322	555	54	60	421	417	473	36	180
13	230	281	426	159	205	538	6	569	85	392
14	194	572	510	20	530	483	34	567	32	329
15	315	489	272	500	576	331	124	258	188	507
16	307	235	432	254	317	105	410	215	88	310
17	277	174	443	491	377	465	97	519	221	382
18	209	17	274	128	348	303	225	67	243	582
19	543	502	201	118	456	395	238	131	591	263
20	578	370	450	527	171	588	477	250	387	333
21	359	42	178	83	565	122	103	375	126	199
22	368	357	197	435	351	480	440	260	437	406
23	27	149	48	341	289	514	190	353	321	59
24	472	229	158	5	391	509	482	31	488	575
25	257	306	253	409	309	442	464	220	16	347
26	66	542	117	237	262	449	587	386	41	564
27	374	367	434	439	405	47	513	320	228	390
28	30	256	408	463	346	116	448	40	366	404
29	319	29	462	447	403	461	460	164	165	107
30	151	166	325	23	108	70	336	152	412	50
31	167	112	552	326	94	524	24	217	343	109
32	143	138	71	78	268	337	90	291	153	558
33	533	413	246	362	51	312	516	168	146	13
34	113	549	10	553	279	192	327	186	213	95
35	301	454	525	176	355	25	57	486	218	585
36	45	344	445	323	110	141	556	144	184	55
37	139	493	61	72	495	422	79	399	418	269
38	379	474	338	63	37	91	546	181	292	467
39	231	154	74	282	559	295	427	534	99	160
40	414	497	206	247	286	539	363	521	7	52
41	424	570	313	505	86	517	223	393	169	81
42	195	147	470	573	14	384	511	114	401	21
43	550	136	531	11	211	484	554	420	35	280
44	204	568	193	19	33	328	271	330	187	234
45	316	214	276	490	96	381	273	302	242	501
46	455	130	577	526	476	332	177	121	125	356
47	350	259	26	340	189	58	157	508	487	305
48	308	219	65	236	586	563	433	46	227	255
49	345	39	318	446	459	106	324	69	411	111

POWER RESIDUES

	0	1	2	3	4	5	6	7	8	9
0	1	3	9	27	81	243	136	408	38	114
1	342	433	113	339	424	86	258	181	543	443
2	143	429	101	303	316	355	472	230	97	291
3	280	247	148	444	146	438	128	384	559	491
4	287	268	211	40	120	360	487	275	232	103
5	309	334	409	41	123	369	514	356	475	239
6	124	372	523	383	556	482	260	187	561	497
7	305	322	373	526	392	583	563	503	323	376
8	535	419	71	213	46	138	414	56	168	504
9	326	385	562	500	314	349	454	176	528	398
10	8	24	72	216	55	165	495	299	304	319
11	364	499	311	340	427	95	285	262	193	579
12	551	467	215	52	156	468	218	61	183	549
13	461	197	591	587	575	539	431	107	321	370
14	517	365	502	320	367	508	338	421	77	231
15	100	300	307	328	391	580	554	476	242	133
16	399	11	33	99	297	298	301	310	337	418
17	68	204	19	57	171	513	353	466	212	43
18	129	387	568	518	368	511	347	448	158	474
19	236	115	345	442	140	420	74	222	73	219
20	64	192	576	542	440	134	402	20	60	180
21	540	434	116	348	451	167	501	317	358	481
22	257	178	534	416	62	186	558	488	278	241
23	130	390	577	545	449	161	483	263	196	588
24	578	548	458	188	564	506	332	403	23	69
25	207	28	84	252	163	489	281	250	157	471
26	227	88	264	199	4	12	36	108	324	379
27	544	446	152	456	182	546	452	170	510	344
28	439	131	393	586	572	530	404	26	78	234
29	109	327	388	571	527	395	592	590	584	566
30	512	350	457	185	555	479	251	160	480	254
31	169	507	335	412	50	150	450	164	492	290
32	277	238	121	363	496	302	313	346	445	149
33	447	155	465	209	34	102	306	325	382	553
34	473	233	106	318	361	490	284	259	184	552
35	470	224	79	237	118	354	469	221	70	210
36	37	111	333	406	32	96	288	271	220	67
37	201	10	30	90	270	217	58	174	522	380
38	547	455	179	537	425	89	267	208	31	93
39	279	244	139	417	65	195	585	569	521	377
40	538	428	98	294	289	274	229	94	282	253
41	166	498	308	331	400	14	42	126	378	541
42	437	125	375	532	410	44	132	396	2	6
43	18	54	162	486	272	223	76	228	91	273
44	226	85	255	172	516	362	493	293	286	265
45	202	13	39	117	351	460	194	582	560	494
46	296	295	292	283	256	175	525	389	574	536
47	422	80	240	127	381	550	464	206	25	75
48	225	82	246	145	435	119	357	478	248	151
49	453	173	519	371	520	374	529	401	17	51

P = 593

INDICES

	0	1	2	3	4	5	6	7	8	9
50	93	216	142	77	89	557	245	311	145	548
51	278	185	300	175	56	584	444	140	183	492
52	494	398	378	62	545	466	73	294	98	496
53	285	520	423	504	222	80	469	383	400	135
54	210	419	203	18	270	233	275	380	241	129
55	475	120	349	339	156	304	64	562	226	38
56	458	68	92	76	244	547	299	583	182	397
57	544	293	284	503	468	134	202	232	240	119
58	155	561	457	75	298	396	283	133	239	560
59	297	132	296							

POWER RESIDUES

	0	1	2	3	4	5	6	7	8	9
50	153	459	191	573	533	413	53	159	477	245
51	142	426	92	276	235	112	336	415	59	177
52	531	407	35	105	315	352	463	203	16	48
53	144	432	110	330	397	5	15	45	135	405
54	29	87	261	190	570	524	386	565	509	341
55	430	104	312	343	436	122	366	505	329	394
56	589	581	557	485	269	214	49	147	441	137
57	411	47	141	423	83	249	154	462	200	7
58	21	63	189	567	515	359	484	266	205	22
59	66	198								

P = 599

INDICES

	0	1	2	3	4	5	6	7	8	9
0		0	262	402	524	4	66	1	188	206
1	266	31	328	352	263	406	450	220	468	92
2	528	403	293	283	590	8	16	10	525	461
3	70	473	114	433	482	5	132	448	354	156
4	192	44	67	139	555	210	545	574	254	2
5	270	24	278	120	272	35	189	494	125	239
6	332	363	137	207	376	356	97	318	146	87
7	267	584	394	517	112	410	18	32	418	245
8	454	412	306	168	329	224	401	265	219	589
9	472	353	209	277	238	96	516	453	264	237
10	532	533	286	26	540	407	382	73	534	567
11	297	252	451	179	158	287	387	558	501	221
12	594	62	27	446	399	12	469	128	40	541
13	20	185	359	93	580	14	408	397	349	512
14	529	378	248	383	58	465	181	404	374	177
15	74	78	280	426	294	477	82	535	507	522
16	118	284	76	194	568	437	430	161	591	106
17	486	298	65	351	527	9	481	43	253	34
18	136	86	17	167	471	452	539	251	500	11
19	358	511	180	425	117	160	526	85	499	159
20	196	122	197	462	548	48	288	489	204	123
21	71	80	46	388	335	143	198	474	231	321
22	559	572	514	463	115	214	441	502	420	415
23	549	434	51	130	222	578	165	49	483	99
24	258	595	324	216	289	6	110	444	63	570
25	274	490	133	314	390	28	302	261	205	449
26	282	69	447	554	23	124	355	393	244	400
27	276	531	72	157	61	39	13	247	176	81
28	193	485	42	470	510	498	47	45	320	440
29	129	257	443	389	68	243	38	41	439	37
30	336	140	340	337	542	367	90	144	556	428
31	141	21	344	346	199	211	171	341	186	492
32	380	475	546	312	338	360	456	371	232	575
33	101	543	94	56	423	322	255	148	368	581
34	150	504	560	3	327	91	15	432	191	573
35	271	362	145	409	305	588	515	25	296	557
36	398	184	348	464	279	521	429	350	135	250
37	116	121	203	142	513	414	164	215	273	260
38	22	530	175	497	442	36	89	345	379	370
39	422	503	190	587	347	249	163	496	421	495
40	458	200	384	227	459	416	126	479	212	59
41	310	201	550	240	153	172	466	316	385	435
42	333	552	342	182	308	228	52	364	597	187
43	405	292	460	131	138	269	493	375	583	417
44	223	208	236	381	178	593	127	579	377	373
45	476	75	105	480	166	357	84	547	79	230
46	213	50	98	109	313	281	392	60	484	319
47	242	339	427	170	311	100	147	326	361	295
48	520	202	259	88	586	457	478	152	551	596
49	268	235	372	83	108	241	325	585	234	233

POWER RESIDUES

	0	1	2	3	4	5	6	7	8	9
0	1	7	49	343	5	35	245	517	25	175
1	27	189	125	276	135	346	26	182	76	532
2	130	311	380	264	51	357	103	122	255	587
3	515	11	77	539	179	55	385	299	296	275
4	128	297	282	177	41	287	212	286	205	237
5	461	232	426	586	508	561	333	534	144	409
6	467	274	121	248	538	172	6	42	294	261
7	30	210	272	107	150	451	162	535	151	458
8	211	279	156	493	456	197	181	69	483	386
9	306	345	19	133	332	527	95	66	462	239
10	475	330	513	596	578	452	169	584	494	463
11	246	524	74	518	32	224	370	194	160	521
12	53	371	201	209	265	58	406	446	127	290
13	233	433	36	252	566	368	180	62	434	43
14	301	310	373	215	307	352	68	476	337	562
15	340	583	487	414	502	519	39	273	114	199
16	195	167	570	396	376	236	454	183	83	581
17	473	316	415	509	568	382	278	149	444	113
18	192	146	423	565	361	131	318	429	8	56
19	392	348	40	280	163	542	200	202	216	314
20	401	411	481	372	208	258	9	63	441	92
21	45	315	408	460	225	377	243	503	526	88
22	17	119	234	440	85	595	571	403	425	579
23	459	218	328	499	498	491	442	99	94	59
24	413	495	470	295	268	79	553	277	142	395
25	369	187	111	178	48	336	555	291	240	482
26	379	257	2	14	98	87	10	70	490	435
27	50	350	54	378	250	552	270	93	52	364
28	152	465	260	23	161	528	102	115	206	244
29	510	575	431	22	154	479	358	110	171	598
30	592	550	256	594	564	354	82	574	424	572
31	410	474	323	464	253	573	417	523	67	469
32	288	219	335	548	242	496	477	344	12	84
33	588	522	60	420	544	214	300	303	324	471
34	302	317	422	558	312	387	313	394	362	138
35	367	173	13	91	38	266	65	455	190	132
36	325	478	351	61	427	593	557	305	338	569
37	389	327	492	449	148	437	64	448	141	388
38	320	443	106	143	402	418	530	116	213	293
39	254	580	466	267	72	504	533	137	360	124
40	269	86	3	21	147	430	15	105	136	353
41	75	525	81	567	375	229	405	439	78	546
42	228	398	390	334	541	193	153	472	309	366
43	166	563	347	33	231	419	537	165	556	298
44	289	226	384	292	247	531	123	262	37	259
45	16	112	185	97	80	560	326	485	400	404
46	432	29	203	223	363	145	416	516	18	126
47	283	184	90	31	217	321	450	155	486	407
48	453	176	34	238	468	281	170	591	543	207
49	251	559	319	436	57	399	397	383	285	198

P = 599

INDICES

	0	1	2	3	4	5	6	7	8	9
50	536	563	154	217	395	537	576	508	54	173
51	290	518	564	102	523	30	467	7	113	155
52	544	119	331	317	111	411	218	95	285	566
53	386	445	19	396	57	77	506	436	64	33
54	538	424	195	488	334	571	419	577	323	569
55	301	553	275	246	509	256	438	366	343	491
56	455	55	149	431	304	183	134	413	174	369
57	162	226	309	315	307	291	582	592	104	229
58	391	169	519	151	107	562	53	29	330	565
59	505	487	300	365	303	225	103	561	299	

POWER RESIDUES

	0	1	2	3	4	5	6	7	8	9
50	188	118	227	391	341	590	536	158	507	554
51	284	191	139	374	222	356	96	73	511	582
52	480	365	159	514	4	28	196	174	20	140
53	381	271	100	101	108	157	500	505	540	186
54	104	129	304	331	520	46	322	457	204	230
55	412	488	421	551	263	44	308	359	117	220
56	342	597	585	501	512	589	529	109	164	549
57	249	545	221	349	47	329	506	547	235	447
58	134	339	576	438	71	497	484	393	355	89
59	24	168	577	445	120	241	489	428		

P = 601

INDICES

	0	1	2	3	4	5	6	7	8	9
0		0	432	304	264	550	136	1	96	8
1	382	157	568	270	433	254	528	485	440	241
2	214	305	589	502	400	500	102	312	265	391
3	86	27	360	461	317	551	272	380	73	574
4	46	179	137	167	421	558	334	112	232	2
5	332	189	534	583	144	107	97	545	223	75
6	518	226	459	9	192	220	293	424	149	206
7	383	65	104	89	212	204	505	158	406	531
8	478	16	11	513	569	435	599	95	253	588
9	390	271	166	331	544	191	64	405	434	165
10	164	414	21	349	366	255	415	43	576	447
11	539	84	529	22	377	452	55	278	507	486
12	350	314	58	483	291	450	441	367	24	471
13	52	194	125	242	256	262	581	19	38	594
14	215	416	497	427	536	341	521	306	44	586
15	36	40	337	493	590	577	238	48	363	287
16	310	503	448	525	443	411	345	160	401	540
17	267	249	431	7	527	501	85	379	420	188
18	222	219	103	530	598	330	163	42	376	313
19	23	261	496	585	237	524	266	378	597	260
20	596	128	246	392	453	129	181	510	198	398
21	87	56	247	369	475	117	408	28	279	393
22	371	155	516	445	361	508	454	174	209	295
23	284	462	487	130	110	62	339	235	318	351
24	182	354	146	320	490	552	315	511	123	217
25	282	33	273	59	199	139	456	563	303	381
26	484	399	26	72	557	533	74	292	88	477
27	94	543	413	575	451	57	470	580	426	35
28	47	442	248	419	329	495	259	180	368	370
29	173	109	353	122	138	25	476	469	418	172
30	468	168	472	118	169	176	325	438	422	53
31	409	473	70	68	480	559	195	29	119	548
32	142	347	335	126	280	170	357	151	275	113
33	243	394	177	388	592	374	233	257	372	326
34	99	184	81	3	263	156	439	499	359	573
35	333	582	517	423	211	15	252	190	20	446
36	54	482	51	18	535	39	362	410	430	187
37	162	584	595	509	474	154	208	61	145	216
38	455	71	93	579	328	108	417	175	69	547
39	356	387	98	498	210	481	429	153	92	546
40	428	296	560	297	78	566	224	537	285	196
41	561	323	13	76	342	463	30	298	230	403
42	519	522	488	120	79	385	201	227	307	131
43	549	567	240	101	460	45	111	143	225	148
44	203	10	587	63	348	538	277	290	193	37
45	340	336	286	344	6	221	41	236	127	197
46	116	515	294	338	319	281	562	556	542	425
47	494	352	171	324	67	141	150	591	183	358
48	14	50	186	207	578	355	152	77	322	229
49	384	239	147	276	343	115	555	66	49	321

POWER RESIDUES

	0	1	2	3	4	5	6	7	8	9
0	1	7	49	343	598	580	454	173	9	63
1	441	82	574	412	480	355	81	567	363	137
2	358	102	113	190	128	295	262	31	217	317
3	416	508	551	251	555	279	150	449	138	365
4	151	456	187	107	148	435	40	280	157	498
5	481	362	130	309	360	116	211	275	122	253
6	569	377	235	443	96	71	497	474	313	388
7	312	381	263	38	266	59	413	487	404	424
8	564	342	591	531	111	176	30	210	268	73
9	511	572	398	382	270	87	8	56	392	340
10	577	433	26	182	72	504	523	55	385	291
11	234	436	47	329	500	495	460	215	303	318
12	423	557	293	248	534	132	323	458	201	205
13	233	429	599	587	503	516	6	42	294	255
14	583	475	320	437	54	378	242	492	439	68
15	476	327	486	397	375	221	345	11	77	539
16	167	568	370	186	100	99	92	43	301	304
17	325	472	299	290	227	387	305	332	521	41
18	287	206	240	478	341	584	482	369	179	51
19	357	95	64	448	131	316	409	459	208	254
20	576	426	578	440	75	525	69	483	376	228
21	394	354	74	518	20	140	379	249	541	181
22	65	455	180	58	406	438	61	427	585	489
23	418	522	48	336	549	237	457	194	156	491
24	432	19	133	330	507	544	202	212	282	171
25	596	566	356	88	15	105	134	337	556	286
26	199	191	135	344	4	28	196	170	589	517
27	13	91	36	252	562	328	493	446	117	218
28	324	465	250	548	230	408	452	159	512	579
29	447	124	267	66	462	229	401	403	417	515
30	600	594	552	258	3	21	147	428	592	538
31	160	519	27	189	121	246	520	34	238	464
32	243	499	488	411	473	306	339	570	384	284
33	185	93	50	350	46	322	451	152	463	236
34	450	145	414	494	453	166	561	321	444	103
35	120	239	471	292	241	485	390	326	479	348
36	32	224	366	158	505	530	104	127	288	213
37	289	220	338	563	335	542	188	114	197	177
38	37	259	10	70	490	425	571	391	333	528
39	90	29	203	219	331	514	593	545	209	261
40	24	168	575	419	529	97	78	546	216	310
41	367	165	554	272	101	106	141	386	298	283
42	178	44	308	353	67	469	278	143	400	396
43	368	172	2	14	98	85	595	559	307	346
44	18	126	281	164	547	223	359	109	162	533
45	125	274	115	204	226	380	256	590	524	62
46	434	33	231	415	501	502	509	558	300	297
47	276	129	302	311	374	214	296	269	80	560
48	314	395	361	123	260	17	119	232	422	550
49	244	506	537	153	470	285	192	142	393	347

P = 601

INDICES

	0	1	2	3	4	5	6	7	8	9
50	114	464	465	134	105	364	491	244	31	466
51	571	90	288	553	395	299	135	269	213	311
52	316	178	231	106	458	205	504	512	389	404
53	365	83	506	449	124	593	520	492	309	159
54	526	218	375	523	245	397	407	444	283	234
55	489	32	302	532	412	34	258	121	467	437
56	479	346	274	373	80	572	251	17	161	60
57	327	386	91	565	12	402	200	100	202	289
58	5	514	541	140	185	228	554	133	570	268
59	457	82	308	396	301	436	250	564	4	132
60	300	0								

POWER RESIDUES

	0	1	2	3	4	5	6	7	8	9
50	25	175	23	161	526	76	532	118	225	373
51	207	247	527	83	581	461	222	352	60	420
52	536	146	421	543	195	163	540	174	16	112
53	183	79	553	265	52	364	144	407	445	110
54	169	582	468	271	94	57	399	389	319	430
55	5	35	245	513	586	496	467	264	45	315
56	402	410	466	257	597	573	405	431	12	84
57	588	510	565	349	39	273	108	155	484	383
58	277	136	351	53	371	193	149	442	89	22
59	154	477	334	535	139	372	200	198	184	86
60										

P = 607

INDICES

	0	1	2	3	4	5	6	7	8	9
0		0	584	1	562	601	585	228	540	2
1	579	446	563	124	206	602	518	37	586	110
2	557	229	424	203	541	596	102	3	184	355
3	580	173	496	447	15	223	564	387	88	125
4	535	544	207	92	402	603	181	438	519	456
5	574	38	80	398	587	441	162	111	333	367
6	558	28	151	230	474	119	425	257	599	204
7	201	494	542	572	365	597	66	68	103	56
8	513	4	522	177	185	32	70	356	380	290
9	581	352	159	174	416	105	497	314	434	448
10	552	324	16	467	58	224	376	244	565	459
11	419	388	140	515	89	198	311	126	345	265
12	536	286	6	545	129	591	208	189	452	93
13	97	524	403	338	235	604	577	108	182	385
14	179	439	472	570	520	350	550	457	343	187
15	575	348	44	39	46	168	81	273	34	399
16	491	431	588	41	500	442	155	72	163	248
17	10	112	48	76	334	218	358	368	268	503
18	559	170	330	29	137	382	152	483	394	231
19	83	317	475	486	292	120	412	214	426	275
20	530	258	302	583	600	539	445	205	36	556
21	202	101	354	495	222	87	543	401	437	573
22	397	161	366	150	118	598	493	364	67	512
23	176	69	289	158	104	433	323	57	243	418
24	514	310	264	5	590	451	523	234	107	178
25	569	549	186	43	167	33	430	499	71	9
26	75	357	502	329	381	393	316	291	213	529
27	582	444	555	353	86	436	160	117	363	175
28	157	322	417	263	450	106	548	166	498	74
29	328	315	528	554	435	362	321	449	165	327
30	553	320	326	325	22	23	17	250	24	468
31	146	18	59	132	251	225	12	25	377	195
32	469	245	409	147	566	114	19	460	478	60
33	420	463	133	389	50	252	141	279	226	516
34	594	13	90	78	26	199	54	378	312	374
35	196	127	336	470	346	489	246	266	481	410
36	537	220	148	287	308	567	7	211	115	546
37	360	20	130	407	461	592	372	479	209	370
38	61	190	295	421	453	63	464	94	270	134
39	98	240	390	525	192	51	404	505	253	339
40	508	142	236	297	280	605	561	227	578	123
41	517	109	423	595	183	172	14	386	534	91
42	180	455	79	440	332	27	473	256	200	571
43	65	55	521	31	379	351	415	313	551	466
44	375	458	139	197	344	285	128	188	96	337
45	576	384	471	349	342	347	45	272	490	40
46	154	247	47	217	267	169	136	482	82	485
47	411	274	301	538	35	100	221	400	396	149
48	492	511	288	432	242	309	589	233	568	42
49	429	8	501	392	212	443	85	116	156	262

POWER RESIDUES

	0	1	2	3	4	5	6	7	8	9
0	1	3	9	27	81	243	122	366	491	259
1	170	510	316	341	416	34	102	306	311	326
2	371	506	304	305	308	317	344	425	61	183
3	549	433	85	255	158	474	208	17	51	153
4	459	163	489	253	152	456	154	462	172	516
5	334	395	578	520	346	431	79	237	104	312
6	329	380	533	385	548	430	76	228	77	231
7	86	258	167	501	289	260	173	519	343	422
8	52	156	468	190	570	496	274	215	38	114
9	342	419	43	129	387	554	448	130	390	563
10	475	211	26	78	234	95	285	248	137	411
11	19	57	171	513	325	368	497	277	224	65
12	195	585	541	409	13	39	117	351	446	124
13	372	509	313	332	389	560	466	184	552	442
14	112	336	401	596	574	508	310	323	362	479
15	223	62	186	558	460	166	498	280	233	92
16	276	221	56	168	504	298	287	254	155	465
17	181	543	415	31	93	279	230	83	249	140
18	420	46	138	414	28	84	252	149	447	127
19	381	536	394	575	511	319	350	443	115	345
20	428	70	210	23	69	207	14	42	126	378
21	527	367	494	268	197	591	559	463	175	525
22	361	476	214	35	105	315	338	407	7	21
23	63	189	567	487	247	134	402	599	583	535
24	391	566	484	238	107	321	356	461	169	507
25	307	314	335	398	587	547	427	67	201	603
26	595	571	499	283	242	119	357	464	178	534
27	388	557	457	157	471	199	597	577	517	337
28	404	605	601	589	553	445	121	363	482	232
29	89	267	194	582	532	382	539	403	602	592
30	562	472	202	606	604	598	580	526	364	485
31	241	116	348	437	97	291	266	191	573	505
32	301	296	281	236	101	303	302	299	290	263
33	182	546	424	58	174	522	352	449	133	399
34	590	556	454	148	444	118	354	455	151	453
35	145	435	91	273	212	29	87	261	176	528
36	370	503	295	278	227	74	222	59	177	531
37	379	530	376	521	349	440	106	318	347	434
38	88	264	185	555	451	139	417	37	111	333
39	392	569	493	265	188	564	478	220	53	159
40	477	217	44	132	396	581	529	373	512	322
41	359	470	196	588	550	436	94	282	239	110
42	330	383	542	412	22	66	198	594	568	490
43	256	161	483	235	98	294	275	218	47	141
44	423	55	165	495	271	206	11	33	99	297
45	284	245	128	384	545	421	49	147	441	109
46	327	374	515	331	386	551	439	103	309	320
47	353	452	142	426	64	192	576	514	328	377
48	524	358	467	187	561	469	193	579	523	355
49	458	160	480	226	71	213	32	96	288	257

P = 607

INDICES

	0	1	2	3	4	5	6	7	8	9
50	547	73	527	361	164	319	21	249	145	131
51	11	194	408	113	477	462	49	278	593	77
52	53	373	335	488	480	219	307	210	359	406
53	371	369	294	62	269	239	191	504	507	296
54	560	122	422	171	533	454	331	255	64	30
55	414	465	138	284	95	383	341	271	153	216
56	135	484	300	99	395	510	241	232	428	391
57	84	261	526	318	144	193	476	277	52	487
58	306	405	293	238	506	121	532	254	413	283
59	340	215	299	509	427	260	143	276	305	237
60	531	282	298	259	304	281	303			

POWER RESIDUES

	0	1	2	3	4	5	6	7	8	9
50	164	492	262	179	537	397	584	538	400	593
51	565	481	229	80	240	113	339	410	16	48
52	144	432	82	246	131	393	572	502	292	269
53	200	600	586	544	418	40	120	360	473	205
54	8	24	72	216	41	123	369	500	286	251
55	146	438	100	300	293	272	209	20	60	180
56	540	406	4	12	36	108	324	365	488	250
57	143	429	73	219	50	150	450	136	408	10
58	30	90	270	203	2	6	18	54	162	486
59	244	125	375	518	340	413	25	75	225	68
60	204	5	15	45	135	405				

P = 613

INDICES

	0	1	2	3	4	5	6	7	8	9
0		0	1	114	2	335	115	124	3	228
1	336	599	116	481	125	449	4	76	229	24
2	337	238	600	273	117	58	482	342	126	70
3	450	399	5	101	77	459	230	540	25	595
4	338	164	239	168	601	563	274	438	118	248
5	59	190	483	157	343	322	127	138	71	243
6	451	84	400	352	6	204	102	414	78	387
7	460	254	231	373	541	172	26	111	596	21
8	339	456	165	187	240	411	169	184	602	212
9	564	605	275	513	439	359	119	590	249	215
10	60	315	191	220	484	573	158	567	344	49
11	323	42	128	89	139	608	72	97	244	200
12	452	586	85	278	401	393	353	265	7	282
13	205	516	103	148	415	65	79	508	388	442
14	461	552	255	468	232	405	374	362	542	380
15	173	532	27	304	112	122	597	447	22	271
16	340	397	457	593	166	436	188	320	241	350
17	412	252	170	19	185	182	603	357	213	218
18	565	40	606	198	276	263	514	63	440	466
19	360	530	120	269	591	318	250	180	216	196
20	61	528	316	194	192	499	221	501	485	11
21	574	223	159	368	568	503	345	523	50	487
22	324	557	43	13	129	286	90	576	140	427
23	609	225	73	55	98	161	245	135	201	370
24	453	209	587	570	86	583	279	505	402	301
25	394	347	354	260	266	525	8	520	283	52
26	206	298	517	489	104	492	149	326	416	477
27	66	559	80	107	509	45	389	548	443	15
28	462	495	553	131	256	473	469	288	233	152
29	406	92	375	35	363	578	543	329	381	142
30	174	292	533	429	28	419	305	611	113	334
31	123	227	598	480	448	75	23	237	272	57
32	341	69	398	100	458	539	594	163	167	562
33	437	247	189	156	321	137	242	83	351	203
34	413	386	253	372	171	110	20	455	186	410
35	183	211	604	512	358	589	214	314	219	572
36	566	48	41	88	607	96	199	585	277	392
37	264	281	515	147	64	507	441	551	467	404
38	361	379	531	303	121	446	270	396	592	435
39	319	349	251	18	181	356	217	39	197	262
40	62	465	529	268	317	179	195	527	193	498
41	500	10	222	367	502	522	486	556	12	285
42	575	426	224	54	160	134	369	208	569	582
43	504	300	346	259	524	519	51	297	488	491
44	325	476	558	106	44	547	14	494	130	472
45	287	151	91	34	577	328	141	291	428	418
46	610	333	226	479	74	236	56	68	99	538
47	162	561	246	155	136	82	202	385	371	109
48	454	409	210	511	588	313	571	47	87	95
49	584	391	280	146	506	550	403	378	302	445

POWER RESIDUES

	0	1	2	3	4	5	6	7	8	9
0	1	2	4	8	16	32	64	128	256	512
1	411	209	418	223	446	279	558	503	393	173
2	346	79	158	316	19	38	76	152	304	608
3	603	593	573	533	453	293	586	559	505	397
4	181	362	111	222	444	275	550	487	361	109
5	218	436	259	518	423	233	466	319	25	50
6	100	200	400	187	374	135	270	540	467	321
7	29	58	116	232	464	315	17	34	68	136
8	272	544	475	337	61	122	244	488	363	113
9	226	452	291	582	551	489	365	117	234	468
10	323	33	66	132	264	528	443	273	546	479
11	345	77	154	308	3	6	12	24	48	96
12	192	384	155	310	7	14	28	56	112	224
13	448	283	566	519	425	237	474	335	57	114
14	228	456	299	598	583	553	493	373	133	266
15	532	451	289	578	543	473	333	53	106	212
16	424	235	470	327	41	82	164	328	43	86
17	172	344	75	150	300	600	587	561	509	405
18	197	394	175	350	87	174	348	83	166	332
19	51	102	204	408	203	406	199	398	183	366
20	119	238	476	339	65	130	260	520	427	241
21	482	351	89	178	356	99	198	396	179	358
22	103	206	412	211	422	231	462	311	9	18
23	36	72	144	288	576	539	465	317	21	42
24	84	168	336	59	118	236	472	331	49	98
25	196	392	171	342	71	142	284	568	523	433
26	253	506	399	185	370	127	254	508	403	193
27	386	159	318	23	46	92	184	368	123	246
28	492	371	129	258	516	419	225	450	287	574
29	535	457	301	602	591	569	525	437	261	522
30	431	249	498	383	153	306	612	611	609	605
31	597	581	549	485	357	101	202	404	195	390
32	167	334	55	110	220	440	267	534	455	297
33	594	575	537	461	309	5	10	20	40	80
34	160	320	27	54	108	216	432	251	502	391
35	169	338	63	126	252	504	395	177	354	95
36	190	380	147	294	588	563	513	413	213	426
37	239	478	343	73	146	292	584	555	497	381
38	149	298	596	579	545	477	341	69	138	276
39	552	491	369	125	250	500	387	161	322	31
40	62	124	248	496	379	145	290	580	547	481
41	349	85	170	340	67	134	268	536	459	305
42	610	607	601	589	565	517	421	229	458	303
43	606	599	585	557	501	389	165	330	47	94
44	188	376	139	278	556	499	385	157	314	15
45	30	60	120	240	480	347	81	162	324	35
46	70	140	280	560	507	401	189	378	143	286
47	572	531	449	285	570	527	441	269	538	463
48	313	13	26	52	104	208	416	219	438	263
49	526	439	265	530	447	281	562	511	409	205

P = 613

INDICES

	0	1	2	3	4	5	6	7	8	9
50	395	434	348	17	355	38	261	464	267	178
51	526	497	9	366	521	555	284	425	53	133
52	207	581	299	258	518	296	490	475	105	546
53	493	471	150	33	327	290	417	332	478	235
54	67	537	560	154	81	384	108	408	510	312
55	46	94	390	145	549	377	444	433	16	37
56	463	177	496	365	554	424	132	580	257	295
57	474	545	470	32	289	331	234	536	153	383
58	407	311	93	144	376	432	36	176	364	423
59	579	294	544	31	330	535	382	310	143	431
60	175	422	293	30	534	309	430	421	29	308
61	420	307	306							

POWER RESIDUES

	0	1	2	3	4	5	6	7	8	9
50	410	207	414	215	430	247	494	375	137	274
51	548	483	353	93	186	372	131	262	524	435
52	257	514	415	217	434	255	510	407	201	402
53	191	382	151	302	604	595	577	541	469	325
54	37	74	148	296	592	571	529	445	277	554
55	495	377	141	282	564	515	417	221	442	271
56	542	471	329	45	90	180	360	107	214	428
57	243	486	359	105	210	420	227	454	295	590
58	567	521	429	245	490	367	121	242	484	355
59	97	194	388	163	326	39	78	156	312	11
60	22	44	88	176	352	91	182	364	115	230
61	460	307								

P = 617

INDICES

	0	1	2	3	4	5	6	7	8	9
0		0	428	1	240	321	429	142	52	2
1	133	114	241	277	570	322	480	387	430	18
2	561	143	542	237	53	26	89	3	382	217
3	134	56	292	115	199	463	242	470	446	278
4	373	414	571	60	354	323	49	460	481	284
5	454	388	517	393	431	435	194	19	29	178
6	562	317	484	144	104	598	543	260	11	238
7	275	540	54	371	282	27	258	256	90	270
8	185	4	226	408	383	92	488	218	166	287
9	135	419	477	57	272	339	293	342	96	116
10	266	609	200	187	329	464	205	213	243	41
11	247	471	6	504	447	558	457	279	606	529
12	374	228	129	415	296	347	572	109	532	61
13	410	125	355	160	72	324	439	306	50	385
14	87	461	352	391	482	538	183	285	94	211
15	455	345	70	389	68	377	518	490	82	394
16	613	379	432	223	38	436	220	148	195	554
17	520	20	300	403	30	168	594	179	99	492
18	563	589	231	318	289	175	485	501	84	145
19	151	45	105	137	154	599	524	396	544	252
20	78	261	421	359	12	119	615	239	141	132
21	276	479	17	541	25	381	55	198	469	372
22	59	48	283	516	434	28	316	103	259	274
23	370	257	269	225	91	165	418	271	341	265
24	186	204	40	5	557	605	227	295	108	409
25	159	438	384	351	537	93	344	67	489	612
26	222	219	553	299	167	98	588	288	500	150
27	136	523	251	420	118	140	478	24	197	58
28	515	315	273	268	164	340	203	556	294	158
29	350	343	611	552	97	499	522	117	23	514
30	267	202	157	610	498	22	201	497	496	188
31	189	509	330	190	302	465	510	575	206	331
32	425	214	191	405	244	303	35	42	466	602
33	248	511	32	472	576	581	7	207	366	505
34	332	170	448	426	112	559	215	444	458	192
35	596	280	406	475	607	245	527	530	304	181
36	375	36	401	229	43	76	130	467	101	416
37	603	535	297	249	313	348	512	494	573	33
38	579	110	473	399	533	577	565	62	582	567
39	411	8	336	126	208	591	356	367	64	161
40	506	363	73	333	233	325	171	584	440	449
41	547	307	427	320	51	113	569	386	560	236
42	88	216	291	462	445	413	353	459	453	392
43	193	177	483	597	10	539	281	255	184	407
44	487	286	476	338	95	608	328	212	246	503
45	456	528	128	346	531	124	71	305	86	390
46	182	210	69	376	81	378	37	147	519	402
47	593	491	230	174	83	44	153	395	77	358
48	614	131	16	380	468	47	433	102	369	224
49	417	264	39	604	107	437	536	66	221	298

POWER RESIDUES

	0	1	2	3	4	5	6	7	8	9
0	1	3	9	27	81	243	112	336	391	556
1	434	68	204	612	602	572	482	212	19	57
2	171	513	305	298	277	214	25	75	225	58
3	174	522	332	379	520	326	361	466	164	492
4	242	109	327	364	475	191	573	485	221	46
5	138	414	8	24	72	216	31	93	279	220
6	43	129	387	544	398	577	497	257	154	462
7	152	456	134	402	589	533	365	478	200	600
8	566	464	158	474	188	564	458	140	420	26
9	78	234	85	255	148	444	98	294	265	178
10	534	368	487	227	64	192	576	494	248	127
11	381	526	344	415	11	33	99	297	274	205
12	615	611	599	563	455	131	393	562	452	122
13	366	481	209	10	30	90	270	193	579	503
14	275	208	7	21	63	189	567	467	167	501
15	269	190	570	476	194	582	512	302	289	250
16	133	399	580	506	284	235	88	264	175	525
17	341	406	601	569	473	185	555	431	59	177
18	531	359	460	146	438	80	240	103	309	310
19	313	322	349	430	56	168	504	278	217	34
20	102	306	301	286	241	106	318	337	394	565
21	461	149	447	107	321	346	421	29	87	261
22	166	498	260	163	489	233	82	246	121	363
23	472	182	546	404	595	551	419	23	69	207
24	4	12	36	108	324	355	448	110	330	373
25	502	272	199	597	557	437	77	231	76	228
26	67	201	603	575	491	239	100	300	283	232
27	79	237	94	282	229	70	210	13	39	117
28	351	436	74	222	49	147	441	89	267	184
29	552	422	32	96	288	247	124	372	499	263
30	172	516	314	325	358	457	137	411	616	614
31	608	590	536	374	505	281	226	61	183	549
32	413	5	15	45	135	405	598	560	446	104
33	312	319	340	403	592	542	392	559	443	95
34	285	238	97	291	256	151	453	125	375	508
35	290	253	142	426	44	132	396	571	479	203
36	609	593	545	401	586	524	338	397	574	488
37	230	73	219	40	120	360	463	155	465	161
38	483	215	28	84	252	139	417	17	51	153
39	459	143	429	53	159	477	197	591	539	383
40	532	362	469	173	519	323	352	439	83	249
41	130	390	553	425	41	123	369	490	236	91
42	273	202	606	584	518	320	343	412	2	6
43	18	54	162	486	224	55	165	495	251	136
44	408	607	587	527	347	424	38	114	342	409
45	610	596	554	428	50	150	450	116	348	427
46	47	141	423	35	105	315	328	367	484	218
47	37	111	333	382	529	353	442	92	276	211
48	16	48	144	432	62	186	558	440	86	258
49	157	471	179	537	377	514	308	307	304	295

P = 617

INDICES

	0	1	2	3	4	5	6	7	8	9
50	587	149	250	139	196	314	163	555	349	551
51	521	513	156	21	495	508	301	574	424	404
52	34	601	31	580	365	169	111	443	595	474
53	526	180	400	75	100	534	312	493	578	398
54	564	566	335	590	63	362	232	583	546	319
55	568	235	290	412	452	176	9	254	486	337
56	327	502	127	123	85	209	80	146	592	173
57	152	357	15	46	368	263	106	65	586	138
58	162	550	155	507	423	600	364	442	525	74
59	311	397	334	361	545	234	451	253	326	122
60	79	172	14	262	585	549	422	441	310	360
61	450	121	13	548	309	120	308			

POWER RESIDUES

	0	1	2	3	4	5	6	7	8	9
50	268	187	561	449	113	339	400	583	515	311
51	316	331	376	511	299	280	223	52	156	468
52	170	510	296	271	196	588	530	356	451	119
53	357	454	128	384	535	371	496	254	145	435
54	71	213	22	66	198	594	548	410	613	605
55	581	509	293	262	169	507	287	244	115	345
56	418	20	60	180	540	386	541	389	550	416
57	14	42	126	378	517	317	334	385	538	380
58	523	335	388	547	407	604	578	500	266	181
59	543	395	568	470	176	528	350	433	65	195
60	585	521	329	370	493	245	118	354	445	101
61	303	292	259	160	480	206				

P = 619

INDICES

	0	1	2	3	4	5	6	7	8	9
0		0	1	75	2	328	76	260	3	150
1	329	121	77	249	261	403	4	417	151	425
2	330	335	122	394	78	38	250	225	262	303
3	404	288	5	196	418	588	152	530	426	324
4	331	526	336	465	123	478	395	63	79	520
5	39	492	251	340	226	449	263	500	304	283
6	405	130	289	410	6	577	197	163	419	469
7	589	180	153	276	531	113	427	381	325	246
8	332	300	527	475	337	127	466	378	124	360
9	479	509	396	363	64	135	80	145	521	271
10	40	482	493	233	252	45	341	318	227	512
11	450	605	264	207	501	104	305	399	284	59
12	406	242	131	601	290	366	411	294	7	540
13	578	442	198	67	164	553	420	487	470	99
14	590	138	181	370	154	13	277	595	532	83
15	114	92	428	567	382	616	326	148	247	415
16	333	36	301	194	528	524	476	518	338	498
17	128	575	467	274	379	298	125	358	361	143
18	480	43	510	205	397	240	364	538	65	485
19	136	11	81	565	146	34	522	496	272	356
20	41	238	483	563	494	236	234	544	253	546
21	46	186	342	255	319	175	228	548	513	351
22	451	48	606	582	265	188	208	214	502	344
23	105	456	306	257	400	391	285	321	60	446
24	407	177	243	375	132	230	602	56	291	550
25	367	89	412	515	295	202	8	353	541	172
26	579	453	443	53	199	50	68	435	165	608
27	554	71	421	584	488	159	471	267	100	438
28	591	190	139	30	182	210	371	168	155	216
29	14	220	278	504	596	611	533	346	84	25
30	115	107	93	557	429	458	568	18	383	308
31	617	74	327	259	149	120	248	402	416	424
32	334	393	37	224	302	287	195	587	529	323
33	525	464	477	62	519	491	339	448	499	282
34	129	409	576	162	468	179	275	112	380	245
35	299	474	126	377	359	508	362	134	144	270
36	481	232	44	317	511	604	206	103	398	58
37	241	600	365	293	539	441	66	552	486	98
38	137	369	12	594	82	91	566	615	147	414
39	35	193	523	517	497	574	273	297	357	142
40	42	204	239	537	484	10	564	33	495	355
41	237	562	235	543	545	185	254	174	547	350
42	47	581	187	213	343	455	256	390	320	445
43	176	374	229	55	549	88	514	201	352	171
44	452	52	49	434	607	70	583	158	266	437
45	189	29	209	167	215	219	503	610	345	24
46	106	556	457	17	307	73	258	119	401	423
47	392	223	286	586	322	463	61	490	447	281
48	408	161	178	111	244	473	376	507	133	269
49	231	316	603	102	57	599	292	440	551	97

POWER RESIDUES

	0	1	2	3	4	5	6	7	8	9
0	1	2	4	8	16	32	64	128	256	512
1	405	191	382	145	290	580	541	463	307	614
2	609	599	579	539	459	299	598	577	535	451
3	283	566	513	407	195	390	161	322	25	50
4	100	200	400	181	362	105	210	420	221	442
5	265	530	441	263	526	433	247	494	369	119
6	238	476	333	47	94	188	376	133	266	532
7	445	271	542	465	311	3	6	12	24	48
8	96	192	384	149	298	596	573	527	435	251
9	502	385	151	302	604	589	559	499	379	139
10	278	556	493	367	115	230	460	301	602	585
11	551	483	347	75	150	300	600	581	543	467
12	315	11	22	44	88	176	352	85	170	340
13	61	122	244	488	357	95	190	380	141	282
14	564	509	399	179	358	97	194	388	157	314
15	9	18	36	72	144	288	576	533	447	275
16	550	481	343	67	134	268	536	453	287	574
17	529	439	259	518	417	215	430	241	482	345
18	71	142	284	568	517	415	211	422	225	450
19	281	562	505	391	163	326	33	66	132	264
20	528	437	255	510	401	183	366	113	226	452
21	285	570	521	423	227	454	289	578	537	455
22	291	582	545	471	323	27	54	108	216	432
23	245	490	361	103	206	412	205	410	201	402
24	185	370	121	242	484	349	79	158	316	13
25	26	52	104	208	416	213	426	233	466	313
26	7	14	28	56	112	224	448	277	554	489
27	359	99	198	396	173	346	73	146	292	584
28	549	479	339	59	118	236	472	325	31	62
29	124	248	496	373	127	254	508	397	175	350
30	81	162	324	29	58	116	232	464	309	618
31	617	615	611	603	587	555	491	363	107	214
32	428	237	474	329	39	78	156	312	5	10
33	20	40	80	160	320	21	42	84	168	336
34	53	106	212	424	229	458	297	594	569	519
35	419	219	438	257	514	409	199	398	177	354
36	89	178	356	93	186	372	125	250	500	381
37	143	286	572	525	431	243	486	353	87	174
38	348	77	154	308	616	613	607	595	571	523
39	427	235	470	321	23	46	92	184	368	117
40	234	468	317	15	30	60	120	240	480	341
41	63	126	252	504	389	159	318	17	34	68
42	136	272	544	469	319	19	38	76	152	304
43	608	597	575	531	443	267	534	449	279	558
44	497	375	131	262	524	429	239	478	337	55
45	110	220	440	261	522	425	231	462	305	610
46	601	583	547	475	331	43	86	172	344	69
47	138	276	552	485	351	83	166	332	45	90
48	180	360	101	202	404	189	378	137	274	548
49	477	335	51	102	204	408	197	394	169	338

P = 619

INDICES

	0	1	2	3	4	5	6	7	8	9
50	368	593	90	614	413	192	516	573	296	141
51	203	536	9	32	354	561	542	184	173	349
52	580	212	454	389	444	373	54	87	200	170
53	51	433	69	157	436	28	166	218	609	23
54	555	16	72	118	422	222	585	462	489	280
55	160	110	472	506	268	315	101	598	439	96
56	592	613	191	572	140	535	31	560	183	348
57	211	388	372	86	169	432	156	27	217	22
58	15	117	221	461	279	109	505	314	597	95
59	612	571	534	559	347	387	85	431	26	21
60	116	460	108	313	94	570	558	386	430	20
61	459	312	569	385	19	311	384	310	309	

POWER RESIDUES

	0	1	2	3	4	5	6	7	8	9
50	57	114	228	456	293	586	553	487	355	91
51	182	364	109	218	436	253	506	393	167	334
52	49	98	196	392	165	330	41	82	164	328
53	37	74	148	296	592	565	511	403	187	374
54	129	258	516	413	207	414	209	418	217	434
55	249	498	377	135	270	540	461	303	606	593
56	567	515	411	203	406	193	386	153	306	612
57	605	591	563	507	395	171	342	65	130	260
58	520	421	223	446	273	546	473	327	35	70
59	140	280	560	501	383	147	294	588	557	495
60	371	123	246	492	365	111	222	444	269	538
61	457	295	590	561	503	387	155	310		

P = 631

INDICES

	0	1	2	3	4	5	6	7	8	9
0		0	98	1	196	576	99	269	294	2
1	44	329	197	191	367	577	392	298	100	181
2	142	270	427	356	295	522	289	3	465	472
3	45	502	490	330	396	215	198	115	279	192
4	240	130	368	420	525	578	454	266	393	538
5	620	299	387	379	101	275	563	182	570	401
6	143	541	600	271	588	137	428	148	494	357
7	313	292	296	287	213	523	377	598	290	336
8	338	4	228	36	466	244	518	473	623	340
9	46	460	552	503	364	127	491	124	6	331
10	88	108	397	407	485	216	477	230	199	257
11	373	116	31	167	280	302	38	193	499	567
12	241	28	9	131	68	468	369	250	56	421
13	235	349	526	450	246	579	592	155	455	12
14	411	267	390	520	394	418	385	539	311	334
15	621	122	475	300	66	448	388	120	434	380
16	436	625	102	74	326	276	134	549	564	382
17	342	183	616	345	571	161	91	402	438	48
18	144	307	558	542	20	61	601	627	462	272
19	225	254	589	71	222	138	104	554	429	80
20	186	149	206	111	495	76	505	358	583	510
21	314	97	575	293	328	366	297	141	355	288
22	471	489	214	278	129	524	265	619	378	562
23	400	599	136	493	291	212	597	337	35	517
24	339	551	126	5	107	484	229	372	166	37
25	566	8	467	55	348	245	154	410	519	384
26	333	474	447	433	624	325	548	341	344	90
27	47	557	60	461	253	221	553	185	110	504
28	509	574	365	354	488	128	618	399	492	596
29	516	125	483	165	7	347	409	332	432	547
30	89	59	220	109	573	487	398	515	164	408
31	546	219	486	163	218	217	532	533	478	171
32	534	231	93	479	200	83	172	258	424	535
33	374	404	232	117	17	94	32	322	480	168
34	440	201	281	177	84	303	443	173	39	50
35	259	194	189	425	500	238	536	568	146	375
36	242	362	405	29	26	233	10	309	118	132
37	159	18	69	204	95	469	560	33	370	152
38	323	251	352	481	57	544	169	422	320	441
39	236	24	202	350	22	282	527	606	178	451
40	284	85	247	63	304	580	209	444	593	529
41	174	156	603	40	456	612	51	13	608	260
42	412	629	195	268	43	190	391	180	426	521
43	464	501	395	114	239	419	453	537	386	274
44	569	540	587	147	312	286	376	335	227	243
45	622	459	363	123	87	406	476	256	30	301
46	498	27	67	249	234	449	591	11	389	417
47	310	121	65	119	435	73	133	381	615	160
48	437	306	19	626	224	70	103	79	205	75
49	582	96	327	140	470	277	264	561	135	211

POWER RESIDUES

	0	1	2	3	4	5	6	7	8	9
0	1	3	9	27	81	243	98	294	251	122
1	366	467	139	417	620	598	532	334	371	482
2	184	552	394	551	391	542	364	461	121	363
3	458	112	336	377	500	238	83	249	116	348
4	413	608	562	424	10	30	90	270	179	537
5	349	416	617	589	505	253	128	384	521	301
6	272	185	555	403	578	472	154	462	124	372
7	485	193	579	475	163	489	205	615	583	487
8	199	597	529	325	344	401	572	454	100	300
9	269	176	528	322	335	374	491	211	2	6
10	18	54	162	486	196	588	502	244	101	303
11	278	203	609	565	433	37	111	333	368	473
12	157	471	151	453	97	291	242	95	285	224
13	41	123	369	476	166	498	232	65	195	585
14	493	217	20	60	180	540	358	443	67	201
15	603	547	379	506	256	137	411	602	544	370
16	479	175	525	313	308	293	248	113	339	386
17	527	319	326	347	410	599	535	343	398	563
18	427	19	57	171	513	277	200	600	538	352
19	425	13	39	117	351	422	4	12	36	108
20	324	341	392	545	373	488	202	606	556	406
21	587	499	235	74	222	35	105	315	314	311
22	302	275	194	582	484	190	570	448	82	246
23	107	321	332	365	464	130	390	539	355	434
24	40	120	360	449	85	255	134	402	575	463
25	127	381	512	274	191	573	457	109	327	350
26	419	626	616	586	496	226	47	141	423	7
27	21	63	189	567	439	55	165	495	223	38
28	114	342	395	554	400	569	445	73	219	26
29	78	234	71	213	8	24	72	216	17	51
30	153	459	115	345	404	581	481	181	543	367
31	470	148	444	70	210	630	628	622	604	550
32	388	533	337	380	509	265	164	492	214	11
33	33	99	297	260	149	447	79	237	80	240
34	89	267	170	510	268	173	519	295	254	131
35	393	548	382	515	283	218	23	69	207	621
36	601	541	361	452	94	282	215	14	42	126
37	378	503	247	110	330	359	446	76	228	53
38	159	477	169	507	259	146	438	52	156	468
39	142	426	16	48	144	432	34	102	306	287
40	230	59	177	531	331	362	455	103	309	296
41	257	140	420	629	625	613	577	469	145	435
42	43	129	387	530	328	353	428	22	66	198
43	594	520	298	263	158	474	160	480	178	534
44	340	389	536	346	407	590	508	262	155	465
45	133	399	566	436	46	138	414	611	571	451
46	91	273	188	564	430	28	84	252	125	375
47	494	220	29	87	261	152	456	106	318	323
48	338	383	518	292	245	104	312	305	284	221
49	32	96	288	233	68	204	612	574	460	118

P = 631

INDICES

	0	1	2	3	4	5	6	7	8	9
50	34	550	106	371	565	54	153	383	446	324
51	343	556	252	184	508	353	617	595	482	346
52	431	58	572	514	545	162	531	170	92	82
53	423	403	16	321	439	176	442	49	188	237
54	145	361	25	308	158	203	559	151	351	543
55	319	23	21	605	283	62	208	528	602	611
56	607	628	42	179	463	113	452	273	586	285
57	226	458	86	255	497	248	590	416	64	72
58	614	305	223	78	581	139	263	210	105	53
59	445	555	507	594	430	513	530	81	15	175
60	187	360	157	150	318	604	207	610	41	112
61	585	457	496	415	613	77	262	52	506	512
62	14	359	317	609	584	414	261	511	316	413
63	315	0								

POWER RESIDUES

	0	1	2	3	4	5	6	7	8	9
50	354	431	31	93	279	206	618	592	514	280
51	209	627	619	595	523	307	290	239	86	258
52	143	429	25	75	225	44	132	396	557	409
53	596	526	316	317	320	329	356	437	49	147
54	441	61	183	549	385	524	310	299	266	167
55	501	241	92	276	197	591	511	271	182	546
56	376	497	229	56	168	504	250	119	357	440
57	58	174	522	304	281	212	5	15	45	135
58	405	584	490	208	624	610	568	442	64	192
59	576	466	136	408	593	517	289	236	77	231
60	62	186	558	412	605	553	397	560	418	623
61	607	559	415	614	580	478	172	516	286	227
62	50	150	450	88	264	161	483	187	561	421
63										

P = 641

INDICES

	0	1	2	3	4	5	6	7	8	9
0		0	470	1	300	230	471	134	130	2
1	60	516	301	352	604	231	600	633	472	407
2	530	135	346	207	131	460	182	3	434	615
3	61	565	430	517	463	364	302	628	237	353
4	360	271	605	69	176	232	37	29	601	268
5	290	634	12	249	473	106	264	408	445	254
6	531	185	395	136	260	582	347	555	293	208
7	194	148	132	598	458	461	67	10	183	192
8	190	4	101	77	435	223	539	616	6	18
9	62	486	507	566	499	637	431	103	98	518
10	120	213	464	56	482	365	79	169	303	521
11	576	629	94	157	238	437	275	354	84	127
12	361	392	15	272	225	50	606	561	90	70
13	412	374	177	541	385	233	123	586	38	243
14	24	30	618	228	602	205	428	269	288	252
15	291	8	537	635	480	155	13	372	22	250
16	20	341	474	216	571	107	547	343	265	64
17	53	409	369	334	446	594	476	255	488	161
18	532	417	316	186	337	218	396	509	329	137
19	467	612	261	74	573	583	568	609	348	495
20	590	556	43	109	294	501	526	209	312	283
21	195	449	549	149	639	299	133	59	351	599
22	406	345	459	433	564	462	627	359	68	36
23	267	11	105	444	184	259	554	193	597	66
24	191	100	222	5	485	498	102	119	55	78
25	520	93	436	83	391	224	560	411	540	122
26	242	617	204	287	7	479	371	19	215	546
27	63	368	593	487	416	336	508	466	73	567
28	494	42	500	311	448	638	58	405	432	626
29	35	104	258	596	99	484	118	519	82	559
30	121	203	478	214	367	415	465	493	310	57
31	625	257	483	81	202	366	492	624	80	491
32	490	170	171	400	304	172	46	522	401	163
33	577	305	377	630	173	145	95	47	534	158
34	523	441	239	402	199	438	164	419	276	578
35	424	355	306	112	85	378	318	128	631	180
36	362	174	247	393	146	188	16	96	167	273
37	48	383	226	535	339	51	159	327	607	524
38	297	562	442	220	91	240	544	71	403	116
39	413	200	398	375	439	422	178	165	325	542
40	420	511	386	277	513	234	579	504	124	425
41	331	587	356	388	39	307	142	244	113	139
42	25	86	279	31	379	453	619	319	469	229
43	129	515	603	632	529	206	181	614	429	363
44	236	270	175	28	289	248	263	253	394	581
45	292	147	457	9	189	76	538	17	506	636
46	97	212	481	168	575	156	274	126	14	49
47	89	373	384	585	23	227	427	251	536	154
48	21	340	570	342	52	333	475	160	315	217
49	328	611	572	608	589	108	525	282	548	298

POWER RESIDUES

	0	1	2	3	4	5	6	7	8	9
0	1	3	9	27	81	243	88	264	151	453
1	77	231	52	156	468	122	366	457	89	267
2	160	480	158	474	140	420	619	575	443	47
3	141	423	628	602	524	290	229	46	138	414
4	601	521	281	202	606	536	326	337	370	469
5	125	375	484	170	510	248	103	309	286	217
6	10	30	90	270	169	507	239	76	228	43
7	129	387	520	278	193	579	455	83	249	106
8	318	313	298	253	118	354	421	622	584	470
9	128	384	511	251	112	336	367	460	98	294
10	241	82	246	97	291	232	55	165	495	203
11	609	545	353	418	613	557	389	526	296	247
12	100	300	259	136	408	583	467	119	357	430
13	8	24	72	216	7	21	63	189	567	419
14	616	566	416	607	539	335	364	451	71	213
15	639	635	623	587	479	155	465	113	339	376
16	487	179	537	329	346	397	550	368	463	107
17	321	322	325	334	361	442	44	132	396	547
18	359	436	26	78	234	61	183	549	365	454
19	80	240	79	237	70	210	630	608	542	344
20	391	532	314	301	262	145	435	23	69	207
21	621	581	461	101	303	268	163	489	185	555
22	383	508	242	85	255	124	372	475	143	429
23	5	15	45	135	405	574	440	38	114	342
24	385	514	260	139	417	610	548	362	445	53
25	159	477	149	447	59	177	531	311	292	235
26	64	192	576	446	56	168	504	230	49	147
27	441	41	123	369	466	116	348	403	568	422
28	625	593	497	209	627	599	515	263	148	444
29	50	150	450	68	204	612	554	380	499	215
30	4	12	36	108	324	331	352	415	604	530
31	308	283	208	624	590	488	182	546	356	427
32	640	638	632	614	560	398	553	377	490	188
33	564	410	589	485	173	519	275	184	552	374
34	481	161	483	167	501	221	22	66	198	594
35	500	218	13	39	117	351	412	595	503	227
36	40	120	360	439	35	105	315	304	271	172
37	516	266	157	471	131	393	538	332	355	424
38	631	611	551	371	472	134	402	565	413	598
39	512	254	121	363	448	62	186	558	392	535
40	323	328	343	388	523	287	220	19	57	171
41	513	257	130	390	529	305	274	181	543	347
42	400	559	395	544	350	409	586	476	146	438
43	32	96	288	223	28	84	252	115	345	394
44	541	341	382	505	233	58	174	522	284	211
45	633	617	569	425	634	620	578	452	74	222
46	25	75	225	34	102	306	277	190	570	428
47	2	6	18	54	162	486	176	528	302	265
48	154	462	104	312	295	244	91	273	178	534
49	320	319	316	307	280	199	597	509	245	94

P = 641

INDICES

	0	1	2	3	4	5	6	7	8	9
50	350	344	563	358	266	443	553	65	221	497
51	54	92	390	410	241	286	370	545	592	335
52	72	41	447	404	34	595	117	558	477	414
53	309	256	201	623	489	399	45	162	376	144
54	533	440	198	418	423	111	317	179	246	187
55	166	382	338	326	296	219	543	115	397	421
56	324	510	512	503	330	387	141	138	278	452
57	468	514	528	613	235	27	262	580	456	75
58	505	211	574	125	88	584	426	153	569	332
59	314	610	588	281	349	357	552	496	389	285
60	591	40	33	557	308	622	44	143	197	110
61	245	381	295	114	323	502	140	451	527	26
62	455	210	87	152	313	280	551	284	32	621
63	196	380	322	450	454	151	550	620	321	150
64	320	0								

POWER RESIDUES

	0	1	2	3	4	5	6	7	8	9
50	282	205	615	563	407	580	458	92	276	187
51	561	401	562	404	571	431	11	33	99	297
52	250	109	327	340	379	496	206	618	572	434
53	20	60	180	540	338	373	478	152	456	86
54	258	133	399	556	386	517	269	166	498	212
55	636	626	596	506	236	67	201	603	527	299
56	256	127	381	502	224	31	93	279	196	588
57	482	164	492	194	582	464	110	330	349	406
58	577	449	65	195	585	473	137	411	592	494
59	200	600	518	272	175	525	293	238	73	219
60	16	48	144	432	14	42	126	378	493	197
61	591	491	191	573	437	29	87	261	142	426
62	637	629	605	533	317	310	289	226	37	111
63	333	358	433	17	51	153	459	95	285	214
64										

P = 643

INDICES

	0	1	2	3	4	5	6	7	8	9
0		0	453	309	264	27	120	530	75	618
1	480	1	573	23	341	336	528	601	429	539
2	291	197	454	490	384	54	476	285	152	536
3	147	520	339	310	412	557	240	61	350	332
4	102	137	8	117	265	3	301	637	195	418
5	507	268	287	278	96	28	605	206	347	119
6	600	151	331	506	150	50	121	447	223	157
7	368	609	51	365	514	363	161	531	143	247
8	555	594	590	122	461	628	570	203	76	82
9	456	553	112	187	448	566	6	352	229	619
10	318	262	79	255	98	224	89	201	549	523
11	481	370	416	437	17	517	158	641	572	489
12	411	2	604	446	142	81	317	369	603	426
13	503	546	574	427	258	312	34	623	610	260
14	179	304	420	24	504	563	176	85	325	52
15	174	389	614	577	342	547	596	393	58	587
16	366	378	405	354	401	337	575	432	272	46
17	439	515	381	154	14	584	529	428	535	101
18	267	330	364	460	565	88	640	602	259	173
19	377	380	459	162	163	359	40	299	430	313
20	129	114	73	424	532	164	66	466	551	540
21	35	492	542	276	12	144	360	408	334	32
22	292	624	181	167	227	30	248	41	470	598
23	328	198	611	296	452	22	383	556	300	205
24	222	246	455	261	415	445	257	562	595	431
25	534	172	128	491	180	295	414	294	237	591
26	314	512	357	509	385	305	238	391	69	92
27	123	130	487	220	434	55	421	592	71	496
28	632	462	115	399	231	233	477	25	315	560
29	374	19	629	74	538	146	136	286	505	513
30	627	5	200	571	425	178	388	404	153	564
31	358	65	407	469	204	533	511	486	398	537
32	177	510	189	498	216	77	165	190	212	525
33	148	86	386	37	243	474	83	67	499	104
34	250	521	326	306	192	184	607	457	467	217
35	395	308	340	53	239	636	346	156	554	552
36	78	436	141	311	175	392	271	100	376	113
37	541	166	451	444	413	390	70	559	626	64
38	188	36	191	635	270	558	615	93	616	501
39	170	449	493	213	110	274	241	578	124	94
40	582	134	567	543	526	621	235	62	343	131
41	617	290	519	7	277	149	362	569	351	548
42	488	502	303	613	353	13	87	39	465	333
43	597	221	171	356	219	230	145	387	485	211
44	103	394	435	450	634	109	620	361	38	484
45	483	138	59	56	494	580	281	319	409	244
46	139	43	9	588	422	214	107	208	263	335
47	475	60	194	118	367	593	111	254	16	80
48	33	84	57	45	266	379	72	275	226	21
49	256	293	68	495	373	4	406	497	242	183

POWER RESIDUES

	0	1	2	3	4	5	6	7	8	9
0	1	11	121	45	495	301	96	413	42	462
1	581	604	214	425	174	628	478	114	611	291
2	629	489	235	13	143	287	585	5	55	605
3	225	546	219	480	136	210	381	333	448	427
4	196	227	568	461	570	483	169	573	516	532
5	65	72	149	353	25	275	453	482	158	452
6	471	37	407	619	379	311	206	337	492	268
7	376	278	486	202	293	8	88	325	360	102
8	479	125	89	336	481	147	331	426	185	106
9	523	609	269	387	399	531	54	594	104	501
10	367	179	40	440	339	514	510	466	625	445
11	394	476	92	369	201	282	530	43	473	59
12	6	66	83	270	398	520	576	549	252	200
13	271	409	641	621	401	553	296	41	451	460
14	559	362	124	78	215	436	295	30	330	415
15	64	61	28	308	173	617	357	69	116	633
16	533	76	193	194	205	326	371	223	524	620
17	390	432	251	189	150	364	146	320	305	140
18	254	222	513	499	345	580	593	93	380	322
19	327	382	344	569	472	48	528	21	231	612
20	302	107	534	87	314	239	57	627	467	636
21	566	439	328	393	465	614	324	349	624	434
22	273	431	240	68	105	512	488	224	535	98
23	435	284	552	285	563	406	608	258	266	354
24	36	396	498	334	459	548	241	79	226	557
25	340	525	631	511	477	103	490	246	134	188
26	139	243	101	468	4	44	484	180	51	561
27	384	366	168	562	395	487	213	414	53	583
28	626	456	515	521	587	27	297	52	572	505
29	411	20	220	491	257	255	233	634	544	197
30	238	46	506	422	141	265	343	558	351	3
31	33	363	135	199	260	288	596	126	100	457
32	526	642	632	522	598	148	342	547	230	601
33	181	62	39	429	218	469	15	165	529	32
34	352	14	154	408	630	500	356	58	638	588
35	38	418	97	424	163	507	433	262	310	195
36	216	447	416	75	182	73	160	474	70	127
37	111	578	571	494	290	618	368	190	161	485
38	191	172	606	236	24	264	332	437	306	151
39	375	267	365	157	441	350	635	555	318	283
40	541	164	518	554	307	162	496	312	217	458
41	537	120	34	374	256	244	112	589	49	539
42	142	276	464	603	203	304	129	133	177	18
43	198	249	167	551	274	442	361	113	600	170
44	584	637	577	560	373	245	123	67	94	391
45	443	372	234	2	22	242	90	347	602	192
46	183	84	281	519	565	428	207	348	613	313
47	228	579	582	615	335	470	26	286	574	527
48	10	110	567	450	449	438	317	272	420	119
49	23	253	211	392	454	493	279	497	323	338

P = 643

INDICES

	0	1	2	3	4	5	6	7	8	9
50	345	99	625	500	581	289	302	355	633	579
51	106	253	225	182	105	282	48	638	402	463
52	125	283	323	90	168	251	320	479	196	338
53	116	95	49	160	202	228	522	410	545	419
54	576	400	583	639	298	550	31	327	245	127
55	508	433	232	135	403	397	524	249	307	140
56	443	269	273	234	568	464	210	482	42	193
57	44	372	288	47	478	544	126	442	371	471
58	185	10	472	279	440	26	527	284	349	417
59	599	608	589	186	97	516	316	622	324	586
60	438	329	458	423	11	29	382	561	236	91
61	631	18	199	468	215	473	606	155	375	63
62	169	133	518	612	218	108	280	207	15	20
63	344	252	322	159	297	396	209	441	348	585
64	630	132	321							

POWER RESIDUES

	0	1	2	3	4	5	6	7	8	9
50	503	389	421	130	144	298	63	50	550	263
51	321	316	261	299	74	171	595	115	622	412
52	31	341	536	109	556	329	404	586	16	176
53	7	77	204	315	250	178	29	319	294	19
54	209	370	212	403	575	538	131	155	419	108
55	545	208	359	91	358	80	237	35	385	377
56	289	607	247	145	309	184	95	402	564	417
57	86	303	118	12	132	166	540	153	397	509
58	455	504	400	542	175	639	599	159	463	592
59	82	259	277	475	81	248	156	430	229	590
60	60	17	187	128	122	56	616	346	591	71
61	138	232	623	423	152	386	388	410	9	99
62	446	405	597	137	221	502	378	300	85	292
63	640	610	280	508	444	383	355	47	517	543
64	186	117								

P = 647

INDICES

	0	1	2	3	4	5	6	7	8	9
0		0	158	366	316	1	524	138	474	86
1	159	169	36	206	296	367	632	60	244	105
2	317	504	327	235	194	2	364	452	454	82
3	525	458	144	535	218	139	402	507	263	572
4	475	100	16	114	485	87	393	519	352	276
5	160	426	522	456	610	170	612	471	240	635
6	37	25	616	224	302	207	47	76	376	601
7	297	65	560	73	19	368	421	307	84	216
8	633	172	258	232	174	61	272	448	643	379
9	245	344	551	178	31	106	510	6	434	255
10	318	545	584	527	34	505	614	446	122	260
11	328	227	124	580	629	236	398	292	147	198
12	195	338	183	466	128	3	382	358	460	480
13	365	473	205	243	234	453	534	262	113	351
14	455	239	223	375	72	83	231	642	177	433
15	526	121	579	146	465	459	242	112	374	176
16	145	373	330	331	416	536	390	188	332	412
17	219	191	430	417	606	140	155	355	537	285
18	403	637	502	391	63	508	336	229	189	590
19	264	622	22	333	164	573	592	569	413	117
20	476	442	57	220	96	101	39	321	192	274
21	17	253	126	431	604	115	280	596	418	439
22	486	266	385	607	282	88	92	498	141	109
23	394	27	556	156	450	520	305	582	356	577
24	353	55	496	538	341	277	624	311	286	598
25	161	248	540	404	516	427	618	408	638	645
26	523	168	631	503	363	457	401	99	392	425
27	611	24	46	64	420	171	271	343	509	544
28	613	226	397	337	381	472	533	238	230	120
29	241	372	389	190	154	636	335	621	591	441
30	38	252	279	265	91	26	304	54	623	247
31	617	167	400	23	270	225	532	371	334	251
32	303	166	531	165	488	208	489	626	574	11
33	48	209	548	593	346	77	490	294	570	300
34	377	627	349	414	588	602	575	361	118	268
35	298	12	313	477	513	66	49	564	443	553
36	561	210	149	58	14	74	549	290	221	186
37	20	594	494	97	387	369	347	288	102	69
38	422	78	134	40	180	308	491	200	322	315
39	85	295	104	193	81	217	571	484	275	609
40	634	301	600	18	215	173	378	30	254	33
41	259	628	197	127	479	233	350	71	432	464
42	175	415	411	605	284	62	589	163	116	95
43	273	603	438	281	108	449	576	340	597	515
44	644	362	424	419	543	380	119	153	440	90
45	246	269	250	487	10	345	299	587	267	512
46	552	13	185	386	68	179	314	80	608	214
47	32	478	463	283	94	107	514	542	89	9
48	511	67	213	93	8	7	50	468	499	51
49	435	565	136	142	469	256	444	203	110	500

POWER RESIDUES

	0	1	2	3	4	5	6	7	8	9
0	1	5	25	125	625	537	97	485	484	479
1	454	329	351	461	364	526	42	210	403	74
2	370	556	192	313	271	61	305	231	508	599
3	407	94	470	409	104	520	12	60	300	206
4	383	621	517	644	632	572	272	66	330	356
5	486	489	504	579	307	241	558	202	363	521
6	17	85	425	184	273	71	355	481	464	379
7	601	417	144	73	365	531	67	335	381	611
8	467	394	29	145	78	390	9	45	225	478
9	449	304	226	483	474	429	204	373	571	267
10	41	205	378	596	392	19	95	475	434	229
11	498	549	157	138	43	215	428	199	348	446
12	289	151	108	540	112	560	212	413	124	620
13	512	619	507	594	382	616	492	519	7	35
14	175	228	493	524	32	160	153	118	590	362
15	516	639	607	447	294	176	233	518	2	10
16	50	250	603	427	194	323	321	311	261	11
17	55	275	81	405	84	420	159	148	93	465
18	384	626	542	122	610	462	369	551	167	188
19	293	171	208	393	24	120	600	412	119	595
20	387	641	617	497	544	132	13	65	325	331
21	361	511	614	482	469	404	79	395	34	170
22	203	368	546	142	63	315	281	111	555	187
23	288	146	83	415	134	23	115	575	287	141
24	58	290	156	133	18	90	450	309	251	608
25	452	319	301	211	408	99	495	534	82	410
26	109	545	137	38	190	303	221	458	349	451
27	314	276	86	430	209	398	49	245	578	302
28	216	433	224	473	424	179	248	593	377	591
29	367	541	117	585	337	391	14	70	350	456
30	339	401	64	320	306	236	533	77	385	631
31	567	247	588	352	466	389	4	20	100	500
32	559	207	388	646	642	622	522	22	110	550
33	162	163	168	193	318	296	186	283	121	605
34	437	244	573	277	91	455	334	376	586	342
35	416	139	48	240	553	177	238	543	127	635
36	587	347	441	264	26	130	3	15	75	375
37	581	317	291	161	158	143	68	340	406	89
38	445	284	126	630	562	222	463	374	576	292
39	166	183	268	46	230	503	574	282	116	580
40	312	266	36	180	253	618	502	569	257	638
41	602	422	169	198	343	421	164	173	218	443
42	274	76	380	606	442	269	51	255	628	552
43	172	213	418	149	98	490	509	604	432	219
44	448	299	201	358	496	539	107	535	87	435
45	234	523	27	135	28	140	53	265	31	155
46	128	640	612	472	419	154	123	615	487	494
47	529	57	285	131	8	40	200	353	471	414
48	129	645	637	597	397	44	220	453	324	326
49	336	386	636	592	372	566	242	563	227	488

P = 647

INDICES

	0	1	2	3	4	5	6	7	8	9
50	319	554	406	395	52	546	562	132	28	436
51	585	211	130	557	566	528	150	42	157	137
52	35	59	326	451	143	506	15	518	521	470
53	615	75	559	306	257	447	550	5	583	445
54	123	291	182	357	204	261	222	641	578	111
55	329	187	429	354	501	228	21	568	56	320
56	125	595	384	497	555	581	495	310	539	407
57	630	98	45	342	396	237	388	620	278	53
58	399	370	530	625	547	293	348	360	312	563
59	148	289	493	287	133	199	103	483	599	29
60	196	70	410	162	437	339	423	152	249	586
61	184	79	462	541	212	467	135	202	405	131
62	129	41	325	517	558	4	181	640	428	567
63	383	309	44	619	529	359	492	482	409	151
64	461	201	324	639	43	481	323			

POWER RESIDUES

	0	1	2	3	4	5	6	7	8	9
50	499	554	182	263	21	105	525	37	185	278
51	96	480	459	354	476	439	254	623	527	47
52	235	528	52	260	6	30	150	103	515	634
53	582	322	316	286	136	33	165	178	243	568
54	252	613	477	444	279	101	505	584	332	366
55	536	92	460	359	501	564	232	513	624	532
56	72	360	506	589	357	491	514	629	557	197
57	338	396	39	195	328	346	436	239	548	152
58	113	565	237	538	102	510	609	457	344	426
59	189	298	196	333	371	561	217	438	249	598
60	402	69	345	431	214	423	174	223	468	399
61	54	270	56	280	106	530	62	310	256	633
62	577	297	191	308	246	583	327	341	411	114
63	570	262	16	80	400	59	295	181	258	643
64	627	547	147	88	440	259				

P = 653

INDICES

	0	1	2	3	4	5	6	7	8	9
0		0	1	443	2	145	444	252	3	234
1	146	314	445	478	253	588	4	529	235	48
2	147	43	315	306	446	290	479	25	254	599
3	589	284	5	105	530	397	236	243	49	269
4	148	439	44	393	316	379	307	544	447	504
5	291	320	480	410	26	459	255	491	600	14
6	590	573	285	486	6	623	106	383	531	97
7	398	345	237	420	244	81	50	566	270	366
8	149	468	440	311	45	22	394	390	317	11
9	380	78	308	75	545	193	448	227	505	548
10	292	426	321	279	481	188	411	196	27	208
11	460	34	256	498	492	451	601	60	15	129
12	591	628	574	230	286	435	487	416	7	184
13	624	508	107	300	384	170	532	512	98	551
14	399	335	346	140	238	92	421	295	245	163
15	82	176	51	111	567	429	271	614	367	201
16	150	558	469	324	441	250	312	586	46	304
17	23	282	395	267	391	542	318	457	12	484
18	381	343	79	364	309	388	76	191	546	277
19	194	32	449	127	228	414	506	168	549	138
20	293	174	427	199	322	584	280	540	482	362
21	189	30	412	136	197	538	28	536	209	211
22	461	355	35	213	257	524	499	463	493	87
23	452	357	602	516	61	37	16	157	130	215
24	592	607	629	259	575	649	231	526	287	102
25	436	501	488	620	417	465	8	224	185	495
26	625	181	509	89	108	555	301	454	385	124
27	171	359	533	521	513	604	99	221	552	518
28	400	403	336	63	347	636	141	39	239	406
29	93	18	422	56	296	159	246	339	164	132
30	83	645	177	217	52	66	112	594	568	70
31	430	609	272	350	615	631	368	373	202	261
32	151	639	559	577	470	116	325	651	442	144
33	251	233	313	477	587	528	47	42	305	289
34	24	598	283	104	396	242	268	438	392	378
35	543	503	319	409	458	490	13	572	485	622
36	382	96	344	419	80	565	365	467	310	21
37	389	10	77	74	192	226	547	425	278	187
38	195	207	33	497	450	59	128	627	229	434
39	415	183	507	299	169	511	550	334	139	91
40	294	162	175	110	428	613	200	557	323	249
41	585	303	281	266	541	456	483	342	363	387
42	190	276	31	126	413	167	137	173	198	583
43	539	361	29	135	537	535	210	354	212	523
44	462	86	356	515	36	156	214	606	258	648
45	525	101	500	619	464	223	494	180	88	554
46	453	123	358	520	603	220	517	402	62	635
47	38	405	17	55	158	338	131	644	216	65
48	593	69	608	349	630	372	260	638	576	115
49	650	143	232	476	527	41	288	597	103	241

POWER RESIDUES

	0	1	2	3	4	5	6	7	8	9
0	1	2	4	8	16	32	64	128	256	512
1	371	89	178	356	59	118	236	472	291	582
2	511	369	85	170	340	27	54	108	216	432
3	211	422	191	382	111	222	444	235	470	287
4	574	495	337	21	42	84	168	336	19	38
5	76	152	304	608	563	473	293	586	519	385
6	117	234	468	283	566	479	305	610	567	481
7	309	618	583	513	373	93	186	372	91	182
8	364	75	150	300	600	547	441	229	458	263
9	526	399	145	290	580	507	361	69	138	276
10	552	451	249	498	343	33	66	132	264	528
11	403	153	306	612	571	489	325	650	647	641
12	629	605	557	461	269	538	423	193	386	119
13	238	476	299	598	543	433	213	426	199	398
14	143	286	572	491	329	5	10	20	40	80
15	160	320	640	627	601	549	445	237	474	295
16	590	527	401	149	298	596	539	425	197	394
17	135	270	540	427	201	402	151	302	604	555
18	457	261	522	391	129	258	516	379	105	210
19	420	187	374	95	190	380	107	214	428	203
20	406	159	318	636	619	585	517	381	109	218
21	436	219	438	223	446	239	478	303	606	559
22	465	277	554	455	257	514	375	97	194	388
23	123	246	492	331	9	18	36	72	144	288
24	576	499	345	37	74	148	296	592	531	409
25	165	330	7	14	28	56	112	224	448	243
26	486	319	638	623	593	533	413	173	346	39
27	78	156	312	624	595	537	421	189	378	103
28	206	412	171	342	31	62	124	248	496	339
29	25	50	100	200	400	147	294	588	523	393
30	133	266	532	411	169	338	23	46	92	184
31	368	83	166	332	11	22	44	88	176	352
32	51	102	204	408	163	326	652	651	649	645
33	637	621	589	525	397	141	282	564	475	297
34	594	535	417	181	362	71	142	284	568	483
35	313	626	599	545	437	221	442	231	462	271
36	542	431	209	418	183	366	79	158	316	632
37	611	569	485	317	634	615	577	501	349	45
38	90	180	360	67	134	268	536	419	185	370
39	87	174	348	43	86	172	344	35	70	140
40	280	560	467	281	562	471	289	578	503	353
41	53	106	212	424	195	390	127	254	508	363
42	73	146	292	584	515	377	101	202	404	155
43	310	620	587	521	389	125	250	500	347	41
44	82	164	328	3	6	12	24	48	96	192
45	384	115	230	460	267	534	415	177	354	55
46	110	220	440	227	454	255	510	367	81	162
47	324	648	643	633	613	573	493	333	13	26
48	52	104	208	416	179	358	63	126	252	504
49	355	57	114	228	456	259	518	383	113	226

P = 653

INDICES

	0	1	2	3	4	5	6	7	8	9
50	437	377	502	408	489	571	621	95	418	564
51	466	20	9	73	225	424	186	206	496	58
52	626	433	182	298	510	333	90	161	109	612
53	556	248	302	265	455	341	386	275	125	166
54	172	582	360	134	534	353	522	85	514	155
55	605	647	100	618	222	179	553	122	519	219
56	401	634	404	54	337	643	64	68	348	371
57	637	114	142	475	40	596	240	376	407	570
58	94	563	19	72	423	205	57	432	297	332
59	160	611	247	264	340	274	165	581	133	352
60	84	154	646	617	178	121	218	633	53	642
61	67	370	113	474	595	375	569	562	71	204
62	431	331	610	263	273	580	351	153	616	120
63	632	641	369	473	374	561	203	330	262	579
64	152	119	640	472	560	329	578	118	471	328
65	117	327	326							

POWER RESIDUES

	0	1	2	3	4	5	6	7	8	9
50	452	251	502	351	49	98	196	392	131	262
51	524	395	137	274	548	443	233	466	279	558
52	463	273	546	439	225	450	247	494	335	17
53	34	68	136	272	544	435	217	434	215	430
54	207	414	175	350	47	94	188	376	99	198
55	396	139	278	556	459	265	530	407	161	322
56	644	635	617	581	509	365	77	154	308	616
57	579	505	357	61	122	244	488	323	646	639
58	625	597	541	429	205	410	167	334	15	30
59	60	120	240	480	307	614	575	497	341	29
60	58	116	232	464	275	550	447	241	482	311
61	622	591	529	405	157	314	628	603	553	453
62	253	506	359	65	130	260	520	387	121	242
63	484	315	630	607	561	469	285	570	487	321
64	642	631	609	565	477	301	602	551	449	245
65	490	327								

P = 659

INDICES

	0	1	2	3	4	5	6	7	8	9
0		0	1	186	2	52	187	405	3	372
1	53	418	188	596	406	238	4	536	373	388
2	54	591	419	160	189	104	597	558	407	501
3	239	399	5	604	537	457	374	32	389	124
4	55	511	592	497	420	424	161	581	190	152
5	105	64	598	301	559	470	408	574	502	622
6	240	428	400	119	6	648	605	365	538	346
7	458	11	375	616	33	290	390	165	125	226
8	56	86	512	49	593	588	498	29	421	298
9	425	343	162	585	582	440	191	307	153	132
10	106	443	65	653	599	643	302	20	560	194
11	471	218	409	201	575	212	503	310	623	283
12	241	178	429	39	401	156	120	466	7	25
13	649	279	606	135	366	610	539	545	347	322
14	459	109	12	356	376	553	617	338	34	446
15	291	139	391	250	166	451	126	68	227	487
16	57	565	87	74	513	656	50	370	594	534
17	589	102	499	602	30	509	422	150	299	572
18	426	646	344	614	163	84	586	296	583	305
19	441	641	192	199	308	176	154	23	133	543
20	107	551	444	248	66	563	654	532	600	148
21	644	82	303	197	21	549	561	146	195	144
22	472	474	219	525	410	476	202	233	576	221
23	213	351	504	527	311	633	624	412	284	316
24	242	478	179	272	430	204	40	326	402	235
25	157	396	121	578	467	116	8	223	26	437
26	650	215	280	463	607	353	136	484	367	506
27	611	638	540	529	546	522	348	313	323	113
28	460	635	110	255	13	626	357	258	377	414
29	554	493	618	286	339	16	35	318	447	98
30	292	244	140	629	392	480	251	94	167	181
31	452	360	127	274	69	171	228	432	488	261
32	58	206	566	266	88	42	75	380	514	328
33	657	185	51	404	371	417	595	237	535	387
34	590	159	103	557	500	398	603	456	31	123
35	510	496	423	580	151	63	300	469	573	621
36	427	118	647	364	345	10	615	289	164	225
37	85	48	587	28	297	342	584	439	306	131
38	442	652	642	19	193	217	200	211	309	282
39	177	38	155	465	24	278	134	609	544	321
40	108	355	552	337	445	138	249	450	67	486
41	564	73	655	369	533	101	601	508	149	571
42	645	613	83	295	304	640	198	175	22	542
43	550	247	562	531	147	81	196	548	145	143
44	473	524	475	232	220	350	526	632	411	315
45	477	271	203	325	234	395	577	115	222	436
46	214	462	352	483	505	637	528	521	312	112
47	634	254	625	257	413	492	285	15	317	97
48	243	628	479	93	180	359	273	170	431	260
49	205	265	41	379	327	184	403	416	236	386

POWER RESIDUES

	0	1	2	3	4	5	6	7	8	9
0	1	2	4	8	16	32	64	128	256	512
1	365	71	142	284	568	477	295	590	521	383
2	107	214	428	197	394	129	258	516	373	87
3	174	348	37	74	148	296	592	525	391	123
4	246	492	325	650	641	623	587	515	371	83
5	166	332	5	10	20	40	80	160	320	640
6	621	583	507	355	51	102	204	408	157	314
7	628	597	535	411	163	326	652	645	631	603
8	547	435	211	422	185	370	81	162	324	648
9	637	615	571	483	307	614	569	479	299	598
10	537	415	171	342	25	50	100	200	400	141
11	282	564	469	279	558	457	255	510	361	63
12	126	252	504	349	39	78	156	312	624	589
13	519	379	99	198	396	133	266	532	405	151
14	302	604	549	439	219	438	217	434	209	418
15	177	354	49	98	196	392	125	250	500	341
16	23	46	92	184	368	77	154	308	616	573
17	487	315	630	601	543	427	195	390	121	242
18	484	309	618	577	495	331	3	6	12	24
19	48	96	192	384	109	218	436	213	426	193
20	386	113	226	452	245	490	321	642	625	591
21	523	387	115	230	460	261	522	385	111	222
22	444	229	458	257	514	369	79	158	316	632
23	605	551	443	227	454	249	498	337	15	30
24	60	120	240	480	301	602	545	431	203	406
25	153	306	612	565	471	283	566	473	287	574
26	489	319	638	617	575	491	323	646	633	607
27	555	451	243	486	313	626	593	527	395	131
28	262	524	389	119	238	476	293	586	513	367
29	75	150	300	600	541	423	187	374	89	178
30	356	53	106	212	424	189	378	97	194	388
31	117	234	468	277	554	449	239	478	297	594
32	529	399	139	278	556	453	247	494	329	658
33	657	655	651	643	627	595	531	403	147	294
34	588	517	375	91	182	364	69	138	276	552
35	445	231	462	265	530	401	143	286	572	485
36	311	622	585	511	363	67	134	268	536	413
37	167	334	9	18	36	72	144	288	576	493
38	327	654	649	639	619	579	499	339	19	38
39	76	152	304	608	557	455	251	502	345	31
40	62	124	248	496	333	7	14	28	56	112
41	224	448	237	474	289	578	497	335	11	22
42	44	88	176	352	45	90	180	360	61	122
43	244	488	317	634	609	559	459	259	518	377
44	95	190	380	101	202	404	149	298	596	533
45	407	155	310	620	581	503	347	35	70	140
46	280	560	461	263	526	393	127	254	508	357
47	55	110	220	440	221	442	225	450	241	482
48	305	610	561	463	267	534	409	159	318	636
49	613	567	475	291	582	505	351	43	86	172

P = 659

INDICES

	0	1	2	3	4	5	6	7	8	9
50	158	556	397	455	122	495	579	62	468	620
51	117	363	9	288	224	47	27	341	438	130
52	651	18	216	210	281	37	464	277	608	320
53	354	336	137	449	485	72	368	100	507	570
54	612	294	639	174	541	246	530	80	547	142
55	523	231	349	631	314	270	324	394	114	435
56	461	482	636	520	111	253	256	491	14	96
57	627	92	358	169	259	264	378	183	415	385
58	555	454	494	61	619	362	287	46	340	129
59	17	209	36	276	319	335	448	71	99	569
60	293	173	245	79	141	230	630	269	393	434
61	481	519	252	490	95	91	168	263	182	384
62	453	60	361	45	128	208	275	334	70	568
63	172	78	229	268	433	518	489	90	262	383
64	59	44	207	333	567	77	267	517	89	382
65	43	332	76	516	381	331	515	330	329	

POWER RESIDUES

	0	1	2	3	4	5	6	7	8	9
50	344	29	58	116	232	464	269	538	417	175
51	350	41	82	164	328	656	653	647	635	611
52	563	467	275	550	441	223	446	233	466	273
53	546	433	207	414	169	338	17	34	68	136
54	272	544	429	199	398	137	274	548	437	215
55	430	201	402	145	290	580	501	343	27	54
56	108	216	432	205	410	161	322	644	629	599
57	539	419	179	358	57	114	228	456	253	506
58	353	47	94	188	376	93	186	372	85	170
59	340	21	42	84	168	336	13	26	52	104
60	208	416	173	346	33	66	132	264	528	397
61	135	270	540	421	183	366	73	146	292	584
62	509	359	59	118	236	472	285	570	481	303
63	606	553	447	235	470	281	562	465	271	542
64	425	191	382	105	210	420	181	362	65	130
65	260	520	381	103	206	412	165	330		

P = 661

INDICES

	0	1	2	3	4	5	6	7	8	9
0		0	1	570	2	38	571	465	3	480
1	39	380	572	633	466	608	4	118	481	159
2	40	375	381	641	573	76	634	390	467	590
3	609	654	5	290	119	503	482	217	160	543
4	41	364	376	386	382	518	642	434	574	270
5	77	28	635	494	391	418	468	69	591	522
6	610	319	655	285	6	11	291	441	120	551
7	504	231	483	512	218	646	161	185	544	257
8	42	300	365	567	377	156	387	500	383	25
9	519	438	643	564	435	197	575	16	271	200
10	78	177	29	145	636	413	495	578	392	224
11	419	127	469	207	70	19	592	453	523	583
12	611	100	320	274	656	114	286	266	7	296
13	12	203	292	624	442	428	121	535	552	81
14	505	344	232	353	484	628	513	180	219	339
15	647	397	162	598	186	32	545	618	258	404
16	43	446	301	148	366	328	568	463	378	606
17	157	639	388	652	501	541	384	432	26	416
18	520	283	439	229	644	255	565	498	436	195
19	198	143	576	125	17	581	272	264	201	426
20	79	351	178	395	30	402	146	461	637	539
21	414	227	496	141	579	424	393	459	225	422
22	420	91	128	93	470	556	208	130	71	64
23	20	95	593	250	454	472	524	167	584	558
24	612	85	101	210	321	308	275	132	657	477
25	115	73	287	361	267	66	8	509	297	22
26	13	410	204	97	293	532	625	595	443	603
27	429	252	122	348	536	456	553	247	82	474
28	506	529	345	526	233	107	354	169	485	236
29	629	586	514	315	181	560	220	110	340	614
30	648	191	398	87	163	357	599	103	187	55
31	33	212	546	172	619	323	259	59	405	310
32	44	488	447	277	302	49	149	134	367	239
33	329	659	569	37	464	479	379	632	607	117
34	158	374	640	75	389	589	653	289	502	216
35	542	363	385	517	433	269	27	493	417	68
36	521	318	284	10	440	550	230	511	645	184
37	256	299	566	155	499	24	437	563	196	15
38	199	176	144	412	577	223	126	206	18	452
39	582	99	273	113	265	295	202	623	427	534
40	80	343	352	627	179	338	396	597	31	617
41	403	445	147	327	462	605	638	651	540	431
42	415	282	228	254	497	194	142	124	580	263
43	425	350	394	401	460	538	226	140	423	458
44	421	90	92	555	129	63	94	249	471	166
45	557	84	209	307	131	476	72	360	65	508
46	21	409	96	531	594	602	251	347	455	246
47	473	528	525	106	168	235	585	314	559	109
48	613	190	86	356	102	54	211	171	322	58
49	309	487	276	48	133	238	658	36	478	631

POWER RESIDUES

	0	1	2	3	4	5	6	7	8	9
0	1	2	4	8	16	32	64	128	256	512
1	363	65	130	260	520	379	97	194	388	115
2	230	460	259	518	375	89	178	356	51	102
3	204	408	155	310	620	579	497	333	5	10
4	20	40	80	160	320	640	619	577	493	325
5	650	639	617	573	485	309	618	575	489	317
6	634	607	553	445	229	458	255	510	359	57
7	114	228	456	251	502	343	25	50	100	200
8	400	139	278	556	451	241	482	303	606	551
9	441	221	442	223	446	231	462	263	526	391
10	121	242	484	307	614	567	473	285	570	479
11	297	594	527	393	125	250	500	339	17	34
12	68	136	272	544	427	193	386	111	222	444
13	227	454	247	494	327	654	647	633	605	549
14	437	213	426	191	382	103	206	412	163	326
15	652	643	625	589	517	373	85	170	340	19
16	38	76	152	304	608	555	449	237	474	287
17	574	487	313	626	591	521	381	101	202	404
18	147	294	588	515	369	77	154	308	616	571
19	481	301	602	543	425	189	378	95	190	380
20	99	198	396	131	262	524	387	113	226	452
21	243	486	311	622	583	505	349	37	74	148
22	296	592	523	385	109	218	436	211	422	183
23	366	71	142	284	568	475	289	578	495	329
24	658	655	649	637	613	565	469	277	554	447
25	233	466	271	542	423	185	370	79	158	316
26	632	603	545	429	197	394	127	254	508	355
27	49	98	196	392	123	246	492	323	646	631
28	601	541	421	181	362	63	126	252	504	347
29	33	66	132	264	528	395	129	258	516	371
30	81	162	324	648	635	609	557	453	245	490
31	319	638	615	569	477	293	586	511	361	61
32	122	244	488	315	630	599	537	413	165	330
33	660	659	657	653	645	629	597	533	405	149
34	298	596	531	401	141	282	564	467	273	546
35	431	201	402	143	286	572	483	305	610	559
36	457	253	506	351	41	82	164	328	656	651
37	641	621	581	501	341	21	42	84	168	336
38	11	22	44	88	176	352	43	86	172	344
39	27	54	108	216	432	203	406	151	302	604
40	547	433	205	410	159	318	636	611	561	461
41	261	522	383	105	210	420	179	358	55	110
42	220	440	219	438	215	430	199	398	135	270
43	540	419	177	354	47	94	188	376	91	182
44	364	67	134	268	536	411	161	322	644	627
45	593	525	389	117	234	468	275	550	439	217
46	434	207	414	167	334	7	14	28	56	112
47	224	448	235	470	279	558	455	249	498	335
48	9	18	36	72	144	288	576	491	321	642
49	623	585	509	357	53	106	212	424	187	374

P = 661

INDICES

	0	1	2	3	4	5	6	7	8	9
50	116	373	74	588	288	215	362	516	268	492
51	67	317	9	549	510	183	298	154	23	562
52	14	175	411	222	205	451	98	112	294	622
53	533	342	626	337	596	616	444	326	604	650
54	430	281	253	193	123	262	349	400	537	139
55	457	89	554	62	248	165	83	306	475	359
56	507	408	530	601	346	245	527	105	234	313
57	108	189	355	53	170	57	486	47	237	35
58	630	372	587	214	515	491	316	548	182	153
59	561	174	221	450	111	621	341	336	615	325
60	649	280	192	261	399	138	88	61	164	305
61	358	407	600	244	104	312	188	52	56	46
62	34	371	213	490	547	152	173	449	620	335
63	324	279	260	137	60	304	406	243	311	51
64	45	370	489	151	448	334	278	136	303	242
65	50	369	150	333	135	241	368	332	240	331
66	330	0								

POWER RESIDUES

	0	1	2	3	4	5	6	7	8	9
50	87	174	348	35	70	140	280	560	459	257
51	514	367	73	146	292	584	507	353	45	90
52	180	360	59	118	236	472	283	566	471	281
53	562	463	265	530	399	137	274	548	435	209
54	418	175	350	39	78	156	312	624	587	513
55	365	69	138	276	552	443	225	450	239	478
56	295	590	519	377	93	186	372	83	166	332
57	3	6	12	24	48	96	192	384	107	214
58	428	195	390	119	238	476	291	582	503	345
59	29	58	116	232	464	267	534	407	153	306
60	612	563	465	269	538	415	169	338	15	30
61	60	120	240	480	299	598	535	409	157	314
62	628	595	529	397	133	266	532	403	145	290
63	580	499	337	13	26	52	104	208	416	171
64	342	23	46	92	184	368	75	150	300	600
65	539	417	173	346	31	62	124	248	496	331
66										

P = 673

INDICES

	0	1	2	3	4	5	6	7	8	9
0		0	182	284	364	1	466	486	546	568
1	183	655	648	296	668	285	56	611	78	395
2	365	98	165	144	158	2	478	180	178	658
3	467	403	238	267	121	487	260	72	577	580
4	547	219	280	229	347	569	326	625	340	300
5	184	223	660	432	362	656	360	7	168	511
6	649	535	585	382	420	297	449	437	303	428
7	669	561	442	496	254	286	87	469	90	9
8	57	464	401	358	462	612	411	270	529	34
9	79	110	508	15	135	396	522	652	482	551
10	366	307	405	526	170	99	614	273	544	265
11	166	356	542	207	189	145	350	192	21	425
12	159	638	45	503	95	3	564	240	602	513
13	479	413	631	209	619	181	485	647	610	164
14	179	237	71	279	624	659	6	584	436	441
15	468	400	269	507	651	404	272	541	191	44
16	239	630	646	70	583	268	540	645	644	592
17	122	291	593	31	452	488	39	123	216	537
18	261	531	292	147	18	73	197	594	317	666
19	578	418	32	187	162	581	664	453	61	139
20	548	49	489	472	587	220	36	40	352	378
21	281	599	124	173	455	230	54	217	447	108
22	348	235	538	416	52	570	389	262	371	384
23	327	81	532	194	374	626	203	293	607	63
24	341	572	148	76	227	301	13	19	277	642
25	185	445	74	127	422	224	112	198	23	558
26	661	554	595	66	141	433	391	318	129	335
27	363	567	667	394	157	657	120	579	346	299
28	361	510	419	427	253	8	461	33	134	550
29	169	264	188	424	94	512	618	163	623	440
30	650	43	582	591	451	536	17	665	161	138
31	586	377	454	107	51	383	373	62	226	641
32	421	557	140	334	156	298	252	549	93	439
33	450	137	50	640	155	438	154	490	102	491
34	304	386	473	114	103	429	213	588	634	492
35	670	476	221	85	305	562	398	37	47	387
36	443	118	41	250	474	497	329	353	200	115
37	255	246	379	314	104	287	499	282	176	430
38	88	524	600	505	214	470	369	125	344	589
39	91	83	174	25	635	10	243	456	321	493
40	58	331	231	27	671	465	654	55	97	477
41	402	259	218	325	222	359	534	448	560	86
42	463	410	109	521	306	613	355	349	637	563
43	412	484	236	5	399	271	629	539	290	38
44	530	196	417	663	48	35	598	53	234	388
45	80	202	571	12	444	111	553	390	566	119
46	509	460	263	617	42	16	376	372	556	251
47	136	153	385	212	475	397	117	328	245	498
48	523	368	82	242	330	653	258	533	409	354
49	483	628	195	597	201	552	459	375	152	116

POWER RESIDUES

	0	1	2	3	4	5	6	7	8	9
0	1	5	25	125	625	433	146	57	285	79
1	395	629	453	246	557	93	465	306	184	247
2	562	118	590	258	617	393	619	403	669	653
3	573	173	192	287	89	445	206	357	439	176
4	207	362	464	301	159	122	610	358	444	201
5	332	314	224	447	216	407	16	80	400	654
6	578	198	317	239	522	591	263	642	518	571
7	163	142	37	185	252	587	243	542	18	90
8	450	231	482	391	609	353	419	76	380	554
9	78	390	604	328	294	124	620	408	21	105
10	525	606	338	344	374	524	601	313	219	422
11	91	455	256	607	343	369	499	476	361	459
12	276	34	170	177	212	387	589	253	592	268
13	667	643	523	596	288	94	470	331	309	199
14	322	264	647	543	23	115	575	183	242	537
15	666	638	498	471	336	334	324	274	24	120
16	600	308	194	297	139	22	110	550	58	290
17	104	520	581	213	392	614	378	544	28	140
18	27	135	2	10	50	250	577	193	292	114
19	570	158	117	585	233	492	441	186	257	612
20	368	494	451	236	507	516	561	113	565	133
21	665	633	473	346	384	574	178	217	412	41
22	205	352	414	51	255	602	318	244	547	43
23	215	402	664	628	448	221	432	141	32	160
24	127	635	483	396	634	478	371	509	526	611
25	363	469	326	284	74	370	504	501	486	411
26	36	180	227	462	291	109	545	33	165	152
27	87	435	156	107	535	656	588	248	567	143
28	42	210	377	539	3	15	75	375	529	626
29	438	171	182	237	512	541	13	65	325	279
30	49	245	552	68	340	354	424	101	505	506
31	511	536	661	613	373	519	576	188	267	662
32	618	398	644	528	621	413	46	230	477	366
33	484	401	659	603	323	269	672	668	648	548
34	48	240	527	616	388	594	278	44	220	427
35	116	580	208	367	489	426	111	555	83	415
36	56	280	54	270	4	20	100	500	481	386
37	584	228	467	316	234	497	466	311	209	372
38	514	551	63	315	229	472	341	359	449	226
39	457	266	657	593	273	19	95	475	356	434
40	151	82	410	31	155	102	510	531	636	488
41	421	86	430	131	655	583	223	442	191	282
42	64	320	254	597	293	119	595	283	69	345
43	379	549	53	265	652	568	148	67	335	329
44	299	149	72	360	454	251	582	218	417	66
45	330	304	174	197	312	214	397	639	503	496
46	461	286	84	420	81	405	6	30	150	77
47	385	579	203	342	364	474	351	409	26	130
48	650	558	98	490	431	136	7	35	175	202
49	337	339	349	399	649	553	73	365	479	376

P = 673

INDICES

	0	1	2	3	4	5	6	7	8	9
50	367	257	627	458	256	308	309	204	604	247
51	406	310	294	575	380	527	205	608	68	315
52	171	605	64	132	105	100	248	342	323	288
53	615	407	573	515	500	274	311	149	517	283
54	545	295	77	143	177	266	576	228	339	431
55	167	381	302	495	89	357	528	14	481	525
56	543	206	20	502	601	208	609	278	435	506
57	190	69	643	30	215	146	316	186	60	471
58	351	172	446	415	370	193	606	75	276	126
59	22	65	128	393	345	426	133	423	622	590
60	160	106	225	333	92	639	101	113	633	84
61	46	249	199	313	175	504	343	24	320	26
62	96	324	559	520	636	4	289	662	233	11
63	565	616	555	211	244	241	408	596	151	457
64	603	574	67	131	322	514	516	142	338	494
65	480	501	434	29	59	414	275	392	621	332
66	632	312	319	519	232	210	150	130	337	28
67	620	518	336							

POWER RESIDUES

	0	1	2	3	4	5	6	7	8	9
50	534	651	563	123	615	383	569	153	92	460
51	281	59	295	129	645	533	646	538	671	663
52	623	423	96	480	381	559	103	515	556	88
53	440	181	232	487	416	61	305	179	222	437
54	166	157	112	560	108	540	8	40	200	327
55	289	99	495	456	261	632	468	321	259	622
56	418	71	355	429	126	630	458	271	9	45
57	225	452	241	532	641	513	546	38	190	277
58	39	195	302	164	147	62	310	204	347	389
59	599	303	169	172	187	262	637	493	446	211
60	382	564	128	640	508	521	586	238	517	566
61	138	17	85	425	106	530	631	463	296	134
62	670	658	598	298	144	47	235	502	491	436
63	161	132	660	608	348	394	624	428	121	605
64	333	319	249	572	168	167	162	137	12	60
65	300	154	97	485	406	11	55	275	29	145
66	52	260	627	443	196	307	189	272	14	70
67	350	404								

P = 677

INDICES

	0	1	2	3	4	5	6	7	8	9
0		0	1	479	2	465	480	319	3	282
1	466	79	481	168	320	268	4	11	283	35
2	467	122	80	575	482	254	169	85	321	229
3	269	385	5	558	12	108	284	134	36	647
4	468	456	123	75	81	71	576	53	483	638
5	255	490	170	313	86	544	322	514	230	580
6	270	63	386	601	6	633	559	191	13	378
7	109	92	285	523	135	57	37	398	648	406
8	469	564	457	503	124	476	76	32	82	105
9	72	487	577	188	54	500	484	358	639	361
10	256	626	491	438	171	587	314	642	87	433
11	545	613	323	196	515	364	231	450	581	330
12	271	158	64	259	387	43	602	672	7	554
13	634	629	560	354	192	550	14	214	379	494
14	110	532	93	247	286	18	524	441	136	224
15	58	183	38	293	399	174	649	298	407	116
16	470	218	565	590	458	347	504	618	125	336
17	477	317	77	266	33	573	83	383	106	645
18	73	51	488	542	578	599	189	90	55	404
19	501	30	485	498	359	436	640	611	362	328
20	257	670	627	548	492	245	439	181	172	114
21	588	616	315	571	643	540	88	28	434	326
22	546	179	614	538	324	536	197	199	516	663
23	365	201	232	277	451	518	582	209	331	665
24	272	97	159	367	65	427	260	203	388	306
25	44	234	603	654	673	279	8	251	555	453
26	635	511	630	520	561	102	355	584	193	155
27	551	211	15	290	215	333	380	596	495	667
28	111	25	533	274	94	303	248	99	287	22
29	19	161	525	148	442	369	137	164	225	67
30	59	394	184	429	39	528	294	262	400	241
31	175	205	650	151	299	390	408	412	117	308
32	471	445	219	46	566	422	591	236	459	372
33	348	605	505	416	619	656	126	140	337	675
34	478	464	318	281	78	167	267	10	34	121
35	574	253	84	228	384	557	107	133	646	455
36	74	70	52	637	489	312	543	513	579	62
37	600	632	190	377	91	522	56	397	405	563
38	502	475	31	104	486	187	499	357	360	625
39	437	586	641	432	612	195	363	449	329	157
40	258	42	671	553	628	353	549	213	493	531
41	246	17	440	223	182	292	173	297	115	217
42	589	346	617	335	316	265	572	382	644	50
43	541	598	89	403	29	497	435	610	327	669
44	547	244	180	113	615	570	539	27	325	178
45	537	535	198	662	200	276	517	208	664	96
46	366	426	202	305	233	653	278	250	452	510
47	519	101	583	154	210	289	332	595	666	24
48	273	302	98	21	160	147	368	163	66	393
49	428	527	261	240	204	150	389	411	307	444

POWER RESIDUES

	0	1	2	3	4	5	6	7	8	9
0	1	2	4	8	16	32	64	128	256	512
1	347	17	34	68	136	272	544	411	145	290
2	580	483	289	578	479	281	562	447	217	434
3	191	382	87	174	348	19	38	76	152	304
4	608	539	401	125	250	500	323	646	615	553
5	429	181	362	47	94	188	376	75	150	300
6	600	523	369	61	122	244	488	299	598	519
7	361	45	90	180	360	43	86	172	344	11
8	22	44	88	176	352	27	54	108	216	432
9	187	374	71	142	284	568	459	241	482	287
10	574	471	265	530	383	89	178	356	35	70
11	140	280	560	443	209	418	159	318	636	595
12	513	349	21	42	84	168	336	672	667	657
13	637	597	517	357	37	74	148	296	592	507
14	337	674	671	665	653	629	581	485	293	586
15	495	313	626	575	473	269	538	399	121	242
16	484	291	582	487	297	594	511	345	13	26
17	52	104	208	416	155	310	620	563	449	221
18	442	207	414	151	302	604	531	385	93	186
19	372	67	134	268	536	395	113	226	452	227
20	454	231	462	247	494	311	622	567	457	237
21	474	271	542	407	137	274	548	419	161	322
22	644	611	545	413	149	298	596	515	353	29
23	58	116	232	464	251	502	327	654	631	585
24	493	309	618	559	441	205	410	143	286	572
25	467	257	514	351	25	50	100	200	400	123
26	246	492	307	614	551	425	173	346	15	30
27	60	120	240	480	283	566	455	233	466	255
28	510	343	9	18	36	72	144	288	576	475
29	273	546	415	153	306	612	547	417	157	314
30	628	579	481	285	570	463	249	498	319	638
31	599	521	365	53	106	212	424	171	342	7
32	14	28	56	112	224	448	219	438	199	398
33	119	238	476	275	550	423	169	338	676	675
34	673	669	661	645	613	549	421	165	330	660
35	643	609	541	405	133	266	532	387	97	194
36	388	99	198	396	115	230	460	243	486	295
37	590	503	329	658	639	601	525	373	69	138
38	276	552	427	177	354	31	62	124	248	496
39	315	630	583	489	301	602	527	377	77	154
40	308	616	555	433	189	378	79	158	316	632
41	587	497	317	634	591	505	333	666	655	633
42	589	501	325	650	623	569	461	245	490	303
43	606	535	393	109	218	436	195	390	103	206
44	412	147	294	588	499	321	642	607	537	397
45	117	234	468	259	518	359	41	82	164	328
46	656	635	593	509	341	5	10	20	40	80
47	160	320	640	603	529	381	85	170	340	3
48	6	12	24	48	96	192	384	91	182	364
49	51	102	204	408	139	278	556	435	193	386

P = 677

INDICES

	0	1	2	3	4	5	6	7	8	9
50	45	421	235	371	604	415	655	139	674	463
51	280	166	9	120	252	227	556	132	454	69
52	636	311	512	61	631	376	521	396	562	474
53	103	186	356	624	585	431	194	448	156	41
54	552	352	212	530	16	222	291	296	216	345
55	334	264	381	49	597	402	496	609	668	243
56	112	569	26	177	534	661	275	207	95	425
57	304	652	249	509	100	153	288	594	23	301
58	20	146	162	392	526	239	149	410	443	420
59	370	414	138	462	165	119	226	131	68	310
60	60	375	395	473	185	623	430	447	40	351
61	529	221	295	344	263	48	401	608	242	568
62	176	660	206	424	651	508	152	593	300	145
63	391	238	409	419	413	461	118	130	309	374
64	472	622	446	350	220	343	47	607	567	659
65	423	507	592	144	237	418	460	129	373	621
66	349	342	606	658	506	143	417	128	620	341
67	657	142	127	340	141	339	338			

POWER RESIDUES

	0	1	2	3	4	5	6	7	8	9
50	95	190	380	83	166	332	664	651	625	573
51	469	261	522	367	57	114	228	456	235	470
52	263	526	375	73	146	292	584	491	305	610
53	543	409	141	282	564	451	225	450	223	446
54	215	430	183	366	55	110	220	440	203	406
55	135	270	540	403	129	258	516	355	33	66
56	132	264	528	379	81	162	324	648	619	561
57	445	213	426	175	350	23	46	92	184	368
58	59	118	236	472	267	534	391	105	210	420
59	163	326	652	627	577	477	277	554	431	185
60	370	63	126	252	504	331	662	647	617	557
61	437	197	394	111	222	444	211	422	167	334
62	668	659	641	605	533	389	101	202	404	131
63	262	524	371	65	130	260	520	363	49	98
64	196	392	107	214	428	179	358	39	78	156
65	312	624	571	465	253	506	335	670	663	649
66	621	565	453	229	458	239	478	279	558	439
67	201	402	127	254	508	339				

P = 683

INDICES

	0	1	2	3	4	5	6	7	8	9
0		0	217	330	434	1	547	265	651	660
1	218	657	82	427	482	331	186	19	195	270
2	435	595	192	399	299	2	644	308	17	128
3	548	149	403	305	236	266	412	165	487	75
4	652	463	130	497	409	661	616	543	516	530
5	219	349	179	120	525	658	234	600	345	602
6	83	448	366	243	620	428	522	550	453	47
7	483	90	629	325	382	332	22	240	292	39
8	187	638	680	642	347	20	32	458	626	159
9	196	10	151	479	78	271	51	510	65	635
10	436	34	566	222	396	596	337	257	60	604
11	193	495	451	477	135	400	562	405	137	284
12	300	632	665	111	583	3	460	174	155	145
13	645	357	57	535	85	309	670	216	264	81
14	18	191	307	402	164	129	542	178	599	365
15	549	628	239	679	457	150	509	565	256	450
16	404	664	173	56	215	306	177	238	564	172
17	237	248	249	226	675	267	161	250	376	553
18	413	29	227	96	368	166	14	676	295	573
19	488	204	268	407	45	76	282	162	170	43
20	653	198	251	393	101	464	439	377	613	245
21	131	230	554	420	474	498	277	414	139	655
22	410	446	30	493	668	662	12	228	352	104
23	617	570	97	538	622	544	354	369	501	588
24	517	322	167	286	200	531	328	15	118	290
25	220	153	677	374	391	350	372	296	362	430
26	180	106	574	7	274	121	70	489	302	253
27	526	315	205	340	433	659	481	269	298	127
28	235	74	408	529	524	601	619	46	381	38
29	346	158	77	634	395	603	134	283	582	144
30	84	80	163	364	456	449	214	171	674	552
31	367	572	44	42	100	244	473	654	667	103
32	621	587	199	289	390	429	273	252	432	126
33	523	37	394	143	455	551	99	102	389	125
34	454	124	465	113	466	48	443	440	210	114
35	484	53	378	182	467	91	593	614	88	49
36	630	540	246	280	444	326	313	132	585	441
37	383	385	231	26	211	333	512	555	108	115
38	23	504	421	425	485	241	624	475	262	54
39	293	418	499	5	379	40	387	278	260	183
40	188	67	415	576	468	639	610	140	318	92
41	681	546	656	185	594	643	148	411	462	615
42	348	233	447	521	89	21	637	31	9	50
43	33	336	494	561	631	459	356	669	190	541
44	627	508	663	176	247	160	28	13	203	281
45	197	438	229	276	445	11	569	353	321	327
46	152	371	105	69	314	480	73	618	157	133
47	79	213	571	472	586	272	36	98	123	442
48	52	592	539	312	384	511	503	623	417	386
49	66	609	545	147	232	636	335	355	507	27

POWER RESIDUES

	0	1	2	3	4	5	6	7	8	9
0	1	5	25	125	625	393	599	263	632	428
1	91	455	226	447	186	247	552	28	140	17
2	85	425	76	380	534	621	373	499	446	181
3	222	427	86	430	101	505	476	331	289	79
4	395	609	313	199	312	194	287	69	345	359
5	429	96	480	351	389	579	163	132	660	568
6	108	540	651	523	566	98	490	401	639	463
7	266	647	503	466	281	39	195	292	94	470
8	301	139	12	60	300	134	670	618	358	424
9	71	355	409	679	663	583	183	232	477	336
10	314	204	337	319	229	462	261	622	378	524
11	571	123	615	343	349	379	529	596	248	557
12	53	265	642	478	341	339	329	279	29	145
13	42	210	367	469	296	114	570	118	590	218
14	407	669	613	333	299	129	645	493	416	31
15	155	92	460	251	572	128	640	468	291	89
16	445	176	197	302	144	37	185	242	527	586
17	198	307	169	162	127	635	443	166	147	52
18	260	617	353	399	629	413	16	80	400	634
19	438	141	22	110	550	18	90	450	201	322
20	244	537	636	448	191	272	677	653	533	616
21	348	374	504	471	306	164	137	2	10	50
22	250	567	103	515	526	581	173	182	227	452
23	211	372	494	421	56	280	34	170	167	152
24	77	385	559	63	315	209	362	444	171	172
25	177	202	327	269	662	578	158	107	535	626
26	398	624	388	574	138	7	35	175	192	277
27	19	95	475	326	264	637	453	216	397	619
28	363	449	196	297	119	595	243	532	611	323
29	249	562	78	390	584	188	257	602	278	24
30	120	600	268	657	553	33	165	142	27	135
31	675	643	483	366	464	271	672	628	408	674
32	638	458	241	522	561	73	365	459	246	547
33	3	15	75	375	509	496	431	106	530	601
34	273	682	678	658	558	58	290	84	420	51
35	255	592	228	457	236	497	436	131	655	543
36	666	598	258	607	303	149	62	310	184	237
37	502	461	256	597	253	582	178	207	352	394
38	604	288	74	370	484	371	489	396	614	338
39	324	254	587	203	332	294	104	520	551	23
40	115	575	143	32	160	117	585	193	282	44
41	220	417	36	180	217	402	644	488	391	589
42	213	382	544	671	623	383	549	13	65	325
43	259	612	328	274	4	20	100	500	451	206
44	347	369	479	346	364	454	221	422	61	305
45	159	112	560	68	340	334	304	154	87	435
46	126	630	418	41	205	342	344	354	404	654
47	538	641	473	316	214	387	569	113	565	93
48	465	276	14	70	350	384	554	38	190	267
49	652	528	591	223	432	111	555	43	215	392

P = 683

INDICES

	0	1	2	3	4	5	6	7	8	9
50	437	568	370	72	212	35	591	502	608	334
51	567	590	589	578	513	223	579	518	647	556
52	397	514	323	63	109	597	224	168	491	116
53	338	580	287	208	24	258	519	201	470	505
54	61	648	532	359	422	605	557	329	650	426
55	194	398	16	304	486	496	515	119	344	242
56	452	324	291	641	625	478	64	221	59	476
57	136	110	154	534	263	401	598	678	255	55
58	563	225	375	95	294	406	169	392	612	419
59	138	492	351	537	500	285	117	373	361	6
60	301	339	297	528	380	633	581	363	673	41
61	666	288	431	142	388	112	209	181	87	279
62	584	25	107	424	261	4	259	575	317	184
63	461	520	8	560	189	175	202	275	320	68
64	156	471	122	311	416	146	506	71	607	577
65	646	62	490	207	469	358	649	303	343	640
66	58	533	254	94	611	536	360	527	672	141
67	86	423	316	559	319	310	606	206	342	93
68	671	558	341							

POWER RESIDUES

	0	1	2	3	4	5	6	7	8	9
50	594	238	507	486	381	539	646	498	441	156
51	97	485	376	514	521	556	48	240	517	536
52	631	423	66	330	284	54	270	667	603	283
53	49	245	542	661	573	133	665	593	233	482
54	361	439	146	47	235	492	411	6	30	150
55	67	335	309	179	212	377	519	546	681	673
56	633	433	116	580	168	157	102	510	501	456
57	231	472	311	189	262	627	403	649	513	516
58	531	606	298	124	620	368	474	321	239	512
59	511	506	481	356	414	21	105	525	576	148
60	57	285	59	295	109	545	676	648	508	491
61	406	664	588	208	357	419	46	230	467	286
62	64	320	234	487	386	564	88	440	151	72
63	360	434	121	605	293	99	495	426	81	405
64	659	563	83	415	26	130	650	518	541	656
65	548	8	40	200	317	219	412	11	55	275
66	9	45	225	442	161	122	610	318	224	437
67	136	680	668	608	308	174	187	252	577	153
68	82	410								

P = 691

INDICES

	0	1	2	3	4	5	6	7	8	9
0		0	591	1	492	318	592	254	393	2
1	219	335	493	431	155	319	294	659	593	105
2	120	255	236	125	394	636	332	3	56	614
3	220	111	195	336	560	572	494	388	6	432
4	21	623	156	52	137	320	26	526	295	508
5	537	660	233	505	594	653	647	106	515	166
6	121	130	12	256	96	59	237	381	461	126
7	473	576	395	213	289	637	597	589	333	118
8	612	4	524	645	57	287	643	615	38	552
9	221	685	617	112	427	423	196	584	409	337
10	438	40	561	656	134	573	406	261	495	141
11	554	389	548	184	7	443	416	433	67	223
12	22	670	31	624	603	264	157	674	687	53
13	650	521	138	359	282	321	362	619	27	174
14	374	527	477	76	296	242	114	509	190	276
15	538	468	498	661	490	429	234	109	19	506
16	513	379	595	285	425	654	546	668	648	172
17	188	107	544	198	516	200	629	167	453	144
18	122	534	586	131	518	16	13	304	328	257
19	324	411	97	202	485	60	310	92	238	81
20	339	382	631	178	462	251	557	127	35	440
21	474	169	307	577	162	370	396	365	42	214
22	455	400	290	580	449	638	85	563	598	146
23	344	590	317	392	334	154	658	119	124	331
24	613	194	571	5	622	136	525	536	504	646
25	165	11	58	460	575	288	588	611	644	642
26	551	616	422	408	39	133	260	553	183	415
27	222	30	263	686	520	281	618	373	75	113
28	275	497	428	18	378	424	667	187	197	628
29	143	585	15	327	410	484	91	338	177	556
30	439	306	369	41	399	448	562	343	391	657
31	330	570	135	503	10	574	610	550	407	259
32	414	262	280	74	496	377	186	142	326	90
33	555	368	447	390	569	9	549	413	73	185
34	89	446	8	72	445	444	99	100	417	353
35	101	434	530	418	68	204	354	224	45	102
36	23	210	435	671	487	531	32	151	419	625
37	607	69	604	62	205	265	229	355	158	480
38	225	675	312	46	688	217	103	54	386	24
39	651	94	211	522	683	436	139	65	672	360
40	240	488	283	542	532	322	79	33	363	83
41	152	620	458	420	28	273	626	175	341	608
42	375	567	70	528	208	605	478	384	63	77
43	271	206	297	299	266	243	633	230	115	403
44	356	510	301	159	191	180	481	277	350	226
45	539	268	676	469	464	313	499	679	47	662
46	245	689	491	253	218	430	293	104	235	635
47	55	110	559	387	20	51	25	507	232	652
48	514	129	95	380	472	212	596	117	523	286
49	37	684	426	583	437	655	405	140	547	442

POWER RESIDUES

	0	1	2	3	4	5	6	7	8	9
0	1	3	9	27	81	243	38	114	342	335
1	314	251	62	186	558	292	185	555	283	158
2	474	40	120	360	389	476	46	138	414	551
3	271	122	366	407	530	208	624	490	88	264
4	101	303	218	654	580	358	383	458	683	667
5	619	475	43	129	387	470	28	84	252	65
6	195	585	373	428	593	397	500	118	354	371
7	422	575	343	338	323	278	143	429	596	406
8	527	199	597	409	536	226	678	652	574	340
9	329	296	197	591	391	482	64	192	576	346
10	347	350	359	386	467	19	57	171	513	157
11	471	31	93	279	146	438	623	487	79	237
12	20	60	180	540	238	23	69	207	621	481
13	61	183	549	265	104	312	245	44	132	396
14	497	109	327	290	179	537	229	687	679	655
15	583	367	410	539	235	14	42	126	378	443
16	638	532	214	642	544	250	59	177	531	211
17	633	517	169	507	139	417	560	298	203	609
18	445	644	550	268	113	339	326	287	170	510
19	148	444	641	541	241	32	96	288	173	519
20	175	525	193	579	355	374	431	602	424	581
21	361	392	485	73	219	657	589	385	464	10
22	30	90	270	119	357	380	449	656	586	376
23	437	620	478	52	156	468	22	66	198	594
24	400	509	145	435	614	460	689	685	673	637
25	529	205	615	463	7	21	63	189	567	319
26	266	107	321	272	125	375	434	611	451	662
27	604	430	599	415	554	280	149	447	650	568
28	322	275	134	402	515	163	489	85	255	74
29	222	666	616	466	16	48	144	432	605	433
30	608	442	635	523	187	561	301	212	636	526
31	196	588	382	455	674	640	538	232	5	15
32	45	135	405	524	190	570	328	293	188	564
33	310	239	26	78	234	11	33	99	297	200
34	600	418	563	307	230	690	688	682	664	610
35	448	653	577	349	356	377	440	629	505	133
36	399	506	136	408	533	217	651	571	331	302
37	215	645	553	277	140	420	569	325	284	161
38	483	67	201	603	427	590	388	473	37	111
39	333	308	233	8	24	72	216	648	562	304
40	221	663	607	439	626	496	106	318	263	98
41	294	191	573	337	320	269	116	348	353	368
42	413	548	262	95	285	164	492	94	282	155
43	465	13	39	117	351	362	395	494	100	300
44	209	627	499	115	345	344	341	332	305	224
45	672	634	520	178	534	220	660	598	412	545
46	253	68	204	612	454	671	631	511	151	453
47	668	622	484	70	210	630	508	142	426	587
48	379	446	647	559	295	194	582	364	401	512
49	154	462	4	12	36	108	324	281	152	456

P = 691

INDICES

	0	1	2	3	4	5	6	7	8	9
50	66	669	602	673	649	358	361	173	476	241
51	189	467	489	108	512	284	545	171	543	199
52	452	533	517	303	323	201	309	80	630	250
53	34	168	161	364	454	579	84	145	316	153
54	123	193	621	535	164	459	587	641	421	132
55	182	29	519	372	274	17	666	627	14	483
56	176	305	398	342	329	502	609	258	279	376
57	325	367	568	412	88	71	98	352	529	203
58	44	209	486	150	606	61	228	479	311	216
59	385	93	682	64	239	541	78	82	457	272
60	340	566	207	383	270	298	632	402	300	179
61	349	267	463	678	244	252	292	634	558	50
62	231	128	471	116	36	582	404	441	601	357
63	475	466	511	170	451	302	308	249	160	578
64	315	192	163	640	181	371	665	482	397	501
65	278	366	87	351	43	149	227	215	681	540
66	456	565	269	401	348	677	291	49	470	581
67	600	465	450	248	314	639	664	500	86	148
68	680	564	347	48	599	247	663	147	346	246
69	345	0								

POWER RESIDUES

	0	1	2	3	4	5	6	7	8	9
50	677	649	565	313	248	53	159	477	49	147
51	441	632	514	160	480	58	174	522	184	552
52	274	131	393	488	82	246	47	141	423	578
53	352	365	404	521	181	543	247	50	150	450
54	659	595	403	518	172	516	166	498	112	336
55	317	260	89	267	110	330	299	206	618	472
56	34	102	306	227	681	661	601	421	572	334
57	311	242	35	105	315	254	71	213	639	535
58	223	669	625	493	97	291	182	546	256	77
59	231	2	6	18	54	162	486	76	228	684
60	670	628	502	124	372	425	584	370	419	566
61	316	257	80	240	29	87	261	92	276	137
62	411	542	244	41	123	369	416	557	289	176
63	528	202	606	436	617	469	25	75	225	675
64	643	547	259	86	258	83	249	56	168	504
65	130	390	479	55	165	495	103	309	236	17
66	51	153	459	686	676	646	556	286	167	501
67	121	363	398	503	127	381	452	665	613	457
68	680	658	592	394	491	91	273	128	384	461
69										

P = 701

INDICES

	0	1	2	3	4	5	6	7	8	9
0		0	1	429	2	638	430	472	3	158
1	639	423	431	112	473	367	4	610	159	100
2	640	201	424	405	432	576	113	587	474	556
3	368	26	5	152	611	410	160	601	101	541
4	641	442	202	458	425	96	406	335	433	244
5	577	339	114	669	588	361	475	529	557	41
6	369	295	27	630	6	50	153	437	612	134
7	411	219	161	617	602	305	102	195	542	481
8	642	316	443	248	203	548	459	285	426	420
9	97	584	407	455	336	38	434	302	245	581
10	578	658	340	168	115	139	670	661	589	255
11	362	330	476	325	530	343	558	270	42	382
12	370	146	296	171	28	514	631	565	7	187
13	51	118	154	572	438	525	613	416	135	142
14	412	64	220	535	162	494	618	673	603	487
15	306	650	103	68	196	664	543	265	482	398
16	643	177	317	592	444	90	249	500	204	224
17	549	258	460	506	286	348	427	470	421	365
18	98	403	585	24	408	539	456	333	337	359
19	39	628	435	217	303	479	246	283	582	36
20	579	166	659	328	341	380	169	563	116	523
21	140	533	671	648	662	396	590	498	256	346
22	363	22	331	626	477	34	326	561	531	394
23	344	624	559	622	271	273	43	210	383	275
24	371	695	147	45	297	182	172	212	29	677
25	515	385	632	128	566	277	8	682	188	373
26	52	14	119	697	155	607	573	149	439	241
27	526	47	614	313	417	299	136	322	143	184
28	413	491	65	174	221	467	536	214	163	520
29	495	31	619	692	674	679	604	310	488	517
30	307	230	651	387	104	233	69	634	197	597
31	665	130	544	654	266	568	483	86	399	279
32	644	390	178	10	318	688	593	684	445	107
33	91	190	250	59	501	375	205	236	225	54
34	550	449	259	16	461	72	507	121	287	78
35	349	699	428	637	471	157	422	111	366	609
36	99	200	404	575	586	555	25	151	409	600
37	540	441	457	95	334	243	338	668	360	528
38	40	294	629	49	436	133	218	616	304	194
39	480	315	247	547	284	419	583	454	37	301
40	580	657	167	138	660	254	329	324	342	269
41	381	145	170	513	564	186	117	571	524	415
42	141	63	534	493	672	486	649	67	663	264
43	397	176	591	89	499	223	257	505	347	469
44	364	402	23	538	332	358	627	216	478	282
45	35	165	327	379	562	522	532	647	395	497
46	345	21	625	33	560	393	623	621	272	209
47	274	694	44	181	211	676	384	127	276	681
48	372	13	696	606	148	240	46	312	298	321
49	183	490	173	466	213	519	30	691	678	309

POWER RESIDUES

	0	1	2	3	4	5	6	7	8	9
0	1	2	4	8	16	32	64	128	256	512
1	323	646	591	481	261	522	343	686	671	641
2	581	461	221	442	183	366	31	62	124	248
3	496	291	582	463	225	450	199	398	95	190
4	380	59	118	236	472	243	486	271	542	383
5	65	130	260	520	339	678	655	609	517	333
6	666	631	561	421	141	282	564	427	153	306
7	612	523	345	690	679	657	613	525	349	698
8	695	689	677	653	605	509	317	634	567	433
9	165	330	660	619	537	373	45	90	180	360
10	19	38	76	152	304	608	515	329	658	615
11	529	357	13	26	52	104	208	416	131	262
12	524	347	694	687	673	645	589	477	253	506
13	311	622	543	385	69	138	276	552	403	105
14	210	420	139	278	556	411	121	242	484	267
15	534	367	33	66	132	264	528	355	9	18
16	36	72	144	288	576	451	201	402	103	206
17	412	123	246	492	283	566	431	161	322	644
18	587	473	245	490	279	558	415	129	258	516
19	331	662	623	545	389	77	154	308	616	531
20	361	21	42	84	168	336	672	643	585	469
21	237	474	247	494	287	574	447	193	386	71
22	142	284	568	435	169	338	676	651	601	501
23	301	602	503	305	610	519	337	674	647	593
24	485	269	538	375	49	98	196	392	83	166
25	332	664	627	553	405	109	218	436	171	342
26	684	667	633	565	429	157	314	628	555	409
27	117	234	468	235	470	239	478	255	510	319
28	638	575	449	197	394	87	174	348	696	691
29	681	661	621	541	381	61	122	244	488	275
30	550	399	97	194	388	75	150	300	600	499
31	297	594	487	273	546	391	81	162	324	648
32	595	489	277	554	407	113	226	452	203	406
33	111	222	444	187	374	47	94	188	376	51
34	102	204	408	115	230	460	219	438	175	350
35	700	699	697	693	685	669	637	573	445	189
36	378	55	110	220	440	179	358	15	30	60
37	120	240	480	259	518	335	670	639	577	453
38	205	410	119	238	476	251	502	303	606	511
39	321	642	583	465	229	458	215	430	159	318
40	636	571	441	181	362	23	46	92	184	368
41	35	70	140	280	560	419	137	274	548	395
42	89	178	356	11	22	44	88	176	352	3
43	6	12	24	48	96	192	384	67	134	268
44	536	371	41	82	164	328	656	611	521	341
45	682	663	625	549	397	93	186	372	43	86
46	172	344	688	675	649	597	493	285	570	439
47	177	354	7	14	28	56	112	224	448	195
48	390	79	158	316	632	563	425	149	298	596
49	491	281	562	423	145	290	580	459	217	434

P = 701

INDICES

	0	1	2	3	4	5	6	7	8	9
50	516	229	386	232	633	596	129	653	567	85
51	278	389	9	687	683	106	189	58	374	235
52	53	448	15	71	120	77	698	636	156	110
53	608	199	574	554	150	599	440	94	242	667
54	527	293	48	132	615	193	314	546	418	453
55	300	656	137	253	323	268	144	512	185	570
56	414	62	492	485	66	263	175	88	222	504
57	468	401	537	357	215	281	164	378	521	646
58	496	20	32	392	620	208	693	180	675	126
59	680	12	605	239	311	320	489	465	518	690
60	308	228	231	595	652	84	388	686	105	57
61	234	447	70	76	635	109	198	553	598	93
62	666	292	131	192	545	452	655	252	267	511
63	569	61	484	262	87	503	400	356	280	377
64	645	19	391	207	179	125	11	238	319	464
65	689	227	594	83	685	56	446	75	108	552
66	92	291	191	451	251	510	60	261	502	355
67	376	18	206	124	237	463	226	82	55	74
68	551	290	450	509	260	354	17	123	462	81
69	73	289	508	353	122	80	288	352	79	351
70	350	0								

POWER RESIDUES

	0	1	2	3	4	5	6	7	8	9
50	167	334	668	635	569	437	173	346	692	683
51	665	629	557	413	125	250	500	299	598	495
52	289	578	455	209	418	135	270	540	379	57
53	114	228	456	211	422	143	286	572	443	185
54	370	39	78	156	312	624	547	393	85	170
55	340	680	659	617	533	365	29	58	116	232
56	464	227	454	207	414	127	254	508	315	630
57	559	417	133	266	532	363	25	50	100	200
58	400	99	198	396	91	182	364	27	54	108
59	216	432	163	326	652	603	505	309	618	535
60	369	37	74	148	296	592	483	265	530	359
61	17	34	68	136	272	544	387	73	146	292
62	584	467	233	466	231	462	223	446	191	382
63	63	126	252	504	307	614	527	353	5	10
64	20	40	80	160	320	640	579	457	213	426
65	151	302	604	507	313	626	551	401	101	202
66	404	107	214	428	155	310	620	539	377	53
67	106	212	424	147	294	588	475	249	498	295
68	590	479	257	514	327	654	607	513	325	650
69	599	497	293	586	471	241	482	263	526	351
70										

P = 709

INDICES

	0	1	2	3	4	5	6	7	8	9
0		0	1	172	2	322	173	52	3	344
1	323	670	174	597	53	494	4	97	345	652
2	324	224	671	511	175	644	598	516	54	68
3	495	199	5	134	98	374	346	583	653	61
4	325	431	225	574	672	666	512	570	176	104
5	645	269	599	81	517	284	55	116	69	180
6	496	337	200	396	6	211	135	92	99	683
7	375	385	347	609	584	108	654	14	62	365
8	326	688	432	309	226	419	575	240	673	169
9	667	649	513	371	571	266	177	89	105	306
10	646	303	270	122	600	546	82	273	518	465
11	285	47	56	380	117	125	70	233	181	149
12	497	632	338	603	201	258	397	616	7	38
13	212	549	136	704	93	130	100	207	684	85
14	376	34	386	559	348	390	610	276	585	24
15	109	190	655	441	15	521	63	332	366	253
16	327	563	689	468	433	456	310	75	227	486
17	420	288	576	449	241	696	674	352	170	50
18	668	492	650	509	514	197	372	59	572	568
19	267	282	178	394	90	383	106	363	307	238
20	647	264	304	120	271	45	123	147	601	614
21	547	128	83	557	274	188	519	251	466	73
22	286	694	48	507	57	280	381	236	118	145
23	126	186	71	505	234	184	182	537	150	539
24	498	589	633	152	339	426	604	541	202	481
25	259	500	398	473	617	591	8	28	39	635
26	213	412	550	154	137	403	705	341	94	641
27	131	428	101	113	208	606	685	166	86	543
28	377	629	35	204	387	438	560	483	349	194
29	391	261	611	248	277	502	586	478	25	400
30	110	626	191	475	656	659	442	619	16	294
31	522	593	64	662	333	10	367	461	254	30
32	328	445	564	41	690	533	469	637	434	622
33	457	215	311	219	76	414	228	19	487	552
34	421	161	289	156	577	297	450	139	242	315
35	697	405	675	525	353	707	171	321	51	343
36	669	596	493	96	651	223	510	643	515	67
37	198	133	373	582	60	430	573	665	569	103
38	268	80	283	115	179	336	395	210	91	682
39	384	608	107	13	364	687	308	418	239	168
40	648	370	265	88	305	302	121	545	272	464
41	46	379	124	232	148	631	602	257	615	37
42	548	703	129	206	84	33	558	389	275	23
43	189	440	520	331	252	562	467	455	74	485
44	287	448	695	351	49	491	508	196	58	567
45	281	393	382	362	237	263	119	44	146	613
46	127	556	187	250	72	693	506	279	235	144
47	185	504	183	536	538	588	151	425	540	480
48	499	472	590	27	634	411	153	402	340	640
49	427	112	605	165	542	628	203	437	482	193

POWER RESIDUES

	0	1	2	3	4	5	6	7	8	9
0	1	2	4	8	16	32	64	128	256	512
1	315	630	551	393	77	154	308	616	523	337
2	674	639	569	429	149	298	596	483	257	514
3	319	638	567	425	141	282	564	419	129	258
4	516	323	646	583	457	205	410	111	222	444
5	179	358	7	14	28	56	112	224	448	187
6	374	39	78	156	312	624	539	369	29	58
7	116	232	464	219	438	167	334	668	627	545
8	381	53	106	212	424	139	278	556	403	97
9	194	388	67	134	268	536	363	17	34	68
10	136	272	544	379	49	98	196	392	75	150
11	300	600	491	273	546	383	57	114	228	456
12	203	406	103	206	412	115	230	460	211	422
13	135	270	540	371	33	66	132	264	528	347
14	694	679	649	589	469	229	458	207	414	119
15	238	476	243	486	263	526	343	686	663	617
16	525	341	682	655	601	493	277	554	399	89
17	178	356	3	6	12	24	48	96	192	384
18	59	118	236	472	235	470	231	462	215	430
19	151	302	604	499	289	578	447	185	370	31
20	62	124	248	496	283	566	423	137	274	548
21	387	65	130	260	520	331	662	615	521	333
22	666	623	537	365	21	42	84	168	336	672
23	635	561	413	117	234	468	227	454	199	398
24	87	174	348	696	683	657	605	501	293	586
25	463	217	434	159	318	636	563	417	125	250
26	500	291	582	455	201	402	95	190	380	51
27	102	204	408	107	214	428	147	294	588	467
28	225	450	191	382	55	110	220	440	171	342
29	684	659	609	509	309	618	527	345	690	671
30	633	557	405	101	202	404	99	198	396	83
31	166	332	664	619	529	349	698	687	665	621
32	533	357	5	10	20	40	80	160	320	640
33	571	433	157	314	628	547	385	61	122	244
34	488	267	534	359	9	18	36	72	144	288
35	576	443	177	354	708	707	705	701	693	677
36	645	581	453	197	394	79	158	316	632	555
37	401	93	186	372	35	70	140	280	560	411
38	113	226	452	195	390	71	142	284	568	427
39	145	290	580	451	193	386	63	126	252	504
40	299	598	487	265	530	351	702	695	681	653
41	597	485	261	522	335	670	631	553	397	85
42	170	340	680	651	593	477	245	490	271	542
43	375	41	82	164	328	656	603	497	285	570
44	431	153	306	612	515	321	642	575	441	173
45	346	692	675	641	573	437	165	330	660	611
46	513	317	634	559	409	109	218	436	163	326
47	652	595	481	253	506	303	606	503	297	594
48	479	249	498	287	574	439	169	338	676	643
49	577	445	181	362	15	30	60	120	240	480

P = 709

INDICES

	0	1	2	3	4	5	6	7	8	9
50	260	247	501	477	399	625	474	658	618	293
51	592	661	9	460	29	444	40	532	636	621
52	214	218	413	18	551	160	155	296	138	314
53	404	524	706	320	342	595	95	222	642	66
54	132	581	429	664	102	79	114	335	209	681
55	607	12	686	417	167	369	87	301	544	463
56	378	231	630	256	36	702	205	32	388	22
57	439	330	561	454	484	447	350	490	195	566
58	392	361	262	43	612	555	249	692	278	143
59	503	535	587	424	479	471	26	410	401	639
60	111	164	627	436	192	246	476	624	657	292
61	660	459	443	531	620	217	17	159	295	313
62	523	319	594	221	65	580	663	78	334	680
63	11	416	368	300	462	230	255	701	31	21
64	329	453	446	489	565	360	42	554	691	142
65	534	423	470	409	638	163	435	245	623	291
66	458	530	216	158	312	318	220	579	77	679
67	415	299	229	700	20	452	488	359	553	141
68	422	408	162	244	290	529	157	317	578	678
69	298	699	451	358	140	407	243	528	316	677
70	698	357	406	527	676	356	526	355	354	

POWER RESIDUES

	0	1	2	3	4	5	6	7	8	9
50	251	502	295	590	471	233	466	223	446	183
51	366	23	46	92	184	368	27	54	108	216
52	432	155	310	620	531	353	706	703	697	685
53	661	613	517	325	650	591	473	237	474	239
54	478	247	494	279	558	407	105	210	420	131
55	262	524	339	678	647	585	461	213	426	143
56	286	572	435	161	322	644	579	449	189	378
57	47	94	188	376	43	86	172	344	688	667
58	625	541	373	37	74	148	296	592	475	241
59	482	255	510	311	622	535	361	13	26	52
60	104	208	416	123	246	492	275	550	391	73
61	146	292	584	459	209	418	127	254	508	307
62	614	519	329	658	607	505	301	602	495	281
63	562	415	121	242	484	259	518	327	654	599
64	489	269	538	367	25	50	100	200	400	91
65	182	364	19	38	76	152	304	608	507	305
66	610	511	313	626	543	377	45	90	180	360
67	11	22	44	88	176	352	704	699	689	669
68	629	549	389	69	138	276	552	395	81	162
69	324	648	587	465	221	442	175	350	700	691
70	673	637	565	421	133	266	532	355		

P = 719

INDICES

	0	1	2	3	4	5	6	7	8	9
0		0	606	42	494	364	648	650	382	84
1	252	1	536	488	538	406	270	143	690	77
2	140	692	607	703	424	10	376	126	426	638
3	294	304	158	43	31	296	578	552	683	530
4	28	105	580	393	495	448	591	491	312	582
5	616	185	264	165	14	365	314	119	526	542
6	182	670	192	16	46	134	649	689	637	27
7	184	191	466	467	440	52	571	651	418	657
8	634	168	711	342	468	507	281	680	383	627
9	336	420	479	346	379	441	200	455	470	85
10	504	245	73	674	152	338	53	362	620	563
11	253	594	202	534	7	349	414	572	430	75
12	70	2	558	147	80	374	622	463	652	435
13	22	41	537	9	577	490	525	26	633	419
14	72	533	79	489	354	284	355	624	328	12
15	658	214	459	227	539	668	306	285	545	207
16	522	635	56	554	599	407	230	50	356	258
17	395	161	169	709	568	660	271	584	515	625
18	224	588	308	712	367	198	234	144	267	58
19	329	672	88	389	343	176	358	251	691	157
20	392	13	133	570	679	469	562	69	40	78
21	226	598	659	233	250	39	508	236	451	509
22	141	631	482	215	90	94	422	282	613	475
23	237	693	302	457	460	137	318	699	681	205
24	676	452	608	210	446	228	35	565	686	384
25	262	707	510	704	351	549	540	222	323	484
26	628	4	647	142	425	529	615	669	465	341
27	378	337	413	462	632	11	521	160	307	388
28	678	38	421	698	685	483	377	37	242	286
29	172	497	243	480	512	188	216	127	618	473
30	546	325	102	287	347	316	115	91	427	716
31	556	208	194	99	173	380	433	260	95	639
32	410	404	523	220	662	498	442	605	487	423
33	295	590	118	636	656	335	244	201	146	576
34	283	305	49	514	57	391	597	481	456	445
35	548	614	159	241	472	555	403	117	513	471
36	112	154	476	44	196	113	600	518	255	189
37	86	97	122	238	32	416	155	408	664	642
38	217	505	560	603	694	297	277	477	231	654
39	64	128	246	83	139	303	579	164	45	51
40	280	454	619	74	21	532	458	553	567	197
41	357	68	450	474	675	706	646	461	684	187
42	114	259	486	575	547	153	121	602	138	531
43	645	601	396	18	124	326	339	62	397	319
44	29	666	519	162	370	273	103	54	696	19
45	700	106	310	256	170	66	501	288	363	269
46	125	682	581	181	190	710	345	151	348	621
47	25	327	206	394	587	87	569	249	93	317
48	564	322	340	677	496	101	98	661	334	596
49	116	254	641	63	453	449	574	123	272	500

POWER RESIDUES

	0	1	2	3	4	5	6	7	8	9
0	1	11	121	612	261	714	664	114	535	133
1	25	275	149	201	54	594	63	693	433	449
2	625	404	130	711	631	470	137	69	40	440
3	526	34	374	519	676	246	549	287	281	215
4	208	131	3	33	363	398	64	704	554	342
5	167	399	75	106	447	603	162	344	189	641
6	580	628	437	493	390	695	455	691	411	207
7	120	601	140	102	403	119	590	19	209	142
8	124	645	624	393	9	99	370	475	192	674
9	224	307	501	478	225	318	622	371	486	313
10	567	485	302	446	592	41	451	647	646	635
11	514	621	360	365	420	306	490	357	332	57
12	627	426	372	497	434	460	27	297	391	706
13	576	584	672	202	65	715	675	235	428	394
14	20	220	263	17	187	619	338	123	634	503
15	500	467	104	425	361	376	541	199	32	352
16	277	171	443	559	397	53	583	661	81	172
17	454	680	290	314	578	606	195	707	587	705
18	565	463	60	660	70	51	561	419	295	369
19	464	71	62	682	312	556	364	409	185	597
20	96	337	112	513	610	239	472	159	311	545
21	243	516	643	602	151	223	296	380	585	683
22	323	677	257	670	180	542	210	153	245	538
23	166	388	673	213	186	608	217	230	373	508
24	555	353	288	292	336	101	392	717	697	477
25	214	197	10	110	491	368	453	669	169	421
26	317	611	250	593	52	572	540	188	630	459
27	16	176	498	445	581	639	558	386	651	690
28	400	86	227	340	145	157	289	303	457	713
29	653	712	642	591	30	330	35	385	640	569
30	507	544	232	395	31	341	156	278	182	564
31	452	658	48	528	56	616	305	479	236	439
32	515	632	481	258	681	301	435	471	148	190
33	652	701	521	698	488	335	90	271	105	436
34	482	269	83	194	696	466	93	304	468	115
35	546	254	637	536	144	146	168	410	196	718
36	708	598	107	458	5	55	605	184	586	694
37	444	570	518	665	125	656	26	286	270	94
38	315	589	8	88	249	582	650	679	279	193
39	685	345	200	43	473	170	432	438	504	511
40	588	716	686	356	321	655	15	165	377	552
41	320	644	613	272	116	557	375	530	78	139
42	91	282	226	329	24	264	28	308	512	599
43	118	579	617	316	600	129	700	510	577	595
44	74	95	326	710	620	349	244	527	45	495
45	412	218	241	494	401	97	348	233	406	152
46	234	417	273	127	678	268	72	73	84	205
47	98	359	354	299	413	229	362	387	662	92
48	293	347	222	285	259	692	422	328	13	143
49	135	47	517	654	4	44	484	291	325	699

P = 719

INDICES

	0	1	2	3	4	5	6	7	8	9
50	150	92	595	149	398	609	592	300	239	585
51	437	399	428	203	110	320	211	492	372	33
52	516	332	610	717	535	702	30	447	313	688
53	417	626	503	593	557	8	353	667	229	583
54	266	156	225	630	301	209	350	528	520	36
55	617	715	409	589	48	240	195	415	276	163
56	566	186	644	665	309	180	586	100	573	299
57	371	687	265	714	643	713	130	438	174	431
58	60	274	385	166	131	218	368	178	400	381
59	76	293	104	263	15	439	506	199	361	429
60	434	71	213	55	708	366	175	561	235	612
61	204	261	3	412	697	511	315	432	604	145
62	444	111	96	559	82	20	705	120	61	695
63	268	24	321	640	148	109	701	352	527	275
64	298	59	292	212	411	81	108	107	550	543
65	386	278	330	290	493	405	375	551	311	541
66	183	167	478	673	6	373	524	623	544	257
67	223	671	132	232	89	136	34	221	464	387
68	171	324	193	219	655	390	402	517	663	653
69	279	67	485	17	369	65	344	248	333	499
70	436	331	502	629	47	179	129	177	360	611
71	443	23	291	289	5	135	401	247	359	

POWER RESIDUES

	0	1	2	3	4	5	6	7	8	9
50	499	456	702	532	100	381	596	85	216	219
51	252	615	294	358	343	178	520	687	367	442
52	548	276	160	322	666	136	58	638	547	265
53	39	429	405	141	113	524	12	132	14	154
54	256	659	59	649	668	158	300	424	350	255
55	648	657	37	407	163	355	310	534	122	623
56	382	607	206	109	480	247	560	408	174	476
57	203	76	117	568	496	423	339	134	36	396
58	42	462	49	539	177	509	566	474	181	553
59	331	46	506	533	111	502	489	346	211	164
60	366	431	427	383	618	327	2	22	242	505
61	522	709	609	228	351	266	50	550	298	402
62	108	469	126	667	147	179	531	89	260	703
63	543	221	274	138	80	161	333	68	29	319
64	633	492	379	574	562	430	416	262	6	66
65	7	77	128	689	389	684	334	79	150	212
66	175	487	324	688	378	563	441	537	155	267
67	61	671	191	663	103	414	240	483	280	204
68	87	238	461	38	418	284	248	571	529	67
69	18	198	21	231	384	629	448	614	283	237
70	450	636	525	23	253	626	415	251	604	173
71	465	82	183	575	573	551	309	523		

P = 727

INDICES

	0	1	2	3	4	5	6	7	8	9
0		0	684	477	642	1	435	424	600	228
1	685	327	393	428	382	478	558	658	186	203
2	643	175	285	438	351	2	386	705	340	319
3	436	307	516	78	616	425	144	511	161	179
4	601	141	133	710	243	229	396	170	309	122
5	686	409	344	96	663	328	298	680	277	173
6	394	334	265	652	474	429	36	358	574	189
7	383	336	102	518	469	479	119	25	137	693
8	559	456	99	415	91	659	668	70	201	241
9	187	126	354	58	128	204	267	248	80	555
10	644	582	367	374	302	176	54	587	621	446
11	286	262	256	50	638	439	235	656	131	356
12	352	654	292	618	223	3	610	716	432	461
13	387	464	720	627	316	706	532	495	147	152
14	341	647	294	29	60	320	476	599	427	185
15	437	339	77	160	709	308	95	276	651	573
16	517	136	414	200	57	79	373	620	49	130
17	617	431	626	146	28	426	159	650	199	48
18	145	198	84	85	312	512	16	259	86	403
19	162	595	225	313	206	180	38	418	513	273
20	602	109	540	17	325	142	332	666	260	530
21	134	14	12	87	545	711	579	5	404	269
22	244	360	220	163	214	230	8	282	596	487
23	397	502	193	226	614	171	89	444	314	571
24	310	528	612	207	250	123	576	631	181	166
25	687	635	568	39	674	410	390	492	419	209
26	345	547	422	514	678	97	585	718	274	82
27	664	191	490	603	453	329	105	551	110	535
28	299	484	605	541	252	681	713	565	18	590
29	278	725	434	326	557	174	385	306	143	140
30	395	408	297	333	35	335	118	455	667	125
31	266	581	53	261	234	653	609	463	531	646
32	475	338	94	135	372	430	158	197	15	594
33	37	108	331	13	578	359	7	501	88	527
34	575	634	389	546	584	190	104	483	712	724
35	384	407	117	580	608	337	157	107	6	633
36	103	406	156	405	42	519	43	466	270	369
37	470	520	700	245	217	480	44	21	361	349
38	120	467	553	221	183	26	271	212	164	451
39	138	370	722	215	376	694	471	400	231	378
40	560	521	67	9	498	457	701	112	283	168
41	100	246	290	597	624	416	218	629	488	304
42	92	481	698	398	696	660	45	32	503	506
43	669	22	537	194	689	71	362	641	227	381
44	202	350	318	615	178	242	121	662	172	473
45	188	468	692	90	240	127	554	301	445	637
46	355	222	460	315	151	59	184	708	572	56
47	129	27	47	311	402	205	272	324	529	544
48	268	213	486	613	570	249	165	673	208	677
49	81	452	534	251	589	556	139	34	124	233

POWER RESIDUES

	0	1	2	3	4	5	6	7	8	9
0	1	5	25	125	625	217	358	336	226	403
1	561	624	212	333	211	328	186	203	288	713
2	657	377	431	701	597	77	385	471	174	143
3	715	667	427	681	497	304	66	330	196	253
4	538	509	364	366	376	426	676	472	179	168
5	113	565	644	312	106	530	469	164	93	465
6	144	720	692	552	579	714	662	402	556	599
7	87	435	721	697	577	704	612	152	33	165
8	98	490	269	618	182	183	188	213	338	236
9	453	84	420	646	322	156	53	265	598	82
10	410	596	72	360	346	276	653	357	331	201
11	278	663	407	581	724	712	652	352	306	76
12	380	446	49	245	498	309	91	455	94	470
13	169	118	590	42	210	323	161	78	390	496
14	299	41	205	298	36	180	173	138	690	542
15	529	464	139	695	567	654	362	356	326	176
16	153	38	190	223	388	486	249	518	409	591
17	47	235	448	59	295	21	105	525	444	39
18	195	248	513	384	466	149	18	90	450	69
19	345	271	628	232	433	711	647	327	181	178
20	163	88	440	19	95	475	194	243	488	259
21	568	659	387	481	224	393	511	374	416	626
22	222	383	461	124	620	192	233	438	9	45
23	225	398	536	499	314	116	580	719	687	527
24	454	89	445	44	220	373	411	601	97	485
25	244	493	284	693	557	604	112	560	619	187
26	208	313	111	555	594	62	310	96	480	219
27	368	386	476	199	268	613	157	58	290	723
28	707	627	227	408	586	22	110	550	569	664
29	412	606	122	610	142	710	642	302	56	280
30	673	457	104	520	419	641	297	31	155	48
31	240	473	184	193	238	463	134	670	442	29
32	145	725	717	677	477	204	293	11	55	275
33	648	332	206	303	61	305	71	355	321	151
34	28	140	700	592	52	260	573	684	512	379
35	441	24	120	600	92	460	119	595	67	335
36	221	378	436	726	722	702	602	102	510	369
37	391	501	324	166	103	515	394	516	399	541
38	524	439	14	70	350	296	26	130	650	342
39	256	553	584	12	60	300	46	230	423	661
40	397	531	474	189	218	363	361	351	301	51
41	255	548	559	614	162	83	415	621	197	258
42	563	634	262	583	7	35	175	148	13	65
43	325	171	128	640	292	6	30	150	23	115
44	575	694	562	629	237	458	109	545	544	539
45	514	389	491	274	643	307	81	405	571	674
46	462	129	645	317	131	655	367	381	451	74
47	370	396	526	449	64	320	146	3	15	75
48	375	421	651	347	281	678	482	229	418	636
49	272	633	257	558	609	137	685	517	404	566

P = 727

INDICES

	0	1	2	3	4	5	6	7	8	9
50	645	371	593	577	526	583	723	607	632	41
51	368	216	348	182	450	375	377	497	167	623
52	303	695	505	688	380	177	472	239	636	150
53	55	401	543	569	676	588	232	525	40	449
54	622	379	149	675	448	447	561	508	411	562
55	287	522	63	391	509	263	68	254	493	412
56	257	10	442	420	563	51	499	154	210	288
57	639	458	671	346	523	440	702	74	548	64
58	236	113	683	423	392	657	284	704	515	510
59	132	169	343	679	264	357	101	24	98	69
60	353	247	366	586	255	655	291	715	719	494
61	293	598	76	275	413	619	625	649	83	258
62	224	417	539	665	11	4	219	281	192	443
63	611	630	567	491	421	717	489	550	604	564
64	433	305	296	454	52	462	93	196	330	500
65	388	482	116	106	155	465	699	20	552	211
66	721	399	66	111	289	628	697	31	536	640
67	317	661	691	300	459	707	46	323	485	672
68	533	33	592	606	347	496	504	238	542	524
69	148	507	62	253	441	153	670	73	682	703
70	342	23	365	714	75	648	538	280	566	549
71	295	195	115	19	65	30	690	322	591	237
72	61	72	364	279	114	321	363			

POWER RESIDUES

	0	1	2	3	4	5	6	7	8	9
50	649	337	231	428	686	522	429	691	547	554
51	589	37	185	198	263	588	32	160	73	365
52	371	401	551	574	689	537	504	339	241	478
53	209	318	136	680	492	279	668	432	706	622
54	202	283	688	532	479	214	343	261	578	709
55	637	277	658	382	456	99	495	294	16	80
56	400	546	549	564	639	287	708	632	252	533
57	484	239	468	159	68	340	246	503	334	216
58	353	311	101	505	344	266	603	107	535	494
59	289	718	682	502	329	191	228	413	611	147
60	8	40	200	273	638	282	683	507	354	316
61	126	630	242	483	234	443	34	170	123	615
62	167	108	540	519	414	616	172	133	665	417
63	631	247	508	359	341	251	528	459	114	570
64	669	437	4	20	100	500	319	141	705	617
65	177	158	63	315	121	605	117	585	17	85
66	425	671	447	54	270	623	207	308	86	430
67	696	572	679	487	254	543	534	489	264	593
68	57	285	698	582	2	10	50	250	523	434
69	716	672	452	79	395	521	424	666	422	656
70	372	406	576	699	587	27	135	675	467	154
71	43	215	348	286	703	607	127	635	267	608
72	132	660	392	506	349	291				

P = 733

INDICES

	0	1	2	3	4	5	6	7	8	9
0		0	321	412	642	195	1	589	231	92
1	516	111	322	473	178	607	552	586	413	78
2	105	269	432	271	643	390	62	504	499	207
3	196	200	141	523	175	52	2	484	399	153
4	426	514	590	101	21	287	592	258	232	446
5	711	266	383	646	93	306	88	490	528	434
6	517	44	521	681	462	668	112	531	496	683
7	373	121	323	262	73	70	720	700	474	706
8	15	184	103	86	179	49	422	619	342	404
9	608	330	181	612	579	273	553	602	35	203
10	300	571	587	99	704	464	235	695	414	339
11	627	164	409	671	79	466	117	565	23	443
12	106	222	365	194	110	585	270	206	51	513
13	257	645	433	667	120	699	85	403	272	570
14	694	670	442	584	644	402	583	126	394	127
15	391	237	309	678	289	395	63	188	295	326
16	336	128	505	640	424	718	407	392	500	214
17	370	170	11	238	208	247	663	114	725	310
18	197	548	651	456	502	679	201	697	168	361
19	594	290	142	243	191	348	356	396	524	39
20	621	211	160	64	176	709	420	363	293	189
21	53	254	556	533	284	296	3	57	660	674
22	216	327	485	416	730	482	260	337	400	546
23	55	380	438	129	154	453	344	386	32	506
24	427	470	543	596	686	641	515	551	431	498
25	174	425	591	382	527	461	372	719	102	341
26	578	299	234	408	22	109	256	84	441	393
27	288	335	406	10	724	501	593	355	159	292
28	283	215	259	437	31	685	173	371	233	440
29	723	282	172	171	447	629	715	615	448	12
30	712	690	558	251	630	239	267	488	610	511
31	716	209	384	8	509	144	616	248	647	318
32	657	375	449	664	94	131	229	19	13	115
33	307	166	728	576	713	726	89	479	535	351
34	691	311	491	303	332	146	559	198	529	97
35	568	245	252	549	435	316	314	123	631	652
36	518	156	137	634	240	457	45	411	91	606
37	268	503	522	152	286	265	489	680	682	69
38	183	618	611	202	463	163	564	193	512	698
39	669	125	677	325	717	169	113	455	360	347
40	210	362	532	673	481	379	385	595	497	460
41	298	83	9	291	684	281	614	250	510	143
42	374	18	575	350	145	244	122	633	605	264
43	617	192	324	346	378	82	249	349	263	81
44	537	538	648	357	74	599	5	539	319	397
45	71	625	581	649	658	525	721	227	135	358
46	376	40	701	654	27	75	450	622	475	388
47	42	600	665	212	707	468	353	6	95	161
48	16	225	59	540	132	65	185	149	275	320
49	230	177	104	61	140	398	20	710	87	520

POWER RESIDUES

	0	1	2	3	4	5	6	7	8	9
0	1	6	36	216	563	446	477	663	313	412
1	273	172	299	328	502	80	480	681	421	327
2	496	44	264	118	708	583	566	464	585	578
3	536	284	238	695	505	98	588	596	644	199
4	461	567	470	621	61	366	730	715	625	85
5	510	128	35	210	527	230	647	217	569	482
6	693	493	26	156	203	485	711	601	674	379
7	75	450	501	74	444	465	591	614	19	114
8	684	439	435	411	267	136	83	498	56	336
9	550	368	9	54	324	478	669	349	628	103
10	618	43	258	82	492	20	120	720	655	265
11	124	11	66	396	177	329	508	116	696	511
12	134	71	426	357	676	391	147	149	161	233
13	665	325	484	705	565	458	549	362	706	571
14	494	32	192	419	315	424	345	604	692	487
15	723	673	373	39	234	671	361	700	535	278
16	202	479	675	385	111	666	331	520	188	395
17	171	293	292	286	250	34	204	491	14	84
18	504	92	552	380	81	486	717	637	157	209
19	521	194	431	387	123	5	30	180	347	616
20	31	186	383	99	594	632	127	29	174	311
21	400	201	473	639	169	281	220	587	590	608
22	716	631	121	726	691	481	687	457	543	326
23	490	8	48	288	262	106	636	151	173	305
24	364	718	643	193	425	351	640	175	317	436
25	417	303	352	646	211	533	266	130	47	282
26	226	623	73	438	429	375	51	306	370	21
27	126	23	138	95	570	488	729	709	589	602
28	680	415	291	280	214	551	374	45	270	154
29	191	413	279	208	515	158	215	557	410	261
30	100	600	668	343	592	620	55	330	514	152
31	179	341	580	548	356	670	355	664	319	448
32	489	2	12	72	432	393	159	221	593	626
33	91	546	344	598	656	271	160	227	629	109
34	654	259	88	528	236	683	433	399	195	437
35	423	339	568	476	657	277	196	443	459	555
36	398	189	401	207	509	122	732	727	697	517
37	170	287	256	70	420	321	460	561	434	405
38	231	653	253	52	312	406	237	689	469	615
39	25	150	167	269	148	155	197	449	495	38
40	228	635	145	137	89	534	272	166	263	112
41	672	367	3	18	108	648	223	605	698	523
42	206	503	86	516	164	251	40	240	707	577
43	530	248	22	132	59	354	658	283	232	659
44	289	268	142	119	714	619	49	294	298	322
45	466	597	650	235	677	397	183	365	724	679
46	409	255	64	384	105	630	115	690	475	651
47	241	713	613	13	78	468	609	722	667	337
48	556	404	225	617	37	222	599	662	307	376
49	57	342	586	584	572	500	68	408	249	28

P = 733

INDICES

	0	1	2	3	4	5	6	7	8	9
50	495	72	14	421	180	34	703	626	116	364
51	50	119	693	582	308	294	423	369	662	650
52	167	190	620	419	555	659	729	54	343	542
53	430	526	577	255	405	158	30	722	714	557
54	609	508	656	228	727	534	331	567	313	136
55	90	285	182	563	676	359	480	297	613	574
56	604	377	536	4	580	134	26	41	352	58
57	274	139	494	702	692	661	554	429	29	655
58	312	675	603	25	493	28	492	217	36	278
59	218	76	304	328	204	638	37	451	333	486
60	301	67	279	623	147	417	572	636	219	476
61	560	731	588	472	77	389	199	483	100	445
62	305	43	530	261	705	48	329	601	98	338
63	465	221	205	666	569	401	236	187	639	213
64	246	547	696	242	38	708	253	56	415	545
65	452	469	550	381	340	108	334	354	436	439
66	628	689	487	7	317	130	165	478	302	96
67	315	155	410	151	68	162	124	454	672	459
68	280	17	632	345	80	598	624	226	653	387
69	467	224	148	60	519	33	118	368	418	541
70	157	507	566	562	573	133	138	428	24	277
71	637	66	635	471	444	47	220	186	241	544
72	107	688	477	150	458	597	223	367	561	276
73	46	687	366							

POWER RESIDUES

	0	1	2	3	4	5	6	7	8	9
50	168	275	184	371	27	162	239	701	541	314
51	418	309	388	129	41	246	10	60	360	694
52	499	62	372	33	198	455	531	254	58	348
53	622	67	402	213	545	338	562	440	441	447
54	483	699	529	242	719	649	229	641	181	353
55	652	247	16	96	576	524	212	539	302	346
56	610	728	703	553	386	117	702	547	350	634
57	139	101	606	704	559	422	333	532	260	94
58	564	452	513	146	143	125	17	102	612	7
59	42	252	46	276	190	407	243	725	685	445
60	471	627	97	582	560	428	369	15	90	540
61	308	382	93	558	416	297	316	430	381	87
62	522	200	467	603	686	451	507	110	660	295
63	304	358	682	427	363	712	607	710	595	638
64	163	245	4	24	144	131	53	318	442	453
65	519	182	359	688	463	579	542	320	454	525
66	218	575	518	176	323	472	633	133	65	390
67	141	113	678	403	219	581	554	392	153	185
68	377	63	378	69	414	285	244	731	721	661
69	301	340	574	512	140	107	642	187	389	135
70	77	462	573	506	104	624	79	474	645	205
71	497	50	300	334	538	296	310	394	165	257
72	76	456	537	290	274	178	335	544	332	526
73	224	611								

P = 739

INDICES

	0	1	2	3	4	5	6	7	8	9
0		0	417	1	96	696	418	253	513	2
1	375	292	97	633	670	697	192	352	419	521
2	54	254	709	499	514	654	312	3	349	385
3	376	182	609	293	31	211	98	684	200	634
4	471	688	671	530	388	698	178	441	193	506
5	333	353	729	69	420	250	28	522	64	454
6	55	525	599	255	288	591	710	494	448	500
7	628	379	515	734	363	655	617	545	313	716
8	150	4	367	511	350	310	209	386	67	597
9	377	148	595	183	120	479	610	171	185	294
10	12	725	32	535	408	212	486	122	99	261
11	667	685	445	476	201	457	481	635	133	605
12	472	584	204	689	278	612	672	81	705	531
13	270	23	389	36	173	699	127	93	179	61
14	307	442	58	187	194	343	413	507	42	460
15	334	234	296	354	224	140	730	220	395	70
16	567	14	421	659	46	251	190	652	29	528
17	727	523	626	714	65	169	484	455	276	34
18	56	232	565	526	274	642	600	644	537	256
19	158	558	289	197	588	592	602	410	711	426
20	429	495	404	638	449	646	214	501	87	75
21	629	116	165	380	539	488	516	435	678	735
22	346	247	364	258	124	656	155	432	618	359
23	136	546	160	101	314	399	550	717	284	339
24	151	560	263	5	621	464	368	416	695	512
25	291	669	351	53	498	311	384	608	210	199
26	687	387	440	332	68	27	453	598	590	447
27	378	362	544	149	510	208	596	594	478	184
28	724	407	121	666	475	480	604	203	611	704
29	22	172	92	306	186	412	459	295	139	394
30	13	45	651	726	713	483	33	564	641	536
31	557	587	409	428	637	213	74	164	487	677
32	246	123	431	135	100	549	338	262	463	694
33	668	497	607	686	331	452	446	543	207	477
34	406	474	202	21	305	458	393	650	482	640
35	586	636	163	245	134	337	693	606	451	206
36	473	304	649	585	244	692	205	648	691	690
37	321	322	279	574	323	613	216	280	673	104
38	575	82	237	324	706	503	614	532	267	217
39	271	113	281	24	89	674	390	571	105	37
40	108	576	174	77	83	700	317	238	128	299
41	325	94	631	707	180	469	504	62	492	615
42	308	118	533	443	582	268	59	40	218	188
43	167	272	195	402	114	344	357	282	414	382
44	25	508	664	90	43	555	675	461	541	391
45	335	242	572	235	111	106	297	490	38	355
46	553	109	225	227	577	141	518	175	731	9
47	78	221	229	84	396	437	701	71	18	318
48	568	579	239	15	680	129	422	720	300	660
49	143	326	47	737	95	252	374	632	191	520

POWER RESIDUES

	0	1	2	3	4	5	6	7	8	9
0	1	3	9	27	81	243	729	709	649	469
1	668	526	100	300	161	483	710	652	478	695
2	607	343	290	131	393	440	581	265	56	168
3	504	34	102	306	179	537	133	399	458	635
4	427	542	148	444	593	301	164	492	737	733
5	721	685	577	253	20	60	180	540	142	426
6	539	139	417	512	58	174	522	88	264	53
7	159	477	692	598	316	209	627	403	470	671
8	535	127	381	404	473	680	562	208	624	394
9	443	590	292	137	411	494	4	12	36	108
10	324	233	699	619	379	398	455	626	400	461
11	644	454	623	391	434	563	211	633	421	524
12	94	282	107	321	224	672	538	136	408	485
13	716	670	532	118	354	323	230	690	592	298
14	155	465	656	490	731	715	667	523	91	273
15	80	240	720	682	568	226	678	556	190	570
16	232	696	610	352	317	212	636	430	551	175
17	525	97	291	134	402	467	662	508	46	138
18	414	503	31	93	279	98	294	143	429	548
19	166	498	16	48	144	432	557	193	579	259
20	38	114	342	287	122	366	359	338	275	86
21	258	35	105	315	206	618	376	389	428	545
22	157	471	674	544	154	462	647	463	650	472
23	677	553	181	543	151	453	620	382	407	482
24	707	643	451	614	364	353	320	221	663	511
25	55	165	495	7	21	63	189	567	223	669
26	529	109	327	242	726	700	622	388	425	536
27	130	390	431	554	184	552	178	534	124	372
28	377	392	437	572	238	714	664	514	64	192
29	576	250	11	33	99	297	152	456	629	409
30	488	725	697	613	361	344	293	140	420	521
31	85	255	26	78	234	702	628	406	479	698
32	616	370	371	374	383	410	491	734	724	694
33	604	334	263	50	150	450	611	355	326	239
34	717	673	541	145	435	566	220	660	502	28
35	84	252	17	51	153	459	638	436	569	229
36	687	583	271	74	222	666	520	82	246	738
37	736	730	712	658	496	10	30	90	270	71
38	213	639	439	578	256	29	87	261	44	132
39	396	449	608	346	299	158	474	683	571	235
40	705	637	433	560	202	606	340	281	104	312
41	197	591	295	146	438	575	247	2	6	18
42	54	162	486	719	679	559	199	597	313	200
43	600	322	227	681	565	217	651	475	686	580
44	262	47	141	423	530	112	336	269	68	204
45	612	358	335	266	59	177	531	115	345	296
46	149	447	602	328	245	735	727	703	631	415
47	506	40	120	360	341	284	113	339	278	95
48	285	116	348	305	176	528	106	318	215	645
49	457	632	418	515	67	201	603	331	254	23

P = 739

INDICES

	0	1	2	3	4	5	6	7	8	9
50	708	653	348	181	30	683	470	529	177	505
51	728	249	63	524	287	493	627	733	616	715
52	366	309	66	147	119	170	11	534	485	260
53	444	456	132	583	277	80	269	35	126	60
54	57	342	41	233	223	219	566	658	189	527
55	625	168	275	231	273	643	157	196	601	425
56	403	645	86	115	538	434	345	257	154	358
57	159	398	283	559	620	415	290	52	383	198
58	439	26	589	361	509	593	723	665	603	703
59	91	411	138	44	712	563	556	427	73	676
60	430	548	462	496	330	542	405	20	392	639
61	162	336	450	303	243	647	320	573	215	103
62	236	502	266	112	88	570	107	76	316	298
63	630	468	491	117	581	39	166	401	356	381
64	663	554	540	241	110	489	552	226	517	8
65	228	436	17	578	679	719	142	736	373	519
66	347	682	176	248	286	732	365	146	10	259
67	131	79	125	341	222	657	624	230	156	424
68	85	433	153	397	619	51	438	360	722	702
69	137	562	72	547	329	19	161	302	319	102
70	265	569	315	467	580	400	662	240	551	7
71	16	718	372	681	285	145	130	340	623	423
72	152	50	721	561	328	301	264	466	661	6
73	371	144	622	49	327	465	370	48	369	

POWER RESIDUES

	0	1	2	3	4	5	6	7	8	9
50	69	207	621	385	416	509	49	147	441	584
51	274	83	249	8	24	72	216	648	466	659
52	499	19	57	171	513	61	183	549	169	507
53	43	129	387	422	527	103	309	188	564	214
54	642	448	605	337	272	77	231	693	601	325
55	236	708	646	460	641	445	596	310	191	573
56	241	723	691	595	307	182	546	160	480	701
57	625	397	452	617	373	380	401	464	653	481
58	704	634	424	533	121	363	350	311	194	582
59	268	65	195	585	277	92	276	89	267	62
60	186	558	196	588	286	119	357	332	257	32
61	96	288	125	375	386	419	518	76	228	684
62	574	244	732	718	676	550	172	516	70	210
63	630	412	497	13	39	117	351	314	203	609
64	349	308	185	555	187	561	205	615	367	362
65	347	302	167	501	25	75	225	675	547	163
66	489	728	706	640	442	587	283	110	330	251
67	14	42	126	378	395	446	599	319	218	654
68	484	713	661	505	37	111	333	260	41	123
69	369	368	365	356	329	248	5	15	45	135
70	405	476	689	589	289	128	384	413	500	22
71	66	198	594	304	173	519	79	237	711	655
72	487	722	688	586	280	101	303	170	510	52
73	156	468	665	517	73	219	657	493		

P = 743

INDICES

	0	1	2	3	4	5	6	7	8	9
0		0	698	354	654	1	310	313	610	708
1	699	50	266	545	269	355	566	39	664	170
2	655	667	6	162	222	2	501	320	225	291
3	311	520	522	404	737	314	620	70	126	157
4	611	450	623	598	704	709	118	142	178	626
5	700	393	457	102	276	51	181	524	247	419
6	267	155	476	279	478	546	360	631	693	516
7	270	76	576	217	26	356	82	363	113	185
8	567	674	406	688	579	40	554	645	660	281
9	665	116	74	132	98	171	134	536	582	16
10	656	678	349	64	413	668	58	739	232	342
11	7	424	137	607	480	163	203	511	375	352
12	223	100	111	62	432	3	235	602	434	210
13	502	288	316	483	587	321	649	617	472	548
14	226	496	32	595	532	292	173	238	724	697
15	312	265	38	5	319	521	69	622	141	456
16	523	475	630	575	362	405	644	73	535	348
17	738	136	510	110	601	315	616	31	237	37
18	621	629	72	509	30	71	88	89	54	633
19	127	13	90	379	492	158	538	55	714	190
20	612	243	634	604	305	451	20	128	369	220
21	624	24	14	430	695	599	188	91	298	571
22	705	584	380	43	93	710	563	493	436	198
23	119	717	159	721	467	143	331	539	308	518
24	179	672	56	286	67	627	18	715	388	300
25	701	345	191	212	558	394	390	613	166	383
26	458	257	244	506	272	103	439	635	543	124
27	277	658	605	470	573	52	428	306	504	486
28	182	302	452	446	730	525	551	21	488	78
29	248	148	129	295	194	420	680	370	653	707
30	268	169	221	290	736	156	703	625	275	418
31	477	515	25	184	578	280	97	15	412	341
32	479	351	431	209	586	547	531	696	318	455
33	361	347	600	36	29	632	491	189	304	219
34	694	570	92	197	466	517	66	299	557	382
35	271	123	572	485	729	77	193	706	735	417
36	577	340	585	454	28	218	465	381	728	416
37	27	415	44	398	45	357	10	94	589	399
38	83	214	711	206	46	364	335	564	448	358
39	114	201	494	642	11	186	670	437	146	95
40	568	463	199	323	590	675	560	120	261	400
41	407	229	718	732	84	689	325	160	176	215
42	580	60	722	108	712	41	386	468	651	207
43	555	396	144	106	47	646	254	332	527	365
44	661	592	540	639	336	282	741	309	49	565
45	666	500	519	619	449	117	392	180	154	359
46	75	81	673	553	115	133	677	57	423	202
47	99	234	287	648	495	172	264	68	474	643
48	135	615	628	87	12	537	242	19	23	187
49	583	562	716	330	671	17	344	389	256	438

POWER RESIDUES

	0	1	2	3	4	5	6	7	8	9
0	1	5	25	125	625	153	22	110	550	521
1	376	394	484	191	212	317	99	495	246	487
2	206	287	692	488	211	312	74	370	364	334
3	184	177	142	710	578	661	333	179	152	17
4	85	425	639	223	372	374	384	434	684	448
5	11	55	275	632	188	197	242	467	106	530
6	421	619	123	615	103	515	346	244	477	156
7	37	185	182	167	92	460	71	355	289	702
8	538	461	76	380	414	584	691	433	186	187
9	192	217	342	224	377	399	509	316	94	470
10	121	605	53	265	582	681	433	679	423	629
11	173	122	610	78	390	464	91	455	46	230
12	407	549	516	351	269	602	38	190	207	292
13	717	613	93	465	96	480	171	112	560	571
14	626	158	47	235	432	674	398	504	291	712
15	588	711	583	686	458	61	305	39	195	232
16	417	599	23	115	575	646	258	547	506	301
17	19	95	475	146	730	678	418	604	48	240
18	457	56	280	657	313	79	395	489	216	337
19	199	252	517	356	294	727	663	343	229	402
20	524	391	469	116	580	671	383	429	659	323
21	129	645	253	522	381	419	609	73	365	339
22	209	302	24	120	600	28	140	700	528	411
23	569	616	108	540	471	126	630	178	147	735
24	703	543	486	201	262	567	606	58	290	707
25	563	586	701	533	436	694	498	261	562	581
26	676	408	554	541	476	151	12	60	300	14
27	70	350	264	577	656	308	54	270	607	63
28	315	89	445	739	723	643	243	472	131	655
29	303	29	145	725	653	293	722	638	218	347
30	249	502	281	662	338	204	277	642	238	447
31	6	30	150	7	35	175	132	660	328	154
32	27	135	675	403	529	416	594	741	733	693
33	493	236	437	699	523	386	444	734	698	518
34	361	319	109	545	496	251	512	331	169	102
35	510	321	119	595	3	15	75	375	389	459
36	66	330	164	77	385	439	709	573	636	208
37	297	742	738	718	618	118	590	721	633	193
38	222	367	349	259	552	531	426	644	248	497
39	256	537	456	51	255	532	431	669	373	379
40	409	559	566	601	33	165	82	410	564	591
41	726	658	318	104	520	371	369	359	309	59
42	295	732	688	468	111	555	546	501	276	637
43	213	322	124	620	128	640	228	397	499	266
44	587	706	558	561	576	651	283	672	388	454
45	41	205	282	667	363	329	159	52	260	557
46	556	551	526	401	519	366	344	234	427	649
47	273	622	138	690	478	161	62	310	64	320
48	114	570	621	133	665	353	279	652	288	697
49	513	336	194	227	392	474	141	705	553	536

P = 743

INDICES

	0	1	2	3	4	5	6	7	8	9
50	657	427	301	550	147	679	168	702	514	96
51	350	530	346	490	569	65	122	192	339	464
52	414	9	213	334	200	669	462	559	228	324
53	59	385	395	253	591	740	499	391	80	676
54	233	263	614	241	561	343	426	167	529	121
55	8	461	384	498	262	425	460	459	442	401
56	138	443	258	250	408	608	402	245	686	230
57	481	139	507	367	719	164	444	273	34	733
58	204	259	104	152	85	512	251	440	150	690
59	376	409	636	683	326	353	609	544	663	161
60	224	403	125	597	177	101	246	278	692	216
61	112	687	659	131	581	63	231	606	374	61
62	433	482	471	594	723	4	140	574	534	109
63	236	508	53	378	713	603	368	429	297	42
64	435	720	307	285	387	211	165	505	542	469
65	503	445	487	294	652	289	274	183	411	208
66	317	35	303	196	556	484	734	453	727	397
67	588	205	447	641	145	322	260	731	175	107
68	650	105	526	638	48	618	153	552	422	647
69	473	86	22	329	255	549	513	489	338	333
70	227	252	79	240	528	497	441	249	685	366
71	33	151	149	682	662	596	691	130	373	593
72	533	377	296	284	541	293	410	195	726	640
73	174	637	421	328	337	239	684	681	372	283
74	725	327	371							

POWER RESIDUES

	0	1	2	3	4	5	6	7	8	9
50	451	26	130	650	278	647	263	572	631	183
51	172	117	585	696	508	311	69	345	239	452
52	31	155	32	160	57	285	682	438	704	548
53	511	326	144	720	628	168	97	485	196	237
54	442	724	648	268	597	13	65	325	139	695
55	503	286	687	463	86	430	664	348	254	527
56	406	544	491	226	387	449	16	80	400	514
57	341	219	352	274	627	163	72	360	314	84
58	420	614	98	490	221	362	324	134	670	378
59	404	534	441	719	623	143	715	603	43	215
60	332	174	127	635	203	272	617	113	565	596
61	8	40	200	257	542	481	176	137	685	453
62	36	180	157	42	210	307	49	245	482	181
63	162	67	335	189	202	267	592	731	683	443
64	729	673	393	479	166	87	435	689	473	136
65	680	428	654	298	4	20	100	500	271	612
66	88	440	714	598	18	90	450	21	105	525
67	396	494	241	462	81	405	539	466	101	505
68	296	737	713	593	736	708	568	611	83	415
69	589	716	608	68	340	214	327	149	2	10
70	50	250	507	306	44	220	357	299	9	45
71	225	382	424	634	198	247	492	231	412	574
72	641	233	422	624	148	740	728	668	368	354
73	284	677	413	579	666	358	304	34	170	107
74	535	446								

P = 751

INDICES

	0	1	2	3	4	5	6	7	8	9
0		0	416	1	82	736	417	651	498	2
1	402	715	83	508	317	737	164	329	418	268
2	68	652	381	532	499	722	174	3	733	577
3	403	527	580	716	745	637	84	272	684	509
4	484	465	318	114	47	738	198	586	165	552
5	388	330	590	60	419	701	399	269	243	406
6	69	560	193	653	246	494	382	727	411	533
7	303	438	500	625	688	723	350	616	175	107
8	150	4	131	455	734	315	530	578	463	386
9	404	409	614	528	252	254	581	224	218	717
10	54	521	746	127	256	638	476	140	85	182
11	367	273	65	583	685	518	659	510	72	230
12	485	680	226	466	609	708	319	298	662	115
13	160	220	48	169	393	739	77	21	199	38
14	719	587	104	473	166	563	291	553	354	56
15	389	96	16	331	282	513	591	9	523	61
16	566	433	420	260	547	702	121	748	400	266
17	731	270	196	699	244	623	129	407	52	180
18	70	296	75	561	280	258	194	294	668	654
19	670	426	247	570	640	495	634	190	383	656
20	470	728	187	478	412	451	543	534	672	233
21	304	446	142	439	556	100	501	428	598	626
22	33	87	689	505	481	724	249	677	351	620
23	184	617	325	214	176	572	488	108	646	369
24	151	357	346	5	642	538	132	26	275	456
25	374	415	735	497	714	316	328	67	531	173
26	576	579	636	683	464	46	585	387	59	398
27	405	192	493	410	437	687	615	149	454	529
28	385	613	253	217	520	255	139	366	582	658
29	229	225	707	661	219	392	20	718	472	290
30	55	15	512	522	432	546	747	730	698	128
31	179	74	257	667	425	639	189	469	477	542
32	232	141	99	597	86	480	676	183	213	487
33	368	345	537	274	414	713	66	575	682	584
34	397	492	686	453	612	519	365	228	660	19
35	289	511	545	697	73	424	468	231	596	675
36	486	536	712	681	491	611	227	288	696	467
37	674	711	610	695	710	709	334	335	320	235
38	336	299	92	321	663	602	236	116	306	337
39	161	111	300	221	606	93	49	448	322	170
40	136	664	394	285	603	740	144	237	78	311
41	117	22	209	307	200	441	338	39	649	162
42	720	743	112	588	558	301	105	461	222	474
43	516	607	167	102	94	564	264	50	292	632
44	449	554	503	323	355	372	171	57	147	137
45	390	430	665	97	343	395	17	594	286	332
46	600	604	283	207	741	514	630	145	592	628
47	238	10	154	79	524	240	312	62	35	118
48	567	30	23	434	12	210	421	89	308	261
49	204	201	548	156	442	703	691	339	122	360

POWER RESIDUES

	0	1	2	3	4	5	6	7	8	9
0	1	3	9	27	81	243	729	685	553	157
1	471	662	484	701	601	301	152	456	617	349
2	296	137	411	482	695	583	247	741	721	661
3	481	692	574	220	660	478	683	547	139	417
4	500	749	745	733	697	589	265	44	132	396
5	437	560	178	534	100	300	149	447	590	268
6	53	159	477	680	538	112	336	257	20	60
7	180	540	118	354	311	182	546	136	408	473
8	668	502	4	12	36	108	324	221	663	487
9	710	628	382	395	434	551	151	453	608	322
10	215	645	433	548	142	426	527	79	237	711
11	631	391	422	515	43	129	387	410	479	686
12	556	166	498	743	727	679	535	103	309	176
13	528	82	246	738	712	634	400	449	596	286
14	107	321	212	636	406	467	650	448	593	277
15	80	240	720	658	472	665	493	728	682	544
16	130	390	419	506	16	48	144	432	545	133
17	399	446	587	259	26	78	234	702	604	310
18	179	537	109	327	230	690	568	202	606	316
19	197	591	271	62	186	558	172	516	46	138
20	414	491	722	664	490	719	655	463	638	412
21	485	704	610	328	233	699	595	283	98	294
22	131	393	428	533	97	291	122	366	347	290
23	119	357	320	209	627	379	386	407	470	659
24	475	674	520	58	174	522	64	192	576	226
25	678	532	94	282	95	285	104	312	185	555
26	163	489	716	646	436	557	169	507	19	57
27	171	513	37	111	333	248	744	730	688	562
28	184	552	154	462	635	403	458	623	367	350
29	299	146	438	563	187	561	181	543	127	381
30	392	425	524	70	210	630	388	413	488	713
31	637	409	476	677	529	85	255	14	42	126
32	378	383	398	443	578	232	696	586	256	17
33	51	153	459	626	376	377	380	389	416	497
34	740	718	652	454	611	331	242	726	676	526
35	76	228	684	550	148	444	581	241	723	667
36	499	746	736	706	616	346	287	110	330	239
37	717	649	445	584	250	750	748	742	724	670
38	508	22	66	198	594	280	89	267	50	150
39	450	599	295	134	402	455	614	340	269	56
40	168	504	10	30	90	270	59	177	531	91
41	273	68	204	612	334	251	2	6	18	54
42	162	486	707	619	355	314	191	573	217	651
43	451	602	304	161	483	698	592	274	71	213
44	639	415	494	731	691	571	211	633	397	440
45	569	205	615	343	278	83	249	747	739	715
46	643	427	530	88	264	41	123	369	356	317
47	200	600	298	143	429	536	106	318	203	609
48	325	224	672	514	40	120	360	329	236	708
49	622	364	341	272	65	195	585	253	8	24

P = 751

INDICES

	0	1	2	3	4	5	6	7	8	9
50	40	749	81	650	401	507	163	267	380	721
51	732	526	744	271	483	113	197	551	589	700
52	242	559	245	726	302	624	349	106	130	314
53	462	408	251	223	53	126	475	181	64	517
54	71	679	608	297	159	168	76	37	103	562
55	353	95	281	8	565	259	120	265	195	622
56	51	295	279	293	669	569	633	655	186	450
57	671	445	555	427	32	504	248	619	324	571
58	645	356	641	25	373	496	327	172	635	45
59	58	191	436	148	384	216	138	657	706	391
60	471	14	431	729	178	666	188	541	98	479
61	212	344	413	574	396	452	364	18	544	423
62	595	535	490	287	673	694	333	234	91	601
63	305	110	605	447	135	284	143	310	208	440
64	648	742	557	460	515	101	263	631	502	371
65	146	429	342	593	599	206	629	627	153	239
66	34	29	11	88	203	155	690	359	80	506
67	379	525	482	550	241	725	348	313	250	125
68	63	678	158	36	352	7	119	621	278	568
69	185	444	31	618	644	24	326	44	435	215
70	705	13	177	540	211	573	363	422	489	693
71	90	109	134	309	647	459	262	370	341	205
72	152	28	202	358	378	549	347	124	157	6
73	277	443	643	43	704	539	362	692	133	458
74	340	27	377	123	276	42	361	457	376	41
75	375	0								

POWER RESIDUES

	0	1	2	3	4	5	6	7	8	9
50	72	216	648	442	575	223	669	505	13	39
51	117	351	302	155	465	644	430	539	115	345
52	284	101	303	158	474	671	511	31	93	279
53	86	258	23	69	207	621	361	332	245	735
54	703	607	319	206	618	352	305	164	492	725
55	673	517	49	147	441	572	214	642	424	521
56	61	183	549	145	435	554	160	480	689	565
57	193	579	235	705	613	337	260	29	87	261
58	32	96	288	113	339	266	47	141	423	518
59	52	156	468	653	457	620	358	323	218	654
60	460	629	385	404	461	632	394	431	542	124
61	372	365	344	281	92	276	77	231	693	577
62	229	687	559	175	525	73	219	657	469	656
63	466	647	439	566	196	588	262	35	105	315
64	194	582	244	732	694	580	238	714	640	418
65	503	7	21	63	189	567	199	597	289	116
66	348	293	128	384	401	452	605	313	188	564
67	190	570	208	624	370	359	326	227	681	541
68	121	363	338	263	38	114	342	275	74	222
69	666	496	737	709	625	373	368	353	308	173
70	519	55	165	495	734	700	598	292	125	375
71	374	371	362	335	254	11	33	99	297	140
72	420	509	25	75	225	675	523	67	201	603
73	307	170	510	28	84	252	5	15	45	135
74	405	464	641	421	512	34	102	306	167	501
75										

P = 757

INDICES

	0	1	2	3	4	5	6	7	8	9
0		0	1	84	2	139	85	124	3	168
1	140	92	86	356	125	223	4	452	169	698
2	141	208	93	581	87	278	357	252	126	105
3	224	647	5	176	453	263	170	689	699	440
4	142	151	209	283	94	307	582	513	88	248
5	279	536	358	476	253	231	127	26	106	540
6	225	570	648	292	6	495	177	427	454	665
7	264	751	171	490	690	362	700	216	441	36
8	143	336	152	350	210	591	284	189	95	682
9	308	480	583	731	514	81	89	695	249	260
10	280	533	537	424	359	347	477	257	254	717
11	232	17	128	329	27	720	107	524	541	576
12	226	184	571	235	649	417	293	54	7	367
13	496	20	178	66	428	391	455	410	666	131
14	265	597	752	448	172	244	491	332	691	325
15	363	240	701	620	217	30	442	743	37	560
16	144	705	337	723	153	315	351	302	211	712
17	592	110	285	115	190	402	96	624	683	527
18	309	552	481	654	584	72	732	544	515	376
19	82	122	90	221	696	579	250	645	261	438
20	281	511	534	229	538	290	425	749	360	34
21	348	187	478	79	258	422	255	15	718	574
22	233	52	18	389	129	446	330	238	28	558
23	721	300	108	400	525	652	542	120	577	436
24	227	747	185	420	572	387	236	298	650	434
25	418	296	294	673	55	675	8	41	368	57
26	497	273	21	677	179	615	67	10	429	195
27	392	43	456	564	411	370	667	606	132	59
28	266	200	598	499	753	165	449	275	173	148
29	245	23	492	487	333	679	692	344	326	181
30	364	407	241	617	702	709	621	69	218	508
31	31	12	443	397	744	431	38	612	561	197
32	145	341	706	394	338	634	724	45	154	637
33	316	458	352	101	303	566	212	727	713	413
34	593	739	111	372	286	48	116	669	191	161
35	403	608	97	157	625	134	684	660	528	61
36	310	640	553	268	482	629	655	202	585	319
37	73	600	733	469	545	501	516	461	377	755
38	83	138	123	167	91	355	222	451	697	207
39	580	277	251	104	646	175	262	688	439	150
40	282	306	512	247	535	475	230	25	539	569
41	291	494	426	664	750	489	361	215	35	335
42	349	590	188	681	479	730	80	694	259	532
43	423	346	256	716	16	328	719	523	575	183
44	234	416	53	366	19	65	390	409	130	596
45	447	243	331	324	239	619	29	742	559	704
46	722	314	301	711	109	114	401	623	526	551
47	653	71	543	375	121	220	578	644	437	510
48	228	289	748	33	186	78	421	14	573	51
49	388	445	237	557	299	399	651	119	435	746

POWER RESIDUES

	0	1	2	3	4	5	6	7	8	9
0	1	2	4	8	16	32	64	128	256	512
1	267	534	311	622	487	217	434	111	222	444
2	131	262	524	291	582	407	57	114	228	456
3	155	310	620	483	209	418	79	158	316	632
4	507	257	514	271	542	327	654	551	345	690
5	623	489	221	442	127	254	508	259	518	279
6	558	359	718	679	601	445	133	266	532	307
7	614	471	185	370	740	723	689	621	485	213
8	426	95	190	380	3	6	12	24	48	96
9	192	384	11	22	44	88	176	352	704	651
10	545	333	666	575	393	29	58	116	232	464
11	171	342	684	611	465	173	346	692	627	497
12	237	474	191	382	7	14	28	56	112	224
13	448	139	278	556	355	710	663	569	381	5
14	10	20	40	80	160	320	640	523	289	578
15	399	41	82	164	328	656	555	353	706	655
16	553	349	698	639	521	285	570	383	9	18
17	36	72	144	288	576	395	33	66	132	264
18	528	299	598	439	121	242	484	211	422	87
19	174	348	696	635	513	269	538	319	638	519
20	281	562	367	734	711	665	573	389	21	42
21	84	168	336	672	587	417	77	154	308	616
22	475	193	386	15	30	60	120	240	480	203
23	406	55	110	220	440	123	246	492	227	454
24	151	302	604	451	145	290	580	403	49	98
25	196	392	27	54	108	216	432	107	214	428
26	99	198	396	35	70	140	280	560	363	726
27	695	633	509	261	522	287	574	391	25	50
28	100	200	400	43	86	172	344	688	619	481
29	205	410	63	126	252	504	251	502	247	494
30	231	462	167	334	668	579	401	45	90	180
31	360	720	683	609	461	165	330	660	563	369
32	738	719	681	605	453	149	298	596	435	113
33	226	452	147	294	588	419	81	162	324	648
34	539	321	642	527	297	594	431	105	210	420
35	83	166	332	664	571	385	13	26	52	104
36	208	416	75	150	300	600	443	129	258	516
37	275	550	343	686	615	473	189	378	756	755
38	753	749	741	725	693	629	501	245	490	223
39	446	135	270	540	323	646	535	313	626	495
40	233	466	175	350	700	643	529	301	602	447
41	137	274	548	339	678	599	441	125	250	500
42	243	486	215	430	103	206	412	67	134	268
43	536	315	630	503	249	498	239	478	199	398
44	39	78	156	312	624	491	225	450	143	286
45	572	387	17	34	68	136	272	544	331	662
46	567	377	754	751	745	733	709	661	565	373
47	746	735	713	669	581	405	53	106	212	424
48	91	182	364	728	699	641	525	293	586	415
49	73	146	292	584	411	65	130	260	520	283

P = 757

INDICES

	0	1	2	3	4	5	6	7	8	9
50	419	386	297	433	295	672	674	40	56	272
51	676	614	9	194	42	563	369	605	58	199
52	498	164	274	147	22	486	678	343	180	406
53	616	708	68	507	11	396	430	611	196	340
54	393	633	44	636	457	100	565	726	412	738
55	371	47	668	160	607	156	133	659	60	639
56	267	628	201	318	599	468	500	460	754	137
57	166	354	450	206	276	103	174	687	149	305
58	246	474	24	568	493	663	488	214	334	589
59	680	729	693	531	345	715	327	522	182	415
60	365	64	408	595	242	323	618	741	703	313
61	710	113	622	550	70	374	219	643	509	288
62	32	77	13	50	444	556	398	118	745	385
63	432	671	39	271	613	193	562	604	198	163
64	146	485	342	405	707	506	395	610	339	632
65	635	99	725	737	46	159	155	658	638	627
66	317	467	459	136	353	205	102	686	304	473
67	567	662	213	588	728	530	714	521	414	63
68	594	322	740	312	112	549	373	642	287	76
69	49	555	117	384	670	270	192	603	162	484
70	404	505	609	631	98	736	158	657	626	466
71	135	204	685	472	661	587	529	520	62	321
72	311	548	641	75	554	383	269	602	483	504
73	630	735	656	465	203	471	586	519	320	547
74	74	382	601	503	734	464	470	518	546	381
75	502	463	517	380	462	379	378			

POWER RESIDUES

	0	1	2	3	4	5	6	7	8	9
50	566	375	750	743	729	701	645	533	309	618
51	479	201	402	47	94	188	376	752	747	737
52	717	677	597	437	117	234	468	179	358	716
53	675	593	429	101	202	404	51	102	204	408
54	59	118	236	472	187	374	748	739	721	685
55	613	469	181	362	724	691	625	493	229	458
56	159	318	636	515	273	546	335	670	583	409
57	61	122	244	488	219	438	119	238	476	195
58	390	23	46	92	184	368	736	715	673	589
59	421	85	170	340	680	603	449	141	282	564
60	371	742	727	697	637	517	277	554	351	702
61	647	537	317	634	511	265	530	303	606	455
62	153	306	612	467	177	354	708	659	561	365
63	730	703	649	541	325	650	543	329	658	559
64	361	722	687	617	477	197	394	31	62	124
65	248	496	235	470	183	366	732	707	657	557
66	357	714	671	585	413	69	138	276	552	347
67	694	631	505	253	506	255	510	263	526	295
68	590	423	89	178	356	712	667	577	397	37
69	74	148	296	592	427	97	194	388	19	38
70	76	152	304	608	459	161	322	644	531	305
71	610	463	169	338	676	595	433	109	218	436
72	115	230	460	163	326	652	547	337	674	591
73	425	93	186	372	744	731	705	653	549	341
74	682	607	457	157	314	628	499	241	482	207
75	414	71	142	284	568	379				

P = 761

INDICES

	0	1	2	3	4	5	6	7	8	9
0		0	726	35	692	180	1	523	658	70
1	146	161	727	155	489	215	624	442	36	302
2	112	558	127	150	693	360	121	105	455	22
3	181	129	590	196	408	703	2	66	268	190
4	78	494	524	119	93	250	116	586	659	286
5	326	477	87	193	71	341	421	337	748	606
6	147	435	95	593	556	335	162	152	374	185
7	669	711	728	363	32	395	234	684	156	636
8	44	140	460	39	490	622	85	57	59	8
9	216	678	82	164	552	482	625	317	252	231
10	292	688	443	695	53	738	159	584	37	203
11	307	101	387	418	303	330	714	225	572	205
12	113	322	401	529	61	540	559	759	522	154
13	301	359	128	65	118	285	340	434	151	362
14	635	621	677	316	694	202	329	321	758	64
15	361	201	200	512	650	309	122	513	602	228
16	10	673	106	651	426	376	5	612	456	310
17	588	372	51	633	23	123	25	641	734	698
18	182	514	644	470	48	246	130	603	518	628
19	448	103	591	229	283	370	218	173	197	11
20	258	187	654	545	409	674	661	220	19	463
21	704	107	125	746	550	299	3	652	169	398
22	273	597	67	427	353	430	384	389	269	377
23	296	719	680	440	191	6	538	671	171	438
24	79	613	288	175	367	466	495	457	27	74
25	506	243	525	311	725	657	488	111	120	589
26	267	92	325	420	94	373	31	43	84	81
27	251	52	306	713	400	521	117	634	328	199
28	601	425	587	24	643	517	282	257	660	124
29	168	352	295	537	287	26	724	266	30	305
30	327	642	167	723	166	615	478	735	616	730
31	275	16	88	699	479	13	568	413	194	183
32	736	619	639	744	72	515	617	238	392	349
33	342	645	731	136	578	332	422	471	276	453
34	554	290	338	49	17	365	599	566	749	247
35	89	260	751	755	607	131	700	240	664	533
36	148	604	480	357	610	543	436	519	14	564
37	212	716	96	629	569	575	484	177	594	449
38	414	34	69	214	557	104	195	189	249	476
39	336	592	184	394	139	56	163	230	737	100
40	224	528	153	284	620	320	511	227	375	371
41	640	469	627	369	186	219	745	397	429	718
42	670	174	73	656	91	42	712	198	516	351
43	265	722	729	12	618	237	135	452	364	259
44	239	356	563	574	33	188	393	99	319	468
45	396	655	350	236	355	98	235	546	343	547
46	262	707	685	410	646	344	406	667	157	675
47	732	548	504	280	637	662	137	263	404	207
48	45	221	579	708	254	497	141	20	333	686
49	432	631	461	464	423	411	753	474	40	705

POWER RESIDUES

	0	1	2	3	4	5	6	7	8	9
0	1	6	36	216	535	166	235	649	89	534
1	160	199	433	315	368	686	311	344	542	208
2	487	639	29	174	283	176	295	248	727	557
3	298	266	74	444	381	3	18	108	648	83
4	498	705	425	267	80	480	597	538	184	343
5	536	172	271	104	624	700	395	87	522	88
6	528	124	744	659	149	133	37	222	571	382
7	9	54	324	422	249	733	593	514	40	240
8	679	269	92	552	268	86	516	52	312	350
9	578	424	261	44	264	62	372	710	455	447
10	399	111	666	191	385	27	162	211	505	747
11	677	257	20	120	720	515	46	276	134	43
12	258	26	156	175	289	212	511	22	132	31
13	186	355	608	604	580	436	333	476	573	394
14	81	486	633	754	719	509	10	60	360	638
15	23	138	67	402	129	13	78	468	525	106
16	636	11	66	396	93	558	304	302	290	218
17	547	238	667	197	421	243	697	377	740	635
18	5	30	180	319	392	69	414	201	445	387
19	39	234	643	53	318	386	33	198	427	279
20	152	151	145	109	654	119	714	479	591	502
21	729	569	370	698	383	15	90	540	196	415
22	207	481	603	574	400	117	702	407	159	193
23	397	99	594	520	76	456	453	435	327	440
24	357	620	676	251	745	665	185	349	572	388
25	45	270	98	588	484	621	682	287	200	439
26	351	584	460	477	579	430	297	260	38	228
27	607	598	544	220	559	310	338	506	753	713
28	473	555	286	194	403	135	49	294	242	691
29	341	524	100	600	556	292	230	619	670	215
30	529	130	19	114	684	299	272	110	660	155
31	169	253	757	737	617	658	143	97	582	448
32	405	147	121	726	551	262	50	300	278	146
33	115	690	335	488	645	65	390	57	342	530
34	136	55	330	458	465	507	759	749	689	329
35	452	429	291	224	583	454	441	363	656	131
36	25	150	139	73	438	345	548	244	703	413
37	195	409	171	265	68	408	165	229	613	634
38	760	755	725	545	226	595	526	112	672	227
39	601	562	328	446	393	75	450	417	219	553
40	274	122	732	587	478	585	466	513	34	204
41	463	495	687	317	380	758	743	653	113	678
42	263	56	336	494	681	281	164	223	577	418
43	225	589	490	657	137	61	366	674	239	673
44	233	637	17	102	612	628	724	539	190	379
45	752	707	437	339	512	28	168	247	721	521
46	82	492	669	209	493	675	245	709	449	411
47	183	337	500	717	497	699	389	51	306	314
48	362	650	95	570	376	734	599	550	256	14
49	84	504	741	641	41	246	715	485	627	718

P = 761

INDICES

	0	1	2	3	4	5	6	7	8	9
50	472	647	209	500	491	108	277	345	691	145
51	623	126	454	407	77	115	86	747	555	668
52	233	459	58	551	291	158	386	571	60	300
53	339	676	757	649	9	4	50	733	47	447
54	217	653	18	549	272	383	679	170	366	505
55	487	324	83	399	600	281	294	29	165	274
56	567	638	391	577	553	598	750	663	609	211
57	483	68	248	138	223	510	626	428	90	264
58	134	562	318	354	261	405	503	403	253	431
59	752	208	690	76	232	385	756	46	271	486
60	293	390	608	222	133	502	689	270	132	580
61	581	741	444	378	701	709	582	314	696	297
62	241	255	742	531	54	720	665	498	445	508
63	739	681	534	142	379	179	160	441	149	21
64	702	493	585	192	605	334	710	683	38	7
65	481	687	583	417	204	539	358	433	315	63
66	308	672	611	632	697	245	102	172	544	462
67	298	596	388	439	437	465	242	110	419	80
68	520	424	256	536	304	614	15	412	743	348
69	331	289	565	754	532	542	715	176	213	475
70	55	527	226	368	717	41	721	451	573	467
71	97	706	666	279	206	496	630	473	499	144
72	114	458	570	648	446	382	323	28	576	210
73	509	561	402	75	485	501	740	313	530	507
74	178	492	682	416	62	244	595	109	535	347
75	541	526	450	278	143	381	560	312	415	346
76	380	0								

POWER RESIDUES

	0	1	2	3	4	5	6	7	8	9
50	503	735	605	586	472	549	250	739	629	730
51	575	406	153	157	181	325	428	285	188	367
52	680	275	128	7	42	252	751	701	401	123
53	738	623	694	359	632	748	683	293	236	655
54	125	750	695	365	668	203	457	459	471	543
55	214	523	94	564	340	518	64	384	21	126
56	756	731	581	442	369	692	347	560	316	374
57	722	527	118	708	443	375	728	563	334	482
58	609	610	616	652	107	642	47	282	170	259
59	32	192	391	63	378	746	671	221	565	346
60	554	280	158	187	361	644	59	354	602	568
61	364	662	167	241	685	305	308	326	434	321
62	404	141	85	510	16	96	576	412	189	373
63	716	491	663	173	277	140	79	474	561	322
64	410	177	301	284	182	331	464	501	723	533
65	154	163	217	541	202	451	423	255	8	48
66	288	206	475	567	358	626	712	467	519	70
67	420	237	661	161	205	469	531	142	91	546
68	232	631	742	647	77	462	489	651	101	606
69	592	508	4	24	144	103	618	664	179	313
70	356	614	640	35	210	499	711	461	483	615
71	646	71	426	273	116	696	371	704	419	231
72	625	706	431	303	296	254	2	12	72	432
73	309	332	470	537	178	307	320	398	105	630
74	736	611	622	688	323	416	213	517	58	348
75	566	352	590	496	693	353	596	532	148	127
76										

P = 769

INDICES

	0	1	2	3	4	5	6	7	8	9
0		0	278	464	556	30	742	459	66	160
1	308	1	252	487	737	494	344	750	438	448
2	586	155	279	227	530	60	765	624	247	113
3	4	682	622	465	260	489	716	679	726	183
4	96	628	433	360	557	190	505	22	40	150
5	338	446	275	271	134	31	525	144	391	175
6	282	43	192	619	132	517	743	237	538	691
7	767	251	226	259	189	524	236	460	461	615
8	374	320	138	503	711	12	638	577	67	462
9	468	178	15	378	300	478	318	393	428	161
10	616	117	724	733	553	185	549	511	412	667
11	309	375	35	588	422	257	669	647	453	441
12	560	2	321	324	470	90	129	101	410	56
13	27	8	253	139	515	654	48	297	201	543
14	277	486	529	488	504	143	537	614	467	116
15	34	323	514	142	738	712	739	314	125	735
16	652	686	598	475	416	495	13	713	221	206
17	290	608	148	288	87	519	345	639	740	99
18	746	18	456	507	293	709	656	751	578	315
19	756	626	596	676	671	213	706	660	439	68
20	126	701	395	572	234	658	243	387	63	449
21	463	736	59	715	21	390	690	373	177	723
22	587	469	653	536	313	220	98	755	700	58
23	535	156	179	687	157	52	731	311	719	195
24	70	425	280	16	599	180	602	167	748	199
25	368	264	407	228	379	476	688	582	334	370
26	305	273	286	122	531	301	417	158	25	262
27	164	93	326	642	575	61	479	496	53	74
28	555	493	764	678	39	174	766	319	14	732
29	421	89	47	613	124	205	745	625	394	714
30	312	51	601	581	24	73	420	50	248	429
31	222	720	249	594	592	649	403	760	245	114
32	162	207	196	430	108	547	753	363	694	481
33	5	617	291	71	223	267	499	584	484	284
34	568	683	118	609	426	721	566	630	365	357
35	29	343	623	725	149	281	250	137	377	552
36	256	128	296	466	734	289	17	595	571	20
37	219	730	166	333	261	554	88	600	593	107
38	266	565	136	570	106	490	186	520	181	650
39	491	209	216	472	170	645	717	550	346	603
40	404	187	211	401	673	350	82	680	512	640
41	168	761	521	634	665	533	341	239	727	413
42	741	749	246	182	337	42	225	502	299	184
43	668	100	200	115	651	607	455	675	233	389
44	97	310	747	369	163	492	46	580	591	546
45	498	629	376	19	265	208	210	633	336	606
46	45	632	434	36	457	408	197	217	435	696
47	330	10	241	361	589	508	229	431	473	37
48	348	398	703	382	558	423	294	380	109	171
49	458	437	112	95	445	191	258	710	477	548

POWER RESIDUES

	0	1	2	3	4	5	6	7	8	9
0	1	11	121	562	30	330	554	711	131	672
1	471	567	85	166	288	92	243	366	181	453
2	369	214	47	517	304	268	641	130	661	350
3	5	55	605	503	150	112	463	479	655	284
4	48	528	425	61	671	460	446	292	136	727
5	307	301	235	278	751	571	129	650	229	212
6	25	275	718	208	750	560	8	88	199	651
7	240	333	587	305	279	762	692	691	680	559
8	766	736	406	621	679	548	645	174	376	291
9	125	606	514	271	674	493	40	440	226	179
10	431	127	628	756	626	734	384	379	324	488
11	754	604	492	29	319	433	149	101	342	686
12	625	723	263	586	294	158	200	662	361	126
13	617	635	64	704	54	594	382	357	82	133
14	694	713	153	145	57	627	745	505	172	354
15	49	539	546	623	701	21	231	234	267	630
16	9	99	320	444	270	663	372	247	410	665
17	394	489	765	725	285	59	649	218	91	232
18	245	388	423	39	429	105	386	401	566	74
19	45	495	62	682	581	239	322	466	512	249
20	432	138	749	549	656	295	169	321	455	391
21	456	402	577	195	607	525	392	467	523	370
22	225	168	310	334	598	426	72	23	253	476
23	622	690	669	438	204	706	76	67	737	417
24	742	472	578	206	728	318	422	28	308	312
25	356	71	12	132	683	592	360	115	496	73
26	34	374	269	652	251	454	380	335	609	547
27	634	53	583	261	564	52	572	140	2	22
28	242	355	60	660	339	653	262	575	173	365
29	170	332	576	184	486	732	362	137	738	428
30	94	265	608	536	513	260	553	700	10	110
31	441	237	300	224	157	189	541	568	96	287
32	81	122	573	151	123	584	272	685	614	602
33	470	556	733	373	258	531	458	424	50	550
34	667	416	731	351	16	176	398	533	480	666
35	405	610	558	755	615	613	591	349	763	703
36	43	473	589	327	521	348	752	582	250	443
37	259	542	579	217	80	111	452	358	93	254
38	487	743	483	699	768	758	648	207	739	439
39	215	58	638	97	298	202	684	603	481	677
40	526	403	588	316	400	555	722	252	465	501
41	128	639	108	419	764	714	164	266	619	657
42	306	290	114	485	721	241	344	708	98	309
43	323	477	633	42	462	468	534	491	18	198
44	640	119	540	557	744	494	51	561	19	209
45	761	681	570	118	529	436	182	464	490	7
46	77	78	89	210	3	33	363	148	90	221
47	124	595	393	478	644	163	255	498	95	276
48	729	329	543	590	338	642	141	13	143	35
49	385	390	445	281	15	165	277	740	450	336

P = 769

INDICES

	0	1	2	3	4	5	6	7	8	9
50	646	409	542	33	685	147	506	670	657	689
51	754	718	198	304	92	763	612	23	648	752
52	583	364	551	218	564	215	400	664	41	454
53	579	335	695	347	436	541	303	563	540	151
54	442	316	371	482	604	697	152	269	85	203
55	339	561	757	306	6	405	331	443	352	79
56	65	447	3	627	274	618	188	11	317	510
57	452	55	276	322	597	287	292	212	242	372
58	699	194	367	272	325	677	123	72	402	362
59	483	356	255	729	135	471	672	532	224	674
60	590	605	329	397	111	32	91	214	302	268
61	351	509	698	355	328	354	526	130	707	418
62	500	83	230	153	527	120	104	145	102	661
63	159	585	681	432	270	131	523	637	392	411
64	440	26	485	513	474	86	708	705	386	176
65	57	69	263	285	641	38	204	419	759	693
66	283	28	127	165	569	169	349	340	501	232
67	545	44	9	702	94	684	762	399	562	84
68	78	451	193	254	396	327	119	522	704	758
69	231	77	76	620	140	573	643	610	635	383
70	307	154	621	359	133	516	235	576	427	666
71	559	7	528	141	415	518	655	659	62	722
72	534	424	406	121	574	173	744	49	244	480
73	567	342	295	332	105	644	81	238	298	388
74	497	631	240	381	444	146	611	663	539	202
75	64	54	366	728	110	353	103	636	385	692
76	544	450	75	358	414	172	80	662	384	

POWER RESIDUES

	0	1	2	3	4	5	6	7	8	9
50	620	668	427	83	144	46	506	183	475	611
51	569	107	408	643	152	134	705	65	715	175
52	387	412	687	636	75	56	616	624	712	142
53	24	264	597	415	720	230	223	146	68	748
54	538	535	502	139	760	670	449	325	499	106
55	397	522	359	104	375	280	4	44	484	710
56	120	551	678	537	524	381	346	730	340	664
57	383	368	203	695	724	274	707	87	188	530
58	447	303	257	520	337	631	20	220	113	474
59	600	448	314	378	313	367	192	574	162	244
60	377	302	246	399	544	601	459	435	171	343
61	697	746	516	293	147	79	100	331	565	63
62	693	702	32	352	27	297	191	563	41	451
63	347	741	461	457	413	698	757	637	86	177
64	409	654	273	696	735	395	500	117	518	315
65	389	434	160	222	135	716	186	508	205	717
66	197	629	767	747	527	414	709	109	430	116
67	507	194	596	404	599	437	193	585	283	37
68	407	632	31	341	675	504	161	233	256	509
69	216	69	759	659	328	532	469	545	612	580
70	228	201	673	482	688	647	196	618	646	185
71	497	84	155	167	299	213	36	396	511	238
72	311	345	719	219	102	353	38	418	753	593
73	371	236	289	103	364	159	211	14	154	156
74	178	420	6	66	726	296	180	442	248	421
75	17	187	519	326	510	227	190	552	689	658
76	317	411	676	515	282	26	286	70		

P = 773

INDICES

	0	1	2	3	4	5	6	7	8	9
0		0	1	21	2	415	22	253	3	42
1	416	510	23	587	254	436	4	704	43	555
2	417	274	511	109	24	58	588	63	255	353
3	437	715	5	531	705	668	44	500	556	608
4	418	239	275	729	512	457	110	656	25	506
5	59	725	589	75	64	153	256	576	354	593
6	438	602	716	295	6	230	532	692	706	130
7	669	265	45	699	501	79	557	763	609	288
8	419	84	240	160	276	347	730	374	513	213
9	458	68	111	736	657	198	26	18	507	552
10	60	665	726	722	590	689	76	157	65	549
11	154	521	257	562	577	524	355	629	594	185
12	439	248	603	260	717	473	296	102	7	750
13	231	565	533	36	693	478	707	484	131	580
14	670	677	266	325	46	768	700	527	502	226
15	80	14	558	746	764	358	610	380	289	96
16	420	362	85	632	241	174	161	301	277	402
17	348	597	731	468	375	311	514	614	214	188
18	459	118	69	623	112	143	737	442	658	316
19	199	426	27	384	19	251	508	434	553	107
20	61	713	666	606	727	654	723	151	591	293
21	690	263	77	286	158	372	66	196	550	720
22	155	519	522	183	258	100	563	476	578	323
23	525	12	356	94	630	299	595	309	186	621
24	440	424	249	105	604	149	261	370	718	181
25	474	10	297	619	103	368	8	366	751	753
26	232	395	566	755	534	490	37	234	694	684
27	479	397	708	89	485	568	132	333	581	757
28	671	648	678	536	267	219	326	492	47	636
29	769	39	701	55	528	236	503	573	227	696
30	81	210	15	686	559	245	747	481	765	743
31	359	399	611	140	381	710	290	193	97	91
32	421	178	363	487	86	645	633	570	242	137
33	175	134	162	542	302	335	278	165	403	583
34	349	453	598	759	732	545	469	673	376	464
35	312	650	515	305	615	680	215	206	189	538
36	460	338	119	269	70	342	624	221	113	281
37	144	328	738	448	443	494	659	168	317	49
38	200	123	427	638	28	406	385	771	20	414
39	252	41	509	586	435	703	554	273	108	57
40	62	352	714	530	667	499	607	238	728	456
41	655	505	724	74	152	575	592	601	294	229
42	691	129	264	698	78	762	287	83	159	346
43	373	212	67	735	197	17	551	664	721	688
44	156	548	520	561	523	628	184	247	259	472
45	101	749	564	35	477	483	579	676	324	767
46	526	225	13	745	357	379	95	361	631	173
47	300	401	596	467	310	613	187	117	622	142
48	441	315	425	383	250	433	106	712	605	653
49	150	292	262	285	371	195	719	518	182	99

POWER RESIDUES

	0	1	2	3	4	5	6	7	8	9
0	1	2	4	8	16	32	64	128	256	512
1	251	502	231	462	151	302	604	435	97	194
2	388	3	6	12	24	48	96	192	384	768
3	763	753	733	693	613	453	133	266	532	291
4	582	391	9	18	36	72	144	288	576	379
5	758	743	713	653	533	293	586	399	25	50
6	100	200	400	27	54	108	216	432	91	182
7	364	728	683	593	413	53	106	212	424	75
8	150	300	600	427	81	162	324	648	523	273
9	546	319	638	503	233	466	159	318	636	499
10	225	450	127	254	508	243	486	199	398	23
11	46	92	184	368	736	699	625	477	181	362
12	724	675	577	381	762	751	729	685	597	421
13	69	138	276	552	331	662	551	329	658	543
14	313	626	479	185	370	740	707	641	509	245
15	490	207	414	55	110	220	440	107	214	428
16	83	166	332	664	555	337	674	575	377	754
17	735	697	621	469	165	330	660	547	321	642
18	511	249	498	223	446	119	238	476	179	358
19	716	659	545	317	634	495	217	434	95	190
20	380	760	747	721	669	565	357	714	655	537
21	301	602	431	89	178	356	712	651	529	285
22	570	367	734	695	617	461	149	298	596	419
23	65	130	260	520	267	534	295	590	407	41
24	82	164	328	656	539	305	610	447	121	242
25	484	195	390	7	14	28	56	112	224	448
26	123	246	492	211	422	71	142	284	568	363
27	726	679	585	397	21	42	84	168	336	672
28	571	369	738	703	633	493	213	426	79	158
29	316	632	491	209	418	63	126	252	504	235
30	470	167	334	668	563	353	706	639	505	237
31	474	175	350	700	627	481	189	378	756	739
32	705	637	501	229	458	143	286	572	371	742
33	711	649	525	277	554	335	670	567	361	722
34	671	569	365	730	687	601	429	85	170	340
35	680	587	401	29	58	116	232	464	155	310
36	620	467	161	322	644	515	257	514	255	510
37	247	494	215	430	87	174	348	696	619	465
38	157	314	628	483	193	386	772	771	769	765
39	757	741	709	645	517	261	522	271	542	311
40	622	471	169	338	676	579	385	770	767	761
41	749	725	677	581	389	5	10	20	40	80
42	160	320	640	507	241	482	191	382	764	755
43	737	701	629	485	197	394	15	30	60	120
44	240	480	187	374	748	723	673	573	373	746
45	719	665	557	341	682	591	409	45	90	180
46	360	720	667	561	349	698	623	473	173	346
47	692	611	449	125	250	500	227	454	135	270
48	540	307	614	455	137	274	548	323	646	519
49	265	530	287	574	375	750	727	681	589	405

P = 773

INDICES

	0	1	2	3	4	5	6	7	8	9
50	475	322	11	93	298	308	620	423	104	148
51	369	180	9	618	367	365	752	394	754	489
52	233	683	396	88	567	332	756	647	535	218
53	491	635	38	54	235	572	695	209	685	244
54	480	742	398	139	709	192	90	177	486	644
55	569	136	133	541	334	164	582	452	758	544
56	672	463	649	304	679	205	537	337	268	341
57	220	280	327	447	493	167	48	122	637	405
58	770	413	40	585	702	272	56	351	529	498
59	237	455	504	73	574	600	228	128	697	761
60	82	345	211	734	16	663	687	547	560	627
61	246	471	748	34	482	675	766	224	744	378
62	360	172	400	466	612	116	141	314	382	432
63	711	652	291	284	194	517	98	321	92	307
64	422	147	179	617	364	393	488	682	87	331
65	646	217	634	53	571	208	243	741	138	191
66	176	643	135	540	163	451	543	462	303	204
67	336	340	279	446	166	121	404	412	584	271
68	350	497	454	72	599	127	760	344	733	662
69	546	626	470	33	674	223	377	171	465	115
70	313	431	651	283	516	320	306	146	616	392
71	681	330	216	52	207	740	190	642	539	450
72	461	203	339	445	120	411	270	496	71	126
73	343	661	625	32	222	170	114	430	282	319
74	145	391	329	51	739	641	449	202	444	410
75	495	125	660	31	169	429	318	390	50	640
76	201	409	124	30	428	389	639	408	29	388
77	407	387	386							

POWER RESIDUES

	0	1	2	3	4	5	6	7	8	9
50	37	74	148	296	592	411	49	98	196	392
51	11	22	44	88	176	352	704	635	497	221
52	442	111	222	444	115	230	460	147	294	588
53	403	33	66	132	264	528	283	566	359	718
54	663	553	333	666	559	345	690	607	441	109
55	218	436	99	198	396	19	38	76	152	304
56	608	443	113	226	452	131	262	524	275	550
57	327	654	535	297	594	415	57	114	228	456
58	139	278	556	339	678	583	393	13	26	52
59	104	208	416	59	118	236	472	171	342	684
60	595	417	61	122	244	488	203	406	39	78
61	156	312	624	475	177	354	708	643	513	253
62	506	239	478	183	366	732	691	609	445	117
63	234	468	163	326	652	531	289	578	383	766
64	759	745	717	661	549	325	650	527	281	562
65	351	702	631	489	205	410	47	94	188	376
66	752	731	689	605	437	101	202	404	35	70
67	140	280	560	347	694	615	457	141	282	564
68	355	710	647	521	269	538	303	606	439	105
69	210	420	67	134	268	536	299	598	423	73
70	146	292	584	395	17	34	68	136	272	544
71	315	630	487	201	402	31	62	124	248	496
72	219	438	103	206	412	51	102	204	408	43
73	86	172	344	688	603	433	93	186	372	744
74	715	657	541	309	618	463	153	306	612	451
75	129	258	516	259	518	263	526	279	558	343
76	686	599	425	77	154	308	616	459	145	290
77	580	387								

P = 787

INDICES

	0	1	2	3	4	5	6	7	8	9
0		0	1	699	2	601	700	544	3	612
1	602	772	701	421	545	514	4	739	613	314
2	603	457	773	254	702	416	422	525	546	656
3	515	678	5	685	740	359	614	538	315	334
4	604	82	458	201	774	427	255	748	703	302
5	417	652	423	275	526	587	547	227	657	575
6	516	279	679	370	6	236	686	38	741	167
7	360	321	615	18	539	329	316	530	335	97
8	605	438	83	385	459	554	202	569	775	719
9	428	179	256	591	749	129	704	376	303	598
10	418	454	653	535	424	272	276	164	527	551
11	588	451	548	244	228	69	658	247	576	497
12	517	758	280	781	680	231	371	109	7	114
13	237	479	687	72	39	340	742	445	168	48
14	361	661	322	407	616	471	19	215	540	250
15	330	583	317	565	531	493	336	579	98	188
16	606	12	439	731	84	500	386	102	460	56
17	555	140	203	520	570	174	776	488	720	712
18	429	761	180	192	257	353	592	725	750	283
19	130	645	705	119	377	149	304	784	599	610
20	419	737	455	414	654	683	536	80	425	300
21	273	225	277	234	165	16	528	436	552	717
22	589	374	452	270	549	242	245	756	229	112
23	70	443	659	469	248	563	577	10	498	54
24	518	486	759	351	281	117	782	735	681	298
25	232	434	372	240	110	467	8	484	115	296
26	238	482	480	88	688	90	73	632	40	690
27	341	509	743	92	446	402	169	75	49	504
28	362	634	662	766	323	42	408	626	617	692
29	472	289	20	343	216	390	541	511	251	675
30	331	745	584	367	318	94	566	126	532	448
31	494	106	337	404	580	185	99	171	189	642
32	607	77	13	267	440	51	732	464	85	506
33	501	623	387	364	103	639	461	636	57	157
34	556	664	141	60	204	768	521	197	571	325
35	175	160	777	44	489	136	721	410	713	559
36	430	628	762	671	181	619	193	667	258	694
37	354	33	593	474	726	144	751	291	284	262
38	131	22	646	63	706	345	120	27	378	218
39	150	207	305	392	785	698	600	543	611	771
40	420	513	738	313	456	253	415	524	655	677
41	684	358	537	333	81	200	426	747	301	651
42	274	586	226	574	278	369	235	37	166	320
43	17	328	529	96	437	384	553	568	718	178
44	590	128	375	597	453	534	271	163	550	450
45	243	68	246	496	757	780	230	108	113	478
46	71	339	444	47	660	406	470	214	249	582
47	564	492	578	187	11	730	499	101	55	139
48	519	173	487	711	760	191	352	724	282	644
49	118	148	783	609	736	413	682	79	299	224

POWER RESIDUES

	0	1	2	3	4	5	6	7	8	9
0	1	2	4	8	16	32	64	128	256	512
1	237	474	161	322	644	501	215	430	73	146
2	292	584	381	762	737	687	587	387	774	761
3	735	683	579	371	742	697	607	427	67	134
4	268	536	285	570	353	706	625	463	139	278
5	556	325	650	513	239	478	169	338	676	565
6	343	686	585	383	766	745	703	619	451	115
7	230	460	133	266	532	277	554	321	642	497
8	207	414	41	82	164	328	656	525	263	526
9	265	530	273	546	305	610	433	79	158	316
10	632	477	167	334	668	549	311	622	457	127
11	254	508	229	458	129	258	516	245	490	193
12	386	772	757	727	667	547	307	614	441	95
13	190	380	760	733	679	571	355	710	633	479
14	171	342	684	581	375	750	713	639	491	195
15	390	780	773	759	731	675	563	339	678	569
16	351	702	617	447	107	214	428	69	138	276
17	552	317	634	481	175	350	700	613	439	91
18	182	364	728	669	551	315	630	473	159	318
19	636	485	183	366	732	677	567	347	694	601
20	415	43	86	172	344	688	589	391	782	777
21	767	747	707	627	467	147	294	588	389	778
22	769	751	715	643	499	211	422	57	114	228
23	456	125	250	500	213	426	65	130	260	520
24	253	506	225	450	113	226	452	117	234	468
25	149	298	596	405	23	46	92	184	368	736
26	685	583	379	758	729	671	555	323	646	505
27	223	446	105	210	420	53	106	212	424	61
28	122	244	488	189	378	756	725	663	539	291
29	582	377	754	721	655	523	259	518	249	498
30	209	418	49	98	196	392	784	781	775	763
31	739	691	595	403	19	38	76	152	304	608
32	429	71	142	284	568	349	698	609	431	75
33	150	300	600	413	39	78	156	312	624	461
34	135	270	540	293	586	385	770	753	719	651
35	515	243	486	185	370	740	693	599	411	35
36	70	140	280	560	333	666	545	303	606	425
37	63	126	252	504	221	442	97	194	388	776
38	765	743	699	611	435	83	166	332	664	541
39	295	590	393	786	785	783	779	771	755	723
40	659	531	275	550	313	626	465	143	286	572
41	357	714	641	495	203	406	25	50	100	200
42	400	13	26	52	104	208	416	45	90	180
43	360	720	653	519	251	502	217	434	81	162
44	324	648	509	231	462	137	274	548	309	618
45	449	111	222	444	101	202	404	21	42	84
46	168	336	672	557	327	654	521	255	510	233
47	466	145	290	580	373	746	705	623	459	131
48	262	524	261	522	257	514	241	482	177	354
49	708	629	471	155	310	620	453	119	238	476

P = 787

INDICES

	0	1	2	3	4	5	6	7	8	9
50	233	15	435	716	373	269	241	755	111	442
51	468	562	9	53	485	350	116	734	297	433
52	239	466	483	295	481	87	89	631	689	508
53	91	401	74	503	633	765	41	625	691	288
54	342	389	510	674	744	366	93	125	447	105
55	403	184	170	641	76	266	50	463	505	622
56	363	638	635	156	663	59	767	196	324	159
57	43	135	409	558	627	670	618	666	693	32
58	473	143	290	261	21	62	344	26	217	206
59	391	697	542	770	512	312	252	523	676	357
60	332	199	746	650	585	573	368	36	319	327
61	95	383	567	177	127	596	533	162	449	67
62	495	779	107	477	338	46	405	213	581	491
63	186	729	100	138	172	710	190	723	643	147
64	608	412	78	223	14	715	268	754	441	561
65	52	349	733	432	465	294	86	630	507	400
66	502	764	624	287	388	673	365	124	104	183
67	640	265	462	621	637	155	58	195	158	134
68	557	669	665	31	142	260	61	25	205	696
69	769	311	522	356	198	649	572	35	326	382
70	176	595	161	66	778	476	45	212	490	728
71	137	709	722	146	411	222	714	753	560	348
72	431	293	629	399	763	286	672	123	182	264
73	620	154	194	133	668	30	259	24	695	310
74	355	648	34	381	594	65	475	211	727	708
75	145	221	752	347	292	398	285	122	263	153
76	132	29	23	309	647	380	64	210	707	220
77	346	397	121	152	28	308	379	209	219	396
78	151	307	208	395	306	394	393			

POWER RESIDUES

	0	1	2	3	4	5	6	7	8	9
50	165	330	660	533	279	558	329	658	529	271
51	542	297	594	401	15	30	60	120	240	480
52	173	346	692	597	407	27	54	108	216	432
53	77	154	308	616	445	103	206	412	37	74
54	148	296	592	397	7	14	28	56	112	224
55	448	109	218	436	85	170	340	680	573	359
56	718	649	511	235	470	153	306	612	437	87
57	174	348	696	605	423	59	118	236	472	157
58	314	628	469	151	302	604	421	55	110	220
59	440	93	186	372	744	701	615	443	99	198
60	396	5	10	20	40	80	160	320	640	493
61	199	398	9	18	36	72	144	288	576	365
62	730	673	559	331	662	537	287	574	361	722
63	657	527	267	534	281	562	337	674	561	335
64	670	553	319	638	489	191	382	764	741	695
65	603	419	51	102	204	408	29	58	116	232
66	464	141	282	564	341	682	577	367	734	681
67	575	363	726	665	543	299	598	409	31	62
68	124	248	496	205	410	33	66	132	264	528
69	269	538	289	578	369	738	689	591	395	3
70	6	12	24	48	96	192	384	768	749	711
71	635	483	179	358	716	645	503	219	438	89
72	178	356	712	637	487	187	374	748	709	631
73	475	163	326	652	517	247	494	201	402	17
74	34	68	136	272	544	301	602	417	47	94
75	188	376	752	717	647	507	227	454	121	242
76	484	181	362	724	661	535	283	566	345	690
77	593	399	11	22	44	88	176	352	704	621
78	455	123	246	492	197	394				

P = 797

INDICES

	0	1	2	3	4	5	6	7	8	9
0		0	1	563	2	279	564	667	3	330
1	280	344	565	144	668	46	4	590	331	361
2	281	434	345	649	566	558	145	97	669	173
3	47	185	5	111	591	150	332	245	362	707
4	282	368	435	716	346	609	650	207	567	538
5	559	357	146	353	98	623	670	128	174	301
6	48	256	186	201	6	423	112	102	592	416
7	151	58	333	220	246	325	363	215	708	785
8	283	660	369	627	436	73	717	736	347	468
9	610	15	651	748	208	640	568	33	539	674
10	560	341	358	94	147	713	354	298	99	322
11	624	12	671	295	129	132	175	474	302	461
12	49	688	257	135	187	41	202	780	7	483
13	424	178	113	232	103	376	593	790	417	477
14	152	770	59	488	334	452	221	305	247	265
15	326	554	364	124	216	464	709	684	786	120
16	284	520	661	52	370	390	628	83	437	288
17	74	691	718	313	737	429	348	68	469	260
18	611	616	16	23	652	524	749	138	209	764
19	641	507	569	158	34	190	540	726	675	396
20	561	665	342	44	359	647	95	183	148	705
21	714	205	355	621	299	199	100	56	323	783
22	625	734	13	638	672	92	296	10	130	459
23	133	778	176	374	475	486	303	552	462	118
24	50	81	689	427	258	21	136	505	188	394
25	42	181	203	197	781	636	8	776	484	116
26	425	503	179	634	114	632	233	235	104	513
27	377	237	594	578	791	106	418	28	478	515
28	153	87	771	379	60	407	489	239	335	384
29	453	596	222	602	306	580	248	441	266	793
30	327	587	555	108	365	535	125	420	217	657
31	465	30	710	292	685	480	787	449	121	517
32	285	65	521	155	662	702	53	89	371	78
33	391	773	629	575	84	381	438	532	289	62
34	75	529	692	409	719	695	314	491	738	275
35	430	241	349	412	69	337	470	228	261	386
36	612	722	617	455	17	499	24	598	653	698
37	525	224	750	754	139	604	210	317	765	308
38	642	547	508	582	570	494	159	250	35	758
39	191	443	541	741	727	268	676	164	397	795
40	562	278	666	329	343	143	45	589	360	433
41	648	557	96	172	184	110	149	244	706	367
42	715	608	206	537	356	352	622	127	300	255
43	200	422	101	415	57	219	324	214	784	659
44	626	72	735	467	14	747	639	32	673	340
45	93	712	297	321	11	294	131	473	460	687
46	134	40	779	482	177	231	375	789	476	769
47	487	451	304	264	553	123	463	683	119	519
48	51	389	82	287	690	312	428	67	259	615
49	22	523	137	763	506	157	189	725	395	664

POWER RESIDUES

	0	1	2	3	4	5	6	7	8	9
0	1	2	4	8	16	32	64	128	256	512
1	227	454	111	222	444	91	182	364	728	659
2	521	245	490	183	366	732	667	537	277	554
3	311	622	447	97	194	388	776	755	713	629
4	461	125	250	500	203	406	15	30	60	120
5	240	480	163	326	652	507	217	434	71	142
6	284	568	339	678	559	321	642	487	177	354
7	708	619	441	85	170	340	680	563	329	658
8	519	241	482	167	334	668	539	281	562	327
9	654	511	225	450	103	206	412	27	54	108
10	216	432	67	134	268	536	275	550	303	606
11	415	33	66	132	264	528	259	518	239	478
12	159	318	636	475	153	306	612	427	57	114
13	228	456	115	230	460	123	246	492	187	374
14	748	699	601	405	13	26	52	104	208	416
15	35	70	140	280	560	323	646	495	193	386
16	772	747	697	597	397	794	791	785	773	749
17	701	605	413	29	58	116	232	464	131	262
18	524	251	502	207	414	31	62	124	248	496
19	195	390	780	763	729	661	525	253	506	215
20	430	63	126	252	504	211	422	47	94	188
21	376	752	707	617	437	77	154	308	616	435
22	73	146	292	584	371	742	687	577	357	714
23	631	465	133	266	532	267	534	271	542	287
24	574	351	702	607	417	37	74	148	296	592
25	387	774	751	705	613	429	61	122	244	488
26	179	358	716	635	473	149	298	596	395	790
27	783	769	741	685	573	349	698	599	401	5
28	10	20	40	80	160	320	640	483	169	338
29	676	555	313	626	455	113	226	452	107	214
30	428	59	118	236	472	147	294	588	379	758
31	719	641	485	173	346	692	587	377	754	711
32	625	453	109	218	436	75	150	300	600	403
33	9	18	36	72	144	288	576	355	710	623
34	449	101	202	404	11	22	44	88	176	352
35	704	611	425	53	106	212	424	51	102	204
36	408	19	38	76	152	304	608	419	41	82
37	164	328	656	515	233	466	135	270	540	283
38	566	335	670	543	289	578	359	718	639	481
39	165	330	660	523	249	498	199	398	796	795
40	793	789	781	765	733	669	541	285	570	343
41	686	575	353	706	615	433	69	138	276	552
42	307	614	431	65	130	260	520	243	486	175
43	350	700	603	409	21	42	84	168	336	672
44	547	297	594	391	782	767	737	677	557	317
45	634	471	145	290	580	363	726	655	513	229
46	458	119	238	476	155	310	620	443	89	178
47	356	712	627	457	117	234	468	139	278	556
48	315	630	463	129	258	516	235	470	143	286
49	572	347	694	591	385	770	743	689	581	365

P = 797

INDICES

	0	1	2	3	4	5	6	7	8	9
50	43	646	182	704	204	620	198	55	782	733
51	637	91	9	458	777	373	485	551	117	80
52	426	20	504	393	180	196	635	775	115	502
53	633	631	234	512	236	577	105	27	514	86
54	378	406	238	383	595	601	579	440	792	586
55	107	534	419	656	29	291	479	448	516	64
56	154	701	88	77	772	574	380	531	61	528
57	408	694	490	274	240	411	336	227	385	721
58	454	498	597	697	223	753	603	316	307	546
59	581	493	249	757	442	740	267	163	794	277
60	328	142	588	432	556	171	109	243	366	607
61	536	351	126	254	421	414	218	213	658	71
62	466	746	31	339	711	320	293	472	686	39
63	481	230	788	768	450	263	122	682	518	388
64	286	311	66	614	522	762	156	724	663	645
65	703	619	54	732	90	457	372	550	79	19
66	392	195	774	501	630	511	576	26	85	405
67	382	600	439	585	533	655	290	447	63	700
68	76	573	530	527	693	273	410	226	720	497
69	696	752	315	545	492	756	739	162	276	141
70	431	170	242	606	350	253	413	212	70	745
71	338	319	471	38	229	767	262	681	387	310
72	613	761	723	644	618	731	456	549	18	194
73	500	510	25	404	599	584	654	446	699	572
74	526	272	225	496	751	544	755	161	140	169
75	605	252	211	744	318	37	766	680	309	760
76	643	730	548	193	509	403	583	445	571	271
77	495	543	160	168	251	743	36	679	759	729
78	192	402	444	270	542	167	742	678	728	401
79	269	166	677	400	165	399	398			

POWER RESIDUES

	0	1	2	3	4	5	6	7	8	9
50	730	663	529	261	522	247	494	191	382	764
51	731	665	533	269	538	279	558	319	638	479
52	161	322	644	491	185	370	740	683	569	341
53	682	567	337	674	551	305	610	423	49	98
54	196	392	784	771	745	693	589	381	762	727
55	657	517	237	474	151	302	604	411	25	50
56	100	200	400	3	6	12	24	48	96	192
57	384	768	739	681	565	333	666	535	273	546
58	295	590	383	766	735	673	549	301	602	407
59	17	34	68	136	272	544	291	582	367	734
60	671	545	293	586	375	750	703	609	421	45
61	90	180	360	720	643	489	181	362	724	651
62	505	213	426	55	110	220	440	83	166	332
63	664	531	265	530	263	526	255	510	223	446
64	95	190	380	760	723	649	501	205	410	23
65	46	92	184	368	736	675	553	309	618	439
66	81	162	324	648	499	201	402	7	14	28
67	56	112	224	448	99	198	396	792	787	777
68	757	717	637	477	157	314	628	459	121	242
69	484	171	342	684	571	345	690	583	369	738
70	679	561	325	650	503	209	418	39	78	156
71	312	624	451	105	210	420	43	86	172	344
72	688	579	361	722	647	497	197	394	788	779
73	761	725	653	509	221	442	87	174	348	696
74	595	393	786	775	753	709	621	445	93	186
75	372	744	691	585	373	746	695	593	389	778
76	759	721	645	493	189	378	756	715	633	469
77	141	282	564	331	662	527	257	514	231	462
78	127	254	508	219	438	79	158	316	632	467
79	137	274	548	299	598	399				

P = 809

INDICES

	0	1	2	3	4	5	6	7	8	9
0		0	138	1	276	666	139	592	414	2
1	804	27	277	210	730	667	552	39	140	508
2	134	593	165	230	415	524	348	3	60	749
3	805	57	690	28	177	450	278	501	646	211
4	272	701	731	714	303	668	368	361	553	376
5	662	40	486	467	141	693	198	509	79	117
6	135	746	195	594	20	68	166	793	315	231
7	588	437	416	516	639	525	784	619	349	108
8	410	4	31	597	61	705	44	750	441	8
9	806	802	506	58	499	366	691	18	514	29
10	800	798	178	253	624	451	605	755	279	180
11	23	502	336	760	647	88	217	212	255	631
12	273	54	76	702	333	382	732	626	158	715
13	206	495	304	292	123	669	453	71	369	385
14	726	362	575	237	554	607	654	377	777	566
15	663	687	114	41	757	723	487	153	246	468
16	548	14	142	281	169	694	735	490	199	420
17	35	510	182	340	80	308	579	118	146	186
18	136	25	132	747	644	359	196	66	637	595
19	504	796	21	629	156	69	652	721	167	338
20	130	794	128	533	316	559	391	232	762	535
21	589	174	743	438	85	572	417	649	318	517
22	161	249	640	321	474	526	90	561	785	479
23	226	620	355	426	350	219	393	109	769	101
24	411	447	192	5	214	234	32	718	471	598
25	520	601	62	257	764	706	296	241	45	285
26	344	751	633	537	442	325	430	9	261	541
27	807	275	591	803	209	551	507	164	523	59
28	56	176	500	271	713	367	375	485	692	78
29	745	19	792	587	515	783	107	30	704	440
30	801	498	17	799	252	604	179	335	87	254
31	53	332	625	205	291	452	384	574	606	776
32	686	756	152	547	280	734	419	181	307	145
33	24	643	65	503	628	651	337	127	558	761
34	173	84	648	160	320	89	478	354	218	768
35	446	213	717	519	256	295	284	632	324	260
36	274	208	163	55	270	374	77	791	782	703
37	497	251	334	52	204	383	775	151	733	306
38	642	627	126	172	159	477	767	716	294	323
39	207	269	790	496	51	774	305	125	476	293
40	268	50	124	267	266	670	671	528	454	672
41	697	72	529	709	370	455	92	386	673	611
42	727	698	312	363	73	563	576	530	223	238
43	710	329	555	371	787	608	456	738	655	93
44	299	378	387	481	778	674	459	567	612	678
45	664	728	228	688	699	660	115	313	617	42
46	364	622	758	74	493	724	564	244	488	577
47	357	154	531	741	247	224	99	469	239	428
48	549	711	585	15	330	684	143	556	352	282
49	372	202	170	788	48	695	609	221	736	457

POWER RESIDUES

	0	1	2	3	4	5	6	7	8	9
0	1	3	9	27	81	243	729	569	89	267
1	801	785	737	593	161	483	640	302	97	291
2	64	192	576	110	330	181	543	11	33	99
3	297	82	246	738	596	170	510	721	545	17
4	51	153	459	568	86	258	774	704	494	673
5	401	394	373	310	121	363	280	31	93	279
6	28	84	252	756	650	332	187	561	65	195
7	585	137	411	424	463	580	122	366	289	58
8	174	522	757	653	341	214	642	308	115	345
9	226	678	416	439	508	715	527	772	698	476
10	619	239	717	533	790	752	638	296	79	237
11	711	515	736	590	152	456	559	59	177	531
12	784	734	584	134	402	397	382	337	202	606
13	200	600	182	546	20	60	180	540	2	6
14	18	54	162	486	649	329	178	534	793	761
15	665	377	322	157	471	604	194	582	128	384
16	343	220	660	362	277	22	66	198	594	164
17	492	667	383	340	211	633	281	34	102	306
18	109	327	172	516	739	599	179	537	802	788
19	746	620	242	726	560	62	186	558	56	168
20	504	703	491	664	374	313	130	390	361	274
21	13	39	117	351	244	732	578	116	348	235
22	705	497	682	428	475	616	230	690	452	547
23	23	69	207	621	245	735	587	143	429	478
24	625	257	771	695	467	592	158	474	613	221
25	663	371	304	103	309	118	354	253	759	659
26	359	268	804	794	764	674	404	403	400	391
27	364	283	40	120	360	271	4	12	36	108
28	324	163	489	658	356	259	777	713	521	754
29	644	314	133	399	388	355	256	768	686	440
30	511	724	554	44	132	396	379	328	175	525
31	766	680	422	457	562	68	204	612	218	654
32	344	223	669	389	358	265	795	767	683	431
33	484	643	311	124	372	307	112	336	199	597
34	173	519	748	626	260	780	722	548	26	78
35	234	702	488	655	347	232	696	470	601	185
36	555	47	141	423	460	571	95	285	46	138
37	414	433	490	661	365	286	49	147	441	514
38	733	581	125	375	316	139	417	442	517	742
39	608	206	618	236	708	506	709	509	718	536
40	799	779	719	539	808	806	800	782	728	566
41	80	240	720	542	8	24	72	216	648	326
42	169	507	712	518	745	617	233	699	479	628
43	266	798	776	710	512	727	563	71	213	639
44	299	88	264	792	758	656	350	241	723	551
45	35	105	315	136	408	415	436	499	688	446
46	529	778	716	530	781	725	557	53	159	477
47	622	248	744	614	224	672	398	385	346	229
48	687	443	520	751	635	287	52	156	468	595
49	167	501	694	464	583	131	393	370	301	94

P = 809

INDICES

	0	1	2	3	4	5	6	7	8	9
50	658	491	739	583	200	656	395	421	94	397
51	36	300	434	511	379	111	183	388	423	341
52	482	288	81	779	771	309	675	96	580	460
53	463	119	568	103	147	613	399	187	679	403
54	137	665	413	26	729	38	133	229	347	748
55	689	449	645	700	302	360	661	466	197	116
56	194	67	314	436	638	618	409	596	43	7
57	505	365	513	797	623	754	22	759	216	630
58	75	381	157	494	122	70	725	236	653	565
59	113	722	245	13	168	489	34	339	578	185
60	131	358	636	795	155	720	129	532	390	534
61	742	571	317	248	473	560	225	425	392	100
62	191	233	470	600	763	240	343	536	429	540
63	590	550	522	175	712	484	744	586	106	439
64	16	603	86	331	290	573	685	546	418	144
65	64	650	557	83	319	353	445	518	283	259
66	162	373	781	250	203	150	641	171	766	322
67	789	773	475	49	265	527	696	708	91	610
68	311	562	222	328	786	737	298	480	458	677
69	227	659	616	621	492	243	356	740	98	427
70	584	683	351	201	47	220	657	582	394	396
71	433	110	422	287	770	95	462	102	398	402
72	412	37	346	448	301	465	193	435	408	6
73	512	753	215	380	121	235	112	12	33	184
74	635	719	389	570	472	424	190	599	342	539
75	521	483	105	602	289	545	63	82	444	258
76	780	149	765	772	264	707	310	327	297	676
77	615	242	97	682	46	581	432	286	461	401
78	345	464	407	752	120	11	634	569	189	538
79	104	544	443	148	263	326	614	681	431	400
80	406	10	188	543	262	680	405	542	404	

POWER RESIDUES

	0	1	2	3	4	5	6	7	8	9
50	282	37	111	333	190	570	92	276	19	57
51	171	513	730	572	98	294	73	219	657	353
52	250	750	632	278	25	75	225	675	407	412
53	427	472	607	203	609	209	627	263	789	749
54	629	269	807	803	791	755	647	323	160	480
55	631	275	16	48	144	432	487	652	338	205
56	615	227	681	425	466	589	149	447	532	787
57	743	611	215	645	317	142	426	469	598	176
58	528	775	707	503	700	482	637	293	70	210
59	630	272	7	21	63	189	567	83	249	747
60	623	251	753	641	305	106	318	145	435	496
61	679	419	448	535	796	770	692	458	565	77
62	231	693	461	574	104	312	127	381	334	193
63	579	119	357	262	786	740	602	188	564	74
64	222	666	380	331	184	552	38	114	342	217
65	651	335	196	588	146	438	505	706	500	691
66	455	556	50	150	450	541	5	15	45	135
67	405	406	409	418	445	526	769	689	449	538
68	805	797	773	701	485	646	320	151	453	550
69	32	96	288	55	165	495	676	410	421	454
70	553	41	123	369	298	85	255	765	677	413
71	430	481	634	284	43	129	387	352	247	741
72	605	197	591	155	465	586	140	420	451	544
73	14	42	126	378	325	166	498	685	437	502
74	697	473	610	212	636	290	61	183	549	29
75	87	261	783	731	575	107	321	154	462	577
76	113	339	208	624	254	762	668	386	349	238
77	714	524	763	671	395	376	319	148	444	523
78	760	662	368	295	76	228	684	434	493	670
79	392	367	292	67	201	603	191	573	101	303
80	100	300	91	273	10	30	90	270		

P = 811

INDICES

	0	1	2	3	4	5	6	7	8	9
0		0	717	1	624	494	718	390	531	2
1	401	118	625	139	297	495	438	55	719	246
2	308	391	25	239	532	178	46	3	204	606
3	402	43	345	119	772	74	626	786	153	140
4	215	504	298	472	742	496	146	165	439	780
5	85	56	763	348	720	612	111	247	513	198
6	309	175	760	392	252	633	26	170	679	240
7	791	689	533	8	693	179	60	508	47	395
8	122	4	411	655	205	549	379	607	649	804
9	403	529	53	44	72	740	346	758	687	120
10	802	685	773	418	670	75	255	775	627	454
11	519	787	18	323	154	733	420	141	105	445
12	216	236	82	505	667	672	299	467	159	473
13	540	675	743	636	77	497	586	210	147	331
14	698	166	596	257	440	290	725	781	600	747
15	86	22	777	57	415	537	764	767	302	349
16	29	629	721	130	318	613	562	38	112	278
17	456	248	286	226	514	568	556	199	711	521
18	310	388	436	176	770	470	761	173	789	393
19	647	756	253	731	665	634	594	20	27	276
20	709	171	592	186	680	188	325	241	577	364
21	792	305	162	690	682	156	534	433	361	9
22	426	194	694	190	735	180	230	134	61	261
23	640	509	327	422	48	659	12	396	352	476
24	123	243	143	5	799	464	412	385	574	656
25	579	107	206	357	374	550	66	619	380	366
26	447	608	582	429	650	32	543	805	794	218
27	404	716	493	530	117	296	54	307	238	45
28	605	344	73	152	503	741	164	84	347	110
29	197	759	632	678	688	692	507	121	654	378
30	803	52	739	686	684	669	774	518	322	419
31	444	81	671	158	674	76	209	697	256	724
32	746	776	536	301	628	317	37	455	225	555
33	520	435	469	788	755	664	19	708	185	324
34	363	161	155	360	193	734	133	639	421	11
35	475	142	463	573	106	373	618	446	428	542
36	217	492	295	237	343	502	83	196	677	506
37	377	738	668	321	80	673	696	745	300	36
38	554	468	663	184	160	192	638	474	572	617
39	541	294	501	676	737	79	744	553	183	637
40	616	500	78	182	499	498	93	94	587	483
41	95	211	232	588	148	339	484	332	271	96
42	699	136	212	167	69	233	597	565	589	258
43	63	149	441	705	340	291	268	485	726	263
44	333	782	101	272	601	488	97	748	642	700
45	87	622	137	23	41	213	778	511	168	58
46	547	70	416	16	234	538	329	598	765	560
47	566	768	729	590	303	424	259	350	383	64
48	30	115	150	630	50	442	722	223	706	131
49	371	341	319	661	292	614	481	269	563	266

POWER RESIDUES

	0	1	2	3	4	5	6	7	8	9
0	1	3	9	27	81	243	729	565	73	219
1	657	349	236	708	502	695	463	578	112	336
2	197	591	151	453	548	22	66	198	594	160
3	480	629	265	795	763	667	379	326	167	501
4	692	454	551	31	93	279	26	78	234	702
5	484	641	301	92	276	17	51	153	459	566
6	76	228	684	430	479	626	256	768	682	424
7	461	572	94	282	35	105	315	134	402	395
8	374	311	122	366	287	50	150	450	539	806
9	796	766	676	406	407	410	419	446	527	770
10	688	442	515	734	580	118	354	251	753	637
11	289	56	168	504	701	481	632	274	11	33
12	99	297	80	240	720	538	803	787	739	595
13	163	489	656	346	227	681	421	452	545	13
14	39	117	351	242	726	556	46	138	414	431
15	482	635	283	38	114	342	215	645	313	128
16	384	341	212	636	286	47	141	423	458	563
17	67	201	603	187	561	61	183	549	25	75
18	225	675	403	398	383	338	203	609	205	615
19	223	669	385	344	221	663	367	290	59	177
20	531	782	724	550	28	84	252	756	646	316
21	137	411	422	455	554	40	120	360	269	807
22	799	775	703	487	650	328	173	519	746	616
23	226	678	412	425	464	581	121	363	278	23
24	69	207	621	241	723	547	19	57	171	513
25	728	562	64	192	576	106	318	143	429	476
26	617	229	687	439	506	707	499	686	436	497
27	680	418	443	518	743	607	199	597	169	507
28	710	508	713	517	740	598	172	516	737	589
29	145	435	494	671	391	362	275	14	42	126
30	378	323	158	474	611	211	633	277	20	60
31	180	540	809	805	793	757	649	325	164	492
32	665	373	308	113	339	206	618	232	696	466
33	587	139	417	440	509	716	526	767	679	415
34	434	491	662	364	281	32	96	288	53	159
35	477	620	238	714	520	749	625	253	759	655
36	343	218	654	340	209	627	259	777	709	505
37	704	490	659	355	254	762	664	370	299	86
38	258	774	700	478	623	247	741	601	181	543
39	7	21	63	189	567	79	237	711	511	722
40	544	10	30	90	270	810	808	802	784	730
41	568	82	246	738	592	154	462	575	103	309
42	116	348	233	699	475	614	220	660	358	263
43	789	745	613	217	651	331	182	546	16	48
44	144	432	485	644	310	119	357	260	780	718
45	532	785	733	577	109	327	170	510	719	535
46	794	760	658	352	245	735	583	127	381	332
47	185	555	43	129	387	350	239	717	529	776
48	706	496	677	409	416	437	500	689	445	524
49	761	661	361	272	5	15	45	135	405	404

P = 811

INDICES

	0	1	2	3	4	5	6	7	8	9
50	486	39	14	727	113	369	264	279	281	334
51	457	398	783	249	526	102	287	283	273	227
52	354	602	515	752	489	569	336	98	557	478
53	749	200	450	643	712	459	701	522	125	88
54	311	809	623	389	400	138	437	245	24	177
55	203	42	771	785	214	471	145	779	762	611
56	512	174	251	169	790	7	59	394	410	548
57	648	528	71	757	801	417	254	453	17	732
58	104	235	666	466	539	635	585	330	595	289
59	599	21	414	766	28	129	561	277	285	567
60	710	387	769	172	646	730	593	275	591	187
61	576	304	681	432	425	189	229	260	326	658
62	351	242	798	384	578	356	65	365	581	31
63	793	715	116	306	604	151	163	109	631	691
64	653	51	683	517	443	157	208	723	535	316
65	224	434	754	707	362	359	132	10	462	372
66	427	491	342	195	376	320	695	35	662	191
67	571	293	736	552	615	181	92	482	231	338
68	270	135	68	564	62	704	267	262	100	487
69	641	621	40	510	546	15	328	559	728	423
70	382	114	49	222	370	660	480	265	13	368
71	280	397	525	282	353	751	335	477	449	458
72	124	808	399	244	202	784	144	610	250	6
73	409	527	800	452	103	465	584	288	413	128
74	284	386	645	274	575	431	228	657	797	355
75	580	714	603	108	652	516	207	315	753	358
76	461	490	375	34	570	551	91	337	67	703
77	99	620	545	558	381	221	479	367	524	750
78	448	807	201	609	408	451	583	127	644	430
79	796	713	651	314	460	33	90	702	544	220
80	523	806	407	126	795	313	89	219	406	312
81	405	0								

POWER RESIDUES

	0	1	2	3	4	5	6	7	8	9
50	401	392	365	284	41	123	369	296	77	231
51	693	457	560	58	174	522	755	643	307	110
52	330	179	537	800	778	712	514	731	571	91
53	273	8	24	72	216	648	322	155	465	584
54	130	390	359	266	798	772	694	460	569	85
55	255	765	673	397	380	329	176	528	773	697
56	469	596	166	498	683	427	470	599	175	525
57	764	670	388	353	248	744	610	208	624	250
58	750	628	262	786	736	586	136	408	413	428
59	473	608	202	606	196	588	142	426	467	590
60	148	444	521	752	634	280	29	87	261	783
61	727	559	55	165	495	674	400	389	356	257
62	771	691	451	542	4	12	36	108	324	161
63	483	638	292	65	195	585	133	399	386	347
64	230	690	448	533	788	742	604	190	570	88
65	264	792	754	640	298	83	249	747	619	235
66	705	493	668	382	335	194	582	124	372	305
67	104	312	125	375	314	131	393	368	293	68
68	204	612	214	642	304	101	303	98	294	71
69	213	639	295	74	222	666	376	317	140	420
70	449	536	797	769	685	433	488	653	337	200
71	600	178	534	791	751	631	271	2	6	18
72	54	162	486	647	319	146	438	503	698	472
73	605	193	579	115	345	224	672	394	371	302
74	95	285	44	132	396	377	320	149	447	530
75	779	715	523	758	652	334	191	573	97	291
76	62	186	558	52	156	468	593	157	471	602
77	184	552	34	102	306	107	321	152	456	557
78	49	147	441	512	725	553	37	111	333	188
79	564	70	210	630	268	804	790	748	622	244
80	732	574	100	300	89	267	801	781	721	541
81										

P = 821

INDICES

	0	1	2	3	4	5	6	7	8	9
0		0	1	621	2	742	622	458	3	422
1	743	357	623	351	459	543	4	527	423	184
2	744	259	358	34	624	664	352	223	460	372
3	544	601	5	158	528	380	424	510	185	152
4	745	486	260	228	359	344	35	241	625	96
5	665	328	353	219	224	279	461	805	373	283
6	545	519	602	60	6	273	159	314	529	655
7	381	798	425	476	511	465	186	815	153	268
8	746	24	487	499	261	449	229	173	360	732
9	345	809	36	402	242	106	626	751	97	779
10	666	758	329	618	354	181	220	377	225	325
11	280	311	462	496	806	776	374	773	284	165
12	546	714	520	287	603	586	61	71	7	29
13	274	168	160	642	315	145	530	198	656	549
14	382	42	799	708	426	294	477	717	512	674
15	466	647	187	129	816	523	154	92	269	20
16	747	492	25	290	488	80	500	537	262	702
17	450	606	230	437	174	302	361	84	733	589
18	346	339	810	320	37	432	403	64	243	681
19	107	393	627	504	752	74	98	566	780	252
20	667	115	759	10	330	408	619	456	355	541
21	182	32	221	599	378	150	226	239	326	277
22	281	58	312	796	463	266	497	171	807	104
23	777	616	375	309	774	163	285	69	166	143
24	547	706	715	645	521	18	288	535	604	300
25	587	318	62	391	72	250	8	454	30	148
26	275	794	169	614	161	141	643	533	316	248
27	146	612	531	610	199	201	657	122	550	203
28	383	557	43	659	800	727	709	124	427	234
29	295	552	478	572	718	205	513	580	675	385
30	467	686	648	559	188	441	130	45	817	419
31	524	661	155	483	93	802	270	473	21	729
32	748	178	493	711	26	195	291	126	489	699
33	81	429	501	112	538	236	263	306	703	297
34	451	138	607	554	231	577	438	480	175	696
35	303	574	362	365	85	720	734	786	590	207
36	347	368	340	515	811	398	321	582	38	88
37	433	677	404	54	65	387	244	723	682	469
38	108	692	394	688	628	737	505	650	753	637
39	75	561	99	789	567	190	781	632	253	443
40	668	593	116	132	760	766	11	47	331	210
41	409	819	620	741	457	421	356	350	542	526
42	183	258	33	663	222	371	600	157	379	509
43	151	485	227	343	240	95	327	218	278	804
44	282	518	59	272	313	654	797	475	464	814
45	267	23	498	448	172	731	808	401	105	750
46	778	757	617	180	376	324	310	495	775	772
47	164	713	286	585	70	28	167	641	144	197
48	548	41	707	293	716	673	646	128	522	91
49	19	491	289	79	536	701	605	436	301	83

POWER RESIDUES

	0	1	2	3	4	5	6	7	8	9
0	1	2	4	8	16	32	64	128	256	512
1	203	406	812	803	785	749	677	533	245	490
2	159	318	636	451	81	162	324	648	475	129
3	258	516	211	422	23	46	92	184	368	736
4	651	481	141	282	564	307	614	407	814	807
5	793	765	709	597	373	746	671	521	221	442
6	63	126	252	504	187	374	748	675	529	237
7	474	127	254	508	195	390	780	739	657	493
8	165	330	660	499	177	354	708	595	369	738
9	655	489	157	314	628	435	49	98	196	392
10	784	747	673	525	229	458	95	190	380	760
11	699	577	333	666	511	201	402	804	787	753
12	685	549	277	554	287	574	327	654	487	153
13	306	612	403	806	791	761	701	581	341	682
14	543	265	530	239	478	135	270	540	259	518
15	215	430	39	78	156	312	624	427	33	66
16	132	264	528	235	470	119	238	476	131	262
17	524	227	454	87	174	348	696	571	321	642
18	463	105	210	420	19	38	76	152	304	608
19	395	790	759	697	573	325	650	479	137	274
20	548	275	550	279	558	295	590	359	718	615
21	409	818	815	809	797	773	725	629	437	53
22	106	212	424	27	54	108	216	432	43	86
23	172	344	688	555	289	578	335	670	519	217
24	434	47	94	188	376	752	683	545	269	538
25	255	510	199	398	796	771	721	621	421	21
26	42	84	168	336	672	523	225	450	79	158
27	316	632	443	65	130	260	520	219	438	55
28	110	220	440	59	118	236	472	123	246	492
29	163	326	652	483	145	290	580	339	678	535
30	249	498	175	350	700	579	337	674	527	233
31	466	111	222	444	67	134	268	536	251	502
32	183	366	732	643	465	109	218	436	51	102
33	204	408	816	811	801	781	741	661	501	181
34	362	724	627	433	45	90	180	360	720	619
35	417	13	26	52	104	208	416	11	22	44
36	88	176	352	704	587	353	706	591	361	722
37	623	425	29	58	116	232	464	107	214	428
38	35	70	140	280	560	299	598	375	750	679
39	537	253	506	191	382	764	707	593	365	730
40	639	457	93	186	372	744	667	513	205	410
41	820	819	817	813	805	789	757	693	565	309
42	618	415	9	18	36	72	144	288	576	331
43	662	503	185	370	740	659	497	173	346	692
44	563	305	610	399	798	775	729	637	453	85
45	170	340	680	539	257	514	207	414	7	14
46	28	56	112	224	448	75	150	300	600	379
47	758	695	569	317	634	447	73	146	292	584
48	347	694	567	313	626	431	41	82	164	328
49	656	491	161	322	644	467	113	226	452	83

P = 821

INDICES

	0	1	2	3	4	5	6	7	8	9
50	588	338	319	431	63	680	392	503	73	565
51	251	114	9	407	455	540	31	598	149	238
52	276	57	795	265	170	103	615	308	162	68
53	142	705	644	17	534	299	317	390	249	453
54	147	793	613	140	532	247	611	609	200	121
55	202	556	658	726	123	233	551	571	204	579
56	384	685	558	440	44	418	660	482	801	472
57	728	177	710	194	125	698	428	111	235	305
58	296	137	553	576	479	695	573	364	719	785
59	206	367	514	397	581	87	676	53	386	722
60	468	691	687	736	649	636	560	788	189	631
61	442	592	131	765	46	209	818	740	420	349
62	525	257	662	370	156	508	484	342	94	217
63	803	517	271	653	474	813	22	447	730	400
64	749	756	179	323	494	771	712	584	27	640
65	196	40	292	672	127	90	490	78	700	435
66	82	337	430	679	502	564	113	406	539	597
67	237	56	264	102	307	67	704	16	298	389
68	452	792	139	246	608	120	555	725	232	570
69	578	684	439	417	481	471	176	193	697	110
70	304	136	575	694	363	784	366	396	86	52
71	721	690	735	635	787	630	591	764	208	739
72	348	256	369	507	341	216	516	652	812	446
73	399	755	322	770	583	639	39	671	89	77
74	434	336	678	563	405	596	55	101	66	15
75	388	791	245	119	724	569	683	416	470	192
76	109	135	693	783	395	51	689	634	629	763
77	738	255	506	215	651	445	754	769	638	670
78	76	335	562	595	100	14	790	118	568	415
79	191	134	782	50	633	762	254	214	444	768
80	669	334	594	13	117	414	133	49	761	213
81	767	333	12	413	48	212	332	412	211	411
82	410	0								

POWER RESIDUES

	0	1	2	3	4	5	6	7	8	9
50	166	332	664	507	193	386	772	723	625	429
51	37	74	148	296	592	363	726	631	441	61
52	122	244	488	155	310	620	419	17	34	68
53	136	272	544	267	534	247	494	167	334	668
54	515	209	418	15	30	60	120	240	480	139
55	278	556	291	582	343	686	551	281	562	303
56	606	391	782	743	665	509	197	394	788	755
57	689	557	293	586	351	702	583	345	690	559
58	297	594	367	734	647	473	125	250	500	179
59	358	716	611	401	802	783	745	669	517	213
60	426	31	62	124	248	496	171	342	684	547
61	273	546	271	542	263	526	231	462	103	206
62	412	3	6	12	24	48	96	192	384	768
63	715	609	397	794	767	713	605	389	778	735
64	649	477	133	266	532	243	486	151	302	604
65	387	774	727	633	445	69	138	276	552	283
66	566	311	622	423	25	50	100	200	400	800
67	779	737	653	485	149	298	596	371	742	663
68	505	189	378	756	691	561	301	602	383	766
69	711	601	381	762	703	585	349	698	575	329
70	658	495	169	338	676	531	241	482	143	286
71	572	323	646	471	121	242	484	147	294	588
72	355	710	599	377	754	687	553	285	570	319
73	638	455	89	178	356	712	603	385	770	719
74	617	413	5	10	20	40	80	160	320	640
75	459	97	194	388	776	731	641	461	101	202
76	404	808	795	769	717	613	405	810	799	777
77	733	645	469	117	234	468	115	230	460	99
78	198	396	792	763	705	589	357	714	607	393
79	786	751	681	541	261	522	223	446	71	142
80	284	568	315	630	439	57	114	228	456	91
81	182	364	728	635	449	77	154	308	616	411
82										

P = 823

INDICES

	0	1	2	3	4	5	6	7	8	9
0		0	364	1	728	327	365	31	270	2
1	691	531	729	284	395	328	634	629	366	669
2	233	32	73	419	271	654	648	3	759	183
3	692	392	176	532	171	358	730	340	211	285
4	597	179	396	107	437	329	783	53	635	62
5	196	630	190	20	367	36	301	670	547	428
6	234	819	756	33	540	611	74	351	535	420
7	722	276	272	113	704	655	575	562	649	252
8	139	4	543	162	760	134	471	184	801	482
9	693	315	325	393	417	174	177	194	426	533
10	560	469	172	552	554	359	384	262	731	614
11	400	341	665	556	212	746	89	286	792	660
12	598	240	361	180	298	159	397	43	82	108
13	153	386	438	700	715	330	77	46	784	166
14	264	54	640	815	636	510	477	63	246	733
15	197	619	117	631	104	719	191	295	616	21
16	503	450	368	354	85	37	526	402	302	568
17	498	671	13	69	548	685	343	429	24	767
18	235	216	679	820	689	667	757	338	781	34
19	538	111	541	313	558	612	790	41	75	508
20	102	352	11	214	536	506	94	421	96	378
21	723	126	748	277	626	434	273	423	156	114
22	764	91	705	514	207	656	98	228	576	487
23	288	563	453	708	650	380	334	253	202	794
24	140	148	604	5	725	389	544	131	662	163
25	523	310	761	128	407	135	446	600	472	371
26	517	185	750	581	802	347	242	483	257	222
27	694	279	441	316	410	363	326	269	530	394
28	628	232	418	647	182	175	357	210	178	436
29	52	195	19	300	427	755	610	534	275	703
30	561	138	161	470	481	324	173	425	468	553
31	261	399	555	88	659	360	158	81	385	714
32	45	263	814	476	732	116	718	615	449	84
33	401	497	68	342	766	678	666	780	110	557
34	40	101	213	93	377	747	433	155	90	206
35	227	287	707	333	793	603	388	661	309	406
36	599	516	580	241	221	440	362	529	231	181
37	209	51	299	609	702	160	323	467	398	658
38	80	44	475	717	83	67	677	109	100	376
39	154	226	332	387	405	579	439	230	50	701
40	466	79	716	676	375	331	578	49	78	374
41	48	47	458	459	785	489	460	167	742	786
42	265	305	490	55	290	461	641	28	168	816
43	798	743	637	565	787	511	520	266	478	494
44	306	64	455	491	247	809	56	734	571	291
45	198	710	462	620	592	642	118	773	29	632
46	652	169	105	188	817	720	250	799	192	382
47	744	296	698	638	617	501	566	22	336	788
48	504	624	512	451	146	521	369	255	267	355
49	753	479	86	812	495	38	204	307	527	321

POWER RESIDUES

	0	1	2	3	4	5	6	7	8	9
0	1	3	9	27	81	243	729	541	800	754
1	616	202	606	172	516	725	529	764	646	292
2	53	159	477	608	178	534	779	691	427	458
3	551	7	21	63	189	567	55	165	495	662
4	340	197	591	127	381	320	137	411	410	407
5	398	371	290	47	141	423	446	515	722	520
6	737	565	49	147	441	500	677	385	332	173
7	519	734	556	22	66	198	594	136	408	401
8	380	317	128	384	329	164	492	653	313	116
9	348	221	663	343	206	618	208	624	226	678
10	388	341	200	600	154	462	563	43	129	387
11	338	191	573	73	219	657	325	152	456	545
12	812	790	724	526	755	619	211	633	253	759
13	631	247	741	577	85	255	765	649	301	80
14	240	720	514	719	511	710	484	629	241	723
15	523	746	592	130	390	347	218	654	316	125
16	375	302	83	249	747	595	139	417	428	461
17	560	34	102	306	95	285	32	96	288	41
18	123	369	284	29	87	261	783	703	463	566
19	52	156	468	581	97	291	50	150	450	527
20	758	628	238	714	496	665	349	224	672	370
21	287	38	114	342	203	609	181	543	806	772
22	670	364	269	807	775	679	391	350	227	681
23	397	368	281	20	60	180	540	797	745	589
24	121	363	266	798	748	598	148	444	509	704
25	466	575	79	237	711	487	638	268	804	766
26	652	310	107	321	140	420	437	488	641	277
27	8	24	72	216	648	298	71	213	639	271
28	813	793	733	553	13	39	117	351	230	690
29	424	449	524	749	601	157	471	590	124	372
30	293	56	168	504	689	421	440	497	668	358
31	251	753	613	193	579	91	273	819	811	787
32	715	499	674	376	305	92	276	5	15	45
33	135	405	392	353	236	708	478	611	187	561
34	37	111	333	176	528	761	637	265	795	739
35	571	67	201	603	163	489	644	286	35	105
36	315	122	366	275	2	6	18	54	162	486
37	635	259	777	685	409	404	389	344	209	627
38	235	705	469	584	106	318	131	393	356	245
39	735	559	31	93	279	14	42	126	378	311
40	110	330	167	501	680	394	359	254	762	640
41	274	822	820	814	796	742	580	94	282	23
42	69	207	621	217	651	307	98	294	59	177
43	531	770	664	346	215	645	289	44	132	396
44	365	272	816	802	760	634	256	768	658	328
45	161	483	626	232	696	442	503	686	412	413
46	416	425	452	533	776	682	400	377	308	101
47	303	86	258	774	676	382	323	146	438	491
48	650	304	89	267	801	757	625	229	687	415
49	422	443	506	695	439	494	659	331	170	510

P = 823

INDICES

	0	1	2	3	4	5	6	7	8	9
50	65	403	674	456	303	796	492	569	771	248
51	499	144	810	672	142	57	14	584	735	70
52	59	572	549	150	292	686	123	199	344	16
53	711	430	606	463	25	589	621	768	586	593
54	236	7	643	217	805	119	680	737	774	821
55	727	30	690	283	633	668	72	653	758	391
56	170	339	596	106	782	61	189	35	546	818
57	539	350	721	112	574	251	542	133	800	314
58	416	193	559	551	383	613	664	745	791	239
59	297	42	152	699	76	165	639	509	245	618
60	103	294	502	353	525	567	12	684	23	215
61	688	337	537	312	789	507	10	505	95	125
62	625	422	763	513	97	486	452	379	201	147
63	724	130	522	127	445	370	749	346	256	278
64	409	268	627	646	356	435	18	754	274	137
65	480	424	260	87	157	713	813	115	448	496
66	765	779	39	92	432	205	706	602	308	515
67	220	528	208	608	322	657	474	66	99	225
68	404	229	465	675	577	373	457	488	741	304
69	289	27	797	564	519	493	454	808	570	709
70	591	772	651	187	249	381	697	500	335	623
71	145	254	752	811	203	320	673	795	770	143
72	141	583	58	149	122	15	605	588	585	6
73	804	736	726	282	71	390	595	60	545	349
74	573	132	415	550	663	238	151	164	244	293
75	524	683	687	311	9	124	762	485	200	129
76	444	345	408	645	17	136	259	712	447	778
77	431	601	219	607	473	224	464	372	740	26
78	518	807	590	186	696	622	751	319	769	582
79	121	587	803	281	594	348	414	237	243	682
80	8	484	443	644	258	777	218	223	739	806
81	695	318	120	280	413	681	442	776	738	317
82	412	775	411							

POWER RESIDUES

	0	1	2	3	4	5	6	7	8	9
50	707	475	602	160	480	617	205	615	199	597
51	145	435	482	623	223	669	361	260	780	694
52	436	485	632	250	750	604	166	498	671	367
53	278	11	33	99	297	68	204	612	190	570
54	64	192	576	82	246	738	568	58	174	522
55	743	583	103	309	104	312	113	339	194	582
56	100	300	77	231	693	433	476	605	169	507
57	698	448	521	740	574	76	228	684	406	395
58	362	263	789	721	517	728	538	791	727	535
59	782	700	454	539	794	736	562	40	120	360
60	257	771	667	355	242	726	532	773	673	373
61	296	65	195	585	109	327	158	474	599	151
62	453	536	785	709	481	620	214	642	280	17
63	51	153	459	554	16	48	144	432	473	596
64	142	426	455	542	803	763	643	283	26	78
65	234	702	460	557	25	75	225	675	379	314
66	119	357	248	744	586	112	336	185	555	19
67	57	171	513	716	502	683	403	386	335	182
68	546	815	799	751	607	175	525	752	610	184
69	552	10	30	90	270	810	784	706	472	593
70	133	399	374	299	74	222	666	352	233	699
71	451	530	767	655	319	134	402	383	326	155
72	465	572	70	210	630	244	732	550	4	12
73	36	108	324	149	447	518	731	547	818	808
74	778	688	418	431	470	587	115	345	212	636
75	262	786	712	490	647	295	62	186	558	28
76	84	252	756	622	220	660	334	179	537	788
77	718	508	701	457	548	821	817	805	769	661
78	337	188	564	46	138	414	419	434	479	614
79	196	588	118	354	239	717	505	692	430	467
80	578	88	264	792	730	544	809	781	697	445
81	512	713	493	656	322	143	429	464	569	61
82	183	549								

P = 827

INDICES

	0	1	2	3	4	5	6	7	8	9
0		0	1	256	2	175	257	561	3	512
1	176	634	258	169	562	431	4	787	513	702
2	177	817	635	312	259	350	170	768	563	281
3	432	234	5	64	788	736	514	773	703	425
4	178	797	818	713	636	687	313	189	260	296
5	351	217	171	813	769	809	564	132	282	677
6	433	206	235	247	6	344	65	467	789	568
7	737	92	515	38	774	606	704	369	426	184
8	179	198	798	80	819	136	714	537	637	71
9	688	730	314	490	190	51	261	627	297	320
10	352	286	218	666	172	166	814	278	770	684
11	810	203	565	366	133	487	283	681	678	522
12	434	442	207	227	236	525	248	500	7	143
13	345	127	66	437	468	117	790	331	569	304
14	738	445	93	803	516	456	39	552	775	210
15	607	753	705	473	370	409	427	230	185	243
16	180	47	199	496	799	239	81	654	820	338
17	137	388	715	528	538	85	638	107	72	614
18	689	251	731	462	315	122	491	595	191	503
19	52	658	262	394	628	600	298	10	321	645
20	353	723	287	16	219	146	667	824	173	510
21	167	785	815	348	279	62	771	795	685	294
22	811	130	204	342	566	36	367	196	134	69
23	488	625	284	164	682	364	679	440	523	141
24	435	329	443	454	208	471	228	45	237	336
25	526	105	249	120	501	392	8	721	144	508
26	346	793	128	34	67	162	438	327	469	334
27	118	719	791	160	332	158	570	572	305	746
28	739	574	446	379	94	307	804	532	517	748
29	457	57	40	741	553	26	776	576	211	481
30	608	448	754	542	706	381	474	760	371	96
31	410	558	428	309	231	422	186	806	244	89
32	181	534	48	663	200	519	497	114	800	750
33	240	651	82	459	655	642	821	59	339	622
34	138	42	389	31	716	743	529	23	539	555
35	86	111	639	28	108	267	73	778	615	270
36	690	578	252	698	732	213	463	76	316	483
37	123	548	492	610	596	781	192	450	504	154
38	53	756	659	618	263	544	395	399	629	708
39	601	273	299	383	11	359	322	476	646	693
40	354	762	724	403	288	373	17	581	220	98
41	147	587	668	412	825	255	174	560	511	633
42	168	430	786	701	816	311	349	767	280	233
43	63	735	772	424	796	712	686	188	295	216
44	812	808	131	676	205	246	343	466	567	91
45	37	605	368	183	197	79	135	536	70	729
46	489	50	626	319	285	665	165	277	683	202
47	365	486	680	521	441	226	524	499	142	126
48	436	116	330	303	444	802	455	551	209	752
49	472	408	229	242	46	495	238	653	337	387

POWER RESIDUES

	0	1	2	3	4	5	6	7	8	9
0	1	2	4	8	16	32	64	128	256	512
1	197	394	788	749	671	515	203	406	812	797
2	767	707	587	347	694	561	295	590	353	706
3	585	343	686	545	263	526	225	450	73	146
4	292	584	341	682	537	247	494	161	322	644
5	461	95	190	380	760	693	559	291	582	337
6	674	521	215	430	33	66	132	264	528	229
7	458	89	178	356	712	597	367	734	641	455
8	83	166	332	664	501	175	350	700	573	319
9	638	449	71	142	284	568	309	618	409	818
10	809	791	755	683	539	251	502	177	354	708
11	589	351	702	577	327	654	481	135	270	540
12	253	506	185	370	740	653	479	131	262	524
13	221	442	57	114	228	456	85	170	340	680
14	533	239	478	129	258	516	205	410	820	813
15	799	771	715	603	379	758	689	551	275	550
16	273	546	265	530	233	466	105	210	420	13
17	26	52	104	208	416	5	10	20	40	80
18	160	320	640	453	79	158	316	632	437	47
19	94	188	376	752	677	527	227	454	81	162
20	324	648	469	111	222	444	61	122	244	488
21	149	298	596	365	730	633	439	51	102	204
22	408	816	805	783	739	651	475	123	246	492
23	157	314	628	429	31	62	124	248	496	165
24	330	660	493	159	318	636	445	63	126	252
25	504	181	362	724	621	415	3	6	12	24
26	48	96	192	384	768	709	591	355	710	593
27	359	718	609	391	782	737	647	467	107	214
28	428	29	58	116	232	464	101	202	404	808
29	789	751	675	523	219	438	49	98	196	392
30	784	741	655	483	139	278	556	285	570	313
31	626	425	23	46	92	184	368	736	645	463
32	99	198	396	792	757	687	547	267	534	241
33	482	137	274	548	269	538	249	498	169	338
34	676	525	223	446	65	130	260	520	213	426
35	25	50	100	200	400	800	773	719	611	395
36	790	753	679	531	235	470	113	226	452	77
37	154	308	616	405	810	793	759	691	555	283
38	566	305	610	393	786	745	663	499	171	342
39	684	541	255	510	193	386	772	717	607	387
40	774	721	615	403	806	785	743	659	491	155
41	310	620	413	826	825	823	819	811	795	763
42	699	571	315	630	433	39	78	156	312	624
43	421	15	30	60	120	240	480	133	266	532
44	237	474	121	242	484	141	282	564	301	602
45	377	754	681	535	243	486	145	290	580	333
46	666	505	183	366	732	637	447	67	134	268
47	536	245	490	153	306	612	397	794	761	695
48	563	299	598	369	738	649	471	115	230	460
49	93	186	372	744	661	495	163	326	652	477

P = 827

INDICES

	0	1	2	3	4	5	6	7	8	9
50	527	84	106	613	250	461	121	594	502	657
51	393	599	9	644	722	15	145	823	509	784
52	347	61	794	293	129	341	35	195	68	624
53	163	363	439	140	328	453	470	44	335	104
54	119	391	720	507	792	33	161	326	333	718
55	159	157	571	745	573	378	306	531	747	56
56	740	25	575	480	447	541	380	759	95	557
57	308	421	805	88	533	662	518	113	749	650
58	458	641	58	621	41	30	742	22	554	110
59	27	266	777	269	577	697	212	75	482	547
60	609	780	449	153	755	617	543	398	707	272
61	382	358	475	692	761	402	372	580	97	586
62	411	254	559	632	429	700	310	766	232	734
63	423	711	187	215	807	675	245	465	90	604
64	182	78	535	728	49	318	664	276	201	485
65	520	225	498	125	115	302	801	550	751	407
66	241	494	652	386	83	612	460	593	656	598
67	643	14	822	783	60	292	340	194	623	362
68	139	452	43	103	390	506	32	325	717	156
69	744	377	530	55	24	479	540	758	556	420
70	87	661	112	649	640	620	29	21	109	265
71	268	696	74	546	779	152	616	397	271	357
72	691	401	579	585	253	631	699	765	733	710
73	214	674	464	603	77	727	317	275	484	224
74	124	301	549	406	493	385	611	592	597	13
75	782	291	193	361	451	102	505	324	155	376
76	54	478	757	419	660	648	619	20	264	695
77	545	151	396	356	400	584	630	764	709	673
78	602	726	274	223	300	405	384	591	12	290
79	360	101	323	375	477	418	647	19	694	150
80	355	583	763	672	725	222	404	590	289	100
81	374	417	18	149	582	671	221	589	99	416
82	148	670	588	415	669	414	413			

POWER RESIDUES

	0	1	2	3	4	5	6	7	8	9
50	127	254	508	189	378	756	685	543	259	518
51	209	418	9	18	36	72	144	288	576	325
52	650	473	119	238	476	125	250	500	173	346
53	692	557	287	574	321	642	457	87	174	348
54	696	565	303	606	385	770	713	599	371	742
55	657	487	147	294	588	349	698	569	311	622
56	417	7	14	28	56	112	224	448	69	138
57	276	552	277	554	281	562	297	594	361	722
58	617	407	814	801	775	723	619	411	822	817
59	807	787	747	667	507	187	374	748	669	511
60	195	390	780	733	639	451	75	150	300	600
61	373	746	665	503	179	358	716	605	383	766
62	705	583	339	678	529	231	462	97	194	388
63	776	725	623	419	11	22	44	88	176	352
64	704	581	335	670	513	199	398	796	765	703
65	579	331	662	497	167	334	668	509	191	382
66	764	701	575	323	646	465	103	206	412	824
67	821	815	803	779	731	635	443	59	118	236
68	472	117	234	468	109	218	436	45	90	180
69	360	720	613	399	798	769	711	595	363	726
70	625	423	19	38	76	152	304	608	389	778
71	729	631	435	43	86	172	344	688	549	271
72	542	257	514	201	402	804	781	735	643	459
73	91	182	364	728	629	431	35	70	140	280
74	560	293	586	345	690	553	279	558	289	578
75	329	658	489	151	302	604	381	762	697	567
76	307	614	401	802	777	727	627	427	27	54
77	108	216	432	37	74	148	296	592	357	714
78	601	375	750	673	519	211	422	17	34	68
79	136	272	544	261	522	217	434	41	82	164
80	328	656	485	143	286	572	317	634	441	55
81	110	220	440	53	106	212	424	21	42	84
82	168	336	672	517	207	414				

P = 829

INDICES

	0	1	2	3	4	5	6	7	8	9
0		0	1	376	2	92	377	213	3	752
1	93	684	378	370	214	468	4	404	753	355
2	94	589	685	488	379	184	371	300	215	603
3	469	531	5	232	405	305	754	197	356	746
4	95	244	590	437	686	16	489	479	380	426
5	185	780	372	351	301	776	216	731	604	576
6	470	798	532	137	6	462	233	220	406	36
7	306	110	755	101	198	560	357	69	747	239
8	96	676	245	735	591	496	438	151	687	705
9	17	583	490	79	480	447	381	762	427	608
10	186	172	781	503	373	681	352	297	302	434
11	777	573	217	557	732	580	605	294	577	617
12	471	540	799	620	533	276	138	257	7	813
13	463	474	234	568	221	392	407	250	37	543
14	307	27	111	226	756	695	102	802	199	85
15	561	520	358	328	70	623	748	180	240	727
16	97	701	677	536	246	324	736	285	592	740
17	497	279	439	662	152	397	688	124	706	141
18	18	265	584	346	491	289	80	260	481	513
19	448	46	382	315	763	10	428	656	609	644
20	187	596	173	816	782	336	504	412	374	211
21	682	466	353	486	298	529	303	744	435	477
22	778	774	574	135	218	108	558	237	733	149
23	581	445	606	501	295	571	578	615	618	255
24	472	390	541	224	800	518	621	725	534	283
25	277	395	139	344	258	44	8	642	814	410
26	464	527	475	133	235	443	569	253	222	723
27	393	42	408	131	251	40	38	453	544	455
28	308	666	28	546	112	823	227	457	757	808
29	696	310	103	637	803	668	200	156	86	30
30	562	650	521	548	359	62	329	114	71	51
31	624	825	749	401	181	229	241	423	728	459
32	98	673	702	759	678	554	537	810	247	692
33	325	698	737	121	286	312	593	208	741	105
34	498	387	280	639	440	128	663	805	153	59
35	398	670	689	205	125	202	707	165	142	158
36	19	710	266	88	585	193	347	32	492	168
37	290	564	81	320	261	652	482	145	514	523
38	449	633	47	550	383	161	316	361	764	365
39	11	64	429	22	657	331	610	718	645	116
40	188	713	597	73	174	768	817	53	783	269
41	337	626	505	789	413	827	375	91	212	751
42	683	369	467	403	354	588	487	183	299	602
43	530	231	304	196	745	243	436	15	478	425
44	779	350	775	730	575	797	136	461	219	35
45	109	100	559	68	238	675	734	495	150	704
46	582	78	446	761	607	171	502	680	296	433
47	572	556	579	293	616	539	619	275	256	812
48	473	567	391	249	542	26	225	694	801	84
49	519	327	622	179	726	700	535	323	284	739

POWER RESIDUES

	0	1	2	3	4	5	6	7	8	9
0	1	2	4	8	16	32	64	128	256	512
1	195	390	780	731	633	437	45	90	180	360
2	720	611	393	786	743	657	485	141	282	564
3	299	598	367	734	639	449	69	138	276	552
4	275	550	271	542	255	510	191	382	764	699
5	569	309	618	407	814	799	769	709	589	349
6	698	567	305	610	391	782	735	641	453	77
7	154	308	616	403	806	783	737	645	461	93
8	186	372	744	659	489	149	298	596	363	726
9	623	417	5	10	20	40	80	160	320	640
10	451	73	146	292	584	339	678	527	225	450
11	71	142	284	568	307	614	399	798	767	705
12	581	333	666	503	177	354	708	587	345	690
13	551	273	546	263	526	223	446	63	126	252
14	504	179	358	716	603	377	754	679	529	229
15	458	87	174	348	696	563	297	594	359	718
16	607	385	770	711	593	357	714	599	369	738
17	647	465	101	202	404	808	787	745	661	493
18	157	314	628	427	25	50	100	200	400	800
19	771	713	597	365	730	631	433	37	74	148
20	296	592	355	710	591	353	706	583	337	674
21	519	209	418	7	14	28	56	112	224	448
22	67	134	268	536	243	486	143	286	572	315
23	630	431	33	66	132	264	528	227	454	79
24	158	316	632	435	41	82	164	328	656	483
25	137	274	548	267	534	239	478	127	254	508
26	187	374	748	667	505	181	362	724	619	409
27	818	807	785	741	653	477	125	250	500	171
28	342	684	539	249	498	167	334	668	507	185
29	370	740	651	473	117	234	468	107	214	428
30	27	54	108	216	432	35	70	140	280	560
31	291	582	335	670	511	193	386	772	715	601
32	373	746	663	497	165	330	660	491	153	306
33	612	395	790	751	673	517	205	410	820	811
34	793	757	685	541	253	506	183	366	732	635
35	441	53	106	212	424	19	38	76	152	304
36	608	387	774	719	609	389	778	727	625	421
37	13	26	52	104	208	416	3	6	12	24
38	48	96	192	384	768	707	585	341	682	535
39	241	482	135	270	540	251	502	175	350	700
40	571	313	626	423	17	34	68	136	272	544
41	259	518	207	414	828	827	825	821	813	797
42	765	701	573	317	634	439	49	98	196	392
43	784	739	649	469	109	218	436	43	86	172
44	344	688	547	265	530	231	462	95	190	380
45	760	691	553	277	554	279	558	287	574	319
46	638	447	65	130	260	520	211	422	15	30
47	60	120	240	480	131	262	524	219	438	47
48	94	188	376	752	675	521	213	426	23	46
49	92	184	368	736	643	457	85	170	340	680

P = 829

INDICES

	0	1	2	3	4	5	6	7	8	9
50	278	661	396	123	140	264	345	288	259	512
51	45	314	9	655	643	595	815	335	411	210
52	465	485	528	743	476	773	134	107	236	148
53	444	500	570	614	254	389	223	517	724	282
54	394	343	43	641	409	526	132	442	252	722
55	41	130	39	452	454	665	545	822	456	807
56	309	636	667	155	29	649	547	61	113	50
57	824	400	228	422	458	672	758	553	809	691
58	697	120	311	207	104	386	638	127	804	58
59	669	204	201	164	157	709	87	192	31	167
60	563	319	651	144	522	632	549	160	360	364
61	63	21	330	717	115	712	72	767	52	268
62	625	788	826	90	750	368	402	587	182	601
63	230	195	242	14	424	349	729	796	460	34
64	99	67	674	494	703	77	760	170	679	432
65	555	292	538	274	811	566	248	25	693	83
66	326	178	699	322	738	660	122	263	287	511
67	313	654	594	334	209	484	742	772	106	147
68	499	613	388	516	281	342	640	525	441	721
69	129	451	664	821	806	635	154	648	60	49
70	399	421	671	552	690	119	206	385	126	57
71	203	163	708	191	166	318	143	631	159	363
72	20	716	711	766	267	787	89	367	586	600
73	194	13	348	795	33	66	493	76	169	431
74	291	273	565	24	82	177	321	659	262	510
75	653	333	483	771	146	612	515	341	524	720
76	450	820	634	647	48	420	551	118	384	56
77	162	190	317	630	362	715	765	786	366	599
78	12	794	65	75	430	272	23	176	658	509
79	332	770	611	340	719	819	646	419	117	55
80	189	629	714	785	598	793	74	271	175	508
81	769	339	818	418	54	628	784	792	270	507
82	338	417	627	791	506	416	790	415	414	

POWER RESIDUES

	0	1	2	3	4	5	6	7	8	9
50	531	233	466	103	206	412	824	819	809	789
51	749	669	509	189	378	756	683	537	245	490
52	151	302	604	379	758	687	545	261	522	215
53	430	31	62	124	248	496	163	326	652	475
54	121	242	484	139	278	556	283	566	303	606
55	383	766	703	577	325	650	471	113	226	452
56	75	150	300	600	371	742	655	481	133	266
57	532	235	470	111	222	444	59	118	236	472
58	115	230	460	91	182	364	728	627	425	21
59	42	84	168	336	672	515	201	402	804	779
60	729	629	429	29	58	116	232	464	99	198
61	396	792	755	681	533	237	474	119	238	476
62	123	246	492	155	310	620	411	822	815	801
63	773	717	605	381	762	695	561	293	586	343
64	686	543	257	514	199	398	796	763	697	565
65	301	602	375	750	671	513	197	394	788	747
66	665	501	173	346	692	555	281	562	295	590
67	351	702	575	321	642	455	81	162	324	648
68	467	105	210	420	11	22	44	88	176	352
69	704	579	329	658	487	145	290	580	331	662
70	495	161	322	644	459	89	178	356	712	595
71	361	722	615	401	802	775	721	613	397	794
72	759	689	549	269	538	247	494	159	318	636
73	443	57	114	228	456	83	166	332	664	499
74	169	338	676	523	217	434	39	78	156	312
75	624	419	9	18	36	72	144	288	576	323
76	646	463	97	194	388	776	723	617	405	810
77	791	753	677	525	221	442	55	110	220	440
78	51	102	204	408	816	803	777	725	621	413
79	826	823	817	805	781	733	637	445	61	122
80	244	488	147	294	588	347	694	559	289	578
81	327	654	479	129	258	516	203	406	812	795
82	761	693	557	285	570	311	622	415		

P = 839

INDICES

	0	1	2	3	4	5	6	7	8	9
0		0	486	192	134	246	678	618	620	384
1	732	1	326	635	266	438	268	699	32	476
2	380	810	487	740	812	492	283	576	752	243
3	86	329	754	193	347	26	518	424	124	827
4	28	515	458	430	135	630	388	586	460	398
5	140	53	769	116	224	247	400	668	729	788
6	572	172	815	164	402	43	679	119	833	94
7	512	309	166	98	72	684	610	619	475	85
8	514	768	163	71	106	107	78	435	621	159
9	278	415	36	521	234	722	108	801	46	385
10	626	128	539	237	417	218	602	79	710	411
11	733	616	48	261	316	148	377	181	436	479
12	220	2	658	707	463	738	650	360	50	622
13	529	695	327	256	605	822	481	440	580	825
14	160	778	795	636	652	489	584	590	558	407
15	332	279	258	245	267	575	123	397	571	308
16	162	520	416	147	649	439	557	307	592	432
17	593	22	564	37	83	272	269	142	645	154
18	764	433	63	364	522	670	169	700	720	356
19	370	131	594	404	449	235	532	338	33	715
20	274	311	614	23	187	761	723	286	65	477
21	704	112	250	501	565	676	358	109	59	290
22	381	496	264	820	534	38	747	798	802	485
23	634	811	25	387	667	832	84	277	127	47
24	706	604	488	122	306	644	355	273	111	263
25	386	305	298	741	8	299	536	222	270	204
26	177	627	343	367	813	362	742	351	253	143
27	470	510	129	607	88	493	228	9	473	713
28	646	780	426	540	443	76	284	295	300	560
29	137	155	232	674	238	196	206	577	55	537
30	818	210	765	320	744	418	731	809	753	429
31	223	42	609	434	45	410	219	694	794	244
32	648	271	168	337	64	289	633	603	297	366
33	87	75	205	808	793	365	240	372	80	453
34	241	330	508	178	212	340	523	422	569	711
35	758	373	755	189	628	555	293	671	640	773
36	412	114	81	194	549	344	12	151	170	61
37	318	734	655	454	348	92	368	40	4	701
38	18	552	617	31	242	27	52	814	97	105
39	721	601	180	49	824	331	519	563	363	448
40	760	357	797	126	262	176	509	425	673	743
41	409	632	371	568	772	317	551	179	125	771
42	352	544	598	132	736	353	149	790	213	828
43	324	254	6	90	595	681	545	378	776	341
44	29	782	144	100	750	405	468	599	182	302
45	524	516	395	471	446	661	450	198	133	437
46	282	423	459	787	511	767	35	236	315	737
47	480	589	570	431	763	130	613	500	533	831
48	354	221	252	712	136	209	608	336	792	339
49	292	150	3	104	759	631	597	89	749	660

POWER RESIDUES

	0	1	2	3	4	5	6	7	8	9
0	1	11	121	492	378	802	432	557	254	277
1	530	796	366	670	658	526	752	721	380	824
2	674	702	171	203	555	232	35	385	40	440
3	645	383	18	198	500	466	92	173	225	797
4	377	791	311	65	715	314	98	239	112	393
5	128	569	386	51	561	298	761	820	630	218
6	720	369	703	182	324	208	610	837	817	597
7	694	83	74	814	564	331	285	618	86	107
8	338	362	626	174	236	79	30	330	274	497
9	433	568	375	769	69	759	798	388	73	803
10	443	678	746	655	493	389	84	85	96	217
11	709	248	211	643	361	615	53	583	540	67
12	737	556	243	156	38	418	403	238	101	272
13	475	191	423	458	4	44	484	290	673	691
14	50	550	177	269	442	667	625	163	115	426
15	491	367	681	779	179	291	684	812	542	89
16	140	701	160	82	63	693	72	792	322	186
17	368	692	61	671	669	647	405	260	343	417
18	392	117	448	733	512	598	705	204	566	353
19	527	763	3	33	363	637	295	728	457	832
20	762	831	751	710	259	332	296	739	578	485
21	301	794	344	428	513	609	826	696	105	316
22	120	481	257	310	54	594	661	559	276	519
23	675	713	292	695	94	195	467	103	294	717
24	336	340	384	29	319	153	5	55	605	782
25	212	654	482	268	431	546	133	624	152	833
26	773	113	404	249	222	764	14	154	16	176
27	258	321	175	247	200	522	708	237	90	151
28	822	652	460	26	286	629	207	599	716	325
29	219	731	490	356	560	287	640	328	252	255
30	288	651	449	744	633	251	244	167	159	71
31	781	201	533	829	729	468	114	415	370	714
32	303	816	586	573	430	535	12	132	613	31
33	341	395	150	811	531	807	487	323	197	489
34	345	439	634	262	365	659	537	34	374	758
35	787	267	420	425	480	246	189	401	216	698
36	127	558	265	398	183	335	329	263	376	780
37	190	412	337	351	505	521	697	116	437	612
38	20	220	742	611	9	99	250	233	46	506
39	532	818	608	815	575	452	777	157	49	539
40	56	616	64	704	193	445	700	149	800	410
41	315	109	360	604	771	91	162	104	305	838
42	828	718	347	461	37	407	282	585	562	309
43	43	473	169	181	313	87	118	459	15	165
44	137	668	636	284	607	804	454	799	399	194
45	456	821	641	339	373	747	666	614	42	462
46	48	528	774	124	525	741	600	727	446	711
47	270	453	788	278	541	78	19	209	621	119
48	470	136	657	515	631	229	2	22	242	145
49	756	765	25	275	508	554	221	753	732	501

P = 839

INDICES

	0	1	2	3	4	5	6	7	8	9
50	34	499	791	659	784	374	389	624	494	506
51	785	716	184	214	708	483	756	587	690	229
52	663	375	275	638	829	464	15	190	461	642
53	10	334	390	312	837	325	739	346	629	399
54	118	474	158	625	615	657	255	651	574	556
55	141	719	714	703	495	24	121	7	361	227
56	294	54	428	647	74	507	188	548	91	51
57	562	672	770	323	781	394	786	762	208	596
58	623	689	641	117	718	427	322	717	724	805
59	682	530	692	774	225	725	541	69	185	287
60	466	546	696	503	413	248	806	444	392	215
61	66	383	379	328	457	115	401	683	77	800
62	709	478	528	777	257	146	82	669	531	285
63	58	484	705	304	342	606	442	195	730	693
64	296	452	757	113	654	30	823	175	550	789
65	775	301	281	588	251	103	783	482	14	345
66	573	226	561	688	691	502	456	145	441	174
67	13	173	726	138	20	230	566	835	101	581
68	727	152	816	542	156	686	664	677	698	751
69	826	139	171	165	70	233	217	376	359	579
70	406	161	21	62	403	186	675	746	276	110
71	203	469	779	231	319	44	288	239	421	639
72	60	17	600	796	567	735	680	467	197	314
73	830	291	498	183	637	836	656	120	547	207
74	804	465	382	527	303	653	102	455	834	697
75	578	202	16	497	526	525	490	582	349	95
76	504	56	200	191	265	491	517	585	728	93
77	513	414	538	260	462	821	583	396	591	153
78	369	310	249	819	666	643	535	350	472	559
79	817	41	167	807	211	554	11	39	96	447
80	408	543	5	99	445	766	612	335	748	505
81	662	333	157	702	73	393	321	68	391	799
82	57	451	280	687	19	685	216	745	420	313
83	803	201	199	259	665	553	611	67	419	

POWER RESIDUES

	0	1	2	3	4	5	6	7	8	9
50	477	213	665	603	760	809	509	565	342	406
51	271	464	70	770	80	41	451	766	36	396
52	161	93	184	346	450	755	754	743	622	130
53	591	628	196	478	224	786	256	299	772	102
54	283	596	683	801	421	436	601	738	567	364
55	648	416	381	835	795	355	549	166	148	789
56	289	662	570	397	172	214	676	724	413	348
57	472	158	60	660	548	155	27	297	750	699
58	138	679	757	776	146	767	47	517	653	471
59	147	778	168	170	192	434	579	496	422	447
60	722	391	106	327	241	134	635	273	486	312
61	76	836	806	476	202	544	111	382	7	77
62	8	88	129	580	507	543	100	261	354	538
63	45	495	411	326	230	13	143	734	523	719
64	358	582	529	785	245	178	280	563	320	164
65	126	547	144	745	644	372	736	545	122	503
66	499	455	810	520	686	834	784	234	57	627
67	185	357	571	408	293	706	215	687	6	66
68	726	435	590	617	75	825	685	823	663	581
69	518	664	592	639	317	131	602	749	688	17
70	187	379	813	553	210	632	240	123	514	620
71	108	349	483	279	552	199	511	587	584	551
72	188	390	95	206	588	595	672	680	768	58
73	638	306	10	110	371	725	424	469	125	536
74	23	253	266	409	304	827	707	226	808	498
75	444	689	28	308	32	352	516	642	350	494
76	400	205	577	474	180	302	805	465	81	52
77	572	419	414	359	593	650	438	623	141	712
78	281	574	441	656	504	510	576	463	59	649
79	427	502	488	334	318	142	723	402	227	819
80	619	97	228	830	740	589	606	793	333	307
81	21	231	24	264	387	62	682	790	300	783
82	223	775	135	646	394	139	690	39	429	524
83	730	479	235	68	748	677	735	534		

P = 853

INDICES

	0	1	2	3	4	5	6	7	8	9
0		0	1	474	2	843	475	603	3	96
1	844	575	476	645	604	465	4	65	97	766
2	845	225	576	310	477	834	646	570	605	451
3	466	712	5	197	66	594	98	117	767	267
4	846	630	226	610	577	87	311	80	478	354
5	835	539	647	413	571	566	606	388	452	392
6	467	248	713	699	6	636	198	304	67	784
7	595	802	99	686	118	456	768	326	268	281
8	847	192	631	744	227	56	611	73	578	125
9	88	396	312	334	81	757	479	749	355	671
10	836	510	540	22	648	216	414	471	572	763
11	567	591	607	536	389	301	453	741	393	668
12	468	298	249	252	714	825	700	347	7	232
13	637	255	199	517	305	561	68	663	785	717
14	596	554	803	368	100	442	687	828	119	155
15	457	790	769	161	327	703	269	502	282	35
16	848	61	193	350	632	188	745	532	228	438
17	57	10	612	485	74	585	579	14	126	235
18	89	656	397	722	313	108	335	640	82	321
19	758	549	480	616	750	258	356	208	672	812
20	837	778	511	202	541	621	23	406	649	489
21	217	520	415	424	472	601	573	463	764	308
22	568	710	592	265	608	78	537	564	390	697
23	302	800	454	279	742	71	394	755	669	20
24	469	589	299	666	250	345	253	559	715	366
25	826	788	701	33	348	530	8	583	233	720
26	638	547	256	810	200	404	518	599	306	263
27	562	798	69	18	664	557	786	528	718	808
28	597	796	555	806	804	379	369	381	101	130
29	443	371	688	172	829	383	120	293	156	103
30	458	361	791	132	770	239	162	445	328	496
31	704	373	270	137	503	690	283	733	36	174
32	849	93	62	831	194	627	351	385	633	683
33	189	122	746	213	533	295	229	660	439	158
34	58	435	11	105	613	775	486	460	75	276
35	586	363	580	401	15	793	127	290	236	134
36	90	680	657	772	398	677	723	241	314	726
37	109	164	336	44	641	447	83	244	322	330
38	759	821	550	498	481	317	617	706	751	29
39	259	375	357	729	209	272	673	817	813	139
40	838	112	779	505	512	183	203	692	542	167
41	622	285	24	143	407	735	650	339	490	38
42	218	148	521	176	416	47	425	851	473	842
43	602	95	574	644	464	64	765	224	309	833
44	569	450	711	196	593	116	266	629	609	86
45	79	353	538	412	565	387	391	247	698	635
46	303	783	801	685	455	325	280	191	743	55
47	72	124	395	333	756	748	670	509	21	215
48	470	762	590	535	300	740	667	297	251	824
49	346	231	254	516	560	662	716	553	367	441

POWER RESIDUES

	0	1	2	3	4	5	6	7	8	9
0	1	2	4	8	16	32	64	128	256	512
1	171	342	684	515	177	354	708	563	273	546
2	239	478	103	206	412	824	795	737	621	389
3	778	703	553	253	506	159	318	636	419	838
4	823	793	733	613	373	746	639	425	850	847
5	841	829	805	757	661	469	85	170	340	680
6	507	161	322	644	435	17	34	68	136	272
7	544	235	470	87	174	348	696	539	225	450
8	47	94	188	376	752	651	449	45	90	180
9	360	720	587	321	642	431	9	18	36	72
10	144	288	576	299	598	343	686	519	185	370
11	740	627	401	802	751	649	445	37	74	148
12	296	592	331	662	471	89	178	356	712	571
13	289	578	303	606	359	718	583	313	626	399
14	798	743	633	413	826	799	745	637	421	842
15	831	809	765	677	501	149	298	596	339	678
16	503	153	306	612	371	742	631	409	818	783
17	713	573	293	586	319	638	423	846	839	825
18	797	741	629	405	810	767	681	509	165	330
19	660	467	81	162	324	648	443	33	66	132
20	264	528	203	406	812	771	689	525	197	394
21	788	723	593	333	666	479	105	210	420	840
22	827	801	749	645	437	21	42	84	168	336
23	672	491	129	258	516	179	358	716	579	305
24	610	367	734	615	377	754	655	457	61	122
25	244	488	123	246	492	131	262	524	195	390
26	780	707	561	269	538	223	446	39	78	156
27	312	624	395	790	727	601	349	698	543	233
28	466	79	158	316	632	411	822	791	729	605
29	357	714	575	297	594	335	670	487	121	242
30	484	115	230	460	67	134	268	536	219	438
31	23	46	92	184	368	736	619	385	770	687
32	521	189	378	756	659	465	77	154	308	616
33	379	758	663	473	93	186	372	744	635	417
34	834	815	777	701	549	245	490	127	254	508
35	163	326	652	451	49	98	196	392	784	715
36	577	301	602	351	702	551	249	498	143	286
37	572	291	582	311	622	391	782	711	569	285
38	570	287	574	295	590	327	654	455	57	114
39	228	456	59	118	236	472	91	182	364	728
40	603	353	706	559	265	530	207	414	828	803
41	753	653	453	53	106	212	424	848	843	833
42	813	773	693	533	213	426	852	851	849	845
43	837	821	789	725	597	341	682	511	169	338
44	676	499	145	290	580	307	614	375	750	647
45	441	29	58	116	232	464	75	150	300	600
46	347	694	535	217	434	15	30	60	120	240
47	480	107	214	428	3	6	12	24	48	96
48	192	384	768	683	513	173	346	692	531	209
49	418	836	819	785	717	581	309	618	383	766

P = 853

INDICES

	0	1	2	3	4	5	6	7	8	9
50	827	154	789	160	702	501	34	60	349	187
51	531	437	9	484	584	13	234	655	721	107
52	639	320	548	615	257	207	811	777	201	620
53	405	488	519	423	600	462	307	709	264	77
54	563	696	799	278	70	754	19	588	665	344
55	558	365	787	32	529	582	719	546	809	403
56	598	262	797	17	556	527	807	795	805	378
57	380	129	370	171	382	292	102	360	131	238
58	444	495	372	136	689	732	173	92	830	626
59	384	682	121	212	294	659	157	434	104	774
60	459	275	362	400	792	289	133	679	771	676
61	240	725	163	43	446	243	329	820	497	316
62	705	28	374	728	271	816	138	111	504	182
63	691	166	284	142	734	338	37	147	175	46
64	850	841	94	643	63	223	832	449	195	115
65	628	85	352	411	386	246	634	782	684	324
66	190	54	123	332	747	508	214	761	534	739
67	296	823	230	515	661	552	440	153	159	500
68	59	186	436	483	12	654	106	319	614	206
69	776	619	487	422	461	708	76	695	277	753
70	587	343	364	31	581	545	402	261	16	526
71	794	377	128	170	291	359	237	494	135	731
72	91	625	681	211	658	433	773	274	399	288
73	678	675	724	42	242	819	315	27	727	815
74	110	181	165	141	337	146	45	840	642	222
75	448	114	84	410	245	781	323	53	331	507
76	760	738	822	514	551	152	499	185	482	653
77	318	205	618	421	707	694	752	342	30	544
78	260	525	376	169	358	493	730	624	210	432
79	273	287	674	41	818	26	814	180	140	145
80	839	221	113	409	780	52	506	737	513	151
81	184	652	204	420	693	341	543	524	168	492
82	623	431	286	40	25	179	144	220	408	51
83	736	150	651	419	340	523	491	430	39	178
84	219	50	149	418	522	429	177	49	417	428
85	48	427	426							

POWER RESIDUES

	0	1	2	3	4	5	6	7	8	9
50	679	505	157	314	628	403	806	759	665	477
51	101	202	404	808	763	673	493	133	266	532
52	211	422	844	835	817	781	709	565	277	554
53	255	510	167	334	668	483	113	226	452	51
54	102	204	408	816	779	705	557	261	522	191
55	382	764	675	497	141	282	564	275	550	247
56	494	135	270	540	227	454	55	110	220	440
57	27	54	108	216	432	11	22	44	88	176
58	352	704	555	257	514	175	350	700	547	241
59	482	111	222	444	35	70	140	280	560	267
60	534	215	430	7	14	28	56	112	224	448
61	43	86	172	344	688	523	193	386	772	691
62	529	205	410	820	787	721	589	325	650	447
63	41	82	164	328	656	459	65	130	260	520
64	187	374	748	643	433	13	26	52	104	208
65	416	832	811	769	685	517	181	362	724	595
66	337	674	495	137	274	548	243	486	119	238
67	476	99	198	396	792	731	609	365	730	607
68	361	722	591	329	658	463	73	146	292	584
69	315	630	407	814	775	697	541	229	458	63
70	126	252	504	155	310	620	387	774	695	537
71	221	442	31	62	124	248	496	139	278	556
72	259	518	183	366	732	611	369	738	623	393
73	786	719	585	317	634	415	830	807	761	669
74	485	117	234	468	83	166	332	664	475	97
75	194	388	776	699	545	237	474	95	190	380
76	760	667	481	109	218	436	19	38	76	152
77	304	608	363	726	599	345	690	527	201	402
78	804	755	657	461	69	138	276	552	251	502
79	151	302	604	355	710	567	281	562	271	542
80	231	462	71	142	284	568	283	566	279	558
81	263	526	199	398	796	739	625	397	794	735
82	617	381	762	671	489	125	250	500	147	294
83	588	323	646	439	25	50	100	200	400	800
84	747	641	429	5	10	20	40	80	160	320
85	640	427								

P = 857

INDICES

	0	1	2	3	4	5	6	7	8	9
0		0	62	1	124	773	63	313	186	2
1	835	47	125	746	375	774	248	845	64	571
2	41	314	109	212	187	690	808	3	437	766
3	836	466	310	48	51	230	126	279	633	747
4	103	666	376	816	171	775	274	411	249	626
5	752	846	14	182	65	820	499	572	828	519
6	42	54	528	315	372	663	110	485	113	213
7	292	220	188	446	341	691	695	360	809	78
8	165	4	728	452	438	762	22	767	233	69
9	837	203	336	467	473	488	311	246	688	49
10	814	12	52	290	76	231	244	242	127	588
11	26	280	561	225	634	129	34	748	581	302
12	104	94	116	667	590	607	377	853	434	817
13	725	585	172	28	547	776	175	595	275	577
14	354	412	282	793	250	683	508	627	403	216
15	753	563	757	847	422	383	15	699	140	183
16	227	525	66	31	790	821	514	620	500	636
17	824	573	84	269	829	147	295	520	131	716
18	43	332	265	55	398	196	529	36	535	316
19	550	771	373	210	308	664	750	517	111	358
20	20	486	74	223	114	583	352	214	138	618
21	293	194	306	221	304	733	189	779	650	447
22	88	735	342	106	623	692	287	722	696	395
23	191	361	96	567	810	328	643	79	364	781
24	166	118	156	5	178	543	729	461	652	453
25	669	503	439	259	59	763	496	449	23	592
26	787	768	647	540	234	99	90	70	609	323
27	838	598	237	204	657	737	337	379	639	468
28	416	802	474	613	344	489	855	123	312	834
29	745	247	570	108	689	436	465	50	278	102
30	815	273	625	13	819	827	53	371	484	291
31	445	694	77	727	761	232	202	472	245	813
32	289	243	587	560	128	580	93	589	852	724
33	27	174	576	281	682	402	562	421	698	226
34	30	513	635	83	146	130	331	397	35	549
35	209	749	357	73	582	137	193	303	778	87
36	105	286	394	95	327	363	117	177	460	668
37	258	495	591	646	98	608	597	656	378	415
38	612	854	833	569	435	277	272	818	370	444
39	726	201	812	586	579	851	173	681	420	29
40	82	330	548	356	136	777	285	326	176	257
41	645	596	414	832	276	369	200	578	680	81
42	355	284	256	413	368	679	283	367	366	794
43	795	711	251	796	841	684	712	783	509	252
44	150	628	797	704	404	842	168	217	685	604
45	754	713	349	564	784	120	758	510	457	848
46	253	601	423	151	158	384	629	298	16	798
47	390	700	705	7	141	405	426	184	843	806
48	228	169	180	526	218	163	67	686	240	32
49	605	545	791	755	523	822	714	533	515	350

POWER RESIDUES

	0	1	2	3	4	5	6	7	8	9
0	1	3	9	27	81	243	729	473	562	829
1	773	605	101	303	52	156	468	547	784	638
2	200	600	86	258	774	608	110	330	133	399
3	340	163	489	610	116	348	187	561	826	764
4	578	20	60	180	540	763	575	11	33	99
5	297	34	102	306	61	183	549	790	656	254
6	762	572	2	6	18	54	162	486	601	89
7	267	801	689	353	202	606	104	312	79	237
8	711	419	400	343	172	516	691	359	220	660
9	266	798	680	326	121	363	232	696	374	265
10	795	671	299	40	120	360	223	669	293	22
11	66	198	594	68	204	612	122	366	241	723
12	455	508	667	287	4	12	36	108	324	115
13	345	178	534	745	521	706	404	355	208	624
14	158	474	565	838	800	686	344	175	525	718
15	440	463	532	739	503	652	242	726	464	535
16	748	530	733	485	598	80	240	720	446	481
17	586	44	132	396	331	136	408	367	244	732
18	482	589	53	159	477	574	8	24	72	216
19	648	230	690	356	211	633	185	555	808	710
20	416	391	316	91	273	819	743	515	688	350
21	193	579	23	69	207	621	149	447	484	595
22	71	213	639	203	609	113	339	160	480	583
23	35	105	315	88	264	792	662	272	816	734
24	488	607	107	321	106	318	97	291	16	48
25	144	432	439	460	523	712	422	409	370	253
26	759	563	832	782	632	182	546	781	629	173
27	519	700	386	301	46	138	414	385	298	37
28	111	333	142	426	421	406	361	226	678	320
29	103	309	70	210	630	176	528	727	467	544
30	775	611	119	357	214	642	212	636	194	582
31	32	96	288	7	21	63	189	567	844	818
32	740	506	661	269	807	707	407	364	235	705
33	401	346	181	543	772	602	92	276	828	770
34	596	74	222	666	284	852	842	812	722	452
35	499	640	206	618	140	420	403	352	199	597
36	77	231	693	365	238	714	428	427	424	415
37	388	307	64	192	576	14	42	126	378	277
38	831	779	623	155	465	538	757	557	814	728
39	470	553	802	692	362	229	687	347	184	552
40	799	683	335	148	444	475	568	847	827	767
41	587	47	141	423	412	379	280	840	806	704
42	398	337	154	462	529	730	476	571	856	854
43	848	830	776	614	128	384	295	28	84	252
44	756	554	805	701	389	310	73	219	657	257
45	771	599	83	249	747	527	724	458	517	694
46	368	247	741	509	670	296	31	93	279	837
47	797	677	317	94	282	846	824	758	560	823
48	755	551	796	674	308	67	201	603	95	285
49	855	851	839	803	695	371	256	768	590	56

P = 857

INDICES

	0	1	2	3	4	5	6	7	8	9
50	731	621	565	154	501	785	321	637	121	463
51	825	759	558	574	511	207	85	458	654	270
52	849	134	830	254	709	148	602	455	296	424
53	161	521	152	556	132	159	671	717	385	673
54	44	630	660	333	299	505	266	17	719	56
55	799	481	399	391	441	197	701	387	530	706
56	478	37	8	261	536	142	675	317	406	740
57	551	427	61	772	185	46	374	844	40	211
58	807	765	309	229	632	665	170	410	751	181
59	498	518	527	662	112	219	340	359	164	451
60	21	68	335	487	687	11	75	241	25	224
61	33	301	115	606	433	584	546	594	353	792
62	507	215	756	382	139	524	789	619	823	268
63	294	715	264	195	534	770	307	516	19	222
64	351	617	305	732	649	734	622	721	190	566
65	642	780	155	542	651	502	58	448	786	539
66	89	322	236	736	638	801	343	122	744	107
67	464	101	624	826	483	693	760	471	288	559
68	92	723	575	401	697	512	145	396	208	72
69	192	86	393	362	459	494	97	655	611	568
70	271	443	811	850	419	329	135	325	644	831
71	199	80	255	678	365	710	840	782	149	703
72	167	603	348	119	456	600	157	297	389	6
73	425	805	179	162	239	544	522	532	730	153
74	320	462	557	206	653	133	708	454	160	555
75	670	672	659	504	718	480	440	386	477	260
76	674	739	60	45	39	764	631	409	497	661
77	339	450	334	10	24	300	432	593	506	381
78	788	267	263	769	18	616	648	720	641	541
79	57	538	235	800	743	100	482	470	91	400
80	144	71	392	493	610	442	418	324	198	677
81	839	702	347	599	388	804	238	531	319	205
82	707	554	658	479	476	738	38	408	338	9
83	431	380	262	615	640	537	742	469	143	492
84	417	676	346	803	318	553	475	407	430	614
85	741	491	345	552	429	490	428			

POWER RESIDUES

	0	1	2	3	4	5	6	7	8	9
50	168	504	655	251	753	545	778	620	146	438
51	457	514	685	341	166	498	637	197	591	59
52	177	531	736	494	625	161	483	592	62	186
53	558	817	737	497	634	188	564	835	791	659
54	263	789	653	245	735	491	616	134	402	349
55	190	570	853	845	821	749	533	742	512	679
56	323	112	336	151	453	502	649	233	699	383
57	292	19	57	171	513	682	332	139	417	394
58	325	118	354	205	615	131	393	322	109	327
59	124	372	259	777	617	137	411	376	271	813
60	725	461	526	721	449	490	613	125	375	268
61	804	698	380	283	849	833	785	641	209	627
62	167	501	646	224	672	302	49	147	441	466
63	541	766	584	38	114	342	169	507	664	278
64	834	788	650	236	708	410	373	262	786	644
65	218	654	248	744	518	697	377	274	822	752
66	542	769	593	65	195	585	41	123	369	250
67	750	536	751	539	760	566	841	809	713	425
68	418	397	334	145	435	448	487	604	98	294
69	25	75	225	675	311	76	228	684	338	157
70	471	556	811	719	443	472	559	820	746	524
71	715	431	436	451	496	631	179	537	754	548
72	787	647	227	681	329	130	390	313	82	246
73	738	500	643	215	645	221	663	275	825	761
74	569	850	836	794	668	290	13	39	117	351
75	196	588	50	150	450	493	622	152	456	511
76	676	314	85	255	765	581	29	87	261	783
77	635	191	573	5	15	45	135	405	358	217
78	651	239	717	437	454	505	658	260	780	626
79	164	492	619	143	429	430	433	442	469	550
80	793	665	281	843	815	731	479	580	26	78
81	234	702	392	319	100	300	43	129	387	304
82	55	165	495	628	170	510	673	305	58	174
83	522	709	413	382	289	10	30	90	270	810
84	716	434	445	478	577	17	51	153	459	520
85	703	395	328	127	381	286				

P = 859

INDICES

	0	1	2	3	4	5	6	7	8	9
0		0	1	119	2	362	120	634	3	238
1	363	387	121	780	635	481	4	800	239	689
2	364	753	388	649	122	724	781	357	636	763
3	482	460	5	506	801	138	240	641	690	41
4	365	106	754	494	389	600	650	112	123	410
5	725	61	782	812	358	749	637	808	764	300
6	483	156	461	14	6	284	507	199	802	768
7	139	84	241	679	642	843	691	163	42	834
8	366	476	107	829	755	304	495	24	390	97
9	601	556	651	579	113	193	124	397	411	625
10	726	487	62	564	783	257	813	545	359	777
11	750	760	638	597	809	153	765	160	301	576
12	484	774	157	225	462	228	15	706	7	613
13	285	130	508	465	200	719	803	92	769	175
14	140	231	85	309	242	267	680	529	643	18
15	844	850	692	180	164	822	43	709	835	73
16	367	425	477	456	108	10	830	189	756	702
17	305	69	496	616	25	500	391	419	98	736
18	602	288	557	275	652	145	580	329	114	133
19	194	620	125	451	398	403	412	511	626	441
20	727	318	488	539	63	468	565	29	784	218
21	258	50	814	203	546	856	360	236	778	798
22	751	722	761	504	639	104	598	408	810	806
23	154	282	766	677	161	474	302	95	577	395
24	485	255	775	595	158	772	226	611	463	90
25	229	265	16	178	707	423	8	700	614	417
26	286	143	131	449	509	316	466	216	201	234
27	720	102	804	675	93	253	770	88	176	698
28	141	314	232	673	86	312	310	740	243	742
29	268	516	681	245	530	662	644	744	19	571
30	845	270	851	606	693	518	181	342	165	683
31	823	523	44	247	710	376	836	532	74	292
32	368	664	426	631	478	646	457	38	109	746
33	11	81	831	21	190	561	757	573	703	716
34	306	847	70	186	497	272	617	438	26	853
35	501	279	392	608	420	446	99	695	737	659
36	603	520	289	35	558	183	276	656	653	344
37	146	588	581	167	330	347	115	685	134	57
38	195	825	621	149	126	525	452	732	399	46
39	404	591	413	249	512	338	627	712	442	584
40	728	378	319	382	489	838	540	170	64	534
41	469	211	566	76	30	333	785	294	219	323
42	259	370	51	350	815	666	204	790	547	428
43	857	118	361	633	237	386	779	480	799	688
44	752	648	723	356	762	459	505	137	640	40
45	105	493	599	111	409	60	811	748	807	299
46	155	13	283	198	767	83	678	842	162	833
47	475	828	303	23	96	555	578	192	396	624
48	486	563	256	544	776	759	596	152	159	575
49	773	224	227	705	612	129	464	718	91	174

POWER RESIDUES

	0	1	2	3	4	5	6	7	8	9
0	1	2	4	8	16	32	64	128	256	512
1	165	330	660	461	63	126	252	504	149	298
2	596	333	666	473	87	174	348	696	533	207
3	414	828	797	735	611	363	726	593	327	654
4	449	39	78	156	312	624	389	778	697	535
5	211	422	844	829	799	739	619	379	758	657
6	455	51	102	204	408	816	773	687	515	171
7	342	684	509	159	318	636	413	826	793	727
8	595	331	662	465	71	142	284	568	277	554
9	249	498	137	274	548	237	474	89	178	356
10	712	565	271	542	225	450	41	82	164	328
11	656	453	47	94	188	376	752	645	431	3
12	6	12	24	48	96	192	384	768	677	495
13	131	262	524	189	378	756	653	447	35	70
14	140	280	560	261	522	185	370	740	621	383
15	766	673	487	115	230	460	61	122	244	488
16	117	234	468	77	154	308	616	373	746	633
17	407	814	769	679	499	139	278	556	253	506
18	153	306	612	365	730	601	343	686	513	167
19	334	668	477	95	190	380	760	661	463	67
20	134	268	536	213	426	852	845	831	803	747
21	635	411	822	785	711	563	267	534	209	418
22	836	813	767	675	491	123	246	492	125	250
23	500	141	282	564	269	538	217	434	9	18
24	36	72	144	288	576	293	586	313	626	393
25	786	713	567	275	550	241	482	105	210	420
26	840	821	783	707	555	251	502	145	290	580
27	301	602	345	690	521	183	366	732	605	351
28	702	545	231	462	65	130	260	520	181	362
29	724	589	319	638	417	834	809	759	659	459
30	59	118	236	472	85	170	340	680	501	143
31	286	572	285	570	281	562	265	530	201	402
32	804	749	639	419	838	817	775	691	523	187
33	374	748	637	415	830	801	743	627	395	790
34	721	583	307	614	369	738	617	375	750	641
35	423	846	833	807	755	651	443	27	54	108
36	216	432	5	10	20	40	80	160	320	640
37	421	842	825	791	723	587	315	630	401	802
38	745	631	403	806	753	647	435	11	22	44
39	88	176	352	704	549	239	478	97	194	388
40	776	693	527	195	390	780	701	543	227	454
41	49	98	196	392	784	709	559	259	518	177
42	354	708	557	255	510	161	322	644	429	858
43	857	855	851	843	827	795	731	603	347	694
44	529	199	398	796	733	607	355	710	561	263
45	526	193	386	772	685	511	163	326	652	445
46	31	62	124	248	496	133	266	532	205	410
47	820	781	703	547	235	470	81	162	324	648
48	437	15	30	60	120	240	480	101	202	404
49	808	757	655	451	43	86	172	344	688	517

P = 859

INDICES

	0	1	2	3	4	5	6	7	8	9
50	230	308	266	528	17	849	179	821	708	72
51	424	455	9	188	701	68	615	499	418	735
52	287	274	144	328	132	619	450	402	510	440
53	317	538	467	28	217	49	202	855	235	797
54	721	503	103	407	805	281	676	473	94	394
55	254	594	771	610	89	264	177	422	699	416
56	142	448	315	215	233	101	674	252	87	697
57	313	672	311	739	741	515	244	661	743	570
58	269	605	517	341	682	522	246	375	531	291
59	663	630	645	37	745	80	20	560	572	715
60	846	185	271	437	852	278	607	445	694	658
61	519	34	182	655	343	587	166	346	684	56
62	824	148	524	731	45	590	248	337	711	583
63	377	381	837	169	533	210	75	332	293	322
64	369	349	665	789	427	117	632	385	479	687
65	647	355	458	136	39	492	110	59	747	298
66	12	197	82	841	832	827	22	554	191	623
67	562	543	758	151	574	223	704	128	717	173
68	307	527	848	820	71	454	187	67	498	734
69	273	327	618	401	439	537	27	48	854	796
70	502	406	280	472	393	593	609	263	421	415
71	447	214	100	251	696	671	738	514	660	569
72	604	340	521	374	290	629	36	79	559	714
73	184	436	277	444	657	33	654	586	345	55
74	147	730	589	336	582	380	168	209	331	321
75	348	788	116	384	686	354	135	491	58	297
76	196	840	826	553	622	542	150	222	127	172
77	526	819	453	66	733	326	400	536	47	795
78	405	471	592	262	414	213	250	670	513	568
79	339	373	628	78	713	435	443	32	585	54
80	729	335	379	208	320	787	383	353	490	296
81	839	552	541	221	171	818	65	325	535	794
82	470	261	212	669	567	372	77	434	31	53
83	334	207	786	352	295	551	220	817	324	793
84	260	668	371	433	52	206	351	550	816	792
85	667	432	205	549	791	431	548	430	429	

POWER RESIDUES

	0	1	2	3	4	5	6	7	8	9
50	175	350	700	541	223	446	33	66	132	264
51	528	197	394	788	717	575	291	582	305	610
52	361	722	585	311	622	385	770	681	503	147
53	294	588	317	634	409	818	777	695	531	203
54	406	812	765	671	483	107	214	428	856	853
55	847	835	811	763	667	475	91	182	364	728
56	597	335	670	481	103	206	412	824	789	719
57	579	299	598	337	674	489	119	238	476	93
58	186	372	744	629	399	798	737	615	371	742
59	625	391	782	705	551	243	486	113	226	452
60	45	90	180	360	720	581	303	606	353	706
61	553	247	494	129	258	516	173	346	692	525
62	191	382	764	669	479	99	198	396	792	725
63	591	323	646	433	7	14	28	56	112	224
64	448	37	74	148	296	592	325	650	441	23
65	46	92	184	368	736	613	367	734	609	359
66	718	577	295	590	321	642	425	850	841	823
67	787	715	571	283	566	273	546	233	466	73
68	146	292	584	309	618	377	754	649	439	19
69	38	76	152	304	608	357	714	569	279	558
70	257	514	169	338	676	493	127	254	508	157
71	314	628	397	794	729	599	339	678	497	135
72	270	540	221	442	25	50	100	200	400	800
73	741	623	387	774	689	519	179	358	716	573
74	287	574	289	578	297	594	329	658	457	55
75	110	220	440	21	42	84	168	336	672	485
76	111	222	444	29	58	116	232	464	69	138
77	276	552	245	490	121	242	484	109	218	436
78	13	26	52	104	208	416	832	805	751	643
79	427	854	849	839	819	779	699	539	219	438
80	17	34	68	136	272	544	229	458	57	114
81	228	456	53	106	212	424	848	837	815	771
82	683	507	155	310	620	381	762	665	471	83
83	166	332	664	469	79	158	316	632	405	810
84	761	663	467	75	150	300	600	341	682	505
85	151	302	604	349	698	537	215	430		

P = 863

INDICES

	0	1	2	3	4	5	6	7	8	9
0		0	592	450	322	1	180	769	52	38
1	593	153	772	99	499	451	644	798	630	444
2	323	357	745	841	502	2	691	488	229	588
3	181	634	374	603	528	770	360	362	174	549
4	53	666	87	558	475	39	571	599	232	676
5	594	386	421	238	218	154	821	32	318	294
6	773	832	364	807	104	100	333	815	258	429
7	500	674	90	189	92	452	766	60	279	27
8	645	76	396	441	679	799	288	176	205	757
9	631	6	301	222	329	445	824	555	406	191
10	324	533	116	66	151	358	830	286	810	848
11	746	812	551	614	624	842	48	137	24	705
12	503	306	562	254	94	3	537	784	696	146
13	692	311	63	351	545	489	850	55	159	839
14	230	187	404	252	682	589	781	264	684	454
15	182	378	496	836	652	635	9	709	619	688
16	375	748	668	662	126	604	171	659	409	198
17	529	482	18	591	768	771	797	744	487	373
18	361	86	598	420	31	363	814	89	59	395
19	175	300	554	115	285	550	136	561	783	62
20	54	403	263	495	708	667	658	17	743	597
21	88	553	560	262	16	559	540	541	578	639
22	476	35	542	266	281	40	344	579	354	778
23	572	510	640	107	729	600	616	477	435	762
24	233	211	36	526	292	677	846	543	686	29
25	595	727	267	132	514	387	426	282	738	269
26	422	626	41	73	655	239	81	345	275	802
27	219	575	580	456	647	155	751	355	569	672
28	822	304	779	480	134	33	844	573	412	734
29	319	143	511	194	856	295	414	641	184	78
30	774	465	108	121	226	833	566	730	382	516
31	365	50	601	316	439	808	349	617	418	741
32	105	736	478	380	398	101	392	436	718	506
33	334	242	763	400	389	816	139	234	790	202
34	259	787	212	583	610	430	321	37	498	443
35	501	587	527	548	474	675	217	293	103	428
36	91	26	678	756	328	190	150	847	623	704
37	93	145	544	838	681	453	651	687	125	197
38	767	372	30	394	284	61	707	596	15	638
39	280	777	728	761	291	28	513	268	654	801
40	646	671	133	733	855	77	225	515	438	740
41	397	505	388	201	609	442	473	427	327	703
42	680	196	283	637	290	800	854	739	608	702
43	289	701	270	720	271	177	308	423	369	721
44	206	714	627	249	272	758	858	42	11	178
45	632	819	74	828	309	7	84	656	508	424
46	302	564	240	215	370	223	699	82	459	722
47	330	297	346	711	207	446	165	276	492	715
48	825	461	803	336	628	556	256	220	22	250
49	407	113	576	524	273	192	416	581	621	759

POWER RESIDUES

	0	1	2	3	4	5	6	7	8	9
0	1	5	25	125	625	536	91	455	549	156
1	780	448	514	844	768	388	214	207	172	860
2	848	788	488	714	118	590	361	79	395	249
3	382	184	57	285	562	221	242	347	9	45
4	225	262	447	509	819	643	626	541	116	580
5	311	692	8	40	200	137	685	836	728	188
6	77	385	199	132	660	711	103	515	849	793
7	513	839	743	263	452	534	81	405	299	632
8	571	266	467	609	456	554	181	42	210	187
9	72	360	74	370	124	620	511	829	693	13
10	65	325	762	358	64	320	737	233	302	647
11	646	641	616	491	729	193	102	510	824	668
12	751	303	652	671	766	378	164	820	648	651
13	666	741	253	402	284	557	196	117	585	336
14	817	633	576	291	592	371	129	645	636	591
15	366	104	520	11	55	275	512	834	718	138
16	690	861	853	813	613	476	654	681	816	628
17	551	166	830	698	38	190	87	435	449	519
18	6	30	150	750	298	627	546	141	705	73
19	365	99	495	749	293	602	421	379	169	845
20	773	413	339	832	708	88	440	474	644	631
21	566	241	342	847	783	463	589	356	54	270
22	487	709	93	465	599	406	304	657	696	28
23	140	700	48	240	337	822	658	701	53	265
24	462	584	331	792	508	814	618	501	779	443
25	489	719	143	715	123	615	486	704	68	340
26	837	733	213	202	147	735	223	252	397	259
27	432	434	444	494	744	268	477	659	706	78
28	390	224	257	422	384	194	107	535	86	430
29	424	394	244	357	59	295	612	471	629	556
30	191	92	460	574	281	542	121	605	436	454
31	544	131	655	686	841	753	313	702	58	290
32	587	346	4	20	100	500	774	418	364	94
33	470	624	531	66	330	787	483	689	856	828
34	688	851	803	563	226	267	472	634	581	316
35	717	133	665	736	228	277	522	21	105	525
36	36	180	37	185	62	310	687	846	778	438
37	464	594	381	179	32	160	800	548	151	755
38	323	752	308	677	796	528	51	255	412	334
39	807	583	326	767	383	189	82	410	324	757
40	333	802	558	201	142	710	98	490	724	168
41	840	748	288	577	296	617	496	754	318	727
42	183	52	260	437	459	569	256	417	359	69
43	345	862	858	838	738	238	327	772	408	314
44	707	83	415	349	19	95	475	649	656	691
45	3	15	75	375	149	745	273	502	784	468
46	614	481	679	806	578	301	642	621	516	854
47	818	638	601	416	354	44	220	237	322	747
48	283	552	171	855	823	663	726	178	27	135
49	675	786	478	664	731	203	152	760	348	14

P = 863

INDICES

	0	1	2	3	4	5	6	7	8	9
50	325	247	457	522	859	534	724	648	244	43
51	117	96	156	70	12	67	468	752	861	179
52	152	643	356	690	633	359	665	570	385	820
53	831	332	673	765	75	287	5	823	532	829
54	811	47	305	536	310	849	186	780	377	8
55	747	170	481	796	85	813	299	135	402	657
56	552	539	34	343	509	615	210	845	726	425
57	625	80	574	750	303	843	142	413	464	565
58	49	348	735	391	241	138	786	320	586	216
59	25	149	144	650	371	706	776	512	670	224
60	504	472	195	853	700	307	713	857	818	83
61	563	698	296	164	460	255	112	415	246	723
62	95	467	642	664	331	4	46	185	169	298
63	538	209	79	141	347	785	148	775	471	712
64	697	111	466	45	208	147	110	109	128	447
65	693	129	122	519	166	312	448	227	236	277
66	64	694	834	485	493	352	130	567	119	716
67	546	123	731	606	826	490	520	383	794	462
68	851	167	517	792	804	56	313	366	340	337
69	160	449	51	98	629	840	228	602	173	557
70	231	237	317	806	257	188	278	440	204	221
71	405	65	809	613	23	253	695	350	158	251
72	683	835	618	661	408	590	486	419	58	114
73	782	494	742	261	577	265	353	106	434	525
74	685	131	737	72	274	455	568	479	411	193
75	183	120	381	315	417	379	717	399	789	582
76	497	547	102	755	622	837	124	393	14	760
77	653	732	437	200	326	636	607	719	368	248
78	10	827	507	214	458	710	491	335	21	523
79	620	521	243	69	860	689	384	764	531	535
80	376	795	401	342	725	749	463	390	585	649
81	669	852	817	163	245	663	168	140	470	44
82	127	518	235	484	118	605	793	791	339	97
83	172	805	203	612	157	660	57	260	433	71
84	410	314	788	754	13	199	367	213	20	68
85	530	341	584	162	469	483	338	611	432	753
86	19	161	431							

POWER RESIDUES

	0	1	2	3	4	5	6	7	8	9
50	70	350	24	120	600	411	329	782	458	564
51	231	292	597	396	254	407	309	682	821	653
52	676	791	503	789	493	739	243	352	34	170
53	850	798	538	101	505	799	543	126	630	561
54	216	217	222	247	372	134	670	761	353	39
55	195	112	560	211	192	97	485	699	43	215
56	212	197	122	610	461	579	306	667	746	278
57	527	46	230	287	572	271	492	734	218	227
58	272	497	759	343	852	808	588	351	29	145
59	725	173	2	10	50	250	387	209	182	47
60	235	312	697	33	165	825	673	776	428	414
61	344	857	833	713	113	565	236	317	722	158
62	790	498	764	368	114	570	261	442	484	694
63	18	90	450	524	31	155	775	423	389	219
64	232	297	622	521	16	80	400	274	507	809
65	593	376	154	770	398	264	457	559	206	167
66	835	723	163	815	623	526	41	205	162	810
67	598	401	279	532	71	355	49	245	362	84
68	420	374	144	720	148	740	248	377	159	795
69	523	26	130	650	661	716	128	640	611	466
70	604	431	429	419	369	119	595	386	204	157
71	785	473	639	606	441	479	669	756	328	777
72	433	439	469	619	506	804	568	251	392	234
73	307	672	771	403	289	582	321	742	258	427
74	409	319	732	208	177	22	110	550	161	805
75	573	276	517	859	843	763	363	89	445	499
76	769	393	239	332	797	533	76	380	174	7
77	35	175	12	60	300	637	596	391	229	282
78	547	146	730	198	127	635	586	341	842	758
79	338	827	683	826	678	801	553	176	17	85
80	425	399	269	482	684	831	703	63	315	712
81	108	540	111	555	186	67	335	812	608	451
82	529	56	280	537	96	480	674	781	453	539
83	106	530	61	305	662	721	153	765	373	139
84	695	23	115	575	286	567	246	367	109	545
85	136	680	811	603	426	404	294	607	446	504
86	794	518								

P = 877

INDICES

	0	1	2	3	4	5	6	7	8	9
0		0	1	686	2	697	687	100	3	496
1	698	861	688	749	101	507	4	225	497	107
2	699	786	862	140	689	518	750	306	102	30
3	508	832	5	671	226	797	498	172	108	559
4	700	532	787	840	863	317	141	773	690	200
5	519	35	751	464	307	682	103	793	31	372
6	509	477	833	596	6	570	672	376	227	826
7	798	268	499	626	173	328	109	85	560	456
8	701	116	533	513	788	46	841	716	864	51
9	318	849	142	642	774	804	691	820	201	481
10	520	385	36	23	752	607	465	345	308	256
11	683	858	104	303	794	837	32	369	373	325
12	510	846	478	342	834	339	597	588	7	650
13	571	600	673	207	377	127	228	433	827	591
14	799	583	269	734	500	727	627	10	174	414
15	329	219	110	721	86	653	561	759	457	274
16	702	240	117	574	534	492	514	528	789	622
17	47	603	842	429	717	618	865	182	52	676
18	319	281	850	287	143	869	643	210	775	406
19	805	739	692	167	821	380	202	487	482	552
20	521	186	386	130	37	353	24	636	753	92
21	608	231	466	78	346	661	309	56	257	436
22	684	98	859	505	105	138	304	830	795	557
23	838	771	33	680	370	594	374	266	326	454
24	511	714	847	802	479	21	343	856	835	323
25	340	586	598	125	589	732	8	217	651	272
26	572	526	601	616	674	285	208	737	378	550
27	128	634	229	659	434	503	828	769	592	452
28	800	854	584	730	270	614	735	632	501	450
29	728	630	628	191	11	193	175	291	415	13
30	330	64	220	195	111	298	722	177	87	709
31	654	293	562	147	760	417	458	363	275	15
32	703	155	241	332	118	391	575	66	535	873
33	493	222	515	668	529	197	790	567	623	113
34	48	817	604	300	843	647	430	724	718	237
35	619	179	866	164	183	89	53	135	677	711
36	320	214	282	656	851	447	288	295	144	152
37	870	564	644	161	211	149	776	779	407	762
38	806	398	740	419	693	782	168	460	822	42
39	381	365	203	410	488	277	483	74	553	17
40	522	765	187	705	387	813	131	157	38	809
41	354	243	25	472	637	334	754	401	93	120
42	609	358	232	393	467	743	79	577	347	544
43	662	68	310	422	57	537	258	247	437	875
44	685	696	99	495	860	748	506	224	106	785
45	139	517	305	29	831	670	796	171	558	531
46	839	316	772	199	34	463	681	792	371	476
47	595	569	375	825	267	625	327	84	455	115
48	512	45	715	50	848	641	803	819	480	384
49	22	606	344	255	857	302	836	368	324	845

POWER RESIDUES

	0	1	2	3	4	5	6	7	8	9
0	1	2	4	8	16	32	64	128	256	512
1	147	294	588	299	598	319	638	399	798	719
2	561	245	490	103	206	412	824	771	665	453
3	29	58	116	232	464	51	102	204	408	816
4	755	633	389	778	679	481	85	170	340	680
5	483	89	178	356	712	547	217	434	868	859
6	841	805	733	589	301	602	327	654	431	862
7	847	817	757	637	397	794	711	545	213	426
8	852	827	777	677	477	77	154	308	616	355
9	710	543	209	418	836	795	713	549	221	442
10	7	14	28	56	112	224	448	19	38	76
11	152	304	608	339	678	479	81	162	324	648
12	419	838	799	721	565	253	506	135	270	540
13	203	406	812	747	617	357	714	551	225	450
14	23	46	92	184	368	736	595	313	626	375
15	750	623	369	738	599	321	642	407	814	751
16	625	373	746	615	353	706	535	193	386	772
17	667	457	37	74	148	296	592	307	614	351
18	702	527	177	354	708	539	201	402	804	731
19	585	293	586	295	590	303	606	335	670	463
20	49	98	196	392	784	691	505	133	266	532
21	187	374	748	619	361	722	567	257	514	151
22	302	604	331	662	447	17	34	68	136	272
23	544	211	422	844	811	745	613	349	698	519
24	161	322	644	411	822	767	657	437	874	871
25	865	853	829	781	685	493	109	218	436	872
26	867	857	837	797	717	557	237	474	71	142
27	284	568	259	518	159	318	636	395	790	703
28	529	181	362	724	571	265	530	183	366	732
29	587	297	594	311	622	367	734	591	305	610
30	343	686	495	113	226	452	27	54	108	216
31	432	864	851	825	773	669	461	45	90	180
32	360	720	563	249	498	119	238	476	75	150
33	300	600	323	646	415	830	783	689	501	125
34	250	500	123	246	492	107	214	428	856	835
35	793	709	541	205	410	820	763	649	421	842
36	807	737	597	317	634	391	782	687	497	117
37	234	468	59	118	236	472	67	134	268	536
38	195	390	780	683	489	101	202	404	808	739
39	601	325	650	423	846	815	753	629	381	762
40	647	417	834	791	705	533	189	378	756	635
41	393	786	695	513	149	298	596	315	630	383
42	766	655	433	866	855	833	789	701	525	173
43	346	692	507	137	274	548	219	438	876	875
44	873	869	861	845	813	749	621	365	730	583
45	289	578	279	558	239	478	79	158	316	632
46	387	774	671	465	53	106	212	424	848	819
47	761	645	413	826	775	673	469	61	122	244
48	488	99	198	396	792	707	537	197	394	788
49	699	521	165	330	660	443	9	18	36	72

P = 877

INDICES

	0	1	2	3	4	5	6	7	8	9
50	341	338	587	649	599	206	126	432	590	582
51	733	726	9	413	218	720	652	758	273	239
52	573	491	527	621	602	428	617	181	675	280
53	286	868	209	405	738	166	379	486	551	185
54	129	352	635	91	230	77	660	55	435	97
55	504	137	829	556	770	679	593	265	453	713
56	801	20	855	322	585	124	731	216	271	525
57	615	284	736	549	633	658	502	768	451	853
58	729	613	631	449	629	190	192	290	12	63
59	194	297	176	708	292	146	416	362	14	154
60	331	390	65	872	221	667	196	566	112	816
61	299	646	723	236	178	163	88	134	710	213
62	655	446	294	151	563	160	148	778	761	397
63	418	781	459	41	364	409	276	73	16	764
64	704	812	156	808	242	471	333	400	119	357
65	392	742	576	543	67	421	536	246	874	695
66	494	747	223	784	516	28	669	170	530	315
67	198	462	791	475	568	824	624	83	114	44
68	49	640	818	383	605	254	301	367	844	337
69	648	205	431	581	725	412	719	757	238	490
70	620	427	180	279	867	404	165	485	184	351
71	90	76	54	96	136	555	678	264	712	19
72	321	123	215	524	283	548	657	767	852	612
73	448	189	289	62	296	707	145	361	153	389
74	871	666	565	815	645	235	162	133	212	445
75	150	159	777	396	780	40	408	72	763	811
76	807	470	399	356	741	542	420	245	694	746
77	783	27	169	314	461	474	823	82	43	639
78	382	253	366	336	204	580	411	756	489	426
79	278	403	484	350	75	95	554	263	18	122
80	523	547	766	611	188	61	706	360	388	665
81	814	234	132	444	158	395	39	71	810	469
82	355	541	244	745	26	313	473	81	638	252
83	335	579	755	425	402	349	94	262	121	546
84	610	60	359	664	233	443	394	70	468	540
85	744	312	80	251	578	424	348	261	545	59
86	663	442	69	539	311	250	423	260	58	441
87	538	249	259	440	248	439	438			

POWER RESIDUES

	0	1	2	3	4	5	6	7	8	9
50	144	288	576	275	550	223	446	15	30	60
51	120	240	480	83	166	332	664	451	25	50
52	100	200	400	800	723	569	261	522	167	334
53	668	459	41	82	164	328	656	435	870	863
54	849	821	765	653	429	858	839	801	725	573
55	269	538	199	398	796	715	553	229	458	39
56	78	156	312	624	371	742	607	337	674	471
57	65	130	260	520	163	326	652	427	854	831
58	785	693	509	141	282	564	251	502	127	254
59	508	139	278	556	235	470	63	126	252	504
60	131	262	524	171	342	684	491	105	210	420
61	840	803	729	581	285	570	263	526	175	350
62	700	523	169	338	676	475	73	146	292	584
63	291	582	287	574	271	542	207	414	828	779
64	681	485	93	186	372	744	611	345	690	503
65	129	258	516	155	310	620	363	726	575	273
66	546	215	430	860	843	809	741	605	333	666
67	455	33	66	132	264	528	179	358	716	555
68	233	466	55	110	220	440	3	6	12	24
69	48	96	192	384	768	659	441	5	10	20
70	40	80	160	320	640	403	806	735	593	309
71	618	359	718	559	241	482	87	174	348	696
72	515	153	306	612	347	694	511	145	290	580
73	283	566	255	510	143	286	572	267	534	191
74	382	764	651	425	850	823	769	661	445	13
75	26	52	104	208	416	832	787	697	517	157
76	314	628	379	758	639	401	802	727	577	277
77	554	231	462	47	94	188	376	752	627	377
78	754	631	385	770	663	449	21	42	84	168
79	336	672	467	57	114	228	456	35	70	140
80	280	560	243	486	95	190	380	760	643	409
81	818	759	641	405	810	743	609	341	682	487
82	97	194	388	776	675	473	69	138	276	552
83	227	454	31	62	124	248	496	115	230	460
84	43	86	172	344	688	499	121	242	484	91
85	182	364	728	579	281	562	247	494	111	222
86	444	11	22	44	88	176	352	704	531	185
87	370	740	603	329	658	439				

P = 881

INDICES

	0	1	2	3	4	5	6	7	8	9
0		0	416	1	832	62	417	671	368	2
1	478	474	833	166	207	63	784	763	418	78
2	14	672	10	617	369	124	582	3	623	435
3	479	863	320	475	299	733	834	302	494	167
4	430	662	208	218	426	64	153	755	785	462
5	540	764	118	131	419	536	159	79	851	769
6	15	236	399	673	736	228	11	752	715	618
7	269	42	370	549	718	125	30	265	583	799
8	846	4	198	726	624	825	634	436	842	404
9	480	837	569	864	291	140	321	806	878	476
10	76	621	300	151	534	734	547	196	835	74
11	72	303	575	249	495	679	387	168	305	554
12	431	68	652	663	815	186	209	577	272	219
13	644	163	427	749	288	65	251	792	154	778
14	685	756	458	640	786	497	85	463	254	629
15	541	587	446	765	681	45	119	699	335	132
16	382	408	420	389	614	537	262	531	160	332
17	361	80	170	282	852	795	378	770	820	145
18	16	307	373	237	105	364	400	357	707	674
19	556	656	737	562	342	229	414	472	12	433
20	492	753	157	226	716	724	567	619	70	552
21	270	790	83	43	612	280	371	654	490	550
22	488	49	719	522	111	126	665	51	31	781
23	215	266	803	812	584	817	721	800	90	173
24	847	774	484	5	188	524	199	244	351	727
25	602	711	625	211	113	826	688	511	635	93
26	180	437	579	128	843	193	285	405	704	277
27	481	274	667	838	328	598	570	99	314	865
28	221	53	292	759	874	141	176	453	322	646
29	33	807	501	855	879	831	670	477	165	783
30	77	9	123	622	862	298	301	429	217	152
31	461	117	535	850	235	735	751	268	548	29
32	798	197	824	841	836	290	805	75	150	546
33	73	574	678	304	67	814	576	643	748	250
34	777	457	496	253	586	680	698	381	388	261
35	331	169	794	819	306	104	356	555	561	413
36	432	156	723	69	789	611	653	487	521	664
37	780	802	816	89	773	187	243	601	210	687
38	92	578	192	703	273	327	98	220	758	175
39	645	500	830	164	8	861	428	460	849	750
40	28	823	289	149	573	66	642	776	252	697
41	260	793	103	560	155	788	486	779	88	242
42	686	191	326	757	499	7	459	27	148	641
43	696	102	787	87	190	498	26	695	86	25
44	24	464	465	526	255	466	58	630	527	347
45	542	256	201	588	467	19	447	59	317	766
46	631	246	682	528	339	46	348	595	120	543
47	353	700	257	692	336	202	506	133	589	729
48	383	468	310	409	20	868	421	448	604	390
49	60	205	615	318	660	538	767	713	263	632

POWER RESIDUES

	0	1	2	3	4	5	6	7	8	9
0	1	3	9	27	81	243	729	425	394	301
1	22	66	198	594	20	60	180	540	739	455
2	484	571	832	734	440	439	436	427	400	319
3	76	228	684	290	870	848	782	584	871	851
4	791	611	71	213	639	155	465	514	661	221
5	663	227	681	281	843	767	539	736	446	457
6	490	589	5	15	45	135	405	334	121	363
7	208	624	110	330	109	327	100	300	19	57
8	171	513	658	212	636	146	438	433	418	373
9	238	714	380	259	777	569	826	716	386	277
10	831	731	431	412	355	184	552	775	563	808
11	662	224	672	254	762	524	691	311	52	156
12	468	523	688	302	25	75	225	675	263	789
13	605	53	159	477	550	769	545	754	500	619
14	95	285	855	803	647	179	537	730	428	403
15	328	103	309	46	138	414	361	202	606	56
16	168	504	631	131	393	298	13	39	117	351
17	172	516	667	239	717	389	286	858	812	674
18	260	780	578	853	797	629	125	375	244	732
19	434	421	382	265	795	623	107	321	82	246
20	738	452	475	544	751	491	592	14	42	126
21	378	253	759	515	664	230	690	308	43	129
22	387	280	840	758	512	655	203	609	65	195
23	585	874	860	818	692	314	61	183	549	766
24	536	727	419	376	247	741	461	502	625	113
25	339	136	408	343	148	444	451	472	535	724
26	410	349	166	498	613	77	231	693	317	70
27	210	630	128	384	271	813	677	269	807	659
28	215	645	173	519	676	266	798	632	134	402
29	325	94	282	846	776	566	817	689	305	34
30	102	306	37	111	333	118	354	181	543	748
31	482	565	814	680	278	834	740	458	493	598
32	32	96	288	864	830	728	422	385	274	822
33	704	350	169	507	640	158	474	541	742	464
34	511	652	194	582	865	833	737	449	466	517
35	670	248	744	470	529	706	356	187	561	802
36	644	170	510	649	185	555	784	590	8	24
37	72	216	648	182	546	757	509	646	176	528
38	703	347	160	480	559	796	626	116	348	163
39	489	586	877	869	845	773	557	790	608	62
40	186	558	793	617	89	267	801	641	161	483
41	568	823	707	359	196	588	2	6	18	54
42	162	486	577	850	788	602	44	132	396	307
43	40	120	360	199	597	29	87	261	783	587
44	880	878	872	854	800	638	152	456	487	580
45	859	815	683	287	861	821	701	341	142	426
46	397	310	49	147	441	442	445	454	481	562
47	805	653	197	591	11	33	99	297	10	30
48	90	270	810	668	242	726	416	367	220	660
49	218	654	200	600	38	114	342	145	435	424

P = 881

INDICES

	0	1	2	3	4	5	6	7	8	9
50	138	532	247	650	161	683	627	333	529	376
51	362	340	224	81	47	213	171	349	509	283
52	596	872	853	121	115	796	544	746	379	354
53	609	771	701	828	821	258	240	146	693	56
54	17	337	690	308	203	136	374	507	744	238
55	134	513	106	590	515	365	730	396	401	384
56	637	358	469	108	708	311	295	675	410	95
57	557	21	592	657	869	741	738	422	182	563
58	449	517	343	605	37	230	391	439	415	61
59	367	473	206	762	13	616	581	434	319	732
60	493	661	425	754	539	130	158	768	398	227
61	714	41	717	264	845	725	633	403	568	139
62	877	620	533	195	71	248	386	553	651	185
63	271	162	287	791	684	639	84	628	445	44
64	334	407	613	530	360	281	377	144	372	363
65	706	655	341	471	491	225	566	551	82	279
66	489	48	110	50	214	811	720	172	483	523
67	350	710	112	510	179	127	284	276	666	597
68	313	52	873	452	32	854	669	782	122	297
69	216	116	234	267	797	840	804	545	677	813
70	747	456	585	380	330	818	355	412	722	610
71	520	801	772	600	91	702	97	174	829	860
72	848	822	572	775	259	559	485	241	325	6
73	147	101	189	694	23	525	57	346	200	18
74	316	245	338	594	352	691	505	728	309	867
75	603	204	659	712	137	649	626	375	223	212
76	508	871	114	745	608	827	239	55	689	135
77	743	512	514	395	636	107	294	94	591	740
78	181	516	36	438	366	761	580	731	424	129
79	397	40	844	402	876	194	385	184	286	638
80	444	406	359	143	705	470	565	278	109	810
81	482	709	178	275	312	451	668	296	233	839
82	676	455	329	411	519	599	96	859	571	558
83	324	100	22	345	315	593	504	866	658	648
84	222	870	607	54	742	394	293	739	35	760
85	423	39	875	183	443	142	564	809	177	450
86	232	454	518	858	323	344	503	647	606	393
87	34	38	442	808	231	857	502	392	441	856
88	440	0								

POWER RESIDUES

	0	1	2	3	4	5	6	7	8	9
50	391	292	876	866	836	746	476	547	760	518
51	673	257	771	551	772	554	781	581	862	824
52	710	368	223	669	245	735	443	448	463	508
53	643	167	501	622	104	312	55	165	495	604
54	50	150	450	469	526	697	329	106	318	73
55	219	657	209	627	119	357	190	570	829	725
56	413	358	193	579	856	806	656	206	618	92
57	276	828	722	404	331	112	336	127	381	262
58	786	596	26	78	234	702	344	151	453	478
59	553	778	572	835	743	467	520	679	275	825
60	713	377	250	750	488	583	868	842	764	530
61	709	365	214	642	164	492	595	23	69	207
62	621	101	303	28	84	252	756	506	637	149
63	447	460	499	616	86	258	774	560	799	635
64	143	429	406	337	130	390	289	867	839	755
65	503	628	122	366	217	651	191	573	838	752
66	494	601	41	123	369	226	678	272	816	686
67	296	7	21	63	189	567	820	698	332	115
68	345	154	462	505	634	140	420	379	256	768
69	542	745	473	538	733	437	430	409	346	157
70	471	532	715	383	268	804	650	188	564	811
71	671	251	753	497	610	68	204	612	74	222
72	666	236	708	362	205	615	83	249	747	479
73	556	787	599	35	105	315	64	192	576	847
74	779	575	844	770	548	763	527	700	338	133
75	399	316	67	201	603	47	141	423	388	283
76	849	785	593	17	51	153	459	496	607	59
77	177	531	712	374	241	723	407	340	139	417
78	370	229	687	299	16	48	144	432	415	364
79	211	633	137	411	352	175	525	694	320	79
80	237	711	371	232	696	326	97	291	873	857
81	809	665	233	699	335	124	372	235	705	353
82	178	534	721	401	322	85	255	765	533	718
83	392	295	4	12	36	108	324	91	273	819
84	695	323	88	264	792	614	80	240	720	398
85	313	58	174	522	685	293	879	875	863	827
86	719	395	304	31	93	279	837	749	485	574
87	841	761	521	682	284	852	794	620	98	294
88										

P = 883

INDICES

	0	1	2	3	4	5	6	7	8	9
0		0	1	301	2	175	302	801	3	602
1	176	563	303	808	802	476	4	72	603	467
2	177	220	564	575	304	350	809	21	803	772
3	477	114	5	864	73	94	604	753	468	227
4	178	785	221	839	565	777	576	591	305	720
5	351	373	810	531	22	738	804	768	773	407
6	478	411	115	521	6	101	865	818	74	876
7	95	252	605	57	754	651	469	482	228	680
8	179	322	786	796	222	247	840	191	566	625
9	778	727	577	415	592	642	306	15	721	283
10	352	207	374	845	811	395	532	459	23	119
11	739	172	805	217	769	750	774	528	408	873
12	479	244	412	204	116	525	522	383	7	258
13	102	154	866	386	819	196	75	550	877	859
14	96	10	253	489	606	65	58	139	755	261
15	652	273	470	674	483	289	229	105	681	832
16	180	494	323	340	787	157	797	571	223	734
17	248	187	841	869	192	269	567	708	626	128
18	779	389	728	712	578	46	416	635	593	822
19	643	430	307	611	16	402	722	199	284	630
20	353	237	208	691	375	78	846	295	812	148
21	396	666	533	553	460	132	24	33	120	358
22	740	880	173	600	806	70	218	348	770	862
23	751	783	775	718	529	766	409	99	874	55
24	480	320	245	623	413	13	205	393	117	215
25	526	242	523	256	384	548	8	63	259	672
26	103	492	155	732	867	706	387	44	820	609
27	197	235	76	146	551	31	878	68	860	716
28	97	318	11	213	254	61	490	704	607	144
29	66	316	59	142	140	582	756	584	262	501
30	653	758	274	508	471	586	675	167	484	264
31	290	50	230	503	106	696	682	655	833	453
32	181	760	495	539	324	276	341	420	788	510
33	158	438	798	473	572	111	224	588	735	518
34	249	677	188	639	842	169	870	380	193	486
35	270	829	568	266	709	427	627	292	129	597
36	780	52	390	545	729	232	713	701	579	505
37	47	450	417	108	636	826	594	698	823	83
38	644	684	431	86	308	657	612	559	17	835
39	403	647	723	455	200	855	285	183	631	687
40	354	762	238	40	209	497	692	434	376	541
41	79	851	847	326	296	89	813	278	149	335
42	397	343	667	311	534	422	554	330	461	790
43	133	660	25	512	34	366	121	160	359	615
44	741	440	881	300	174	800	601	562	807	475
45	71	466	219	574	349	20	771	113	863	93
46	752	226	784	838	776	590	719	372	530	737
47	767	406	410	520	100	817	875	251	56	650
48	481	679	321	795	246	190	624	726	414	641
49	14	282	206	844	394	458	118	171	216	749

POWER RESIDUES

	0	1	2	3	4	5	6	7	8	9
0	1	2	4	8	16	32	64	128	256	512
1	141	282	564	245	490	97	194	388	776	669
2	455	27	54	108	216	432	864	845	807	731
3	579	275	550	217	434	868	853	823	763	643
4	403	806	729	575	267	534	185	370	740	597
5	311	622	361	722	561	239	478	73	146	292
6	584	285	570	257	514	145	290	580	277	554
7	225	450	17	34	68	136	272	544	205	410
8	820	757	631	379	758	633	383	766	649	415
9	830	777	671	459	35	70	140	280	560	237
10	474	65	130	260	520	157	314	628	373	746
11	609	335	670	457	31	62	124	248	496	109
12	218	436	872	861	839	795	707	531	179	358
13	716	549	215	430	860	837	791	699	515	147
14	294	588	293	586	289	578	273	546	209	418
15	836	789	695	507	131	262	524	165	330	660
16	437	874	865	847	811	739	595	307	614	345
17	690	497	111	222	444	5	10	20	40	80
18	160	320	640	397	794	705	527	171	342	684
19	485	87	174	348	696	509	135	270	540	197
20	394	788	693	503	123	246	492	101	202	404
21	808	733	583	283	566	249	498	113	226	452
22	21	42	84	168	336	672	461	39	78	156
23	312	624	365	730	577	271	542	201	402	804
24	725	567	251	502	121	242	484	85	170	340
25	680	477	71	142	284	568	253	506	129	258
26	516	149	298	596	309	618	353	706	529	175
27	350	700	517	151	302	604	325	650	417	834
28	785	687	491	99	198	396	792	701	519	155
29	310	620	357	714	545	207	414	828	773	663
30	443	3	6	12	24	48	96	192	384	768
31	653	423	846	809	735	587	291	582	281	562
32	241	482	81	162	324	648	413	826	769	655
33	427	854	825	767	651	419	838	793	703	523
34	163	326	652	421	842	801	719	555	227	454
35	25	50	100	200	400	800	717	551	219	438
36	876	869	855	827	771	659	435	870	857	831
37	779	675	467	51	102	204	408	816	749	615
38	347	694	505	127	254	508	133	266	532	181
39	362	724	565	247	494	105	210	420	840	797
40	711	539	195	390	780	677	471	59	118	236
41	472	61	122	244	488	93	186	372	744	605
42	327	654	425	850	817	751	619	355	710	537
43	191	382	764	645	407	814	745	607	331	662
44	441	882	881	879	875	867	851	819	755	627
45	371	742	601	319	638	393	786	689	495	107
46	214	428	856	829	775	667	451	19	38	76
47	152	304	608	333	666	449	15	30	60	120
48	240	480	77	154	308	616	349	698	513	143
49	286	572	261	522	161	322	644	405	810	737

P = 883

INDICES

	0	1	2	3	4	5	6	7	8	9
50	527	872	243	203	524	382	257	153	385	195
51	549	858	9	488	64	138	260	272	673	288
52	104	831	493	339	156	570	733	186	868	268
53	707	127	388	711	45	634	821	429	610	401
54	198	629	236	690	77	294	147	665	552	131
55	32	357	879	599	69	347	861	782	717	765
56	98	54	319	622	12	392	214	241	255	547
57	62	671	491	731	705	43	608	234	145	30
58	67	715	317	212	60	703	143	315	141	581
59	583	500	757	507	585	166	263	49	502	695
60	654	452	759	538	275	419	509	437	472	110
61	587	517	676	638	168	379	485	828	265	426
62	291	596	51	544	231	700	504	449	107	825
63	697	82	683	85	656	558	834	646	454	854
64	182	686	761	39	496	433	540	850	325	88
65	277	334	342	310	421	329	789	659	511	365
66	159	614	439	299	799	561	474	465	573	19
67	112	92	225	837	589	371	736	405	519	816
68	250	649	678	794	189	725	640	281	843	457
69	170	748	871	202	381	152	194	857	487	137
70	271	287	830	338	569	185	267	126	710	633
71	428	400	628	689	293	664	130	356	598	346
72	781	764	53	621	391	240	546	670	730	42
73	233	29	714	211	702	314	580	499	506	165
74	48	694	451	537	418	436	109	516	637	378
75	827	425	595	543	699	448	824	81	84	557
76	645	853	685	38	432	849	87	333	309	328
77	658	364	613	298	560	464	18	91	836	370
78	404	815	648	793	724	280	456	747	201	151
79	856	136	286	337	184	125	632	399	688	663
80	355	345	763	620	239	669	41	28	210	313
81	498	164	693	536	435	515	377	424	542	447
82	80	556	852	37	848	332	327	363	297	463
83	90	369	814	792	279	746	150	135	336	124
84	398	662	344	619	668	27	312	163	535	514
85	423	446	555	36	331	362	462	368	791	745
86	134	123	661	618	26	162	513	445	35	361
87	367	744	122	617	161	444	360	743	616	443
88	742	442	441							

POWER RESIDUES

	0	1	2	3	4	5	6	7	8	9
50	591	299	598	313	626	369	738	593	303	606
51	329	658	433	866	849	815	747	611	339	678
52	473	63	126	252	504	125	250	500	117	234
53	468	53	106	212	424	848	813	743	603	323
54	646	409	818	753	623	363	726	569	255	510
55	137	274	548	213	426	852	821	759	635	387
56	774	665	447	11	22	44	88	176	352	704
57	525	167	334	668	453	23	46	92	184	368
58	736	589	295	590	297	594	305	610	337	674
59	465	47	94	188	376	752	621	359	718	553
60	223	446	9	18	36	72	144	288	576	269
61	538	193	386	772	661	439	878	873	863	843
62	803	723	563	243	486	89	178	356	712	541
63	199	398	796	709	535	187	374	748	613	343
64	686	489	95	190	380	760	637	391	782	681
65	479	75	150	300	600	317	634	385	770	657
66	431	862	841	799	715	547	211	422	844	805
67	727	571	259	518	153	306	612	341	682	481
68	79	158	316	632	381	762	641	399	798	713
69	543	203	406	812	741	599	315	630	377	754
70	625	367	734	585	287	574	265	530	177	354
71	708	533	183	366	732	581	279	558	233	466
72	49	98	196	392	784	685	487	91	182	364
73	728	573	263	526	169	338	676	469	55	110
74	220	440	880	877	871	859	835	787	691	499
75	115	230	460	37	74	148	296	592	301	602
76	321	642	401	802	721	559	235	470	57	114
77	228	456	29	58	116	232	464	45	90	180
78	360	720	557	231	462	41	82	164	328	656
79	429	858	833	783	683	483	83	166	332	664
80	445	7	14	28	56	112	224	448	13	26
81	52	104	208	416	832	781	679	475	67	134
82	268	536	189	378	756	629	375	750	617	351
83	702	521	159	318	636	389	778	673	463	43
84	86	172	344	688	493	103	206	412	824	765
85	647	411	822	761	639	395	790	697	511	139
86	278	556	229	458	33	66	132	264	528	173
87	346	692	501	119	238	476	69	138	276	552
88	221	442								

P = 887

INDICES

	0	1	2	3	4	5	6	7	8	9
0		0	746	66	606	1	812	226	466	132
1	747	342	672	740	86	67	326	49	878	496
2	607	292	202	827	532	2	600	198	832	565
3	813	107	186	408	795	227	738	354	356	806
4	467	751	152	34	62	133	687	316	392	452
5	748	115	460	37	58	343	692	562	425	236
6	673	765	853	358	46	741	268	29	655	7
7	87	884	598	113	214	68	216	568	666	93
8	327	264	611	258	12	50	780	631	808	205
9	879	80	547	173	176	497	252	397	312	474
10	608	70	861	335	320	293	783	84	804	44
11	203	420	552	469	422	828	285	872	96	275
12	533	684	625	817	713	3	218	520	792	100
13	601	587	128	722	775	199	515	372	753	554
14	833	382	744	196	458	566	859	518	74	300
15	814	570	76	181	428	108	526	417	839	103
16	187	167	124	154	471	409	118	16	758	594
17	796	628	640	644	491	228	668	302	65	465
18	739	877	826	831	407	355	33	391	36	424
19	357	654	112	665	257	807	172	311	334	803
20	468	95	816	791	721	752	195	73	180	838
21	153	757	643	64	830	35	664	333	790	179
22	63	789	280	281	412	134	329	572	282	845
23	688	634	145	413	732	317	842	159	135	287
24	393	848	544	330	485	453	677	350	573	324
25	749	266	78	283	380	116	652	662	846	580
26	461	697	447	689	874	38	582	271	635	704
27	59	591	375	146	232	344	613	183	414	239
28	693	439	242	733	604	563	56	91	318	98
29	426	463	719	843	378	237	820	540	160	681
30	674	260	430	136	822	766	41	729	288	401
31	854	621	386	394	277	359	699	866	849	21
32	47	150	27	545	870	742	14	110	331	542
33	269	717	864	486	762	30	618	647	454	535
34	656	449	488	678	500	8	504	362	351	121
35	88	52	528	574	162	885	811	341	325	291
36	599	106	737	750	686	114	691	764	267	883
37	215	263	779	79	251	69	782	419	284	683
38	217	586	514	381	858	569	525	166	117	627
39	667	876	32	653	171	94	194	756	663	788
40	328	633	841	847	676	265	651	696	581	590
41	612	438	55	462	819	259	40	620	698	149
42	13	716	617	448	503	51	810	105	690	262
43	781	585	524	875	193	632	650	437	39	715
44	809	584	649	583	140	206	141	366	272	482
45	880	207	189	636	432	81	142	338	705	247
46	548	367	494	60	5	174	273	456	592	255
47	177	483	702	376	19	498	881	169	147	138
48	253	208	708	233	404	398	190	771	345	220
49	313	637	537	614	210	475	433	224	184	560

POWER RESIDUES

	0	1	2	3	4	5	6	7	8	9
0	1	5	25	125	625	464	546	69	345	838
1	642	549	84	420	326	743	167	835	627	474
2	596	319	708	879	847	687	774	322	723	67
3	335	788	392	186	43	215	188	53	265	438
4	416	306	643	554	109	545	64	320	713	17
5	85	425	351	868	792	412	286	543	54	270
6	463	541	44	220	213	178	3	15	75	375
7	101	505	751	207	148	740	152	760	252	373
8	91	455	501	731	107	535	14	70	350	863
9	767	287	548	79	395	201	118	590	289	558
10	129	645	564	159	795	427	361	31	155	775
11	327	748	192	73	365	51	255	388	166	830
12	602	349	858	742	162	810	502	736	132	660
13	639	534	9	45	225	238	303	628	479	621
14	444	446	456	506	756	232	273	478	616	419
15	321	718	42	210	163	815	527	861	757	237
16	298	603	354	883	867	787	387	161	805	477
17	611	394	196	93	465	551	94	470	576	219
18	208	153	765	277	498	716	32	160	800	452
19	486	656	619	434	396	206	143	715	27	135
20	675	714	22	110	550	89	445	451	481	631
21	494	696	819	547	74	370	76	380	126	630
22	489	671	694	809	497	711	7	35	175	875
23	827	587	274	483	641	544	59	295	588	279
24	508	766	282	523	841	657	624	459	521	831
25	607	374	96	480	626	469	571	194	83	415
26	301	618	429	371	81	405	251	368	66	330
27	763	267	448	466	556	119	595	314	683	754
28	222	223	228	253	378	116	580	239	308	653
29	604	359	21	105	525	851	707	874	822	562
30	149	745	177	885	877	837	637	524	846	682
31	749	197	98	490	676	719	47	235	288	553
32	104	520	826	582	249	358	16	80	400	226
33	243	328	753	217	198	103	515	801	457	511
34	781	357	11	55	275	488	666	669	684	759
35	247	348	853	717	37	185	38	190	63	315
36	688	779	347	848	692	799	447	461	531	881
37	857	737	137	685	764	272	473	591	294	583
38	254	383	141	705	864	772	312	673	704	859
39	747	187	48	240	313	678	729	97	485	651
40	594	309	658	629	484	646	569	184	33	165
41	825	577	224	233	278	503	741	157	785	377
42	111	555	114	570	189	58	290	563	154	770
43	302	623	454	496	706	869	797	437	411	281
44	518	816	532	886	882	862	762	262	423	341
45	818	542	49	245	338	803	467	561	144	720
46	52	260	413	291	568	179	8	40	200	113
47	565	164	820	552	99	495	701	844	672	699
48	834	622	449	471	581	244	333	778	342	823
49	567	174	870	802	462	536	19	95	475	601

P = 887

INDICES

	0	1	2	3	4	5	6	7	8	9
50	609	82	126	415	824	71	143	660	240	727
51	862	339	512	694	522	336	706	658	440	710
52	321	248	557	243	307	294	549	156	734	768
53	784	368	442	605	131	85	495	531	564	794
54	805	61	451	57	235	45	6	213	92	11
55	204	175	473	319	43	421	274	712	99	774
56	553	457	299	427	102	470	593	490	464	406
57	423	256	802	720	837	829	178	411	844	731
58	286	484	323	379	579	873	703	231	238	603
59	97	377	680	821	400	276	20	869	541	761
60	534	499	120	161	290	685	882	250	682	857
61	626	170	787	675	589	818	148	502	261	192
62	714	139	481	431	246	4	254	18	137	403
63	219	209	559	823	726	521	709	306	767	130
64	793	234	10	42	773	101	405	836	730	578
65	602	399	760	289	856	588	191	245	402	725
66	129	772	577	855	724	723	346	506	622	347
67	776	221	478	387	507	200	314	596	395	623
68	516	638	309	278	348	373	538	25	360	777
69	754	615	364	700	222	555	211	800	867	479
70	834	476	798	850	388	383	434	296	22	508
71	745	225	671	48	201	197	185	353	151	315
72	459	561	852	28	597	567	610	630	546	396
73	860	83	551	871	624	519	127	371	743	517
74	75	416	123	15	639	301	825	390	111	310
75	815	72	642	332	279	571	144	158	543	349
76	77	661	446	270	374	182	241	90	718	539
77	429	728	385	865	26	109	863	646	487	361
78	527	340	736	763	778	418	513	165	31	755
79	840	695	54	619	616	104	523	436	648	365
80	188	337	493	455	701	168	707	770	536	223
81	125	659	511	657	556	155	441	530	450	212
82	472	711	298	489	801	410	322	230	679	868
83	119	249	786	501	480	17	558	305	9	835
84	759	244	576	505	477	595	308	24	363	799
85	797	295	670	352	851	629	550	370	122	389
86	641	157	445	89	384	645	735	164	53	435
87	492	769	510	529	297	229	785	304	575	23
88	669	369	444	163	509	303	443			

POWER RESIDUES

	0	1	2	3	4	5	6	7	8	9
50	344	833	617	424	346	843	667	674	709	884
51	872	812	512	786	382	136	680	739	147	735
52	127	635	514	796	432	386	156	780	352	873
53	817	537	24	120	600	339	808	492	686	769
54	297	598	329	758	242	323	728	92	460	526
55	856	732	112	560	139	695	814	522	836	632
56	499	721	57	285	538	29	145	725	77	385
57	151	755	227	248	353	878	842	662	649	584
58	259	408	266	443	441	431	381	131	655	614
59	409	271	468	566	169	845	677	724	72	360
60	26	130	650	589	284	533	4	20	100	500
61	726	82	410	276	493	691	794	422	336	793
62	417	311	668	679	734	122	610	389	171	855
63	727	87	435	401	231	268	453	491	681	744
64	172	860	752	212	173	865	777	337	798	442
65	436	406	256	393	191	68	340	813	517	811
66	507	761	257	398	216	193	78	390	176	880
67	852	712	12	60	300	613	404	246	343	828
68	592	299	608	379	121	605	364	46	230	263
69	428	366	56	280	513	791	407	261	418	316
70	693	804	472	586	269	458	516	806	482	636
71	519	821	557	124	620	439	421	331	768	292
72	573	204	133	665	664	659	634	509	771	307
73	648	579	234	283	528	866	782	362	36	180
74	13	65	325	738	142	710	2	10	50	250
75	363	41	205	138	690	789	397	211	168	840
76	652	599	334	783	367	61	305	638	529	871
77	807	487	661	644	559	134	670	689	784	372
78	86	430	376	106	530	876	832	612	399	221
79	218	203	128	640	539	34	170	850	702	849
80	697	824	572	199	108	540	39	195	88	440
81	426	356	6	30	150	750	202	123	615	414
82	296	593	304	633	504	746	182	23	115	575
83	214	183	28	140	700	839	647	574	209	158
84	790	402	236	293	578	229	258	403	241	318
85	703	854	722	62	310	663	654	609	384	146
86	730	102	510	776	332	773	317	698	829	597
87	324	733	117	585	264	433	391	181	18	90
88	450	476	606	369	71	355				

P = 907

INDICES

	0	1	2	3	4	5	6	7	8	9
0		0	1	295	2	245	296	629	3	590
1	246	183	297	326	630	540	4	203	591	852
2	247	18	184	78	298	490	327	885	631	13
3	541	443	5	478	204	874	592	101	853	621
4	248	514	19	437	185	835	79	231	299	352
5	491	498	328	546	886	428	632	241	14	97
6	542	369	444	313	6	571	479	719	205	373
7	875	584	593	599	102	785	854	812	622	217
8	249	274	515	113	20	448	438	308	186	410
9	836	49	80	738	232	191	300	67	353	773
10	492	317	499	563	329	263	547	42	887	418
11	429	396	633	745	242	323	15	10	98	832
12	543	366	370	809	445	735	314	415	7	732
13	572	523	480	575	720	224	206	605	374	756
14	876	526	585	509	594	258	600	647	103	483
15	786	157	855	793	813	688	623	578	218	841
16	250	707	275	288	516	723	114	801	21	652
17	449	536	439	227	309	213	187	392	411	505
18	837	209	50	664	81	346	739	386	233	608
19	192	54	301	675	68	866	354	377	774	847
20	493	108	318	642	500	759	564	668	330	129
21	264	764	548	879	43	682	888	166	419	894
22	430	529	397	85	634	174	746	904	243	588
23	324	201	16	488	11	476	99	512	833	350
24	544	239	367	569	371	597	810	272	446	408
25	736	65	315	261	416	743	8	364	733	730
26	573	603	524	256	481	791	576	705	721	650
27	225	390	207	344	606	673	375	106	757	127
28	877	164	527	172	586	486	510	237	595	406
29	259	362	601	789	648	342	104	162	484	404
30	787	160	158	612	856	614	794	335	814	858
31	689	32	624	616	579	558	219	796	842	196
32	251	337	708	149	276	816	289	713	517	860
33	724	143	115	691	802	58	22	34	653	134
34	450	626	537	75	440	618	228	425	310	581
35	214	305	188	560	393	829	412	221	506	154
36	838	798	210	661	51	844	665	679	82	198
37	347	269	740	253	387	124	234	339	609	29
38	193	710	55	72	302	151	676	121	69	278
39	867	281	355	818	378	462	775	291	848	870
40	494	715	109	769	319	519	643	284	501	862
41	760	900	565	726	669	358	331	145	130	825
42	265	117	765	821	549	693	880	92	44	804
43	683	381	889	60	167	553	420	24	895	465
44	431	36	530	470	398	655	86	778	635	136
45	175	697	747	452	905	294	244	628	589	182
46	325	539	202	851	17	77	489	884	12	442
47	477	873	100	620	513	436	834	230	351	497
48	545	427	240	96	368	312	570	718	372	583
49	598	784	811	216	273	112	447	307	409	48

POWER RESIDUES

	0	1	2	3	4	5	6	7	8	9
0	1	2	4	8	16	32	64	128	256	512
1	117	234	468	29	58	116	232	464	21	42
2	84	168	336	672	437	874	841	775	643	379
3	758	609	311	622	337	674	441	882	857	807
4	707	507	107	214	428	856	805	703	499	91
5	182	364	728	549	191	382	764	621	335	670
6	433	866	825	743	579	251	502	97	194	388
7	776	645	383	766	625	343	686	465	23	46
8	92	184	368	736	565	223	446	892	877	847
9	787	667	427	854	801	695	483	59	118	236
10	472	37	74	148	296	592	277	554	201	402
11	804	701	495	83	166	332	664	421	842	777
12	647	387	774	641	375	750	593	279	558	209
13	418	836	765	623	339	678	449	898	889	871
14	835	763	619	331	662	417	834	761	615	323
15	646	385	770	633	359	718	529	151	302	604
16	301	602	297	594	281	562	217	434	868	829
17	751	595	283	566	225	450	900	893	879	851
18	795	683	459	11	22	44	88	176	352	704
19	501	95	190	380	760	613	319	638	369	738
20	569	231	462	17	34	68	136	272	544	181
21	362	724	541	175	350	700	493	79	158	316
22	632	357	714	521	135	270	540	173	346	692
23	477	47	94	188	376	752	597	287	574	241
24	482	57	114	228	456	5	10	20	40	80
25	160	320	640	373	746	585	263	526	145	290
26	580	253	506	105	210	420	840	773	639	371
27	742	577	247	494	81	162	324	648	389	778
28	649	391	782	657	407	814	721	535	163	326
29	652	397	794	681	455	3	6	12	24	48
30	96	192	384	768	629	351	702	497	87	174
31	348	696	485	63	126	252	504	101	202	404
32	808	709	511	115	230	460	13	26	52	104
33	208	416	832	757	607	307	614	321	642	377
34	754	601	295	590	273	546	185	370	740	573
35	239	478	49	98	196	392	784	661	415	830
36	753	599	291	582	257	514	121	242	484	61
37	122	244	488	69	138	276	552	197	394	788
38	669	431	862	817	727	547	187	374	748	589
39	271	542	177	354	708	509	111	222	444	888
40	869	831	755	603	299	598	289	578	249	498
41	89	178	356	712	517	127	254	508	109	218
42	436	872	837	767	627	347	694	481	55	110
43	220	440	880	853	799	691	475	43	86	172
44	344	688	469	31	62	124	248	496	85	170
45	340	680	453	906	905	903	899	891	875	843
46	779	651	395	790	673	439	878	849	791	675
47	443	886	865	823	739	571	235	470	33	66
48	132	264	528	149	298	596	285	570	233	466
49	25	50	100	200	400	800	693	479	51	102

P = 907

INDICES

	0	1	2	3	4	5	6	7	8	9
50	737	190	66	772	316	562	262	41	417	395
51	744	322	9	831	365	808	734	414	731	522
52	574	223	604	755	525	508	257	646	482	156
53	792	687	577	840	706	287	722	800	651	535
54	226	212	391	504	208	663	345	385	607	53
55	674	865	376	846	107	641	758	667	128	763
56	878	681	165	893	528	84	173	903	587	200
57	487	475	511	349	238	568	596	271	407	64
58	260	742	363	729	602	255	790	704	649	389
59	343	672	105	126	163	171	485	236	405	361
60	788	341	161	403	159	611	613	334	857	31
61	615	557	795	195	336	148	815	712	859	142
62	690	57	33	133	625	74	617	424	580	304
63	559	828	220	153	797	660	843	678	197	268
64	252	123	338	28	709	71	150	120	277	280
65	817	461	290	869	714	768	518	283	861	899
66	725	357	144	824	116	820	692	91	803	380
67	59	552	23	464	35	469	654	777	135	696
68	451	293	627	181	538	850	76	883	441	872
69	619	435	229	496	426	95	311	717	582	783
70	215	111	306	47	189	771	561	40	394	321
71	830	807	413	521	222	754	507	645	155	686
72	839	286	799	534	211	503	662	384	52	864
73	845	640	666	762	680	892	83	902	199	474
74	348	567	270	63	741	728	254	703	388	671
75	125	170	235	360	340	402	610	333	30	556
76	194	147	711	141	56	132	73	423	303	827
77	152	659	677	267	122	27	70	119	279	460
78	868	767	282	898	356	823	819	90	379	551
79	463	468	776	695	292	180	849	882	871	434
80	495	94	716	782	110	46	770	39	320	806
81	520	753	644	685	285	533	502	383	863	639
82	761	891	901	473	566	62	727	702	670	169
83	359	401	332	555	146	140	131	422	826	658
84	266	26	118	459	766	897	822	89	550	467
85	694	179	881	433	93	781	45	38	805	752
86	684	532	382	638	890	472	61	701	168	400
87	554	139	421	657	25	458	896	88	466	178
88	432	780	37	751	531	637	471	700	399	138
89	656	457	87	177	779	750	636	699	137	456
90	176	749	698	455	748	454	453			

POWER RESIDUES

	0	1	2	3	4	5	6	7	8	9
50	204	408	816	725	543	179	358	716	525	143
51	286	572	237	474	41	82	164	328	656	405
52	810	713	519	131	262	524	141	282	564	221
53	442	884	861	815	723	539	171	342	684	461
54	15	30	60	120	240	480	53	106	212	424
55	848	789	671	435	870	833	759	611	315	630
56	353	706	505	103	206	412	824	741	575	243
57	486	65	130	260	520	133	266	532	157	314
58	628	349	698	489	71	142	284	568	229	458
59	9	18	36	72	144	288	576	245	490	73
60	146	292	584	261	522	137	274	548	189	378
61	756	605	303	606	305	610	313	626	345	690
62	473	39	78	156	312	624	341	682	457	7
63	14	28	56	112	224	448	896	885	863	819
64	731	555	203	406	812	717	527	147	294	588
65	269	538	169	338	676	445	890	873	839	771
66	635	363	726	545	183	366	732	557	207	414
67	828	749	591	275	550	193	386	772	637	367
68	734	561	215	430	860	813	719	531	155	310
69	620	333	666	425	850	793	679	451	902	897
70	887	867	827	747	587	267	534	161	322	644
71	381	762	617	327	654	401	802	697	487	67
72	134	268	536	165	330	660	413	826	745	583
73	259	518	129	258	516	125	250	500	93	186
74	372	744	581	255	510	113	226	452	904	901
75	895	883	859	811	715	523	139	278	556	205
76	410	820	733	559	211	422	844	781	655	403
77	806	705	503	99	198	396	792	677	447	894
78	881	855	803	699	491	75	150	300	600	293
79	586	265	530	153	306	612	317	634	361	722
80	537	167	334	668	429	858	809	711	515	123
81	246	492	77	154	308	616	325	650	393	786
82	665	423	846	785	663	419	838	769	631	355
83	710	513	119	238	476	45	90	180	360	720
84	533	159	318	636	365	730	553	199	398	796
85	685	463	19	38	76	152	304	608	309	618
86	329	658	409	818	729	551	195	390	780	653
87	399	798	689	471	35	70	140	280	560	213
88	426	852	797	687	467	27	54	108	216	432
89	864	821	735	563	219	438	876	845	783	659
90	411	822	737	567	227	454				

P = 911

INDICES

	0	1	2	3	4	5	6	7	8	9
0		0	110	288	220	92	398	65	330	576
1	202	525	508	188	175	380	440	1	686	182
2	312	353	635	154	618	184	298	864	285	361
3	490	602	550	813	111	157	796	901	292	476
4	422	396	463	432	745	668	264	49	728	130
5	294	289	408	656	64	617	395	470	471	373
6	600	750	712	641	660	280	13	689	221	442
7	267	320	906	104	101	472	402	590	586	393
8	532	242	506	495	573	93	542	649	855	606
9	778	253	374	890	159	274	838	171	240	191
10	404	899	399	774	518	445	766	742	174	601
11	727	279	505	190	580	246	581	764	483	66
12	710	140	860	684	822	276	751	115	770	720
13	390	333	123	247	799	46	331	663	552	647
14	377	337	430	713	106	453	214	418	211	58
15	582	149	512	577	700	694	696	204	503	34
16	642	219	352	291	616	905	605	765	683	376
17	203	758	652	627	759	249	55	661	716	803
18	888	761	363	128	484	83	90	526	269	19
19	384	653	38	882	281	568	350	9	301	481
20	514	67	99	426	509	488	884	730	628	707
21	555	14	876	608	852	524	284	667	711	392
22	837	189	389	417	615	760	300	523	690	782
23	356	878	691	133	874	141	593	681	176	448
24	820	436	250	530	60	222	794	370	22	783
25	386	670	861	679	225	381	880	544	830	56
26	500	27	443	117	233	748	357	894	909	685
27	156	407	441	541	773	709	662	699	757	268
28	487	388	447	879	540	562	823	461	216	2
29	563	459	324	717	528	465	321	479	168	342
30	692	497	259	277	622	842	687	824	810	152
31	804	347	806	907	314	733	613	134	144	886
32	752	120	329	183	462	372	401	889	726	114
33	105	218	715	567	875	781	793	116	486	478
34	313	217	868	195	762	534	737	102	869	43
35	359	142	165	833	771	412	826	354	3	317
36	88	364	871	428	473	196	238	96	594	62
37	193	721	200	340	636	564	379	549	129	12
38	494	403	763	798	148	682	82	98	391	592
39	678	155	460	621	119	485	411	199	591	535
40	624	36	177	790	209	334	536	516	619	325
41	598	41	84	438	840	587	738	25	817	449
42	665	787	124	625	76	185	718	815	52	91
43	634	475	394	103	777	741	821	336	502	248
44	37	706	299	529	499	698	527	346	725	533
45	870	11	410	437	633	345	800	178	892	865
46	466	415	78	270	801	72	243	44	74	754
47	251	492	703	47	791	366	286	322	558	849
48	20	179	546	507	360	263	640	531	170	579
49	332	210	904	362	480	283	132	385	893	539

POWER RESIDUES

	0	1	2	3	4	5	6	7	8	9
0	1	17	289	358	620	519	624	587	869	197
1	616	451	379	66	211	854	853	836	547	189
2	480	872	248	572	614	417	712	261	793	727
3	516	573	631	706	159	881	401	440	192	531
4	828	411	610	349	467	651	135	473	753	47
5	799	829	428	899	707	176	259	759	149	711
6	244	504	369	807	54	7	119	201	684	696
7	900	724	465	617	468	668	424	831	462	566
8	512	505	386	185	412	627	638	825	360	654
9	186	429	5	85	534	879	367	773	387	202
10	701	74	347	433	73	330	144	626	621	536
11	2	34	578	716	329	127	337	263	827	394
12	321	902	758	132	422	797	795	761	183	378
13	49	833	496	233	317	834	513	522	675	543
14	121	235	351	501	318	851	802	880	384	151
15	745	822	309	698	23	391	270	35	595	94
16	687	747	856	887	503	352	518	607	298	511
17	488	97	738	703	108	14	238	402	457	481
18	889	537	19	323	25	425	848	751	13	221
19	113	99	772	370	824	343	365	739	720	397
20	372	858	10	170	157	847	734	635	774	404
21	491	148	694	866	146	660	288	341	331	161
22	4	68	245	521	658	254	674	526	743	788
23	642	893	605	264	844	683	679	611	366	756
24	98	755	81	466	634	757	115	133	439	175
25	242	470	702	91	636	791	693	849	768	302
26	579	733	618	485	46	782	540	70	279	188
27	463	583	801	863	95	704	125	303	596	111
28	65	194	565	495	216	28	476	804	3	51
29	867	163	38	646	50	850	785	591	26	442
30	226	198	633	740	737	686	730	567	529	794
31	744	805	20	340	314	783	557	359	637	808
32	71	296	477	821	292	409	576	682	662	322
33	8	136	490	131	405	508	437	141	575	665
34	373	875	299	528	777	455	447	311	732	601
35	196	599	162	21	357	603	230	266	878	350
36	484	29	493	182	361	671	475	787	625	604
37	247	555	325	59	92	653	169	140	558	376
38	15	255	691	815	190	497	250	606	281	222
39	130	388	219	79	432	56	41	697	6	102
40	823	326	76	381	100	789	659	271	52	884
41	452	396	355	569	563	461	549	223	147	677
42	577	699	40	680	628	655	203	718	363	705
43	142	592	43	731	584	818	241	453	413	644
44	16	272	69	262	810	105	874	282	239	419
45	746	839	598	145	643	910	894	622	553	291
46	392	287	324	42	714	295	460	532	845	700
47	57	58	75	364	722	431	39	663	339	297
48	494	199	650	118	184	395	338	280	205	752
49	30	510	471	719	380	83	500	301	562	444

P = 911

INDICES

	0	1	2	3	4	5	6	7	8	9
50	496	143	780	164	61	81	789	664	335	632
51	491	169	80	136	654	866	30	574	166	5
52	610	223	137	846	553	537	227	603	343	308
53	858	39	467	584	94	834	109	181	795	655
54	266	648	517	139	551	693	651	18	883	416
55	819	543	772	458	809	371	867	316	378	620
56	597	814	498	414	557	282	79	307	650	413
57	672	768	23	31	571	338	326	420	112	260
58	673	560	569	271	434	856	827	7	638	784
59	575	297	431	599	589	158	278	769	452	351
60	802	349	607	355	369	232	387	167	732	714
61	42	237	797	623	24	776	10	73	262	779
62	4	108	457	671	6	368	107	85	424	902
63	843	32	723	302	244	207	254	318	86	896
64	862	611	230	454	439	812	293	688	572	898
65	482	45	511	375	89	425	836	680	224	406
66	215	841	328	477	825	339	677	515	75	705
67	891	365	903	631	226	138	596	419	588	236
68	423	811	327	235	68	755	305	160	872	844
69	644	382	847	256	212	739	69	397	153	421
70	469	100	252	173	275	429	33	54	881	554
71	522	59	26	756	464	805	113	736	427	493
72	198	839	474	724	71	545	538	29	583	818
73	306	433	348	261	206	510	704	304	172	197
74	303	658	831	228	310	150	450	161	746	807
75	674	187	489	48	659	241	239	245	122	57
76	604	127	513	666	873	669	908	561	258	885
77	792	832	192	97	208	786	501	344	702	578
78	788	845	265	315	570	296	731	367	229	405
79	595	255	521	28	309	126	701	125	645	50
80	734	272	146	629	287	311	900	63	319	854
81	444	859	646	695	626	383	729	614	435	829
82	708	323	151	400	194	87	548	118	40	51
83	697	77	848	131	135	857	17	556	559	451
84	775	722	897	676	234	468	735	205	186	257
85	295	145	828	16	15	850	162	519	201	863
86	744	749	585	273	504	719	213	290	887	8
87	851	877	21	747	446	341	612	566	358	95
88	147	35	816	740	409	753	639	163	609	180
89	808	767	637	231	456	895	835	630	643	53
90	70	657	121	785	520	853	547	675	743	565
91	455	0								

POWER RESIDUES

	0	1	2	3	4	5	6	7	8	9
50	260	776	438	158	864	112	82	483	12	204
51	735	652	152	762	200	667	407	542	104	857
52	904	792	710	227	215	11	187	446	294	443
53	243	487	80	449	345	399	406	525	726	499
54	284	273	86	551	257	725	482	906	826	377
55	32	544	138	524	709	210	837	564	478	838
56	581	767	285	290	375	909	877	333	195	582
57	784	574	648	84	517	590	9	153	779	489
58	114	116	150	728	533	862	78	415	678	594
59	77	398	389	236	368	790	676	560	410	593
60	60	109	31	527	760	166	89	602	213	888
61	520	641	876	316	817	224	164	55	24	408
62	559	393	304	613	400	423	814	173	208	803
63	897	673	509	454	430	22	374	892	588	886
64	486	63	160	898	690	798	812	139	541	87
65	568	546	172	191	514	539	53	901	741	754
66	64	177	276	137	507	420	763	217	45	765
67	251	623	570	580	750	907	843	666	390	253
68	657	237	385	168	123	269	18	306	647	67
69	228	232	300	545	155	813	156	830	445	277
70	154	796	778	472	736	669	441	209	820	275
71	120	218	62	143	609	332	178	293	426	865
72	129	371	841	632	723	448	328	110	48	816
73	207	786	608	315	800	846	717	346	416	695
74	883	435	107	908	860	44	748	873	265	861
75	61	126	320	885	469	685	713	278	171	174
76	225	181	344	382	117	167	106	891	571	597
77	128	354	552	274	103	840	615	434	90	619
78	502	335	229	249	589	903	775	421	780	506
79	403	474	770	336	246	538	36	612	383	134
80	456	464	600	179	310	715	312	749	890	554
81	308	681	645	33	561	427	882	418	729	550
82	240	436	124	286	307	664	356	586	852	819
83	258	742	771	353	535	896	656	220	96	721
84	414	661	305	630	689	781	523	692	832	479
85	855	870	214	905	809	88	585	835	530	811
86	122	252	640	859	27	459	515	556	342	348
87	450	362	688	764	234	334	212	871	231	283
88	256	708	193	548	206	769	319	868	180	327
89	93	670	458	498	267	895	639	842	649	101
90	806	37	629	672	492	165	72	313	766	268
91										

P = 919

INDICES

	0	1	2	3	4	5	6	7	8	9
0		0	30	141	60	158	171	1	90	282
1	188	874	201	552	31	299	120	6	312	199
2	218	142	904	670	231	316	582	423	61	132
3	329	545	150	97	36	159	342	773	229	693
4	248	479	172	437	16	440	700	842	261	2
5	346	147	612	765	453	114	91	340	162	196
6	359	220	575	283	180	710	127	168	66	811
7	189	426	372	695	803	457	259	875	723	849
8	278	564	509	674	202	164	467	273	46	403
9	470	553	730	686	872	357	291	877	32	238
10	376	365	177	726	642	300	795	652	483	293
11	144	914	121	668	370	828	192	834	226	7
12	389	830	250	620	605	474	313	787	210	578
13	740	488	157	200	198	581	96	247	841	452
14	219	65	456	508	402	290	725	143	833	604
15	487	840	289	288	905	703	753	499	879	906
16	308	671	594	25	539	255	704	503	232	186
17	194	481	497	754	303	317	76	337	433	532
18	500	332	583	361	760	13	716	880	902	424
19	387	184	321	542	907	851	62	887	268	101
20	406	309	395	133	207	637	756	34	672	155
21	330	856	825	567	682	595	513	546	323	836
22	174	558	26	822	151	598	698	355	400	540
23	858	98	222	492	864	82	256	72	37	713
24	419	380	860	705	280	160	650	751	635	815
25	504	104	343	626	817	305	240	233	608	774
26	770	414	518	140	187	5	230	544	228	439
27	611	195	126	694	277	272	871	364	482	827
28	249	577	95	507	486	498	538	480	432	12
29	320	100	755	566	173	354	863	379	634	304
30	517	438	870	506	319	378	318	807	17	867
31	733	808	783	77	529	441	909	9	18	88
32	338	793	701	205	624	868	55	434	569	843
33	285	662	734	137	533	326	262	589	216	809
34	224	501	511	3	527	51	784	109	333	69
35	347	57	106	78	367	584	463	148	562	738
36	530	398	362	53	613	853	391	442	790	761
37	43	766	746	265	910	615	14	684	454	182
38	417	10	214	717	351	115	572	719	19	494
39	881	676	92	629	917	89	298	903	131	341
40	436	345	339	179	425	722	163	729	237	794
41	667	388	786	197	64	832	702	593	185	75
42	360	386	886	206	855	322	597	221	712	649
43	625	769	543	276	576	431	353	869	866	908
44	204	284	588	526	56	561	852	745	181	571
45	628	435	728	63	385	711	430	587	570	429
46	888	111	128	889	252	844	522	269	894	169
47	112	640	286	393	102	515	67	129	743	663
48	449	407	410	812	890	117	735	84	310	166
49	190	253	680	138	781	396	665	427	845	819

POWER RESIDUES

	0	1	2	3	4	5	6	7	8	9
0	1	7	49	343	563	265	17	119	833	317
1	381	829	289	185	376	794	44	308	318	388
2	878	632	748	641	811	163	222	635	769	788
3	2	14	98	686	207	530	34	238	747	634
4	762	739	578	370	752	669	88	616	636	776
5	837	345	577	363	703	326	444	351	619	657
6	4	28	196	453	414	141	68	476	575	349
7	605	559	237	740	585	419	176	313	353	633
8	755	690	235	726	487	652	888	702	319	395
9	8	56	392	906	828	282	136	33	231	698
10	291	199	474	561	251	838	352	626	706	347
11	591	461	470	533	55	385	857	485	638	790
12	16	112	784	893	737	564	272	66	462	477
13	582	398	29	203	502	757	704	333	493	694
14	263	3	21	147	110	770	795	51	357	661
15	32	224	649	867	555	209	544	132	5	35
16	245	796	58	406	85	595	489	666	67	469
17	526	6	42	294	220	621	671	102	714	403
18	64	448	379	815	191	418	169	264	10	70
19	490	673	116	812	170	271	59	413	134	19
20	133	12	84	588	440	323	423	204	509	806
21	128	896	758	711	382	836	338	528	20	140
22	61	427	232	705	340	542	118	826	268	38
23	266	24	168	257	880	646	846	408	99	693
24	256	873	597	503	764	753	676	137	40	280
25	122	854	464	491	680	165	236	733	536	76
26	532	48	336	514	841	373	773	816	198	467
27	512	827	275	87	609	587	433	274	80	560
28	244	789	9	63	441	330	472	547	153	152
29	145	96	672	109	763	746	627	713	396	15
30	105	735	550	174	299	255	866	548	160	201
31	488	659	18	126	882	660	25	175	306	304
32	290	192	425	218	607	573	335	507	792	30
33	210	551	181	348	598	510	813	177	320	402
34	57	399	36	252	845	401	50	350	612	608
35	580	384	850	436	295	227	670	95	665	60
36	420	183	362	696	277	101	707	354	640	804
37	114	798	72	504	771	802	100	700	305	297
38	241	768	781	872	590	454	421	190	411	120
39	840	366	724	473	554	202	495	708	361	689
40	228	677	144	89	623	685	200	481	610	594
41	482	617	643	825	261	908	842	380	822	240
42	761	732	529	27	189	404	71	497	722	459
43	456	435	288	178	327	451	400	43	301	269
44	45	315	367	731	522	897	765	760	725	480
45	603	545	139	54	378	808	142	75	525	918
46	912	870	576	356	654	902	800	86	602	538
47	90	630	734	543	125	875	611	601	531	41
48	287	171	278	108	756	697	284	150	131	917
49	905	821	233	712	389	885	681	172	285	157

P = 919

INDICES

	0	1	2	3	4	5	6	7	8	9
50	534	644	134	243	373	523	656	327	847	208
51	335	696	270	622	263	884	638	798	804	895
52	800	590	444	757	548	458	170	551	217	422
53	35	478	260	113	574	810	258	673	469	876
54	641	913	225	473	156	451	724	287	307	502
55	302	331	901	850	394	154	512	821	857	71
56	279	103	607	4	125	826	537	565	516	806
57	528	792	568	325	510	68	462	52	42	683
58	350	675	130	721	785	74	596	275	203	744
59	384	110	893	514	409	165	664	242	334	797
60	547	477	468	450	900	70	536	324	349	274
61	408	476	348	777	837	778	47	411	897	58
62	763	175	838	404	813	632	107	296	559	779
63	471	891	21	79	39	27	48	554	118	708
64	368	23	823	412	731	736	235	585	654	152
65	898	687	85	689	464	646	599	59	873	311
66	315	149	692	699	764	358	167	802	563	45
67	356	176	292	191	619	739	246	401	839	878
68	254	496	531	715	541	405	33	681	557	399
69	81	859	814	239	139	610	363	485	99	633
70	377	782	87	54	136	223	108	366	397	789
71	614	213	493	297	178	666	592	854	768	865
72	560	727	428	521	392	448	83	780	643	846
73	883	443	421	257	472	301	820	124	791	41
74	73	892	796	535	776	762	295	38	22	653
75	645	691	44	245	714	80	484	135	212	767
76	447	420	40	294	244	446	747	748	381	28
77	145	374	602	266	749	861	49	915	524	678
78	911	382	706	555	122	657	659	616	29	281
79	119	669	328	772	15	146	161	709	371	848
80	466	685	375	651	369	829	209	580	455	603
81	752	24	193	336	759	183	267	636	824	835
82	697	491	418	750	816	413	227	271	94	11
83	862	505	732	8	623	661	215	50	105	737
84	390	264	416	718	916	344	236	831	885	648
85	352	525	627	586	251	639	742	116	679	818
86	655	621	799	550	573	912	306	153	606	805
87	461	720	383	241	899	475	896	631	20	707
88	234	688	314	801	618	495	556	609	86	788
89	591	520	882	123	775	690	211	445	601	677
90	658	771	465	579	758	490	93	660	415	647
91	741	549	460	630	617	519	600	489	459	

POWER RESIDUES

	0	1	2	3	4	5	6	7	8	9
50	180	341	549	167	250	831	303	283	143	82
51	574	342	556	216	593	475	568	300	262	915
52	891	723	466	505	778	851	443	344	570	314
53	360	682	179	334	500	743	606	566	286	164
54	229	684	193	432	267	31	217	600	524	911
55	863	527	13	91	637	783	886	688	221	628
56	720	445	358	668	81	567	293	213	572	328
57	458	449	386	864	534	62	434	281	129	903
58	807	135	26	182	355	647	853	457	442	337
59	521	890	716	417	162	215	586	426	225	656
60	916	898	772	809	149	124	868	562	258	887
61	695	270	52	364	710	375	787	914	884	674
62	123	861	513	834	324	430	253	852	450	393
63	913	877	625	699	298	248	817	205	516	855
64	471	540	104	728	501	750	655	909	849	429
65	246	803	107	749	648	860	506	785	900	786
66	907	835	331	479	596	496	715	410	113	791
67	23	161	208	537	83	581	391	899	779	858
68	492	687	214	579	377	801	93	651	881	653
69	895	751	662	39	273	73	511	820	226	663
70	46	322	416	155	166	243	782	879	639	797
71	65	455	428	239	754	683	186	383	843	387
72	871	583	405	78	546	146	103	721	452	407
73	92	644	832	310	332	486	645	839	359	675
74	130	910	856	478	589	447	372	766	767	774
75	823	247	810	156	173	292	206	523	904	814
76	184	369	745	620	664	53	371	759	718	431
77	260	901	793	37	259	894	744	613	615	629
78	727	494	701	312	346	584	412	127	889	709
79	368	738	571	321	409	106	742	599	517	862
80	520	883	667	74	518	869	569	307	311	339
81	535	69	483	624	692	249	824	254	859	499
82	736	557	223	642	818	212	565	279	115	805
83	121	847	415	148	117	819	219	614	622	678
84	151	138	47	329	465	498	729	508	799	79
85	553	195	446	365	717	424	211	558	230	691
86	242	775	830	296	234	719	438	309	325	437
87	302	276	94	658	11	77	539	97	679	158
88	187	390	892	730	515	848	422	197	460	463
89	484	631	741	592	468	519	876	618	650	874
90	604	552	188	397	22	154	159	194	439	316
91	374	780	865	541	111	777	844	394		

P = 929

INDICES

	0	1	2	3	4	5	6	7	8	9
0		0	810	1	692	876	811	505	574	2
1	758	142	693	857	387	877	456	721	812	728
2	640	506	24	872	575	824	739	3	269	126
3	759	169	338	143	603	453	694	332	610	858
4	522	443	388	697	834	878	754	430	457	82
5	706	722	621	12	813	90	151	729	8	421
6	641	902	51	507	220	805	25	543	485	873
7	335	418	576	711	214	825	492	647	740	35
8	404	4	325	778	270	669	579	127	716	564
9	760	434	636	170	312	676	339	613	892	144
10	588	174	604	344	503	454	822	601	695	619
11	900	333	33	714	611	820	818	859	303	298
12	523	284	784	444	861	772	389	481	102	698
13	687	652	835	305	425	879	367	254	755	329
14	217	431	300	71	458	74	593	83	96	106
15	707	525	374	723	529	117	622	46	845	13
16	286	449	814	199	207	91	660	828	152	786
17	551	730	461	736	9	401	598	422	446	191
18	642	163	316	903	518	280	52	863	194	508
19	558	791	221	746	495	806	774	203	26	77
20	470	544	56	631	486	391	226	874	385	870
21	336	441	704	419	483	645	577	674	501	712
22	782	650	215	104	843	826	596	278	493	629
23	702	648	700	237	741	378	185	36	180	239
24	405	689	166	5	666	30	326	657	743	779
25	654	133	271	86	363	670	912	380	580	837
26	569	128	534	680	717	888	187	565	307	319
27	761	353	249	435	136	38	637	427	211	171
28	99	114	313	867	182	677	881	20	340	514
29	884	614	475	241	893	369	906	145	916	801
30	589	274	407	175	256	850	605	109	411	345
31	927	691	504	757	856	455	727	23	823	268
32	168	602	331	521	696	753	81	620	89	7
33	901	219	542	334	710	491	34	324	668	715
34	433	311	612	587	343	821	618	32	819	302
35	283	860	480	686	304	366	328	299	73	95
36	524	528	45	285	198	659	785	460	400	445
37	162	517	862	557	745	773	76	55	390	384
38	440	482	673	781	103	595	628	699	377	179
39	688	665	656	653	85	911	836	533	887	306
40	352	135	426	98	866	880	513	474	368	915
41	273	255	108	926	756	726	267	330	752	88
42	218	709	323	432	586	617	301	479	365	72
43	527	197	459	161	556	75	383	672	594	376
44	664	84	532	351	97	512	914	107	725	751
45	708	585	478	526	160	382	375	531	511	724
46	584	159	530	583	582	118	119	66	623	120
47	260	47	67	839	846	624	62	14	121	244
48	287	261	571	450	48	561	815	68	548	200
49	840	130	208	847	539	92	625	923	661	63

POWER RESIDUES

	0	1	2	3	4	5	6	7	8	9
0	1	3	9	27	81	243	729	329	58	174
1	522	637	53	159	477	502	577	802	548	715
2	287	861	725	317	22	66	198	594	853	701
3	245	735	347	112	336	79	237	711	275	825
4	617	922	908	866	740	362	157	471	484	523
5	640	62	186	558	745	377	202	606	889	809
6	569	778	476	499	568	775	467	472	487	532
7	667	143	429	358	145	435	376	199	597	862
8	728	326	49	147	441	394	253	759	419	328
9	55	165	495	556	739	359	148	444	403	280
10	840	662	128	384	223	669	149	447	412	307
11	921	905	857	713	281	843	671	155	465	466
12	469	478	505	586	829	629	29	87	261	783
13	491	544	703	251	753	401	274	822	608	895
14	827	623	11	33	99	297	891	815	587	832
15	638	56	168	504	583	820	602	877	773	461
16	454	433	370	181	543	700	242	726	320	31
17	93	279	837	653	101	303	909	869	749	389
18	238	714	284	852	698	236	708	266	798	536
19	679	179	537	682	188	564	763	431	364	163
20	489	538	685	197	591	844	674	164	492	547
21	712	278	834	644	74	222	666	140	420	331
22	64	192	576	799	539	688	206	618	925	917
23	893	821	605	886	800	542	697	233	699	239
24	717	293	879	779	479	508	595	856	710	272
25	816	590	841	665	137	411	304	912	878	776
26	470	481	514	613	910	872	758	416	319	28
27	84	252	756	410	301	903	851	695	227	681
28	185	555	736	350	121	363	160	480	511	604
29	883	791	515	616	919	899	839	659	119	357
30	142	426	349	118	354	133	399	268	804	554
31	733	341	94	282	846	680	182	546	709	269
32	807	563	760	422	337	82	246	738	356	139
33	417	322	37	111	333	70	210	630	32	96
34	288	864	734	344	103	309	927	923	911	875
35	767	443	400	271	813	581	814	584	823	611
36	904	854	704	254	762	428	355	136	408	295
37	885	797	533	670	152	456	439	388	235	705
38	257	771	455	436	379	208	624	14	42	126
39	378	205	615	916	890	812	578	805	557	742
40	368	175	525	646	80	240	720	302	906	860
41	722	308	924	914	884	794	524	643	71	213
42	639	59	177	531	664	134	402	277	831	635
43	47	141	423	340	91	273	819	599	868	746
44	380	211	633	41	123	369	178	534	673	161
45	483	520	631	35	105	315	16	48	144	432
46	367	172	516	619	928	926	920	902	848	686
47	200	600	871	755	407	292	876	770	452	427
48	352	127	381	214	642	68	204	612	907	863
49	731	335	76	228	684	194	582	817	593	850

P = 929

INDICES

	0	1	2	3	4	5	6	7	8	9
50	536	829	15	765	153	122	896	787	245	682
51	552	288	794	731	262	292	462	572	719	737
52	451	832	10	49	416	402	562	890	599	816
53	770	423	69	372	447	549	189	192	201	224
54	643	841	235	164	131	567	317	209	18	904
55	848	854	519	540	309	281	93	398	53	626
56	909	864	924	321	195	662	749	509	64	60
57	559	537	763	792	830	768	222	16	396	747
58	766	355	496	154	357	807	123	148	775	897
59	251	204	788	498	27	246	798	78	683	437
60	471	553	156	545	289	232	57	795	138	632
61	732	359	487	263	919	392	293	40	227	463
62	809	875	573	141	386	720	639	871	738	125
63	337	452	609	442	833	429	705	11	150	420
64	50	804	484	417	213	646	403	777	578	563
65	635	675	891	173	502	600	899	713	817	297
66	783	771	101	651	424	253	216	70	592	105
67	373	116	844	448	206	827	550	735	597	190
68	315	279	193	790	494	202	469	630	225	869
69	703	644	500	649	842	277	701	236	184	238
70	165	29	742	132	362	379	568	679	186	318
71	248	37	210	113	181	19	883	240	905	800
72	406	849	410	690	855	22	167	520	80	6
73	541	490	667	310	342	31	282	685	327	94
74	44	658	399	516	744	54	439	780	627	178
75	655	910	886	134	865	473	272	925	266	87
76	322	616	364	196	555	671	663	350	913	750
77	477	381	510	158	581	65	259	838	61	243
78	570	560	547	129	538	922	535	764	895	681
79	793	291	718	831	415	889	769	371	188	223
80	234	566	17	853	308	397	908	320	748	59
81	762	767	395	354	356	147	250	497	797	436
82	155	231	137	358	918	39	808	140	638	124
83	608	428	149	803	212	776	634	172	898	296
84	100	252	591	115	205	734	314	789	468	868
85	499	276	183	28	361	678	247	112	882	799
86	409	21	79	489	341	684	43	515	438	177
87	885	472	265	615	554	349	476	157	258	242
88	546	921	894	290	414	370	233	852	907	58
89	394	146	796	230	917	139	607	802	633	295
90	590	733	467	275	360	111	408	488	42	176
91	264	348	257	920	413	851	393	229	606	294
92	466	110	41	347	412	228	465	346	464	

POWER RESIDUES

	0	1	2	3	4	5	6	7	8	9
50	692	218	654	104	312	7	21	63	189	567
51	772	458	445	406	289	867	743	371	184	552
52	727	323	40	120	360	151	453	430	361	154
53	462	457	442	397	262	786	500	571	784	494
54	553	730	332	67	201	603	880	782	488	535
55	676	170	510	601	874	764	434	373	190	570
56	781	485	526	649	89	267	801	545	706	260
57	780	482	517	622	8	24	72	216	648	86
58	258	774	464	463	460	451	424	343	100	300
59	900	842	668	146	438	385	226	678	176	528
60	655	107	321	34	102	306	918	896	830	632
61	38	114	342	97	291	873	761	425	346	109
62	327	52	156	468	475	496	559	748	386	229
63	687	203	609	898	836	650	92	276	828	626
64	20	60	180	540	691	215	645	77	231	693
65	221	663	131	393	250	750	392	247	741	365
66	166	498	565	766	440	391	244	732	338	85
67	255	765	437	382	217	651	95	285	855	707
68	263	789	509	598	865	737	353	130	390	241
69	723	311	4	12	36	108	324	43	129	387
70	232	696	230	690	212	636	50	150	450	421
71	334	73	219	657	113	339	88	264	792	518
72	625	17	51	153	459	448	415	316	19	57
73	171	513	610	901	845	677	173	519	628	26
74	78	234	702	248	744	374	193	579	808	566
75	769	449	418	325	46	138	414	313	10	30
76	90	270	810	572	787	503	580	811	575	796
77	530	661	125	375	196	588	835	647	83	249
78	747	383	220	660	122	366	169	507	592	847
79	683	191	573	790	512	607	892	818	596	859
80	719	299	897	833	641	65	195	585	826	620
81	2	6	18	54	162	486	529	658	116	348
82	115	345	106	318	25	75	225	675	167	501
83	574	793	521	634	44	132	396	259	777	473
84	490	541	694	224	672	158	474	493	550	721
85	305	915	887	803	551	724	314	13	39	117
86	351	124	372	187	561	754	404	283	849	689
87	209	627	23	69	207	621	5	15	45	135
88	405	286	858	716	290	870	752	398	265	795
89	527	652	98	294	882	788	506	589	838	656
90	110	330	61	183	549	718	296	888	806	560
91	751	395	256	768	446	409	298	894	824	614
92	913	881	785	497	562	757	413	310		

P = 937

INDICES

	0	1	2	3	4	5	6	7	8	9
0		0	904	932	872	1	900	851	840	928
1	905	257	868	572	819	933	808	178	896	602
2	873	847	225	741	836	2	540	924	787	620
3	901	418	776	253	146	852	864	398	570	568
4	841	159	815	703	193	929	709	59	804	766
5	906	174	508	218	892	258	755	598	588	43
6	869	696	386	843	744	573	221	117	114	737
7	820	715	832	296	366	934	538	172	536	325
8	809	920	127	111	783	179	671	616	161	558
9	897	487	677	414	27	603	772	284	734	249
10	874	327	142	445	476	848	186	548	860	201
11	226	394	723	817	566	742	556	564	11	93
12	837	514	664	155	354	3	811	421	712	699
13	541	490	189	517	85	925	82	310	705	13
14	788	55	683	829	800	621	264	762	334	271
15	902	922	506	170	140	419	504	37	293	214
16	777	656	888	195	95	254	79	609	751	208
17	147	594	639	363	584	853	129	39	526	346
18	865	307	455	692	645	399	382	435	931	839
19	571	895	740	786	252	569	702	803	217	587
20	842	113	295	535	110	160	413	733	444	859
21	816	10	154	711	516	704	828	333	169	292
22	194	750	362	525	691	930	785	216	534	443
23	710	168	524	533	532	60	915	321	61	666
24	805	52	482	916	632	767	123	238	322	107
25	907	181	779	62	389	175	680	551	667	313
26	509	612	458	806	157	219	485	554	53	77
27	893	826	50	483	278	259	673	658	917	410
28	756	499	23	633	651	599	797	74	768	356
29	589	280	232	124	730	44	302	245	239	377
30	870	618	890	323	474	697	138	344	108	441
31	387	408	472	908	5	844	261	823	182	877
32	745	544	624	780	856	574	163	197	63	910
33	222	759	47	390	577	118	719	370	176	813
34	115	675	562	681	607	738	331	480	552	230
35	821	560	97	668	7	716	494	89	314	792
36	833	268	275	510	423	297	660	99	613	151
37	367	133	350	459	403	935	899	256	807	846
38	539	417	863	158	708	173	754	695	220	714
39	537	919	670	486	771	326	185	393	555	513
40	810	489	81	54	263	921	503	655	78	593
41	128	306	381	894	701	112	412	9	827	749
42	784	167	914	51	122	180	679	611	484	825
43	672	498	796	279	301	617	137	407	260	543
44	162	758	718	674	330	559	493	267	659	132
45	898	416	753	918	184	488	502	305	411	166
46	678	497	136	757	492	415	501	496	500	32
47	28	33	883	24	289	604	29	210	634	879
48	773	34	20	652	450	285	884	430	600	191
49	735	25	91	798	206	250	290	630	75	728

POWER RESIDUES

	0	1	2	3	4	5	6	7	8	9
0	1	5	25	125	625	314	633	354	833	417
1	211	118	590	139	695	664	509	671	544	846
2	482	536	806	282	473	491	581	94	470	476
3	506	656	469	471	481	531	781	157	785	177
4	885	677	574	59	295	538	816	332	723	804
5	272	423	241	268	403	141	705	714	759	47
6	235	238	253	328	703	704	709	734	859	547
7	861	557	911	807	287	498	616	269	408	166
8	830	402	136	680	589	134	670	539	821	357
9	848	492	586	119	595	164	820	352	823	367
10	898	742	899	747	924	872	612	249	308	603
11	204	83	415	201	68	340	763	67	335	738
12	879	647	424	246	293	528	766	82	410	176
13	880	652	449	371	918	842	462	436	306	593
14	154	770	102	510	676	569	34	170	850	502
15	636	369	908	792	212	123	615	264	383	41
16	205	88	440	326	693	654	459	421	231	218
17	153	765	77	385	51	255	338	753	17	85
18	425	251	318	653	454	396	106	530	776	132
19	660	489	571	44	220	163	815	327	698	679
20	584	109	545	851	507	661	494	596	169	845
21	477	511	681	594	159	795	227	198	53	265
22	388	66	330	713	754	22	110	550	876	632
23	349	808	292	523	741	894	722	799	247	298
24	553	891	707	724	809	297	548	866	582	99
25	495	601	194	33	165	825	377	11	55	275
26	438	316	643	404	146	730	839	447	361	868
27	592	149	745	914	822	362	873	617	274	433
28	291	518	716	769	97	485	551	881	657	474
29	496	606	219	158	790	202	73	365	888	692
30	649	434	296	543	841	457	411	181	905	777
31	137	685	614	259	358	853	517	711	744	909
32	797	237	248	303	578	79	395	101	505	651
33	444	346	793	217	148	740	889	697	674	559
34	921	857	537	811	307	598	179	895	727	824
35	372	923	867	587	124	620	289	508	666	519
36	721	794	222	173	865	577	74	370	913	817
37	337	748	929	897	737	874	622	299	558	916
38	832	412	186	930	902	762	62	310	613	254
39	333	728	829	397	111	555	901	757	37	185
40	925	877	637	374	933	917	837	437	311	618
41	279	458	416	206	93	465	451	381	31	155
42	775	127	635	364	883	667	524	746	919	847
43	487	561	931	907	787	187	935	927	887	687
44	624	309	608	229	208	103	515	701	694	659
45	484	546	856	532	786	182	910	802	262	373
46	928	892	712	749	934	922	862	562	936	932
47	912	812	312	623	304	583	104	520	726	819
48	347	798	242	273	428	266	393	91	455	401
49	131	655	464	446	356	843	467	461	431	281

P = 937

INDICES

	0	1	2	3	4	5	6	7	8	9
50	875	605	149	769	747	328	30	204	357	16
51	143	211	648	590	519	446	635	316	281	359
52	477	880	580	233	426	849	774	596	125	546
53	187	35	453	731	522	549	21	342	45	87
54	861	653	794	303	18	202	451	69	246	688
55	227	286	641	240	626	395	885	71	378	339
56	724	431	467	871	927	818	601	835	619	145
57	567	192	765	891	42	743	736	365	324	782
58	557	26	248	475	200	565	92	353	698	84
59	12	799	270	139	213	94	207	583	345	644
60	838	251	586	109	858	515	291	690	442	531
61	665	631	106	388	312	156	76	277	409	650
62	355	729	376	473	440	4	876	855	909	576
63	812	606	229	6	791	422	150	402	845	707
64	713	770	512	262	592	700	748	121	824	300
65	542	329	131	183	165	491	31	288	878	449
66	190	205	727	746	15	518	358	425	545	521
67	86	17	687	625	338	926	144	41	781	199
68	83	212	643	857	530	311	649	439	575	790
69	706	591	299	164	448	14	520	337	198	529
70	789	447	528	64	65	56	636	242	911	66
71	684	317	462	223	57	830	282	662	760	637
72	801	360	236	48	243	622	478	348	391	912
73	265	881	628	578	67	763	581	374	119	685
74	335	234	101	720	318	272	427	103	371	463
75	903	850	867	177	224	923	775	397	814	58
76	507	597	385	116	831	171	126	615	676	283
77	141	547	722	563	663	420	188	309	682	761
78	505	36	887	608	638	38	454	434	739	802
79	294	732	153	332	361	215	523	320	481	237
80	778	550	457	553	49	657	22	73	231	244
81	889	343	471	822	623	196	46	369	561	479
82	96	88	274	98	349	255	862	694	669	392
83	80	654	380	8	913	610	795	406	717	266
84	752	304	135	495	882	209	19	429	90	629
85	148	203	647	315	579	595	452	341	793	68
86	640	70	466	834	764	364	247	352	269	582
87	585	689	105	276	375	854	228	401	511	120
88	130	287	726	424	686	40	642	438	298	336
89	527	241	461	661	235	347	627	373	100	102
90	866	396	384	614	721	308	886	433	152	319
91	456	72	470	368	273	693	379	405	134	428
92	646	340	465	351	104	400	725	437	460	372
93	383	432	469	404	464	436	468			

POWER RESIDUES

	0	1	2	3	4	5	6	7	8	9
50	468	466	456	406	156	780	152	760	52	260
51	363	878	642	399	121	605	214	133	665	514
52	696	669	534	796	232	223	178	890	702	699
53	684	609	234	233	228	203	78	390	76	380
54	26	130	650	439	321	668	529	771	107	535
55	801	257	348	803	267	398	116	580	89	445
56	351	818	342	773	117	585	114	570	39	195
57	38	190	13	65	325	688	629	334	733	854
58	522	736	869	597	174	870	602	199	58	290
59	513	691	644	409	171	855	527	761	57	285
60	488	566	19	95	475	501	631	344	783	167
61	835	427	261	368	903	767	87	435	301	568
62	29	145	725	814	322	673	554	896	732	849
63	497	611	244	283	478	516	706	719	784	172
64	860	552	886	682	599	184	920	852	512	686
65	619	284	483	541	831	407	161	805	277	448
66	366	893	717	774	122	610	239	258	353	828
67	392	86	430	276	443	341	768	92	460	426
68	256	343	778	142	710	739	884	672	549	871
69	607	224	183	915	827	387	61	305	588	129
70	645	414	196	43	215	138	690	639	384	46
71	230	213	128	640	389	71	355	838	442	336
72	743	904	772	112	560	926	882	662	499	621
73	294	533	791	207	98	490	576	69	345	788
74	192	23	115	575	64	320	663	504	646	419
75	221	168	840	452	386	56	280	463	441	331
76	718	779	147	735	864	572	49	245	288	503
77	641	394	96	480	526	756	32	160	800	252
78	323	678	579	84	420	226	193	28	140	700
79	689	634	359	858	542	836	432	286	493	591
80	144	720	789	197	48	240	263	378	16	80
81	400	126	630	339	758	42	210	113	565	14
82	70	350	813	317	648	429	271	418	216	143
83	715	764	72	360	863	567	24	120	600	189
84	8	40	200	63	315	638	379	21	105	525
85	751	7	35	175	875	627	324	683	604	209
86	108	540	826	382	36	180	900	752	12	60
87	300	563	4	20	100	500	626	319	658	479
88	521	731	844	472	486	556	906	782	162	810
89	302	573	54	270	413	191	18	90	450	376
90	6	30	150	750	2	10	50	250	313	628
91	329	708	729	834	422	236	243	278	453	391
92	81	405	151	755	27	135	675	564	9	45
93	225	188	3	15	75	375				

P = 941

INDICES

	0	1	2	3	4	5	6	7	8	9
0		0	1	583	2	192	584	881	3	226
1	193	403	585	433	882	775	4	459	227	781
2	194	524	404	799	586	384	434	809	883	898
3	776	97	5	46	460	133	228	90	782	76
4	195	142	525	728	405	418	800	276	587	822
5	385	102	435	206	810	595	884	424	899	579
6	777	129	98	167	6	625	47	171	461	442
7	134	264	229	510	91	27	783	344	77	296
8	196	452	143	10	526	651	729	541	406	379
9	419	374	801	680	277	33	588	705	823	629
10	386	249	103	186	436	716	207	178	811	909
11	596	673	885	557	425	51	900	659	580	400
12	778	806	130	725	99	576	168	24	7	371
13	626	175	48	722	172	61	462	286	443	64
14	135	859	265	836	230	150	511	465	92	162
15	28	19	784	685	345	289	78	356	297	789
16	197	740	453	446	144	238	11	485	527	866
17	652	67	730	121	542	325	407	222	380	138
18	420	506	375	712	802	282	681	862	278	750
19	34	690	589	394	706	268	824	213	630	618
20	387	754	250	839	104	334	187	85	437	244
21	717	233	208	847	179	920	812	38	910	153
22	597	892	674	350	886	610	558	514	426	852
23	52	927	901	694	660	468	581	879	401	773
24	779	797	807	95	131	74	726	274	100	593
25	577	165	169	262	25	294	8	539	372	31
26	627	184	176	671	49	398	723	22	173	59
27	62	834	463	17	287	787	444	483	65	323
28	136	710	860	688	266	616	837	83	231	918
29	151	348	512	925	466	771	93	272	163	292
30	29	669	20	832	785	321	686	81	346	769
31	290	830	79	828	357	359	298	550	790	361
32	198	761	741	300	454	817	447	552	145	217
33	239	792	12	316	486	363	528	491	867	200
34	653	500	68	763	731	634	122	743	543	564
35	326	302	408	937	223	456	381	43	139	819
36	421	622	507	449	376	702	713	554	803	368
37	283	147	682	737	863	219	279	391	751	241
38	35	607	691	794	590	536	395	14	707	915
39	269	318	825	758	214	488	631	934	619	365
40	388	533	755	530	251	644	840	493	105	254
41	335	869	188	520	86	202	438	647	245	655
42	718	158	234	502	209	843	848	70	180	479
43	921	765	813	496	39	733	911	640	154	636
44	598	108	893	124	675	571	351	745	887	257
45	611	545	559	602	515	566	427	338	853	328
46	53	310	928	304	902	872	695	410	661	112
47	469	939	582	191	880	225	402	432	774	458
48	780	523	798	383	808	897	96	45	132	89
49	75	141	727	417	275	821	101	205	594	423

POWER RESIDUES

	0	1	2	3	4	5	6	7	8	9
0	1	2	4	8	16	32	64	128	256	512
1	83	166	332	664	387	774	607	273	546	151
2	302	604	267	534	127	254	508	75	150	300
3	600	259	518	95	190	380	760	579	217	434
4	868	795	649	357	714	487	33	66	132	264
5	528	115	230	460	920	899	857	773	605	269
6	538	135	270	540	139	278	556	171	342	684
7	427	854	767	593	245	490	39	78	156	312
8	624	307	614	287	574	207	414	828	715	489
9	37	74	148	296	592	243	486	31	62	124
10	248	496	51	102	204	408	816	691	441	882
11	823	705	469	938	935	929	917	893	845	749
12	557	173	346	692	443	886	831	721	501	61
13	122	244	488	35	70	140	280	560	179	358
14	716	491	41	82	164	328	656	371	742	543
15	145	290	580	219	438	876	811	681	421	842
16	743	545	149	298	596	251	502	63	126	252
17	504	67	134	268	536	131	262	524	107	214
18	428	856	771	601	261	522	103	206	412	824
19	707	473	5	10	20	40	80	160	320	640
20	339	678	415	830	719	497	53	106	212	424
21	848	755	569	197	394	788	635	329	658	375
22	750	559	177	354	708	475	9	18	36	72
23	144	288	576	211	422	844	747	553	165	330
24	660	379	758	575	209	418	836	731	521	101
25	202	404	808	675	409	818	695	449	898	855
26	769	597	253	506	71	142	284	568	195	390
27	780	619	297	594	247	494	47	94	188	376
28	752	563	185	370	740	539	137	274	548	155
29	310	620	299	598	255	510	79	158	316	632
30	323	646	351	702	463	926	911	881	821	701
31	461	922	903	865	789	637	333	666	391	782
32	623	305	610	279	558	175	350	700	459	918
33	895	849	757	573	205	410	820	699	457	914
34	887	833	725	509	77	154	308	616	291	582
35	223	446	892	843	745	549	157	314	628	315
36	630	319	638	335	670	399	798	655	369	738
37	535	129	258	516	91	182	364	728	515	89
38	178	356	712	483	25	50	100	200	400	800
39	659	377	754	567	193	386	772	603	265	530
40	119	238	476	11	22	44	88	176	352	704
41	467	934	927	913	885	829	717	493	45	90
42	180	360	720	499	57	114	228	456	912	883
43	825	709	477	13	26	52	104	208	416	832
44	723	505	69	138	276	552	163	326	652	363
45	726	511	81	162	324	648	355	710	479	17
46	34	68	136	272	544	147	294	588	235	470
47	940	939	937	933	925	909	877	813	685	429
48	858	775	609	277	554	167	334	668	395	790
49	639	337	674	407	814	687	433	866	791	641

P = 941

INDICES

	0	1	2	3	4	5	6	7	8	9
50	578	128	166	624	170	441	263	509	26	343
51	295	451	9	650	540	378	373	679	32	704
52	628	248	185	715	177	908	672	556	50	658
53	399	805	724	575	23	370	174	721	60	285
54	63	858	835	149	464	161	18	684	288	355
55	788	739	445	237	484	865	66	120	324	221
56	137	505	711	281	861	749	689	393	267	212
57	617	753	838	333	84	243	232	846	919	37
58	152	891	349	609	513	851	926	693	467	878
59	772	796	94	73	273	592	164	261	293	538
60	30	183	670	397	21	58	833	16	786	482
61	322	709	687	615	82	917	347	924	770	271
62	291	668	831	320	80	768	829	827	358	549
63	360	760	299	816	551	216	791	315	362	490
64	199	499	762	633	742	563	301	936	455	42
65	818	621	448	701	553	367	146	736	218	390
66	240	606	793	535	13	914	317	757	487	933
67	364	532	529	643	492	253	868	519	201	646
68	654	157	501	842	69	478	764	495	732	639
69	635	107	123	570	744	256	544	601	565	337
70	327	309	303	871	409	111	938	190	224	431
71	457	522	382	896	44	88	140	416	820	204
72	422	127	623	440	508	342	450	649	377	678
73	703	247	714	907	555	657	804	574	369	720
74	284	857	148	160	683	354	738	236	864	119
75	220	504	280	748	392	211	752	332	242	845
76	36	890	608	850	692	877	795	72	591	260
77	537	182	396	57	15	481	708	614	916	923
78	270	667	319	767	826	548	759	815	215	314
79	489	498	632	562	935	41	620	700	366	735
80	389	605	534	913	756	932	531	642	252	518
81	645	156	841	477	494	638	106	569	255	600
82	336	308	870	110	189	430	521	895	87	415
83	203	126	439	341	648	677	246	906	656	573
84	719	856	159	353	235	118	503	747	210	331
85	844	889	849	876	71	259	181	56	480	613
86	922	666	766	547	814	313	497	561	40	699
87	734	604	912	931	641	517	155	476	637	568
88	599	307	109	429	894	414	125	340	676	905
89	572	855	352	117	746	330	888	875	258	55
90	612	665	546	312	560	698	603	930	516	475
91	567	306	428	413	339	904	854	116	329	874
92	54	664	311	697	929	474	305	412	903	115
93	873	663	696	473	411	114	662	472	113	471
94	470	0								

POWER RESIDUES

	0	1	2	3	4	5	6	7	8	9
50	341	682	423	846	751	561	181	362	724	507
51	73	146	292	584	227	454	908	875	809	677
52	413	826	711	481	21	42	84	168	336	672
53	403	806	671	401	802	663	385	770	599	257
54	514	87	174	348	696	451	902	863	785	629
55	317	634	327	654	367	734	527	113	226	452
56	904	867	793	645	349	698	455	910	879	817
57	693	445	890	839	737	533	125	250	500	59
58	118	236	472	3	6	12	24	48	96	192
59	384	768	595	249	498	55	110	220	440	880
60	819	697	453	906	871	801	661	381	762	583
61	225	450	900	859	777	613	285	570	199	398
62	796	651	361	722	503	65	130	260	520	99
63	198	396	792	643	345	690	439	878	815	689
64	437	874	807	673	405	810	679	417	834	727
65	513	85	170	340	680	419	838	735	529	117
66	234	468	936	931	921	901	861	781	621	301
67	602	263	526	111	222	444	888	835	729	517
68	93	186	372	744	547	153	306	612	283	566
69	191	382	764	587	233	466	932	923	905	869
70	797	653	365	730	519	97	194	388	776	611
71	281	562	183	366	732	523	105	210	420	840
72	739	537	133	266	532	123	246	492	43	86
73	172	344	688	435	870	799	657	373	746	551
74	161	322	644	347	694	447	894	847	753	565
75	189	378	756	571	201	402	804	667	393	786
76	631	321	642	343	686	431	862	783	625	309
77	618	295	590	239	478	15	30	60	120	240
78	480	19	38	76	152	304	608	275	550	159
79	318	636	331	662	383	766	591	241	482	23
80	46	92	184	368	736	531	121	242	484	27
81	54	108	216	432	864	787	633	325	650	359
82	718	495	49	98	196	392	784	627	313	626
83	311	622	303	606	271	542	143	286	572	203
84	406	812	683	425	850	759	577	213	426	852
85	763	585	229	458	916	891	841	741	541	141
86	282	564	187	374	748	555	169	338	676	411
87	822	703	465	930	919	897	853	765	589	237
88	474	7	14	28	56	112	224	448	896	851
89	761	581	221	442	884	827	713	485	29	58
90	116	232	464	928	915	889	837	733	525	109
91	218	436	872	803	665	389	778	615	289	578
92	215	430	860	779	617	293	586	231	462	924
93	907	873	805	669	397	794	647	353	706	471
94										

P = 947

INDICES

	0	1	2	3	4	5	6	7	8	9
0		0	1	914	2	867	915	649	3	882
1	868	307	916	841	650	835	4	215	883	125
2	869	617	308	453	917	788	842	850	651	593
3	836	798	5	275	216	570	884	939	126	809
4	870	22	618	165	309	803	454	253	918	352
5	789	183	843	712	851	228	652	93	594	437
6	837	589	799	585	6	762	276	705	217	421
7	571	549	885	106	940	756	127	10	810	30
8	871	818	23	382	619	136	166	561	310	644
9	804	544	455	766	254	46	919	531	353	243
10	790	663	184	460	844	538	713	68	852	280
11	229	907	653	635	94	374	595	777	438	864
12	838	614	590	936	800	709	586	418	7	133
13	763	660	277	774	706	771	218	267	422	193
14	572	221	550	202	886	514	107	320	941	270
15	757	526	128	151	11	719	811	425	31	680
16	872	156	819	829	24	196	383	259	620	736
17	137	61	167	575	562	491	311	405	645	449
18	805	224	545	557	456	860	767	522	255	553
19	47	82	920	16	532	730	354	205	244	51
20	791	673	664	296	185	889	461	389	845	432
21	539	931	714	517	69	86	853	501	281	74
22	230	110	908	699	654	724	636	334	95	323
23	375	924	596	360	778	174	439	944	865	880
24	839	213	615	786	591	273	937	20	801	350
25	710	91	587	760	419	104	8	816	134	642
26	764	529	661	536	278	633	775	612	707	131
27	772	265	219	512	268	149	423	154	194	734
28	573	403	222	858	551	14	203	671	887	430
29	515	499	108	722	321	358	942	211	271	348
30	758	814	527	631	129	510	152	401	12	428
31	720	209	812	508	426	506	32	34	681	900
32	873	36	157	340	820	683	830	248	25	902
33	197	486	384	875	260	626	621	38	737	603
34	138	159	62	55	168	342	576	286	563	822
35	492	745	312	685	406	470	646	832	450	795
36	806	250	225	582	546	27	558	43	457	904
37	861	415	768	199	523	677	256	488	554	79
38	48	386	83	696	921	877	17	101	533	262
39	731	668	355	628	206	897	245	623	52	742
40	792	40	674	693	665	739	297	300	186	605
41	890	235	462	140	390	303	846	161	433	752
42	540	64	932	189	715	57	518	292	70	170
43	87	608	854	344	502	482	282	578	75	893
44	231	288	111	115	909	565	700	238	655	824
45	725	329	637	494	335	465	96	747	324	119
46	376	314	925	143	597	687	361	367	779	408
47	175	393	440	472	945	913	866	648	881	306
48	840	834	214	124	616	452	787	849	592	797
49	274	569	938	808	21	164	802	252	351	182

POWER RESIDUES

	0	1	2	3	4	5	6	7	8	9
0	1	2	4	8	16	32	64	128	256	512
1	77	154	308	616	285	570	193	386	772	597
2	247	494	41	82	164	328	656	365	730	513
3	79	158	316	632	317	634	321	642	337	674
4	401	802	657	367	734	521	95	190	380	760
5	573	199	398	796	645	343	686	425	850	753
6	559	171	342	684	421	842	737	527	107	214
7	428	856	765	583	219	438	876	805	663	379
8	758	569	191	382	764	581	215	430	860	773
9	599	251	502	57	114	228	456	912	877	807
10	667	387	774	601	255	510	73	146	292	584
11	221	442	884	821	695	443	886	825	703	459
12	918	889	831	715	483	19	38	76	152	304
13	608	269	538	129	258	516	85	170	340	680
14	413	826	705	463	926	905	863	779	611	275
15	550	153	306	612	277	554	161	322	644	341
16	682	417	834	721	495	43	86	172	344	688
17	429	858	769	591	235	470	940	933	919	891
18	835	723	499	51	102	204	408	816	685	423
19	846	745	543	139	278	556	165	330	660	373
20	746	545	143	286	572	197	394	788	629	311
21	622	297	594	241	482	17	34	68	136	272
22	544	141	282	564	181	362	724	501	55	110
23	220	440	880	813	679	411	822	697	447	894
24	841	735	523	99	198	396	792	637	327	654
25	361	722	497	47	94	188	376	752	557	167
26	334	668	389	778	609	271	542	137	274	548
27	149	298	596	245	490	33	66	132	264	528
28	109	218	436	872	797	647	347	694	441	882
29	817	687	427	854	761	575	203	406	812	677
30	407	814	681	415	830	713	479	11	22	44
31	88	176	352	704	461	922	897	847	747	547
32	147	294	588	229	458	916	885	823	699	451
33	902	857	767	587	227	454	908	869	791	635
34	323	646	345	690	433	866	785	623	299	598
35	249	498	49	98	196	392	784	621	295	590
36	233	466	932	917	887	827	707	467	934	921
37	895	843	739	531	115	230	460	920	893	839
38	731	515	83	166	332	664	381	762	577	207
39	414	828	709	471	942	937	927	907	867	787
40	627	307	614	281	562	177	354	708	469	938
41	929	911	875	803	659	371	742	537	127	254
42	508	69	138	276	552	157	314	628	309	618
43	289	578	209	418	836	725	503	59	118	236
44	472	944	941	935	923	899	851	755	563	179
45	358	716	485	23	46	92	184	368	736	525
46	103	206	412	824	701	455	910	873	799	651
47	355	710	473	946	945	943	939	931	915	883
48	819	691	435	870	793	639	331	662	377	754
49	561	175	350	700	453	906	865	783	619	291

P = 947

INDICES

	0	1	2	3	4	5	6	7	8	9
50	711	227	92	436	588	584	761	704	420	548
51	105	755	9	29	817	381	135	560	643	543
52	765	45	530	242	662	459	537	67	279	906
53	634	373	776	863	613	935	708	417	132	659
54	773	770	266	192	220	201	513	319	269	525
55	150	718	424	679	155	828	195	258	735	60
56	574	490	404	448	223	556	859	521	552	81
57	15	729	204	50	672	295	888	388	431	930
58	516	85	500	73	109	698	723	333	322	923
59	359	173	943	879	212	785	272	19	349	90
60	759	103	815	641	528	535	632	611	130	264
61	511	148	153	733	402	857	13	670	429	498
62	721	357	210	347	813	630	509	400	427	208
63	507	505	33	899	35	339	682	247	901	485
64	874	625	37	602	158	54	341	285	821	744
65	684	469	831	794	249	581	26	42	903	414
66	198	676	487	78	385	695	876	100	261	667
67	627	896	622	741	39	692	738	299	604	234
68	139	302	160	751	63	188	56	291	169	607
69	343	481	577	892	287	114	564	237	823	328
70	493	464	746	118	313	142	686	366	407	392
71	471	912	647	305	833	123	451	848	796	568
72	807	163	251	181	226	435	583	703	547	754
73	28	380	559	542	44	241	458	66	905	372
74	862	934	416	658	769	191	200	318	524	717
75	678	827	257	59	489	447	555	520	80	728
76	49	294	387	929	84	72	697	332	922	172
77	878	784	18	89	102	640	534	610	263	147
78	732	856	669	497	356	346	629	399	207	504
79	898	338	246	484	624	601	53	284	743	468
80	793	580	41	413	675	77	694	99	666	895
81	740	691	298	233	301	750	187	290	606	480
82	891	113	236	327	463	117	141	365	391	911
83	304	122	847	567	162	180	434	702	753	379
84	541	240	65	371	933	657	190	317	716	826
85	58	446	519	727	293	928	71	331	171	783
86	88	639	609	146	855	496	345	398	503	337
87	483	600	283	467	579	412	76	98	894	690
88	232	749	289	479	112	326	116	364	910	121
89	566	179	701	378	239	370	656	316	825	445
90	726	927	330	782	638	145	495	397	336	599
91	466	411	97	689	748	478	325	363	120	178
92	377	369	315	444	926	781	144	396	598	410
93	688	477	362	177	368	443	780	395	409	476
94	176	442	394	475	441	474	473			

POWER RESIDUES

	0	1	2	3	4	5	6	7	8	9
50	582	217	434	868	789	631	315	630	313	626
51	305	610	273	546	145	290	580	213	426	852
52	757	567	187	374	748	549	151	302	604	261
53	522	97	194	388	776	605	263	526	105	210
54	420	840	733	519	91	182	364	728	509	71
55	142	284	568	189	378	756	565	183	366	732
56	517	87	174	348	696	445	890	833	719	491
57	35	70	140	280	560	173	346	692	437	874
58	801	655	363	726	505	63	126	252	504	61
59	122	244	488	29	58	116	232	464	928	909
60	871	795	643	339	678	409	818	689	431	862
61	777	607	267	534	121	242	484	21	42	84
62	168	336	672	397	794	641	335	670	393	786
63	625	303	606	265	530	113	226	452	904	861
64	775	603	259	518	89	178	356	712	477	7
65	14	28	56	112	224	448	896	845	743	539
66	131	262	524	101	202	404	808	669	391	782
67	617	287	574	201	402	804	661	375	750	553
68	159	318	636	325	650	353	706	465	930	913
69	879	811	675	403	806	665	383	766	585	223
70	446	892	837	727	507	67	134	268	536	125
71	250	500	53	106	212	424	848	749	551	155
72	310	620	293	586	225	450	900	853	759	571
73	195	390	780	613	279	558	169	338	676	405
74	810	673	399	798	649	351	702	457	914	881
75	815	683	419	838	729	511	75	150	300	600
76	253	506	65	130	260	520	93	186	372	744
77	541	135	270	540	133	266	532	117	234	468
78	936	925	903	859	771	595	243	486	25	50
79	100	200	400	800	653	359	718	489	31	62
80	124	248	496	45	90	180	360	720	493	39
81	78	156	312	624	301	602	257	514	81	162
82	324	648	349	698	449	898	849	751	555	163
83	326	652	357	714	481	15	30	60	120	240
84	480	13	26	52	104	208	416	832	717	487
85	27	54	108	216	432	864	781	615	283	566
86	185	370	740	533	119	238	476	5	10	20
87	40	80	160	320	640	333	666	385	770	593
88	239	478	9	18	36	72	144	288	576	205
89	410	820	693	439	878	809	671	395	790	633
90	319	638	329	658	369	738	529	111	222	444
91	888	829	711	475	3	6	12	24	48	96
92	192	384	768	589	231	462	924	901	855	763
93	579	211	422	844	741	535	123	246	492	37
94	74	148	296	592	237	474				

P = 953

INDICES

	0	1	2	3	4	5	6	7	8	9
0		0	126	1	252	47	127	804	378	2
1	173	311	253	342	930	48	504	246	128	257
2	299	805	437	363	379	94	468	3	104	892
3	174	665	630	312	372	851	254	486	383	343
4	425	286	931	843	563	49	489	519	505	656
5	220	247	594	824	129	358	230	258	66	926
6	300	811	791	806	756	389	438	546	498	364
7	25	308	380	386	612	95	509	163	469	270
8	551	4	412	590	105	293	17	893	689	157
9	175	194	615	666	645	304	631	73	782	313
10	346	85	373	942	720	852	950	171	255	102
11	484	487	356	754	384	410	192	344	100	98
12	426	622	937	287	917	141	932	428	882	844
13	515	878	564	109	672	50	624	275	490	447
14	151	520	434	653	506	939	512	657	738	323
15	221	868	635	248	289	712	595	660	396	825
16	677	215	130	919	538	359	716	529	231	684
17	419	259	143	166	67	898	815	927	283	495
18	301	934	320	812	741	533	792	557	771	807
19	430	79	757	206	199	390	908	583	439	884
20	472	547	211	744	499	333	116	365	846	568
21	26	326	124	309	297	890	381	517	228	387
22	610	588	613	83	482	96	880	273	510	710
23	536	164	318	77	470	566	226	271	224	701
24	552	59	748	5	111	703	413	599	91	591
25	267	947	106	674	554	294	56	795	18	338
26	641	894	52	61	690	871	235	158	798	35
27	176	626	750	195	401	405	616	460	573	667
28	277	7	646	243	560	305	779	138	632	492
29	113	74	638	135	783	21	864	314	449	705
30	347	695	42	86	761	858	374	153	415	943
31	838	774	721	453	786	853	522	601	951	251
32	803	172	341	503	256	436	93	103	664	371
33	485	424	842	488	655	593	357	65	810	755
34	545	24	385	508	269	411	292	688	193	644
35	72	345	941	949	101	355	409	99	621	916
36	427	514	108	623	446	433	938	737	867	288
37	659	676	918	715	683	142	897	282	933	740
38	556	429	205	907	883	210	332	845	325	296
39	516	609	82	879	709	317	565	223	58	110
40	598	266	673	55	337	51	870	797	625	400
41	459	276	242	778	491	637	20	448	694	760
42	152	837	452	521	250	340	435	663	423	654
43	64	544	507	291	643	940	354	620	513	445
44	736	658	714	896	739	204	209	324	608	708
45	222	597	54	869	399	241	636	693	836	249
46	662	63	290	353	444	713	203	607	596	398
47	692	661	352	202	397	351	350	826	827	873
48	678	828	185	216	874	120	131	679	237	920
49	829	766	539	186	725	360	217	160	717	875

POWER RESIDUES

	0	1	2	3	4	5	6	7	8	9
0	1	3	9	27	81	243	729	281	843	623
1	916	842	620	907	815	539	664	86	258	774
2	416	295	885	749	341	70	210	630	937	905
3	809	521	610	877	725	269	807	515	592	823
4	563	736	302	906	812	530	637	5	15	45
5	135	405	262	786	452	403	256	768	398	241
6	723	263	789	461	430	337	58	174	522	613
7	886	752	350	97	291	873	713	233	699	191
8	573	766	392	223	669	101	303	909	821	557
9	718	248	744	326	25	75	225	675	119	357
10	118	354	109	327	28	84	252	756	362	133
11	399	244	732	290	870	704	206	618	901	797
12	485	502	553	706	212	636	2	6	18	54
13	162	486	505	562	733	293	879	731	287	861
14	677	125	375	172	516	595	832	590	817	545
15	682	140	420	307	921	857	665	89	267	801
16	497	538	661	77	231	693	173	519	604	859
17	671	107	321	10	30	90	270	810	524	619
18	904	806	512	583	796	482	493	526	625	922
19	860	674	116	348	91	273	819	551	700	194
20	582	793	473	466	445	382	193	579	784	446
21	385	202	606	865	689	161	483	496	535	652
22	50	150	450	397	238	714	236	708	218	654
23	56	168	504	559	724	266	798	488	511	580
24	787	455	412	283	849	641	17	51	153	459
25	424	319	4	12	36	108	324	19	57	171
26	513	586	805	509	574	769	401	250	750	344
27	79	237	711	227	681	137	411	280	840	614
28	889	761	377	178	534	649	41	123	369	154
29	462	433	346	85	255	765	389	214	642	20
30	60	180	540	667	95	285	855	659	71	213
31	639	11	33	99	297	891	767	395	232	696
32	182	546	685	149	447	388	211	633	946	932
33	890	764	386	205	615	892	770	404	259	777
34	425	322	13	39	117	351	100	300	900	794
35	476	475	472	463	436	355	112	336	55	165
36	495	532	643	23	69	207	621	910	824	566
37	745	329	34	102	306	918	848	638	8	24
38	72	216	648	38	114	342	73	219	657	65
39	195	585	802	500	547	688	158	474	469	454
40	409	274	822	560	727	275	825	569	754	356
41	115	345	82	246	738	308	924	866	692	170
42	510	577	778	428	331	40	120	360	127	381
43	190	570	757	365	142	426	325	22	66	198
44	594	829	581	790	464	439	364	139	417	298
45	894	776	422	313	939	911	827	575	772	410
46	277	831	587	808	518	601	850	644	26	78
47	234	702	200	600	847	635	952	950	944	926
48	872	710	224	672	110	330	37	111	333	46
49	138	414	289	867	695	179	537	658	68	204

P = 953

INDICES

	0	1	2	3	4	5	6	7	8	9
50	393	530	121	698	232	132	800	685	680	263
51	420	238	182	260	921	37	144	830	464	167
52	767	31	68	540	178	899	187	911	816	726
53	45	928	361	628	284	218	924	496	161	15
54	302	718	752	935	876	149	321	394	527	813
55	531	197	742	122	586	534	699	89	793	233
56	403	558	133	40	772	801	369	808	686	407
57	431	681	905	80	264	457	758	421	618	207
58	239	442	200	183	764	391	261	462	909	922
59	147	584	38	903	440	145	575	885	831	577
60	473	465	821	548	168	669	212	768	887	745
61	32	861	500	69	279	334	541	833	117	179
62	12	366	900	9	847	188	579	569	912	732
63	27	817	648	327	727	475	125	46	377	310
64	929	245	298	362	467	891	629	850	382	285
65	562	518	219	823	229	925	790	388	497	307
66	611	162	550	589	16	156	614	303	781	84
67	719	170	483	753	191	97	936	140	881	877
68	671	274	150	652	511	322	634	711	395	214
69	537	528	418	165	814	494	319	532	770	78
70	198	582	471	743	115	567	123	889	227	587
71	481	272	535	76	225	700	747	702	90	946
72	553	794	640	60	234	34	749	404	572	6
73	559	137	112	134	863	704	41	857	414	773
74	785	600	802	502	92	370	841	592	809	23
75	268	687	71	948	408	915	107	432	866	675
76	682	281	555	906	331	295	81	316	57	265
77	336	796	458	777	19	759	451	339	422	543
78	642	619	735	895	208	707	53	240	835	62
79	443	606	691	201	349	872	184	119	236	765
80	724	159	392	697	799	262	181	36	463	30
81	177	910	44	627	923	14	751	148	526	196
82	585	88	402	39	368	406	904	456	617	441
83	763	461	146	902	574	576	820	668	886	860
84	278	832	11	8	578	731	647	474	376	244
85	466	849	561	822	789	306	549	155	780	169
86	190	139	670	651	633	213	417	493	769	581
87	114	888	480	75	746	945	639	33	571	136
88	862	856	784	501	840	22	70	914	865	280
89	330	315	335	776	450	542	734	706	834	605
90	348	118	723	696	180	29	43	13	525	87
91	367	455	762	901	819	859	10	730	375	848
92	788	154	189	650	416	580	479	944	570	855
93	839	913	329	775	733	604	722	28	524	454
94	818	729	787	649	478	854	328	603	523	728
95	477	602	476							

POWER RESIDUES

	0	1	2	3	4	5	6	7	8	9
50	612	883	743	323	16	48	144	432	343	76
51	228	684	146	438	361	130	390	217	651	47
52	141	423	316	948	938	908	818	548	691	167
53	501	550	697	185	555	712	230	690	164	492
54	523	616	895	779	431	340	67	201	603	856
55	662	80	240	720	254	762	380	187	561	730
56	284	852	650	44	132	396	235	705	209	627
57	928	878	728	278	834	596	835	599	844	626
58	925	869	701	197	591	820	554	709	221	663
59	83	249	747	335	52	156	468	451	400	247
60	741	317	951	947	935	899	791	467	448	391
61	220	660	74	222	666	92	276	828	578	781
62	437	358	121	363	136	408	271	813	533	646
63	32	96	288	864	686	152	456	415	292	876
64	722	260	780	434	349	94	282	846	632	943
65	923	863	683	143	429	334	49	147	441	370
66	157	471	460	427	328	31	93	279	837	605
67	862	680	134	402	253	759	371	160	480	487
68	508	571	760	374	169	507	568	751	347	88
69	264	792	470	457	418	301	903	803	503	556
70	715	239	717	245	735	299	897	785	449	394
71	229	687	155	465	442	373	166	498	541	670
72	104	312	936	902	800	494	529	634	949	941
73	917	845	629	934	896	782	440	367	148	444
74	379	184	552	703	203	609	874	716	242	726
75	272	816	542	673	113	339	64	192	576	775
76	419	304	912	830	584	799	491	520	607	868
77	698	188	564	739	311	933	893	773	413	286
78	858	668	98	294	882	740	314	942	920	854
79	656	62	186	558	721	257	771	407	268	804
80	506	565	742	320	7	21	63	189	567	748
81	338	61	183	549	694	176	528	631	940	914
82	836	602	853	653	53	159	477	478	481	490
83	517	598	841	617	898	788	458	421	310	930
84	884	746	332	43	129	387	208	624	919	851
85	647	35	105	315	945	929	881	737	305	915
86	839	611	880	734	296	888	758	368	151	453
87	406	265	795	479	484	499	544	679	131	393
88	226	678	128	384	199	597	838	608	871	707
89	215	645	29	87	261	783	443	376	175	525
90	622	913	833	593	826	572	763	383	196	588
91	811	527	628	931	887	755	359	124	372	163
92	489	514	589	814	536	655	59	177	531	640
93	14	42	126	378	181	543	676	122	366	145
94	435	352	103	309	927	875	719	251	753	353
95	106	318								

P = 967

INDICES

	0	1	2	3	4	5	6	7	8	9
0		0	374	237	748	1	611	67	156	474
1	375	888	19	883	441	238	530	498	848	605
2	749	304	296	771	393	2	291	711	815	699
3	612	64	904	159	872	68	256	193	13	154
4	157	105	678	491	670	475	179	445	767	134
5	376	735	665	518	119	889	223	842	107	724
6	20	910	438	541	312	884	533	741	280	42
7	442	270	630	448	567	239	387	955	528	103
8	531	948	479	680	86	499	865	936	78	97
9	849	950	553	301	819	606	175	828	508	396
10	750	116	143	166	73	305	892	757	493	933
11	297	430	597	868	250	772	481	391	132	565
12	394	810	318	342	812	3	915	944	686	728
13	292	792	907	672	149	712	654	572	416	544
14	816	682	644	805	38	700	822	371	941	320
15	613	782	761	6	363	65	902	840	477	755
16	905	838	356	277	853	160	88	423	460	800
17	873	113	273	625	344	69	452	961	471	146
18	257	920	358	181	927	194	675	420	227	778
19	14	501	549	856	236	155	882	847	770	814
20	158	12	490	766	517	106	540	279	447	527
21	679	77	300	507	165	492	867	131	341	685
22	671	415	804	940	5	476	276	459	624	470
23	180	226	855	769	765	446	506	340	939	623
24	768	938	218	219	692	135	716	522	220	917
25	377	411	323	693	352	736	94	162	136	260
26	666	207	200	717	315	519	80	334	523	185
27	120	609	62	221	946	890	790	900	918	538
28	224	92	90	378	52	843	213	172	412	30
29	108	99	230	324	745	725	349	633	694	688
30	21	558	190	353	169	911	380	425	737	403
31	439	152	310	95	248	542	851	776	163	621
32	313	28	246	137	730	885	651	204	261	512
33	534	54	462	667	797	742	834	433	208	139
34	281	952	487	201	647	43	33	330	718	294
35	443	628	826	316	369	271	845	802	520	60
36	631	244	328	81	732	449	555	878	335	579
37	568	585	83	524	794	240	601	616	186	636
38	388	215	875	121	923	956	264	965	610	887
39	529	303	290	63	255	104	178	734	222	909
40	532	269	386	947	864	949	174	115	891	429
41	480	809	914	791	653	681	821	781	901	837
42	87	112	451	919	674	500	881	11	539	76
43	866	414	275	225	505	937	715	410	93	206
44	79	608	789	91	212	98	348	557	379	151
45	850	27	650	53	833	951	32	627	844	243
46	554	584	600	214	263	302	177	268	173	808
47	820	111	880	413	714	607	347	26	31	583
48	176	110	346	109	592	829	593	659	100	514
49	509	830	124	231	896	397	594	337	325	656

POWER RESIDUES

	0	1	2	3	4	5	6	7	8	9
0	1	5	25	125	625	224	153	765	924	752
1	859	427	201	38	190	950	882	542	776	12
2	60	300	533	731	754	869	477	451	321	638
3	289	478	456	346	763	914	702	609	144	720
4	699	594	69	345	758	889	577	951	887	567
5	901	637	284	453	331	688	539	761	904	652
6	359	828	272	393	31	155	775	7	35	175
7	875	507	601	104	520	666	429	211	88	440
8	266	363	848	372	893	597	84	420	166	830
9	282	443	281	438	256	313	598	89	445	291
10	488	506	596	79	395	41	205	58	290	483
11	481	471	421	171	855	407	101	505	591	54
12	270	383	948	872	492	526	696	579	961	937
13	817	217	118	590	49	245	258	323	648	339
14	728	739	794	102	510	616	179	895	607	134
15	670	449	311	588	39	195	8	40	200	33
16	165	825	257	318	623	214	103	515	641	304
17	553	831	287	468	406	96	480	466	396	46
18	230	183	915	707	634	269	378	923	747	834
19	302	543	781	37	185	925	757	884	552	826
20	262	343	748	839	327	668	439	261	338	723
21	714	669	444	286	463	381	938	822	242	243
22	248	273	398	56	280	433	231	188	940	832
23	292	493	531	721	704	619	194	3	15	75
24	375	908	672	459	361	838	322	643	314	603
25	114	570	916	712	659	394	36	180	900	632
26	259	328	673	464	386	963	947	867	467	401
27	71	355	808	172	860	432	226	163	815	207
28	68	340	733	764	919	727	734	769	944	852
29	392	26	130	650	349	778	22	110	550	816
30	212	93	465	391	21	105	525	691	554	836
31	312	593	64	320	633	264	353	798	122	610
32	149	745	824	252	293	498	556	846	362	843
33	347	768	939	827	267	368	873	497	551	821
34	237	218	123	615	174	870	482	476	446	296
35	513	631	254	303	548	806	162	810	182	910
36	682	509	611	154	770	949	877	517	651	354
37	803	147	735	774	2	10	50	250	283	448
38	306	563	881	537	751	854	402	76	380	933
39	797	117	585	24	120	600	99	495	541	771
40	954	902	642	309	578	956	912	692	559	861
41	437	251	288	473	431	221	138	690	549	811
42	187	935	807	167	835	307	568	906	662	409
43	111	555	841	337	718	689	544	786	62	310
44	583	14	70	350	783	47	235	208	73	365
45	858	422	176	880	532	726	729	744	819	227
46	168	840	332	693	564	886	562	876	512	626
47	229	178	890	582	9	45	225	158	790	82
48	410	116	580	966	962	942	842	342	743	814
49	202	43	215	108	540	766	929	777	17	85

P = 967

INDICES

	0	1	2	3	4	5	6	7	8	9
50	751	660	785	746	697	117	101	71	726	361
51	144	515	468	350	536	167	510	367	634	862
52	74	831	581	695	574	306	125	562	689	576
53	893	232	454	22	708	758	897	383	559	56
54	494	398	17	191	436	934	595	570	354	418
55	298	338	198	170	308	431	326	963	912	408
56	598	657	466	381	464	869	752	49	426	705
57	251	661	587	738	546	773	786	46	404	127
58	482	747	473	440	604	392	698	871	153	669
59	133	118	723	311	41	566	102	85	96	818
60	395	72	932	249	564	811	727	148	543	37
61	319	362	754	852	799	343	145	926	777	235
62	813	516	526	164	684	4	469	764	622	691
63	916	351	259	314	184	945	537	51	29	744
64	687	168	402	247	620	729	511	796	138	646
65	293	368	59	731	578	793	635	922	886	254
66	908	863	428	652	836	673	75	504	205	211
67	150	832	242	262	807	713	582	591	513	895
68	655	696	360	535	861	573	575	707	55	435
69	417	307	407	463	704	545	126	603	668	40
70	817	563	36	798	234	683	690	183	743	619
71	645	577	253	835	210	806	894	860	434	703
72	39	233	618	209	702	701	455	285	140	456
73	823	23	929	282	286	372	709	663	953	141
74	942	759	959	488	457	321	898	188	202	824
75	614	384	9	648	24	783	560	196	44	930
76	762	57	589	34	283	7	495	641	331	287
77	364	399	638	719	373	66	18	497	295	710
78	903	192	677	444	664	841	437	740	629	954
79	478	935	552	827	142	756	596	390	317	943
80	906	571	643	370	760	839	355	422	272	960
81	357	419	548	846	489	278	299	130	803	458
82	854	339	217	521	322	161	199	333	61	899
83	89	171	229	632	189	424	309	775	245	203
84	461	432	486	329	825	801	327	877	82	615
85	874	964	289	733	385	114	913	780	450	10
86	274	409	788	556	649	626	599	267	879	25
87	345	658	123	336	784	70	467	366	580	561
88	453	382	16	569	197	962	465	48	586	45
89	472	870	722	84	931	147	753	925	525	763
90	258	50	401	795	58	921	427	503	241	590
91	359	706	406	602	35	182	252	859	617	284
92	928	662	958	187	8	195	588	640	637	496
93	676	739	551	389	642	421	547	129	216	332
94	228	774	485	876	288	779	787	266	122	365
95	15	47	721	924	400	502	405	858	957	639
96	550	128	484	265	720	857	483			

POWER RESIDUES

	0	1	2	3	4	5	6	7	8	9
50	425	191	955	907	667	434	236	213	98	490
51	516	646	329	678	489	511	621	204	53	265
52	358	823	247	268	373	898	622	209	78	390
53	16	80	400	66	330	683	514	636	279	428
54	206	63	315	608	139	695	574	936	812	192
55	960	932	792	92	460	366	863	447	301	538
56	756	879	527	701	604	119	595	74	370	883
57	547	801	137	685	524	686	529	711	654	369
58	878	522	676	479	461	371	888	572	926	762
59	909	677	484	486	496	546	796	112	560	866
60	462	376	913	697	584	19	95	475	441	271
61	388	6	30	150	750	849	377	918	722	709
62	644	319	628	239	228	173	865	457	351	788
63	72	360	833	297	518	656	379	928	772	959
64	927	767	934	802	142	710	649	344	753	864
65	452	326	663	414	136	680	499	561	871	487
66	501	571	921	737	784	52	260	333	698	589
67	44	220	133	665	424	186	930	782	42	210
68	83	415	141	705	624	219	128	640	299	528
69	706	629	244	253	298	523	681	504	586	29
70	145	725	724	719	694	569	911	687	534	736
71	779	27	135	675	474	436	246	263	348	773
72	964	952	892	592	59	295	508	606	129	645
73	324	653	364	853	397	51	255	308	573	931
74	787	67	335	708	639	294	503	581	4	20
75	100	500	566	896	612	159	795	107	535	741
76	804	152	760	899	627	234	203	48	240	233
77	198	23	115	575	941	837	317	618	189	945
78	857	417	151	755	874	502	576	946	862	442
79	276	413	131	655	374	903	647	334	703	614
80	169	845	357	818	222	143	715	674	469	411
81	121	605	124	620	199	28	140	700	599	94
82	470	416	146	730	749	844	352	793	97	485
83	491	521	671	454	336	713	664	419	161	805
84	157	785	57	285	458	356	813	197	18	90
85	450	316	613	164	820	232	193	965	957	917
86	717	684	519	661	404	86	430	216	113	565
87	891	587	34	170	850	382	943	847	367	868
88	472	426	196	13	65	325	658	389	11	55
89	275	408	106	530	716	679	494	536	746	829
90	277	418	156	780	32	160	800	132	660	399
91	61	305	558	856	412	126	630	249	278	423
92	181	905	657	384	953	897	617	184	920	732
93	759	894	602	109	545	791	87	435	241	238
94	223	148	740	799	127	635	274	403	81	405
95	91	455	341	738	789	77	385	958	922	742
96	809	177	885	557	851	387				

P = 971

INDICES

	0	1	2	3	4	5	6	7	8	9
0		0	325	646	650	392	1	610	5	322
1	717	563	326	190	935	68	330	502	647	632
2	72	286	888	266	651	784	515	968	290	211
3	393	601	655	239	827	32	2	292	957	836
4	397	509	611	381	243	714	591	44	6	250
5	139	178	840	340	323	955	615	308	536	153
6	718	62	926	932	10	582	564	759	182	912
7	357	301	327	213	617	460	312	203	191	425
8	722	644	834	458	936	894	706	857	568	412
9	69	800	916	277	369	54	331	738	575	885
10	464	119	503	406	195	678	665	168	648	395
11	310	938	940	269	633	658	861	512	478	142
12	73	156	387	185	281	206	287	709	335	57
13	907	198	889	272	114	390	507	201	267	685
14	682	690	626	753	652	603	538	896	942	687
15	785	96	637	824	528	23	516	695	750	16
16	77	876	969	609	189	631	783	600	291	380
17	249	954	61	758	212	424	893	799	737	405
18	394	657	155	708	271	684	602	95	694	608
19	379	423	656	94	93	258	900	543	240	259
20	789	435	444	821	828	901	731	588	520	225
21	33	544	20	947	493	773	3	241	720	859
22	635	692	293	260	295	136	594	767	958	790
23	13	849	216	671	837	436	803	101	467	873
24	398	445	481	320	712	642	510	822	606	134
25	531	559	612	829	64	570	660	628	382	902
26	262	533	523	964	244	732	597	88	439	28
27	715	589	832	476	526	377	592	521	40	923
28	37	174	45	226	951	700	108	149	7	34
29	928	414	863	755	251	545	297	561	42	456
30	140	21	421	765	962	454	179	948	853	82
31	348	796	841	494	50	354	105	881	341	774
32	402	814	231	164	324	4	934	71	514	654
33	956	242	138	614	925	181	616	721	705	915
34	574	194	309	860	386	334	113	681	537	636
35	749	188	248	892	154	693	92	788	730	19
36	719	294	12	802	480	605	63	261	596	831
37	39	950	927	296	420	852	49	401	933	137
38	704	385	748	91	11	595	419	703	418	254
39	583	768	255	844	868	817	565	959	584	918
40	144	540	760	791	769	66	176	855	183	14
41	256	847	86	763	913	850	845	361	550	432
42	358	217	869	366	345	316	302	672	818	429
43	128	555	328	838	566	279	75	898	214	437
44	960	572	47	84	618	804	585	363	620	373
45	461	102	919	742	122	222	313	468	145	500
46	338	410	204	874	541	669	26	452	192	399
47	761	371	158	944	426	446	792	662	228	350
48	723	482	770	552	806	160	645	321	67	285
49	967	238	835	713	177	307	931	911	459	643

POWER RESIDUES

	0	1	2	3	4	5	6	7	8	9
0	1	6	36	216	325	8	48	288	757	658
1	64	384	362	230	409	512	159	954	869	359
2	212	301	835	155	930	725	466	854	269	643
3	945	815	35	210	289	763	694	280	709	370
4	278	697	298	817	47	282	721	442	710	376
5	314	913	623	825	95	570	507	129	774	760
6	676	172	61	366	254	553	405	488	15	90
7	540	327	20	120	720	436	674	160	960	905
8	575	537	309	883	443	716	412	530	267	631
9	873	383	356	194	193	187	151	906	581	573
10	525	237	451	764	700	316	925	695	286	745
11	586	603	705	346	134	804	940	785	826	101
12	606	723	454	782	808	964	929	719	430	638
13	915	635	897	527	249	523	225	379	332	50
14	300	829	119	714	400	458	806	952	857	287
15	751	622	819	59	354	182	121	726	472	890
16	485	968	953	863	323	967	947	827	107	642
17	939	779	790	856	281	715	406	494	51	306
18	865	335	68	408	506	123	738	544	351	164
19	13	78	468	866	341	104	624	831	131	786
20	832	137	822	77	462	830	125	750	616	783
21	814	29	174	73	438	686	232	421	584	591
22	633	885	455	788	844	209	283	727	478	926
23	701	322	961	911	611	753	634	891	491	33
24	198	217	331	44	264	613	765	706	352	170
25	49	294	793	874	389	392	410	518	195	199
26	223	367	260	589	621	813	23	138	828	113
27	678	184	133	798	904	569	501	93	558	435
28	668	124	744	580	567	489	21	126	756	652
29	28	168	37	222	361	224	373	296	805	946
30	821	71	426	614	771	742	568	495	57	342
31	110	660	76	456	794	880	425	608	735	526
32	243	487	9	54	324	2	12	72	432	650
33	16	96	576	543	345	128	768	724	460	818
34	53	318	937	767	718	424	602	699	310	889
35	479	932	737	538	315	919	659	70	420	578
36	555	417	560	447	740	556	423	596	663	94
37	564	471	884	449	752	628	855	275	679	190
38	169	43	258	577	549	381	344	122	732	508
39	135	810	5	30	180	109	654	40	240	469
40	872	377	320	949	839	179	103	618	795	886
41	461	824	89	534	291	775	766	712	388	386
42	374	302	841	191	175	79	474	902	557	429
43	632	879	419	572	519	201	235	439	692	268
44	637	909	599	681	202	241	475	908	593	645
45	957	887	467	860	305	859	299	823	83	498
46	75	450	758	664	100	600	687	238	457	800
47	916	641	933	743	574	531	273	667	118	708
48	364	242	481	944	809	970	965	935	755	646
49	963	923	683	214	313	907	587	609	741	562

P = 971

INDICES

	0	1	2	3	4	5	6	7	8	9
50	856	276	884	677	937	511	184	56	389	689
51	895	823	15	630	953	798	707	607	257	434
52	587	946	858	135	848	100	319	133	569	532
53	87	475	922	699	413	560	764	81	353	813
54	70	613	914	333	187	787	801	830	851	384
55	702	843	917	65	846	360	365	428	278	571
56	362	741	499	668	370	661	551	284	306	275
57	55	629	433	99	474	80	332	383	359	740
58	283	98	739	903	218	904	110	496	576	263
59	870	219	622	448	886	534	367	905	781	442
60	465	524	346	111	746	548	120	965	317	497
61	779	234	504	245	303	577	208	639	407	733
62	673	264	151	52	196	598	819	871	375	794
63	679	89	430	220	236	131	666	440	129	623
64	727	471	169	29	556	449	489	809	649	716
65	329	887	289	826	396	590	839	535	9	356
66	311	833	567	368	463	664	939	477	280	906
67	506	625	941	527	76	782	60	736	270	378
68	899	443	519	492	634	593	215	466	711	530
69	659	522	438	525	36	107	862	41	961	347
70	104	230	513	924	573	112	247	729	479	38
71	48	747	417	867	143	175	85	549	344	127
72	74	46	619	121	337	25	157	227	805	966
73	930	883	388	952	586	318	921	352	186	701
74	364	498	305	473	282	109	621	780	745	778
75	207	150	374	235	726	488	288	8	462	505
76	59	518	710	35	103	246	416	343	336	929
77	920	304	744	725	58	415	743	578	579	171
78	908	864	123	209	580	117	199	756	223	640
79	172	879	890	252	314	408	909	697	273	546
80	469	734	865	776	115	298	146	674	124	484
81	391	562	501	265	210	31	508	43	339	152
82	581	300	202	457	411	53	118	167	268	141
83	205	197	200	752	686	22	875	599	757	404
84	683	422	542	820	224	772	691	766	670	872
85	641	558	627	963	27	376	173	148	754	455
86	453	795	880	163	653	180	193	680	891	18
87	604	949	400	90	253	816	539	854	762	431
88	315	554	897	83	372	221	409	451	943	349
89	159	237	910	676	688	797	945	132	698	812
90	786	842	427	667	274	79	97	495	447	441
91	547	233	638	51	793	130	470	808	825	355
92	663	624	735	491	529	106	229	728	866	126
93	24	882	351	472	777	487	517	342	724	170
94	116	878	696	775	483	30	299	166	751	403
95	771	557	147	162	17	815	553	450	675	811
96	78	232	807	490	125	486	877	165	161	810
97	485	0								

POWER RESIDUES

	0	1	2	3	4	5	6	7	8	9
50	459	812	17	102	612	759	670	136	816	41
51	246	505	117	702	328	26	156	936	761	682
52	208	277	691	262	601	693	274	673	154	924
53	689	250	529	261	595	657	58	348	146	876
54	401	464	842	197	211	295	799	910	605	717
55	418	566	483	956	881	431	644	951	851	251
56	535	297	811	11	66	396	434	662	88	528
57	255	559	441	704	340	98	588	615	777	778
58	784	820	65	390	398	446	734	520	207	271
59	655	46	276	685	226	385	368	266	625	837
60	167	31	186	145	870	365	248	517	189	163
61	7	42	252	541	333	56	336	74	444	722
62	448	746	592	639	921	671	142	852	257	571
63	513	165	19	114	684	220	349	152	912	617
64	789	850	245	499	81	486	3	18	108	648
65	4	24	144	864	329	32	192	181	115	690
66	256	565	477	920	665	106	636	903	563	465
67	848	233	427	620	807	958	893	503	105	630
68	867	347	140	840	185	139	834	149	894	509
69	141	846	221	355	188	157	942	797	898	533
70	285	739	550	387	380	338	86	516	183	127
71	762	688	244	493	45	270	649	10	60	360
72	218	337	80	480	938	773	754	640	927	707
73	358	206	265	619	801	922	677	178	97	582
74	579	561	453	776	772	748	604	711	382	350
75	158	948	833	143	858	293	787	838	173	67
76	402	470	878	413	536	303	847	227	391	404
77	482	950	845	215	319	943	803	934	749	610
78	747	598	675	166	25	150	900	545	357	200
79	229	403	476	914	629	861	311	895	515	177
80	91	546	363	236	445	728	484	962	917	647
81	969	959	899	539	321	955	875	395	428	626
82	843	203	247	511	153	918	653	34	204	253
83	547	369	272	661	82	492	39	234	433	656
84	52	312	901	551	393	416	554	411	524	231
85	415	548	375	308	877	407	500	87	522	219
86	343	116	696	292	781	802	928	713	394	422
87	590	627	849	239	463	836	161	966	941	791
88	862	317	931	731	502	99	594	651	22	132
89	792	868	353	176	85	510	147	882	437	680
90	196	205	259	583	585	597	669	130	780	796
91	892	497	69	414	542	339	92	552	399	452
92	770	736	532	279	703	334	62	372	290	769
93	730	496	63	378	326	14	84	504	111	666
94	112	672	148	888	473	896	521	213	307	871
95	371	284	733	514	171	55	330	38	228	397
96	440	698	304	853	263	607	729	490	27	162
97										

P = 977

INDICES

	0	1	2	3	4	5	6	7	8	9
0		0	50	1	100	593	51	142	150	2
1	643	658	101	327	192	594	200	406	52	231
2	693	143	708	953	151	210	377	3	242	522
3	644	344	250	659	456	735	102	705	281	328
4	743	967	193	124	758	595	27	500	201	284
5	260	407	427	413	53	275	292	232	572	947
6	694	288	394	144	300	920	709	624	506	954
7	785	214	152	403	755	211	331	800	378	909
8	793	4	41	130	243	23	174	523	808	368
9	645	469	77	345	550	824	251	963	334	660
10	310	16	457	746	477	736	463	678	103	98
11	325	706	342	741	282	570	622	329	21	548
12	744	340	338	968	444	803	194	178	350	125
13	970	64	759	373	674	596	556	398	28	446
14	835	501	264	9	202	139	453	285	805	567
15	261	651	381	408	850	937	428	196	959	414
16	843	119	54	925	91	276	180	159	293	654
17	73	233	224	237	573	352	858	948	418	912
18	695	47	519	289	127	322	395	88	600	145
19	874	603	301	972	37	921	384	533	710	435
20	360	625	66	664	507	584	796	955	527	889
21	786	761	513	215	728	717	153	486	148	404
22	375	733	756	411	392	212	791	366	332	676
23	620	801	672	7	379	117	71	910	598	531
24	794	715	390	5	388	877	42	558	494	131
25	853	879	244	635	228	24	400	307	175	847
26	44	524	114	111	809	30	423	369	724	560
27	646	578	606	470	448	868	78	940	496	346
28	885	185	551	837	314	825	59	133	252	812
29	189	964	503	821	335	564	855	661	617	304
30	311	266	701	17	431	881	458	779	900	747
31	11	269	478	768	246	737	33	864	464	204
32	893	679	169	637	104	537	975	99	141	642
33	326	199	230	707	209	241	343	455	704	742
34	123	26	283	426	274	571	287	299	623	784
35	402	330	908	40	22	807	468	549	962	309
36	745	462	97	341	569	20	339	443	177	969
37	372	555	445	263	138	804	650	849	195	842
38	924	179	653	223	351	417	46	126	87	873
39	971	383	434	65	583	526	760	727	485	374
40	410	790	675	671	116	597	714	387	557	852
41	634	399	846	113	29	723	577	447	939	884
42	836	58	811	502	563	616	265	430	778	10
43	767	32	203	168	536	140	198	208	454	122
44	425	286	783	907	806	961	461	568	442	371
45	262	649	841	652	416	86	382	582	726	409
46	670	713	851	845	722	938	57	562	429	766
47	167	197	121	782	960	441	648	415	581	669
48	844	56	765	120	440	580	55	439	438	926
49	927	543	92	928	608	277	544	356	181	93

POWER RESIDUES

	0	1	2	3	4	5	6	7	8	9
0	1	3	9	27	81	243	729	233	699	143
1	429	310	930	836	554	685	101	303	909	773
2	365	118	354	85	255	765	341	46	138	414
3	265	795	431	316	948	890	716	194	582	769
4	353	82	246	738	260	780	386	181	543	652
5	2	6	18	54	162	486	481	466	421	286
6	858	620	883	695	131	393	202	606	841	569
7	730	236	708	170	510	553	682	92	276	828
8	530	613	862	632	919	803	455	388	187	561
9	706	164	492	499	520	583	772	362	109	327
10	4	12	36	108	324	972	962	932	842	572
11	739	263	789	413	262	786	404	235	705	161
12	483	472	439	340	43	129	387	184	552	679
13	83	249	747	287	861	629	910	776	374	145
14	435	328	7	21	63	189	567	724	218	654
15	8	24	72	216	648	967	947	887	707	167
16	501	526	601	826	524	595	808	470	433	322
17	966	944	878	680	86	258	774	368	127	381
18	166	498	517	574	745	281	843	575	748	290
19	870	656	14	42	126	378	157	471	436	331
20	16	48	144	432	319	957	917	797	437	334
21	25	75	225	675	71	213	639	940	866	644
22	955	911	779	383	172	516	571	736	254	762
23	332	19	57	171	513	562	709	173	519	580
24	763	335	28	84	252	756	314	942	872	662
25	32	96	288	864	638	937	857	617	874	668
26	50	150	450	373	142	426	301	903	755	311
27	933	845	581	766	344	55	165	495	508	547
28	664	38	114	342	49	147	441	346	61	183
29	549	670	56	168	504	535	628	907	767	347
30	64	192	576	751	299	897	737	257	771	359
31	100	300	900	746	284	852	602	829	533	622
32	889	713	185	555	688	110	330	13	39	117
33	351	76	228	684	98	294	882	692	122	366
34	121	363	112	336	31	93	279	837	557	694
35	128	384	175	525	598	817	497	514	565	718
36	200	600	823	515	568	727	227	681	89	267
37	801	449	370	133	399	220	660	26	78	234
38	702	152	456	391	196	588	787	407	244	732
39	242	726	224	672	62	186	558	697	137	411
40	256	768	350	73	219	657	17	51	153	459
41	400	223	669	53	159	477	454	385	178	534
42	625	898	740	266	798	440	343	52	156	468
43	427	304	912	782	392	199	597	814	488	487
44	484	475	448	367	124	372	139	417	274	822
45	512	559	700	146	438	337	34	102	306	918
46	800	446	361	106	318	954	908	770	356	91
47	273	819	503	532	619	880	686	104	312	936
48	854	608	847	587	784	398	217	651	976	974
49	968	950	896	734	248	744	278	834	548	667

P = 977

INDICES

	0	1	2	3	4	5	6	7	8	9
50	903	160	929	472	294	609	685	655	278	917
51	74	545	450	234	357	363	225	182	897	238
52	94	870	574	904	164	353	161	750	859	930
53	80	949	473	318	419	295	774	913	610	942
54	696	686	628	48	656	691	520	279	498	290
55	918	753	128	75	14	323	546	348	396	451
56	935	89	235	517	601	358	887	146	364	69
57	875	226	109	604	183	187	302	898	862	973
58	239	272	38	95	553	922	871	483	385	575
59	614	534	905	839	711	165	667	436	354	683
60	361	162	316	626	751	933	67	860	481	665
61	931	827	508	81	829	585	950	257	797	474
62	61	956	319	510	528	420	818	890	296	135
63	787	775	83	762	914	771	514	611	254	216
64	943	831	729	697	219	718	687	814	154	629
65	587	487	49	592	149	657	191	405	692	952
66	376	521	249	734	280	966	757	499	259	412
67	291	946	393	919	505	213	754	799	792	129
68	173	367	76	823	333	15	476	677	324	740
69	621	547	337	802	349	63	673	397	834	8
70	452	566	380	936	958	118	90	158	72	236
71	857	911	518	321	599	602	36	532	359	663
72	795	888	512	716	147	732	391	365	619	6
73	70	530	389	876	493	878	227	306	43	110
74	422	559	605	867	495	184	313	132	188	820
75	854	303	700	880	899	268	245	863	892	636
76	974	641	229	240	703	25	273	298	401	39
77	467	308	96	19	176	554	137	848	923	222
78	45	872	433	525	484	789	115	386	633	112
79	576	883	810	615	777	31	535	207	424	906
80	460	370	840	85	725	712	721	561	166	781
81	647	668	764	579	437	542	607	355	902	471
82	684	916	449	362	896	869	163	749	79	317
83	773	941	627	690	497	752	13	347	934	516
84	886	68	108	186	861	271	552	482	613	838
85	666	682	315	932	480	826	828	256	60	509
86	817	134	82	770	253	830	218	813	586	591
87	190	951	248	965	258	945	504	798	172	822
88	475	739	336	62	833	565	957	157	856	320
89	35	662	511	731	618	529	492	305	421	866
90	312	819	699	267	891	640	702	297	466	18
91	136	221	432	788	632	882	776	206	459	84
92	720	780	763	541	901	915	895	748	772	689
93	12	515	107	270	612	681	479	255	816	769
94	217	590	247	944	171	738	832	156	34	730
95	491	865	698	639	465	220	631	205	719	540
96	894	688	106	680	815	589	170	155	490	638
97	630	539	105	588	489	538	488			

POWER RESIDUES

	0	1	2	3	4	5	6	7	8	9
50	47	141	423	292	876	674	68	204	612	859
51	623	892	722	212	636	931	839	563	712	182
52	546	661	29	87	261	783	395	208	624	895
53	731	239	717	197	591	796	434	325	975	971
54	959	923	815	491	496	511	556	691	119	357
55	94	282	846	584	775	371	136	408	247	741
56	269	807	467	424	295	885	701	149	447	364
57	115	345	58	174	522	589	790	416	271	813
58	485	478	457	394	205	615	868	650	973	965
59	941	869	653	5	15	45	135	405	238	714
60	188	564	715	191	573	742	272	816	494	505
61	538	637	934	848	590	793	425	298	894	728
62	230	690	116	348	67	201	603	832	542	649
63	970	956	914	788	410	253	759	323	969	953
64	905	761	329	10	30	90	270	810	476	451
65	376	151	453	382	169	507	544	655	11	33
66	99	297	891	719	203	609	850	596	811	479
67	460	403	232	696	134	402	229	687	107	321
68	963	935	851	599	820	506	541	646	961	929
69	833	545	658	20	60	180	540	643	952	902
70	752	302	906	764	338	37	111	333	22	66
71	198	594	805	461	406	241	723	215	645	958
72	920	806	464	415	268	804	458	397	214	642
73	949	893	725	221	663	35	105	315	945	881
74	689	113	339	40	120	360	103	309	927	827
75	527	604	835	551	676	74	222	666	44	132
76	396	211	633	922	812	482	469	430	313	939
77	863	635	928	830	536	631	916	794	428	307
78	921	809	473	442	349	70	210	630	913	785
79	401	226	678	80	240	720	206	618	877	677
80	77	231	693	125	375	148	444	355	88	264
81	792	422	289	867	647	964	938	860	626	901
82	749	293	879	683	95	285	855	611	856	614
83	865	641	946	884	698	140	420	283	849	593
84	802	452	379	160	480	463	412	259	777	377
85	154	462	409	250	750	296	888	710	176	528
86	607	844	578	757	317	951	899	743	275	825
87	521	586	781	389	190	570	733	245	735	251
88	753	305	915	791	419	280	840	566	721	209
89	627	904	758	320	960	926	824	518	577	754
90	308	924	818	500	523	592	799	443	352	79
91	237	711	179	537	634	925	821	509	550	673
92	65	195	585	778	380	163	489	490	493	502
93	529	610	853	605	838	560	703	155	465	418
94	277	831	539	640	943	875	671	59	177	531
95	616	871	659	23	69	207	621	886	704	158
96	474	445	358	97	291	873	665	41	123	369
97	130	390	193	579	760	326				

P = 983

INDICES

	0	1	2	3	4	5	6	7	8	9
0		0	674	76	366	1	750	100	58	152
1	675	255	442	471	774	77	732	61	826	146
2	367	176	929	684	134	2	163	228	466	323
3	751	710	424	331	735	101	518	504	820	547
4	59	848	850	66	621	153	376	190	808	200
5	676	137	837	970	902	256	158	222	15	306
6	443	841	402	252	116	472	23	852	427	760
7	775	463	210	755	196	78	512	355	239	150
8	733	304	540	29	542	62	740	399	313	602
9	827	571	68	786	864	147	500	287	874	407
10	368	535	811	497	529	177	662	706	594	31
11	930	580	832	583	896	685	689	623	980	161
12	135	510	533	924	94	3	926	273	790	142
13	164	414	697	246	544	229	119	525	452	84
14	467	266	155	726	884	324	447	276	870	343
15	752	96	204	213	47	711	913	589	824	64
16	425	784	978	724	232	332	703	378	234	942
17	736	298	432	488	91	102	5	382	294	803
18	519	729	263	917	742	505	478	316	556	328
19	821	956	192	334	961	548	566	673	99	441
20	60	928	227	423	503	849	189	836	221	401
21	851	209	354	539	398	67	286	810	705	831
22	622	532	272	696	524	154	275	203	588	977
23	377	431	381	262	315	191	672	226	835	353
24	809	271	202	380	225	201	616	617	768	105
25	677	792	618	939	947	138	482	769	816	604
26	838	475	106	394	389	971	920	678	236	420
27	903	169	793	647	217	257	144	619	758	862
28	159	882	940	959	829	223	418	948	576	122
29	16	363	139	944	950	307	562	483	35	173
30	444	166	770	611	878	842	887	817	721	573
31	403	109	605	54	281	253	516	839	738	578
32	117	782	476	207	670	473	416	107	906	290
33	24	599	395	656	70	853	908	390	634	659
34	428	965	972	300	124	761	180	921	765	40
35	776	699	679	436	74	464	968	237	495	788
36	211	292	421	586	937	756	609	904	434	18
37	197	88	170	43	8	79	248	794	20	953
38	513	349	648	627	866	356	26	218	653	666
39	240	745	258	490	365	151	773	145	133	322
40	734	546	620	199	901	305	115	759	195	149
41	541	601	863	406	528	30	895	160	93	141
42	543	83	883	342	46	63	231	941	90	802
43	741	327	960	440	502	400	397	830	523	976
44	314	352	224	104	946	603	388	419	216	861
45	828	121	949	172	877	572	280	577	669	289
46	69	658	123	39	73	787	936	17	7	952
47	865	665	364	321	900	148	527	140	45	801
48	501	975	945	860	876	288	72	951	899	800
49	875	799	308	384	309	408	460	563	779	385

POWER RESIDUES

	0	1	2	3	4	5	6	7	8	9
0	1	5	25	125	625	176	880	468	374	887
1	503	549	779	946	798	58	290	467	369	862
2	378	907	603	66	330	667	386	947	803	83
3	415	109	545	759	846	298	507	569	879	463
4	349	762	861	373	882	478	424	154	770	901
5	573	899	563	849	313	582	944	788	8	40
6	200	17	85	425	159	795	43	215	92	460
7	334	687	486	464	354	787	3	15	75	375
8	892	528	674	421	139	695	526	664	371	872
9	428	174	870	418	124	620	151	755	826	198
10	7	35	175	875	443	249	262	327	652	311
11	572	894	538	724	671	406	64	320	617	136
12	680	451	289	462	344	737	736	731	706	581
13	939	763	866	398	24	120	600	51	255	292
14	477	419	129	645	276	397	19	95	475	409
15	79	395	9	45	225	142	710	601	56	280
16	417	119	595	26	130	650	301	522	644	271
17	372	877	453	299	512	594	21	105	525	659
18	346	747	786	981	973	933	733	716	631	206
19	47	235	192	960	868	408	74	370	867	403
20	49	245	242	227	152	760	851	323	632	211
21	72	360	817	153	765	876	448	274	387	952
22	828	208	57	285	442	244	237	202	27	135
23	675	426	164	820	168	840	268	357	802	78
24	390	967	903	583	949	813	133	665	376	897
25	553	799	63	315	592	11	55	275	392	977
26	953	833	233	182	910	618	141	705	576	914
27	638	241	222	127	635	226	147	735	726	681
28	456	314	587	969	913	633	216	97	485	459
29	329	662	361	822	178	890	518	624	171	855
30	343	732	711	606	81	405	59	295	492	494
31	504	554	804	88	440	234	187	935	743	766
32	881	473	399	29	145	725	676	431	189	945
33	793	33	165	825	193	965	893	533	699	546
34	764	871	423	149	745	776	931	723	666	381
35	922	678	441	239	212	77	385	942	778	941
36	773	916	648	291	472	394	4	20	100	500
37	534	704	571	889	513	599	46	230	167	835
38	243	232	177	885	493	499	529	679	446	264
39	337	702	561	839	263	332	677	436	214	87
40	435	209	62	310	567	869	413	99	495	509
41	579	929	713	616	131	655	326	647	286	447
42	269	362	827	203	32	160	800	68	340	717
43	636	231	172	860	368	857	353	782	961	873
44	433	199	12	60	300	517	619	146	730	701
45	556	814	138	690	501	539	729	696	531	689
46	496	514	604	71	355	792	28	140	700	551
47	789	13	65	325	642	261	322	627	186	930
48	718	641	256	297	502	544	754	821	173	865
49	393	982	978	958	858	358	807	103	515	609

P = 983

INDICES

	0	1	2	3	4	5	6	7	8	9
50	369	454	484	10	310	536	631	36	639	409
51	812	855	174	374	461	498	508	445	296	564
52	530	614	167	560	780	178	86	771	81	386
53	663	458	612	337	370	707	910	879	112	455
54	595	715	843	805	485	32	339	888	891	11
55	931	469	818	250	311	581	450	722	554	537
56	833	392	574	52	632	584	651	404	521	37
57	897	372	110	50	640	686	268	606	796	410
58	690	129	55	243	813	624	636	282	642	856
59	981	749	254	731	175	162	709	517	847	375
60	136	157	840	22	462	511	303	739	570	499
61	534	661	579	688	509	925	413	118	265	446
62	95	912	783	702	297	4	728	477	955	565
63	927	188	208	285	531	274	430	671	270	615
64	791	481	474	919	168	143	881	417	362	561
65	165	886	108	515	781	415	598	907	964	179
66	698	967	291	608	87	247	348	25	744	772
67	545	114	600	894	82	230	326	396	351	387
68	120	279	657	935	664	526	974	71	798	459
69	453	630	854	507	613	85	457	909	714	338
70	468	449	391	650	371	267	128	635	748	708
71	156	302	660	412	911	727	187	429	480	880
72	885	597	966	347	113	325	278	973	629	456
73	448	127	301	186	596	277	126	125	692	716
74	871	693	762	318	844	344	717	181	682	806
75	753	872	922	868	486	97	694	766	645	33
76	205	763	41	131	340	214	319	777	558	889
77	48	845	700	360	892	712	345	680	358	12
78	914	718	437	551	932	590	182	75	57	470
79	825	683	465	330	819	65	807	969	14	251
80	426	754	238	28	312	785	873	496	593	582
81	979	923	789	245	451	725	869	212	823	723
82	233	487	293	916	555	333	98	422	220	538
83	704	695	587	261	834	379	767	938	815	393
84	235	646	757	958	575	943	34	610	720	53
85	737	206	905	655	633	299	764	435	494	585
86	433	42	19	626	652	489	132	198	194	405
87	92	341	89	439	522	103	215	171	668	38
88	6	320	44	859	898	383	778	9	638	373
89	295	559	80	336	111	804	890	249	553	51
90	520	49	795	242	641	730	846	21	569	687
91	264	701	954	284	269	918	361	514	963	607
92	743	893	350	934	797	506	713	649	747	411
93	479	346	628	185	691	317	681	867	644	130
94	557	359	357	550	56	329	13	27	592	244
95	822	915	219	260	814	957	719	654	493	625
96	193	438	667	858	637	335	552	241	568	283
97	962	933	746	184	643	549	591	259	492	857
98	567	183	491							

POWER RESIDUES

	0	1	2	3	4	5	6	7	8	9
50	96	480	434	204	37	185	925	693	516	614
51	121	605	76	380	917	653	316	597	36	180
52	900	568	874	438	224	137	685	476	414	104
53	520	634	221	122	610	101	505	559	829	213
54	82	410	84	420	134	670	401	39	195	975
55	943	783	966	898	558	824	188	940	768	891
56	523	649	296	497	519	629	196	980	968	908
57	608	91	455	309	562	844	288	457	319	612
58	111	555	809	113	565	859	363	832	228	157
59	785	976	948	808	108	540	734	721	656	331
60	672	411	89	445	259	312	577	919	663	366
61	847	303	532	694	521	639	246	247	252	277
62	402	44	220	117	585	959	863	383	932	728
63	691	506	564	854	338	707	586	964	888	508
64	574	904	588	974	938	758	841	273	382	927
65	703	566	864	388	957	853	333	682	461	339
66	712	611	106	530	684	471	389	962	878	458
67	324	637	236	197	2	10	50	250	267	352
68	777	936	748	791	23	115	575	909	613	116
69	580	934	738	741	756	831	223	132	660	351
70	772	911	623	166	830	218	107	535	709	596
71	31	155	775	926	698	541	739	746	781	956
72	848	308	557	819	163	815	143	715	626	181
73	905	593	16	80	400	34	170	850	318	607
74	86	430	184	920	668	391	972	928	708	591
75	6	30	150	750	801	73	365	842	278	407
76	69	345	742	761	856	348	757	836	248	257
77	302	527	669	396	14	70	350	767	886	498
78	524	654	321	622	161	805	93	465	359	812
79	128	640	251	272	377	902	578	924	688	491
80	489	479	429	179	895	543	749	796	48	240
81	217	102	510	584	954	838	258	307	552	794
82	38	190	950	818	158	790	18	90	450	284
83	437	219	112	560	834	238	207	52	260	317
84	602	61	305	542	744	771	906	598	41	205
85	42	210	67	335	692	511	589	979	963	883
86	483	449	279	412	94	470	384	937	753	816
87	148	740	751	806	98	490	484	454	304	537
88	719	646	281	422	144	720	651	306	547	769
89	896	548	774	921	673	416	114	570	884	488
90	474	404	54	270	367	852	328	657	336	697
91	536	714	621	156	780	951	823	183	915	643
92	266	347	752	811	123	615	126	630	201	22
93	110	550	784	971	923	683	466	364	837	253
94	282	427	169	845	293	482	444	254	287	452
95	294	487	469	379	912	628	191	955	843	283
96	432	194	970	918	658	341	722	661	356	797
97	53	265	342	727	686	481	439	229	162	810
98	118	590								

P = 991

INDICES

	0	1	2	3	4	5	6	7	8	9
0		0	772	219	554	694	1	899	336	438
1	476	571	773	986	681	913	118	465	220	164
2	258	128	353	983	555	398	768	657	463	942
3	695	100	890	790	247	603	2	669	936	215
4	40	839	900	284	135	142	765	921	337	808
5	180	684	550	944	439	275	245	383	724	308
6	477	300	872	347	672	690	572	758	29	212
7	385	528	774	409	451	617	718	480	987	6
8	812	876	621	911	682	169	66	171	907	697
9	914	895	547	319	703	858	119	147	590	19
10	952	678	466	729	332	822	726	520	221	533
11	57	888	27	330	165	687	506	434	90	374
12	259	152	82	68	654	102	129	62	454	503
13	472	47	354	73	540	361	801	486	984	806
14	167	150	310	567	556	646	191	37	233	641
15	399	663	500	903	262	794	769	312	778	173
16	594	892	658	490	403	494	693	570	464	982
17	941	602	838	920	943	307	689	527	479	910
18	696	857	677	519	329	373	101	46	485	566
19	640	793	891	569	919	909	372	792	791	850
20	734	977	460	851	248	543	511	431	114	735
21	604	968	508	747	302	978	3	9	315	628
22	829	461	670	950	799	836	112	852	937	558
23	469	699	288	249	216	625	862	225	156	544
24	41	598	924	105	854	512	840	160	436	140
25	874	432	901	564	834	388	236	115	285	578
26	254	390	819	736	136	648	845	916	322	605
27	143	755	583	124	268	969	766	870	588	538
28	939	509	922	586	92	87	349	748	338	930
29	428	366	963	303	809	12	15	238	423	979
30	181	193	445	897	282	4	685	661	44	948
31	576	10	551	826	94	51	560	316	945	523
32	376	739	674	629	440	394	272	752	185	830
33	276	553	475	117	352	462	246	39	764	549
34	723	671	384	717	620	906	702	951	725	26
35	89	653	471	800	309	232	261	593	692	837
36	478	328	639	371	459	113	301	828	111	287
37	155	853	873	235	818	321	267	938	348	962
38	422	281	575	559	673	184	351	722	701	470
39	691	458	154	266	574	700	573	515	632	292
40	516	289	759	96	242	580	633	250	30	643
41	325	705	293	217	213	615	886	35	517	626
42	386	364	750	369	290	863	529	209	84	786
43	760	226	775	815	781	865	97	157	410	53
44	611	256	243	545	452	401	732	860	581	42
45	618	420	884	882	634	599	719	203	340	132
46	251	925	481	413	70	23	31	106	988	667
47	407	531	644	855	7	562	928	392	326	513
48	813	665	380	121	706	841	877	188	636	709
49	294	161	622	417	932	713	218	437	912	127

POWER RESIDUES

	0	1	2	3	4	5	6	7	8	9
0	1	6	36	216	305	839	79	474	862	217
1	311	875	295	779	710	296	785	746	512	99
2	594	591	573	465	808	884	349	112	672	68
3	408	466	814	920	565	417	520	147	882	337
4	40	240	449	712	308	857	187	131	786	752
5	548	315	899	439	652	939	679	110	660	987
6	967	847	127	762	608	675	86	516	123	738
7	464	802	848	133	798	824	980	925	595	597
8	609	681	122	732	428	586	543	285	719	350
9	118	708	284	713	314	893	403	436	634	831
10	31	186	125	750	536	243	467	820	956	781
11	722	368	226	365	208	257	551	333	16	96
12	576	483	916	541	273	647	909	499	21	126
13	756	572	459	772	668	44	264	593	585	537
14	249	503	45	270	629	801	842	97	582	519
15	141	846	121	726	392	370	238	437	640	867
16	247	491	964	829	19	114	684	140	840	85
17	510	87	522	159	954	769	650	927	607	669
18	50	300	809	890	385	328	977	907	487	940
19	685	146	876	301	815	926	601	633	825	986
20	961	811	902	457	760	596	603	645	897	427
21	580	507	69	414	502	39	234	413	496	3
22	18	108	648	915	535	237	431	604	651	933
23	643	885	355	148	888	373	256	545	297	791
24	782	728	404	442	670	56	336	34	204	233
25	407	460	778	704	260	569	441	664	20	120
26	720	356	154	924	589	561	393	376	274	653
27	945	715	326	965	835	55	330	989	979	919
28	559	381	304	833	43	258	557	369	232	401
29	424	562	399	412	490	958	793	794	800	836
30	61	366	214	293	767	638	855	175	59	354
31	142	852	157	942	697	218	317	911	511	93
32	558	375	268	617	729	410	478	886	361	184
33	113	678	104	624	771	662	8	48	288	737
34	458	766	632	819	950	745	506	63	378	286
35	725	386	334	22	132	792	788	764	620	747
36	518	135	810	896	421	544	291	755	566	423
37	556	363	196	185	119	714	320	929	619	741
38	482	910	505	57	342	70	420	538	255	539
39	261	575	477	880	325	959	799	830	25	150
40	900	445	688	164	984	949	739	470	838	73
41	438	646	903	463	796	812	908	493	976	901
42	451	724	380	298	797	818	944	709	290	749
43	530	207	251	515	117	702	248	497	9	54
44	324	953	763	614	711	302	821	962	817	938
45	673	74	444	682	128	768	644	891	391	364
46	202	221	335	28	168	17	102	612	699	230
47	389	352	130	780	716	332	10	60	360	178
48	77	462	790	776	692	188	137	822	968	853
49	163	978	913	523	165	990	985	955	775	686

P = 991

INDICES

	0	1	2	3	4	5	6	7	8	9
50	656	789	214	141	683	382	346	211	616	875
51	170	318	18	821	887	433	67	502	360	149
52	36	902	172	493	601	526	518	565	908	976
53	430	746	627	835	698	224	104	139	387	389
54	915	123	537	86	365	237	896	947	50	738
55	751	116	548	905	652	592	370	286	320	280
56	721	265	291	579	704	34	368	785	864	255
57	859	881	131	22	530	391	120	708	712	788
58	210	820	148	525	745	138	85	737	591	264
59	784	21	787	137	20	78	205	79	761	649
60	953	196	965	206	227	846	679	178	64	80
61	776	917	467	843	443	762	816	323	730	378
62	358	650	782	606	333	796	608	954	866	144
63	823	973	342	197	98	756	727	804	305	966
64	158	584	521	230	456	207	411	125	222	879
65	176	228	54	269	534	741	957	847	612	970
66	58	771	335	680	257	767	889	935	134	179
67	244	871	28	450	811	65	546	589	331	56
68	505	81	453	539	166	190	499	777	402	940
69	688	676	484	918	733	510	507	314	798	468
70	861	923	435	833	253	844	582	587	91	427
71	14	444	43	93	375	271	474	763	619	88
72	260	638	110	817	421	350	153	631	241	324
73	885	749	83	780	610	731	883	339	69	406
74	927	379	635	931	655	345	17	359	600	429
75	103	536	49	651	720	367	130	711	744	783
76	204	964	63	442	357	607	341	304	455	175
77	956	334	133	810	504	498	483	797	252	13
78	473	109	240	609	926	16	48	743	356	955
79	482	239	355	296	297	867	414	424	74	396
80	298	145	71	980	541	596	868	824	24	182
81	362	201	415	974	32	194	802	448	425	343
82	107	446	487	959	75	198	989	898	985	163
83	397	99	668	283	807	274	299	757	408	5
84	168	894	146	728	532	686	151	61	72	805
85	645	662	311	489	981	306	856	45	568	849
86	542	967	8	949	557	624	597	159	563	577
87	647	754	869	585	929	11	192	660	825	522
88	393	552	38	716	25	231	327	827	234	961
89	183	457	514	95	642	614	363	208	814	52
90	400	419	202	412	666	561	664	187	416	126
91	381	317	501	492	975	223	122	946	904	279
92	33	880	707	524	263	77	195	177	842	377
93	795	972	803	229	878	740	770	934	449	55
94	189	675	313	832	426	270	637	630	779	405
95	344	535	710	441	174	497	108	742	295	395
96	595	200	447	958	162	273	893	60	488	848
97	623	753	659	715	960	613	418	186	491	278
98	76	971	933	831	404	496	199	59	714	277
99	495	0								

POWER RESIDUES

	0	1	2	3	4	5	6	7	8	9
50	152	912	517	129	774	680	116	696	212	281
51	695	206	245	479	892	397	400	418	526	183
52	107	642	879	319	923	583	525	177	71	426
53	574	471	844	109	654	951	751	542	279	683
54	134	804	860	205	239	443	676	92	552	339
55	52	312	881	331	4	24	144	864	229	383
56	316	905	475	868	253	527	189	143	858	193
57	167	11	66	396	394	382	310	869	259	563
58	405	448	706	272	641	873	283	707	278	677
59	98	588	555	357	160	960	805	866	241	455
60	748	524	171	35	210	269	623	765	626	783
61	734	440	658	975	895	415	508	75	450	718
62	344	82	492	970	865	235	419	532	219	323
63	947	727	398	406	454	742	488	946	721	362
64	190	149	894	409	472	850	145	870	265	599
65	621	753	554	351	124	744	500	27	162	972
66	877	307	851	151	906	481	904	469	832	37
67	222	341	64	384	322	941	691	182	101	606
68	663	14	84	504	51	306	845	115	690	176
69	65	390	358	166	5	30	180	89	534	231
70	395	388	346	94	564	411	484	922	577	489
71	952	757	578	495	988	973	883	343	76	456
72	754	560	387	340	58	348	106	636	843	103
73	618	735	446	694	200	209	263	587	549	321
74	935	655	957	787	758	584	531	213	287	731
75	422	550	327	971	871	271	635	837	67	402
76	430	598	615	717	338	46	276	665	26	156
77	936	661	2	12	72	432	610	687	158	948
78	733	434	622	759	590	567	429	592	579	501
79	33	198	197	191	155	930	625	777	698	224
80	353	136	816	932	637	849	139	834	49	294
81	773	674	80	480	898	433	616	723	374	262
82	581	513	105	630	807	878	313	887	367	220
83	329	983	943	703	254	533	225	359	172	41
84	246	485	928	613	705	266	605	657	969	859
85	199	203	227	371	244	473	856	181	95	570
86	447	700	236	425	568	435	628	795	806	872
87	277	671	62	372	250	509	81	486	934	649
88	921	571	453	736	452	730	416	514	111	666
89	32	192	161	966	841	91	546	303	827	7
90	42	252	521	153	918	553	345	88	528	195
91	179	83	498	15	90	540	267	611	693	194
92	173	47	282	701	242	461	784	740	476	874
93	289	743	494	982	937	667	38	228	377	280
94	689	170	29	174	53	318	917	547	309	863
95	223	347	100	600	627	789	770	656	963	823
96	974	889	379	292	761	602	639	861	211	275
97	659	981	931	631	813	914	529	201	215	299
98	803	854	169	23	138	828	13	78	468	826
99										

P = 997

INDICES

	0	1	2	3	4	5	6	7	8	9
0		0	201	6	402	465	207	1	603	12
1	666	817	408	580	202	471	804	371	213	524
2	867	7	22	248	609	930	781	18	403	743
3	672	954	9	823	572	466	414	183	725	586
4	72	469	208	853	223	477	449	161	810	2
5	135	377	982	142	219	286	604	530	944	832
6	873	697	159	13	210	49	28	132	773	254
7	667	302	615	728	384	936	926	818	787	92
8	273	24	670	90	409	836	58	749	424	890
9	678	581	650	960	362	989	15	846	203	829
10	336	910	578	157	187	472	343	62	420	294
11	487	189	805	855	731	713	149	592	37	372
12	78	638	898	475	360	399	214	917	411	859
13	250	770	229	525	333	483	974	226	455	110
14	868	167	503	401	816	212	929	8	585	448
15	141	872	131	383	23	423	988	577	293	148
16	474	249	225	815	871	292	291	258	610	164
17	41	536	259	262	950	931	625	838	95	611
18	879	683	782	703	851	648	165	192	563	19
19	194	241	216	42	51	55	404	441	34	234
20	537	138	115	744	779	934	358	260	388	345
21	673	479	544	308	263	322	621	955	495	734
22	688	951	390	568	10	942	60	986	932	120
23	914	824	350	145	793	626	238	98	573	565
24	279	919	839	30	103	467	676	108	561	96
25	600	595	415	69	122	842	612	552	64	184
26	451	755	971	880	430	607	726	896	534	686
27	684	347	179	587	427	751	656	783	311	966
28	73	515	368	81	704	995	602	470	21	742
29	413	852	134	529	209	301	786	835	649	828
30	342	854	77	916	332	166	584	422	224	163
31	624	702	193	440	778	478	494	941	349	564
32	675	68	450	895	426	514	20	300	76	162
33	493	894	492	195	459	597	811	196	365	861
34	242	775	737	3	460	719	463	217	155	129
35	136	598	826	153	43	767	296	378	812	267
36	84	52	884	644	983	197	904	181	56	481
37	849	143	366	892	393	405	764	327	220	862
38	395	923	442	125	417	287	243	865	252	35
39	256	619	605	776	642	557	235	45	435	531
40	738	352	339	538	316	489	945	4	980	908
41	139	232	559	833	461	555	589	116	546	445
42	874	720	680	173	745	305	509	698	464	407
43	523	780	822	71	160	218	696	772	935	669
44	889	14	156	486	591	359	769	454	211	130
45	147	290	261	878	191	50	137	387	321	389
46	119	237	29	599	551	429	346	310	994	133
47	827	583	439	674	299	458	774	154	766	883
48	480	763	124	255	44	315	231	545	304	821
49	668	768	877	118	309	298	762	303	297	795

POWER RESIDUES

	0	1	2	3	4	5	6	7	8	9
0	1	7	49	343	407	855	3	21	147	32
1	224	571	9	63	441	96	672	716	27	189
2	326	288	22	154	81	567	978	864	66	462
3	243	704	940	598	198	389	729	118	826	797
4	594	170	193	354	484	397	785	510	579	65
5	455	194	361	533	740	195	368	582	86	602
6	226	585	107	749	258	809	678	758	321	253
7	774	433	40	280	963	759	328	302	120	840
8	895	283	984	906	360	526	691	849	958	724
9	83	581	79	553	880	178	249	746	237	662
10	646	534	747	244	711	989	941	605	247	732
11	139	973	829	818	741	202	417	925	493	460
12	229	606	254	781	482	383	687	821	762	349
13	449	152	67	469	292	50	350	456	201	410
14	876	150	53	371	603	233	634	450	159	116
15	812	699	905	353	477	348	442	103	721	62
16	434	47	329	309	169	186	305	141	987	927
17	507	558	915	423	967	787	524	677	751	272
18	907	367	575	37	259	816	727	104	728	111
19	777	454	187	312	190	333	337	365	561	936
20	570	2	14	98	686	814	713	6	42	294
21	64	448	145	18	126	882	192	347	435	54
22	378	652	576	44	308	162	137	959	731	132
23	924	486	411	883	199	396	778	461	236	655
24	597	191	340	386	708	968	794	573	23	161
25	130	910	388	722	69	483	390	736	167	172
26	207	452	173	214	501	516	621	359	519	642
27	506	551	866	80	560	929	521	656	604	240
28	683	793	566	971	815	720	55	385	701	919
29	451	166	165	158	109	763	356	498	495	474
30	327	295	71	497	488	425	981	885	213	494
31	467	278	949	661	639	485	404	834	853	986
32	920	458	215	508	565	964	766	377	645	527
33	698	898	304	134	938	584	100	700	912	402
34	820	755	300	106	742	209	466	271	900	318
35	232	627	401	813	706	954	696	884	206	445
36	124	868	94	658	618	338	372	610	282	977
37	857	17	119	833	846	937	577	51	357	505
38	544	817	734	153	74	518	635	457	208	459
39	222	557	908	374	624	380	666	674	730	125
40	875	143	4	28	196	375	631	429	12	84
41	588	128	896	290	36	252	767	384	694	870
42	108	756	307	155	88	616	324	274	921	465
43	264	851	972	822	769	398	792	559	922	472
44	313	197	382	680	772	419	939	591	149	46
45	322	260	823	776	447	138	966	780	475	334
46	344	414	904	346	428	5	35	245	718	41
47	287	15	105	735	160	123	861	45	315	211
48	480	369	589	135	945	633	443	110	770	405
49	841	902	332	330	316	218	529	712	996	990

P = 997

INDICES

	0	1	2	3	4	5	6	7	8	9
50	801	264	796	807	616	379	270	170	323	802
51	47	729	813	542	753	622	265	978	385	268
52	652	276	956	797	176	937	85	329	631	496
53	808	844	927	53	101	527	735	617	887	819
54	885	635	548	689	380	759	788	645	628	709
55	952	271	857	93	984	654	512	391	171	437
56	274	198	716	658	569	324	282	25	905	962
57	200	11	803	247	671	182	222	376	943	48
58	614	91	57	959	335	61	730	637	410	482
59	502	447	987	814	40	837	850	240	33	933
60	543	733	59	144	278	107	121	754	533	750
61	367	741	785	915	623	940	425	893	364	718
62	825	266	903	891	394	864	641	351	979	554
63	679	406	695	485	146	386	550	582	765	314
64	876	794	269	541	651	328	100	634	627	653
65	715	961	221	958	501	239	277	740	363	863
66	694	313	99	957	693	990	396	991	660	574
67	798	518	16	924	397	948	566	177	66	847
68	443	992	976	280	938	691	204	126	661	722
69	920	86	664	830	418	575	356	840	330	151
70	337	288	799	707	31	632	354	911	244	519
71	968	104	497	206	579	866	17	571	468	809
72	285	158	253	925	89	677	845	186	188	36
73	398	228	109	928	382	473	257	949	682	562
74	54	114	344	620	567	913	97	102	594	63
75	606	178	965	601	528	341	421	777	67	75
76	596	736	128	295	643	848	326	416	618	434
77	488	558	444	508	70	888	453	190	236	993
78	457	123	820	761	806	46	977	175	843	886
79	758	856	436	281	246	613	636	39	732	532
80	939	902	553	549	540	714	739	692	517	65
81	690	663	150	353	205	284	185	381	113	593
82	340	127	433	452	760	757	38	539	662	112
83	756	789	790	373	317	723	747	972	646	791
84	79	490	921	521	881	629	374	639	946	87
85	506	431	710	318	899	5	665	370	608	953
86	724	476	981	831	27	727	272	748	361	909
87	419	712	897	858	973	400	140	576	870	535
88	94	647	215	233	357	307	687	985	792	918
89	560	841	970	685	655	80	412	834	331	701
90	348	513	491	860	462	152	83	180	392	922
91	251	556	338	907	588	172	522	771	590	289
92	320	428	438	882	230	117	800	169	752	275
93	630	526	547	708	511	657	199	375	334	446
94	32	106	784	717	640	484	875	633	500	312
95	659	947	975	721	355	706	967	570	88	227
96	681	912	964	74	325	507	456	174	245	901
97	516	283	432	111	746	520	505	369	26	711
98	869	306	969	700	82	906	319	168	510	105
99	499	705	963	900	504	699	498			

POWER RESIDUES

	0	1	2	3	4	5	6	7	8	9
50	948	654	590	142	994	976	850	965	773	426
51	988	934	556	901	325	281	970	808	671	709
52	975	843	916	430	19	133	931	535	754	293
53	57	399	799	608	268	879	171	200	403	827
54	804	643	513	600	212	487	418	932	542	803
55	636	464	257	802	629	415	911	395	771	412
56	890	248	739	188	319	239	676	744	223	564
57	957	717	34	238	669	695	877	157	102	714
58	13	91	637	471	306	148	39	273	914	416
59	918	444	117	819	748	251	760	335	351	463
60	250	753	286	8	56	392	750	265	858	24
61	168	179	256	795	580	72	504	537	768	391
62	743	216	515	614	310	176	235	648	548	845
63	930	528	705	947	647	541	796	587	121	847
64	944	626	394	764	363	547	838	881	185	298
65	92	644	520	649	555	894	276	935	563	950
66	668	688	828	811	692	856	10	70	490	439
67	82	574	30	210	473	320	246	725	90	630
68	422	960	738	181	270	893	269	886	220	543
69	810	685	807	664	660	632	436	61	427	995
70	983	899	311	183	284	991	955	703	933	549
71	852	979	871	115	805	650	562	943	619	345
72	421	953	689	835	860	38	266	865	73	511
73	586	114	798	601	219	536	761	342	400	806
74	657	611	289	29	203	424	974	836	867	87
75	609	275	928	514	607	261	830	825	790	545
76	824	783	496	481	376	638	478	355	491	446
77	131	917	437	68	476	341	393	757	314	204
78	431	26	182	277	942	612	296	78	546	831
79	832	839	888	234	641	499	502	523	670	702
80	926	500	509	572	16	112	784	503	530	719
81	48	336	358	512	593	163	144	11	77	539
82	782	489	432	33	231	620	352	470	299	99
83	693	863	59	413	897	297	85	595	177	242
84	697	891	255	788	531	726	97	679	765	370
85	596	184	291	43	301	113	791	552	873	129
86	903	339	379	659	625	387	715	20	140	980
87	878	164	151	60	420	946	640	492	453	180
88	263	844	923	479	362	540	789	538	775	440
89	89	623	373	617	331	323	267	872	122	854
90	993	969	801	622	366	568	985	913	409	869
91	101	707	961	745	230	613	303	127	889	241
92	690	842	909	381	673	723	76	532	733	146
93	25	175	228	599	205	438	75	525	684	800
94	615	317	225	578	58	406	848	951	675	737
95	174	221	550	859	31	217	522	663	653	583
96	93	651	569	992	962	752	279	956	710	982
97	892	262	837	874	136	952	682	786	517	628
98	408	862	52	364	554	887	227	592	156	95
99	665	667	681	779	468	285				

P = 1009

INDICES

	0	1	2	3	4	5	6	7	8	9
0		0	886	102	764	694	988	788	642	204
1	572	1	866	357	666	796	520	457	82	273
2	450	890	887	345	744	380	235	306	544	514
3	674	563	398	103	335	474	968	770	151	459
4	328	140	768	609	765	898	223	501	622	568
5	258	559	113	109	184	695	422	375	392	27
6	552	87	441	992	276	43	989	472	213	447
7	352	634	846	699	648	482	29	789	337	733
8	206	408	18	1003	646	143	487	616	643	169
9	776	137	101	665	379	967	500	391	446	205
10	136	436	437	318	999	576	995	523	62	844
11	573	872	300	438	253	31	270	561	913	237
12	430	2	973	242	319	66	870	146	154	711
13	929	825	867	53	350	1000	91	982	325	684
14	230	603	512	358	724	200	577	670	526	555
15	360	842	915	661	667	249	215	996	611	211
16	84	125	286	79	904	797	881	304	524	714
17	21	477	365	534	494	160	521	129	47	63
18	654	809	15	189	987	456	543	458	257	86
19	845	1002	378	575	269	145	324	554	83	476
20	14	574	314	294	315	834	196	549	877	274
21	454	537	873	736	401	295	948	343	722	801
22	451	814	750	301	178	584	316	176	131	405
23	917	891	148	529	439	187	791	835	115	857
24	308	638	888	510	851	254	120	630	197	97
25	952	434	748	346	24	245	32	517	589	550
26	807	718	703	853	745	803	939	271	228	716
27	878	726	977	239	860	381	203	449	562	767
28	108	275	481	486	390	61	236	928	602	914
29	78	493	455	323	548	721	404	307	433	702
30	238	389	720	538	793	781	539	37	545	420
31	127	431	93	754	874	678	489	794	89	515
32	970	625	3	730	164	737	965	946	782	281
33	675	922	759	974	182	158	402	784	592	540
34	907	564	355	348	243	133	412	296	372	49
35	38	663	399	156	7	320	933	339	949	111
36	532	546	687	104	901	385	67	1007	865	344
37	334	897	421	471	336	168	135	871	972	52
38	723	248	880	128	256	475	453	813	147	509
39	23	802	202	927	432	419	969	921	354	155
40	900	167	452	920	192	94	172	771	193	620
41	712	76	74	815	427	689	755	786	152	95
42	332	930	415	705	751	837	614	875	279	460
43	173	288	826	984	221	302	600	618	679	443
44	329	772	692	868	628	863	179	657	56	490
45	462	141	194	944	54	831	9	585	283	763
46	795	234	769	621	26	351	407	100	317	252
47	65	90	669	610	713	653	1001	313	735	177
48	186	119	516	227	766	77	388	92	729	181
49	132	932	1006	971	508	899	75	414	983	627

POWER RESIDUES

	0	1	2	3	4	5	6	7	8	9
0	1	11	121	322	515	620	766	354	867	456
1	980	690	527	752	200	182	993	833	82	902
2	841	170	861	390	254	776	464	59	649	76
3	836	115	256	798	706	703	670	307	350	823
4	981	701	648	65	715	802	750	178	949	349
5	812	860	379	133	454	958	448	892	731	978
6	668	285	108	179	960	470	125	366	999	899
7	808	816	904	863	412	496	411	485	290	163
8	784	552	18	198	160	751	189	61	671	318
9	471	136	487	312	405	419	573	249	721	868
10	467	92	3	33	363	966	536	851	280	53
11	583	359	922	52	572	238	600	546	961	481
12	246	688	505	510	565	161	762	310	383	177
13	938	228	490	345	768	376	100	91	1001	921
14	41	451	925	85	935	195	127	388	232	534
15	829	38	418	562	128	399	353	856	335	658
16	175	916	995	855	324	537	862	401	375	89
17	979	679	406	430	694	571	227	479	224	446
18	870	489	334	647	54	594	480	235	567	183
19	1004	954	404	408	452	936	206	248	710	747
20	145	586	392	276	9	99	80	880	599	535
21	840	159	740	68	748	156	707	714	791	629
22	865	434	738	46	506	521	686	483	268	930
23	140	531	796	684	461	26	286	119	300	273
24	985	745	123	344	757	255	787	585	381	155
25	696	593	469	114	245	677	384	188	50	550
26	1005	965	525	730	967	547	972	602	568	194
27	116	267	919	19	209	281	64	704	681	428
28	672	329	592	458	1002	932	162	773	431	705
29	692	549	994	844	203	215	347	790	618	744
30	112	223	435	749	167	828	27	297	240	622
31	788	596	502	477	202	204	226	468	103	124
32	355	878	577	293	196	138	509	554	40	440
33	804	772	420	584	370	34	374	78	858	357
34	900	819	937	217	369	23	253	765	343	746
35	134	465	70	770	398	342	735	13	143	564
36	150	641	997	877	566	172	883	632	898	797
37	695	582	348	801	739	57	627	843	192	94
38	25	275	1007	987	767	365	988	778	486	301
39	284	97	58	638	964	514	609	645	32	352
40	845	214	336	669	296	229	501	466	81	891
41	720	857	346	779	497	422	606	612	678	395
42	309	372	56	616	722	879	588	414	518	653
43	120	311	394	298	251	743	101	102	113	234
44	556	62	682	439	793	651	98	69	759	277
45	20	220	402	386	210	292	185	17	187	39
46	429	683	450	914	973	613	689	516	631	887
47	676	373	67	737	35	385	199	171	872	511
48	576	282	75	825	1003	943	283	86	946	316
49	449	903	852	291	174	905	874	533	818	926

P = 1009

INDICES

	0	1	2	3	4	5	6	7	8	9
50	830	406	312	728	626	122	224	816	910	326
51	123	479	918	579	395	4	467	502	428	636
52	685	225	596	892	581	262	731	12	623	690
53	681	231	817	497	149	209	106	165	594	569
54	756	821	604	911	855	530	117	265	738	291
55	259	787	81	513	327	558	440	698	645	966
56	994	560	153	683	359	124	364	188	268	833
57	947	175	114	96	806	725	480	322	792	677
58	964	783	371	110	333	247	201	919	426	836
59	599	656	282	251	185	931	311	578	580	208
60	116	697	267	676	598	696	416	956	671	396
61	659	858	417	465	923	936	423	706	298	527
62	5	651	309	957	979	760	632	376	752	219
63	556	468	367	639	672	840	975	925	393	838
64	848	361	503	571	889	397	608	183	42	28
65	615	445	843	429	824	511	660	903	159	542
66	553	876	800	916	637	747	852	859	60	403
67	36	88	280	906	662	686	470	255	418	171
68	785	278	442	461	233	668	226	507	121	466
69	11	593	290	993	174	370	250	597	935	631
70	924	41	541	35	277	289	34	216	893	742
71	198	937	811	908	217	44	827	959	997	582
72	410	98	424	740	565	894	990	985	779	612
73	263	58	953	707	885	356	743	473	222	374
74	212	732	775	435	299	241	349	199	214	303
75	46	85	13	536	749	528	850	244	938	448
76	601	701	126	624	758	347	6	384	134	812
77	353	619	331	287	691	943	25	652	387	413
78	909	635	680	820	80	682	805	246	310	955
79	297	218	847	444	799	905	232	369	33	958
80	778	373	45	700	330	819	798	818	70	518
81	980	587	50	828	649	773	71	882	498	341
82	590	761	962	39	960	483	693	519	305	150
83	567	551	633	17	664	998	30	869	981	525
84	210	20	808	377	293	400	583	790	629	588
85	715	107	492	719	753	163	157	411	338	864
86	51	22	166	73	704	220	862	8	99	734
87	180	829	478	595	496	854	557	363	321	425
88	207	658	650	366	570	823	746	469	506	934
89	741	409	57	774	535	757	942	804	368	69
90	340	566	19	491	72	495	822	941	940	640
91	709	950	895	1004	463	883	161	605	641	272
92	673	139	112	991	647	142	499	522	912	710
93	229	841	285	533	986	144	195	342	130	856
94	951	717	976	485	547	780	488	945	591	48
95	531	896	879	926	191	688	613	617	55	762
96	64	118	1005	727	394	261	105	264	644	832
97	963	655	266	464	978	839	607	902	59	170
98	10	40	810	739	884	240	849	383	386	954
99	777	586	961	16	292	162	861	362	505	68

POWER RESIDUES

	0	1	2	3	4	5	6	7	8	9
50	96	47	517	642	1008	998	888	687	494	389
51	243	655	142	553	29	319	482	257	809	827
52	16	176	927	107	168	839	148	619	755	233
53	545	950	360	933	173	894	753	211	303	306
54	339	702	659	186	28	308	361	944	294	207
55	259	831	60	660	197	149	630	876	555	51
56	561	117	278	31	341	724	901	830	49	539
57	884	643	10	110	201	193	105	146	597	513
58	598	524	719	846	225	457	991	811	849	258
59	820	948	338	691	538	873	522	697	604	590
60	436	760	288	141	542	917	1006	976	646	43
61	473	158	729	956	426	650	87	957	437	771
62	409	463	48	528	763	321	504	499	444	848
63	247	699	626	832	71	781	519	664	241	633
64	909	918	8	88	968	558	84	924	74	814
65	882	621	777	475	180	971	591	447	881	610
66	656	153	674	351	834	93	14	154	685	472
67	147	608	634	920	30	330	603	579	315	438
68	782	530	785	563	139	520	675	362	955	415
69	529	774	442	826	5	55	605	601	557	73
70	803	761	299	262	864	423	617	733	1000	910
71	929	129	410	474	169	850	269	941	261	853
72	302	295	218	380	144	575	271	963	503	488
73	323	526	741	79	869	478	213	325	548	983
74	723	890	709	736	24	264	886	665	252	754
75	222	424	628	854	313	416	540	895	764	332
76	625	821	959	459	4	44	484	279	42	462
77	37	407	441	815	893	742	90	990	800	728
78	945	305	328	581	337	680	417	551	7	77
79	847	236	578	304	317	460	15	165	806	794
80	662	219	391	265	897	786	574	260	842	181
81	982	712	769	387	221	413	507	532	807	805
82	783	541	906	885	654	131	432	716	813	871
83	500	455	969	569	205	237	589	425	639	975
84	635	931	151	652	109	190	72	792	640	986
85	756	244	666	263	875	544	939	239	611	667
86	274	996	866	445	859	368	12	132	443	837
87	126	377	111	212	314	427	661	208	270	952
88	382	166	817	915	984	734	2	22	242	644
89	21	231	523	708	725	912	951	371	45	495
90	400	364	977	657	164	795	673	340	713	780
91	508	543	928	118	289	152	663	230	512	587
92	403	397	331	614	700	637	953	393	287	130
93	421	595	491	356	889	698	615	711	758	266
94	908	907	896	775	453	947	327	570	216	358
95	911	940	250	732	989	789	607	623	799	717
96	824	992	822	970	580	326	559	95	36	396
97	320	493	378	122	333	636	942	272	974	624
98	810	838	137	498	433	727	934	184	6	66
99	726	923	63	693	560	106	157	718	835	104

P = 1009

INDICES

	0	1	2	3	4	5	6	7	8	9
100	708	138	284	484	190	260	606	382	504	

POWER RESIDUES

	0	1	2	3	4	5	6	7	8	9
100	135	476	191	83	913	962	492	367		

P = 1013

INDICES

	0	1	2	3	4	5	6	7	8	9
0		0	363	1	726	757	364	821	77	2
1	108	594	727	830	172	758	440	349	365	464
2	471	822	957	198	78	502	181	3	535	809
3	109	525	803	595	712	566	728	675	827	831
4	834	225	173	386	308	759	561	877	441	630
5	865	350	544	406	366	339	898	465	160	265
6	472	741	888	823	154	575	958	837	63	199
7	929	798	79	842	26	503	178	403	182	354
8	185	4	588	128	536	94	749	810	671	624
9	110	639	924	526	228	209	804	784	993	596
10	216	399	713	241	907	567	769	357	729	295
11	702	676	249	724	828	955	523	832	628	158
12	835	176	92	226	239	247	174	936	517	387
13	938	489	309	273	188	760	426	51	562	519
14	280	878	149	412	442	554	193	631	389	300
15	866	499	541	351	766	270	545	940	717	407
16	548	7	367	708	951	340	491	736	899	648
17	457	466	100	138	161	311	22	266	987	377
18	473	478	1002	742	275	420	889	943	591	824
19	572	921	155	190	135	576	344	284	959	114
20	579	838	762	618	64	982	604	200	258	46
21	930	428	120	799	720	131	80	334	658	843
22	53	167	27	968	612	504	75	347	179	564
23	306	404	886	796	183	622	991	355	521	245
24	186	410	539	5	455	375	589	282	602	129
25	610	794	537	792	287	95	880	32	750	484
26	289	811	852	105	672	151	636	625	551	97
27	111	72	789	640	414	84	925	495	882	527
28	643	962	229	444	512	210	775	34	805	698
29	917	785	556	693	994	10	752	597	663	16
30	217	195	862	400	904	486	714	417	117	242
31	633	690	908	531	291	568	68	381	770	391
32	911	358	370	813	730	320	59	296	302	686
33	703	976	854	677	87	582	250	868	1011	725
34	820	107	829	439	463	956	501	534	524	711
35	674	833	385	560	629	543	338	159	740	153
36	836	928	841	177	353	587	93	670	638	227
37	783	215	240	768	294	248	954	627	175	238
38	935	937	272	425	518	148	553	388	498	765
39	939	547	707	490	647	99	310	986	477	274
40	942	571	189	343	113	761	981	257	427	719
41	333	52	967	74	563	885	621	520	409	454
42	281	609	791	879	483	851	150	550	71	413
43	494	642	443	774	697	555	9	662	194	903
44	416	632	530	67	390	369	319	301	975	86
45	867	819	438	500	710	384	542	739	927	352
46	669	782	767	953	237	271	147	497	546	646
47	985	941	342	980	718	966	884	408	608	482
48	549	493	773	8	902	529	368	974	818	709
49	738	668	952	146	645	341	965	607	492	901

POWER RESIDUES

	0	1	2	3	4	5	6	7	8	9
0	1	3	9	27	81	243	729	161	483	436
1	295	885	629	874	596	775	299	897	665	982
2	920	734	176	528	571	700	74	222	666	985
3	929	761	257	771	287	861	557	658	961	857
4	545	622	853	533	586	745	209	627	868	578
5	721	137	411	220	660	967	875	599	784	326
6	978	908	698	68	204	612	823	443	316	948
7	818	428	271	813	413	226	678	8	24	72
8	216	648	931	767	275	825	449	334	1002	980
9	914	716	122	366	85	255	765	269	807	395
10	172	516	535	592	763	263	789	341	10	30
11	90	270	810	404	199	597	778	308	924	746
12	212	636	895	659	964	866	572	703	83	249
13	747	215	645	922	740	194	582	733	173	519
14	544	619	844	506	505	502	493	466	385	142
15	426	265	795	359	64	192	576	715	119	357
16	58	174	522	553	646	925	749	221	663	976
17	902	680	14	42	126	378	121	363	76	228
18	684	26	78	234	702	80	240	720	134	402
19	193	579	724	146	438	301	903	683	23	69
20	207	621	850	524	559	664	979	911	707	95
21	285	855	539	604	799	371	100	300	900	674
22	1009	1001	977	905	689	41	123	369	94	282
23	846	512	523	556	655	952	830	464	379	124
24	372	103	309	927	755	239	717	125	375	112
25	336	1008	998	968	878	608	811	407	208	624
26	859	551	640	907	695	59	177	531	580	727
27	155	465	382	133	399	184	552	643	916	722
28	140	420	247	741	197	591	760	254	762	260
29	780	314	942	800	374	109	327	981	917	725
30	149	447	328	984	926	752	230	690	44	132
31	396	175	525	562	673	1006	992	950	824	446
32	325	975	899	671	1000	974	896	662	973	893
33	653	946	812	410	217	651	940	794	356	55
34	165	495	472	403	196	588	751	227	681	17
35	51	153	459	364	79	237	711	107	321	963
36	863	563	676	2	6	18	54	162	486	445
37	322	966	872	590	757	245	735	179	537	598
38	781	317	951	827	455	352	43	129	387	148
39	444	319	957	845	509	514	529	574	709	101
40	303	909	701	77	231	693	53	159	477	418
41	241	723	143	429	274	822	440	307	921	737
42	185	555	652	943	803	383	136	408	211	633
43	886	632	883	623	856	542	613	826	452	343
44	16	48	144	432	283	849	521	550	637	898
45	668	991	947	815	419	244	732	170	510	517
46	538	601	790	344	19	57	171	513	526	565
47	682	20	60	180	540	607	808	398	181	543
48	616	835	479	424	259	777	305	915	719	131
49	393	166	498	481	430	277	831	467	388	151

P = 1013

INDICES

	0	1	2	3	4	5	6	7	8	9
50	973	737	145	964	900	144	143	649	650	394
51	458	651	231	467	395	998	101	459	847	139
52	652	446	162	232	203	312	468	874	23	396
53	514	267	999	43	988	102	914	378	460	212
54	474	848	435	479	140	40	1003	653	777	743
55	447	261	276	163	858	421	233	36	890	204
56	1006	944	313	361	592	469	807	825	875	896
57	573	24	126	922	397	700	156	515	49	191
58	268	949	136	1000	919	577	44	656	345	989
59	373	285	103	787	960	915	14	115	379	57
60	580	461	558	839	213	933	763	475	255	619
61	849	695	65	436	780	983	480	816	605	141
62	996	201	41	433	259	1004	894	47	654	12
63	931	778	431	429	744	681	121	448	754	800
64	262	746	721	277	733	132	164	599	81	859
65	683	335	422	330	659	234	665	844	37	123
66	54	891	327	168	205	18	28	1007	450	969
67	945	323	613	314	219	505	362	756	76	593
68	171	348	470	197	180	808	802	565	826	224
69	307	876	864	405	897	264	887	574	62	797
70	25	402	184	127	748	623	923	208	992	398
71	906	356	701	723	522	157	91	246	516	488
72	187	50	279	411	192	299	540	269	716	6
73	950	735	456	137	21	376	1001	419	590	920
74	134	283	578	617	603	45	119	130	657	166
75	611	346	305	795	990	244	538	374	601	793
76	286	31	288	104	635	96	788	83	881	961
77	511	33	916	692	751	15	861	485	116	689
78	290	380	910	812	58	685	853	581	1010	106
79	462	533	673	559	337	152	840	586	637	214
80	293	626	934	424	552	764	706	98	476	570
81	112	256	332	73	620	453	790	850	70	641
82	696	661	415	66	318	85	437	383	926	781
83	236	496	984	979	883	481	772	528	817	667
84	644	606	972	963	142	393	230	997	846	445
85	202	873	513	42	913	211	434	39	776	260
86	857	35	1005	360	806	895	125	699	48	948
87	918	655	372	786	13	56	557	932	254	694
88	779	815	995	432	893	11	430	680	753	745
89	732	598	682	329	664	122	326	17	449	322
90	218	755	170	196	801	223	863	263	61	401
91	747	207	905	722	90	487	278	298	715	734
92	20	418	133	616	118	165	304	243	600	30
93	634	82	510	691	860	688	909	684	1009	532
94	336	585	292	423	705	569	331	452	69	660
95	317	382	235	978	771	666	971	392	845	872
96	912	38	856	359	124	947	371	55	253	814
97	892	679	731	328	325	321	169	222	60	206
98	89	297	19	615	303	29	509	687	1008	584
99	704	451	316	977	970	871	855	946	252	678

POWER RESIDUES

	0	1	2	3	4	5	6	7	8	9
50	453	346	25	75	225	675	1012	1010	1004	986
51	932	770	284	852	530	577	718	128	384	139
52	417	238	714	116	348	31	93	279	837	485
53	442	313	939	791	347	28	84	252	756	242
54	726	152	456	355	52	156	468	391	160	480
55	427	268	804	386	145	435	292	876	602	793
56	353	46	138	414	229	687	35	105	315	945
57	809	401	190	570	697	65	195	585	742	200
58	600	787	335	1005	989	941	797	365	82	246
59	738	188	564	679	11	33	99	297	891	647
60	928	758	248	744	206	618	841	497	478	421
61	250	750	224	672	1003	983	923	743	203	609
62	814	416	235	705	89	267	801	377	118	354
63	49	147	441	310	930	764	266	798	368	91
64	273	819	431	280	840	494	469	394	169	507
65	508	511	520	547	628	871	587	748	218	654
66	949	821	437	298	894	656	955	839	491	460
67	367	88	264	792	350	37	111	333	999	971
68	887	635	892	650	937	785	329	987	935	779
69	311	933	773	293	879	611	820	434	289	867
70	575	712	110	330	990	944	806	392	163	489
71	454	349	34	102	306	918	728	158	474	409
72	214	642	913	713	113	339	4	12	36	108
73	324	972	890	644	919	731	167	501	490	457
74	358	61	183	549	634	889	641	910	704	86
75	258	774	296	888	638	901	677	5	15	45
76	135	405	202	606	805	389	154	462	373	106
77	318	954	836	482	433	286	858	548	631	880
78	614	829	461	370	97	291	873	593	766	272
79	816	422	253	759	251	753	233	699	71	213
80	639	904	686	32	96	288	864	566	685	29
81	87	261	783	323	969	881	617	838	488	451
82	340	7	21	63	189	567	688	38	114	342
83	13	39	117	351	40	120	360	67	201	603
84	796	362	73	219	657	958	848	518	541	610
85	817	425	262	786	332	996	962	860	554	649
86	934	776	302	906	692	50	150	450	337	1011
87	1007	995	959	851	527	568	691	47	141	423
88	256	768	278	834	476	415	232	696	62	186
89	558	661	970	884	626	865	569	694	56	168
90	504	499	484	439	304	912	710	104	312	936
91	782	320	960	854	536	595	772	290	870	584
92	739	191	573	706	92	276	828	458	361	70
93	210	630	877	605	802	380	127	381	130	390
94	157	471	400	187	561	670	997	965	869	581
95	730	164	492	463	376	115	345	22	66	198
96	594	769	281	843	503	496	475	412	223	669
97	994	956	842	500	487	448	331	993	953	833
98	473	406	205	615	832	470	397	178	534	589
99	754	236	708	98	294	882	620	847	515	532

P = 1013

INDICES

	0	1	2	3	4	5	6	7	8	9
100	324	221	88	614	508	583	315	870	251	220
101	507	869	506							

POWER RESIDUES

	0	1	2	3	4	5	6	7	8	9
100	583	736	182	546	625	862	560	667	988	938
101	788	338								

P = 1019

INDICES

	0	1	2	3	4	5	6	7	8	9
0		0	1	958	2	10	959	363	3	898
1	11	756	960	289	364	968	4	48	899	542
2	12	303	757	114	961	20	290	838	365	138
3	969	324	5	696	49	373	900	701	543	229
4	13	939	304	346	758	908	115	211	962	726
5	21	1006	291	927	839	766	366	482	139	465
6	970	851	325	243	6	299	697	923	50	54
7	374	165	901	594	702	978	544	101	230	732
8	14	778	940	681	305	58	347	78	759	784
9	909	652	116	264	212	552	963	206	727	636
10	22	378	1007	745	292	313	928	995	840	154
11	767	641	367	630	483	124	140	169	466	411
12	971	494	852	879	326	30	244	446	7	286
13	300	135	698	905	924	848	51	98	55	261
14	375	151	166	27	902	148	595	666	703	598
15	979	180	545	946	102	334	231	669	733	867
16	15	477	779	489	941	706	682	616	306	578
17	59	422	348	601	79	383	760	405	785	825
18	910	982	653	791	117	711	265	804	213	183
19	553	505	964	320	207	239	728	548	637	442
20	23	863	379	501	1008	949	746	1012	293	280
21	314	890	929	105	996	356	841	687	155	534
22	768	337	642	953	368	918	631	130	484	234
23	125	41	141	585	170	221	467	672	412	750
24	972	255	495	718	853	736	880	831	327	621
25	31	457	245	870	447	1016	8	896	287	46
26	301	18	136	694	699	937	906	724	925	480
27	849	297	52	592	99	776	56	782	262	204
28	376	311	152	628	167	492	28	284	903	96
29	149	146	596	944	667	475	704	576	599	403
30	980	709	181	318	546	861	947	278	103	685
31	335	916	232	583	670	253	734	619	868	894
32	16	935	478	590	780	309	490	94	942	574
33	707	859	683	581	617	933	307	572	579	570
34	60	62	423	71	349	64	602	817	80	425
35	384	109	761	73	406	175	786	351	826	199
36	911	66	983	434	654	604	792	1000	118	819
37	712	272	266	82	805	988	214	427	184	526
38	554	386	506	360	965	111	321	226	208	763
39	240	162	729	75	549	742	638	408	443	845
40	24	177	864	613	380	788	502	439	1009	353
41	950	38	747	828	1013	691	294	201	281	472
42	315	913	891	91	930	68	106	196	997	985
43	357	159	842	436	688	88	156	656	535	659
44	769	606	338	395	643	794	954	538	369	1002
45	919	677	632	120	131	662	485	821	235	886
46	126	714	42	772	142	274	586	566	171	268
47	222	609	468	84	673	562	413	807	751	341
48	973	990	256	417	496	216	719	398	854	429
49	737	191	881	186	832	646	328	528	622	811

POWER RESIDUES

	0	1	2	3	4	5	6	7	8	9
0	1	2	4	8	16	32	64	128	256	512
1	5	10	20	40	80	160	320	640	261	522
2	25	50	100	200	400	800	581	143	286	572
3	125	250	500	1000	981	943	867	715	411	822
4	625	231	462	924	829	639	259	518	17	34
5	68	136	272	544	69	138	276	552	85	170
6	340	680	341	682	345	690	361	722	425	850
7	681	343	686	353	706	393	786	553	87	174
8	348	696	373	746	473	946	873	727	435	870
9	721	423	846	673	327	654	289	578	137	274
10	548	77	154	308	616	213	426	852	685	351
11	702	385	770	521	23	46	92	184	368	736
12	453	906	793	567	115	230	460	920	821	623
13	227	454	908	797	575	131	262	524	29	58
14	116	232	464	928	837	655	291	582	145	290
15	580	141	282	564	109	218	436	872	725	431
16	862	705	391	782	545	71	142	284	568	117
17	234	468	936	853	687	355	710	401	802	585
18	151	302	604	189	378	756	493	986	953	887
19	755	491	982	945	871	723	427	854	689	359
20	718	417	834	649	279	558	97	194	388	776
21	533	47	94	188	376	752	485	970	921	823
22	627	235	470	940	861	703	387	774	529	39
23	78	156	312	624	229	458	916	813	607	195
24	390	780	541	63	126	252	504	1008	997	975
25	931	843	667	315	630	241	482	964	909	799
26	579	139	278	556	93	186	372	744	469	938
27	857	695	371	742	465	930	841	663	307	614
28	209	418	836	653	287	574	129	258	516	13
29	26	52	104	208	416	832	645	271	542	65
30	130	260	520	21	42	84	168	336	672	325
31	650	281	562	105	210	420	840	661	303	606
32	193	386	772	525	31	62	124	248	496	992
33	965	911	803	587	155	310	620	221	442	884
34	749	479	958	897	775	531	43	86	172	344
35	688	357	714	409	818	617	215	430	860	701
36	383	766	513	7	14	28	56	112	224	448
37	896	773	527	35	70	140	280	560	101	202
38	404	808	597	175	350	700	381	762	505	1010
39	1001	983	947	875	731	443	886	753	487	974
40	929	839	659	299	598	177	354	708	397	794
41	569	119	238	476	952	885	751	483	966	913
42	807	595	171	342	684	349	698	377	754	489
43	978	937	855	691	363	726	433	866	713	407
44	814	609	199	398	796	573	127	254	508	1016
45	1013	1007	995	971	923	827	635	251	502	1004
46	989	959	899	779	539	59	118	236	472	944
47	869	719	419	838	657	295	590	161	322	644
48	269	538	57	114	228	456	912	805	591	163
49	326	652	285	570	121	242	484	968	917	815

P = 1019

INDICES

	0	1	2	3	4	5	6	7	8	9
50	32	556	458	797	246	388	871	518	448	508
51	1017	957	9	362	897	755	288	967	47	541
52	302	113	19	837	137	323	695	372	700	228
53	938	345	907	210	725	1005	926	765	481	464
54	850	242	298	922	53	164	593	977	100	731
55	777	680	57	77	783	651	263	551	205	635
56	377	744	312	994	153	640	629	123	168	410
57	493	878	29	445	285	134	904	847	97	260
58	150	26	147	665	597	179	945	333	668	866
59	476	488	705	615	577	421	600	382	404	824
60	981	790	710	803	182	504	319	238	547	441
61	862	500	948	1011	279	889	104	355	686	533
62	336	952	917	129	233	40	584	220	671	749
63	254	717	735	830	620	456	869	1015	895	45
64	17	693	936	723	479	296	591	775	781	203
65	310	627	491	283	95	145	943	474	575	402
66	708	317	860	277	684	915	582	252	618	893
67	934	589	308	93	573	858	580	932	571	569
68	61	70	63	816	424	108	72	174	350	198
69	65	433	603	999	818	271	81	987	426	525
70	385	359	110	225	762	161	74	741	407	844
71	176	612	787	438	352	37	827	690	200	471
72	912	90	67	195	984	158	435	87	655	658
73	605	394	793	537	1001	676	119	661	820	885
74	713	771	273	565	267	608	83	561	806	340
75	989	416	215	397	428	190	185	645	527	810
76	555	796	387	517	507	956	361	754	966	540
77	112	836	322	371	227	344	209	1004	764	463
78	241	921	163	976	730	679	76	650	550	634
79	743	993	639	122	409	877	444	133	846	259
80	25	664	178	332	865	487	614	420	381	823
81	789	802	503	237	440	499	1010	888	354	532
82	951	128	39	219	748	716	829	455	1014	44
83	692	722	295	774	202	626	282	144	473	401
84	316	276	914	251	892	588	92	857	931	568
85	69	815	107	173	197	432	998	270	986	524
86	358	224	160	740	843	611	437	36	689	470
87	89	194	157	86	657	393	536	675	660	884
88	770	564	607	560	339	415	396	189	644	809
89	795	516	955	753	539	835	370	343	1003	462
90	920	975	678	649	633	992	121	876	132	258
91	663	331	486	419	822	801	236	498	887	531
92	127	218	715	454	43	721	773	625	143	400
93	275	250	587	856	567	814	172	431	269	523
94	223	739	610	35	469	193	85	392	674	883
95	563	559	414	188	808	515	752	834	342	461
96	974	648	991	875	257	330	418	800	497	530
97	217	453	720	624	399	249	855	813	430	522
98	738	34	192	391	882	558	187	514	833	460
99	647	874	329	799	529	452	623	248	812	521

POWER RESIDUES

	0	1	2	3	4	5	6	7	8	9
50	611	203	406	812	605	191	382	764	509	1018
51	1017	1015	1011	1003	987	955	891	763	507	1014
52	1009	999	979	939	859	699	379	758	497	994
53	969	919	819	619	219	438	876	733	447	894
54	769	519	19	38	76	152	304	608	197	394
55	788	557	95	190	380	760	501	1002	985	951
56	883	747	475	950	881	743	467	934	849	679
57	339	678	337	674	329	658	297	594	169	338
58	676	333	666	313	626	233	466	932	845	671
59	323	646	273	546	73	146	292	584	149	298
60	596	173	346	692	365	730	441	882	745	471
61	942	865	711	403	806	593	167	334	668	317
62	634	249	498	996	973	927	835	651	283	566
63	113	226	452	904	789	559	99	198	396	792
64	565	111	222	444	888	757	495	990	961	903
65	787	555	91	182	364	728	437	874	729	439
66	878	737	455	910	801	583	147	294	588	157
67	314	628	237	474	948	877	735	451	902	785
68	551	83	166	332	664	309	618	217	434	868
69	717	415	830	641	263	526	33	66	132	264
70	528	37	74	148	296	592	165	330	660	301
71	602	185	370	740	461	922	825	631	243	486
72	972	925	831	643	267	534	49	98	196	392
73	784	549	79	158	316	632	245	490	980	941
74	863	707	395	790	561	103	206	412	824	629
75	239	478	956	893	767	515	11	22	44	88
76	176	352	704	389	778	537	55	110	220	440
77	880	741	463	926	833	647	275	550	81	162
78	324	648	277	554	89	178	356	712	405	810
79	601	183	366	732	445	890	761	503	1006	993
80	967	915	811	603	187	374	748	477	954	889
81	759	499	998	977	935	851	683	347	694	369
82	738	457	914	809	599	179	358	716	413	826
83	633	247	494	988	957	895	771	523	27	54
84	108	216	432	864	709	399	798	577	135	270
85	540	61	122	244	488	976	933	847	675	331
86	662	305	610	201	402	804	589	159	318	636
87	253	506	1012	1005	991	963	907	795	571	123
88	246	492	984	949	879	739	459	918	817	615
89	211	422	844	669	319	638	257	514	9	18
90	36	72	144	288	576	133	266	532	45	90
91	180	360	720	421	842	665	311	622	225	450
92	900	781	543	67	134	268	536	53	106	212
93	424	848	677	335	670	321	642	265	530	41
94	82	164	328	656	293	586	153	306	612	205
95	410	820	621	223	446	892	765	511	3	6
96	12	24	48	96	192	384	768	517	15	30
97	60	120	240	480	960	901	783	547	75	150
98	300	600	181	362	724	429	858	697	375	750
99	481	962	905	791	563	107	214	428	856	693

P = 1019

INDICES

	0	1	2	3	4	5	6	7	8	9
100	33	390	557	513	459	873	798	451	247	520
101	389	512	872	450	519	511	449	510	509	

POWER RESIDUES

	0	1	2	3	4	5	6	7	8	9
100	367	734	449	898	777	535	51	102	204	408
101	816	613	207	414	828	637	255	510		

P = 1021

INDICES

	0	1	2	3	4	5	6	7	8	9
0		0	333	270	666	688	603	243	999	540
1	1	16	936	585	576	958	312	926	873	565
2	334	513	349	368	249	356	918	810	909	182
3	271	47	645	286	239	931	186	49	898	855
4	667	310	846	787	682	208	701	236	582	486
5	689	176	231	521	123	704	222	835	515	457
6	604	406	380	783	978	253	619	884	572	638
7	244	744	519	444	382	626	211	259	168	18
8	1000	60	643	950	159	594	100	452	1015	320
9	541	828	14	317	569	233	915	685	819	556
10	2	525	509	539	564	181	854	485	456	637
11	17	319	555	636	148	36	848	105	790	149
12	937	32	739	580	713	24	96	199	291	37
13	586	831	952	808	197	478	905	647	971	849
14	577	506	57	601	852	870	777	756	715	106
15	959	963	544	446	592	735	501	945	351	791
16	313	611	393	694	976	974	263	472	492	150
17	927	85	433	323	785	599	328	727	653	938
18	874	670	141	676	347	737	650	942	902	33
19	566	441	228	44	1018	523	132	8	889	740
20	335	134	858	425	842	998	872	908	897	581
21	514	571	167	1014	818	455	789	290	970	714
22	350	491	652	901	888	896	969	480	481	25
23	369	529	161	164	438	924	103	288	482	97
24	250	679	365	330	52	154	913	130	26	200
25	357	770	429	384	532	864	624	597	370	292
26	919	722	144	401	265	189	121	590	530	38
27	811	117	218	78	980	372	284	806	162	587
28	910	893	839	673	390	503	934	553	165	832
29	183	955	90	297	69	125	28	826	439	953
30	272	10	276	795	877	74	779	242	925	809
31	48	235	834	883	258	451	684	484	104	198
32	646	755	944	471	726	941	7	907	289	479
33	287	129	596	589	805	552	825	241	483	906
34	240	63	418	729	766	306	656	64	98	648
35	932	375	661	628	40	412	986	419	251	972
36	187	110	1003	302	474	112	1009	730	680	850
37	50	764	983	549	255	294	215	767	366	578
38	899	469	774	21	561	947	377	307	331	507
39	856	274	465	81	341	706	202	657	53	58
40	668	891	467	632	171	748	758	65	155	602
41	311	917	185	700	221	618	210	99	914	853
42	847	95	904	776	500	262	327	649	131	871
43	788	968	102	912	623	120	283	933	27	778
44	683	6	824	655	985	1008	214	376	201	757
45	209	326	282	213	813	496	814	662	358	716
46	702	733	862	410	494	1005	497	629	771	107
47	237	195	436	803	621	921	815	41	430	960
48	583	634	1012	881	698	353	663	413	385	964
49	487	12	226	88	463	224	359	987	533	545

POWER RESIDUES

	0	1	2	3	4	5	6	7	8	9
0	1	10	100	1000	811	963	441	326	197	949
1	301	968	491	826	92	920	11	110	79	790
2	753	383	767	523	125	229	248	438	296	918
3	1012	931	121	189	869	522	115	129	269	648
4	354	477	686	734	193	909	922	31	310	37
5	370	637	244	398	917	1002	831	142	399	927
6	81	810	953	341	347	407	1007	881	642	294
7	898	812	973	541	305	1008	891	742	273	688
8	754	393	867	502	936	171	689	764	493	846
9	292	878	612	1015	961	421	126	239	348	417
10	86	860	432	236	318	117	149	469	606	955
11	361	547	365	587	765	503	946	271	668	554
12	435	266	618	54	540	295	908	912	952	331
13	247	428	196	939	201	989	701	884	672	594
14	835	182	799	843	262	578	675	624	114	119
15	169	669	564	535	245	408	1017	981	621	84
16	840	232	278	738	233	288	838	212	78	780
17	653	404	977	581	705	924	51	510	1016	971
18	521	105	29	290	858	412	36	360	537	265
19	608	975	561	505	966	471	626	134	319	127
20	249	448	396	897	802	873	562	515	45	450
21	416	76	760	453	446	376	697	844	272	678
22	654	414	56	560	495	866	492	836	192	899
23	822	52	520	95	950	311	47	470	616	34
24	340	337	307	7	70	700	874	572	615	24
25	240	358	517	65	650	374	677	644	314	77
26	770	553	425	166	639	264	598	875	582	715
27	3	30	300	958	391	847	302	978	591	805
28	903	862	452	436	276	718	33	330	237	328
29	217	128	259	548	375	687	744	293	888	712
30	994	751	363	567	565	545	345	387	807	923
31	41	410	16	160	579	685	724	93	930	111
32	89	890	732	173	709	964	451	426	176	739
33	243	388	817	2	20	200	979	601	905	882
34	652	394	877	602	915	982	631	184	819	22
35	220	158	559	485	766	513	25	250	458	496
36	876	592	815	1003	841	242	378	717	23	230
37	258	538	275	708	954	351	447	386	797	823
38	62	620	74	740	253	488	796	813	983	641
39	284	798	833	162	599	885	682	694	814	993
40	741	263	588	775	603	925	61	610	995	761
41	463	546	355	487	786	713	1004	851	342	357
42	507	986	671	584	735	203	1009	901	842	252
43	478	696	834	172	699	864	472	636	234	298
44	938	191	889	722	73	730	153	509	1006	871
45	542	315	87	870	532	215	108	59	590	795
46	803	883	662	494	856	392	857	402	957	381
47	747	323	167	649	364	577	665	524	135	329
48	227	228	238	338	317	107	49	490	816	1013
49	941	221	168	659	464	556	455	466	576	655

P = 1021

INDICES

	0	1	2	3	4	5	6	7	8	9
50	690	742	83	115	762	193	717	420	865	447
51	177	687	957	355	930	207	703	252	625	593
52	232	180	35	23	477	869	734	973	598	736
53	522	997	454	895	923	153	863	188	371	502
54	124	73	450	940	551	305	411	111	293	946
55	705	747	617	261	119	1007	495	1004	920	352
56	223	192	206	868	152	304	1006	303	723	792
57	836	719	247	711	886	724	498	475	145	314
58	516	173	268	537	423	793	630	113	402	612
59	458	278	361	641	139	837	772	1010	266	394
60	605	337	343	404	609	720	108	731	190	695
61	407	821	92	665	575	248	238	681	122	977
62	381	158	568	563	147	712	196	851	591	975
63	784	346	1017	841	817	887	437	51	531	264
64	979	389	68	876	257	725	804	765	39	473
65	254	560	340	170	220	499	622	984	812	493
66	620	697	462	761	929	476	922	550	118	151
67	885	422	138	608	574	146	816	256	219	928
68	573	750	396	993	751	315	42	295	79	86
69	639	797	989	799	397	517	431	216	981	434
70	245	136	708	614	994	174	961	768	373	324
71	745	558	299	415	752	269	584	367	285	786
72	520	782	443	949	316	538	635	579	807	600
73	445	693	322	675	43	424	1013	900	163	329
74	383	400	77	672	296	794	882	470	588	728
75	627	301	548	20	80	631	699	775	911	654
76	212	409	802	880	87	114	354	22	894	939
77	260	867	710	536	640	403	664	562	840	875
78	169	760	607	992	798	613	414	948	674	671
79	19	879	535	991	990	459	386	378	391	142
80	1001	860	204	460	800	279	965	308	504	677
81	61	4	71	387	398	362	488	332	935	348
82	644	845	230	379	518	642	13	508	554	738
83	951	56	543	392	432	140	227	857	166	651
84	160	364	428	143	217	838	89	275	833	943
85	595	417	660	1002	982	773	464	466	184	903
86	101	823	281	861	435	1011	225	82	956	34
87	453	449	616	205	246	267	360	342	91	567
88	1016	67	339	461	137	395	988	707	298	442
89	321	76	547	801	709	606	534	203	70	229
90	542	427	659	280	615	338	546	658	126	45
91	829	527	127	966	995	344	691	54	29	1019
92	15	512	46	309	175	405	743	59	827	524
93	318	31	830	505	962	610	84	669	440	133
94	570	490	528	678	769	721	116	892	954	9
95	234	754	128	62	374	109	763	468	273	890
96	916	94	967	5	325	732	194	633	11	741
97	686	179	996	72	746	191	718	172	277	336
98	820	157	345	388	559	696	421	749	796	135
99	557	781	692	399	300	408	866	759	878	859

POWER RESIDUES

	0	1	2	3	4	5	6	7	8	9
50	424	156	539	285	808	933	141	389	827	102
51	1020	1011	921	21	210	58	580	695	824	72
52	720	53	530	195	929	101	1010	911	942	231
53	268	638	254	498	896	792	773	583	725	103
54	9	90	900	832	152	499	906	892	752	373
55	667	544	335	287	828	112	99	990	711	984
56	651	384	777	623	104	19	190	879	622	94
57	940	211	68	680	674	614	14	140	379	727
58	123	209	48	480	716	13	130	279	748	333
59	267	628	154	519	85	850	332	257	528	175
60	729	143	409	6	60	600	895	782	673	604
61	935	161	589	785	703	904	872	552	415	66
62	660	474	656	434	256	518	75	750	353	467
63	586	755	403	967	481	726	113	109	69	690
64	774	593	825	82	820	32	320	137	349	427
65	186	839	222	178	759	443	346	397	907	902
66	852	352	457	486	776	613	4	40	400	937
67	181	789	743	283	788	733	183	809	943	241
68	368	617	44	440	316	97	970	511	5	50
69	500	916	992	731	163	609	985	661	484	756
70	413	46	460	516	55	550	395	887	702	894
71	772	573	625	124	219	148	459	506	976	571
72	605	945	261	568	575	645	324	177	749	343
73	367	607	965	461	526	155	529	185	829	122
74	199	969	501	926	71	710	974	551	405	987
75	681	684	714	1014	951	321	147	449	406	997
76	781	663	504	956	371	647	344	377	707	944
77	251	468	596	855	382	757	423	146	439	306
78	1018	991	721	63	630	174	719	43	430	216
79	118	159	569	585	745	303	988	691	784	693
80	804	893	762	473	646	334	277	728	133	309
81	27	270	658	454	456	476	676	634	214	98
82	980	611	1005	861	442	336	297	928	91	910
83	932	131	289	848	312	57	570	595	845	282
84	778	633	204	1019	1001	821	42	420	116	139
85	369	627	144	419	106	39	390	837	202	999
86	801	863	462	536	255	508	996	771	563	525
87	145	429	206	18	180	779	643	304	998	791
88	763	483	746	313	67	670	574	635	224	198
89	959	401	947	281	768	533	225	208	38	380
90	737	223	188	859	422	136	339	327	207	28
91	280	758	433	246	418	96	960	411	26	260
92	558	475	666	534	235	308	17	170	679	664
93	514	35	350	437	286	818	12	120	179	769
94	543	325	187	849	322	157	549	385	787	723
95	83	830	132	299	948	291	868	512	15	150
96	479	706	934	151	489	806	913	962	431	226
97	218	138	359	527	165	629	164	619	64	640
98	274	698	854	372	657	444	356	497	886	692
99	794	793	783	683	704	914	972	531	205	8

P = 1021

INDICES

	0	1	2	3	4	5	6	7	8	9
100	3	844	55	363	416	822	448	66	75	426
101	526	511	30	489	753	93	178	156	780	843
102	510	0								

POWER RESIDUES

	0	1	2	3	4	5	6	7	8	9
100	80	800	853	362	557	465	566	555	445	366
101	597	865	482	736	213	88	880	632	194	919
102										

P = 1031

INDICES

	0	1	2	3	4	5	6	7	8	9
0		0	796	606	562	384	372	235	328	182
1	150	302	138	734	1	990	94	295	978	345
2	946	841	68	1026	934	768	500	788	797	1020
3	756	965	890	908	61	619	744	617	111	310
4	712	119	607	96	864	566	792	538	700	470
5	534	901	266	74	554	686	563	951	786	1017
6	522	77	731	417	656	88	674	25	857	602
7	385	101	510	696	383	344	907	537	76	343
8	478	364	915	996	373	679	892	596	630	479
9	332	969	558	541	304	729	466	442	236	484
10	300	176	667	365	32	195	870	160	320	867
11	452	193	329	334	717	380	552	916	783	530
12	288	604	873	725	497	122	183	147	422	702
13	884	997	440	580	821	142	623	790	368	36
14	151	114	897	6	276	374	462	46	149	933
15	110	265	673	477	303	319	872	622	109	680
16	244	231	130	217	681	262	762	133	139	438
17	445	527	658	893	362	1003	396	593	245	754
18	98	314	735	683	324	1001	307	597	70	1023
19	495	8	232	805	208	694	2	923	250	875
20	66	631	972	225	433	503	131	178	828	647
21	991	550	636	707	956	480	86	170	633	272
22	218	1029	989	1019	95	950	100	678	483	333
23	146	113	318	437	682	922	549	949	296	297
24	54	1008	370	970	639	854	491	49	263	572
25	918	741	979	298	943	255	188	559	468	852
26	650	172	763	279	206	458	346	55	587	4
27	938	542	389	545	556	40	134	1005	832	117
28	947	1009	910	644	663	305	802	354	42	590
29	140	18	228	582	842	371	945	60	699	730
30	906	331	31	782	439	461	243	361	69	971
31	85	145	638	467	388	801	905	387	446	292
32	10	766	1027	640	926	472	1013	443	447	773
33	28	20	528	799	929	409	935	855	204	940
34	211	237	293	705	424	986	659	574	128	518
35	769	492	162	191	359	485	11	106	520	186
36	894	690	80	180	501	50	449	809	90	301
37	767	309	73	24	363	728	866	724	789	264
38	261	753	804	177	1028	921	571	278	1004	17
39	460	291	798	573	689	727	16	668	641	156
40	862	52	397	669	738	748	1021	919	199	426
41	269	366	927	222	974	350	594	642	413	524
42	757	742	316	720	402	33	473	312	722	612
43	246	157	882	1011	966	980	399	341	38	196
44	1014	652	795	93	755	863	785	509	891	299
45	716	421	896	871	444	323	249	635	99	53
46	942	586	909	944	84	925	203	161	448	260
47	688	198	315	398	715	83	62	256	63	415
48	850	321	774	837	136	826	736	670	405	823
49	620	189	257	285	845	868	29	336	338	627

POWER RESIDUES

	0	1	2	3	4	5	6	7	8	9
0	1	14	196	682	269	673	143	971	191	612
1	320	356	860	699	507	912	396	389	291	981
2	331	510	954	984	373	67	938	760	330	496
3	758	302	104	425	795	820	139	915	438	977
4	275	757	288	939	774	526	147	1027	975	247
5	365	986	401	459	240	267	645	782	638	684
6	297	34	476	478	506	898	200	738	22	308
7	188	570	763	372	53	742	78	61	854	615
8	362	944	844	475	464	310	216	962	65	910
9	368	1028	989	443	16	224	43	602	180	458
10	226	71	994	513	996	541	357	874	895	158
11	150	38	532	231	141	943	830	279	813	41
12	574	819	125	719	787	708	633	614	348	748
13	162	206	822	167	276	771	484	590	12	168
14	290	967	135	859	685	311	230	127	747	148
15	10	140	929	634	628	544	399	431	879	965
16	107	467	352	804	946	872	867	797	848	531
17	217	976	261	561	637	670	101	383	207	836
18	363	958	9	126	733	983	359	902	256	491
19	688	353	818	111	523	105	439	991	471	408
20	557	581	917	466	338	608	264	603	194	654
21	908	340	636	656	936	732	969	163	220	1018
22	849	545	413	627	530	203	780	610	292	995
23	527	161	192	626	516	7	98	341	650	852
24	587	1001	611	306	160	178	430	865	769	456
25	198	710	661	1006	681	255	477	492	702	549
26	469	380	165	248	379	151	52	728	913	410
27	585	973	219	1004	653	894	144	985	387	263
28	589	1029	1003	639	698	493	716	745	120	649
29	838	391	319	342	664	17	238	239	253	449
30	100	369	11	154	94	285	897	186	542	371
31	39	546	427	823	181	472	422	753	232	155
32	108	481	548	455	184	514	1010	737	8	112
33	537	301	90	229	113	551	497	772	498	786
34	694	437	963	79	75	19	266	631	586	987
35	415	655	922	536	287	925	578	875	909	354
36	832	307	174	374	81	103	411	599	138	901
37	242	295	6	84	145	999	583	945	858	671
38	115	579	889	74	5	70	980	317	314	272
39	715	731	955	998	569	749	176	402	473	436
40	949	914	424	781	624	488	646	796	834	335
41	566	707	619	418	697	479	520	63	882	1007
42	695	451	128	761	344	692	409	571	777	568
43	735	1011	751	204	794	806	974	233	169	304
44	132	817	97	327	454	170	318	328	468	366
45	1000	597	110	509	940	788	722	829	265	617
46	390	305	146	1013	779	596	96	313	258	519
47	49	686	325	426	809	1016	821	153	80	89
48	215	948	900	228	99	355	846	503	856	643
49	754	246	351	790	750	190	598	124	705	591

P = 1031

INDICES

	0	1	2	3	4	5	6	7	8	9
50	684	739	507	487	745	560	64	14	709	453
51	21	931	984	103	325	749	234	840	618	469
52	416	536	968	194	529	579	45	230	1002	1022
53	224	169	112	853	851	544	353	330	800	772
54	704	105	308	920	155	221	311	651	322	259
55	836	335	930	578	771	577	598	200	913	830
56	713	173	775	963	676	718	410	599	429	394
57	71	427	568	614	120	764	838	959	356	381
58	936	201	814	376	1024	270	348	240	608	280
59	137	499	711	553	856	914	465	451	496	367
60	672	761	97	207	827	988	548	917	205	831
61	227	242	9	928	127	79	865	459	737	412
62	881	784	941	714	404	506	233	223	154	912
63	567	347	671	126	153	531	212	174	58	283
64	806	975	532	489	793	56	406	513	692	289
65	238	776	779	274	209	351	213	878	539	588
66	824	252	816	605	294	964	565	1016	695	595
67	175	379	701	5	621	526	1000	874	706	677
68	1007	254	3	643	59	144	471	939	190	808
69	752	726	425	719	340	420	924	414	284	13
70	535	543	258	962	958	498	987	411	125	512
71	251	525	807	961	902	390	286	903	982	123
72	660	600	456	584	876	758	976	954	267	546
73	846	391	215	184	575	430	886	327	67	743
74	533	655	75	557	869	287	820	148	129	395
75	494	432	632	317	490	649	555	41	30	904
76	27	423	519	72	570	861	973	721	794	248
77	687	135	337	983	44	703	770	428	813	464
78	226	403	57	778	564	1006	339	124	455	885
79	493	569	812	811	434	34	407	167	952	833
80	628	661	848	998	163	615	435	610	504	474
81	514	733	787	118	685	601	995	441	192	121
82	35	476	132	313	693	646	1018	948	740	457
83	116	581	360	765	408	517	179	723	290	747
84	523	1010	508	585	82	822	486	839	168	220
85	829	613	239	760	78	911	488	877	378	143
86	12	960	953	654	648	247	777	166	732	645
87	746	759	165	624	107	357	834	818	992	158
88	780	625	418	664	561	977	889	791	521	382
89	629	666	551	883	275	108	657	306	65	955
90	482	369	187	937	662	698	637	1012	210	358
91	89	803	15	268	401	37	895	202	849	844
92	708	967	352	835	675	355	710	547	880	152
93	691	815	999	751	957	981	214	819	26	43
94	454	847	994	115	81	377	164	888	481	400
95	879	993	858	591	22	392	859	898	181	1025
96	616	900	87	342	540	159	603	141	932	216
97	592	7	502	271	436	48	171	39	589	781
98	386	19	985	185	23	277	51	349	611	92
99	634	197	825	626	102	229	104	576	393	375

POWER RESIDUES

	0	1	2	3	4	5	6	7	8	9
50	26	364	972	205	808	1002	625	502	842	447
51	72	1008	709	647	810	1030	1017	835	349	762
52	358	888	60	840	419	711	675	171	332	524
53	119	635	642	740	50	700	521	77	47	658
54	964	93	271	701	535	273	729	927	606	236
55	211	892	116	593	54	756	274	743	92	257
56	505	884	4	56	784	666	45	630	572	791
57	764	386	249	393	347	734	997	555	553	525
58	133	831	293	1009	723	843	461	268	659	978
59	289	953	970	177	416	669	87	187	556	567
60	721	815	69	966	121	663	3	42	588	1015
61	807	988	429	851	573	805	960	37	518	35
62	490	674	157	136	873	881	993	499	800	890
63	88	201	752	218	990	457	212	906	312	244
64	323	398	417	683	283	869	825	209	864	755
65	260	547	441	1019	863	741	64	896	172	346
66	720	801	904	284	883	1021	891	102	397	403
67	487	632	600	152	66	924	564	679	227	85
68	159	164	234	183	500	814	55	770	470	394
69	361	930	648	824	195	668	73	1022	905	298
70	48	672	129	775	540	343	678	213	920	508
71	926	592	40	560	623	474	450	114	565	693
72	423	767	428	837	377	123	691	395	375	95
73	299	62	868	811	13	182	486	618	404	501
74	828	251	421	739	36	504	870	839	405	515
75	1024	933	690	381	179	444	30	420	725	871
76	853	601	166	262	575	833	321	370	25	350
77	776	554	539	329	482	562	651	866	783	652
78	880	979	303	118	621	446	58	812	27	378
79	137	887	46	644	768	442	2	28	392	333
80	538	315	286	911	382	193	640	712	689	367
81	1014	793	792	778	582	931	662	1020	877	937
82	746	134	845	489	660	992	485	604	208	850
83	559	609	278	799	876	923	550	483	576	847
84	517	21	294	1023	919	494	730	941	802	918
85	480	534	259	533	245	337	594	68	952	956
86	1012	765	400	445	44	616	376	109	495	744
87	106	453	156	122	677	199	724	857	657	950
88	928	620	432	893	130	789	736	1025	947	886
89	32	448	86	173	360	916	452	142	957	1026
90	961	51	714	717	759	316	300	76	33	462
91	282	855	629	558	595	82	117	607	250	407
92	543	385	235	197	696	465	324	412	613	334
93	552	511	968	149	24	336	580	903	270	687
94	339	622	460	254	463	296	20	280	827	237
95	225	57	798	862	727	899	214	934	704	577
96	861	713	703	563	665	31	434	921	522	91
97	243	309	202	766	414	641	726	885	18	252
98	435	935	718	773	512	982	345	706	605	222
99	15	210	878	951	942	816	83	131	803	932

P = 1031

INDICES

	0	1	2	3	4	5	6	7	8	9
100	450	241	505	282	273	1015	253	419	511	583
101	326	431	860	463	810	609	475	516	219	653
102	817	665	697	843	750	887	899	47	91	281
103	515	0								

POWER RESIDUES

	0	1	2	3	4	5	6	7	8	9
100	676	185	528	175	388	277	785	680	241	281
101	841	433	907	326	440	1005	667	59	826	223
102	29	406	529	189	584	959	23	322	384	221
103										

P = 1033

INDICES

	0	1	2	3	4	5	6	7	8	9
0		0	364	14	728	1	378	66	60	28
1	365	565	742	673	430	15	424	446	392	176
2	729	80	929	335	74	2	5	42	794	841
3	379	302	788	579	810	67	756	252	540	687
4	61	574	444	442	261	29	699	103	438	132
5	366	460	369	345	406	566	126	190	173	449
6	743	282	666	94	120	674	943	263	142	349
7	431	773	88	651	616	16	904	631	19	221
8	425	56	938	26	808	447	806	855	625	357
9	393	739	31	316	467	177	802	245	496	593
10	730	486	824	165	733	81	709	919	770	857
11	930	266	490	912	554	336	537	701	813	512
12	75	98	646	588	1030	3	458	902	484	456
13	6	987	275	242	627	43	506	34	713	161
14	795	117	105	206	452	842	1015	146	980	299
15	380	8	236	474	995	303	383	877	585	359
16	789	401	420	704	270	580	390	440	140	314
17	811	204	138	655	187	68	989	463	721	196
18	757	999	71	296	395	253	680	1011	831	108
19	541	534	134	657	609	688	860	953	957	23
20	62	277	850	907	156	575	529	363	65	741
21	445	928	41	787	251	443	102	368	189	665
22	262	87	630	937	854	30	244	823	918	489
23	700	645	901	274	33	104	145	235	876	419
24	439	137	462	70	1010	133	952	849	362	40
25	367	629	822	900	234	461	848	821	820	318
26	370	869	319	480	639	346	606	371	991	746
27	407	764	870	753	398	567	45	320	525	330
28	127	11	481	897	469	191	570	640	816	892
29	174	259	347	465	510	450	312	607	663	1008
30	744	508	372	500	600	283	838	992	327	179
31	667	200	747	969	209	95	949	408	723	374
32	121	933	765	622	784	675	36	871	634	169
33	944	563	754	280	804	264	504	399	678	926
34	143	867	568	198	502	350	1019	46	551	416
35	432	715	321	1023	827	774	53	526	560	247
36	89	352	331	112	435	652	660	128	759	602
37	617	411	12	792	343	17	163	482	472	719
38	905	916	898	523	498	632	1021	470	973	613
39	20	781	192	1001	285	222	289	571	387	256
40	426	797	641	975	182	57	239	817	520	595
41	939	48	893	515	727	27	429	175	73	840
42	809	686	260	131	405	448	119	348	615	220
43	807	356	466	592	732	856	553	511	1029	455
44	626	160	451	298	994	358	269	313	186	195
45	394	107	608	22	155	740	250	664	853	488
46	32	418	1009	39	233	317	638	745	397	329
47	468	891	509	1007	599	178	208	373	783	168
48	803	925	501	415	826	246	434	601	342	718
49	497	612	284	255	181	594	726	839	404	219

POWER RESIDUES

	0	1	2	3	4	5	6	7	8	9
0	1	5	25	125	625	26	130	650	151	755
1	676	281	372	827	3	15	75	375	842	78
2	390	917	453	199	995	843	83	415	9	45
3	225	92	460	234	137	685	326	597	919	463
4	249	212	27	135	675	276	347	702	411	1022
5	978	758	691	356	747	636	81	405	992	828
6	8	40	200	1000	868	208	7	35	175	875
7	243	182	910	418	24	120	600	934	538	624
8	21	105	525	559	729	546	664	221	72	360
9	767	736	581	839	63	315	542	644	121	605
10	959	663	216	47	235	142	710	451	189	945
11	593	899	363	782	811	956	648	141	705	426
12	64	320	567	769	746	631	56	280	367	802
13	911	423	49	245	192	960	668	241	172	860
14	168	840	68	340	667	236	147	735	576	814
15	971	723	516	514	504	454	204	1020	968	708
16	441	139	695	376	847	103	515	509	479	329
17	612	994	838	58	290	417	19	95	475	309
18	512	494	404	987	803	916	448	174	870	218
19	57	285	392	927	503	449	179	895	343	682
20	311	522	544	654	171	855	143	715	476	314
21	537	619	1029	1013	933	533	599	929	513	499
22	429	79	395	942	578	824	1021	973	733	566
23	764	721	506	464	254	237	152	760	701	406
24	997	853	133	665	226	97	485	359	762	711
25	456	214	37	185	925	493	399	962	678	291
26	422	44	220	67	335	642	111	555	709	446
27	164	820	1001	873	233	132	660	201	1005	893
28	333	632	61	305	492	394	937	553	699	396
29	947	603	949	613	999	863	183	915	443	149
30	745	626	31	155	775	776	781	806	931	523
31	549	679	296	447	169	845	93	465	259	262
32	277	352	727	536	614	1004	888	308	507	469
33	279	362	777	786	831	23	115	575	809	946
34	598	924	488	374	837	53	265	292	427	69
35	345	692	361	772	761	706	431	89	445	159
36	795	876	248	207	2	10	50	250	217	52
37	260	267	302	477	319	562	744	621	6	30
38	150	750	651	156	780	801	906	398	957	653
39	166	830	18	90	450	184	920	468	274	337
40	652	161	805	926	498	424	54	270	317	552
41	694	371	822	1011	923	483	349	712	461	239
42	162	810	951	623	16	80	400	967	703	416
43	14	70	350	717	486	364	787	836	48	240
44	167	835	43	215	42	210	17	85	425	59
45	295	442	144	720	501	439	129	645	126	630
46	51	255	242	177	885	293	432	94	470	284
47	387	902	378	857	153	765	726	531	589	879
48	263	282	377	852	128	640	101	505	459	229
49	112	560	734	571	789	846	98	490	384	887

P = 1033

INDICES

	0	1	2	3	4	5	6	7	8	9
50	731	454	993	194	154	487	232	328	598	167
51	825	717	180	218	153	166	152	668	682	669
52	734	696	201	309	683	82	844	748	1003	670
53	710	477	970	215	735	920	323	210	78	697
54	771	800	96	1013	202	858	85	950	762	310
55	931	1017	409	287	684	267	889	724	694	83
56	491	1025	375	984	845	913	229	122	833	749
57	555	493	934	548	1004	337	148	766	224	671
58	538	92	623	910	711	702	829	785	874	478
59	814	967	676	110	971	513	1027	37	340	216
60	76	982	872	291	736	99	864	635	964	921
61	647	776	170	293	324	589	691	945	543	211
62	1031	377	564	423	79	4	301	755	573	698
63	459	125	281	942	772	903	55	805	738	801
64	485	708	265	536	97	457	986	505	116	1014
65	7	382	400	389	203	988	998	679	533	859
66	276	528	927	101	86	243	644	144	136	951
67	628	847	868	605	763	44	10	569	258	311
68	507	837	199	948	932	35	562	503	866	1018
69	714	52	351	659	410	162	915	1020	780	288
70	796	238	47	428	685	118	355	552	159	268
71	106	249	417	637	890	207	924	433	611	725
72	453	231	716	151	695	843	476	322	799	84
73	1016	888	1024	228	492	147	91	828	966	1026
74	981	863	775	690	376	300	124	54	707	985
75	381	997	527	643	846	9	836	561	51	914
76	237	354	248	923	230	475	887	90	862	123
77	996	835	353	886	834	304	305	332	977	750
78	384	306	113	883	556	878	333	436	649	494
79	586	978	653	955	935	360	751	661	620	549
80	790	385	129	184	1005	402	307	760	546	338
81	421	114	603	778	149	705	884	618	959	767
82	271	557	412	961	225	581	879	13	59	672
83	391	334	793	578	539	441	437	344	172	93
84	141	650	18	25	624	315	495	164	769	911
85	812	587	483	241	712	205	979	473	584	703
86	139	654	720	295	830	656	956	906	64	786
87	188	936	917	273	875	69	361	899	819	479
88	990	752	524	896	815	464	662	499	326	968
89	722	621	633	279	677	197	550	1022	559	111
90	758	791	471	522	972	1000	386	974	519	514
91	72	130	614	591	1028	297	185	21	852	38
92	396	1006	782	414	341	254	403	193	597	217
93	681	308	1002	214	77	1012	761	286	693	983
94	832	547	223	909	873	109	339	290	963	292
95	542	422	572	941	737	535	115	388	532	100
96	135	604	257	947	865	658	779	427	158	636
97	610	150	798	227	965	689	706	642	50	922
98	861	885	976	882	648	954	619	183	545	777
99	958	960	58	577	171	24	768	240	583	294

POWER RESIDUES

	0	1	2	3	4	5	6	7	8	9
50	303	482	344	687	336	647	136	680	301	472
51	294	437	119	595	909	413	1032	1028	1008	908
52	408	1007	903	383	882	278	357	752	661	206
53	1030	1018	958	658	191	955	643	116	580	834
54	38	190	950	618	1024	988	808	941	573	799
55	896	348	707	436	114	570	784	821	1006	898
56	358	757	686	331	622	11	55	275	342	677
57	286	397	952	628	41	205	1025	993	833	33
58	165	825	1026	998	858	158	790	851	123	615
59	1009	913	433	99	495	409	1012	928	508	474
60	304	487	369	812	961	673	266	297	452	194
61	970	718	491	389	912	428	74	370	817	986
62	798	891	323	582	844	88	440	134	670	251
63	222	77	385	892	328	607	969	713	466	264
64	287	402	977	753	666	231	122	610	984	788
65	841	73	365	792	861	173	865	193	965	693
66	366	797	886	298	457	219	62	310	517	519
67	529	579	829	13	65	325	592	894	338	657
68	186	930	518	524	554	704	421	39	195	975
69	743	616	1014	938	558	724	521	539	629	46
70	230	117	585	859	163	815	976	748	641	106
71	530	584	854	138	690	351	722	511	489	379
72	862	178	890	318	557	719	496	414	4	20
73	100	500	434	104	520	534	604	954	638	91
74	455	209	12	60	300	467	269	312	527	569
75	779	796	881	273	332	627	36	180	900	368
76	807	936	548	674	271	322	577	819	996	848
77	108	540	634	71	355	742	611	989	813	966
78	698	391	922	478	324	587	869	213	32	160
79	800	901	373	832	28	140	700	401	972	728
80	541	639	96	480	334	637	86	430	84	420
81	34	170	850	118	590	884	288	407	1002	878
82	258	257	252	227	102	510	484	354	737	586
83	864	188	940	568	774	771	756	681	306	497
84	419	29	145	725	526	564	754	671	256	247
85	202	1010	918	458	224	87	435	109	545	659
86	196	980	768	741	606	964	688	341	672	261
87	272	327	602	944	588	874	238	157	785	826
88	1031	1023	983	783	816	981	773	766	731	556
89	714	471	289	412	1027	1003	883	283	382	877
90	253	232	127	635	76	380	867	203	1015	943
91	583	849	113	565	759	696	381	872	228	107
92	535	609	979	763	716	481	339	662	211	22
93	110	550	684	321	572	794	871	223	82	410
94	1017	953	633	66	330	617	1019	963	683	316
95	547	669	246	197	985	793	866	198	990	818
96	991	823	1016	948	608	974	738	591	889	313
97	532	594	904	388	907	403	982	778	791	856
98	148	740	601	939	563	749	646	131	655	176
99	880	268	307	502	444	154	770	751	656	181

P = 1033

INDICES

	0	1	2	3	4	5	6	7	8	9
100	63	272	818	895	325	278	558	521	518	590
101	851	413	596	213	692	908	962	940	531	946
102	157	226	49	881	544	576	582	894	517	212
103	530	880	516							

POWER RESIDUES

	0	1	2	3	4	5	6	7	8	9
100	905	393	932	528	574	804	921	473	299	462
101	244	187	935	543	649	146	730	551	689	346
102	697	386	897	353	732	561	739	596	914	438
103	124	620								

P = 1039

INDICES

	0	1	2	3	4	5	6	7	8	9
0		0	232	1	464	762	233	158	696	2
1	994	877	465	386	390	763	928	1000	234	670
2	188	159	71	219	697	486	618	3	622	296
3	995	569	122	878	194	920	466	936	902	387
4	420	423	391	1018	303	764	451	172	929	316
5	718	1001	850	1009	235	601	854	671	528	1023
6	189	789	801	160	354	110	72	988	426	220
7	114	893	698	91	130	487	96	1035	619	598
8	652	4	655	34	623	724	212	297	535	869
9	996	544	683	570	404	394	123	783	548	879
10	950	859	195	565	44	921	203	613	467	7
11	833	937	48	588	903	981	760	388	217	120
12	421	716	1021	424	1033	210	392	42	586	1019
13	342	344	304	828	182	765	658	1013	452	433
14	346	173	87	225	930	20	323	317	362	306
15	719	76	328	1002	229	293	851	31	830	1010
16	884	377	236	37	887	602	266	184	855	772
17	956	672	444	286	529	644	767	1024	63	687
18	190	977	776	790	915	660	802	839	636	161
19	626	380	355	925	1015	111	780	1030	73	60
20	144	989	53	454	427	147	797	221	276	509
21	115	166	435	894	845	742	699	727	239	92
22	27	348	131	372	280	488	820	399	97	479
23	175	1036	992	668	620	934	449	599	352	89
24	653	542	948	5	215	40	656	18	227	35
25	442	975	624	58	274	725	818	932	213	56
26	574	298	576	960	536	733	22	870	414	472
27	997	300	890	545	207	325	684	794	665	571
28	578	260	405	106	319	395	457	581	124	962
29	252	784	555	364	549	747	594	880	538	605
30	951	138	308	860	560	513	196	735	461	566
31	525	721	45	430	263	922	24	15	204	135
32	78	614	609	632	468	872	269	8	81	330
33	834	969	498	938	416	712	49	102	1004	589
34	150	408	904	474	676	982	518	231	761	695
35	876	389	999	187	218	617	295	121	919	901
36	422	302	171	717	1008	853	1022	800	109	425
37	892	129	1034	651	33	211	868	682	393	547
38	858	43	612	832	587	759	119	1020	209	585
39	343	181	1012	345	224	322	305	327	292	829
40	376	886	183	955	285	766	686	775	659	635
41	379	1014	1029	143	453	796	508	434	741	238
42	347	279	398	174	667	448	88	947	39	226
43	974	273	931	573	959	21	471	889	324	664
44	259	318	580	251	363	593	604	307	512	460
45	720	262	14	77	631	268	329	497	711	1003
46	407	675	230	875	186	294	900	170	852	108
47	128	32	681	857	831	118	584	1011	321	291
48	885	284	774	378	142	507	237	397	447	38
49	272	958	888	258	250	603	459	13	267	710

POWER RESIDUES

	0	1	2	3	4	5	6	7	8	9
0	1	3	9	27	81	243	729	109	327	981
1	865	517	512	497	452	317	951	775	247	741
2	145	435	266	798	316	948	766	220	660	941
3	745	157	471	374	83	249	747	163	489	428
4	245	735	127	381	104	312	936	730	112	336
5	1008	946	760	202	606	779	259	777	253	759
6	199	597	752	178	534	563	650	911	655	926
7	700	22	66	198	594	743	151	453	320	960
8	802	328	984	874	544	593	740	142	426	239
9	717	73	219	657	932	718	76	228	684	1013
10	961	805	337	1011	955	787	283	849	469	368
11	65	195	585	716	70	210	630	851	475	386
12	119	357	32	96	288	864	514	503	470	371
13	74	222	666	959	799	319	957	793	301	903
14	631	854	484	413	200	600	761	205	615	806
15	340	1020	982	868	526	539	578	695	7	21
16	63	189	567	662	947	763	211	633	860	502
17	467	362	47	141	423	230	690	1031	1015	967
18	823	391	134	402	167	501	464	353	20	60
19	180	540	581	704	34	102	306	918	676	989
20	889	589	728	106	318	954	784	274	822	388
21	125	375	86	258	774	244	732	118	354	23
22	69	207	621	824	394	143	429	248	744	154
23	462	347	2	6	18	54	162	486	419	218
24	654	923	691	1034	1024	994	904	634	863	511
25	494	443	290	870	532	557	632	857	493	440
26	281	843	451	314	942	748	166	498	455	326
27	978	856	490	431	254	762	208	624	833	421
28	224	672	977	853	481	404	173	519	518	515
29	506	479	398	155	465	356	29	87	261	783
30	271	813	361	44	132	396	149	447	302	906
31	640	881	565	656	929	709	49	147	441	284
32	852	478	395	146	438	275	825	397	152	456
33	329	987	883	571	674	983	871	535	566	659
34	938	736	130	390	131	393	140	420	221	663
35	950	772	238	714	64	192	576	689	1028	1006
36	940	742	148	444	293	879	559	638	875	547
37	602	767	223	669	968	826	400	161	483	410
38	191	573	680	1001	925	697	13	39	117	351
39	14	42	126	378	95	285	855	487	422	227
40	681	1004	934	724	94	282	846	460	341	1023
41	991	895	607	782	268	804	334	1002	928	706
42	40	120	360	41	123	369	68	204	612	797
43	313	939	739	139	417	212	636	869	529	548
44	605	776	250	750	172	516	509	488	425	236
45	708	46	138	414	203	609	788	286	858	496
46	449	308	924	694	4	12	36	108	324	972
47	838	436	269	807	343	1029	1009	949	769	229
48	687	1022	988	886	580	701	25	75	225	675
49	986	880	562	647	902	628	845	457	332	996

P = 1039

INDICES

	0	1	2	3	4	5	6	7	8	9
50	674	185	169	127	856	583	290	773	506	446
51	957	249	12	673	126	289	445	11	288	287
52	806	807	530	964	808	645	154	531	768	438
53	965	1025	254	809	64	337	646	688	704	155
54	191	786	532	978	84	769	777	369	439	791
55	557	966	916	756	1026	661	897	255	803	366
56	810	840	492	65	637	312	338	162	551	647
57	627	333	689	381	813	705	356	749	156	926
58	484	192	1016	848	787	112	596	533	781	201
59	979	1031	826	85	74	882	770	61	837	778
60	145	843	370	990	540	440	54	412	792	455
61	745	558	428	607	967	148	693	917	798	866
62	757	222	953	1027	277	972	662	510	495	898
63	116	140	256	167	247	804	436	702	367	895
64	310	811	846	824	841	743	864	493	700	862
65	66	728	501	638	240	68	313	93	562	339
66	28	912	163	349	730	552	132	515	648	373
67	944	628	281	503	334	489	198	690	821	941
68	382	400	640	814	98	737	706	480	908	357
69	176	242	750	1037	463	157	993	385	927	669
70	70	485	621	568	193	935	419	1017	450	315
71	849	600	527	788	353	987	113	90	95	597
72	654	723	534	543	403	782	949	564	202	6
73	47	980	216	715	1032	41	341	827	657	432
74	86	19	361	75	228	30	883	36	265	771
75	443	643	62	976	914	838	625	924	779	59
76	52	146	275	165	844	726	26	371	819	478
77	991	933	351	541	214	17	441	57	817	55
78	575	732	413	299	206	793	577	105	456	961
79	554	746	537	137	559	734	524	429	23	134
80	608	871	80	968	415	101	149	473	517	694
81	998	616	918	301	1007	799	891	650	867	546
82	611	758	208	180	223	326	375	954	685	634
83	1028	795	740	278	666	946	973	572	470	663
84	579	592	511	261	630	496	406	874	899	107
85	680	117	320	283	141	396	271	257	458	709
86	168	582	505	248	125	10	805	963	153	437
87	253	336	703	785	83	368	556	755	896	365
88	491	311	550	332	812	748	483	847	595	200
89	825	881	836	842	539	411	744	606	692	865
90	952	971	494	139	246	701	309	823	863	861
91	500	67	561	911	729	514	943	502	197	940
92	639	736	907	241	462	384	69	567	418	314
93	526	986	94	722	402	563	46	714	340	431
94	360	29	264	642	913	923	51	164	25	477
95	350	16	816	731	205	104	553	136	523	133
96	79	100	516	615	1006	649	610	179	374	633
97	739	945	469	591	629	873	679	282	270	708
98	504	9	152	335	82	754	490	331	482	199
99	835	410	691	970	245	822	499	910	942	939

POWER RESIDUES

	0	1	2	3	4	5	6	7	8	9
50	910	652	917	673	980	862	508	485	416	209
51	627	842	448	305	915	667	962	808	346	1038
52	1036	1030	1012	958	796	310	930	712	58	174
53	522	527	542	587	722	88	264	792	298	894
54	604	773	241	723	91	273	819	379	98	294
55	882	568	665	956	790	292	876	550	611	794
56	304	912	658	935	727	103	309	927	703	31
57	93	279	837	433	260	780	262	786	280	840
58	442	287	861	505	476	389	128	384	113	339
59	1017	973	841	445	296	888	586	719	79	237
60	711	55	165	495	446	299	897	613	800	322
61	966	820	382	107	321	963	811	355	26	78
62	234	702	28	84	252	756	190	570	671	974
63	844	454	323	969	829	409	188	564	653	920
64	682	1007	943	751	175	525	536	569	668	965
65	817	373	80	240	720	82	246	738	136	408
66	185	555	626	839	439	278	834	424	233	699
67	19	57	171	513	500	461	344	1032	1018	976
68	850	472	377	92	276	828	406	179	537	572
69	677	992	898	616	809	349	8	24	72	216
70	648	905	637	872	538	575	686	1019	979	859
71	499	458	335	1005	937	733	121	363	50	150
72	450	311	933	721	85	255	765	217	651	914
73	664	953	781	265	795	307	921	685	1016	970
74	832	418	215	645	896	610	791	295	885	577
75	692	1037	1033	1021	985	877	553	620	821	385
76	116	348	5	15	45	135	405	176	528	545
77	596	749	169	507	482	407	182	546	599	758
78	196	588	725	97	291	873	541	584	713	61
79	183	549	608	785	277	831	415	206	618	815
80	367	62	186	558	635	866	520	521	524	533
81	560	641	884	574	683	1010	952	778	256	768
82	226	678	995	907	643	890	592	737	133	399
83	158	474	383	110	330	990	892	598	755	187
84	561	644	893	601	764	214	642	887	583	710
85	52	156	468	365	56	168	504	473	380	101
86	303	909	649	908	646	899	619	818	376	89
87	267	801	325	975	847	463	350	11	33	99
88	297	891	595	746	160	480	401	164	492	437
89	272	816	370	71	213	639	878	556	629	848
90	466	359	38	114	342	1026	1000	922	688	1025
91	997	913	661	944	754	184	552	617	812	358
92	35	105	315	945	757	193	579	698	16	48
93	144	432	257	771	235	705	37	111	333	999
94	919	679	998	916	670	971	835	427	242	726
95	100	300	900	622	827	403	170	510	491	434
96	263	789	289	867	523	530	551	614	803	331
97	993	901	625	836	430	251	753	181	543	590
98	731	115	345	1035	1027	1003	931	715	67	201
99	603	770	232	696	10	30	90	270	810	352

P = 1039

INDICES

	0	1	2	3	4	5	6	7	8	9
100	906	383	417	985	401	713	359	641	50	476
101	815	103	522	99	1005	178	738	590	678	707
102	151	753	481	409	244	909	905	984	358	475
103	521	177	677	752	243	983	520	751	519	

POWER RESIDUES

	0	1	2	3	4	5	6	7	8	9
100	17	51	153	459	338	1014	964	814	364	53
101	159	477	392	137	411	194	582	707	43	129
102	387	122	366	59	177	531	554	623	830	412
103	197	591	734	124	372	77	231	693		

P = 1049

INDICES

	0	1	2	3	4	5	6	7	8	9
0		0	596	1	144	98	597	255	740	2
1	694	418	145	140	851	99	288	757	598	152
2	242	256	1014	227	741	196	736	3	399	476
3	695	841	884	419	305	353	146	265	748	141
4	838	21	852	540	562	100	823	657	289	510
5	792	758	284	176	599	516	995	153	24	590
6	243	960	389	257	432	238	1015	987	901	228
7	949	189	742	724	861	197	296	673	737	350
8	386	4	617	555	400	855	88	477	110	7
9	696	395	371	842	205	250	885	180	58	420
10	340	1019	306	1030	880	354	772	610	147	375
11	64	266	543	358	749	325	620	142	138	1012
12	839	836	508	22	985	294	853	203	1028	541
13	834	832	563	407	535	101	449	965	824	565
14	497	658	785	558	290	574	272	511	409	866
15	793	485	892	759	221	939	285	537	946	177
16	982	482	600	116	165	517	103	584	996	280
17	403	154	684	345	25	451	706	591	603	647
18	244	716	991	961	967	363	390	127	801	258
19	846	631	433	826	776	239	654	858	1016	1025
20	936	988	567	731	902	119	578	229	428	570
21	950	499	320	190	158	638	743	48	971	725
22	660	897	862	917	91	198	954	1038	297	787
23	921	674	168	522	738	755	734	351	560	174
24	387	187	384	5	56	608	618	292	533	556
25	890	480	401	645	799	856	576	636	89	520
26	382	478	380	905	111	274	1003	8	83	907
27	697	209	1045	396	513	614	372	446	113	843
28	45	53	206	411	333	251	106	276	886	466
29	122	181	868	926	59	688	1005	421	414	367
30	341	795	33	1020	440	10	307	503	817	1031
31	487	95	881	587	85	355	494	581	773	894
32	530	611	30	909	148	336	712	376	761	912
33	65	470	699	267	132	37	544	223	876	359
34	999	211	750	765	232	326	941	215	621	71
35	1047	143	254	693	139	287	151	1013	195	398
36	840	304	264	837	539	822	509	283	515	23
37	959	431	986	948	723	295	349	616	854	109
38	394	204	179	339	1029	771	374	542	324	137
39	835	984	202	833	406	448	564	784	573	408
40	484	220	536	981	115	102	279	683	450	602
41	715	966	126	845	825	653	1024	566	118	427
42	498	157	47	659	916	953	786	167	754	559
43	186	55	291	889	644	575	519	379	273	82
44	208	512	445	44	410	105	465	867	687	413
45	794	439	502	486	586	493	893	29	335	760
46	469	131	222	998	764	940	70	253	286	194
47	303	538	282	958	947	348	108	178	770	323
48	983	405	783	483	980	278	601	125	652	117
49	156	915	166	185	888	518	81	444	104	686

POWER RESIDUES

	0	1	2	3	4	5	6	7	8	9
0	1	3	9	27	81	243	729	89	267	801
1	305	915	647	892	578	685	1006	920	662	937
2	713	41	123	369	58	174	522	517	502	457
3	322	966	800	302	906	620	811	335	1005	917
4	653	910	632	847	443	280	840	422	217	651
5	904	614	793	281	843	431	244	732	98	294
6	882	548	595	736	110	330	990	872	518	505
7	466	349	1047	1043	1031	995	887	563	640	871
8	515	496	439	268	804	314	942	728	86	258
9	774	224	672	967	803	311	933	701	5	15
10	45	135	405	166	498	445	286	858	476	379
11	88	264	792	278	834	404	163	489	418	205
12	615	796	290	870	512	487	412	187	561	634
13	853	461	334	1002	908	626	829	389	118	354
14	13	39	117	351	4	12	36	108	324	972
15	818	356	19	57	171	513	490	421	214	642
16	877	533	550	601	754	164	492	427	232	696
17	1039	1019	959	779	239	717	53	159	477	382
18	97	291	873	521	514	493	430	241	723	71
19	213	639	868	506	469	358	25	75	225	675
20	976	830	392	127	381	94	282	846	440	271
21	813	341	1023	971	815	347	1041	1025	977	833
22	401	154	462	337	1011	935	707	23	69	207
23	621	814	344	1032	998	896	590	721	65	195
24	585	706	20	60	180	540	571	664	943	731
25	95	285	855	467	352	7	21	63	189	567
26	652	907	623	820	362	37	111	333	999	899
27	599	748	146	438	265	795	287	861	485	406
28	169	507	472	367	52	156	468	355	16	48
29	144	432	247	741	125	375	76	228	684	1003
30	911	635	856	470	361	34	102	306	918	656
31	919	659	928	686	1009	929	689	1018	956	770
32	212	636	859	479	388	115	345	1035	1007	923
33	671	964	794	284	852	458	325	975	827	383
34	100	300	900	602	757	173	519	508	475	376
35	79	237	711	35	105	315	945	737	113	339
36	1017	953	761	185	555	616	799	299	897	593
37	730	92	276	828	386	109	327	981	845	437
38	262	786	260	780	242	726	80	240	720	62
39	186	558	625	826	380	91	273	819	359	28
40	84	252	756	170	510	481	394	133	399	148
41	444	283	849	449	298	894	584	703	11	33
42	99	297	891	575	676	979	839	419	208	624
43	823	371	64	192	576	679	988	866	500	451
44	304	912	638	865	497	442	277	831	395	136
45	408	175	525	526	529	538	565	646	889	569
46	658	925	677	982	848	446	289	867	503	460
47	331	993	881	545	586	709	29	87	261	783
48	251	753	161	483	400	151	453	310	930	692
49	1027	983	851	455	316	948	746	140	420	211

P = 1049

INDICES

	0	1	2	3	4	5	6	7	8	9
50	438	585	28	468	997	69	193	281	347	769
51	404	979	124	155	184	80	685	27	68	346
52	978	183	26	977	976	452	453	550	707	454
53	870	592	551	161	604	708	679	648	455	928
54	245	871	805	717	593	473	992	552	61	962
55	162	628	968	605	1042	364	709	690	391	680
56	641	128	649	77	802	456	1007	259	929	459
57	847	246	702	632	872	423	434	806	14	827
58	718	810	777	594	416	240	474	746	655	993
59	236	859	553	369	1017	62	1010	1026	963	270
60	937	163	343	989	629	934	568	969	1036	732
61	606	797	903	1043	51	120	365	815	579	710
62	35	230	691	262	429	392	135	571	681	1022
63	951	642	42	500	129	301	321	650	442	191
64	78	974	159	803	626	639	457	12	744	1008
65	932	49	260	40	972	930	309	726	460	311
66	661	848	18	898	247	505	863	703	728	918
67	633	330	92	873	819	199	424	462	955	435
68	547	1039	807	1033	298	15	313	788	828	316
69	922	719	489	675	811	663	169	778	667	523
70	595	97	739	417	850	756	241	226	735	475
71	883	352	747	20	561	656	791	175	994	589
72	388	237	900	188	860	672	385	554	87	6
73	370	249	57	1018	879	609	63	357	619	1011
74	507	293	1027	831	534	964	496	557	271	865
75	891	938	945	481	164	583	402	344	705	646
76	990	362	800	630	775	857	935	730	577	569
77	319	637	970	896	90	1037	920	521	733	173
78	383	607	532	479	798	635	381	904	1002	906
79	1044	613	112	52	332	275	121	925	1004	366
80	32	9	816	94	84	580	529	908	711	911
81	698	36	875	210	231	214	1046	692	150	397
82	263	821	514	430	722	615	393	338	373	136
83	201	447	572	219	114	682	714	844	1023	426
84	46	952	753	54	643	378	207	43	464	412
85	501	492	334	130	763	252	302	957	107	322
86	782	277	651	914	887	443	437	467	192	768
87	123	79	67	182	975	549	869	160	678	927
88	804	472	60	627	1041	689	640	76	1006	458
89	701	422	13	809	415	745	235	368	1009	269
90	342	933	1035	796	50	814	34	261	134	1021
91	41	300	441	973	625	11	931	39	308	310
92	17	504	727	329	818	461	546	1032	312	315
93	488	662	666	96	849	225	882	19	790	588
94	899	671	86	248	878	356	506	830	495	864
95	944	582	704	361	774	729	318	895	919	172
96	531	634	1001	612	331	924	31	93	528	910
97	874	213	149	820	721	337	200	218	713	425
98	752	377	463	491	762	956	781	913	436	767
99	66	548	677	471	1040	75	700	808	234	268

POWER RESIDUES

	0	1	2	3	4	5	6	7	8	9
50	633	850	452	307	921	665	946	740	122	366
51	49	147	441	274	822	368	55	165	495	436
52	259	777	233	699	1048	1046	1040	1022	968	806
53	320	960	782	248	744	134	402	157	471	364
54	43	129	387	112	336	1008	926	680	991	875
55	527	532	547	592	727	83	249	747	143	429
56	238	714	44	132	396	139	417	202	606	769
57	209	627	832	398	145	435	256	768	206	618
58	805	317	951	755	167	501	454	313	939	719
59	59	177	531	544	583	700	2	6	18	54
60	162	486	409	178	534	553	610	781	245	735
61	107	321	963	791	275	825	377	82	246	738
62	116	348	1044	1034	1004	914	644	883	551	604
63	763	191	573	670	961	785	257	771	215	645
64	886	560	631	844	434	253	759	179	537	562
65	637	862	488	415	196	588	715	47	141	423
66	220	660	931	695	1036	1010	932	698	1045	1037
67	1013	941	725	77	231	693	1030	992	878	536
68	559	628	835	407	172	516	499	448	295	885
69	557	622	817	353	10	30	90	270	810	332
70	996	890	572	667	952	758	176	528	535	556
71	619	808	326	978	836	410	181	543	580	691
72	1024	974	824	374	73	219	657	922	668	955
73	767	203	609	778	236	708	26	78	234	702
74	8	24	72	216	648	895	587	712	38	114
75	342	1026	980	842	428	235	705	17	51	153
76	459	328	984	854	464	343	1029	989	869	509
77	478	385	106	318	954	764	194	582	697	1042
78	1028	986	860	482	397	142	426	229	687	1012
79	938	716	50	150	450	301	903	611	784	254
80	762	188	564	643	880	542	577	682	997	893
81	581	694	1033	1001	905	617	802	308	924	674
82	973	821	365	46	138	414	193	579	688	1015
83	947	743	131	393	130	390	121	363	40	120
84	360	31	93	279	837	413	190	570	661	934
85	704	14	42	126	378	85	255	765	197	591
86	724	74	222	666	949	749	149	447	292	876
87	530	541	574	673	970	812	338	1014	944	734
88	104	312	936	710	32	96	288	864	494	433
89	250	750	152	456	319	957	773	221	663	940
90	722	68	204	612	787	263	789	269	807	323
91	969	809	329	987	863	491	424	223	669	958
92	776	230	690	1021	965	797	293	879	539	568
93	655	916	650	901	605	766	200	600	751	155
94	465	346	1038	1016	950	752	158	474	373	70
95	210	630	841	425	226	678	985	857	473	370
96	61	183	549	598	745	137	411	184	552	607
97	772	218	654	913	641	874	524	523	520	511
98	484	403	160	480	391	124	372	67	201	603
99	760	182	546	589	718	56	168	504	463	340

P = 1049

INDICES

	0	1	2	3	4	5	6	7	8	9
100	1034	813	133	299	624	38	16	328	545	314
101	665	224	789	670	877	829	943	360	317	171
102	1000	923	527	212	720	217	751	490	780	766
103	676	74	233	812	623	327	664	669	942	170
104	526	216	779	73	622	668	525	72	524	

POWER RESIDUES

	0	1	2	3	4	5	6	7	8	9
100	1020	962	788	266	798	296	888	566	649	898
101	596	739	119	357	22	66	198	594	733	101
102	303	909	629	838	416	199	597	742	128	384
103	103	309	927	683	1000	902	608	775	227	681
104	994	884	554	613	790	272	816	350		

P = 1051

INDICES

	0	1	2	3	4	5	6	7	8	9
0		0	27	265	54	116	292	1	81	530
1	143	766	319	17	28	381	108	689	557	985
2	170	266	793	1037	346	232	44	795	55	992
3	408	599	135	1031	716	117	584	851	1012	282
4	197	337	293	114	820	646	14	421	373	2
5	259	954	71	360	822	882	82	200	1019	209
6	435	914	626	531	162	133	8	158	743	252
7	144	697	611	439	878	497	1039	767	309	854
8	224	10	364	38	320	805	141	207	847	370
9	673	18	41	864	448	51	400	392	29	246
10	286	719	981	648	98	382	387	842	849	139
11	909	66	109	711	227	103	1046	547	236	690
12	462	482	941	602	653	348	558	561	189	379
13	160	709	35	986	185	911	770	565	279	833
14	171	686	724	783	638	58	466	267	905	605
15	524	291	16	169	794	715	336	372	881	625
16	251	1038	37	672	391	97	65	235	347	34
17	832	465	168	250	234	233	874	474	397	745
18	700	875	45	129	68	967	891	405	475	796
19	78	809	427	550	419	398	56	417	273	491
20	313	423	746	993	1008	453	675	517	125	701
21	409	988	414	962	869	230	876	600	166	704
22	936	706	93	46	136	762	738	204	254	332
23	130	1032	23	111	574	537	263	69	717	522
24	489	678	509	275	968	118	629	1002	680	303
25	375	892	585	753	588	20	216	458	406	852
26	187	472	736	996	62	476	1013	635	212	178
27	938	977	797	283	592	998	306	146	860	79
28	198	385	713	1006	751	316	810	338	665	328
29	85	657	493	428	294	325	932	511	632	4
30	551	115	318	984	43	1030	196	420	821	913
31	742	496	363	369	399	647	908	546	652	708
32	278	57	15	624	64	249	699	404	418	422
33	124	229	92	331	262	274	374	457	61	976
34	859	315	492	3	195	368	277	403	261	314
35	260	812	901	866	501	813	424	955	772	829
36	727	920	902	747	72	555	156	1044	95	867
37	994	361	918	478	432	613	502	1009	823	926
38	105	826	836	814	454	883	577	644	446	781
39	425	676	83	974	444	970	300	956	518	201
40	340	801	450	616	773	126	1020	567	1035	609
41	480	830	702	210	544	154	152	48	728	410
42	436	149	1015	951	441	921	989	915	896	1048
43	257	244	903	415	627	323	193	972	731	748
44	963	532	733	595	120	486	73	870	163	667
45	789	53	765	556	231	134	281	13	359	434
46	157	877	9	846	50	980	138	1045	601	159
47	564	637	290	880	96	167	744	890	549	312
48	516	868	705	253	536	508	302	215	995	937
49	145	750	656	631	1029	362	707	698	330	858

POWER RESIDUES

	0	1	2	3	4	5	6	7	8	9
0	1	7	49	343	299	1042	988	610	66	462
1	81	567	816	457	46	322	152	13	91	637
2	255	734	934	232	573	858	751	2	14	98
3	686	598	1033	925	169	132	924	162	83	581
4	914	92	644	304	26	182	223	510	417	817
5	464	95	665	451	4	28	196	321	145	1015
6	799	338	264	797	324	166	111	777	184	237
7	608	52	364	446	1020	834	583	928	190	279
8	902	8	56	392	642	290	979	547	676	528
9	543	648	332	222	503	368	474	165	104	728
10	892	989	617	115	805	380	558	753	16	112
11	784	233	580	907	43	301	5	35	245	664
12	444	1006	736	948	330	208	405	733	927	183
13	230	559	760	65	455	32	224	517	466	109
14	763	86	602	10	70	490	277	888	961	421
15	845	660	416	810	415	803	366	460	67	469
16	130	910	64	448	1034	932	218	475	172	153
17	20	140	980	554	725	871	842	639	269	832
18	569	830	555	732	920	134	938	260	769	128
19	896	1017	813	436	950	344	306	40	280	909
20	57	399	691	633	227	538	613	87	609	59
21	413	789	268	825	520	487	256	741	983	575
22	872	849	688	612	80	560	767	114	798	331
23	215	454	25	175	174	167	118	826	527	536
24	599	1040	974	512	431	915	99	693	647	325
25	173	160	69	483	228	545	662	430	908	50
26	350	348	334	236	601	3	21	147	1029	897
27	1024	862	779	198	335	243	650	346	320	138
28	966	456	39	273	860	765	100	700	696	668
29	472	151	6	42	294	1007	743	997	673	507
30	396	670	486	249	692	640	276	881	912	78
31	546	669	479	200	349	341	285	944	302	12
32	84	588	963	435	943	295	1014	792	289	972
33	498	333	229	552	711	773	156	41	287	958
34	400	698	682	570	837	604	24	168	125	875
35	870	835	590	977	533	578	893	996	666	458
36	53	371	495	312	82	574	865	800	345	313
37	89	623	157	48	336	250	699	689	619	129
38	903	15	105	735	941	281	916	106	742	990
39	624	164	97	679	549	690	626	178	195	314
40	96	672	500	347	327	187	258	755	30	210
41	419	831	562	781	212	433	929	197	328	194
42	307	47	329	201	356	390	628	192	293	1000
43	694	654	374	516	459	60	420	838	611	73
44	511	424	866	807	394	656	388	614	94	658
45	402	712	780	205	384	586	949	337	257	748
46	1032	918	120	840	625	171	146	1022	848	681
47	563	788	261	776	177	188	265	804	373	509
48	410	768	121	847	674	514	445	1013	785	240
49	629	199	342	292	993	645	311	75	525	522

P = 1051

INDICES

	0	1	2	3	4	5	6	7	8	9
50	402	500	919	94	612	835	780	299	615	479
51	47	440	243	730	485	764	433	137	879	515
52	214	1028	499	614	763	498	1023	238	89	1024
53	503	739	1040	354	662	958	239	1010	205	768
54	965	572	1004	90	824	255	310	87	619	394
55	1025	927	333	855	173	182	887	504	106	131
56	225	670	412	470	740	827	1033	11	778	180
57	343	1041	837	24	365	219	692	621	355	815
58	112	39	684	76	520	663	455	575	321	534
59	352	682	959	884	538	806	659	756	31	240
60	578	264	142	688	345	598	1011	645	70	208
61	7	438	223	206	447	718	848	102	940	378
62	769	782	523	371	390	464	396	966	426	490
63	674	961	935	203	573	677	679	19	735	177
64	305	1005	84	510	42	495	651	248	91	975
65	276	865	726	1043	431	825	445	969	449	608
66	151	950	256	971	119	52	358	979	289	311
67	301	630	401	298	484	1027	88	957	1003	393
68	886	469	342	620	519	681	30	597	222	377
69	395	202	304	247	430	949	288	1026	341	376
70	287	785	839	786	928	802	893	720	528	1017
71	840	334	451	586	982	899	799	787	856	617
72	754	649	947	943	929	174	774	589	99	540
73	582	803	183	127	21	383	122	924	894	888
74	1021	217	388	296	945	721	505	568	459	843
75	640	26	529	107	1036	407	850	819	953	1018
76	132	610	853	140	863	285	841	226	481	188
77	910	723	604	335	671	831	473	67	808	272
78	452	413	703	737	110	488	1001	587	471	211
79	997	712	327	931	983	741	545	63	228	60
80	367	900	828	155	477	104	643	443	800	1034
81	153	1014	1047	192	594	788	12	49	636	548
82	507	655	857	779	729	213	237	661	571	618
83	181	411	179	691	75	351	755	344	437	939
84	463	934	176	650	1042	150	978	483	468	221
85	948	838	1016	798	942	581	923	944	25	952
86	284	603	271	1000	930	366	442	593	654	570
87	350	175	220	922	999	349	758	759	775	693
88	990	307	559	872	760	590	622	916	147	562
89	513	776	100	356	897	861	190	269	694	541
90	816	1049	80	380	792	991	583	113	258	199
91	161	696	308	804	40	245	386	710	461	560
92	184	685	904	714	36	33	873	128	77	416
93	1007	987	165	761	22	521	628	752	186	634
94	591	384	664	324	317	912	907	623	123	456
95	194	811	771	554	917	925	576	973	339	566
96	543	148	895	322	732	666	280	845	563	889
97	535	749	329	834	242	514	1022	353	964	86
98	172	669	777	218	683	533	658	687	6	101
99	389	960	734	494	725	607	357	297	885	596

POWER RESIDUES

	0	1	2	3	4	5	6	7	8	9
50	501	354	376	530	557	746	1018	820	485	242
51	643	297	1028	890	975	519	480	207	398	684
52	584	935	239	622	150	1050	1044	1002	708	752
53	9	63	441	985	589	970	484	235	594	1005
54	729	899	1038	960	414	796	317	117	819	478
55	193	300	1049	1037	953	365	453	18	126	882
56	919	127	889	968	470	137	959	407	747	1025
57	869	828	541	634	234	587	956	386	600	1047
58	1023	855	730	906	36	252	713	787	254	727
59	885	940	274	867	814	443	999	687	605	31
60	217	468	123	861	772	149	1043	995	659	409
61	761	72	504	375	523	508	403	719	829	548
62	683	577	886	947	323	159	62	434	936	246
63	671	493	298	1035	939	267	818	471	144	1008
64	750	1046	1016	806	387	607	45	315	103	721
65	843	646	318	124	868	821	492	291	986	596
66	1019	827	534	585	942	288	965	449	1041	981
67	561	774	163	90	630	206	391	635	241	636
68	248	685	591	984	582	921	141	987	603	17
69	119	833	576	879	898	1031	911	71	497	326
70	180	209	412	782	219	482	221	496	319	131
71	917	113	791	282	923	155	34	238	615	101
72	707	745	1011	771	142	994	652	360	418	824
73	513	438	964	442	992	638	262	783	226	531
74	564	795	310	68	476	179	202	363	439	971
75	491	284	937	253	720	836	597	1026	876	877
76	884	933	225	524	515	452	11	77	539	620
77	136	952	358	404	726	878	891	982	568	823
78	506	389	621	143	1001	701	703	717	815	450
79	1048	1030	904	22	154	27	189	272	853	716
80	808	401	705	731	913	85	595	1012	778	191
81	286	951	351	355	383	579	900	1045	1009	757
82	44	308	54	378	544	655	381	565	802	359
83	411	775	170	139	973	505	382	572	851	702
84	710	766	107	749	1039	967	463	88	616	108
85	756	37	259	762	79	553	718	822	499	340
86	278	895	1010	764	93	651	353	369	481	214
87	447	1027	883	926	176	181	216	461	74	518
88	473	158	55	385	593	998	680	556	739	969
89	477	186	251	706	738	962	428	894	1003	715
90	801	352	362	432	922	148	1036	946	316	110
91	770	135	945	309	61	427	887	954	372	502
92	361	425	873	856	737	955	379	551	704	724
93	864	793	296	1021	841	632	220	489	270	839
94	618	122	854	723	857	744	1004	722	850	695
95	661	423	859	758	51	357	397	677	535	592
96	991	631	213	440	978	540	627	185	244	657
97	395	663	437	957	393	649	339	271	846	667
98	465	102	714	794	303	19	133	931	211	426
99	880	905	29	203	370	488	263	790	275	874

P = 1051

INDICES

	0	1	2	3	4	5	6	7	8	9
100	429	784	527	898	946	539	121	295	639	818
101	862	722	807	487	326	59	642	191	506	660
102	74	933	467	580	270	569	757	871	512	268
103	791	695	460	32	164	633	906	553	542	844
104	241	668	5	606	526	817	641	579	790	552
105	525	0								

POWER RESIDUES

	0	1	2	3	4	5	6	7	8	9
100	863	786	247	678	542	641	283	930	204	377
101	537	606	38	266	811	422	852	709	759	58
102	406	740	976	526	529	550	697	675	521	494
103	305	33	231	566	809	408	754	23	161	76
104	532	571	844	653	367	467	116	812	429	901
105										

P = 1061

INDICES

	0	1	2	3	4	5	6	7	8	9
0		0	1	167	2	244	168	476	3	334
1	245	602	169	925	477	411	4	495	335	748
2	246	643	603	878	170	488	926	501	478	689
3	412	510	5	769	496	720	336	540	749	32
4	247	378	644	1049	604	578	879	428	171	952
5	489	662	927	284	502	846	479	915	690	725
6	413	205	511	810	6	109	770	598	497	1045
7	721	651	337	85	541	655	750	18	33	101
8	248	668	379	470	645	739	1050	856	605	307
9	579	341	880	677	429	992	172	626	953	936
10	490	947	663	795	928	887	285	89	503	444
11	847	707	480	800	916	62	691	199	726	971
12	414	144	206	545	512	732	811	45	7	156
13	110	392	771	164	599	745	498	717	1046	659
14	722	595	652	467	338	933	86	59	542	389
15	656	56	751	829	19	754	34	273	102	451
16	249	294	669	832	380	1013	471	27	646	790
17	740	22	1051	180	857	964	606	892	308	757
18	580	320	342	372	881	784	678	37	430	977
19	993	571	173	458	627	276	954	1036	937	1056
20	491	765	948	105	664	622	796	152	929	290
21	888	454	286	818	90	233	504	986	445	252
22	848	360	708	258	481	822	801	297	917	401
23	63	185	692	684	200	672	727	268	972	355
24	415	94	145	835	207	136	546	613	513	637
25	733	383	812	420	46	906	8	237	157	1016
26	111	1023	393	862	772	528	165	474	600	409
27	746	876	499	508	718	30	1047	426	660	844
28	723	808	596	649	653	99	468	854	339	990
29	934	793	87	705	60	969	543	43	390	743
30	657	465	57	54	752	449	830	25	20	962
31	755	370	35	569	274	1054	103	150	452	231
32	250	256	295	183	670	353	833	611	381	904
33	1014	860	472	874	28	842	647	852	791	967
34	741	52	23	368	1052	229	181	609	858	840
35	965	366	607	364	893	895	309	78	758	897
36	581	436	321	311	343	329	373	80	882	712
37	785	760	679	523	38	899	431	554	978	583
38	994	212	572	438	174	262	459	323	628	118
39	277	313	955	559	1037	345	938	1003	1057	331
40	492	485	766	375	949	912	106	82	665	304
41	623	884	797	141	153	714	930	826	291	787
42	889	781	455	762	287	983	819	681	91	634
43	234	525	505	805	987	40	446	566	253	901
44	849	226	361	433	709	551	259	556	482	301
45	823	980	802	223	298	585	918	588	402	996
46	64	128	186	214	693	921	685	574	201	14
47	673	440	728	591	269	176	973	618	356	264
48	416	405	95	461	146	870	836	325	208	999
49	137	630	547	124	614	120	514	67	638	279

POWER RESIDUES

	0	1	2	3	4	5	6	7	8	9
0	1	2	4	8	16	32	64	128	256	512
1	1024	987	913	765	469	938	815	569	77	154
2	308	616	171	342	684	307	614	167	334	668
3	275	550	39	78	156	312	624	187	374	748
4	435	870	679	297	594	127	254	508	1016	971
5	881	701	341	682	303	606	151	302	604	147
6	294	588	115	230	460	920	779	497	994	927
7	793	525	1050	1039	1017	973	885	709	357	714
8	367	734	407	814	567	73	146	292	584	107
9	214	428	856	651	241	482	964	867	673	285
10	570	79	158	316	632	203	406	812	563	65
11	130	260	520	1040	1019	977	893	725	389	778
12	495	990	919	777	493	986	911	761	461	922
13	783	505	1010	959	857	653	245	490	980	899
14	737	413	826	591	121	242	484	968	875	689
15	317	634	207	414	828	595	129	258	516	1032
16	1003	945	829	597	133	266	532	3	6	12
17	24	48	96	192	384	768	475	950	839	617
18	173	346	692	323	646	231	462	924	787	513
19	1026	991	921	781	501	1002	943	825	589	117
20	234	468	936	811	561	61	122	244	488	976
21	891	721	381	762	463	926	791	521	1042	1023
22	985	909	757	453	906	751	441	882	703	345
23	690	319	638	215	430	860	659	257	514	1028
24	995	929	797	533	5	10	20	40	80	160
25	320	640	219	438	876	691	321	642	223	446
26	892	723	385	770	479	958	855	649	237	474
27	948	835	609	157	314	628	195	390	780	499
28	998	935	809	557	53	106	212	424	848	635
29	209	418	836	611	161	322	644	227	454	908
30	755	449	898	735	409	818	575	89	178	356
31	712	363	726	391	782	503	1006	951	841	621
32	181	362	724	387	774	487	974	887	713	365
33	730	399	798	535	9	18	36	72	144	288
34	576	91	182	364	728	395	790	519	1038	1015
35	969	877	693	325	650	239	478	956	851	641
36	221	442	884	707	353	706	351	702	343	686
37	311	622	183	366	732	403	806	551	41	82
38	164	328	656	251	502	1004	947	833	605	149
39	298	596	131	262	524	1048	1035	1009	957	853
40	645	229	458	916	771	481	962	863	665	269
41	538	15	30	60	120	240	480	960	859	657
42	253	506	1012	963	865	669	277	554	47	94
43	188	376	752	443	886	711	361	722	383	766
44	471	942	823	585	109	218	436	872	683	305
45	610	159	318	636	211	422	844	627	193	386
46	772	483	966	871	681	301	602	143	286	572
47	83	166	332	664	267	534	7	14	28	56
48	112	224	448	896	731	401	802	543	25	50
49	100	200	400	800	539	17	34	68	136	272

P = 1061

INDICES

	0	1	2	3	4	5	6	7	8	9
50	734	194	384	315	813	131	421	957	47	518
51	907	561	9	189	238	1039	158	1030	1017	347
52	112	217	1024	940	394	71	863	1005	773	696
53	529	1059	166	243	475	333	601	924	410	494
54	747	642	877	487	500	688	509	768	719	539
55	31	377	1048	577	427	951	661	283	845	914
56	724	204	809	108	597	1044	650	84	654	17
57	100	667	469	738	855	306	340	676	991	625
58	935	946	794	886	88	443	706	799	61	198
59	970	143	544	731	44	155	391	163	744	716
60	658	594	466	932	58	388	55	828	753	272
61	450	293	831	1012	26	789	21	179	963	891
62	756	319	371	783	36	976	570	457	275	1035
63	1055	764	104	621	151	289	453	817	232	985
64	251	359	257	821	296	400	184	683	671	267
65	354	93	834	135	612	636	382	419	905	236
66	1015	1022	861	527	473	408	875	507	29	425
67	843	807	648	98	853	989	792	704	968	42
68	742	464	53	448	24	961	369	568	1053	149
69	230	255	182	352	610	903	859	873	841	851
70	966	51	367	228	608	839	365	363	894	77
71	896	435	310	328	79	711	759	522	898	553
72	582	211	437	261	322	117	312	558	344	1002
73	330	484	374	911	81	303	883	140	713	825
74	786	780	761	982	680	633	524	804	39	565
75	900	225	432	550	555	300	979	222	584	587
76	995	127	213	920	573	13	439	590	175	617
77	263	404	460	869	324	998	629	123	119	66
78	278	193	314	130	956	517	560	188	1038	1029
79	346	216	939	70	1004	695	1058	242	332	923
80	493	641	486	687	767	538	376	576	950	282
81	913	203	107	1043	83	16	666	737	305	675
82	624	945	885	442	798	197	142	730	154	162
83	715	593	931	387	827	271	292	1011	788	178
84	890	318	782	975	456	1034	763	620	288	816
85	984	358	820	399	682	266	92	134	635	418
86	235	1021	526	407	506	424	806	97	988	703
87	41	463	447	960	567	148	254	351	902	872
88	850	50	227	838	362	76	434	327	710	521
89	552	210	260	116	557	1001	483	910	302	139
90	824	779	981	632	803	564	224	549	299	221
91	586	126	919	12	589	616	403	868	997	122
92	65	192	129	516	187	1028	215	69	694	241
93	922	640	686	537	575	281	202	1042	15	736
94	674	944	441	196	729	161	592	386	270	1010
95	177	317	974	1033	619	815	357	398	265	133
96	417	1020	406	423	96	702	462	959	147	350
97	871	49	837	75	326	520	209	115	1000	909
98	138	778	631	563	548	220	125	11	615	867
99	121	191	515	1027	68	240	639	536	280	1041

POWER RESIDUES

	0	1	2	3	4	5	6	7	8	9
50	544	27	54	108	216	432	864	667	273	546
51	31	62	124	248	496	992	923	785	509	1018
52	975	889	717	373	746	431	862	663	265	530
53	1060	1059	1057	1053	1045	1029	997	933	805	549
54	37	74	148	296	592	123	246	492	984	907
55	753	445	890	719	377	754	447	894	727	393
56	786	511	1022	983	905	749	437	874	687	313
57	626	191	382	764	467	934	807	553	45	90
58	180	360	720	379	758	455	910	759	457	914
59	767	473	946	831	601	141	282	564	67	134
60	268	536	11	22	44	88	176	352	704	347
61	694	327	654	247	494	988	915	769	477	954
62	847	633	205	410	820	579	97	194	388	776
63	491	982	903	745	429	858	655	249	498	996
64	931	801	541	21	42	84	168	336	672	283
65	566	71	142	284	568	75	150	300	600	139
66	278	556	51	102	204	408	816	571	81	162
67	324	648	235	470	940	819	577	93	186	372
68	744	427	854	647	233	466	932	803	545	29
69	58	116	232	464	928	795	529	1058	1055	1049
70	1037	1013	965	869	677	293	586	111	222	444
71	888	715	369	738	415	830	599	137	274	548
72	35	70	140	280	560	59	118	236	472	944
73	827	593	125	250	500	1000	939	817	573	85
74	170	340	680	299	598	135	270	540	19	38
75	76	152	304	608	155	310	620	179	358	716
76	371	742	423	846	631	201	402	804	547	33
77	66	132	264	528	1056	1051	1041	1021	981	901
78	741	421	842	623	185	370	740	419	838	615
79	169	338	676	291	582	103	206	412	824	587
80	113	226	452	904	747	433	866	671	281	562
81	63	126	252	504	1008	955	849	637	213	426
82	852	643	225	450	900	739	417	834	607	153
83	306	612	163	326	652	243	486	972	883	705
84	349	698	335	670	279	558	55	110	220	440
85	880	699	337	674	287	574	87	174	348	696
86	331	662	263	526	1052	1043	1025	989	917	773
87	485	970	879	697	333	666	271	542	23	46
88	92	184	368	736	411	822	583	105	210	420
89	840	619	177	354	708	355	710	359	718	375
90	750	439	878	695	329	658	255	510	1020	979
91	897	733	405	810	559	57	114	228	456	912
92	763	465	930	799	537	13	26	52	104	208
93	416	832	603	145	290	580	99	198	396	792
94	523	1046	1031	1001	941	821	581	101	202	404
95	808	555	49	98	196	392	784	507	1014	967
96	873	685	309	618	175	350	700	339	678	295
97	590	119	238	476	952	843	625	189	378	756
98	451	902	743	425	850	639	217	434	868	675
99	289	578	95	190	380	760	459	918	775	489

P = 1061

INDICES

	0	1	2	3	4	5	6	7	8	9
100	735	943	195	160	385	1009	316	1032	814	397
101	132	1019	422	701	958	349	48	74	519	114
102	908	777	562	219	10	866	190	1026	239	535
103	1040	942	159	1008	1031	396	1018	700	348	73
104	113	776	218	865	1025	534	941	1007	395	699
105	72	775	864	533	1006	698	774	532	697	531
106	530	0								

POWER RESIDUES

	0	1	2	3	4	5	6	7	8	9
100	978	895	729	397	794	527	1054	1047	1033	1005
101	949	837	613	165	330	660	259	518	1036	1011
102	961	861	661	261	522	1044	1027	993	925	789
103	517	1034	1007	953	845	629	197	394	788	515
104	1030	999	937	813	565	69	138	276	552	43
105	86	172	344	688	315	630	199	398	796	531
106										

P = 1063

INDICES

	0	1	2	3	4	5	6	7	8	9
0		0	1048	1	1034	939	1049	118	1020	2
1	925	718	1035	390	104	940	1006	900	1050	986
2	911	119	704	742	1021	816	376	3	90	481
3	926	709	992	719	886	1057	1036	444	972	391
4	897	687	105	219	690	941	728	308	1007	236
5	802	901	362	683	1051	595	76	987	467	543
6	912	7	695	120	978	267	705	58	872	743
7	1043	108	1022	52	430	817	958	836	377	115
8	883	4	673	616	91	777	205	482	676	966
9	927	508	714	710	294	863	993	316	222	720
10	788	289	887	325	348	1058	669	255	1037	140
11	581	445	62	195	973	619	453	392	529	1018
12	898	374	1055	688	681	693	106	881	964	220
13	253	451	691	42	44	942	858	761	729	278
14	1029	309	94	46	1008	358	38	237	416	262
15	803	400	944	902	822	586	363	918	101	684
16	869	860	1052	259	659	596	602	551	77	780
17	763	988	191	298	468	934	662	544	952	731
18	913	755	494	8	700	321	696	556	280	121
19	849	629	979	876	302	268	208	1031	706	464
20	774	59	275	599	873	564	311	744	334	642
21	1044	612	655	109	241	96	1023	827	126	53
22	567	228	431	485	48	818	181	83	959	796
23	605	837	439	1010	378	185	515	116	1004	814
24	884	217	360	5	1041	113	674	314	667	617
25	679	40	92	398	867	778	950	554	206	562
26	239	483	437	215	677	560	28	967	30	418
27	928	147	844	509	747	472	715	969	264	711
28	1015	35	295	771	80	864	32	805	994	738
29	344	317	24	168	223	420	402	721	248	70
30	789	337	386	290	930	946	888	624	808	326
31	572	783	349	149	904	1059	87	592	670	137
32	855	256	846	824	1038	144	245	141	645	426
33	582	511	588	446	537	997	63	892	766	196
34	749	365	974	354	177	620	284	172	454	474
35	920	393	648	502	530	1047	938	1019	717	103
36	899	910	741	375	480	991	1056	971	686	689
37	307	801	682	75	542	694	266	871	107	429
38	835	882	615	204	965	713	862	221	288	347
39	254	580	194	452	1017	1054	692	963	450	43
40	760	1028	45	37	261	943	585	100	859	658
41	550	762	297	661	730	493	320	279	628	301
42	1030	773	598	310	641	654	95	125	227	47
43	82	604	1009	514	813	359	112	666	39	866
44	553	238	214	27	417	843	471	263	34	79
45	804	343	167	401	69	385	945	807	782	903
46	591	854	823	244	425	587	996	765	364	176
47	171	919	501	937	102	740	990	685	800	541
48	870	834	203	861	346	193	1053	449	1027	260
49	99	549	660	319	300	597	653	226	603	812

POWER RESIDUES

	0	1	2	3	4	5	6	7	8	9
0	1	3	9	27	81	243	729	61	183	549
1	584	689	1004	886	532	533	536	545	572	653
2	896	562	623	806	292	876	502	443	266	798
3	268	804	286	858	448	281	843	403	146	438
4	251	753	133	399	134	402	143	429	224	672
5	953	733	73	219	657	908	598	731	67	201
6	603	746	112	336	1008	898	568	641	860	454
7	299	897	565	632	833	373	56	168	504	449
8	284	852	430	227	681	980	814	316	948	718
9	28	84	252	756	142	426	215	645	872	490
10	407	158	474	359	14	42	126	378	71	213
11	639	854	436	245	735	79	237	711	7	21
12	63	189	567	638	851	427	218	654	899	571
13	650	887	535	542	563	626	815	319	957	745
14	109	327	981	817	325	975	799	271	813	313
15	939	691	1010	904	586	695	1022	940	694	1019
16	931	667	938	688	1001	877	505	452	293	879
17	511	470	347	1041	997	865	469	344	1032	970
18	784	226	678	971	787	235	705	1052	1030	964
19	766	172	516	485	392	113	339	1017	925	649
20	884	526	515	482	383	86	258	774	196	588
21	701	1040	994	856	442	263	789	241	723	43
22	129	387	98	294	882	520	497	428	221	663
23	926	652	893	553	596	725	49	147	441	260
24	780	214	642	863	463	326	978	808	298	894
25	556	605	752	130	390	107	321	963	763	163
26	489	404	149	447	278	834	376	65	195	585
27	692	1013	913	613	776	202	606	755	139	417
28	188	564	629	824	346	1038	988	838	388	101
29	303	909	601	740	94	282	846	412	173	519
30	494	419	194	582	683	986	832	370	47	141
31	423	206	618	791	247	741	97	291	873	493
32	416	185	555	602	743	103	309	927	655	902
33	580	677	968	778	208	624	809	301	903	583
34	686	995	859	451	290	870	484	389	104	312
35	936	682	983	823	343	1029	961	757	145	435
36	242	726	52	156	468	341	1023	943	703	1046
37	1012	910	604	749	121	363	26	78	234	702
38	1043	1003	883	523	506	455	302	906	592	713
39	13	39	117	351	1053	1033	973	793	253	759
40	151	453	296	888	538	551	590	707	1058	1048
41	1018	928	658	911	607	758	148	444	269	807
42	295	885	529	524	509	464	329	987	835	379
43	74	222	666	935	679	974	796	262	786	232
44	696	1025	949	721	37	111	333	999	871	487
45	398	131	393	116	348	1044	1006	892	550	587
46	698	1031	967	775	199	597	728	58	174	522
47	503	446	275	825	349	1047	1015	919	631	830
48	364	29	87	261	783	223	669	944	706	1055
49	1039	991	847	415	182	546	575	662	923	643

P = 1063

INDICES

	0	1	2	3	4	5	6	7	8	9
50	665	552	26	470	78	166	384	781	853	424
51	764	170	936	989	540	202	192	1026	548	299
52	225	664	469	383	423	935	201	547	663	422
53	546	545	14	15	953	132	16	732	404	954
54	914	1000	133	756	830	17	495	723	733	9
55	458	405	701	233	955	322	250	915	697	609
56	1001	557	21	134	281	72	757	122	66	831
57	850	129	18	630	791	496	980	522	724	877
58	330	734	303	339	10	269	154	459	209	633
59	406	1032	388	702	707	895	234	465	56	956
60	775	292	323	60	372	251	276	414	916	600
61	932	698	874	273	610	565	794	1002	312	948
62	558	745	769	22	335	570	135	643	890	282
63	1045	478	73	613	578	758	656	626	123	110
64	841	67	242	499	832	97	810	851	1024	199
65	130	828	231	19	127	328	631	54	412	792
66	568	576	497	229	574	981	432	161	523	486
67	983	725	49	785	878	819	752	331	182	434
68	735	84	351	304	960	638	340	797	163	11
69	606	151	270	838	158	155	440	525	460	1011
70	906	210	379	368	634	186	488	407	516	1061
71	1033	117	924	389	1005	985	703	815	89	708
72	885	443	896	218	727	235	361	594	466	6
73	977	57	1042	51	957	114	672	776	675	507
74	293	315	787	324	668	139	61	618	528	373
75	680	880	252	41	857	277	93	357	415	399
76	821	917	868	258	601	779	190	933	951	754
77	699	555	848	875	207	463	274	563	333	611
78	240	826	566	484	180	795	438	184	1003	216
79	1040	313	678	397	949	561	436	559	29	146
80	746	968	1014	770	31	737	23	419	247	336
81	929	623	571	148	86	136	845	143	644	510
82	536	891	748	353	283	473	647	1046	716	909
83	479	970	306	74	265	428	614	712	287	579
84	1016	962	759	36	584	657	296	492	627	772
85	640	124	81	513	111	865	213	842	33	342
86	68	806	590	243	995	175	500	739	799	833
87	345	448	98	318	652	811	25	165	852	169
88	539	1025	224	382	200	421	13	131	403	999
89	829	722	457	232	249	608	20	71	65	128
90	790	521	329	338	153	632	387	894	55	291
91	371	413	931	272	793	947	768	569	889	477
92	577	625	840	498	809	198	230	327	411	575
93	573	160	982	784	751	433	350	637	162	150
94	157	524	905	367	487	1060	923	984	88	442
95	726	593	976	50	671	506	786	138	527	879
96	856	356	820	257	189	753	847	462	332	825
97	179	183	1039	396	435	145	1013	736	246	622
98	85	142	535	352	646	908	305	427	286	961
99	583	491	639	512	212	341	589	174	798	447

POWER RESIDUES

	0	1	2	3	4	5	6	7	8	9
50	866	472	353	1059	1051	1027	955	739	91	273
51	819	331	993	853	433	236	708	1061	1057	1045
52	1009	901	577	668	941	697	1028	958	748	118
53	354	1062	1060	1054	1036	982	820	334	1002	880
54	514	479	374	59	177	531	530	527	518	491
55	410	167	501	440	257	771	187	561	620	797
56	265	795	259	777	205	615	782	220	660	917
57	625	812	310	930	664	929	661	920	634	839
58	391	110	330	990	844	406	155	465	332	996
59	862	460	317	951	727	55	165	495	422	203
60	609	764	166	498	431	230	690	1007	895	559
61	614	779	211	633	836	382	83	249	747	115
62	345	1035	979	811	307	921	637	848	418	191
63	573	656	905	589	704	1049	1021	937	685	992
64	850	424	209	627	818	328	984	826	352	1056
65	1042	1000	874	496	425	212	636	845	409	164
66	492	413	176	528	521	500	437	248	744	106
67	318	954	736	82	246	738	88	264	792	250
68	750	124	372	53	159	477	368	41	123	369
69	44	132	396	125	375	62	186	558	611	770
70	184	552	593	716	22	66	198	594	719	31
71	93	279	837	385	92	276	828	358	11	33
72	99	297	891	547	578	671	950	724	46	138
73	414	179	537	548	581	680	977	805	289	867
74	475	362	23	69	207	621	800	274	822	340
75	1020	934	676	965	769	181	543	566	635	842
76	400	137	411	170	510	467	338	1014	916	622
77	803	283	849	421	200	600	737	85	255	765
78	169	507	458	311	933	673	956	742	100	300
79	900	574	659	914	616	785	229	687	998	868
80	478	371	50	150	450	287	861	457	308	924
81	646	875	499	434	239	717	25	75	225	675
82	962	760	154	462	323	969	781	217	651	890
83	544	569	644	869	481	380	77	231	693	1016
84	922	640	857	445	272	816	322	966	772	190
85	570	647	878	508	461	320	960	754	136	408
86	161	483	386	95	285	855	439	254	762	160
87	480	377	68	204	612	773	193	579	674	959
88	751	127	381	80	240	720	34	102	306	918
89	628	821	337	1011	907	595	722	40	120	360
90	17	51	153	459	314	942	700	1037	985	829
91	361	20	60	180	540	557	608	761	157	471
92	350	1050	1024	946	712	10	30	90	270	810
93	304	912	610	767	175	525	512	473	356	5
94	15	45	135	405	152	456	305	915	619	794
95	256	768	178	534	539	554	599	734	76	228
96	684	989	841	397	128	384	89	267	801	277
97	831	367	38	114	342	1026	952	730	64	192
98	576	665	932	670	947	715	19	57	171	513
99	476	365	32	96	288	864	466	335	1005	889

P = 1063

INDICES

	0	1	2	3	4	5	6	7	8	9
100	651	164	538	381	12	998	456	607	64	520
101	152	893	370	271	767	476	839	197	410	159
102	750	636	156	366	922	441	975	505	526	355
103	188	461	178	395	1012	621	534	907	285	490
104	211	173	650	380	455	519	369	475	409	635
105	921	504	187	394	533	489	649	518	408	503
106	532	517	531							

POWER RESIDUES

	0	1	2	3	4	5	6	7	8	9
100	541	560	617	788	238	714	16	48	144	432
101	233	699	1034	976	802	280	840	394	119	357
102	8	24	72	216	648	881	517	488	401	140
103	420	197	591	710	4	12	36	108	324	972
104	790	244	732	70	210	630	827	355	2	6
105	18	54	162	486	395	122	366	35	105	315
106	945	709								

P = 1069

INDICES

	0	1	2	3	4	5	6	7	8	9
0		0	867	202	666	256	1	707	465	404
1	55	259	868	1058	506	458	264	824	203	686
2	922	909	58	497	667	512	857	606	305	1044
3	257	369	63	461	623	963	2	690	485	192
4	721	947	708	557	925	660	296	371	466	346
5	311	1026	656	16	405	515	104	888	843	1038
6	56	841	168	43	930	246	260	1006	422	699
7	762	742	869	399	489	714	284	966	1059	184
8	520	808	746	65	507	12	356	178	724	734
9	459	697	95	571	170	942	265	74	145	663
10	110	449	825	671	455	97	883	1013	204	854
11	314	892	971	786	687	753	642	394	837	463
12	923	518	640	81	1035	768	910	85	729	759
13	45	978	59	325	805	862	221	141	498	92
14	561	573	541	249	668	232	198	548	288	684
15	513	695	83	160	765	625	858	618	1051	218
16	319	136	607	162	545	717	932	471	306	1048
17	879	22	155	902	1045	151	523	172	533	255
18	258	823	496	1043	962	946	370	15	1037	245
19	741	965	64	733	941	448	1012	785	462	767
20	977	140	248	683	624	135	470	901	254	945
21	964	784	682	944	812	813	3	8	653	601
22	113	814	691	40	770	916	585	4	486	28
23	552	100	441	9	193	627	636	386	262	654
24	722	1033	317	1010	439	602	948	676	834	267
25	567	114	709	756	952	214	528	815	558	329
26	912	380	777	692	926	272	124	936	604	41
27	661	860	20	899	1008	771	297	594	959	773
28	360	917	372	445	340	76	48	586	467	580
29	31	276	1065	5	347	226	87	865	483	487
30	312	196	494	651	950	29	1027	620	564	873
31	424	553	657	377	417	299	850	101	17	235
32	118	147	1003	442	406	502	1029	1056	344	10
33	516	616	731	26	270	194	105	107	847	988
34	678	628	889	1053	1022	955	701	637	844	390
35	1018	596	322	387	1039	998	332	665	54	263
36	57	304	622	720	295	655	842	929	761	283
37	745	723	169	109	882	970	836	1034	44	220
38	540	287	764	318	931	154	532	961	740	1011
39	247	253	811	112	584	440	261	438	566	527
40	776	603	1007	359	47	1064	482	949	423	849
41	1002	343	269	677	700	321	53	294	744	835
42	763	739	583	775	481	268	743	480	611	451
43	612	568	870	350	875	434	452	115	400	632
44	980	750	613	710	490	990	907	886	569	757
45	715	138	384	897	871	953	285	292	895	362
46	351	215	967	984	240	827	876	529	1060	645
47	426	820	435	816	185	130	61	420	453	559
48	521	680	832	338	116	330	809	609	238	364
49	401	913	747	800	475	919	633	381	66	409

POWER RESIDUES

	0	1	2	3	4	5	6	7	8	9
0	1	6	36	216	227	293	689	927	217	233
1	329	905	85	510	922	187	53	318	839	758
2	272	563	171	1026	811	590	333	929	229	305
3	761	290	671	819	638	621	519	976	511	928
4	223	269	545	63	378	130	780	404	286	647
5	675	843	782	416	358	10	60	360	22	132
6	792	476	718	32	192	83	498	850	824	668
7	801	530	1042	907	97	582	285	641	639	627
8	555	123	738	152	912	127	762	296	707	1035
9	865	914	139	834	728	92	552	105	630	573
10	231	317	833	722	56	336	947	337	953	373
11	100	600	393	220	251	437	484	766	320	851
12	830	704	1017	757	266	527	1024	799	518	970
13	475	712	1065	1045	925	205	161	966	451	568
14	201	137	822	656	729	98	588	321	857	866
15	920	175	1050	955	385	172	1032	847	806	560
16	153	918	163	978	523	1000	655	723	62	372
17	94	564	177	1062	1027	817	626	549	87	522
18	994	619	507	904	79	474	706	1029	829	698
19	981	541	39	234	335	941	301	737	146	876
20	980	535	3	18	108	648	681	879	998	643
21	651	699	987	577	255	461	628	561	159	954
22	379	136	816	620	513	940	295	701	999	649
23	687	915	145	870	944	319	845	794	488	790
24	464	646	669	807	566	189	65	390	202	143
25	858	872	956	391	208	179	5	30	180	11
26	66	396	238	359	16	96	576	249	425	412
27	334	935	265	521	988	583	291	677	855	854
28	848	812	596	369	76	456	598	381	148	888
29	1052	967	457	604	417	364	46	276	587	315
30	821	650	693	951	361	28	168	1008	703	1011
31	721	50	300	731	110	660	753	242	383	160
32	960	415	352	1043	913	133	798	512	934	259
33	485	772	356	1067	1057	997	637	615	483	760
34	284	635	603	411	328	899	49	294	695	963
35	433	460	622	525	1012	727	86	516	958	403
36	280	611	459	616	489	796	500	862	896	31
37	186	47	282	623	531	1048	943	313	809	578
38	261	497	844	788	452	574	237	353	1049	949
39	349	1025	805	554	117	702	1005	685	903	73
40	438	490	802	536	9	54	324	875	974	499
41	856	860	884	1028	823	662	765	314	815	614
42	477	724	68	408	310	791	470	682	885	1034
43	859	878	992	607	435	472	694	957	397	244
44	395	232	323	869	938	283	629	567	195	101
45	606	429	436	478	730	104	624	537	15	90
46	540	33	198	119	714	8	48	288	659	747
47	206	167	1002	667	795	494	826	680	873	962
48	427	424	406	298	719	38	228	299	725	74
49	444	526	1018	763	302	743	182	23	138	828

P = 1069

INDICES

	0	1	2	3	4	5	6	7	8	9
50	366	673	981	778	508	705	555	182	751	693
51	13	38	327	224	614	927	357	630	128	36
52	711	273	179	164	576	353	491	125	725	994
53	71	374	991	937	735	201	403	457	908	605
54	460	191	659	1025	887	42	698	713	807	177
55	570	662	96	891	393	80	758	861	572	547
56	159	217	716	21	171	1042	244	447	139	900
57	943	600	915	99	385	1009	266	213	379	935
58	898	772	75	275	864	650	872	298	146	1055
59	25	987	954	595	664	719	282	969	286	960
60	111	526	1063	342	293	774	450	433	749	885
61	896	361	826	819	419	337	363	918	672	181
62	223	35	352	373	456	1024	176	79	216	446
63	98	934	649	986	968	341	884	336	34	78
64	985	77	1014	209	802	1015	241	49	205	229
65	301	210	828	587	855	166	143	803	877	468
66	315	957	415	1016	530	581	893	473	69	242
67	1061	32	972	795	974	50	646	277	787	781
68	477	206	427	1066	688	397	852	230	821	6
69	754	578	500	302	436	348	643	703	189	211
70	817	227	395	308	121	829	186	88	838	591
71	797	588	131	866	464	505	921	856	62	484
72	924	310	103	167	421	488	519	355	94	144
73	454	313	641	639	728	804	560	197	82	1050
74	544	878	522	495	1036	940	976	469	681	652
75	769	551	635	316	833	951	911	123	19	958
76	339	30	86	493	563	416	117	1028	730	846
77	1021	1017	331	621	760	881	539	531	810	565
78	46	1001	52	582	610	874	979	906	383	894
79	239	425	60	831	237	474	365	554	326	127
80	575	70	402	658	806	392	158	243	914	378
81	863	24	281	1062	748	418	222	175	648	33
82	801	300	142	414	68	973	476	851	499	188
83	120	796	920	102	93	727	543	975	634	18
84	562	1020	538	51	382	236	574	157	280	647
85	67	119	542	537	279	278	410	148	250	430
86	411	788	367	1004	669	90	149	782	674	443
87	233	996	251	478	982	407	199	598	431	207
88	779	503	549	904	412	428	509	1030	289	792
89	789	1067	706	1057	685	511	368	689	556	345
90	514	840	1005	398	183	11	696	73	670	853
91	752	517	84	324	91	231	694	617	161	1047
92	150	822	14	732	766	134	783	7	39	27
93	626	1032	675	755	328	271	859	593	444	579
94	225	195	619	376	234	501	615	106	1052	389
95	997	303	928	108	219	153	252	437	358	848
96	320	738	479	349	631	989	137	291	983	644
97	129	679	608	799	408	704	37	629	163	993
98	200	190	712	890	546	1041	599	212	274	1054
99	718	525	432	818	180	1023	933	335	208	228

POWER RESIDUES

	0	1	2	3	4	5	6	7	8	9
50	692	945	325	881	1010	715	14	84	504	886
51	1040	895	25	150	900	55	330	911	121	726
52	80	480	742	176	1056	991	601	399	256	467
53	664	777	386	178	1068	1063	1033	853	842	776
54	380	142	852	836	740	164	984	559	147	882
55	1016	751	230	311	797	506	898	43	258	479
56	736	140	840	764	308	779	398	250	431	448
57	550	93	558	141	846	800	524	1006	691	939
58	289	665	783	422	394	226	287	653	711	1059
59	1009	709	1047	937	277	593	351	1037	877	986
60	571	219	245	401	268	539	27	162	972	487
61	784	428	430	442	514	946	331	917	157	942
62	307	773	362	34	204	155	930	235	341	977
63	517	964	439	496	838	752	236	347	1013	733
64	122	732	116	696	969	469	676	849	818	632
65	585	303	749	218	239	365	52	312	803	542
66	45	270	551	99	594	357	4	24	144	864
67	908	103	618	501	868	932	247	413	340	971
68	481	748	212	203	149	894	19	114	684	897
69	37	222	263	509	916	151	906	91	546	69
70	414	346	1007	697	975	505	892	7	42	252
71	443	520	982	547	75	450	562	165	990	595
72	363	40	240	371	88	528	1030	835	734	128
73	768	332	923	193	89	534	1066	1051	961	421
74	388	190	71	426	418	370	82	492	814	608
75	441	508	910	115	690	933	253	449	556	129
76	774	368	70	420	382	154	924	199	125	750
77	224	275	581	279	605	423	400	262	503	880
78	1004	679	867	926	211	197	113	678	861	890
79	1064	1039	889	1058	1003	673	831	710	1053	973
80	493	820	644	657	735	134	804	548	81	486
81	778	392	214	215	221	257	473	700	993	613
82	471	688	921	181	17	102	612	465	652	705
83	1023	793	482	754	248	419	376	118	708	1041
84	901	61	366	58	348	1019	769	338	959	409
85	316	827	686	909	109	654	717	26	156	936
86	271	557	135	810	584	297	713	2	12	72
87	432	454	586	309	785	434	466	658	741	170
88	1020	775	374	106	636	609	447	544	57	342
89	983	553	111	666	789	458	610	453	580	273
90	569	207	173	1038	883	1022	787	446	538	21
91	126	756	260	491	808	572	225	281	617	495
92	832	716	20	120	720	44	264	515	952	367
93	64	384	166	996	631	579	267	533	1060	1015
94	745	194	95	570	213	209	185	41	246	407
95	304	755	254	455	592	345	1001	661	759	278
96	599	387	184	35	210	191	77	462	634	597
97	375	112	672	825	674	837	746	200	131	786
98	440	502	874	968	463	640	633	591	339	965
99	445	532	1054	979	529	1036	871	950	355	1061

P = 1069

INDICES

	0	1	2	3	4	5	6	7	8	9
100	165	956	472	794	780	396	577	702	307	590
101	504	309	354	638	1049	939	550	122	492	845
102	880	1000	905	830	126	391	23	174	413	187
103	726	1019	156	536	429	89	995	597	903	791
104	510	839	72	323	1046	133	1031	592	375	388
105	152	737	290	798	992	1040	524	334	793	589
106	938	999	173	535	790	132	736	333	534	

POWER RESIDUES

	0	1	2	3	4	5	6	7	8	9
100	1021	781	410	322	863	902	67	402	274	575
101	243	389	196	107	642	645	663	771	350	1031
102	841	770	344	995	625	543	51	306	767	326
103	887	1046	931	241	377	124	744	188	59	354
104	1055	985	565	183	29	174	1044	919	169	1014
105	739	158	948	343	989	589	327	893	13	78
106	468	670	813	602	405	292	683	891		

P = 1087

INDICES

	0	1	2	3	4	5	6	7	8	9
0		0	758	1	430	957	759	519	102	2
1	629	921	431	7	191	958	860	882	760	1029
2	301	520	593	21	103	828	765	3	949	257
3	630	911	532	922	554	390	432	477	701	8
4	1059	298	192	146	265	959	779	195	861	1038
5	500	883	437	245	761	792	621	1030	1015	611
6	302	161	583	521	204	964	594	641	226	22
7	62	178	104	230	149	829	373	354	766	838
8	731	4	1056	638	950	753	904	258	1023	55
9	631	526	451	912	953	900	533	1009	710	923
10	172	268	555	944	109	391	1003	796	433	458
11	464	478	293	603	702	978	687	9	283	315
12	1060	756	919	299	255	699	193	619	962	147
13	636	449	266	462	313	960	984	986	780	726
14	820	196	936	928	862	128	988	1039	907	289
15	501	654	45	884	26	782	438	998	510	246
16	403	540	762	242	728	793	310	537	622	14
17	425	1031	576	822	1016	261	695	612	813	877
18	303	870	198	162	123	348	584	717	625	522
19	572	938	205	505	681	965	382	141	595	37
20	930	642	1026	776	227	169	616	23	867	864
21	63	118	675	179	468	17	105	344	130	231
22	136	889	150	1078	1051	830	275	990	374	58
23	650	355	359	895	767	66	1041	839	1073	562
24	732	412	428	5	591	909	1057	1036	1013	639
25	371	751	951	942	291	754	634	724	905	996
26	308	259	121	503	1024	116	134	56	1071	1034
27	632	114	656	527	658	663	452	90	398	913
28	492	47	954	529	608	901	600	817	534	678
29	886	1010	660	323	711	482	579	924	1047	28
30	173	665	326	269	803	32	556	852	784	945
31	454	568	110	363	670	392	182	440	1004	92
32	75	797	212	825	434	835	1000	459	400	714
33	465	409	1068	479	209	512	294	915	772	604
34	97	746	703	471	248	979	494	235	688	515
35	1019	10	367	405	284	49	485	316	549	85
36	1061	972	542	757	956	101	920	190	881	300
37	20	764	256	531	389	700	297	264	194	499
38	244	620	610	582	963	225	177	148	353	730
39	637	903	54	450	899	709	267	108	795	463
40	602	686	314	918	698	961	448	312	985	819
41	927	987	288	44	781	509	539	727	536	424
42	821	694	876	197	347	624	937	680	140	929
43	775	615	863	674	16	129	888	1050	989	649
44	894	1040	561	427	908	1012	750	290	723	307
45	502	133	1033	655	662	397	46	607	816	885
46	322	578	27	325	31	783	567	669	439	74
47	824	999	713	1067	511	771	745	247	234	1018
48	404	484	84	541	100	880	763	388	263	243
49	581	176	729	53	708	794	685	697	311	926

POWER RESIDUES

	0	1	2	3	4	5	6	7	8	9
0	1	3	9	27	81	243	729	13	39	117
1	351	1053	985	781	169	507	434	215	645	848
2	370	23	69	207	621	776	154	462	299	897
3	517	464	305	915	571	626	791	199	597	704
4	1025	901	529	500	413	152	456	281	843	355
5	1065	1021	889	493	392	89	267	801	229	687
6	974	748	70	210	630	803	235	705	1028	910
7	556	581	656	881	469	320	960	706	1031	919
8	583	662	899	523	482	359	1077	1057	997	817
9	277	831	319	957	697	1004	838	340	1020	886
10	484	365	8	24	72	216	648	857	397	104
11	312	936	634	815	271	813	265	795	211	633
12	812	262	786	184	552	569	620	773	145	435
13	218	654	875	451	266	798	220	660	893	505
14	428	197	591	686	971	739	43	129	387	74
15	222	666	911	559	590	683	962	712	1049	973
16	745	61	183	549	560	593	692	989	793	205
17	615	758	100	300	900	526	491	386	71	213
18	639	830	316	948	670	923	595	698	1007	847
19	367	14	42	126	378	47	141	423	182	546
20	551	566	611	746	64	192	576	641	836	334
21	1002	832	322	966	724	1085	1081	1069	1033	925
22	601	716	1061	1009	853	385	68	204	612	749
23	73	219	657	884	478	347	1041	949	673	932
24	622	779	163	489	380	53	159	477	344	1032
25	922	592	689	980	766	124	372	29	87	261
26	783	175	525	488	377	44	132	396	101	303
27	909	553	572	629	800	226	678	947	667	914
28	568	617	764	118	354	1062	1012	862	412	149
29	447	254	762	112	336	1008	850	376	41	123
30	369	20	60	180	540	533	512	449	260	780
31	166	498	407	134	402	119	357	1071	1039	943
32	655	878	460	293	879	463	302	906	544	545
33	548	557	584	665	908	550	563	602	719	1070
34	1036	934	628	797	217	651	866	424	185	555
35	578	647	854	388	77	231	693	992	802	232
36	696	1001	829	313	939	643	842	352	1056	994
37	808	250	750	76	228	684	965	721	1076	1054
38	988	790	196	588	677	944	658	887	487	374
39	35	105	315	945	661	896	514	455	278	834
40	328	984	778	160	480	353	1059	1003	835	331
41	993	805	241	723	1082	1072	1042	952	682	959
42	703	1022	892	502	419	170	510	443	242	726
43	4	12	36	108	324	972	742	52	156	468
44	317	951	679	950	676	941	649	860	406	131
45	393	92	276	828	310	930	616	761	109	327
46	981	769	133	399	110	330	990	796	214	642
47	839	343	1029	913	565	608	737	37	111	333
48	999	823	295	885	481	356	1068	1030	916	574
49	635	818	280	840	346	1038	940	646	851	379

P = 1087

INDICES

	0	1	2	3	4	5	6	7	8	9
50	43	538	423	875	623	139	614	15	1049	893
51	426	749	306	1032	396	815	577	30	668	823
52	1066	744	1017	83	879	262	175	707	696	42
53	874	613	892	305	814	667	743	878	706	873
54	304	742	872	871	328	329	199	847	330	163
55	335	200	124	271	848	349	70	331	585	153
56	164	718	805	336	626	474	201	523	280	125
57	573	34	272	939	489	849	206	969	350	506
58	558	71	682	80	332	966	1081	586	383	854
59	154	142	251	165	596	186	719	38	786	806
60	931	220	337	643	1084	627	1027	947	475	777
61	790	202	228	1054	524	170	456	281	617	982
62	126	24	240	574	868	570	35	865	342	273
63	64	589	940	119	112	490	676	1045	850	180
64	833	207	469	365	970	18	497	351	106	446
65	507	345	672	559	131	320	72	232	386	683
66	137	394	81	890	740	333	151	278	967	1079
67	184	1082	1052	238	587	831	444	384	276	442
68	855	991	418	155	375	857	143	59	1006	252
69	651	810	166	356	993	597	360	94	187	896
70	691	720	768	420	39	67	77	787	1042	737
71	807	840	157	932	1074	799	221	563	843	338
72	733	377	644	413	214	1085	429	518	628	6
73	859	1028	592	827	948	910	553	476	1058	145
74	778	1037	436	791	1014	160	203	640	61	229
75	372	837	1055	752	1022	525	952	1008	171	943
76	1002	457	292	977	282	755	254	618	635	461
77	983	725	935	127	906	653	25	997	402	241
78	309	13	575	260	812	869	122	716	571	504
79	381	36	1025	168	866	117	467	343	135	1077
80	274	57	358	65	1072	411	590	1035	370	941
81	633	995	120	115	1070	113	657	89	491	528
82	599	677	659	481	1046	664	802	851	453	362
83	181	91	211	834	399	408	208	914	96	470
84	493	514	366	48	548	971	955	189	19	530
85	296	498	609	224	352	902	898	107	601	917
86	447	818	287	508	535	693	346	679	774	673
87	887	648	560	1011	722	132	661	606	321	324
88	566	73	712	770	233	483	99	387	580	52
89	684	925	422	138	1048	748	395	29	1065	82
90	174	41	891	666	705	741	327	846	334	270
91	69	152	804	473	279	33	488	968	557	79
92	1080	853	250	185	785	219	1083	946	789	1053
93	455	981	239	569	341	588	111	1044	832	364
94	496	445	671	319	385	393	739	277	183	237
95	443	441	417	856	1005	809	992	93	690	419
96	76	736	156	798	842	376	213	517	858	826
97	552	144	435	159	60	836	1021	1007	1001	976
98	253	460	934	652	401	12	811	715	380	167
99	466	1076	357	410	369	994	1069	88	598	480

POWER RESIDUES

	0	1	2	3	4	5	6	7	8	9
50	50	150	450	263	789	193	579	650	863	415
51	158	474	335	1005	841	349	1047	967	727	7
52	21	63	189	567	614	755	91	273	819	283
53	849	373	32	96	288	864	418	167	501	416
54	161	483	362	1086	1084	1078	1060	1006	844	358
55	1074	1048	970	736	34	102	306	918	580	653
56	872	442	239	717	1064	1018	880	466	311	933
57	625	788	190	570	623	782	172	516	461	296
58	888	490	383	62	186	558	587	674	935	631
59	806	244	732	22	66	198	594	695	998	820
60	286	858	400	113	339	1017	877	457	284	852
61	382	59	177	531	506	431	206	618	767	127
62	381	56	168	504	425	188	564	605	728	10
63	30	90	270	810	256	768	130	390	83	249
64	747	67	201	603	722	1079	1063	1015	871	439
65	230	690	983	775	151	453	272	816	274	822
66	292	876	454	275	825	301	903	535	518	467
67	314	942	652	869	433	212	636	821	289	867
68	427	194	582	659	890	496	401	116	348	1044
69	958	700	1013	865	421	176	528	497	404	125
70	375	38	114	342	1026	904	538	527	494	395
71	98	294	882	472	329	987	787	187	561	596
72	701	1016	874	448	257	771	139	417	164	492
73	389	80	240	720	1073	1045	961	709	1040	946
74	664	905	541	536	521	476	341	1023	895	511
75	446	251	753	85	255	765	121	363	2	6
76	18	54	162	486	371	26	78	234	702	1019
77	883	475	338	1014	868	430	203	609	740	46
78	138	414	155	465	308	924	598	707	1034	928
79	610	743	55	165	495	398	107	321	963	715
80	1058	1000	826	304	912	562	599	710	1043	955
81	691	986	784	178	534	515	458	287	861	409
82	140	420	173	519	470	323	969	733	25	75
83	225	675	938	640	833	325	975	751	79	237
84	711	1046	964	718	1067	1027	907	547	554	575
85	638	827	307	921	589	680	953	685	968	730
86	16	48	144	432	209	627	794	208	624	785
87	181	543	542	539	530	503	422	179	537	524
88	485	368	17	51	153	459	290	870	436	221
89	663	902	532	509	440	233	699	1010	856	394
90	95	285	855	391	86	258	774	148	444	245
91	735	31	93	279	837	337	1011	859	403	122
92	366	11	33	99	297	891	499	410	143	429
93	200	600	713	1052	982	772	142	426	191	573
94	632	809	253	759	103	309	927	607	734	28
95	84	252	756	94	282	846	364	5	15	45
96	135	405	128	384	65	195	585	668	917	577
97	644	845	361	1083	1075	1051	979	763	115	345
98	1035	931	619	770	136	408	137	411	146	438
99	227	681	956	694	995	811	259	777	157	471

P = 1087

INDICES

	0	1	2	3	4	5	6	7	8	9
100	801	361	210	407	95	513	547	188	295	223
101	897	916	286	692	773	647	721	605	565	769
102	98	51	421	747	1064	40	704	845	68	472
103	487	78	249	218	788	980	340	1043	495	318
104	738	236	416	808	689	735	841	516	551	158
105	1020	975	933	11	379	1075	368	87	800	406
106	546	222	285	646	564	50	1063	844	486	217
107	339	317	415	734	550	974	378	86	545	645
108	1062	216	414	973	544	215	543			

POWER RESIDUES

	0	1	2	3	4	5	6	7	8	9
100	326	978	760	106	318	954	688	977	757	97
101	291	873	445	248	744	58	174	522	479	350
102	1050	976	754	88	264	792	202	606	731	19
103	57	171	513	452	269	807	247	741	49	147
104	441	236	708	1037	937	637	824	298	894	508
105	437	224	672	929	613	752	82	246	738	40
106	120	360	1080	1066	1024	898	520	473	332	996
107	814	268	804	238	714	1055	991	799	223	669
108	920	586	671	926	604	725				

P = 1091

INDICES

	0	1	2	3	4	5	6	7	8	9
0		0	1	520	2	370	521	998	3	1040
1	371	298	522	660	999	890	4	1059	1041	14
2	372	428	299	136	523	740	661	470	1000	283
3	891	788	5	818	1060	278	1042	213	15	90
4	373	624	429	899	300	320	137	780	524	906
5	741	489	662	961	471	668	1001	534	284	877
6	892	1047	789	948	6	1030	819	555	1061	656
7	279	316	1043	202	214	170	16	206	91	981
8	374	990	625	407	430	339	900	803	301	159
9	321	568	138	218	781	384	525	770	907	248
10	742	74	490	131	663	798	962	602	472	174
11	669	733	1002	809	535	506	285	610	878	967
12	893	596	1048	54	790	20	949	712	7	329
13	1031	351	820	1012	556	840	1062	367	657	425
14	280	210	317	958	1044	653	203	336	215	71
15	171	607	17	1009	207	68	92	95	982	391
16	375	44	991	833	626	98	408	183	431	230
17	340	1054	901	985	804	648	302	307	160	1083
18	322	394	569	477	139	583	219	267	782	378
19	385	147	526	34	771	460	908	47	249	700
20	743	1075	75	191	491	994	132	86	664	312
21	799	127	963	836	603	179	473	696	175	722
22	670	629	734	153	1003	690	810	1020	536	101
23	507	726	286	934	611	60	879	411	968	293
24	894	165	597	420	1049	186	55	674	791	927
25	21	256	950	434	713	859	8	401	330	121
26	1032	233	352	633	821	241	1013	679	557	343
27	841	451	1063	1088	368	1038	658	1057	426	738
28	281	816	211	622	318	904	959	532	1045	1028
29	654	200	204	988	337	157	216	768	72	796
30	172	807	608	594	18	327	1010	365	208	651
31	69	1007	93	42	96	228	983	305	392	581
32	376	32	45	1073	992	310	834	694	627	688
33	99	932	409	163	184	925	432	399	231	239
34	341	1086	1055	814	902	1026	986	766	805	325
35	649	40	303	30	308	686	161	397	1084	1024
36	323	28	395	26	570	572	478	941	140	574
37	584	869	220	480	268	540	783	943	379	707
38	386	142	148	854	527	576	35	849	772	586
39	461	105	909	871	48	261	250	222	701	442
40	744	482	1076	358	76	270	192	511	492	542
41	995	887	133	785	87	777	665	945	313	978
42	800	381	128	730	964	709	837	955	604	388
43	180	645	474	144	697	83	176	150	723	290
44	671	856	630	448	735	529	154	591	1004	578
45	691	922	811	37	1021	938	537	851	102	439
46	508	774	727	642	287	588	935	639	612	463
47	61	615	880	107	412	754	969	911	294	466
48	895	873	166	564	598	50	421	64	1050	263
49	187	718	56	252	675	618	792	224	928	762

POWER RESIDUES

	0	1	2	3	4	5	6	7	8	9
0	1	2	4	8	16	32	64	128	256	512
1	1024	957	823	555	19	38	76	152	304	608
2	125	250	500	1000	909	727	363	726	361	722
3	353	706	321	642	193	386	772	453	906	721
4	351	702	313	626	161	322	644	197	394	788
5	485	970	849	607	123	246	492	984	877	663
6	235	470	940	789	487	974	857	623	155	310
7	620	149	298	596	101	202	404	808	525	1050
8	1009	927	763	435	870	649	207	414	828	565
9	39	78	156	312	624	157	314	628	165	330
10	660	229	458	916	741	391	782	473	946	801
11	511	1022	953	815	539	1078	1065	1039	987	883
12	675	259	518	1036	981	871	651	211	422	844
13	597	103	206	412	824	557	23	46	92	184
14	368	736	381	762	433	866	641	191	382	764
15	437	874	657	223	446	892	693	295	590	89
16	178	356	712	333	666	241	482	964	837	583
17	75	150	300	600	109	218	436	872	653	215
18	430	860	629	167	334	668	245	490	980	869
19	647	203	406	812	533	1066	1041	991	891	691
20	291	582	73	146	292	584	77	154	308	616
21	141	282	564	37	74	148	296	592	93	186
22	372	744	397	794	497	994	897	703	315	630
23	169	338	676	261	522	1044	997	903	715	339
24	678	265	530	1060	1029	967	843	595	99	198
25	396	792	493	986	881	671	251	502	1004	917
26	743	395	790	489	978	865	639	187	374	748
27	405	810	529	1058	1025	959	827	563	35	70
28	140	280	560	29	58	116	232	464	928	765
29	439	878	665	239	478	956	821	551	11	22
30	44	88	176	352	704	317	634	177	354	708
31	325	650	209	418	836	581	71	142	284	568
32	45	90	180	360	720	349	698	305	610	129
33	258	516	1032	973	855	619	147	294	588	85
34	170	340	680	269	538	1076	1061	1031	971	851
35	611	131	262	524	1048	1005	919	747	403	806
36	521	1042	993	895	699	307	614	137	274	548
37	5	10	20	40	80	160	320	640	189	378
38	756	421	842	593	95	190	380	760	429	858
39	625	159	318	636	181	362	724	357	714	337
40	674	257	514	1028	965	839	587	83	166	332
41	664	237	474	948	805	519	1038	985	879	667
42	243	486	972	853	615	139	278	556	21	42
43	84	168	336	672	253	506	1012	933	775	459
44	918	745	399	798	505	1010	929	767	443	886
45	681	271	542	1084	1077	1063	1035	979	867	643
46	195	390	780	469	938	785	479	958	825	559
47	27	54	108	216	432	864	637	183	366	732
48	373	746	401	802	513	1026	961	831	571	51
49	102	204	408	816	541	1082	1073	1055	1019	947

P = 1091

INDICES

	0	1	2	3	4	5	6	7	8	9
50	22	703	257	883	951	444	435	750	714	746
51	860	110	9	484	402	501	331	1078	122	415
52	1033	360	234	864	353	78	634	757	822	272
53	242	827	1014	194	680	972	558	513	344	114
54	842	494	452	914	1064	544	1089	519	369	997
55	1039	297	659	889	1058	13	427	135	739	469
56	282	787	817	277	212	89	623	898	319	779
57	905	488	960	667	533	876	1046	947	1029	554
58	655	315	201	169	205	980	989	406	338	802
59	158	567	217	383	769	247	73	130	797	601
60	173	732	808	505	609	966	595	53	19	711
61	328	350	1011	839	366	424	209	957	652	335
62	70	606	1008	67	94	390	43	832	97	182
63	229	1053	984	647	306	1082	393	476	582	266
64	377	146	33	459	46	699	1074	190	993	85
65	311	126	835	178	695	721	628	152	689	1019
66	100	725	933	59	410	292	164	419	185	673
67	926	255	433	858	400	120	232	632	240	678
68	342	450	1087	1037	1056	737	815	621	903	531
69	1027	199	987	156	767	795	806	593	326	364
70	650	1006	41	227	304	580	31	1072	309	693
71	687	931	162	924	398	238	1085	813	1025	765
72	324	39	29	685	396	1023	27	25	571	940
73	573	868	479	539	942	706	141	853	575	848
74	585	104	870	260	221	441	481	357	269	510
75	541	886	784	776	944	977	380	729	708	954
76	387	644	143	82	149	289	855	447	528	590
77	577	921	36	937	850	438	773	641	587	638
78	462	614	106	753	910	465	872	563	49	63
79	262	717	251	617	223	761	702	882	443	749
80	745	109	483	500	1077	414	359	863	77	756
81	271	826	193	971	512	113	493	913	543	518
82	996	296	888	12	134	468	786	276	88	897
83	778	487	666	875	946	553	314	168	979	405
84	801	566	382	246	129	600	731	504	965	52
85	710	349	838	423	956	334	605	66	389	831
86	181	1052	646	1081	475	265	145	458	698	189
87	84	125	177	720	151	1018	724	58	291	418
88	672	254	857	119	631	677	449	1036	736	620
89	530	198	155	794	592	363	1005	226	579	1071
90	692	930	923	237	812	764	38	684	1022	24
91	939	867	538	705	852	847	103	259	440	356
92	509	885	775	976	728	953	643	81	288	446
93	589	920	936	437	640	637	613	752	464	562
94	62	716	616	760	881	748	108	499	413	862
95	755	825	970	112	912	517	295	11	467	275
96	896	486	874	552	167	404	565	245	599	503
97	51	348	422	333	65	830	1051	1080	264	457
98	188	124	719	1017	57	417	253	118	676	1035
99	619	197	793	362	225	1070	929	236	763	683

POWER RESIDUES

	0	1	2	3	4	5	6	7	8	9
50	803	515	1030	969	847	603	115	230	460	920
51	749	407	814	537	1074	1057	1023	955	819	547
52	3	6	12	24	48	96	192	384	768	445
53	890	689	287	574	57	114	228	456	912	733
54	375	750	409	818	545	1090	1089	1087	1083	1075
55	1059	1027	963	835	579	67	134	268	536	1072
56	1053	1015	939	787	483	966	841	591	91	182
57	364	728	365	730	369	738	385	770	449	898
58	705	319	638	185	370	740	389	778	465	930
59	769	447	894	697	303	606	121	242	484	968
60	845	599	107	214	428	856	621	151	302	604
61	117	234	468	936	781	471	942	793	495	990
62	889	687	283	566	41	82	164	328	656	221
63	442	884	677	263	526	1052	1013	935	779	467
64	934	777	463	926	761	431	862	633	175	350
65	700	309	618	145	290	580	69	138	276	552
66	13	26	52	104	208	416	832	573	55	110
67	220	440	880	669	247	494	988	885	679	267
68	534	1068	1045	999	907	723	355	710	329	658
69	225	450	900	709	327	654	217	434	868	645
70	199	398	796	501	1002	913	735	379	758	425
71	850	609	127	254	508	1016	941	791	491	982
72	873	655	219	438	876	661	231	462	924	757
73	423	846	601	111	222	444	888	685	279	558
74	25	50	100	200	400	800	509	1018	945	799
75	507	1014	937	783	475	950	809	527	1054	1017
76	943	795	499	998	905	719	347	694	297	594
77	97	194	388	776	461	922	753	415	830	569
78	47	94	188	376	752	413	826	561	31	62
79	124	248	496	992	893	695	299	598	105	210
80	420	840	589	87	174	348	696	301	602	113
81	226	452	904	717	343	686	281	562	33	66
82	132	264	528	1056	1021	951	811	531	1062	1033
83	975	859	627	163	326	652	213	426	852	613
84	135	270	540	1080	1069	1047	1003	915	739	387
85	774	457	914	737	383	766	441	882	673	255
86	510	1020	949	807	523	1046	1001	911	731	371
87	742	393	786	481	962	833	575	59	118	236
88	472	944	797	503	1006	921	751	411	822	553
89	15	30	60	120	240	480	960	829	567	43
90	86	172	344	688	285	570	49	98	196	392
91	784	477	954	817	543	1086	1081	1071	1051	1011
92	931	771	451	902	713	335	670	249	498	996
93	901	711	331	662	233	466	932	773	455	910
94	729	367	734	377	754	417	834	577	63	126
95	252	504	1008	925	759	427	854	617	143	286
96	572	53	106	212	424	848	605	119	238	476
97	952	813	535	1070	1049	1007	923	755	419	838
98	585	79	158	316	632	173	346	692	293	586
99	81	162	324	648	205	410	820	549	7	14

P = 1091

INDICES

	0	1	2	3	4	5	6	7	8	9
100	23	866	704	846	258	355	884	975	952	80
101	445	919	436	636	751	561	715	759	747	498
102	861	824	111	516	10	274	485	551	403	244
103	502	347	332	829	1079	456	123	1016	416	117
104	1034	196	361	1069	235	682	865	845	354	974
105	79	918	635	560	758	497	823	515	273	550
106	243	346	828	455	1015	116	195	1068	681	844
107	973	917	559	496	514	549	345	454	115	1067
108	843	916	495	548	453	1066	915	547	1065	546
109	545	0								

POWER RESIDUES

	0	1	2	3	4	5	6	7	8	9
100	28	56	112	224	448	896	701	311	622	153
101	306	612	133	266	532	1064	1037	983	875	659
102	227	454	908	725	359	718	345	690	289	578
103	65	130	260	520	,1040	989	887	683	275	550
104	9	18	36	72	144	288	576	61	122	244
105	488	976	861	631	171	342	684	277	554	17
106	34	68	136	272	544	1088	1085	1079	1067	1043
107	995	899	707	323	646	201	402	804	517	1034
108	977	863	635	179	358	716	341	682	273	546
109										

P = 1093

INDICES

	0	1	2	3	4	5	6	7	8	9
0		0	687	624	282	1	219	620	969	156
1	688	336	906	112	215	625	564	793	843	305
2	283	152	1023	240	501	2	799	780	902	256
3	220	894	159	960	388	621	438	573	992	736
4	970	527	839	295	618	157	927	120	96	148
5	689	325	394	131	375	337	497	929	943	597
6	907	250	489	776	846	113	555	134	1075	864
7	216	823	33	62	168	626	587	956	331	989
8	565	312	122	649	434	794	982	880	213	734
9	844	732	522	426	807	306	783	1009	835	492
10	284	507	1012	634	1081	153	818	98	1062	482
11	1024	105	92	977	524	241	538	268	192	321
12	502	672	937	59	84	3	371	533	441	919
13	800	826	150	925	821	781	670	747	459	428
14	903	744	418	448	720	257	749	772	855	615
15	221	364	182	949	551	895	1018	691	584	755
16	160	860	999	568	809	961	244	1059	29	224
17	389	461	577	664	475	622	900	129	329	632
18	439	947	327	874	117	574	21	37	402	308
19	993	1004	378	986	604	737	430	515	87	288
20	971	758	102	876	607	528	229	396	676	641
21	840	445	413	355	785	296	657	422	77	686
22	619	905	792	1022	779	158	572	838	119	393
23	928	488	133	32	955	121	879	521	1008	1011
24	97	91	267	936	532	149	746	417	771	181
25	690	998	1058	576	128	326	36	377	514	101
26	395	412	421	791	837	132	520	266	416	1057
27	376	420	265	264	342	338	54	343	23	1050
28	498	612	339	454	13	930	43	55	315	494
29	944	541	344	707	367	598	450	24	210	352
30	908	915	1051	39	869	251	544	499	146	166
31	490	82	613	473	286	777	179	340	350	592
32	847	722	455	6	594	114	163	14	404	740
33	556	206	931	729	654	135	716	44	911	509
34	1076	138	56	768	172	865	259	316	70	849
35	217	892	495	310	816	824	1016	945	227	486
36	34	610	542	204	1014	63	469	345	804	683
37	169	751	708	175	724	627	1089	368	995	1086
38	588	65	599	965	1065	957	581	451	199	636
39	332	1033	25	358	110	990	774	211	975	457
40	566	400	353	1006	789	313	471	909	202	197
41	123	279	916	125	1083	650	271	1052	236	185
42	435	857	40	276	8	795	1042	870	380	1072
43	983	347	252	697	17	881	764	545	281	155
44	214	304	500	255	387	735	617	147	374	596
45	845	863	167	988	433	733	806	491	1080	481
46	523	320	83	918	820	427	719	614	550	754
47	808	223	474	631	116	307	603	287	606	640
48	784	685	778	392	954	1010	531	180	127	100
49	836	1056	341	1049	12	493	366	351	868	165

POWER RESIDUES

	0	1	2	3	4	5	6	7	8	9
0	1	5	25	125	625	939	323	522	424	1027
1	763	536	494	284	327	542	524	434	1077	1013
2	693	186	930	278	297	392	867	1056	908	168
3	840	921	233	72	360	707	256	187	935	303
4	422	1017	713	286	337	592	774	591	769	566
5	644	1034	798	711	276	287	342	617	899	123
6	615	889	73	365	732	381	812	781	626	944
7	348	647	1049	873	1086	1058	918	218	1090	1078
8	1018	718	311	462	124	620	914	198	990	578
9	704	241	112	560	614	884	48	240	107	535
10	489	259	202	1010	678	111	555	589	759	516
11	394	877	13	65	325	532	474	184	920	228
12	47	235	82	410	957	413	972	488	254	177
13	885	53	265	232	67	335	582	724	341	612
14	874	1091	1083	1043	843	936	308	447	49	245
15	132	660	21	105	525	439	9	45	225	32
16	160	800	721	326	537	499	309	452	74	370
17	757	506	344	627	949	373	772	581	719	316
18	487	249	152	760	521	419	1002	638	1004	648
19	1054	898	118	590	764	541	519	409	952	388
20	847	956	408	947	363	722	331	562	624	934
21	298	397	892	88	440	14	70	350	657	6
22	30	150	750	471	169	845	946	358	697	206
23	1030	778	611	869	1066	958	418	997	613	879
24	23	115	575	689	166	830	871	1076	1008	668
25	61	305	432	1067	963	443	29	145	725	346
26	637	999	623	929	273	272	267	242	117	585
27	739	416	987	563	629	959	423	1022	738	411
28	962	438	4	20	100	500	314	477	199	995
29	603	829	866	1051	883	43	215	1075	1003	643
30	1029	773	586	744	441	19	95	475	189	945
31	353	672	81	405	932	288	347	642	1024	748
32	461	119	595	789	666	51	255	182	910	178
33	890	78	390	857	1006	658	11	55	275	282
34	317	492	274	277	292	367	742	431	1062	938
35	318	497	299	402	917	213	1065	953	393	872
36	1081	1033	793	686	151	755	496	294	377	792
37	681	126	630	964	448	54	270	257	192	960
38	428	1047	863	1036	808	761	526	444	34	170
39	850	971	483	229	52	260	207	1035	803	736
40	401	912	188	940	328	547	549	559	609	859
41	1016	708	261	212	1060	928	268	247	142	710
42	271	262	217	1085	1053	893	93	465	139	695
43	196	980	528	454	84	420	1007	663	36	180
44	900	128	640	1014	698	211	1055	903	143	715
45	296	387	842	931	283	322	517	399	902	138
46	690	171	855	996	608	854	991	583	729	366
47	737	406	937	313	472	174	870	1071	983	543
48	529	459	109	545	539	509	359	702	231	62
49	310	457	99	495	289	352	667	56	280	307

P = 1093

INDICES

	0	1	2	3	4	5	6	7	8	9
50	285	591	593	739	653	508	171	848	815	485
51	1013	682	723	1085	1064	635	109	456	788	196
52	1082	184	7	1071	16	154	386	595	432	480
53	819	753	115	639	953	99	11	164	652	484
54	1063	195	15	479	952	483	951	405	1029	406
55	1025	561	741	517	1030	106	710	557	645	407
56	93	661	207	273	1026	978	49	932	700	562
57	525	553	730	536	742	242	1002	655	89	518
58	539	177	136	467	1031	269	302	717	1054	107
59	193	47	45	831	711	322	897	912	1039	558
60	503	887	510	290	646	673	726	1077	464	408
61	938	232	139	238	94	60	833	57	853	662
62	85	1020	769	262	208	4	68	173	973	274
63	372	629	866	1069	1027	534	1037	260	187	979
64	442	713	317	299	50	920	693	71	189	933
65	801	1046	850	760	701	827	1091	218	335	563
66	151	798	893	437	526	926	324	496	249	554
67	822	586	311	981	731	782	506	817	104	537
68	671	370	825	669	743	748	363	1017	859	243
69	460	899	946	20	1003	429	757	228	444	656
70	904	571	487	878	90	745	997	35	411	519
71	419	53	611	42	540	449	914	543	81	178
72	721	162	205	715	137	258	891	1015	609	468
73	750	1088	64	580	1032	773	399	470	278	270
74	856	1041	346	763	303	616	862	805	319	718
75	222	602	684	530	1055	365	590	170	681	108
76	183	385	752	10	194	950	560	709	660	48
77	552	1001	176	301	46	896	886	725	231	832
78	1019	67	628	1036	712	692	1045	1090	797	323
79	585	505	369	362	898	756	570	996	52	913
80	161	890	1087	398	1040	861	601	589	384	559
81	1000	885	66	1044	504	569	889	600	884	888
82	810	811	966	922	511	962	812	1066	678	291
83	245	967	958	941	647	1060	923	582	872	674
84	30	512	452	144	727	225	963	200	695	1078
85	390	813	637	643	465	462	1067	333	667	409
86	578	679	1034	382	939	665	292	26	704	233
87	476	246	359	73	140	623	968	111	842	239
88	901	959	991	294	95	130	942	775	1074	61
89	330	648	212	425	834	633	1061	976	191	58
90	440	924	458	447	854	948	583	567	28	663
91	328	873	401	985	86	875	675	354	76	1021
92	118	31	1007	935	770	575	513	790	415	263
93	22	453	314	706	209	38	145	472	349	5
94	403	728	910	767	69	309	226	203	803	174
95	994	964	198	357	974	1005	201	124	235	275
96	379	696	280	254	373	987	1079	917	549	630
97	605	391	126	1048	867	738	814	1084	787	1070
98	431	638	651	478	1028	516	644	272	699	535
99	88	466	1053	830	1038	289	463	237	852	261

POWER RESIDUES

	0	1	2	3	4	5	6	7	8	9
50	442	24	120	600	814	791	676	101	505	339
51	602	824	841	926	258	197	985	553	579	709
52	266	237	92	460	114	570	664	41	205	1025
53	753	486	244	127	635	989	573	679	116	580
54	714	291	362	717	306	437	1092	1088	1068	968
55	468	154	770	571	669	66	330	557	599	809
56	766	551	569	659	16	80	400	907	163	815
57	796	701	226	37	185	925	253	172	860	1021
58	733	386	837	906	158	790	671	76	380	807
59	756	501	319	502	324	527	449	59	295	382
60	817	806	751	476	194	970	478	204	1020	728
61	361	712	281	312	467	149	745	446	44	220
62	7	35	175	875	3	15	75	375	782	631
63	969	473	179	895	103	515	389	852	981	533
64	479	209	1045	853	986	558	604	834	891	83
65	415	982	538	504	334	577	699	216	1080	1028
66	768	561	619	909	173	865	1046	858	1011	683
67	136	680	121	605	839	916	208	1040	828	861
68	1026	758	511	369	752	481	219	2	10	50
69	250	157	785	646	1044	848	961	433	1072	988
70	568	654	1084	1048	868	1061	933	293	372	767
71	556	594	784	641	1019	723	336	587	749	466
72	144	720	321	512	374	777	606	844	941	333
73	572	674	91	455	89	445	39	195	975	503
74	329	552	574	684	141	705	246	137	685	146
75	730	371	762	531	469	159	795	696	201	1005
76	653	1079	1023	743	436	1087	1063	943	343	622
77	924	248	147	735	396	887	63	315	482	224
78	27	135	675	96	480	214	1070	978	518	404
79	927	263	222	17	85	425	1032	788	661	26
80	130	650	1064	948	368	747	456	94	470	164
81	820	821	826	851	976	508	354	677	106	530
82	464	134	670	71	355	682	131	655	1089	1073
83	993	593	779	616	894	98	490	264	227	42
84	210	1050	878	18	90	450	64	320	507	349
85	652	1074	998	618	904	148	740	421	1012	688
86	161	805	746	451	69	345	632	974	498	304
87	427	1042	838	911	183	915	203	1015	703	236
88	87	435	1082	1038	818	811	776	601	819	816
89	801	726	351	662	31	155	775	596	794	691
90	176	880	28	140	700	221	12	60	300	407
91	942	338	597	799	716	301	412	967	463	129
92	645	1039	823	836	901	133	665	46	230	57
93	285	332	567	649	1059	923	243	122	610	864
94	1041	833	886	58	290	357	692	181	905	153
95	765	546	544	534	484	234	77	385	832	881
96	33	165	825	846	951	383	822	831	876	8
97	40	200	1000	628	954	398	897	113	565	639
98	1009	673	86	430	1057	913	193	965	453	79
99	395	882	38	190	950	378	797	706	251	162

P = 1093

INDICES

	0	1	2	3	4	5	6	7	8	9
100	972	1068	186	298	188	759	334	436	248	980
101	103	668	858	19	443	877	410	41	80	714
102	608	579	277	762	318	529	680	9	659	300
103	230	1035	796	361	51	397	383	1043	883	921
104	677	940	871	143	694	642	666	381	703	72
105	841	293	1073	424	190	446	27	984	75	934
106	414	705	348	766	802	356	234	253	548	1047
107	786	477	698	829	851	297	247	18	79	761
108	658	360	882	142	702	423	74	765	547	828
109	78	141	546							

POWER RESIDUES

	0	1	2	3	4	5	6	7	8	9
100	810	771	576	694	191	955	403	922	238	97
101	485	239	102	510	364	727	356	687	156	780
102	621	919	223	22	110	550	564	634	984	548
103	554	584	734	391	862	1031	783	636	994	598
104	804	741	426	1037	813	786	651	1069	973	493
105	279	302	417	992	588	754	491	269	252	167
106	835	896	108	540	514	384	827	856	1001	633
107	979	523	429	1052	888	68	340	607	849	966
108	458	104	520	414	977	513	379	802	731	376
109	787	656								

P = 1097

INDICES

	0	1	2	3	4	5	6	7	8	9
0		0	132	1	264	1003	133	555	396	2
1	39	1019	265	731	687	1004	528	854	134	617
2	171	556	55	26	397	910	863	3	819	254
3	40	351	660	1020	986	462	266	691	749	732
4	303	36	688	789	187	1005	158	1050	529	14
5	1042	855	995	1068	135	926	951	618	386	876
6	172	962	483	557	792	638	56	930	22	27
7	594	204	398	772	823	911	881	478	864	411
8	435	4	168	1047	820	761	921	255	319	537
9	41	190	290	352	86	524	661	665	146	1021
10	78	764	987	343	31	463	104	512	267	1064
11	1058	692	1083	981	750	1029	518	733	1008	313
12	304	942	1094	37	615	817	689	156	924	790
13	770	166	188	76	1062	1006	154	152	159	608
14	726	1051	336	654	530	161	904	15	955	128
15	1043	296	1013	856	610	258	996	673	543	1069
16	567	581	136	728	300	927	83	939	952	366
17	893	619	1053	195	387	369	451	877	669	441
18	173	338	322	963	422	598	484	777	218	558
19	656	977	793	829	797	639	278	628	57	532
20	210	931	896	809	23	1039	475	28	163	540
21	595	233	236	205	644	696	399	906	100	773
22	94	489	824	227	119	912	17	842	882	622
23	65	479	650	115	865	957	44	412	445	239
24	436	360	1074	5	130	1017	169	252	747	1048
25	949	636	821	1045	288	762	1056	311	922	150
26	902	256	298	193	320	975	208	538	98	840
27	42	1015	286	191	284	833	291	755	740	353
28	858	835	87	198	468	525	786	591	662	612
29	293	666	1036	647	147	783	1087	1022	260	757
30	79	248	428	765	49	869	988	998	742	344
31	390	847	32	1090	805	464	675	355	105	177
32	699	513	713	375	268	545	860	1065	432	509
33	1059	578	215	693	1071	837	1084	372	498	982
34	1025	274	751	569	89	1030	327	402	519	493
35	501	734	583	200	1009	111	801	314	573	718
36	305	138	470	943	454	679	1095	263	554	38
37	730	527	616	54	909	818	350	985	690	302
38	788	157	13	994	925	385	961	791	929	593
39	771	880	410	167	760	318	189	85	664	77
40	342	103	1063	1082	1028	1007	941	614	155	769
41	75	153	607	335	160	954	295	609	672	566
42	727	82	365	1052	368	668	337	421	776	655
43	828	277	531	895	1038	162	232	643	905	93
44	226	16	621	649	956	444	359	129	251	948
45	1044	1055	149	297	974	97	1014	283	754	857
46	197	785	611	1035	782	259	247	48	997	389
47	1089	674	176	712	544	431	577	1070	371	1024
48	568	326	492	582	110	572	137	453	262	729
49	53	349	301	12	384	928	879	759	84	341

POWER RESIDUES

	0	1	2	3	4	5	6	7	8	9
0	1	3	9	27	81	243	729	1090	1076	1034
1	908	530	493	382	49	147	441	226	678	937
2	617	754	68	204	612	739	23	69	207	621
3	766	104	312	936	614	745	41	123	369	10
4	30	90	270	810	236	708	1027	887	467	304
5	912	542	529	490	373	22	66	198	594	685
6	958	680	943	635	808	230	690	973	725	1078
7	1040	926	584	655	868	410	133	399	100	300
8	900	506	421	166	498	397	94	282	846	344
9	1032	902	512	439	220	660	883	455	268	804
10	218	654	865	401	106	318	954	668	907	527
11	484	355	1065	1001	809	233	699	1000	806	224
12	672	919	563	592	679	940	626	781	149	447
13	244	732	2	6	18	54	162	486	361	1083
14	1055	971	719	1060	986	764	98	294	882	452
15	259	777	137	411	136	408	127	381	46	138
16	414	145	435	208	624	775	131	393	82	246
17	738	20	60	180	540	523	472	319	957	677
18	934	608	727	1084	1058	980	746	44	132	396
19	91	273	819	263	789	173	519	460	283	849
20	353	1059	983	755	71	213	639	820	266	798
21	200	600	703	1012	842	332	996	794	188	564
22	595	688	967	707	1024	878	440	223	669	910
23	536	511	436	211	633	802	212	636	811	239
24	717	1054	968	710	1033	905	521	466	301	903
25	515	448	247	741	29	87	261	783	155	465
26	298	894	488	367	4	12	36	108	324	972
27	722	1069	1013	845	341	1023	875	431	196	588
28	667	904	518	457	274	822	272	816	254	762
29	92	276	828	290	870	416	151	453	262	786
30	164	492	379	40	120	360	1080	1046	944	638
31	817	257	771	119	357	1071	1019	863	395	88
32	264	792	182	546	541	526	481	346	1038	920
33	566	601	706	1021	869	413	142	426	181	543
34	532	499	400	103	309	927	587	664	895	491
35	376	31	93	279	837	317	951	659	880	446
36	241	723	1072	1022	872	422	169	507	424	175
37	525	478	337	1011	839	323	969	713	1042	932
38	602	709	1030	896	494	385	58	174	522	469
39	310	930	596	691	976	734	8	24	72	216
40	648	847	347	1041	929	593	682	949	653	862
41	392	79	237	711	1036	914	548	547	544	535
42	508	427	184	552	559	580	643	832	302	906
43	524	475	328	984	758	80	240	720	1063	995
44	791	179	537	514	445	238	714	1045	941	629
45	790	176	528	487	364	1092	1082	1052	962	692
46	979	743	35	105	315	945	641	826	284	852
47	362	1086	1064	998	800	206	618	757	77	231
48	693	982	752	62	186	558	577	634	805	221
49	663	892	482	349	1047	947	647	844	338	1014

P = 1097

INDICES

	0	1	2	3	4	5	6	7	8	9
50	1081	940	768	606	953	671	81	367	420	827
51	894	231	92	620	443	250	1054	973	282	196
52	1034	246	388	175	430	370	325	109	452	52
53	11	878	340	767	670	419	230	442	972	1033
54	174	324	51	339	418	971	323	417	416	964
55	965	871	423	966	887	599	872	722	485	424
56	990	778	967	122	219	888	330	559	600	1000
57	657	873	918	978	723	936	794	486	744	830
58	425	506	798	991	72	640	779	346	279	968
59	915	629	123	405	58	220	392	533	889	632
60	211	331	380	932	560	849	897	601	181	810
61	1001	685	24	658	34	1040	874	20	476	919
62	522	29	979	1092	164	724	126	541	937	449
63	596	795	807	234	487	63	237	745	309	206
64	831	466	645	426	845	697	507	496	400	799
65	677	907	992	408	101	73	564	774	641	357
66	95	780	710	490	347	1079	825	280	107	228
67	969	885	120	916	504	913	630	179	18	124
68	61	843	406	708	883	59	701	623	221	703
69	66	393	459	480	534	515	651	890	625	116
70	633	737	866	212	715	958	332	223	45	381
71	243	413	933	377	446	561	705	240	850	142
72	437	898	270	361	602	68	1075	182	586	6
73	811	547	131	1002	395	1018	686	853	170	25
74	862	253	659	461	748	35	186	1049	1041	1067
75	950	875	482	637	21	203	822	477	434	1046
76	920	536	289	523	145	763	30	511	1057	980
77	517	312	1093	816	923	165	1061	151	725	653
78	903	127	1012	257	542	580	299	938	892	194
79	450	440	321	597	217	976	796	627	209	808
80	474	539	235	695	99	488	118	841	64	114
81	43	238	1073	1016	746	635	287	310	901	192
82	207	839	285	832	739	834	467	590	292	646
83	1086	756	427	868	741	846	804	354	698	374
84	859	508	214	836	497	273	88	401	500	199
85	800	717	469	678	553	526	908	984	787	993
86	960	592	409	317	663	102	1027	613	74	334
87	294	565	364	667	775	276	1037	642	225	648
88	358	947	148	96	753	784	781	47	1088	711
89	576	1023	491	571	261	348	383	758	1080	605
90	80	826	91	249	281	245	429	108	10	766
91	229	1032	50	970	415	870	886	721	989	121
92	329	999	917	935	743	505	71	345	914	404
93	391	631	379	848	180	684	33	19	521	1091
94	125	448	806	62	308	465	844	495	676	407
95	563	356	709	1078	106	884	503	178	60	707
96	700	702	458	514	624	736	714	222	242	376
97	704	141	269	67	585	546	394	852	861	460
98	185	1066	481	202	433	535	144	510	516	815
99	1060	652	1011	579	891	439	216	626	473	694

POWER RESIDUES

	0	1	2	3	4	5	6	7	8	9
50	848	350	1050	956	674	925	581	646	841	329
51	987	767	107	321	963	695	988	770	116	348
52	1044	938	620	763	95	285	855	371	16	48
53	144	432	199	597	694	985	761	89	267	801
54	209	627	784	158	474	325	975	731	1096	1094
55	1088	1070	1016	854	368	7	21	63	189	567
56	604	715	1048	950	656	871	419	160	480	343
57	1029	893	485	358	1074	1028	890	476	331	993
58	785	161	483	352	1056	974	728	1087	1067	1007
59	827	287	861	389	70	210	630	793	185	555
60	568	607	724	1075	1031	899	503	412	139	417
61	154	462	289	867	407	124	372	19	57	171
62	513	442	229	687	964	698	997	797	197	591
63	676	931	599	700	1003	815	251	753	65	195
64	585	658	877	437	214	642	829	293	879	443
65	232	696	991	779	143	429	190	570	613	742
66	32	96	288	864	398	97	291	873	425	178
67	534	505	418	157	471	316	948	650	853	365
68	1095	1091	1079	1043	935	611	736	14	42	126
69	378	37	111	333	999	803	215	645	838	320
70	960	686	961	689	970	716	1051	959	683	952
71	662	889	473	322	966	704	1015	851	359	1077
72	1037	917	557	574	625	778	140	420	163	489
73	370	13	39	117	351	1053	965	701	1006	824
74	278	834	308	924	578	637	814	248	744	38
75	114	342	1026	884	458	277	831	299	897	497
76	394	85	255	765	101	303	909	533	502	409
77	130	390	73	219	657	874	428	187	561	586
78	661	886	464	295	885	461	286	858	380	43
79	129	387	64	192	576	631	796	194	582	649
80	850	356	1068	1010	836	314	942	632	799	203
81	609	730	1093	1085	1061	989	773	125	375	28
82	84	252	756	74	222	666	901	509	430	193
83	579	640	823	275	825	281	843	335	1005	821
84	269	807	227	681	946	644	835	311	933	605
85	718	1057	977	737	17	51	153	459	280	840
86	326	978	740	26	78	234	702	1009	833	305
87	915	551	556	571	616	751	59	177	531	496
88	391	76	228	684	955	671	916	554	565	598
89	697	994	788	170	510	43	202	606	721	1066
90	1004	818	260	780	146	438	217	651	856	374
91	25	75	225	675	928	590	673	922	572	619
92	760	86	258	774	128	384	55	165	495	388
93	67	201	603	712	1039	923	575	628	787	167
94	501	406	121	363	1089	1073	1025	881	449	250
95	750	56	168	504	415	148	444	235	705	1018
96	860	386	61	183	549	550	553	562	589	670
97	913	545	538	517	454	265	795	191	573	622
98	769	113	339	1017	857	377	34	102	306	918
99	560	583	652	859	383	52	156	468	307	921

P = 1097

INDICES

	0	1	2	3	4	5	6	7	8	9
100	117	113	1072	634	900	838	738	589	1085	867
101	803	373	213	272	499	716	552	983	959	316
102	1026	333	363	275	224	946	752	46	575	570
103	382	604	90	244	9	1031	414	720	328	934
104	70	403	378	683	520	447	307	494	562	1077
105	502	706	457	735	241	140	584	851	184	201
106	143	814	1010	438	472	112	899	588	802	271
107	551	315	362	945	574	603	8	719	69	682
108	306	1076	456	139	183	813	471	587	550	944
109	7	681	455	812	549	680	548			

POWER RESIDUES

	0	1	2	3	4	5	6	7	8	9
100	569	610	733	5	15	45	135	405	118	354
101	1062	992	782	152	456	271	813	245	735	11
102	33	99	297	891	479	340	1020	866	404	115
103	345	1035	911	539	520	463	292	876	434	205
104	615	748	50	150	450	253	759	83	249	747
105	47	141	423	172	516	451	256	768	110	330
106	990	776	134	402	109	327	981	749	53	159
107	477	334	1002	812	242	726	1081	1049	953	665
108	898	500	403	112	336	1008	830	296	888	470
109	313	939	623	772	122	366				

P = 1103

INDICES

	0	1	2	3	4	5	6	7	8	9
0		0	190	356	380	1	546	1021	570	712
1	191	525	736	421	109	357	760	870	902	839
2	381	275	715	1088	926	2	611	1068	299	624
3	547	431	950	881	1060	1022	1092	474	1029	777
4	571	414	465	848	905	713	176	178	14	940
5	192	124	801	1018	156	526	489	93	814	63
6	737	752	621	631	38	422	1071	222	148	342
7	110	121	180	764	664	358	117	444	967	247
8	761	322	604	1056	655	871	1038	980	1095	837
9	903	340	366	787	368	840	204	16	28	135
10	382	45	314	22	991	276	106	139	346	781
11	716	830	679	877	283	1089	1004	31	253	789
12	927	1050	942	770	811	3	821	961	228	102
13	612	507	159	758	412	1069	338	1002	532	142
14	300	534	311	946	370	625	954	194	854	267
15	548	808	307	480	634	432	55	1012	437	272
16	951	1007	512	8	794	882	144	50	845	842
17	1061	449	126	427	68	1023	183	419	1027	629
18	1093	875	530	6	556	475	977	293	558	987
19	1030	302	394	1082	206	778	218	803	325	896
20	572	578	235	543	504	415	212	698	79	262
21	466	564	296	477	329	849	536	350	971	18
22	906	189	1020	735	869	714	1067	949	473	464
23	177	800	92	620	221	179	443	603	979	365
24	15	313	138	678	30	941	960	158	1001	310
25	193	306	1011	511	49	125	418	529	292	393
26	802	234	697	295	349	1019	948	91	602	137
27	157	1010	528	696	90	527	722	723	332	41
28	490	997	724	244	501	94	34	333	560	638
29	815	372	42	1064	384	64	1044	491	457	407
30	738	767	998	401	497	753	670	725	824	378
31	622	154	245	989	100	632	627	502	462	47
32	39	495	95	607	702	423	198	35	984	97
33	1072	911	334	84	240	223	1035	561	1032	131
34	149	956	639	859	316	343	617	816	258	684
35	111	387	373	1100	609	122	115	43	819	806
36	181	576	1065	304	720	765	196	385	746	24
37	665	937	65	404	483	359	748	1045	75	704
38	118	215	492	922	584	445	170	458	396	784
39	968	856	408	863	993	248	515	739	1086	12
40	762	26	768	852	425	323	733	999	694	455
41	605	256	402	1084	888	1057	269	498	452	278
42	656	595	754	890	486	872	667	671	519	200
43	1039	674	726	964	540	981	59	825	208	1075
44	1096	550	379	711	108	838	925	623	1059	776
45	904	939	155	62	37	341	663	246	654	836
46	367	134	990	780	282	788	810	101	411	141
47	369	266	633	271	793	841	67	628	555	986
48	205	895	503	261	328	17	868	463	220	364
49	29	309	48	392	348	136	89	40	500	637

POWER RESIDUES

	0	1	2	3	4	5	6	7	8	9
0	1	5	25	125	625	919	183	915	163	815
1	766	521	399	892	48	240	97	485	219	1095
2	1063	903	103	515	369	742	401	902	98	490
3	244	117	585	719	286	327	532	454	64	320
4	497	279	292	357	682	101	505	319	492	254
5	167	835	866	1021	693	156	780	591	749	436
6	1077	973	453	59	295	372	757	476	174	870
7	1041	793	656	1074	958	378	787	626	924	208
8	1040	788	631	949	333	562	604	814	761	496
9	274	267	232	57	285	322	507	329	542	504
10	314	467	129	645	1019	683	106	530	444	14
11	70	350	647	1029	733	356	677	76	380	797
12	676	71	355	672	51	255	172	860	991	543
13	509	339	592	754	461	99	495	269	242	107
14	535	469	139	695	166	830	841	896	68	340
15	597	779	586	724	311	452	54	270	247	132
16	660	1094	1058	878	1081	993	553	559	589	739
17	386	827	826	821	796	671	46	230	47	235
18	72	360	697	176	880	1091	1043	803	706	221
19	2	10	50	250	147	735	366	727	326	527
20	429	1042	798	681	96	480	194	970	438	1087
21	1023	703	206	1030	738	381	802	701	196	980
22	488	234	67	335	572	654	1064	908	128	640
23	994	558	584	714	261	202	1010	638	984	508
24	334	567	629	939	283	312	457	79	395	872
25	1051	843	906	118	590	744	411	952	348	637
26	979	483	209	1045	813	756	471	149	745	416
27	977	473	159	795	666	21	105	525	419	992
28	548	534	464	114	570	644	1014	658	1084	1008
29	628	934	258	187	935	263	212	1060	888	28
30	140	700	191	955	363	712	251	152	760	491
31	249	142	710	241	102	510	344	617	879	1086
32	1018	678	81	405	922	198	990	538	484	214
33	1070	938	278	287	332	557	579	689	136	680
34	91	455	69	345	622	904	108	540	494	264
35	217	1085	1013	653	1059	883	3	15	75	375
36	772	551	549	539	489	239	92	460	94	470
37	144	720	291	352	657	1079	983	503	309	442
38	4	20	100	500	294	367	732	351	652	1054
39	858	981	493	259	192	960	388	837	876	1071
40	943	303	412	957	373	762	501	299	392	857
41	976	468	134	670	41	205	1025	713	256	177
42	885	13	65	325	522	404	917	173	865	1016
43	668	31	155	775	566	624	914	158	790	641
44	999	583	709	236	77	385	822	801	696	171
45	855	966	418	987	523	409	942	298	387	832
46	851	946	318	487	229	42	210	1050	838	881
47	1096	1068	928	228	37	185	925	213	1065	913
48	153	765	516	374	767	526	424	1017	673	56
49	280	297	382	807	726	321	502	304	417	982

P = 1103

INDICES

	0	1	2	3	4	5	6	7	8	9
50	383	406	496	377	99	46	701	96	239	130
51	315	683	608	805	719	23	482	703	583	783
52	992	11	424	454	887	277	485	199	539	1074
53	107	775	36	835	281	140	792	985	327	363
54	347	636	98	129	718	782	886	1073	280	362
55	717	361	912	166	913	831	522	335	231	167
56	680	649	85	898	914	878	434	241	691	832
57	284	587	224	658	523	1090	750	1036	828	336
58	1005	975	562	441	232	32	152	1033	574	168
59	254	57	132	866	681	790	647	150	597	650
60	928	1047	957	934	86	1051	591	640	687	899
61	943	599	860	580	915	771	1014	317	568	879
62	812	1054	344	756	435	4	77	618	290	242
63	822	82	817	920	692	962	652	259	237	833
64	229	439	685	918	285	103	797	112	892	588
65	613	706	388	353	225	508	72	374	287	659
66	160	930	1101	545	524	759	274	610	430	1091
67	413	175	123	488	751	1070	120	116	321	1037
68	339	203	44	105	829	1003	1049	820	506	337
69	533	953	807	54	1006	143	448	182	874	976
70	301	217	577	211	563	535	188	1066	799	442
71	312	959	305	417	233	947	1009	721	996	33
72	371	1043	766	669	153	626	494	197	910	1034
73	955	616	386	114	575	195	936	747	214	169
74	855	514	25	732	255	268	594	666	673	58
75	549	924	938	662	133	809	265	66	894	867
76	308	88	405	700	682	481	10	484	774	791
77	635	885	360	521	648	433	586	749	974	151
78	56	646	1046	590	598	1013	1053	76	81	651
79	438	796	705	71	929	273	174	119	202	1048
80	952	447	216	187	958	1008	1042	493	615	935
81	513	593	923	264	87	9	884	585	645	1052
82	795	173	446	1041	592	883	172	171	1078	641
83	145	1079	459	708	688	51	642	397	468	900
84	846	146	785	251	944	843	1080	969	676	600
85	1062	460	857	744	861	450	709	409	390	581
86	127	689	864	566	916	428	52	994	730	772
87	69	643	249	728	1015	1024	398	516	163	318
88	184	469	740	355	569	420	901	1087	298	880
89	1028	847	13	1017	813	630	147	763	966	1055
90	1094	786	27	21	345	876	252	769	227	757
91	531	945	853	479	436	7	844	426	1026	5
92	557	1081	324	542	78	476	970	734	472	619
93	978	677	1000	510	291	294	601	695	331	243
94	559	1063	456	400	823	988	461	606	983	83
95	1031	858	257	1099	818	303	745	403	74	921
96	395	862	1085	851	693	1083	451	889	518	963
97	207	710	1058	61	653	779	410	270	554	260
98	219	391	499	376	238	804	582	453	538	834
99	326	128	279	165	230	897	690	657	827	440

POWER RESIDUES

	0	1	2	3	4	5	6	7	8	9
50	498	284	317	482	204	1020	688	131	655	1069
51	933	253	162	810	741	396	877	1076	968	428
52	1037	773	556	574	664	11	55	275	272	257
53	182	910	138	690	141	705	216	1080	988	528
54	434	1067	923	203	1015	663	6	30	150	750
55	441	1102	1098	1078	978	478	184	920	188	940
56	288	337	582	704	211	1055	863	1006	618	884
57	8	40	200	1000	588	734	361	702	201	1005
58	613	859	986	518	384	817	776	571	649	1039
59	783	606	824	811	746	421	1002	598	784	611
60	849	936	268	237	82	410	947	323	512	354
61	667	26	130	650	1044	808	731	346	627	929
62	233	62	310	447	29	145	725	316	477	179
63	895	63	315	472	154	770	541	499	289	342
64	607	829	836	871	1046	818	781	596	774	561
65	599	789	636	974	458	84	420	997	573	659
66	1089	1033	753	456	74	370	747	426	1027	723
67	306	427	1032	748	431	1052	848	931	243	112
68	560	594	764	511	349	642	1004	608	834	861
69	996	568	634	964	408	937	273	262	207	1035
70	763	506	324	517	379	792	651	1049	833	856
71	971	443	9	45	225	22	110	550	544	514
72	364	717	276	277	282	307	432	1057	873	1056
73	868	1031	743	406	927	223	12	60	300	397
74	882	1101	1093	1053	853	956	368	737	376	777
75	576	674	61	305	422	1007	623	909	133	665
76	16	80	400	897	73	365	722	301	402	907
77	123	615	869	1036	768	531	449	39	195	975
78	463	109	545	519	389	842	901	93	465	119
79	595	769	536	474	164	820	791	646	1024	708
80	231	52	260	197	985	513	359	692	151	755
81	466	124	620	894	58	290	347	632	954	358
82	687	126	630	944	308	437	1082	998	578	684
83	111	555	569	639	989	533	459	89	445	19
84	95	475	169	845	916	168	840	891	43	215
85	1075	963	403	912	148	740	391	852	951	343
86	612	854	961	393	862	1001	593	759	486	224
87	17	85	425	1022	698	181	905	113	565	619
88	889	33	165	825	816	771	546	524	414	967
89	423	1012	648	1034	758	481	199	995	563	609
90	839	886	18	90	450	44	220	1100	1088	1028
91	728	331	552	554	564	614	864	1011	643	1009
92	633	959	383	812	751	446	24	120	600	794
93	661	1099	1083	1003	603	809	736	371	752	451
94	49	245	122	610	844	911	143	715	266	227
95	32	160	800	691	146	730	341	602	804	711
96	246	127	635	969	433	1062	898	78	390	847
97	926	218	1090	1038	778	581	699	186	930	238
98	87	435	1072	948	328	537	479	189	945	313
99	462	104	520	394	867	1026	718	281	302	407

P = 1103

INDICES

	0	1	2	3	4	5	6	7	8	9
100	573	865	596	933	686	579	567	755	289	919
101	236	917	891	352	286	544	429	487	320	104
102	505	53	873	210	798	416	995	668	909	113
103	213	731	672	661	893	699	773	520	973	589
104	80	70	201	186	614	263	644	1040	1077	707
105	467	250	675	743	389	565	729	727	162	354
106	297	1016	965	20	226	478	1025	541	471	509
107	330	399	982	1098	73	850	517	60	553	375
108	537	164	826	932	288	351	319	209	908	660
109	972	185	1076	742	161	19	470	1097	552	931
110	907	741	551							

POWER RESIDUES

	0	1	2	3	4	5	6	7	8	9
100	932	248	137	685	116	580	694	161	805	716
101	271	252	157	785	616	874	1061	893	53	265
102	222	7	35	175	875	1066	918	178	890	38
103	190	950	338	587	729	336	577	679	86	430
104	1047	823	806	721	296	377	782	601	799	686
105	121	605	819	786	621	899	83	415	972	448
106	34	170	850	941	293	362	707	226	27	135
107	675	66	330	547	529	439	1092	1048	828	831
108	846	921	193	965	413	962	398	887	23	115
109	575	669	36	180	900	88	440	1097	1073	953
110	353	662								

P = 1109

INDICES

	0	1	2	3	4	5	6	7	8	9
0		0	1	219	2	594	220	311	3	438
1	595	910	221	1100	312	813	4	1078	439	164
2	596	530	911	925	222	80	1101	657	313	700
3	814	979	5	21	1079	905	440	294	165	211
4	597	1006	531	445	912	1032	926	1050	223	622
5	81	189	1102	580	658	396	314	383	701	57
6	815	1025	980	749	6	586	22	844	1080	36
7	906	653	441	53	295	299	166	113	212	461
8	598	876	1007	268	532	564	446	919	913	231
9	1033	303	927	90	1051	758	224	175	623	240
10	82	199	190	420	1103	16	581	170	659	123
11	397	513	315	1043	384	411	702	430	58	281
12	816	712	1026	117	981	674	750	641	7	664
13	587	468	23	475	845	143	1081	543	37	216
14	907	161	654	902	442	186	54	841	296	265
15	300	237	167	408	114	465	213	838	462	799
16	599	128	877	802	1008	615	269	504	533	1092
17	565	602	447	987	920	391	914	276	232	131
18	1034	151	304	136	928	888	91	880	1052	968
19	759	74	225	402	176	805	624	941	241	344
20	83	1063	200	1011	191	492	421	255	1104	1074
21	17	618	582	872	171	1039	660	182	124	272
22	398	1070	514	734	316	518	1044	507	385	954
23	412	332	703	828	431	536	59	680	282	960
24	817	738	713	1095	1027	108	118	156	982	487
25	675	568	751	727	642	783	8	320	665	605
26	588	30	469	935	24	66	476	450	846	573
27	144	632	1082	522	544	990	38	552	217	309
28	908	811	162	923	655	977	903	209	443	1048
29	187	394	55	747	842	651	297	459	266	917
30	301	756	238	418	168	511	409	279	115	639
31	466	141	214	900	839	235	463	797	800	502
32	600	389	129	134	878	72	803	342	1009	253
33	616	1037	270	732	505	330	534	958	1093	154
34	566	781	603	933	448	630	988	307	921	207
35	392	649	915	416	277	139	233	500	132	340
36	1035	328	152	931	305	647	137	338	929	336
37	889	891	92	376	881	893	1053	692	969	94
38	760	860	75	378	226	707	403	883	177	482
39	806	895	625	687	942	1055	242	788	345	694
40	84	832	1064	971	201	362	1012	96	192	947
41	493	762	422	368	256	862	1105	435	1075	77
42	18	1003	619	380	583	50	873	228	172	13
43	1040	709	661	540	183	405	125	1089	273	885
44	399	1060	1071	179	515	825	735	484	317	63
45	519	808	1045	456	508	897	386	250	955	627
46	413	325	333	689	704	684	829	944	432	47
47	537	1057	60	247	681	244	283	1018	961	790
48	818	286	739	347	714	769	1096	696	1028	1021
49	109	86	119	670	157	834	983	964	488	1066

POWER RESIDUES

	0	1	2	3	4	5	6	7	8	9
0	1	2	4	8	16	32	64	128	256	512
1	1024	939	769	429	858	607	105	210	420	840
2	571	33	66	132	264	528	1056	1003	897	685
3	261	522	1044	979	849	589	69	138	276	552
4	1104	1099	1089	1069	1029	949	789	469	938	767
5	425	850	591	73	146	292	584	59	118	236
6	472	944	779	449	898	687	265	530	1060	1011
7	913	717	325	650	191	382	764	419	838	567
8	25	50	100	200	400	800	491	982	855	601
9	93	186	372	744	379	758	407	814	519	1038
10	967	825	541	1082	1055	1001	893	677	245	490
11	980	851	593	77	154	308	616	123	246	492
12	984	859	609	109	218	436	872	635	161	322
13	644	179	358	716	323	646	183	366	732	355
14	710	311	622	135	270	540	1080	1051	993	877
15	645	181	362	724	339	678	247	494	988	867
16	625	141	282	564	19	38	76	152	304	608
17	107	214	428	856	603	97	194	388	776	443
18	886	663	217	434	868	627	145	290	580	51
19	102	204	408	816	523	1046	983	857	605	101
20	202	404	808	507	1014	919	729	349	698	287
21	574	39	78	156	312	624	139	278	556	3
22	6	12	24	48	96	192	384	768	427	854
23	599	89	178	356	712	315	630	151	302	604
24	99	198	396	792	475	950	791	473	946	783
25	457	914	719	329	658	207	414	828	547	1094
26	1079	1049	989	869	629	149	298	596	83	166
27	332	664	219	438	876	643	177	354	708	307
28	614	119	238	476	952	795	481	962	815	521
29	1042	975	841	573	37	74	148	296	592	75
30	150	300	600	91	182	364	728	347	694	279
31	558	7	14	28	56	112	224	448	896	683
32	257	514	1028	947	785	461	922	735	361	722
33	335	670	231	462	924	739	369	738	367	734
34	359	718	327	654	199	398	796	483	966	823
35	537	1074	1039	969	829	549	1098	1087	1065	1021
36	933	757	405	810	511	1022	935	761	413	826
37	543	1086	1063	1017	925	741	373	746	383	766
38	423	846	583	57	114	228	456	912	715	321
39	642	175	350	700	291	582	55	110	220	440
40	880	651	193	386	772	435	870	631	153	306
41	612	115	230	460	920	731	353	706	303	606
42	103	206	412	824	539	1078	1047	985	861	613
43	117	234	468	936	763	417	834	559	9	18
44	36	72	144	288	576	43	86	172	344	688
45	267	534	1068	1027	945	781	453	906	703	297
46	594	79	158	316	632	155	310	620	131	262
47	524	1048	987	865	621	133	266	532	1064	1019
48	929	749	389	778	447	894	679	249	498	996
49	883	657	205	410	820	531	1062	1015	921	733

P = 1109

INDICES

	0	1	2	3	4	5	6	7	8	9
50	676	723	569	973	752	793	728	203	643	856
51	784	364	9	821	321	1014	666	852	606	98
52	589	289	31	194	470	610	936	949	25	742
53	67	495	477	998	451	764	847	350	574	424
54	145	102	633	370	1083	717	523	258	545	355
55	991	864	39	772	553	1107	218	593	310	437
56	909	1099	812	1077	163	529	924	79	656	699
57	978	20	904	293	210	1005	444	1031	1049	621
58	188	579	395	382	56	1024	748	585	843	35
59	652	52	298	112	460	875	267	563	918	230
60	302	89	757	174	239	198	419	15	169	122
61	512	1042	410	429	280	711	116	673	640	663
62	467	474	142	542	215	160	901	185	840	264
63	236	407	464	837	798	127	801	614	503	1091
64	601	986	390	275	130	150	135	887	879	967
65	73	401	804	940	343	1062	1010	491	254	1073
66	617	871	1038	181	271	1069	733	517	506	953
67	331	827	535	679	959	737	1094	107	155	486
68	567	726	782	319	604	29	934	65	449	572
69	631	521	989	551	308	810	922	976	208	1047
70	393	746	650	458	916	755	417	510	278	638
71	140	899	234	796	501	388	133	71	341	252
72	1036	731	329	957	153	780	932	629	306	206
73	648	415	138	499	339	327	930	646	337	335
74	890	375	892	691	93	859	377	706	882	481
75	894	686	1054	787	693	831	970	361	95	946
76	761	367	861	434	76	1002	379	49	227	12
77	708	539	404	1088	884	1059	178	824	483	62
78	807	455	896	249	626	324	688	683	943	46
79	1056	246	243	1017	789	285	346	768	695	1020
80	85	669	833	963	1065	722	972	792	202	855
81	363	820	1013	851	97	288	193	609	948	741
82	494	997	763	349	423	101	369	716	257	354
83	863	771	1106	592	436	1098	1076	528	78	698
84	19	292	1004	1030	620	578	381	1023	584	34
85	51	111	874	562	229	88	173	197	14	121
86	1041	428	710	672	662	473	541	159	184	263
87	406	836	126	613	1090	985	274	149	886	966
88	400	939	1061	490	1072	870	180	1068	516	952
89	826	678	736	106	485	725	318	28	64	571
90	520	550	809	975	1046	745	457	754	509	637
91	898	795	387	70	251	730	956	779	628	205
92	414	498	326	645	334	374	690	858	705	480
93	685	786	830	360	945	366	433	1001	48	11
94	538	1087	1058	823	61	454	248	323	682	45
95	245	1016	284	767	1019	668	962	721	791	854
96	819	850	287	608	740	996	348	100	715	353
97	770	591	1097	527	697	291	1029	577	1022	33
98	110	561	87	196	120	427	671	472	158	262
99	835	612	984	148	965	938	489	869	1067	951

POWER RESIDUES

	0	1	2	3	4	5	6	7	8	9
50	357	714	319	638	167	334	668	227	454	908
51	707	305	610	111	222	444	888	667	225	450
52	900	691	273	546	1092	1075	1041	973	837	565
53	21	42	84	168	336	672	235	470	940	771
54	433	866	623	137	274	548	1096	1083	1057	1005
55	901	693	277	554	1108	1107	1105	1101	1093	1077
56	1045	981	853	597	85	170	340	680	251	502
57	1004	899	689	269	538	1076	1043	977	845	581
58	53	106	212	424	848	587	65	130	260	520
59	1040	971	833	557	5	10	20	40	80	160
60	320	640	171	342	684	259	518	1036	963	817
61	525	1050	991	873	637	165	330	660	211	422
62	844	579	49	98	196	392	784	459	918	727
63	345	690	271	542	1084	1059	1009	909	709	309
64	618	127	254	508	1016	923	737	365	730	351
65	702	295	590	71	142	284	568	27	54	108
66	216	432	864	619	129	258	516	1032	955	801
67	493	986	863	617	125	250	500	1000	891	673
68	237	474	948	787	465	930	751	393	786	463
69	926	743	377	754	399	798	487	974	839	569
70	29	58	116	232	464	928	747	385	770	431
71	862	615	121	242	484	968	827	545	1090	1071
72	1033	957	805	501	1002	895	681	253	506	1012
73	915	721	333	666	223	446	892	675	241	482
74	964	819	529	1058	1007	905	701	293	586	63
75	126	252	504	1008	907	705	301	602	95	190
76	380	760	411	822	535	1070	1031	953	797	485
77	970	831	553	1106	1103	1097	1085	1061	1013	917
78	725	341	682	255	510	1020	931	753	397	794
79	479	958	807	505	1010	911	713	317	634	159
80	318	636	163	326	652	195	390	780	451	902
81	695	281	562	15	30	60	120	240	480	960
82	811	513	1026	943	777	445	890	671	233	466
83	932	755	401	802	495	990	871	633	157	314
84	628	147	294	588	67	134	268	536	1072	1035
85	961	813	517	1034	959	809	509	1018	927	745
86	381	762	415	830	551	1102	1095	1081	1053	997
87	885	661	213	426	852	595	81	162	324	648
88	187	374	748	387	774	439	878	647	185	370
89	740	371	742	375	750	391	782	455	910	711
90	313	626	143	286	572	35	70	140	280	560
91	11	22	44	88	176	352	704	299	598	87
92	174	348	696	283	566	23	46	92	184	368
93	736	363	726	343	686	263	526	1052	995	881
94	653	197	394	788	467	934	759	409	818	527
95	1054	999	889	669	229	458	916	723	337	674
96	239	478	956	803	497	994	879	649	189	378
97	756	403	806	503	1006	903	697	285	570	31
98	62	124	248	496	992	875	641	173	346	692
99	275	550	1100	1091	1073	1037	965	821	533	1066

P = 1109

INDICES

	0	1	2	3	4	5	6	7	8	9
100	677	105	724	27	570	549	974	744	753	636
101	794	69	729	778	204	497	644	373	857	479
102	785	359	365	1000	10	1086	822	453	322	44
103	1015	766	667	720	853	849	607	995	99	352
104	590	526	290	576	32	560	195	426	471	261
105	611	147	937	868	950	104	26	548	743	635
106	68	777	496	372	478	358	999	1085	452	43
107	765	719	848	994	351	525	575	559	425	260
108	146	867	103	547	634	776	371	357	1084	42
109	718	993	524	558	259	866	546	775	356	41
110	992	557	865	774	40	556	773	555	554	

POWER RESIDUES

	0	1	2	3	4	5	6	7	8	9
100	1023	937	765	421	842	575	41	82	164	328
101	656	203	406	812	515	1030	951	793	477	954
102	799	489	978	847	585	61	122	244	488	976
103	843	577	45	90	180	360	720	331	662	215
104	430	860	611	113	226	452	904	699	289	578
105	47	94	188	376	752	395	790	471	942	775
106	441	882	655	201	402	804	499	998	887	665
107	221	442	884	659	209	418	836	563	17	34
108	68	136	272	544	1088	1067	1025	941	773	437
109	874	639	169	338	676	243	486	972	835	561
110	13	26	52	104	208	416	832	555		

P = 1117

INDICES

	0	1	2	3	4	5	6	7	8	9
0		0	1	1104	2	753	1105	346	3	1092
1	754	465	1106	612	347	741	4	299	1093	435
2	755	334	466	62	1107	390	613	1080	348	863
3	742	580	5	453	300	1099	1094	162	436	600
4	756	232	335	503	467	729	63	474	1108	692
5	391	287	614	226	1081	102	349	423	864	683
6	743	1016	581	322	6	249	454	167	301	50
7	1100	431	1095	283	163	378	437	811	601	676
8	757	1068	233	382	336	1052	504	851	468	144
9	730	958	64	568	475	72	1109	484	693	441
10	392	82	288	655	615	1087	227	278	1082	884
11	103	150	350	974	424	815	865	588	684	645
12	744	930	1017	220	582	27	323	637	7	491
13	250	605	455	781	168	717	302	889	51	192
14	1101	462	432	1077	1096	500	284	680	164	375
15	379	955	438	275	812	217	602	189	677	214
16	758	408	1069	761	234	90	383	268	337	108
17	1053	411	505	129	852	736	469	671	145	1072
18	731	33	959	1004	65	915	569	764	476	310
19	73	874	1110	243	485	237	694	260	442	822
20	393	155	83	93	289	985	656	38	616	900
21	1088	386	228	419	279	140	1083	926	885	271
22	104	911	151	922	351	366	975	340	425	711
23	816	799	866	355	589	111	685	664	646	964
24	745	831	931	1056	1018	329	221	1047	583	370
25	28	414	324	527	638	1040	8	700	492	508
26	251	839	606	805	456	979	782	132	169	788
27	718	1009	303	946	890	855	52	532	193	556
28	1102	344	463	739	433	60	1078	578	1097	598
29	501	472	285	100	681	320	165	429	376	674
30	380	849	956	70	439	653	276	148	813	643
31	218	635	603	715	190	1075	678	953	215	212
32	759	266	409	734	1070	1002	762	872	235	820
33	91	36	384	138	269	920	338	797	109	962
34	1054	1045	412	1038	506	803	130	1007	853	554
35	737	576	470	318	672	68	146	633	1073	210
36	732	870	34	918	960	1036	1005	574	66	208
37	916	572	570	13	765	15	477	359	311	767
38	74	625	875	17	1111	448	244	479	486	403
39	238	361	695	593	261	313	443	175	823	769
40	394	516	156	76	84	705	94	627	290	115
41	986	877	657	1029	39	19	617	180	901	1113
42	1089	296	387	450	229	689	420	246	280	1065
43	141	481	1084	971	927	488	886	497	272	405
44	105	668	912	240	152	897	923	363	352	828
45	367	697	976	943	341	595	426	650	712	263
46	817	794	800	315	867	205	356	445	590	513
47	112	177	686	968	665	825	647	202	965	771
48	746	774	832	396	932	121	1057	518	1019	749
49	330	158	222	46	1048	78	584	777	371	86

POWER RESIDUES

	0	1	2	3	4	5	6	7	8	9
0	1	2	4	8	16	32	64	128	256	512
1	1024	931	745	373	746	375	750	383	766	415
2	830	543	1086	1055	993	869	621	125	250	500
3	1000	883	649	181	362	724	331	662	207	414
4	828	539	1078	1039	961	805	493	986	855	593
5	69	138	276	552	1104	1091	1065	1013	909	701
6	285	570	23	46	92	184	368	736	355	710
7	303	606	95	190	380	760	403	806	495	990
8	863	609	101	202	404	808	499	998	879	641
9	165	330	660	203	406	812	507	1014	911	705
10	293	586	55	110	220	440	880	643	169	338
11	676	235	470	940	763	409	818	519	1038	959
12	801	485	970	823	529	1058	999	881	645	173
13	346	692	267	534	1068	1019	921	725	333	666
14	215	430	860	603	89	178	356	712	307	614
15	111	222	444	888	659	201	402	804	491	982
16	847	577	37	74	148	296	592	67	134	268
17	536	1072	1027	937	757	397	794	471	942	767
18	417	834	551	1102	1087	1057	997	877	637	157
19	314	628	139	278	556	1112	1107	1097	1077	1037
20	957	797	477	954	791	465	930	743	369	738
21	359	718	319	638	159	318	636	155	310	620
22	123	246	492	984	851	585	53	106	212	424
23	848	579	41	82	164	328	656	195	390	780
24	443	886	655	193	386	772	427	854	591	65
25	130	260	520	1040	963	809	501	1002	887	657
26	197	394	788	459	918	719	321	642	167	334
27	668	219	438	876	635	153	306	612	107	214
28	428	856	595	73	146	292	584	51	102	204
29	408	816	515	1030	943	769	421	842	567	17
30	34	68	136	272	544	1088	1059	1001	885	653
31	189	378	756	395	790	463	926	735	353	706
32	295	590	63	126	252	504	1008	899	681	245
33	490	980	843	569	21	42	84	168	336	672
34	227	454	908	699	281	562	7	14	28	56
35	112	224	448	896	675	233	466	932	747	377
36	754	391	782	447	894	671	225	450	900	683
37	249	498	996	875	633	149	298	596	75	150
38	300	600	83	166	332	664	211	422	844	571
39	25	50	100	200	400	800	483	966	815	513
40	1026	935	753	389	778	439	878	639	161	322
41	644	171	342	684	251	502	1004	891	665	213
42	426	852	587	57	114	228	456	912	707	297
43	594	71	142	284	568	19	38	76	152	304
44	608	99	198	396	792	467	934	751	385	770
45	423	846	575	33	66	132	264	528	1056	995
46	873	629	141	282	564	11	22	44	88	176
47	352	704	291	582	47	94	188	376	752	387
48	774	431	862	607	97	194	388	776	435	870
49	623	129	258	516	1032	947	777	437	874	631

P = 1117

INDICES

	0	1	2	3	4	5	6	7	8	9
50	29	256	415	707	325	835	528	96	639	998
51	1041	629	9	399	701	292	493	939	509	117
52	252	935	840	988	607	724	806	879	457	124
53	980	659	783	844	133	1031	170	1060	789	41
54	719	540	1010	21	304	521	947	619	891	992
55	856	182	53	1022	533	903	194	545	557	1115
56	1103	752	345	1091	464	611	740	298	434	333
57	61	389	1079	862	579	452	1098	161	599	231
58	502	728	473	691	286	225	101	422	682	1015
59	321	248	166	49	430	282	377	810	675	1067
60	381	1051	850	143	957	567	71	483	440	81
61	654	1086	277	883	149	973	814	587	644	929
62	219	26	636	490	604	780	716	888	191	461
63	1076	499	679	374	954	274	216	188	213	407
64	760	89	267	107	410	128	735	670	1071	32
65	1003	914	763	309	873	242	236	259	821	154
66	92	984	37	899	385	418	139	925	270	910
67	921	365	339	710	798	354	110	663	963	830
68	1055	328	1046	369	413	526	1039	699	507	838
69	804	978	131	787	1008	945	854	531	555	343
70	738	59	577	597	471	99	319	428	673	848
71	69	652	147	642	634	714	1074	952	211	265
72	733	1001	871	819	35	137	919	796	961	1044
73	1037	802	1006	553	575	317	67	632	209	869
74	917	1035	573	207	571	12	14	358	766	624
75	16	447	478	402	360	592	312	174	768	515
76	75	704	626	114	876	1028	18	179	1112	295
77	449	688	245	1064	480	970	487	496	404	667
78	239	896	362	827	696	942	594	649	262	793
79	314	204	444	512	176	967	824	201	770	773
80	395	120	517	748	157	45	77	776	85	255
81	706	834	95	997	628	398	291	938	116	934
82	987	723	878	123	658	843	1030	1059	40	539
83	20	520	618	991	181	1021	902	544	1114	751
84	1090	610	297	332	388	861	451	160	230	727
85	690	224	421	1014	247	48	281	809	1066	1050
86	142	566	482	80	1085	882	972	586	928	25
87	489	779	887	460	498	373	273	187	406	88
88	106	127	669	31	913	308	241	258	153	983
89	898	417	924	909	364	709	353	662	829	327
90	368	525	698	837	977	786	944	530	342	58
91	596	98	427	847	651	641	713	951	264	1000
92	818	136	795	1043	801	552	316	631	868	1034
93	206	11	357	623	446	401	591	173	514	703
94	113	1027	178	294	687	1063	969	495	666	895
95	826	941	648	792	203	511	966	200	772	119
96	747	44	775	254	833	996	397	937	933	722
97	122	842	1058	538	519	990	1020	543	750	609
98	331	860	159	726	223	1013	47	808	1049	565
99	79	881	585	24	778	459	372	186	87	126

POWER RESIDUES

	0	1	2	3	4	5	6	7	8	9
50	145	290	580	43	86	172	344	688	259	518
51	1036	955	793	469	938	759	401	802	487	974
52	831	545	1090	1063	1009	901	685	253	506	1012
53	907	697	277	554	1108	1099	1081	1045	973	829
54	541	1082	1047	977	837	557	1114	1111	1105	1093
55	1069	1021	925	733	349	698	279	558	1116	1115
56	1113	1109	1101	1085	1053	989	861	605	93	186
57	372	744	371	742	367	734	351	702	287	574
58	31	62	124	248	496	992	867	617	117	234
59	468	936	755	393	786	455	910	703	289	578
60	39	78	156	312	624	131	262	524	1048	979
61	841	565	13	26	52	104	208	416	832	547
62	1094	1071	1025	933	749	381	762	407	814	511
63	1022	927	737	357	714	311	622	127	254	508
64	1016	915	713	309	618	119	238	476	952	787
65	457	914	711	305	610	103	206	412	824	531
66	1062	1007	897	677	237	474	948	779	441	882
67	647	177	354	708	299	598	79	158	316	632
68	147	294	588	59	118	236	472	944	771	425
69	850	583	49	98	196	392	784	451	902	687
70	257	514	1028	939	761	405	810	503	1006	895
71	673	229	458	916	715	313	626	135	270	540
72	1080	1043	969	821	525	1050	983	849	581	45
73	90	180	360	720	323	646	175	350	700	283
74	566	15	30	60	120	240	480	960	803	489
75	978	839	561	5	10	20	40	80	160	320
76	640	163	326	652	187	374	748	379	758	399
77	798	479	958	799	481	962	807	497	994	871
78	625	133	266	532	1064	1011	905	693	269	538
79	1076	1035	953	789	461	922	727	337	674	231
80	462	924	731	345	690	263	526	1052	987	857
81	597	77	154	308	616	115	230	460	920	723
82	329	658	199	398	796	475	950	783	449	898
83	679	241	482	964	811	505	1010	903	689	261
84	522	1044	971	825	533	1066	1015	913	709	301
85	602	87	174	348	696	275	550	1100	1083	1049
86	981	845	573	29	58	116	232	464	928	739
87	361	722	327	654	191	382	764	411	822	527
88	1054	991	865	613	109	218	436	872	627	137
89	274	548	1096	1075	1033	949	781	445	890	663
90	209	418	836	555	1110	1103	1089	1061	1005	893
91	669	221	442	884	651	185	370	740	363	726
92	335	670	223	446	892	667	217	434	868	619
93	121	242	484	968	819	521	1042	967	817	517
94	1034	951	785	453	906	695	273	546	1092	1067
95	1017	917	717	317	634	151	302	604	91	182
96	364	728	339	678	239	478	956	795	473	946
97	775	433	866	615	113	226	452	904	691	265
98	530	1060	1003	889	661	205	410	820	523	1046
99	975	833	549	1098	1079	1041	965	813	509	1018

P = 1117

INDICES

	0	1	2	3	4	5	6	7	8	9
100	30	307	257	982	416	908	708	661	326	524
101	836	785	529	57	97	846	640	950	999	135
102	1042	551	630	1033	10	622	400	172	702	1026
103	293	1062	494	894	940	791	510	199	118	43
104	253	995	936	721	841	537	989	542	608	859
105	725	1012	807	564	880	23	458	185	125	306
106	981	907	660	523	784	56	845	949	134	550
107	1032	621	171	1025	1061	893	790	198	42	994
108	720	536	541	858	1011	563	22	184	305	906
109	522	55	948	549	620	1024	892	197	993	535
110	857	562	183	905	54	548	1023	196	534	561
111	904	547	195	560	546	559	558			

POWER RESIDUES

	0	1	2	3	4	5	6	7	8	9
100	919	721	325	650	183	366	732	347	694	271
101	542	1084	1051	985	853	589	61	122	244	488
102	976	835	553	1106	1095	1073	1029	941	765	413
103	826	535	1070	1023	929	741	365	730	343	686
104	255	510	1020	923	729	341	682	247	494	988
105	859	601	85	170	340	680	243	486	972	827
106	537	1074	1031	945	773	429	858	599	81	162
107	324	648	179	358	716	315	630	143	286	572
108	27	54	108	216	432	864	611	105	210	420
109	840	563	9	18	36	72	144	288	576	35
110	70	140	280	560	3	6	12	24	48	96
111	192	384	768	419	838	559				

P = 1123

INDICES

	0	1	2	3	4	5	6	7	8	9
0		0	1	197	2	243	198	510	3	394
1	244	177	199	527	511	440	4	186	395	866
2	245	707	178	104	200	486	528	591	512	401
3	441	675	5	374	187	753	396	647	867	724
4	246	1096	708	276	179	637	105	43	201	1020
5	487	383	529	98	592	420	513	1063	402	818
6	442	652	676	904	6	770	375	940	188	301
7	754	523	397	633	648	683	868	687	725	236
8	247	788	1097	213	709	429	277	598	180	782
9	638	1037	106	872	44	1109	202	897	1021	571
10	488	583	384	67	530	950	99	415	593	691
11	421	844	514	266	1064	347	403	921	819	696
12	443	354	653	171	677	729	905	973	7	473
13	771	119	376	254	941	834	189	27	302	735
14	755	240	524	704	398	644	634	95	649	298
15	684	426	869	580	688	918	726	251	237	295
16	248	614	789	1007	1098	617	214	717	710	1054
17	430	138	278	792	599	996	181	1015	783	261
18	639	1010	1038	849	107	890	873	363	45	1101
19	1110	1028	203	555	898	967	1022	620	572	325
20	489	15	584	911	385	217	68	498	531	1043
21	951	506	100	720	416	519	594	63	692	830
22	422	713	845	321	515	880	267	1078	1065	1057
23	348	884	404	465	922	286	820	433	697	154
24	444	854	355	985	654	141	172	271	678	410
25	730	133	906	281	974	626	8	546	474	35
26	772	795	120	1082	377	341	255	979	942	602
27	835	161	190	112	28	663	303	999	736	1069
28	756	1120	241	392	525	184	705	484	399	372
29	645	1094	635	1018	96	1061	650	768	299	631
30	685	786	427	780	870	895	581	948	689	264
31	919	352	727	471	252	25	238	642	296	578
32	249	612	615	1052	790	1013	1008	888	1099	553
33	618	13	215	1041	718	61	711	878	1055	463
34	431	852	139	408	279	544	793	339	600	110
35	997	1118	182	370	1016	766	784	893	262	469
36	640	610	1011	551	1039	876	850	542	108	368
37	891	608	874	366	364	926	46	928	1102	314
38	1111	48	1029	331	204	930	556	670	899	1104
39	968	290	1023	316	621	479	573	1113	326	451
40	490	50	16	80	585	1031	912	824	386	333
41	218	224	69	206	499	456	532	932	1044	744
42	952	558	507	437	101	672	721	40	417	901
43	520	233	595	1106	64	841	693	970	831	701
44	423	292	714	993	846	1025	322	495	516	318
45	881	151	268	623	1079	158	1066	481	1058	777
46	349	575	885	58	405	1115	466	539	923	328
47	287	448	821	453	434	230	698	492	155	55
48	445	52	855	811	356	18	986	858	655	82
49	142	800	173	587	272	814	679	1033	411	167

POWER RESIDUES

	0	1	2	3	4	5	6	7	8	9
0	1	2	4	8	16	32	64	128	256	512
1	1024	925	727	331	662	201	402	804	485	970
2	817	511	1022	921	719	315	630	137	274	548
3	1096	1069	1015	907	691	259	518	1036	949	775
4	427	854	585	47	94	188	376	752	381	762
5	401	802	481	962	801	479	958	793	463	926
6	729	335	670	217	434	868	613	103	206	412
7	824	525	1050	977	831	539	1078	1033	943	763
8	403	806	489	978	833	543	1086	1049	975	827
9	531	1062	1001	879	635	147	294	588	53	106
10	212	424	848	573	23	46	92	184	368	736
11	349	698	273	546	1092	1061	999	875	627	131
12	262	524	1048	973	823	523	1046	969	815	507
13	1014	905	687	251	502	1004	885	647	171	342
14	684	245	490	980	837	551	1102	1081	1039	955
15	787	451	902	681	239	478	956	789	455	910
16	697	271	542	1084	1045	967	811	499	998	873
17	623	123	246	492	984	845	567	11	22	44
18	88	176	352	704	285	570	17	34	68	136
19	272	544	1088	1053	983	843	563	3	6	12
20	24	48	96	192	384	768	413	826	529	1058
21	993	863	603	83	166	332	664	205	410	820
22	517	1034	945	767	411	822	521	1042	961	799
23	475	950	777	431	862	601	79	158	316	632
24	141	282	564	5	10	20	40	80	160	320
25	640	157	314	628	133	266	532	1064	1005	887
26	651	179	358	716	309	618	113	226	452	904
27	685	247	494	988	853	583	43	86	172	344
28	688	253	506	1012	901	679	235	470	940	757
29	391	782	441	882	641	159	318	636	149	298
30	596	69	138	276	552	1104	1085	1047	971	819
31	515	1030	937	751	379	758	393	786	449	898
32	673	223	446	892	661	199	398	796	469	938
33	753	383	766	409	818	513	1026	929	735	347
34	694	265	530	1060	997	871	619	115	230	460
35	920	717	311	622	121	242	484	968	813	503
36	1006	889	655	187	374	748	373	746	369	738
37	353	706	289	578	33	66	132	264	528	1056
38	989	855	587	51	102	204	408	816	509	1018
39	913	703	283	566	9	18	36	72	144	288
40	576	29	58	116	232	464	928	733	343	686
41	249	498	996	869	615	107	214	428	856	589
42	55	110	220	440	880	637	151	302	604	85
43	170	340	680	237	474	948	773	423	846	569
44	15	30	60	120	240	480	960	797	471	942
45	761	399	798	473	946	769	415	830	537	1074
46	1025	927	731	339	678	233	466	932	741	359
47	718	313	626	129	258	516	1032	941	759	395
48	790	457	914	705	287	574	25	50	100	200
49	400	800	477	954	785	447	894	665	207	414

P = 1123

INDICES

	0	1	2	3	4	5	6	7	8	9
50	731	914	134	359	907	826	282	129	975	388
51	627	21	9	335	547	310	475	220	36	989
52	773	226	796	125	121	71	1083	861	378	208
53	342	90	256	501	980	658	943	458	603	75
54	836	534	162	85	191	934	113	961	29	1046
55	664	145	304	746	1000	1087	737	954	1070	803
56	757	560	1121	196	242	509	393	176	526	439
57	185	865	706	103	485	590	400	674	373	752
58	646	723	1095	275	636	42	1019	382	97	419
59	1062	817	651	903	769	939	300	522	632	682
60	686	235	787	212	428	597	781	1036	871	1108
61	896	570	582	66	949	414	690	843	265	346
62	920	695	353	170	728	972	472	118	253	833
63	26	734	239	703	643	94	297	425	579	917
64	250	294	613	1006	616	716	1053	137	791	995
65	1014	260	1009	848	889	362	1100	1027	554	966
66	619	324	14	910	216	497	1042	505	719	518
67	62	829	712	320	879	1077	1056	883	464	285
68	432	153	853	984	140	270	409	132	280	625
69	545	34	794	1081	340	978	601	160	111	662
70	998	1068	1119	391	183	483	371	1093	1017	1060
71	767	630	785	779	894	947	263	351	470	24
72	641	577	611	1051	1012	887	552	12	1040	60
73	877	462	851	407	543	338	109	1117	369	765
74	892	468	609	550	875	541	367	607	365	925
75	927	313	47	330	929	669	1103	289	315	478
76	1112	450	49	79	1030	823	332	223	205	455
77	931	743	557	436	671	39	900	232	1105	840
78	969	700	291	992	1024	494	317	150	622	157
79	480	776	574	57	1114	538	327	447	452	229
80	491	54	51	810	17	857	81	799	586	813
81	1032	166	913	358	825	128	387	20	334	309
82	219	988	225	124	70	860	207	89	500	657
83	457	74	533	84	933	960	1045	144	745	1086
84	953	802	559	195	508	175	438	864	102	589
85	673	751	722	274	41	381	418	816	902	938
86	521	681	234	211	596	1035	1107	569	65	413
87	842	345	694	169	971	117	832	733	702	93
88	424	916	293	1005	715	136	994	259	847	361
89	1026	965	323	909	496	504	517	828	319	1076
90	882	284	152	983	269	131	624	33	1080	977
91	159	661	1067	390	482	1092	1059	629	778	946
92	350	23	576	1050	886	11	59	461	406	337
93	1116	764	467	549	540	606	924	312	329	668
94	288	477	449	78	822	222	454	742	435	38
95	231	839	699	991	493	149	156	775	56	537
96	446	228	53	809	856	798	812	165	357	127
97	19	308	987	123	859	88	656	73	83	959
98	143	1085	801	194	174	863	588	750	273	380
99	815	937	680	210	1034	568	412	344	168	116

POWER RESIDUES

	0	1	2	3	4	5	6	7	8	9
50	828	533	1066	1009	895	667	211	422	844	565
51	7	14	28	56	112	224	448	896	669	215
52	430	860	597	71	142	284	568	13	26	52
53	104	208	416	832	541	1082	1041	959	795	467
54	934	745	367	734	345	690	257	514	1028	933
55	743	363	726	329	658	193	386	772	421	842
56	561	1122	1121	1119	1115	1107	1091	1059	995	867
57	611	99	198	396	792	461	922	721	319	638
58	153	306	612	101	202	404	808	493	986	849
59	575	27	54	108	216	432	864	605	87	174
60	348	696	269	538	1076	1029	935	747	371	742
61	361	722	321	642	161	322	644	165	330	660
62	197	394	788	453	906	689	255	510	1020	917
63	711	299	598	73	146	292	584	45	90	180
64	360	720	317	634	145	290	580	37	74	148
65	296	592	61	122	244	488	976	829	535	1070
66	1017	911	699	275	550	1100	1077	1031	939	755
67	387	774	425	850	577	31	62	124	248	496
68	992	861	599	75	150	300	600	77	154	308
69	616	109	218	436	872	621	119	238	476	952
70	781	439	878	633	143	286	572	21	42	84
71	168	336	672	221	442	884	645	167	334	668
72	213	426	852	581	39	78	156	312	624	125
73	250	500	1000	877	631	139	278	556	1112	1101
74	1079	1035	947	771	419	838	553	1106	1089	1055
75	987	851	579	35	70	140	280	560	1120	1117
76	1111	1099	1075	1027	931	739	355	710	297	594
77	65	130	260	520	1040	957	791	459	918	713
78	303	606	89	178	356	712	301	602	81	162
79	324	648	173	346	692	261	522	1044	965	807
80	491	982	841	559	1118	1113	1103	1083	1043	963
81	803	483	966	809	495	990	857	591	59	118
82	236	472	944	765	407	814	505	1010	897	671
83	219	438	876	629	135	270	540	1080	1037	951
84	779	435	870	617	111	222	444	888	653	183
85	366	732	341	682	241	482	964	805	487	974
86	825	527	1054	985	847	571	19	38	76	152
87	304	608	93	186	372	744	365	730	337	674
88	225	450	900	677	231	462	924	725	327	654
89	185	370	740	357	714	305	610	97	194	388
90	776	429	858	593	63	126	252	504	1008	893
91	663	203	406	812	501	1002	881	639	155	310
92	620	117	234	468	936	749	375	750	377	754
93	385	770	417	834	545	1090	1057	991	859	595
94	67	134	268	536	1072	1021	919	715	307	614
95	105	210	420	840	557	1114	1105	1087	1051	979
96	835	547	1094	1065	1007	891	659	195	390	780
97	437	874	625	127	254	508	1016	909	695	267
98	534	1068	1013	903	683	243	486	972	821	519
99	1038	953	783	443	886	649	175	350	700	277

P = 1123

INDICES

	0	1	2	3	4	5	6	7	8	9
100	732	92	915	1004	135	258	360	964	908	503
101	827	1075	283	982	130	32	976	660	389	1091
102	628	945	22	1049	10	460	336	763	548	605
103	311	667	476	77	221	741	37	838	990	148
104	774	536	227	808	797	164	126	307	122	87
105	72	958	1084	193	862	749	379	936	209	567
106	343	115	91	1003	257	963	502	1074	981	31
107	659	1090	944	1048	459	762	604	666	76	740
108	837	147	535	807	163	306	86	957	192	748
109	935	566	114	1002	962	1073	30	1089	1047	761
110	665	739	146	806	305	956	747	565	1001	1072
111	1088	760	738	805	955	564	1071	759	804	563
112	758	562	561							

POWER RESIDUES

	0	1	2	3	4	5	6	7	8	9
100	554	1108	1093	1063	1003	883	643	163	326	652
101	181	362	724	325	650	177	354	708	293	586
102	49	98	196	392	784	445	890	657	191	382
103	764	405	810	497	994	865	607	91	182	364
104	728	333	666	209	418	836	549	1098	1073	1023
105	923	723	323	646	169	338	676	229	458	916
106	709	295	590	57	114	228	456	912	701	279
107	558	1116	1109	1095	1067	1011	899	675	227	454
108	908	693	263	526	1052	981	839	555	1110	1097
109	1071	1019	915	707	291	582	41	82	164	328
110	656	189	378	756	389	778	433	866	609	95
111	190	380	760	397	794	465	930	737	351	702
112	281	562								

P = 1129

INDICES

	0	1	2	3	4	5	6	7	8	9
0		0	298	1114	596	772	284	530	894	1100
1	1070	1	582	991	828	758	64	809	270	903
2	240	516	299	930	880	416	161	1086	1126	449
3	1056	987	362	1115	1107	174	568	411	73	977
4	538	905	814	404	597	744	100	812	50	1060
5	714	795	459	112	256	773	296	889	747	555
6	226	153	157	502	660	635	285	261	277	916
7	472	466	866	913	709	402	371	531	147	666
8	836	1072	75	287	1112	453	702	435	895	135
9	1042	393	398	973	1110	547	348	720	230	1101
10	1012	833	1093	595	757	160	410	49	554	471
11	1071	397	594	58	59	574	1045	963	853	211
12	524	2	451	891	455	60	800	856	958	390
13	933	742	583	305	559	730	575	785	86	479
14	770	798	764	992	36	93	83	1046	1007	736
15	700	900	669	781	829	631	445	1090	964	98
16	6	332	242	52	373	759	585	8	282	854
17	751	875	1000	673	733	946	65	541	433	1053
18	212	684	691	139	696	55	143	810	280	488
19	845	525	646	165	1018	621	528	956	271	351
20	182	247	3	979	263	549	893	902	1055	904
21	458	501	708	452	347	48	852	389	769	899
22	241	672	695	620	892	388	356	640	357	420
23	872	517	215	924	133	456	23	652	509	641
24	822	727	300	1058	749	704	61	766	753	273
25	358	28	1098	931	26	439	128	801	688	941
26	103	421	1040	499	881	884	603	121	857	80
27	1028	712	873	379	1083	417	384	484	777	959
28	1068	740	1096	518	1062	533	162	307	334	490
29	391	706	381	936	216	199	177	1087	1034	793
30	998	934	70	819	967	925	1079	505	1127	581
31	929	1106	743	295	260	146	134	1011	396	450
32	304	35	630	584	540	279	350	457	671	214
33	1057	25	883	383	306	1033	580	303	24	44
34	1049	988	45	462	170	560	971	345	1031	653
35	116	949	363	1050	839	110	731	197	223	1037
36	510	678	982	1116	989	557	437	576	994	877
37	353	642	441	520	1108	46	578	312	786	908
38	15	842	823	254	944	175	463	376	188	87
39	919	611	826	728	126	310	569	171	649	291
40	480	723	545	850	301	716	149	412	561	244
41	847	771	63	1085	72	1059	225	465	74	972
42	756	573	799	784	1006	97	750	683	645	978
43	346	387	22	765	687	79	1067	705	69	294
44	539	1032	970	196	993	907	918	722	62	783
45	686	906	654	886	938	37	655	314	718	767
46	42	40	815	117	513	617	94	887	431	791
47	754	1076	321	405	950	191	807	84	939	13
48	1120	274	1025	318	598	364	228	897	1047	38
49	1002	184	359	130	1064	745	1051	996	571	1008

POWER RESIDUES

	0	1	2	3	4	5	6	7	8	9
0	1	11	121	202	1093	733	160	631	167	708
1	1014	993	762	479	753	380	793	820	1117	997
2	806	963	432	236	338	331	254	536	251	503
3	1017	1026	1125	1085	645	321	144	455	489	863
4	461	555	460	544	339	342	375	738	215	107
5	48	528	163	664	530	185	906	934	113	114
6	125	246	448	412	16	176	807	974	553	438
7	302	1064	414	38	418	82	902	890	758	435
8	269	701	937	146	477	731	138	389	892	780
9	677	673	629	145	466	610	1065	425	159	620
10	46	506	1050	260	602	977	586	801	908	956
11	355	518	53	583	768	545	350	463	577	702
12	948	267	679	695	871	549	394	947	256	558
13	493	907	945	234	316	89	979	608	1043	183
14	884	692	838	186	917	1055	315	78	858	406
15	1079	579	724	61	671	607	1032	62	682	728
16	105	26	286	888	736	193	994	773	600	955
17	344	397	980	619	35	385	848	296	998	817
18	1084	634	200	1071	491	885	703	959	388	881
19	659	475	709	1025	1114	964	443	357	540	295
20	987	696	882	670	596	911	989	718	1124	1074
21	524	119	180	851	329	232	294	976	575	680
22	706	992	751	358	551	416	60	660	486	830
23	98	1078	568	603	988	707	1003	872	560	515
24	20	220	162	653	409	1112	942	201	1082	612
25	1087	667	563	548	383	826	54	594	889	747
26	314	67	737	204	1115	975	564	559	504	1028
27	18	198	1049	249	481	775	622	68	748	325
28	188	939	168	719	6	66	726	83	913	1011
29	960	399	1002	861	439	313	56	616	2	22
30	242	404	1057	337	320	133	334	287	899	857
31	395	958	377	760	457	511	1105	865	483	797
32	864	472	676	662	508	1072	502	1006	905	923
33	1121	1041	161	642	288	910	978	597	922	1110
34	920	1088	678	684	750	347	430	214	96	1056
35	326	199	1060	370	683	739	226	228	250	492
36	896	824	32	352	485	819	1106	876	604	999
37	828	76	836	164	675	651	387	870	538	273
38	745	292	954	333	276	778	655	431	225	217
39	129	290	932	91	1001	850	318	111	92	1012
40	971	520	75	825	43	473	687	783	710	1036
41	106	37	407	1090	700	926	25	275	767	534
42	229	261	613	1098	788	765	512	1116	986	685
43	761	468	632	178	829	87	957	366	639	255
44	547	372	705	981	630	156	587	812	1029	29
45	319	122	213	85	935	124	235	327	210	52
46	572	647	343	386	859	417	71	781	688	794
47	831	109	70	770	567	592	867	505	1039	139
48	400	1013	982	641	277	789	776	633	189	950
49	289	921	1099	799	886	714	1080	590	845	263

P = 1129

INDICES

	0	1	2	3	4	5	6	7	8	9
50	656	1122	326	29	268	477	101	840	324	663
51	737	315	426	861	1099	239	986	813	111	659
52	401	701	719	553	210	932	797	668	51	732
53	54	527	901	768	419	821	27	1039	378	1061
54	198	1078	1010	670	43	115	677	440	253	125
55	715	224	682	68	782	41	1075	1024	129	267
56	238	796	1038	252	266	830	816	474	232	802
57	831	693	460	511	605	218	632	118	788	151
58	689	817	1004	113	679	607	106	446	514	762
59	497	942	475	591	257	983	204	337	1091	618
60	168	615	104	233	368	774	1117	155	137	965
61	95	675	249	422	803	535	297	990	879	173
62	99	888	276	665	1041	832	593	890	558	92
63	444	7	432	487	181	500	694	923	748	438
64	602	483	333	792	928	34	882	461	838	556
65	577	375	648	243	755	386	969	885	512	190
66	227	995	323	658	53	1077	681	251	604	606
67	203	154	878	91	601	374	322	90	342	122
68	219	626	158	354	343	429	760	406	468	1103
69	858	633	141	503	643	123	201	586	951	910
70	414	81	119	186	661	442	220	235	9	192
71	408	638	1029	789	495	636	521	627	207	283
72	808	1125	976	713	152	865	286	1109	159	1044
73	855	85	735	5	874	690	164	262	47	355
74	651	752	940	1027	739	380	818	259	278	579
75	344	222	876	14	610	544	1084	1005	78	917
76	313	430	12	1001	1121	425	552	418	114	1074
77	473	787	761	167	674	275	486	927	385	680
78	89	467	909	407	1124	734	1026	609	424	485
79	608	588	867	16	469	870	947	319	589	493
80	778	107	1021	914	843	1104	20	66	599	868
81	1014	960	447	698	710	824	859	179	542	365
82	17	563	1069	515	361	403	255	634	370	434
83	229	470	523	741	763	780	372	945	142	955
84	1054	898	871	726	1097	498	1082	532	176	504
85	395	213	1048	948	981	519	943	309	148	464
86	644	293	685	39	320	317	1063	476	985	667
87	377	124	237	692	1003	590	367	534	592	922
88	837	189	202	625	140	185	494	864	163	258
89	77	1073	88	587	1020	697	360	779	1081	308
90	984	921	76	920	952	328	56	131	108	805
91	335	205	953	288	612	911	1016	144	1065	1022
92	340	491	338	329	1113	827	415	567	811	746
93	915	835	392	1092	57	454	729	82	1089	281
94	1052	844	246	707	619	132	703	127	120	776
95	489	997	1105	629	382	169	109	436	311	187
96	290	846	572	21	195	937	616	806	896	570
97	662	400	526	1009	67	265	217	105	336	136
98	172	443	482	647	657	600	428	200	234	206
99	1043	650	221	11	166	1123	869	19	178	369

POWER RESIDUES

	0	1	2	3	4	5	6	7	8	9
50	635	211	63	693	849	307	1119	1019	1048	238
51	360	573	658	464	588	823	21	231	283	855
52	373	716	1102	832	120	191	972	531	196	1027
53	7	77	847	285	877	615	1120	1030	40	440
54	324	177	818	1095	755	402	1035	95	1045	205
55	1126	1096	766	523	108	59	649	365	628	134
56	345	408	1101	821	1128	1118	1008	927	36	396
57	969	498	962	421	115	136	367	650	376	749
58	336	309	12	132	323	166	697	893	791	798
59	875	593	878	626	112	103	4	44	484	808
60	985	674	640	266	668	574	669	585	790	787
61	754	391	914	1022	1081	601	966	465	599	944
62	223	195	1016	1015	1004	883	681	717	1113	953
63	322	155	576	691	827	65	715	1091	711	1047
64	227	239	371	694	860	428	192	983	652	398
65	991	740	237	349	452	456	500	984	663	519
66	64	704	970	509	1083	623	79	869	527	152
67	543	328	221	173	774	611	1076	546	361	584
68	779	666	552	427	181	862	450	434	258	580
69	735	182	873	571	636	222	184	895	813	1040
70	150	521	86	946	245	437	291	943	212	74
71	814	1051	271	723	50	550	405	1068	458	522
72	97	1067	447	401	1024	1103	843	241	393	936
73	135	356	529	174	785	732	149	510	1094	744
74	281	833	131	312	45	495	929	58	638	244
75	426	170	741	248	470	654	420	104	15	165
76	686	772	589	834	142	433	247	459	533	218
77	140	411	5	55	605	1010	949	278	800	897
78	835	153	554	449	423	137	378	771	578	713
79	1069	469	643	299	1031	51	561	526	141	422
80	126	257	569	614	1109	909	967	476	720	17
81	187	928	47	517	42	462	566	581	746	303
82	1075	535	240	382	815	1062	392	925	14	154
83	565	570	625	101	1111	931	80	880	648	354
84	507	1061	381	804	941	190	961	410	1123	1063
85	403	1046	216	118	169	730	127	268	690	816
86	1073	513	1127	1107	887	725	72	792	809	996
87	795	842	230	272	734	171	752	369	672	618
88	24	264	646	332	265	657	453	467	621	57
89	627	123	224	206	8	88	968	487	841	219
90	151	532	207	19	209	41	451	445	379	782
91	699	915	1033	73	803	930	69	759	446	390
92	903	901	879	637	233	305	1097	777	644	310
93	23	253	525	130	301	1053	293	965	454	478
94	742	259	591	856	384	837	175	796	853	351
95	474	698	904	912	1000	839	197	1038	128	279
96	811	1018	1037	117	158	609	1054	304	1086	656
97	442	346	419	93	1023	1092	722	39	429	203
98	1104	854	362	595	900	868	516	31	341	364
99	617	13	143	444	368	661	497	951	300	1042

P = 1129

INDICES

	0	1	2	3	4	5	6	7	8	9
100	954	394	292	236	624	1019	327	1015	566	1088
101	775	289	399	481	10	623	622	30	961	507
102	1035	1118	613	974	724	193	31	529	269	448
103	537	794	156	912	1111	546	409	962	957	478
104	699	331	999	138	1017	548	851	639	508	272
105	102	711	1095	935	966	145	349	302	1030	1036
106	352	841	825	849	71	96	1066	721	717	790
107	1119	183	325	860	209	820	676	1023	231	150
108	496	614	248	664	180	33	968	250	341	1102
109	413	637	975	4	738	543	551	926	423	492
110	1013	562	522	725	980	316	366	863	1080	804
111	339	834	245	628	194	264	427	18	565	506
112	536	330	1094	848	208	32	550	862	564	

POWER RESIDUES

	0	1	2	3	4	5	6	7	8	9
100	172	763	490	874	582	757	424	148	499	973
101	542	317	100	1100	810	1007	916	1044	194	1005
102	894	802	919	1077	557	482	786	743	270	712
103	1058	348	441	335	298	1020	1059	359	562	537
104	262	624	90	990	729	116	147	488	852	340
105	353	496	940	179	840	208	30	330	243	415
106	49	539	284	866	494	918	1066	436	280	822
107	10	110	81	891	769	556	471	665	541	306
108	1108	898	846	274	756	413	27	297	1009	938
109	157	598	933	102	1122	1052	282	844	252	514
110	9	99	1089	689	805	952	311	34	374	727
111	94	1034	84	924	3	33	363	606	1021	1070
112	480	764	501	995	784	721	28	308		

P = 1151

INDICES

	0	1	2	3	4	5	6	7	8	9
0		0	428	802	856	858	80	390	134	454
1	136	1106	508	875	818	510	562	1	882	315
2	564	42	384	731	936	566	153	106	96	612
3	938	513	990	758	429	98	160	918	743	527
4	992	131	470	30	812	162	9	370	214	780
5	994	803	581	126	534	814	524	1117	1040	48
6	216	969	941	844	268	583	36	1082	857	383
7	526	523	588	589	196	218	21	346	955	1069
8	270	908	559	288	898	859	458	264	90	355
9	590	115	437	165	798	23	642	367	58	410
10	272	461	81	351	1009	900	554	197	962	258
11	92	570	952	481	395	439	318	179	476	391
12	644	1062	247	933	219	274	122	255	696	832
13	1011	792	464	705	360	964	135	105	811	968
14	954	22	951	831	1016	320	1017	432	624	1147
15	646	983	449	455	774	221	233	766	347	928
16	698	1121	186	321	987	466	716	492	176	600
17	137	769	886	976	692	956	518	850	783	841
18	1018	1078	543	621	865	626	593	1107	76	496
19	451	203	1070	310	795	235	486	433	838	1100
20	700	734	889	1002	509	989	779	35	287	271
21	178	359	982	175	625	888	240	903	686	241
22	520	876	998	1027	230	1020	909	279	823	947
23	867	1148	746	1110	607	78	904	721	819	1104
24	1072	826	340	560	675	488	211	40	647	1090
25	702	151	550	687	683	511	1124	652	110	158
26	289	1066	70	129	892	984	1133	7	788	1087
27	242	801	563	917	533	522	89	899	246	967
28	232	975	450	34	229	825	109	521	294	2
29	748	19	295	336	860	906	1052	62	425	456
30	1074	420	261	113	877	677	883	640	52	3
31	649	459	661	755	44	552	775	473	206	568
32	1126	999	399	316	614	291	749	1060	265	760
33	894	120	1144	222	920	790	604	727	1028	133
34	565	469	47	20	164	91	254	1015	1120	782
35	234	981	946	210	128	231	61	43	119	1119
36	296	630	356	714	971	297	1049	767	143	585
37	1054	516	1021	763	385	1076	504	337	924	591
38	879	1057	631	201	348	54	738	484	73	910
39	663	732	914	444	861	777	116	190	378	357
40	1128	929	12	238	167	616	280	874	937	369
41	267	907	57	438	463	1146	715	620	699	902
42	606	150	787	824	260	567	603	209	1053	483
43	166	149	668	972	181	1122	1114	1046	669	1064
44	948	84	154	1131	276	63	305	799	658	834
45	298	87	187	635	707	973	101	868	225	107
46	145	1094	426	17	24	1023	388	1050	1035	322
47	506	418	182	1136	1149	881	97	580	382	457
48	350	643	104	773	768	75	988	997	1103	1123
49	916	747	639	613	468	118	1075	913	368	602

POWER RESIDUES

	0	1	2	3	4	5	6	7	8	9
0	1	17	289	309	649	674	1099	267	1086	46
1	782	633	402	1079	1078	1061	772	463	965	291
2	343	76	141	95	464	982	580	652	725	815
3	43	731	917	626	283	207	66	1122	658	827
4	247	746	21	357	314	734	968	342	59	1003
5	937	966	308	632	385	790	769	412	98	515
6	698	356	297	445	659	844	536	1055	670	1031
7	262	1001	903	388	841	485	188	894	235	542
8	6	102	583	703	441	591	839	451	761	276
9	88	345	110	719	713	611	28	476	35	595
10	907	456	846	570	482	137	27	459	897	286
11	258	933	898	303	547	91	396	977	495	358
12	331	1023	126	991	733	951	53	901	354	263
13	1018	41	697	339	8	136	10	170	588	788
14	735	985	631	368	501	460	914	575	567	431
15	421	251	814	26	442	608	1128	760	259	950
16	36	612	45	765	344	93	430	404	1113	505
17	528	919	660	861	825	213	168	554	210	117
18	838	434	472	1118	590	822	162	452	778	565
19	397	994	784	667	980	546	74	107	668	997
20	835	383	756	191	945	1102	318	802	973	427
21	353	246	729	883	48	816	60	1020	75	124
22	957	155	333	1057	704	458	880	1148	1100	284
23	224	355	280	156	350	195	1013	1107	403	1096
24	216	219	270	1137	913	558	278	122	923	728
25	866	910	507	562	346	127	1008	1022	109	702
26	424	302	530	953	87	328	972	410	64	1088
27	80	209	100	549	125	974	444	642	555	227
28	406	1147	1083	1146	1066	857	757	208	83	260
29	967	325	921	694	288	292	360	365	450	744
30	1138	930	847	587	771	446	676	1133	845	553
31	193	979	529	936	949	19	323	887	116	821
32	145	163	469	1067	874	1046	517	732	934	915
33	592	856	740	1070	925	762	293	377	654	759
34	242	661	878	1114	522	817	77	158	384	773
35	480	103	600	992	750	89	362	399	1028	211
36	134	1127	743	1121	641	538	1089	97	498	409
37	47	799	922	711	577	601	1009	1039	398	1011
38	1073	976	478	69	22	374	603	1043	466	1016
39	7	119	872	1012	1090	114	787	718	696	322
40	870	978	512	647	640	521	800	939	1000	886
41	99	532	987	665	946	1119	607	1111	471	1101
42	301	513	664	929	830	298	462	948	2	34
43	578	618	147	197	1047	534	1021	92	413	115
44	804	1007	1005	971	393	926	779	582	686	152
45	282	190	928	813	9	153	299	479	86	311
46	683	101	566	414	132	1093	165	503	494	341
47	42	714	628	317	785	684	118	855	723	781
48	616	113	770	429	387	824	196	1030	245	712
49	594	890	167	537	1072	959	189	911	524	851

P = 1151

INDICES

	0	1	2	3	4	5	6	7	8	9
50	1130	144	579	467	978	169	1115	252	1111	852
51	939	979	402	421	1080	59	538	326	586	628
52	717	405	344	1047	498	608	557	514	170	312
53	262	502	411	1006	435	1055	66	493	365	736
54	670	530	79	730	991	1116	195	114	961	273
55	950	927	517	309	177	278	674	1065	245	905
56	660	759	253	713	878	189	462	148	657	1022
57	103	601	537	1005	949	147	722	374	430	1112
58	26	678	447	82	723	1037	764	303	138	828
59	184	85	330	820	490	99	853	752	884	1092
60	352	375	848	386	689	770	541	416	155	654
61	1105	95	161	940	1068	641	480	1010	431	986
62	1077	837	887	745	1089	1132	33	1073	472	919
63	980	142	53	11	901	1113	634	505	996	977
64	404	364	277	536	827	540	744	403	1042	4
65	719	555	27	943	338	500	693	1043	38	64
66	172	341	548	528	422	413	650	193	198	679
67	68	925	1032	957	5	672	306	574	561	757
68	993	1081	897	460	475	963	448	599	592	1001
69	519	720	682	800	293	676	398	132	60	762
70	662	873	259	83	224	880	638	851	556	729
71	659	373	489	94	471	539	547	756	397	93
72	724	741	1058	478	784	28	1142	835	249	212
73	725	31	327	124	45	140	571	1038	1013	632
74	332	842	944	362	299	855	41	742	813	587
75	354	553	932	953	765	691	202	286	1019	339
76	157	88	335	648	1059	163	629	923	776	56
77	482	304	16	349	912	1079	501	960	188	446
78	1091	479	10	718	192	474	872	396	139	931
79	55	871	544	694	618	636	806	703	785	371
80	406	809	207	545	440	829	666	739	595	622
81	1044	1140	708	453	152	29	215	345	797	569
82	695	319	185	840	485	174	866	39	891	974
83	424	551	1143	781	1048	200	1127	619	180	86
84	1034	74	578	627	65	308	102	302	688	836
85	995	499	1031	1000	637	477	331	285	911	870
86	594	173	577	869	1096	684	250	804	609	1025
87	400	807	392	821	324	664	1097	1108	342	1138
88	226	817	512	213	582	558	409	317	704	645
89	491	864	733	685	77	549	1086	108	112	1125
90	726	127	515	72	615	786	1063	100	1135	915
91	251	497	529	244	146	329	653	32	535	171
92	573	292	372	248	854	334	445	805	452	423
93	301	1095	816	111	328	815	313	50	750	407
94	934	753	846	862	610	204	414	1084	427	314
95	159	125	525	263	1008	1061	810	220	885	495
96	778	1026	1071	651	532	18	51	290	46	1118
97	503	443	266	208	275	1093	381	117	401	311
98	194	712	25	751	1067	141	1041	412	896	761
99	546	123	353	922	191	808	796	199	1030	1024

POWER RESIDUES

	0	1	2	3	4	5	6	7	8	9
50	655	776	531	970	376	637	470	1084	12	204
51	15	255	882	31	527	902	371	552	176	690
52	220	287	275	71	56	952	70	39	663	912
53	541	1140	964	274	54	918	643	572	516	715
54	645	606	1094	182	792	803	990	716	662	895
55	252	831	315	751	106	651	708	526	885	82
56	243	678	16	272	20	340	25	425	319	819
57	111	736	1002	920	677	1150	1134	862	842	502
58	477	52	884	65	1105	369	518	749	72	73
59	90	379	688	186	860	808	1075	1010	1056	687
60	169	571	499	426	336	1108	420	234	525	868
61	944	1085	29	493	324	904	405	1130	794	837
62	417	183	809	1092	148	214	185	843	519	766
63	361	382	739	1053	636	453	795	854	706	492
64	307	615	96	481	120	889	150	248	763	310
65	666	963	257	916	609	1145	1049	568	448	710
66	560	312	700	390	875	1063	806	1041	432	438
67	540	1123	675	1116	556	244	695	305	581	669
68	1014	1124	692	254	865	893	218	253	848	604
69	1060	755	174	656	793	820	128	1025	160	418
70	200	1098	250	797	888	133	1110	454	812	1143
71	1015	1141	981	563	363	416	166	520	783	650
72	691	237	576	584	720	730	900	337	1125	709
73	543	23	391	892	201	1115	539	1106	386	807
74	1058	721	747	38	646	623	232	491	290	326
75	938	983	597	941	1034	313	717	679	33	561
76	329	989	699	373	586	754	157	367	484	171
77	605	1077	1044	483	154	316	768	395	960	206
78	49	833	349	178	724	798	905	422	268	1103
79	335	1091	131	1076	1027	194	996	818	94	447
80	693	271	3	51	867	927	796	871	995	801
81	956	138	44	748	55	935	932	881	14	238
82	593	873	1029	228	423	285	241	644	589	805
83	1024	143	129	1042	449	727	849	621	198	1064
84	823	179	741	1087	63	1071	942	1051	602	1026
85	177	707	509	596	924	745	4	68	5	85
86	294	394	943	1068	891	184	826	230	457	863
87	859	791	786	701	407	13	221	304	564	380
88	705	475	18	306	598	958	172	622	215	202
89	1132	828	264	1035	330	1006	988	682	84	277
90	105	634	419	217	236	559	295	411	81	226
91	389	858	774	497	392	909	490	273	37	629
92	334	1074	993	767	378	671	1048	551	159	401
93	1062	789	752	123	940	1017	24	408	30	510
94	613	62	1054	653	742	1104	352	229	440	574
95	550	142	112	753	140	78	175	673	1082	1129
96	777	548	108	685	135	1144	1032	279	139	61
97	1037	364	433	455	829	281	173	639	504	511
98	630	351	212	151	265	1052	619	164	486	205
99	32	544	40	680	50	850	638	487	222	321

P = 1151

INDICES

	0	1	2	3	4	5	6	7	8	9
100	408	71	572	49	1007	442	895	441	256	376
101	597	379	393	236	680	710	389	935	130	1039
102	217	436	257	121	830	697	849	794	358	822
103	487	69	966	1051	754	893	1014	970	1056	377
104	1145	667	833	387	772	1129	325	434	926	656
105	1036	847	985	633	942	67	598	223	740	1012
106	690	15	930	665	839	1033	284	323	863	1134
107	333	845	494	380	921	596	793	771	14	13
108	1098	1101	958	282	507	611	8	843	269	366
109	394	791	623	465	542	1099	239	1109	701	6
110	228	419	205	789	945	584	737	237	605	1045
111	706	417	1102	168	343	735	673	1004	183	415
112	1088	363	37	671	681	728	1141	361	156	959
113	617	1139	890	307	576	1137	1085	243	300	1083
114	531	711	1029	709	965	655	283	281	227	1003
115	575	0								

POWER RESIDUES

	0	1	2	3	4	5	6	7	8	9
100	853	689	203	1149	1117	573	533	1004	954	104
101	617	130	1059	738	1036	347	144	146	180	758
102	225	372	569	465	999	869	961	223	338	1142
103	998	852	672	1065	840	468	1050	585	737	1019
104	58	986	648	657	810	1109	437	523	834	366
105	467	1033	296	428	370	535	1038	381	722	764
106	327	955	121	906	439	557	261	984	614	79
107	192	962	240	627	300	496	375	620	181	775
108	514	681	67	1139	947	1136	896	269	1120	624
109	249	780	599	975	461	931	864	876	1080	1095
110	199	1081	1112	488	239	610	11	187	877	1097
111	233	508	579	635	436	506	545	57	969	359
112	348	161	435	489	256	899	320	836	400	1045
113	500	443	625	266	1069	908	473	1135	879	1131
114	811	1126	726	832	332	1040	415	149	231	474
115										

P = 1153

INDICES

	0	1	2	3	4	5	6	7	8	9
0		0	124	430	248	1	554	39	372	860
1	125	806	678	258	163	431	496	91	984	155
2	249	469	930	880	802	2	382	138	287	818
3	555	875	620	84	215	40	1108	255	279	688
4	373	290	593	234	1054	861	1004	928	926	78
5	126	521	506	480	262	807	411	585	942	1041
6	679	399	999	899	744	259	208	648	339	158
7	164	171	80	1087	379	432	403	845	812	189
8	497	568	414	697	717	92	358	96	26	1142
9	985	297	1128	153	1052	156	1050	128	202	514
10	250	363	645	19	630	470	604	1148	386	198
11	931	685	535	179	709	881	1066	1118	13	130
12	803	460	523	720	1123	3	1023	993	868	664
13	383	674	332	194	772	139	463	789	282	494
14	288	206	295	1064	204	819	59	508	503	316
15	556	435	527	951	969	876	936	799	313	910
16	621	919	692	63	538	85	821	457	841	516
17	216	1015	482	903	220	41	150	319	114	211
18	1109	670	421	829	100	256	277	897	24	177
19	280	61	22	599	252	689	326	264	638	888
20	374	1078	487	857	769	291	143	588	754	961
21	594	777	728	601	120	235	510	914	322	365
22	1055	349	809	854	659	862	303	407	833	947
23	1005	123	38	677	90	929	137	619	254	592
24	927	505	584	998	647	79	844	413	95	1127
25	127	644	1147	534	1117	522	992	331	788	294
26	507	526	798	691	456	481	318	420	896	21
27	263	486	587	727	913	808	406	37	618	583
28	412	1146	330	797	419	586	36	329	328	182
29	943	558	183	1059	632	1042	627	944	440	1138
30	680	273	559	793	651	400	1075	184	1093	449
31	1000	49	1060	266	923	900	437	633	1034	472
32	745	426	1043	246	816	260	187	628	662	967
33	209	767	945	1115	581	649	965	441	640	609
34	340	529	1139	117	606	159	1027	681	344	750
35	165	396	274	46	443	172	238	560	335	549
36	81	310	794	890	545	1088	953	652	224	1150
37	380	519	401	361	1021	433	148	1076	301	642
38	404	271	185	394	146	846	723	1094	376	885
39	813	971	450	1104	388	190	762	1001	1012	624
40	498	848	50	1133	611	569	981	1061	893	1101
41	415	67	267	1080	712	698	878	924	1085	200
42	718	501	901	636	852	93	725	438	244	342
43	359	1010	634	781	1038	97	446	1035	489	108
44	27	938	473	872	933	1143	978	746	783	974
45	986	1096	427	865	531	298	957	1044	1071	229
46	1129	575	247	859	162	154	801	817	214	687
47	1053	77	261	1040	743	157	378	188	716	1141
48	1051	513	629	197	708	129	1122	663	771	493
49	203	315	968	909	537	515	219	210	99	176

POWER RESIDUES

	0	1	2	3	4	5	6	7	8	9
0	1	5	25	125	625	819	636	874	911	1096
1	868	881	946	118	590	644	914	1111	943	103
2	515	269	192	960	188	940	88	440	1047	623
3	809	586	624	814	611	749	286	277	232	7
4	35	175	875	916	1121	993	353	612	754	311
5	402	857	826	671	1049	633	859	836	721	146
6	730	191	955	163	815	616	774	411	902	1051
7	643	909	1086	818	631	849	786	471	49	245
8	72	360	647	929	33	165	825	666	1024	508
9	234	17	85	425	972	248	87	435	1022	498
10	184	920	1141	1093	853	806	571	549	439	1042
11	598	684	1114	958	178	890	991	343	562	504
12	214	1070	738	231	2	10	50	250	97	485
13	119	595	669	1039	583	609	739	236	27	135
14	675	1069	733	206	1030	538	384	767	376	727
15	176	880	941	93	465	19	95	475	69	345
16	572	554	464	14	70	350	597	679	1089	833
17	706	71	355	622	804	561	499	189	945	113
18	565	519	289	292	307	382	757	326	477	79
19	395	822	651	949	133	665	1019	483	109	545
20	419	942	98	490	144	720	141	705	66	330
21	497	179	895	1016	468	34	170	850	791	496
22	174	870	891	996	368	687	1129	1033	553	459
23	1142	1098	878	931	43	215	1075	763	356	627
24	829	686	1124	1008	428	987	323	462	4	20
25	100	500	194	970	238	37	185	925	13	65
26	325	472	54	270	197	985	313	412	907	1076
27	768	381	752	301	352	607	729	186	930	38
28	190	950	138	690	1144	1108	928	28	140	700
29	41	205	1025	513	259	142	710	91	455	1122
30	998	378	737	226	1130	1038	578	584	614	764
31	361	652	954	158	790	491	149	745	266	177
32	885	966	218	1090	838	731	196	980	288	287
33	282	257	132	660	994	358	637	879	936	68
34	340	547	429	992	348	587	629	839	736	221
35	1105	913	1106	918	1131	1043	603	709	86	430
36	997	373	712	101	505	219	1095	863	856	821
37	646	924	8	40	200	1000	388	787	476	74
38	370	697	26	130	650	944	108	540	394	817
39	626	824	661	999	383	762	351	602	704	61
40	305	372	707	76	380	747	276	227	1135	1063
41	703	56	280	247	82	410	897	1026	518	284
42	267	182	910	1091	843	756	321	452	1107	923
43	3	15	75	375	722	151	755	316	427	982
44	298	337	532	354	617	779	436	1027	523	309
45	392	807	576	574	564	514	264	167	835	716
46	121	605	719	136	680	1094	858	831	696	21
47	105	525	319	442	1057	673	1059	683	1109	933
48	53	265	172	860	841	746	271	202	1010	438
49	1037	573	559	489	139	695	16	80	400	847

P = 1153

INDICES

	0	1	2	3	4	5	6	7	8	9
50	251	887	768	960	119	364	658	946	89	591
51	646	1126	1116	293	455	20	912	582	418	181
52	631	1137	650	448	922	471	815	966	580	608
53	605	749	442	548	544	1149	1020	641	145	884
54	387	623	610	1100	711	199	851	341	1037	107
55	932	973	530	228	161	686	742	1140	707	492
56	536	175	118	590	454	180	921	607	543	883
57	710	106	160	491	453	882	452	1028	306	1029
58	1067	736	682	134	307	1119	31	345	756	1030
59	14	694	751	1112	1068	131	564	166	110	737
60	804	1106	397	356	683	461	917	275	775	135
61	524	34	47	963	308	721	65	444	573	1120
62	1124	1018	173	29	32	4	390	239	1047	346
63	1024	74	561	55	757	994	6	336	596	1031
64	869	540	550	70	15	665	370	82	940	695
65	384	192	311	827	752	675	786	795	1091	1113
66	333	392	891	779	1069	195	87	546	705	132
67	773	53	1089	475	565	140	764	954	733	167
68	464	837	653	477	111	790	241	225	730	738
69	283	823	1151	553	805	495	468	381	874	1107
70	289	1003	520	410	398	207	170	402	567	357
71	296	1049	362	603	684	1065	459	1022	673	462
72	205	58	434	935	918	820	1014	149	669	276
73	60	325	1077	142	776	509	348	302	122	136
74	504	843	643	991	525	317	485	405	1145	35
75	557	626	272	1074	48	436	425	186	766	964
76	528	1026	395	237	309	952	518	147	270	722
77	970	761	847	980	66	877	500	724	1009	445
78	937	977	1095	956	574	800	76	377	512	1121
79	314	218	886	657	1125	911	1136	814	748	1019
80	622	850	972	741	174	920	105	451	735	30
81	693	563	1105	916	33	64	1017	389	73	5
82	539	369	191	785	391	86	52	763	836	240
83	822	467	1002	169	1048	458	57	1013	324	347
84	842	484	625	424	1025	517	760	499	976	75
85	217	1135	849	104	562	1016	368	51	466	56
86	483	759	1134	367	758	904	905	612	10	995
87	221	906	570	988	7	42	613	982	232	337
88	151	11	1062	839	597	320	996	894	1057	1032
89	115	222	1102	1083	870	212	907	416	1098	541
90	1110	571	68	703	551	671	989	268	655	71
91	422	8	1081	351	16	830	43	713	353	666
92	101	614	699	429	371	257	983	879	286	83
93	278	233	925	479	941	898	338	1086	811	696
94	25	152	201	18	385	178	12	719	867	193
95	281	1063	502	950	312	62	840	902	113	828
96	23	598	637	856	753	600	321	853	832	676
97	253	997	94	533	787	690	895	726	617	796
98	327	1058	439	792	1092	265	1033	245	661	1114
99	639	116	343	45	334	889	223	360	300	393

POWER RESIDUES

	0	1	2	3	4	5	6	7	8	9
50	776	421	952	148	740	241	52	260	147	735
51	216	1080	788	481	99	495	169	845	766	371
52	702	51	255	122	610	744	261	152	760	341
53	552	454	1117	973	253	112	560	494	164	820
54	641	899	1036	568	534	364	667	1029	533	359
55	642	904	1061	693	6	30	150	750	291	302
56	357	632	854	811	596	674	1064	708	81	405
57	872	901	1046	618	784	461	1152	1148	1128	1028
58	528	334	517	279	242	57	285	272	207	1035
59	563	509	239	42	210	1050	638	884	961	193
60	965	213	1065	713	106	530	344	567	529	339
61	542	404	867	876	921	1146	1118	978	278	237
62	32	160	800	541	399	842	751	296	327	482
63	104	520	294	317	432	1007	423	962	198	990
64	338	537	379	742	251	102	510	244	67	335
65	522	304	367	682	1104	908	1081	793	506	224
66	1120	988	328	487	129	645	919	1136	1068	728
67	181	905	1066	718	131	655	969	233	12	60
68	300	347	582	604	714	111	555	469	39	195
69	975	263	162	810	591	649	939	83	415	922
70	1151	1143	1103	903	1056	668	1034	558	484	114
71	570	544	414	917	1126	1018	478	84	420	947
72	123	615	769	386	777	426	977	273	212	1060
73	688	1134	1058	678	1084	808	581	599	689	1139
74	1083	803	556	474	64	320	447	1082	798	531
75	349	592	654	964	208	1040	588	634	864	861
76	846	771	396	827	676	1074	758	331	502	204
77	1020	488	134	670	1044	608	734	211	1055	663
78	1009	433	1012	448	1087	823	656	974	258	137
79	685	1119	983	303	362	657	979	283	262	157
80	785	466	24	120	600	694	11	55	275	222
81	1110	938	78	390	797	526	324	467	29	145
82	725	166	830	691	1149	1133	1053	653	959	183
83	915	1116	968	228	1140	1088	828	681	1099	883
84	956	168	840	741	246	77	385	772	401	852
85	801	546	424	967	223	1115	963	203	1015	463
86	9	45	225	1125	1013	453	1112	948	128	640
87	894	1011	443	1062	698	31	155	775	416	927
88	23	115	575	569	539	389	792	501	199	995
89	363	662	1004	408	887	976	268	187	935	63
90	315	422	957	173	865	866	871	896	1021	493
91	159	795	516	274	217	1085	813	606	724	161
92	805	566	524	314	417	932	48	240	47	235
93	22	110	550	444	1067	723	156	780	441	1052
94	648	934	58	290	297	332	507	229	1145	1113
95	953	153	765	366	677	1079	783	456	1127	1023
96	503	209	1045	613	759	336	527	329	492	154
97	770	391	802	551	449	1092	848	781	446	1077
98	773	406	877	926	18	90	450	1097	873	906
99	1071	743	256	127	635	869	886	971	243	62

P = 1153

INDICES

	0	1	2	3	4	5	6	7	8	9
100	375	1103	1011	1132	892	1079	1084	635	243	780
101	488	871	782	864	1070	858	213	1039	715	196
102	770	908	98	959	88	292	417	447	579	547
103	144	1099	1036	227	706	589	542	490	305	133
104	755	1111	109	355	774	962	572	28	1046	54
105	595	69	939	826	1090	778	704	474	732	476
106	729	552	873	409	566	602	672	934	668	141
107	121	990	1144	1073	765	236	269	979	1008	955
108	511	656	747	740	734	915	72	784	835	168
109	323	423	975	103	465	366	9	987	231	838
110	1056	1082	1097	702	654	350	352	428	285	478
111	810	17	866	949	112	855	831	532	616	791
112	660	44	299	1131	242	863	714	958	578	226
113	304	354	1045	825	731	408	667	1072	1007	739
114	834	102	230	701	284	948	615	1130	577	824
115	1006	700	576							

POWER RESIDUES

	0	1	2	3	4	5	6	7	8	9
100	310	397	832	701	46	230	1150	1138	1078	778
101	431	1002	398	837	726	171	855	816	621	799
102	536	374	717	126	630	844	761	346	577	579
103	589	639	889	986	318	437	1032	548	434	1017
104	473	59	295	322	457	1132	1048	628	834	711
105	96	480	94	470	44	220	1100	888	981	293
106	312	407	882	951	143	715	116	580	594	664
107	1014	458	1137	1073	753	306	377	732	201	1005
108	413	912	1101	893	1006	418	937	73	365	672
109	1054	658	984	308	387	782	451	1102	898	1031
110	543	409	892	1001	393	812	601	699	36	180
111	900	1041	593	659	989	333	512	254	117	585
112	619	789	486	124	620	794	511	249	92	460
113	1147	1123	1003	403	862	851	796	521	299	342
114	557	479	89	445	1072	748	281	252	107	535
115	369	692								

P = 1163

INDICES

	0	1	2	3	4	5	6	7	8	9
0		0	1085	720	1008	1	643	471	931	278
1	1086	320	566	269	394	721	854	603	201	939
2	1009	29	243	925	489	2	192	998	317	369
3	644	1021	777	1040	526	472	124	414	862	989
4	932	985	1114	668	166	279	848	564	412	942
5	1087	161	115	477	921	321	240	497	292	756
6	567	650	944	749	700	270	963	467	449	483
7	395	725	47	309	337	722	785	791	912	684
8	855	556	908	187	1037	604	591	1089	89	955
9	202	740	771	579	487	940	335	596	865	598
10	1010	376	84	905	38	30	400	74	844	966
11	244	1134	163	535	420	926	215	547	679	1074
12	490	640	573	543	867	3	672	150	623	226
13	193	576	886	248	390	999	372	117	406	973
14	318	122	648	589	1132	370	232	500	260	600
15	645	510	708	881	714	1022	835	810	607	35
16	778	234	479	353	831	1041	110	172	960	538
17	527	55	514	1103	1012	473	12	314	878	893
18	125	729	663	208	694	415	502	923	410	307
19	863	541	258	1101	519	990	788	296	521	378
20	933	25	299	840	7	986	828	41	1123	97
21	1115	262	323	283	1159	669	767	330	889	1029
22	167	872	1057	992	86	280	458	897	343	781
23	849	349	138	1084	470	565	602	242	997	776
24	413	1113	563	114	496	943	466	46	790	907
25	1088	770	595	83	73	162	546	572	149	885
26	116	647	499	707	809	478	171	513	313	662
27	922	257	295	298	40	322	329	1056	896	137
28	241	562	45	594	571	498	512	294	1055	44
29	293	154	155	432	423	757	183	156	523	32
30	568	1139	433	1096	631	651	804	424	637	463
31	945	710	758	1109	733	750	530	184	1120	689
32	701	794	157	380	402	271	276	524	754	1035
33	964	388	33	692	95	468	883	569	461	93
34	450	179	1140	251	437	484	1026	434	935	76
35	396	105	1097	1061	237	726	801	632	816	452
36	48	716	652	198	586	310	131	805	617	101
37	338	948	425	27	846	723	333	638	230	53
38	786	870	464	255	181	792	1024	946	442	288
39	913	366	711	134	219	685	444	759	301	968
40	856	212	1110	128	222	557	763	734	1092	1142
41	909	837	751	65	1126	188	1046	531	20	929
42	1038	290	185	842	246	605	206	1121	1082	147
43	592	635	690	814	253	1090	812	702	952	1156
44	90	58	795	552	980	956	915	158	9	1136
45	203	143	381	68	820	741	266	403	704	439
46	772	609	272	900	61	580	1007	277	393	938
47	488	368	525	988	165	941	920	755	699	482
48	336	683	1036	954	486	597	37	965	419	1073
49	866	225	389	972	1131	599	713	34	830	537

POWER RESIDUES

	0	1	2	3	4	5	6	7	8	9
0	1	5	25	125	625	799	506	204	1020	448
1	1077	733	176	880	911	1066	678	1064	668	1014
2	418	927	1146	1078	738	201	1005	373	702	21
3	105	525	299	332	497	159	795	486	104	520
4	274	207	1035	523	289	282	247	72	360	637
5	859	806	541	379	732	171	855	786	441	1042
6	558	464	1157	1133	1013	413	902	1021	453	1102
7	858	801	516	254	107	535	349	582	584	594
8	644	894	981	253	102	510	224	1120	948	88
9	440	1037	533	339	532	334	507	209	1045	573
10	539	369	682	1084	768	351	592	634	844	731
11	166	830	661	979	243	52	260	137	685	1099
12	843	726	141	705	36	180	900	1011	403	852
13	771	366	667	1009	393	802	521	279	232	1160
14	1148	1088	788	451	1092	808	551	429	982	258
15	127	635	849	756	291	292	297	322	447	1072
16	708	51	255	112	560	474	44	220	1100	848
17	751	266	167	835	686	1104	868	851	766	341
18	542	384	757	296	317	422	947	83	415	912
19	1071	703	26	130	650	924	1131	1003	363	652
20	934	18	90	450	1087	783	426	967	183	915
21	1086	778	401	842	721	116	580	574	544	394
22	807	546	404	857	796	491	129	645	899	1006
23	378	727	146	730	161	805	536	354	607	709
24	56	280	237	22	110	550	424	957	133	665
25	999	343	552	434	1007	383	752	271	192	960
26	148	740	211	1055	623	789	456	1117	933	13
27	65	325	462	1147	1083	763	326	467	9	45
28	225	1125	973	213	1065	673	1039	543	389	782
29	421	942	58	290	287	272	197	985	273	202
30	1010	398	827	646	904	1031	503	189	945	73
31	365	662	984	268	177	885	936	28	140	700
32	11	55	275	212	1060	648	914	1081	753	276
33	217	1085	773	376	717	96	480	74	370	687
34	1109	893	976	228	1140	1048	588	614	744	231
35	1155	1123	963	163	815	586	604	694	1144	1068
36	688	1114	918	1101	853	776	391	792	471	29
37	145	725	136	680	1074	718	101	505	199	995
38	323	452	1097	833	676	1054	618	764	331	492
39	134	670	1024	468	14	70	350	587	609	719
40	106	530	324	457	1122	958	138	690	1124	968
41	188	940	48	240	37	185	925	1136	1028	488
42	114	570	524	294	307	372	697	1159	1143	1063
43	663	989	293	302	347	572	534	344	557	459
44	1132	1008	388	777	396	817	596	654	944	68
45	340	537	359	632	834	681	1079	743	226	1130
46	998	338	527	309	382	747	246	67	335	512
47	234	7	35	175	875	886	941	53	265	162
48	810	561	479	69	345	562	484	94	470	24
49	120	600	674	1044	568	514	244	57	285	262

P = 1163

INDICES

	0	1	2	3	4	5	6	7	8	9
50	1011	892	693	306	518	377	6	96	1158	1028
51	85	780	469	775	495	906	72	884	808	661
52	39	136	570	43	422	31	630	462	732	688
53	401	1034	94	92	436	75	236	451	585	100
54	845	52	180	287	218	967	221	1141	1125	928
55	245	146	252	1155	979	1135	819	438	60	937
56	164	481	485	1072	1130	536	517	1027	494	660
57	421	687	435	99	217	927	978	936	1129	659
58	216	658	77	797	78	548	355	397	346	798
59	680	1016	106	1002	79	1075	446	1098	1117	549
60	491	1066	1062	745	356	641	1019	238	554	398
61	574	833	727	826	347	544	560	802	386	799
62	868	761	633	264	681	4	1032	817	656	1017
63	673	675	453	982	107	151	1043	49	612	1003
64	624	1151	717	620	80	227	303	653	325	1076
65	194	1050	199	666	447	577	677	587	958	1099
66	887	112	311	430	1118	249	615	132	18	550
67	391	970	806	285	492	1000	384	618	16	1067
68	373	455	102	917	1063	118	174	339	360	746
69	407	1106	949	1069	357	974	858	426	1161	642
70	319	853	28	191	1020	123	984	847	160	239
71	649	962	724	784	555	590	739	334	375	399
72	1133	214	639	671	575	371	121	231	509	834
73	233	109	54	11	728	501	540	787	24	827
74	261	766	871	457	348	601	1112	465	769	545
75	646	170	256	328	561	511	153	182	1138	803
76	709	529	793	275	387	882	178	1025	104	800
77	715	130	947	332	869	1023	365	443	211	762
78	836	1045	289	205	634	811	57	914	142	265
79	608	1006	367	919	682	36	224	712	891	5
80	779	71	135	629	1033	235	51	220	145	818
81	480	516	686	977	657	354	1015	445	1065	1018
82	832	559	760	1031	674	1042	1150	302	1049	676
83	111	614	969	383	454	173	1105	857	852	983
84	961	738	213	120	108	539	765	1111	169	152
85	528	177	129	364	1044	56	1005	223	70	50
86	515	1014	558	1149	613	1104	737	764	176	1004
87	1013	736	735	874	625	474	875	1093	1079	1152
88	13	626	1143	822	718	315	475	910	903	621
89	879	876	838	341	81	894	1094	752	1059	228
90	126	1080	66	697	304	730	1153	1127	743	654
91	664	14	189	507	326	209	627	1047	362	1077
92	695	1144	532	994	195	416	823	21	1146	1051
93	503	719	930	268	200	924	316	1039	861	667
94	411	476	291	748	448	308	911	186	88	578
95	864	904	843	534	678	542	622	247	405	588
96	259	880	606	352	959	1102	877	207	409	1100
97	520	839	1122	282	888	991	342	1083	996	113
98	789	82	148	706	312	297	895	593	1054	431
99	522	1095	636	1108	1119	379	753	691	460	250

POWER RESIDUES

	0	1	2	3	4	5	6	7	8	9
50	147	735	186	930	1161	1153	1113	913	1076	728
51	151	755	286	267	172	860	811	566	504	194
52	970	198	990	298	327	472	34	170	850	761
53	316	417	922	1121	953	113	565	499	169	845
54	736	191	955	123	615	749	256	117	585	599
55	669	1019	443	1052	608	714	81	405	862	821
56	616	754	281	242	47	235	12	60	300	337
57	522	284	257	122	610	724	131	655	949	93
58	465	1162	1158	1138	1038	538	364	657	959	143
59	715	86	430	987	283	252	97	485	99	495
60	149	745	236	17	85	425	962	158	790	461
61	1142	1058	638	864	831	666	1004	368	677	1059
62	643	889	956	128	640	874	881	916	1091	803
63	526	304	357	622	784	431	992	308	377	722
64	121	605	699	6	30	150	750	261	142	710
65	61	305	362	647	909	1056	628	814	581	579
66	569	519	269	182	910	1061	653	939	43	215
67	1075	723	126	630	824	631	829	656	954	118
68	590	624	794	481	79	395	812	571	529	319
69	432	997	333	502	184	920	1111	903	1026	478
70	64	320	437	1022	458	1127	983	263	152	760
71	311	392	797	496	154	770	361	642	884	931
72	3	15	75	375	712	71	355	612	734	181
73	905	1036	528	314	407	872	871	866	841	716
74	91	455	1112	908	1051	603	689	1119	943	63
75	315	412	897	996	328	477	59	295	312	397
76	822	621	779	406	867	846	741	216	1080	748
77	251	92	460	1137	1033	513	239	32	160	800
78	511	229	1145	1073	713	76	380	737	196	980
79	248	77	385	762	321	442	1047	583	589	619
80	769	356	617	759	306	367	672	1034	518	264
81	157	785	436	1017	433	1002	358	627	809	556
82	454	1107	883	926	1141	1053	613	739	206	1030
83	498	164	820	611	729	156	780	411	892	971
84	203	1015	423	952	108	540	374	707	46	230
85	1150	1098	838	701	16	80	400	837	696	1154
86	1118	938	38	190	950	98	490	124	620	774
87	381	742	221	1105	873	876	891	966	178	890
88	961	153	765	336	517	259	132	660	974	218
89	1090	798	501	179	895	986	278	227	1135	1023
90	463	1152	1108	888	951	103	515	249	82	410
91	887	946	78	390	787	446	1067	683	1089	793
92	476	54	270	187	935	23	115	575	549	419
93	932	8	40	200	1000	348	577	559	469	19
94	95	475	49	245	62	310	387	772	371	692
95	1134	1018	438	1027	483	89	445	1062	658	964
96	168	840	711	66	330	487	109	545	399	832
97	671	1029	493	139	695	1149	1093	813	576	554
98	444	1057	633	839	706	41	205	1025	473	39
99	195	975	223	1115	923	1126	978	238	27	135

P = 1163

INDICES

	0	1	2	3	4	5	6	7	8	9
100	934	1060	815	197	616	26	229	254	441	133
101	300	127	1091	64	19	841	1081	813	951	551
102	8	67	703	899	392	987	698	953	418	971
103	829	305	1157	774	807	42	731	91	584	286
104	1124	1154	59	1071	493	98	1128	796	345	1001
105	1116	744	553	825	385	263	655	981	611	619
106	324	665	957	429	17	284	15	916	359	1068
107	1160	190	159	783	374	670	508	10	23	456
108	768	327	1137	274	103	331	210	204	141	918
109	890	628	144	976	1064	1030	1048	382	851	119
110	168	363	69	1148	175	873	1078	821	902	340
111	1058	696	742	506	361	993	1145	267	860	747
112	87	533	404	351	408	281	995	705	1053	1107
113	459	196	440	63	950	898	417	773	583	1070
114	344	824	610	428	358	782	22	273	140	975
115	850	1147	901	505	859	350	1052	62	582	427
116	139	504	581							

POWER RESIDUES

	0	1	2	3	4	5	6	7	8	9
100	675	1049	593	639	869	856	791	466	4	20
101	100	500	174	870	861	816	591	629	819	606
102	704	31	155	775	386	767	346	567	509	219
103	1095	823	626	804	531	329	482	84	420	937
104	33	165	825	636	854	781	416	917	1096	828
105	651	929	1156	1128	988	288	277	222	1110	898
106	1001	353	602	684	1094	818	601	679	1069	693
107	1139	1043	563	489	119	595	649	919	1106	878
108	901	1016	428	977	233	2	10	50	250	87
109	435	1012	408	877	896	991	303	352	597	659
110	969	193	965	173	865	836	691	1129	993	313
111	402	847	746	241	42	210	1050	598	664	994
112	318	427	972	208	1040	548	414	907	1046	578
113	564	494	144	720	111	555	449	1082	758	301
114	342	547	409	882	921	1116	928	1151	1103	863
115	826	641	879	906	1041	553	439	1032	508	214
116	1070	698								

P = 1171

INDICES

	0	1	2	3	4	5	6	7	8	9
0		0	1	155	2	598	156	805	3	310
1	599	201	157	846	806	753	4	668	311	902
2	600	960	202	348	158	26	847	465	807	185
3	754	1072	5	356	669	233	312	841	903	1001
4	601	126	961	719	203	908	349	1146	159	440
5	27	823	848	981	466	799	808	1057	186	880
6	755	1010	1073	1115	6	274	357	1092	670	503
7	234	814	313	736	842	181	904	1006	1002	53
8	602	620	127	89	962	96	720	340	204	545
9	909	481	350	57	1147	330	160	63	441	511
10	28	1139	824	117	849	388	982	1125	467	606
11	800	996	809	112	1058	946	187	1156	881	303
12	756	402	1011	281	1074	624	1116	1082	7	874
13	275	863	358	537	1093	1063	671	763	504	292
14	235	131	815	1047	314	783	737	595	843	957
15	182	838	905	978	1007	500	1003	93	54	1136
16	603	1153	621	534	128	954	90	951	963	522
17	97	42	721	966	341	831	205	1035	546	492
18	910	525	482	1165	351	269	58	869	1148	100
19	331	455	161	105	64	429	442	45	512	192
20	29	77	1140	990	825	724	118	658	850	1103
21	389	174	983	969	1126	147	468	707	607	891
22	801	344	997	795	810	336	113	299	1059	834
23	947	1161	188	143	1157	574	882	208	304	730
24	757	71	403	775	1012	1038	282	578	1075	244
25	625	364	1117	549	1083	251	8	460	875	476
26	276	495	864	886	359	409	538	700	1094	913
27	1064	923	672	636	764	227	505	528	293	212
28	236	559	132	414	816	485	1048	931	315	166
29	784	218	738	1168	596	308	844	666	958	24
30	183	354	839	124	906	438	979	1055	1008	272
31	501	734	1004	618	94	543	55	61	1137	386
32	604	110	1154	400	622	872	535	761	129	781
33	955	976	91	1151	952	520	964	1033	523	267
34	98	103	43	75	722	1101	967	705	342	334
35	832	141	206	69	1036	242	547	458	493	407
36	911	634	526	557	483	164	1166	664	352	436
37	270	616	59	108	870	779	1149	1031	101	1099
38	332	67	456	632	162	434	106	1029	65	432
39	430	1016	443	1018	46	651	513	445	193	692
40	30	1020	78	748	1141	48	991	1042	826	653
41	725	918	119	515	659	687	851	447	1104	565
42	390	195	175	286	984	694	970	645	1127	32
43	148	856	469	1022	708	938	608	80	892	582
44	802	750	345	1069	998	1143	796	1112	811	50
45	337	327	114	993	300	1079	1060	1044	835	1133
46	948	828	1162	452	189	655	144	792	1158	727
47	575	248	883	920	209	928	305	121	731	383
48	758	517	72	138	404	661	776	629	1013	689
49	1039	684	283	853	579	1109	1076	449	245	380

POWER RESIDUES

	0	1	2	3	4	5	6	7	8	9
0	1	2	4	8	16	32	64	128	256	512
1	1024	877	583	1166	1161	1151	1131	1091	1011	851
2	531	1062	953	735	299	598	25	50	100	200
3	400	800	429	858	545	1090	1009	847	523	1046
4	921	671	171	342	684	197	394	788	405	810
5	449	898	625	79	158	316	632	93	186	372
6	744	317	634	97	194	388	776	381	762	353
7	706	241	482	964	757	343	686	201	402	804
8	437	874	577	1154	1137	1103	1035	899	627	83
9	166	332	664	157	314	628	85	170	340	680
10	189	378	756	341	682	193	386	772	373	746
11	321	642	113	226	452	904	637	103	206	412
12	824	477	954	737	303	606	41	82	164	328
13	656	141	282	564	1128	1085	999	827	483	966
14	761	351	702	233	466	932	693	215	430	860
15	549	1098	1025	879	587	3	6	12	24	48
16	96	192	384	768	365	730	289	578	1156	1141
17	1111	1051	931	691	211	422	844	517	1034	897
18	623	75	150	300	600	29	58	116	232	464
19	928	685	199	398	796	421	842	513	1026	881
20	591	11	22	44	88	176	352	704	237	474
21	948	725	279	558	1116	1061	951	731	291	582
22	1164	1157	1143	1115	1059	947	723	275	550	1100
23	1029	887	603	35	70	140	280	560	1120	1069
24	967	763	355	710	249	498	996	821	471	942
25	713	255	510	1020	869	567	1134	1097	1023	875
26	579	1158	1145	1119	1067	963	755	339	678	185
27	370	740	309	618	65	130	260	520	1040	909
28	647	123	246	492	984	797	423	846	521	1042
29	913	655	139	278	556	1112	1053	935	699	227
30	454	908	645	119	238	476	952	733	295	590
31	9	18	36	72	144	288	576	1152	1133	1095
32	1019	867	563	1126	1081	991	811	451	902	633
33	95	190	380	760	349	698	225	450	900	629
34	87	174	348	696	221	442	884	597	23	46
35	92	184	368	736	301	602	33	66	132	264
36	528	1056	941	711	251	502	1004	837	503	1006
37	841	511	1022	873	575	1150	1129	1087	1003	835
38	499	998	825	479	958	745	319	638	105	210
39	420	840	509	1018	865	559	1118	1065	959	747
40	323	646	121	242	484	968	765	359	718	265
41	530	1060	949	727	283	566	1132	1093	1015	859
42	547	1094	1017	863	555	1110	1049	927	683	195
43	390	780	389	778	385	770	369	738	305	610
44	49	98	196	392	784	397	794	417	834	497
45	994	817	463	926	681	191	382	764	357	714
46	257	514	1028	885	599	27	54	108	216	432
47	864	557	1114	1057	943	715	259	518	1036	901
48	631	91	182	364	728	285	570	1140	1109	1047
49	923	675	179	358	716	261	522	1044	917	663

P = 1171

INDICES

	0	1	2	3	4	5	6	7	8	9
50	626	1106	365	368	1118	567	550	677	1084	392
51	252	371	9	197	461	715	876	177	477	1121
52	277	288	496	38	865	986	887	570	360	696
53	410	20	539	972	701	553	1095	647	914	641
54	1065	1129	924	680	673	34	637	420	765	150
55	228	1087	506	858	529	424	294	471	213	395
56	237	1024	560	322	133	710	415	255	817	940
57	486	769	1049	610	932	374	316	82	167	260
58	785	894	219	12	739	584	1169	154	597	804
59	309	200	845	752	667	901	959	347	25	464
60	184	1071	355	232	840	1000	125	718	907	1145
61	439	822	980	798	1056	879	1009	1114	273	1091
62	502	813	735	180	1005	52	619	88	95	339
63	544	480	56	329	62	510	1138	116	387	1124
64	605	995	111	945	1155	302	401	280	623	1081
65	873	862	536	1062	762	291	130	1046	782	594
66	956	837	977	499	92	1135	1152	533	953	950
67	521	41	965	830	1034	491	524	1164	268	868
68	99	454	104	428	44	191	76	989	723	657
69	1102	173	968	146	706	890	343	794	335	298
70	833	1160	142	573	207	729	70	774	1037	577
71	243	363	548	250	459	475	494	885	408	699
72	912	922	635	226	527	211	558	413	484	930
73	165	217	1167	307	665	23	353	123	437	1054
74	271	733	617	542	60	385	109	399	871	760
75	780	975	1150	519	1032	266	102	74	1100	704
76	333	140	68	241	457	406	633	556	163	663
77	435	615	107	778	1030	1098	66	631	433	1028
78	431	1015	1017	650	444	691	1019	747	47	1041
79	652	917	514	686	446	564	194	285	693	644
80	31	855	1021	937	79	581	749	1068	1142	1111
81	49	326	992	1078	1043	1132	827	451	654	791
82	726	247	919	927	120	382	516	137	660	628
83	688	683	852	1108	448	379	1105	367	566	676
84	391	370	196	714	176	1120	287	37	985	569
85	695	19	971	552	646	640	1128	679	33	419
86	149	1086	857	423	470	394	1023	321	709	254
87	939	768	609	373	81	259	893	11	583	153
88	803	199	751	900	346	463	1070	231	999	717
89	1144	821	797	878	1113	1090	812	179	51	87
90	338	479	328	509	115	1123	994	944	301	279
91	1080	861	1061	290	1045	593	836	498	1134	532
92	949	40	829	490	1163	867	453	427	190	988
93	656	172	145	889	793	297	1159	572	728	773
94	576	362	249	474	884	698	921	225	210	412
95	929	216	306	22	122	1053	732	541	384	398
96	759	974	518	265	73	703	139	240	405	555
97	662	614	777	1097	630	1027	1014	649	690	746
98	1040	916	685	563	284	643	854	936	580	1067
99	1110	325	1077	1131	450	790	246	926	381	136

POWER RESIDUES

	0	1	2	3	4	5	6	7	8	9
50	155	310	620	69	138	276	552	1104	1037	903
51	635	99	198	396	792	413	826	481	962	753
52	335	670	169	338	676	181	362	724	277	554
53	1108	1045	919	667	163	326	652	133	266	532
54	1064	957	743	315	630	89	178	356	712	253
55	506	1012	853	535	1070	969	767	363	726	281
56	562	1124	1077	983	795	419	838	505	1010	849
57	527	1054	937	703	235	470	940	709	247	494
58	988	805	439	878	585	1170	1169	1167	1163	1155
59	1139	1107	1043	915	659	147	294	588	5	10
60	20	40	80	160	320	640	109	218	436	872
61	573	1146	1121	1071	971	771	371	742	313	626
62	81	162	324	648	125	250	500	1000	829	487
63	974	777	383	766	361	722	273	546	1092	1013
64	855	539	1078	985	799	427	854	537	1074	977
65	783	395	790	409	818	465	930	689	207	414
66	828	485	970	769	367	734	297	594	17	34
67	68	136	272	544	1088	1005	839	507	1014	857
68	543	1086	1001	831	491	982	793	415	830	489
69	978	785	399	798	425	850	529	1058	945	719
70	267	534	1068	965	759	347	694	217	434	868
71	565	1130	1089	1007	843	515	1030	889	607	43
72	86	172	344	688	205	410	820	469	938	705
73	239	478	956	741	311	622	73	146	292	584
74	1168	1165	1159	1147	1123	1075	979	787	403	806
75	441	882	593	15	30	60	120	240	480	960
76	749	327	654	137	274	548	1096	1021	871	571
77	1142	1113	1055	939	707	243	486	972	773	375
78	750	329	658	145	290	580	1160	1149	1127	1083
79	995	819	467	934	697	223	446	892	613	55
80	110	220	440	880	589	7	14	28	56	112
81	224	448	896	621	71	142	284	568	1136	1101
82	1031	891	611	51	102	204	408	816	461	922
83	673	175	350	700	229	458	916	661	151	302
84	604	37	74	148	296	592	13	26	52	104
85	208	416	832	493	986	801	431	862	553	1106
86	1041	911	651	131	262	524	1048	925	679	187
87	374	748	325	650	129	258	516	1032	893	615
88	59	118	236	472	944	717	263	526	1052	933
89	695	219	438	876	581	1162	1153	1135	1099	1027
90	883	595	19	38	76	152	304	608	45	90
91	180	360	720	269	538	1076	981	791	411	822
92	473	946	721	271	542	1084	997	823	475	950
93	729	287	574	1148	1125	1079	987	803	435	870
94	569	1138	1105	1039	907	643	115	230	460	920
95	669	167	334	668	165	330	660	149	298	596
96	21	42	84	168	336	672	173	346	692	213
97	426	852	533	1066	961	751	331	662	153	306
98	612	53	106	212	424	848	525	1050	929	687
99	203	406	812	453	906	641	111	222	444	888

P = 1171

INDICES

	0	1	2	3	4	5	6	7	8	9
100	627	682	1107	378	366	675	369	713	1119	36
101	568	18	551	639	678	418	1085	422	393	320
102	253	767	372	258	10	152	198	899	462	230
103	716	820	877	1089	178	86	478	508	1122	943
104	278	860	289	592	497	531	39	489	866	426
105	987	171	888	296	571	772	361	473	697	224
106	411	215	21	1052	540	397	973	264	702	239
107	554	613	1096	1026	648	745	915	562	642	935
108	1066	324	1130	789	925	135	681	377	674	712
109	35	17	638	417	421	319	766	257	151	898
110	229	819	1088	85	507	942	859	591	530	488
111	425	170	295	771	472	223	214	1051	396	263
112	238	612	1025	744	561	934	323	788	134	376
113	711	16	416	318	256	897	818	84	941	590
114	487	169	770	222	1050	262	611	743	933	787
115	375	15	317	896	83	589	168	221	261	742
116	786	14	895	588	220	741	13	587	740	586
117	585	0								

POWER RESIDUES

	0	1	2	3	4	5	6	7	8	9
100	605	39	78	156	312	624	77	154	308	616
101	61	122	244	488	976	781	391	782	393	786
102	401	802	433	866	561	1122	1073	975	779	387
103	774	377	754	337	674	177	354	708	245	490
104	980	789	407	814	457	914	657	143	286	572
105	1144	1117	1063	955	739	307	614	57	114	228
106	456	912	653	135	270	540	1080	989	807	443
107	886	601	31	62	124	248	496	992	813	455
108	910	649	127	254	508	1016	861	551	1102	1033
109	895	619	67	134	268	536	1072	973	775	379
110	758	345	690	209	418	836	501	1002	833	495
111	990	809	447	894	617	63	126	252	504	1008
112	845	519	1038	905	639	107	214	428	856	541
113	1082	993	815	459	918	665	159	318	636	101
114	202	404	808	445	890	609	47	94	188	376
115	752	333	666	161	322	644	117	234	468	936
116	701	231	462	924	677	183	366	732	293	586
117										

P = 1181

INDICES

	0	1	2	3	4	5	6	7	8	9
0		0	835	177	490	914	1012	1	145	354
1	569	160	667	1007	836	1091	980	964	9	625
2	224	178	995	774	322	648	662	531	491	889
3	746	487	635	337	619	915	844	722	280	4
4	1059	436	1013	283	650	88	429	954	1157	2
5	303	1141	317	686	186	1074	146	802	544	366
6	401	960	142	355	290	741	1172	639	274	951
7	570	878	499	617	377	825	1115	161	839	579
8	714	708	91	379	668	698	1118	1066	305	1085
9	923	1008	84	664	609	359	812	887	837	514
10	1138	1000	796	407	1152	1092	341	920	1021	1029
11	729	899	981	1162	457	508	199	181	21	965
12	56	320	615	613	977	382	10	516	1125	460
13	396	1071	827	626	294	265	1109	1143	606	216
14	225	1131	533	1167	154	623	272	179	32	15
15	480	386	770	138	996	221	494	680	234	863
16	369	775	363	468	926	71	34	76	323	834
17	353	979	773	745	721	649	1140	543	740	498
18	578	1117	663	1137	919	456	319	1124	264	532
19	14	493	467	352	542	918	492	168	169	1175
20	793	816	655	890	451	170	62	1128	807	785
21	747	866	1176	1055	575	17	676	488	684	794
22	384	791	554	848	636	1002	817	105	112	520
23	163	338	1034	656	1016	688	856	756	620	1102
24	891	588	1155	885	270	916	268	452	632	556
25	37	643	845	934	171	875	780	238	115	723
26	51	63	726	560	482	420	281	82	1129	12
27	1100	987	764	5	798	808	261	717	1051	841
28	1060	902	786	102	188	536	822	437	989	748
29	278	1064	1107	454	1014	100	867	691	850	601
30	135	284	41	1177	425	694	973	464	651	584
31	1056	1045	149	388	335	89	1069	576	518	1049
32	24	1097	430	409	18	475	123	26	581	955
33	906	677	869	1076	911	373	1158	766	489	159
34	8	647	634	3	428	685	400	638	376	707
35	304	358	795	1028	198	612	395	1142	153	385
36	233	70	772	497	318	351	792	1127	574	790
37	111	687	1154	555	779	559	1099	716	187	1063
38	849	693	148	1048	122	1075	7	637	197	69
39	573	558	147	68	1003	313	1004	392	830	803
40	448	818	471	314	310	442	545	882	106	252
41	1005	140	897	367	783	113	462	393	440	938
42	402	1094	521	128	831	432	710	961	230	164
43	852	804	331	1024	143	800	339	219	449	932
44	39	356	446	1035	209	819	503	192	291	1037
45	657	596	472	563	940	742	947	1017	175	315
46	998	478	1173	630	689	398	311	207	671	640
47	343	857	511	443	411	93	275	1040	757	603
48	546	549	243	952	810	621	540	883	1105	645
49	571	930	1103	673	107	248	287	879	211	892

POWER RESIDUES

	0	1	2	3	4	5	6	7	8	9
0	1	7	49	343	39	273	730	386	340	18
1	126	882	269	702	190	149	1043	215	324	1087
2	523	118	826	1058	320	1059	327	1108	670	1147
3	943	696	148	1036	166	1162	1048	250	569	440
4	718	302	933	626	839	1149	957	794	834	1114
5	712	260	639	930	605	692	120	840	1156	1006
6	1137	873	206	261	646	979	948	731	393	389
7	361	165	1155	999	1088	530	167	1169	1097	593
8	608	713	267	688	92	644	965	850	45	315
9	1024	82	574	475	963	836	1128	810	946	717
10	295	884	283	800	876	227	408	494	1096	586
11	559	370	228	415	543	258	625	832	1100	614
12	755	561	384	326	1101	621	804	904	423	599
13	650	1007	1144	922	549	300	919	528	153	1071
14	411	515	62	434	676	8	56	392	382	312
15	1003	1116	726	358	144	1008	1151	971	892	339
16	11	77	539	230	429	641	944	703	197	198
17	205	254	597	636	909	458	844	3	21	147
18	1029	117	819	1009	1158	1020	54	378	284	807
19	925	570	447	767	645	972	899	388	354	116
20	812	960	815	981	962	829	1079	467	907	444
21	746	498	1124	782	750	526	139	973	906	437
22	697	155	1085	509	20	140	980	955	780	736
23	428	634	895	360	158	1106	656	1049	257	618
24	783	757	575	482	1012	1179	1167	1083	495	1103
25	635	902	409	501	1145	929	598	643	958	801
26	883	276	751	533	188	135	945	710	246	541
27	244	527	146	1022	68	476	970	885	290	849
28	38	266	681	43	301	926	577	496	1110	684
29	64	448	774	694	134	938	661	1084	502	1152
30	978	941	682	50	350	88	616	769	659	1070
31	404	466	900	395	403	459	851	52	364	186
32	121	847	24	168	1176	1146	936	647	986	997
33	1074	432	662	1091	551	314	1017	33	231	436
34	690	106	742	470	928	591	594	615	762	610
35	727	365	193	170	9	63	441	725	351	95
36	665	1112	698	162	1134	852	59	413	529	160
37	1120	754	554	335	1164	1062	348	74	518	83
38	581	524	125	875	220	359	151	1057	313	1010
39	1165	1069	397	417	557	356	130	910	465	893
40	346	60	420	578	503	1159	1027	103	721	323
41	1080	474	956	787	785	771	673	1168	1090	544
42	265	674	1175	1139	887	304	947	724	344	46
43	322	1073	425	613	748	512	41	287	828	1072
44	418	564	405	473	949	738	442	732	400	438
45	704	204	247	548	293	870	185	114	798	862
46	129	903	416	550	307	968	871	192	163	1141
47	901	402	452	802	890	325	1094	572	461	865
48	150	1050	264	667	1126	796	848	31	217	338
49	4	28	196	191	156	1092	558	363	179	72

P = 1181

INDICES

	0	1	2	3	4	5	6	7	8	9
50	872	253	298	404	500	734	589	1011	1006	223
51	530	618	435	1156	1073	141	950	1114	378	922
52	886	1151	898	20	381	826	215	271	137	368
53	75	720	1116	263	917	654	784	675	847	162
54	755	269	642	114	419	763	840	821	453	134
55	463	334	1096	580	372	633	706	394	496	110
56	715	121	557	829	441	896	937	709	1023	38
57	191	939	477	670	92	242	644	286	403	529
58	1113	380	719	846	762	1095	109	936	669	1112
59	935	345	522	79	346	699	505	172	256	129
60	970	523	1119	993	876	54	832	682	80	1067
61	349	781	628	433	119	347	306	1031	239	1147
62	711	125	700	1086	984	116	43	962	1170	506
63	924	1053	724	1043	231	250	173	1009	704	52
64	859	165	752	257	85	194	64	327	853	526
65	130	665	958	727	861	805	236	971	610	308
66	561	296	332	968	524	360	731	483	566	1025
67	28	1120	813	416	421	1179	144	1090	994	888
68	843	282	302	801	289	877	838	697	83	513
69	340	1161	55	515	293	1130	31	220	362	833
70	1139	1136	13	167	450	865	683	1001	1033	1101
71	267	933	50	81	797	901	988	99	40	583
72	1068	408	905	765	427	357	152	350	1153	1062
73	6	67	447	881	782	1093	229	799	445	1036
74	946	629	342	1039	809	929	210	733	434	921
75	214	262	754	820	371	120	1022	241	718	1111
76	504	992	348	1030	983	1052	703	193	957	307
77	730	415	842	696	292	1135	1032	900	904	1061
78	228	1038	213	240	982	414	903	413	658	737
79	1148	1163	659	787	47	597	485	712	458	738
80	103	259	473	777	126	509	1149	189	1145	564
81	97	701	200	1164	537	202	941	908	1087	182
82	660	823	975	743	552	985	22	788	438	205
83	948	894	117	966	48	990	95	1018	593	44
84	57	598	749	1079	176	568	963	321	486	279
85	87	316	365	1171	616	713	1065	608	999	1020
86	507	614	459	1108	1166	479	679	925	978	739
87	455	466	1174	61	1054	383	104	1015	587	631
88	874	725	11	260	101	277	690	424	1044	517
89	474	868	158	399	1027	232	1126	778	692	196
90	312	470	251	461	127	851	218	208	595	174
91	397	510	602	539	672	871	1010	1072	1150	136
92	653	641	133	705	828	190	285	761	344	255
93	53	627	1146	42	1042	858	326	860	295	565
94	1178	301	512	30	166	266	98	426	66	444
95	928	753	1110	702	695	227	412	46	258	1144
96	201	974	204	94	1078	86	607	1165	465	586
97	276	157	195	217	538	652	760	1041	300	65
98	226	203	585	759	758	1082	328	1132	942	1057
99	1083	604	1122	854	534	909	1046	329	547	73

POWER RESIDUES

	0	1	2	3	4	5	6	7	8	9
50	504	1166	1076	446	760	596	629	860	115	805
51	911	472	942	689	99	693	127	889	318	1045
52	229	422	592	601	664	1105	649	1000	1095	579
53	510	27	189	142	994	1053	285	814	974	913
54	486	1040	194	177	58	406	480	998	1081	481
55	1005	1130	824	1044	222	373	249	562	391	375
56	263	660	1077	453	809	939	668	1133	845	10
57	70	490	1068	390	368	214	317	1038	180	79
58	553	328	1115	719	309	982	969	878	241	506
59	1180	1174	1132	838	1142	908	451	795	841	1163
60	1055	299	912	479	991	1032	138	966	857	94
61	658	1063	355	123	861	122	854	73	511	34
62	238	485	1033	145	1015	19	133	931	612	741
63	463	879	248	555	342	32	224	387	347	67
64	469	921	542	251	576	489	1061	341	25	175
65	44	308	975	920	535	202	233	450	788	792
66	820	1016	26	182	93	651	1014	12	84	588
67	573	468	914	493	1089	537	216	331	1136	866
68	157	1099	607	706	218	345	53	371	235	464
69	886	297	898	381	305	954	773	687	85	595
70	622	811	953	766	638	923	556	349	81	567
71	426	620	797	855	80	560	377	277	758	582
72	531	174	37	259	632	881	262	653	1028	110
73	770	666	1119	747	505	1173	1125	789	799	869
74	178	65	455	823	1037	173	30	210	289	842
75	1170	1104	642	951	752	540	237	478	984	983
76	976	927	584	545	272	723	337	1178	1160	1034
77	152	1064	362	172	23	161	1127	803	897	374
78	256	611	734	414	536	209	282	793	827	1065
79	369	221	366	200	219	352	102	714	274	737
80	435	683	57	399	431	655	1042	208	275	744
81	484	1026	96	672	1161	1041	201	226	401	445
82	753	547	286	821	1023	75	525	132	924	563
83	398	424	606	699	169	2	14	98	686	78
84	546	279	772	680	36	252	583	538	223	380
85	298	905	430	648	993	1046	236	471	935	640
86	937	654	1035	159	1113	705	211	296	891	332
87	1143	915	500	1138	880	255	604	685	71	497
88	1117	733	407	487	1047	243	520	97	679	29
89	203	240	499	1131	831	1093	565	412	522	111
90	777	715	281	786	778	722	330	1129	817	995
91	1060	334	1157	1013	5	35	245	534	195	184
92	107	749	519	90	630	867	164	1148	950	745
93	491	1075	439	711	253	590	587	566	419	571
94	454	816	988	1011	1172	1118	740	456	830	1086
95	516	69	483	1019	47	329	1122	768	652	1021
96	61	427	627	846	17	119	833	1107	663	1098
97	600	657	1056	306	961	822	1030	124	868	171
98	16	112	784	764	624	825	1051	271	716	288
99	835	1121	761	603	678	22	154	1078	460	858

P = 1181

INDICES

	0	1	2	3	4	5	6	7	8	9
100	527	1168	1088	150	1133	550	59	131	155	183
101	389	943	244	913	666	624	661	336	1058	953
102	185	959	273	824	90	1084	811	406	728	180
103	976	1070	605	622	769	862	33	744	577	1123
104	541	815	806	16	553	519	855	884	36	237
105	481	986	1050	535	1106	600	972	387	23	25
106	910	646	375	611	771	789	1098	1047	572	391
107	309	139	439	431	330	931	502	562	997	206
108	410	548	1104	247	297	222	949	19	74	674
109	418	333	495	895	476	528	108	78	969	681
110	118	124	1169	249	751	525	235	967	27	1089
111	288	1160	361	864	49	582	151	880	945	732
112	370	991	956	1134	212	736	484	776	96	907
113	551	893	592	567	364	1019	678	60	873	423
114	1026	469	594	870	132	254	325	29	927	45
115	1077	156	299	1081	1121	72	58	912	184	405
116	768	814	35	599	374	390	501	246	417	77
117	750	1159	944	735	591	422	324	1080	767	245
118	590	0								

POWER RESIDUES

	0	1	2	3	4	5	6	7	8	9
100	101	707	225	394	396	410	508	13	91	637
101	916	507	6	42	294	877	234	457	837	1135
102	859	108	756	568	433	669	1140	894	353	109
103	763	617	776	708	232	443	739	449	781	743
104	477	977	934	633	888	311	996	1067	383	319
105	1052	278	765	631	874	213	310	989	1018	40
106	280	779	729	379	291	856	87	609	720	316
107	1031	131	917	514	55	385	333	1150	964	843
108	1177	1153	985	990	1025	89	623	818	1002	1109
109	677	15	105	735	421	585	552	321	1066	376
110	270	709	239	492	1082	488	1054	292	863	136
111	952	759	589	580	517	76	532	181	86	602
112	671	1154	992	1039	187	128	896	367	207	268
113	695	141	987	1004	1123	775	701	183	100	700
114	176	51	357	137	959	808	932	619	790	806
115	918	521	104	728	372	242	513	48	336	1171
116	1111	691	113	791	813	967	864	143	1001	1102
117	628	853	66	462	872	199	212	303	940	675
118										

P = 1187

INDICES

	0	1	2	3	4	5	6	7	8	9
0		0	1	646	2	1111	647	781	3	106
1	1112	432	648	500	782	571	4	1125	107	225
2	1113	241	433	790	649	1036	501	752	783	231
3	572	473	5	1078	1126	706	108	48	226	1146
4	1114	956	242	342	434	31	791	205	650	376
5	1037	585	502	401	753	357	784	871	232	261
6	573	1151	474	887	6	425	1079	118	1127	250
7	707	1174	109	814	49	496	227	27	1147	23
8	1115	212	957	847	243	1050	343	877	435	665
9	32	95	792	1119	206	150	651	735	377	538
10	1038	388	586	914	503	166	402	87	754	216
11	358	694	785	352	872	715	233	606	262	720
12	574	864	1152	416	475	961	888	921	7	988
13	426	490	1080	1006	119	677	1128	685	251	1086
14	708	851	1175	932	110	156	815	1022	50	1108
15	497	238	228	45	28	398	1148	247	24	1047
16	1116	385	213	603	958	1003	848	1105	244	1000
17	1051	331	344	1054	878	631	436	907	666	298
18	33	334	96	611	793	1159	1120	371	207	347
19	151	902	652	177	736	1071	378	1057	539	134
20	1039	764	389	1012	587	881	915	896	504	657
21	167	562	403	634	88	267	755	68	217	274
22	359	439	695	777	786	1142	353	1170	873	910
23	716	673	234	1101	607	130	263	669	721	78
24	575	182	865	858	1153	301	417	725	476	307
25	962	16	889	36	922	510	8	452	989	829
26	427	337	491	82	1081	326	1007	125	120	99
27	678	319	1129	741	686	282	252	614	1087	579
28	709	292	852	948	1176	796	933	551	111	1064
29	157	195	816	1162	1023	186	51	1184	1109	104
30	498	1123	239	1034	229	1076	46	954	29	374
31	399	869	1149	423	248	812	25	210	1048	663
32	1117	733	386	164	214	350	604	862	959	986
33	1004	683	849	154	1106	43	245	383	1001	998
34	1052	905	332	1157	345	175	1055	762	879	655
35	632	66	437	1140	908	1099	667	180	299	305
36	34	450	335	324	97	739	612	290	794	1062
37	1160	1182	1121	1074	372	421	208	731	348	984
38	152	381	903	173	653	1138	178	448	737	1060
39	1072	729	379	1136	1058	1134	540	542	135	466
40	1040	544	765	973	390	137	1013	480	588	468
41	882	145	916	1042	897	772	505	546	658	61
42	168	767	563	311	404	975	635	746	89	392
43	268	942	756	139	69	802	218	1015	275	966
44	360	482	440	529	696	590	778	568	787	470
45	1143	202	354	884	1171	20	874	147	911	691
46	717	918	674	929	235	1044	1102	628	608	899
47	131	893	264	774	670	75	722	507	79	316
48	576	548	183	1031	866	660	859	40	1154	63
49	302	287	418	170	726	463	477	769	308	939

POWER RESIDUES

	0	1	2	3	4	5	6	7	8	9
0	1	2	4	8	16	32	64	128	256	512
1	1024	861	535	1070	953	719	251	502	1004	821
2	455	910	633	79	158	316	632	77	154	308
3	616	45	90	180	360	720	253	506	1012	837
4	487	974	761	335	670	153	306	612	37	74
5	148	296	592	1184	1181	1175	1163	1139	1091	995
6	803	419	838	489	978	769	351	702	217	434
7	868	549	1098	1009	831	475	950	713	239	478
8	956	725	263	526	1052	917	647	107	214	428
9	856	525	1050	913	639	91	182	364	728	269
10	538	1076	965	743	299	598	9	18	36	72
11	144	288	576	1152	1117	1047	907	627	67	134
12	268	536	1072	957	727	267	534	1068	949	711
13	235	470	940	693	199	398	796	405	810	433
14	866	545	1090	993	799	411	822	457	914	641
15	95	190	380	760	333	666	145	290	580	1160
16	1133	1079	971	755	323	646	105	210	420	840
17	493	986	785	383	766	345	690	193	386	772
18	357	714	241	482	964	741	295	590	1180	1173
19	1159	1131	1075	963	739	291	582	1164	1141	1095
20	1003	819	451	902	617	47	94	188	376	752
21	317	634	81	162	324	648	109	218	436	872
22	557	1114	1041	895	603	19	38	76	152	304
23	608	29	58	116	232	464	928	669	151	302
24	604	21	42	84	168	336	672	157	314	628
25	69	138	276	552	1104	1021	855	523	1046	905
26	623	59	118	236	472	944	701	215	430	860
27	533	1066	945	703	219	438	876	565	1130	1073
28	959	731	275	550	1100	1013	839	491	982	777
29	367	734	281	562	1124	1061	935	683	179	358
30	716	245	490	980	773	359	718	249	498	996
31	805	423	846	505	1010	833	479	958	729	271
32	542	1084	981	775	363	726	265	530	1060	933
33	679	171	342	684	181	362	724	261	522	1044
34	901	615	43	86	172	344	688	189	378	756
35	325	650	113	226	452	904	621	55	110	220
36	440	880	573	1146	1105	1023	859	531	1062	937
37	687	187	374	748	309	618	49	98	196	392
38	784	381	762	337	674	161	322	644	101	202
39	404	808	429	858	529	1058	929	671	155	310
40	620	53	106	212	424	848	509	1018	849	511
41	1022	857	527	1054	921	655	123	246	492	984
42	781	375	750	313	626	65	130	260	520	1040
43	893	599	11	22	44	88	176	352	704	221
44	442	884	581	1162	1137	1087	987	787	387	774
45	361	722	257	514	1028	869	551	1102	1017	847
46	507	1014	841	495	990	793	399	798	409	818
47	449	898	609	31	62	124	248	496	992	797
48	407	814	441	882	577	1154	1121	1055	923	659
49	131	262	524	1048	909	631	75	150	300	600

P = 1187

INDICES

	0	1	2	3	4	5	6	7	8	9
50	963	565	17	926	890	313	37	460	923	406
51	511	409	9	977	453	839	990	637	830	514
52	428	748	338	257	492	91	83	412	1082	394
53	327	367	1008	270	126	12	121	944	100	808
54	679	758	320	980	1130	141	742	525	687	71
55	283	456	253	804	615	619	1088	220	580	842
56	710	1017	293	557	853	277	949	993	1177	968
57	797	623	934	362	552	640	112	484	1065	823
58	158	442	196	833	817	531	1163	1092	1024	698
59	187	517	52	592	1185	645	1110	780	105	431
60	499	570	1124	224	240	789	1035	751	230	472
61	1077	705	47	1145	955	341	30	204	375	584
62	400	356	870	260	1150	886	424	117	249	1173
63	813	495	26	22	211	846	1049	876	664	94
64	1118	149	734	537	387	913	165	86	215	693
65	351	714	605	719	863	415	960	920	987	489
66	1005	676	684	1085	850	931	155	1021	1107	237
67	44	397	246	1046	384	602	1002	1104	999	330
68	1053	630	906	297	333	610	1158	370	346	901
69	176	1070	1056	133	763	1011	880	895	656	561
70	633	266	67	273	438	776	1141	1169	909	672
71	1100	129	668	77	181	857	300	724	306	15
72	35	509	451	828	336	81	325	124	98	318
73	740	281	613	578	291	947	795	550	1063	194
74	1161	185	1183	103	1122	1033	1075	953	373	868
75	422	811	209	662	732	163	349	861	985	682
76	153	42	382	997	904	1156	174	761	654	65
77	1139	1098	179	304	449	323	738	289	1061	1181
78	1073	420	730	983	380	172	1137	447	1059	728
79	1135	1133	541	465	543	972	136	479	467	144
80	1041	771	545	60	766	310	974	745	391	941
81	138	801	1014	965	481	528	589	567	469	201
82	883	19	146	690	917	928	1043	627	898	892
83	773	74	506	315	547	1030	659	39	62	286
84	169	462	768	938	564	925	312	459	405	408
85	976	838	636	513	747	256	90	411	393	366
86	269	11	943	807	757	979	140	524	70	455
87	803	618	219	841	1016	556	276	992	967	622
88	361	639	483	822	441	832	530	1091	697	516
89	591	644	779	430	569	223	788	750	471	704
90	1144	340	203	583	355	259	885	116	1172	494
91	21	845	875	93	148	536	912	85	692	713
92	718	414	919	488	675	1084	930	1020	236	396
93	1045	601	1103	329	629	296	609	369	900	1069
94	132	1010	894	560	265	272	775	1168	671	128
95	76	856	723	14	508	827	80	123	317	280
96	577	946	549	193	184	102	1032	952	867	810
97	661	162	860	681	41	996	1155	760	64	1097
98	303	322	288	1180	419	982	171	446	727	1132
99	464	971	478	143	770	59	309	744	940	800

POWER RESIDUES

	0	1	2	3	4	5	6	7	8	9
50	13	26	52	104	208	416	832	477	954	721
51	255	510	1020	853	519	1038	889	591	1182	1177
52	1167	1147	1107	1027	867	547	1094	1001	815	443
53	886	585	1170	1153	1119	1051	915	643	99	198
54	396	792	397	794	401	802	417	834	481	962
55	737	287	574	1148	1109	1031	875	563	1126	1065
56	943	699	211	422	844	501	1002	817	447	894
57	601	15	30	60	120	240	480	960	733	279
58	558	1116	1045	903	619	51	102	204	408	816
59	445	890	593	1186	1185	1183	1179	1171	1155	1123
60	1059	931	675	163	326	652	117	234	468	936
61	685	183	366	732	277	554	1108	1029	871	555
62	1110	1033	879	571	1142	1097	1007	827	467	934
63	681	175	350	700	213	426	852	517	1034	881
64	575	1150	1113	1039	891	595	3	6	12	24
65	48	96	192	384	768	349	698	209	418	836
66	485	970	753	319	638	89	178	356	712	237
67	474	948	709	231	462	924	661	135	270	540
68	1080	973	759	331	662	137	274	548	1096	1005
69	823	459	918	649	111	222	444	888	589	1178
70	1169	1151	1115	1043	899	611	35	70	140	280
71	560	1120	1053	919	651	115	230	460	920	653
72	119	238	476	952	717	247	494	988	789	391
73	782	377	754	321	642	97	194	388	776	365
74	730	273	546	1092	997	807	427	854	521	1042
75	897	607	27	54	108	216	432	864	541	1082
76	977	767	347	694	201	402	804	421	842	497
77	994	801	415	830	473	946	705	223	446	892
78	597	7	14	28	56	112	224	448	896	605
79	23	46	92	184	368	736	285	570	1140	1093
80	999	811	435	870	553	1106	1025	863	539	1078
81	969	751	315	630	73	146	292	584	1168	1149
82	1111	1035	883	579	1158	1129	1071	955	723	259
83	518	1036	885	583	1166	1145	1103	1019	851	515
84	1030	873	559	1118	1049	911	635	83	166	332
85	664	141	282	564	1128	1069	951	715	243	486
86	972	757	327	654	121	242	484	968	749	311
87	622	57	114	228	456	912	637	87	174	348
88	696	205	410	820	453	906	625	63	126	252
89	504	1008	829	471	942	697	207	414	828	469
90	938	689	191	382	764	341	682	177	354	708
91	229	458	916	645	103	206	412	824	461	922
92	657	127	254	508	1016	845	503	1006	825	463
93	926	665	143	286	572	1144	1101	1015	843	499
94	998	809	431	862	537	1074	961	735	283	566
95	1132	1077	967	747	307	614	41	82	164	328
96	656	125	250	500	1000	813	439	878	569	1138
97	1089	991	795	403	806	425	850	513	1026	865
98	543	1086	985	783	379	758	329	658	129	258
99	516	1032	877	567	1134	1081	975	763	339	678

P = 1187

INDICES

	0	1	2	3	4	5	6	7	8	9
100	964	527	566	200	18	689	927	626	891	73
101	314	1029	38	285	461	937	924	458	407	837
102	512	255	410	365	10	806	978	523	454	617
103	840	555	991	621	638	821	831	1090	515	643
104	429	222	749	703	339	582	258	115	493	844
105	92	535	84	712	413	487	1083	1019	395	600
106	328	295	368	1068	1009	559	271	1167	127	855
107	13	826	122	279	945	192	101	951	809	161
108	680	995	759	1096	321	1179	981	445	1131	970
109	142	58	743	799	526	199	688	625	72	1028
110	284	936	457	836	254	364	805	522	616	554
111	620	820	1089	642	221	702	581	114	843	534
112	711	486	1018	599	294	1067	558	1166	854	825
113	278	191	950	160	994	1095	1178	444	969	57
114	798	198	624	1027	935	835	363	521	553	819
115	641	701	113	533	485	598	1066	1165	824	190
116	159	1094	443	56	197	1026	834	520	818	700
117	532	597	1164	189	1093	55	1025	519	699	596
118	188	54	518	595	53	594	593			

POWER RESIDUES

	0	1	2	3	4	5	6	7	8	9
100	169	338	676	165	330	660	133	266	532	1064
101	941	695	203	406	812	437	874	561	1122	1057
102	927	667	147	294	588	1176	1165	1143	1099	1011
103	835	483	966	745	303	606	25	50	100	200
104	400	800	413	826	465	930	673	159	318	636
105	85	170	340	680	173	346	692	197	394	788
106	389	778	369	738	289	578	1156	1125	1063	939
107	691	195	390	780	373	746	305	610	33	66
108	132	264	528	1056	925	663	139	278	556	1112
109	1037	887	587	1174	1161	1135	1083	979	771	355
110	710	233	466	932	677	167	334	668	149	298
111	596	5	10	20	40	80	160	320	640	93
112	186	372	744	301	602	17	34	68	136	272
113	544	1088	989	791	395	790	393	786	385	770
114	353	706	225	450	900	613	39	78	156	312
115	624	61	122	244	488	976	765	343	686	185
116	370	740	293	586	1172	1157	1127	1067	947	707
117	227	454	908	629	71	142	284	568	1136	1085
118	983	779	371	742	297	594				

P = 1193

INDICES

	0	1	2	3	4	5	6	7	8	9
0		0	588	1	1176	699	589	175	572	2
1	95	116	1177	258	763	700	1160	327	590	999
2	683	176	704	951	573	206	846	3	159	634
3	96	901	556	117	915	874	1178	42	395	259
4	79	1138	764	1149	100	701	347	980	1161	350
5	794	328	242	1087	591	815	747	1000	30	171
6	684	512	297	177	1144	957	705	860	311	952
7	270	436	574	834	630	207	983	291	847	468
8	667	4	534	734	160	1026	545	635	688	324
9	97	433	935	902	376	506	557	53	938	118
10	190	1014	916	1164	830	875	483	448	1179	473
11	211	43	143	678	396	458	618	260	759	502
12	80	232	1100	1139	885	905	765	196	540	1150
13	353	165	101	1174	256	702	899	77	348	28
14	858	981	1024	374	1162	141	230	351	26	24
15	795	128	379	329	879	408	243	797	1056	1088
16	63	1126	592	663	1122	816	130	994	748	516
17	422	1001	1133	415	31	381	84	172	912	509
18	685	455	1021	513	331	741	298	443	964	178
19	1094	987	1145	881	641	958	334	123	706	603
20	778	861	410	809	312	645	560	953	226	1115
21	271	245	1071	437	1036	656	575	1076	1061	835
22	799	585	631	744	731	208	74	1119	984	1058
23	1046	292	14	56	848	487	155	469	1090	1081
24	668	478	820	5	496	1049	535	65	281	735
25	301	790	161	1067	784	1027	1128	236	546	217
26	941	636	753	401	689	594	570	325	844	872
27	98	1085	295	434	665	322	936	446	616	903
28	254	372	377	1124	420	507	962	121	558	654
29	729	54	818	788	939	870	614	119	612	17
30	191	132	716	1015	967	19	917	890	275	1165
31	996	344	831	187	193	876	452	223	484	750
32	651	449	522	134	1180	464	59	474	518	1155
33	212	181	718	44	390	367	144	424	1104	679
34	1010	1017	397	525	529	459	1003	974	619	825
35	969	261	672	851	760	1135	308	503	1097	21
36	81	806	1043	233	417	341	1101	338	919	1140
37	137	70	886	33	1031	906	360	892	766	150
38	490	197	383	695	541	990	277	1151	37	249
39	354	86	922	166	711	1167	102	1183	1191	1175
40	174	94	257	1159	998	703	205	158	900	914
41	41	78	1148	346	349	241	814	29	511	1143
42	859	269	833	982	467	533	1025	687	432	375
43	52	189	1163	482	472	142	457	758	231	884
44	195	352	1173	898	27	1023	140	25	127	878
45	796	62	662	129	515	1132	380	911	454	330
46	442	1093	880	333	602	409	644	225	244	1035
47	1075	798	743	73	1057	13	486	1089	477	495
48	64	300	1066	1127	216	752	593	843	1084	664
49	445	253	1123	961	653	817	869	611	131	966

POWER RESIDUES

	0	1	2	3	4	5	6	7	8	9
0	1	3	9	27	81	243	729	994	596	595
1	592	583	556	475	232	696	895	299	897	305
2	915	359	1077	845	149	447	148	444	139	417
3	58	174	522	373	1119	971	527	388	1164	1106
4	932	410	37	111	333	999	611	640	727	988
5	578	541	430	97	291	873	233	699	904	326
6	978	548	451	160	480	247	741	1030	704	919
7	371	1113	953	473	226	678	841	137	411	40
8	120	360	1080	854	176	528	391	1173	1133	1013
9	653	766	1105	929	401	10	30	90	270	810
10	44	132	396	1188	1178	1148	1058	788	1171	1127
11	995	599	604	619	664	799	11	33	99	297
12	891	287	861	197	591	580	547	448	151	453
13	166	498	301	903	323	969	521	370	1110	944
14	446	145	435	112	336	1008	638	721	970	524
15	379	1137	1025	689	874	236	708	931	407	28
16	84	252	756	1075	839	131	393	1179	1151	1067
17	815	59	177	531	400	7	21	63	189	567
18	508	331	993	593	586	565	502	313	939	431
19	100	300	900	314	942	440	127	381	1143	1043
20	743	1036	722	973	533	406	25	75	225	675
21	832	110	330	990	584	559	484	259	777	1138
22	1028	698	901	317	951	467	208	624	679	844
23	146	438	121	363	1089	881	257	771	1120	974
24	536	415	52	156	468	211	633	706	925	389
25	1167	1115	959	491	280	840	134	402	13	39
26	117	351	1053	773	1126	992	590	577	538	421
27	70	210	630	697	898	308	924	386	1158	1088
28	878	248	744	1039	731	1000	614	649	754	1069
29	821	77	231	693	886	272	816	62	186	558
30	481	250	750	1057	785	1162	1100	914	356	1068
31	818	68	204	612	643	736	1015	659	784	1159
32	1091	887	275	825	89	267	801	17	51	153
33	459	184	552	463	196	588	571	520	367	1101
34	917	365	1095	899	311	933	413	46	138	414
35	49	147	441	130	390	1170	1124	986	572	523
36	376	1128	998	608	631	700	907	335	1005	629
37	694	889	281	843	143	429	94	282	846	152
38	456	175	525	382	1146	1052	770	1117	965	509
39	334	1002	620	667	808	38	114	342	1026	692
40	883	263	789	1174	1136	1022	680	847	155	465
41	202	606	625	682	853	173	519	364	1092	890
42	284	852	170	510	337	1011	647	748	1051	767
43	1108	938	428	91	273	819	71	213	639	724
44	979	551	460	187	561	490	277	831	107	321
45	963	503	316	948	458	181	543	436	115	345
46	1035	719	964	506	325	975	539	424	79	237
47	711	940	434	109	327	981	557	478	241	723
48	976	542	433	106	318	954	476	235	705	922
49	380	1140	1034	716	955	479	244	732	1003	623

P = 1193

INDICES

	0	1	2	3	4	5	6	7	8	9
50	889	995	186	451	749	521	463	517	180	389
51	423	1009	524	1002	824	671	1134	1096	805	416
52	337	136	32	359	149	382	989	36	85	710
53	1182	173	1158	204	913	1147	240	510	268	466
54	686	51	481	456	883	1172	1022	126	61	514
55	910	441	332	643	1034	742	12	476	299	215
56	842	444	960	868	965	185	520	179	1008	823
57	1095	336	358	988	709	1157	1146	267	50	882
58	125	909	642	11	214	959	184	1007	335	708
59	266	124	10	183	707	9	8	604	605	111
60	779	606	720	862	112	931	411	780	363	810
61	607	46	313	721	286	646	863	550	561	113
62	392	954	932	499	227	412	775	1116	781	369
63	272	364	1040	246	811	895	1072	608	146	438
64	47	928	1037	314	1110	657	722	426	576	287
65	1052	1077	647	90	1062	864	1106	836	551	317
66	800	562	769	586	114	681	632	393	978	745
67	955	628	732	933	1012	209	500	538	75	228
68	406	1120	413	1019	985	776	1113	1059	1117	153
69	1047	782	399	293	370	727	15	273	221	57
70	365	527	849	1041	68	488	247	1189	156	812
71	531	470	896	660	1091	1073	493	1082	609	461
72	669	147	202	479	439	840	821	48	1005	6
73	929	284	497	1038	926	1050	315	976	536	1111
74	725	66	658	200	282	723	621	736	427	623
75	302	577	948	791	288	827	162	1053	738	1068
76	1078	567	785	648	971	1028	91	429	1129	1063
77	386	237	865	263	547	1107	625	218	837	945
78	942	552	674	637	318	304	754	801	107	402
79	563	853	690	770	579	595	587	698	571	115
80	762	326	682	950	845	633	555	873	394	1137
81	99	979	793	1086	746	170	296	956	310	435
82	629	290	666	733	544	323	934	505	937	1013
83	829	447	210	677	617	501	1099	904	539	164
84	255	76	857	373	229	23	378	407	1055	1125
85	1121	993	421	414	83	508	1020	740	963	986
86	640	122	777	808	559	1114	1070	655	1060	584
87	730	1118	1045	55	154	1080	819	1048	280	789
88	783	235	940	400	569	871	294	321	615	371
89	419	120	728	787	613	16	715	18	274	343
90	192	222	650	133	58	1154	717	366	1103	1016
91	528	973	968	850	307	20	1042	340	918	69
92	1030	891	489	694	276	248	921	1166	1190	93
93	997	157	40	345	813	1142	832	532	431	188
94	471	757	194	897	139	877	661	1131	453	1092
95	601	224	1074	72	485	494	1065	751	1083	252
96	652	610	888	450	462	388	523	670	804	135
97	148	35	1181	203	239	465	480	1171	60	440
98	1033	475	841	867	519	822	357	1156	49	908
99	213	1006	265	182	7	110	719	930	362	45

POWER RESIDUES

	0	1	2	3	4	5	6	7	8	9
50	676	835	119	357	1071	827	95	285	855	179
51	537	418	61	183	549	454	169	507	328	984
52	566	505	322	966	512	343	1029	701	910	344
53	1032	710	937	425	82	246	738	1021	677	838
54	128	384	1152	1070	824	86	258	774	1129	1001
55	617	658	781	1150	1064	806	32	96	288	864
56	206	618	661	790	1177	1145	1049	761	1090	884
57	266	798	8	24	72	216	648	751	1060	794
58	1189	1181	1157	1085	869	221	663	796	2	6
59	18	54	162	486	265	795	1192	1190	1184	1166
60	1112	950	464	199	597	598	601	610	637	718
61	961	497	298	894	296	888	278	834	116	348
62	1044	746	1045	749	1054	776	1135	1019	671	820
63	74	222	666	805	29	87	261	783	1156	1082
64	860	194	582	553	466	205	615	652	763	1096
65	902	320	960	494	289	867	215	645	742	1033
66	713	946	452	163	489	274	822	80	240	720
67	967	515	352	1056	782	1153	1073	833	113	339
68	1017	665	802	20	60	180	540	427	88	264
69	792	1183	1163	1103	923	383	1149	1061	797	5
70	15	45	135	405	22	66	198	594	589	574
71	529	394	1182	1160	1094	896	302	906	332	996
72	602	613	646	745	1042	740	1027	695	892	290
73	870	224	672	823	83	249	747	1048	758	1081
74	857	185	555	472	223	669	814	56	168	504
75	319	957	485	262	786	1165	1109	941	437	118
76	354	1062	800	14	42	126	378	1134	1016	662
77	793	1186	1172	1130	1004	626	685	862	200	600
78	607	628	691	880	254	762	1093	893	293	879
79	251	753	1066	812	50	150	450	157	471	220
80	660	787	1168	1118	968	518	361	1083	863	203
81	609	634	709	934	416	55	165	495	292	876
82	242	726	985	569	514	349	1047	755	1072	830
83	104	312	936	422	73	219	657	778	1141	1037
84	725	982	560	487	268	804	26	78	234	702
85	913	353	1059	791	1180	1154	1076	842	140	420
86	67	201	603	616	655	772	1123	983	563	496
87	295	885	269	807	35	105	315	945	449	154
88	462	193	579	544	439	124	372	1116	962	500
89	307	921	377	1131	1007	635	712	943	443	136
90	408	31	93	279	837	125	375	1125	989	581
91	550	457	178	534	409	34	102	306	918	368
92	1104	926	392	1176	1142	1040	734	1009	641	730
93	997	605	622	673	826	92	276	828	98	294
94	882	260	780	1147	1055	779	1144	1046	752	1063
95	803	23	69	207	621	670	817	65	195	585
96	562	493	286	858	188	564	499	304	912	350
97	1050	764	1099	911	347	1041	737	1018	668	811
98	47	141	423	76	228	684	859	191	573	526
99	385	1155	1079	851	167	501	310	930	404	19

P = 1193

INDICES

	0	1	2	3	4	5	6	7	8	9
100	285	549	391	498	774	368	1039	894	145	927
101	1109	425	1051	89	1105	316	768	680	977	627
102	1011	537	405	1018	1112	152	398	726	220	526
103	67	1188	530	659	492	460	201	839	1004	283
104	925	975	724	199	620	622	947	826	737	566
105	970	428	385	262	624	944	673	303	106	852
106	578	697	761	949	554	1136	792	169	309	289
107	543	504	828	676	1098	163	856	22	1054	992
108	82	739	639	807	1069	583	1044	1079	279	234
109	568	320	418	786	714	342	649	1153	1102	972
110	306	339	1029	693	920	92	39	1141	430	756
111	138	1130	600	71	1064	251	887	387	803	34
112	238	1170	1032	866	356	907	264	109	361	548
113	773	893	1108	88	767	626	404	151	219	1187
114	491	838	924	198	946	565	384	943	105	696
115	553	168	542	675	855	991	638	582	278	319
116	713	1152	305	692	38	755	599	250	802	1169
117	355	108	772	87	403	1186	923	564	104	167
118	854	581	712	691	598	1168	771	1185	103	580
119	597	1184	596							

POWER RESIDUES

	0	1	2	3	4	5	6	7	8	9
100	57	171	513	346	1038	728	991	587	568	511
101	340	1020	674	829	101	303	909	341	1023	683
102	856	182	546	445	142	426	85	255	765	1102
103	920	374	1122	980	554	469	214	642	733	1006
104	632	703	916	362	1086	872	230	690	877	245
105	735	1012	650	757	1078	848	158	474	229	687
106	868	218	654	769	1114	956	482	253	759	1084
107	866	212	636	715	952	470	217	651	760	1087
108	875	239	717	958	488	271	813	53	159	477
109	238	714	949	461	190	570	517	358	1074	836
110	122	366	1098	908	338	1014	656	775	1132	1010
111	644	739	1024	686	865	209	627	688	871	227
112	681	850	164	492	283	849	161	483	256	768
113	1111	947	455	172	516	355	1065	809	41	123
114	369	1107	935	419	64	192	576	535	412	43
115	129	387	1161	1097	905	329	987	575	532	403
116	16	48	144	432	103	309	927	395	1185	1169
117	1121	977	545	442	133	399	4	12	36	108
118	324	972	530	397	1191	1187	1175	1139	1031	707
119	928	398								

P = 1201

INDICES

	0	1	2	3	4	5	6	7	8	9
0		0	1132	388	1064	842	320	450	996	776
1	774	1	252	429	382	30	928	577	708	438
2	706	838	1133	1149	184	484	361	1164	314	1007
3	1162	179	860	389	509	92	640	317	370	817
4	638	1045	770	74	1065	418	1081	477	116	900
5	416	965	293	759	1096	843	246	826	939	732
6	1094	932	111	26	792	71	321	134	441	337
7	24	943	572	61	249	872	302	451	749	298
8	570	352	977	1035	702	219	6	195	997	36
9	350	879	1013	567	409	80	48	665	832	777
10	348	949	897	1040	225	480	691	783	1028	531
11	775	705	178	769	758	791	871	5	664	1027
12	1026	2	864	233	43	126	1158	763	724	462
13	3	957	253	888	66	806	373	84	269	840
14	1156	865	875	430	504	649	1193	88	181	380
15	804	654	234	153	383	1021	681	1047	230	1147
16	502	399	284	44	909	31	967	1010	634	858
17	151	14	1138	324	127	934	929	1120	1168	1043
18	282	1071	811	120	945	1159	499	578	341	414
19	12	1123	1180	354	597	459	764	718	709	730
20	280	522	881	257	829	687	972	725	157	439
21	412	951	623	131	715	916	960	629	463	449
22	707	1006	637	964	110	60	701	79	690	4
23	723	839	803	398	1137	119	596	686	959	78
24	958	222	1134	740	796	542	165	867	1175	223
25	58	254	1090	1150	695	607	656	1060	394	767
26	1135	583	889	1116	185	401	820	424	1198	862
27	738	741	305	67	16	485	201	103	772	955
28	1088	1187	797	1073	807	468	362	295	436	1154
29	581	1053	1125	543	20	374	113	1165	312	378
30	736	524	586	137	166	574	85	100	315	228
31	953	210	613	1101	979	868	162	270	1079	1008
32	434	1171	331	1015	216	913	1176	919	841	927
33	1163	369	899	1093	942	976	566	224	790	1157
34	83	180	1146	150	1070	1179	256	714	59	595
35	866	393	861	1087	1052	585	1100	215	975	255
36	214	876	1003	390	743	903	52	560	877	621
37	1091	9	431	1189	510	514	273	236	346	1004
38	1144	1151	1055	505	1112	93	286	850	529	721
39	391	526	696	145	650	1140	641	986	662	76
40	212	744	454	608	813	1194	189	318	761	1173
41	619	472	904	1182	657	677	89	28	371	1058
42	344	923	883	53	555	1061	63	182	647	818
43	848	625	892	444	561	1037	395	387	381	483
44	639	476	938	336	569	878	896	768	42	805
45	1192	1046	633	1042	11	521	622	963	1136	541
46	655	423	771	1153	735	209	330	1092	1069	584
47	51	235	528	75	618	922	891	335	10	208
48	890	746	154	787	1066	307	672	747	728	432
49	474	1117	97	384	799	419	1107	193	155	925

POWER RESIDUES

	0	1	2	3	4	5	6	7	8	9
0	1	11	121	130	229	117	86	946	798	371
1	478	454	190	889	171	680	274	612	727	791
2	294	832	745	989	70	770	63	693	417	984
3	15	165	614	749	1033	554	89	979	1161	761
4	1165	805	448	124	163	592	507	773	96	1056
5	807	470	366	423	1050	741	945	787	250	348
6	225	73	803	426	1083	1104	134	273	601	606
7	661	65	715	659	43	473	399	786	239	227
8	95	1045	686	340	137	306	964	996	147	416
9	973	1095	35	385	632	947	809	492	608	683
10	307	975	1117	277	645	1090	1181	981	1183	1003
11	224	62	682	296	854	987	48	528	1004	235
12	183	812	525	971	1073	994	125	174	713	637
13	1002	213	1142	552	67	737	901	303	931	633
14	958	930	622	837	800	393	720	714	648	1123
15	343	170	669	153	482	498	674	208	1087	1148
16	618	793	316	1074	1005	246	304	942	754	1088
17	1159	739	923	545	1191	1091	1192	1102	112	31
18	341	148	427	1094	24	264	502	718	692	406
19	863	1086	1137	497	663	87	957	919	501	707
20	571	276	634	969	1051	752	1066	917	479	465
21	311	1019	400	797	360	357	324	1162	772	85
22	935	677	241	249	337	104	1144	574	309	997
23	158	537	1103	123	152	471	377	544	1180	970
24	1062	873	1196	1146	596	551	56	616	771	74
25	814	547	12	132	251	359	346	203	1032	543
26	1169	849	932	644	1079	1060	851	954	886	138
27	317	1085	1126	376	533	1059	840	833	756	1110
28	200	999	180	779	162	581	386	643	1068	939
29	721	725	769	52	572	287	755	1099	79	869
30	1152	662	76	836	789	272	590	485	531	1037
31	598	573	298	876	28	308	986	37	407	874
32	6	66	726	780	173	702	516	872	1185	1025
33	466	322	1140	530	1026	477	443	69	759	1143
34	563	188	867	1130	420	1017	378	555	100	1100
35	90	990	81	891	193	922	534	1070	961	963
36	985	26	286	744	978	1150	640	1035	576	331
37	38	418	995	136	295	843	866	1119	299	887
38	149	438	14	154	493	619	804	437	3	33
39	363	390	687	351	258	436	1193	1113	233	161
40	570	265	513	839	822	635	980	1172	882	94
41	1034	565	210	1109	189	878	50	550	45	495
42	641	1046	697	461	267	535	1081	1082	1093	13
43	143	372	489	575	320	1118	288	766	19	209
44	1098	68	748	1022	433	1160	750	1044	675	219
45	7	77	847	910	402	819	602	617	782	195
46	944	776	129	218	1197	1157	717	681	285	733
47	857	1020	411	918	490	586	441	47	517	883
48	105	1155	695	439	25	275	623	848	921	523
49	949	831	734	868	1141	541	1147	607	672	186

P = 1201

INDICES

	0	1	2	3	4	5	6	7	8	9
50	1190	198	186	1127	1022	591	1082	46	627	788
51	539	511	588	402	992	682	326	478	699	712
52	1067	615	515	489	821	122	1048	756	117	1098
53	333	308	752	274	356	425	1130	231	794	901
54	670	495	673	259	237	173	1199	251	1148	508
55	417	245	133	748	35	347	704	863	887	503
56	1020	966	1119	340	729	411	1005	802	739	694
57	400	200	294	311	227	433	368	1145	1086	742
58	513	285	985	760	1057	847	475	632	1152	617
59	306	1106	45	698	1097	669	244	1118	310	1056
60	668	68	456	910	518	844	69	497	98	645
61	506	906	17	552	32	1075	247	457	160	385
62	885	1113	142	486	545	968	1033	827	911	894
63	800	1000	94	139	202	405	1011	129	940	519
64	366	420	1103	287	263	104	947	635	148	733
65	845	1017	1108	548	851	599	773	837	859	73
66	1095	70	301	194	831	530	1025	956	874	152
67	908	933	498	717	156	448	722	221	1089	1115
68	15	467	112	99	1078	926	82	392	1002	1188
69	1111	1139	188	27	646	482	1191	422	527	786
70	798	590	325	755	793	507	1019	199	984	697
71	517	1074	1032	128	147	72	907	466	187	754
72	146	290	808	610	935	291	322	18	675	1128
73	835	651	1184	469	492	930	809	135	553	171
74	1023	55	1141	536	363	22	1121	611	442	33
75	446	592	205	642	168	296	278	1169	936	338
76	1076	39	1083	981	987	995	437	1161	1044	292
77	25	248	218	47	782	663	461	1155	653	283
78	323	944	458	971	628	689	77	57	582	304
79	1072	19	573	161	918	789	594	213	8	1054
80	144	812	676	62	386	41	540	50	745	96
81	1126	991	121	1129	250	886	693	512	1105	455
82	551	544	404	946	836	873	1114	1110	589	1031
83	609	491	21	277	1160	652	303	143	990	403
84	276	814	855	375	815	500	1185	452	487	261
85	993	266	1195	659	114	856	579	470	750	546
86	780	683	557	190	824	1166	376	342	493	299
87	969	563	327	241	319	576	313	816	415	931
88	571	1034	408	479	870	762	268	379	501	13
89	810	353	828	915	700	685	1174	766	737	1186
90	1124	136	978	912	565	713	974	620	1143	525
91	453	1181	554	1036	895	962	1068	207	473	197
92	587	488	355	172	703	801	1085	616	667	905
93	141	138	262	598	1024	220	1001	785	516	289
94	1183	535	167	994	460	56	7	95	550	490
95	854	658	823	575	267	765	1142	196	140	534
96	822	358	678	359	86	1196	719	537	998	203
97	239	123	604	90	679	101	660	710	364	37
98	406	107	1049	1063	29	360	316	115	731	23
99	351	1012	1039	757	125	372	87	229	857	281

POWER RESIDUES

	0	1	2	3	4	5	6	7	8	9
50	845	888	160	559	144	383	610	705	549	34
51	374	511	817	580	375	522	938	710	604	639
52	1024	455	201	1010	301	909	391	698	472	388
53	665	109	1199	1179	959	941	743	967	1029	510
54	806	459	245	293	821	624	859	1042	653	1178
55	948	820	613	738	912	424	1061	862	1075	1016
56	367	434	1171	871	1174	904	336	93	1023	444
57	80	880	72	792	305	953	875	17	187	856
58	1009	290	788	261	469	355	302	920	512	828
59	701	505	751	1055	796	349	236	194	933	655
60	1200	1190	1080	1071	972	1084	1115	255	403	830
61	723	747	1011	312	1030	521	927	589	474	410
62	907	369	456	212	1131	431	1138	508	784	217
63	1186	1036	587	452	168	647	1112	222	40	440
64	36	396	753	1077	1038	609	694	428	1105	145
65	394	731	835	778	151	460	256	414	951	853
66	976	1128	398	775	118	97	1067	928	600	595
67	540	1136	486	542	1158	728	802	415	962	974
68	1106	156	515	861	1064	895	237	205	1054	785
69	228	106	1166	816	569	254	392	709	593	518
70	894	226	84	924	556	111	20	220	18	198
71	977	1139	519	905	347	214	1153	673	197	966
72	1018	389	676	230	128	207	1076	1027	488	564
73	199	988	59	649	1134	464	300	898	270	568
74	243	271	579	364	401	808	481	487	553	78
75	858	1031	532	1048	719	703	527	993	114	53
76	583	408	885	127	196	955	897	259	447	113
77	42	462	278	656	10	110	9	99	1089	1170
78	860	1053	774	107	1177	937	699	483	509	795
79	338	115	64	704	538	1114	244	282	700	494
80	630	925	567	232	150	449	135	284	722	736
81	890	182	801	404	841	844	877	39	429	1116
82	266	524	960	952	864	1097	57	627	892	204
83	1043	664	98	1078	1049	730	824	657	21	231
84	139	328	5	55	605	650	1145	585	430	1127
85	387	654	1189	1069	950	842	855	998	169	658
86	32	352	269	557	122	141	350	247	315	1063
87	884	116	75	825	668	142	361	368	445	91
88	1001	202	1021	422	1039	620	815	558	133	262
89	480	476	432	1149	629	914	446	102	1122	332
90	49	539	1125	365	412	929	611	716	670	164
91	603	628	903	325	1173	893	215	1164	794	327
92	1195	1135	475	421	1028	499	685	329	16	176
93	735	879	61	671	175	724	758	1132	442	58
94	638	1013	334	71	781	184	823	646	1101	101
95	1111	211	1120	310	1008	279	667	131	240	238
96	216	1175	915	457	223	51	561	166	625	870
97	1163	783	206	1065	906	358	335	82	902	314
98	1052	763	1187	1047	708	582	397	764	1198	1168
99	838	811	514	850	943	765	8	88	968	1040

P = 1201

INDICES

	0	1	2	3	4	5	6	7	8	9
100	1122	880	130	109	118	164	1059	1197	954	580
101	523	612	1014	941	1178	1099	559	345	720	211
102	471	882	443	568	520	329	334	727	924	538
103	614	751	258	34	410	367	631	309	644	884
104	999	1102	547	830	447	81	421	983	753	834
105	54	204	980	781	688	593	49	1104	1030	275
106	265	556	240	869	684	973	206	666	288	853
107	357	603	1062	124	163	558	726	643	833	264
108	602	426	427	64	605	271	191	158	169	778
109	105	175	1131	428	183	91	1080	825	440	297
110	349	948	177	232	65	648	680	1009	1167	413
111	279	950	636	397	795	606	819	102	435	377
112	952	1170	898	149	1051	902	272	849	661	1172
113	343	624	937	1041	734	921	671	192	626	711
114	332	494	132	339	226	846	243	496	159	893
115	365	1016	300	716	1077	481	1018	465	674	170
116	445	38	217	970	917	40	692	1109	989	260
117	779	562	407	914	564	961	1084	784	549	533
118	238	106	1038	108	1177	328	630	982	1029	852
119	601	174	176	396	1050	920	242	464	988	532
120	600	0								

POWER RESIDUES

	0	1	2	3	4	5	6	7	8	9
100	631	936	688	362	379	566	221	29	319	1107
101	167	636	991	92	1012	323	1151	651	1156	706
102	560	155	504	740	934	666	120	119	108	1188
103	1058	829	712	626	881	83	913	435	1182	992
104	103	1133	453	179	768	41	451	157	526	982
105	1194	1124	354	291	799	382	599	584	419	1006
106	257	425	1072	983	4	44	484	520	916	468
107	344	181	790	283	711	615	760	1154	684	318
108	1096	46	506	762	1176	926	578	353	280	678
109	252	370	467	333	60	660	54	594	529	1015
110	356	313	1041	642	1057	818	591	496	652	1167
111	827	690	384	621	826	679	263	491	597	562
112	177	746	1000	191	900	292	810	503	729	813
113	536	1092	2	22	242	260	458	234	172	691
114	395	742	956	908	380	577	342	159	548	23
115	253	381	588	463	289	777	140	339	126	185
116	834	767	30	330	27	297	865	1108	178	757
117	1121	321	1129	409	896	248	326	1184	1014	345
118	192	911	413	940	732	846	899	281	689	373
119	500	696	450	146	405	852	965	1007	268	546
120										

P = 1213

INDICES

	0	1	2	3	4	5	6	7	8	9
0		0	1	928	2	209	929	256	3	644
1	210	662	930	744	257	1137	4	15	645	922
2	211	1184	663	1087	931	418	745	360	258	236
3	1138	148	5	378	16	465	646	837	923	460
4	212	89	1185	992	664	853	1088	1111	932	512
5	419	943	746	1054	361	871	259	638	237	773
6	1139	45	149	900	6	953	379	217	17	803
7	466	308	647	243	838	134	924	918	461	939
8	213	76	90	80	1186	224	993	1164	665	121
9	854	1000	1089	1076	1112	1131	933	188	513	94
10	420	888	944	157	747	181	1055	590	362	201
11	872	553	260	476	639	84	238	176	774	271
12	1140	112	46	1017	150	627	901	428	7	708
13	954	1190	380	1178	218	569	18	779	804	279
14	467	827	309	194	648	445	244	228	839	575
15	135	812	925	659	919	357	462	989	940	770
16	214	131	77	997	91	587	81	1014	1187	276
17	225	354	994	351	1165	674	666	489	122	1168
18	855	105	1001	973	1090	1046	1077	677	1113	616
19	1132	1106	934	548	189	669	514	1037	95	599
20	421	1145	889	492	945	298	158	519	748	372
21	182	125	1056	24	591	1201	363	404	202	1171
22	873	759	554	910	261	1062	477	858	640	414
23	85	634	239	117	177	108	775	655	272	1042
24	1141	400	113	1004	47	721	1018	454	151	1008
25	628	976	902	537	429	1152	8	438	709	1093
26	955	880	1191	735	381	51	1179	1049	219	171
27	570	100	19	716	780	1080	805	785	280	792
28	468	725	828	680	310	847	195	345	649	30
29	446	1116	245	693	229	982	840	1022	576	619
30	136	36	813	604	926	254	660	1135	920	1085
31	358	146	463	458	990	1109	941	869	771	898
32	215	306	132	937	78	1162	998	1129	92	155
33	588	551	82	269	1015	426	1188	567	277	192
34	226	810	355	768	995	1012	352	672	1166	971
35	675	1104	667	597	490	517	123	1199	1169	908
36	856	632	106	1040	1002	452	974	1150	1091	733
37	1047	98	1078	790	678	343	1114	980	617	602
38	1133	144	1107	896	935	1127	549	424	190	766
39	670	1102	515	906	1038	1148	96	341	600	894
40	422	1100	1146	892	890	285	493	287	946	541
41	299	495	159	1029	520	289	749	1207	373	948
42	183	703	126	543	1057	433	25	301	592	1122
43	1202	497	364	65	405	161	203	797	1172	1031
44	874	1156	760	522	555	330	911	291	262	502
45	1063	751	478	528	859	1209	641	12	415	375
46	86	509	635	950	240	73	118	185	178	473
47	109	705	776	442	656	128	273	486	1043	545
48	1142	369	401	1059	114	397	1005	435	48	713
49	722	27	1019	251	455	303	152	564	1009	594

POWER RESIDUES

	0	1	2	3	4	5	6	7	8	9
0	1	2	4	8	16	32	64	128	256	512
1	1024	835	457	914	615	17	34	68	136	272
2	544	1088	963	713	213	426	852	491	982	751
3	289	578	1156	1099	985	757	301	602	1204	1195
4	1177	1141	1069	925	637	61	122	244	488	976
5	739	265	530	1060	907	601	1202	1191	1169	1125
6	1037	861	509	1018	823	433	866	519	1038	863
7	513	1026	839	465	930	647	81	162	324	648
8	83	166	332	664	115	230	460	920	627	41
9	82	164	328	656	99	198	396	792	371	742
10	271	542	1084	955	697	181	362	724	235	470
11	940	667	121	242	484	968	723	233	466	932
12	651	89	178	356	712	211	422	844	475	950
13	687	161	322	644	75	150	300	600	1200	1187
14	1161	1109	1005	797	381	762	311	622	31	62
15	124	248	496	992	771	329	658	103	206	412
16	824	435	870	527	1054	895	577	1154	1095	977
17	741	269	538	1076	939	665	117	234	468	936
18	659	105	210	420	840	467	934	655	97	194
19	388	776	339	678	143	286	572	1144	1075	937
20	661	109	218	436	872	531	1062	911	609	5
21	10	20	40	80	160	320	640	67	134	268
22	536	1072	931	649	85	170	340	680	147	294
23	588	1176	1139	1065	917	621	29	58	116	232
24	464	928	643	73	146	292	584	1168	1123	1033
25	853	493	986	759	305	610	7	14	28	56
26	112	224	448	896	579	1158	1103	993	773	333
27	666	119	238	476	952	691	169	338	676	139
28	278	556	1112	1011	809	405	810	407	814	415
29	830	447	894	575	1150	1087	961	709	205	410
30	820	427	854	495	990	767	321	642	71	142
31	284	568	1136	1059	905	597	1194	1175	1137	1061
32	909	605	1210	1207	1201	1189	1165	1117	1021	829
33	445	890	567	1134	1055	897	581	1162	1111	1009
34	805	397	794	375	750	287	574	1148	1083	953
35	693	173	346	692	171	342	684	155	310	620
36	27	54	108	216	432	864	515	1030	847	481
37	962	711	209	418	836	459	918	623	33	66
38	132	264	528	1056	899	585	1170	1127	1041	869
39	525	1050	887	561	1122	1031	849	485	970	727
40	241	482	964	715	217	434	868	523	1046	879
41	545	1090	967	721	229	458	916	619	25	50
42	100	200	400	800	387	774	335	670	127	254
43	508	1016	819	425	850	487	974	735	257	514
44	1028	843	473	946	679	145	290	580	1160	1107
45	1001	789	365	730	247	494	988	763	313	626
46	39	78	156	312	624	35	70	140	280	560
47	1120	1027	841	469	938	663	113	226	452	904
48	595	1190	1167	1121	1029	845	477	954	695	177
49	354	708	203	406	812	411	822	431	862	511

P = 1213

INDICES

	0	1	2	3	4	5	6	7	8	9
50	629	730	977	1124	903	1097	538	1204	430	62
51	1153	499	9	70	439	366	710	561	1094	67
52	956	959	881	407	1192	390	736	163	382	962
53	52	205	1180	833	1050	799	220	884	172	1174
54	571	583	101	1033	20	410	717	876	781	689
55	1081	1158	806	1195	786	762	281	699	793	524
56	469	393	726	557	829	685	681	332	311	739
57	848	913	196	822	346	293	650	166	31	264
58	447	336	1117	504	246	385	694	1065	230	1070
59	983	753	841	965	1023	480	577	315	620	530
60	137	55	37	861	814	321	605	1211	927	208
61	255	643	661	743	1136	14	921	1183	1086	417
62	359	235	147	377	464	836	459	88	991	852
63	1110	511	942	1053	870	637	772	44	899	952
64	216	802	307	242	133	917	938	75	79	223
65	1163	120	999	1075	1130	187	93	887	156	180
66	589	200	552	475	83	175	270	111	1016	626
67	427	707	1189	1177	568	778	278	826	193	444
68	227	574	811	658	356	988	769	130	996	586
69	1013	275	353	350	673	488	1167	104	972	1045
70	676	615	1105	547	668	1036	598	1144	491	297
71	518	371	124	23	1200	403	1170	758	909	1061
72	857	413	633	116	107	654	1041	399	1003	720
73	453	1007	975	536	1151	437	1092	879	734	50
74	1048	170	99	715	1079	784	791	724	679	846
75	344	29	1115	692	981	1021	618	35	603	253
76	1134	1084	145	457	1108	868	897	305	936	1161
77	1128	154	550	268	425	566	191	809	767	1011
78	671	970	1103	596	516	1198	907	631	1039	451
79	1149	732	97	789	342	979	601	143	895	1126
80	423	765	1101	905	1147	340	893	1099	891	284
81	286	540	494	1028	288	1206	947	702	542	432
82	300	1121	496	64	160	796	1030	1155	521	329
83	290	501	750	527	1208	11	374	508	949	72
84	184	472	704	441	127	485	544	368	1058	396
85	434	712	26	250	302	563	593	729	1123	1096
86	1203	61	498	69	365	560	66	958	406	389
87	162	961	204	832	798	883	1173	582	1032	409
88	875	688	1157	1194	761	698	523	392	556	684
89	331	738	912	821	292	165	263	335	503	384
90	1064	1069	752	964	479	314	529	54	860	320
91	1210	207	642	742	13	1182	416	234	376	835
92	87	851	510	1052	636	43	951	801	241	916
93	74	222	119	1074	186	886	179	199	474	174
94	110	625	706	1176	777	825	443	573	657	987
95	129	585	274	349	487	103	1044	614	546	1035
96	1143	296	370	22	402	757	1060	412	115	653
97	398	719	1006	535	436	878	49	169	714	783
98	723	845	28	691	1020	34	252	1083	456	867
99	304	1160	153	267	565	808	1010	969	595	1197

POWER RESIDUES

	0	1	2	3	4	5	6	7	8	9
50	1022	831	449	898	583	1166	1119	1025	837	461
51	922	631	49	98	196	392	784	355	710	207
52	414	828	443	886	559	1118	1023	833	453	906
53	599	1198	1183	1153	1093	973	733	253	506	1012
54	811	409	818	423	846	479	958	703	193	386
55	772	331	662	111	222	444	888	563	1126	1039
56	865	517	1034	855	497	994	775	337	674	135
57	270	540	1080	947	681	149	298	596	1192	1171
58	1129	1045	877	541	1082	951	689	165	330	660
59	107	214	428	856	499	998	783	353	706	199
60	398	796	379	758	303	606	1212	1211	1209	1205
61	1197	1181	1149	1085	957	701	189	378	756	299
62	598	1196	1179	1145	1077	941	669	125	250	500
63	1000	787	361	722	231	462	924	635	57	114
64	228	456	912	611	9	18	36	72	144	288
65	576	1152	1091	969	725	237	474	948	683	153
66	306	612	11	22	44	88	176	352	704	195
67	390	780	347	694	175	350	700	187	374	748
68	283	566	1132	1051	889	565	1130	1047	881	549
69	1098	983	753	293	586	1172	1131	1049	885	557
70	1114	1015	817	421	842	471	942	671	129	258
71	516	1032	851	489	978	743	273	546	1092	971
72	729	245	490	980	747	281	562	1124	1035	857
73	501	1002	791	369	738	263	526	1052	891	569
74	1138	1063	913	613	13	26	52	104	208	416
75	832	451	902	591	1182	1151	1089	965	717	221
76	442	884	555	1110	1007	801	389	778	343	686
77	159	318	636	59	118	236	472	944	675	137
78	274	548	1096	979	745	277	554	1108	1003	793
79	373	746	279	558	1116	1019	825	437	874	535
80	1070	927	641	69	138	276	552	1104	995	777
81	341	682	151	302	604	1208	1203	1193	1173	1133
82	1053	893	573	1146	1079	945	677	141	282	564
83	1128	1043	873	533	1066	919	625	37	74	148
84	296	592	1184	1155	1097	981	749	285	570	1140
85	1067	921	629	45	90	180	360	720	227	454
86	908	603	1206	1199	1185	1157	1101	989	765	317
87	634	55	110	220	440	880	547	1094	975	737
88	261	522	1044	875	537	1074	935	657	101	202
89	404	808	403	806	399	798	383	766	319	638
90	63	126	252	504	1008	803	393	786	359	718
91	223	446	892	571	1142	1071	929	645	77	154
92	308	616	19	38	76	152	304	608	3	6
93	12	24	48	96	192	384	768	323	646	79
94	158	316	632	51	102	204	408	816	419	838
95	463	926	639	65	130	260	520	1040	867	521
96	1042	871	529	1058	903	593	1186	1159	1105	997
97	781	349	698	183	366	732	251	502	1004	795
98	377	754	295	590	1180	1147	1081	949	685	157
99	314	628	43	86	172	344	688	163	326	652

P = 1213

INDICES

	0	1	2	3	4	5	6	7	8	9
100	630	450	731	788	978	142	1125	764	904	339
101	1098	283	539	1027	1205	701	431	1120	63	795
102	1154	328	500	526	10	507	71	471	440	484
103	367	395	711	249	562	728	1095	60	68	559
104	957	388	960	831	882	581	408	687	1193	697
105	391	683	737	820	164	334	383	1068	963	313
106	53	319	206	741	1181	233	834	850	1051	42
107	800	915	221	1073	885	198	173	624	1175	824
108	572	986	584	348	102	613	1034	295	21	756
109	411	652	718	534	877	168	782	844	690	33
110	1082	866	1159	266	807	968	1196	449	787	141
111	763	338	282	1026	700	1119	794	327	525	506
112	470	483	394	248	727	59	558	387	830	580
113	686	696	682	819	333	1067	312	318	740	232
114	849	41	914	1072	197	623	823	985	347	612
115	294	755	651	533	167	843	32	865	265	967
116	448	140	337	1025	1118	326	505	482	247	58
117	386	579	695	818	1066	317	231	40	1071	622
118	984	611	754	532	842	864	966	139	1024	325
119	481	57	578	817	316	39	621	610	531	863
120	138	324	56	816	38	609	862	323	815	608
121	322	607	606							

POWER RESIDUES

	0	1	2	3	4	5	6	7	8	9
100	91	182	364	728	243	486	972	731	249	498
101	996	779	345	690	167	334	668	123	246	492
102	984	755	297	594	1188	1163	1113	1013	813	413
103	826	439	878	543	1086	959	705	197	394	788
104	363	726	239	478	956	699	185	370	740	267
105	534	1068	923	633	53	106	212	424	848	483
106	966	719	225	450	900	587	1174	1135	1057	901
107	589	1178	1143	1073	933	653	93	186	372	744
108	275	550	1100	987	761	309	618	23	46	92
109	184	368	736	259	518	1036	859	505	1010	807
110	401	802	391	782	351	702	191	382	764	315
111	630	47	94	188	376	752	291	582	1164	1115
112	1017	821	429	858	503	1006	799	385	770	327
113	654	95	190	380	760	307	614	15	30	60
114	120	240	480	960	707	201	402	804	395	790
115	367	734	255	510	1020	827	441	882	551	1102
116	991	769	325	650	87	174	348	696	179	358
117	716	219	438	876	539	1078	943	673	133	266
118	532	1064	915	617	21	42	84	168	336	672
119	131	262	524	1048	883	553	1106	999	785	357
120	714	215	430	860	507	1014	815	417	834	455
121	910	607								

P = 1217

INDICES

	0	1	2	3	4	5	6	7	8	9
0		0	216	1	432	819	217	113	648	2
1	1035	1059	433	87	329	820	864	679	218	528
2	35	114	59	203	649	422	303	3	545	886
3	1036	1168	1080	1060	895	932	434	588	744	88
4	251	267	330	150	275	821	419	516	865	226
5	638	680	519	13	219	662	761	529	1102	1161
6	36	1182	168	115	80	906	60	233	1111	204
7	1148	964	650	1186	804	423	960	1172	304	868
8	467	4	483	941	546	282	366	887	491	557
9	1037	200	635	1169	732	131	1081	188	442	1061
10	854	994	896	95	735	933	229	1016	435	983
11	878	589	977	460	745	1022	102	89	161	792
12	252	902	182	268	384	25	331	194	296	151
13	1122	134	276	641	449	822	111	862	420	893
14	148	517	1180	1146	866	489	186	227	1020	382
15	639	1178	1176	681	172	771	520	656	1084	14
16	683	316	220	239	699	663	1157	144	762	174
17	498	530	582	712	1103	535	707	1162	773	321
18	37	525	416	1183	851	191	169	522	948	116
19	347	139	81	336	404	907	658	107	61	594
20	1070	234	1210	999	1112	1086	311	205	951	371
21	1149	9	445	965	16	969	651	65	1199	1187
22	1094	766	805	685	1193	424	676	272	961	439
23	22	1173	318	308	305	119	377	869	1008	1064
24	468	222	1118	5	398	1045	484	615	600	942
25	241	1141	547	46	410	283	512	292	367	701
26	122	888	350	839	492	832	857	558	665	693
27	1038	817	327	201	1078	265	636	1159	1109	1170
28	364	129	733	458	180	132	146	380	1082	142
29	705	189	402	997	443	764	20	1062	598	290
30	855	263	178	995	176	785	897	627	388	96
31	987	787	736	500	872	934	84	248	230	729
32	899	1017	532	1207	436	509	455	984	915	629
33	879	584	157	590	360	1052	978	918	390	461
34	714	1011	746	339	798	1023	928	98	103	1105
35	751	90	923	475	162	567	989	793	537	755
36	253	1056	741	903	632	789	183	709	1067	269
37	407	126	385	1049	738	26	1164	973	332	1074
38	563	195	355	502	297	775	552	152	620	29
39	1123	882	874	135	323	471	277	910	810	642
40	70	936	450	39	210	823	1215	431	112	1034
41	86	863	527	58	421	544	1167	894	587	250
42	149	418	225	518	661	1101	1181	79	232	1147
43	1185	959	867	482	281	490	199	731	187	853
44	94	228	982	976	1021	160	901	383	193	1121
45	640	110	892	1179	488	1019	1177	171	655	682
46	238	1156	173	581	534	772	524	850	521	346
47	335	657	593	1209	1085	950	8	15	64	1093
48	684	675	438	317	118	1007	221	397	614	240
49	45	511	700	349	831	664	816	1077	1158	363

POWER RESIDUES

	0	1	2	3	4	5	6	7	8	9
0	1	3	9	27	81	243	729	970	476	211
1	633	682	829	53	159	477	214	642	709	910
2	296	888	230	690	853	125	375	1125	941	389
3	1167	1067	767	1084	818	20	60	180	540	403
4	1209	1193	1145	1001	569	490	253	759	1060	746
5	1021	629	670	793	1162	1052	722	949	413	22
6	66	198	594	565	478	217	651	736	991	539
7	400	1200	1166	1064	758	1057	737	994	548	427
8	64	192	576	511	316	948	410	13	39	117
9	351	1053	725	958	440	103	309	927	347	1041
10	689	850	116	348	1044	698	877	197	591	556
11	451	136	408	7	21	63	189	567	484	235
12	705	898	260	780	1123	935	371	1113	905	281
13	843	95	285	855	131	393	1179	1103	875	191
14	573	502	289	867	167	501	286	858	140	420
15	43	129	387	1161	1049	713	922	332	996	554
16	445	118	354	1062	752	1039	683	832	62	186
17	558	457	154	462	169	507	304	912	302	906
18	284	852	122	366	1098	860	146	438	97	291
19	873	185	555	448	127	381	1143	995	551	436
20	91	273	819	23	69	207	621	646	721	946
21	404	1212	1202	1172	1082	812	2	6	18	54
22	162	486	241	723	952	422	49	147	441	106
23	318	954	428	67	201	603	592	559	460	163
24	489	250	750	1033	665	778	1117	917	317	951
25	419	40	120	360	1080	806	1201	1169	1073	785
26	1138	980	506	301	903	275	825	41	123	369
27	1107	887	227	681	826	44	132	396	1188	1130
28	956	434	85	255	765	1078	800	1183	1115	911
29	299	897	257	771	1096	854	128	384	1152	1022
30	632	679	820	26	78	234	702	889	233	699
31	880	206	618	637	694	865	161	483	232	696
32	871	179	537	394	1182	1112	902	272	816	14
33	42	126	378	1134	968	470	193	579	520	343
34	1029	653	742	1009	593	562	469	190	570	493
35	262	786	1141	989	533	382	1146	1004	578	517
36	334	1002	572	499	280	840	86	258	774	1105
37	881	209	627	664	775	1108	890	236	708	907
38	287	861	149	447	124	372	1116	914	308	924
39	338	1014	608	607	604	595	568	487	244	732
40	979	503	292	876	194	582	529	370	1110	896
41	254	762	1069	773	1102	872	182	546	421	46
42	138	414	25	75	225	675	808	1207	1187	1127
43	947	407	4	12	36	108	324	972	482	229
44	687	844	98	294	882	212	636	691	856	134
45	402	1206	1184	1118	920	326	978	500	283	849
46	113	339	1017	617	634	685	838	80	240	720
47	943	395	1185	1121	929	353	1059	743	1012	602
48	589	550	433	82	246	738	997	557	454	145
49	435	88	264	792	1159	1043	695	868	170	510

P = 1217

INDICES

	0	1	2	3	4	5	6	7	8	9
50	457	145	141	401	763	597	262	175	626	986
51	499	83	728	531	508	914	583	359	917	713
52	338	927	1104	922	566	536	1055	631	708	406
53	1048	1163	1073	354	774	619	881	322	909	69
54	38	1214	1033	526	543	586	417	660	78	1184
55	481	198	852	981	159	192	109	487	170	237
56	580	523	345	592	949	63	674	117	396	44
57	348	815	362	140	596	625	82	507	358	337
58	921	1054	405	1072	618	908	1213	542	659	480
59	980	108	236	344	62	395	814	595	506	920
60	1071	1212	479	235	394	505	1211	393	392	1000
61	1001	603	1113	1002	843	1087	604	463	312	1114
62	1203	206	1003	670	952	844	716	372	1088	51
63	1150	605	300	10	464	1013	446	313	945	966
64	1115	690	17	1204	748	970	207	956	652	1004
65	725	66	671	341	1200	953	1131	1188	845	778
66	1095	717	800	767	373	244	806	1089	576	686
67	52	1025	1194	1151	1134	425	606	646	677	301
68	930	273	11	166	962	465	555	440	1014	100
69	23	447	1144	1174	314	496	319	946	105	309
70	967	1191	306	1116	1139	120	691	1107	378	18
71	783	870	1205	155	1009	749	753	1065	971	550
72	469	208	56	223	957	92	1119	653	848	6
73	1005	829	399	726	925	1046	67	76	485	672
74	623	616	342	477	601	1201	49	943	954	1129
75	242	1132	164	1142	1189	781	548	846	74	47
76	779	569	411	1096	571	284	718	32	513	801
77	991	293	768	413	368	374	836	702	245	795
78	123	807	1098	889	1090	259	351	577	539	840
79	687	573	493	53	1126	833	1026	757	858	1195
80	286	559	1152	1029	666	1135	255	694	426	720
81	1039	607	215	818	647	1058	328	678	34	202
82	302	885	1079	931	743	266	274	515	637	12
83	760	1160	167	905	1110	963	803	1171	466	940
84	365	556	634	130	441	993	734	1015	877	459
85	101	791	181	24	295	133	448	861	147	1145
86	185	381	1175	770	1083	315	698	143	497	711
87	706	320	415	190	947	138	403	106	1069	998
88	310	370	444	968	1198	765	1192	271	21	307
89	376	1063	1117	1044	599	1140	409	291	121	838
90	856	692	326	264	1108	128	179	379	704	996
91	19	289	177	784	387	786	871	247	898	1206
92	454	628	156	1051	389	1010	797	97	750	474
93	988	754	740	788	1066	125	737	972	562	501
94	551	28	873	470	809	935	209	430	85	57
95	1166	249	224	1100	231	958	280	730	93	975
96	900	1120	891	1018	654	1155	533	849	334	1208
97	7	1092	437	1006	613	510	830	1076	456	400
98	261	985	727	913	916	926	565	630	1047	353
99	880	68	1032	585	77	197	158	486	579	591

POWER RESIDUES

	0	1	2	3	4	5	6	7	8	9
50	313	939	383	1149	1013	605	598	577	514	325
51	975	491	256	768	1087	827	47	141	423	52
52	156	468	187	561	466	181	543	412	19	57
53	171	513	322	966	464	175	525	358	1074	788
54	1147	1007	587	544	415	28	84	252	756	1051
55	719	940	386	1158	1040	686	841	89	267	801
56	1186	1124	938	380	1140	986	524	355	1065	761
57	1066	764	1075	791	1156	1034	668	787	1144	998
58	560	463	172	516	331	993	545	418	37	111
59	333	999	563	472	199	597	574	505	298	894
60	248	744	1015	611	616	631	676	811	1216	1214
61	1208	1190	1136	974	488	247	741	1006	584	535
62	388	1164	1058	740	1003	575	508	307	921	329
63	987	527	364	1092	842	92	276	828	50	150
64	450	133	399	1197	1157	1037	677	814	8	24
65	72	216	648	727	964	458	157	471	196	588
66	547	424	55	165	495	268	804	1195	1151	1019
67	623	652	739	1000	566	481	226	678	817	17
68	51	153	459	160	480	223	669	790	1153	1025
69	641	706	901	269	807	1204	1178	1100	866	164
70	492	259	777	1114	908	290	870	176	528	367
71	1101	869	173	519	340	1020	626	661	766	1081
72	809	1210	1196	1154	1028	650	733	982	512	319
73	957	437	94	282	846	104	312	936	374	1122
74	932	362	1086	824	38	114	342	1026	644	715
75	928	350	1050	716	931	359	1077	797	1174	1088
76	830	56	168	504	295	885	221	663	772	1099
77	863	155	465	178	534	385	1155	1031	659	760
78	1063	755	1048	710	913	305	915	311	933	365
79	1095	851	119	357	1071	779	1120	926	344	1032
80	662	769	1090	836	74	222	666	781	1126	944
81	398	1194	1148	1010	596	571	496	271	813	5
82	15	45	135	405	1215	1211	1199	1163	1055	731
83	976	494	265	795	1168	1070	776	1111	899	263
84	789	1150	1016	614	625	658	757	1054	728	967
85	467	184	552	439	100	300	900	266	798	1177
86	1097	857	137	411	16	48	144	432	79	237
87	711	916	314	942	392	1176	1094	848	110	330
88	990	536	391	1173	1085	821	29	87	261	783
89	1132	962	452	139	417	34	102	306	918	320
90	960	446	121	363	1089	833	65	195	585	538
91	397	1191	1139	983	515	328	984	518	337	1011
92	599	580	523	352	1056	734	985	521	346	1038
93	680	823	35	105	315	945	401	1203	1175	1091
94	839	83	249	747	1024	638	697	874	188	564
95	475	208	624	655	748	1027	647	724	955	431
96	76	228	684	835	71	213	639	700	883	215
97	645	718	937	377	1131	959	443	112	336	1008
98	590	553	442	109	327	981	509	310	930	356
99	1068	770	1093	845	101	303	909	293	879	203

P = 1217

INDICES

	0	1	2	3	4	5	6	7	8	9
100	673	43	361	624	357	1053	617	541	979	343
101	813	919	478	504	391	602	842	462	1202	669
102	715	50	299	1012	944	689	747	955	724	340
103	1130	777	799	243	575	1024	1133	645	929	165
104	554	99	1143	495	104	1190	1138	1106	782	154
105	752	549	55	91	847	828	924	75	622	476
106	48	1128	163	780	73	568	570	31	990	412
107	835	794	1097	258	538	572	1125	756	285	1028
108	254	719	214	1057	33	884	742	514	759	904
109	802	939	633	992	876	790	294	860	184	769
110	697	710	414	137	1068	369	1197	270	375	1043
111	408	837	325	127	703	288	386	246	453	1050
112	796	473	739	124	561	27	808	429	1165	1099
113	279	974	890	1154	333	1091	612	1075	260	912
114	564	352	1031	196	578	42	356	540	812	503
115	841	668	298	688	723	776	574	644	553	494
116	1137	153	54	827	621	1127	72	30	834	257
117	1124	1027	213	883	758	938	875	859	696	136
118	1196	1042	324	287	452	472	560	428	278	1153
119	611	911	1030	41	811	667	722	643	1136	826
120	71	256	212	937	695	1041	451	427	610	40
121	721	825	211	1040	609	824	608			

POWER RESIDUES

	0	1	2	3	4	5	6	7	8	9
100	609	610	613	622	649	730	973	485	238	714
101	925	341	1023	635	688	847	107	321	963	455
102	148	444	115	345	1035	671	796	1171	1079	803
103	1192	1142	992	542	409	10	30	90	270	810
104	1213	1205	1181	1109	893	245	735	988	530	373
105	1119	923	335	1005	581	526	361	1083	815	11
106	33	99	297	891	239	717	934	368	1104	878
107	200	600	583	532	379	1137	977	497	274	822
108	32	96	288	864	158	474	205	615	628	667
109	784	1135	971	479	220	660	763	1072	782	1129
110	953	425	58	174	522	349	1047	707	904	278
111	834	68	204	612	619	640	703	892	242	726
112	961	449	130	390	1170	1076	794	1165	1061	749
113	1030	656	751	1036	674	805	1198	1160	1046	704
114	895	251	753	1042	692	859	143	429	70	210
115	630	673	802	1189	1133	965	461	166	498	277
116	831	59	177	531	376	1128	950	416	31	93
117	279	837	77	231	693	862	152	456	151	453
118	142	426	61	183	549	430	73	219	657	754
119	1045	701	886	224	672	799	1180	1106	884	218
120	654	745	1018	620	643	712	919	323	969	473
121	202	606	601	586	541	406				

P = 1223

INDICES

	0	1	2	3	4	5	6	7	8	9
0		0	464	156	928	1	620	842	170	312
1	465	58	1084	1192	84	157	634	740	776	1113
2	929	998	522	181	326	2	434	468	548	372
3	621	569	1098	214	1204	843	18	861	355	126
4	171	221	240	1176	986	313	645	177	790	462
5	466	896	898	136	932	59	1012	47	836	858
6	1085	1060	1033	1154	340	1193	678	575	446	337
7	85	505	482	36	103	158	819	900	590	809
8	635	624	685	365	704	741	418	528	228	97
9	777	812	1109	725	641	1114	32	385	926	370
10	930	807	138	108	140	999	600	1198	174	879
11	523	1017	254	871	511	182	78	282	100	360
12	327	116	302	377	275	3	396	934	804	110
13	435	63	1142	733	1039	469	910	153	801	236
14	549	333	969	28	946	373	500	618	567	1010
15	622	598	61	1052	142	570	1054	44	51	292
16	1099	1023	1088	454	1149	215	829	701	1168	1162
17	1205	203	882	853	992	844	692	1014	561	1001
18	19	144	54	1216	351	862	1189	798	1105	88
19	356	891	496	1184	849	127	168	212	834	363
20	172	731	49	1214	602	222	572	493	604	1171
21	241	556	1064	661	440	1177	638	189	121	192
22	987	710	259	784	718	314	113	838	975	1200
23	646	1056	542	224	746	178	564	965	824	1158
24	791	164	580	780	766	463	841	1083	739	521
25	467	1097	860	239	176	897	46	1032	574	481
26	899	684	527	1108	384	137	1197	253	281	301
27	933	1141	152	968	617	60	43	1087	700	881
28	1013	53	797	495	211	48	492	1063	188	258
29	837	541	964	579	1082	859	1031	526	252	151
30	1086	796	1062	963	525	1061	294	295	606	264
31	1034	70	296	666	508	1155	515	607	756	430
32	341	132	265	631	330	1194	918	1035	391	1019
33	679	1101	71	1173	1165	576	410	297	404	1027
34	447	627	667	82	124	338	95	509	234	1147
35	86	438	1156	382	256	506	1025	516	243	955
36	483	1004	608	272	518	37	458	757	815	533
37	104	978	431	595	40	159	347	342	552	873
38	820	1090	133	558	960	901	426	266	91	245
39	591	921	632	219	676	810	76	331	827	889
40	636	162	1195	539	513	625	456	919	1066	772
41	686	309	1036	478	957	366	1068	392	413	1048
42	705	15	1020	489	306	742	1125	680	904	184
43	419	1151	1102	663	653	529	585	72	656	485
44	229	774	1174	444	723	98	26	1166	1182	119
45	778	279	577	754	80	813	217	411	442	1208
46	1110	943	298	673	1006	726	688	405	1210	195
47	642	200	1028	12	207	1115	66	448	400	284
48	33	831	628	1179	1044	386	22	668	8	610
49	927	311	83	1112	325	371	1203	125	985	461

POWER RESIDUES

	0	1	2	3	4	5	6	7	8	9
0	1	5	25	125	625	679	949	1076	488	1217
1	1193	1073	473	1142	818	421	882	741	36	180
2	900	831	486	1207	1143	823	446	1007	143	715
3	1129	753	96	480	1177	993	73	365	602	564
4	374	647	789	276	157	785	256	57	285	202
5	1010	158	790	281	182	910	881	736	11	55
6	275	152	760	131	655	829	476	1157	893	796
7	311	332	437	962	1141	813	396	757	116	580
8	454	1047	343	492	14	70	350	527	189	945
9	1056	388	717	1139	803	346	507	89	445	1002
10	118	590	504	74	370	627	689	999	103	515
11	129	645	779	226	1130	758	121	605	579	449
12	1022	218	1090	558	344	497	39	195	975	1206
13	1138	798	321	382	687	989	53	265	102	510
14	104	520	154	770	181	905	856	611	609	599
15	549	299	272	137	685	979	3	15	75	375
16	652	814	401	782	241	1205	1133	773	196	980
17	8	40	200	1000	108	540	254	47	235	1175
18	983	23	115	575	429	922	941	1036	288	217
19	1085	533	219	1095	583	469	1122	718	1144	828
20	471	1132	768	171	855	606	584	474	1147	843
21	546	284	197	985	33	165	825	456	1057	393
22	742	41	205	1025	233	1165	933	996	88	440
23	977	1216	1188	1048	348	517	139	695	1029	253
24	42	210	1050	358	567	389	722	1164	928	971
25	1186	1038	298	267	112	560	354	547	289	222
26	1110	658	844	551	309	322	387	712	1114	678
27	944	1051	363	592	514	124	620	654	824	451
28	1032	268	117	585	479	1172	968	1171	963	1146
29	838	521	159	795	306	307	312	337	462	1087
30	543	269	122	610	604	574	424	897	816	411
31	832	491	9	45	225	1125	733	1219	1203	1123
32	723	1169	953	1096	588	494	24	120	600	554
33	324	397	762	141	705	1079	503	69	345	502
34	64	320	377	662	864	651	809	376	657	839
35	526	184	920	931	986	38	190	950	1081	513
36	119	595	529	199	995	83	415	852	591	509
37	99	495	29	145	725	1179	1003	123	615	629
38	699	1049	353	542	264	97	485	1202	1118	698
39	1044	328	417	862	641	759	126	630	704	1074
40	478	1167	943	1046	338	467	1112	668	894	801
41	336	457	1062	418	867	666	884	751	86	430
42	927	966	1161	913	896	811	386	707	1089	553
43	319	372	637	739	26	130	650	804	351	532
44	214	1070	458	1067	443	992	68	340	477	1162
45	918	921	936	1011	163	815	406	807	366	607
46	589	499	49	245	2	10	50	250	27	135
47	675	929	976	1211	1163	923	946	1061	413	842
48	541	259	72	360	577	439	972	1191	1063	423
49	892	791	286	207	1035	283	192	960	1131	763

P = 1223

INDICES

	0	1	2	3	4	5	6	7	8	9
50	931	857	339	336	102	808	703	96	640	369
51	139	878	510	359	274	109	1038	235	945	1009
52	141	291	1148	1161	991	1000	350	87	848	362
53	601	1170	439	191	717	1199	745	1157	765	520
54	175	480	383	300	616	880	210	257	1081	150
55	524	263	507	429	329	1018	1164	1026	123	1146
56	255	954	517	532	39	872	959	244	675	888
57	512	771	956	1047	305	183	652	484	722	118
58	79	1207	1005	194	206	283	1043	609	324	460
59	101	368	273	1008	990	361	716	519	615	149
60	328	1145	38	887	304	117	205	459	989	148
61	303	147	758	914	759	378	1070	816	728	915
62	276	649	534	939	760	4	1130	105	972	379
63	397	884	979	712	1071	935	1220	432	894	817
64	805	394	596	690	729	111	1095	41	794	916
65	436	345	160	1123	277	64	855	348	261	650
66	1143	1128	343	866	535	734	415	553	407	940
67	1040	1118	874	1135	761	470	868	821	269	5
68	911	994	1091	786	1131	154	546	134	588	106
69	802	1050	559	1212	973	237	698	961	389	380
70	550	537	902	752	398	334	846	427	720	885
71	970	1121	267	750	980	29	707	92	197	713
72	947	950	246	320	1072	374	736	592	982	936
73	501	694	922	316	1221	619	57	633	997	433
74	568	17	220	644	895	1011	1059	677	504	818
75	623	417	811	31	806	599	1016	77	115	395
76	62	909	332	499	597	1053	1022	828	202	691
77	143	1188	890	167	730	571	555	637	709	112
78	1055	563	163	840	1096	45	683	1196	1140	42
79	52	491	540	1030	795	293	69	514	131	917
80	1100	409	626	94	437	1024	1003	457	977	346
81	1089	425	920	75	161	455	308	1067	14	1124
82	1150	584	773	25	278	216	942	687	199	65
83	830	21	310	1202	856	702	877	1037	290	349
84	1169	744	479	209	262	1163	953	958	770	651
85	1206	1042	367	715	1144	204	146	1069	648	1129
86	883	1219	393	1094	344	854	1127	414	1117	867
87	993	545	1049	697	536	845	1120	706	949	735
88	693	56	16	1058	416	1015	908	1021	1187	554
89	562	682	490	68	408	1002	424	307	583	941
90	20	876	743	952	1041	145	1218	1126	544	1119
91	55	907	681	423	875	1217	906	905	450	1136
92	352	451	185	475	762	863	1137	420	248	471
93	1190	353	1152	226	869	799	452	1103	659	822
94	1106	186	664	402	270	89	476	654	671	6
95	357	763	530	322	912	892	864	586	748	995
96	497	1138	73	288	1092	1185	421	657	286	787
97	850	249	486	1078	1132	128	472	230	1074	155
98	169	1191	775	180	547	213	354	1175	789	135
99	835	1153	445	35	589	364	227	724	925	107

POWER RESIDUES

	0	1	2	3	4	5	6	7	8	9
50	146	730	1204	1128	748	71	355	552	314	347
51	512	114	570	404	797	316	357	562	364	597
52	539	249	22	110	550	304	297	262	87	435
53	952	1091	563	369	622	664	874	701	1059	403
54	792	291	232	1160	908	871	686	984	28	140
55	700	1054	378	667	889	776	211	1055	383	692
56	1014	178	890	781	236	1180	1008	148	740	31
57	155	775	206	1030	258	67	335	452	1037	293
58	242	1210	1158	898	821	436	957	1116	688	994
59	78	390	727	1189	1053	373	642	764	151	755
60	106	530	204	1020	208	1040	308	317	362	587
61	489	1222	1218	1198	1098	598	544	274	147	735
62	6	30	150	750	81	405	802	341	482	1187
63	1043	323	392	737	16	80	400	777	216	1080
64	508	94	470	1127	743	46	230	1150	858	621
65	659	849	576	434	947	1066	438	967	1166	938
66	1021	213	1065	433	942	1041	313	342	487	1212
67	1168	948	1071	463	1092	568	394	747	66	330
68	427	912	891	786	261	82	410	827	466	1107
69	643	769	176	880	731	1209	1153	873	696	1034
70	278	167	835	506	84	420	877	716	1134	778
71	221	1105	633	719	1149	853	596	534	224	1120
72	708	1094	578	444	997	93	465	1102	618	644
73	774	201	1005	133	665	879	726	1184	1028	248
74	17	85	425	902	841	536	234	1170	958	1121
75	713	1119	703	1069	453	1042	318	367	612	614
76	624	674	924	951	1086	538	244	1220	1208	1148
77	848	571	409	822	441	982	18	90	450	1027
78	243	1215	1183	1023	223	1115	683	969	1176	988
79	48	240	1200	1108	648	794	301	282	187	935
80	1006	138	690	1004	128	640	754	101	505	79
81	395	752	91	455	1052	368	617	639	749	76
82	380	677	939	1026	238	1190	1058	398	767	166
83	830	481	1182	1018	198	990	58	290	227	1135
84	783	246	7	35	175	875	706	1084	528	194
85	970	1181	1013	173	865	656	834	501	59	295
86	252	37	185	925	956	1111	663	869	676	934
87	1001	113	565	379	672	914	901	836	511	109
88	545	279	172	860	631	709	1099	603	569	399
89	772	191	955	1106	638	744	51	255	52	260
90	77	385	702	1064	428	917	916	911	886	761
91	136	680	954	1101	613	619	649	799	326	407
92	812	391	732	1214	1178	998	98	490	4	20
93	100	500	54	270	127	635	729	1199	1103	623
94	669	899	826	461	1082	518	144	720	1154	878
95	721	1159	903	846	561	359	572	414	847	566
96	384	697	1039	303	292	237	1185	1033	273	142
97	710	1104	628	694	1024	228	1140	808	371	632
98	714	1124	728	1194	1078	498	44	220	1100	608
99	594	524	174	870	681	959	1126	738	21	105

P = 1223

INDICES

	0	1	2	3	4	5	6	7	8	9
100	173	870	99	376	803	732	800	27	566	1051
101	50	453	1167	852	560	1215	1104	1183	833	1213
102	603	660	120	783	974	223	823	779	738	238
103	573	1107	280	967	699	494	187	578	251	962
104	605	665	755	630	390	1172	403	81	233	381
105	242	271	814	594	551	557	90	218	826	538
106	1065	477	412	488	903	662	655	443	1181	753
107	441	672	1209	11	399	1178	7	1111	984	335
108	639	358	944	1160	847	190	764	299	1080	428
109	122	531	674	1046	721	193	323	1007	614	886
110	988	913	727	938	971	711	893	689	793	1122
111	260	865	406	1134	268	785	587	1211	388	751
112	719	749	196	319	981	315	996	643	503	30
113	114	498	201	166	708	839	1139	1029	130	93
114	976	74	13	24	198	1201	289	208	769	714
115	647	1093	1116	696	948	1057	1186	67	582	951
116	543	422	449	474	247	225	658	401	670	321
117	747	287	285	1077	1073	179	788	34	924	375
118	565	851	832	782	737	966	250	629	232	593
119	825	487	1180	10	983	1159	1079	1045	613	937
120	792	1133	387	318	502	165	129	23	768	695
121	581	473	669	1076	923	781	231	9	612	317
122	767	1075	611							

POWER RESIDUES

	0	1	2	3	4	5	6	7	8	9
100	525	179	895	806	361	582	464	1097	593	519
101	149	745	56	280	177	885	756	111	555	329
102	422	887	766	161	805	356	557	339	472	1137
103	793	296	257	62	310	327	412	837	516	134
104	670	904	851	586	484	1197	1093	573	419	872
105	691	1009	153	765	156	780	231	1155	883	746
106	61	305	302	287	212	1060	408	817	416	857
107	616	634	724	1174	978	1221	1213	1173	973	1196
108	1088	548	294	247	12	60	300	277	162	810
109	381	682	964	1151	863	646	784	251	32	160
110	800	331	432	937	1016	188	940	1031	263	92
111	460	1077	493	19	95	475	1152	868	671	909
112	876	711	1109	653	819	426	907	866	661	859
113	626	684	974	1201	1113	673	919	926	961	1136
114	788	271	132	660	854	601	559	349	522	164
115	820	431	932	991	63	315	352	537	239	1195
116	1083	523	169	845	556	334	447	1012	168	840
117	531	209	1045	333	442	987	43	215	1075	483
118	1192	1068	448	1017	193	965	1156	888	771	186
119	930	981	13	65	325	402	787	266	107	535
120	229	1145	833	496	34	170	850	581	459	1072
121	468	1117	693	1019	203	1015	183	915	906	861
122	636	734								

P = 1229

INDICES

	0	1	2	3	4	5	6	7	8	9
0		0	1	603	2	182	604	126	3	1206
1	183	473	605	1135	127	785	4	815	1207	515
2	184	729	474	553	606	364	1136	581	128	357
3	786	288	5	1076	816	308	1208	769	516	510
4	185	442	730	850	475	160	554	832	607	252
5	365	190	1137	244	582	655	129	1118	358	682
6	787	408	289	104	6	89	1077	1188	817	1156
7	309	273	1209	1018	770	967	517	599	511	304
8	186	1184	443	447	731	997	851	960	476	688
9	161	33	555	891	833	697	608	98	253	451
10	366	824	191	749	1138	911	245	50	583	927
11	656	144	130	882	1119	735	359	1113	683	941
12	788	946	409	1045	290	546	105	259	7	225
13	90	1001	1078	641	1189	763	818	24	1157	496
14	310	207	274	380	1210	539	1019	855	771	152
15	968	112	518	793	600	470	512	578	305	847
16	187	679	1185	964	444	30	448	47	732	1042
17	998	493	852	467	961	490	477	57	689	480
18	162	390	34	1011	556	951	892	60	834	707
19	698	457	609	283	99	692	254	842	452	318
20	367	563	825	483	192	624	750	531	1139	988
21	912	165	246	876	51	1032	584	414	928	393
22	657	722	145	323	131	342	883	37	1120	1163
23	736	1202	360	438	1114	1014	684	907	942	20
24	789	1038	947	559	410	434	1046	422	291	1050
25	547	954	106	1026	260	372	8	1175	226	895
26	91	335	1002	669	1079	426	642	63	1190	177
27	764	1151	819	636	25	837	1158	330	497	266
28	311	295	208	710	275	72	381	568	1211	402
29	540	701	1020	502	856	864	772	1054	153	460
30	969	976	113	199	519	590	794	612	601	124
31	471	783	513	551	579	286	306	508	848	830
32	188	653	680	102	1186	271	965	302	445	958
33	31	695	449	747	48	142	733	939	1043	257
34	999	761	494	378	853	110	468	845	962	45
35	491	488	478	1009	58	455	690	316	481	529
36	163	1030	391	321	35	1200	1012	18	557	420
37	952	370	893	667	61	1149	835	264	708	566
38	699	862	458	197	610	781	284	828	100	300
39	693	140	255	376	843	486	453	527	319	16
40	368	1147	564	195	826	138	484	14	193	12
41	625	627	751	808	532	629	1140	1099	989	753
42	913	213	166	810	247	1179	877	534	52	983
43	1033	631	585	934	415	1142	929	1068	394	1101
44	658	230	723	991	146	870	324	755	132	80
45	343	915	884	715	38	215	1121	899	1164	168
46	737	1225	1203	812	361	1073	439	249	1115	86
47	1015	1181	685	95	908	879	943	222	21	536
48	790	676	1039	54	948	280	560	985	411	339
49	435	1035	1047	1172	423	633	292	399	1051	587

POWER RESIDUES

	0	1	2	3	4	5	6	7	8	9
0	1	2	4	8	16	32	64	128	256	512
1	1024	819	409	818	407	814	399	798	367	734
2	239	478	956	683	137	274	548	1096	963	697
3	165	330	660	91	182	364	728	227	454	908
4	587	1174	1119	1009	789	349	698	167	334	668
5	107	214	428	856	483	966	703	177	354	708
6	187	374	748	267	534	1068	907	585	1170	1111
7	993	757	285	570	1140	1051	873	517	1034	839
8	449	898	567	1134	1039	849	469	938	647	65
9	130	260	520	1040	851	473	946	663	97	194
10	388	776	323	646	63	126	252	504	1008	787
11	345	690	151	302	604	1208	1187	1145	1061	893
12	557	1114	999	769	309	618	7	14	28	56
13	112	224	448	896	563	1126	1023	817	405	810
14	391	782	335	670	111	222	444	888	547	1094
15	959	689	149	298	596	1192	1155	1081	933	637
16	45	90	180	360	720	211	422	844	459	918
17	607	1214	1199	1169	1109	989	749	269	538	1076
18	923	617	5	10	20	40	80	160	320	640
19	51	102	204	408	816	403	806	383	766	303
20	606	1212	1195	1161	1093	957	685	141	282	564
21	1128	1027	825	421	842	455	910	591	1182	1135
22	1041	853	477	954	679	129	258	516	1032	835
23	441	882	535	1070	911	593	1186	1143	1057	885
24	541	1082	935	641	53	106	212	424	848	467
25	934	639	49	98	196	392	784	339	678	127
26	254	508	1016	803	377	754	279	558	1116	1003
27	777	325	650	71	142	284	568	1136	1043	857
28	485	970	711	193	386	772	315	630	31	62
29	124	248	496	992	755	281	562	1124	1019	809
30	389	778	327	654	79	158	316	632	35	70
31	140	280	560	1120	1011	793	357	714	199	398
32	796	363	726	223	446	892	555	1110	991	753
33	277	554	1108	987	745	261	522	1044	859	489
34	978	727	225	450	900	571	1142	1055	881	533
35	1066	903	577	1154	1079	929	629	29	58	116
36	232	464	928	627	25	50	100	200	400	800
37	371	742	255	510	1020	811	393	786	343	686
38	143	286	572	1144	1059	889	549	1098	967	705
39	181	362	724	219	438	876	523	1046	863	497
40	994	759	289	578	1156	1083	937	645	61	122
41	244	488	976	723	217	434	868	507	1014	799
42	369	738	247	494	988	747	265	530	1060	891
43	553	1106	983	737	245	490	980	731	233	466
44	932	635	41	82	164	328	656	83	166	332
45	664	99	198	396	792	355	710	191	382	764
46	299	598	1196	1163	1097	965	701	173	346	692
47	155	310	620	11	22	44	88	176	352	704
48	179	358	716	203	406	812	395	790	351	702
49	175	350	700	171	342	684	139	278	556	1112

P = 1229

INDICES

	0	1	2	3	4	5	6	7	8	9
50	548	650	955	936	107	1006	1027	417	261	778
51	373	1144	9	1096	1176	931	227	77	896	1070
52	92	673	336	396	1003	1093	670	1103	1080	1106
53	427	660	643	349	64	232	1191	1083	178	725
54	765	240	1152	993	820	1109	637	148	26	386
55	838	872	1159	430	331	326	498	120	267	757
56	312	663	296	134	209	1064	711	82	276	646
57	73	345	382	1060	569	917	1212	352	403	886
58	541	573	702	717	1021	67	503	40	857	803
59	865	217	773	235	1055	1123	154	921	461	901
60	970	1194	977	1166	114	1128	200	170	520	1086
61	591	739	795	1216	613	1227	602	181	125	1205
62	472	1134	784	814	514	728	552	363	580	356
63	287	1075	307	768	509	441	849	159	831	251
64	189	243	654	1117	681	407	103	88	1187	1155
65	272	1017	966	598	303	1183	446	996	959	687
66	32	890	696	97	450	823	748	910	49	926
67	143	881	734	1112	940	945	1044	545	258	224
68	1000	640	762	23	495	206	379	538	854	151
69	111	792	469	577	846	678	963	29	46	1041
70	492	466	489	56	479	389	1010	950	59	706
71	456	282	691	841	317	562	482	623	530	987
72	164	875	1031	413	392	721	322	341	36	1162
73	1201	437	1013	906	19	1037	558	433	421	1049
74	953	1025	371	1174	894	334	668	425	62	176
75	1150	635	836	329	265	294	709	71	567	401
76	700	501	863	1053	459	975	198	589	611	123
77	782	550	285	507	829	652	101	270	301	957
78	694	746	141	938	256	760	377	109	844	44
79	487	1008	454	315	528	1029	320	1199	17	419
80	369	666	1148	263	565	861	196	780	827	299
81	139	375	485	526	15	1146	194	137	13	11
82	626	807	628	1098	752	212	809	1178	533	982
83	630	933	1141	1067	1100	229	990	869	754	79
84	914	714	214	898	167	1224	811	1072	248	85
85	1180	94	878	221	535	675	53	279	984	338
86	1034	1171	632	398	586	649	935	1005	416	777
87	1143	1095	930	76	1069	672	395	1092	1102	1105
88	659	348	231	1082	724	239	992	1108	147	385
89	871	429	325	119	756	662	133	1063	81	645
90	344	1059	916	351	885	572	716	66	39	802
91	216	234	1122	920	900	1193	1165	1127	169	1085
92	738	1215	1226	180	1204	1133	813	727	362	355
93	1074	767	440	158	250	242	1116	406	87	1154
94	1016	597	1182	995	686	889	96	822	909	925
95	880	1111	944	544	223	639	22	205	537	150
96	791	576	677	28	1040	465	55	388	949	705
97	281	840	561	622	986	874	412	720	340	1161
98	436	905	1036	432	1048	1024	1173	333	424	175
99	634	328	293	70	400	500	1052	974	588	122

POWER RESIDUES

	0	1	2	3	4	5	6	7	8	9
50	995	761	293	586	1172	1115	1001	773	317	634
51	39	78	156	312	624	19	38	76	152	304
52	608	1216	1203	1177	1125	1021	813	397	794	359
53	718	207	414	828	427	854	479	958	687	145
54	290	580	1160	1091	953	677	125	250	500	1000
55	771	313	626	23	46	92	184	368	736	243
56	486	972	715	201	402	804	379	758	287	574
57	1148	1067	905	581	1162	1095	961	693	157	314
58	628	27	54	108	216	432	864	499	998	767
59	305	610	1220	1211	1193	1157	1085	941	653	77
60	154	308	616	3	6	12	24	48	96	192
61	384	768	307	614	1228	1227	1225	1221	1213	1197
62	1165	1101	973	717	205	410	820	411	822	415
63	830	431	862	495	990	751	273	546	1092	955
64	681	133	266	532	1064	899	569	1138	1047	865
65	501	1002	775	321	642	55	110	220	440	880
66	531	1062	895	561	1122	1015	801	373	746	263
67	526	1052	875	521	1042	855	481	962	695	161
68	322	644	59	118	236	472	944	659	89	178
69	356	712	195	390	780	331	662	95	190	380
70	760	291	582	1164	1099	969	709	189	378	756
71	283	566	1132	1035	841	453	906	583	1166	1103
72	977	725	221	442	884	539	1078	927	625	21
73	42	84	168	336	672	115	230	460	920	611
74	1222	1215	1201	1173	1117	1005	781	333	666	103
75	206	412	824	419	838	447	894	559	1118	1007
76	785	341	682	135	270	540	1080	931	633	37
77	74	148	296	592	1184	1139	1049	869	509	1018
78	807	385	770	311	622	15	30	60	120	240
79	480	960	691	153	306	612	1224	1219	1209	1189
80	1149	1069	909	589	1178	1127	1025	821	413	826
81	423	846	463	926	623	17	34	68	136	272
82	544	1088	947	665	101	202	404	808	387	774
83	319	638	47	94	188	376	752	275	550	1100
84	971	713	197	394	788	347	694	159	318	636
85	43	86	172	344	688	147	294	588	1176	1123
86	1017	805	381	762	295	590	1180	1131	1033	837
87	445	890	551	1102	975	721	213	426	852	475
88	950	671	113	226	452	904	579	1158	1087	945
89	661	93	186	372	744	259	518	1036	843	457
90	914	599	1198	1167	1105	981	733	237	474	948
91	667	105	210	420	840	451	902	575	1150	1071
92	913	597	1194	1159	1089	949	669	109	218	436
93	872	515	1030	831	433	866	503	1006	783	337
94	674	119	238	476	952	675	121	242	484	968
95	707	185	370	740	251	502	1004	779	329	658
96	87	174	348	696	163	326	652	75	150	300
97	600	1200	1171	1113	997	765	301	602	1204	1179
98	1129	1029	829	429	858	487	974	719	209	418
99	836	443	886	543	1086	943	657	85	170	340

P = 1229

INDICES

	0	1	2	3	4	5	6	7	8	9
100	549	506	651	269	956	745	937	759	108	43
101	1007	314	1028	1198	418	665	262	860	779	298
102	374	525	1145	136	10	806	1097	211	1177	981
103	932	1066	228	868	78	713	897	1223	1071	84
104	93	220	674	278	337	1170	397	648	1004	776
105	1094	75	671	1091	1104	347	1081	238	1107	384
106	428	118	661	1062	644	1058	350	571	65	801
107	233	919	1192	1126	1084	1214	179	1132	726	354
108	766	157	241	405	1153	596	994	888	821	924
109	1110	543	638	204	149	575	27	464	387	704
110	839	621	873	719	1160	904	431	1023	332	174
111	327	69	499	973	121	505	268	744	758	42
112	313	1197	664	859	297	524	135	805	210	980
113	1065	867	712	1222	83	219	277	1169	647	775
114	74	1090	346	237	383	117	1061	1057	570	800
115	918	1125	1213	1131	353	156	404	595	887	923
116	542	203	574	463	703	620	718	903	1022	173
117	68	972	504	743	41	1196	858	523	804	979
118	866	1221	218	1168	774	1089	236	116	1056	799
119	1124	1130	155	594	922	202	462	619	902	172
120	971	742	1195	522	978	1220	1167	1088	115	798
121	1129	593	201	618	171	741	521	1219	1087	797
122	592	617	740	1218	796	616	1217	615	614	

POWER RESIDUES

	0	1	2	3	4	5	6	7	8	9
100	680	131	262	524	1048	867	505	1010	791	353
101	706	183	366	732	235	470	940	651	73	146
102	292	584	1168	1107	985	741	253	506	1012	795
103	361	722	215	430	860	491	982	735	241	482
104	964	699	169	338	676	123	246	492	984	739
105	249	498	996	763	297	594	1188	1147	1065	901
106	573	1146	1063	897	565	1130	1031	833	437	874
107	519	1038	847	465	930	631	33	66	132	264
108	528	1056	883	537	1074	919	609	1218	1207	1185
109	1141	1053	877	525	1050	871	513	1026	823	417
110	834	439	878	527	1054	879	529	1058	887	545
111	1090	951	673	117	234	468	936	643	57	114
112	228	456	912	595	1190	1151	1073	917	605	1210
113	1191	1153	1077	925	621	13	26	52	104	208
114	416	832	435	870	511	1022	815	401	802	375
115	750	271	542	1084	939	649	69	138	276	552
116	1104	979	729	229	458	916	603	1206	1183	1137
117	1045	861	493	986	743	257	514	1028	827	425
118	850	471	942	655	81	162	324	648	67	134
119	268	536	1072	915	601	1202	1175	1121	1013	797
120	365	730	231	462	924	619	9	18	36	72
121	144	288	576	1152	1075	921	613	1226	1223	1217
122	1205	1181	1133	1037	845	461	922	615		

P = 1231

INDICES

	0	1	2	3	4	5	6	7	8	9
0		0	454	1	908	1196	455	1184	132	2
1	420	690	909	624	408	1197	586	435	456	318
2	874	1185	1144	233	133	1162	1078	3	862	830
3	421	1134	1040	691	889	1150	910	344	772	625
4	98	194	409	986	368	1198	687	769	587	1138
5	386	436	302	61	457	656	86	319	54	177
6	375	431	358	1186	264	590	1145	91	113	234
7	374	313	134	1215	798	1163	1226	644	1079	105
8	552	4	648	441	863	401	210	831	822	789
9	422	578	1141	1135	1223	284	1041	1027	362	692
10	840	24	890	287	756	1151	515	382	911	965
11	1110	345	540	219	773	199	508	626	631	389
12	99	150	885	195	812	1128	410	205	718	987
13	1044	915	369	272	545	1199	567	452	688	872
14	828	770	767	84	588	796	439	1139	22	1108
15	387	716	450	437	1098	1100	303	1030	559	62
16	1006	187	458	1083	1102	657	895	1019	87	18
17	855	320	664	305	55	1116	46	178	13	1190
18	876	956	1032	432	365	310	359	1125	447	1187
19	738	561	265	145	251	591	816	68	1146	504
20	64	92	478	784	114	160	741	235	1210	1008
21	375	695	969	314	836	952	135	1088	189	1216
22	334	1059	799	1157	994	1164	673	460	1227	859
23	653	645	962	564	1080	735	1085	106	843	329
24	553	497	604	5	109	1104	649	942	36	442
25	352	167	864	923	659	402	1172	491	211	298
26	268	832	139	897	823	27	726	790	999	807
27	423	846	1021	579	906	622	1142	1132	96	1136
28	52	89	1224	399	1221	285	538	148	1042	870
29	20	1028	893	1114	363	143	476	693	332	857
30	841	940	1170	25	904	397	891	938	322	288
31	324	946	757	277	254	1152	1013	666	516	290
32	230	383	641	753	912	556	307	966	326	723
33	1111	227	119	346	243	57	541	948	472	220
34	79	594	774	1092	1118	200	759	122	509	979
35	340	627	500	48	632	279	467	390	414	482
36	100	636	180	151	256	1181	886	428	819	196
37	764	15	813	1154	349	1129	901	224	411	607
38	1192	206	1015	32	719	610	599	988	705	878
39	1045	668	40	916	522	71	370	712	958	273
40	518	246	546	528	932	1200	8	1034	568	292
41	614	453	1195	131	689	407	434	873	232	1077
42	829	1039	1149	771	193	367	768	385	60	85
43	176	357	589	112	312	797	643	551	440	209
44	788	1140	283	361	23	755	381	1109	218	507
45	388	884	1127	717	914	544	451	827	83	438
46	1107	449	1099	558	186	1101	1018	854	304	45
47	1189	1031	309	446	560	250	67	63	783	740
48	1007	968	951	188	1058	993	459	652	563	1084
49	328	603	1103	35	166	658	490	267	896	725

POWER RESIDUES

	0	1	2	3	4	5	6	7	8	9
0	1	3	9	27	81	243	729	956	406	1218
1	1192	1114	880	178	534	371	1113	877	169	507
2	290	870	148	444	101	303	909	265	795	1154
3	1000	538	383	1149	985	493	248	744	1001	541
4	392	1176	1066	736	977	469	176	528	353	1059
5	715	914	280	840	58	174	522	335	1005	553
6	428	53	159	477	200	600	569	476	197	591
7	542	395	1185	1093	817	1220	1198	1132	934	340
8	1020	598	563	458	143	429	56	168	504	281
9	843	67	201	603	578	503	278	834	40	120
10	360	1080	778	1103	847	79	237	711	902	244
11	732	965	433	68	204	612	605	584	521	332
12	996	526	347	1041	661	752	1025	613	608	593
13	548	413	8	24	72	216	648	713	908	262
14	786	1127	919	295	885	193	579	506	287	861
15	121	363	1089	805	1184	1090	808	1193	1117	889
16	205	615	614	611	602	575	494	251	753	1028
17	622	635	674	791	1142	964	430	59	177	531
18	362	1086	796	1157	1009	565	464	161	483	218
19	654	731	962	424	41	123	369	1107	859	115
20	345	1035	643	698	863	127	381	1143	967	439
21	86	258	774	1091	811	1202	1144	970	448	113
22	339	1017	589	536	377	1131	931	331	993	517
23	320	960	418	23	69	207	621	632	665	764
24	1061	721	932	334	1002	544	401	1203	1147	979
25	475	194	582	515	314	942	364	1092	814	1211
26	1171	1051	691	842	64	192	576	497	260	780
27	1109	865	133	399	1197	1129	925	313	939	355
28	1065	733	968	442	95	285	855	103	309	927
29	319	957	409	1227	1219	1195	1123	907	259	777
30	1100	838	52	156	468	173	519	326	978	472
31	185	555	434	71	213	639	686	827	19	57
32	171	513	308	924	310	930	328	984	490	239
33	717	920	298	894	220	660	749	1016	586	527
34	350	1050	688	833	37	111	333	999	535	374
35	1122	904	250	750	1019	595	554	431	62	186
36	558	443	98	294	882	184	552	425	44	132
37	396	1188	1102	844	70	210	630	659	746	1007
38	559	446	107	321	963	427	50	150	450	119
39	357	1071	751	1022	604	581	512	305	915	283
40	849	85	255	765	1064	730	959	415	14	42
41	126	378	1134	940	358	1074	760	1049	685	824
42	10	30	90	270	810	1199	1135	943	367	1101
43	841	61	183	549	416	17	51	153	459	146
44	438	83	249	747	1010	568	473	188	564	461
45	152	456	137	411	2	6	18	54	162	486
46	227	681	812	1205	1153	997	529	356	1068	742
47	995	523	338	1014	580	509	296	888	202	606
48	587	530	359	1077	769	1076	766	1067	739	986
49	496	257	771	1082	784	1121	901	241	723	938

P = 1231

INDICES

	0	1	2	3	4	5	6	7	8	9
50	806	1020	621	95	88	1220	147	19	1113	475
51	856	1169	396	321	945	253	665	229	752	306
52	722	118	56	471	593	1117	121	339	47	466
53	481	179	1180	818	14	348	223	1191	31	598
54	877	39	70	957	245	931	1033	613	130	433
55	1076	1148	366	59	356	311	550	787	360	380
56	506	1126	543	82	448	185	853	1188	445	66
57	739	950	992	562	602	165	266	805	94	146
58	474	395	252	751	117	592	338	480	817	222
59	597	69	930	129	1147	355	786	505	81	852
60	65	991	164	93	394	116	479	596	128	785
61	851	163	115	127	162	161	776	777	742	730
62	778	236	170	743	1211	1094	731	1009	708	779
63	376	680	237	696	1120	171	970	532	744	315
64	684	1212	837	202	1095	953	1207	732	136	867
65	1010	1089	761	709	190	881	780	1217	1177	377
66	335	124	681	1060	573	238	800	1063	697	1158
67	511	1121	995	975	172	1165	926	971	674	981
68	533	461	1048	745	1228	418	316	860	342	685
69	654	262	1213	646	576	838	963	629	203	565
70	794	1096	1081	662	954	736	502	1208	1086	671
71	733	107	921	137	844	50	868	330	936	1011
72	554	241	1090	498	634	762	605	703	710	6
73	405	191	110	281	882	1105	43	781	650	488
74	1218	943	469	1178	37	1074	378	443	803	336
75	353	392	125	168	678	682	865	1175	1061	924
76	416	574	660	919	239	403	486	801	1173	484
77	1064	492	1053	698	212	1066	1159	299	102	512
78	269	1003	1122	833	494	996	140	638	976	898
79	525	173	824	1055	1166	28	182	927	727	1204
80	972	791	700	675	1000	153	982	808	156	534
81	424	214	462	847	258	1049	1022	74	746	580
82	1068	1229	907	1183	419	623	585	317	1143	1161
83	861	1133	888	343	97	985	686	1137	301	655
84	53	430	263	90	373	1214	1225	104	647	400
85	821	577	1222	1026	839	286	514	964	539	198
86	630	149	811	204	1043	271	566	871	766	795
87	21	715	1097	1029	1005	1082	894	17	663	1115
88	12	955	364	1124	737	144	815	503	477	159
89	1209	694	835	1087	333	1156	672	858	961	734
90	842	496	108	941	351	922	1171	297	138	26
91	998	845	905	1131	51	398	537	869	892	142
92	331	939	903	937	323	276	1012	289	640	555
93	325	226	242	947	78	1091	758	978	499	278
94	413	635	255	427	763	1153	900	606	1014	609
95	704	667	521	711	517	527	7	291	1194	406
96	231	1038	192	384	175	111	642	208	282	754
97	217	883	913	826	1106	557	1017	44	308	249
98	782	967	1057	651	327	34	489	724	620	1219
99	1112	1168	944	228	721	470	120	465	1179	347

POWER RESIDUES

	0	1	2	3	4	5	6	7	8	9
50	352	1056	706	887	199	597	560	449	116	348
51	1044	670	779	1106	856	106	318	954	400	1200
52	1138	952	394	1182	1084	790	1139	955	403	1209
53	1165	1033	637	680	809	1196	1126	916	286	858
54	112	336	1008	562	455	134	402	1206	1156	1006
55	556	437	80	240	720	929	325	975	463	158
56	474	191	573	488	233	699	866	136	408	1224
57	1210	1168	1042	664	761	1052	694	851	91	273
58	819	1226	1216	1186	1096	826	16	48	144	432
59	65	195	585	524	341	1023	607	590	539	386
60	1158	1012	574	491	242	726	947	379	1137	949
61	385	1155	1003	547	410	1230	1228	1222	1204	1150
62	988	502	275	825	13	39	117	351	1053	697
63	860	118	354	1062	724	941	361	1083	787	1130
64	928	322	966	436	77	231	693	848	82	246
65	738	983	487	230	690	839	55	165	495	254
66	762	1055	703	878	172	516	317	951	391	1173
67	1057	709	896	226	678	803	1178	1072	754	1031
68	631	662	755	1034	640	689	836	46	138	414
69	11	33	99	297	891	211	633	668	773	1088
70	802	1175	1063	727	950	388	1164	1030	628	653
71	728	953	397	1191	1111	871	151	453	128	384
72	1152	994	520	329	987	499	266	798	1163	1027
73	619	626	647	710	899	235	705	884	190	570
74	479	206	618	623	638	683	818	1223	1207	1159
75	1015	583	518	323	969	445	104	312	936	346
76	1038	652	725	944	370	1110	868	142	426	47
77	141	423	38	114	342	1026	616	617	620	629
78	656	737	980	478	203	609	596	557	440	89
79	267	801	1172	1054	700	869	145	435	74	222
80	666	767	1070	748	1013	577	500	269	807	1190
81	1108	862	124	372	1116	886	196	588	533	368
82	1104	850	88	264	792	1145	973	457	140	420
83	29	87	261	783	1118	892	214	642	695	854
84	100	300	900	238	714	911	271	813	1208	1162
85	1024	610	599	566	467	170	510	299	897	229
86	687	830	28	84	252	756	1037	649	716	917
87	289	867	139	417	20	60	180	540	389	1167
88	1039	655	734	971	451	122	366	1098	832	34
89	102	306	918	292	876	166	498	263	789	1136
90	946	376	1128	922	304	912	274	822	4	12
91	36	108	324	972	454	131	393	1179	1075	763
92	1058	712	905	253	759	1046	676	797	1160	1018
93	592	545	404	1212	1174	1060	718	923	307	921
94	301	903	247	741	992	514	311	933	337	1011
95	571	482	215	645	704	881	181	543	398	1194
96	1120	898	232	696	857	109	327	981	481	212
97	636	677	800	1169	1045	673	788	1133	937	349
98	1047	679	806	1187	1099	835	43	129	387	1161
99	1021	601	572	485	224	672	785	1124	910	268

P = 1231

INDICES

	0	1	2	3	4	5	6	7	8	9
100	30	38	244	612	1075	58	549	379	542	184
101	444	949	601	804	473	750	337	221	929	354
102	80	990	393	595	850	126	775	729	169	1093
103	707	679	1119	531	683	201	1206	866	760	880
104	1176	123	572	1062	510	974	925	980	1047	417
105	341	261	575	628	793	661	501	670	920	49
106	935	240	633	702	404	280	42	487	468	1073
107	802	391	677	1174	415	918	485	483	1052	1065
108	101	1002	493	637	524	1054	181	1203	699	152
109	155	213	257	73	1067	1182	584	1160	887	984
110	300	429	372	103	820	1025	513	197	810	270
111	765	714	1004	16	11	1123	814	158	834	1155
112	960	495	350	296	997	1130	536	141	902	275
113	639	225	77	977	412	426	899	608	520	526
114	1193	1037	174	207	216	825	1016	248	1056	33
115	619	1167	720	464	29	611	548	183	600	749
116	928	989	849	728	706	530	1205	879	571	973
117	1046	260	792	669	934	701	41	1072	676	917
118	1051	1001	523	1202	154	72	583	983	371	1024
119	809	713	10	157	959	295	535	274	76	425
120	519	1036	215	247	618	463	547	748	848	529
121	570	259	933	1071	1050	1201	582	1023	9	294
122	75	1035	617	747	569	1070	581	293	616	1069
123	615	0								

POWER RESIDUES

	0	1	2	3	4	5	6	7	8	9
100	804	1181	1081	781	1112	874	160	480	209	627
101	650	719	926	316	948	382	1146	976	466	167
102	501	272	816	1217	1189	1105	853	97	291	873
103	157	471	182	546	407	1221	1201	1141	961	421
104	32	96	288	864	130	390	1170	1048	682	815
105	1214	1180	1078	772	1085	793	1148	982	484	221
106	663	758	1043	667	770	1079	775	1094	820	1229
107	1225	1213	1177	1069	745	1004	550	419	26	78
108	234	702	875	163	489	236	708	893	217	651
109	722	935	343	1029	625	644	701	872	154	462
110	155	465	164	492	245	735	974	460	149	447
111	110	330	990	508	293	879	175	525	344	1032
112	634	671	782	1115	883	187	561	452	125	375
113	1125	913	277	831	31	93	279	837	49	147
114	441	92	276	828	22	66	198	594	551	422
115	35	105	315	945	373	1119	895	223	669	776
116	1097	829	25	75	225	675	794	1151	991	511
117	302	906	256	768	1073	757	1040	658	743	998
118	532	365	1095	823	7	21	63	189	567	470
119	179	537	380	1140	958	412	5	15	45	135
120	405	1215	1183	1087	799	1166	1036	646	707	890
121	208	624	641	692	845	73	219	657	740	989
122	505	284	852	94	282	846	76	228	684	821
123										

P = 1237

INDICES

	0	1	2	3	4	5	6	7	8	9
0		0	1	1012	2	317	1013	1117	3	788
1	318	1050	1014	33	1118	93	4	1096	789	269
2	319	893	1051	988	1015	634	34	564	1119	1229
3	94	692	5	826	1097	198	790	1032	270	1045
4	320	405	894	325	1052	1105	989	677	1016	998
5	635	872	35	419	565	131	1120	45	1230	344
6	95	159	693	669	6	350	827	521	1098	764
7	199	852	791	142	1033	410	271	931	1046	560
8	321	340	406	1146	895	177	326	1005	1053	906
9	1106	1150	990	468	678	586	1017	982	999	602
10	636	238	873	840	36	1210	420	899	566	1074
11	132	808	1121	1199	46	69	1231	821	345	977
12	96	864	160	181	694	951	670	508	7	101
13	351	1060	828	150	522	881	1099	1068	765	330
14	200	453	853	1083	792	310	143	774	1034	484
15	411	608	272	648	932	1009	1047	266	561	195
16	322	869	341	518	407	1143	1147	599	896	66
17	178	1057	327	771	1006	515	1054	120	907	123
18	1107	213	1151	1171	991	113	469	910	679	445
19	587	755	1018	165	983	126	1000	972	603	1166
20	637	297	239	1110	874	722	841	540	37	83
21	1211	216	421	628	900	642	567	573	1075	1154
22	133	1129	809	461	1122	186	1200	1174	47	55
23	70	707	1232	1092	822	994	346	336	978	1195
24	97	306	865	116	161	79	182	302	695	922
25	952	472	671	802	509	1189	8	699	102	913
26	352	781	1061	729	829	736	151	682	523	249
27	882	28	1100	926	1069	448	766	717	331	244
28	201	579	454	590	854	362	1084	286	793	956
29	311	758	144	966	775	661	1035	378	485	1021
30	412	206	609	14	273	476	649	168	933	616
31	1010	1115	1048	91	267	986	562	690	196	1043
32	323	675	870	129	342	667	519	850	408	558
33	1144	1003	1148	584	600	838	897	806	67	975
34	179	506	1058	879	328	1081	772	606	1007	193
35	516	597	1055	513	121	1169	908	753	124	1164
36	1108	538	214	640	1152	459	1172	705	992	1193
37	114	300	470	1187	911	727	680	26	446	242
38	588	284	756	659	1019	12	166	1113	984	1041
39	127	848	1001	836	973	877	604	595	1167	1162
40	638	703	298	725	240	657	1111	846	875	1160
41	723	844	842	225	541	227	38	106	84	543
42	1212	258	217	229	422	494	629	40	901	859
43	643	108	568	917	574	86	1076	21	1155	545
44	134	550	1130	1214	810	1223	462	260	1123	356
45	187	219	1201	384	1175	231	48	746	56	424
46	71	367	708	496	1233	785	1093	631	823	402
47	995	42	347	139	337	903	979	1207	1196	861
48	98	1065	307	645	866	63	117	110	162	294
49	80	570	183	1089	303	919	696	733	923	576

POWER RESIDUES

	0	1	2	3	4	5	6	7	8	9
0	1	2	4	8	16	32	64	128	256	512
1	1024	811	385	770	303	606	1212	1187	1137	1037
2	837	437	874	511	1022	807	377	754	271	542
3	1084	931	625	13	26	52	104	208	416	832
4	427	854	471	942	647	57	114	228	456	912
5	587	1174	1111	985	733	229	458	916	595	1190
6	1143	1049	861	485	970	703	169	338	676	115
7	230	460	920	603	1206	1175	1113	989	741	245
8	490	980	723	209	418	836	435	870	503	1006
9	775	313	626	15	30	60	120	240	480	960
10	683	129	258	516	1032	827	417	834	431	862
11	487	974	711	185	370	740	243	486	972	707
12	177	354	708	179	358	716	195	390	780	323
13	646	55	110	220	440	880	523	1046	855	473
14	946	655	73	146	292	584	1168	1099	961	685
15	133	266	532	1064	891	545	1090	943	649	61
16	122	244	488	976	715	193	386	772	307	614
17	1228	1219	1201	1165	1093	949	661	85	170	340
18	680	123	246	492	984	731	225	450	900	563
19	1126	1015	793	349	698	159	318	636	35	70
20	140	280	560	1120	1003	769	301	602	1204	1171
21	1105	973	709	181	362	724	211	422	844	451
22	902	567	1134	1031	825	413	826	415	830	423
23	846	455	910	583	1166	1095	953	669	101	202
24	404	808	379	758	279	558	1116	995	753	269
25	538	1076	915	593	1186	1135	1033	829	421	842
26	447	894	551	1102	967	697	157	314	628	19
27	38	76	152	304	608	1216	1195	1153	1069	901
28	565	1130	1023	809	381	762	287	574	1148	1059
29	881	525	1050	863	489	978	719	201	402	804
30	371	742	247	494	988	739	241	482	964	691
31	145	290	580	1160	1083	929	621	5	10	20
32	40	80	160	320	640	43	86	172	344	688
33	139	278	556	1112	987	737	237	474	948	659
34	81	162	324	648	59	118	236	472	944	651
35	65	130	260	520	1040	843	449	898	559	1118
36	999	761	285	570	1140	1043	849	461	922	607
37	1214	1191	1145	1053	869	501	1002	767	297	594
38	1188	1139	1041	845	453	906	575	1150	1063	889
39	541	1082	927	617	1234	1231	1225	1213	1189	1141
40	1045	853	469	938	639	41	82	164	328	656
41	75	150	300	600	1200	1163	1089	941	645	53
42	106	212	424	848	459	918	599	1198	1159	1081
43	925	613	1226	1215	1193	1149	1061	885	533	1066
44	895	553	1106	975	713	189	378	756	275	550
45	1100	963	689	141	282	564	1128	1019	801	365
46	730	223	446	892	547	1094	951	665	93	186
47	372	744	251	502	1004	771	305	610	1220	1203
48	1169	1101	965	693	149	298	596	1192	1147	1057
49	877	517	1034	831	425	850	463	926	615	1230

P = 1237

INDICES

	0	1	2	3	4	5	6	7	8	9
50	953	375	473	88	672	555	803	1078	510	535
51	1190	23	9	833	700	1157	103	491	914	547
52	353	743	782	136	1062	291	730	552	830	740
53	737	1132	152	438	683	1216	524	1135	250	812
54	883	390	29	1225	1101	155	927	464	1070	947
55	449	262	767	441	718	1125	332	798	245	358
56	202	686	580	189	455	280	591	221	855	1219
57	363	1203	1085	531	287	386	794	527	957	1177
58	312	1027	759	233	145	1138	967	50	776	961
59	662	748	1036	253	379	58	486	942	1022	426
60	413	815	207	73	610	1181	15	369	274	886
61	477	710	650	431	169	498	934	393	617	1235
62	1011	316	1116	787	1049	32	92	1095	268	892
63	987	633	563	1228	691	825	197	1031	1044	404
64	324	1104	676	997	871	418	130	44	343	158
65	668	349	520	763	851	141	409	930	559	339
66	1145	176	1004	905	1149	467	585	981	601	237
67	839	1209	898	1073	807	1198	68	820	976	863
68	180	950	507	100	1059	149	880	1067	329	452
69	1082	309	773	483	607	647	1008	265	194	868
70	517	1142	598	65	1056	770	514	119	122	212
71	1170	112	909	444	754	164	125	971	1165	296
72	1109	721	539	82	215	627	641	572	1153	1128
73	460	185	1173	54	706	1091	993	335	1194	305
74	115	78	301	921	471	801	1188	698	912	780
75	728	735	681	248	27	925	447	716	243	578
76	589	361	285	955	757	965	660	377	1020	205
77	13	475	167	615	1114	90	985	689	1042	674
78	128	666	849	557	1002	583	837	805	974	505
79	878	1080	605	192	596	512	1168	752	1163	537
80	639	458	704	1192	299	1186	726	25	241	283
81	658	11	1112	1040	847	835	876	594	1161	702
82	724	656	845	1159	843	224	226	105	542	257
83	228	493	39	858	107	916	85	20	544	549
84	1213	1222	259	355	218	383	230	745	423	366
85	495	784	630	401	41	138	902	1206	860	1064
86	644	62	109	293	569	1088	918	732	575	374
87	87	554	1077	534	22	832	1156	490	546	742
88	135	290	551	739	1131	437	1215	1134	811	389
89	1224	154	463	946	261	440	1124	797	357	685
90	188	279	220	1218	1202	530	385	526	1176	1026
91	232	1137	49	960	747	252	57	941	425	814
92	72	1180	368	885	709	430	497	392	1234	315
93	786	31	1094	891	632	1227	824	1030	403	1103
94	996	417	43	157	348	762	140	929	338	175
95	904	466	980	236	1208	1072	1197	819	862	949
96	99	148	1066	451	308	482	646	264	867	1141
97	64	769	118	211	111	443	163	970	295	720
98	81	626	571	1127	184	53	1090	334	304	77
99	920	800	697	779	734	247	924	715	577	360

POWER RESIDUES

	0	1	2	3	4	5	6	7	8	9
50	1223	1209	1181	1125	1013	789	341	682	127	254
51	508	1016	795	353	706	175	350	700	163	326
52	652	67	134	268	536	1072	907	577	1154	1071
53	905	573	1146	1055	873	509	1018	799	361	722
54	207	414	828	419	838	439	878	519	1038	839
55	441	882	527	1054	871	505	1010	783	329	658
56	79	158	316	632	27	54	108	216	432	864
57	491	982	727	217	434	868	499	998	759	281
58	562	1124	1011	785	333	666	95	190	380	760
59	283	566	1132	1027	817	397	794	351	702	167
60	334	668	99	198	396	792	347	694	151	302
61	604	1208	1179	1121	1005	773	309	618	1236	1235
62	1233	1229	1221	1205	1173	1109	981	725	213	426
63	852	467	934	631	25	50	100	200	400	800
64	363	726	215	430	860	483	966	695	153	306
65	612	1224	1211	1185	1133	1029	821	405	810	383
66	766	295	590	1180	1123	1009	781	325	650	63
67	126	252	504	1008	779	321	642	47	94	188
68	376	752	267	534	1068	899	561	1122	1007	777
69	317	634	31	62	124	248	496	992	747	257
70	514	1028	819	401	802	367	734	231	462	924
71	611	1222	1207	1177	1117	997	757	277	554	1108
72	979	721	205	410	820	403	806	375	750	263
73	526	1052	867	497	994	751	265	530	1060	883
74	529	1058	879	521	1042	847	457	914	591	1182
75	1127	1017	797	357	714	191	382	764	291	582
76	1164	1091	945	653	69	138	276	552	1104	971
77	705	173	346	692	147	294	588	1176	1115	993
78	749	261	522	1044	851	465	930	623	9	18
79	36	72	144	288	576	1152	1067	897	557	1114
80	991	745	253	506	1012	787	337	674	111	222
81	444	888	539	1078	919	601	1202	1167	1097	957
82	677	117	234	468	936	635	33	66	132	264
83	528	1056	875	513	1026	815	393	786	335	670
84	103	206	412	824	411	822	407	814	391	782
85	327	654	71	142	284	568	1136	1035	833	429
86	858	479	958	679	121	242	484	968	699	161
87	322	644	51	102	204	408	816	395	790	343
88	686	135	270	540	1080	923	609	1218	1199	1161
89	1085	933	629	21	42	84	168	336	672	107
90	214	428	856	475	950	663	89	178	356	712
91	187	374	748	259	518	1036	835	433	866	495
92	990	743	249	498	996	755	273	546	1092	947
93	657	77	154	308	616	1232	1227	1217	1197	1157
94	1077	917	597	1194	1151	1065	893	549	1098	959
95	681	125	250	500	1000	763	289	578	1156	1075
96	913	589	1178	1119	1001	765	293	586	1172	1107
97	977	717	197	394	788	339	678	119	238	476
98	952	667	97	194	388	776	315	630	23	46
99	92	184	368	736	235	470	940	643	49	98

P = 1237

INDICES

	0	1	2	3	4	5	6	7	8	9
100	954	964	376	204	474	614	89	688	673	665
101	556	582	804	504	1079	191	511	751	536	457
102	1191	1185	24	282	10	1039	834	593	701	655
103	1158	223	104	256	492	857	915	19	548	1221
104	354	382	744	365	783	400	137	1205	1063	61
105	292	1087	731	373	553	533	831	489	741	289
106	738	436	1133	388	153	945	439	796	684	278
107	1217	529	525	1025	1136	959	251	940	813	1179
108	884	429	391	314	30	890	1226	1029	1102	416
109	156	761	928	174	465	235	1071	818	948	147
110	450	481	263	1140	768	210	442	969	719	625
111	1126	52	333	76	799	778	246	714	359	963
112	203	613	687	664	581	503	190	750	456	1184
113	281	1038	592	654	222	255	856	18	1220	381
114	364	399	1204	60	1086	372	532	488	288	435
115	387	944	795	277	528	1024	958	939	1178	428
116	313	889	1028	415	760	173	234	817	146	480
117	1139	209	968	624	51	75	777	713	962	612
118	663	502	749	1183	1037	653	254	17	380	398
119	59	371	487	434	943	276	1023	938	427	888
120	414	172	816	479	208	623	74	712	611	501
121	1182	652	16	397	370	433	275	937	887	171
122	478	622	711	500	651	396	432	936	170	621
123	499	395	935	620	394	619	618			

POWER RESIDUES

	0	1	2	3	4	5	6	7	8	9
100	196	392	784	331	662	87	174	348	696	155
101	310	620	3	6	12	24	48	96	192	384
102	768	299	598	1196	1155	1073	909	581	1162	1087
103	937	637	37	74	148	296	592	1184	1131	1025
104	813	389	778	319	638	39	78	156	312	624
105	11	22	44	88	176	352	704	171	342	684
106	131	262	524	1048	859	481	962	687	137	274
107	548	1096	955	673	109	218	436	872	507	1014
108	791	345	690	143	286	572	1144	1051	865	493
109	986	735	233	466	932	627	17	34	68	136
110	272	544	1088	939	641	45	90	180	360	720
111	203	406	812	387	774	311	622	7	14	28
112	56	112	224	448	896	555	1110	983	729	221
113	442	884	531	1062	887	537	1074	911	585	1170
114	1103	969	701	165	330	660	83	166	332	664
115	91	182	364	728	219	438	876	515	1030	823
116	409	818	399	798	359	718	199	398	796	355
117	710	183	366	732	227	454	908	579	1158	1079
118	921	605	1210	1183	1129	1021	805	373	746	255
119	510	1020	803	369	738	239	478	956	675	113
120	226	452	904	571	1142	1047	857	477	954	671
121	105	210	420	840	443	886	535	1070	903	569
122	1138	1039	841	445	890	543	1086	935	633	29
123	58	116	232	464	928	619				

P = 1249

INDICES

	0	1	2	3	4	5	6	7	8	9
0		0	856	750	464	722	358	1	72	252
1	330	191	1214	586	857	224	928	496	1108	173
2	1186	751	1047	15	822	196	194	1002	465	347
3	1080	82	536	941	104	723	716	148	1029	88
4	794	965	359	1133	655	974	871	184	430	2
5	1052	1246	1050	441	610	913	73	923	1203	203
6	688	1033	938	253	144	60	549	649	960	765
7	331	487	324	200	1004	946	637	192	944	544
8	402	504	573	864	1215	1218	741	1097	263	517
9	582	587	479	832	1040	895	38	628	858	443
10	660	806	854	1244	658	225	49	757	218	237
11	521	898	929	791	531	737	811	838	1059	497
12	296	382	641	467	546	918	1109	421	1000	635
13	916	703	157	174	257	476	568	52	373	604
14	1187	934	95	777	1180	1069	1056	752	612	227
15	554	269	245	748	1048	804	552	1177	152	1191
16	10	16	112	841	181	415	472	1025	823	1172
17	826	425	349	404	705	197	1119	953	125	463
18	190	1107	195	535	87	870	440	687	648	1003
19	503	262	894	853	236	810	466	915	51	1179
20	268	151	414	348	462	439	852	267	266	364
21	1081	138	905	1237	365	607	1074	83	1093	950
22	129	1082	506	159	537	448	399	433	139	560
23	345	942	419	1117	446	906	667	46	105	512
24	1152	557	1238	6	249	724	75	759	154	366
25	526	884	717	206	29	720	608	1242	243	149
26	524	599	311	1075	1013	1163	1030	19	1113	564
27	84	575	176	89	908	387	1229	1094	212	334
28	795	1078	542	998	951	397	385	966	788	992
29	677	130	664	352	360	925	220	1193	1083	601
30	162	1134	1125	308	1101	507	356	911	656	746
31	412	882	160	286	785	975	1008	957	799	538
32	866	259	872	669	968	782	449	987	1037	185
33	23	482	80	400	633	123	431	1227	780	293
34	434	273	33	3	1205	239	12	140	313	288
35	1053	340	727	377	561	1209	981	1247	71	223
36	1046	346	715	1132	1051	922	143	486	943	1217
37	478	442	48	790	295	420	256	933	611	803
38	111	1171	1118	534	502	914	461	137	1092	447
39	418	511	74	205	523	18	907	1077	787	924
40	1124	745	1007	668	22	1226	1204	339	70	921
41	47	802	460	204	1123	338	1122	106	1220	570
42	689	107	994	436	513	692	845	1034	1221	279
43	215	1153	682	302	939	571	701	188	558	210
44	985	254	690	900	114	1239	1015	977	145	108
45	56	1156	7	1019	41	61	995	1139	168	250
46	1201	755	550	437	27	306	725	743	54	650
47	514	679	275	76	902	369	961	693	120	1146
48	760	734	165	766	846	102	862	155	1105	343
49	332	1035	931	843	367	1165	1010	488	1222	652

POWER RESIDUES

	0	1	2	3	4	5	6	7	8	9
0	1	7	49	343	1152	570	243	452	666	915
1	160	1120	346	1173	717	23	161	1127	395	267
2	620	593	404	330	1061	1182	780	464	750	254
3	529	1205	941	342	1145	521	1149	549	96	672
4	957	454	680	1013	846	926	237	410	372	106
5	742	198	137	959	468	778	450	652	817	723
6	65	455	687	1062	1189	829	807	653	824	772
7	408	358	8	56	392	246	473	813	695	1118
8	332	1075	31	217	270	641	740	184	39	273
9	662	887	1213	997	734	142	994	713	1244	1214
10	1004	783	485	897	34	238	417	421	449	645
11	768	380	162	1134	444	610	523	1163	647	782
12	478	848	940	335	1096	178	1246	1228	1102	220
13	291	788	520	1142	500	1002	769	387	211	228
14	347	1180	766	366	64	448	638	719	37	259
15	564	201	158	1106	248	487	911	132	924	223
16	312	935	300	851	961	482	876	1136	458	708
17	1209	969	538	19	133	931	272	655	838	870
18	1094	164	1148	542	47	329	1054	1133	437	561
19	180	11	77	539	26	182	25	175	1225	1081
20	73	511	1079	59	413	393	253	522	1156	598
21	439	575	278	697	1132	430	512	1086	108	756
22	296	823	765	359	15	105	735	149	1043	1056
23	1147	535	1247	1235	1151	563	194	109	763	345
24	1166	668	929	258	557	152	1064	1203	927	244
25	459	715	9	63	441	589	376	134	938	321
26	998	741	191	88	616	565	208	207	200	151
27	1057	1154	584	341	1138	472	806	646	775	429
28	505	1037	1014	853	975	580	313	942	349	1194
29	864	1052	1119	339	1124	374	120	840	884	1192
30	850	954	433	533	1233	1137	465	757	303	872
31	1108	262	585	348	1187	815	709	1216	1018	881
32	1171	703	1174	724	72	504	1030	965	510	1072
33	10	70	490	932	279	704	1181	773	415	407
34	351	1208	962	489	925	230	361	29	203	172
35	1204	934	293	802	618	579	306	893	6	42
36	294	809	667	922	209	214	249	494	960	475
37	827	793	555	138	966	517	1121	353	1222	1060
38	1175	731	121	847	933	286	753	275	676	985
39	650	803	625	628	649	796	576	285	746	226
40	333	1082	80	560	173	1211	983	636	705	1188
41	822	758	310	921	202	165	1155	591	390	232
42	375	127	889	1227	1095	171	1197	885	1199	899
43	48	336	1103	227	340	1131	423	463	743	205
44	186	53	371	99	693	1104	234	389	225	326
45	1033	986	657	852	968	531	1219	1039	1028	951
46	412	386	204	179	4	28	196	123	861	1031
47	972	559	166	1162	640	733	135	945	370	92
48	644	761	331	1068	1231	1123	367	71	497	981
49	622	607	502	1016	867	1073	17	119	833	835

P = 1249

INDICES

	0	1	2	3	4	5	6	7	8	9
50	134	527	492	1022	325	280	1062	674	885	710
51	328	201	216	1175	850	718	1099	375	1005	1154
52	132	35	207	116	1167	947	683	578	621	30
53	771	455	638	303	875	231	721	1213	172	193
54	940	793	183	609	1032	959	945	572	516	37
55	1243	520	837	545	702	372	1068	244	1190	471
56	403	189	686	235	150	265	606	505	559	666
57	5	525	1241	1012	574	211	396	663	600	355
58	285	865	986	632	272	312	1208	714	1216	255
59	533	417	1076	21	801	1219	691	681	209	1014
60	1018	1200	742	901	733	1104	1164	491	709	1098
61	115	770	1212	1031	519	1189	264	1240	354	1207
62	20	1017	490	518	1016	392	1142	1114	393	644
63	583	978	616	888	565	1143	407	588	146	739
64	474	85	1115	540	480	109	277	118	576	394
65	390	833	57	67	595	177	645	452	1041	1157
66	879	592	90	584	936	896	8	362	241	909
67	979	1224	39	1020	835	1198	388	617	1149	629
68	42	1183	1129	1230	889	774	859	62	813	1027
69	1095	566	868	444	996	78	1169	213	1144	619
70	661	1140	1196	321	335	408	1233	807	169	316
71	817	796	589	97	855	251	927	14	1079	147
72	654	1245	1202	59	323	543	740	831	659	756
73	530	381	999	475	94	226	551	840	825	952
74	86	261	50	438	904	949	398	1116	1151	758
75	28	598	1112	386	541	991	219	307	411	956
76	967	481	779	238	726	222	142	789	110	136
77	522	744	69	337	993	278	700	899	55	1138
78	26	678	119	101	930	651	1061	1174	131	577
79	874	792	515	371	685	665	395	631	532	680
80	732	769	353	391	615	738	276	66	878	361
81	834	1182	812	77	1195	315	926	58	529	839
82	903	597	410	221	68	1137	1060	370	731	65
83	1194	596	730	498	962	499	828	1084	178	671
84	297	694	963	580	602	646	44	383	121	500
85	300	163	453	283	642	1147	829	698	1135	1042
86	1071	468	761	1085	290	1126	1158	494	547	735
87	179	1235	309	880	1044	919	166	672	1066	1102
88	593	319	1110	767	298	427	508	91	970	422
89	847	695	623	357	585	1185	1001	103	964	429
90	912	937	764	636	863	581	627	657	897	1058
91	917	156	603	1055	747	9	1024	704	1106	647
92	809	413	363	1073	158	344	45	248	883	242
93	1162	175	333	384	351	161	910	784	258	1036
94	122	32	287	980	1131	477	932	501	510	786
95	1225	459	569	844	301	984	976	40	754	53
96	368	164	342	1009	1021	327	374	1166	454	171
97	958	836	470	605	1011	284	713	800	1199	708
98	1188	489	643	406	539	389	451	935	1223	1148
99	773	867	618	1232	96	653	830	93	260	1150

POWER RESIDUES

	0	1	2	3	4	5	6	7	8	9
50	849	947	384	190	81	567	222	305	886	1206
51	948	391	239	424	470	792	548	89	623	614
52	551	110	770	394	260	571	250	501	1009	818
53	730	114	798	590	383	183	32	224	319	984
54	643	754	282	725	79	553	124	868	1080	66
55	462	736	156	1092	150	1050	1105	241	438	568
56	229	354	1229	1109	269	634	691	1090	136	952
57	419	435	547	82	574	271	648	789	527	1191
58	843	905	90	630	663	894	13	91	637	712
59	1237	1165	661	880	1164	654	831	821	751	261
60	578	299	844	912	139	973	566	215	256	543
61	54	378	148	1036	1007	804	632	677	992	699
62	1146	528	1198	892	1248	1242	1200	906	97	679
63	1006	797	583	334	1089	129	903	76	532	1226
64	1088	122	854	982	629	656	845	919	188	67
65	469	785	499	995	720	44	308	907	104	728
66	100	700	1153	577	292	795	569	236	403	323
67	1012	839	877	1143	507	1051	1112	290	781	471
68	799	597	432	526	1184	794	562	187	60	420
69	442	596	425	477	841	891	1241	1193	857	1003
70	776	436	554	131	917	174	1218	1032	979	608
71	509	1065	1210	976	587	362	36	252	515	1107
72	255	536	5	35	245	466	764	352	1215	1011
73	832	828	800	604	481	869	1087	115	805	639
74	726	86	602	467	771	401	309	914	153	1071
75	3	21	147	1029	958	461	729	107	749	247
76	480	862	1038	1021	902	69	483	883	1185	801
77	611	530	1212	990	685	1048	1091	143	1001	762
78	338	1117	325	1026	937	314	949	398	288	767
79	373	113	791	541	40	280	711	1230	1116	318
80	977	594	411	379	155	1085	101	707	1202	920
81	195	116	812	688	1069	1238	1172	710	1223	1067
82	1224	1074	24	168	1176	738	170	1190	836	856
83	996	727	93	651	810	674	971	552	117	819
84	737	163	1141	493	953	426	484	890	1234	1144
85	514	1100	206	193	102	714	2	14	98	686
86	1055	1140	486	904	83	581	320	991	692	1097
87	185	46	322	1005	790	534	1240	1186	808	660
88	873	1115	311	928	251	508	1058	1161	633	684
89	1041	1042	1049	1098	192	95	665	908	111	777
90	443	603	474	820	744	212	235	396	274	669
91	936	307	900	55	385	197	130	910	125	875
92	1129	409	365	57	399	295	816	716	16	112
93	784	492	946	377	141	987	664	901	62	434
94	540	33	231	368	78	546	75	525	1177	745
95	219	284	739	177	1239	1179	759	317	970	545
96	68	476	834	842	898	41	287	760	324	1019
97	888	1220	1046	1077	45	315	956	447	631	670
98	943	356	1243	1207	955	440	582	327	1040	1035
99	1000	755	289	774	422	456	694	1111	283	732

P = 1249

INDICES

	0	1	2	3	4	5	6	7	8	9
100	990	778	135	699	100	873	630	614	1181	528
101	1136	729	670	43	282	1070	493	1043	318	969
102	1184	763	1057	1023	1072	1161	783	1130	458	753
103	326	469	707	450	1231	989	613	281	762	457
104	988	890	891	228	1063	1086	972	1038	775	892
105	555	675	291	1090	186	860	229	270	886	1127
106	379	24	63	1064	246	711	1159	819	483	814
107	1087	749	329	495	821	81	1028	973	1049	202
108	548	199	401	1096	1039	805	217	736	640	634
109	567	776	553	1176	180	424	124	869	893	1178
110	851	1236	128	432	445	556	153	719	310	563
111	1228	997	676	1192	1100	881	798	781	79	292
112	11	376	1045	485	294	1170	1091	17	1006	920
113	1121	435	214	187	113	1155	167	305	274	1145
114	861	842	133	673	849	34	620	230	182	36
115	1067	234	4	662	271	416	208	1103	1211	1206
116	1141	887	473	117	594	591	240	1197	1128	1026
117	1168	320	816	13	322	380	824	948	1111	955
118	141	336	25	1173	684	768	877	314	409	64
119	827	579	299	697	289	1234	1065	426	622	428
120	626	1054	808	247	350	31	509	983	341	170
121	712	405	772	92	99	728	317	1160	706	456
122	971	1089	378	818	820	198	639	423	127	562
123	797	484	1120	304	848	233	1210	590	815	954
124	876	696	625	982	98	1088	126	232	624	

POWER RESIDUES

	0	1	2	3	4	5	6	7	8	9
100	128	896	27	189	74	518	1128	402	316	963
101	496	974	573	264	599	446	624	621	600	453
102	673	964	503	1023	916	167	1169	689	1076	38
103	266	613	544	61	427	491	939	328	1047	1084
104	94	658	859	1017	874	1122	360	22	154	1078
105	52	364	50	350	1201	913	146	1022	909	118
106	826	786	506	1044	1063	1196	878	1150	556	145
107	1015	860	1024	923	216	263	592	397	281	718
108	30	210	221	298	837	863	1045	1070	1245	1221
109	1053	1126	388	218	277	690	1083	87	609	516
110	1114	304	879	1157	605	488	918	181	18	126
111	882	1178	752	268	627	642	747	233	382	176
112	1232	1130	416	414	400	302	865	1059	1168	682
113	1027	944	363	43	301	858	1010	825	779	457
114	701	1160	626	635	698	1139	479	855	989	678
115	999	748	240	431	519	1135	451	659	866	1066
116	1217	1025	930	265	606	495	967	524	1170	696
117	1125	381	169	1183	787	513	1093	157	1099	199
118	144	1008	811	681	1020	895	20	140	980	615
119	558	159	1113	297	830	814	702	1167	675	978
120	601	460	722	58	406	344	1159	619	586	355
121	1236	1158	612	537	12	84	588	369	85	595
122	418	428	498	988	671	950	405	337	1110	276
123	683	1034	993	706	1195	871	1101	213	242	445
124	617	572	257	550	103	721	51	357		

P = 1259

INDICES

	0	1	2	3	4	5	6	7	8	9
0		0	1	1096	2	76	1097	246	3	934
1	77	1151	1098	679	247	1172	4	14	935	973
2	78	84	1152	1128	1099	152	680	772	248	119
3	1173	265	5	989	15	322	936	614	974	517
4	79	833	85	350	1153	1010	1129	563	1100	492
5	153	1110	681	838	773	1227	249	811	120	623
6	1174	1068	266	1180	6	755	990	532	16	966
7	323	38	937	292	615	1248	975	139	518	72
8	80	610	834	962	86	90	351	1215	1154	1061
9	1011	925	1130	103	564	1049	1101	580	493	827
10	154	94	1111	659	682	160	839	312	774	652
11	1228	452	250	740	812	1204	121	355	624	260
12	1175	1044	1069	671	267	228	1181	1074	7	188
13	756	1033	991	1219	533	848	17	375	967	956
14	324	401	39	572	938	195	293	330	616	1158
15	1249	478	976	948	140	341	519	464	73	676
16	81	116	611	1007	835	1065	963	136	87	100
17	91	649	352	225	1216	398	1155	461	1062	222
18	1012	1015	926	906	1131	690	104	1165	565	1018
19	1050	272	1102	884	581	593	494	929	828	287
20	155	370	95	365	1112	909	660	804	683	866
21	161	407	840	1134	313	426	775	511	653	130
22	1229	693	453	233	251	1086	741	820	813	107
23	1205	1235	122	1117	356	639	625	1168	261	559
24	1176	68	1045	448	1070	568	672	394	268	800
25	229	555	1182	1021	1075	1186	8	604	189	860
26	757	1053	1034	173	992	914	1220	899	534	275
27	849	1025	18	763	376	45	968	1105	957	1199
28	325	217	402	443	40	887	573	1079	939	28
29	196	418	294	584	331	699	617	665	1159	549
30	1250	596	479	1190	977	1144	949	892	141	497
31	342	541	520	873	465	1256	74	932	677	12
32	82	150	117	987	612	831	1008	490	836	809
33	1066	753	964	290	137	608	88	1059	101	578
34	92	158	650	738	353	1042	226	186	1217	373
35	399	193	1156	946	462	114	1063	98	223	459
36	1013	688	1016	882	927	368	907	864	1132	509
37	691	1084	105	1115	1166	66	566	798	1019	602
38	1051	912	273	761	1103	215	885	26	582	663
39	594	1142	495	871	930	148	829	807	288	1057
40	156	1040	371	944	96	686	366	507	1113	796
41	910	213	661	869	805	1038	684	794	867	792
42	162	164	408	239	841	166	1135	56	314	410
43	427	177	776	241	512	33	654	843	131	282
44	1230	168	694	485	454	1137	234	996	252	58
45	1087	726	742	316	821	1001	814	412	108	786
46	1206	429	1236	918	123	179	1118	201	357	778
47	640	302	626	243	1169	1125	262	514	560	1224
48	1177	35	69	1212	1046	656	449	257	1071	845
49	569	475	673	133	395	903	269	284	801	423

POWER RESIDUES

	0	1	2	3	4	5	6	7	8	9
0	1	2	4	8	16	32	64	128	256	512
1	1024	789	319	638	17	34	68	136	272	544
2	1088	917	575	1150	1041	823	387	774	289	578
3	1156	1053	847	435	870	481	962	665	71	142
4	284	568	1136	1013	767	275	550	1100	941	623
5	1246	1233	1207	1155	1051	843	427	854	449	898
6	537	1074	889	519	1038	817	375	750	241	482
7	964	669	79	158	316	632	5	10	20	40
8	80	160	320	640	21	42	84	168	336	672
9	85	170	340	680	101	202	404	808	357	714
10	169	338	676	93	186	372	744	229	458	916
11	573	1146	1033	807	355	710	161	322	644	29
12	58	116	232	464	928	597	1194	1129	999	739
13	219	438	876	493	986	713	167	334	668	77
14	154	308	616	1232	1205	1151	1043	827	395	790
15	321	642	25	50	100	200	400	800	341	682
16	105	210	420	840	421	842	425	850	441	882
17	505	1010	761	263	526	1052	845	431	862	465
18	930	601	1202	1145	1031	803	347	694	129	258
19	516	1032	805	351	702	145	290	580	1160	1061
20	863	467	934	609	1218	1177	1095	931	603	1206
21	1153	1047	835	411	822	385	770	281	562	1124
22	989	719	179	358	716	173	346	692	125	250
23	500	1000	741	223	446	892	525	1050	841	423
24	846	433	866	473	946	633	7	14	28	56
25	112	224	448	896	533	1066	873	487	974	689
26	119	238	476	952	645	31	62	124	248	496
27	992	725	191	382	764	269	538	1076	893	527
28	1054	849	439	878	497	994	729	199	398	796
29	333	666	73	146	292	584	1168	1077	895	531
30	1062	865	471	942	625	1250	1241	1223	1187	1115
31	971	683	107	214	428	856	453	906	553	1106
32	953	647	35	70	140	280	560	1120	981	703
33	147	294	588	1176	1093	927	595	1190	1121	983
34	707	155	310	620	1240	1221	1183	1107	955	651
35	43	86	172	344	688	117	234	468	936	613
36	1226	1193	1127	995	731	203	406	812	365	730
37	201	402	804	349	698	137	274	548	1096	933
38	607	1214	1169	1079	899	539	1078	897	535	1070
39	881	503	1006	753	247	494	988	717	175	350
40	700	141	282	564	1128	997	735	211	422	844
41	429	858	457	914	569	1138	1017	775	291	582
42	1164	1069	879	499	998	737	215	430	860	461
43	922	585	1170	1081	903	547	1094	929	599	1198
44	1137	1015	771	283	566	1132	1005	751	243	486
45	972	685	111	222	444	888	517	1034	809	359
46	718	177	354	708	157	314	628	1256	1253	1247
47	1235	1211	1163	1067	875	491	982	705	151	302
48	604	1208	1157	1055	851	443	886	513	1026	793
49	327	654	49	98	196	392	784	309	618	1236

P = 1259

INDICES

	0	1	2	3	4	5	6	7	8	9
50	230	1232	556	391	1183	170	1022	1196	1076	696
51	1187	538	9	487	605	735	190	456	861	63
52	758	1139	1054	504	1035	236	174	279	993	998
53	915	299	1221	254	900	388	535	60	276	385
54	850	1089	1026	853	19	728	764	435	377	744
55	46	1092	969	318	1106	528	958	823	1200	1029
56	326	1003	218	589	403	816	444	856	41	414
57	888	983	574	110	1080	22	940	788	29	722
58	197	1208	419	731	295	431	585	718	332	1238
59	700	767	618	920	666	336	1160	125	550	438
60	1251	181	597	208	480	1120	1191	380	978	203
61	1145	1242	950	359	893	747	142	780	498	712
62	343	642	542	49	521	304	874	704	466	628
63	1257	1095	75	245	933	1150	678	1171	13	972
64	83	1127	151	771	118	264	988	321	613	516
65	832	349	1009	562	491	1109	837	1226	810	622
66	1067	1179	754	531	965	37	291	1247	138	71
67	609	961	89	1214	1060	924	102	1048	579	826
68	93	658	159	311	651	451	739	1203	354	259
69	1043	670	227	1073	187	1032	1218	847	374	955
70	400	571	194	329	1157	477	947	340	463	675
71	115	1006	1064	135	99	648	224	397	460	221
72	1014	905	689	1164	1017	271	883	592	928	286
73	369	364	908	803	865	406	1133	425	510	129
74	692	232	1085	819	106	1234	1116	638	1167	558
75	67	447	567	393	799	554	1020	1185	603	859
76	1052	172	913	898	274	1024	762	44	1104	1198
77	216	442	886	1078	27	417	583	698	664	548
78	595	1189	1143	891	496	540	872	1255	931	11
79	149	986	830	489	808	752	289	607	1058	577
80	157	737	1041	185	372	192	945	113	97	458
81	687	881	367	863	508	1083	1114	65	797	601
82	911	760	214	25	662	1141	870	147	806	1056
83	1039	943	685	506	795	212	868	1037	793	791
84	163	238	165	55	409	176	240	32	842	281
85	167	484	1136	995	57	725	315	1000	411	785
86	428	917	178	200	777	301	242	1124	513	1223
87	34	1211	655	256	844	474	132	902	283	422
88	1231	390	169	1195	695	537	486	734	455	62
89	1138	503	235	278	997	298	253	387	59	384
90	1088	852	727	434	743	1091	317	527	822	1028
91	1002	588	815	855	413	982	109	21	787	721
92	1207	730	430	717	1237	766	919	335	124	437
93	180	207	1119	379	202	1241	358	746	779	711
94	641	48	303	703	627	1094	244	1149	1170	971
95	1126	770	263	320	515	348	561	1108	1225	621
96	1178	530	36	1246	70	960	1213	923	1047	825
97	657	310	450	1202	258	669	1072	1031	846	954
98	570	328	476	339	674	1005	134	647	396	220
99	904	1163	270	591	285	363	802	405	424	128

POWER RESIDUES

	0	1	2	3	4	5	6	7	8	9
50	1213	1167	1075	891	523	1046	833	407	814	369
51	738	217	434	868	477	954	649	39	78	156
52	312	624	1248	1237	1215	1171	1083	907	555	1110
53	961	663	67	134	268	536	1072	885	511	1022
54	785	311	622	1244	1229	1199	1139	1019	779	299
55	598	1196	1133	1007	755	251	502	1004	749	239
56	478	956	653	47	94	188	376	752	245	490
57	980	701	143	286	572	1144	1029	799	339	678
58	97	194	388	776	293	586	1172	1085	911	563
59	1126	993	727	195	390	780	301	602	1204	1149
60	1039	819	379	758	257	514	1028	797	335	670
61	81	162	324	648	37	74	148	296	592	1184
62	1109	959	659	59	118	236	472	944	629	1258
63	1257	1255	1251	1243	1227	1195	1131	1003	747	235
64	470	940	621	1242	1225	1191	1123	987	715	171
65	342	684	109	218	436	872	485	970	681	103
66	206	412	824	389	778	297	594	1188	1117	975
67	691	123	246	492	984	709	159	318	636	13
68	26	52	104	208	416	832	405	810	361	722
69	185	370	740	221	442	884	509	1018	777	295
70	590	1180	1101	943	627	1254	1249	1239	1219	1179
71	1099	939	619	1238	1217	1175	1091	923	587	1174
72	1089	919	579	1158	1057	855	451	902	545	1090
73	921	583	1166	1073	887	515	1030	801	343	686
74	113	226	452	904	549	1098	937	615	1230	1201
75	1143	1027	795	331	662	65	130	260	520	1040
76	821	383	766	273	546	1092	925	591	1182	1105
77	951	643	27	54	108	216	432	864	469	938
78	617	1234	1209	1159	1059	859	459	918	577	1154
79	1049	839	419	838	417	834	409	818	377	754
80	249	498	996	733	207	414	828	397	794	329
81	658	57	114	228	456	912	565	1130	1001	743
82	227	454	908	557	1114	969	679	99	198	396
83	792	325	650	41	82	164	328	656	53	106
84	212	424	848	437	874	489	978	697	135	270
85	540	1080	901	543	1086	913	567	1134	1009	759
86	259	518	1036	813	367	734	209	418	836	413
87	826	393	786	313	626	1252	1245	1231	1203	1147
88	1035	811	363	726	193	386	772	285	570	1140
89	1021	783	307	614	1228	1197	1135	1011	763	267
90	534	1068	877	495	990	721	183	366	732	205
91	410	820	381	762	265	530	1060	861	463	926
92	593	1186	1113	967	675	91	182	364	728	197
93	394	788	317	634	9	18	36	72	144	288
94	576	1152	1045	831	403	806	353	706	153	306
95	612	1224	1189	1119	979	699	139	278	556	1112
96	965	671	83	166	332	664	69	138	276	552
97	1104	949	639	19	38	76	152	304	608	1216
98	1173	1087	915	571	1142	1025	791	323	646	33
99	66	132	264	528	1056	853	447	894	529	1058

P = 1259

INDICES

	0	1	2	3	4	5	6	7	8	9
100	231	818	1233	637	557	446	392	553	1184	858
101	171	897	1023	43	1197	441	1077	416	697	547
102	1188	890	539	1254	10	985	488	751	606	576
103	736	184	191	112	457	880	862	1082	64	600
104	759	24	1140	146	1055	942	505	211	1036	790
105	237	54	175	31	280	483	994	724	999	784
106	916	199	300	1123	1222	1210	255	473	901	421
107	389	1194	536	733	61	502	277	297	386	383
108	851	433	1090	526	1027	587	854	981	20	720
109	729	716	765	334	436	206	378	1240	745	710
110	47	702	1093	1148	970	769	319	347	1107	620
111	529	1245	959	922	824	309	1201	668	1030	953
112	327	338	1004	646	219	1162	590	362	404	127
113	817	636	445	552	857	896	42	440	415	546
114	889	1253	984	750	575	183	111	879	1081	599
115	23	145	941	210	789	53	30	482	723	783
116	198	1122	1209	472	420	1193	732	501	296	382
117	432	525	586	980	719	715	333	205	1239	709
118	701	1147	768	346	619	1244	921	308	667	952
119	337	645	1161	361	126	635	551	895	439	545
120	1252	749	182	878	598	144	209	52	481	782
121	1121	471	1192	500	381	524	979	714	204	708
122	1146	345	1243	307	951	644	360	634	894	544
123	748	877	143	51	781	470	499	523	713	707
124	344	306	643	633	543	876	50	469	522	706
125	305	632	875	468	705	631	467	630	629	

POWER RESIDUES

	0	1	2	3	4	5	6	7	8	9
100	857	455	910	561	1122	985	711	163	326	652
101	45	90	180	360	720	181	362	724	189	378
102	756	253	506	1012	765	271	542	1084	909	559
103	1118	977	695	131	262	524	1048	837	415	830
104	401	802	345	690	121	242	484	968	677	95
105	190	380	760	261	522	1044	829	399	798	337
106	674	89	178	356	712	165	330	660	61	122
107	244	488	976	693	127	254	508	1016	773	287
108	574	1148	1037	815	371	742	225	450	900	541
109	1082	905	551	1102	945	631	3	6	12	24
110	48	96	192	384	768	277	554	1108	957	655
111	51	102	204	408	816	373	746	233	466	932
112	605	1210	1161	1063	867	475	950	641	23	46
113	92	184	368	736	213	426	852	445	890	521
114	1042	825	391	782	305	610	1220	1181	1103	947
115	635	11	22	44	88	176	352	704	149	298
116	596	1192	1125	991	723	187	374	748	237	474
117	948	637	15	30	60	120	240	480	960	661
118	63	126	252	504	1008	757	255	510	1020	781
119	303	606	1212	1165	1071	883	507	1014	769	279
120	558	1116	973	687	115	230	460	920	581	1162
121	1065	871	483	966	673	87	174	348	696	133
122	266	532	1064	869	479	958	657	55	110	220
123	440	880	501	1002	745	231	462	924	589	1178
124	1097	935	611	1222	1185	1111	963	667	75	150
125	300	600	1200	1141	1023	787	315	630		

P = 1277

INDICES

	0	1	2	3	4	5	6	7	8	9
0		0	1	669	2	661	670	1113	3	62
1	662	244	671	356	1114	54	4	1200	63	128
2	663	506	245	404	672	46	357	731	1115	392
3	55	815	5	913	1201	498	64	841	129	1025
4	664	493	507	301	246	723	405	1186	673	950
5	47	593	358	627	732	905	1116	797	393	261
6	56	772	816	1175	6	1017	914	512	1202	1073
7	499	1213	65	778	842	715	130	81	1026	990
8	665	124	494	589	508	585	302	1061	247	339
9	724	193	406	208	1187	789	674	286	951	306
10	48	984	594	460	359	1167	628	442	733	144
11	906	234	1117	319	798	1065	394	418	262	1037
12	57	488	773	1162	817	707	1176	1089	7	970
13	1018	251	915	1241	513	116	1203	822	1074	933
14	500	579	1214	600	66	1053	779	343	843	1220
15	716	432	131	1262	82	200	1027	1141	991	20
16	666	241	125	728	495	298	590	258	509	712
17	586	190	303	439	1062	1159	248	930	340	197
18	725	187	194	165	407	226	209	168	1188	568
19	790	219	675	1005	287	410	952	757	307	557
20	49	1181	985	229	595	1154	461	466	360	372
21	1168	212	629	606	443	962	734	652	145	171
22	907	280	235	102	1118	108	320	1191	799	892
23	1066	750	395	1094	419	571	263	383	1038	471
24	58	42	489	793	774	335	1163	484	818	1258
25	708	222	1177	648	1090	1254	8	618	971	678
26	1019	454	252	744	916	12	1242	1008	514	541
27	117	365	1204	862	823	290	1075	72	934	877
28	501	622	580	413	1215	182	601	330	67	1124
29	1054	955	780	527	344	922	844	975	1221	760
30	717	138	433	377	132	157	1263	310	83	1129
31	201	273	1028	682	1142	560	992	698	21	636
32	667	1111	242	52	126	402	729	813	496	1023
33	299	1184	591	903	259	1173	510	1211	713	988
34	587	1059	191	787	304	458	440	232	1063	1035
35	1160	1087	249	114	931	598	341	430	198	18
36	726	256	188	1157	195	163	166	217	408	555
37	227	464	210	960	169	100	1189	748	569	469
38	791	482	220	1252	676	742	1006	363	288	875
39	411	328	953	920	758	375	308	271	558	634
40	50	811	1182	1171	986	785	230	1085	596	16
41	1155	215	462	98	467	1250	361	326	373	632
42	1169	1083	213	1248	630	1246	607	609	444	1269
43	963	611	735	852	653	446	146	532	172	1271
44	908	1012	281	965	236	1000	103	613	1119	1106
45	109	737	321	1101	1192	854	800	518	893	655
46	1067	1235	751	448	396	869	1095	148	420	349
47	572	534	264	545	384	174	1039	689	472	1273
48	59	1197	43	910	490	947	794	1014	775	121
49	336	283	1164	316	485	967	819	1050	1259	238

POWER RESIDUES

	0	1	2	3	4	5	6	7	8	9
0	1	2	4	8	16	32	64	128	256	512
1	1024	771	265	530	1060	843	409	818	359	718
2	159	318	636	1272	1267	1257	1237	1197	1117	957
3	637	1274	1271	1265	1253	1229	1181	1085	893	509
4	1018	759	241	482	964	651	25	50	100	200
5	400	800	323	646	15	30	60	120	240	480
6	960	643	9	18	36	72	144	288	576	1152
7	1027	777	277	554	1108	939	601	1202	1127	977
8	677	77	154	308	616	1232	1187	1097	917	557
9	1114	951	625	1250	1223	1169	1061	845	413	826
10	375	750	223	446	892	507	1014	751	225	450
11	900	523	1046	815	353	706	135	270	540	1080
12	883	489	978	679	81	162	324	648	19	38
13	76	152	304	608	1216	1155	1033	789	301	602
14	1204	1131	985	693	109	218	436	872	467	934
15	591	1182	1087	897	517	1034	791	305	610	1220
16	1163	1049	821	365	730	183	366	732	187	374
17	748	219	438	876	475	950	623	1246	1215	1153
18	1029	781	285	570	1140	1003	729	181	362	724
19	171	342	684	91	182	364	728	179	358	716
20	155	310	620	1240	1203	1129	981	685	93	186
21	372	744	211	422	844	411	822	367	734	191
22	382	764	251	502	1004	731	185	370	740	203
23	406	812	347	694	111	222	444	888	499	998
24	719	161	322	644	11	22	44	88	176	352
25	704	131	262	524	1048	819	361	722	167	334
26	668	59	118	236	472	944	611	1222	1167	1057
27	837	397	794	311	622	1244	1211	1145	1013	749
28	221	442	884	491	982	687	97	194	388	776
29	275	550	1100	923	569	1138	999	721	165	330
30	660	43	86	172	344	688	99	198	396	792
31	307	614	1228	1179	1081	885	493	986	695	113
32	226	452	904	531	1062	847	417	834	391	782
33	287	574	1148	1019	761	245	490	980	683	89
34	178	356	712	147	294	588	1176	1075	873	469
35	938	599	1198	1119	961	645	13	26	52	104
36	208	416	832	387	774	271	542	1084	891	505
37	1010	743	209	418	836	395	790	303	606	1212
38	1147	1017	757	237	474	948	619	1238	1199	1121
39	965	653	29	58	116	232	464	928	579	1158
40	1039	801	325	650	23	46	92	184	368	736
41	195	390	780	283	566	1132	987	697	117	234
42	468	936	595	1190	1103	929	581	1162	1047	817
43	357	714	151	302	604	1208	1139	1001	725	173
44	346	692	107	214	428	856	435	870	463	926
45	575	1150	1023	769	261	522	1044	811	345	690
46	103	206	412	824	371	742	207	414	828	379
47	758	239	478	956	635	1270	1263	1249	1221	1165
48	1053	829	381	762	247	494	988	699	121	242
49	484	968	659	41	82	164	328	656	35	70

P = 1277

INDICES

	0	1	2	3	4	5	6	7	8	9
50	709	927	223	1002	1178	369	649	105	1091	39
51	1255	615	9	859	619	1121	972	154	679	1108
52	1020	1208	455	111	253	552	745	739	917	808
53	13	323	1243	849	1009	1103	515	866	542	1194
54	118	1047	366	856	1205	805	863	802	824	834
55	291	520	1076	827	73	895	935	89	878	657
56	502	837	623	1069	581	980	414	1237	1216	294
57	183	753	602	888	331	450	68	523	1125	398
58	1055	426	956	871	781	1079	528	1097	345	943
59	923	150	845	830	976	422	1222	1226	761	351
60	718	76	139	574	434	1149	378	536	133	898
61	158	266	1264	1230	311	547	84	938	1130	386
62	202	1135	274	176	1029	92	683	1041	1143	765
63	561	691	993	881	699	474	22	30	637	1275
64	668	660	1112	61	243	355	53	1199	127	505
65	403	45	730	391	814	912	497	840	1024	492
66	300	722	1185	949	592	626	904	796	260	771
67	1174	1016	511	1072	1212	777	714	80	989	123
68	588	584	1060	338	192	207	788	285	305	983
69	459	1166	441	143	233	318	1064	417	1036	487
70	1161	706	1088	969	250	1240	115	821	932	578
71	599	1052	342	1219	431	1261	199	1140	19	240
72	727	297	257	711	189	438	1158	929	196	186
73	164	225	167	567	218	1004	409	756	556	1180
74	228	1153	465	371	211	605	961	651	170	279
75	101	107	1190	891	749	1093	570	382	470	41
76	792	334	483	1257	221	647	1253	617	677	453
77	743	11	1007	540	364	861	289	71	876	621
78	412	181	329	1123	954	526	921	974	759	137
79	376	156	309	1128	272	681	559	697	635	1110
80	51	401	812	1022	1183	902	1172	1210	987	1058
81	786	457	231	1034	1086	113	597	429	17	255
82	1156	162	216	554	463	959	99	747	468	481
83	1251	741	362	874	327	919	374	270	633	810
84	1170	784	1084	15	214	97	1249	325	631	1082
85	1247	1245	608	1268	610	851	445	531	1270	1011
86	964	999	612	1105	736	1100	853	517	654	1234
87	447	868	147	348	533	544	173	688	1272	1196
88	909	946	1013	120	282	315	966	1049	237	926
89	1001	368	104	38	614	858	1120	153	1107	1207
90	110	551	738	807	322	848	1102	865	1193	1046
91	855	804	801	833	519	826	894	88	656	836
92	1068	979	1236	293	752	887	449	522	397	425
93	870	1078	1096	942	149	829	421	1225	350	75
94	573	1148	535	897	265	1229	546	937	385	1134
95	175	91	1040	764	690	880	473	29	1274	659
96	60	354	1198	504	44	390	911	839	491	721
97	948	625	795	770	1015	1071	776	79	122	583
98	337	206	284	982	1165	142	317	416	486	705
99	968	1239	820	577	1051	1218	1260	1139	239	296

POWER RESIDUES

	0	1	2	3	4	5	6	7	8	9
50	140	280	560	1120	963	649	21	42	84	168
51	336	672	67	134	268	536	1072	867	457	914
52	551	1102	927	577	1154	1031	785	293	586	1172
53	1067	857	437	874	471	942	607	1214	1151	1025
54	773	269	538	1076	875	473	946	615	1230	1183
55	1089	901	525	1050	823	369	738	199	398	796
56	315	630	1260	1243	1209	1141	1005	733	189	378
57	756	235	470	940	603	1206	1135	993	709	141
58	282	564	1128	979	681	85	170	340	680	83
59	166	332	664	51	102	204	408	816	355	710
60	143	286	572	1144	1011	745	213	426	852	427
61	854	431	862	447	894	511	1022	767	257	514
62	1028	779	281	562	1124	971	665	53	106	212
63	424	848	419	838	399	798	319	638	1276	1275
64	1273	1269	1261	1245	1213	1149	1021	765	253	506
65	1012	747	217	434	868	459	918	559	1118	959
66	641	5	10	20	40	80	160	320	640	3
67	6	12	24	48	96	192	384	768	259	518
68	1036	795	313	626	1252	1227	1177	1077	877	477
69	954	631	1262	1247	1217	1157	1037	797	317	634
70	1268	1259	1241	1205	1133	989	701	125	250	500
71	1000	723	169	338	676	75	150	300	600	1200
72	1123	969	661	45	90	180	360	720	163	326
73	652	27	54	108	216	432	864	451	902	527
74	1054	831	385	770	263	526	1052	827	377	754
75	231	462	924	571	1142	1007	737	197	394	788
76	299	598	1196	1115	953	629	1258	1239	1201	1125
77	973	669	61	122	244	488	976	675	73	146
78	292	584	1168	1059	841	405	810	343	686	95
79	190	380	760	243	486	972	667	57	114	228
80	456	912	547	1094	911	545	1090	903	529	1058
81	839	401	802	327	654	31	62	124	248	496
82	992	707	137	274	548	1096	915	553	1106	935
83	593	1186	1095	913	549	1098	919	561	1122	967
84	657	37	74	148	296	592	1184	1091	905	533
85	1066	855	433	866	455	910	543	1086	895	513
86	1026	775	273	546	1092	907	537	1074	871	465
87	930	583	1166	1055	833	389	778	279	558	1116
88	955	633	1266	1255	1233	1189	1101	925	573	1146
89	1015	753	229	458	916	555	1110	943	609	1218
90	1159	1041	805	333	666	55	110	220	440	880
91	483	966	655	33	66	132	264	528	1056	835
92	393	786	295	590	1180	1083	889	501	1002	727
93	177	354	708	139	278	556	1112	947	617	1234
94	1191	1105	933	589	1178	1079	881	485	970	663
95	49	98	196	392	784	291	582	1164	1051	825
96	373	746	215	430	860	443	886	495	990	703
97	129	258	516	1032	787	297	594	1188	1099	921
98	565	1130	983	689	101	202	404	808	339	678
99	79	158	316	632	1264	1251	1225	1173	1069	861

P = 1277

INDICES

	0	1	2	3	4	5	6	7	8	9
100	710	437	928	185	224	566	1003	755	1179	1152
101	370	604	650	278	106	890	1092	381	40	333
102	1256	646	616	452	10	539	860	70	620	180
103	1122	525	973	136	155	1127	680	696	1109	400
104	1021	901	1209	1057	456	1033	112	428	254	161
105	553	958	746	480	740	873	918	269	809	783
106	14	96	324	1081	1244	1267	850	530	1010	998
107	1104	1099	516	1233	867	347	543	687	1195	945
108	119	314	1048	925	367	37	857	152	1206	550
109	806	847	864	1045	803	832	825	87	835	978
110	292	886	521	424	1077	941	828	1224	74	1147
111	896	1228	936	1133	90	763	879	28	658	353
112	503	389	838	720	624	769	1070	78	582	205
113	981	141	415	704	1238	576	1217	1138	295	436
114	184	565	754	1151	603	277	889	380	332	645
115	451	538	69	179	524	135	1126	695	399	900
116	1056	1032	427	160	957	479	872	268	782	95
117	1080	1266	529	997	1098	1232	346	686	944	313
118	924	36	151	549	846	1044	831	86	977	885
119	423	940	1223	1146	1227	1132	762	27	352	388
120	719	768	77	204	140	703	575	1137	435	564
121	1150	276	379	644	537	178	134	694	899	1031
122	159	478	267	94	1265	996	1231	685	312	35
123	548	1043	85	884	939	1145	1131	26	387	767
124	203	702	1136	563	275	643	177	693	1030	477
125	93	995	684	34	1042	883	1144	25	766	701
126	562	642	692	476	994	33	882	24	700	641
127	475	32	23	640	31	639	638			

POWER RESIDUES

	0	1	2	3	4	5	6	7	8	9
100	445	890	503	1006	735	193	386	772	267	534
101	1068	859	441	882	487	974	671	65	130	260
102	520	1040	803	329	658	39	78	156	312	624
103	1248	1219	1161	1045	813	349	698	119	238	476
104	952	627	1254	1231	1185	1093	909	541	1082	887
105	497	994	711	145	290	580	1160	1043	809	341
106	682	87	174	348	696	115	230	460	920	563
107	1126	975	673	69	138	276	552	1104	931	585
108	1170	1063	849	421	842	407	814	351	702	127
109	254	508	1016	755	233	466	932	587	1174	1071
110	865	453	906	535	1070	863	449	898	519	1038
111	799	321	642	7	14	28	56	112	224	448
112	896	515	1030	783	289	578	1156	1035	793	309
113	618	1236	1195	1113	949	621	1242	1207	1137	997
114	717	157	314	628	1256	1235	1193	1109	941	605
115	1210	1143	1009	741	205	410	820	363	726	175
116	350	700	123	246	492	984	691	105	210	420
117	840	403	806	335	670	63	126	252	504	1008
118	739	201	402	804	331	662	47	94	188	376
119	752	227	454	908	539	1078	879	481	962	647
120	17	34	68	136	272	544	1088	899	521	1042
121	807	337	674	71	142	284	568	1136	995	713
122	149	298	596	1192	1107	937	597	1194	1111	945
123	613	1226	1175	1073	869	461	922	567	1134	991
124	705	133	266	532	1064	851	425	850	423	846
125	415	830	383	766	255	510	1020	763	249	498
126	996	715	153	306	612	1224	1171	1065	853	429
127	858	439	878	479	958	639				

P = 1279

INDICES

	0	1	2	3	4	5	6	7	8	9
0		0	46	1	92	910	47	712	138	2
1	956	57	93	79	758	911	184	188	48	1077
2	1002	713	103	430	139	542	125	3	804	491
3	957	949	230	58	234	344	94	1118	1123	80
4	1048	1106	759	378	149	912	476	314	185	146
5	588	189	171	1212	49	967	850	1078	537	974
6	1003	611	995	714	276	989	104	887	280	431
7	390	591	140	296	1164	543	1169	769	126	88
8	1094	4	1152	1240	805	1098	424	492	195	1217
9	958	791	522	950	360	709	231	608	192	59
10	634	155	235	924	217	345	1258	817	95	398
11	1013	1119	896	676	1124	62	583	81	1020	900
12	1049	114	657	1107	1041	174	760	963	322	379
13	1035	1271	150	511	933	913	326	1113	477	163
14	436	315	637	136	186	123	342	147	1210	993
15	589	1092	1215	190	815	581	172	931	134	1213
16	1140	1142	50	404	1198	968	8	940	851	158
17	1144	1079	470	207	538	1254	241	975	1263	52
18	1004	20	837	612	568	750	996	245	406	715
19	755	1103	277	706	654	990	238	1200	105	412
20	680	888	201	1203	281	738	970	432	263	1134
21	391	671	26	592	863	10	141	383	444	297
22	1059	267	1165	927	942	544	722	1193	1170	662
23	108	770	629	853	127	1224	1066	89	946	534
24	1095	893	160	5	703	1056	1153	1156	1087	1241
25	220	1146	806	487	1009	1099	368	415	425	552
26	1081	493	39	462	196	844	557	1218	979	472
27	959	259	372	792	1159	599	523	348	209	951
28	482	1128	361	694	683	710	182	540	232	376
29	169	609	388	86	193	606	1256	60	1039	509
30	635	1090	1138	156	1261	243	236	736	861	925
31	627	891	218	550	977	346	180	604	1259	548
32	1186	818	1188	1265	96	621	450	399	1244	1026
33	1014	820	54	1120	986	519	897	339	204	677
34	1190	1006	1125	858	516	63	253	306	584	1267
35	22	82	287	419	1021	223	31	901	98	839
36	1050	876	66	115	883	1206	658	623	614	1108
37	796	646	1042	500	291	175	452	570	761	1275
38	801	964	1149	395	323	401	752	380	700	256
39	1036	618	284	1272	1246	998	151	833	458	512
40	726	529	934	1028	247	914	1249	1175	327	809
41	784	1114	1016	408	478	872	309	164	1180	741
42	437	822	717	316	72	730	638	45	909	137
43	56	757	187	1001	429	124	490	229	343	1122
44	1105	148	313	587	1211	849	973	994	988	279
45	590	1163	768	1093	1239	423	1216	521	708	191
46	154	216	816	1012	675	582	899	656	173	321
47	1270	932	1112	435	135	341	992	1214	580	133
48	1141	1197	939	1143	206	240	51	836	749	405
49	1102	653	1199	679	1202	969	1133	25	9	443

POWER RESIDUES

	0	1	2	3	4	5	6	7	8	9
0	1	3	9	27	81	243	729	908	166	498
1	215	645	656	689	788	1085	697	812	1157	913
2	181	543	350	1050	592	497	212	636	629	608
3	545	356	1068	646	659	698	815	1166	940	262
4	786	1079	679	758	995	427	2	6	18	54
5	162	486	179	537	332	996	430	11	33	99
6	297	891	115	345	1035	547	362	1086	700	821
7	1184	994	424	1272	1258	1216	1090	712	857	13
8	39	117	351	1053	601	524	293	879	79	237
9	711	854	4	12	36	108	324	972	358	1074
10	664	713	860	22	66	198	594	503	230	690
11	791	1094	724	893	121	363	1089	709	848	1265
12	1237	1153	901	145	435	26	78	234	702	827
13	1202	1048	586	479	158	474	143	429	8	24
14	72	216	648	665	716	869	49	147	441	44
15	132	396	1188	1006	460	101	303	909	169	507
16	242	726	899	139	417	1251	1195	1027	523	290
17	870	52	156	468	125	375	1125	817	1172	958
18	316	948	286	858	16	48	144	432	17	51
19	153	459	98	294	882	88	264	792	1097	733
20	920	202	606	539	338	1014	484	173	519	278
21	834	1223	1111	775	1046	580	461	104	312	936
22	250	750	971	355	1065	637	632	617	572	437
23	32	96	288	864	34	102	306	918	196	588
24	485	176	528	305	915	187	561	404	1212	1078
25	676	749	968	346	1038	556	389	1167	943	271
26	813	1160	922	208	624	593	500	221	663	710
27	851	1274	1264	1234	1144	874	64	192	576	449
28	68	204	612	557	392	1176	970	352	1056	610
29	551	374	1122	808	1145	877	73	219	657	692
30	797	1112	778	1055	607	542	347	1041	565	416
31	1248	1186	1000	442	47	141	423	1269	1249	1189
32	1009	469	128	384	1152	898	136	408	1224	1114
33	784	1073	661	704	833	1220	1102	748	965	337
34	1011	475	146	438	35	105	315	945	277	831
35	1214	1084	694	803	1130	832	1217	1093	721	884
36	94	282	846	1259	1219	1099	739	938	256	768
37	1025	517	272	816	1169	949	289	867	43	129
38	387	1161	925	217	651	674	743	950	292	876
39	70	210	630	611	554	383	1149	889	109	327
40	981	385	1155	907	163	489	188	564	413	1239
41	1159	919	199	597	512	257	771	1034	544	353
42	1059	619	578	455	86	258	774	1043	571	434
43	23	69	207	621	584	473	140	420	1260	1222
44	1108	766	1019	499	218	654	683	770	1031	535
45	326	978	376	1128	826	1199	1039	559	398	1194
46	1024	514	263	789	1088	706	839	1238	1156	910
47	172	516	269	807	1142	868	46	138	414	1242
48	1168	946	280	840	1241	1165	937	253	759	998
49	436	29	87	261	783	1070	652	677	752	977

P = 1279

INDICES

	0	1	2	3	4	5	6	7	8	9
50	266	941	1192	107	852	1065	533	159	1055	1086
51	1145	1008	414	1080	461	556	471	371	598	208
52	1127	682	539	168	85	1255	508	1137	242	860
53	890	976	603	1185	1264	449	1025	53	518	203
54	1005	515	305	21	418	30	838	65	1205	613
55	645	290	569	800	394	751	255	283	997	457
56	528	246	1174	783	407	308	740	716	729	908
57	756	428	228	1104	586	972	278	767	422	707
58	215	674	655	1269	434	991	132	938	239	748
59	652	1201	24	265	106	532	1085	413	555	597
60	681	84	1136	889	1184	1024	202	304	29	1204
61	289	393	282	527	782	739	907	227	971	421
62	673	433	937	651	264	1084	596	1135	1023	28
63	392	781	226	672	650	595	27	225	594	593
64	1232	1233	864	666	1234	11	33	865	142	1031
65	667	384	496	1235	445	903	12	298	1072	34
66	1060	332	866	268	100	143	1166	921	1032	928
67	565	668	943	841	385	545	250	497	723	42
68	1236	1194	1052	446	1171	745	904	663	562	13
69	109	878	299	771	352	1073	630	16	35	854
70	68	1061	128	917	333	1225	465	867	1067	117
71	269	90	77	101	947	1046	144	535	885	1167
72	1096	358	922	894	112	1033	161	1208	929	6
73	1252	566	704	199	669	1057	660	944	1154	366
74	842	1157	692	386	1088	625	546	1242	337	251
75	221	881	498	1147	616	724	807	1178	43	488
76	847	1237	1010	1110	1195	1100	441	1053	369	506
77	447	416	798	1172	426	213	746	553	302	905
78	1082	648	664	494	330	563	40	560	14	463
79	1044	110	197	690	879	845	504	300	558	502
80	772	1219	575	353	980	774	1074	473	293	631
81	960	812	17	260	1221	36	373	177	855	793
82	830	69	1160	577	1062	600	454	129	524	1229
83	918	349	355	334	210	572	1226	952	787	466
84	483	982	868	1129	763	1068	362	826	118	695
85	776	270	684	1277	91	711	955	78	183	1076
86	102	541	803	948	233	1117	1047	377	475	145
87	170	966	536	610	275	886	389	295	1168	87
88	1151	1097	194	790	359	607	633	923	1257	397
89	895	61	1019	113	1040	962	1034	510	325	162
90	636	122	1209	1091	814	930	1139	403	7	157
91	469	1253	1262	19	567	244	754	705	237	411
92	200	737	262	670	862	382	1058	926	721	661
93	628	1223	945	892	702	1155	219	486	367	551
94	38	843	978	258	1158	347	481	693	181	375
95	387	605	1038	1089	1260	735	626	549	179	547
96	1187	620	1243	819	985	338	1189	857	252	1266
97	286	222	97	875	882	622	795	499	451	1274
98	1148	400	699	617	1245	832	725	1027	1248	808
99	1015	871	1179	821	71	44	55	1000	489	1121

POWER RESIDUES

	0	1	2	3	4	5	6	7	8	9
50	373	1119	799	1118	796	1109	769	1028	526	299
51	897	133	399	1197	1033	541	344	1032	538	335
52	1005	457	92	276	828	1205	1057	613	560	401
53	1203	1051	595	506	239	717	872	58	174	522
54	287	861	25	75	225	675	746	959	319	957
55	313	939	259	777	1052	598	515	266	798	1115
56	787	1082	688	785	1076	670	731	914	184	552
57	377	1131	835	1226	1120	802	1127	823	1190	1012
58	478	155	465	116	348	1044	574	443	50	150
59	450	71	213	639	638	635	626	599	518	275
60	825	1196	1030	532	317	951	295	885	97	291
61	873	61	183	549	368	1104	754	983	391	1173
62	961	325	975	367	1101	745	956	310	930	232
63	696	809	1148	886	100	300	900	142	426	1278
64	1276	1270	1252	1198	1036	550	371	1113	781	1064
65	634	623	590	491	194	582	467	122	366	1098
66	736	929	229	687	782	1067	643	650	671	734
67	923	211	633	620	581	464	113	339	1017	493
68	200	600	521	284	852	1277	1273	1261	1225	1117
69	793	1100	742	947	283	849	1268	1246	1180	982
70	388	1164	934	244	732	917	193	579	458	95
71	285	855	7	21	63	189	567	422	1266	1240
72	1162	928	226	678	755	986	400	1200	1042	568
73	425	1275	1267	1243	1171	955	307	921	205	615
74	566	419	1257	1213	1081	685	776	1049	589	488
75	185	555	386	1158	916	190	570	431	14	42
76	126	378	1134	844	1253	1201	1045	577	452	77
77	231	693	800	1121	805	1136	850	1271	1255	1207
78	1063	631	614	563	410	1230	1132	838	1235	1147
79	883	91	273	819	1178	976	370	1110	772	1037
80	553	380	1140	862	28	84	252	756	989	409
81	1227	1123	811	1154	904	154	462	107	321	963
82	331	993	421	1263	1231	1135	847	1262	1228	1126
83	820	1181	985	397	1191	1015	487	182	546	359
84	1077	673	740	941	265	795	1106	760	1001	445
85	56	168	504	233	699	818	1175	967	343	1029
86	529	308	924	214	642	647	662	707	842	1247
87	1183	991	415	1245	1177	973	361	1083	691	794
88	1103	751	974	364	1092	718	875	67	201	603
89	530	311	933	241	723	890	112	336	1008	466
90	119	357	1071	655	686	779	1058	616	569	428
91	5	15	45	135	405	1215	1087	703	830	1211
92	1075	667	722	887	103	309	927	223	669	728
93	905	157	471	134	402	1206	1060	622	587	482
94	167	501	224	672	737	932	238	714	863	31
95	93	279	837	1232	1138	856	10	30	90	270
96	810	1151	895	127	381	1143	871	55	165	495
97	206	618	575	446	59	177	531	314	942	268
98	804	1133	841	1244	1174	964	334	1002	448	65
99	195	585	476	149	447	62	186	558	395	1185

P = 1279

INDICES

	0	1	2	3	4	5	6	7	8	9
100	312	848	987	1162	1238	520	153	1011	898	320
101	1111	340	579	1196	205	835	1101	678	1132	442
102	1191	1064	1054	1007	460	370	1126	167	507	859
103	602	448	517	514	417	64	644	799	254	456
104	1173	307	728	427	585	766	214	1268	131	747
105	23	531	554	83	1183	303	288	526	906	420
106	936	1083	1022	780	649	224	1231	665	32	1030
107	495	902	1071	331	99	920	564	840	249	41
108	1051	744	561	877	351	15	67	916	464	116
109	76	1045	884	357	111	1207	1251	198	659	365
110	691	624	336	880	615	1177	846	1109	440	505
111	797	212	301	647	329	559	1043	689	503	501
112	574	773	292	811	1220	176	829	576	453	1228
113	354	571	786	981	762	825	775	1276	954	1075
114	802	1116	474	965	274	294	1150	789	632	396
115	1018	961	324	121	813	402	468	18	753	410
116	261	381	720	1222	701	485	37	257	480	374
117	1037	734	178	619	984	856	285	874	794	1273
118	698	831	1247	870	70	999	311	1161	152	319
119	578	834	1131	1063	459	166	601	513	643	455
120	727	765	130	530	1182	525	935	779	1230	1029
121	1070	919	248	743	350	915	75	356	1250	364
122	335	1176	439	211	328	688	573	810	828	1227
123	785	824	953	1115	273	788	1017	120	467	409
124	719	484	479	733	983	873	697	869	310	318
125	1130	165	642	764	1181	778	1069	742	74	363
126	438	687	827	823	272	119	718	732	696	317
127	641	777	73	686	271	731	640	685	639	

POWER RESIDUES

	0	1	2	3	4	5	6	7	8	9
100	997	433	20	60	180	540	341	1023	511	254
101	762	1007	463	110	330	990	412	1236	1150	892
102	118	354	1062	628	605	536	329	987	403	1209
103	1069	649	668	725	896	130	390	1170	952	298
104	894	124	372	1116	790	1091	715	866	40	120
105	360	1080	682	767	1022	508	245	735	926	220
106	660	701	824	1193	1021	505	236	708	845	1256
107	1210	1072	658	695	806	1139	859	19	57	171
108	513	260	780	1061	625	596	509	248	744	953
109	301	903	151	453	80	240	720	881	85	255
110	765	1016	490	191	573	440	41	123	369	1107
111	763	1010	472	137	411	1233	1141	865	37	111
112	333	999	439	38	114	342	1026	520	281	843
113	1250	1192	1018	496	209	627	602	527	302	906
114	160	480	161	483	170	510	251	753	980	382
115	1146	880	82	246	738	935	247	741	944	274
116	822	1187	1003	451	74	222	666	719	878	76
117	228	684	773	1040	562	407	1221	1105	757	992
118	418	1254	1204	1054	604	533	320	960	322	966
119	340	1020	502	227	681	764	1013	481	164	492
120	197	591	494	203	609	548	365	1095	727	902
121	148	444	53	159	477	152	456	89	267	801
122	1124	814	1163	931	235	705	836	1229	1129	829
123	1208	1066	640	641	644	653	680	761	1004	454
124	83	249	747	962	328	984	394	1182	988	406
125	1218	1096	730	911	175	525	296	888	106	318
126	954	304	912	178	534	323	969	349	1047	583
127	470	131	393	1179	979	379	1137	853		

P = 1283

INDICES

	0	1	2	3	4	5	6	7	8	9
0		0	1	1214	2	565	1215	1027	3	1146
1	566	406	1216	1014	1028	497	4	864	1147	280
2	567	959	407	817	1217	1130	1015	1078	1029	1260
3	498	602	5	338	865	310	1148	906	281	946
4	568	1255	960	529	408	429	818	591	1218	772
5	1131	796	1016	1112	1079	971	1030	212	1261	90
6	499	965	603	891	6	297	339	927	866	749
7	311	59	1149	737	907	1062	282	151	947	917
8	569	1010	1256	425	961	147	530	1192	409	519
9	430	759	819	534	592	845	1219	34	773	270
10	1132	766	797	16	1017	242	1113	66	1080	1196
11	972	838	1031	803	213	100	1262	878	91	609
12	500	812	966	1187	604	413	892	1089	7	461
13	298	512	340	25	928	361	867	626	750	782
14	312	523	60	138	1150	543	738	704	908	115
15	1063	418	283	728	152	1167	948	434	918	1044
16	570	562	1011	956	1257	903	426	1109	962	746
17	148	144	531	763	1193	875	410	22	520	112
18	431	900	760	897	820	189	535	1270	593	823
19	846	52	1220	1121	35	229	774	192	271	1227
20	1133	859	767	1005	798	538	17	681	1018	686
21	243	290	1114	1273	67	1094	1081	347	1197	669
22	973	596	839	1038	1032	994	804	984	214	826
23	101	83	1263	167	879	1156	92	849	610	485
24	501	1023	813	942	967	55	1188	12	605	357
25	414	1105	893	1223	1090	79	8	718	462	651
26	299	1124	513	722	341	395	26	451	929	38
27	362	584	868	691	627	254	751	232	783	466
28	313	401	524	1057	61	777	139	1000	1151	446
29	544	1248	739	195	705	655	909	202	116	549
30	1064	274	419	698	284	248	729	328	153	1230
31	1168	303	949	1241	435	174	919	1136	1045	384
32	571	1280	563	1144	1012	862	957	1128	1258	336
33	904	1253	427	770	1110	210	963	295	747	735
34	149	1008	145	517	532	32	764	240	1194	801
35	876	810	411	459	23	624	521	541	113	726
36	432	560	901	744	761	20	898	187	821	1119
37	190	857	536	684	1271	345	594	992	824	165
38	847	1021	53	355	1221	716	1122	393	36	689
39	230	399	775	444	193	200	272	246	1228	1239
40	1134	1278	860	334	768	293	1006	30	799	457
41	539	558	18	1117	682	990	1019	714	687	442
42	244	1276	291	455	1115	712	1274	710	68	70
43	1095	634	1082	72	348	475	1198	1097	670	933
44	974	636	597	886	840	1084	1039	47	1033	74
45	995	379	805	350	985	42	215	477	827	660
46	102	1200	84	1181	1264	1099	168	159	880	672
47	1157	366	93	935	850	128	611	976	486	220
48	502	638	1024	494	814	599	943	588	968	888
49	56	914	1189	842	13	835	606	1086	358	135

POWER RESIDUES

	0	1	2	3	4	5	6	7	8	9
0	1	2	4	8	16	32	64	128	256	512
1	1024	765	247	494	988	693	103	206	412	824
2	365	730	177	354	708	133	266	532	1064	845
3	407	814	345	690	97	194	388	776	269	538
4	1076	869	455	910	537	1074	865	447	894	505
5	1010	737	191	382	764	245	490	980	677	71
6	142	284	568	1136	989	695	107	214	428	856
7	429	858	433	866	449	898	513	1026	769	255
8	510	1020	757	231	462	924	565	1130	977	671
9	59	118	236	472	944	605	1210	1137	991	699
10	115	230	460	920	557	1114	945	607	1214	1145
11	1007	731	179	358	716	149	298	596	1192	1101
12	919	555	1110	937	591	1182	1081	879	475	950
13	617	1234	1185	1087	891	499	998	713	143	286
14	572	1144	1005	727	171	342	684	85	170	340
15	680	77	154	308	616	1232	1181	1079	875	467
16	934	585	1170	1057	831	379	758	233	466	932
17	581	1162	1041	799	315	630	1260	1237	1191	1099
18	915	547	1094	905	527	1054	825	367	734	185
19	370	740	197	394	788	293	586	1172	1061	839
20	395	790	297	594	1188	1093	903	523	1046	809
21	335	670	57	114	228	456	912	541	1082	881
22	479	958	633	1266	1249	1215	1147	1011	739	195
23	390	780	277	554	1108	933	583	1166	1049	815
24	347	694	105	210	420	840	397	794	305	610
25	1220	1157	1031	779	275	550	1100	917	551	1102
26	921	559	1118	953	623	1246	1209	1135	987	691
27	99	198	396	792	301	602	1204	1125	967	651
28	19	38	76	152	304	608	1216	1149	1015	747
29	211	422	844	405	810	337	674	65	130	260
30	520	1040	797	311	622	1244	1205	1127	971	659
31	35	70	140	280	560	1120	957	631	1262	1241
32	1199	1115	947	611	1222	1161	1039	795	307	614
33	1228	1173	1063	843	403	806	329	658	33	66
34	132	264	528	1056	829	375	750	217	434	868
35	453	906	529	1058	833	383	766	249	498	996
36	709	135	270	540	1080	877	471	942	601	1202
37	1121	959	635	1270	1257	1231	1179	1075	867	451
38	902	521	1042	801	319	638	1276	1269	1255	1227
39	1171	1059	835	387	774	265	530	1060	837	391
40	782	281	562	1124	965	647	11	22	44	88
41	176	352	704	125	250	500	1000	717	151	302
42	604	1208	1133	983	683	83	166	332	664	45
43	90	180	360	720	157	314	628	1256	1229	1175
44	1067	851	419	838	393	786	289	578	1156	1029
45	775	267	534	1068	853	423	846	409	818	353
46	706	129	258	516	1032	781	279	558	1116	949
47	615	1230	1177	1071	859	435	870	457	914	545
48	1090	897	511	1022	761	239	478	956	629	1258
49	1233	1183	1083	883	483	966	649	15	30	60

P = 1283

INDICES

	0	1	2	3	4	5	6	7	8	9
50	415	1041	1106	872	894	49	1224	678	1091	1035
51	80	482	9	76	719	581	463	997	652	695
52	300	381	1125	207	514	807	723	184	342	352
53	396	1236	27	987	452	631	930	44	39	1178
54	363	217	585	832	869	479	692	181	628	829
55	255	258	752	662	233	121	784	104	467	261
56	314	1202	402	1074	525	86	1058	755	62	1183
57	778	1163	140	1266	1001	665	1152	1101	447	1053
58	545	170	1249	236	740	161	196	554	706	882
59	656	124	910	674	203	1174	117	1159	550	787
60	1065	368	275	791	420	95	699	107	285	937
61	249	323	730	852	329	470	154	130	1231	1069
62	1169	613	304	264	950	978	1242	618	436	488
63	175	317	920	222	1137	372	1046	504	385	1205
64	572	640	1281	1213	564	1026	1145	405	1013	496
65	863	279	958	816	1129	1077	1259	601	337	309
66	905	945	1254	528	428	590	771	795	1111	970
67	211	89	964	890	296	926	748	58	736	1061
68	150	916	1009	424	146	1191	518	758	533	844
69	33	269	765	15	241	65	1195	837	802	99
70	877	608	811	1186	412	1088	460	511	24	360
71	625	781	522	137	542	703	114	417	727	1166
72	433	1043	561	955	902	1108	745	143	762	874
73	21	111	899	896	188	1269	822	51	1120	228
74	191	1226	858	1004	537	680	685	289	1272	1093
75	346	668	595	1037	993	983	825	82	166	1155
76	848	484	1022	941	54	11	356	1104	1222	78
77	717	650	1123	721	394	450	37	583	690	253
78	231	465	400	1056	776	999	445	1247	194	654
79	201	548	273	697	247	327	1229	302	1240	173
80	1135	383	1279	1143	861	1127	335	1252	769	209
81	294	734	1007	516	31	239	800	809	458	623
82	540	725	559	743	19	186	1118	856	683	344
83	991	164	1020	354	715	392	688	398	443	199
84	245	1238	1277	333	292	29	456	557	1116	989
85	713	441	1275	454	711	709	69	633	71	474
86	1096	932	635	885	1083	46	73	378	349	41
87	476	659	1199	1180	1098	158	671	365	934	127
88	975	219	637	493	598	587	887	913	841	834
89	1085	134	1040	871	48	677	1034	481	75	580
90	996	694	380	206	806	183	351	1235	986	630
91	43	1177	216	831	478	180	828	257	661	120
92	103	260	1201	1073	85	754	1182	1162	1265	664
93	1100	1052	169	235	160	553	881	123	673	1173
94	1158	786	367	790	94	106	936	322	851	469
95	129	1068	612	263	977	617	487	316	221	371
96	503	1204	639	1212	1025	404	495	278	815	1076
97	600	308	944	527	589	794	969	88	889	925
98	57	1060	915	423	1190	757	843	268	14	64
99	836	98	607	1185	1087	510	359	780	136	702

POWER RESIDUES

	0	1	2	3	4	5	6	7	8	9
50	120	240	480	960	637	1274	1265	1247	1211	1139
51	995	707	131	262	524	1048	813	343	686	89
52	178	356	712	141	282	564	1128	973	663	43
53	86	172	344	688	93	186	372	744	205	410
54	820	357	714	145	290	580	1160	1037	791	299
55	598	1196	1109	935	587	1174	1065	847	411	822
56	361	722	161	322	644	5	10	20	40	80
57	160	320	640	1280	1277	1271	1259	1235	1187	1091
58	899	515	1030	777	271	542	1084	885	487	974
59	665	47	94	188	376	752	221	442	884	485
60	970	657	31	62	124	248	496	992	701	119
61	238	476	952	621	1242	1201	1119	955	627	1254
62	1225	1167	1051	819	355	710	137	274	548	1096
63	909	535	1070	857	431	862	441	882	481	962
64	641	1282	1281	1279	1275	1267	1251	1219	1155	1027
65	771	259	518	1036	789	295	590	1180	1077	871
66	459	918	553	1106	929	575	1150	1017	751	219
67	438	876	469	938	593	1186	1089	895	507	1014
68	745	207	414	828	373	746	209	418	836	389
69	778	273	546	1092	901	519	1038	793	303	606
70	1212	1141	999	715	147	294	588	1176	1069	855
71	427	854	425	850	417	834	385	770	257	514
72	1028	773	263	526	1052	821	359	718	153	306
73	612	1224	1165	1047	811	339	678	73	146	292
74	584	1168	1053	823	363	726	169	338	676	69
75	138	276	552	1104	925	567	1134	985	687	91
76	182	364	728	173	346	692	101	202	404	808
77	333	666	49	98	196	392	784	285	570	1140
78	997	711	139	278	556	1112	941	599	1198	1113
79	943	603	1206	1129	975	667	51	102	204	408
80	816	349	698	113	226	452	904	525	1050	817
81	351	702	121	242	484	968	653	23	46	92
82	184	368	736	189	378	756	229	458	916	549
83	1098	913	543	1086	889	495	990	697	111	222
84	444	888	493	986	689	95	190	380	760	237
85	474	948	613	1226	1169	1055	827	371	742	201
86	402	804	325	650	17	34	68	136	272	544
87	1088	893	503	1006	729	175	350	700	117	234
88	468	936	589	1178	1073	863	443	886	489	978
89	673	63	126	252	504	1008	733	183	366	732
90	181	362	724	165	330	660	37	74	148	296
91	592	1184	1085	887	491	982	681	79	158	316
92	632	1264	1245	1207	1131	979	675	67	134	268
93	536	1072	861	439	878	473	946	609	1218	1153
94	1023	763	243	486	972	661	39	78	156	312
95	624	1248	1213	1143	1003	723	163	326	652	21
96	42	84	168	336	672	61	122	244	488	976
97	669	55	110	220	440	880	477	954	625	1250
98	1217	1151	1019	755	227	454	908	533	1066	849
99	415	830	377	754	225	450	900	517	1034	785

P = 1283

INDICES

	0	1	2	3	4	5	6	7	8	9
100	416	1165	1042	954	1107	142	873	110	895	1268
101	50	227	1225	1003	679	288	1092	667	1036	982
102	81	1154	483	940	10	1103	77	649	720	449
103	582	252	464	1055	998	1246	653	547	696	326
104	301	172	382	1142	1126	1251	208	733	515	238
105	808	622	724	742	185	855	343	163	353	391
106	397	198	1237	332	28	556	988	440	453	708
107	632	473	931	884	45	377	40	658	1179	157
108	364	126	218	492	586	912	833	133	870	676
109	480	579	693	205	182	1234	629	1176	830	179
110	256	119	259	1072	753	1161	663	1051	234	552
111	122	1172	785	789	105	321	468	1067	262	616
112	315	370	1203	1211	403	277	1075	307	526	793
113	87	924	1059	422	756	267	63	97	1184	509
114	779	701	1164	953	141	109	1267	226	1002	287
115	666	981	1153	939	1102	648	448	251	1054	1245
116	546	325	171	1141	1250	732	237	621	741	854
117	162	390	197	331	555	439	707	472	883	376
118	657	156	125	491	911	132	675	578	204	1233
119	1175	178	118	1071	1160	1050	551	1171	788	320
120	1066	615	369	1210	276	306	792	923	421	266
121	96	508	700	952	108	225	286	980	938	647
122	250	1244	324	1140	731	620	853	389	330	438
123	471	375	155	490	131	577	1232	177	1070	1049
124	1170	319	614	1209	305	922	265	507	951	224
125	979	646	1243	1139	619	388	437	374	489	576
126	176	1048	318	1208	921	506	223	645	1138	387
127	373	575	1047	1207	505	644	386	574	1206	643
128	573	642	641							

POWER RESIDUES

	0	1	2	3	4	5	6	7	8	9
100	287	574	1148	1013	743	203	406	812	341	682
101	81	162	324	648	13	26	52	104	208	416
102	832	381	762	241	482	964	645	7	14	28
103	56	112	224	448	896	509	1018	753	223	446
104	892	501	1002	721	159	318	636	1272	1261	1239
105	1195	1107	931	579	1158	1033	783	283	566	1132
106	981	679	75	150	300	600	1200	1117	951	619
107	1238	1193	1103	923	563	1126	969	655	27	54
108	108	216	432	864	445	890	497	994	705	127
109	254	508	1016	749	215	430	860	437	874	465
110	930	577	1154	1025	767	251	502	1004	725	167
111	334	668	53	106	212	424	848	413	826	369
112	738	193	386	772	261	522	1044	805	327	654
113	25	50	100	200	400	800	317	634	1268	1253
114	1223	1163	1043	803	323	646	9	18	36	72
115	144	288	576	1152	1021	759	235	470	940	597
116	1194	1105	927	571	1142	1001	719	155	310	620
117	1240	1197	1111	939	595	1190	1097	911	539	1078
118	873	463	926	569	1138	993	703	123	246	492
119	984	685	87	174	348	696	109	218	436	872
120	461	922	561	1122	961	639	1278	1273	1263	1243
121	1203	1123	963	643	3	6	12	24	48	96
122	192	384	768	253	506	1012	741	199	398	796
123	309	618	1236	1189	1095	907	531	1062	841	399
124	798	313	626	1252	1221	1159	1035	787	291	582
125	1164	1045	807	331	662	41	82	164	328	656
126	29	58	116	232	464	928	573	1146	1009	735
127	187	374	748	213	426	852	421	842	401	802
128	321	642								

P = 1289

INDICES

	0	1	2	3	4	5	6	7	8	9
0		0	1016	273	744	790	1	4	472	546
1	518	431	1017	683	1020	1063	200	1099	274	1006
2	246	277	159	168	745	292	411	819	748	152
3	791	678	1216	704	827	794	2	495	734	956
4	1262	240	5	497	1175	48	1184	71	473	8
5	20	84	139	998	547	1221	476	1279	1168	387
6	519	839	406	550	944	185	432	1126	555	441
7	522	801	1018	18	223	565	462	435	684	736
8	990	1092	1256	756	1021	601	225	425	903	121
9	1064	687	912	951	1087	508	201	709	1024	977
10	1036	62	1100	625	1155	1067	726	417	275	1277
11	949	768	204	109	1007	958	896	1229	115	1103
12	247	862	567	513	134	1082	278	1132	672	770
13	1201	1047	160	1010	854	321	283	574	169	832
14	250	344	529	1114	746	942	1034	281	1239	881
15	293	1264	190	357	163	180	412	876	464	1271
16	718	172	820	591	984	206	484	887	749	78
17	329	264	1241	36	153	296	631	660	1137	642
18	792	799	415	1112	640	1285	679	242	815	823
19	236	469	1217	402	437	458	752	1060	705	1151
20	764	111	1078	156	828	1030	353	714	883	149
21	795	811	454	1074	145	1287	3	682	1005	291
22	677	494	496	7	1220	838	1125	17	735	600
23	686	708	624	1276	957	861	1131	1009	831	941
24	1263	875	590	77	295	798	241	401	1150	1029
25	810	681	6	599	860	874	400	598	498	499
26	929	698	775	909	1176	500	738	394	582	974
27	49	930	11	960	302	723	1185	699	560	1224
28	1266	106	72	776	257	781	842	244	474	910
29	670	982	762	1129	9	1177	967	1250	609	851
30	21	501	992	335	1206	341	85	739	1179	898
31	1196	1236	140	395	604	52	192	177	999	583
32	446	690	1188	817	548	975	319	262	712	75
33	1222	50	212	1041	615	628	477	931	1094	382
34	57	1109	1280	12	969	1231	1052	233	1169	961
35	24	214	359	1057	388	303	865	88	370	825
36	520	724	527	1135	143	808	840	1186	368	786
37	1013	1002	407	700	1258	67	543	835	551	561
38	1252	117	197	621	945	1225	130	1043	165	938
39	186	1267	480	32	788	238	433	107	879	1283
40	492	596	1127	73	806	594	1172	926	556	777
41	758	847	81	391	442	258	611	1105	1165	299
42	523	782	539	617	182	103	802	843	1161	99
43	1015	471	1019	245	410	1215	733	1174	19	475
44	405	554	222	989	224	911	1023	1154	948	895
45	566	671	853	249	1033	189	463	983	328	630
46	414	814	436	763	352	453	1004	1219	685	1130
47	589	1149	859	928	737	10	559	256	669	966
48	991	1178	603	445	318	211	1093	968	23	864
49	526	367	1257	1251	129	479	878	805	757	610

POWER RESIDUES

	0	1	2	3	4	5	6	7	8	9
0	1	6	36	216	7	42	252	223	49	294
1	475	272	343	769	747	615	1112	227	73	438
2	50	300	511	488	350	811	999	838	1161	521
3	548	710	393	1069	1258	1103	173	1038	1072	1276
4	1211	821	1059	1198	743	591	968	652	45	270
5	331	697	315	601	1028	1012	916	340	751	639
6	1256	1091	101	606	1058	1192	707	375	961	610
7	1082	47	282	403	1129	329	685	243	169	1014
8	928	412	1183	653	51	306	547	704	357	853
9	1251	1061	1210	815	1023	982	736	549	716	429
10	1285	1265	1145	425	1261	1121	281	397	1093	113
11	678	201	1206	791	879	118	708	381	997	826
12	1089	89	534	626	1178	623	1160	515	512	494
13	386	1027	1006	880	124	744	597	1004	868	52
14	312	583	920	364	895	214	1284	1259	1109	209
15	1254	1079	29	174	1044	1108	203	1218	863	22
16	132	792	885	154	924	388	1039	1078	23	138
17	828	1101	161	966	640	1262	1127	317	613	1100
18	155	930	424	1255	1085	65	390	1051	1150	455
19	152	912	316	607	1064	1228	923	382	1003	862
20	16	96	576	878	112	672	165	990	784	837
21	1155	485	332	703	351	817	1035	1054	1168	563
22	800	933	442	74	444	86	516	518	530	602
23	1034	1048	1132	347	793	891	190	1140	395	1081
24	41	246	187	1122	287	433	20	120	720	453
25	140	840	1173	593	980	724	477	284	415	1201
26	761	699	327	673	171	1026	1000	844	1197	737
27	555	752	645	3	18	108	648	21	126	756
28	669	147	882	136	816	1029	1018	952	556	758
29	681	219	25	150	900	244	175	1050	1144	419
30	1225	905	274	355	841	1179	629	1196	731	519
31	536	638	1250	1055	1174	599	1016	940	484	326
32	667	135	810	993	802	945	514	506	458	170
33	1020	964	628	1190	695	303	529	596	998	832
34	1125	305	541	668	141	846	1209	809	987	766
35	729	507	464	206	1236	971	670	153	918	352
36	823	1071	1270	1175	605	1052	1156	491	368	919
37	358	859	1287	1277	1217	857	1275	1205	785	843
38	1191	701	339	745	603	1040	1084	59	354	835
39	1143	413	1189	689	267	313	589	956	580	902
40	256	247	193	1158	503	440	62	372	943	502
41	434	26	156	936	460	182	1092	107	642	1274
42	1199	749	627	1184	659	87	522	554	746	609
43	1076	11	66	396	1087	77	462	194	1164	539
44	656	69	414	1195	725	483	320	631	1208	803
45	951	550	722	465	212	1272	1187	677	195	1170
46	575	872	76	456	158	948	532	614	1106	191
47	1146	431	8	48	288	439	56	336	727	495
48	392	1063	1222	887	166	996	820	1053	1162	527
49	584	926	400	1111	221	37	222	43	258	259

P = 1289

INDICES

	0	1	2	3	4	5	6	7	8	9
50	538	1160	409	404	1022	852	327	351	588	558
51	602	22	128	537	326	127	226	502	227	309
52	657	29	426	993	503	569	637	489	904	336
53	228	933	466	923	122	1207	310	915	702	439
54	1065	342	658	1072	1027	779	688	86	30	97
55	451	1158	913	740	427	270	288	1212	952	1180
56	994	515	1122	219	1088	899	504	1096	1273	892
57	509	1197	570	742	1260	460	202	1237	638	675
58	398	760	710	141	490	731	857	586	1025	396
59	905	45	695	253	978	605	337	136	579	315
60	1037	53	229	384	720	364	63	193	934	429
61	69	754	1101	178	467	15	907	849	626	1000
62	924	987	964	125	1156	584	123	422	332	306
63	1068	447	1208	1084	1193	634	727	691	311	59
64	174	920	418	1189	916	272	545	1062	276	818
65	703	955	47	83	1278	549	440	564	1091	424
66	950	976	1066	767	1228	512	769	320	343	280
67	356	1270	205	263	659	1111	822	457	110	713
68	1073	290	837	707	1008	76	1028	873	697	393
69	959	1223	780	981	1249	334	897	51	689	261
70	1040	381	1230	213	87	1134	785	66	116	1042
71	31	1282	593	846	1104	616	98	1214	553	1153
72	248	629	452	1148	255	444	863	478	1159	350
73	536	308	568	932	914	1071	96	269	514	1095
74	741	674	730	44	135	383	428	14	986	421
75	1083	58	271	954	563	766	279	1110	289	872
76	980	260	1133	1281	1213	1147	349	1070	673	13
77	953	871	1146	870	771	970	1181	772	666	1246
78	1202	1232	995	971	208	378	1048	1053	516	1182
79	1254	113	161	234	1123	773	607	613	1011	1170
80	220	667	324	449	855	962	1089	1247	534	347
81	322	25	900	1203	654	93	284	215	505	1233
82	486	41	575	360	1097	996	119	1080	170	1058
83	1274	972	339	1107	833	389	893	209	27	1210
84	251	304	510	379	267	868	345	866	1198	1049
85	1119	663	530	89	571	1054	889	375	1115	371
86	743	517	199	158	747	826	1261	1183	138	1167
87	943	521	461	1255	902	1086	1035	725	203	114
88	133	1200	282	528	1238	162	717	483	1240	1136
89	639	235	751	1077	882	144	676	1124	623	830
90	294	809	399	774	581	301	1265	841	761	608
91	1205	1195	191	1187	711	614	56	1051	358	369
92	142	1012	542	196	164	787	491	1171	80	1164
93	181	1014	732	221	947	1032	413	1003	858	668
94	317	525	877	408	587	325	656	636	465	701
95	1026	450	287	1121	1272	1259	397	856	694	578
96	719	68	906	963	331	1192	173	544	46	1090
97	1227	355	821	836	696	1248	1039	784	592	552
98	254	535	95	729	985	562	979	348	1145	665
99	207	1253	606	323	533	653	485	118	338	26

POWER RESIDUES

	0	1	2	3	4	5	6	7	8	9
50	265	301	517	524	566	818	1041	1090	95	570
51	842	1185	665	123	738	561	788	861	10	60
52	360	871	70	420	1231	941	490	362	883	142
53	852	1245	1025	994	808	981	730	513	500	422
54	1243	1013	922	376	967	646	9	54	324	655
55	63	378	979	718	441	68	408	1159	509	476
56	278	379	985	754	657	75	450	122	732	525
57	572	854	1257	1097	137	822	1065	1234	959	598
58	1010	904	268	319	625	1172	587	944	508	470
59	242	163	978	712	405	1141	401	1117	257	253
60	229	85	510	482	314	595	992	796	909	298
61	499	416	1207	797	915	334	715	423	1249	1049
62	1138	383	1009	898	232	103	618	1130	335	721
63	459	176	1056	1180	635	1232	947	526	578	890
64	184	1104	179	1074	1288	1283	1253	1073	1282	1247
65	1037	1066	1240	995	814	1017	946	520	542	674
66	177	1062	1216	851	1239	989	778	801	939	478
67	290	451	128	768	741	579	896	220	31	186
68	1116	251	217	13	78	468	230	91	546	698
69	321	637	1244	1019	958	592	974	688	261	277
70	373	949	538	650	33	198	1188	683	231	97
71	582	914	328	679	207	1242	1007	886	160	960
72	604	1046	1120	275	361	877	106	636	1238	983
73	742	585	932	436	38	228	79	474	266	307
74	553	740	573	860	4	24	144	864	28	168
75	1008	892	196	1176	611	1088	83	498	410	1171
76	581	908	292	463	200	1200	755	663	111	666
77	129	774	777	795	903	262	283	409	1165	545
78	692	285	421	1237	977	706	369	925	394	1075
79	5	30	180	1080	35	210	1260	1115	245	181
80	1086	71	426	1267	1157	497	404	1135	365	901
81	250	211	1266	1151	461	188	1128	323	649	27
82	162	972	676	189	1134	359	865	34	204	1224
83	899	238	139	834	1137	377	973	682	225	61
84	366	907	286	427	1273	1193	713	411	1177	617
85	1124	299	505	452	134	804	957	586	938	472
86	254	235	121	726	489	356	847	1215	845	1203
87	773	771	759	687	255	241	157	942	496	398
88	1099	149	894	208	1248	1043	1102	167	1002	856
89	1269	1169	569	836	1149	449	116	696	309	565
90	812	1005	874	88	528	590	962	616	1118	263
91	289	445	92	552	734	537	644	1286	1271	1181
92	641	1268	1163	533	620	1142	407	1153	473	260
93	271	337	733	531	608	1070	1264	1139	389	1045
94	1114	239	145	870	64	384	1015	934	448	110
95	660	93	558	770	753	651	39	234	115	690
96	273	349	805	963	622	1154	479	296	487	344
97	775	783	831	1119	269	325	661	99	594	986
98	760	693	291	457	164	984	748	621	1148	443
99	80	480	302	523	560	782	825	1083	53	318

P = 1289

INDICES

	0	1	2	3	4	5	6	7	8	9
100	266	1118	888	198	137	901	132	716	750	622
101	580	1204	55	541	79	946	316	655	286	693
102	330	1226	1038	94	1144	532	265	131	54	285
103	1143	1142	1242	1044	230	216	1243	650	37	166
104	385	506	1045	885	154	939	721	1234	231	619
105	297	187	365	487	217	313	632	1268	64	42
106	1244	91	661	481	194	576	651	1140	1138	33
107	935	361	38	647	643	789	430	1098	167	151
108	793	239	70	997	386	184	800	434	755	120
109	507	61	416	108	1102	1081	1046	573	1113	880
110	179	171	886	35	641	1284	468	1059	155	148
111	1286	493	16	1275	940	797	680	597	908	973
112	722	105	243	1128	850	340	1235	176	816	74
113	627	1108	232	1056	824	807	1001	834	620	937
114	237	595	925	390	298	102	470	1173	988	894
115	188	813	1218	927	965	210	366	804	403	557
116	126	28	488	922	438	778	1157	1211	218	891
117	459	759	585	252	314	363	753	848	124	305
118	633	919	1061	82	423	511	1269	456	706	392
119	333	380	65	845	1152	443	307	268	43	420
120	765	259	1069	869	1245	377	112	612	448	346
121	92	40	1079	1106	1209	867	662	374	157	1166
122	1085	1199	482	1076	829	300	1194	1050	195	1163
123	1031	524	635	1120	577	1191	354	783	728	664
124	652	1117	715	540	692	531	1141	649	884	618
125	312	90	1139	646	150	183	60	572	34	147
126	796	104	175	1055	936	101	812	803	921	890
127	362	918	455	844	419	376	39	373	1075	1162
128	1190	1116	648	645	146	100	917	372	644	

POWER RESIDUES

	0	1	2	3	4	5	6	7	8	9
100	619	1136	371	937	466	218	19	114	684	237
101	133	798	921	370	931	430	2	12	72	432
102	14	84	504	446	98	588	950	544	686	249
103	205	1230	935	454	146	876	100	600	1022	976
104	700	333	709	387	1033	1042	1096	131	786	849
105	1227	917	346	787	855	1263	1133	353	829	1107
106	197	1182	647	15	90	540	662	105	630	1202
107	767	735	543	680	213	1278	1223	893	202	1212
108	827	1095	125	750	633	1220	875	94	564	806
109	969	658	81	486	338	739	567	824	1077	17
110	102	612	1094	119	714	417	1213	833	1131	341
111	757	675	183	1098	143	858	1281	1241	1001	850
112	1233	953	562	794	897	226	67	402	1123	293
113	469	236	127	762	705	363	889	178	1068	1252
114	1067	1246	1031	1030	1024	988	772	765	723	471
115	248	199	1194	719	447	104	624	1166	551	728
116	501	428	1279	1229	929	418	1219	869	58	348
117	799	927	406	1147	437	44	264	295	481	308
118	559	776	789	867	46	276	367	913	322	643
119	1280	1235	965	634	1226	911	310	571	848	1221
120	881	130	780	813	1011	910	304	535	632	1214
121	839	1167	557	764	717	435	32	192	1152	467
122	224	55	330	691	279	385	1021	970	664	117
123	702	345	781	819	1047	1126	311	577	884	148
124	888	172	1032	1036	1060	1204	779	807	975	694
125	297	493	380	991	790	873	82	492	374	955
126	574	866	40	240	151	906	280	391	1057	1186
127	671	159	954	568	830	1113	233	109	654	57
128	342	763	711	399	1105	185	1110	215		

P = 1291

INDICES

	0	1	2	3	4	5	6	7	8	9
0		0	1	77	2	312	78	532	3	154
1	313	965	79	818	533	389	4	1238	155	50
2	314	609	966	187	80	624	819	231	534	67
3	990	355	5	1042	1239	844	156	448	51	895
4	315	604	610	255	967	466	188	90	81	1064
5	625	25	820	615	232	1277	535	127	68	856
6	391	349	356	686	6	1130	1043	750	1240	264
7	845	18	157	32	449	701	52	207	896	872
8	316	308	605	444	611	260	256	144	968	578
9	467	60	189	432	91	362	82	217	1065	1119
10	626	148	26	553	821	921	616	1098	233	1159
11	1278	525	536	1051	128	499	69	972	857	480
12	392	640	350	681	357	936	687	941	7	332
13	1131	1027	1044	582	751	543	1241	559	265	806
14	846	167	19	493	158	379	33	1141	450	471
15	702	1086	53	102	208	667	897	196	873	692
16	317	719	309	815	606	64	445	463	612	346
17	261	204	257	429	145	1156	969	933	579	164
18	468	193	61	426	190	760	433	913	92	763
19	363	946	83	1149	218	1207	1066	436	1120	784
20	627	827	149	599	27	916	554	341	822	1015
21	922	1191	617	95	1099	567	234	887	1160	109
22	1279	766	526	12	537	778	1052	1230	129	366
23	500	284	70	1020	973	402	858	949	481	415
24	393	589	641	385	351	86	682	868	358	521
25	937	489	688	1152	942	337	8	411	333	980
26	1132	221	1028	1058	1045	927	583	655	752	1210
27	544	984	1242	137	560	299	266	1069	807	509
28	847	1106	168	45	20	439	494	1136	159	1186
29	380	294	34	1123	1142	1168	451	1196	472	1005
30	703	787	1087	225	54	661	103	39	209	630
31	668	733	898	248	197	998	874	830	693	1032
32	318	1175	720	1288	310	152	816	1236	607	622
33	65	1040	446	602	464	1062	613	125	347	1128
34	262	30	205	306	258	576	430	215	146	919
35	1157	1049	970	638	934	330	580	557	165	377
36	469	100	194	717	62	344	427	931	191	758
37	761	1147	434	825	914	1013	93	885	764	776
38	364	1018	947	587	84	519	1150	409	219	925
39	1208	135	1067	1104	437	1184	1121	1194	785	659
40	628	246	828	1173	150	620	600	123	28	574
41	917	636	555	98	342	756	823	883	1016	517
42	923	1102	1192	244	618	572	96	881	1100	570
43	568	1214	235	1216	888	456	1161	237	110	742
44	1280	1218	767	1264	527	890	13	548	538	458
45	779	279	1053	1163	1231	372	130	239	367	179
46	501	112	285	988	71	744	1021	1201	974	1282
47	403	273	859	1220	950	674	482	769	416	1246
48	394	1266	590	796	642	529	386	184	352	892
49	87	1274	683	15	869	141	359	550	522	477

POWER RESIDUES

	0	1	2	3	4	5	6	7	8	9
0	1	2	4	8	16	32	64	128	256	512
1	1024	757	223	446	892	493	986	681	71	142
2	284	568	1136	981	671	51	102	204	408	816
3	341	682	73	146	292	584	1168	1045	799	307
4	614	1228	1165	1039	787	283	566	1132	973	655
5	19	38	76	152	304	608	1216	1141	991	691
6	91	182	364	728	165	330	660	29	58	116
7	232	464	928	565	1130	969	647	3	6	12
8	24	48	96	192	384	768	245	490	980	669
9	47	94	188	376	752	213	426	852	413	826
10	361	722	153	306	612	1224	1157	1023	755	219
11	438	876	461	922	553	1106	921	551	1102	913
12	535	1070	849	407	814	337	674	57	114	228
13	456	912	533	1066	841	391	782	273	546	1092
14	893	495	990	689	87	174	348	696	101	202
15	404	808	325	650	9	18	36	72	144	288
16	576	1152	1013	735	179	358	716	141	282	564
17	1128	965	639	1278	1265	1239	1187	1083	875	459
18	918	545	1090	889	487	974	657	23	46	92
19	184	368	736	181	362	724	157	314	628	1256
20	1221	1151	1011	731	171	342	684	77	154	308
21	616	1232	1173	1055	819	347	694	97	194	388
22	776	261	522	1044	797	303	606	1212	1133	975
23	659	27	54	108	216	432	864	437	874	457
24	914	537	1074	857	423	846	401	802	313	626
25	1252	1213	1135	979	667	43	86	172	344	688
26	85	170	340	680	69	138	276	552	1104	917
27	543	1086	881	471	942	593	1186	1081	871	451
28	902	513	1026	761	231	462	924	557	1114	937
29	583	1166	1041	791	291	582	1164	1037	783	275
30	550	1100	909	527	1054	817	343	686	81	162
31	324	648	5	10	20	40	80	160	320	640
32	1280	1269	1247	1203	1115	939	587	1174	1057	823
33	355	710	129	258	516	1032	773	255	510	1020
34	749	207	414	828	365	730	169	338	676	61
35	122	244	488	976	661	31	62	124	248	496
36	992	693	95	190	380	760	229	458	916	541
37	1082	873	455	910	529	1058	825	359	718	145
38	290	580	1160	1029	767	243	486	972	653	15
39	30	60	120	240	480	960	629	1258	1225	1159
40	1027	763	235	470	940	589	1178	1065	839	387
41	774	257	514	1028	765	239	478	956	621	1242
42	1193	1095	899	507	1014	737	183	366	732	173
43	346	692	93	186	372	744	197	394	788	285
44	570	1140	989	687	83	166	332	664	37	74
45	148	296	592	1184	1077	863	435	870	449	898
46	505	1010	729	167	334	668	45	90	180	360
47	720	149	298	596	1192	1093	895	499	998	705
48	119	238	476	952	613	1226	1161	1031	771	251
49	502	1004	717	143	286	572	1144	997	703	115

P = 1291

INDICES

	0	1	2	3	4	5	6	7	8	9
50	938	540	490	1083	689	460	1153	423	943	781
51	338	564	9	281	412	865	334	1055	981	506
52	1133	1165	222	730	1029	1233	1059	303	1046	374
53	928	1010	584	132	656	120	753	241	1211	739
54	545	369	985	270	1243	181	138	1080	561	503
55	300	117	267	114	1070	837	808	287	510	1073
56	848	990	1107	708	169	73	46	840	21	746
57	440	1115	495	1023	1137	811	160	1203	1187	1226
58	381	976	295	290	35	1284	1124	326	1143	405
59	1169	513	452	275	1197	792	473	861	1006	1076
60	704	1222	788	904	1088	952	226	851	55	676
61	662	908	104	484	40	993	210	771	631	1259
62	669	418	734	1110	899	1248	249	1092	198	396
63	999	711	875	1268	831	1253	694	592	1033	172
64	319	798	1176	956	721	644	1289	76	311	531
65	153	964	817	388	1237	49	608	186	623	230
66	66	354	1041	843	447	894	603	254	465	89
67	1063	24	614	1276	126	855	348	685	1129	749
68	263	17	31	700	206	871	307	443	259	143
69	577	59	431	361	216	1118	147	552	920	1097
70	1158	524	1050	498	971	479	639	680	935	940
71	331	1026	581	542	558	805	166	492	378	1140
72	470	1085	101	666	195	691	718	814	63	462
73	345	203	428	1155	932	163	192	425	759	912
74	762	945	1148	1206	435	783	826	598	915	340
75	1014	1190	94	566	886	108	765	11	777	1229
76	365	283	1019	401	948	414	588	384	85	867
77	520	488	1151	336	410	979	220	1057	926	654
78	1209	983	136	298	1068	508	1105	44	438	1135
79	1185	293	1122	1167	1195	1004	786	224	660	38
80	629	732	247	997	829	1031	1174	1287	151	1235
81	621	1039	601	1061	124	1127	29	305	575	214
82	918	1048	637	329	556	376	99	716	343	930
83	757	1146	824	1012	884	775	1017	586	518	408
84	924	134	1103	1183	1193	658	245	1172	619	122
85	573	635	97	755	882	516	1101	243	571	880
86	569	1213	1215	455	236	741	1217	1263	889	547
87	457	278	1162	371	238	178	111	987	743	1200
88	1281	272	1219	673	768	1245	1265	795	528	183
89	891	1273	14	140	549	476	539	1082	459	422
90	780	563	280	864	1054	505	1164	729	1232	302
91	373	1009	131	119	240	738	368	269	180	1079
92	502	116	113	836	286	1072	989	707	72	839
93	745	1114	1022	810	1202	1225	975	289	1283	325
94	404	512	274	791	860	1075	1221	903	951	850
95	675	907	483	992	770	1258	417	1109	1247	1091
96	395	710	1267	1252	591	171	797	955	643	75
97	530	963	387	48	185	229	353	842	893	253
98	88	23	1275	854	684	748	16	699	870	442
99	142	58	360	1117	551	1096	523	497	478	679

POWER RESIDUES

	0	1	2	3	4	5	6	7	8	9
50	230	460	920	549	1098	905	519	1038	785	279
51	558	1116	941	591	1182	1073	855	419	838	385
52	770	249	498	996	701	111	222	444	888	485
53	970	649	7	14	28	56	112	224	448	896
54	501	1002	713	135	270	540	1080	869	447	894
55	497	994	697	103	206	412	824	357	714	137
56	274	548	1096	901	511	1022	753	215	430	860
57	429	858	425	850	409	818	345	690	89	178
58	356	712	133	266	532	1064	837	383	766	241
59	482	964	637	1274	1257	1223	1155	1019	747	203
60	406	812	333	666	41	82	164	328	656	21
61	42	84	168	336	672	53	106	212	424	848
62	405	810	329	658	25	50	100	200	400	800
63	309	618	1236	1181	1071	851	411	822	353	706
64	121	242	484	968	645	1290	1289	1287	1283	1275
65	1259	1227	1163	1035	779	267	534	1068	845	399
66	798	305	610	1220	1149	1007	723	155	310	620
67	1240	1189	1087	883	475	950	609	1218	1145	999
68	707	123	246	492	984	677	63	126	252	504
69	1008	725	159	318	636	1272	1253	1215	1139	987
70	683	75	150	300	600	1200	1109	927	563	1126
71	961	631	1262	1233	1175	1059	827	363	726	161
72	322	644	1288	1285	1279	1267	1243	1195	1099	907
73	523	1046	801	311	622	1244	1197	1103	915	539
74	1078	865	439	878	465	930	569	1138	985	679
75	67	134	268	536	1072	853	415	830	369	738
76	185	370	740	189	378	756	221	442	884	477
77	954	617	1234	1177	1063	835	379	758	225	450
78	900	509	1018	745	199	398	796	301	602	1204
79	1117	943	595	1190	1089	887	483	966	641	1282
80	1273	1255	1219	1147	1003	715	139	278	556	1112
81	933	575	1150	1009	727	163	326	652	13	26
82	52	104	208	416	832	373	746	201	402	804
83	317	634	1268	1245	1199	1107	923	555	1110	929
84	567	1134	977	663	35	70	140	280	560	1120
85	949	607	1214	1137	983	675	59	118	236	472
86	944	597	1194	1097	903	515	1030	769	247	494
87	988	685	79	158	316	632	1264	1237	1183	1075
88	859	427	854	417	834	377	754	217	434	868
89	445	890	489	978	665	39	78	156	312	624
90	1248	1205	1119	947	603	1206	1121	951	611	1222
91	1153	1015	739	187	374	748	205	410	820	349
92	698	105	210	420	840	389	778	265	530	1060
93	829	367	734	177	354	708	125	250	500	1000
94	709	127	254	508	1016	741	191	382	764	237
95	474	948	605	1210	1129	967	643	1286	1281	1271
96	1251	1211	1131	971	651	11	22	44	88	176
97	352	704	117	234	468	936	581	1162	1033	775
98	259	518	1036	781	271	542	1084	877	463	926
99	561	1122	953	615	1230	1169	1047	803	315	630

P = 1291

INDICES

	0	1	2	3	4	5	6	7	8	9
100	939	1025	541	804	491	1139	1084	665	690	813
101	461	202	1154	162	424	911	944	1205	782	597
102	339	1189	565	107	10	1228	282	400	413	383
103	866	487	335	978	1056	653	982	297	507	43
104	1134	292	1166	1003	223	37	731	996	1030	1286
105	1234	1038	1060	1126	304	213	1047	328	375	715
106	929	1145	1011	774	585	407	133	1182	657	1171
107	121	634	754	515	242	879	1212	454	740	1262
108	546	277	370	177	986	1199	271	672	1244	794
109	182	1272	139	475	1081	421	562	863	504	728
110	301	1008	118	737	268	1078	115	835	1071	706
111	838	1113	809	1224	288	324	511	790	1074	902
112	849	906	991	1257	1108	1090	709	1251	170	954
113	74	962	47	228	841	252	22	853	747	698
114	441	57	1116	1095	496	678	1024	803	1138	664
115	812	201	161	910	1204	596	1188	106	1227	399
116	382	486	977	652	296	42	291	1002	36	995
117	1285	1037	1125	212	327	714	1144	773	406	1181
118	1170	633	514	878	453	1261	276	176	1198	671
119	793	1271	474	420	862	727	1007	736	1077	834
120	705	1112	1223	323	789	901	905	1256	1089	1250
121	953	961	227	251	852	697	56	1094	677	802
122	663	200	909	595	105	398	485	651	41	1001
123	994	1036	211	713	772	1180	632	877	1260	175
124	670	1270	419	726	735	833	1111	322	900	1255
125	1249	960	250	696	1093	801	199	594	397	650
126	1000	1035	712	1179	876	174	1269	725	832	321
127	1254	959	695	800	593	649	1034	1178	173	724
128	320	958	799	648	1177	723	957	647	722	646
129	645	0								

POWER RESIDUES

	0	1	2	3	4	5	6	7	8	9
100	1260	1229	1167	1043	795	299	598	1196	1101	911
101	531	1062	833	375	750	209	418	836	381	762
102	233	466	932	573	1146	1001	711	131	262	524
103	1048	805	319	638	1276	1261	1231	1171	1051	811
104	331	662	33	66	132	264	528	1056	821	351
105	702	113	226	452	904	517	1034	777	263	526
106	1052	813	335	670	49	98	196	392	784	277
107	554	1108	925	559	1118	945	599	1198	1105	919
108	547	1094	897	503	1006	721	151	302	604	1208
109	1125	959	627	1254	1217	1143	995	699	107	214
110	428	856	421	842	393	786	281	562	1124	957
111	623	1246	1201	1111	931	571	1142	993	695	99
112	198	396	792	293	586	1172	1053	815	339	678
113	65	130	260	520	1040	789	287	574	1148	1005
114	719	147	294	588	1176	1061	831	371	742	193
115	386	772	253	506	1012	733	175	350	700	109
116	218	436	872	453	906	521	1042	793	295	590
117	1180	1069	847	403	806	321	642	1284	1277	1263
118	1235	1179	1067	843	395	790	289	578	1156	1021
119	751	211	422	844	397	794	297	594	1188	1085
120	879	467	934	577	1154	1017	743	195	390	780
121	269	538	1076	861	431	862	433	866	441	882
122	473	946	601	1202	1113	935	579	1158	1025	759
123	227	454	908	525	1050	809	327	654	17	34
124	68	136	272	544	1088	885	479	958	625	1250
125	1209	1127	963	635	1270	1249	1207	1123	955	619
126	1238	1185	1079	867	443	886	481	962	633	1266
127	1241	1191	1091	891	491	982	673	55	110	220
128	440	880	469	938	585	1170	1049	807	323	646
129										

P = 1297

INDICES

	0	1	2	3	4	5	6	7	8	9
0		0	478	8	956	819	486	230	138	16
1	1	627	964	6	708	827	616	107	494	404
2	479	238	1105	296	146	342	484	24	1186	599
3	9	103	1094	635	585	1049	972	77	882	14
4	957	1029	716	869	287	835	774	514	624	460
5	820	115	962	844	502	150	368	412	1077	191
6	487	1026	581	246	276	825	1113	390	1063	304
7	231	558	154	909	555	350	64	857	492	667
8	139	32	211	783	1194	926	51	607	765	55
9	17	236	1252	111	992	1223	1102	318	938	643
10	2	610	593	710	144	1057	26	986	980	959
11	628	85	846	523	890	1115	259	22	669	337
12	965	1254	208	1037	1059	1161	724	671	754	877
13	7	5	295	634	868	843	245	908	782	110
14	709	522	1036	633	632	122	91	468	1033	271
15	828	565	542	123	39	922	970	243	1145	852
16	617	526	510	92	689	158	1261	1172	376	12
17	108	420	529	469	1085	572	1243	199	533	705
18	495	427	714	1034	434	896	589	734	174	254
19	405	727	284	272	796	833	120	1277	1121	872
20	480	398	1088	829	1071	552	1188	312	622	1031
21	239	265	504	566	168	392	162	333	141	917
22	1106	113	563	543	28	358	1001	339	72	371
23	297	865	737	124	500	37	1147	675	815	422
24	147	1081	436	40	686	1279	219	410	241	791
25	343	545	1202	923	1149	934	1232	793	59	307
26	485	615	483	971	773	367	1112	63	50	1101
27	25	258	723	244	90	969	1260	1242	588	119
28	1187	161	1000	1146	218	1231	1111	1259	1110	214
29	600	326	569	853	946	1010	215	651	749	302
30	10	1099	1043	618	1020	549	601	1292	517	718
31	104	536	152	527	721	1065	327	291	34	1226
32	1095	994	1004	511	988	348	570	967	1167	744
33	636	364	443	93	354	1209	854	455	490	531
34	586	730	898	690	1007	1123	947	576	267	983
35	1050	30	425	159	677	81	1011	345	1183	450
36	973	808	905	1262	1192	432	216	760	912	1045
37	78	1074	1067	1173	1212	1169	652	605	732	1257
38	883	679	1205	377	762	380	750	885	1274	647
39	15	403	598	13	459	190	303	666	54	642
40	958	336	876	109	270	851	11	704	253	871
41	1030	916	370	421	790	306	1100	118	213	301
42	717	1225	743	530	982	449	1044	1256	646	641
43	870	300	640	470	811	130	619	700	99	471
44	288	476	591	1086	1041	874	1021	279	506	812
45	836	360	183	573	817	1055	550	547	849	131
46	775	43	47	1244	1215	930	602	136	978	620
47	515	251	329	200	1153	746	1293	860	900	701
48	625	83	263	534	914	1137	518	681	1164	100
49	461	1235	697	706	888	166	719	788	1269	472

POWER RESIDUES

	0	1	2	3	4	5	6	7	8	9
0	1	10	100	1000	921	131	13	130	3	30
1	300	406	169	393	39	390	9	90	900	1218
2	507	1179	117	1170	27	270	106	1060	224	943
3	351	916	81	810	318	586	672	235	1053	154
4	243	1133	954	461	719	705	565	462	729	805
5	268	86	860	818	398	89	890	1118	804	258
6	1283	1157	1194	267	76	760	1115	774	1255	877
7	988	801	228	983	751	1025	1171	37	370	1106
8	684	355	956	481	919	111	1110	724	755	1065
9	274	146	163	333	736	875	968	601	822	438
10	489	999	911	31	310	506	1169	17	170	403
11	139	93	930	221	913	51	510	1209	417	279
12	196	663	145	153	233	1033	1251	837	588	692
13	435	459	699	505	1159	1214	467	779	8	80
14	800	218	883	1048	104	1040	24	240	1103	654
15	55	550	312	526	72	720	715	665	165	353
16	936	281	216	863	848	698	495	1059	214	843
17	648	1292	1247	797	188	583	642	1232	647	1282
18	1147	1094	564	452	629	1102	644	1252	847	688
19	395	59	590	712	635	1162	1244	767	1185	177
20	473	839	608	892	1138	1004	961	531	122	1220
21	527	82	820	418	289	296	366	1066	284	246
22	1163	1254	867	888	1098	604	852	738	895	1168
23	7	70	700	515	1259	917	91	910	21	210
24	803	248	1183	157	273	136	63	630	1112	744
25	955	471	819	408	189	593	742	935	271	116
26	1160	1224	567	482	929	211	813	348	886	1078
27	404	149	193	633	1142	1044	64	640	1212	447
28	579	602	832	538	192	623	1042	44	440	509
29	1199	317	576	572	532	132	23	230	1003	951
30	431	419	299	396	69	690	415	259	1293	1257
31	897	1188	207	773	1245	777	1285	1177	97	970
32	621	1022	1141	1034	1261	937	291	316	566	472
33	829	508	1189	217	873	948	401	119	1190	227
34	973	651	25	250	1203	357	976	681	325	656
35	75	750	1015	1071	334	746	975	671	225	953
36	451	619	1002	941	331	716	675	265	56	560
37	412	229	993	851	728	795	168	383	1236	687
38	385	1256	887	1088	504	1149	1114	764	1155	1174
39	67	670	215	853	748	995	871	928	201	713
40	645	1262	947	391	19	190	603	842	638	1192
41	247	1173	57	570	512	1229	617	982	741	925
42	171	413	239	1093	554	352	926	181	513	1239
43	717	685	365	1056	184	543	242	1123	854	758
44	1095	574	552	332	726	775	1265	977	691	425
45	359	996	881	1028	1201	337	776	1275	1077	394
46	49	490	1009	1011	1031	1231	637	1182	147	173
47	433	439	499	1099	614	952	441	519	2	20
48	200	703	545	262	26	260	6	60	600	812
49	338	786	78	780	18	180	503	1139	1014	1061

P = 1297

INDICES

	0	1	2	3	4	5	6	7	8	9
50	821	1180	1023	496	384	133	105	20	331	289
51	116	1139	414	428	1271	233	537	1141	785	477
52	963	1104	1093	715	961	580	153	210	1251	592
53	845	207	294	1035	541	509	528	713	283	1087
54	503	562	736	435	1201	482	722	999	568	1042
55	151	1003	442	897	424	904	1066	1204	597	875
56	369	742	639	590	182	46	328	262	696	1022
57	413	1092	293	735	441	638	292	803	692	280
58	1078	1013	804	175	1047	841	35	1207	128	507
59	192	1285	693	255	1129	1156	1227	880	780	813
60	488	97	281	406	225	777	1096	953	202	837
61	1027	520	1079	728	474	560	995	416	1196	361
62	582	320	1014	285	630	684	1005	1039	1199	184
63	247	1219	805	273	769	194	512	466	408	574
64	277	997	176	797	186	400	989	178	170	818
65	826	341	1048	834	149	824	349	925	1222	1056
66	1114	1160	842	121	921	157	571	895	832	551
67	391	357	36	1278	933	366	968	1230	1009	548
68	1064	347	1208	1122	80	431	1168	379	189	850
69	305	448	129	873	1054	929	745	1136	165	132
70	232	579	508	481	903	45	637	840	1155	776
71	559	683	193	399	823	156	365	430	928	44
72	155	940	1286	1089	87	941	444	1061	374	48
73	910	976	694	830	1238	1287	94	1017	227	1245
74	556	418	256	1072	249	1090	355	799	394	1216
75	351	74	1130	553	1083	88	1210	1151	439	931
76	65	1176	1157	1189	387	942	855	197	1240	603
77	858	801	1228	313	67	445	456	315	1125	137
78	493	1185	881	623	1076	1062	491	764	937	979
79	668	753	781	1032	1144	375	532	173	1120	621
80	140	71	814	240	58	49	587	1109	748	516
81	33	1166	489	266	1182	911	731	1273	53	252
82	212	645	98	505	848	977	899	1163	1268	330
83	784	1250	282	567	596	695	691	127	779	201
84	1195	1198	407	169	1221	831	1008	188	164	1154
85	927	373	226	393	438	1239	1124	936	1119	747
86	52	1267	778	163	1118	1288	948	222	1289	1294
87	608	396	1097	334	1178	95	577	69	949	861
88	766	452	954	142	1069	1018	268	382	223	901
89	56	659	203	918	757	228	984	310	1290	702
90	18	951	838	1107	661	1246	1051	663	1295	626
91	237	102	1028	114	1025	557	31	235	609	84
92	1253	4	521	564	525	419	426	726	397	264
93	112	864	1080	544	614	257	160	325	1098	535
94	993	363	729	29	807	1073	678	402	335	915
95	1224	299	475	359	42	250	82	1234	1179	1138
96	1103	206	561	1002	741	1091	1012	1284	96	519
97	319	1218	996	340	1159	356	346	447	578	682
98	939	975	417	73	1175	800	1184	752	70	1165
99	644	1249	1197	372	1266	395	451	658	950	101

POWER RESIDUES

	0	1	2	3	4	5	6	7	8	9
50	234	1043	54	540	212	823	448	589	702	535
51	162	323	636	1172	47	470	809	308	486	969
52	611	922	141	113	1130	924	161	313	536	172
53	423	339	796	178	483	939	311	516	1269	1017
54	1091	534	152	223	933	251	1213	457	679	305
55	456	669	205	753	1045	74	740	915	71	710
56	615	962	541	222	923	151	213	833	548	292
57	326	666	175	453	639	1202	347	876	978	701
58	525	62	620	1012	1041	34	340	806	278	186
59	563	442	529	102	1020	1121	834	558	392	29
60	290	306	466	769	1205	377	1176	87	870	918
61	101	1010	1021	1131	934	261	16	160	303	436
62	469	799	208	783	48	480	909	11	110	1100
63	624	1052	144	143	133	33	330	706	575	562
64	432	429	399	99	990	821	428	389	1296	1287
65	1197	297	376	1166	1284	1167	1294	1267	997	891
66	1128	904	1258	907	1288	1207	397	79	790	118
67	1180	127	1270	1027	1191	237	1073	354	946	381
68	1216	487	979	711	625	1062	244	1143	1054	164
69	343	836	578	592	732	835	568	492	1029	1211
70	437	479	899	1208	407	179	493	1039	14	140
71	103	1030	1221	537	182	523	42	420	309	496
72	1069	314	546	272	126	1260	927	191	613	942
73	341	816	378	1186	187	573	542	232	1023	1151
74	1134	964	561	422	329	696	475	859	808	298
75	386	1266	987	791	128	1280	1127	894	1158	1204
76	367	1076	384	1246	787	88	880	1018	1101	634
77	1152	1144	1064	264	46	460	709	605	862	838
78	598	792	138	83	830	518	1289	1217	497	1079
79	414	249	1193	257	1273	1057	194	643	1242	747
80	985	771	1225	577	582	632	1132	944	361	1016
81	1081	434	449	599	802	238	1083	454	649	5
82	50	500	1109	714	655	65	650	15	150	203
83	733	845	668	195	653	45	450	609	902	1238
84	707	585	662	135	53	530	112	1120	824	458
85	689	405	159	293	336	766	1175	77	770	1215
86	477	879	1008	1001	931	231	1013	1051	134	43
87	430	409	199	693	445	559	402	129	1290	1227
88	597	782	38	380	1206	387	1276	1087	494	1049
89	114	1140	1024	1161	1234	667	185	553	342	826
90	478	889	1108	704	555	362	1026	1181	137	73
91	730	815	368	1086	484	949	411	219	893	1148
92	1104	664	155	253	1233	657	85	850	718	695
93	465	759	1105	674	255	1253	857	788	98	980
94	721	725	765	1165	1274	1067	294	346	866	878
95	998	901	1228	607	882	1038	4	40	400	109
96	1090	524	52	520	12	120	1200	327	676	275
97	156	263	36	360	1006	981	731	825	468	789
98	108	1080	424	349	896	1178	107	1070	324	646
99	1272	1047	94	940	321	616	972	641	1222	547

P = 1297

INDICES

	0	1	2	3	4	5	6	7	8	9
100	3	863	362	298	205	1217	974	1248	862	462
101	611	463	583	866	498	352	809	539	767	1236
102	594	612	321	738	892	75	906	673	453	698
103	711	464	1015	125	323	1131	1263	1133	955	707
104	145	584	286	501	275	554	1193	991	143	889
105	1058	867	631	38	688	1084	433	795	1070	167
106	27	499	685	1148	772	89	217	945	1019	720
107	987	353	1006	676	1191	1211	761	458	269	789
108	981	810	1040	816	1214	1152	913	887	383	1270
109	960	540	1200	423	181	440	1046	1128	224	473
110	629	768	185	148	920	932	79	1053	902	822
111	86	1237	248	1082	386	66	1075	1143	57	1181
112	847	595	1220	437	1117	1177	1068	756	660	1024
113	524	613	806	41	740	1158	1174	1265	204	497
114	891	322	274	687	771	1190	1213	180	919	385
115	1116	739	770	1280	1281	388	1170	61	758	134
116	260	893	195	220	1282	943	653	655	229	106
117	23	76	513	411	389	856	606	317	985	21
118	670	907	467	242	1171	198	733	1276	311	332
119	338	674	409	792	62	1241	1258	650	1291	290
120	966	454	575	344	759	604	884	665	703	117
121	1255	699	278	546	135	859	680	787	19	1140
122	209	712	998	1203	261	802	1206	879	952	415
123	1038	465	177	924	894	1229	378	1135	839	429
124	1060	1016	798	1150	196	314	763	172	1108	1272
125	1162	126	187	935	221	68	381	309	662	234
126	725	324	401	1233	1283	446	751	657	1247	538
127	672	1132	990	794	944	457	886	1127	1052	1142
128	755	1264	179	60	654	316	1275	649	664	786
129	878	1134	171	308	656	1126	648			

POWER RESIDUES

	0	1	2	3	4	5	6	7	8	9
100	282	226	963	551	322	626	1072	344	846	678
101	295	356	966	581	622	1032	1241	737	885	1068
102	304	446	569	502	1129	914	61	610	912	41
103	410	209	793	148	183	533	142	123	1230	627
104	1082	444	549	302	426	369	1096	584	652	35
105	350	906	1278	1107	694	455	659	105	1050	124
106	1240	727	785	68	680	315	556	372	1126	884
107	1058	204	743	945	371	1116	784	58	580	612
108	932	241	1113	754	1055	174	443	539	202	723
109	745	965	571	522	32	320	606	872	938	301
110	416	269	96	960	521	22	220	903	1248	807
111	288	286	266	66	660	115	1150	1124	864	858
112	798	198	683	345	856	778	1295	1277	1097	594
113	752	1035	1271	1037	1291	1237	697	485	959	511
114	1219	517	1279	1117	794	158	283	236	1063	254
115	1243	757	1085	474	849	708	595	762	1135	974
116	661	125	1250	827	488	989	811	328	686	375
117	1156	1184	167	373	1136	984	761	1125	874	958
118	501	1119	814	358	986	781	28	280	206	763
119	1145	1074	364	1046	84	840	618	992	841	628
120	1092	544	252	1223	557	382	1226	587	682	335
121	756	1075	374	1146	1084	464	749	1005	971	631
122	1122	844	658	95	950	421	319	596	772	1235
123	677	285	256	1263	957	491	1019	1111	734	855
124	768	1195	277	176	463	739	905	1268	1007	991
125	831	528	92	920	121	1210	427	379	1196	287
126	276	166	363	1036	1281	1137	994	861	828	498
127	1089	514	1249	817	388	1286	1187	197	673	245
128	1153	1154	1164	1264	967	591	722	735	865	868
129	898	1198	307	476	869	908				

p = 1301

INDICES

	0	1	2	3	4	5	6	7	8	9
0		0	1	263	2	406	264	801	3	526
1	407	1090	265	1136	802	669	4	712	527	462
2	408	1064	1091	982	266	812	1137	789	803	370
3	670	235	5	53	713	1207	528	1007	463	99
4	409	1085	1065	1070	1092	932	983	1166	267	302
5	813	975	1138	754	790	196	804	725	371	1122
6	671	1294	236	27	6	242	54	991	714	1245
7	1208	1105	529	609	1008	1075	464	591	100	353
8	410	1052	1086	785	1066	1118	1071	633	1093	44
9	933	637	984	498	1167	868	268	1223	303	316
10	814	429	976	627	1139	170	755	1097	791	536
11	197	1270	805	1231	726	88	372	362	1123	213
12	672	880	1295	48	237	1218	28	478	7	33
13	243	119	55	1263	992	1195	715	838	1246	937
14	1209	129	1106	926	530	776	610	565	1009	1183
15	1076	1145	465	1238	592	641	101	279	354	1017
16	411	483	1053	260	1087	459	786	1204	1067	972
17	1119	988	1072	782	634	313	1094	85	45	116
18	934	562	638	257	985	113	499	502	1168	290
19	869	1027	269	12	1224	505	304	599	317	183
20	815	1254	430	1171	977	191	628	208	1140	252
21	171	293	756	68	1098	176	792	1036	537	872
22	198	548	1271	743	806	38	1232	1030	727	345
23	89	854	373	959	363	272	1124	616	214	999
24	673	512	881	15	1296	708	49	298	238	1048
25	1219	1227	29	772	479	81	8	248	34	508
26	244	896	120	396	56	1160	1264	307	993	686
27	1196	384	716	900	839	602	1247	660	938	761
28	1210	733	130	320	1107	1131	927	586	531	124
29	777	186	611	681	566	228	1010	579	1184	818
30	1077	571	1146	692	466	400	1239	1257	593	890
31	642	73	102	950	280	433	355	701	1018	160
32	412	60	484	1174	1054	648	261	799	1088	667
33	460	980	787	233	1205	97	1068	1164	973	194
34	1120	25	989	1103	1073	351	783	631	635	866
35	314	625	1095	1268	86	211	46	476	117	1193
36	935	924	563	1143	639	1015	258	1202	986	311
37	114	255	500	1025	503	181	1169	206	291	174
38	870	741	1028	852	270	997	13	296	1225	79
39	506	394	305	382	600	759	318	584	184	226
40	816	690	1255	71	431	158	1172	797	978	95
41	192	1101	629	623	209	1191	1141	1200	253	179
42	172	850	294	392	757	224	69	795	1099	1189
43	177	390	793	388	1037	1039	538	144	873	1041
44	199	828	549	540	1272	450	744	146	807	720
45	39	875	1233	108	1031	1043	728	945	346	201
46	90	823	855	830	374	904	960	551	364	492
47	273	542	1125	860	617	1274	215	1280	1000	452
48	674	843	513	746	882	329	16	148	1297	523
49	709	809	50	1082	299	722	239	606	1049	41

POWER RESIDUES

	0	1	2	3	4	5	6	7	8	9
0	1	2	4	8	16	32	64	128	256	512
1	1024	747	193	386	772	243	486	972	643	1286
2	1271	1241	1181	1061	821	341	682	63	126	252
3	504	1008	715	129	258	516	1032	763	225	450
4	900	499	998	695	89	178	356	712	123	246
5	492	984	667	33	66	132	264	528	1056	811
6	321	642	1284	1267	1233	1165	1029	757	213	426
7	852	403	806	311	622	1244	1187	1073	845	389
8	778	255	510	1020	739	177	354	708	115	230
9	460	920	539	1078	855	409	818	335	670	39
10	78	156	312	624	1248	1195	1089	877	453	906
11	511	1022	743	185	370	740	179	358	716	131
12	262	524	1048	795	289	578	1156	1011	721	141
13	282	564	1128	955	609	1218	1135	969	637	1274
14	1247	1193	1085	869	437	874	447	894	487	974
15	647	1294	1287	1273	1245	1189	1077	853	405	810
16	319	638	1276	1251	1201	1101	901	501	1002	703
17	105	210	420	840	379	758	215	430	860	419
18	838	375	750	199	398	796	291	582	1164	1027
19	753	205	410	820	339	678	55	110	220	440
20	880	459	918	535	1070	839	377	754	207	414
21	828	355	710	119	238	476	952	603	1206	1111
22	921	541	1082	863	425	850	399	798	295	590
23	1180	1059	817	333	666	31	62	124	248	496
24	992	683	65	130	260	520	1040	779	257	514
25	1028	755	209	418	836	371	742	183	366	732
26	163	326	652	3	6	12	24	48	96	192
27	384	768	235	470	940	579	1158	1015	729	157
28	314	628	1256	1211	1121	941	581	1162	1023	745
29	189	378	756	211	422	844	387	774	247	494
30	988	675	49	98	196	392	784	267	534	1068
31	835	369	738	175	350	700	99	198	396	792
32	283	566	1132	963	625	1250	1199	1097	893	485
33	970	639	1278	1255	1209	1117	933	565	1130	959
34	617	1234	1167	1033	765	229	458	916	531	1062
35	823	345	690	79	158	316	632	1264	1227	1153
36	1005	709	117	234	468	936	571	1142	983	665
37	29	58	116	232	464	928	555	1110	919	537
38	1074	847	393	786	271	542	1084	867	433	866
39	431	862	423	846	391	782	263	526	1052	803
40	305	610	1220	1139	977	653	5	10	20	40
41	80	160	320	640	1280	1259	1217	1133	965	629
42	1258	1215	1129	957	613	1226	1151	1001	701	101
43	202	404	808	315	630	1260	1219	1137	973	645
44	1290	1279	1257	1213	1125	949	597	1194	1087	873
45	445	890	479	958	615	1230	1159	1017	733	165
46	330	660	19	38	76	152	304	608	1216	1131
47	961	621	1242	1183	1065	829	357	714	127	254
48	508	1016	731	161	322	644	1288	1275	1249	1197
49	1093	885	469	938	575	1150	999	697	93	186

P = 1301

INDICES

	0	1	2	3	4	5	6	7	8	9
50	1220	167	1228	877	30	835	773	1235	480	969
51	82	110	9	1251	249	1033	35	956	509	1045
52	245	1157	897	730	121	576	397	947	57	664
53	1161	348	1265	921	308	203	994	379	687	92
54	1197	221	385	825	717	942	901	857	840	520
55	603	832	1248	1154	661	376	939	1151	762	906
56	1211	765	734	962	131	337	321	553	1108	909
57	1132	366	928	1290	587	494	532	1214	125	275
58	778	286	187	544	612	768	682	1127	567	697
59	229	862	1011	737	580	619	1185	446	819	1276
60	1078	965	572	217	1147	1286	693	1282	467	134
61	401	1002	1240	424	1258	454	594	340	891	676
62	643	471	74	845	103	324	951	515	281	419
63	434	748	356	556	702	884	1019	138	161	331
64	413	1111	61	18	485	439	1175	150	1055	912
65	649	1299	262	405	800	525	1089	1135	668	711
66	461	1063	981	811	788	369	234	52	1206	1006
67	98	1084	1069	931	1165	301	974	753	195	724
68	1121	1293	26	241	990	1244	1104	608	1074	590
69	352	1051	784	1117	632	43	636	497	867	1222
70	315	428	626	169	1096	535	1269	1230	87	361
71	212	879	47	1217	477	32	118	1262	1194	837
72	936	128	925	775	564	1182	1144	1237	640	278
73	1016	482	259	458	1203	971	987	781	312	84
74	115	561	256	112	501	289	1026	11	504	598
75	182	1253	1170	190	207	251	292	67	175	1035
76	871	547	742	37	1029	344	853	958	271	615
77	998	511	14	707	297	1047	1226	771	80	247
78	507	895	395	1159	306	685	383	899	601	659
79	760	732	319	1130	585	123	185	680	227	578
80	817	570	691	399	1256	889	72	949	432	700
81	159	59	1173	647	798	666	979	232	96	1163
82	193	24	1102	350	630	865	624	1267	210	475
83	1192	923	1142	1014	1201	310	254	1024	180	205
84	173	740	851	996	295	78	393	381	758	583
85	225	689	70	157	796	94	1100	622	1190	1199
86	178	849	391	223	794	1188	389	387	1038	143
87	1040	827	539	449	145	719	874	107	1042	944
88	200	822	829	903	550	491	541	859	1273	1279
89	451	842	745	328	147	522	808	1081	721	605
90	40	166	876	834	1234	968	109	1250	1032	955
91	1044	1156	729	575	946	663	347	920	202	378
92	91	220	824	941	856	519	831	1153	375	1150
93	905	764	961	336	552	908	365	1289	493	1213
94	274	285	543	767	1126	696	861	736	618	445
95	1275	964	216	1285	1281	133	1001	423	453	339
96	675	470	844	323	514	418	747	555	883	137
97	330	1110	17	438	149	911	1298	404	524	1134
98	710	1062	810	368	51	1005	1083	930	300	752
99	723	1292	240	1243	607	589	1050	1116	42	496

POWER RESIDUES

	0	1	2	3	4	5	6	7	8	9
50	372	744	187	374	748	195	390	780	259	518
51	1036	771	241	482	964	627	1254	1207	1113	925
52	549	1098	895	489	978	655	9	18	36	72
53	144	288	576	1152	1003	705	109	218	436	872
54	443	886	471	942	583	1166	1031	761	221	442
55	884	467	934	567	1134	967	633	1266	1231	1161
56	1021	741	181	362	724	147	294	588	1176	1051
57	801	301	602	1204	1107	913	525	1050	799	297
58	594	1188	1075	849	397	794	287	574	1148	995
59	689	77	154	308	616	1232	1163	1025	749	197
60	394	788	275	550	1100	899	497	994	687	73
61	146	292	584	1168	1035	769	237	474	948	595
62	1190	1079	857	413	826	351	702	103	206	412
63	824	347	694	87	174	348	696	91	182	364
64	728	155	310	620	1240	1179	1057	813	325	650
65	1300	1299	1297	1293	1285	1269	1237	1173	1045	789
66	277	554	1108	915	529	1058	815	329	658	15
67	30	60	120	240	480	960	619	1238	1175	1049
68	797	293	586	1172	1043	785	269	538	1076	851
69	401	802	303	606	1212	1123	945	589	1178	1055
70	809	317	634	1268	1235	1169	1037	773	245	490
71	980	659	17	34	68	136	272	544	1088	875
72	449	898	495	990	679	57	114	228	456	912
73	523	1046	791	281	562	1124	947	593	1186	1071
74	841	381	762	223	446	892	483	966	631	1262
75	1223	1145	989	677	53	106	212	424	848	395
76	790	279	558	1116	931	561	1122	943	585	1170
77	1039	777	253	506	1012	723	145	290	580	1160
78	1019	737	173	346	692	83	166	332	664	27
79	54	108	216	432	864	427	854	407	814	327
80	654	7	14	28	56	112	224	448	896	491
81	982	663	25	50	100	200	400	800	299	598
82	1196	1091	881	461	922	543	1086	871	441	882
83	463	926	551	1102	903	505	1010	719	137	274
84	548	1096	891	481	962	623	1246	1191	1081	861
85	421	842	383	766	231	462	924	547	1094	887
86	473	946	591	1182	1063	825	349	698	95	190
87	380	760	219	438	876	451	902	503	1006	711
88	121	242	484	968	635	1270	1239	1177	1053	805
89	309	618	1236	1171	1041	781	261	522	1044	787
90	273	546	1092	883	465	930	559	1118	935	569
91	1138	975	649	1298	1295	1289	1277	1253	1205	1109
92	917	533	1066	831	361	722	143	286	572	1144
93	987	673	45	90	180	360	720	139	278	556
94	1112	923	545	1090	879	457	914	527	1054	807
95	313	626	1252	1203	1105	909	517	1034	767	233
96	466	932	563	1126	951	601	1202	1103	905	509
97	1018	735	169	338	676	51	102	204	408	816
98	331	662	23	46	92	184	368	736	171	342
99	684	67	134	268	536	1072	843	385	770	239

P = 1301

INDICES

	0	1	2	3	4	5	6	7	8	9
100	1221	427	168	534	1229	360	878	1216	31	1261
101	836	127	774	1181	1236	277	481	457	970	780
102	83	560	111	288	10	597	1252	189	250	66
103	1034	546	36	343	957	614	510	706	1046	770
104	246	894	1158	684	898	658	731	1129	122	679
105	577	569	398	888	948	699	58	646	665	231
106	1162	23	349	864	1266	474	922	1013	309	1023
107	204	739	995	77	380	582	688	156	93	621
108	1198	848	222	1187	386	142	826	448	718	106
109	943	821	902	490	858	1278	841	327	521	1080
110	604	165	833	967	1249	954	1155	574	662	919
111	377	219	940	518	1152	1149	763	335	907	1288
112	1212	284	766	695	735	444	963	1284	132	422
113	338	469	322	417	554	136	1109	437	910	403
114	1133	1061	367	1004	929	751	1291	1242	588	1115
115	495	426	533	359	1215	1260	126	1180	276	456
116	779	559	287	596	188	65	545	342	613	705
117	769	893	683	657	1128	678	568	887	698	645
118	230	22	863	473	1012	1022	738	76	581	155
119	620	847	1186	141	447	105	820	489	1277	326
120	1079	164	966	953	573	918	218	517	1148	334
121	1287	283	694	443	1283	421	468	416	135	436
122	402	1060	1003	750	1241	1114	425	358	1259	1179
123	455	558	595	64	341	704	892	656	677	886
124	644	21	472	1021	75	154	846	140	104	488
125	325	163	952	917	516	333	282	442	420	415
126	435	1059	749	1113	357	1178	557	63	703	655
127	885	20	1020	153	139	487	162	916	332	441
128	414	1058	1112	1177	62	654	19	152	486	915
129	440	1057	1176	653	151	914	1056	652	913	651
130	650	0								

POWER RESIDUES

	0	1	2	3	4	5	6	7	8	9
100	478	956	611	1222	1143	985	669	37	74	148
101	296	592	1184	1067	833	365	730	159	318	636
102	1272	1243	1185	1069	837	373	746	191	382	764
103	227	454	908	515	1030	759	217	434	868	435
104	870	439	878	455	910	519	1038	775	249	498
105	996	691	81	162	324	648	1296	1291	1281	1261
106	1221	1141	981	661	21	42	84	168	336	672
107	43	86	172	344	688	75	150	300	600	1200
108	1099	897	493	986	671	41	82	164	328	656
109	11	22	44	88	176	352	704	107	214	428
110	856	411	822	343	686	71	142	284	568	1136
111	971	641	1282	1263	1225	1149	997	693	85	170
112	340	680	59	118	236	472	944	587	1174	1047
113	793	285	570	1140	979	657	13	26	52	104
114	208	416	832	363	726	151	302	604	1208	1115
115	929	557	1114	927	553	1106	911	521	1042	783
116	265	530	1060	819	337	674	47	94	188	376
117	752	203	406	812	323	646	1292	1283	1265	1229
118	1157	1013	725	149	298	596	1192	1083	865	429
119	858	415	830	359	718	135	270	540	1080	859
120	417	834	367	734	167	334	668	35	70	140
121	280	560	1120	939	577	1154	1007	713	125	250
122	500	1000	699	97	194	388	776	251	502	1004
123	707	113	226	452	904	507	1014	727	153	306
124	612	1224	1147	993	685	69	138	276	552	1104
125	907	513	1026	751	201	402	804	307	614	1228
126	1155	1009	717	133	266	532	1064	827	353	706
127	111	222	444	888	475	950	599	1198	1095	889
128	477	954	607	1214	1127	953	605	1210	1119	937
129	573	1146	991	681	61	122	244	488	976	651
130										

P = 1303

INDICES

	0	1	2	3	4	5	6	7	8	9
0		0	922	381	542	609	1	655	162	762
1	229	399	923	574	275	990	1084	249	382	259
2	1151	1036	19	824	543	1218	194	1143	1197	853
3	610	1297	704	780	1171	1264	2	851	1181	955
4	771	58	656	615	941	69	444	679	163	8
5	838	630	1116	103	763	1008	817	640	473	1241
6	230	936	917	115	324	1183	400	1002	791	1205
7	884	185	924	17	471	297	801	1054	575	522
8	391	222	980	134	276	858	235	1234	561	1016
9	991	1229	64	376	299	868	1085	733	930	1161
10	458	957	250	730	736	343	1025	1289	383	988
11	628	1232	437	482	260	131	93	34	861	904
12	1152	798	556	439	537	525	1037	1202	1246	996
13	803	426	20	914	622	450	411	773	825	1005
14	504	1060	1107	973	544	160	939	389	91	419
15	1219	55	421	1011	674	604	195	1168	142	484
16	11	177	1144	1140	600	87	1056	618	1198	1148
17	478	1021	1157	60	854	571	181	320	636	834
18	611	1300	849	15	986	158	1298	648	1221	496
19	488	516	705	810	353	262	550	146	781	336
20	78	81	577	206	1172	667	350	284	356	658
21	1265	199	645	566	909	1224	3	650	608	398
22	248	823	852	1263	57	678	102	1240	1182	184
23	1053	133	1015	867	956	1288	481	903	524	425
24	772	972	418	603	176	617	59	833	157	515
25	145	205	657	1223	822	1239	866	424	616	204
26	423	313	46	314	942	712	534	95	242	47
27	70	507	31	308	393	315	445	371	625	757
28	124	943	680	1130	727	1249	593	713	164	498
29	1082	1114	559	535	9	548	1013	240	39	96
30	839	1270	977	36	41	243	631	406	294	1111
31	224	48	1117	739	788	724	1064	71	104	1252
32	933	368	1099	508	764	490	760	67	220	32
33	1009	494	676	311	238	309	818	829	768	863
34	98	394	641	663	777	512	982	316	474	1136
35	191	415	1103	446	1242	794	256	1285	454	372
36	231	518	920	1179	469	626	937	847	606	820
37	1080	758	918	1256	268	906	841	125	116	24
38	108	281	136	944	325	361	430	75	1275	681
39	1184	1073	170	807	1068	1131	401	707	1258	1295
40	1000	728	1003	569	197	831	1128	1250	792	1071
41	287	1154	1272	594	1206	743	1278	84	278	714
42	885	1041	1121	139	265	165	186	289	529	52
43	844	499	925	812	270	541	228	1083	18	1196
44	1170	770	443	1115	472	323	883	800	979	560
45	298	457	1024	436	860	536	802	410	1106	90
46	673	10	1055	1156	635	985	487	549	576	355
47	908	247	101	1014	523	175	144	865	45	241
48	392	123	592	558	38	40	223	1063	1098	219
49	237	97	981	1102	453	468	1079	840	135	1274

POWER RESIDUES

	0	1	2	3	4	5	6	7	8	9
0	1	6	36	216	1296	1261	1051	1094	49	294
1	461	160	960	548	682	183	1098	73	438	22
2	132	792	843	1149	379	971	614	1078	1256	1021
3	914	272	329	671	117	702	303	515	484	298
4	485	304	521	520	514	478	262	269	311	563
5	772	723	429	1271	1111	151	906	224	41	246
6	173	1038	1016	884	92	552	706	327	659	45
7	270	317	599	988	716	387	1019	902	200	1200
8	685	201	1206	721	417	1199	679	165	990	728
9	459	148	888	116	696	267	299	491	340	737
10	513	472	226	53	318	605	1024	932	380	977
11	650	1294	1249	979	662	63	378	965	578	862
12	1263	1063	1166	481	280	377	959	542	646	1270
13	1105	115	690	231	83	498	382	989	722	423
14	1235	895	158	948	476	250	197	1182	577	856
15	1227	847	1173	523	532	586	910	248	185	1110
16	145	870	8	48	288	425	1247	967	590	934
17	392	1049	1082	1280	1165	475	244	161	966	584
18	898	176	1056	1124	229	71	426	1253	1003	806
19	927	350	797	873	26	156	936	404	1121	211
20	1266	1081	1274	1129	259	251	203	1218	793	849
21	1185	595	964	572	826	1047	1070	1208	733	489
22	328	665	81	486	310	557	736	507	436	10
23	60	360	857	1233	883	86	516	490	334	701
24	297	479	268	305	527	556	730	471	220	17
25	102	612	1066	1184	589	928	356	833	1089	19
26	114	684	195	1170	505	424	1241	931	374	941
27	434	1301	1291	1231	871	14	84	504	418	1205
28	715	381	983	686	207	1242	937	410	1157	427
29	1259	1039	1022	920	308	545	664	75	450	94
30	564	778	759	645	1264	1069	1202	697	273	335
31	707	333	695	261	263	275	347	779	765	681
32	177	1062	1160	445	64	384	1001	794	855	1221
33	811	957	530	574	838	1119	199	1194	649	1288
34	1213	763	669	105	630	1174	529	568	802	903
35	206	1236	901	194	1164	469	208	1248	973	626
36	1150	385	1007	830	1071	1214	769	705	321	623
37	1132	277	359	851	1197	667	93	558	742	543
38	652	3	18	108	648	1282	1177	547	676	147
39	882	80	480	274	341	743	549	688	219	11
40	66	396	1073	1226	841	1137	307	539	628	1162
41	457	136	816	987	710	351	803	909	242	149
42	894	152	912	260	257	239	131	786	807	933
43	386	1013	866	1287	1207	727	453	112	672	123
44	738	519	508	442	46	276	353	815	981	674
45	135	810	951	494	358	845	1161	451	100	600
46	994	752	603	1012	860	1251	991	734	495	364
47	881	74	444	58	348	785	801	897	170	1020
48	908	236	113	678	159	954	512	466	190	1140
49	325	647	1276	1141	331	683	189	1134	289	431

P = 1303

INDICES

	0	1	2	3	4	5	6	7	8	9
50	1067	999	1127	1271	277	264	843	227	442	978
51	859	672	486	100	44	37	236	1078	1126	441
52	43	42	1235	153	968	952	1236	244	562	346
53	332	701	154	632	1017	596	1164	1215	969	407
54	992	552	127	379	953	295	1230	387	13	396
55	1237	1112	65	1177	1293	539	245	225	377	1189
56	1046	1029	563	49	300	1091	750	877	347	1118
57	869	1208	213	897	333	740	1086	148	118	1191
58	702	789	734	502	179	643	155	725	931	254
59	168	527	633	1065	1162	211	961	717	1018	72
60	459	686	890	462	597	105	958	745	963	587
61	1165	1253	251	783	26	1048	1216	934	731	912
62	1146	665	970	369	737	1134	359	1039	408	1100
63	344	1089	684	580	993	509	1026	582	872	947
64	553	765	1290	1280	719	303	128	491	384	338
65	110	1031	380	761	989	1035	1142	779	954	68
66	629	639	114	1204	296	221	1233	375	1160	342
67	1231	33	438	995	449	1059	388	1010	483	86
68	1020	319	14	495	261	80	283	565	397	677
69	132	902	602	514	1238	312	94	307	756	1248
70	1113	239	35	1110	723	367	66	310	862	511
71	414	1284	1178	819	905	280	74	806	1294	830
72	1153	83	138	51	540	769	799	435	89	984
73	246	864	557	218	467	998	226	99	440	951
74	700	1214	378	395	538	1028	876	896	1190	642
75	526	716	461	586	1047	664	1038	579	946	302
76	1030	778	1203	341	1058	318	564	513	1247	366
77	1283	805	50	983	997	1213	895	585	301	317
78	804	584	693	694	1092	475	427	887	688	695
79	751	1137	21	208	327	1093	878	192	915	928
80	620	476	348	416	623	786	189	428	1119	1104
81	451	330	748	888	870	447	412	874	691	689
82	1209	1243	774	1043	892	696	214	795	826	1174
83	363	752	898	257	1006	1227	1200	1138	334	1286
84	505	404	661	22	741	455	1061	151	1187	209
85	1087	373	1108	949	1211	328	149	232	974	1123
86	464	1094	119	519	545	669	432	879	1192	921
87	161	274	1150	193	703	1180	940	837	816	916
88	790	470	390	234	63	929	735	627	92	555
89	1245	621	503	938	420	141	599	477	180	848
90	1220	352	77	349	644	607	56	1052	480	417
91	156	821	422	533	30	624	726	1081	1012	976
92	293	787	932	759	675	767	776	190	255	919
93	605	267	107	429	169	1257	196	286	1277	1120
94	528	269	1169	882	1023	1105	634	907	143	591
95	1097	452	1066	842	485	1125	967	331	1163	126
96	12	1292	1045	749	212	117	178	167	960	889
97	962	25	1145	358	683	871	718	109	1141	113
98	1159	448	1019	282	601	755	722	413	73	137
99	88	466	699	875	460	945	1057	1282	894	692

POWER RESIDUES

	0	1	2	3	4	5	6	7	8	9
50	1283	1183	583	892	140	840	1131	271	323	635
51	1204	709	345	767	693	249	191	1146	361	863
52	1269	1099	79	474	238	125	750	591	940	428
53	1265	1075	1238	913	266	293	455	124	744	555
54	724	435	4	24	144	864	1275	1135	295	467
55	196	1176	541	640	1234	889	122	732	483	292
56	449	88	528	562	766	687	213	1278	1153	403
57	1115	175	1050	1088	13	78	468	202	1212	757
58	633	1192	637	1216	781	777	753	609	1048	1076
59	1244	949	482	286	413	1175	535	604	1018	896
60	164	984	692	243	155	930	368	905	218	5
61	30	180	1080	1268	1093	43	258	245	167	1002
62	800	891	134	804	915	278	365	887	110	660
63	51	306	533	592	946	464	178	1068	1196	661
64	57	342	749	585	904	212	1272	1117	187	1122
65	217	1302	1297	1267	1087	7	42	252	209	1254
66	1009	842	1143	343	755	621	1120	205	1230	865
67	1281	1171	511	460	154	924	332	689	225	47
68	282	389	1031	974	632	1186	601	1000	788	819
69	1005	818	999	782	783	789	825	1041	1034	992
70	740	531	580	874	32	192	1152	397	1079	1262
71	1057	1130	265	287	419	1211	751	597	976	644
72	1258	1033	986	704	315	587	916	284	401	1103
73	103	618	1102	97	582	886	104	624	1138	313
74	575	844	1155	415	1187	607	1036	1004	812	963
75	566	790	831	1077	1250	985	698	279	371	923
76	326	653	9	54	324	641	1240	925	338	725
77	441	40	240	137	822	1023	926	344	761	657
78	33	198	1188	613	1072	1220	805	921	314	581
79	880	68	408	1145	355	827	1053	1106	121	726
80	447	76	456	130	780	771	717	393	1055	1118
81	193	1158	433	1295	1255	1015	878	56	336	713
82	369	911	254	221	23	138	828	1059	1142	337
83	719	405	1127	247	179	1074	1232	877	50	300
84	497	376	953	506	430	1277	1147	367	899	182
85	1092	37	222	29	174	1044	1052	1100	85	510
86	454	118	708	339	731	477	256	233	95	570
87	814	975	638	1222	817	993	746	567	796	867
88	1293	1243	943	446	70	420	1217	787	813	969
89	602	1006	824	1035	998	776	747	573	832	1083
90	1286	1201	691	237	119	714	375	947	470	214
91	1284	1189	619	1108	133	798	879	62	372	929
92	362	869	2	12	72	432	1289	1219	799	885
93	98	588	922	320	617	1096	61	366	893	146
94	876	44	264	281	383	995	758	639	1228	853
95	1209	739	525	544	658	39	234	101	606	1030
96	968	596	970	608	1042	1040	1028	956	524	538
97	622	1126	241	143	858	1239	919	302	509	448
98	82	492	346	773	729	465	184	1104	109	654
99	15	90	540	634	1198	673	129	774	735	501

P = 1303

INDICES

	0	1	2	3	4	5	6	7	8	9
100	687	326	619	188	747	690	891	362	1199	660
101	1186	1210	463	431	1149	815	62	1244	598	76
102	479	29	292	775	106	1276	1022	1096	966	1044
103	959	682	1158	721	698	893	746	1185	61	291
104	965	697	964	1074	855	1267	1075	215	588	171
105	572	6	856	796	1166	808	182	710	1268	827
106	1254	1069	321	121	1076	1175	252	1132	637	305
107	216	364	784	402	835	531	589	753	27	708
108	612	201	172	899	1049	1259	1301	654	573	258
109	1217	1296	850	614	7	1007	935	1001	16	521
110	857	1228	732	729	987	130	797	1201	913	1004
111	159	54	1167	1139	1147	570	1299	647	809	335
112	666	198	649	1262	183	1287	971	832	1222	203
113	711	506	370	1129	497	547	1269	405	738	1251
114	489	493	828	662	1135	793	517	846	1255	23
115	360	1072	706	568	1070	742	1040	288	811	1195
116	322	456	409	1155	354	174	122	1062	1101	1273
117	263	671	1077	152	345	595	551	386	1176	1188
118	1090	1207	147	501	253	210	685	744	782	911
119	1133	1088	581	1279	337	1034	638	374	994	85
120	79	901	306	1109	510	279	82	434	217	950
121	1027	715	578	340	365	1212	583	886	207	927
122	785	329	873	1042	1173	1226	403	150	948	1122
123	668	273	836	233	554	140	351	1051	532	975
124	766	266	285	881	590	1124	1291	166	357	112
125	754	465	1281	187	659	814	28	1095	720	290
126	1266	5	709	120	304	530	200	653	613	520
127	129	53	646	1261	202	546	492	845	567	1194
128	173	670	385	500	910	1033	900	433	339	926
129	1225	272	1050	880	111	813	4	652	1260	1193
130	1032	271	651							

POWER RESIDUES

	0	1	2	3	4	5	6	7	8	9
100	400	1097	67	402	1109	139	834	1095	55	330
101	677	153	918	296	473	232	89	534	598	982
102	680	171	1026	944	452	106	636	1210	745	561
103	760	651	1300	1285	1195	655	21	126	756	627
104	1156	421	1223	823	1029	962	560	754	615	1084
105	1292	1237	907	230	77	462	166	996	764	675
106	141	846	1167	487	316	593	952	500	394	1061
107	1154	409	1151	391	1043	1046	1064	1172	517	496
108	370	917	290	437	16	96	576	850	1191	631
109	1180	565	784	795	861	1257	1027	950	488	322
110	629	1168	493	352	809	945	458	142	852	1203
111	703	309	551	700	291	443	52	312	569	808
112	939	422	1229	859	1245	955	518	502	406	1133
113	283	395	1067	1190	625	1144	349	791	837	1113
114	163	978	656	27	162	972	620	1114	169	1014
115	872	20	120	720	411	1163	463	172	1032	980
116	668	99	594	958	536	610	1054	1112	157	942
117	440	34	204	1224	829	1065	1178	553	712	363
118	875	38	228	65	390	1037	1010	848	1179	559
119	748	579	868	1299	1279	1159	439	28	168	1008
120	836	1107	127	762	663	69	414	1181	571	820
121	1011	854	1215	775	741	537	616	1090	25	150
122	900	188	1128	253	215	1290	1225	835	1101	91
123	546	670	111	666	87	522	526	550	694	255
124	227	59	354	821	1017	890	128	768	699	285
125	407	1139	319	611	1060	1148	373	935	398	1085
126	1298	1273	1123	223	35	210	1260	1045	1058	1136
127	301	503	412	1169	499	388	1025	938	416	1193
128	643	1252	997	770	711	357	839	1125	235	107
129	642	1246	961	554	718	399	1091	31	186	1116
130	181	1086								

P = 1307

INDICES

	0	1	2	3	4	5	6	7	8	9
0		0	1	296	2	227	297	864	3	592
1	228	535	298	1061	865	523	4	1214	593	1266
2	229	1160	536	1052	299	454	1062	888	866	1141
3	524	1025	5	831	1215	1091	594	1166	1267	51
4	230	222	1161	37	537	819	1053	1032	300	422
5	455	204	1063	139	889	762	867	256	1142	709
6	525	555	1026	150	6	1288	832	602	1216	42
7	1092	1201	595	271	1167	750	1268	93	52	686
8	231	1184	223	1156	1162	135	38	131	538	343
9	820	619	1054	15	1033	187	301	645	423	1127
10	456	542	205	250	1064	81	140	101	890	1008
11	763	156	868	124	257	1279	1143	347	710	772
12	526	1070	556	518	1027	681	151	285	7	333
13	1289	68	833	824	603	1115	1217	1228	43	928
14	1093	22	1202	290	596	62	272	718	1168	623
15	751	471	1269	500	94	1252	53	854	687	435
16	232	610	1185	946	224	1058	1157	1138	1163	816
17	136	552	39	90	132	12	539	1005	344	678
18	821	19	620	851	1055	87	16	443	1034	446
19	188	966	302	979	646	278	424	1037	1128	480
20	457	898	543	699	206	449	251	338	1065	495
21	82	578	141	191	102	264	891	583	1009	567
22	764	969	157	728	869	1046	125	465	258	305
23	1280	389	1144	322	348	1259	711	982	773	1294
24	527	631	1071	174	557	649	519	1021	1028	146
25	682	183	152	281	286	431	8	962	334	724
26	1290	427	69	1082	834	366	825	639	604	1040
27	1116	73	1218	915	1229	989	44	1131	929	311
28	1094	196	23	663	1203	483	291	1086	597	1122
29	63	941	273	460	719	936	1169	117	624	807
30	752	901	472	838	1270	782	501	31	95	546
31	1253	801	54	107	855	377	688	702	436	370
32	233	397	611	1174	1186	209	947	1304	225	590
33	1059	1212	1158	452	1139	829	1164	220	817	420
34	137	254	553	1286	40	269	91	1182	133	341
35	13	643	540	79	1006	122	345	1068	679	331
36	822	1226	20	60	621	498	852	608	1056	814
37	88	1003	17	85	444	977	1035	896	447	493
38	189	581	967	1044	303	320	980	629	647	144
39	279	960	425	364	1038	913	1129	194	481	1120
40	458	115	899	780	544	105	700	395	207	588
41	450	218	252	267	339	77	1066	1224	496	812
42	83	894	579	318	142	362	192	113	103	586
43	265	1222	892	360	584	358	1010	1012	568	1238
44	765	1014	970	240	158	570	729	919	870	1240
45	1047	757	126	767	466	846	259	1016	306	796
46	1281	972	390	1233	1145	242	323	737	349	160
47	1260	1150	712	572	983	414	774	731	1295	993
48	528	921	632	906	1072	872	175	1104	558	1242
49	650	861	520	1049	1022	48	1029	759	147	1198

POWER RESIDUES

	0	1	2	3	4	5	6	7	8	9
0	1	2	4	8	16	32	64	128	256	512
1	1024	741	175	350	700	93	186	372	744	181
2	362	724	141	282	564	1128	949	591	1182	1057
3	807	307	614	1228	1149	991	675	43	86	172
4	344	688	69	138	276	552	1104	901	495	990
5	673	39	78	156	312	624	1248	1189	1071	835
6	363	726	145	290	580	1160	1013	719	131	262
7	524	1048	789	271	542	1084	861	415	830	353
8	706	105	210	420	840	373	746	185	370	740
9	173	346	692	77	154	308	616	1232	1157	1007
10	707	107	214	428	856	405	810	313	626	1252
11	1197	1087	867	427	854	401	802	297	594	1188
12	1069	831	355	710	113	226	452	904	501	1002
13	697	87	174	348	696	85	170	340	680	53
14	106	212	424	848	389	778	249	498	996	685
15	63	126	252	504	1008	709	111	222	444	888
16	469	938	569	1138	969	631	1262	1217	1127	947
17	587	1174	1041	775	243	486	972	637	1274	1241
18	1175	1043	779	251	502	1004	701	95	190	380
19	760	213	426	852	397	794	281	562	1124	941
20	575	1150	993	679	51	102	204	408	816	325
21	650	1300	1293	1279	1251	1195	1083	859	411	822
22	337	674	41	82	164	328	656	5	10	20
23	40	80	160	320	640	1280	1253	1199	1091	875
24	443	886	465	930	553	1106	905	503	1006	705
25	103	206	412	824	341	682	57	114	228	456
26	912	517	1034	761	215	430	860	413	826	345
27	690	73	146	292	584	1168	1029	751	195	390
28	780	253	506	1012	717	127	254	508	1016	725
29	143	286	572	1144	981	655	3	6	12	24
30	48	96	192	384	768	229	458	916	525	1050
31	793	279	558	1116	925	543	1086	865	423	846
32	385	770	233	466	932	557	1114	921	535	1070
33	833	359	718	129	258	516	1032	757	207	414
34	828	349	698	89	178	356	712	117	234	468
35	936	565	1130	953	599	1198	1089	871	435	870
36	433	866	425	850	393	786	265	530	1060	813
37	319	638	1276	1245	1183	1059	811	315	630	1260
38	1213	1119	931	555	1110	913	519	1038	769	231
39	462	924	541	1082	857	407	814	321	642	1284
40	1261	1215	1123	939	571	1142	977	647	1294	1281
41	1255	1203	1099	891	475	950	593	1186	1065	823
42	339	678	49	98	196	392	784	261	522	1044
43	781	255	510	1020	733	159	318	636	1272	1237
44	1167	1027	747	187	374	748	189	378	756	205
45	410	820	333	666	25	50	100	200	400	800
46	293	586	1172	1037	767	227	454	908	509	1018
47	729	151	302	604	1208	1109	911	515	1030	753
48	199	398	796	285	570	1140	973	639	1278	1249
49	1191	1075	843	379	758	209	418	836	365	730

P = 1307

INDICES

	0	1	2	3	4	5	6	7	8	9
50	683	128	184	247	153	769	282	1112	287	468
51	432	1135	9	848	963	477	335	261	725	386
52	1291	1018	428	1079	70	308	1083	933	835	798
53	367	1301	826	1283	640	328	605	974	1041	957
54	1117	392	74	315	1219	1235	916	843	1230	1147
55	990	1101	45	244	1132	383	930	325	312	1098
56	1095	739	197	671	24	351	664	742	1204	162
57	484	404	292	1262	1087	200	598	1152	1123	1275
58	64	714	942	674	274	574	461	170	720	985
59	937	27	1170	416	118	999	625	776	808	354
60	753	733	902	1194	473	1297	839	667	1271	995
61	783	787	502	530	32	745	96	923	547	694
62	1254	634	802	1207	55	908	108	791	856	1074
63	378	165	689	874	703	512	437	177	371	487
64	234	1106	398	506	612	560	1175	407	1187	1244
65	210	879	948	652	1305	295	226	863	591	534
66	1060	522	1213	1265	1159	1051	453	887	1140	1024
67	830	1090	1165	50	221	36	818	1031	471	203
68	138	761	255	708	554	149	1287	601	41	1200
69	270	749	92	685	1183	1155	134	130	342	618
70	14	186	644	1126	541	249	80	100	1007	155
71	123	1278	346	771	1069	517	680	284	332	67
72	823	1114	1227	927	21	289	61	717	622	470
73	499	1251	853	434	609	945	1057	1137	815	551
74	89	11	1004	677	18	850	86	442	445	965
75	978	277	1036	479	897	698	448	337	494	577
76	190	263	582	566	968	727	1045	464	304	388
77	321	1258	981	1293	630	173	648	1020	145	182
78	280	430	961	723	426	1081	365	638	1039	72
79	914	988	1130	310	195	662	482	1085	1121	940
80	459	935	116	806	900	837	781	30	545	800
81	106	376	701	369	396	1173	208	1303	589	1211
82	451	828	219	419	253	1285	268	1181	340	642
83	78	121	1067	330	1225	59	497	607	813	1002
84	84	976	895	492	580	1043	319	628	143	959
85	363	912	193	1119	114	779	104	394	587	217
86	266	76	1223	811	893	317	361	112	585	1221
87	359	357	1011	1237	1013	239	569	918	1239	756
88	766	845	1015	795	971	1232	241	736	159	1149
89	571	413	730	992	920	905	871	1103	1241	860
90	1048	47	758	1197	127	246	768	1111	467	1134
91	847	476	260	385	1017	1078	307	932	797	1300
92	1282	327	973	956	391	314	1234	842	1146	1100
93	243	382	324	1097	738	670	350	741	161	403
94	1261	199	1151	1274	713	673	573	169	984	26
95	415	998	775	353	732	1193	1296	666	994	786
96	529	744	922	693	633	1206	907	790	1073	164
97	873	511	176	486	1105	505	559	406	1243	878
98	651	294	862	533	521	1264	1050	886	1023	1089
99	49	35	1030	202	760	707	148	600	1199	748

POWER RESIDUES

	0	1	2	3	4	5	6	7	8	9
50	153	306	612	1224	1141	975	643	1286	1265	1223
51	1139	971	635	1270	1233	1159	1011	715	123	246
52	492	984	661	15	30	60	120	240	480	960
53	613	1226	1145	983	659	11	22	44	88	176
54	352	704	101	202	404	808	309	618	1236	1165
55	1023	739	171	342	684	61	122	244	488	976
56	645	1290	1273	1239	1171	1035	763	219	438	876
57	445	890	473	946	585	1170	1033	759	211	422
58	844	381	762	217	434	868	429	858	409	818
59	329	658	9	18	36	72	144	288	576	1152
60	997	687	67	134	268	536	1072	837	367	734
61	161	322	644	1288	1269	1231	1155	1003	699	91
62	182	364	728	149	298	596	1192	1077	847	387
63	774	241	482	964	621	1242	1177	1047	787	267
64	534	1068	829	351	702	97	194	388	776	245
65	490	980	653	1306	1305	1303	1299	1291	1275	1243
66	1179	1051	795	283	566	1132	957	607	1214	1121
67	935	563	1126	945	583	1166	1025	743	179	358
68	716	125	250	500	1000	693	79	158	316	632
69	1264	1221	1135	963	619	1238	1169	1031	755	203
70	406	812	317	634	1268	1229	1151	995	683	59
71	118	236	472	944	581	1162	1017	727	147	294
72	588	1176	1045	783	259	518	1036	765	223	446
73	892	477	954	601	1202	1097	887	467	934	561
74	1122	937	567	1134	961	615	1230	1153	999	691
75	75	150	300	600	1200	1093	879	451	902	497
76	994	681	55	110	220	440	880	453	906	505
77	1010	713	119	238	476	952	597	1194	1081	855
78	403	806	305	610	1220	1133	959	611	1222	1137
79	967	627	1254	1201	1095	883	459	918	529	1058
80	809	311	622	1244	1181	1055	803	299	598	1196
81	1085	863	419	838	369	738	169	338	676	45
82	90	180	360	720	133	266	532	1064	821	335
83	670	33	66	132	264	528	1056	805	303	606
84	1212	1117	927	547	1094	881	455	910	513	1026
85	745	183	366	732	157	314	628	1256	1205	1103
86	899	491	982	657	7	14	28	56	112	224
87	448	896	485	970	633	1266	1225	1143	979	651
88	1302	1297	1287	1267	1227	1147	987	667	27	54
89	108	216	432	864	421	842	377	754	201	402
90	804	301	602	1204	1101	895	483	966	625	1250
91	1193	1079	851	395	790	273	546	1092	877	447
92	894	481	962	617	1234	1161	1015	723	139	278
93	556	1112	917	527	1054	801	295	590	1180	1053
94	799	291	582	1164	1021	735	163	326	652	1304
95	1301	1295	1283	1259	1211	1115	923	539	1078	849
96	391	782	257	514	1028	749	191	382	764	221
97	442	884	461	922	537	1074	841	375	750	193
98	386	772	237	474	948	589	1178	1049	791	275
99	550	1100	893	479	958	609	1218	1129	951	595

P = 1307

INDICES

	0	1	2	3	4	5	6	7	8	9
100	684	1154	129	617	185	1125	248	99	154	1277
101	770	516	283	66	1113	926	288	716	469	1250
102	433	944	1136	550	10	676	849	441	964	276
103	478	697	336	576	262	565	726	463	387	1257
104	1292	172	1019	181	429	722	1080	637	71	987
105	309	661	1084	939	934	805	836	29	799	375
106	368	1172	1302	1210	827	418	1284	1180	641	120
107	329	58	606	1001	975	491	1042	627	958	911
108	1118	778	393	216	75	810	316	111	1220	356
109	1236	238	917	755	844	794	1231	735	1148	412
110	991	904	1102	859	46	1196	245	1110	1133	475
111	384	1077	931	1299	326	955	313	841	1099	381
112	1096	669	740	402	198	1273	672	168	25	997
113	352	1192	665	785	743	692	1205	789	163	510
114	485	504	405	877	293	532	1263	885	1088	34
115	201	706	599	747	1153	616	1124	98	1276	515
116	65	925	715	1249	943	549	675	440	275	696
117	575	564	462	1256	171	180	721	636	986	660
118	938	804	28	374	1171	1209	417	1179	119	57
119	1000	490	626	910	777	215	809	110	355	237
120	754	793	734	411	903	858	1195	1109	474	1076
121	1298	954	840	380	668	401	1272	167	996	1191
122	784	691	788	509	503	876	531	884	33	705
123	746	615	97	514	924	1248	548	439	695	563
124	1255	179	635	659	803	373	1208	1178	56	489
125	909	214	109	236	792	410	857	1108	1075	953
126	379	400	166	1190	690	508	875	883	704	614
127	513	1247	438	562	178	658	372	1177	488	213
128	235	409	1107	952	399	1189	507	882	613	1246
129	561	657	1176	212	408	951	1188	881	1245	656
130	211	950	880	655	949	654	653			

POWER RESIDUES

	0	1	2	3	4	5	6	7	8	9
100	1190	1073	839	371	742	177	354	708	109	218
101	436	872	437	874	441	882	457	914	521	1042
102	777	247	494	988	669	31	62	124	248	496
103	992	677	47	94	188	376	752	197	394	788
104	269	538	1076	845	383	766	225	450	900	493
105	986	665	23	46	92	184	368	736	165	330
106	660	13	26	52	104	208	416	832	357	714
107	121	242	484	968	629	1258	1209	1111	915	523
108	1046	785	263	526	1052	797	287	574	1148	989
109	671	35	70	140	280	560	1120	933	559	1118
110	929	551	1102	897	487	974	641	1282	1257	1207
111	1107	907	507	1014	721	135	270	540	1080	853
112	399	798	289	578	1156	1005	703	99	198	396
113	792	277	554	1108	909	511	1022	737	167	334
114	668	29	58	116	232	464	928	549	1098	889
115	471	942	577	1154	1001	695	83	166	332	664
116	21	42	84	168	336	672	37	74	148	296
117	592	1184	1061	815	323	646	1292	1277	1247	1187
118	1067	827	347	694	81	162	324	648	1296	1285
119	1263	1219	1131	955	603	1206	1105	903	499	998
120	689	71	142	284	568	1136	965	623	1246	1185
121	1063	819	331	662	17	34	68	136	272	544
122	1088	869	431	862	417	834	361	722	137	274
123	548	1096	885	463	926	545	1090	873	439	878
124	449	898	489	978	649	1298	1289	1271	1235	1163
125	1019	731	155	310	620	1240	1173	1039	771	235
126	470	940	573	1146	985	663	19	38	76	152
127	304	608	1216	1125	943	579	1158	1009	711	115
128	230	460	920	533	1066	825	343	686	65	130
129	260	520	1040	773	239	478	956	605	1210	1113
130	919	531	1062	817	327	654				

P = 1319

INDICES

	0	1	2	3	4	5	6	7	8	9
0		0	18	692	36	1208	710	298	54	66
1	1226	682	728	1	316	582	72	905	84	476
2	1244	990	700	863	746	1098	19	758	334	1019
3	600	556	90	56	923	188	102	1217	494	693
4	1262	867	1008	1078	718	1274	881	1017	764	596
5	1116	279	37	930	776	572	352	1168	1037	949
6	618	163	574	364	108	1209	74	1064	941	237
7	206	124	120	465	1235	472	512	980	711	1159
8	1280	132	885	1312	1026	795	1096	393	736	808
9	1292	299	899	1248	1035	366	782	377	614	748
10	1134	50	297	1243	55	880	948	119	794	613
11	590	591	370	489	1186	753	1055	67	967	1203
12	636	46	181	241	592	988	382	29	126	452
13	1227	817	92	774	1082	648	959	371	255	216
14	224	391	142	683	138	909	483	1288	1253	634
15	490	1196	530	971	998	446	729	969	1177	304
16	1298	1161	150	1187	903	1264	12	851	1044	2
17	813	542	1114	1155	411	78	754	323	826	435
18	1310	398	317	855	917	1107	1266	269	1053	1056
19	384	1104	800	1110	395	583	632	320	766	937
20	1152	438	68	1317	315	757	1261	929	73	1158
21	898	879	966	816	137	968	812	854	631	1157
22	608	906	609	1084	388	1164	507	368	1204	1180
23	771	354	1073	449	85	907	985	533	1221	43
24	654	637	64	824	199	486	259	477	610	686
25	1006	877	400	227	47	169	144	374	470	197
26	1245	1085	835	805	110	820	792	182	1100	129
27	666	212	977	991	389	462	273	184	234	622
28	242	1206	409	892	160	1058	701	1165	156	492
29	927	1069	501	593	1306	839	1271	122	652	864
30	508	58	1214	742	548	53	989	922	1016	617
31	464	1095	747	369	987	254	1195	902	322	383
32	1316	811	1179	63	168	1099	1205	1305	921	1315
33	1282	1172	30	1283	869	954	1062	983	20	1181
34	831	1238	560	894	1132	127	1173	201	429	944
35	96	759	772	1212	341	14	844	577	453	31
36	10	952	416	738	335	355	873	598	935	933
37	1125	1228	1284	1119	287	362	1071	1020	1074	284
38	402	721	1122	780	818	870	1128	1144	413	497
39	601	450	650	191	338	1049	784	93	955	148
40	1170	1022	456	557	86	22	17	581	333	866
41	775	1063	1279	1247	947	1202	91	908	1176	541
42	916	319	897	1083	984	685	834	461	155	57
43	986	1304	830	1211	872	283	649	21	1175	1303
44	626	662	924	534	627	698	1102	8	406	960
45	1182	231	525	570	386	189	1222	663	1198	345
46	789	734	372	832	1091	1138	467	193	103	44
47	925	343	1003	442	551	256	1239	996	61	275
48	672	1218	655	535	82	267	842	768	217	561
49	504	306	277	606	495	638	628	422	704	134

POWER RESIDUES

	0	1	2	3	4	5	6	7	8	9
0	1	13	169	878	862	654	588	1049	447	535
1	360	723	166	839	355	658	640	406	2	26
2	338	437	405	1308	1176	779	894	1070	720	127
3	332	359	710	1316	1280	812	4	52	676	874
4	810	1297	1033	239	469	821	121	254	664	718
5	101	1313	1241	305	8	104	33	429	301	1275
6	747	478	938	323	242	508	9	117	202	1307
7	1163	610	16	208	66	858	602	1231	175	956
8	557	646	484	1016	18	234	404	1295	1007	1220
9	32	416	132	397	1204	1143	350	593	1114	1292
10	968	713	36	468	808	1271	695	1121	64	832
11	264	794	1089	967	700	1186	909	1265	617	107
12	72	936	297	1223	71	923	128	345	528	269
13	859	615	81	1053	499	1211	1234	214	144	553
14	594	1127	142	527	256	690	1056	538	399	1230
15	162	787	998	1103	1149	428	288	1106	1188	935
16	284	1054	512	61	793	1076	798	1141	324	255
17	677	887	979	856	576	893	1057	551	568	789
18	1024	122	267	833	277	963	648	510	35	455
19	639	393	1152	467	795	1102	1136	259	729	244
20	534	347	554	607	1296	1020	70	910	1278	786
21	985	934	271	885	953	518	139	488	1068	694
22	1108	1214	1273	721	140	501	1237	253	651	549
23	542	451	587	1036	278	976	817	69	897	1109
24	1227	123	280	1002	1155	506	1302	1098	1084	902
25	1174	753	556	633	315	138	475	899	1135	246
26	560	685	991	1012	1285	877	849	485	1029	187
27	1112	1266	630	276	950	479	951	492	1120	51
28	663	705	1251	435	379	970	739	374	905	1213
29	1260	552	581	958	583	984	921	102	7	91
30	1183	870	758	621	159	748	491	1107	1201	1104
31	1162	597	1166	649	523	204	14	182	1047	421
32	197	1242	318	177	982	895	1083	889	1005	1194
33	1013	1298	1046	408	28	364	775	842	394	1165
34	636	354	645	471	847	459	691	1069	707	1277
35	773	816	56	728	231	365	788	1011	1272	708
36	1290	942	375	918	63	819	95	1235	227	313
37	112	137	462	730	257	703	1225	97	1261	565
38	750	517	126	319	190	1151	454	626	224	274
39	924	141	514	87	1131	194	1203	1130	181	1034
40	252	638	380	983	908	1252	448	548	529	282
41	1028	174	943	388	1087	941	362	749	504	1276
42	760	647	497	1185	896	1096	1058	564	737	348
43	567	776	855	563	724	179	1008	1233	201	1294
44	994	1051	473	873	797	1128	155	696	1134	233
45	391	1126	129	358	697	1147	402	1269	669	783
46	946	427	275	937	310	73	949	466	782	933
47	258	716	75	975	804	1219	19	247	573	854
48	550	555	620	146	579	932	245	547	516	113
49	150	631	289	1119	38	494	1146	389	1100	1110

P = 1319

INDICES

	0	1	2	3	4	5	6	7	8	9
50	1024	225	895	1010	418	1258	245	694	65	699
51	187	763	162	1234	392	1133	488	381	215	529
52	1263	825	1103	314	853	770	823	143	128	408
53	838	1015	810	868	200	9	1118	1127	147	1278
54	684	1174	230	1090	995	503	1009	487	407	229
55	480	177	291	139	202	481	252	80	640	1079
56	260	961	1224	433	427	379	910	430	178	1039
57	1076	964	719	478	1183	643	174	587	510	484
58	945	292	1087	294	519	1275	611	232	6	1032
59	857	1012	1289	97	140	1093	670	311	882	687
60	526	708	76	1130	1232	1254	760	203	566	691
61	71	1018	1007	571	940	131	1034	118	635	773
62	482	303	1113	1106	765	878	387	532	1005	804
63	272	491	1213	253	920	1237	340	597	401	190
64	16	540	829	697	1197	342	81	421	186	313
65	1117	228	1223	642	5	707	939	531	15	641
66	1300	674	1190	280	48	664	1301	564	887	458
67	972	845	1080	740	1001	538	38	170	1199	675
68	849	1060	1256	999	578	261	912	554	1150	931
69	145	346	1191	1046	219	106	447	454	962	1141
70	114	1294	777	375	790	281	1230	348	359	730
71	32	1225	862	101	595	573	471	735	49	1185
72	28	223	970	11	434	799	756	630	353	198
73	373	665	891	1270	616	1178	953	428	951	286
74	1143	1169	1246	833	1302	524	1137	60	305	417
75	380	837	1089	251	1038	1086	1092	565	302	919
76	420	1299	739	911	1140	861	798	950	836	1139
77	888	1066	1146	350	1162	336	431	889	515	25
78	619	806	468	459	668	859	209	151	356	179
79	1067	787	802	164	111	194	973	444	166	604
80	1188	874	1040	1147	474	1051	575	821	104	846
81	40	724	35	904	599	1077	351	236	884	365
82	793	45	1081	1287	1297	1154	1265	936	965	1163
83	1220	876	109	183	926	741	1194	1314	559	13
84	934	720	337	580	915	1210	1101	344	1002	266
85	703	762	852	1126	479	432	173	1031	75	130
86	1004	539	4	563	848	1045	1229	1184	890	523
87	301	1065	667	443	39	1286	1193	265	3	1285
88	644	516	680	1308	942	213	552	171	645	327
89	716	814	1120	175	26	325	424	238	978	257
90	1200	517	249	750	543	288	588	620	404	116
91	207	992	1240	676	681	745	1216	1115	363	511
92	807	296	752	125	390	997	850	1309	1109	1260
93	1156	1072	485	469	211	159	121	463	62	1061
94	943	415	361	412	1021	946	460	625	569	466
95	274	276	1257	214	1014	994	79	1075	293	669
96	690	1112	1236	185	673	1000	553	113	100	755
97	285	1088	860	514	786	473	235	1219	579	172
98	522	679	324	403	295	210	624	689	513	623
99	656	262	646	546	440	827	722	520	152	657

POWER RESIDUES

	0	1	2	3	4	5	6	7	8	9
50	1240	292	1158	545	490	1094	1032	226	300	1262
51	578	919	76	988	973	778	881	901	1161	584
52	997	1090	980	869	745	452	600	1205	1156	519
53	152	657	627	237	443	483	1003	1168	675	861
54	641	419	171	904	1200	1091	993	1038	304	1314
55	1254	474	886	966	687	1017	31	403	1282	838
56	342	489	1081	863	667	757	608	1309	1189	948
57	453	613	55	715	62	806	1245	357	684	978
58	843	407	15	195	1216	1299	1059	577	906	1226
59	110	111	124	293	1171	714	49	637	367	814
60	30	390	1113	1279	799	1154	493	1133	220	222
61	248	586	1023	109	98	1274	734	309	60	780
62	907	1239	279	989	986	947	440	444	496	1172
63	727	218	196	1229	149	618	120	241	495	1159
64	558	659	653	575	880	888	992	1025	135	436
65	392	1139	298	1236	240	482	990	999	1116	1318
66	1306	1150	441	457	665	731	270	872	784	959
67	596	1153	480	964	661	679	913	1317	1293	981
68	882	914	11	143	540	425	249	599	1192	987
69	960	609	3	39	507	1315	1267	643	445	509
70	22	286	1080	850	498	1198	1065	655	601	1218
71	6	78	1014	1311	1215	1286	890	1018	44	572
72	841	381	996	1077	811	1310	1202	1117	12	156
73	709	1303	1111	1253	461	717	88	1144	363	762
74	673	835	303	1301	1085	915	24	312	99	1287
75	903	1187	922	115	176	969	726	205	27	351
76	606	1283	851	511	48	624	198	1255	487	1055
77	525	230	352	619	133	410	54	702	1212	1247
78	383	1022	96	1248	396	1191	974	791	1050	460
79	704	1238	266	820	108	85	1105	1175	766	725
80	192	1177	792	1063	629	263	781	920	89	1157
81	532	321	216	170	891	1031	213	131	384	1035
82	265	807	1258	526	243	521	178	995	1064	642
83	432	340	463	743	426	262	768	751	530	295
84	1197	1052	486	1042	356	671	809	1284	864	680
85	926	167	852	524	217	183	1060	590	1075	785
86	972	765	712	23	299	1249	409	41	533	334
87	385	1048	434	366	801	1180	831	251	625	211
88	105	46	598	1179	818	82	1066	668	770	777
89	868	732	283	1041	343	502	1250	422	210	92
90	1196	1039	317	164	813	17	221	235	417	145
91	566	763	686	1004	1181	844	420	184	1073	759
92	634	328	307	34	442	470	834	290	1132	207
93	53	689	1043	369	840	368	827	199	1268	656
94	614	68	884	940	349	580	945	414	106	59
95	767	738	361	736	335	398	1217	1312	1228	136
96	449	561	698	1160	571	828	212	118	215	157
97	722	153	670	796	1115	1305	1137	272	898	1122
98	77	1001	1142	337	424	236	430	314	125	306
99	21	273	911	1291	955	544	477	925	154	683

P = 1319

INDICES

	0	1	2	3	4	5	6	7	8	9
100	1042	981	243	536	913	328	1028	88	436	1123
101	1276	357	263	330	712	1207	83	555	717	1167
102	205	1311	781	612	180	647	1252	1160	410	268
103	1151	815	506	42	399	819	233	1068	547	901
104	1281	893	843	932	1121	1048	332	318	871	7
105	788	441	841	133	161	769	146	176	426	586
106	856	1129	1033	803	828	706	886	1059	218	347
107	27	1269	1136	918	1145	858	165	723	1296	1313
108	702	562	1192	326	248	744	1108	414	1013	112
109	521	545	1027	1166	505	1047	425	1268	247	1267
110	498	1290	195	153	309	796	157	307	220	239
111	499	732	270	602	98	974	658	727	1097	493
112	278	107	979	1291	1242	1054	451	141	445	1043
113	397	394	928	607	448	258	196	976	1057	651
114	1094	167	982	95	737	1070	496	455	1201	154
115	661	385	192	671	605	244	528	809	502	639
116	963	518	310	70	1105	339	312	1189	537	1149
117	1293	594	629	1142	250	797	24	801	1050	883
118	875	914	1030	300	1307	423	115	751	158	568
119	1111	785	688	1041	329	1251	900	840	705	1295
120	544	308	726	396	94	527	1148	1029	1250	1249
121	1272	135	778	289	221	714	584	956	709	475
122	89	1273	1036	123	1025	376	589	240	958	633
123	149	77	1052	437	136	367	653	226	791	621
124	500	52	321	1171	1131	576	1124	779	783	865
125	896	282	405	733	550	767	1023	1233	822	1277
126	290	378	509	1011	1231	117	271	696	938	457
127	1255	105	358	222	615	59	419	349	208	603
128	34	1153	558	761	847	264	715	749	1215	1259
129	360	993	99	678	439	87	204	41	331	585
130	1135	743	246	731	1241	975	660	69	23	567
131	725	713	957	51	549	695	33	677	659	

POWER RESIDUES

	0	1	2	3	4	5	6	7	8	9
100	965	674	848	472	860	628	250	612	42	546
101	503	1263	591	1088	954	531	308	47	611	29
102	377	944	401	1256	500	1224	84	1092	1006	1207
103	1182	857	589	1062	616	94	1222	58	754	569
104	802	1193	1000	1129	168	865	693	1095	1045	395
105	1178	805	1232	188	1125	116	189	1138	285	1067
106	681	939	336	411	67	871	771	790	1037	291
107	1145	376	931	232	378	957	570	815	43	559
108	672	822	134	423	223	261	755	582	971	752
109	543	464	756	595	1140	311	86	1118	25	325
110	268	846	446	522	191	1164	623	185	1086	928
111	193	1190	961	622	172	917	50	650	536	373
112	892	1044	382	1009	1246	370	853	537	386	1061
113	603	1244	344	515	100	1300	1072	746	465	769
114	764	699	1173	740	387	1074	772	803	1206	1169
115	688	1030	200	1281	825	173	930	219	209	79
116	1027	161	774	829	225	287	1093	1019	57	741
117	400	1243	331	346	541	438	418	158	735	322
118	229	339	450	574	867	719	114	163	800	1167
119	662	692	1082	876	836	316	151	644	458	678
120	900	1148	415	119	228	326	281	1015	5	65
121	845	433	353	632	302	1288	916	37	481	977
122	830	238	456	652	562	711	10	130	371	866
123	706	1264	604	1257	513	74	962	635	341	476
124	912	1304	1124	103	20	260	742	413	93	1209
125	1208	1195	1026	148	605	1270	682	952	505	1289
126	929	206	40	520	165	826	186	1099	1097	1071
127	733	296	1210	1221	45	585	1010	1259	539	412
128	80	1040	330	333	372	879	875	823	147	592
129	1101	1123	90	1170	701	1199	1078	824	160	761
130	660	666	744	439	431	327	294	1184	883	927
131	180	1021	83	1079	837	329	320	203		

P = 1321

INDICES

	0	1	2	3	4	5	6	7	8	9
0		0	242	144	484	1102	386	565	726	288
1	24	8	628	1	807	1246	968	715	530	1019
2	266	709	250	841	870	884	243	432	1049	238
3	168	728	1210	152	957	347	772	556	1261	145
4	508	1058	951	1220	492	70	1083	713	1112	1130
5	1126	859	485	920	674	1110	1291	1163	480	1251
6	410	459	970	853	132	1103	394	753	1199	985
7	589	30	1014	695	798	1028	183	573	387	855
8	750	576	1300	917	1193	497	142	382	734	881
9	312	566	5	872	955	801	34	1069	52	296
10	48	65	1101	529	727	491	1162	588	916	33
11	32	700	213	1039	85	623	722	289	173	1280
12	652	16	701	1202	1212	666	1095	175	374	44
13	25	644	636	264	995	214	121	1106	1227	961
14	831	857	272	9	1256	20	937	1274	1040	1298
15	1270	973	425	1003	815	510	629	1037	1097	1064
16	992	86	818	649	222	1254	1159	520	115	2
17	739	1307	384	127	624	129	976	75	1123	1294
18	554	769	808	603	247	338	1114	723	1197	997
19	1043	403	276	923	1311	1247	294	1235	538	449
20	290	897	307	803	23	840	771	1129	969	1027
21	733	64	84	174	830	1002	1158	1293	275	839
22	274	716	942	329	455	1172	1281	672	327	534
23	865	717	964	187	531	495	415	999	202	653
24	894	280	258	720	943	912	124	1020	134	1061
25	908	1272	17	849	417	641	616	330	286	1121
26	267	526	886	1264	878	702	506	1025	1237	1088
27	456	1175	363	710	28	892	149	350	1203	1016
28	1073	91	1099	1173	514	945	251	303	178	110
29	262	1213	1179	154	196	1033	1282	440	220	842
30	192	465	1215	209	667	241	1245	1048	1057	673
31	752	749	871	1161	1279	635	19	1096	1306	246
32	1234	732	328	414	1060	885	891	177	464	1278
33	176	980	81	844	762	535	357	1268	244	1183
34	981	736	229	375	626	767	369	269	866	544
35	371	433	1218	82	317	1132	45	104	216	139
36	796	718	1011	160	1050	477	845	790	489	26
37	580	165	36	823	965	810	119	239	1239	763
38	1285	319	645	900	518	355	1165	188	233	11
39	169	236	536	788	157	637	780	541	691	408
40	532	689	1139	729	549	358	1045	564	265	151
41	1082	1250	1013	496	51	699	1211	1105	1269	648
42	975	996	306	1001	326	279	416	1024	1072	153
43	1244	245	80	766	215	164	517	540	1081	1000
44	516	98	958	582	1184	663	571	122	697	99
45	94	1066	203	1117	914	348	569	982	776	1147
46	1107	826	959	1055	1206	654	429	606	773	1318
47	737	1181	657	1228	1241	583	444	1208	895	578
48	1136	557	522	230	500	851	962	687	1185	793
49	1154	281	366	953	1262	78	376	595	1303	832

POWER RESIDUES

	0	1	2	3	4	5	6	7	8	9
0	1	13	169	876	820	92	1196	1017	11	143
1	538	389	1094	1012	1267	619	121	252	634	316
2	145	564	727	204	10	130	369	834	274	920
3	71	923	110	109	96	1248	372	873	781	906
4	1210	1199	1056	518	129	356	665	719	100	1300
5	1048	414	98	1274	710	1304	1100	1090	960	591
6	1078	804	1205	1134	211	101	1313	1217	1290	918
7	45	585	1000	1111	1233	177	980	851	495	1151
8	432	332	353	626	212	114	161	772	789	1010
9	1241	281	1011	1254	450	566	753	542	441	449
10	553	584	987	942	357	678	888	976	799	1140
11	289	1115	1285	853	521	168	863	651	537	376
12	925	136	447	527	246	556	623	173	928	175
13	954	513	64	832	248	582	961	604	1247	359
14	704	1226	86	1118	3	39	507	1307	1139	276
15	946	409	33	429	293	1167	640	394	1159	536
16	363	756	581	948	435	371	860	612	30	390
17	1107	1181	822	118	213	127	330	327	288	1102
18	1116	1298	1022	76	988	955	526	233	387	1068
19	674	836	300	1258	502	1242	294	1180	809	1270
20	658	628	238	452	592	1091	973	760	633	303
21	1297	1009	1228	112	135	434	358	691	1057	531
22	298	1232	164	811	1296	996	1059	557	636	342
23	483	995	1046	388	1081	843	391	1120	29	377
24	938	305	2	26	338	431	319	184	1071	713
25	22	286	1076	778	867	703	1213	1238	242	504
26	1268	632	290	1128	133	408	20	260	738	347
27	548	519	142	525	220	218	192	1175	744	425
28	241	491	1099	1077	791	1036	258	712	9	117
29	200	1279	775	828	196	1227	99	1287	879	859
30	599	1182	835	287	1089	947	422	202	1305	1113
31	1259	515	90	1170	679	901	1145	354	639	381
32	990	981	864	664	706	1252	424	228	322	223
33	257	699	1161	562	701	1187	900	1132	185	1084
34	882	898	1106	1168	653	563	714	35	455	631
35	277	959	578	909	1249	385	1042	336	405	1302
36	1074	752	529	272	894	1054	497	1112	1246	346
37	535	350	587	1026	128	343	496	1164	601	1208
38	1173	718	87	1131	172	915	6	78	1014	1293
39	957	552	571	818	66	858	586	1013	1280	788
40	997	1072	726	191	1162	575	870	742	399	1224
41	60	780	893	1041	323	236	426	254	660	654
42	576	883	911	1275	723	152	655	589	1052	466
43	774	815	27	351	600	1195	1004	1163	588	1039
44	297	1219	1316	1256	476	904	1184	861	625	199
45	1266	606	1273	697	1135	224	270	868	716	61
46	793	1062	596	1143	328	301	1271	671	797	1114
47	1272	684	966	669	771	776	841	365	782	919
48	58	754	555	610	4	52	676	862	638	368
49	821	105	44	572	831	235	413	85	1105	1155

P = 1321

INDICES

	0	1	2	3	4	5	6	7	8	9
50	1150	664	194	1053	259	1167	1091	146	659	627
51	883	1260	858	131	572	311	528	721	43	271
52	509	114	768	1310	1128	273	186	123	1120	362
53	944	219	748	1059	1267	370	159	118	10	1138
54	698	1071	97	913	605	1135	952	1090	270	747
55	1134	1257	391	100	592	482	125	227	1258	1221
56	1315	867	333	345	21	821	95	1141	756	1021
57	1187	392	493	547	545	405	420	938	352	1067
58	504	162	135	928	101	71	396	372	438	427
59	1275	59	204	632	682	1062	462	593	1084	300
60	434	378	707	1041	137	1118	451	1006	909	947
61	483	714	167	1219	1290	984	1299	800	915	15
62	994	1273	991	126	1113	448	83	1171	201	1271
63	877	349	261	208	18	1277	228	1131	488	318
64	156	563	974	765	570	1146	656	850	1302	1259
65	1127	117	1133	344	419	426	706	983	200	562
66	418	1078	1222	860	323	46	1086	1079	1004	473
67	777	467	599	642	190	1316	486	1230	105	314
68	1223	816	978	1148	471	888	617	678	868	921
69	1009	217	611	861	511	743	1108	453	786	331
70	613	334	675	255	140	639	324	630	559	827
71	54	1143	287	249	346	1111	458	797	381	47
72	1038	1094	960	424	1253	1122	402	22	1292	864
73	719	615	1087	1098	1032	1056	731	761	268	795
74	822	1164	407	1012	278	1080	1065	1205	1207	1153
75	1052	527	361	96	481	755	161	681	1005	993
76	207	655	561	598	887	785	1142	1252	760	1051
77	597	474	87	930	430	292	475	1265	253	757
78	411	38	478	670	778	819	1030	607	399	88
79	879	284	1022	460	783	846	933	468	650	108
80	774	1169	931	703	61	1188	971	1232	791	198
81	600	223	1287	1319	806	431	507	919	393	854
82	4	490	172	643	1255	1036	738	602	293	1026
83	941	494	133	525	27	302	191	1160	890	1182
84	1217	476	1238	235	548	1104	1243	581	568	1317
85	521	77	658	113	1266	1089	1314	546	395	299
86	166	447	487	116	322	1229	1008	254	457	863
87	406	754	759	37	782	1231	3	524	1242	298
88	758	1176	340	421	1200	1177	824	875	106	740
89	905	584	813	412	364	1076	939	986	341	966
90	336	315	1308	609	445	551	39	711	1156	353
91	590	422	811	925	1224	385	1018	1209	69	479
92	29	1192	1068	31	1201	120	1297	817	128	1196
93	896	829	671	893	848	505	1015	1178	240	1305
94	979	625	103	579	899	779	150	305	163	696
95	825	1240	686	1149	130	185	1137	390	820	351
96	58	136	799	876	764	705	472	977	742	558
97	1093	1031	1204	206	929	1029	107	1286	1035	889
98	76	321	523	904	608	1017	1195	102	184	741
99	320	836	618	1124	837	231	225	400	1074	988

POWER RESIDUES

	0	1	2	3	4	5	6	7	8	9
50	484	1008	1215	1264	580	935	266	816	40	520
51	155	694	1096	1038	284	1050	440	436	384	1029
52	167	850	482	982	877	833	261	751	516	103
53	18	234	400	1237	229	335	392	1133	198	1253
54	437	397	1198	1043	349	574	857	573	844	404
55	1289	905	1197	1030	180	1019	37	481	969	708
56	1278	762	659	641	407	7	91	1183	848	456
57	644	446	514	77	1001	1124	81	1053	479	943
58	370	847	443	475	891	1015	1306	1126	107	70
59	910	1262	554	597	1156	497	1177	770	763	672
60	810	1283	827	183	1058	544	467	787	984	903
61	1171	692	1070	700	1174	731	256	686	992	1007
62	1202	1095	1025	115	174	941	344	509	12	156
63	707	1265	593	1104	1142	315	132	395	1172	705
64	1239	255	673	823	131	382	1003	1150	419	163
65	798	1127	120	239	465	761	646	472	852	508
66	1320	1308	1152	445	501	1229	125	304	1310	1178
67	783	932	227	309	54	702	1200	1069	687	1005
68	1176	757	594	1117	1311	1191	952	487	1047	401
69	1250	398	1211	1212	1225	73	949	448	540	415
70	111	122	265	803	1192	965	656	602	1221	21
71	273	907	1223	47	611	17	221	231	361	730
72	243	517	116	187	1110	1220	8	104	31	403
73	1276	736	321	210	88	1144	341	470	826	170
74	889	989	968	695	1109	1207	1160	549	532	311
75	80	1040	310	67	871	755	568	779	880	872
76	768	737	334	379	964	643	433	345	522	181
77	1032	206	36	468	800	1153	458	670	784	945
78	396	1185	874	794	1075	765	698	1148	393	1146
79	367	808	1257	489	1073	739	360	717	74	962
80	617	95	1235	203	1318	1282	814	14	182	1045
81	375	912	1288	892	1028	154	681	927	162	785
82	958	565	740	373	886	950	461	709	1291	931
83	214	140	499	1203	1108	1194	991	994	1033	219
84	205	23	299	1245	333	366	795	1088	934	253
85	647	485	1021	63	819	79	1027	141	512	51
86	663	693	1083	869	729	230	348	561	688	1018
87	24	312	93	1209	1186	887	963	630	264	790
88	1023	89	1157	510	25	325	262	764	685	979
89	838	326	275	933	240	478	930	201	1292	944
90	383	1016	1319	1295	983	890	1002	1137	250	608
91	1299	1035	245	543	454	618	108	83	1079	817
92	53	689	1031	193	1188	913	1301	1061	583	974
93	773	802	1179	796	1101	1103	1129	146	577	896
94	1080	830	222	244	530	285	1063	609	1312	1204
95	1121	42	546	493	1125	94	1222	34	442	462
96	722	139	486	1034	232	374	899	1119	16	208
97	62	806	1231	151	642	420	176	967	682	940
98	331	340	457	657	615	69	897	1093	999	1098
99	1064	622	160	759	620	134	421	189	1136	237

P = 1321

INDICES

	0	1	2	3	4	5	6	7	8	9
100	72	574	906	646	436	679	1295	619	501	211
101	89	92	13	397	388	585	901	7	869	555
102	1125	852	182	880	1100	622	373	856	814	519
103	553	922	770	838	963	911	285	1174	513	439
104	751	413	356	543	1010	809	232	688	50	1023
105	515	1116	428	577	365	1166	42	218	604	226
106	1186	927	461	946	990	1276	1301	1077	189	677
107	612	248	401	794	360	784	252	283	60	918
108	940	234	1313	862	339	1075	1155	1191	847	304
109	57	205	1194	987	12	621	512	1115	989	282
110	56	934	179	935	633	498	342	170	834	744
111	724	73	367	309	469	111	180	683	143	967
112	237	950	1109	1198	575	954	587	651	263	936
113	1063	383	337	537	63	454	998	907	1263	148
114	109	1214	634	463	735	316	789	1284	787	1044
115	647	79	662	775	1180	499	594	882	1309	158
116	746	332	404	437	377	1289	1170	155	343	1085
117	313	610	638	380	614	277	680	596	669	932
118	197	171	301	567	446	781	874	335	924	1296
119	1304	685	704	1034	835	435	6	552	542	41
120	676	1312	620	833	949	62	1283	745	379	873
121	40	692	693	256	1248	502	1151	67	1189	441
122	725	708	956	712	409	694	141	295	212	665
123	1226	972	221	74	1042	802	1157	533	257	640
124	1236	90	195	1047	1233	843	368	138	35	354
125	690	1249	325	539	93	1054	443	792	193	310
126	1119	1070	591	1140	503	631	450	14	260	1145
127	199	466	470	452	53	423	730	1152	560	291
128	398	1168	805	601	1216	112	1007	297	812	550
129	68	828	898	389	1092	903	224	210	181	910
130	49	926	359	1190	55	308	586	147	661	1288
131	668	684	948	66	1225	1046	442	1144	804	902
132	660	0								

POWER RESIDUES

	0	1	2	3	4	5	6	7	8	9
100	439	423	215	153	668	758	607	1286	866	690
101	1044	362	743	412	72	936	279	985	916	19
102	247	569	792	1049	427	267	829	209	75	975
103	786	971	734	295	1193	978	825	157	720	113
104	148	603	1234	190	1149	406	1315	1243	307	28
105	364	769	750	503	1255	463	735	308	41	533
106	324	249	595	1130	159	746	451	579	922	97
107	1261	541	428	280	998	1085	895	1067	661	667
108	745	438	410	46	598	1169	666	732	269	855
109	547	506	1294	970	721	126	317	158	733	282
110	1024	102	5	65	845	417	137	460	696	1122
111	55	715	48	624	186	1097	1051	453	605	1260
112	528	259	725	178	993	1020	50	650	524	207
113	49	637	355	652	550	545	480	956	539	402
114	1263	567	766	711	1317	1269	645	459	683	953
115	500	1216	1277	749	490	1086	908	1236	216	166
116	837	313	106	57	741	386	1055	505	1281	801
117	1166	627	225	283	1037	271	881	885	937	292
118	1154	471	839	339	444	488	1060	570	805	1218
119	1303	1087	921	84	1092	986	929	188	1123	68
120	884	924	123	278	972	747	464	748	477	917
121	32	416	124	291	1141	302	1284	840	352	613
122	43	559	662	680	914	1314	1230	138	473	865
123	677	875	807	1244	320	197	1240	268	842	378
124	951	474	878	846	430	306	15	195	1214	1251
125	411	59	767	724	165	824	144	551	558	649
126	511	38	494	1138	263	777	854	534	337	418
127	150	629	251	621	147	590	1065	635	329	314
128	119	226	296	1206	1147	380	977	812	1309	1165
129	614	56	728	217	179	1006	1189	926	149	616
130	82	1066	648	498	1190	939	318	171	902	1158
131	523	194	1201	1082	856	560	675	849	469	813
132										

P = 1327

INDICES

	0	1	2	3	4	5	6	7	8	9
0		0	750	1	174	97	751	417	924	2
1	847	58	175	298	1167	98	348	940	752	63
2	271	418	808	947	925	194	1048	3	591	46
3	848	1015	1098	59	364	514	176	1247	813	299
4	1021	989	1168	1062	232	99	371	130	349	834
5	944	941	472	1219	753	155	15	64	796	1227
6	272	616	439	419	522	395	809	27	1114	948
7	1264	745	926	209	671	195	237	475	1049	734
8	445	4	413	978	592	1037	486	47	982	826
9	849	715	1121	1016	880	160	1099	1174	258	60
10	368	206	365	1203	1222	515	643	224	177	551
11	905	1248	765	1197	814	1044	220	300	651	31
12	1022	116	40	990	1189	291	1169	1206	1272	1063
13	1145	756	233	480	777	100	538	215	372	898
14	688	131	169	356	350	143	959	835	95	1165
15	945	1096	987	942	1225	1112	473	484	158	1220
16	1195	38	754	686	1163	156	402	404	16	596
17	461	65	1236	466	797	611	406	1228	250	917
18	273	518	139	617	545	18	440	998	304	420
19	910	430	523	508	598	396	1008	55	810	392
20	1118	28	956	463	1115	1086	627	949	646	121
21	1265	528	67	746	974	1159	927	106	1301	210
22	329	1238	672	633	189	196	621	1089	238	705
23	468	476	970	1320	1050	227	75	735	781	799
24	446	606	866	5	790	931	414	361	613	979
25	1041	166	593	1005	630	1038	696	408	487	338
26	569	48	180	741	983	1316	1230	827	201	655
27	850	494	1288	716	965	252	1122	699	322	1017
28	112	952	881	885	919	161	1106	80	1100	554
29	893	1175	383	275	259	1324	845	61	589	1245
30	369	153	520	207	411	713	366	549	649	1204
31	536	141	1223	684	1234	516	908	390	644	104
32	619	225	788	1003	178	492	110	552	587	547
33	906	490	1152	1249	1154	124	766	244	20	1198
34	1211	1073	815	1251	660	1045	1216	442	221	774
35	35	301	1156	863	652	842	1000	32	341	377
36	1023	126	1268	117	889	306	41	1283	1295	991
37	768	310	1190	1308	422	292	1054	344	1170	246
38	334	1207	1180	912	1273	572	1258	1064	22	531
39	1146	561	432	757	805	831	234	1200	1142	481
40	542	525	778	1313	380	101	1213	1305	539	1030
41	510	216	51	318	373	1075	70	899	871	600
42	689	1184	1278	132	817	1134	170	1033	398	357
43	583	1026	351	1253	856	144	725	1010	960	183
44	1079	836	662	749	96	923	57	1166	939	270
45	946	1047	45	1097	513	812	988	231	129	943
46	1218	14	1226	438	394	1113	744	670	474	444
47	977	485	825	1120	159	257	205	1221	223	904
48	1196	219	30	39	290	1271	755	776	214	687
49	355	958	1164	986	1111	157	37	1162	403	460

POWER RESIDUES

	0	1	2	3	4	5	6	7	8	9
0	1	3	9	27	81	243	729	860	1253	1105
1	661	656	641	596	461	56	168	504	185	555
2	338	1014	388	1164	838	1187	907	67	201	603
3	482	119	357	1071	559	350	1050	496	161	483
4	122	366	1098	640	593	452	29	87	261	783
5	1022	412	1236	1054	508	197	591	446	11	33
6	99	297	891	19	57	171	513	212	636	581
7	416	1248	1090	616	521	236	708	797	1064	538
8	287	861	1256	1114	688	737	884	1325	1321	1309
9	1273	1165	841	1196	934	148	444	5	15	45
10	135	405	1215	991	319	957	217	651	626	551
11	326	978	280	840	1193	925	121	363	1089	613
12	512	209	627	554	335	1005	361	1083	595	458
13	47	141	423	1269	1153	805	1088	610	503	182
14	546	311	933	145	435	1305	1261	1129	733	872
15	1289	1213	985	301	903	55	165	495	158	474
16	95	285	855	1238	1060	526	251	753	932	142
17	426	1278	1180	886	4	12	36	108	324	972
18	262	786	1031	439	1317	1297	1237	1057	517	224
19	672	689	740	893	25	75	225	675	698	767
20	974	268	804	1085	601	476	101	303	909	73
21	219	657	644	605	488	137	411	1233	1045	481
22	116	348	1044	478	107	321	963	235	705	788
23	1037	457	44	132	396	1188	910	76	228	684
24	725	848	1217	997	337	1011	379	1137	757	944
25	178	534	275	825	1148	790	1043	475	98	294
26	882	1319	1303	1255	1111	679	710	803	1082	592
27	449	20	60	180	540	293	879	1310	1276	1174
28	868	1277	1177	877	1304	1258	1120	706	791	1046
29	484	125	375	1125	721	836	1181	889	13	39
30	117	351	1053	505	188	564	365	1095	631	566
31	371	1113	685	728	857	1244	1078	580	413	1239
32	1063	535	278	834	1175	871	1286	1204	958	220
33	660	653	632	569	380	1140	766	971	259	777
34	1004	358	1074	568	377	1131	739	890	16	48
35	144	432	1296	1234	1048	490	143	429	1287	1207
36	967	247	741	896	34	102	306	918	100	300
37	900	46	138	414	1242	1072	562	359	1077	577
38	404	1212	982	292	876	1301	1249	1093	625	548
39	317	951	199	597	464	65	195	585	428	1284
40	1198	940	166	498	167	501	176	528	257	771
41	986	304	912	82	246	738	887	7	21	63
42	189	567	374	1122	712	809	1100	646	611	506
43	191	573	392	1176	874	1295	1231	1039	463	62
44	186	558	347	1041	469	80	240	720	833	1172
45	862	1259	1123	715	818	1127	727	854	1235	1051
46	499	170	510	203	609	500	173	519	230	690
47	743	902	52	156	468	77	231	693	752	929
48	133	399	1197	937	157	471	86	258	774	995
49	331	993	325	975	271	813	1112	682	719	830

P = 1327

INDICES

	0	1	2	3	4	5	6	7	8	9
50	465	405	916	138	17	303	429	597	54	1117
51	462	626	120	66	1158	1300	1237	188	1088	467
52	1319	74	798	865	930	612	165	629	407	568
53	740	1229	654	1287	251	321	951	918	79	892
54	274	844	1244	519	712	648	140	1233	389	618
55	1002	109	546	1151	123	19	1072	659	441	34
56	862	999	376	1267	305	1294	309	421	343	333
57	911	1257	530	431	830	1141	524	379	1304	509
58	317	69	599	1277	1133	397	1025	855	1009	1078
59	748	56	269	44	811	128	13	393	669	976
60	1119	204	903	29	1270	213	957	1110	1161	464
61	137	428	1116	119	1299	1087	73	929	628	739
62	1286	950	891	1243	647	388	108	122	658	861
63	1266	308	332	529	1140	1303	68	1132	854	747
64	43	12	975	902	212	1160	427	1298	928	1285
65	1242	107	860	331	1302	853	11	211	1297	1241
66	330	10	1240	1239	576	577	673	993	578	634
67	874	674	190	639	994	197	770	579	622	265
68	635	1090	497	875	239	312	675	706	84	191
69	469	731	640	477	1192	995	971	603	198	1321
70	785	771	1051	1310	580	228	287	623	76	1291
71	266	736	424	636	782	453	1091	800	1127	498
72	447	294	876	607	692	240	867	456	313	6
73	1056	676	791	148	707	932	719	85	415	346
74	192	362	1060	470	614	1262	732	980	1172	641
75	1042	1187	478	167	1094	1193	594	248	996	1006
76	1084	972	631	968	604	1039	336	199	697	1104
77	1322	409	682	786	488	1209	772	339	1281	1052
78	570	803	1311	49	1182	581	181	937	229	742
79	255	288	984	914	624	1317	566	77	1231	1070
80	1292	828	1275	267	202	135	737	656	1130	425
81	851	574	637	495	729	783	1289	1125	454	717
82	1260	1092	966	680	801	253	1068	1128	1123	1066
83	499	700	820	448	323	501	295	1018	24	877
84	113	92	608	953	702	693	882	533	241	886
85	558	868	920	822	457	162	1148	314	1107	1137
86	7	81	450	1057	1101	563	677	555	280	792
87	894	325	149	1176	434	708	384	283	933	276
88	503	720	260	759	86	1325	173	416	846	297
89	347	62	807	193	590	1014	363	1246	1070	1061
90	370	833	471	154	795	615	521	26	1263	208
91	236	733	412	1036	981	714	879	1173	367	1202
92	642	550	764	1043	650	115	1188	1205	1144	479
93	537	897	168	142	94	1095	1224	483	1194	685
94	401	595	1235	610	249	517	544	997	909	507
95	1007	391	955	1085	645	527	973	105	328	632
96	620	704	969	226	780	605	789	360	1040	1004
97	695	337	179	1315	200	493	964	698	111	884
98	1105	553	382	1323	588	152	410	548	535	683
99	907	103	787	491	586	489	1153	243	1210	1250

POWER RESIDUES

	0	1	2	3	4	5	6	7	8	9
50	1163	835	1178	880	1313	1285	1201	949	193	579
51	410	1230	1036	454	35	105	315	945	181	543
52	302	906	64	192	576	401	1203	955	211	633
53	572	389	1167	847	1214	988	310	930	136	408
54	1224	1018	400	1200	946	184	552	329	987	307
55	921	109	327	981	289	867	1274	1168	850	1223
56	1015	391	1173	865	1268	1150	796	1061	529	260
57	780	1013	385	1155	811	1106	664	665	668	677
58	704	785	1028	430	1290	1216	994	328	984	298
59	894	28	84	252	756	941	169	507	194	582
60	419	1257	1117	697	764	965	241	723	842	1199
61	943	175	525	248	744	905	61	183	549	320
62	960	226	678	707	794	1055	511	206	618	527
63	254	762	959	223	669	680	713	812	1109	673
64	692	749	920	106	318	954	208	624	545	308
65	924	118	354	1062	532	269	807	1094	628	557
66	344	1032	442	1326	1324	1318	1300	1246	1084	598
67	467	74	222	666	671	686	731	866	1271	1159
68	823	1142	772	989	313	939	163	489	140	420
69	1260	1126	724	845	1208	970	256	768	977	277
70	831	1166	844	1205	961	229	687	734	875	1298
71	1240	1066	544	305	915	91	273	819	1130	736
72	881	1316	1294	1228	1030	436	1308	1270	1156	814
73	1115	691	746	911	79	237	711	806	1091	619
74	530	263	789	1040	466	71	213	639	590	443
75	2	6	18	54	162	486	131	393	1179	883
76	1322	1312	1282	1192	922	112	336	1008	370	1110
77	676	701	776	1001	349	1047	487	134	402	1206
78	964	238	714	815	1118	700	773	992	322	966
79	244	732	869	1280	1186	904	58	174	522	239
80	717	824	1145	781	1016	394	1182	892	22	66
81	198	594	455	38	114	342	1026	424	1272	1162
82	832	1169	853	1232	1042	472	89	267	801	1076
83	574	395	1185	901	49	147	441	1323	1315	1291
84	1219	1003	355	1065	541	296	888	10	30	90
85	270	810	1103	655	638	587	434	1302	1252	1102
86	652	629	560	353	1059	523	242	726	851	1226
87	1024	418	1254	1108	670	683	722	839	1190	916
88	94	282	846	1211	979	283	849	1220	1006	364
89	1092	622	539	290	870	1283	1195	931	139	417
90	1251	1099	643	602	479	110	330	990	316	948
91	190	570	383	1149	793	1052	502	179	537	284
92	852	1229	1033	445	8	24	72	216	648	617
93	524	245	735	878	1307	1267	1147	787	1034	448
94	17	51	153	459	50	150	450	23	69	207
95	621	536	281	843	1202	952	202	606	491	146
96	438	1314	1288	1210	976	274	822	1139	763	962
97	232	696	761	956	214	642	599	470	83	249
98	747	914	88	264	792	1049	493	152	456	41
99	123	369	1107	667	674	695	758	947	187	561

P = 1327

INDICES

	0	1	2	3	4	5	6	7	8	9
100	1215	773	1155	841	340	125	888	1282	767	1307
101	1053	245	1179	571	21	560	804	1199	541	1312
102	1212	1029	50	1074	870	1183	816	1032	582	1252
103	724	182	661	922	938	1046	512	230	1217	437
104	743	443	824	256	222	218	289	775	354	985
105	36	459	915	302	53	625	1157	187	1318	864
106	164	567	653	320	78	843	711	1232	1001	1150
107	1071	33	375	1293	342	1256	829	378	316	1276
108	1024	1077	268	127	668	203	1269	1109	136	118
109	72	738	890	387	657	307	1139	1131	42	901
110	426	1284	859	852	1296	9	575	992	873	638
111	769	264	496	311	83	730	1191	602	784	1309
112	286	1290	423	452	1126	293	691	455	1055	147
113	718	345	1059	1261	1171	1186	1093	247	1083	967
114	335	1103	681	1208	1280	802	1181	936	254	913
115	565	1069	1274	134	1129	573	728	1124	1259	679
116	1067	1065	819	500	23	91	701	532	557	821
117	1147	1136	449	562	279	324	433	282	502	758
118	172	296	806	1013	1019	832	794	25	235	1035
119	878	1201	763	114	1143	896	93	482	400	609
120	543	506	954	526	327	703	779	359	694	1314
121	963	883	381	151	534	102	585	242	1214	840
122	887	1306	1178	559	540	1028	869	1031	723	921
123	511	436	823	217	353	458	52	186	163	319
124	710	1149	374	1255	315	1076	667	1108	71	386
125	1138	900	858	8	872	263	82	601	285	451
126	690	146	1058	1185	1082	1102	1279	935	564	133
127	727	678	818	90	556	1135	278	281	171	1012
128	793	1034	762	895	399	505	326	358	962	150
129	584	839	1177	1027	722	435	352	185	709	1254
130	666	385	857	262	284	145	1081	934	726	89
131	277	1011	761	504	961	838	721	184	665	261
132	1080	88	760	837	664	87	663			

POWER RESIDUES

	0	1	2	3	4	5	6	7	8	9
100	356	1068	550	323	969	253	759	950	196	588
101	437	1311	1279	1183	895	31	93	279	837	1184
102	898	40	120	360	1080	586	431	1293	1225	1021
103	409	1227	1027	427	1281	1189	913	85	255	765
104	968	250	750	923	115	345	1035	451	26	78
105	234	702	779	1010	376	1128	730	863	1262	1132
106	742	899	43	129	387	1161	829	1160	826	1151
107	799	1070	556	341	1023	415	1245	1081	589	440
108	1320	1306	1264	1138	760	953	205	615	518	227
109	681	716	821	1136	754	935	151	453	32	96
110	288	864	1265	1141	769	980	286	858	1247	1087
111	607	494	155	465	68	204	612	509	200	600
112	473	92	276	828	1157	817	1124	718	827	1154
113	808	1097	637	584	425	1275	1171	859	1250	1096
114	634	575	398	1194	928	130	390	1170	856	1241
115	1069	553	332	996	334	1002	352	1056	514	215
116	645	608	497	164	492	149	447	14	42	126
117	378	1134	748	917	97	291	873	1292	1222	1012
118	382	1146	784	1025	421	1263	1135	751	926	124
119	372	1116	694	755	938	160	480	113	339	1017
120	397	1191	919	103	309	927	127	381	1143	775
121	998	340	1020	406	1218	1000	346	1038	460	53
122	159	477	104	312	936	154	462	59	177	531
123	266	798	1067	547	314	942	172	516	221	663
124	662	659	650	623	542	299	897	37	111	333
125	999	343	1029	433	1299	1243	1075	571	386	1158
126	820	1133	745	908	70	210	630	563	362	1086
127	604	485	128	384	1152	802	1079	583	422	1266
128	1144	778	1007	367	1101	649	620	533	272	816
129	1121	709	800	1073	565	368	1104	658	647	614
130	515	218	654	635	578	407	1221	1009	373	1119
131	703	782	1019	403	1209	973	265	795	1058	520
132	233	699	770	983	295	885				

P = 1361

INDICES

	0	1	2	3	4	5	6	7	8	9
0		0	126	1	252	1036	127	423	378	2
1	1162	161	253	152	549	1037	504	500	128	43
2	1288	424	287	114	379	712	278	3	675	443
3	1163	948	630	162	626	99	254	869	169	153
4	54	896	550	407	413	1038	240	1043	505	846
5	838	501	404	222	129	1197	801	44	569	818
6	1289	436	1074	425	756	1188	288	1176	752	115
7	225	890	380	235	995	713	295	584	279	308
8	180	4	1022	338	676	176	533	444	539	1281
9	1164	575	366	949	1169	1079	631	132	972	163
10	964	1033	627	815	530	100	348	1011	255	649
11	1323	870	927	103	170	1150	695	154	944	923
12	55	322	562	897	1200	388	551	93	882	408
13	1314	19	414	466	1302	1039	878	200	241	641
14	351	1044	1016	313	506	119	361	847	1121	606
15	839	804	421	502	710	624	405	402	434	223
16	306	537	130	346	1148	1198	464	1014	802	304
17	302	45	659	1096	570	1135	665	819	47	512
18	1290	66	701	437	492	545	1075	661	1295	426
19	1205	636	757	59	258	1189	1098	1065	289	207
20	1090	1177	1159	866	753	572	941	116	656	204
21	226	272	474	891	1137	83	381	11	775	236
22	89	652	996	667	1053	714	229	1233	296	25
23	1276	585	821	742	280	719	1070	309	1049	108
24	181	49	448	5	688	522	1023	195	1326	339
25	514	1352	677	275	219	177	1008	1299	534	1292
26	80	445	145	1244	540	1258	592	1282	68	148
27	1165	1131	1004	576	326	873	367	703	767	950
28	477	737	1170	453	1142	1080	439	1319	632	1000
29	245	133	487	854	973	494	1247	164	732	266
30	965	830	930	1034	547	112	628	894	836	816
31	750	582	531	1077	528	101	560	17	349	604
32	432	1012	663	543	256	864	472	650	1274	106
33	1324	1297	590	871	1140	852	928	580	430	104
34	428	1109	171	1269	785	1151	1222	1111	696	1207
35	1261	155	791	249	945	566	173	924	638	461
36	56	86	192	323	827	1271	563	759	618	898
37	671	645	1201	1127	787	389	61	595	552	372
38	1331	94	762	1153	883	260	185	409	384	937
39	1315	614	1224	20	1191	1344	415	981	333	467
40	1216	1113	1303	1100	1285	1040	992	1030	879	621
41	698	201	1067	1241	242	14	782	642	330	1209
42	352	291	398	1045	600	1212	1017	859	1263	314
43	209	71	507	393	137	120	901	157	362	1092
44	215	848	778	1309	1122	957	793	607	1179	1228
45	840	1057	355	805	1359	251	422	1161	151	503
46	42	286	711	674	947	625	868	53	406	239
47	845	403	1196	568	435	755	1175	224	234	294
48	307	1021	175	538	574	1168	131	963	814	347
49	648	926	1149	943	321	1199	92	1313	465	877

POWER RESIDUES

	0	1	2	3	4	5	6	7	8	9
0	1	3	9	27	81	243	729	826	1117	629
1	526	217	651	592	415	1245	1013	317	951	131
2	393	1179	815	1084	530	229	687	700	739	856
3	1207	899	1336	1286	1136	686	697	730	829	1126
4	656	607	460	19	57	171	513	178	534	241
5	723	808	1063	467	40	120	360	1080	518	193
6	579	376	1128	662	625	514	181	543	268	804
7	1051	431	1293	1157	749	886	1297	1169	785	994
8	260	780	979	215	645	574	361	1083	527	220
9	660	619	496	127	381	1143	707	760	919	35
10	105	315	945	113	339	1017	329	987	239	717
11	790	1009	305	915	23	69	207	621	502	145
12	435	1305	1193	857	1210	908	2	6	18	54
13	162	486	97	291	873	1258	1052	434	1302	1184
14	830	1129	665	634	541	262	786	997	269	807
15	1060	458	13	39	117	351	1053	437	1311	1211
16	911	11	33	99	297	891	1312	1214	920	38
17	114	342	1026	356	1068	482	85	255	765	934
18	80	240	720	799	1036	386	1158	752	895	1324
19	1250	1028	362	1086	536	247	741	862	1225	953
20	137	411	1233	977	209	627	520	199	597	430
21	1290	1148	722	805	1054	440	1320	1238	992	254
22	762	925	53	159	477	70	210	630	529	226
23	678	673	658	613	478	73	219	657	610	469
24	46	138	414	1242	1004	290	870	1249	1025	353
25	1059	455	4	12	36	108	324	972	194	582
26	385	1155	743	868	1243	1007	299	897	1330	1268
27	1082	524	211	633	538	253	759	916	26	78
28	234	702	745	874	1261	1061	461	22	66	198
29	594	421	1263	1067	479	76	228	684	691	712
30	775	964	170	510	169	507	160	480	79	237
31	711	772	955	143	429	1287	1139	695	724	811
32	1072	494	121	363	1089	545	274	822	1105	593
33	418	1254	1040	398	1194	860	1219	935	83	249
34	747	880	1279	1115	623	508	163	489	106	318
35	954	140	420	1260	1058	452	1356	1346	1316	1226
36	956	146	438	1314	1220	938	92	276	828	1123
37	647	580	379	1137	689	706	757	910	8	24
38	72	216	648	583	388	1164	770	949	125	375
39	1125	653	598	433	1299	1175	803	1048	422	1266
40	1076	506	157	471	52	156	468	43	129	387
41	1161	761	922	44	132	396	1188	842	1165	773
42	958	152	456	7	21	63	189	567	340	1020
43	338	1014	320	960	158	474	61	183	549	286
44	858	1213	917	29	87	261	783	988	242	726
45	817	1090	548	283	849	1186	836	1147	719	796
46	1027	359	1077	509	166	498	133	399	1197	869
47	1246	1016	326	978	212	636	547	280	840	1159
48	755	904	1351	1331	1271	1091	551	292	876	1267
49	1079	515	184	552	295	885	1294	1160	758	913

P = 1361

INDICES

	0	1	2	3	4	5	6	7	8	9
50	640	1015	118	1120	803	709	401	305	345	463
51	303	658	1134	46	65	491	660	1204	58	1097
52	206	1158	571	655	271	1136	10	88	666	228
53	24	820	718	1048	48	687	194	513	274	1007
54	1291	144	1257	67	1130	325	702	476	452	438
55	999	486	493	731	829	546	893	749	1076	559
56	603	662	863	1273	1296	1139	579	427	1268	1221
57	1206	790	565	637	85	826	758	670	1126	60
58	371	761	259	383	613	1190	980	1215	1099	991
59	620	1066	13	329	290	599	858	208	392	900
60	1091	777	956	1178	1056	1358	1160	41	673	867
61	238	1195	754	233	1020	573	962	647	942	91
62	876	117	708	344	657	64	1203	205	654	9
63	227	717	686	273	143	1129	475	998	730	892
64	558	862	1138	1267	789	84	669	370	382	979
65	990	12	598	391	776	1055	40	237	232	961
66	90	707	63	653	716	142	997	557	1266	668
67	978	597	1054	231	706	715	556	977	230	555
68	554	1234	1235	910	297	1236	35	26	911	374
69	1277	298	1348	586	1237	317	822	36	1333	743
70	27	770	281	912	917	720	375	96	1071	1278
71	692	310	299	1062	1050	1349	764	109	587	458
72	182	1238	212	50	318	1155	449	823	953	6
73	37	907	689	1334	885	523	744	1337	1024	28
74	797	196	771	262	1327	282	1253	340	913	74
75	515	918	187	1353	721	480	678	376	498	276
76	97	411	220	1072	888	178	1279	970	1009	693
77	386	1300	311	419	535	300	510	1293	1063	939
78	81	1051	740	446	1350	78	146	765	1317	1245
79	110	526	541	588	1107	1259	459	616	593	183
80	1342	1283	1239	396	69	213	1226	149	51	1173
81	1166	319	1118	1132	1156	22	1005	450	747	577
82	824	611	327	954	1193	874	7	728	368	38
83	140	704	908	1346	768	690	456	951	1335	1251
84	478	886	417	738	524	1340	1171	745	726	454
85	1338	983	1143	1025	985	1081	29	123	440	798
86	335	1320	197	1145	633	772	519	1001	263	469
87	246	1328	1027	134	283	811	488	1254	1218	855
88	341	987	974	914	904	495	75	1115	1248	516
89	1083	165	919	1086	733	188	1305	267	1354	31
90	966	722	1183	831	481	1102	931	679	125	1035
91	377	160	548	499	1287	113	277	442	629	98
92	168	895	412	1042	837	221	800	817	1073	1187
93	751	889	994	583	179	337	532	1280	365	1078
94	971	1032	529	1010	1322	102	694	922	561	387
95	881	18	1301	199	350	312	360	605	420	623
96	433	536	1147	1013	301	1095	664	511	700	544
97	1294	635	257	1064	1089	865	940	203	473	82
98	774	651	1052	1232	1275	741	1069	107	447	521
99	1325	1351	218	1298	79	1243	591	147	1003	872

POWER RESIDUES

	0	1	2	3	4	5	6	7	8	9
50	17	51	153	459	16	48	144	432	1296	1166
51	776	967	179	537	250	750	889	1306	1196	866
52	1237	989	245	735	844	1171	791	1012	314	942
53	104	312	936	86	258	774	961	161	483	88
54	264	792	1015	323	969	185	555	304	912	14
55	42	126	378	1134	680	679	676	667	640	559
56	316	948	122	366	1098	572	355	1065	473	58
57	174	522	205	615	484	91	273	819	1096	566
58	337	1011	311	933	77	231	693	718	793	1018
59	332	996	266	798	1033	377	1131	671	652	595
60	424	1272	1094	560	319	957	149	447	1341	1301
61	1181	821	1102	584	391	1173	797	1030	368	1104
62	590	409	1227	959	155	465	34	102	306	918
63	32	96	288	864	1231	971	191	573	358	1074
64	500	139	417	1251	1031	371	1113	617	490	109
65	327	981	221	663	628	523	208	624	511	172
66	516	187	561	322	966	176	528	223	669	646
67	577	370	1110	608	463	28	84	252	756	907
68	1360	1358	1352	1334	1280	1118	632	535	244	732
69	835	1144	710	769	946	116	348	1044	410	1230
70	968	182	546	277	831	1132	674	661	622	505
71	154	462	25	75	225	675	664	631	532	235
72	705	754	901	1342	1304	1190	848	1183	827	1120
73	638	553	298	894	1321	1241	1001	281	843	1168
74	782	985	233	699	736	847	1180	818	1093	557
75	310	930	68	204	612	475	64	192	576	367
76	1101	581	382	1146	716	787	1000	278	834	1141
77	701	742	865	1234	980	218	654	601	442	1326
78	1256	1046	416	1248	1022	344	1032	374	1122	644
79	571	352	1056	446	1338	1292	1154	740	859	1216
80	926	56	168	504	151	453	1359	1355	1343	1307
81	1199	875	1264	1070	488	103	309	927	59	177
82	531	232	696	727	820	1099	575	364	1092	554
83	301	903	1348	1322	1244	1010	308	924	50	150
84	450	1350	1328	1262	1064	470	49	147	441	1323
85	1247	1019	335	1005	293	879	1276	1106	596	427
86	1281	1121	641	562	325	975	203	609	466	37
87	111	333	999	275	825	1114	620	499	136	408
88	1224	950	128	384	1152	734	841	1162	764	931
89	71	213	639	556	307	921	41	123	369	1107
90	599	436	1308	1202	884	1291	1151	731	832	1135
91	683	688	703	748	883	1288	1142	704	751	892
92	1315	1223	947	119	357	1071	491	112	336	1008
93	302	906	1357	1349	1325	1253	1037	389	1167	779
94	976	206	618	493	118	354	1062	464	31	93
95	279	837	1150	728	823	1108	602	445	1335	1283
96	1127	659	616	487	100	300	900	1339	1295	1163
97	767	940	98	294	882	1285	1133	677	670	649
98	586	397	1191	851	1192	854	1201	881	1282	1124
99	650	589	406	1218	932	74	222	666	637	550

P = 1361

INDICES

	0	1	2	3	4	5	6	7	8	9
100	766	736	1141	1318	244	853	1246	265	929	111
101	835	581	527	16	431	542	471	105	589	851
102	429	1108	784	1110	1260	248	172	460	191	1270
103	617	644	786	594	1330	1152	184	936	1223	1343
104	332	1112	1284	1029	697	1240	781	1208	397	1211
105	1262	70	136	156	214	1308	792	1227	354	250
106	150	285	946	52	844	567	1174	293	174	1167
107	813	925	320	1312	639	1119	400	462	1133	490
108	57	1157	270	87	23	1047	193	1006	1256	324
109	451	485	828	748	602	1272	578	1220	564	825
110	1125	760	612	1214	619	328	857	899	955	1357
111	672	1194	1019	646	875	343	1202	8	685	1128
112	729	861	788	369	989	390	39	960	62	141
113	1265	596	705	976	553	909	34	373	1347	316
114	1332	769	916	95	691	1061	763	457	211	1154
115	952	906	884	1336	796	261	1252	73	186	479
116	497	410	887	969	385	418	509	938	739	77
117	1316	525	1106	615	1341	395	1225	1172	1117	21
118	746	610	1192	727	139	1345	455	1250	416	1339
119	725	982	984	122	334	1144	518	468	1026	810
120	1217	986	903	1114	1082	1085	1304	30	1182	1101
121	124	159	1286	441	167	1041	799	1186	993	336
122	364	1031	1321	921	880	198	359	622	1146	1094
123	699	634	1088	202	773	1231	1068	520	217	1242
124	1002	735	243	264	834	15	470	850	783	247
125	190	643	1329	935	331	1028	780	1210	135	1307
126	353	284	843	292	812	1311	399	489	269	1046
127	1255	484	601	1219	1124	1213	856	1356	1018	342
128	684	860	988	959	1264	975	33	315	915	1060
129	210	905	795	72	496	968	508	76	1105	394
130	1116	609	138	1249	724	121	517	809	902	1084
131	1181	158	166	1185	363	920	358	1093	1087	1230
132	216	734	833	849	189	934	779	1306	842	1310
133	268	483	1123	1355	683	958	32	1059	794	967
134	1104	608	723	808	1180	1184	357	1229	832	933
135	841	482	682	1058	1103	807	356	932	681	806
136	680	0								

POWER RESIDUES

	0	1	2	3	4	5	6	7	8	9
100	289	867	1240	998	272	816	1087	539	256	768
101	943	107	321	963	167	501	142	426	1278	1112
102	614	481	82	246	738	853	1198	872	1255	1043
103	407	1221	941	101	303	909	5	15	45	135
104	405	1215	923	47	141	423	1269	1085	533	238
105	714	781	982	224	672	655	604	451	1353	1337
106	1289	1145	713	778	973	197	591	412	1236	986
107	236	708	763	928	62	186	558	313	939	95
108	285	855	1204	890	1309	1205	893	1318	1232	974
109	200	600	439	1317	1229	965	173	519	196	588
110	403	1209	905	1354	1340	1298	1172	794	1021	341
111	1023	347	1041	401	1203	887	1300	1178	812	1075
112	503	148	444	1332	1274	1100	578	373	1119	635
113	544	271	813	1078	512	175	525	214	642	565
114	334	1002	284	852	1195	863	1228	962	164	492
115	115	345	1035	383	1149	725	814	1081	521	202
116	606	457	10	30	90	270	810	1069	485	94
117	282	846	1177	809	1066	476	67	201	603	448
118	1344	1310	1208	902	1345	1313	1217	929	65	195
119	585	394	1182	824	1111	611	472	55	165	495
120	124	372	1116	626	517	190	570	349	1047	419
121	1257	1049	425	1275	1103	587	400	1200	878	1273
122	1097	569	346	1038	392	1176	806	1057	449	1347
123	1319	1235	983	227	681	682	685	694	721	802
124	1045	413	1239	995	263	789	1006	296	888	1303
125	1187	839	1156	746	877	1270	1088	542	265	795
126	1024	350	1050	428	1284	1130	668	643	568	343
127	1029	365	1095	563	328	984	230	690	709	766
128	937	89	267	801	1042	404	1212	914	20	60
129	180	540	259	777	970	188	564	331	993	257
130	771	952	134	402	1206	896	1327	1259	1055	443
131	1329	1265	1073	497	130	390	1170	788	1003	287
132	861	1222	944	110	330	990	248	744	871	1252
133	1034	380	1140	698	733	838	1153	737	850	1189
134	845	1174	800	1039	395	1185	833	1138	692	715
135	784	991	251	753	898	1333	1277	1109	605	454
136										

P = 1367

INDICES

	0	1	2	3	4	5	6	7	8	9
0		0	740	878	114	1	252	873	854	390
1	741	851	992	1037	247	879	228	1327	1130	122
2	115	385	225	44	366	2	411	1268	987	262
3	253	596	968	363	701	874	504	1053	862	549
4	855	567	1125	788	965	391	784	535	1106	380
5	742	839	1151	440	642	852	361	1000	1002	14
6	993	460	1336	1263	342	1038	1103	470	75	922
7	248	325	1244	1359	427	880	236	358	1289	1088
8	229	780	1307	1004	499	1328	162	1140	339	772
9	1131	544	158	108	1275	123	480	826	1120	1241
10	116	288	213	633	525	386	1180	695	16	1071
11	226	565	1101	542	374	45	376	61	754	834
12	367	336	1200	79	710	3	637	768	1082	300
13	412	942	477	995	1210	1269	815	137	296	669
14	988	47	1065	522	618	263	733	1258	1167	704
15	254	1147	976	351	1098	597	663	394	462	1318
16	969	917	154	1092	681	364	378	425	1239	708
17	702	512	902	473	514	875	1079	892	146	184
18	505	1292	1284	1338	898	1054	848	812	649	775
19	863	63	1220	38	200	550	494	119	615	904
20	856	1348	1028	1135	953	568	7	434	1265	973
21	1126	719	554	1203	69	789	756	103	445	871
22	966	998	1305	693	475	392	1282	432	1114	621
23	785	1236	1116	344	801	536	128	600	208	218
24	1107	836	1076	292	574	381	819	1159	84	516
25	743	417	11	895	142	840	456	623	1040	560
26	1152	652	316	467	1217	441	369	284	584	907
27	643	308	189	56	877	853	1036	1129	43	986
28	362	861	787	1105	439	1001	1262	74	1358	1288
29	1003	338	107	1119	632	15	541	753	78	1081
30	994	295	521	1166	350	461	1091	1238	472	145
31	1337	648	37	614	1134	1264	1202	444	692	1113
32	343	207	291	83	894	1039	466	583	55	42
33	1104	1357	1118	77	1165	471	613	691	82	54
34	76	81	1252	1253	276	923	1213	271	1254	148
35	249	939	453	277	266	326	886	346	924	808
36	1245	244	666	1214	658	1360	712	174	272	957
37	428	1313	222	1255	186	881	23	1299	149	590
38	237	280	803	250	594	359	778	1178	940	661
39	1290	5	1234	454	859	1089	1355	884	278	507
40	230	486	722	267	402	781	509	538	327	793
41	1308	1015	747	887	1174	1005	639	181	347	31
42	500	330	93	925	1294	1329	577	1333	809	34
43	163	232	130	1246	843	1141	1185	166	245	547
44	340	770	372	667	679	773	67	216	1215	1286
45	1132	52	656	659	1172	545	488	602	1361	1229
46	159	716	610	713	490	109	1084	1189	175	1343
47	1276	1272	868	273	1340	124	948	830	958	736
48	481	724	210	429	450	827	1032	397	1314	604
49	1121	302	193	223	533	1242	824	1198	1256	900

POWER RESIDUES

	0	1	2	3	4	5	6	7	8	9
0	1	5	25	125	625	391	588	206	1030	1049
1	1144	252	1260	832	59	295	108	540	1333	1197
2	517	1218	622	376	513	1198	522	1243	747	1001
3	904	419	728	906	429	778	1156	312	193	965
4	724	886	329	278	23	115	575	141	705	791
5	1221	637	451	888	339	328	273	1365	1357	1317
6	1117	117	585	191	955	674	636	446	863	214
7	1070	1249	777	1151	287	68	340	333	298	123
8	615	341	338	323	248	1240	732	926	529	1278
9	922	509	1178	422	743	981	804	1286	962	709
10	811	1321	1137	217	1085	1324	1152	292	93	465
11	958	689	711	821	4	20	100	500	1133	197
12	985	824	19	95	475	1008	939	594	236	1180
13	432	793	1231	687	701	771	1121	137	685	691
14	721	871	254	1270	882	309	178	890	349	378
15	523	1248	772	1126	162	810	1316	1112	92	460
16	933	564	86	430	783	1181	437	818	1356	1312
17	1092	1359	1327	1167	367	468	973	764	1086	1329
18	1177	417	718	856	179	895	374	503	1148	272
19	1360	1332	1192	492	1093	1364	1352	1292	992	859
20	194	970	749	1011	954	669	611	321	238	1190
21	482	1043	1114	102	510	1183	447	868	239	1195
22	507	1168	372	493	1098	22	110	550	16	80
23	400	633	431	788	1206	562	76	380	533	1298
24	1022	1009	944	619	361	438	823	14	70	350
25	383	548	6	30	150	750	1016	979	794	1236
26	712	826	29	145	725	891	354	403	648	506
27	1163	347	368	473	998	889	344	353	398	623
28	381	538	1323	1147	267	1335	1207	567	101	505
29	1158	322	243	1215	607	301	138	690	716	846
30	129	645	491	1088	1339	1227	667	601	271	1355
31	1307	1067	1234	702	776	1146	262	1310	1082	1309
32	1077	1284	952	659	561	71	355	408	673	631
33	421	738	956	679	661	571	121	605	291	88
34	440	833	64	320	233	1165	357	418	723	881
35	304	153	765	1091	1354	1302	1042	1109	77	385
36	558	56	280	33	165	825	24	120	600	266
37	1330	1182	442	843	114	570	116	580	166	830
38	49	245	1225	657	551	21	105	525	1258	822
39	9	45	225	1125	157	785	1191	487	1068	1239
40	727	901	404	653	531	1288	972	759	1061	1204
41	552	26	130	650	516	1213	597	251	1255	807
42	1301	1037	1084	1319	1127	167	835	74	370	483
43	1048	1139	227	1135	207	1035	1074	1269	877	284
44	53	265	1325	1157	317	218	1090	1349	1277	917
45	484	1053	1164	352	393	598	256	1280	932	559
46	61	305	158	790	1216	612	326	263	1315	1107
47	67	335	308	173	865	224	1120	132	660	566
48	96	480	1033	1064	1219	627	401	638	456	913
49	464	953	664	586	196	980	799	1261	837	84

P = 1367

INDICES

	0	1	2	3	4	5	6	7	8	9
50	117	1303	1157	187	751	289	269	220	882	91
51	214	866	1196	24	1363	634	414	20	1300	1351
52	526	982	26	150	1056	387	1207	557	591	88
53	1181	404	1109	238	1024	696	1324	1062	281	1231
54	17	944	1048	804	929	1072	796	1365	251	850
55	227	384	410	595	503	566	783	838	360	459
56	1102	324	235	779	161	543	479	287	1179	564
57	375	335	636	941	814	46	732	1146	662	916
58	377	511	1078	1291	847	62	493	1347	6	718
59	755	997	1281	1235	127	835	818	416	455	651
60	368	307	1035	860	1261	337	540	294	1090	647
61	1201	206	465	1356	612	80	1212	938	885	243
62	711	1312	22	279	777	4	1354	485	508	1014
63	638	329	576	231	1184	769	66	51	487	715
64	1083	1271	947	723	1031	301	823	1302	268	865
65	413	981	1206	403	1323	943	795	383	782	323
66	478	334	731	510	492	996	817	306	539	205
67	1211	1311	1353	328	65	1270	822	980	794	333
68	816	1310	821	1309	626	138	627	133	1016	111
69	297	139	587	748	1011	670	628	528	888	1222
70	989	134	313	1175	1193	48	1017	1161	1006	99
71	1066	112	260	640	1086	523	298	1096	182	951
72	619	140	984	348	40	264	588	400	32	1170
73	734	749	86	501	914	1259	1012	1321	331	1191
74	1168	671	687	94	962	705	629	28	926	202
75	255	529	763	1295	673	1148	889	518	1330	407
76	977	1223	1020	578	177	352	990	1051	1334	1138
77	1099	135	152	810	552	598	314	72	35	689
78	664	1176	745	164	608	395	1194	1060	233	1345
79	463	49	729	131	258	1319	1018	1058	1247	496
80	970	1162	1226	844	96	918	1007	419	1142	1043
81	155	100	1249	1186	1278	1093	1067	910	167	934
82	682	113	389	246	121	365	261	700	548	964
83	379	641	13	341	921	426	1087	498	771	1274
84	1240	524	1070	373	833	709	299	1209	668	617
85	703	1097	1317	680	707	513	183	897	774	199
86	903	952	972	68	870	474	620	800	217	573
87	515	141	559	1216	906	876	985	438	1287	631
88	1080	349	144	1133	1112	893	41	1164	53	275
89	147	265	807	657	956	185	589	593	660	858
90	506	401	792	1173	30	1293	33	842	546	678
91	1285	1171	1228	489	1342	1339	735	449	603	532
92	899	750	90	1362	1350	1055	87	1023	1230	928
93	849	502	458	160	563	813	915	846	717	126
94	650	1260	646	611	242	776	1013	1183	714	1030
95	864	1322	322	491	204	64	332	625	110	1010
96	1221	1192	98	1085	950	39	1169	913	1190	961
97	201	672	406	176	1137	551	688	607	1344	257
98	495	95	1042	1277	933	120	963	920	1273	832
99	616	706	198	869	572	905	630	1111	274	955

POWER RESIDUES

	0	1	2	3	4	5	6	7	8	9
50	420	733	931	554	36	180	900	399	628	406
51	663	581	171	855	174	870	249	1245	757	1051
52	1154	302	143	715	841	104	520	1233	697	751
53	1021	1004	919	494	1103	47	235	1175	407	668
54	606	296	113	565	91	455	908	439	828	39
55	195	975	774	1136	212	1060	1199	527	1268	872
56	259	1295	1007	934	569	111	555	41	205	1025
57	1024	1019	994	869	244	1220	632	426	763	1081
58	1304	1052	1159	327	268	1340	1232	692	726	896
59	379	528	1273	897	384	553	31	155	775	1141
60	237	1185	457	918	489	1078	1289	977	784	1186
61	462	943	614	336	313	198	990	849	144	720
62	866	229	1145	257	1285	957	684	686	696	746
63	996	879	294	103	515	1208	572	126	630	416
64	713	831	54	270	1350	1282	942	609	311	188
65	940	599	261	1305	1057	1184	452	893	364	453
66	898	389	578	156	780	1166	362	443	848	139
67	695	741	971	754	1036	1079	1294	1002	909	444
68	853	164	820	1366	1362	1342	1242	742	976	779
69	1161	337	318	223	1115	107	535	1308	1072	1259
70	827	34	170	850	149	745	991	854	169	845
71	124	620	366	463	948	639	461	938	589	211
72	1055	1174	402	643	481	1038	1089	1344	1252	792
73	1226	662	576	146	730	916	479	1028	1039	1094
74	2	10	50	250	1250	782	1176	412	693	731
75	921	504	1153	297	118	590	216	1080	1299	1027
76	1034	1069	1244	752	1026	1029	1044	1119	127	635
77	441	838	89	445	858	189	945	624	386	563
78	81	405	658	556	46	230	1150	282	43	215
79	1075	1274	902	409	678	656	546	1363	1347	1267
80	867	234	1170	382	543	1348	1272	892	359	428
81	773	1131	187	935	574	136	680	666	596	246
82	1230	682	676	646	496	1113	97	485	1058	1189
83	477	1018	989	844	119	595	241	1205	557	51
84	255	1275	907	434	803	1281	937	584	186	930
85	549	11	55	275	8	40	200	1000	899	394
86	603	281	38	190	950	649	511	1188	472	993
87	864	219	1095	7	35	175	875	274	3	15
88	75	375	508	1173	397	618	356	413	698	756
89	1046	1129	177	885	324	253	1265	857	184	920
90	499	1128	172	860	199	995	874	269	1345	1257
91	817	1351	1287	967	734	936	579	161	805	1291
92	987	834	69	345	358	423	748	1006	929	544
93	1353	1297	1017	984	819	1361	1337	1217	617	351
94	388	573	131	655	541	1338	1222	642	476	1013
95	964	719	861	204	1020	999	894	369	478	1023
96	1014	969	744	986	829	44	220	1100	32	160
97	800	1266	862	209	1045	1124	152	760	1066	1229
98	677	651	521	1238	722	876	279	28	140	700
99	766	1096	12	60	300	133	665	591	221	1105

P = 1367

INDICES

	0	1	2	3	4	5	6	7	8	9
100	857	29	677	1341	531	1349	927	562	125	241
101	1029	203	1009	949	960	1136	256	932	831	571
102	954	530	240	959	570	569	764	759	737	765
103	8	1296	1154	482	760	435	674	421	725	738
104	1266	1149	356	211	766	974	890	1026	430	9
105	1127	519	581	451	1297	720	1331	654	828	1155
106	555	408	1144	1033	483	1204	978	311	398	761
107	70	1224	698	1315	436	790	1021	320	605	675
108	757	579	318	1122	422	104	178	1045	303	726
109	446	353	170	194	739	872	991	1326	224	1267
110	967	1052	1124	534	1150	999	1335	469	1243	357
111	1306	1139	157	825	212	694	1100	60	1199	767
112	476	136	1064	1257	975	393	153	424	901	891
113	1283	811	1219	118	1027	433	553	102	1304	431
114	1115	599	1075	1158	10	622	315	283	188	1128
115	786	73	106	752	520	1237	36	443	290	582
116	1117	690	1251	270	452	345	665	173	221	1298
117	802	1177	1233	883	721	537	746	180	92	1332
118	129	165	371	215	655	601	609	1188	867	829
119	209	396	192	1197	1156	219	1195	19	25	556
120	1108	1061	1047	1364	409	837	234	286	635	1145
121	1077	1346	1280	415	1034	293	464	937	21	484
122	575	50	946	1301	1205	382	730	305	1352	979
123	820	132	586	527	312	1160	259	1095	983	399
124	85	1320	686	27	762	517	1019	1050	151	71
125	744	1059	728	1057	1225	418	1248	909	388	699
126	12	497	1069	1208	1316	896	971	799	558	437
127	143	1163	806	592	791	841	1227	448	89	1022
128	457	845	645	1182	321	624	97	912	405	606
129	1041	919	197	1110	676	561	1008	931	239	758
130	1153	420	355	1025	580	653	1143	310	697	319
131	317	1044	169	1325	1123	468	156	59	1063	423
132	1218	101	1074	282	105	442	1250	172	1232	179
133	370	1187	191	18	1046	285	1279	936	945	304
134	585	1094	685	1049	727	908	1068	798	805	447
135	644	911	196	930	354	309	168	58	1073	171
136	190	935	684	797	195	57	683			

POWER RESIDUES

	0	1	2	3	4	5	6	7	8	9
100	57	285	58	290	83	415	708	806	1296	1012
101	959	694	736	946	629	411	688	706	796	1246
102	762	1076	1279	927	534	1303	1047	1134	202	1010
103	949	644	486	1063	1214	602	276	13	65	325
104	258	1290	982	809	1311	1087	1334	1202	542	1343
105	1247	767	1101	37	185	925	524	1253	797	1251
106	787	1201	537	1318	1122	142	710	816	1346	1262
107	842	109	545	1358	1322	1142	242	1210	582	176
108	880	299	128	640	466	963	714	836	79	395
109	608	306	163	815	1341	1237	717	851	154	770
110	1116	112	560	66	330	283	48	240	1200	532
111	1293	997	884	319	228	1140	232	1160	332	293
112	98	490	1083	1314	1102	42	210	1050	1149	277
113	18	90	450	883	314	203	1015	974	769	1111
114	87	435	808	1306	1062	1209	577	151	755	1041
115	1104	52	260	1300	1032	1059	1194	502	1143	247
116	1235	707	801	1271	887	334	303	148	740	966
117	729	911	454	903	414	703	781	1171	387	568
118	106	530	1283	947	634	436	813	1331	1187	467
119	968	739	961	704	786	1196	512	1193	497	1118
120	122	610	316	213	1065	1224	652	526	1263	847
121	134	670	616	346	363	448	873	264	1320	1132
122	192	960	699	761	1071	1254	802	1276	912	459
123	928	539	1328	1172	392	593	231	1155	307	168
124	840	99	495	1108	72	360	433	798	1256	812
125	1326	1162	342	343	348	373	498	1123	147	735
126	941	604	286	63	315	208	1040	1099	27	135
127	675	641	471	988	839	94	470	983	814	1336
128	1212	592	226	1130	182	910	449	878	289	78
129	390	583	181	905	424	753	1031	1054	1169	377
130	518	1223	647	501	1138	222	1110	82	410	683
131	681	671	621	371	488	1073	1264	852	159	795
132	1241	737	951	654	536	1313	1097	17	85	425
133	758	1056	1179	427	768	1106	62	310	183	915
134	474	1003	914	469	978	789	1211	587	201	1005
135	924	519	1228	672	626	396	613	331	288	73
136	365	458	923	514	1203	547				

P = 1373

INDICES

	0	1	2	3	4	5	6	7	8	9
0		0	1	955	2	1317	956	228	3	538
1	1318	166	957	933	229	900	4	298	539	90
2	1319	1183	167	698	958	1262	934	121	230	503
3	901	1056	5	1121	299	173	540	1030	91	516
4	1320	884	1184	950	168	483	699	129	959	456
5	1263	1253	935	383	122	111	231	1045	504	1364
6	902	203	1057	766	6	878	1122	488	300	281
7	174	182	541	139	1031	845	92	394	517	1289
8	1321	1076	885	1165	1185	243	951	86	169	1249
9	484	1161	700	639	130	35	960	1357	457	704
10	1264	655	1254	52	936	1128	384	978	123	607
11	112	613	232	27	1046	643	505	99	1365	526
12	903	332	204	467	1058	1207	767	792	7	533
13	879	134	1123	318	489	66	301	323	282	352
14	175	1084	183	1099	542	448	140	39	1032	153
15	846	377	93	836	395	1001	518	782	1290	1338
16	1322	926	1077	964	886	1066	1166	341	1186	494
17	244	628	952	163	87	118	170	947	1250	1361
18	485	842	1162	1158	701	975	640	464	131	349
19	36	998	961	625	1358	461	458	728	705	1091
20	1265	71	656	731	1255	829	53	1236	937	256
21	1129	708	385	1137	979	895	124	1284	608	1094
22	113	1231	614	1275	233	428	28	1268	1047	416
23	644	1349	506	306	100	74	1366	872	527	619
24	904	555	333	659	205	401	468	1023	1059	748
25	1208	734	768	864	793	1198	8	910	534	1258
26	880	1041	135	1245	1124	328	319	832	490	971
27	67	1280	302	744	324	56	283	1012	353	222
28	176	60	1085	1239	184	990	1100	1112	543	596
29	449	940	141	755	40	1309	1033	287	154	259
30	847	1178	378	238	94	148	837	1132	396	1007
31	1002	1217	519	1016	783	711	1291	440	1339	669
32	1323	561	927	388	1078	823	965	190	887	357
33	1067	1140	1167	196	342	433	1187	574	495	982
34	245	1222	629	684	953	226	164	898	88	696
35	119	1054	171	514	948	127	1251	109	1362	764
36	486	180	843	1287	1163	84	1159	33	702	50
37	976	611	641	524	465	790	132	64	350	1097
38	37	375	999	1336	962	339	626	116	1359	1156
39	462	996	459	1089	729	1234	706	893	1092	1273
40	1266	1347	72	617	657	1021	732	1196	1256	1243
41	830	1278	54	220	1237	1110	938	1307	257	236
42	1130	1215	709	667	386	188	1138	431	980	682
43	896	1052	125	762	1285	31	609	788	1095	1334
44	114	994	1232	1271	615	1194	1276	1108	234	665
45	429	1050	29	1332	1269	1106	1048	1104	417	419
46	645	363	1350	421	507	584	307	647	101	716
47	75	365	1367	1116	873	1352	528	921	620	423
48	905	591	556	509	334	1302	660	586	206	547
49	402	309	469	801	1024	649	1060	410	749	103

POWER RESIDUES

	0	1	2	3	4	5	6	7	8	9
0	1	2	4	8	16	32	64	128	256	512
1	1024	675	1350	1327	1281	1189	1005	637	1274	1175
2	977	581	1162	951	529	1058	743	113	226	452
3	904	435	870	367	734	95	190	380	760	147
4	294	588	1176	979	585	1170	967	561	1122	871
5	369	738	103	206	412	824	275	550	1100	827
6	281	562	1124	875	377	754	135	270	540	1080
7	787	201	402	804	235	470	940	507	1014	655
8	1310	1247	1121	869	365	730	87	174	348	696
9	19	38	76	152	304	608	1216	1059	745	117
10	234	468	936	499	998	623	1246	1119	865	357
11	714	55	110	220	440	880	387	774	175	350
12	700	27	54	108	216	432	864	355	710	47
13	94	188	376	752	131	262	524	1048	723	73
14	146	292	584	1168	963	553	1106	839	305	610
15	1220	1067	761	149	298	596	1192	1011	649	1298
16	1223	1073	773	173	346	692	11	22	44	88
17	176	352	704	35	70	140	280	560	1120	867
18	361	722	71	142	284	568	1136	899	425	850
19	327	654	1308	1243	1113	853	333	666	1332	1291
20	1209	1045	717	61	122	244	488	976	579	1158
21	943	513	1026	679	1358	1343	1313	1253	1133	893
22	413	826	279	558	1116	859	345	690	7	14
23	28	56	112	224	448	896	419	838	303	606
24	1212	1051	729	85	170	340	680	1360	1347	1321
25	1269	1165	957	541	1082	791	209	418	836	299
26	598	1196	1019	665	1330	1287	1201	1029	685	1370
27	1367	1361	1349	1325	1277	1181	989	605	1210	1047
28	721	69	138	276	552	1104	835	297	594	1188
29	1003	633	1266	1159	945	517	1034	695	17	34
30	68	136	272	544	1088	803	233	466	932	491
31	982	591	1182	991	609	1218	1063	753	133	266
32	532	1064	755	137	274	548	1096	819	265	530
33	1060	747	121	242	484	968	563	1126	879	385
34	770	167	334	668	1336	1299	1225	1077	781	189
35	378	756	139	278	556	1112	851	329	658	1316
36	1259	1145	917	461	922	471	942	511	1022	671
37	1342	1311	1249	1125	877	381	762	151	302	604
38	1208	1043	713	53	106	212	424	848	323	646
39	1292	1211	1049	725	77	154	308	616	1232	1091
40	809	245	490	980	587	1174	975	577	1154	935
41	497	994	615	1230	1087	801	229	458	916	459
42	918	463	926	479	958	543	1086	799	225	450
43	900	427	854	335	670	1340	1307	1241	1109	845
44	317	634	1268	1163	953	533	1066	759	145	290
45	580	1160	947	521	1042	711	49	98	196	392
46	784	195	390	780	187	374	748	123	246	492
47	984	595	1190	1007	641	1282	1191	1009	645	1290
48	1207	1041	709	45	90	180	360	720	67	134
49	268	536	1072	771	169	338	676	1352	1331	1289

P = 1373

INDICES

	0	1	2	3	4	5	6	7	8	9
50	1209	1296	735	718	769	600	865	77	794	812
51	1199	367	9	211	911	1369	535	295	1259	1118
52	881	453	1042	875	136	1073	1246	1354	1125	24
53	329	530	320	445	833	923	491	944	972	622
54	68	253	1281	425	303	552	745	907	325	741
55	57	593	284	145	1013	558	354	571	223	511
56	177	47	61	336	1086	1344	1240	1304	185	759
57	991	662	1101	581	1113	588	544	407	597	208
58	450	21	941	549	142	44	756	404	41	1146
59	1310	311	1034	1149	288	471	155	674	260	803
60	848	1313	1179	1026	379	277	239	651	95	314
61	149	1062	838	724	1133	412	397	1037	1008	751
62	1003	819	1218	105	520	1152	1017	1211	784	1328
63	712	1298	1292	291	441	737	1340	17	670	720
64	1324	474	562	771	928	478	389	602	1079	158
65	824	867	966	1173	191	79	888	677	358	796
66	1068	566	1141	814	1168	263	197	1201	343	858
67	434	369	1188	806	575	11	496	775	983	213
68	246	851	1223	913	630	268	685	1371	954	1316
69	227	537	165	932	899	297	89	1182	697	1261
70	120	502	1055	1120	172	1029	515	883	949	482
71	128	455	1252	382	110	1044	1363	202	765	877
72	487	280	181	138	844	393	1288	1075	1164	242
73	85	1248	1160	638	34	1356	703	654	51	1127
74	977	606	612	26	642	98	525	331	466	1206
75	791	532	133	317	65	322	351	1083	1098	447
76	38	152	376	835	1000	781	1337	925	963	1065
77	340	493	627	162	117	946	1360	841	1157	974
78	463	348	997	624	460	727	1090	70	730	828
79	1235	255	707	1136	894	1283	1093	1230	1274	427
80	1267	415	1348	305	73	871	618	554	658	400
81	1022	747	733	863	1197	909	1257	1040	1244	327
82	831	970	1279	743	55	1011	221	59	1238	989
83	1111	595	939	754	1308	286	258	1177	237	147
84	1131	1006	1216	1015	710	439	668	560	387	822
85	189	356	1139	195	432	573	981	1221	683	225
86	897	695	1053	513	126	108	763	179	1286	83
87	32	49	610	523	789	63	1096	374	1335	338
88	115	1155	995	1088	1233	892	1272	1346	616	1020
89	1195	1242	1277	219	1109	1306	235	1214	666	187
90	430	681	1051	761	30	787	1333	993	1270	1193
91	1107	664	1049	1331	1105	1103	418	362	420	583
92	646	715	364	1115	1351	920	422	590	508	1301
93	585	546	308	800	648	409	102	1295	717	599
94	76	811	366	210	1368	294	1117	452	874	1072
95	1353	23	529	444	922	943	621	252	424	551
96	906	740	592	144	557	570	510	46	335	1343
97	1303	758	661	580	587	406	207	20	548	43
98	403	1145	310	1148	470	673	802	1312	1025	276
99	650	313	1061	723	411	1036	750	818	104	1151

POWER RESIDUES

	0	1	2	3	4	5	6	7	8	9
50	1205	1037	701	29	58	116	232	464	928	483
51	966	559	1118	863	353	706	39	78	156	312
52	624	1248	1123	873	373	746	119	238	476	952
53	531	1062	751	129	258	516	1032	691	9	18
54	36	72	144	288	576	1152	931	489	978	583
55	1166	959	545	1090	807	241	482	964	555	1110
56	847	321	642	1284	1195	1017	661	1322	1271	1169
57	965	557	1114	855	337	674	1348	1323	1273	1173
58	973	573	1146	919	465	930	487	974	575	1150
59	927	481	962	551	1102	831	289	578	1156	939
60	505	1010	647	1294	1215	1057	741	109	218	436
61	872	371	742	111	222	444	888	403	806	239
62	478	956	539	1078	783	193	386	772	171	342
63	684	1368	1363	1353	1333	1293	1213	1053	733	93
64	186	372	744	115	230	460	920	467	934	495
65	990	607	1214	1055	737	101	202	404	808	243
66	486	972	571	1142	911	449	898	423	846	319
67	638	1276	1179	985	597	1194	1015	657	1314	1255
68	1137	901	429	858	343	686	1372	1371	1369	1365
69	1357	1341	1309	1245	1117	861	349	698	23	46
70	92	184	368	736	99	198	396	792	211	422
71	844	315	630	1260	1147	921	469	938	503	1006
72	639	1278	1183	993	613	1226	1079	785	197	394
73	788	203	406	812	251	502	1004	635	1270	1167
74	961	549	1098	823	273	546	1092	811	249	498
75	996	619	1238	1103	833	293	586	1172	971	569
76	1138	903	433	866	359	718	63	126	252	504
77	1008	643	1286	1199	1025	677	1354	1335	1297	1221
78	1069	765	157	314	628	1256	1139	905	437	874
79	375	750	127	254	508	1016	659	1318	1263	1153
80	933	493	986	599	1198	1023	673	1346	1319	1265
81	1157	941	509	1018	663	1326	1279	1185	997	621
82	1242	1111	849	325	650	1300	1227	1081	789	205
83	410	820	267	534	1068	763	153	306	612	1224
84	1075	777	181	362	724	75	150	300	600	1200
85	1027	681	1362	1351	1329	1285	1197	1021	669	1338
86	1303	1233	1093	813	253	506	1012	651	1302	1231
87	1089	805	237	474	948	523	1046	719	65	130
88	260	520	1040	707	41	82	164	328	656	1312
89	1251	1129	885	397	794	215	430	860	347	694
90	15	30	60	120	240	480	960	547	1094	815
91	257	514	1028	683	1366	1359	1345	1317	1261	1149
92	925	477	954	535	1070	767	161	322	644	1288
93	1203	1033	693	13	26	52	104	208	416	832
94	291	582	1164	955	537	1074	775	177	354	708
95	43	86	172	344	688	3	6	12	24	48
96	96	192	384	768	163	326	652	1304	1235	1097
97	821	269	538	1076	779	185	370	740	107	214
98	428	856	339	678	1356	1339	1305	1237	1101	829
99	285	570	1140	907	441	882	391	782	191	382

P = 1373

INDICES

	0	1	2	3	4	5	6	7	8	9
100	1210	1327	1297	290	736	16	719	473	770	477
101	601	157	866	1172	78	676	795	565	813	262
102	1200	857	368	805	10	774	212	850	912	267
103	1370	1315	536	931	296	1181	1260	501	1119	1028
104	882	481	454	381	1043	201	876	279	137	392
105	1074	241	1247	637	1355	653	1126	605	25	97
106	330	1205	531	316	321	1082	446	151	834	780
107	924	1064	492	161	945	840	973	347	623	726
108	69	827	254	1135	1282	1229	426	414	304	870
109	553	399	746	862	908	1039	326	969	742	1010
110	58	988	594	753	285	1176	146	1005	1014	438
111	559	821	355	194	572	1220	224	694	512	107
112	178	82	48	522	62	373	337	1154	1087	891
113	1345	1019	1241	218	1305	1213	186	680	760	786
114	992	1192	663	1330	1102	361	582	714	1114	919
115	589	1300	545	799	408	1294	598	810	209	293
116	451	1071	22	443	942	251	550	739	143	569
117	45	1342	757	579	405	19	42	1144	1147	672
118	1311	275	312	722	1035	817	1150	1326	289	15
119	472	476	156	1171	675	564	261	856	804	773
120	849	266	1314	930	1180	500	1027	480	380	200
121	278	391	240	636	652	604	96	1204	315	1081
122	150	779	1063	160	839	346	725	826	1134	1228
123	413	869	398	861	1038	968	1009	987	752	1175
124	1004	437	820	193	1219	693	106	81	521	372
125	1153	890	1018	217	1212	679	785	1191	1329	360
126	713	918	1299	798	1293	809	292	1070	442	250
127	738	568	1341	578	18	1143	671	274	721	816
128	1325	14	475	1170	563	855	772	265	929	499
129	479	199	390	635	603	1203	1080	778	159	345
130	825	1227	868	860	967	986	1174	436	192	692
131	80	371	889	216	678	1190	359	917	797	808
132	1069	249	567	577	1142	273	815	13	1169	854
133	264	498	198	634	1202	777	344	1226	859	985
134	435	691	370	215	1189	916	807	248	576	272
135	12	853	497	633	776	1225	984	690	214	915
136	247	271	852	632	1224	689	914	270	631	688
137	269	687	686							

POWER RESIDUES

	0	1	2	3	4	5	6	7	8	9
100	764	155	310	620	1240	1107	841	309	618	1236
101	1099	825	277	554	1108	843	313	626	1252	1131
102	889	405	810	247	494	988	603	1206	1039	705
103	37	74	148	296	592	1184	995	617	1234	1095
104	817	261	522	1044	715	57	114	228	456	912
105	451	902	431	862	351	702	31	62	124	248
106	496	992	611	1222	1071	769	165	330	660	1320
107	1267	1161	949	525	1050	727	81	162	324	648
108	1296	1219	1065	757	141	282	564	1128	883	393
109	786	199	398	796	219	438	876	379	758	143
110	286	572	1144	915	457	914	455	910	447	894
111	415	830	287	574	1148	923	473	946	519	1038
112	703	33	66	132	264	528	1056	739	105	210
113	420	840	307	614	1228	1083	793	213	426	852
114	331	662	1324	1275	1177	981	589	1178	983	593
115	1186	999	625	1250	1127	881	389	778	183	366
116	732	91	182	364	728	83	166	332	664	1328
117	1283	1193	1013	653	1306	1239	1105	837	301	602
118	1204	1035	697	21	42	84	168	336	672	1344
119	1315	1257	1141	909	445	890	407	814	255	510
120	1020	667	1334	1295	1217	1061	749	125	250	500
121	1000	627	1254	1135	897	421	842	311	622	1244
122	1115	857	341	682	1364	1355	1337	1301	1229	1085
123	797	221	442	884	395	790	207	414	828	283
124	566	1132	891	409	818	263	526	1052	731	89
125	178	356	712	51	102	204	408	816	259	518
126	1036	699	25	50	100	200	400	800	227	454
127	908	443	886	399	798	223	446	892	411	822
128	271	542	1084	795	217	434	868	363	726	79
129	158	316	632	1264	1155	937	501	1002	631	1262
130	1151	929	485	970	567	1134	895	417	834	295
131	590	1180	987	601	1202	1031	689	5	10	20
132	40	80	160	320	640	1280	1187	1001	629	1258
133	1143	913	453	906	439	878	383	766	159	318
134	636	1272	1171	969	565	1130	887	401	802	231
135	462	924	475	950	527	1054	735	97	194	388
136	776	179	358	716	59	118	236	472	944	515
137	1030	687								

P = 1381

INDICES

	0	1	2	3	4	5	6	7	8	9
0		0	1	292	2	958	293	884	3	584
1	959	869	294	1320	885	1250	4	904	585	43
2	960	1176	870	818	295	536	1321	876	886	573
3	1251	723	5	1161	905	462	586	492	44	232
4	961	415	1177	263	871	162	819	702	296	388
5	537	1196	1322	1041	877	447	887	335	574	167
6	1252	52	724	88	6	898	1162	145	906	1110
7	463	652	587	250	493	828	45	373	233	1210
8	962	1168	416	347	1178	482	264	865	872	259
9	163	824	820	1015	703	1001	297	623	389	73
10	538	276	1197	547	1323	754	1042	1019	878	646
11	448	784	888	932	336	396	575	524	168	408
12	1253	358	53	707	725	114	89	515	7	555
13	899	383	1163	927	146	454	907	600	1111	1005
14	464	994	653	809	588	151	251	680	494	1067
15	829	976	46	108	374	301	234	801	1211	1333
16	963	322	1169	1060	417	739	348	849	1179	1260
17	483	627	265	289	866	40	873	459	260	1193
18	164	142	825	344	821	70	1016	393	704	380
19	1002	677	298	1057	624	1190	390	1187	74	790
20	539	437	277	77	1198	1373	548	22	1324	912
21	755	793	1043	944	1020	1221	879	227	647	542
22	449	844	785	660	889	1120	933	440	337	1281
23	397	665	576	611	525	280	169	122	409	748
24	1254	605	359	80	54	1346	708	1363	726	639
25	115	1201	90	307	516	774	8	29	556	1376
26	900	1157	384	894	1164	619	928	551	147	318
27	455	1053	908	1116	601	25	1112	424	1006	1307
28	465	717	995	1327	654	1293	810	1299	589	428
29	152	915	252	220	681	1125	495	365	1068	758
30	830	1147	977	568	47	1010	109	796	375	839
31	302	1288	235	1243	802	1046	1212	240	1334	62
32	964	1311	323	947	1170	476	1061	938	418	206
33	740	1023	349	1076	850	1103	1180	469	1261	1224
34	484	212	628	1272	266	688	290	882	867	1248
35	41	816	874	721	460	230	261	700	1194	445
36	165	86	143	650	826	1208	345	863	822	999
37	71	545	1017	782	394	406	705	513	381	452
38	1003	807	678	974	299	1331	1058	847	625	38
39	1191	342	391	675	1188	788	75	20	791	1219
40	540	658	438	663	278	746	78	1361	1199	772
41	1374	892	549	1051	23	1305	1325	1297	913	1123
42	756	566	794	1286	1044	60	945	936	1021	1101
43	1222	1270	880	814	228	443	648	861	543	404
44	450	972	845	340	786	1217	661	1359	890	1303
45	1121	1284	934	1268	441	402	338	1357	1282	400
46	398	1089	666	1091	577	593	612	668	526	1029
47	281	1093	170	1132	123	579	410	245	749	595
48	1255	432	606	614	360	201	81	670	55	1352
49	1347	528	709	97	1364	1031	727	156	640	283

POWER RESIDUES

	0	1	2	3	4	5	6	7	8	9
0	1	2	4	8	16	32	64	128	256	512
1	1024	667	1334	1287	1193	1005	629	1258	1135	889
2	397	794	207	414	828	275	550	1100	819	257
3	514	1028	675	1350	1319	1257	1133	885	389	778
4	175	350	700	19	38	76	152	304	608	1216
5	1051	721	61	122	244	488	976	571	1142	903
6	425	850	319	638	1276	1171	961	541	1082	783
7	185	370	740	99	198	396	792	203	406	812
8	243	486	972	563	1126	871	361	722	63	126
9	252	504	1008	635	1270	1159	937	493	986	591
10	1182	983	585	1170	959	537	1074	767	153	306
11	612	1224	1067	753	125	250	500	1000	619	1238
12	1095	809	237	474	948	515	1030	679	1358	1335
13	1289	1197	1013	645	1290	1199	1017	653	1306	1231
14	1081	781	181	362	724	67	134	268	536	1072
15	763	145	290	580	1160	939	497	994	607	1214
16	1047	713	45	90	180	360	720	59	118	236
17	472	944	507	1014	647	1294	1207	1033	685	1370
18	1359	1337	1293	1205	1029	677	1354	1327	1273	1165
19	949	517	1034	687	1374	1367	1353	1325	1269	1157
20	933	485	970	559	1118	855	329	658	1316	1251
21	1121	861	341	682	1364	1347	1313	1245	1109	837
22	293	586	1172	963	545	1090	799	217	434	868
23	355	710	39	78	156	312	624	1248	1115	849
24	317	634	1268	1155	929	477	954	527	1054	727
25	73	146	292	584	1168	955	529	1058	735	89
26	178	356	712	43	86	172	344	688	1376	1371
27	1361	1341	1301	1221	1061	741	101	202	404	808
28	235	470	940	499	998	615	1230	1079	777	173
29	346	692	3	6	12	24	48	96	192	384
30	768	155	310	620	1240	1099	817	253	506	1012
31	643	1286	1191	1001	621	1242	1103	825	269	538
32	1076	771	161	322	644	1288	1195	1009	637	1274
33	1167	953	525	1050	719	57	114	228	456	912
34	443	886	391	782	183	366	732	83	166	332
35	664	1328	1275	1169	957	533	1066	751	121	242
36	484	968	555	1110	839	297	594	1188	995	609
37	1218	1055	729	77	154	308	616	1232	1083	785
38	189	378	756	131	262	524	1048	715	49	98
39	196	392	784	187	374	748	115	230	460	920
40	459	918	455	910	439	878	375	750	119	238
41	476	952	523	1046	711	41	82	164	328	656
42	1312	1243	1105	829	277	554	1108	835	289	578
43	1156	931	481	962	543	1086	791	201	402	804
44	227	454	908	435	870	359	718	55	110	220
45	440	880	379	758	135	270	540	1080	779	177
46	354	708	35	70	140	280	560	1120	859	337
47	674	1348	1315	1249	1117	853	325	650	1300	1219
48	1057	733	85	170	340	680	1360	1339	1297	1213
49	1045	709	37	74	148	296	592	1184	987	593

P = 1381

INDICES

	0	1	2	3	4	5	6	7	8	9
50	116	1141	1202	1095	91	1234	308	172	517	1339
51	775	1134	9	919	30	125	557	191	1377	581
52	901	533	1158	412	385	332	895	247	1165	256
53	620	751	929	355	552	597	148	105	319	1257
54	456	67	1054	434	909	224	1117	608	602	636
55	26	616	1113	714	425	362	1007	1240	1308	203
56	466	685	718	83	996	510	1328	672	655	769
57	1294	57	811	969	1300	1354	590	1129	429	1349
58	153	1231	916	530	253	102	221	711	682	766
59	1126	99	496	499	366	1366	1069	1082	759	1033
60	831	502	1148	729	978	1316	569	158	48	369
61	1011	642	110	990	797	285	376	1369	840	118
62	303	314	1289	1143	236	1072	1244	1204	803	16
63	1047	1097	1213	1085	241	93	1335	328	63	1236
64	965	762	1312	310	324	133	948	174	1171	1036
65	477	519	1062	137	939	1341	419	834	207	777
66	741	856	1024	1136	350	505	1077	11	851	952
67	1104	921	1181	1151	470	32	1262	185	1225	127
68	485	732	213	559	629	178	1273	193	267	981
69	689	1379	291	957	883	583	868	1319	1249	903
70	42	1175	817	535	875	572	722	1160	461	491
71	231	414	262	161	701	387	1195	1040	446	334
72	166	51	87	897	144	1109	651	249	827	372
73	1209	1167	346	481	864	258	823	1014	1000	622
74	72	275	546	753	1018	645	783	931	395	523
75	407	357	706	113	514	554	382	926	453	599
76	1004	993	808	150	679	1066	975	107	300	800
77	1332	321	1059	738	848	1259	626	288	39	458
78	1192	141	343	69	392	379	676	1056	1189	1186
79	789	436	76	1372	21	911	792	943	1220	226
80	541	843	659	1119	439	1280	664	610	279	121
81	747	604	79	1345	1362	638	1200	306	773	28
82	1375	1156	893	618	550	317	1052	1115	24	423
83	1306	716	1326	1292	1298	427	914	219	1124	364
84	757	1146	567	1009	795	838	1287	1242	1045	239
85	61	1310	946	475	937	205	1022	1075	1102	468
86	1223	211	1271	687	881	1247	815	720	229	699
87	444	85	649	1207	862	998	544	781	405	512
88	451	806	973	1330	846	37	341	674	787	19
89	1218	657	662	745	1360	771	891	1050	1304	1296
90	1122	565	1285	59	935	1100	1269	813	442	860
91	403	971	339	1216	1358	1302	1283	1267	401	1356
92	399	1088	1090	592	667	1028	1092	1131	578	244
93	594	431	613	200	669	1351	527	96	1030	155
94	282	1140	1094	1233	171	1338	1133	918	124	190
95	580	532	411	331	246	255	750	354	596	104
96	1256	66	433	223	607	635	615	713	361	1239
97	202	684	82	509	671	768	56	968	1353	1128
98	1348	1230	529	101	710	765	98	498	1365	1081
99	1032	501	728	1315	157	368	641	989	284	1368

POWER RESIDUES

	0	1	2	3	4	5	6	7	8	9
50	1186	991	601	1202	1023	665	1330	1279	1177	973
51	565	1130	879	377	754	127	254	508	1016	651
52	1302	1223	1065	749	117	234	468	936	491	982
53	583	1166	951	521	1042	703	25	50	100	200
54	400	800	219	438	876	371	742	103	206	412
55	824	267	534	1068	755	129	258	516	1032	683
56	1366	1351	1321	1261	1141	901	421	842	303	606
57	1212	1043	705	29	58	116	232	464	928	475
58	950	519	1038	695	9	18	36	72	144	288
59	576	1152	923	465	930	479	958	535	1070	759
60	137	274	548	1096	811	241	482	964	547	1094
61	807	233	466	932	483	966	551	1102	823	265
62	530	1060	739	97	194	388	776	171	342	684
63	1368	1355	1329	1277	1173	965	549	1098	815	249
64	498	996	611	1222	1063	745	109	218	436	872
65	363	726	71	142	284	568	1136	891	401	802
66	223	446	892	403	806	231	462	924	467	934
67	487	974	567	1134	887	393	786	191	382	764
68	147	294	588	1176	971	561	1122	863	345	690
69	1380	1379	1377	1373	1365	1349	1317	1253	1125	869
70	357	714	47	94	188	376	752	123	246	492
71	984	587	1174	967	553	1106	831	281	562	1124
72	867	353	706	31	62	124	248	496	992	603
73	1206	1031	681	1362	1343	1305	1229	1077	773	165
74	330	660	1320	1259	1137	893	405	810	239	478
75	956	531	1062	743	105	210	420	840	299	598
76	1196	1011	641	1282	1183	985	589	1178	975	569
77	1138	895	409	818	255	510	1020	659	1318	1255
78	1129	877	373	746	111	222	444	888	395	790
79	199	398	796	211	422	844	307	614	1228	1075
80	769	157	314	628	1256	1131	881	381	762	143
81	286	572	1144	907	433	866	351	702	23	46
82	92	184	368	736	91	182	364	728	75	150
83	300	600	1200	1019	657	1314	1247	1113	845	309
84	618	1236	1091	801	221	442	884	387	774	167
85	334	668	1336	1291	1201	1021	661	1322	1263	1145
86	909	437	874	367	734	87	174	348	696	11
87	22	44	88	176	352	704	27	54	108	216
88	432	864	347	694	7	14	28	56	112	224
89	448	896	411	822	263	526	1052	723	65	130
90	260	520	1040	699	17	34	68	136	272	544
91	1088	795	209	418	836	291	582	1164	947	513
92	1026	671	1342	1303	1225	1069	757	133	266	532
93	1064	747	113	226	452	904	427	854	327	654
94	1308	1235	1089	797	213	426	852	323	646	1292
95	1203	1025	669	1338	1295	1209	1037	693	5	10
96	20	40	80	160	320	640	1280	1179	977	573
97	1146	911	441	882	383	766	151	302	604	1208
98	1035	689	1378	1375	1369	1357	1333	1285	1189	997
99	613	1226	1071	761	141	282	564	1128	875	369

P = 1381

INDICES

	0	1	2	3	4	5	6	7	8	9
100	117	313	1142	1071	1203	15	1096	1084	92	327
101	1235	761	309	132	173	1035	518	136	1340	833
102	776	855	1135	504	10	951	920	1150	31	184
103	126	731	558	177	192	980	1378	956	582	1318
104	902	1174	534	571	1159	490	413	160	386	1039
105	333	50	896	1108	248	371	1166	480	257	1013
106	621	274	752	644	930	522	356	112	553	925
107	598	992	149	1065	106	799	320	737	1258	287
108	457	140	68	378	1055	1185	435	1371	910	942
109	225	842	1118	1279	609	120	603	1344	637	305
110	27	1155	617	316	1114	422	715	1291	426	218
111	363	1145	1008	837	1241	238	1309	474	204	1074
112	467	210	686	1246	719	698	84	1206	997	780
113	511	805	1329	36	673	18	656	744	770	1049
114	1295	564	58	1099	812	859	970	1215	1301	1266
115	1355	1087	591	1027	1130	243	430	199	1350	95
116	154	1139	1232	1337	917	189	531	330	254	353
117	103	65	222	634	712	1238	683	508	767	967
118	1127	1229	100	764	497	1080	500	1314	367	988
119	1367	312	1070	14	1083	326	760	131	1034	135
120	832	854	503	950	1149	183	730	176	979	955
121	1317	1173	570	489	159	1038	49	1107	370	479
122	1012	273	643	521	111	924	991	1064	798	736
123	286	139	377	1184	1370	941	841	1278	119	1343
124	304	1154	315	421	1290	217	1144	836	237	473
125	1073	209	1245	697	1205	779	804	35	17	743
126	1048	563	1098	858	1214	1265	1086	1026	242	198
127	94	1138	1336	188	329	352	64	633	1237	507
128	966	1228	763	1079	1313	987	311	13	325	130
129	134	853	949	182	175	954	1172	488	1037	1106
130	478	272	520	923	1063	735	138	1183	940	1277
131	1342	1153	420	216	835	472	208	696	778	34
132	742	562	857	1264	1025	197	1137	187	351	632
133	506	1227	1078	986	12	129	852	181	953	487
134	1105	271	922	734	1182	1276	1152	215	471	695
135	33	561	1263	196	186	631	1226	985	128	180
136	486	270	733	1275	214	694	560	195	630	984
137	179	269	1274	693	194	983	268	692	982	691
138	690	0								

POWER RESIDUES

	0	1	2	3	4	5	6	7	8	9
100	738	95	190	380	760	139	278	556	1112	843
101	305	610	1220	1059	737	93	186	372	744	107
102	214	428	856	331	662	1324	1267	1153	925	469
103	938	495	990	599	1198	1015	649	1298	1215	1049
104	717	53	106	212	424	848	315	630	1260	1139
105	897	413	826	271	542	1084	787	193	386	772
106	163	326	652	1304	1227	1073	765	149	298	596
107	1192	1003	625	1250	1119	857	333	666	1332	1283
108	1185	989	597	1194	1007	633	1266	1151	921	461
109	922	463	926	471	942	503	1006	631	1262	1143
110	905	429	858	335	670	1340	1299	1217	1053	725
111	69	138	276	552	1104	827	273	546	1092	803
112	225	450	900	419	838	295	590	1180	979	577
113	1154	927	473	946	511	1022	663	1326	1271	1161
114	941	501	1002	623	1246	1111	841	301	602	1204
115	1027	673	1346	1311	1241	1101	821	261	522	1044
116	707	33	66	132	264	528	1056	731	81	162
117	324	648	1296	1211	1041	701	21	42	84	168
118	336	672	1344	1307	1233	1085	789	197	394	788
119	195	390	780	179	358	716	51	102	204	408
120	816	251	502	1004	627	1254	1127	873	365	730
121	79	158	316	632	1264	1147	913	445	890	399
122	798	215	430	860	339	678	1356	1331	1281	1181
123	981	581	1162	943	505	1010	639	1278	1175	969
124	557	1114	847	313	626	1252	1123	865	349	698
125	15	30	60	120	240	480	960	539	1078	775
126	169	338	676	1352	1323	1265	1149	917	453	906
127	431	862	343	686	1372	1363	1345	1309	1237	1093
128	805	229	458	916	451	902	423	846	311	622
129	1244	1107	833	285	570	1140	899	417	834	287
130	574	1148	915	449	898	415	830	279	558	1116
131	851	321	642	1284	1187	993	605	1210	1039	697
132	13	26	52	104	208	416	832	283	566	1132
133	883	385	770	159	318	636	1272	1163	945	509
134	1018	655	1310	1239	1097	813	245	490	980	579
135	1158	935	489	978	575	1150	919	457	914	447
136	894	407	814	247	494	988	595	1190	999	617
137	1234	1087	793	205	410	820	259	518	1036	691
138										

P = 1399

INDICES

	0	1	2	3	4	5	6	7	8	9
0		0	324	339	648	268	663	1288	972	678
1	592	1206	987	1	214	607	1296	873	1002	848
2	916	229	132	292	1311	536	325	1017	538	352
3	931	401	222	147	1197	158	1326	116	1172	340
4	1240	1168	553	769	456	946	616	275	237	1178
5	860	1212	649	603	1341	76	862	1187	676	960
6	1255	356	725	568	546	269	471	743	123	631
7	482	711	252	838	440	875	98	1096	664	688
8	166	1356	94	114	877	1141	1093	691	780	638
9	1270	1289	940	740	599	1116	561	255	104	486
10	1184	393	138	555	973	497	927	272	267	1001
11	400	455	1186	481	113	560	1000	679	1284	763
12	181	1014	680	109	1049	804	892	1215	870	1108
13	593	745	795	738	1067	1285	447	459	955	785
14	806	614	1035	1207	576	620	1162	119	764	697
15	1199	1261	422	153	22	669	988	934	1012	942
16	490	182	282	843	418	415	438	295	1201	2
17	67	128	19	334	1015	426	1104	1299	962	573
18	196	206	215	695	1264	384	1064	681	923	907
19	42	136	885	1046	579	608	428	327	810	74
20	110	1082	717	242	462	38	879	970	1297	656
21	821	774	1251	1050	596	1037	591	291	1325	1177
22	724	874	779	392	112	1214	805	152	437	572
23	884	37	1324	36	1003	543	210	1027	1087	893
24	505	1010	1338	297	1004	48	433	849	1373	453
25	1128	1007	1216	100	141	82	1194	544	34	6
26	917	1030	1069	1308	1119	871	1062	977	1391	374
27	211	887	771	230	783	344	1279	645	1109	1079
28	1130	395	938	1028	1359	57	133	1058	900	348
29	944	594	88	203	443	1228	1088	825	1021	293
30	125	659	187	732	746	624	477	179	346	894
31	993	720	1312	170	1258	836	1336	796	1266	160
32	814	611	506	323	606	537	1167	1340	742	165
33	739	926	762	794	619	1011	127	1263	326	820
34	391	209	452	1068	343	899	658	1257	1339	390
35	750	1018	30	751	225	979	1286	1102	897	866
36	520	298	530	1353	539	1106	1019	1381	190	448
37	708	493	1388	92	1005	1143	1247	353	1231	31
38	366	156	460	90	1209	1364	1370	49	903	286
39	932	1165	752	1084	651	956	1134	259	398	1077
40	434	788	8	402	1041	226	566	1322	786	379
41	362	798	1203	850	1294	382	223	1124	980	1395
42	1145	807	1098	953	177	11	1374	246	920	148
43	1361	1287	915	146	615	959	251	1140	103	454
44	1048	458	1198	842	1103	906	716	1036	436	1009
45	140	976	1129	202	476	159	761	898	896	492
46	1208	258	361	952	250	1008	360	1383	1327	633
47	867	1273	534	577	1351	1384	13	1281	1217	833
48	829	117	1334	521	264	523	621	386	1328	1182
49	372	101	757	1225	1173	754	299	601	777	1163

POWER RESIDUES

	0	1	2	3	4	5	6	7	8	9
0	1	13	169	798	581	558	259	569	402	1029
1	786	425	1328	476	592	701	719	953	1197	172
2	837	1088	154	603	844	1179	1337	593	714	888
3	352	379	730	1096	258	556	233	231	205	1266
4	1069	1306	190	1071	1332	528	1268	1095	245	387
5	834	1049	1046	1007	500	904	560	285	907	599
6	792	503	943	1067	1280	1251	874	170	811	750
7	1356	840	1127	661	199	1188	55	715	901	521
8	1177	1311	255	517	1125	635	1260	991	292	998
9	383	782	373	652	82	1066	1267	1082	76	988
10	253	491	787	438	98	1274	1173	1259	978	123
11	200	1201	224	114	83	1079	37	481	657	147
12	512	1060	1189	68	884	300	1102	336	171	824
13	919	755	22	286	920	768	191	1084	102	1326
14	450	254	504	956	1236	679	433	33	429	1380
15	1152	986	227	153	590	675	381	756	35	455
16	319	1349	749	1343	671	329	80	1040	929	885
17	313	1271	1134	752	1382	1178	1324	424	1315	307
18	1193	120	161	694	628	1169	1207	302	1128	674
19	368	587	636	1273	1160	1090	180	941	1041	942
20	1054	1111	453	293	1011	552	181	954	1210	341
21	236	270	712	862	14	182	967	1379	1139	817
22	828	971	32	416	1211	354	405	1068	1293	21
23	273	751	1369	1009	526	1242	757	48	624	1117
24	531	1307	203	1240	731	1109	427	1354	814	789
25	464	436	72	936	976	97	1261	1004	461	397
26	964	1340	632	1221	484	696	654	108	5	65
27	845	1192	107	1391	1295	47	611	948	1132	726
28	1044	981	162	707	797	568	389	860	1387	1243
29	770	217	23	299	1089	167	772	243	361	496
30	852	1283	1290	1381	1165	1155	1025	734	1148	934
31	950	1158	1064	1241	744	1278	1225	536	1372	1048
32	1033	838	1101	323	2	26	338	197	1162	1116
33	518	1138	804	659	173	850	1257	952	1184	3
34	39	507	995	344	275	777	308	1206	289	959
35	1275	1186	29	377	704	758	61	793	516	1112
36	466	462	410	1133	739	1213	380	743	1265	1056
37	1137	791	490	774	269	699	693	615	1000	409
38	1120	570	415	1198	185	1006	487	735	1161	1103
39	349	340	223	101	1313	281	855	1322	398	977
40	110	31	403	1042	955	1223	510	1034	851	1270
41	1121	583	584	597	766	165	746	1304	164	733
42	1135	765	152	577	506	982	175	876	196	1149
43	947	1119	557	246	400	1003	448	228	166	759
44	74	962	1314	294	1024	721	979	136	369	600
45	805	672	342	249	439	111	44	572	441	137
46	382	769	204	1253	900	508	1008	513	1073	1358
47	866	66	858	1361	905	573	454	306	1180	1350
48	762	113	70	910	638	1299	99	1287	1342	658
49	160	681	459	371	626	1143	869	105	1365	957

P = 1399

INDICES

	0	1	2	3	4	5	6	7	8	9
50	54	634	1331	61	142	661	424	341	465	531
51	406	728	120	467	868	823	358	83	330	673
52	1241	79	1354	1126	1393	765	234	1274	45	584
53	1195	240	1386	1169	1301	540	317	912	698	986
54	535	1171	1211	545	1095	1269	554	999	1107	1034
55	668	1200	205	578	969	723	35	432	5	770
56	56	1020	719	605	1262	749	1352	1246	285	7
57	381	919	457	475	1382	828	1224	423	672	1385
58	1268	4	918	411	412	947	527	191	767	1249
59	154	666	14	27	1149	1031	1345	413	617	59
60	449	702	983	23	511	1282	1056	759	1070	581
61	948	276	801	709	503	377	670	790	1218	557
62	1317	1309	1044	528	238	1072	494	995	184	989
63	1160	834	262	1113	1120	85	192	1179	484	1389
64	1138	1054	935	856	830	1376	647	872	930	768
65	861	630	93	1115	266	1013	1066	118	489	333
66	1063	73	1250	1213	1086	1006	1118	644	943	731
67	1335	164	451	978	189	155	650	1321	1144	145
68	715	491	533	522	776	727	1392	911	667	604
69	1223	1248	982	376	183	1053	265	643	714	375
70	1074	15	1342	964	354	882	1075	283	549	524
71	1303	1366	212	693	28	77	1221	1232	1190	16
72	844	445	622	1349	854	888	279	1150	863	636
73	32	244	1343	419	307	387	514	551	772	364
74	1032	1188	817	367	314	965	416	792	1329	162
75	69	231	173	1346	677	131	157	236	355	439
76	690	1183	480	891	784	421	414	961	135	461
77	290	883	296	1193	373	937	1227	345	610	618
78	1256	519	91	1369	1076	1202	10	102	975	249
79	1280	371	60	357	583	1210	722	284	3	1148
80	758	1316	1112	646	332	450	726	713	1365	853
81	550	68	890	1226	248	1111	1110	219	703	569
82	686	1371	1122	525	129	683	1174	1156	220	1080
83	706	984	547	653	50	563	1304	20	321	755
84	71	704	1131	734	24	270	1277	904	501	1367
85	335	408	300	1253	570	396	1244	512	472	1234
86	287	1397	213	1016	1239	602	470	687	939	496
87	1283	744	575	933	66	694	427	655	778	542
88	1372	1029	782	1057	124	169	1166	819	29	1105
89	1230	1164	1040	1123	1360	841	760	632	1333	753
90	464	78	1300	998	55	474	526	58	800	1071
91	483	629	1085	1320	1222	963	1220	635	816	130
92	134	518	582	712	685	652	1276	1233	574	168
93	1332	628	684	1059	309	949	253	1060	957	509
94	1191	197	199	62	858	1175	901	430	277	839
95	310	1135	337	17	207	404	143	499	1157	349
96	1153	802	441	950	260	1314	845	216	588	662
97	847	221	945	675	710	876	254	399	108	446
98	696	281	425	922	1081	595	151	504	99	1061
99	1078	87	623	1265	925	342	1101	707	89	1133

POWER RESIDUES

	0	1	2	3	4	5	6	7	8	9
50	1249	848	1231	614	987	240	322	1388	1256	939
51	1015	604	857	1348	736	1174	1272	1147	921	781
52	360	483	683	485	709	823	906	586	623	1104
53	362	509	1021	682	472	540	25	325	28	364
54	535	1359	879	235	257	543	64	832	1023	708
55	810	737	1187	42	546	103	1339	619	1052	1085
56	115	96	1248	835	1062	1215	406	1081	63	819
57	854	1309	229	179	928	872	144	473	553	194
58	1123	609	922	794	529	1281	1264	1043	968	1392
59	1308	216	10	130	291	985	214	1383	1191	94
60	1222	497	865	53	689	563	324	15	195	1136
61	778	321	1375	1087	141	434	46	598	779	334
62	145	486	722	992	305	1167	1181	1363	931	911
63	651	69	897	469	501	917	729	1083	89	1157
64	1051	1072	1345	697	667	277	803	646	4	52
65	676	394	925	833	1036	877	209	1318	346	301
66	1115	505	969	6	78	1014	591	688	550	155
67	616	1013	578	519	1151	973	58	754	9	117
68	122	187	1032	825	932	924	820	867	79	1027
69	760	87	1131	713	875	183	980	149	538	1398
70	1386	1230	601	818	841	1140	830	997	370	613
71	974	71	923	807	698	680	446	202	1227	562
72	311	1245	796	555	220	62	806	685	511	1047
73	1020	669	303	1141	843	1166	1168	1194	133	330
74	93	1209	328	67	871	131	304	1154	1012	565
75	350	353	392	899	495	839	1114	492	800	607
76	896	456	332	119	148	525	1229	588	649	43
77	559	272	738	1200	211	1344	684	498	878	222
78	88	1144	882	274	764	139	408	1107	401	1016
79	617	1026	747	1317	333	132	317	1323	411	1146
80	908	612	961	1301	125	226	140	421	1276	1199
81	198	1175	1285	1316	320	1362	918	742	1252	887
82	339	210	1331	515	1099	297	1063	1228	575	480
83	644	1377	1113	479	631	1208	315	1297	73	949
84	1145	895	443	163	720	966	1366	970	19	247
85	413	1172	1246	809	724	1018	643	1364	944	1080
86	50	650	56	728	1070	1319	359	470	514	1086
87	128	265	647	17	221	75	975	84	1092	206
88	1279	1238	705	771	230	192	1097	271	725	1031
89	812	763	126	239	309	1219	458	358	457	345
90	288	946	1106	388	847	1218	445	189	1058	1163
91	1129	687	537	1385	1217	432	20	260	582	571
92	428	1367	983	188	1045	994	331	106	1378	1126
93	648	30	390	873	157	642	1351	775	282	868
94	92	1196	159	668	290	972	45	585	610	935
95	963	1327	463	423	1302	138	395	938	1002	435
96	59	767	178	915	703	745	1291	1394	1334	554
97	207	1292	8	104	1352	788	451	267	673	355
98	418	1237	692	602	831	1010	539	12	156	629
99	1182	1376	1100	310	1232	627	1156	1038	903	547

P = 1399

INDICES

	0	1	2	3	4	5	6	7	8	9
100	378	1097	958	435	257	1350	385	53	466	233
101	985	204	748	671	665	510	789	1159	855	1065
102	730	532	1052	548	444	306	791	689	1192	9
103	1147	889	682	320	407	1238	654	1229	997	1219
104	167	198	403	587	280	924	52	729	319	51
105	1089	640	558	1357	200	1042	369	1151	908	1090
106	121	1025	564	826	312	1318	95	63	227	40
107	864	43	641	468	1236	1305	1022	1205	1310	115
108	859	567	97	637	137	559	869	613	21	294
109	195	1045	878	1176	1323	47	33	886	1358	824
110	992	322	126	389	529	1142	902	787	1293	245
111	1047	201	359	832	756	660	329	239	1094	431
112	380	410	1344	580	1043	84	929	72	188	910
113	1073	692	278	363	172	420	609	370	331	218
114	705	733	1243	495	781	840	799	517	308	429
115	1152	674	150	1132	747	305	996	639	311	1204
116	194	388	328	909	1242	304	735	625	736	185
117	1271	1136	851	106	515	811	1091	80	175	25
118	478	626	990	1290	338	1295	351	552	75	122
119	1355	598	271	180	737	1161	941	18	383	809
120	773	111	1026	1127	1307	1278	347	186	835	741
121	208	224	1380	365	1083	565	1394	914	905	895
122	1272	263	600	405	1125	316	1033	718	827	766
123	701	502	994	1137	1114	1117	144	981	881	1189
124	243	313	235	289	1368	721	852	1121	562	500
125	1396	65	818	463	1319	1275	508	336	1313	107
126	86	256	1158	1146	586	368	39	96	46	1292
127	409	171	516	193	105	350	808	1379	315	880
128	64	585	1378	301	1259	812	1180	487	1154	1099
129	302	966	971	228	1196	274	1254	837	1092	485
130	1185	803	954	1260	417	1298	41	241	590	571
131	1337	81	1390	394	442	178	813	793	657	865
132	1387	1363	397	797	176	1139	139	951	12	1181
133	1330	822	44	1170	968	1245	1267	26	1055	556
134	261	1375	488	163	775	642	1302	1348	513	161
135	479	936	974	1315	247	1155	70	1252	469	541
136	1039	473	815	627	857	498	846	921	1100	232
137	1051	1237	318	1024	1235	612	991	831	928	217
138	149	303	174	597	1306	913	700	288	507	1291
139	1377	273	589	1362	967	1347	1038	1023	699	

POWER RESIDUES

	0	1	2	3	4	5	6	7	8	9
100	116	109	18	234	244	374	665	251	465	449
101	241	335	158	655	121	174	863	27	351	366
102	561	298	1076	1397	1373	1061	1202	237	283	881
103	261	595	740	1226	549	142	447	215	1396	1360
104	892	404	1055	1124	622	1091	193	1110	440	124
105	213	1370	1022	695	641	1338	606	883	287	933
106	937	989	266	660	186	1019	656	134	343	262
107	608	909	625	1130	700	706	784	399	990	279
108	829	984	201	1214	393	912	664	238	296	1050
109	1059	1176	1298	86	1118	544	77	1001	422	1289
110	1368	996	357	444	176	889	365	548	129	278
111	816	815	802	633	1234	653	95	1235	666	264
112	634	1247	822	893	417	1224	523	1203	250	452
113	280	842	1153	999	396	951	1171	1233	640	1325
114	437	85	1105	375	678	420	1263	1030	799	594
115	727	1057	1150	960	1288	1355	827	958	1262	1017
116	630	1195	146	499	891	391	886	326	41	533
117	1333	541	38	494	826	945	1093	219	49	637
118	1286	1329	489	761	100	1300	112	57	741	1239
119	718	940	1028	773	256	530	1294	34	442	150
120	551	168	785	412	1159	1077	11	143	460	384
121	795	542	51	663	225	127	252	478	618	1039
122	916	716	914	690	576	493	813	776	295	1037
123	890	378	717	927	859	1374	1074	1371	1035	864
124	40	520	1164	1142	856	1335	567	376	691	589
125	662	212	1357	853	1296	60	780	347	314	1284
126	1303	151	564	337	184	993	318	1336	580	545
127	90	1170	1220	471	527	1255	926	846	1205	276
128	790	477	605	870	118	135	356	431	7	91
129	1183	1389	1269	1108	414	1185	16	208	1305	177
130	902	534	1346	710	836	1075	1384	1204	263	621
131	1078	24	312	1258	965	1353	801	620	1065	1254
132	913	677	407	1094	232	218	36	468	488	748
133	1330	502	930	898	482	670	316	1310	242	348
134	327	54	702	732	1122	596	753	1395	1347	723
135	1005	474	566	363	522	1190	81	1053	1098	284
136	894	430	1393	1321	385	808	711	849	1244	783
137	386	821	880	248	426	1341	645	1390	1282	1277
138	1212	367	574	467	475	579	532	1320	372	639
139	1312	268	686	524	1216	419	1250	861		

P = 1409

INDICES

	0	1	2	3	4	5	6	7	8	9
0		0	58	1	116	954	59	32	174	2
1	1012	298	117	131	90	955	232	990	60	1139
2	1070	33	356	1094	175	500	189	3	148	53
3	1013	1246	290	299	1048	986	118	916	1197	132
4	1128	611	91	713	414	956	1152	395	233	64
5	558	991	247	353	61	1252	206	1140	111	1265
6	1071	1077	1304	34	348	1085	357	729	1106	1095
7	1044	636	176	1329	974	501	1255	330	190	71
8	1186	4	669	476	149	536	771	54	472	723
9	1014	163	1210	1247	453	685	291	197	122	300
10	616	864	1049	209	305	987	411	633	119	43
11	1310	917	264	940	1198	640	169	133	1323	1022
12	1129	596	1135	612	1362	46	92	523	406	714
13	1143	1400	415	1171	787	957	1164	1232	1153	831
14	1102	396	694	429	234	1007	1387	65	1032	400
15	559	1260	1313	992	388	792	248	114	129	354
16	1244	1126	62	109	727	1253	534	451	207	262
17	594	1141	829	1030	112	532	530	1266	781	920
18	1072	1366	221	1078	1268	462	1305	1288	511	35
19	743	848	349	783	255	1086	180	277	358	904
20	674	730	922	85	1107	157	267	1096	363	29
21	1045	1074	469	637	691	259	177	1278	101	1330
22	1368	1121	975	1281	322	502	998	1040	1256	223
23	698	331	227	943	191	1349	1381	72	1080	441
24	1187	857	654	5	1193	1018	670	1270	12	477
25	104	138	150	1392	581	537	464	1112	772	948
26	1201	55	50	203	473	1307	1229	724	845	98
27	1015	1219	1222	164	1290	798	1211	1333	889	1248
28	1160	1274	454	513	752	686	487	643	292	572
29	1065	198	37	660	123	811	1090	301	458	1225
30	617	745	1318	865	1371	623	1050	546	446	210
31	850	433	306	702	172	988	187	984	412	351
32	1302	634	1184	721	120	631	167	44	785	427
33	1311	1124	592	918	509	275	265	257	320	941
34	652	136	1199	96	887	641	1088	621	170	719
35	590	134	588	1293	1324	182	839	1023	978	1295
36	1130	870	16	597	279	875	1136	1149	1326	613
37	520	385	1363	360	1346	47	569	184	93	517
38	801	524	906	496	407	1284	841	715	313	1357
39	1144	676	238	1401	335	1025	416	804	962	1172
40	732	970	788	1377	980	958	143	1214	1165	924
41	215	1233	325	1297	1154	22	421	832	87	608
42	1103	682	1132	397	527	82	695	1109	749	430
43	317	872	235	605	1336	1008	159	825	1388	505
44	18	66	1179	481	1033	269	1339	401	380	599
45	560	909	1056	1261	1098	1117	1314	492	281	993
46	756	892	389	365	285	793	1001	877	249	761
47	1407	115	31	1011	130	231	1138	355	499	147
48	1245	1047	915	1127	712	1151	63	246	1251	110
49	1076	347	728	1043	1328	1254	70	668	535	471

POWER RESIDUES

	0	1	2	3	4	5	6	7	8	9
0	1	3	9	27	81	243	729	778	925	1366
1	1280	1022	248	744	823	1060	362	1086	440	1320
2	1142	608	415	1245	917	1342	1208	806	1009	209
3	627	472	7	21	63	189	567	292	876	1219
4	839	1108	506	109	327	981	125	375	1125	557
5	262	786	949	29	87	261	783	940	2	6
6	18	54	162	486	49	147	441	1323	1151	635
7	496	79	237	711	724	763	880	1231	875	1216
8	830	1081	425	1275	1007	203	609	418	1254	944
9	14	42	126	378	1134	584	343	1029	269	807
10	1012	218	654	553	250	750	841	1114	524	163
11	489	58	174	522	157	471	4	12	36	108
12	324	972	98	294	882	1237	893	1270	992	158
13	474	13	39	117	351	1053	341	1023	251	753
14	850	1141	605	406	1218	836	1099	479	28	84
15	252	756	859	1168	686	649	538	205	615	436
16	1308	1106	500	91	273	819	1048	326	978	116
17	348	1044	314	942	8	24	72	216	648	535
18	196	588	355	1065	377	1131	575	316	948	26
19	78	234	702	697	682	637	502	97	291	873
20	1210	812	1027	263	789	958	56	168	504	103
21	309	927	1372	1298	1076	410	1230	872	1207	803
22	1000	182	546	229	687	652	547	232	696	679
23	628	475	16	48	144	432	1296	1070	392	1176
24	710	721	754	853	1150	632	487	52	156	468
25	1404	1394	1364	1274	1004	194	582	337	1011	215
26	645	526	169	507	112	336	1008	206	618	445
27	1335	1187	743	820	1051	335	1005	197	591	364
28	1092	458	1374	1304	1094	464	1392	1358	1256	950
29	32	96	288	864	1183	731	784	943	11	33
30	99	297	891	1264	974	104	312	936	1399	1379
31	1319	1139	599	388	1164	674	613	430	1290	1052
32	338	1014	224	672	607	412	1236	890	1261	965
33	77	231	693	670	601	394	1182	728	775	916
34	1339	1199	779	928	1375	1307	1103	491	64	192
35	576	319	957	53	159	477	22	66	198	594
36	373	1119	539	208	624	463	1389	1349	1229	869
37	1198	776	919	1348	1226	860	1171	695	676	619
38	448	1344	1214	824	1063	371	1113	521	154	462
39	1386	1340	1202	788	955	47	141	423	1269	989
40	149	447	1341	1205	797	982	128	384	1152	638
41	505	106	318	954	44	132	396	1188	746	829
42	1078	416	1248	926	1369	1289	1049	329	987	143
43	429	1287	1043	311	933	1390	1352	1238	896	1279
44	1019	239	717	742	817	1042	308	924	1363	1271
45	995	167	501	94	282	846	1129	569	298	894
46	1273	1001	185	555	256	768	895	1276	1010	212
47	636	499	88	264	792	967	83	249	747	832
48	1087	443	1329	1169	689	658	565	286	858	1165
49	677	622	457	1371	1295	1067	383	1149	629	478

P = 1409

INDICES

	0	1	2	3	4	5	6	7	8	9
50	162	452	196	615	208	410	42	263	639	1322
51	595	1361	522	1142	1170	1163	830	693	1006	1031
52	1259	387	113	1243	108	533	261	828	531	780
53	1365	1267	1287	742	782	179	903	921	156	362
54	1073	690	1277	1367	1280	997	222	226	1348	1079
55	856	1192	1269	103	1391	463	947	49	1306	844
56	1218	1289	1332	1159	512	486	571	36	810	457
57	744	1370	545	849	701	186	350	1183	630	784
58	1123	508	256	651	95	1087	718	587	181	977
59	869	278	1148	519	359	568	516	905	1283	312
60	675	334	803	731	1376	142	923	324	21	86
61	681	526	1108	316	604	158	504	1178	268	379
62	908	1097	491	755	364	1000	760	30	230	498
63	1046	711	245	1075	1042	69	470	195	409	638
64	1360	1169	692	1258	1242	260	779	1286	178	155
65	689	1279	225	855	102	946	843	1331	485	809
66	1369	700	1182	1122	650	717	976	1147	567	1282
67	333	1375	323	680	315	503	378	490	999	229
68	710	1041	194	1359	1257	778	154	224	945	484
69	699	649	1146	332	679	377	228	193	777	944
70	648	678	192	647	646	1350	1351	896	1382	1352
71	240	73	897	932	1081	1383	1036	442	1353	1403
72	1188	241	928	858	74	553	655	898	337	6
73	933	295	1194	1082	1207	1019	1384	1027	671	1037
74	578	1271	443	272	13	1354	418	478	1404	665
75	105	1189	627	139	242	806	151	929	575	1393
76	859	882	582	75	964	538	554	1396	465	656
77	1342	1113	899	1174	773	338	371	949	7	342
78	1202	934	734	56	296	1068	51	1195	393	204
79	1083	972	474	1208	862	1308	1020	404	1230	1385
80	790	725	1028	219	846	672	27	99	1038	1379
81	1016	579	201	1220	1272	1063	1223	444	982	165
82	273	885	1291	14	383	799	1355	960	1212	419
83	80	1334	479	1054	890	1405	145	1249	666	40
84	1161	106	740	1275	1190	1216	455	628	585	514
85	140	602	753	243	1167	687	807	565	488	152
86	375	644	930	926	293	576	663	573	1394	369
87	1066	860	217	199	883	78	38	583	563	661
88	76	1235	124	965	1237	812	539	817	1091	555
89	327	302	1397	126	459	466	438	1226	657	1299
90	618	1343	967	746	1114	912	1319	900	1156	866
91	1175	1239	1372	774	550	624	339	24	1051	372
92	814	547	950	767	447	8	423	211	343	541
93	851	1203	1059	434	935	834	307	735	819	703
94	57	953	173	297	89	989	1069	1093	188	52
95	289	985	1196	610	413	394	557	352	205	1264
96	1303	1084	1105	635	973	329	1185	475	770	722
97	1209	684	121	863	304	632	1309	939	168	1021
98	1134	45	405	1399	786	1231	1101	428	1386	399
99	1312	791	128	1125	726	450	593	1029	529	919

POWER RESIDUES

	0	1	2	3	4	5	6	7	8	9
50	25	75	225	675	616	439	1317	1133	581	334
51	1002	188	564	283	849	1138	596	379	1137	593
52	370	1110	512	127	381	1143	611	424	1272	998
53	176	528	175	525	166	498	85	255	765	886
54	1249	929	1378	1316	1130	572	307	921	1354	1244
55	914	1333	1181	725	766	889	1258	956	50	150
56	450	1350	1232	878	1225	857	1162	668	595	376
57	1128	566	289	867	1192	758	865	1186	740	811
58	1024	254	762	877	1222	848	1135	587	352	1056
59	350	1050	332	996	170	510	121	363	1089	449
60	1347	1223	851	1144	614	433	1299	1079	419	1257
61	953	41	123	369	1107	503	100	300	900	1291
62	1055	347	1041	305	915	1336	1190	752	847	1132
63	578	325	975	107	321	963	71	213	639	508
64	115	345	1035	287	861	1174	704	703	700	691
65	664	583	340	1020	242	726	769	898	1285	1037
66	293	879	1228	866	1189	749	838	1105	497	82
67	246	738	805	1006	200	600	391	1173	701	694
68	673	610	421	1263	971	95	285	855	1156	650
69	541	214	642	517	142	426	1278	1016	230	690
70	661	574	313	939	1408	1406	1400	1382	1328	1166
71	680	631	484	43	129	387	1161	665	586	349
72	1047	323	969	89	267	801	994	164	492	67
73	201	603	400	1200	782	937	1402	1388	1346	1220
74	842	1117	533	190	570	301	903	1300	1082	428
75	1284	1034	284	852	1147	623	460	1380	1322	1148
76	626	469	1407	1403	1391	1355	1247	923	1360	1262
77	968	86	258	774	913	1330	1172	698	685	646
78	529	178	534	193	579	328	984	134	402	1206
79	800	991	155	465	1395	1367	1283	1031	275	825
80	1066	380	1140	602	397	1191	755	856	1159	659
81	568	295	885	1246	920	1351	1235	887	1252	938
82	1405	1397	1373	1301	1085	437	1311	1115	527	172
83	516	139	417	1251	935	1396	1370	1292	1058	356
84	1068	386	1158	656	559	268	804	1003	191	573
85	310	930	1381	1325	1157	653	550	241	723	760
86	871	1204	794	973	101	303	909	1318	1136	590
87	361	1083	431	1293	1061	365	1095	467	1401	1385
88	1337	1193	761	874	1213	821	1054	344	1032	278
89	834	1093	461	1383	1331	1175	707	712	727	772
90	907	1312	1118	536	199	597	382	1146	620	451
91	1353	1241	905	1306	1100	482	37	111	333	999
92	179	537	202	606	409	1227	863	1180	722	757
93	862	1177	713	730	781	934	1393	1361	1265	977
94	113	339	1017	233	699	688	655	556	259	777
95	922	1357	1253	941	5	15	45	135	405	1215
96	827	1072	398	1194	764	883	1240	902	1297	1073
97	401	1203	791	964	74	222	666	589	358	1074
98	404	1212	818	1045	317	951	35	105	315	945
99	17	51	153	459	1377	1313	1121	545	226	678

P = 1409

INDICES

	0	1	2	3	4	5	6	7	8	9
100	220	461	510	847	254	276	673	84	266	28
101	468	258	100	1120	321	1039	697	942	1380	440
102	653	1017	11	137	580	1111	1200	202	1228	97
103	1221	797	888	1273	751	642	1064	659	1089	1224
104	1317	622	445	432	171	983	1301	720	166	426
105	591	274	319	135	886	620	589	1292	838	1294
106	15	874	1325	384	1345	183	800	495	840	1356
107	237	1024	961	969	979	1213	214	1296	420	607
108	1131	81	748	871	1335	824	17	480	1338	598
109	1055	1116	280	891	284	876	1406	1010	1137	146
110	914	1150	1250	346	1327	667	161	614	41	1321
111	521	1162	1005	386	107	827	1364	741	902	361
112	1276	996	1347	1191	1390	48	1217	1158	570	456
113	544	185	629	507	94	586	868	518	515	311
114	802	141	20	525	603	1177	907	754	759	497
115	244	68	408	1168	1241	1285	688	854	842	808
116	1181	716	566	1374	314	489	709	1358	153	483
117	1145	376	776	677	645	895	239	931	1035	1402
118	927	552	336	294	1206	1026	577	271	417	664
119	626	805	574	881	963	1395	1341	1173	370	341
120	733	1067	392	971	861	403	789	218	26	1378
121	200	1062	981	884	382	959	79	1053	144	39
122	739	1215	584	601	1166	564	374	925	662	368
123	216	77	562	1234	1236	816	326	125	437	1298
124	966	911	1155	1238	549	23	813	766	422	540
125	1058	833	818	952	88	1092	288	609	556	1263
126	1104	328	769	683	303	938	1133	1398	1100	398
127	127	449	528	460	253	83	467	1119	696	439
128	10	1110	1227	796	750	658	1316	431	1300	425
129	318	619	837	873	1344	494	236	968	213	606
130	747	823	1337	1115	283	1009	913	345	160	1320
131	1004	826	901	995	1389	1157	543	506	867	310
132	19	1176	758	67	1240	853	1180	1373	708	482
133	775	894	1034	551	1205	270	625	880	1340	340
134	391	402	25	1061	381	1052	738	600	373	367
135	561	815	436	910	548	765	1057	951	287	1262
136	768	937	1099	448	252	1118	9	795	1315	424
137	836	493	212	822	282	344	1003	994	542	309
138	757	852	707	893	1204	879	390	1060	737	366
139	435	764	286	936	251	794	835	821	1002	308
140	706	878	736	763	250	820	705	762	704	

POWER RESIDUES

	0	1	2	3	4	5	6	7	8	9
100	625	466	1398	1376	1310	1112	518	145	435	1305
101	1097	473	10	30	90	270	810	1021	245	735
102	796	979	119	357	1071	395	1185	737	802	997
103	173	519	148	444	1332	1178	716	739	808	1015
104	227	681	634	493	70	210	630	481	34	102
105	306	918	1345	1217	833	1090	452	1356	1250	932
106	1387	1343	1211	815	1036	290	870	1201	785	946
107	20	60	180	540	211	633	490	61	183	549
108	238	714	733	790	961	65	195	585	346	1038
109	296	888	1255	947	23	69	207	621	454	1362
110	1268	986	140	420	1260	962	68	204	612	427
111	1281	1025	257	771	904	1303	1091	455	1365	1277
112	1013	221	663	580	331	993	161	483	40	120
113	360	1080	422	1266	980	122	366	1098	476	19
114	57	171	513	130	390	1170	692	667	592	367
115	1101	485	46	138	414	1242	908	1315	1127	563
116	280	840	1111	515	136	408	1224	854	1153	641
117	514	133	399	1197	773	910	1321	1145	617	442
118	1326	1160	662	577	322	966	80	240	720	751
119	844	1123	551	244	732	787	952	38	114	342
120	1026	260	780	931	1384	1334	1184	734	793	970
121	92	276	828	1075	407	1221	845	1126	560	271
122	813	1030	272	816	1039	299	897	1282	1028	266
123	798	985	137	411	1233	881	1234	884	1243	911
124	1324	1154	644	523	160	480	31	93	279	837
125	1102	488	55	165	495	76	228	684	643	520
126	151	453	1359	1259	959	59	177	531	184	552
127	247	741	814	1033	281	843	1120	542	217	651
128	544	223	669	598	385	1155	647	532	187	561
129	274	822	1057	353	1059	359	1077	413	1239	899
130	1288	1046	320	960	62	186	558	265	795	976
131	110	330	990	152	456	1368	1286	1040	302	906
132	1309	1109	509	118	354	1062	368	1104	494	73
133	219	657	562	277	831	1084	434	1302	1088	446
134	1338	1196	770	901	1294	1064	374	1122	548	235
135	705	706	709	718	745	826	1069	389	1167	683
136	640	511	124	372	1116	530	181	543	220	660
137	571	304	912	1327	1163	671	604	403	1209	809
138	1018	236	708	715	736	799	988	146	438	1314
139	1124	554	253	759	868	1195	767	892	1267	983
140	131	393	1179	719	748	835	1096	470		

P = 1423

INDICES

	0	1	2	3	4	5	6	7	8	9
0		0	66	1	132	537	67	957	198	2
1	603	787	133	989	1023	538	264	869	68	413
2	669	958	853	96	199	1074	1055	3	1089	285
3	604	1261	330	788	935	72	134	1101	479	990
4	735	61	1024	55	919	539	162	1096	265	492
5	1140	870	1121	195	69	1324	1155	414	351	47
6	670	1284	1327	959	396	104	854	17	1001	97
7	138	43	200	432	1167	1075	545	322	1056	643
8	801	4	127	1397	1090	1406	121	286	985	1158
9	605	524	228	1262	1162	950	331	1214	558	789
10	1206	1112	936	812	1187	73	261	52	135	1211
11	1390	1102	1221	595	480	633	417	991	113	404
12	736	152	1350	62	1393	189	1025	979	462	56
13	170	703	920	1370	83	540	1067	303	163	896
14	204	1097	109	354	266	822	498	493	1233	836
15	1141	1105	611	871	388	376	1122	1312	709	196
16	867	1053	70	917	193	1325	41	799	1156	556
17	50	415	187	81	352	609	1051	48	1224	1226
18	671	876	590	1285	294	216	1328	234	1228	960
19	1016	1297	397	1376	1280	105	624	673	855	358
20	1272	18	1178	1242	1002	598	878	98	1253	1200
21	139	534	327	44	118	592	201	796	1277	433
22	34	436	1168	628	1287	1076	661	506	546	1136
23	699	323	483	296	1057	211	179	644	470	720
24	802	29	218	5	1416	1029	128	1402	37	1398
25	255	1330	1091	883	1045	1407	528	337	122	636
26	236	287	769	309	986	732	14	1159	149	1230
27	606	1175	1133	525	369	439	229	653	962	1263
28	270	242	1163	372	175	951	420	1018	332	316
29	888	1215	564	487	559	584	1299	790	902	1085
30	1207	1012	1171	1113	677	399	937	684	454	813
31	442	383	1188	994	1378	74	775	955	262	1072
32	933	53	1119	1282	136	641	983	1212	259	631
33	1391	1368	107	1103	865	554	1222	232	622	596
34	116	626	481	27	253	634	147	651	418	582
35	675	992	1117	1366	114	580	1290	405	1292	857
36	737	826	942	153	656	969	1351	407	360	63
37	282	1152	1394	1387	300	190	1294	1274	1026	1130
38	1082	980	1363	1079	463	859	20	57	1346	1238
39	171	965	690	704	739	1180	921	1193	424	1371
40	1338	744	84	828	1244	541	1308	466	1068	1334
41	664	304	944	1004	164	512	1319	897	1266	751
42	205	155	600	1098	393	521	110	819	184	355
43	658	880	267	681	862	823	1343	509	499	971
44	100	494	502	450	1234	273	694	837	1353	1255
45	1142	848	727	1106	572	1061	612	409	1202	872
46	765	23	389	223	549	377	362	141	1123	974
47	277	1313	245	842	710	65	536	197	786	1022
48	868	668	95	1054	284	329	71	478	60	918
49	1095	1139	194	1154	46	1326	103	1000	42	1166

POWER RESIDUES

	0	1	2	3	4	5	6	7	8	9
0	1	3	9	27	81	243	729	764	869	1184
1	706	695	662	563	266	798	971	67	201	603
2	386	1158	628	461	1383	1303	1063	343	1029	241
3	723	746	815	1022	220	660	557	248	744	809
4	1004	166	498	71	213	639	494	59	177	531
5	170	510	107	321	963	43	129	387	1161	637
6	488	41	123	369	1107	475	2	6	18	54
7	162	486	35	105	315	945	1412	1390	1324	1126
8	532	173	519	134	402	1206	772	893	1256	922
9	1343	1183	703	686	635	482	23	69	207	621
10	440	1320	1114	496	65	195	585	332	996	142
11	426	1278	988	118	354	1062	340	1020	214	642
12	503	86	258	774	899	1274	976	82	246	738
13	791	950	4	12	36	108	324	972	70	210
14	630	467	1401	1357	1225	829	1064	346	1038	268
15	804	989	121	363	1089	421	1263	943	1406	1372
16	1270	964	46	138	414	1242	880	1217	805	992
17	130	390	1170	664	569	284	852	1133	553	236
18	708	701	680	617	428	1284	1006	172	516	125
19	375	1125	529	164	492	53	159	477	8	24
20	72	216	648	521	140	420	1260	934	1379	1291
21	1027	235	705	692	653	536	185	555	242	726
22	755	842	1103	463	1389	1321	1117	505	92	276
23	828	1061	337	1011	187	561	260	780	917	1328
24	1138	568	281	843	1106	472	1416	1402	1360	1234
25	856	1145	589	344	1032	250	750	827	1058	328
26	984	106	318	954	16	48	144	432	1296	1042
27	280	840	1097	445	1335	1159	631	470	1410	1384
28	1306	1072	370	1110	484	29	87	261	783	926
29	1355	1219	811	1010	184	552	233	699	674	599
30	374	1122	520	137	411	1233	853	1136	562	263
31	789	944	1409	1381	1297	1045	289	867	1178	688
32	641	500	77	231	693	656	545	212	636	485
33	32	96	288	864	1169	661	560	257	771	890
34	1247	895	1262	940	1397	1345	1189	721	740	797
35	968	58	174	522	143	429	1287	1015	199	597
36	368	1104	466	1398	1348	1198	748	821	1040	274
37	822	1043	283	849	1124	526	155	465	1395	1339
38	1171	667	578	311	933	1376	1282	1000	154	462
39	1386	1312	1090	424	1272	970	64	192	576	305
40	915	1322	1120	514	119	357	1071	367	1101	457
41	1371	1267	955	19	57	171	513	116	348	1044
42	286	858	1151	607	398	1194	736	785	932	1373
43	1273	973	73	219	657	548	221	663	566	275
44	825	1052	310	930	1367	1255	919	1334	1156	622
45	443	1329	1141	577	308	924	1349	1201	757	848
46	1121	517	128	384	1152	610	407	1221	817	1028
47	238	714	719	734	779	914	1319	1111	487	38
48	114	342	1026	232	696	665	572	293	879	1214
49	796	965	49	147	441	1323	1123	523	146	438

P = 1423

INDICES

	0	1	2	3	4	5	6	7	8	9
50	321	800	1396	120	1157	227	949	557	1111	1186
51	51	1389	594	416	403	1349	188	461	702	82
52	302	203	353	497	835	610	375	708	1052	192
53	798	49	80	1050	1225	589	215	1227	1296	1279
54	672	1271	1241	877	1199	326	591	1276	435	1286
55	505	698	295	178	719	217	1028	36	1329	1044
56	336	235	308	13	1229	1132	438	961	241	174
57	1017	887	486	1298	1084	1170	398	453	382	1377
58	954	932	1281	982	630	106	553	621	625	252
59	650	674	1365	1289	856	941	968	359	1151	299
60	1273	1081	1078	19	1237	689	1179	423	743	1243
61	465	663	1003	1318	750	599	520	183	879	861
62	508	99	449	693	1254	726	1060	1201	22	548
63	140	276	841	535	1021	94	328	59	1138	45
64	999	320	119	948	1185	593	1348	701	202	834
65	707	797	1049	214	1278	1240	325	434	697	718
66	35	335	12	437	173	485	1169	381	931	629
67	620	649	1288	967	298	1077	688	742	662	749
68	182	507	692	1059	547	840	93	1137	319	1184
69	700	706	213	324	717	11	484	930	648	297
70	741	181	1058	92	1183	212	10	647	180	1182
71	646	645	1356	1357	471	891	1358	721	923	472
72	803	347	892	30	1008	1359	219	1195	722	6
73	1035	924	1417	1411	473	1030	426	804	129	1258
74	348	1403	1218	893	38	1373	31	1399	366	1009
75	256	577	1360	1331	1340	220	1092	458	1196	884
76	1148	723	1046	746	7	1408	1145	1036	529	567
77	925	338	86	1418	123	913	1412	637	1304	474
78	237	830	1031	288	756	427	770	1039	805	310
79	1246	130	987	851	1259	733	490	349	15	543
80	1404	1160	810	1219	150	168	894	1231	1310	39
81	607	292	1374	1176	532	32	1134	468	1400	526
82	730	367	370	562	1010	440	1070	257	230	145
83	578	654	1385	1361	963	1336	1332	1264	817	1341
84	271	570	221	243	666	1093	1164	1109	459	373
85	587	1197	176	306	885	952	250	1149	421	518
86	724	1019	946	1047	333	618	747	317	928	8
87	889	1006	1409	1216	575	1146	565	1302	1037	488
88	166	530	560	1383	568	585	516	926	1300	514
89	339	791	760	87	903	341	1419	1086	1321	124
90	1208	1064	914	1013	793	1413	1172	899	638	1114
91	1127	1305	678	762	475	400	1268	238	938	446
92	831	685	89	1032	455	753	289	814	615	757
93	443	905	428	384	207	771	1189	782	1040	995
94	343	806	1379	157	311	75	908	1247	776	1421
95	131	956	602	988	263	412	852	1073	1088	1260
96	934	1100	734	54	161	491	1120	1323	350	1283
97	395	16	137	431	544	642	126	1405	984	523
98	1161	1213	1205	811	260	1210	1220	632	112	151
99	1392	978	169	1369	1066	895	108	821	1232	1104

POWER RESIDUES

	0	1	2	3	4	5	6	7	8	9
50	1314	1096	442	1326	1132	550	227	681	620	437
51	1311	1087	415	1245	889	1244	886	1235	859	1154
52	616	425	1275	979	91	273	819	1034	256	768
53	881	1220	814	1019	211	633	476	5	15	45
54	135	405	1215	799	974	76	228	684	629	464
55	1392	1330	1144	586	335	1005	169	507	98	294
56	882	1223	823	1046	292	876	1205	769	884	1229
57	841	1100	454	1362	1240	874	1199	751	830	1067
58	355	1065	349	1047	295	885	1232	850	1127	535
59	182	546	215	645	512	113	339	1017	205	615
60	422	1266	952	10	30	90	270	810	1007	175
61	525	152	456	1368	1258	928	1361	1237	865	1172
62	670	587	338	1014	196	588	341	1023	223	669
63	584	329	987	115	345	1035	259	777	908	1301
64	1057	325	975	79	237	711	710	707	698	671
65	590	347	1041	277	831	1070	364	1092	430	1290
66	1024	226	678	611	410	1230	844	1109	481	20
67	60	180	540	197	591	350	1050	304	912	1313
68	1093	433	1299	1051	307	921	1340	1174	676	605
69	392	1176	682	623	446	1338	1168	658	551	230
70	690	647	518	131	393	1179	691	650	527	158
71	474	1422	1420	1414	1396	1342	1180	694	659	554
72	239	717	728	761	860	1157	625	452	1356	1222
73	820	1037	265	795	962	40	120	360	1080	394
74	1182	700	677	608	401	1203	763	866	1175	679
75	614	419	1257	925	1352	1210	784	929	1364	1246
76	892	1253	913	1316	1102	460	1380	1294	1036	262
77	786	935	1382	1300	1054	316	948	1421	1417	1405
78	1369	1261	937	1388	1318	1108	478	11	33	99
79	297	891	1250	904	1289	1021	217	651	530	167
80	501	80	240	720	737	788	941	1400	1354	1216
81	802	983	103	309	927	1358	1228	838	1091	427
82	1281	997	145	435	1305	1069	361	1083	403	1209
83	781	920	1337	1165	649	524	149	447	1341	1177
84	685	632	473	1419	1411	1387	1315	1099	451	1353
85	1213	793	956	22	66	198	594	359	1077	385
86	1155	619	434	1302	1060	334	1002	160	480	17
87	51	153	459	1377	1285	1009	181	543	206	618
88	431	1293	1033	253	759	854	1139	571	290	870
89	1187	715	722	743	806	995	139	417	1251	907
90	1298	1048	298	894	1259	931	1370	1264	946	1415
91	1399	1351	1207	775	902	1283	1003	163	489	44
92	132	396	1188	718	731	770	887	1238	868	1181
93	697	668	581	320	960	34	102	306	918	1331
94	1147	595	362	1086	412	1236	862	1163	643	506
95	95	285	855	1142	580	317	951	7	21	63
96	189	567	278	834	1079	391	1173	673	596	365
97	1095	439	1317	1105	469	1407	1375	1279	991	127
98	381	1143	583	326	978	88	264	792	953	13
99	39	117	351	1053	313	939	1394	1336	1162	640

P = 1423

INDICES

	0	1	2	3	4	5	6	7	8	9
100	387	1311	866	916	40	555	186	608	1223	875
101	293	233	1015	1375	623	357	1177	597	1252	533
102	117	795	33	627	660	1135	482	210	469	28
103	1415	1401	254	882	527	635	768	731	148	1174
104	368	652	269	371	419	315	563	583	901	1011
105	676	683	441	993	774	1071	1118	640	258	1367
106	864	231	115	26	146	581	1116	579	1291	825
107	655	406	281	1386	1293	1129	1362	858	1345	964
108	738	1192	1337	827	1307	1333	943	511	1265	154
109	392	818	657	680	1342	970	501	272	1352	847
110	571	408	764	222	361	973	244	64	785	667
111	283	477	1094	1153	102	1165	1395	226	1110	1388
112	402	460	301	496	374	191	79	588	1295	1270
113	1198	1275	504	177	1027	1043	307	1131	240	886
114	1083	452	953	981	552	251	1364	940	1150	1080
115	1236	422	464	1317	519	860	448	725	21	275
116	1020	58	998	947	1347	833	1048	1239	696	334
117	172	380	619	966	687	748	691	839	318	705
118	716	929	740	91	9	1181	1355	890	922	346
119	1007	1194	1034	1410	425	1257	1217	1372	365	576
120	1339	457	1147	745	1144	566	85	912	1303	829
121	755	1038	1245	850	489	542	809	167	1309	291
122	531	467	729	561	1069	144	1384	1335	816	569
123	665	1108	586	305	249	517	945	617	927	1005
124	574	1301	165	1382	515	513	759	340	1320	1063
125	792	898	1126	761	1267	445	88	752	614	904
126	206	781	342	156	907	1420	601	411	1087	1099
127	160	1322	394	430	125	522	1204	1209	111	977
128	1065	820	386	915	185	874	1014	356	1251	794
129	659	209	1414	881	767	1173	268	314	900	682
130	773	639	863	25	1115	824	280	1128	1344	1191
131	1306	510	391	679	500	846	763	972	784	476
132	101	225	401	495	78	1269	503	1042	239	451
133	551	939	1235	1316	447	274	997	832	695	379
134	686	838	715	90	1354	345	1033	1256	364	456
135	1143	911	754	849	808	290	728	143	815	1107
136	248	616	573	1381	758	1062	1125	444	613	780
137	906	410	159	429	1203	976	385	873	1250	208
138	766	313	772	24	279	1190	390	845	783	224
139	77	1041	550	1315	996	378	714	344	363	910
140	807	142	247	1380	1124	779	158	975	1249	312
141	278	844	76	1314	713	909	246	778	1248	843
142	712	777	711							

POWER RESIDUES

	0	1	2	3	4	5	6	7	8	9
100	497	68	204	612	413	1239	871	1190	724	749
101	824	1049	301	903	1286	1012	190	570	287	861
102	1160	634	479	14	42	126	378	1134	556	245
103	735	782	923	1346	1192	730	767	878	1211	787
104	938	1391	1327	1135	559	254	762	863	1166	652
105	533	176	528	161	483	26	78	234	702	683
106	626	455	1365	1249	901	1280	994	136	408	1224
107	826	1055	319	957	25	75	225	675	602	383
108	1149	601	380	1140	574	299	897	1268	958	28
109	84	252	756	845	1112	490	47	141	423	1269
110	961	37	111	333	999	151	453	1359	1231	847
111	1118	508	101	303	909	1304	1066	352	1056	322
112	966	52	156	468	1404	1366	1252	910	1307	1075
113	379	1137	565	272	816	1025	229	687	638	491
114	50	150	450	1350	1204	766	875	1202	760	857
115	1148	598	371	1113	493	56	168	504	89	267
116	801	980	94	282	846	1115	499	74	222	666
117	575	302	906	1295	1039	271	813	1016	202	606
118	395	1185	709	704	689	644	509	104	312	936
119	1385	1309	1081	397	1191	727	758	851	1130	544
120	209	627	458	1374	1276	982	100	300	900	1277
121	985	109	327	981	97	291	873	1196	742	803
122	986	112	336	1008	178	534	179	537	188	564
123	269	807	998	148	444	1332	1150	604	389	1167
124	655	542	203	609	404	1212	790	947	1418	1408
125	1378	1288	1018	208	624	449	1347	1195	739	794
126	959	31	93	279	837	1088	418	1254	916	1325
127	1129	541	200	600	377	1131	547	218	654	539
128	194	582	323	969	61	183	549	224	672	593
129	356	1068	358	1074	376	1128	538	191	573	296
130	888	1241	877	1208	778	911	1310	1084	406	1218
131	808	1001	157	471	1413	1393	1333	1153	613	416
132	1248	898	1271	967	55	165	495	62	186	558
133	251	753	836	1085	409	1227	835	1082	400	1200
134	754	839	1094	436	1308	1078	388	1164	646	515
135	122	366	1098	448	1344	1186	712	713	716	725
136	752	833	1076	382	1146	592	353	1059	331	993
137	133	399	1197	745	812	1013	193	579	314	942
138	1403	1363	1243	883	1226	832	1073	373	1119	511
139	110	330	990	124	372	1116	502	83	249	747
140	818	1031	247	741	800	977	85	255	765	872
141	1193	733	776	905	1292	1030	244	732	773	896
142	1265	949								

P = 1427

INDICES

	0	1	2	3	4	5	6	7	8	9
0		0	1	1184	2	1227	1185	382	3	942
1	1228	634	1186	748	383	985	4	1284	943	1354
2	1229	140	635	737	1187	1028	749	700	384	1134
3	986	1401	5	392	1285	183	944	924	1355	506
4	1230	1246	141	324	636	743	738	1011	1188	764
5	1029	1042	750	728	701	435	385	1112	1135	160
6	987	1163	1402	1324	6	549	393	376	1286	495
7	184	1292	945	589	925	786	1356	1016	507	997
8	1231	458	1247	859	142	1085	325	892	637	467
9	744	1130	739	1159	1012	1155	1189	825	765	150
10	1030	1078	1043	602	751	1367	729	909	702	1193
11	436	682	386	819	1113	538	1136	264	161	240
12	988	1268	1164	1004	1403	829	1325	1065	7	82
13	550	1175	394	310	377	501	1287	597	496	409
14	185	769	1293	1382	946	935	590	522	926	96
15	787	1057	1357	800	1017	1202	508	154	998	486
16	1232	1119	459	288	1248	193	860	414	143	70
17	1086	870	326	1034	893	1410	638	1344	468	1224
18	745	137	1131	921	740	725	1160	492	1013	1082
19	1156	1075	1190	261	826	307	766	93	151	190
20	1031	134	1079	90	1044	1047	603	253	752	562
21	1368	647	730	1050	910	125	703	357	1194	347
22	437	606	683	1421	387	544	820	77	1114	256
23	539	774	1137	662	265	812	162	755	241	623
24	989	169	1269	216	1165	565	1005	676	1404	617
25	830	1238	1326	1371	1066	843	8	779	83	1306
26	551	650	1176	1298	395	529	311	225	378	733
27	502	431	1288	888	598	236	497	1053	410	917
28	186	121	770	672	1294	913	1383	202	947	1142
29	936	583	591	128	523	1387	927	1334	97	59
30	788	706	1058	836	1358	964	801	901	1018	360
31	1203	206	509	695	155	1125	999	1197	487	342
32	1233	667	1120	1212	460	350	289	951	1249	1393
33	194	1313	861	440	415	177	144	282	71	577
34	1087	609	871	1146	327	296	1035	1217	894	686
35	1411	22	639	270	1345	1093	469	1424	1225	940
36	746	1282	138	1026	1132	390	922	1244	741	762
37	726	1110	1161	547	493	587	1014	456	1083	465
38	1157	823	1076	1365	1191	817	262	1266	827	80
39	308	595	767	933	94	798	152	1117	191	68
40	1032	1342	135	723	1080	259	91	132	1045	560
41	1048	355	604	542	254	660	753	167	563	615
42	1369	777	648	527	731	886	1051	119	911	1140
43	126	1332	704	962	358	693	1195	665	348	1391
44	438	280	607	294	684	268	1422	1280	388	760
45	545	454	821	815	78	931	1115	1340	257	558
46	540	165	775	884	1138	960	663	278	266	758
47	813	1338	163	958	756	956	242	244	624	44
48	990	246	170	877	1270	626	217	101	1166	46
49	566	980	1006	992	677	1377	1405	248	618	426

POWER RESIDUES

	0	1	2	3	4	5	6	7	8	9
0	1	2	4	8	16	32	64	128	256	512
1	1024	621	1242	1057	687	1374	1321	1215	1003	579
2	1158	889	351	702	1404	1381	1335	1243	1059	691
3	1382	1337	1247	1067	707	1414	1401	1375	1323	1219
4	1011	595	1190	953	479	958	489	978	529	1058
5	689	1378	1329	1231	1035	643	1286	1145	863	299
6	598	1196	965	503	1006	585	1170	913	399	798
7	169	338	676	1352	1277	1127	827	227	454	908
8	389	778	129	258	516	1032	637	1274	1121	815
9	203	406	812	197	394	788	149	298	596	1192
10	957	487	974	521	1042	657	1314	1201	975	523
11	1046	665	1330	1233	1039	651	1302	1177	927	427
12	854	281	562	1124	821	215	430	860	293	586
13	1172	917	407	814	201	402	804	181	362	724
14	21	42	84	168	336	672	1344	1261	1095	763
15	99	198	396	792	157	314	628	1256	1085	743
16	59	118	236	472	944	461	922	417	834	241
17	482	964	501	1002	577	1154	881	335	670	1340
18	1253	1079	731	35	70	140	280	560	1120	813
19	199	398	796	165	330	660	1320	1213	999	571
20	1142	857	287	574	1148	869	311	622	1244	1061
21	695	1390	1353	1279	1131	835	243	486	972	517
22	1034	641	1282	1137	847	267	534	1068	709	1418
23	1409	1391	1355	1283	1139	851	275	550	1100	773
24	119	238	476	952	477	954	481	962	497	994
25	561	1122	817	207	414	828	229	458	916	405
26	810	193	386	772	117	234	468	936	445	890
27	353	706	1412	1397	1367	1307	1187	947	467	934
28	441	882	337	674	1348	1269	1111	795	163	326
29	652	1304	1181	935	443	886	345	690	1380	1333
30	1239	1051	675	1350	1273	1119	811	195	390	780
31	133	266	532	1064	701	1402	1377	1327	1227	1027
32	627	1254	1081	735	43	86	172	344	688	1376
33	1325	1223	1019	611	1222	1017	607	1214	1001	575
34	1150	873	319	638	1276	1125	823	219	438	876
35	325	650	1300	1173	919	411	822	217	434	868
36	309	618	1236	1045	663	1326	1225	1023	619	1238
37	1049	671	1342	1257	1087	747	67	134	268	536
38	1072	717	7	14	28	56	112	224	448	896
39	365	730	33	66	132	264	528	1056	685	1370
40	1313	1199	971	515	1030	633	1266	1105	783	139
41	278	556	1112	797	167	334	668	1336	1245	1063
42	699	1398	1369	1311	1195	963	499	998	569	1138
43	849	271	542	1084	741	55	110	220	440	880
44	333	666	1332	1237	1047	667	1334	1241	1055	683
45	1366	1305	1183	939	451	902	377	754	81	162
46	324	648	1296	1165	903	379	758	89	178	356
47	712	1424	1421	1415	1403	1379	1331	1235	1043	659
48	1318	1209	991	555	1110	793	159	318	636	1272
49	1117	807	187	374	748	69	138	276	552	1104

P = 1427

INDICES

	0	1	2	3	4	5	6	7	8	9
50	831	172	1239	63	1327	879	1372	1254	1067	1272
51	844	971	9	628	780	403	84	219	1307	792
52	552	103	651	109	1177	1168	1299	1259	396	48
53	530	1102	312	568	226	710	379	982	734	1398
54	503	1008	432	1321	1289	994	889	1152	599	679
55	237	1062	498	1379	1054	483	411	1407	918	1072
56	187	250	122	1418	771	620	673	840	1295	428
57	914	199	1384	833	203	339	948	174	1143	19
58	937	1241	584	1362	592	65	129	657	524	1329
59	1388	1277	928	881	1335	41	98	1374	60	968
60	789	1256	707	1318	1059	1069	837	336	1359	1274
61	965	333	802	846	902	805	1019	973	361	368
62	1204	11	207	849	510	630	696	320	156	782
63	1126	905	1000	405	1198	866	488	86	343	808
64	1234	221	668	55	1121	1309	1213	1022	461	794
65	351	115	290	554	952	976	1250	105	1394	479
66	195	653	1314	364	862	111	441	445	416	1179
67	178	371	145	1170	283	302	72	1301	578	1207
68	1088	1261	610	449	872	398	1147	14	328	50
69	297	29	1036	532	1218	210	895	1104	687	420
70	1412	314	23	852	640	570	271	34	1346	228
71	1094	513	470	712	1425	1183	1226	381	941	633
72	747	984	1283	1353	139	736	1027	699	1133	1400
73	391	182	923	505	1245	323	742	1010	763	1041
74	727	434	1111	159	1162	1323	548	375	494	1291
75	588	785	1015	996	457	858	1084	891	466	1129
76	1158	1154	824	149	1077	601	1366	908	1192	681
77	818	537	263	239	1267	1003	828	1064	81	1174
78	309	500	596	408	768	1381	934	521	95	1056
79	799	1201	153	485	1118	287	192	413	69	869
80	1033	1409	1343	1223	136	920	724	491	1081	1074
81	260	306	92	189	133	89	1046	252	561	646
82	1049	124	356	346	605	1420	543	76	255	773
83	661	811	754	622	168	215	564	675	616	1237
84	1370	842	778	1305	649	1297	528	224	732	430
85	887	235	1052	916	120	671	912	201	1141	582
86	127	1386	1333	58	705	835	963	900	359	205
87	694	1124	1196	341	666	1211	349	950	1392	1312
88	439	176	281	576	608	1145	295	1216	685	21
89	269	1092	1423	939	1281	1025	389	1243	761	1109
90	546	586	455	464	822	1364	816	1265	79	594
91	932	797	1116	67	1341	722	258	131	559	354
92	541	659	166	614	776	526	885	118	1139	1331
93	961	692	664	1390	279	293	267	1279	759	453
94	814	930	1339	557	164	883	959	277	757	1337
95	957	955	243	43	245	876	625	100	45	979
96	991	1376	247	425	171	62	878	1253	1271	970
97	627	402	218	791	102	108	1167	1258	47	1101
98	567	709	981	1397	1007	1320	993	1151	678	1061
99	1378	482	1406	1071	249	1417	619	839	427	198

POWER RESIDUES

	0	1	2	3	4	5	6	7	8	9
50	781	135	270	540	1080	733	39	78	156	312
51	624	1248	1069	711	1422	1417	1407	1387	1347	1267
52	1107	787	147	294	588	1176	925	423	846	265
53	530	1060	693	1386	1345	1263	1099	771	115	230
54	460	920	413	826	225	450	900	373	746	65
55	130	260	520	1040	653	1306	1185	943	459	918
56	409	818	209	418	836	245	490	980	533	1066
57	705	1410	1393	1359	1291	1155	883	339	678	1356
58	1285	1143	859	291	582	1164	901	375	750	73
59	146	292	584	1168	909	391	782	137	274	548
60	1096	765	103	206	412	824	221	442	884	341
61	682	1364	1301	1175	923	419	838	249	498	996
62	565	1130	833	239	478	956	485	970	513	1026
63	625	1250	1073	719	11	22	44	88	176	352
64	704	1408	1389	1351	1275	1123	819	211	422	844
65	261	522	1044	661	1322	1217	1007	587	1174	921
66	415	830	233	466	932	437	874	321	642	1284
67	1141	855	283	566	1132	837	247	494	988	549
68	1098	769	111	222	444	888	349	698	1396	1365
69	1303	1179	931	435	870	313	626	1252	1077	727
70	27	54	108	216	432	864	301	602	1204	981
71	535	1070	713	1426	1425	1423	1419	1411	1395	1363
72	1299	1171	915	403	806	185	370	740	53	106
73	212	424	848	269	538	1076	725	23	46	92
74	184	368	736	45	90	180	360	720	13	26
75	52	104	208	416	832	237	474	948	469	938
76	449	898	369	738	49	98	196	392	784	141
77	282	564	1128	829	231	462	924	421	842	257
78	514	1028	629	1258	1089	751	75	150	300	600
79	1200	973	519	1038	649	1298	1169	911	395	790
80	153	306	612	1224	1021	615	1230	1033	639	1278
81	1129	831	235	470	940	453	906	385	770	113
82	226	452	904	381	762	97	194	388	776	125
83	250	500	1000	573	1146	865	303	606	1212	997
84	567	1134	841	255	510	1020	613	1226	1025	623
85	1246	1065	703	1406	1385	1343	1259	1091	755	83
86	166	332	664	1328	1229	1031	635	1270	1113	799
87	171	342	684	1368	1309	1191	955	483	966	505
88	1010	593	1186	945	463	926	425	850	273	546
89	1092	757	87	174	348	696	1392	1357	1287	1147
90	867	307	614	1228	1029	631	1262	1097	767	107
91	214	428	856	285	570	1140	853	279	558	1116
92	805	183	366	732	37	74	148	296	592	1184
93	941	455	910	393	786	145	290	580	1160	893
94	359	718	9	18	36	72	144	288	576	1152
95	877	327	654	1308	1189	951	475	950	473	946
96	465	930	433	866	305	610	1220	1013	599	1198
97	969	511	1022	617	1234	1041	655	1310	1193	959
98	491	982	537	1074	721	15	30	60	120	240
99	480	960	493	986	545	1090	753	79	158	316

P = 1427

INDICES

	0	1	2	3	4	5	6	7	8	9
100	832	338	173	18	1240	1361	64	656	1328	1276
101	880	40	1373	967	1255	1317	1068	335	1273	332
102	845	804	972	367	10	848	629	319	781	904
103	404	865	85	807	220	54	1308	1021	793	114
104	553	975	104	478	652	363	110	444	1178	370
105	1169	301	1300	1206	1260	448	397	13	49	28
106	531	209	1103	419	313	851	569	33	227	512
107	711	1182	380	632	983	1352	735	698	1399	181
108	504	322	1009	1040	433	158	1322	374	1290	784
109	995	857	890	1128	1153	148	600	907	680	536
110	238	1002	1063	1173	499	407	1380	520	1055	1200
111	484	286	412	868	1408	1222	919	490	1073	305
112	188	88	251	645	123	345	1419	75	772	810
113	621	214	674	1236	841	1304	1296	223	429	234
114	915	670	200	581	1385	57	834	899	204	1123
115	340	1210	949	1311	175	575	1144	1215	20	1091
116	938	1024	1242	1108	585	463	1363	1264	593	796
117	66	721	130	353	658	613	525	117	1330	691
118	1389	292	1278	452	929	556	882	276	1336	954
119	42	875	99	978	1375	424	61	1252	969	401
120	790	107	1257	1100	708	1396	1319	1150	1060	481
121	1070	1416	838	197	337	17	1360	655	1275	39
122	966	1316	334	331	803	366	847	318	903	864
123	806	53	1020	113	974	477	362	443	369	300
124	1205	447	12	27	208	418	850	32	511	1181
125	631	1351	697	180	321	1039	157	373	783	856
126	1127	147	906	535	1001	1172	406	519	1199	285
127	867	1221	489	304	87	644	344	74	809	213
128	1235	1303	222	233	669	580	56	898	1122	1209
129	1310	574	1214	1090	1023	1107	462	1263	795	720
130	352	612	116	690	291	451	555	275	953	874
131	977	423	1251	400	106	1099	1395	1149	480	1415
132	196	16	654	38	1315	330	365	317	863	52
133	112	476	442	299	446	26	417	31	1180	1350
134	179	1038	372	855	146	534	1171	518	284	1220
135	303	643	73	212	1302	232	579	897	1208	573
136	1089	1106	1262	719	611	689	450	274	873	422
137	399	1098	1148	1414	15	37	329	316	51	475
138	298	25	30	1349	1037	854	533	517	1219	642
139	211	231	896	572	1105	718	688	273	421	1097
140	1413	36	315	474	24	1348	853	516	641	230
141	571	717	272	1096	35	473	1347	515	229	716
142	1095	472	514	715	471	714	713			

POWER RESIDUES

	0	1	2	3	4	5	6	7	8	9
100	632	1264	1101	775	123	246	492	984	541	1082
101	737	47	94	188	376	752	77	154	308	616
102	1232	1037	647	1294	1161	895	363	726	25	50
103	100	200	400	800	173	346	692	1384	1341	1255
104	1083	739	51	102	204	408	816	205	410	820
105	213	426	852	277	554	1108	789	151	302	604
106	1208	989	551	1102	777	127	254	508	1016	605
107	1210	993	559	1118	809	191	382	764	101	202
108	404	808	189	378	756	85	170	340	680	1360
109	1293	1159	891	355	710	1420	1413	1399	1371	1315
110	1203	979	531	1062	697	1394	1361	1295	1163	899
111	371	742	57	114	228	456	912	397	794	161
112	322	644	1288	1149	871	315	630	1260	1093	759
113	91	182	364	728	29	58	116	232	464	928
114	429	858	289	578	1156	885	343	686	1372	1317
115	1207	987	547	1094	761	95	190	380	760	93
116	186	372	744	61	122	244	488	976	525	1050
117	673	1346	1265	1103	779	131	262	524	1048	669
118	1338	1249	1071	715	3	6	12	24	48	96
119	192	384	768	109	218	436	872	317	634	1268
120	1109	791	155	310	620	1240	1053	679	1358	1289
121	1151	875	323	646	1292	1157	887	347	694	1388
122	1349	1271	1115	803	179	358	716	5	10	20
123	40	80	160	320	640	1280	1133	839	251	502
124	1004	581	1162	897	367	734	41	82	164	328
125	656	1312	1197	967	507	1014	601	1202	977	527
126	1054	681	1362	1297	1167	907	387	774	121	242
127	484	968	509	1018	609	1218	1009	591	1182	937
128	447	894	361	722	17	34	68	136	272	544
129	1088	749	71	142	284	568	1136	845	263	526
130	1052	677	1354	1281	1135	843	259	518	1036	645
131	1290	1153	879	331	662	1324	1221	1015	603	1206
132	985	543	1086	745	63	126	252	504	1008	589
133	1178	929	431	862	297	594	1188	949	471	942
134	457	914	401	802	177	354	708	1416	1405	1383
135	1339	1251	1075	723	19	38	76	152	304	608
136	1216	1005	583	1166	905	383	766	105	210	420
137	840	253	506	1012	597	1194	961	495	990	553
138	1106	785	143	286	572	1144	861	295	590	1180
139	933	439	878	329	658	1316	1205	983	539	1078
140	729	31	62	124	248	496	992	557	1114	801
141	175	350	700	1400	1373	1319	1211	995	563	1126
142	825	223	446	892	357	714				

P = 1429

INDICES

	0	1	2	3	4	5	6	7	8	9
0		0	527	902	1054	948	1	320	153	376
1	47	1103	528	278	847	422	680	1294	903	398
2	574	1222	202	1306	1055	468	805	1278	1374	227
3	949	1211	1207	577	393	1268	2	1095	925	1180
4	1101	161	321	184	729	1324	405	163	154	640
5	995	768	1332	677	377	623	473	1300	754	1365
6	48	213	310	696	306	1226	1104	1122	920	780
7	367	516	529	637	194	1370	24	1423	279	131
8	200	752	688	323	848	814	711	1129	1256	982
9	423	598	932	685	690	1346	681	383	1167	51
10	94	289	1295	859	431	742	1204	1361	904	964
11	1150	569	1000	823	399	826	1281	654	464	186
12	575	778	740	1063	837	1416	1223	818	833	1086
13	325	853	203	718	221	798	19	604	1307	419
14	894	1065	1043	1381	1056	1175	1164	114	721	166
15	469	705	551	242	522	731	806	1018	658	151
16	727	198	1279	549	1215	97	850	1246	1375	556
17	1341	774	1238	457	228	788	355	839	81	749
18	950	245	1125	1115	31	615	1212	969	1217	170
19	445	1326	1208	673	910	700	266	1389	578	396
20	621	596	816	547	394	1109	1386	254	958	73
21	1269	1262	303	1418	460	1132	3	103	63	111
22	249	144	1096	1311	99	844	1350	407	926	1336
23	1353	897	380	496	1181	1111	991	1033	713	947
24	1102	1293	1305	226	1267	160	162	676	1364	1225
25	515	1422	322	981	1345	288	1360	822	185	1415
26	852	603	1380	165	730	197	1245	456	748	614
27	1325	1388	546	72	1131	143	406	495	946	159
28	1421	821	164	613	142	820	480	481	155	1160
29	274	1285	263	482	641	885	1248	953	693	156
30	996	504	1232	1191	1078	1161	769	256	1049	333
31	1258	275	1333	499	117	216	1185	1286	678	1330
32	1254	835	725	264	378	746	1076	438	314	483
33	624	402	1377	43	345	642	474	412	1083	297
34	440	886	1301	960	337	300	984	1249	755	237
35	1315	128	882	954	1366	36	608	1088	1276	694
36	49	796	772	252	224	157	214	126	558	537
37	1142	997	311	1070	68	890	316	505	697	75
38	972	292	425	1233	307	943	1200	560	9	1192
39	1227	1172	793	327	488	1079	1105	525	923	192
40	1148	1162	1123	61	1343	272	1074	770	921	628
41	208	78	485	257	781	1271	57	1321	600	1050
42	368	662	361	539	830	334	517	533	987	855
43	231	1259	530	137	630	649	590	276	638	812
44	776	1016	671	1334	195	502	410	1068	626	500
45	1371	1264	449	179	934	118	25	566	435	1144
46	452	217	1424	913	907	205	1023	1186	280	14
47	210	492	90	1287	132	866	1240	1053	46	679
48	201	1373	392	1100	404	1331	753	305	366	23
49	687	1255	689	93	1203	999	463	836	324	18

POWER RESIDUES

	0	1	2	3	4	5	6	7	8	9
0	1	6	36	216	1296	631	928	1281	541	388
1	899	1107	926	1269	469	1385	1165	1274	499	136
2	816	609	796	489	76	456	1307	697	1324	799
3	507	184	1104	908	1161	1250	355	701	1348	943
4	1371	1081	770	333	569	556	478	10	60	360
5	731	99	594	706	1378	1123	1022	416	1067	686
6	1258	403	989	218	1308	703	1360	1015	374	815
7	603	760	273	209	1254	379	845	783	411	1037
8	506	178	1068	692	1294	619	856	849	807	555
9	472	1403	1273	493	100	600	742	165	990	224
10	1344	919	1227	217	1302	667	1144	1148	1172	1316
11	751	219	1314	739	147	882	1005	314	455	1301
12	661	1108	932	1305	685	1252	367	773	351	677
13	1204	79	474	1415	1345	925	1263	433	1169	1298
14	643	1000	284	275	221	1326	811	579	616	838
15	741	159	954	8	48	288	299	365	761	279
16	245	41	246	47	282	263	149	894	1077	746
17	189	1134	1088	812	585	652	1054	608	790	453
18	1289	589	676	1198	43	258	119	714	1426	1411
19	1321	781	399	965	74	444	1235	265	161	966
20	80	480	22	132	792	465	1361	1021	410	1031
21	470	1391	1201	61	366	767	315	461	1337	877
22	975	134	804	537	364	755	243	29	174	1044
23	548	430	1151	1190	1424	1399	1249	349	665	1132
24	1076	740	153	918	1221	181	1086	800	513	220
25	1320	775	363	749	207	1242	307	413	1049	578
26	610	802	525	292	323	509	196	1176	1340	895
27	1083	782	405	1001	290	311	437	1193	13	78
28	468	1379	1129	1058	632	934	1317	757	255	101
29	606	778	381	857	855	843	771	339	605	772
30	345	641	988	212	1272	487	64	384	875	963
31	62	372	803	531	328	539	376	827	675	1192
32	7	42	252	83	498	130	780	393	929	1287
33	577	604	766	309	425	1121	1010	344	635	952
34	1425	1405	1285	565	532	334	575	592	694	1306
35	691	1288	583	640	982	176	1056	620	862	885
36	1023	422	1103	902	1125	1034	488	70	420	1091
37	830	693	1300	655	1072	716	9	54	324	515
38	232	1392	1207	97	582	634	946	1389	1189	1418
39	1363	1033	482	34	204	1224	199	1194	19	114
40	684	1246	331	557	484	46	276	227	1362	1027
41	446	1247	337	593	700	1342	907	1155	1214	139
42	834	717	15	90	540	382	863	891	1059	638
43	970	104	624	886	1029	458	1319	769	327	533
44	340	611	808	561	508	190	1140	1124	1028	452
45	1283	553	460	1331	841	759	267	173	1038	512
46	214	1284	559	496	118	708	1390	1195	25	150
47	900	1113	962	56	336	587	664	1126	1040	524
48	286	287	293	329	545	412	1043	542	394	935
49	1323	793	471	1397	1237	277	233	1398	1243	313

P = 1429

INDICES	0	1	2	3	4	5	6	7	8	9
50	1042	720	521	726	849	1237	80	30	444	265
51	815	957	459	248	1349	379	712	1266	514	1359
52	1379	747	1130	1420	479	262	692	1077	1257	1184
53	724	313	344	439	983	881	1275	223	1141	315
54	424	8	487	1147	1073	484	599	829	230	589
55	670	625	933	451	1022	89	45	403	686	462
56	520	443	1348	1378	691	343	1140	1072	669	44
57	1347	668	1007	800	1008	346	682	330	259	147
58	801	643	384	352	790	174	1009	475	1168	181
59	1412	863	347	413	52	1134	1220	1298	683	1084
60	95	594	1031	70	331	298	290	1319	177	21
61	260	441	1296	734	783	583	148	887	860	85
62	357	1156	802	1302	432	936	1026	975	644	961
63	743	5	284	736	385	338	1205	918	429	892
64	353	301	1362	140	1252	606	791	985	905	1040
65	1273	1005	175	1250	965	373	841	1013	1010	756
66	1151	120	929	1046	476	238	570	105	872	785
67	1169	1316	1001	510	939	318	182	129	824	703
68	967	1309	1413	883	400	124	59	810	864	955
69	827	350	83	371	348	1367	1282	27	764	1398
70	414	37	655	65	1409	585	53	609	465	1290
71	563	507	1135	1089	187	901	375	421	1221	1277
72	576	1179	1323	767	1299	695	779	1369	751	1128
73	684	50	741	568	653	1062	1085	797	1064	113
74	241	150	96	773	838	1114	169	699	595	253
75	1417	110	843	896	1032	225	1224	287	602	455
76	71	158	819	1284	952	1190	332	215	834	437
77	42	296	299	127	1087	251	536	889	291	559
78	326	191	271	77	1320	538	854	648	1015	1067
79	178	1143	204	491	1052	1099	22	998	719	29
80	247	1358	261	312	222	1146	588	88	442	1071
81	799	146	173	862	1297	69	20	582	1155	974
82	735	891	605	1004	1012	1045	784	317	1308	809
83	370	1397	584	506	420	766	1127	1061	149	698
84	895	454	1189	295	888	76	1066	1098	1357	87
85	861	973	1044	1396	1060	294	86	293	1382	633
86	758	1383	358	426	1057	1405	664	634	1157	1234
87	1176	1400	1117	759	803	308	1165	219	1339	1384
88	1303	944	115	1313	1198	359	433	1201	722	1138
89	1029	427	937	561	167	269	1153	1058	1027	10
90	470	543	363	1406	976	1193	706	416	33	665
91	645	1228	552	1426	1093	635	962	1173	243	101
92	979	1158	744	794	523	135	12	1235	6	328
93	732	1038	122	1177	285	489	807	1403	541	1401
94	737	1080	1019	39	617	1118	386	1106	659	915
95	1393	760	339	526	152	846	573	804	1206	924
96	728	994	472	309	919	193	199	710	931	1166
97	430	1149	1280	739	832	220	893	1163	550	657
98	1214	1340	354	1124	1216	909	620	1385	302	62
99	98	1352	990	1304	1363	1344	851	1244	545	945

POWER RESIDUES	0	1	2	3	4	5	6	7	8	9
50	449	1265	445	1241	301	377	833	711	1408	1303
51	673	1180	1364	1039	518	250	71	426	1127	1046
52	560	502	154	924	1257	397	953	2	12	72
53	432	1163	1262	427	1133	1082	776	369	785	423
54	1109	938	1341	901	1119	998	272	203	1218	163
55	978	152	912	1185	1394	1219	169	1014	368	779
56	387	893	1071	710	1402	1267	457	1313	733	111
57	666	1138	1112	956	20	120	720	33	198	1188
58	1412	1327	817	615	832	705	1372	1087	806	549
59	436	1187	1406	1291	601	748	201	1206	91	546
60	418	1079	758	261	137	822	645	1012	356	707
61	1384	1159	1238	283	269	185	1110	944	1377	1117
62	986	200	1200	55	330	551	448	1259	409	1025
63	434	1175	1334	859	867	915	1203	73	438	1199
64	49	294	335	581	628	910	1173	1322	787	435
65	1181	1370	1075	734	117	702	1354	979	158	948
66	1401	1261	421	1097	866	909	1167	1286	571	568
67	550	442	1223	193	1158	1232	247	53	318	479
68	16	96	576	598	730	93	558	490	82	492
69	94	564	526	298	359	725	63	378	839	747
70	195	1170	1304	679	1216	151	906	1149	1178	1352
71	967	86	516	238	1428	1423	1393	1213	133	798
72	501	148	888	1041	530	322	503	160	960	44
73	264	155	930	1293	613	820	633	940	1353	973
74	122	732	105	630	922	1245	325	521	268	179
75	1074	728	81	486	58	348	659	1096	860	873
76	951	1419	1369	1069	698	1330	835	723	51	306
77	407	1013	362	743	171	1026	440	1211	121	726
78	69	414	1055	614	826	669	1156	1220	175	1050
79	584	646	1018	392	923	1251	361	737	135	810
80	573	580	622	874	957	26	156	936	1329	829
81	687	1264	439	1205	85	510	202	1212	127	762
82	285	281	257	113	678	1210	115	690	1282	547
83	424	1115	974	128	768	321	497	124	744	177
84	1062	656	1078	752	225	1350	955	14	84	504
85	166	996	260	131	786	429	1145	1154	1208	103
86	618	850	813	591	688	1270	475	1421	1381	1141
87	1130	1064	668	1150	1184	1388	1183	1382	1147	1166
88	1280	535	352	683	1240	295	341	617	844	777
89	375	821	639	976	140	840	753	231	1386	1171
90	1310	715	3	18	108	648	1030	464	1355	985
91	194	1164	1268	463	1349	949	1407	1297	637	964
92	68	408	1019	398	959	38	228	1368	1063	662
93	1114	968	92	552	454	1295	625	892	1065	674
94	1186	1400	1255	385	881	999	278	239	5	30
95	180	1080	764	297	353	689	1276	511	208	1248
96	343	629	916	1209	109	654	1066	680	1222	187
97	1122	1016	380	851	819	627	904	1137	1106	920
98	1233	253	89	534	346	647	1024	428	1139	1118
99	992	236	1416	1351	961	50	300	371	797	495

P = 1429

INDICES

	0	1	2	3	4	5	6	7	8	9
100	141	273	1247	1231	1048	116	1253	1075	1376	1082
101	336	1314	607	771	557	67	971	1199	792	922
102	1342	207	56	360	986	629	775	409	448	434
103	906	209	1239	391	365	1202	1041	79	458	513
104	478	723	1274	486	229	1021	519	1139	1006	258
105	789	1411	1219	1030	176	782	356	1025	283	428
106	1251	1272	840	928	871	938	966	58	82	763
107	1408	562	374	1322	750	652	240	168	842	601
108	951	41	535	270	1014	1051	246	587	172	1154
109	1011	369	1126	1188	1356	1059	757	663	1116	1338
110	1197	1028	1152	362	32	1092	978	11	121	540
111	616	1392	572	471	930	831	1213	619	989	544
112	1047	335	970	55	447	364	477	518	1218	282
113	870	1407	239	534	171	1355	1196	977	571	988
114	446	869	1195	1194	106	856	1327	878	107	707
115	873	232	1209	1120	857	417	786	1260	674	611
116	1328	34	1170	531	911	16	879	666	1317	138
117	701	899	108	646	1002	631	267	1036	708	1229
118	511	650	1390	876	874	553	940	591	579	388
119	233	1427	319	277	397	467	1210	1094	183	639
120	622	212	1121	636	130	813	597	382	858	963
121	825	777	817	717	418	1174	704	1017	548	555
122	787	244	968	672	395	1108	1261	102	1310	1335
123	1110	1292	675	980	1414	196	1387	494	612	1159
124	884	503	255	498	1329	745	401	411	959	236
125	35	795	125	1069	74	942	1171	524	60	627
126	1270	661	532	136	811	501	1263	565	912	13
127	865	1372	304	92	17	1236	956	1265	1419	1183
128	880	7	828	450	461	342	667	329	351	180
129	1133	593	1318	733	84	935	4	917	139	1039
130	372	119	104	509	702	123	349	26	64	1289
131	900	1178	1368	567	112	1113	109	286	1283	436
132	250	190	647	490	28	1145	145	581	1003	808
133	765	453	1097	1395	632	1404	1399	218	1312	1137
134	268	542	415	1425	100	134	1037	1402	38	914
135	845	993	709	738	656	908	1351	1243	1230	1081
136	66	206	408	390	512	1020	1410	1024	927	762
137	651	40	586	1187	1337	1091	1391	618	54	281
138	1354	868	877	1119	610	15	898	1035	875	387
139	466	211	381	716	554	1107	1291	493	497	235
140	941	660	564	91	1182	341	592	916	508	1288
141	1112	189	580	1394	1136	133	992	1242	389	761
142	1090	867	1034	715	234	340	188	1241	714	

POWER RESIDUES

	0	1	2	3	4	5	6	7	8	9
100	112	672	1174	1328	823	651	1048	572	574	586
101	658	1090	824	657	1084	788	441	1217	157	942
102	1365	1045	554	466	1367	1057	626	898	1101	890
103	1053	602	754	237	1422	1387	1177	1346	931	1299
104	649	1036	500	142	852	825	663	1120	1004	308
105	419	1085	794	477	4	24	144	864	897	1095
106	854	837	735	123	738	141	846	789	447	1253
107	373	809	567	544	406	1007	326	527	304	395
108	941	1359	1009	338	599	736	129	774	357	713
109	1420	1375	1105	914	1197	37	222	1332	847	795
110	483	40	240	11	66	396	947	1395	1225	205
111	1230	235	1410	1315	745	183	1098	872	945	1383
112	1153	1202	67	402	983	182	1092	836	729	87
113	522	274	215	1290	595	712	1414	1339	889	1047
114	566	538	370	791	459	1325	805	543	400	971
115	110	660	1102	896	1089	818	621	868	921	1239
116	289	305	401	977	146	876	969	98	588	670
117	1162	1256	391	917	1215	145	870	933	1311	721
118	39	234	1404	1279	529	316	467	1373	1093	842
119	765	303	389	905	1143	1142	1136	1100	884	1017
120	386	887	1035	494	106	636	958	32	192	1152
121	1196	31	186	1116	980	164	984	188	1128	1052
122	596	718	21	126	756	249	65	390	911	1179
123	1358	1003	302	383	869	927	1275	505	172	1032
124	476	1427	1417	1357	997	266	167	1002	296	347
125	653	1060	644	1006	320	491	88	528	310	431
126	1157	1226	211	1266	451	1277	517	244	35	210
127	1260	415	1061	650	1042	536	358	719	27	162
128	972	116	696	1318	763	291	317	473	1409	1309
129	709	1396	1231	241	17	102	612	814	597	724
130	57	342	623	880	993	242	23	138	828	681
131	1228	223	1338	883	1011	350	671	1168	1292	607
132	784	417	1073	722	45	270	191	1146	1160	1244
133	319	485	52	312	443	1229	229	1374	1099	878
134	981	170	1020	404	995	254	95	570	562	514
135	226	1356	991	230	1380	1135	1094	848	801	519
136	256	107	642	994	248	59	354	695	1312	727
137	75	450	1271	481	28	168	1008	332	563	520
138	262	143	858	861	879	987	206	1236	271	197
139	1182	1376	1111	950	1413	1333	853	831	699	1336
140	871	939	1347	937	1335	865	903	1131	1070	704
141	1366	1051	590	682	1234	259	125	750	213	1278
142	523	280	251	77	462	1343	913	1191		

P = 1433

INDICES

	0	1	2	3	4	5	6	7	8	9
0		0	1016	1	600	511	1017	1297	184	2
1	95	354	601	268	881	512	1200	761	1018	1309
2	1111	1298	1370	1333	185	1022	1284	3	465	155
3	96	1096	784	355	345	376	602	1258	893	269
4	695	640	882	1242	954	513	917	521	1201	1162
5	606	762	868	297	1019	865	49	1310	1171	1292
6	1112	911	680	1299	368	779	1371	702	1361	1334
7	1392	1305	186	324	842	1023	477	219	1285	52
8	279	4	224	1325	466	1272	826	156	538	950
9	97	133	501	1097	105	388	785	858	746	356
10	190	1144	346	553	452	377	1313	1330	603	216
11	449	1259	1065	334	894	412	755	270	876	626
12	696	708	495	641	264	101	883	964	1384	1243
13	363	1262	955	1174	286	514	945	488	918	431
14	976	522	889	622	1202	666	1340	1163	426	1215
15	607	124	61	763	1235	175	869	393	1068	298
16	1295	1198	1020	343	1240	866	909	1390	50	536
17	856	1311	410	262	1172	887	122	1293	534	532
18	1113	328	1149	912	85	337	681	1115	1121	1300
19	1404	204	369	1075	442	780	330	438	1372	114
20	1206	703	728	20	1362	1151	137	1335	36	231
21	1393	1089	897	1306	914	321	187	961	1232	325
22	33	1029	843	87	649	1024	1350	1004	478	991
23	1428	220	339	75	1286	1032	460	53	210	415
24	280	683	292	5	79	241	225	145	1280	1326
25	1117	739	467	255	548	1273	968	631	827	1123
26	1379	157	846	1081	539	808	758	951	1302	743
27	98	58	529	134	72	1376	502	1406	15	1098
28	560	670	106	1223	473	389	206	505	786	90
29	250	859	924	273	747	371	10	357	799	169
30	191	1107	1140	1145	1077	1422	347	1267	819	554
31	1191	1416	453	444	1409	378	652	982	1314	509
32	879	1331	782	638	604	1290	1359	217	824	386
33	450	332	493	1260	974	1213	1066	1388	120	335
34	440	18	895	1027	1426	413	1278	629	756	1374
35	471	271	1138	1414	877	384	118	627	116	833
36	697	1186	1344	709	733	835	496	1208	1101	642
37	1353	162	265	692	699	102	705	423	884	725
38	988	965	1220	1188	1385	730	659	1244	26	41
39	364	662	1346	1263	22	563	956	1007	1130	1175
40	790	711	287	1364	312	515	1036	180	946	852
41	735	489	1153	1157	919	404	1052	432	1247	837
42	977	139	673	523	481	351	890	776	498	623
43	1337	259	1203	1001	545	667	816	1210	1341	38
44	1049	1164	613	1167	427	29	1103	1216	233	109
45	608	994	934	125	588	644	62	1395	575	764
46	1012	1321	1236	237	1355	176	1091	67	870	567
47	616	394	44	164	1069	899	1226	299	1431	599
48	1296	94	267	1199	1308	1369	1021	464	1095	344
49	1257	694	1241	916	1161	867	864	1170	910	367

POWER RESIDUES

	0	1	2	3	4	5	6	7	8	9
0	1	3	9	27	81	243	729	754	829	1054
1	296	888	1231	827	1048	278	834	1069	341	1023
2	203	609	394	1182	680	607	388	1164	626	445
3	1335	1139	551	220	660	547	208	624	439	1317
4	1085	389	1167	635	472	1416	1382	1280	974	56
5	168	504	79	237	711	700	667	568	271	813
6	1006	152	456	1368	1238	848	1111	467	1401	1337
7	1145	569	274	822	1033	233	699	664	559	244
8	732	763	856	1135	539	184	552	223	669	574
9	289	867	1168	638	481	10	30	90	270	810
10	997	125	375	1125	509	94	282	846	1105	449
11	1347	1175	659	544	199	597	358	1074	356	1068
12	338	1014	176	528	151	453	1359	1211	767	868
13	1171	647	508	91	273	819	1024	206	618	421
14	1263	923	1336	1142	560	247	741	790	937	1378
15	1268	938	1381	1277	965	29	87	261	783	916
16	1315	1079	371	1113	473	1419	1391	1307	1055	299
17	897	1258	908	1291	1007	155	465	1395	1319	1091
18	407	1221	797	958	8	24	72	216	648	511
19	100	300	900	1267	935	1372	1250	884	1219	791
20	940	1387	1295	1019	191	573	286	858	1141	557
21	238	714	709	694	649	514	109	327	981	77
22	231	693	646	505	82	24	738	781	910	1297
23	1025	209	627	448	1344	116	632	463	1389	1301
24	1037	245	735	772	883	1216	782	913	1306	1052
25	290	870	1177	665	562	253	759	844	1099	431
26	1293	1013	173	519	124	372	1116	482	13	39
27	117	351	1053	293	879	1204	746	805	982	80
28	240	720	727	748	811	1000	134	402	1206	752
29	823	1036	242	726	745	802	973	53	159	477
30	1431	1427	1415	1379	1271	947	1408	1358	1208	758
31	841	1090	404	1212	770	877	1198	728	751	820
32	1027	215	645	502	73	219	657	538	181	543
33	196	588	331	993	113	339	1017	185	555	232
34	696	655	532	163	489	34	102	306	918	1321
35	1097	425	1275	959	11	33	99	297	891	1240
36	854	1129	521	130	390	1170	644	499	64	192
37	576	295	885	1222	800	967	35	105	315	945
38	1402	1340	1154	596	355	1065	329	987	95	285
39	855	1132	530	157	471	1413	1373	1253	893	1246
40	872	1183	683	616	415	1245	869	1174	656	535
41	172	516	115	345	1035	239	717	718	721	730
42	757	838	1081	377	1131	527	148	444	1332	1130
43	524	139	417	1251	887	1228	818	1021	197	591
44	340	1020	194	582	313	939	1384	1286	992	110
45	330	990	104	312	936	1375	1259	911	1300	1034
46	236	708	691	640	487	28	84	252	756	835
47	1072	350	1050	284	852	1123	503	76	228	684
48	619	424	1272	950	1417	1385	1289	1001	137	411
49	1233	833	1066	332	996	122	366	1098	428	1284

P = 1433

INDICES

	0	1	2	3	4	5	6	7	8	9
50	701	1391	323	476	51	223	1271	537	132	104
51	857	189	552	1312	215	1064	411	875	707	263
52	963	362	1173	944	430	888	665	425	123	1234
53	392	1294	342	908	535	409	886	533	327	84
54	1114	1403	1074	329	113	727	1150	35	1088	913
55	960	32	86	1349	990	338	1031	209	682	78
56	144	1116	254	967	1122	845	807	1301	57	71
57	1405	559	1222	205	89	923	370	798	1106	1076
58	1266	1190	443	651	508	781	1289	823	331	973
59	1387	439	1026	1277	1373	1137	383	115	1185	732
60	1207	1352	691	704	724	1219	729	25	661	21
61	1006	789	1363	1035	851	1152	403	1246	138	480
62	775	1336	1000	815	37	612	28	232	993	587
63	1394	1011	236	1090	566	43	898	1430	93	1307
64	463	1256	915	863	366	322	222	131	188	214
65	874	962	943	664	1233	341	408	326	1402	112
66	34	959	1348	1030	77	253	844	56	558	88
67	797	1265	650	1288	972	1025	1136	1184	1351	723
68	24	1005	1034	402	479	999	611	992	1010	565
69	1429	462	862	221	213	942	340	1401	958	76
70	55	796	1287	1135	722	1033	998	1009	461	212
71	1400	54	1134	997	211	1133	1132	416	417	927
72	281	418	770	684	928	1177	293	282	317	6
73	419	571	80	771	792	242	685	1056	226	929
74	937	146	1178	713	1281	294	276	1327	283	1195
75	1118	318	289	740	7	635	468	420	309	256
76	572	1366	549	81	804	1274	772	128	969	793
77	314	632	243	750	828	686	1042	1124	1057	517
78	1380	227	246	158	930	904	847	938	1038	1082
79	147	199	540	1179	591	809	714	182	759	1282
80	374	952	295	678	1303	277	948	744	1328	753
81	99	284	620	59	1196	854	530	1119	436	135
82	319	647	73	290	737	1377	741	13	503	8
83	1420	1407	636	491	16	469	831	1099	421	657
84	561	310	1155	671	257	1047	107	573	65	1224
85	1367	1159	474	550	360	390	82	1086	207	805
86	921	506	1275	689	787	773	585	91	129	406
87	251	970	400	860	794	1398	925	315	1054	274
88	633	802	748	244	197	372	751	434	11	829
89	1045	358	687	398	800	1043	1249	170	1125	1251
90	192	1058	578	1108	518	839	1141	1381	172	1146
91	228	457	1078	247	979	1423	159	1127	348	931
92	596	1268	905	141	820	848	1253	555	939	767
93	1192	1039	675	1417	1083	194	454	148	151	445
94	200	525	1410	541	1060	379	1180	305	653	592
95	483	983	810	580	1315	715	1015	510	183	353
96	880	760	1110	1332	1283	154	783	375	892	639
97	953	520	605	296	48	1291	679	778	1360	1304
98	841	218	278	1324	825	949	500	387	745	1143
99	451	1329	448	333	754	625	494	100	1383	1261

POWER RESIDUES

	0	1	2	3	4	5	6	7	8	9
50	986	92	276	828	1051	287	861	1150	584	319
51	957	5	15	45	135	405	1215	779	904	1279
52	971	47	141	423	1269	941	1390	1304	1046	272
53	816	1015	179	537	178	534	169	507	88	264
54	792	943	1396	1322	1100	434	1302	1040	254	762
55	853	1126	512	103	309	927	1348	1178	668	571
56	280	840	1087	395	1185	689	634	469	1407	1355
57	1199	731	760	847	1108	458	1374	1256	902	1273
58	953	1426	1412	1370	1244	866	1165	629	454	1362
59	1220	794	949	1414	1376	1262	920	1327	1115	479
60	4	12	36	108	324	972	50	150	450	1350
61	1184	686	625	442	1326	1112	470	1410	1364	1226
62	812	1003	143	429	1287	995	119	357	1071	347
63	1041	257	771	880	1207	755	832	1063	323	969
64	41	123	369	1107	455	1365	1229	821	1030	224
65	672	583	316	948	1411	1367	1235	839	1084	386
66	1158	608	391	1173	653	526	145	435	1305	1049
67	281	843	1096	422	1266	932	1363	1223	803	976
68	62	186	558	241	723	736	775	892	1243	863
69	1156	602	373	1119	491	40	120	360	1080	374
70	1122	500	67	201	603	376	1128	518	121	363
71	1089	401	1203	743	796	955	1432	1430	1424	1406
72	1352	1190	704	679	604	379	1137	545	202	606
73	385	1155	599	364	1092	410	1230	824	1039	251
74	753	826	1045	269	807	988	98	294	882	1213
75	773	886	1225	809	994	116	348	1044	266	798
76	961	17	51	153	459	1377	1265	929	1354	1196
77	722	733	766	865	1162	620	427	1281	977	65
78	195	585	322	966	32	96	288	864	1159	611
79	400	1200	734	769	874	1189	701	670	577	298
80	894	1249	881	1210	764	859	1144	566	265	795
81	952	1423	1403	1343	1163	623	436	1308	1058	308
82	924	1339	1151	587	328	984	86	258	774	889
83	1234	836	1075	359	1077	365	1095	419	1257	905
84	1282	980	74	222	666	565	262	786	925	1342
85	1160	614	409	1227	815	1012	170	510	97	291
86	873	1186	692	643	496	55	165	495	52	156
87	468	1404	1346	1172	650	517	118	354	1062	320
88	960	14	42	126	378	1134	536	175	525	142
89	426	1278	968	38	114	342	1026	212	636	475
90	1425	1409	1361	1217	785	922	1333	1133	533	166
91	498	61	183	549	214	642	493	46	138	414
92	1242	860	1147	575	292	876	1195	719	724	739
93	784	919	1324	1106	452	1356	1202	740	787	928
94	1351	1187	695	652	523	136	408	1224	806	985
95	89	267	801	970	44	132	396	1188	698	661
96	550	217	651	520	127	381	1143	563	256	768
97	871	1180	674	589	334	1002	140	420	1260	914
98	1309	1061	317	951	1420	1394	1316	1082	380	1140
99	554	229	687	628	451	1353	1193	713	706	685

P = 1433

INDICES

	0	1	2	3	4	5	6	7	8	9
100	285	487	975	621	1339	1214	60	174	1067	1197
101	1239	1389	855	261	121	531	1148	336	1120	203
102	441	437	1205	19	136	230	896	320	1231	1028
103	648	1003	1427	74	459	414	291	240	1279	738
104	547	630	1378	1080	757	742	528	1375	14	669
105	472	504	249	272	9	168	1139	1421	818	1415
106	1408	981	878	637	1358	385	492	1212	119	17
107	1425	628	470	1413	117	832	1343	834	1100	161
108	698	422	987	1187	658	40	1345	562	1129	710
109	311	179	734	1156	1051	836	672	350	497	258
110	544	1209	1048	1166	1102	108	933	643	574	1320
111	1354	66	615	163	1225	598	266	1368	1094	693
112	1160	1169	700	475	1270	103	551	1063	706	361
113	429	424	391	907	885	83	1073	726	1087	31
114	989	208	143	966	806	70	1221	922	1105	1189
115	507	822	1386	1276	382	731	690	1218	660	788
116	850	1245	774	814	27	586	235	42	92	1255
117	365	130	873	663	407	111	1347	252	557	1264
118	971	1183	23	401	610	564	861	941	957	795
119	721	1008	1399	996	1131	926	769	1176	316	570
120	791	1055	936	712	275	1194	288	634	308	1365
121	803	127	313	749	1041	516	245	903	1037	198
122	590	181	373	677	947	752	619	853	435	646
123	736	12	1419	490	830	656	1154	1046	64	1158
124	359	1085	920	688	584	405	399	1397	1053	801
125	196	433	1044	397	1248	1250	577	838	171	456
126	978	1126	595	140	1252	766	674	193	150	524
127	1059	304	482	579	1014	352	1109	153	891	519
128	47	777	840	1323	499	1142	447	624	1382	486
129	1338	173	1238	260	1147	202	1204	229	1230	1002
130	458	239	546	1079	527	668	248	167	817	980
131	1357	1211	1424	1412	1342	160	986	39	1128	178
132	1050	349	543	1165	932	1319	614	597	1093	1168
133	1269	1062	428	906	1072	30	142	69	1104	821
134	381	1217	849	813	234	1254	872	110	556	1182
135	609	940	720	995	768	569	935	1193	307	126
136	1040	902	589	676	618	645	1418	655	63	1084
137	583	1396	195	396	576	455	594	765	149	303
138	1013	152	46	1322	446	485	1237	201	1229	238
139	526	166	1356	1411	985	177	542	1318	1092	1061
140	1071	68	380	812	871	1181	719	568	306	901
141	617	654	582	395	593	302	45	484	1228	165
142	984	1317	1070	811	718	900	581	301	1227	1316
143	717	300	716							

POWER RESIDUES

	0	1	2	3	4	5	6	7	8	9
100	622	433	1299	1031	227	681	610	397	1191	707
101	688	631	460	1380	1274	956	2	6	18	54
102	162	486	25	75	225	675	592	343	1029	221
103	663	556	235	705	682	613	406	1218	788	931
104	1360	1214	776	895	1252	890	1237	845	1102	440
105	1320	1094	416	1248	878	1201	737	778	901	1270
106	944	1399	1331	1127	515	112	336	1008	158	474
107	1422	1400	1334	1136	542	193	579	304	912	1303
108	1043	263	789	934	1369	1241	857	1138	548	211
109	633	466	1398	1328	1118	488	31	93	279	837
110	1078	368	1104	446	1338	1148	578	301	903	1276
111	962	20	60	180	540	187	561	250	750	817
112	1018	188	564	259	777	898	1261	917	1318	1088
113	398	1194	716	715	712	703	676	595	352	1056
114	302	906	1285	989	101	303	909	1294	1016	182
115	546	205	615	412	1236	842	1093	413	1239	851
116	1120	494	49	147	441	1323	1103	443	1329	1121
117	497	58	174	522	133	399	1197	725	742	793
118	946	1405	1349	1181	677	598	361	1083	383	1149
119	581	310	930	1357	1205	749	814	1009	161	483
120	16	48	144	432	1296	1022	200	600	367	1101
121	437	1311	1067	335	1005	149	447	1341	1157	605
122	382	1146	572	283	849	1114	476	1428	1418	1388
123	1298	1028	218	654	529	154	462	1386	1292	1010
124	164	492	43	129	387	1161	617	418	1254	896
125	1255	899	1264	926	1345	1169	641	490	37	111
126	333	999	131	393	1179	671	580	307	921	1330
127	1124	506	85	255	765	862	1153	593	346	1038
128	248	744	799	964	26	78	234	702	673	586
129	325	975	59	177	531	160	480	7	21	63
130	189	567	268	804	979	71	213	639	484	19
131	57	171	513	106	318	954	1429	1421	1397	1325
132	1109	461	1383	1283	983	83	249	747	808	991
133	107	321	963	23	69	207	621	430	1290	1004
134	146	438	1314	1076	362	108	392	1176	662	553
135	226	678	601	370	1110	464	1392	1310	1064	326
136	978	68	204	612	403	1209	761	850	1117	485
137	22	66	198	594	349	1047	275	825	1042	260
138	780	907	1288	998	128	384	1152	590	337	1011
139	167	501	70	210	630	45	1371	1247	875	1192
140	710	697	658	541	190	570	277	831	1060	314
141	942	1393	1313	1073	353	105	311	933	1366	1232
142	830	1057	305	915	1312	1070	344	1032	230	690
143	637	478								

P = 1439

INDICES

	0	1	2	3	4	5	6	7	8	9
0		0	706	676	1412	870	1382	1	680	1352
1	138	907	650	1026	707	108	1386	975	620	448
2	844	677	175	223	1356	302	294	590	1413	1337
3	814	816	654	145	243	871	1326	1148	1154	264
4	112	1260	1383	1418	881	784	929	1242	624	2
5	1008	213	1000	809	1296	339	681	1124	605	1024
6	82	384	84	1353	1360	458	851	696	949	899
7	139	323	594	1271	416	978	422	908	970	1074
8	818	1266	528	1157	651	407	686	575	149	879
9	52	1027	197	54	510	1318	1330	1278	708	821
10	276	314	919	1407	268	109	77	317	564	1306
11	1045	386	1387	1226	392	1093	1311	940	292	976
12	788	376	1090	498	790	1172	621	1195	628	656
13	1164	1237	119	449	1402	22	217	42	167	583
14	845	480	1029	495	1300	769	539	678	1122	75
15	246	185	1128	889	176	248	238	1099	342	47
16	86	224	534	61	1234	1015	425	8	1357	614
17	1113	362	1392	378	1281	303	855	262	147	40
18	758	672	295	1060	903	580	760	444	1216	591
19	586	199	598	867	546	1134	1414	800	89	209
20	982	1372	1020	1338	187	692	675	137	974	1355
21	815	1153	783	999	1023	850	1270	817	574	509
22	313	563	1092	1089	655	216	494	245	1098	1233
23	361	146	579	597	208	674	998	312	244	207
24	56	57	1082	504	358	872	1204	36	58	395
25	440	752	1327	1130	463	1083	1334	25	1362	1149
26	432	1251	505	639	825	241	1155	117	670	359
27	728	500	923	265	748	1209	873	1145	1289	730
28	113	92	1186	1205	297	556	1201	1261	568	512
29	37	516	1245	862	1384	456	390	59	781	1249
30	952	1419	891	990	396	1254	157	460	882	645
31	954	441	944	1189	367	785	1048	1107	753	806
32	792	993	930	1423	1240	1328	767	544	502	1243
33	283	400	1131	1062	714	128	625	334	1320	464
34	381	285	1068	3	660	331	1084	958	549	725
35	1009	178	123	1335	968	1193	853	214	746	1421
36	26	896	1378	1052	1001	703	328	1363	171	1174
37	1286	810	28	835	1150	410	484	925	1297	934
38	1292	433	905	80	1304	340	135	1332	1252	966
39	402	1198	682	475	68	506	795	101	915	1125
40	250	1041	640	404	288	698	606	617	893	826
41	1398	718	1381	1025	843	589	242	1259	623	338
42	83	898	421	1156	51	1277	267	385	291	1171
43	118	582	538	888	85	7	1280	671	1215	1133
44	1019	1354	1269	1088	360	311	357	751	1361	240
45	922	729	1200	861	951	459	366	992	501	127
46	1067	724	852	1051	1285	924	1303	1197	914	697
47	1380	337	266	887	1018	750	950	723	913	749
48	762	736	763	900	350	710	1210	937	1064	737
49	140	1005	472	874	742	253	764	324	1101	1367

POWER RESIDUES

	0	1	2	3	4	5	6	7	8	9
0	1	7	49	343	962	978	1090	435	167	1169
1	988	1160	925	719	716	695	548	958	950	894
2	502	636	135	945	859	257	360	1081	372	1165
3	960	964	992	1188	1121	652	247	290	591	1259
4	179	1253	137	959	957	943	845	159	1113	596
5	1294	424	90	630	93	651	240	241	248	297
6	640	163	1141	792	1227	1394	1124	673	394	1319
7	599	1315	571	1119	638	149	1043	106	742	877
8	383	1242	60	420	62	434	160	1120	645	198
9	1386	1068	281	528	818	1409	1229	1408	1222	1359
10	879	397	1340	746	905	579	1175	1030	15	105
11	735	828	40	280	521	769	1066	267	430	132
12	924	712	667	352	1025	1419	1299	459	335	906
13	586	1224	1373	977	1083	386	1263	207	10	70
14	490	552	986	1146	827	33	231	178	1246	88
15	616	1434	1404	1194	1163	946	866	306	703	604
16	1350	816	1395	1131	722	737	842	138	966	1006
17	1286	368	1137	764	1031	22	154	1078	351	1018
18	1370	956	936	796	1255	151	1057	204	1428	1362
19	900	544	930	754	961	971	1041	92	644	191
20	1337	725	758	989	1167	974	1062	239	234	199
21	1393	1117	624	51	357	1060	225	136	952	908
22	600	1322	620	23	161	1127	694	541	909	607
23	1371	963	985	1139	778	1129	708	639	156	1092
24	449	265	416	34	238	227	150	1050	155	1085
25	400	1361	893	495	587	1231	1422	1320	606	1364
26	914	642	177	1239	39	273	472	426	104	728
27	779	1136	757	982	1118	631	100	700	583	1203
28	1226	1387	1075	330	871	341	948	880	404	1389
29	1089	428	118	826	26	182	1274	284	549	965
30	999	1237	25	175	1225	1380	1026	1426	1348	802
31	1297	445	237	220	101	707	632	107	749	926
32	726	765	1038	71	497	601	1329	669	366	1123
33	666	345	976	1076	337	920	684	471	419	55
34	385	1256	158	1106	547	951	901	551	979	1097
35	484	510	692	527	811	1360	886	446	244	269
36	444	230	171	1197	1184	1093	456	314	759	996
37	1216	1317	585	1217	1324	634	121	847	173	1211
38	1282	340	941	831	61	427	111	777	1122	659
39	296	633	114	798	1269	249	304	689	506	664
40	331	878	390	1291	403	1382	1040	85	595	1287
41	375	1186	1107	554	1000	1244	74	518	748	919
42	677	422	76	532	846	166	1162	939	817	1402
43	1180	1065	260	381	1228	1401	1173	1016	1356	858
44	250	311	738	849	187	1309	529	825	19	133
45	931	761	1010	1314	564	1070	295	626	65	455
46	307	710	653	254	339	934	782	1157	904	572
47	1126	687	492	566	1084	393	1312	550	972	1048
48	141	987	1153	876	376	1193	1156	897	523	783
49	1164	953	915	649	226	143	1001	1251	123	861

P = 1439

INDICES

	0	1	2	3	4	5	6	7	8	9
100	414	496	1390	561	726	804	169	1257	1301	837
101	452	1010	1104	986	558	770	437	1140	179	802
102	1057	1342	540	961	1308	124	306	662	1437	679
103	107	174	1336	1325	1417	1007	1123	1359	322	969
104	406	196	820	76	1225	787	1194	1401	479	1121
105	247	533	613	854	1059	585	799	186	1152	573
106	215	578	206	1203	1129	431	116	747	91	567
107	455	890	644	1047	1422	282	333	659	177	745
108	702	27	933	134	474	249	616	842	897	290
109	6	1268	239	365	1050	1379	722	349	1004	1100
110	1183	601	1053	1344	847	1433	343	412	1119	1002
111	524	1221	1263	48	609	521	704	211	274	73
112	87	34	388	329	66	1086	470	225	1160	235
113	1364	163	1179	876	535	1115	271	172	700	233
114	530	62	778	1109	1175	665	143	526	1235	756
115	1231	1287	542	482	1275	1016	486	467	811	832
116	11	570	426	154	490	29	984	204	1219	9
117	1078	1389	836	436	960	106	1358	1224	532	1151
118	430	643	744	615	364	1182	411	608	33	1159
119	1114	777	755	485	153	1077	1223	363	776	775
120	926	963	1031	279	1393	927	1316	1298	865	1080
121	514	379	964	1213	935	1374	370	373	1282	1032
122	1228	1293	98	551	131	304	280	64	434	96
123	636	255	856	1394	1411	906	619	301	653	263
124	928	808	81	695	415	1265	148	1317	918	1305
125	1310	497	1163	41	1299	184	341	1014	1391	39
126	759	866	981	136	1022	562	1097	673	1081	394
127	1333	638	727	1144	296	515	780	1253	943	805
128	766	1061	380	957	967	895	170	409	904	965
129	794	403	1397	1258	50	581	1214	310	1199	126
130	1302	886	761	936	741	683	1168	838	518	445
131	1375	1347	476	1340	453	71	1217	371	1095	69
132	257	1011	221	592	374	1111	507	668	1105	326
133	587	1283	1036	796	828	987	688	200	1033	995
134	102	1427	559	611	599	1229	773	916	308	771
135	160	868	1294	1405	1126	1370	438	1247	547	99
136	355	251	189	1141	259	1135	552	1313	1042	858
137	180	230	1415	132	1177	641	634	803	1103	801
138	305	1324	405	1400	1058	577	90	281	932	289
139	721	1343	523	210	65	162	699	664	541	831
140	983	435	429	607	152	962	864	1373	97	95
141	618	694	1309	1013	1021	637	942	894	1396	125
142	1167	1339	256	667	827	1426	307	1369	188	857
143	633	1399	720	663	151	693	1395	1425	719	

POWER RESIDUES

	0	1	2	3	4	5	6	7	8	9
100	52	364	1109	568	1098	491	559	1035	50	350
101	1011	1321	613	1413	1257	165	1155	890	474	440
102	202	1414	1264	214	59	413	13	91	637	142
103	994	1202	1219	1338	732	807	1332	690	513	713
104	674	401	1368	942	838	110	770	1073	316	773
105	1094	463	363	1102	519	755	968	1020	1384	1054
106	183	1281	333	892	488	538	888	460	342	955
107	929	747	912	628	79	553	993	1195	1170	995
108	1209	1268	242	255	346	983	1125	680	443	223
109	122	854	222	115	805	1318	592	1266	228	157
110	1099	498	608	1378	1012	1328	662	317	780	1143
111	806	1325	641	170	1190	1135	750	933	775	1108
112	561	1049	148	1036	57	399	1354	844	152	1064
113	253	332	885	439	195	1365	921	691	520	762
114	1017	1363	907	593	1273	277	500	622	37	259
115	374	1179	1058	211	38	266	423	83	581	1189
116	1128	701	590	1252	130	910	614	1420	1306	508
117	678	429	125	875	369	1144	813	1374	984	1132
118	729	786	1185	1100	505	657	282	535	867	313
119	752	947	873	355	1046	127	889	467	391	1298
120	452	286	563	1063	246	283	542	916	656	275
121	486	524	790	1213	1296	438	188	1316	578	1168
122	981	1111	582	1196	1177	1044	113	791	1220	1345
123	781	1150	855	229	164	1148	841	131	917	663
124	324	829	47	329	864	292	605	1357	865	299
125	654	261	388	1277	305	696	555	1007	1293	417
126	41	287	570	1112	589	1245	81	567	1091	442
127	216	73	511	699	576	1154	883	425	97	679
128	436	174	1218	1331	683	464	370	1151	862	278
129	507	671	380	1221	1352	830	54	378	1207	1254
130	144	1008	1300	466	384	1249	109	763	1024	1412
131	1250	116	812	1367	935	789	1206	1247	95	665
132	338	927	733	814	1381	1033	36	252	325	836
133	96	672	387	1270	256	353	1032	29	203	1421
134	1313	557	1021	1391	1103	526	804	1311	543	923
135	705	618	9	63	441	209	24	168	1176	1037
136	64	448	258	367	1130	715	688	499	615	1427
137	1355	851	201	1407	1215	1310	536	874	362	1095
138	470	412	6	42	294	619	16	112	784	1171
139	1002	1258	172	1204	1233	1436	1418	1292	410	1431
140	1383	1047	134	938	810	1353	837	103	721	730
141	793	1234	4	28	196	1372	970	1034	43	301
142	668	359	1074	323	822	1437	1425	1341	753	954
143	922	698	569	1105	540	902	558	1028		

P = 1439

	INDICES											POWER RESIDUES									
	0	1	2	3	4	5	6	7	8	9		0	1	2	3	4	5	6	7	8	9
50	1146	684	20	901	595	1184	398	1290	1169	911	50	271	458	328	857	243	262	395	1326	648	219
51	351	1272	602	1038	731	839	630	711	417	1054	51	94	658	289	584	1210	1275	291	598	1308	522
52	1138	114	519	488	1211	979	1345	353	93	446	52	776	1115	610	1392	1110	575	1147	834	82	574
53	947	938	423	848	823	1187	1376	716	1065	909	53	1140	785	1178	1051	162	1134	743	884	432	146
54	1434	227	1206	1348	191	738	971	344	16	298	54	1022	1398	1152	869	327	850	194	1358	872	348
55	477	347	141	1075	413	1256	557	1341	1436	1006	55	997	1223	1366	928	740	863	285	556	1014	1342
56	819	1120	798	1202	454	658	473	1267	1003	1432	56	760	1003	1265	221	108	756	975	1069	288	577
57	1262	72	469	875	529	525	1274	569	1218	105	57	1161	932	768	1059	218	87	609	1385	1061	232
58	743	1158	1222	278	513	372	130	254	652	1264	58	185	1295	431	139	973	1055	190	1330	676	415
59	1162	38	1096	1143	765	408	49	885	517	70	59	27	189	1323	627	72	504	650	233	192	1344
60	220	325	687	610	159	1246	258	229	1102	576	60	774	1101	512	706	625	58	406	1403	1187	1114
61	522	830	863	1012	1166	1368	150	705	1351	1385	61	603	1343	767	1052	169	1183	1086	407	1410	1236
62	222	813	1147	880	212	604	457	593	1073	685	62	18	126	882	418	48	336	913	635	128	896
63	53	275	316	391	375	627	21	1028	74	237	63	516	734	821	1430	1376	998	1230	1415	1271	263
64	60	1112	261	902	198	88	691	782	508	493	64	402	1375	991	1181	1072	309	724	751	940	824
65	596	55	35	462	1250	669	1208	1185	511	389	65	12	84	588	1238	32	224	129	903	565	1077
66	989	953	1106	1239	399	1319	330	122	1420	327	66	344	969	1027	1433	1397	1145	820	1423	1327	655
67	834	1291	1331	67	1040	892	588	420	1170	1279	67	268	437	181	1267	235	206	3	21	147	1029
68	1087	921	991	1284	336	912	709	471	1366	397	68	8	56	392	1305	501	629	86	602	1336	718
69	1037	1137	352	822	226	15	1255	797	1431	1273	69	709	646	205	1435	1411	1243	67	469	405	1396
70	277	1161	884	158	829	1350	603	315	236	690	70	1138	771	1080	365	1116	617	2	14	98	686
71	461	988	121	1039	920	1365	14	883	689	13	71	485	517	741	870	334	899	537	881	411	1438
72	732	1408	164	733	646	201	320	840	269	1180	72	1432	1390	1096	477	461	349	1004	1272	270	451
73	1409	955	1034	1322	631	110	877	165	442	996	73	279	514	720	723	744	891	481	489	545	937
74	554	712	78	536	734	945	103	1071	418	318	74	803	1304	494	580	1182	1079	358	1067	274	479
75	1116	647	1190	1428	193	1055	565	272	202	368	75	475	447	251	318	787	1192	1149	848	180	1260
76	560	451	1139	1307	173	321	786	612	572	115	76	186	1302	480	482	496	594	1280	326	843	145
77	1046	701	841	1049	600	1118	520	387	234	270	77	1015	1349	809	1346	788	1199	1198	1191	1142	799
78	1108	1230	466	489	1388	531	1181	754	774	1315	78	1276	298	647	212	45	315	766	1045	120	840
79	1212	1227	63	1410	807	917	183	980	393	779	79	124	868	320	801	1290	396	1333	697	562	1056
80	956	793	309	740	1346	1094	1110	1035	994	772	80	197	1379	1019	1377	1005	1279	319	794	1241	53
81	1404	354	1312	1176	1323	931	161	428	94	941	81	371	1158	911	621	30	210	31	217	80	560
82	666	632	1424	869	649	447	293	144	111	1241	82	1042	99	693	534	860	264	409	1424	1334	704
83	1295	383	948	977	527	878	1329	1406	1044	939	83	611	1399	1159	918	670	373	1172	1009	1307	515
84	789	1236	166	768	1127	46	424	377	757	443	84	727	772	1087	414	20	140	980	1104	533	853
85	545	1371	973	849	1091	1232	997	503	439	24	85	215	66	462	356	1053	176	1232	1429	1369	949
86	824	499	1288	555	1244	1248	156	1188	791	543	86	887	453	293	612	1406	1208	1261	193	1351	823
87	713	284	548	1192	1377	1173	483	79	401	100	87	5	35	245	276	493	573	1133	736	835	89
88	287	717	622	1276	537	1132	356	860	1066	1196	88	623	44	308	717	702	597	1301	473	433	153
89	1017	735	1063	252	19	910	629	487	946	715	89	1071	302	675	408	1417	1285	361	1088	421	69
90	190	346	1435	657	468	104	129	1142	219	228	90	483	503	643	184	1288	382	1235	11	77	539
91	1165	812	1072	626	260	492	1207	1238	833	419	91	895	509	685	478	468	398	1347	795	1248	102
92	335	1136	1430	1349	120	12	319	1321	553	1070	92	714	681	450	272	465	377	1200	1205	1240	46
93	192	450	571	1117	465	1314	182	739	1403	427	93	322	815	1388	1082	379	1214	1303	487	531	839
94	648	382	1043	45	972	23	155	1191	286	859	94	117	819	1416	1278	312	745	898	530	832	68
95	18	345	218	491	1429	1069	181	44	17	43	95	476	454	300	661	310	731	800	1283	347	990
96	30	194	4	231	31	299	168	985	1056	661	96	1174	1023	1405	1201	1212	1289	389	1284	354	1039
97	1416	195	478	584	205	566	332	133	5	348	97	78	546	944	852	208	17	119	833	75	525
98	846	1220	273	1085	1178	232	142	481	10	203	98	797	1262	200	1400	1166	967	1013	1335	711	660
99	959	642	32	1076	1030	1079	369	550	635	300	99	303	682	457	321	808	1339	739	856	236	213

P = 1447

INDICES

	0	1	2	3	4	5	6	7	8	9
0		0	68	1	136	285	69	1350	204	2
1	353	74	137	1272	1418	286	272	976	70	294
2	421	1351	142	162	205	570	1340	3	40	809
3	354	398	340	75	1044	189	138	1032	362	1273
4	489	671	1419	688	210	287	230	1401	273	1254
5	638	977	1408	992	71	359	108	295	877	916
6	422	771	466	1352	408	111	143	1307	1112	163
7	257	305	206	851	1100	571	430	1424	1341	1223
8	557	4	739	1331	41	1261	756	810	278	613
9	355	1176	298	399	23	579	341	1364	1322	76
10	706	826	1045	1036	30	190	1060	1005	139	1251
11	427	1033	176	316	363	447	945	1274	984	880
12	490	148	839	672	534	855	1420	1287	476	689
13	179	718	211	198	1375	288	1180	348	231	665
14	325	1402	373	1346	274	1094	919	1255	1168	335
15	639	999	498	978	46	683	1409	319	1291	993
16	625	66	72	419	807	360	1399	106	109	1098
17	1329	296	824	425	878	474	346	917	681	805
18	423	1242	1244	772	366	1317	467	1050	91	1353
19	647	1246	409	1160	1432	112	1390	485	144	890
20	774	1308	894	713	1113	956	1104	164	98	368
21	258	450	1128	306	1073	973	207	302	1319	852
22	495	802	1101	459	244	572	384	469	431	59
23	515	1425	1013	462	1342	240	1052	1224	948	480
24	558	654	216	5	907	93	740	120	602	1332
25	923	847	42	236	1355	1262	544	510	757	936
26	247	811	786	649	279	1277	266	614	1443	37
27	356	736	1248	1177	416	644	299	904	733	400
28	393	411	24	778	441	580	1414	575	342	506
29	1162	1365	987	1231	1323	1201	1236	77	403	1434
30	707	592	1067	827	566	1056	1046	1439	114	1037
31	751	1300	31	699	387	191	1359	1392	1061	883
32	693	1006	134	1270	140	396	487	1252	875	1305
33	428	1259	21	1034	174	146	177	663	1166	317
34	1397	472	364	1158	892	448	493	57	946	118
35	542	1275	414	776	985	590	749	881	873	661
36	491	588	1310	149	1312	1136	840	1215	434	673
37	1385	896	535	151	1118	856	159	635	1421	27
38	715	1288	1314	1125	477	263	1228	690	54	1115
39	180	1138	12	719	553	62	212	1266	958	199
40	842	183	1376	224	962	289	781	1106	1181	1217
41	1024	349	1172	820	232	170	166	666	436	1369
42	326	1088	518	1403	1196	100	374	675	1141	1347
43	1041	768	275	444	370	1095	1387	456	920	901
44	563	1256	870	260	1169	898	527	336	312	1428
45	640	745	452	1000	537	15	499	1152	127	979
46	583	1130	47	153	1081	684	530	952	1410	1211
47	308	320	1120	762	1292	864	1016	994	548	1075
48	626	858	722	67	284	203	73	1417	975	420
49	161	1339	808	339	188	361	670	209	1400	637

POWER RESIDUES

	0	1	2	3	4	5	6	7	8	9
0	1	3	9	27	81	243	729	740	773	872
1	1169	613	392	1176	634	455	1365	1201	709	680
2	593	332	996	94	282	846	1091	379	1137	517
3	104	312	936	1361	1189	673	572	269	807	974
4	28	84	252	756	821	1016	154	462	1386	1264
5	898	1247	847	1094	388	1164	598	347	1041	229
6	687	614	395	1185	661	536	161	483	2	6
7	18	54	162	486	11	33	99	297	891	1226
8	784	905	1268	910	1283	955	1418	1360	1186	664
9	545	188	564	245	735	758	827	1034	208	624
10	425	1275	931	1346	1144	538	167	501	56	168
11	504	65	195	585	308	924	1325	1081	349	1047
12	247	741	776	881	1196	694	635	458	1374	1228
13	790	923	1322	1072	322	966	4	12	36	108
14	324	972	22	66	198	594	335	1005	121	363
15	1089	373	1119	463	1389	1273	925	1328	1090	376
16	1128	490	23	69	207	621	416	1248	850	1103
17	415	1245	841	1076	334	1002	112	336	1008	130
18	390	1170	616	401	1203	715	698	647	494	35
19	105	315	945	1388	1270	916	1301	1009	133	399
20	1197	697	644	485	8	24	72	216	648	497
21	44	132	396	1188	670	563	242	726	731	746
22	791	926	1331	1099	403	1209	733	752	809	980
23	46	138	414	1242	832	1049	253	759	830	1043
24	235	705	668	557	224	672	569	260	780	893
25	1232	802	959	1430	1396	1294	988	70	210	630
26	443	1329	1093	385	1155	571	266	798	947	1394
27	1288	970	16	48	144	432	1296	994	88	264
28	792	929	1340	1126	484	5	15	45	135	405
29	1215	751	806	971	19	57	171	513	92	276
30	828	1037	217	651	506	71	213	639	470	1410
31	1336	1114	448	1344	1138	520	113	339	1017	157
32	471	1413	1345	1141	529	140	420	1260	886	1211
33	739	770	863	1142	532	149	447	1341	1129	493
34	32	96	288	864	1145	541	176	528	137	411
35	1233	805	968	10	30	90	270	810	983	55
36	165	495	38	114	342	1026	184	552	209	627
37	434	1302	1012	142	426	1278	940	1373	1225	781
38	896	1241	829	1040	226	678	587	314	942	1379
39	1243	835	1058	280	840	1073	325	975	31	93
40	279	837	1064	298	894	1235	811	986	64	192
41	576	281	843	1082	352	1056	274	822	1019	163
42	489	20	60	180	540	173	519	110	330	990
43	76	228	684	605	368	1104	418	1254	868	1157
44	577	284	852	1109	433	1299	1003	115	345	1035
45	211	633	452	1356	1174	628	437	1311	1039	223
46	669	560	233	699	650	503	62	186	558	227
47	681	596	341	1023	175	525	128	384	1152	562
48	239	717	704	665	548	197	591	326	978	40
49	120	360	1080	346	1038	220	660	533	152	456

P = 1447

INDICES

	0	1	2	3	4	5	6	7	8	9
50	991	107	915	465	110	1111	304	1099	1423	556
51	1330	755	612	297	578	1321	825	29	1004	426
52	315	944	879	838	854	475	717	1374	347	324
53	1345	918	334	497	682	1290	65	806	105	1328
54	424	345	804	1243	1316	90	1245	1431	484	773
55	712	1103	367	1127	972	1318	801	243	468	514
56	461	1051	479	215	92	601	846	1354	509	246
57	648	265	36	1247	643	732	410	440	574	1161
58	1230	1235	1433	1066	1055	113	1299	386	1391	692
59	1269	486	1304	20	145	1165	471	891	56	541
60	775	748	660	1309	1135	433	895	1117	634	714
61	1124	1227	1114	11	61	957	182	961	1105	1023
62	819	165	1368	517	99	1140	767	369	455	562
63	259	526	1427	451	14	126	1129	1080	951	307
64	761	1015	1074	721	202	974	1338	187	208	990
65	464	303	555	611	1320	1003	943	853	1373	1344
66	496	64	1327	803	89	483	1102	971	242	460
67	214	845	245	35	731	573	1234	1054	385	1268
68	19	470	540	659	432	633	1226	60	960	818
69	516	766	561	1426	125	950	1014	201	186	463
70	610	942	1343	1326	482	241	844	730	1053	18
71	658	1225	817	560	949	185	941	481	729	657
72	559	940	656	655	1378	1379	217	1282	1380	6
73	1204	218	908	226	1283	94	502	1381	741	330
74	7	121	964	1205	603	620	219	1333	1186	909
75	924	291	227	848	703	1284	43	1239	95	237
76	783	503	1356	1155	1382	1263	1193	742	545	1108
77	331	511	1296	8	758	968	122	937	1183	965
78	248	379	1206	812	80	604	787	1219	621	650
79	130	220	280	597	1334	1278	1026	1187	267	931
80	910	615	251	925	1444	351	292	38	1030	228
81	357	406	849	737	1174	704	1249	982	1285	1178
82	1092	44	417	822	1240	645	888	96	300	382
83	238	905	234	784	734	391	504	401	1437	1357
84	394	172	1156	412	586	1383	25	52	1264	779
85	168	1194	442	868	743	581	1209	546	1415	668
86	1109	576	836	332	343	710	512	507	438	1297
87	1163	1133	9	1366	524	759	988	1371	969	1232
88	631	123	1324	815	938	1202	328	1184	1237	1191
89	966	78	595	249	404	1090	380	1435	50	1207
90	708	522	813	593	520	81	1068	1147	605	828
91	83	788	567	1405	1220	1057	195	622	1047	1070
92	651	1440	1198	131	115	156	221	1038	1149	281
93	752	102	598	1301	1020	1335	32	607	1279	700
94	376	1027	388	833	1188	192	830	268	1360	677
95	932	1393	1084	911	1062	85	616	884	1143	252
96	694	796	926	1007	790	1445	135	1349	352	1271
97	271	293	141	569	39	397	1043	1031	488	687
98	229	1253	1407	358	876	770	407	1306	256	850
99	429	1222	738	1260	277	1175	22	1363	705	1035

POWER RESIDUES

	0	1	2	3	4	5	6	7	8	9
50	1368	1210	736	761	836	1061	289	867	1154	568
51	257	771	866	1151	559	230	690	623	422	1266
52	904	1265	901	1256	874	1175	631	446	1338	1120
53	466	1398	1300	1006	124	372	1116	454	1362	1192
54	682	599	350	1050	256	768	857	1124	478	1434
55	1408	1330	1096	394	1182	652	509	80	240	720
56	713	692	629	440	1320	1066	304	912	1289	973
57	25	75	225	675	578	287	861	1136	514	95
58	285	855	1118	460	1380	1246	844	1085	361	1083
59	355	1065	301	903	1262	892	1229	793	932	1349
60	1153	565	248	744	785	908	1277	937	1364	1198
61	700	653	512	89	267	801	956	1421	1369	1213
62	745	788	917	1304	1018	160	480	1440	1426	1384
63	1258	880	1193	685	608	377	1131	499	50	150
64	450	1350	1156	574	275	825	1028	190	570	263
65	789	920	1313	1045	241	723	722	719	710	683
66	602	359	1077	337	1011	139	417	1251	859	1130
67	496	41	123	369	1107	427	1281	949	1400	1306
68	1024	178	534	155	465	1395	1291	979	43	129
69	387	1161	589	320	960	1433	1405	1321	1069	313
70	939	1370	1216	754	815	998	100	300	900	1253
71	865	1148	550	203	609	380	1140	526	131	393
72	1179	643	482	1446	1444	1438	1420	1366	1204	718
73	707	674	575	278	834	1055	271	813	992	82
74	246	738	767	854	1115	451	1353	1165	601	356
75	1068	310	930	1343	1135	511	86	258	774	875
76	1178	640	473	1419	1363	1195	691	626	431	1293
77	985	61	183	549	200	600	353	1059	283	849
78	1100	406	1218	760	833	1052	262	786	911	1286
79	964	1445	1441	1429	1393	1285	961	1436	1414	1348
80	1150	556	221	663	542	179	537	164	492	29
81	87	261	783	902	1259	883	1202	712	689	620
82	413	1239	823	1022	172	516	101	303	909	1280
83	946	1391	1279	943	1382	1252	862	1139	523	122
84	366	1098	400	1200	706	671	566	251	753	812
85	989	73	219	657	524	125	375	1125	481	1443
86	1435	1411	1339	1123	475	1425	1381	1249	853	1112
87	442	1326	1084	358	1074	328	984	58	174	522
88	119	357	1071	319	957	1424	1378	1240	826	1031
89	199	597	344	1032	202	606	371	1113	445	1335
90	1111	439	1317	1057	277	831	1046	244	732	749
91	800	953	1412	1342	1132	502	59	177	531	146
92	438	1314	1048	250	750	803	962	1439	1423	1375
93	1231	799	950	1403	1315	1051	259	777	884	1205
94	721	716	701	656	521	116	348	1044	238	714
95	695	638	467	1401	1309	1033	205	615	398	1194
96	688	617	404	1212	742	779	890	1223	775	878
97	1187	667	554	215	645	488	17	51	153	459
98	1377	1237	817	1004	118	354	1062	292	876	1181
99	649	500	53	159	477	1431	1399	1303	1015	151

P = 1447

INDICES

	0	1	2	3	4	5	6	7	8	9
100	1059	1250	175	446	983	147	533	1286	178	197
101	1179	664	372	1093	1167	998	45	318	624	418
102	1398	1097	823	473	680	1241	365	1049	646	1159
103	1389	889	893	955	97	449	1072	301	494	458
104	383	58	1012	239	947	653	906	119	922	235
105	543	935	785	1276	1442	735	415	903	392	777
106	1413	505	986	1200	402	591	565	1438	750	698
107	1358	882	133	395	874	1258	173	662	1396	1157
108	492	117	413	589	872	587	1311	1214	1384	150
109	158	26	1313	262	53	1137	552	1265	841	223
110	780	1216	1171	169	435	1087	1195	674	1040	443
111	1386	900	869	897	311	744	536	1151	582	152
112	529	1210	1119	863	547	857	283	1416	160	338
113	669	636	914	1110	1422	754	577	28	314	837
114	716	323	333	1289	104	344	1315	1430	711	1126
115	800	513	478	600	508	264	642	439	1229	1065
116	1298	691	1303	1164	55	747	1134	1116	1123	10
117	181	1022	1367	1139	454	525	13	1079	760	720
118	1337	989	554	1002	1372	63	88	970	213	34
119	1233	1267	539	632	959	765	124	200	609	1325
120	843	17	816	184	728	939	1377	1281	1203	225
121	501	329	963	619	1185	290	702	1238	782	1154
122	1192	1107	1295	967	1182	378	79	1218	129	596
123	1025	930	250	350	1029	405	1173	981	1091	821
124	887	381	233	390	1436	171	585	51	167	867
125	1208	667	835	709	437	1132	523	1370	630	814
126	327	1190	594	1089	49	521	519	1146	82	1404
127	194	1069	1197	155	1148	101	1019	606	375	832
128	829	676	1083	84	1142	795	789	1348	270	568
129	1042	686	1406	769	255	1221	276	1362	1058	445
130	532	196	371	997	623	1096	679	1048	1388	954
131	1071	457	1011	652	921	934	1441	902	1412	1199
132	564	697	132	1257	1395	116	871	1213	157	261
133	551	222	1170	1086	1039	899	310	1150	528	862
134	282	337	913	753	313	322	103	1429	799	599
135	641	1064	1302	746	1122	1021	453	1078	1336	1001
136	87	33	538	764	608	16	727	1280	500	618
137	701	1153	1294	377	128	929	1028	980	886	389
138	584	866	834	1131	629	1189	48	1145	193	154
139	1018	831	1082	794	269	685	254	1361	531	996
140	678	953	1010	933	1411	696	1394	1212	550	1085
141	309	861	912	321	798	1063	1121	1077	86	763
142	726	617	1293	928	885	865	628	1144	1017	793
143	253	995	1009	695	549	860	797	1076	725	927
144	627	792	1008	859	724	791	723			

POWER RESIDUES

	0	1	2	3	4	5	6	7	8	9
100	453	1359	1183	655	518	107	321	963	1442	1432
101	1402	1312	1042	232	696	641	476	1428	1390	1276
102	934	1355	1171	619	410	1230	796	941	1376	1234
103	808	977	37	111	333	999	103	309	927	1334
104	1108	430	1290	976	34	102	306	918	1307	1027
105	187	561	236	708	677	584	305	915	1298	1000
106	106	318	954	1415	1351	1159	583	302	906	1271
107	919	1310	1036	214	642	479	1437	1417	1357	1177
108	637	464	1392	1282	952	1409	1333	1105	421	1263
109	895	1238	820	1013	145	435	1305	1021	169	507
110	74	222	666	551	206	618	407	1221	769	860
111	1133	505	68	204	612	389	1167	607	374	1122
112	472	1416	1354	1168	610	383	1149	553	212	636
113	461	1383	1255	871	1166	604	365	1095	391	1173
114	625	428	1284	958	1427	1387	1267	907	1274	928
115	1337	1117	457	1371	1219	763	842	1079	343	1029
116	193	579	290	870	1163	595	338	1014	148	444
117	1332	1102	412	1236	814	995	91	273	819	1010
118	136	408	1224	778	887	1214	748	797	944	1385
119	1261	889	1220	766	851	1106	424	1272	922	1319
120	1063	295	885	1208	730	743	782	899	1250	856
121	1121	469	1407	1327	1087	367	1101	409	1227	787
122	914	1295	991	79	237	711	686	611	386	1158
123	580	293	879	1190	676	581	296	888	1217	757
124	824	1025	181	543	182	546	191	573	272	816
125	1001	109	327	981	49	147	441	1323	1075	331
126	993	85	255	765	848	1097	397	1191	679	590
127	323	969	13	39	117	351	1053	265	795	938
128	1367	1207	727	734	755	818	1007	127	381	1143
129	535	158	474	1422	1372	1222	772	869	1160	586
130	311	933	1352	1162	592	329	987	67	201	603
131	362	1086	364	1092	382	1146	544	185	555	218
132	654	515	98	294	882	1199	703	662	539	170
133	510	83	249	747	794	935	1358	1180	646	491
134	26	78	234	702	659	530	143	429	1287	967
135	7	21	63	189	567	254	762	839	1070	316
136	948	1397	1297	997	97	291	873	1172	622	419
137	1257	877	1184	658	527	134	402	1206	724	725
138	728	737	764	845	1088	370	1110	436	1308	1030
139	196	588	317	951	1406	1324	1078	340	1020	166
140	498	47	141	423	1269	913	1292	982	52	156
141	468	1404	1318	1060	286	858	1127	487	14	42
142	126	378	1134	508	77	231	693	632	449	1347
143	1147	547	194	582	299	897	1244	838	1067	307
144	921	1316	1054	268	804	965				

P = 1451

INDICES

	0	1	2	3	4	5	6	7	8	9
0		0	1	822	2	114	823	583	3	194
1	115	1038	824	977	584	936	4	717	195	653
2	116	1405	1039	1399	825	228	978	1016	585	496
3	937	1003	5	410	718	697	196	379	654	349
4	117	32	1406	320	1040	308	1400	1270	826	1166
5	229	89	979	1275	1017	1152	586	25	497	597
6	938	152	1004	777	6	1091	411	360	719	771
7	698	162	197	78	380	1050	655	171	350	1026
8	118	388	33	125	1407	831	321	1318	1041	287
9	309	110	1401	375	1271	767	827	516	1167	1232
10	230	520	90	335	980	69	1276	686	1018	466
11	1153	1201	587	668	26	63	498	1171	598	1300
12	939	626	153	854	1005	342	778	704	7	1142
13	1092	1252	412	1236	361	1130	720	998	772	762
14	699	642	163	565	198	610	79	538	381	234
15	1051	482	656	911	172	1117	351	1185	1027	647
16	119	532	389	1260	34	524	126	785	1408	504
17	832	847	322	1082	1319	811	1042	1419	288	1375
18	310	94	111	974	1402	493	376	305	1272	149
19	768	168	828	372	517	463	1168	339	1233	639
20	231	1182	521	1079	91	146	336	143	981	241
21	70	395	1277	984	687	434	1019	136	467	900
22	1154	244	1202	570	588	422	669	189	27	73
23	64	993	499	1177	1172	1384	599	398	1301	619
24	940	16	627	1210	154	1280	855	180	1006	947
25	343	329	779	987	705	203	8	737	1143	962
26	1093	690	1253	1331	413	1389	1237	1109	362	437
27	1131	1438	721	932	999	1266	773	1022	763	1197
28	700	561	643	807	164	139	566	615	199	1434
29	611	1338	80	470	539	711	382	604	235	926
30	1052	903	483	1342	657	266	912	1293	173	1157
31	1118	866	352	1362	1186	891	1028	247	648	84
32	120	58	533	1370	390	1205	1261	1288	35	403
33	525	1427	127	573	786	474	1409	1058	505	40
34	833	591	848	299	323	885	1083	50	1320	425
35	812	543	1043	1072	1420	276	289	672	1376	209
36	311	1306	95	1448	112	192	975	715	1403	226
37	494	408	377	30	306	1164	1273	23	150	1089
38	769	76	169	386	829	285	373	514	518	67
39	464	666	1169	624	340	1140	1234	996	640	608
40	232	909	1183	530	522	502	1080	1417	92	491
41	147	370	337	1180	144	239	982	134	242	420
42	71	1175	396	14	1278	945	985	735	688	1387
43	435	930	1020	559	137	1432	468	602	901	264
44	1155	1360	245	56	1203	401	571	1056	589	883
45	423	1070	670	1304	190	224	28	21	74	283
46	65	622	994	907	500	489	1178	132	1173	943
47	1385	557	600	1358	399	881	1302	19	620	487
48	941	1356	17	1354	628	630	1211	743	155	632
49	1281	217	856	1213	181	1346	1007	745	948	578

POWER RESIDUES

	0	1	2	3	4	5	6	7	8	9
0	1	2	4	8	16	32	64	128	256	512
1	1024	597	1194	937	423	846	241	482	964	477
2	954	457	914	377	754	57	114	228	456	912
3	373	746	41	82	164	328	656	1312	1173	895
4	339	678	1356	1261	1071	691	1382	1313	1175	899
5	347	694	1388	1325	1199	947	443	886	321	642
6	1284	1117	783	115	230	460	920	389	778	105
7	210	420	840	229	458	916	381	762	73	146
8	292	584	1168	885	319	638	1276	1101	751	51
9	102	204	408	816	181	362	724	1448	1445	1439
10	1427	1403	1355	1259	1067	683	1366	1281	1111	771
11	91	182	364	728	5	10	20	40	80	160
12	320	640	1280	1109	767	83	166	332	664	1328
13	1205	959	467	934	417	834	217	434	868	285
14	570	1140	829	207	414	828	205	410	820	189
15	378	756	61	122	244	488	976	501	1002	553
16	1106	761	71	142	284	568	1136	821	191	382
17	764	77	154	308	616	1232	1013	575	1150	849
18	247	494	988	525	1050	649	1298	1145	839	227
19	454	908	365	730	9	18	36	72	144	288
20	576	1152	853	255	510	1020	589	1178	905	359
21	718	1436	1421	1391	1331	1211	971	491	982	513
22	1026	601	1202	953	455	910	369	738	25	50
23	100	200	400	800	149	298	596	1192	933	415
24	830	209	418	836	221	442	884	317	634	1268
25	1085	719	1438	1425	1399	1347	1243	1035	619	1238
26	1025	599	1198	945	439	878	305	610	1220	989
27	527	1054	657	1314	1177	903	355	710	1420	1389
28	1327	1203	955	459	918	385	770	89	178	356
29	712	1424	1397	1343	1235	1019	587	1174	897	343
30	686	1372	1293	1135	819	187	374	748	45	90
31	180	360	720	1440	1429	1407	1363	1275	1099	747
32	43	86	172	344	688	1376	1301	1151	851	251
33	502	1004	557	1114	777	103	206	412	824	197
34	394	788	125	250	500	1000	549	1098	745	39
35	78	156	312	624	1248	1045	639	1278	1105	759
36	67	134	268	536	1072	693	1386	1321	1191	931
37	411	822	193	386	772	93	186	372	744	37
38	74	148	296	592	1184	917	383	766	81	162
39	324	648	1296	1141	831	211	422	844	237	474
40	948	445	890	329	658	1316	1181	911	371	742
41	33	66	132	264	528	1056	661	1322	1193	935
42	419	838	225	450	900	349	698	1396	1341	1231
43	1011	571	1142	833	215	430	860	269	538	1076
44	701	1402	1353	1255	1059	667	1334	1217	983	515
45	1030	609	1218	985	519	1038	625	1250	1049	647
46	1294	1137	823	195	390	780	109	218	436	872
47	293	586	1172	893	335	670	1340	1229	1007	563
48	1126	801	151	302	604	1208	965	479	958	465
49	930	409	818	185	370	740	29	58	116	232

P = 1451

INDICES

	0	1	2	3	4	5	6	7	8	9
50	344	157	330	1125	780	634	988	1326	706	1283
51	204	661	9	219	738	449	1144	858	963	454
52	1094	1215	691	1226	1254	183	1332	270	414	1348
53	1390	791	1238	1009	1110	800	363	747	438	754
54	1132	950	1439	916	722	580	933	1396	1000	346
55	1267	1149	774	159	1023	1315	764	332	1198	1297
56	701	1127	562	479	644	782	808	971	165	636
57	140	431	567	990	616	177	200	1328	1435	1194
58	612	708	1339	863	81	1285	471	296	540	206
59	712	1161	383	663	605	1414	236	11	927	261
60	1053	221	904	554	484	740	1343	1122	658	451
61	267	797	913	1146	1294	968	174	860	1158	258
62	1119	965	867	870	353	456	1363	1063	1187	1096
63	892	873	1029	1217	248	818	649	693	85	356
64	121	1228	59	1248	534	1256	1371	459	391	185
65	1206	958	1262	1334	1289	1366	36	272	404	510
66	526	416	1428	1066	128	1350	574	445	787	1392
67	475	1190	1410	793	1059	1244	506	1240	41	1099
68	834	1011	592	105	849	1112	300	895	324	802
69	886	45	1084	365	51	876	1321	749	426	549
70	813	440	544	1032	1044	756	1073	1103	1421	1134
71	277	1220	290	952	673	679	1377	1441	210	251
72	312	918	1307	838	96	724	1449	821	113	582
73	193	1037	976	935	716	652	1404	1398	227	1015
74	495	1002	409	696	378	348	31	319	307	1269
75	1165	88	1274	1151	24	596	151	776	1090	359
76	770	161	77	1049	170	1025	387	124	830	1317
77	286	109	374	766	515	1231	519	334	68	685
78	465	1200	667	62	1170	1299	625	853	341	703
79	1141	1251	1235	1129	997	761	641	564	609	537
80	233	481	910	1116	1184	646	531	1259	523	784
81	503	846	1081	810	1418	1374	93	973	492	304
82	148	167	371	462	338	638	1181	1078	145	142
83	240	394	983	433	135	899	243	569	421	188
84	72	992	1176	1383	397	618	15	1209	1279	179
85	946	328	986	202	736	961	689	1330	1388	1108
86	436	1437	931	1265	1021	1196	560	806	138	614
87	1433	1337	469	710	603	925	902	1341	265	1292
88	1156	865	1361	890	246	83	57	1369	1204	1287
89	402	1426	572	473	1057	39	590	298	884	49
90	424	542	1071	275	671	208	1305	1447	191	714
91	225	407	29	1163	22	1088	75	385	284	513
92	66	665	623	1139	995	607	908	529	501	1416
93	490	369	1179	238	133	419	1174	13	944	734
94	1386	929	558	1431	601	263	1359	55	400	1055
95	882	1069	1303	223	20	282	621	906	488	131
96	942	556	1357	880	18	486	1355	1353	629	742
97	631	216	1212	1345	744	577	156	1124	633	1325
98	1282	660	218	448	857	453	1214	1225	182	269
99	1347	790	1008	799	746	753	949	915	579	1395

POWER RESIDUES

	0	1	2	3	4	5	6	7	8	9
50	464	928	405	810	169	338	676	1352	1253	1055
51	659	1318	1185	919	387	774	97	194	388	776
52	101	202	404	808	165	330	660	1320	1189	927
53	403	806	161	322	644	1288	1125	799	147	294
54	588	1176	901	351	702	1404	1357	1263	1075	699
55	1398	1345	1239	1027	603	1206	961	471	942	433
56	866	281	562	1124	797	143	286	572	1144	837
57	223	446	892	333	666	1332	1213	975	499	998
58	545	1090	729	7	14	28	56	112	224	448
59	896	341	682	1364	1277	1103	755	59	118	236
60	472	944	437	874	297	594	1188	925	399	798
61	145	290	580	1160	869	287	574	1148	845	239
62	478	956	461	922	393	786	121	242	484	968
63	485	970	489	978	505	1010	569	1138	825	199
64	398	796	141	282	564	1128	805	159	318	636
65	1272	1093	735	19	38	76	152	304	608	1216
66	981	511	1022	593	1186	921	391	782	113	226
67	452	904	357	714	1428	1405	1359	1267	1083	715
68	1430	1409	1367	1283	1115	779	107	214	428	856
69	261	522	1044	637	1274	1097	743	35	70	140
70	280	560	1120	789	127	254	508	1016	581	1162
71	873	295	590	1180	909	367	734	17	34	68
72	136	272	544	1088	725	1450	1449	1447	1443	1435
73	1419	1387	1323	1195	939	427	854	257	514	1028
74	605	1210	969	487	974	497	994	537	1074	697
75	1394	1337	1223	995	539	1078	705	1410	1369	1287
76	1123	795	139	278	556	1112	773	95	190	380
77	760	69	138	276	552	1104	757	63	126	252
78	504	1008	565	1130	809	167	334	668	1336	1221
79	991	531	1062	673	1346	1241	1031	611	1222	993
80	535	1070	689	1378	1305	1159	867	283	566	1132
81	813	175	350	700	1400	1349	1247	1043	635	1270
82	1089	727	3	6	12	24	48	96	192	384
83	768	85	170	340	680	1360	1269	1087	723	1446
84	1441	1431	1411	1371	1291	1131	811	171	342	684
85	1368	1285	1119	787	123	246	492	984	517	1034
86	617	1234	1017	583	1166	881	311	622	1244	1037
87	623	1246	1041	631	1262	1073	695	1390	1329	1207
88	963	475	950	449	898	345	690	1380	1309	1167
89	883	315	630	1260	1069	687	1374	1297	1143	835
90	219	438	876	301	602	1204	957	463	926	401
91	802	153	306	612	1224	997	543	1086	721	1442
92	1433	1415	1379	1307	1163	875	299	598	1196	941
93	431	862	273	546	1092	733	15	30	60	120
94	240	480	960	469	938	425	850	249	498	996
95	541	1082	713	1426	1401	1351	1251	1051	651	1302
96	1153	855	259	518	1036	621	1242	1033	615	1230
97	1009	567	1134	817	183	366	732	13	26	52
98	104	208	416	832	213	426	852	253	506	1012
99	573	1146	841	231	462	924	397	794	137	274

P = 1451

INDICES

	0	1	2	3	4	5	6	7	8	9
100	345	1148	158	1314	331	1296	1126	478	781	970
101	635	430	989	176	1327	1193	707	862	1284	295
102	205	1160	662	1413	10	260	220	553	739	1121
103	450	796	1145	967	859	257	964	869	455	1062
104	1095	872	1216	817	692	355	1227	1247	1255	458
105	184	957	1333	1365	271	509	415	1065	1349	444
106	1391	1189	792	1243	1239	1098	1010	104	1111	894
107	801	44	364	875	748	548	439	1031	755	1102
108	1133	1219	951	678	1440	250	917	837	723	820
109	581	1036	934	651	1397	1014	1001	695	347	318
110	1268	87	1150	595	775	358	160	1048	1024	123
111	1316	108	765	1230	333	684	1199	61	1298	852
112	702	1250	1128	760	563	536	480	1115	645	1258
113	783	845	809	1373	972	303	166	461	637	1077
114	141	393	432	898	568	187	991	1382	617	1208
115	178	327	201	960	1329	1107	1436	1264	1195	805
116	613	1336	709	924	1340	1291	864	889	82	1368
117	1286	1425	472	38	297	48	541	274	207	1446
118	713	406	1162	1087	384	512	664	1138	606	528
119	1415	368	237	418	12	733	928	1430	262	54
120	1054	1068	222	281	905	130	555	879	485	1352
121	741	215	1344	576	1123	1324	659	447	452	1224
122	268	789	798	752	914	1394	1147	1313	1295	477
123	969	429	175	1192	861	294	1159	1412	259	552
124	1120	795	966	256	868	1061	871	816	354	1246
125	457	956	1364	508	1064	443	1188	1242	1097	103
126	893	43	874	547	1030	1101	1218	677	249	836
127	819	1035	650	1013	694	317	86	594	357	1047
128	122	107	1229	683	60	851	1249	759	535	1114
129	1257	844	1372	302	460	1076	392	897	186	1381
130	1207	326	959	1106	1263	804	1335	923	1290	888
131	1367	1424	37	47	273	1445	405	1086	511	1137
132	527	367	417	732	1429	53	1067	280	129	878
133	1351	214	575	1323	446	1223	788	751	1393	1312
134	476	428	1191	293	1411	551	794	255	1060	815
135	1245	955	507	442	1241	102	42	546	1100	676
136	835	1034	1012	316	593	1046	106	682	850	758
137	1113	843	301	1075	896	1380	325	1105	803	922
138	887	1423	46	1444	1085	1136	366	731	52	279
139	877	213	1322	1222	750	1311	427	292	550	254
140	814	954	441	101	545	675	1033	315	1045	681
141	757	842	1074	1379	1104	921	1422	1443	1135	730
142	278	212	1221	1310	291	253	953	100	674	314
143	680	841	1378	920	1442	729	211	1309	252	99
144	313	840	919	728	1308	98	839	727	97	726
145	725	0								

POWER RESIDUES

	0	1	2	3	4	5	6	7	8	9
100	548	1096	741	31	62	124	248	496	992	533
101	1066	681	1362	1273	1095	739	27	54	108	216
102	432	864	277	554	1108	765	79	158	316	632
103	1264	1077	703	1406	1361	1271	1091	731	11	22
104	44	88	176	352	704	1408	1365	1279	1107	763
105	75	150	300	600	1200	949	447	894	337	674
106	1348	1245	1039	627	1254	1057	663	1326	1201	951
107	451	902	353	706	1412	1373	1295	1139	827	203
108	406	812	173	346	692	1384	1317	1183	915	379
109	758	65	130	260	520	1040	629	1258	1065	679
110	1358	1265	1079	707	1414	1377	1303	1155	859	267
111	534	1068	685	1370	1289	1127	803	155	310	620
112	1240	1029	607	1214	977	503	1006	561	1122	793
113	135	270	540	1080	709	1418	1385	1319	1187	923
114	395	790	129	258	516	1032	613	1226	1001	551
115	1102	753	55	110	220	440	880	309	618	1236
116	1021	591	1182	913	375	750	49	98	196	392
117	784	117	234	468	936	421	842	233	466	932
118	413	826	201	402	804	157	314	628	1256	1061
119	671	1342	1233	1015	579	1158	865	279	558	1116
120	781	111	222	444	888	325	650	1300	1149	847
121	243	486	972	493	986	521	1042	633	1266	1081
122	711	1422	1393	1335	1219	987	523	1046	641	1282
123	1113	775	99	198	396	792	133	266	532	1064
124	677	1354	1257	1063	675	1350	1249	1047	643	1286
125	1121	791	131	262	524	1048	645	1290	1129	807
126	163	326	652	1304	1157	863	275	550	1100	749
127	47	94	188	376	752	53	106	212	424	848
128	245	490	980	509	1018	585	1170	889	327	654
129	1308	1165	879	307	614	1228	1005	559	1118	785
130	119	238	476	952	453	906	361	722	1444	1437
131	1423	1395	1339	1227	1003	555	1110	769	87	174
132	348	696	1392	1333	1215	979	507	1014	577	1154
133	857	263	526	1052	653	1306	1161	871	291	582
134	1164	877	303	606	1212	973	495	990	529	1058
135	665	1330	1209	967	483	966	481	962	473	946
136	441	882	313	626	1252	1053	655	1310	1169	887
137	323	646	1292	1133	815	179	358	716	1432	1413
138	1375	1299	1147	843	235	470	940	429	858	265
139	530	1060	669	1338	1225	999	547	1094	737	23
140	46	92	184	368	736	21	42	84	168	336
141	672	1344	1237	1023	595	1190	929	407	814	177
142	354	708	1416	1381	1311	1171	891	331	662	1324
143	1197	943	435	870	289	578	1156	861	271	542
144	1084	717	1434	1417	1383	1315	1179	907	363	726
145										

P = 1453

INDICES

	0	1	2	3	4	5	6	7	8	9
0		0	1	812	2	517	813	840	3	172
1	518	1408	814	1420	841	1329	4	106	173	1174
2	519	200	1409	1168	815	1034	1421	984	842	503
3	1330	541	5	768	107	1357	174	464	1175	780
4	520	994	201	65	1410	689	1169	913	816	228
5	1035	918	1422	1151	985	473	843	534	504	375
6	1331	593	542	1012	6	485	769	243	108	528
7	1358	975	175	321	465	394	1176	796	781	1094
8	521	344	995	821	202	623	66	1315	1411	1225
9	690	808	1170	1353	914	239	817	124	229	128
10	1036	665	919	1293	1423	717	1152	1300	986	932
11	474	1276	844	36	535	233	505	140	376	946
12	1332	1364	594	354	543	99	1013	161	7	877
13	486	132	770	562	244	49	109	1029	529	1220
14	1359	273	976	1376	176	1020	322	1040	466	1398
15	395	16	1177	278	797	1058	782	1074	1095	511
16	522	556	345	669	996	1285	822	863	203	1388
17	624	1346	67	1251	1316	422	1412	1187	1226	923
18	691	1240	809	1405	1171	981	1354	62	915	372
19	240	391	818	805	125	1297	230	351	129	1217
20	1037	1055	666	1343	920	59	1294	1340	1424	1130
21	718	1427	1153	335	1301	582	987	1381	933	1133
22	475	74	1277	146	845	1206	37	721	536	1007
23	234	156	506	386	141	1430	377	454	947	1087
24	1333	753	1365	1156	595	745	355	1142	544	181
25	100	338	1014	1124	162	1435	8	412	878	1304
26	487	675	133	738	771	216	563	585	245	1195
27	50	438	110	168	1030	990	530	317	1221	713
28	1360	1025	274	1384	977	1051	1377	382	177	212
29	1021	936	323	297	1041	892	467	940	1399	1136
30	396	905	17	25	1178	1110	279	478	798	653
31	1059	402	783	327	1075	77	1096	253	512	459
32	523	660	557	1280	346	1002	670	292	997	301
33	1286	149	823	636	864	760	204	1441	1389	848
34	625	497	1347	1068	68	1045	1252	1209	1317	1258
35	423	952	1413	266	1188	40	1227	306	924	830
36	692	896	1241	724	810	838	1406	1327	1172	1166
37	982	539	1355	778	63	911	916	471	373	1010
38	241	973	392	1092	819	1313	806	237	126	1291
39	1298	1274	231	944	352	159	130	47	1218	1374
40	1038	14	1056	509	667	861	1344	420	921	1403
41	60	389	1295	1215	1341	1338	1425	580	1131	144
42	719	154	1428	1085	1154	1140	336	1433	1302	736
43	583	436	988	711	1382	380	934	890	1134	23
44	476	400	75	457	1278	290	147	758	846	1066
45	1207	950	38	828	722	1325	537	909	1008	1090
46	235	1272	157	1372	507	418	387	1336	142	1083
47	1431	434	378	21	455	756	948	1323	1088	1370
48	1334	432	754	1368	1366	641	1157	643	596	29
49	746	1159	356	609	1143	645	545	363	182	598

POWER RESIDUES

	0	1	2	3	4	5	6	7	8	9
0	1	2	4	8	16	32	64	128	256	512
1	1024	595	1190	927	401	802	151	302	604	1208
2	963	473	946	439	878	303	606	1212	971	489
3	978	503	1006	559	1118	783	113	226	452	904
4	355	710	1420	1387	1321	1189	925	397	794	135
5	270	540	1080	707	1414	1375	1297	1141	829	205
6	410	820	187	374	748	43	86	172	344	688
7	1376	1299	1145	837	221	442	884	315	630	1260
8	1067	681	1362	1271	1089	725	1450	1447	1441	1429
9	1405	1357	1261	1069	685	1370	1287	1121	789	125
10	250	500	1000	547	1094	735	17	34	68	136
11	272	544	1088	723	1446	1439	1425	1397	1341	1229
12	1005	557	1114	775	97	194	388	776	99	198
13	396	792	131	262	524	1048	643	1286	1119	785
14	117	234	468	936	419	838	223	446	892	331
15	662	1324	1195	937	421	842	231	462	924	395
16	790	127	254	508	1016	579	1158	863	273	546
17	1092	731	9	18	36	72	144	288	576	1152
18	851	249	498	996	539	1078	703	1406	1359	1265
19	1077	701	1402	1351	1249	1045	637	1274	1095	737
20	21	42	84	168	336	672	1344	1235	1017	581
21	1162	871	289	578	1156	859	265	530	1060	667
22	1334	1215	977	501	1002	551	1102	751	49	98
23	196	392	784	115	230	460	920	387	774	95
24	190	380	760	67	134	268	536	1072	691	1382
25	1311	1169	885	317	634	1268	1083	713	1426	1399
26	1345	1237	1021	589	1178	903	353	706	1412	1371
27	1289	1125	797	141	282	564	1128	803	153	306
28	612	1224	995	537	1074	695	1390	1327	1201	949
29	445	890	327	654	1308	1163	873	293	586	1172
30	891	329	658	1316	1179	905	357	714	1428	1403
31	1353	1253	1053	653	1306	1159	865	277	554	1108
32	763	73	146	292	584	1168	883	313	626	1252
33	1051	649	1298	1143	833	213	426	852	251	502
34	1004	555	1110	767	81	162	324	648	1296	1139
35	825	197	394	788	123	246	492	984	515	1030
36	607	1214	975	497	994	535	1070	687	1374	1295
37	1137	821	189	378	756	59	118	236	472	944
38	435	870	287	574	1148	843	233	466	932	411
39	822	191	382	764	75	150	300	600	1200	947
40	441	882	311	622	1244	1035	617	1234	1015	577
41	1154	855	257	514	1028	603	1206	959	465	930
42	407	814	175	350	700	1400	1347	1241	1029	605
43	1210	967	481	962	471	942	431	862	271	542
44	1084	715	1430	1407	1361	1269	1085	717	1434	1415
45	1377	1301	1149	845	237	474	948	443	886	319
46	638	1276	1099	745	37	74	148	296	592	1184
47	915	377	754	55	110	220	440	880	307	614
48	1228	1003	553	1106	759	65	130	260	520	1040
49	627	1254	1055	657	1314	1175	897	341	682	1364

P = 1453

INDICES

	0	1	2	3	4	5	6	7	8	9
50	101	223	339	31	1015	1182	1125	748	163	1105
51	1436	1161	9	706	413	358	879	869	1305	611
52	488	1114	676	1145	134	1234	739	647	772	884
53	217	547	564	962	586	365	246	283	1196	184
54	51	1264	439	600	111	1449	169	103	1031	765
55	991	225	531	482	318	341	1222	121	714	33
56	1361	874	1026	1017	275	553	1385	1184	978	802
57	1052	1127	1378	1203	383	750	178	409	213	165
58	1022	209	937	1107	324	657	298	1438	1042	263
59	893	1163	468	1310	941	11	1400	577	1137	708
60	397	1063	906	415	18	429	26	360	1179	703
61	1111	881	280	1446	479	871	799	406	654	1307
62	1060	700	403	613	784	616	328	490	1076	570
63	78	1116	1097	787	254	678	513	196	460	1147
64	524	619	661	136	558	1394	1281	1236	347	331
65	1003	741	671	313	293	649	998	493	302	774
66	1287	857	150	886	824	1079	637	219	865	958
67	761	549	205	573	1442	566	1390	853	849	964
68	626	81	498	588	1348	94	1069	367	69	1119
69	1046	248	1253	968	1210	285	1318	1100	1259	1198
70	424	191	953	186	1414	790	267	53	1189	630
71	41	1266	1228	257	307	441	925	447	831	602
72	693	681	897	113	1242	85	725	1451	811	516
73	839	171	1407	1419	1328	105	1173	199	1167	1033
74	983	502	540	767	1356	463	779	993	64	688
75	912	227	917	1150	472	533	374	592	1011	484
76	242	527	974	320	393	795	1093	343	820	622
77	1314	1224	807	1352	238	123	127	664	1292	716
78	1299	931	1275	35	232	139	945	1363	353	98
79	160	876	131	561	48	1028	1219	272	1375	1019
80	1039	1397	15	277	1057	1073	510	555	668	1284
81	862	1387	1345	1250	421	1186	922	1239	1404	980
82	61	371	390	804	1296	350	1216	1054	1342	58
83	1339	1129	1426	334	581	1380	1132	73	145	1205
84	720	1006	155	385	1429	453	1086	752	1155	744
85	1141	180	337	1123	1434	411	1303	674	737	215
86	584	1194	437	167	989	316	712	1024	1383	1050
87	381	211	935	296	891	939	1135	904	24	1109
88	477	652	401	326	76	252	458	659	1279	1001
89	291	300	148	635	759	1440	847	496	1067	1044
90	1208	1257	951	265	39	305	829	895	723	837
91	1326	1165	538	777	910	470	1009	972	1091	1312
92	236	1290	1273	943	158	46	1373	13	508	860
93	419	1402	388	1214	1337	579	143	153	1084	1139
94	1432	735	435	710	379	889	22	399	456	289
95	757	1065	949	827	1324	908	1089	1271	1371	417
96	1335	1082	433	20	755	1322	1369	431	1367	640
97	642	28	1158	608	644	362	597	222	30	1181
98	747	1104	1160	705	357	868	610	1113	1144	1233
99	646	883	546	961	364	282	183	1263	599	1448

POWER RESIDUES

	0	1	2	3	4	5	6	7	8	9
50	1275	1097	741	29	58	116	232	464	928	403
51	806	159	318	636	1272	1091	729	5	10	20
52	40	80	160	320	640	1280	1107	761	69	138
53	276	552	1104	755	57	114	228	456	912	371
54	742	31	62	124	248	496	992	531	1062	671
55	1342	1231	1009	565	1130	807	161	322	644	1288
56	1123	793	133	266	532	1064	675	1350	1247	1041
57	629	1258	1063	673	1346	1239	1025	597	1194	935
58	417	834	215	430	860	267	534	1068	683	1366
59	1279	1105	757	61	122	244	488	976	499	998
60	543	1086	719	1438	1423	1393	1333	1213	973	493
61	986	519	1038	623	1246	1039	625	1250	1047	641
62	1282	1111	769	85	170	340	680	1360	1267	1081
63	709	1418	1383	1313	1173	893	333	666	1332	1211
64	969	485	970	487	974	495	990	527	1054	655
65	1310	1167	881	309	618	1236	1019	585	1170	887
66	321	642	1284	1115	777	101	202	404	808	163
67	326	652	1304	1155	857	261	522	1044	635	1270
68	1087	721	1442	1431	1409	1365	1277	1101	749	45
69	90	180	360	720	1440	1427	1401	1349	1245	1037
70	621	1242	1031	609	1218	983	513	1026	599	1198
71	943	433	866	279	558	1116	779	105	210	420
72	840	227	454	908	363	726	1452	1451	1449	1445
73	1437	1421	1389	1325	1197	941	429	858	263	526
74	1052	651	1302	1151	849	245	490	980	507	1014
75	575	1150	847	241	482	964	475	950	447	894
76	335	670	1340	1227	1001	549	1098	743	33	66
77	132	264	528	1056	659	1318	1183	913	373	746
78	39	78	156	312	624	1248	1043	633	1266	1079
79	705	1410	1367	1281	1109	765	77	154	308	616
80	1232	1011	569	1138	823	193	386	772	91	182
81	364	728	3	6	12	24	48	96	192	384
82	768	83	166	332	664	1328	1203	953	453	906
83	359	718	1436	1419	1385	1317	1181	909	365	730
84	7	14	28	56	112	224	448	896	339	678
85	1356	1259	1065	677	1354	1255	1057	661	1322	1191
86	929	405	810	167	334	668	1336	1219	985	517
87	1034	615	1230	1007	561	1122	791	129	258	516
88	1032	611	1222	991	529	1058	663	1326	1199	945
89	437	874	295	590	1180	907	361	722	1444	1435
90	1417	1381	1309	1165	877	301	602	1204	955	457
91	914	375	750	47	94	188	376	752	51	102
92	204	408	816	179	358	716	1432	1411	1369	1285
93	1117	781	109	218	436	872	291	582	1164	875
94	297	594	1188	923	393	786	119	238	476	952
95	451	902	351	702	1404	1355	1257	1061	669	1338
96	1223	993	533	1066	679	1358	1263	1073	693	1386
97	1319	1185	917	381	762	71	142	284	568	1136
98	819	185	370	740	27	54	108	216	432	864
99	275	550	1100	747	41	82	164	328	656	1312

P = 1453

INDICES

	0	1	2	3	4	5	6	7	8	9
100	102	764	224	481	340	120	32	873	1016	552
101	1183	801	1126	1202	749	408	164	208	1106	656
102	1437	262	1162	1309	10	576	707	1062	414	428
103	359	702	880	1445	870	405	1306	699	612	615
104	489	569	1115	786	677	195	1146	618	135	1393
105	1235	330	740	312	648	492	773	856	885	1078
106	218	957	548	572	565	852	963	80	587	93
107	366	1118	247	967	284	1099	1197	190	185	789
108	52	629	1265	256	440	446	601	680	112	84
109	1450	515	170	1418	104	198	1032	501	766	462
110	992	687	226	1149	532	591	483	526	319	794
111	342	621	1223	1351	122	663	715	930	34	138
112	1362	97	875	560	1027	271	1018	1396	276	1072
113	554	1283	1386	1249	1185	1238	979	370	803	349
114	1053	57	1128	333	1379	72	1204	1005	384	452
115	751	743	179	1122	410	673	214	1193	166	315
116	1023	1049	210	295	938	903	1108	651	325	251
117	658	1000	299	634	1439	495	1043	1256	264	304
118	894	836	1164	776	469	971	1311	1289	942	45
119	12	859	1401	1213	578	152	1138	734	709	888
120	398	288	1064	826	907	1270	416	1081	19	1321
121	430	639	27	607	361	221	1180	1103	704	867
122	1112	1232	882	960	281	1262	1447	763	480	119
123	872	551	800	1201	407	207	655	261	1308	575
124	1061	427	701	1444	404	698	614	568	785	194
125	617	1392	329	311	491	855	1077	956	571	851
126	79	92	1117	966	1098	189	788	628	255	445
127	679	83	514	1417	197	500	461	686	1148	590
128	525	793	620	1350	662	929	137	96	559	270
129	1395	1071	1282	1248	1237	369	348	56	332	71
130	1004	451	742	1121	672	1192	314	1048	294	902
131	650	250	999	633	494	1255	303	835	775	970
132	1288	44	858	1212	151	733	887	287	825	1269
133	1080	1320	638	606	220	1102	866	1231	959	1261
134	762	118	550	1200	206	260	574	426	1443	697
135	567	193	1391	310	854	955	850	91	965	188
136	627	444	82	1416	499	685	589	792	1349	928
137	95	269	1070	1247	368	55	70	450	1120	1191
138	1047	901	249	632	1254	834	969	43	1211	732
139	286	1268	1319	605	1101	1230	1260	117	1199	259
140	425	696	192	309	954	90	187	443	1415	684
141	791	927	268	1246	54	449	1190	900	631	833
142	42	731	1267	604	1229	116	258	695	308	89
143	442	683	926	1245	448	899	832	730	603	115
144	694	88	682	1244	898	729	114	87	1243	728
145	86	727	726							

POWER RESIDUES

	0	1	2	3	4	5	6	7	8	9
100	1171	889	325	650	1300	1147	841	229	458	916
101	379	758	63	126	252	504	1008	563	1126	799
102	145	290	580	1160	867	281	562	1124	795	137
103	274	548	1096	739	25	50	100	200	400	800
104	147	294	588	1176	899	345	690	1380	1307	1161
105	869	285	570	1140	827	201	402	804	155	310
106	620	1240	1027	601	1202	951	449	898	343	686
107	1372	1291	1129	805	157	314	628	1256	1059	665
108	1330	1207	961	469	938	423	846	239	478	956
109	459	918	383	766	79	158	316	632	1264	1075
110	697	1394	1335	1217	981	509	1018	583	1166	879
111	305	610	1220	987	521	1042	631	1262	1071	689
112	1378	1303	1153	853	253	506	1012	571	1142	831
113	209	418	836	219	438	876	299	598	1196	939
114	425	850	247	494	988	523	1046	639	1278	1103
115	753	53	106	212	424	848	243	486	972	491
116	982	511	1022	591	1182	911	369	738	23	46
117	92	184	368	736	19	38	76	152	304	608
118	1216	979	505	1010	567	1134	815	177	354	708
119	1416	1379	1305	1157	861	269	538	1076	699	1398
120	1343	1233	1013	573	1146	839	225	450	900	347
121	694	1388	1323	1193	933	413	826	199	398	796
122	139	278	556	1112	771	89	178	356	712	1424
123	1395	1337	1221	989	525	1050	647	1294	1135	817
124	181	362	724	1448	1443	1433	1413	1373	1293	1133
125	813	173	346	692	1384	1315	1177	901	349	698
126	1396	1339	1225	997	541	1082	711	1422	1391	1329
127	1205	957	461	922	391	782	111	222	444	888
128	323	646	1292	1131	809	165	330	660	1320	1187
129	921	389	778	103	206	412	824	195	390	780
130	107	214	428	856	259	518	1036	619	1238	1023
131	593	1186	919	385	770	87	174	348	696	1392
132	1331	1209	965	477	954	455	910	367	734	15
133	30	60	120	240	480	960	467	934	415	830
134	207	414	828	203	406	812	171	342	684	1368
135	1283	1113	773	93	186	372	744	35	70	140
136	280	560	1120	787	121	242	484	968	483	966
137	479	958	463	926	399	798	143	286	572	1144
138	835	217	434	868	283	566	1132	811	169	338
139	676	1352	1251	1049	645	1290	1127	801	149	298
140	596	1192	931	409	818	183	366	732	11	22
141	44	88	176	352	704	1408	1363	1273	1093	733
142	13	26	52	104	208	416	832	211	422	844
143	235	470	940	427	854	255	510	1020	587	1174
144	895	337	674	1348	1243	1033	613	1226	999	545
145	1090	727								

P = 1459

INDICES

	0	1	2	3	4	5	6	7	8	9
0		0	723	1	1446	798	724	1176	711	2
1	63	958	1447	1036	441	799	1434	915	725	770
2	786	1177	223	1072	712	138	301	3	1164	1328
3	64	1351	699	959	180	516	1448	1126	35	1037
4	51	925	442	1279	946	800	337	101	1435	894
5	861	916	1024	432	726	298	429	771	593	1296
6	787	86	616	1178	1422	376	224	576	903	1073
7	1239	980	713	672	391	139	758	676	302	1130
8	774	4	190	1249	1165	255	544	1329	211	1269
9	65	754	1060	1352	824	110	700	1376	159	960
10	126	1088	181	1203	289	517	1155	596	1449	135
11	1021	1127	1152	485	36	412	1316	1038	561	633
12	52	458	809	926	1339	936	443	387	687	1280
13	1099	496	947	488	1299	801	168	477	338	281
14	504	102	245	536	1436	668	1395	895	1114	1288
15	862	853	23	917	1399	691	1025	1064	395	433
16	39	790	727	709	913	299	514	944	430	614
17	978	772	1267	157	594	1314	934	1297	534	21
18	788	976	19	87	325	466	617	415	89	1179
19	833	362	1423	1002	641	377	882	327	225	1235
20	849	577	353	1046	904	265	468	1074	1012	270
21	1240	1007	420	981	1319	619	714	1069	858	673
22	286	493	392	463	417	140	1208	1381	759	260
23	1135	677	581	91	303	899	1284	1131	1356	143
24	775	1041	1181	5	74	234	191	348	604	1250
25	201	835	1166	572	1110	256	1410	525	545	844
26	364	1330	1219	1367	212	1230	1211	1270	564	1425
27	66	220	891	755	1200	1096	1061	322	1004	1353
28	1227	657	825	877	968	111	1259	643	701	372
29	1391	1377	660	1384	160	636	379	961	553	650
30	127	997	118	1089	746	884	182	1418	664	1204
31	1414	1360	290	357	329	518	1118	1103	1156	828
32	762	597	55	227	1450	1174	1432	136	178	1277
33	1022	84	1237	1128	209	1374	1153	410	1337	486
34	243	851	37	612	532	413	880	263	1317	461
35	579	1039	199	842	562	320	1257	634	744	355
36	53	82	241	459	742	12	810	14	1048	927
37	1189	150	1340	971	1138	937	812	906	444	783
38	98	388	1085	684	688	16	267	1281	1364	1388
39	1100	529	147	497	1050	470	948	1292	500	489
40	114	680	1300	929	1076	802	311	626	169	1309
41	988	478	1191	1014	339	589	277	282	993	1081
42	505	152	272	103	1143	1053	246	1262	584	537
43	1342	1242	1437	767	334	669	123	384	1396	973
44	1009	896	1216	369	1115	609	1186	1289	1140	422
45	863	425	473	854	646	94	24	939	983	918
46	400	28	1400	509	1304	692	814	1321	1026	294
47	164	1065	549	779	396	908	621	434	866	951
48	40	704	306	791	446	716	728	722	797	710
49	957	440	914	785	1071	300	1327	698	515	34

POWER RESIDUES

	0	1	2	3	4	5	6	7	8	9
0	1	3	9	27	81	243	729	728	725	716
1	689	608	365	1095	367	1101	385	1155	547	182
2	546	179	537	152	456	1368	1186	640	461	1383
3	1231	775	866	1139	499	38	114	342	1026	160
4	480	1440	1402	1288	946	1379	1219	739	758	815
5	986	40	120	360	1080	322	966	1439	1399	1279
6	919	1298	976	10	30	90	270	810	971	1454
7	1444	1414	1324	1054	244	732	737	752	797	932
8	1337	1093	361	1083	331	993	61	183	549	188
9	564	233	699	638	455	1365	1177	613	380	1140
10	502	47	141	423	1269	889	1208	706	659	518
11	95	285	855	1106	400	1200	682	587	302	906
12	1259	859	1118	436	1308	1006	100	300	900	1241
13	805	956	1409	1309	1009	109	327	981	25	75
14	225	675	566	239	717	692	617	392	1176	610
15	371	1113	421	1263	871	1154	544	173	519	98
16	294	882	1187	643	470	1410	1312	1018	136	408
17	1224	754	803	950	1391	1255	847	1082	328	984
18	34	102	306	918	1295	967	1442	1408	1306	1000
19	82	246	738	755	806	959	1418	1336	1090	352
20	1056	250	750	791	914	1283	931	1334	1084	334
21	1002	88	264	792	917	1292	958	1415	1327	1063
22	271	813	980	22	66	198	594	323	969	1448
23	1426	1360	1162	568	245	735	746	779	878	1175
24	607	362	1086	340	1020	142	426	1278	916	1289
25	949	1388	1246	820	1001	85	255	765	836	1049
26	229	687	602	347	1041	205	615	386	1158	556
27	209	627	422	1266	880	1181	625	416	1248	826
28	1019	139	417	1251	835	1046	220	660	521	104
29	312	936	1349	1129	469	1407	1303	991	55	165
30	495	26	78	234	702	647	482	1446	1420	1342
31	1108	406	1218	736	749	788	905	1256	850	1091
32	355	1065	277	831	1034	184	552	197	591	314
33	942	1367	1183	631	434	1302	988	46	138	414
34	1242	808	965	1436	1390	1252	838	1055	247	741
35	764	833	1040	202	606	359	1077	313	939	1358
36	1156	550	191	573	260	780	881	1184	634	443
37	1329	1069	289	867	1142	508	65	195	585	296
38	888	1205	697	632	437	1311	1015	127	381	1143
39	511	74	222	666	539	158	474	1422	1348	1126
40	460	1380	1222	748	785	896	1229	769	848	1085
41	337	1011	115	345	1035	187	561	224	672	557
42	212	636	449	1347	1123	451	1353	1141	505	56
43	168	504	53	159	477	1431	1375	1207	703	650
44	491	14	42	126	378	1134	484	1452	1438	1396
45	1270	892	1217	733	740	761	824	1013	121	363
46	1089	349	1047	223	669	548	185	555	206	618
47	395	1185	637	452	1356	1150	532	137	411	1233
48	781	884	1193	661	524	113	339	1017	133	399
49	1197	673	560	221	663	530	131	393	1179	619

P = 1459

INDICES

	0	1	2	3	4	5	6	7	8	9
50	924	945	100	860	431	428	1295	615	375	902
51	979	390	675	773	1248	543	1268	1059	109	158
52	1087	288	595	1020	484	1315	632	808	935	686
53	495	1298	476	503	535	1394	1287	22	690	394
54	789	912	943	977	156	933	20	18	465	88
55	361	640	326	848	1045	467	269	419	618	857
56	492	416	1380	1134	90	1283	142	1180	233	603
57	834	1109	524	363	1366	1210	1424	890	1095	1003
58	656	967	642	1390	1383	378	649	117	883	663
59	1359	328	1102	761	226	1431	1276	1236	1373	1336
60	850	531	262	578	841	1256	354	240	11	1047
61	149	1137	905	97	683	266	1387	146	469	499
62	679	1075	625	987	1013	276	1080	271	1052	583
63	1241	333	383	1008	368	1185	421	472	93	982
64	27	1303	1320	163	778	620	950	305	715	796
65	439	1070	697	923	859	1294	901	674	542	108
66	287	483	807	494	502	1286	393	942	932	464
67	639	1044	418	491	1133	141	602	523	1209	1094
68	966	1382	116	1358	760	1275	1335	261	1255	10
69	1136	682	145	678	986	1079	582	382	1184	92
70	1302	777	304	438	922	900	107	806	1285	931
71	1043	1132	522	965	1357	1334	9	144	1078	1183
72	776	921	805	1042	964	8	1182	804	7	6
73	735	736	75	453	737	235	313	76	192	47
74	454	349	873	738	605	628	236	1251	403	314
75	202	556	77	836	171	193	1167	1033	48	573
76	821	455	1111	1311	350	257	1407	874	1411	407
77	739	526	990	606	546	31	629	845	653	237
78	365	480	1252	1331	870	404	1220	1147	315	1368
79	1193	203	213	1122	557	1231	1223	78	1212	1016
80	837	1271	1403	172	565	130	194	1426	341	1168
81	67	1444	1034	221	1349	49	892	591	574	756
82	253	822	1201	1150	456	1097	279	1112	1062	512
83	1312	323	1000	351	1005	284	258	1354	346	1408
84	1228	1198	875	658	995	1412	826	176	408	878
85	318	740	969	1083	527	112	1307	991	1260	121
86	607	644	507	547	702	955	32	373	1057	630
87	1392	154	846	1378	1107	654	661	1371	238	1385
88	274	366	161	695	481	637	1092	1253	380	105
89	1332	962	451	871	554	819	405	651	1145	1221
90	128	1347	1148	998	1196	316	119	1055	1369	1090
91	817	1194	747	749	204	885	248	214	183	60
92	1123	1419	751	558	665	1264	1232	1205	569	1224
93	1415	206	79	1361	586	1213	291	1324	1017	358
94	887	838	330	539	1272	519	44	1404	1119	250
95	173	1104	1344	566	1157	1160	131	829	216	195
96	763	1244	1427	598	1029	342	56	185	1169	228
97	1439	68	1451	1457	1445	1175	62	1035	1433	769
98	222	137	1163	1350	179	1125	50	1278	336	893
99	1023	297	592	85	1421	575	1238	671	757	1129

POWER RESIDUES

	0	1	2	3	4	5	6	7	8	9
50	398	1194	664	533	140	420	1260	862	1127	463
51	1389	1249	829	1028	166	498	35	105	315	945
52	1376	1210	712	677	572	257	771	854	1103	391
53	1173	601	344	1032	178	534	143	429	1287	943
54	1370	1192	658	515	86	258	774	863	1130	472
55	1416	1330	1072	298	894	1223	751	794	923	1310
56	1012	118	354	1062	268	804	953	1400	1282	928
57	1325	1057	253	759	818	995	67	201	603	350
58	1050	232	696	629	428	1284	934	1343	1111	415
59	1245	817	992	58	174	522	107	321	963	1430
60	1372	1198	676	569	248	744	773	860	1121	445
61	1335	1087	343	1029	169	507	62	186	558	215
62	645	476	1428	1366	1180	622	407	1221	745	776
63	869	1148	526	119	357	1071	295	885	1196	670
64	551	194	582	287	861	1124	454	1362	1168	586
65	299	897	1232	778	875	1166	580	281	843	1070
66	292	876	1169	589	308	924	1313	1021	145	435
67	1305	997	73	219	657	512	77	231	693	620
68	401	1203	691	614	383	1149	529	128	384	1152
69	538	155	465	1395	1267	883	1190	652	497	32
70	96	288	864	1133	481	1443	1411	1315	1027	163
71	489	8	24	72	216	648	485	1455	1447	1423
72	1351	1135	487	2	6	18	54	162	486	1458
73	1456	1450	1432	1378	1216	730	731	734	743	770
74	851	1094	364	1092	358	1074	304	912	1277	913
75	1280	922	1307	1003	91	273	819	998	76	228
76	684	593	320	960	1421	1345	1117	433	1299	979
77	19	57	171	513	80	240	720	701	644	473
78	1419	1339	1099	379	1137	493	20	60	180	540
79	161	483	1449	1429	1369	1189	649	488	5	15
80	45	135	405	1215	727	722	707	662	527	122
81	366	1098	376	1128	466	1398	1276	910	1271	895
82	1226	760	821	1004	94	282	846	1079	319	957
83	1412	1318	1036	190	570	251	753	800	941	1364
84	1174	604	353	1059	259	777	872	1157	553	200
85	600	341	1023	151	453	1359	1159	559	218	654
86	503	50	150	450	1350	1132	478	1434	1384	1234
87	784	893	1220	742	767	842	1067	283	849	1088
88	346	1038	196	588	305	915	1286	940	1361	1165
89	577	272	816	989	49	147	441	1323	1051	235
90	705	656	509	68	204	612	377	1131	475	1425
91	1357	1153	541	164	492	17	51	153	459	1377
92	1213	721	704	653	500	41	123	369	1107	403
93	1209	709	668	545	176	528	125	375	1125	457
94	1371	1195	667	542	167	501	44	132	396	1188
95	646	479	1437	1393	1261	865	1136	490	11	33
96	99	297	891	1214	724	713	680	581	284	852
97	1097	373	1119	439	1317	1033	181	543	170	510
98	71	213	639	458	1374	1204	694	623	410	1230
99	772	857	1112	418	1254	844	1073	301	903	1250

P = 1459

INDICES

	0	1	2	3	4	5	6	7	8	9
100	189	254	210	753	823	1375	125	1202	1154	134
101	1151	411	560	457	1338	386	1098	487	167	280
102	244	667	1113	852	1398	1063	38	708	513	613
103	1266	1313	533	975	324	414	832	1001	881	1234
104	352	264	1011	1006	1318	1068	285	462	1207	259
105	580	898	1355	1040	73	347	200	571	1409	843
106	1218	1229	563	219	1199	321	1226	876	1258	371
107	659	635	552	996	745	1417	1413	356	1117	827
108	54	1173	177	83	208	409	242	611	879	460
109	198	319	743	81	741	13	1188	970	811	782
110	1084	15	1363	528	1049	1291	113	928	310	1308
111	1190	588	992	151	1142	1261	1341	766	122	972
112	1215	608	1139	424	645	938	399	508	813	293
113	548	907	865	703	445	721	956	784	1326	33
114	99	427	374	389	1247	1058	1086	1019	631	685
115	475	1393	689	911	155	17	360	847	268	856
116	1379	1282	232	1108	1365	889	655	1389	648	662
117	1101	1430	1372	530	840	239	148	96	1386	498
118	624	275	1051	332	367	471	26	162	949	795
119	696	1293	541	482	501	941	638	490	601	1093
120	115	1274	1254	681	985	381	1301	437	106	930
121	521	1333	1077	920	963	803	734	452	312	46
122	872	627	402	555	170	1032	820	1310	1406	406
123	989	30	652	479	869	1146	1192	1121	1222	1015
124	1402	129	340	1443	1348	590	252	1149	278	511
125	999	283	345	1197	994	175	317	1082	1306	120
126	506	954	1056	153	1106	1370	273	694	1091	104
127	450	818	1144	1346	1195	1054	816	748	247	59
128	750	1263	568	205	585	1323	886	538	43	249
129	1343	1159	215	1243	1028	184	1438	1456	61	768
130	1162	1124	335	296	1420	670	188	752	124	133
131	559	385	166	666	1397	707	1265	974	831	1233
132	1010	1067	1206	897	72	570	1217	218	1225	370
133	551	1416	1116	1172	207	610	197	80	1187	781
134	1362	1290	309	587	1141	765	1214	423	398	292
135	864	720	1325	426	1246	1018	474	910	359	855
136	231	888	647	1429	839	95	623	331	25	794
137	540	940	600	1273	984	436	520	919	733	45
138	401	1031	1405	29	868	1120	1401	1442	251	510
139	344	174	1305	953	1105	693	449	1345	815	58
140	567	1322	42	1158	1027	1455	1161	295	187	132
141	165	706	830	1066	71	217	550	1171	196	780
142	308	764	397	719	1245	909	230	1428	622	793
143	599	435	732	1030	867	1441	343	952	448	57
144	41	1454	186	705	70	1170	307	718	229	792
145	731	1440	447	1453	69	717	730	1452	729	

POWER RESIDUES

	0	1	2	3	4	5	6	7	8	9
100	832	1037	193	579	278	834	1043	211	633	440
101	1320	1042	208	624	413	1239	799	938	1355	1147
102	523	110	330	990	52	156	468	1404	1294	964
103	1433	1381	1225	757	812	977	13	39	117	351
104	1053	241	723	710	671	554	203	609	368	1104
105	394	1182	628	425	1275	907	1262	868	1145	517
106	92	276	828	1025	157	471	1413	1321	1045	217
107	651	494	23	69	207	621	404	1212	718	695
108	626	419	1257	853	1100	382	1146	520	101	303
109	909	1268	886	1199	679	578	275	825	1016	130
110	390	1170	592	317	951	1394	1264	874	1163	571
111	254	762	827	1022	148	444	1332	1078	316	948
112	1385	1237	793	920	1301	985	37	111	333	999
113	79	237	711	674	563	230	690	611	374	1122
114	448	1344	1114	424	1272	898	1235	787	902	1247
115	823	1010	112	336	1008	106	318	954	1403	1291
116	955	1406	1300	982	28	84	252	756	809	968
117	1445	1417	1333	1081	325	975	7	21	63	189
118	567	242	726	719	698	635	446	1338	1096	370
119	1110	412	1236	790	911	1274	904	1253	841	1064
120	274	822	1007	103	309	927	1322	1048	226	678
121	575	266	798	935	1346	1120	442	1326	1060	262
122	786	899	1238	796	929	1328	1066	280	840	1061
123	265	795	926	1319	1039	199	597	332	996	70
124	210	630	431	1293	961	1424	1354	1144	514	83
125	249	747	782	887	1202	688	605	356	1068	286
126	858	1115	427	1281	925	1316	1030	172	516	89
127	267	801	944	1373	1201	685	596	329	987	43
128	129	387	1161	565	236	708	665	536	149	447
129	1341	1105	397	1191	655	506	59	177	531	134
130	402	1206	700	641	464	1392	1258	856	1109	409
131	1227	763	830	1031	175	525	116	348	1044	214
132	642	467	1401	1285	937	1352	1138	496	29	87
133	261	783	890	1211	715	686	599	338	1014	124
134	372	1116	430	1290	952	1397	1273	901	1244	814
135	983	31	93	279	837	1052	238	714	683	590
136	311	933	1340	1102	388	1164	574	263	789	908
137	1265	877	1172	598	335	1005	97	291	873	1160
138	562	227	681	584	293	879	1178	616	389	1167
139	583	290	870	1151	535	146	438	1314	1024	154
140	462	1386	1240	802	947	1382	1228	766	839	1058
141	256	768	845	1076	310	930	1331	1075	307	921
142	1304	994	64	192	576	269	807	962	1427	1363
143	1171	595	326	978	16	48	144	432	1296	970
144	1451	1435	1387	1243	811	974	4	12	36	108
145	324	972	1457	1453	1441	1405	1297	973		

P = 1471

INDICES

	0	1	2	3	4	5	6	7	8	9
0		0	1056	415	642	1228	1	1223	228	830
1	814	1276	1057	1341	809	173	1284	952	416	1404
2	400	168	862	1014	643	986	927	1245	395	331
3	1229	723	870	221	538	981	2	844	990	286
4	1456	1226	1224	1027	448	588	600	821	229	976
5	572	1367	513	946	831	1034	1451	349	1387	1126
6	815	1315	309	583	456	1099	1277	1023	124	1429
7	567	232	1058	141	430	1401	576	1029	1342	1295
8	1042	190	812	598	810	710	613	746	34	272
9	174	1094	186	1138	407	1162	1285	376	562	636
10	158	275	953	257	99	1396	532	436	417	225
11	620	1259	1037	450	1405	772	973	701	712	705
12	401	1082	901	171	1365	744	169	1359	42	1442
13	685	688	863	1157	609	1003	1180	196	1015	111
14	153	1236	1288	1147	644	89	1197	1391	16	590
15	987	942	162	312	615	481	928	1292	881	1361
16	628	767	1246	547	398	1449	184	40	396	1212
17	296	764	199	1253	332	739	1090	71	1328	793
18	1230	51	680	260	1242	602	724	758	1463	998
19	748	121	871	1383	1432	44	148	1168	222	854
20	1214	1438	1331	84	539	984	1313	374	1155	1210
21	982	248	118	647	22	785	3	476	1281	556
22	206	823	845	421	623	346	36	959	991	1110
23	358	1444	559	875	287	579	298	240	291	108
24	1457	250	668	605	487	734	1227	1275	951	1013
25	330	980	1225	820	945	1125	1098	231	1028	597
26	271	1161	274	435	449	704	743	687	195	1146
27	589	480	766	39	1252	792	601	120	1167	83
28	1209	784	822	958	874	107	733	979	230	434
29	1145	791	783	978	977	884	1072	1051	176	885
30	573	780	528	690	1218	1073	1368	698	201	672
31	67	1052	514	649	878	341	467	177	947	137
32	214	851	353	886	832	857	133	640	1454	574
33	1035	14	1240	204	1096	781	1452	264	798	865
34	1352	529	350	729	1255	1187	839	691	1388	24
35	325	1116	676	1219	1127	1460	914	1120	379	1074
36	816	1338	1107	27	266	1369	1316	508	828	586
37	188	699	310	996	344	1159	1049	202	584	1416
38	334	304	1177	673	457	787	969	387	1018	68
39	1100	496	1204	1103	754	1053	1278	59	440	102
40	800	515	1024	594	917	1418	1140	650	125	807
41	570	611	899	879	1430	356	741	526	796	342
42	568	5	1304	181	1174	468	233	1068	1078	92
43	371	178	1059	519	62	504	867	948	142	935
44	1262	336	409	138	431	30	7	1005	209	215
45	1402	1032	1092	1357	545	852	577	478	696	727
46	1414	354	1030	1132	145	896	461	887	1343	776
47	165	237	1354	833	1296	920	1347	306	1164	858
48	1043	715	1306	1182	254	134	191	1134	73	962
49	320	641	813	1283	861	394	537	1455	599	512

POWER RESIDUES

	0	1	2	3	4	5	6	7	8	9
0	1	6	36	216	1296	421	1055	446	1205	1346
1	721	1384	949	1281	331	515	148	888	915	1077
2	578	526	214	1284	349	623	796	363	707	1300
3	445	1199	1310	505	88	528	226	1356	781	273
4	167	1002	128	768	195	1170	1136	932	1179	1190
5	1256	181	1086	632	850	687	1180	1196	1292	397
6	911	1053	434	1133	914	1071	542	310	389	863
7	765	177	1062	488	1457	1387	967	1389	979	1461
8	1411	1111	782	279	203	1218	1424	1189	1250	145
9	870	807	429	1103	734	1462	1417	1147	998	104
10	624	802	399	923	1125	866	783	285	239	1434
11	1249	139	834	591	604	682	1150	1016	212	1272
12	277	191	1146	992	68	408	977	1449	1339	679
13	1132	908	1035	326	485	1439	1279	319	443	1187
14	1238	73	438	1157	1058	464	1313	523	196	1176
15	1172	1148	1004	140	840	627	820	507	100	600
16	658	1006	152	912	1059	470	1349	739	21	126
17	756	123	738	15	90	540	298	317	431	1115
18	806	423	1067	518	166	996	92	552	370	749
19	81	486	1445	1315	535	268	137	822	519	172
20	1032	308	377	791	333	527	220	1320	565	448
21	1217	1418	1153	1034	320	449	1223	1454	1369	859
22	741	33	198	1188	1244	109	654	982	8	48
23	288	257	71	426	1085	626	814	471	1355	775
24	237	1422	1177	1178	1184	1220	1436	1261	211	1266
25	241	1446	1321	571	484	1433	1243	103	618	766
26	183	1098	704	1282	337	551	364	713	1336	661
27	1024	260	89	534	262	101	606	694	1222	1448
28	1333	643	916	1083	614	742	39	234	1404	1069
29	530	238	1428	1213	1394	1009	170	1020	236	1416
30	1141	962	1359	799	381	815	477	1391	991	62
31	372	761	153	918	1095	686	1174	1160	1076	572
32	490	1469	1459	1399	1039	350	629	832	579	532
33	250	29	174	1044	380	809	441	1175	1166	1112
34	788	315	419	1043	374	773	225	1350	745	57
35	342	581	544	322	461	1295	415	1019	230	1380
36	925	1137	938	1215	1406	1081	602	670	1078	584
37	562	430	1109	770	207	1242	97	582	550	358
38	677	1120	836	603	676	1114	800	387	851	693
39	1216	1412	1117	818	495	28	168	1008	164	984
40	20	120	720	1378	913	1065	506	94	564	442
41	1181	1202	1328	613	736	3	18	108	648	946
42	1263	223	1338	673	1096	692	1210	1376	901	993
43	74	444	1193	1274	289	263	107	642	910	1047
44	398	917	1089	650	958	1335	655	988	44	264
45	113	678	1126	872	819	501	64	384	833	585
46	568	466	1325	595	628	826	543	316	425	1079
47	590	598	646	934	1191	1262	217	1302	457	1271
48	271	155	930	1167	1118	824	531	244	1464	1429
49	1219	1430	1225	1466	1441	1291	391	875	837	609

P = 1471

INDICES

	0	1	2	3	4	5	6	7	8	9
50	1386	455	566	575	811	33	406	157	531	1036
51	711	1364	684	1179	1287	15	614	627	183	198
52	1327	1241	747	147	1330	1154	21	205	35	558
53	290	486	329	1097	273	194	1251	1208	732	782
54	175	1217	66	466	352	1453	1095	1351	838	675
55	378	265	187	1048	1176	1017	753	799	1139	898
56	795	1173	370	866	408	208	544	1413	460	1353
57	1163	253	319	536	565	530	1286	1326	20	328
58	731	351	377	752	369	459	564	730	563	657
59	470	113	658	1256	637	463	1232	1269	471	1188
60	159	825	366	383	114	840	276	1380	804	499
61	659	692	954	413	284	1399	1257	1389	258	554
62	1123	789	638	25	100	502	235	155	464	326
63	1397	889	53	663	1233	1117	533	847	1193	1062
64	1270	677	437	281	1409	1200	472	1220	418	932
65	443	891	1189	1128	226	446	1040	971	160	1461
66	621	269	1070	1238	826	915	1260	1345	682	836
67	367	1121	1038	423	1320	761	384	380	451	129
68	938	1374	115	1075	1406	1424	315	55	841	817
69	773	1421	425	389	277	1339	974	708	1080	1290
70	1381	1108	702	778	262	994	805	28	713	625
71	1046	655	500	267	706	905	1435	523	660	1370
72	402	10	924	665	693	1317	1083	631	1322	1020
73	955	509	902	907	94	1149	414	829	172	167
74	1244	220	285	587	1366	348	582	1428	1400	189
75	745	1137	635	1395	1258	700	170	1441	1002	1235
76	1390	311	1360	1448	763	70	259	997	43	1437
77	373	646	555	345	1443	239	604	1012	1124	1160
78	686	38	82	106	790	1050	689	671	340	850
79	639	203	864	1186	1115	1119	26	585	1158	303
80	386	1102	101	1417	610	525	180	91	503	335
81	1004	1356	726	895	236	305	1181	961	393	454
82	156	1178	197	1153	485	1207	465	674	1016	1172
83	1412	535	327	458	112	1268	382	498	1398	788
84	154	662	1061	1199	890	970	1237	835	760	1373
85	54	388	1289	993	654	522	664	1019	1148	219
86	1427	1394	1234	69	645	1011	105	849	1118	1101
87	90	894	453	1206	534	497	1198	1372	521	1393
88	848	1205	1392	1298	1465	1299	1194	1104	17	1112
89	1086	1466	1063	755	591	551	1265	1300	1271	1054
90	988	428	618	1195	678	1279	943	1143	131	1105
91	438	60	163	404	64	18	282	441	313	922
92	1000	1113	1410	103	616	360	718	1087	1201	801
93	482	910	47	1467	473	516	929	1008	362	1064
94	1221	1025	1293	770	940	756	419	595	882	12
95	506	592	933	918	1362	1349	750	552	444	1419
96	629	1446	301	1266	892	1141	768	76	1310	1301
97	1190	651	1247	1334	720	1272	1129	126	548	78
98	1376	1055	227	808	399	926	869	989	447	571
99	1450	308	123	429	1041	612	185	561	98	619

POWER RESIDUES

	0	1	2	3	4	5	6	7	8	9
50	712	1330	625	808	435	1139	950	1287	367	731
51	1444	1309	499	52	312	401	935	1197	1298	433
52	1127	878	855	717	1360	805	417	1031	302	341
53	575	508	106	636	874	831	573	496	34	204
54	1224	1460	1405	1075	566	454	1253	163	978	1455
55	1375	895	957	1329	619	772	219	1314	529	232
56	1392	997	98	588	586	574	502	70	420	1049
57	410	989	50	300	329	503	76	456	1265	235
58	1410	1105	746	63	378	797	369	743	45	270
59	149	894	951	1293	403	947	1269	259	83	498
60	46	276	185	1110	776	243	1458	1393	1003	134
61	804	411	995	86	516	154	924	1131	902	999
62	110	660	1018	224	1344	709	1312	517	160	960
63	1347	727	1420	1165	1106	752	99	594	622	790
64	327	491	4	24	144	864	771	213	1278	313
65	407	971	1413	1123	854	711	1324	589	592	610
66	718	1366	841	633	856	723	1396	1021	242	1452
67	1357	787	309	383	827	549	352	641	904	1011
68	182	1092	668	1066	512	130	780	267	131	786
69	303	347	611	724	1402	1057	458	1277	307	371
70	755	117	702	1270	265	119	714	1342	697	1240
71	85	510	118	708	1306	481	1415	1135	926	1143
72	974	1431	1231	31	186	1116	812	459	1283	343
73	587	580	538	286	245	1470	1465	1435	1255	175
74	1050	416	1025	266	125	750	87	522	190	1140
75	956	1323	583	556	394	893	945	1257	187	1122
76	848	675	1108	764	171	1026	272	161	966	1383
77	943	1245	115	690	1198	1304	469	1343	703	1276
78	301	335	539	292	281	215	1290	385	839	621
79	784	291	275	179	1074	560	418	1037	338	557
80	400	929	1161	1082	608	706	1294	409	983	14
81	84	504	82	492	10	60	360	689	1192	1268
82	253	47	282	221	1326	601	664	1042	368	737
83	9	54	324	473	1367	847	669	1072	548	346
84	605	688	1186	1232	37	222	1332	637	880	867
85	789	321	455	1259	199	1194	1280	325	479	1403
86	1063	494	22	132	792	339	563	436	1145	986
87	32	192	1152	1028	284	233	1398	1033	314	413
88	1007	158	948	1275	295	299	323	467	1331	631
89	844	651	964	1371	871	813	465	1319	559	412
90	1001	122	732	1450	1345	715	1348	733	1456	1381
91	931	1173	1154	1040	356	665	1048	404	953	1305
92	475	1379	919	1101	722	1390	985	26	156	936
93	1203	1334	649	952	1299	439	1163	1094	680	1138
94	944	1251	151	906	1023	254	53	318	437	1151
95	1022	248	17	102	612	730	1438	1273	283	227
96	1362	817	489	1463	1423	1183	1214	1400	1045	386
97	845	657	1000	116	696	1234	49	294	293	287
98	251	35	210	1260	205	1230	25	150	900	987
99	38	228	1368	853	705	1288	373	767	189	1134

P = 1471

INDICES

	0	1	2	3	4	5	6	7	8	9
100	972	900	41	608	152	1196	161	880	397	295
101	1089	679	1462	1431	1213	1312	117	1280	622	357
102	297	667	950	944	270	742	765	1166	873	1144
103	1071	527	200	877	213	132	1239	797	1254	324
104	913	1106	827	343	333	968	1203	439	916	569
105	740	1303	1077	61	1261	6	1091	695	144	164
106	1346	1305	72	860	1385	405	683	182	1329	289
107	1250	65	837	1175	794	543	318	19	368	469
108	1231	365	803	283	1122	234	52	1192	1408	442
109	1039	1069	681	1319	937	314	424	1079	261	1045
110	1434	923	1321	93	1243	581	634	1001	762	372
111	603	81	339	1114	385	179	725	392	484	1411
112	381	1060	759	653	1426	104	452	520	1464	1085
113	1264	617	130	63	999	717	46	361	939	505
114	749	300	1309	719	1375	868	122	97	151	1088
115	116	949	872	212	912	1202	1076	143	1384	1249
116	317	802	1407	936	1433	633	338	483	1425	1263
117	45	1308	150	911	316	337	149	242	243	48
118	56	410	1169	965	244	1468	842	139	223	87
119	49	474	818	432	855	1336	57	517	774	31
120	1215	1324	411	930	1422	8	1439	1184	1170	1009
121	426	1006	1332	293	966	363	390	210	85	490
122	245	1065	278	216	540	492	1469	1222	1340	1403
123	985	722	843	1026	975	1033	1314	1022	140	1294
124	709	1093	375	256	224	771	1081	1358	1156	110
125	88	941	1291	546	1211	738	50	757	1382	853
126	983	247	475	420	1109	578	249	1274	819	596
127	703	479	119	957	433	883	779	697	648	136
128	856	13	263	728	23	1459	1337	507	995	1415
129	786	495	58	593	806	355	4	1067	518	934
130	29	1031	477	1131	775	919	714	1133	1282	511
131	32	1363	626	146	557	193	1216	1350	1047	897
132	207	252	1325	751	656	462	824	1379	412	553
133	501	888	846	280	931	445	268	1344	422	128
134	1423	1420	707	777	624	904	9	630	906	166
135	347	1136	1440	1447	1436	238	37	670	1185	302
136	524	1355	960	1152	1171	1267	661	834	992	218
137	1010	893	1371	1297	1111	550	427	1142	403	921
138	359	909	1007	769	11	1348	1445	75	1333	77
139	925	307	560	607	294	1311	666	1165	876	323
140	967	1302	694	859	288	542	364	1191	1318	1044
141	580	80	391	652	1084	716	299	96	211	1248
142	632	1307	241	964	86	1335	1323	1183	292	489
143	491	721	1021	255	109	737	246	1273	956	135
144	1458	494	1066	1130	510	192	251	1378	279	127
145	903	1135	669	1151	217	549	908	74	606	322
146	541	79	95	963	488	736	493	1377	1150	321
147	735	0								

POWER RESIDUES

	0	1	2	3	4	5	6	7	8	9
100	920	1107	758	135	810	447	1211	1382	937	1209
101	1370	865	777	249	23	138	828	555	388	857
102	729	1432	1237	67	402	941	1233	43	258	77
103	462	1301	451	1235	55	330	509	112	672	1090
104	656	994	80	480	1409	1099	710	1318	553	376
105	785	297	311	395	899	981	2	12	72	432
106	1121	842	639	892	939	1221	1442	1297	427	1091
107	662	1030	296	305	359	683	1156	1052	428	1097
108	698	1246	121	726	1414	1129	890	927	1149	1010
109	176	1056	452	1241	91	546	334	533	256	65
110	390	869	801	393	887	909	1041	362	701	1264
111	229	1374	889	921	1113	794	351	635	868	795
112	357	671	1084	620	778	255	59	354	653	976
113	1443	1303	463	1307	487	1451	1351	751	93	558
114	406	965	1377	907	1029	290	269	143	858	735
115	1468	1453	1363	823	525	208	1248	133	798	375
116	779	261	95	570	478	1397	1027	278	197	1182
117	1208	1364	829	561	424	1073	554	382	821	513
118	136	816	483	1427	1207	1358	793	345	599	652
119	970	1407	1087	638	886	903	1005	146	876	843
120	645	928	1155	1046	392	881	873	825	537	280
121	209	1254	169	1014	200	1200	1316	541	304	353
122	647	940	1227	7	42	252	41	246	5	30
123	180	1080	596	634	862	759	141	846	663	1036
124	332	521	184	1104	740	27	162	972	1419	1159
125	1070	536	274	173	1038	344	593	616	754	111
126	666	1054	440	1169	1130	896	963	1365	835	597
127	640	898	975	1437	1267	247	11	66	396	905
128	1017	218	1308	493	16	96	576	514	142	852
129	699	1252	157	942	1239	79	474	1373	883	885
130	897	969	1401	1051	422	1061	482	1421	1171	1142
131	968	1395	1015	206	1236	61	366	725	1408	1093
132	674	1102	728	1426	1201	1322	577	520	178	1068
133	524	202	1212	1388	973	1425	1195	1286	361	695
134	1228	13	78	468	1337	667	1060	476	1385	955
135	1317	547	340	569	472	1361	811	453	1247	127
136	762	159	954	1311	511	124	744	51	306	365
137	719	1372	877	849	681	1144	980	1467	1447	1327
138	607	700	1258	193	1158	1064	500	58	348	617
139	760	147	882	879	861	753	105	630	838	615
140	748	75	450	1229	19	114	684	1162	1088	644
141	922	1119	830	567	460	1289	379	803	405	959
142	1341	691	1204	1340	685	1168	1124	860	747	69
143	414	1013	194	1164	1100	716	1354	769	201	1206
144	1352	757	129	774	231	1386	961	1353	763	165
145	990	56	336	545	328	497	40	240	1440	1285
146	355	659	1012	188	1128	884	891	933	1185	1226
147										

P = 1481

INDICES

	0	1	2	3	4	5	6	7	8	9
0		0	1268	1	1056	1118	1269	624	844	2
1	906	1415	1057	240	412	1119	632	340	1270	1451
2	694	625	1203	534	845	756	28	3	200	187
3	907	1471	420	1416	128	262	1058	258	1239	241
4	482	800	413	583	991	1120	322	114	633	1248
5	544	341	1296	1281	1271	1053	1468	1452	1455	1253
6	695	235	1259	626	208	1358	1204	161	1396	535
7	50	281	846	671	46	757	1027	559	29	723
8	270	4	588	450	201	1458	371	188	779	80
9	908	864	110	1472	1382	1089	421	1129	1036	1417
10	332	489	129	569	1084	263	1069	1408	1059	708
11	841	259	1256	77	1240	172	1243	242	1041	964
12	483	1350	23	801	1047	394	414	1006	1476	584
13	1146	1287	992	595	1429	1121	1184	93	323	698
14	1318	115	69	175	634	1305	459	1249	1314	576
15	545	761	815	342	347	1109	1297	654	511	1282
16	58	1158	1272	1150	376	1054	238	1201	1469	480
17	1246	1453	159	1025	1456	1380	567	1254	1348	1144
18	696	1312	652	236	1378	1376	1260	275	1170	627
19	877	750	209	1262	917	1359	824	245	1205	895
20	120	162	277	811	1397	438	357	536	872	1386
21	51	1172	857	282	1196	221	847	615	496	672
22	629	580	47	1126	1044	758	1345	435	1028	879
23	1440	560	1031	1401	30	1232	829	724	752	1065
24	271	1213	1138	5	1291	886	589	211	835	451
25	182	967	202	469	794	1459	1264	446	372	882
26	934	189	1075	1340	780	919	383	81	1217	806
27	909	36	972	865	1361	691	111	43	486	1473
28	1106	649	1383	826	1337	1090	1443	1424	422	680
29	1093	1130	247	254	1037	891	1102	1418	364	774
30	333	1207	549	490	603	1353	130	153	135	570
31	897	408	1085	563	442	264	299	1446	1070	122
32	1326	1409	946	311	1060	996	938	709	164	738
33	842	338	26	260	989	1279	1257	279	268	78
34	1034	1406	1241	392	1427	173	813	1156	1244	1142
35	1168	243	355	219	1042	1399	1136	965	932	804
36	484	1422	1100	1351	440	309	24	1404	1166	802
37	1164	425	1048	359	63	395	958	427	415	686
38	665	1007	538	765	1477	197	1050	585	705	1181
39	1147	874	612	1288	33	361	993	352	683	596
40	1388	1225	1430	231	65	1122	599	193	1185	53
41	226	94	145	397	324	88	660	699	1174	303
42	1319	1235	960	116	645	1096	70	859	984	176
43	9	429	635	1391	403	1306	284	505	460	1115
44	417	1250	368	74	1315	1198	914	577	832	688
45	546	735	1133	762	223	502	816	100	667	343
46	1228	295	348	849	819	1110	1189	1009	1298	785
47	1020	655	617	518	512	727	540	1283	853	250
48	59	498	1001	1159	926	767	1273	1433	1079	1151
49	674	103	377	527	1479	1055	623	905	239	631

POWER RESIDUES

	0	1	2	3	4	5	6	7	8	9
0	1	3	9	27	81	243	729	706	637	430
1	1290	908	1243	767	820	979	1456	1406	1256	806
2	937	1330	1028	122	366	1098	332	996	26	78
3	234	702	625	394	1182	584	271	813	958	1393
4	1217	689	586	277	831	1012	74	222	666	517
5	70	210	630	409	1227	719	676	547	160	480
6	1440	1358	1112	374	1122	404	1212	674	541	142
7	426	1278	872	1135	443	1329	1025	113	339	1017
8	89	267	801	922	1285	893	1198	632	415	1245
9	773	838	1033	137	411	1233	737	730	709	646
10	457	1371	1151	491	1473	1457	1409	1265	833	1018
11	92	276	828	1003	47	141	423	1269	845	1054
12	200	600	319	957	1390	1208	662	505	34	102
13	306	918	1273	857	1090	308	924	1291	911	1252
14	794	901	1222	704	631	412	1236	746	757	790
15	889	1186	596	307	921	1282	884	1171	551	172
16	516	67	201	603	328	984	1471	1451	1391	1211
17	671	532	115	345	1035	143	429	1287	899	1216
18	686	577	250	750	769	826	997	29	87	261
19	783	868	1123	407	1221	701	622	385	1155	503
20	28	84	252	756	787	880	1159	515	64	192
21	576	247	741	742	745	754	781	862	1105	353
22	1059	215	645	454	1362	1124	410	1230	728	703
23	628	403	1209	665	514	61	183	549	166	498
24	13	39	117	351	1053	197	591	292	876	1147
25	479	1437	1349	1085	293	879	1156	506	37	111
26	333	999	35	105	315	945	1354	1100	338	1014
27	80	240	720	679	556	187	561	202	606	337
28	1011	71	213	639	436	1308	962	1405	1253	797
29	910	1249	785	874	1141	461	1383	1187	599	316
30	948	1363	1127	419	1257	809	946	1357	1109	365
31	1095	323	969	1426	1316	986	1477	1469	1445	1373
32	1157	509	46	138	414	1242	764	811	952	1375
33	1163	527	100	300	900	1219	695	604	331	993
34	17	51	153	459	1377	1169	545	154	462	1386
35	1196	626	397	1191	611	352	1056	206	618	373
36	1119	395	1185	593	298	894	1201	641	442	1326
37	1016	86	258	774	841	1042	164	492	1476	1466
38	1436	1346	1076	266	798	913	1258	812	955	1384
39	1190	608	343	1029	125	375	1125	413	1239	755
40	784	871	1132	434	1302	944	1351	1091	311	933
41	1318	992	14	42	126	378	1134	440	1320	998
42	32	96	288	864	1111	371	1113	377	1131	431
43	1293	917	1270	848	1063	227	681	562	205	615
44	364	1092	314	942	1345	1073	257	771	832	1015
45	83	249	747	760	799	916	1267	839	1036	146
46	438	1314	980	1459	1415	1283	887	1180	578	253
47	759	796	907	1240	758	793	898	1213	677	550
48	169	507	40	120	360	1080	278	834	1021	101
49	303	909	1246	776	847	1060	218	654	481	1443

P = 1481

INDICES

	0	1	2	3	4	5	6	7	8	9
50	1450	1202	755	199	1470	127	257	481	582	321
51	1247	1295	1052	1454	234	207	160	49	670	1026
52	722	587	1457	778	863	1381	1128	331	568	1068
53	707	1255	171	1040	1349	1046	1005	1145	594	1183
54	697	68	1304	1313	760	346	653	57	1149	237
55	479	158	1379	1347	1311	1377	274	876	1261	823
56	894	276	437	871	1171	1195	614	628	1125	1344
57	878	1030	1231	751	1212	1290	210	181	468	1263
58	881	1074	918	1216	35	1360	42	1105	825	1442
59	679	246	890	363	1206	602	152	896	562	298
60	121	945	995	163	337	988	278	1033	391	812
61	1141	354	1398	931	1421	439	1403	1163	358	957
62	685	537	196	704	873	32	351	1387	230	598
63	52	144	87	1173	1234	644	858	8	1390	283
64	1114	367	1197	831	734	222	99	1227	848	1188
65	784	616	726	852	497	925	1432	673	526	622
66	630	754	126	581	1294	233	48	721	777	1127
67	1067	170	1045	593	67	759	56	478	1346	273
68	822	436	1194	1124	1029	1211	180	880	1215	41
69	1441	889	601	561	944	336	1032	1140	930	1402
70	956	195	31	229	143	1233	7	1113	830	98
71	1187	725	924	525	753	1293	720	1066	592	55
72	272	1193	1210	1214	888	943	1139	955	228	6
73	97	923	1292	591	1192	887	954	96	590	953
74	952	212	213	1330	836	214	147	452	1331	552
75	183	837	746	968	215	399	203	148	474	470
76	453	1012	795	1332	326	1460	553	13	1265	184
77	1465	447	838	90	373	747	493	883	969	771
78	935	216	662	190	400	292	1076	204	1301	1341
79	149	701	781	475	140	920	471	289	384	454
80	1176	82	1013	606	1218	796	19	807	1333	305
81	910	327	387	37	1461	788	973	554	1321	866
82	14	1370	1362	1266	1413	692	185	1237	112	1466
83	1356	44	448	108	487	839	962	1474	91	457
84	1107	374	1023	650	748	118	1384	494	433	827
85	884	792	1338	970	647	1091	772	133	1444	936
86	1277	1425	217	1098	423	663	1179	681	191	658
87	1094	401	72	1131	293	1018	248	1077	903	255
88	205	861	1038	1302	156	892	1342	466	1103	150
89	986	1419	702	85	365	782	620	775	476	178
90	334	141	523	1208	921	950	550	472	11	491
91	290	138	604	385	1368	1354	455	431	131	1177
92	1016	154	83	521	136	1014	637	571	607	639
93	898	1219	977	409	797	1393	1086	20	573	564
94	808	1437	443	1334	405	265	306	609	300	911
95	515	1447	328	1308	1071	388	641	123	38	717
96	1327	1462	286	1410	789	900	947	974	714	312
97	555	507	1061	1322	1221	997	867	730	939	15
98	462	710	1371	979	165	1363	315	739	1267	1117
99	843	1414	411	339	693	533	27	186	419	261

POWER RESIDUES

	0	1	2	3	4	5	6	7	8	9
50	1367	1139	455	1365	1133	437	1311	971	1432	1334
51	1040	158	474	1422	1304	950	1369	1145	473	1419
52	1295	923	1288	902	1225	713	658	493	1479	1475
53	1463	1427	1319	995	23	69	207	621	382	1146
54	476	1428	1322	1004	50	150	450	1350	1088	302
55	906	1237	749	766	817	970	1429	1325	1013	77
56	231	693	598	313	939	1336	1046	176	528	103
57	309	927	1300	938	1333	1037	149	447	1341	1061
58	221	663	508	43	129	387	1161	521	82	246
59	738	733	718	673	538	133	399	1197	629	406
60	1218	692	595	304	912	1255	803	928	1303	947
61	1360	1118	392	1176	566	217	651	472	1416	1286
62	896	1207	659	496	7	21	63	189	567	220
63	660	499	16	48	144	432	1296	926	1297	929
64	1306	956	1387	1199	635	424	1272	854	1081	281
65	843	1048	182	546	157	471	1413	1277	869	1126
66	416	1248	782	865	1114	380	1140	458	1374	1160
67	518	73	219	657	490	1470	1448	1382	1184	590
68	289	867	1120	398	1194	620	379	1137	449	1347
69	1079	275	825	994	20	60	180	540	139	417
70	1251	791	892	1195	623	388	1164	530	109	327
71	981	1462	1424	1310	968	1423	1307	959	1396	1226
72	716	667	520	79	237	711	652	475	1425	1313
73	977	1450	1388	1202	644	451	1353	1097	329	987
74	1480	1478	1472	1454	1400	1238	752	775	844	1051
75	191	573	238	714	661	502	25	75	225	675
76	544	151	453	1359	1115	383	1149	485	1455	1403
77	1247	779	856	1087	299	897	1210	668	523	88
78	264	792	895	1204	650	469	1407	1259	815	964
79	1411	1271	851	1072	254	762	805	934	1321	1001
80	41	123	369	1107	359	1077	269	807	940	1339
81	1055	203	609	346	1038	152	456	1368	1142	464
82	1392	1214	680	559	196	588	283	849	1066	236
83	708	643	448	1344	1070	248	744	751	772	835
84	1024	110	330	990	8	24	72	216	648	463
85	1389	1205	653	478	1434	1340	1058	212	636	427
86	1281	881	1162	524	91	273	819	976	1447	1379
87	1175	563	208	624	391	1173	557	190	570	229
88	687	580	259	777	850	1069	245	735	724	691
89	592	295	885	1174	560	199	597	310	930	1309
90	965	1414	1280	878	1153	497	10	30	90	270
91	810	949	1366	1136	446	1338	1052	194	582	265
92	795	904	1231	731	712	655	484	1452	1394	1220
93	698	613	358	1074	260	780	859	1096	326	978
94	1453	1397	1229	725	694	601	322	966	1417	1289
95	905	1234	740	739	736	727	700	619	376	1128
96	422	1266	836	1027	119	357	1071	251	753	778
97	853	1078	272	816	967	1420	1298	932	1315	983
98	1468	1442	1364	1130	428	1284	890	1189	605	334
99	1002	44	132	396	1188	602	325	975	1444	1370

P = 1481

INDICES

	0	1	2	3	4	5	6	7	8	9
100	1238	799	990	113	543	1280	1467	1252	1258	1357
101	1395	280	45	558	269	449	370	79	109	1088
102	1035	488	1083	1407	840	76	1242	963	22	393
103	1475	1286	1428	92	1317	174	458	575	814	1108
104	510	1157	375	1200	1245	1024	566	1143	651	1375
105	1169	749	916	244	119	810	356	1385	856	220
106	495	579	1043	434	1439	1400	828	1064	1137	885
107	834	966	793	445	933	1339	382	805	971	690
108	485	648	1336	1423	1092	253	1101	773	548	1352
109	134	407	441	1445	1325	310	937	737	25	1278
110	267	1405	1426	1155	1167	218	1135	803	1099	308
111	1165	424	62	426	664	764	1049	1180	611	360
112	682	1224	64	192	225	396	659	302	959	1095
113	983	428	402	504	416	73	913	687	1132	501
114	666	294	818	1008	1019	517	539	249	1000	766
115	1078	102	1478	904	1449	198	256	320	1051	206
116	669	586	862	330	706	1039	1004	1182	1303	345
117	1148	157	1310	875	893	870	613	1343	1230	1289
118	467	1073	34	1104	678	362	151	297	994	987
119	390	353	1420	1162	684	703	350	597	86	643
120	1389	366	733	1226	783	851	1431	621	125	232
121	776	169	66	477	821	1123	179	40	600	335
122	929	194	142	1112	1186	524	719	54	1209	942
123	227	922	1191	95	951	1329	146	551	745	398
124	473	1011	325	12	1464	89	492	770	661	291
125	1300	700	139	288	1175	605	18	304	386	787
126	1320	1369	1412	1236	1355	107	961	456	1022	117
127	432	791	646	132	1276	1097	1178	657	71	1017
128	902	860	155	465	985	84	619	177	522	949
129	10	137	1367	430	1015	520	636	638	976	1392
130	572	1436	404	608	514	1307	640	716	285	899
131	713	506	1220	729	461	978	314	1116	410	532
132	418	798	542	1251	1394	557	369	1087	1082	75
133	21	1285	1316	574	509	1199	565	1374	915	809
134	855	578	1438	1063	833	444	381	689	1335	252
135	547	406	1324	736	266	1154	1134	307	61	763
136	610	1223	224	301	982	503	912	500	817	516
137	999	101	1448	319	668	329	1003	344	1309	869
138	1229	1072	677	296	389	1161	349	642	732	850
139	124	168	820	39	928	1111	718	941	1190	1328
140	744	1010	1463	769	1299	287	17	786	1411	106
141	1021	790	1275	656	901	464	618	948	1366	519
142	975	1435	513	715	712	728	313	531	541	556
143	1081	1284	508	1373	854	1062	380	251	1323	1153
144	60	1222	981	499	998	318	1002	868	676	1160
145	731	167	927	940	743	768	16	105	1274	463
146	1365	1434	711	530	1080	1372	379	1152	980	317
147	675	166	742	104	1364	529	378	316	741	528
148	740	0								

POWER RESIDUES

	0	1	2	3	4	5	6	7	8	9
100	1148	482	1446	1376	1166	536	127	381	1143	467
101	1401	1241	761	802	925	1294	920	1279	875	1144
102	470	1410	1268	842	1045	173	519	76	228	684
103	571	232	696	607	340	1020	98	294	882	1165
104	533	118	354	1062	224	672	535	124	372	1116
105	386	1158	512	55	165	495	4	12	36	108
106	324	972	1435	1343	1067	239	717	670	529	106
107	318	954	1381	1181	581	262	786	877	1150	488
108	1464	1430	1328	1022	104	312	936	1327	1019	95
109	285	855	1084	290	870	1129	425	1275	863	1108
110	362	1086	296	888	1183	587	280	840	1039	155
111	465	1395	1223	707	640	439	1317	989	5	15
112	45	135	405	1215	683	568	223	669	526	97
113	291	873	1138	452	1356	1106	356	1068	242	726
114	697	610	349	1047	179	537	130	390	1170	548
115	163	489	1467	1439	1355	1103	347	1041	161	483
116	1449	1385	1193	617	370	1110	368	1104	350	1050
117	188	564	211	633	418	1254	800	919	1276	866
118	1117	389	1167	539	136	408	1224	710	649	466
119	1398	1232	734	721	682	565	214	642	445	1335
120	1043	167	501	22	66	198	594	301	903	1228
121	722	685	574	241	723	688	583	268	804	931
122	1312	974	1441	1361	1121	401	1203	647	460	1380
123	1178	572	235	705	634	421	1263	827	1000	38
124	114	342	1026	116	348	1044	170	510	49	147
125	441	1323	1007	59	177	531	112	336	1008	62
126	186	558	193	579	256	768	823	988	2	6
127	18	54	162	486	1458	1412	1274	860	1099	335
128	1005	53	159	477	1431	1331	1031	131	393	1179
129	575	244	732	715	664	511	52	156	468	1404
130	1250	788	883	1168	542	145	435	1305	953	1378
131	1172	554	181	543	148	444	1332	1034	140	420
132	1260	818	973	1438	1352	1094	320	960	1399	1235
133	743	748	763	808	943	1348	1082	284	852	1075
134	263	789	886	1177	569	226	678	553	178	534
135	121	363	1089	305	915	1264	830	1009	65	195
136	585	274	822	985	1474	1460	1418	1292	914	1261
137	821	982	1465	1433	1337	1049	185	555	184	552
138	175	525	94	282	846	1057	209	627	400	1200
139	638	433	1299	935	1324	1010	68	204	612	355
140	1065	233	699	616	367	1101	341	1023	107	321
141	963	1408	1262	824	991	11	33	99	297	891
142	1192	614	361	1083	287	861	1102	344	1032	134
143	402	1206	656	487	1461	1421	1301	941	1342	1064
144	230	690	589	286	858	1093	317	951	1372	1154
145	500	19	57	171	513	58	174	522	85	255
146	765	814	961	1402	1244	770	829	1006	56	168
147	504	31	93	279	837	1030	128	384	1152	494
148										

P = 1483

INDICES

	0	1	2	3	4	5	6	7	8	9
0		0	1	1283	2	515	1284	188	3	1084
1	516	83	1285	1434	189	316	4	1348	1085	987
2	517	1471	84	818	1286	1030	1435	885	190	1076
3	317	710	5	1366	1349	703	1086	24	988	1235
4	518	1325	1472	863	85	117	819	1466	1287	376
5	1031	1149	1436	1292	886	598	191	788	1077	1196
6	318	442	711	1272	6	467	1367	259	1350	619
7	704	14	1087	1042	25	831	989	271	1236	98
8	519	686	1326	480	1473	381	864	877	86	451
9	118	140	820	511	1467	20	1288	615	377	1167
10	1032	1171	1150	395	1437	504	1293	127	887	674
11	599	1307	192	978	789	1333	1078	1036	1197	54
12	319	166	443	1126	712	63	1273	40	7	664
13	468	648	1368	1175	260	1400	1351	1203	620	736
14	705	1267	15	35	1088	109	1043	177	26	1154
15	832	369	990	950	272	1225	1237	361	99	1093
16	520	1006	687	1143	1327	399	481	915	1474	1386
17	382	589	865	423	878	1218	87	997	452	405
18	119	1441	141	243	821	539	512	1431	1468	1073
19	21	114	1289	439	616	268	378	508	1168	671
20	1033	60	1172	1264	1151	358	396	420	1438	1070
21	505	355	1294	1297	128	1378	888	898	675	843
22	600	1300	1308	1048	193	632	979	1105	790	131
23	1334	72	1079	1320	1037	499	1198	1381	55	1315
24	320	963	167	487	444	891	1127	939	713	281
25	64	1016	1274	901	41	182	8	1394	665	212
26	469	678	649	218	1369	325	1176	252	261	846
27	1401	233	1352	1423	1204	1113	621	603	737	312
28	706	1462	1268	94	16	1303	36	31	1089	1214
29	110	416	1044	1311	178	229	27	968	1155	770
30	833	1051	370	972	991	957	951	921	273	196
31	1226	572	1238	811	362	305	100	635	1094	1159
32	521	1410	1007	853	688	982	1144	475	1328	172
33	400	350	482	1108	916	774	1475	657	1387	779
34	383	793	590	564	866	1134	424	759	879	134
35	1219	837	88	753	998	529	453	1337	406	723
36	120	492	1442	1449	142	75	244	1055	822	927
37	540	1480	513	1082	1432	1346	1469	1028	1074	1364
38	22	1323	115	374	1290	786	440	465	617	1040
39	269	684	379	449	509	613	1169	502	672	976
40	1034	164	61	662	1173	1201	1265	107	1152	948
41	359	1004	397	1384	421	995	1439	537	1071	437
42	506	58	356	1068	1295	896	1298	630	129	1318
43	1379	961	889	279	899	1392	676	323	844	1421
44	601	1460	1301	1212	1309	966	1049	955	194	809
45	633	1408	980	170	1106	655	791	1132	132	751
46	1335	490	73	925	1080	1026	1321	784	1038	447
47	500	162	1199	946	1382	535	56	894	1316	277
48	321	1458	964	807	168	1130	488	1024	445	944
49	892	1456	1128	942	940	200	714	202	282	388

POWER RESIDUES

	0	1	2	3	4	5	6	7	8	9
0	1	2	4	8	16	32	64	128	256	512
1	1024	565	1130	777	71	142	284	568	1136	789
2	95	190	380	760	37	74	148	296	592	1184
3	885	287	574	1148	813	143	286	572	1144	805
4	127	254	508	1016	549	1098	713	1426	1369	1255
5	1027	571	1142	801	119	238	476	952	421	842
6	201	402	804	125	250	500	1000	517	1034	585
7	1170	857	231	462	924	365	730	1460	1437	1391
8	1299	1115	747	11	22	44	88	176	352	704
9	1408	1333	1183	883	283	566	1132	781	79	158
10	316	632	1264	1045	607	1214	945	407	814	145
11	290	580	1160	837	191	382	764	45	90	180
12	360	720	1440	1397	1311	1139	795	107	214	428
13	856	229	458	916	349	698	1396	1309	1135	787
14	91	182	364	728	1456	1429	1375	1267	1051	619
15	1238	993	503	1006	529	1058	633	1266	1049	615
16	1230	977	471	942	401	802	121	242	484	968
17	453	906	329	658	1316	1149	815	147	294	588
18	1176	869	255	510	1020	557	1114	745	7	14
19	28	56	112	224	448	896	309	618	1236	989
20	495	990	497	994	505	1010	537	1074	665	1330
21	1177	871	259	518	1036	589	1178	873	263	526
22	1052	621	1242	1001	519	1038	593	1186	889	295
23	590	1180	877	271	542	1084	685	1370	1257	1031
24	579	1158	833	183	366	732	1464	1445	1407	1331
25	1179	875	267	534	1068	653	1306	1129	775	67
26	134	268	536	1072	661	1322	1161	839	195	390
27	780	77	154	308	616	1232	981	479	958	433
28	866	249	498	996	509	1018	553	1106	729	1458
29	1433	1383	1283	1083	683	1366	1249	1015	547	1094
30	705	1410	1337	1191	899	315	630	1260	1037	591
31	1182	881	279	558	1116	749	15	30	60	120
32	240	480	960	437	874	265	530	1060	637	1274
33	1065	647	1294	1105	727	1454	1425	1367	1251	1019
34	555	1110	737	1474	1465	1447	1411	1339	1195	907
35	331	662	1324	1165	847	211	422	844	205	410
36	820	157	314	628	1256	1029	575	1150	817	151
37	302	604	1208	933	383	766	49	98	196	392
38	784	85	170	340	680	1360	1237	991	499	998
39	513	1026	569	1138	793	103	206	412	824	165
40	330	660	1320	1157	831	179	358	716	1432	1381
41	1279	1075	667	1334	1185	887	291	582	1164	845
42	207	414	828	173	346	692	1384	1285	1087	691
43	1382	1281	1079	675	1350	1217	951	419	838	193
44	386	772	61	122	244	488	976	469	938	393
45	786	89	178	356	712	1424	1365	1247	1011	539
46	1078	673	1346	1209	935	387	774	65	130	260
47	520	1040	597	1194	905	327	654	1308	1133	783
48	83	166	332	664	1328	1173	863	243	486	972
49	461	922	361	722	1444	1405	1327	1171	859	235

P = 1483

INDICES

	0	1	2	3	4	5	6	7	8	9
50	65	716	1017	152	1275	204	902	1187	42	284
51	183	1230	9	390	1395	910	666	67	213	224
52	470	718	679	1063	650	1019	219	576	1370	154
53	326	798	1177	1277	253	642	262	206	847	459
54	1402	904	234	1242	1353	1189	1424	298	1205	44
55	1114	581	622	286	604	340	738	185	313	815
56	707	1232	1463	595	1269	11	95	874	17	392
57	1304	51	37	1397	32	366	1090	912	1215	240
58	111	668	417	1375	1045	69	1312	936	179	215
59	230	309	28	226	969	569	1156	472	771	561
60	834	720	1052	1343	371	681	973	104	992	1065
61	958	1418	952	652	922	159	274	1021	197	149
62	1227	221	573	639	1239	578	812	871	363	1372
63	306	558	101	156	636	555	1095	328	1160	1098
64	522	800	1411	1248	1008	1179	854	331	689	1279
65	983	699	1145	255	476	1163	1329	644	173	1139
66	401	264	351	1101	483	208	1109	412	917	849
67	775	525	1476	461	658	433	1388	1404	780	803
68	384	906	794	294	591	236	565	1414	867	1244
69	1135	429	425	1355	760	1251	880	1191	135	1121
70	1220	1426	838	1011	89	300	754	1359	999	1207
71	530	1182	454	46	1338	550	407	1116	724	857
72	121	583	493	764	1443	624	1450	334	143	288
73	76	729	245	606	1056	692	823	342	928	1255
74	541	740	1481	1282	514	187	1083	82	1433	315
75	1347	986	1470	817	1029	884	1075	709	1365	702
76	23	1234	1324	862	116	1465	375	1148	1291	597
77	787	1195	441	1271	466	258	618	13	1041	830
78	270	97	685	479	380	876	450	139	510	19
79	614	1166	1170	394	503	126	673	1306	977	1332
80	1035	53	165	1125	62	39	663	647	1174	1399
81	1202	735	1266	34	108	176	1153	368	949	1224
82	360	1092	1005	1142	398	914	1385	588	422	1217
83	996	404	1440	242	538	1430	1072	113	438	267
84	507	670	59	1263	357	419	1069	354	1296	1377
85	897	842	1299	1047	631	1104	130	71	1319	498
86	1380	1314	962	486	890	938	280	1015	900	181
87	1393	211	677	217	324	251	845	232	1422	1112
88	602	311	1461	93	1302	30	1213	415	1310	228
89	967	769	1050	971	956	920	195	571	810	304
90	634	1158	1409	852	981	474	171	349	1107	773
91	656	778	792	563	1133	758	133	836	752	528
92	1336	722	491	1448	74	1054	926	1479	1081	1345
93	1027	1363	1322	373	785	464	1039	683	448	612
94	501	975	163	661	1200	106	947	1003	1383	994
95	536	436	57	1067	895	629	1317	960	278	1391
96	322	1420	1459	1211	965	954	808	1407	169	654
97	1131	750	489	924	1025	783	446	161	945	534
98	893	276	1457	806	1129	1023	943	1455	941	199
99	201	387	715	151	203	1186	283	1229	389	909

POWER RESIDUES

	0	1	2	3	4	5	6	7	8	9
50	470	940	397	794	105	210	420	840	197	394
51	788	93	186	372	744	5	10	20	40	80
52	160	320	640	1280	1077	671	1342	1201	919	355
53	710	1420	1357	1231	979	475	950	417	834	185
54	370	740	1480	1477	1471	1459	1435	1387	1291	1099
55	715	1430	1377	1271	1059	635	1270	1057	631	1262
56	1041	599	1198	913	343	686	1372	1261	1039	595
57	1190	897	311	622	1244	1005	527	1054	625	1250
58	1017	551	1102	721	1442	1401	1319	1155	827	171
59	342	684	1368	1253	1023	563	1126	769	55	110
60	220	440	880	277	554	1108	733	1466	1449	1415
61	1347	1211	939	395	790	97	194	388	776	69
62	138	276	552	1104	725	1450	1417	1351	1219	955
63	427	854	225	450	900	317	634	1268	1053	623
64	1246	1009	535	1070	657	1314	1145	807	131	262
65	524	1048	613	1226	969	455	910	337	674	1348
66	1213	943	403	806	129	258	516	1032	581	1162
67	841	199	398	796	109	218	436	872	261	522
68	1044	605	1210	937	391	782	81	162	324	648
69	1296	1109	735	1470	1457	1431	1379	1275	1067	651
70	1302	1121	759	35	70	140	280	560	1120	757
71	31	62	124	248	496	992	501	1002	521	1042
72	601	1202	921	359	718	1436	1389	1295	1107	731
73	1462	1441	1399	1315	1147	811	139	278	556	1112
74	741	1482	1481	1479	1475	1467	1451	1419	1355	1227
75	971	459	918	353	706	1412	1341	1199	915	347
76	694	1388	1293	1103	723	1446	1409	1335	1187	891
77	299	598	1196	909	335	670	1340	1197	911	339
78	678	1356	1229	975	467	934	385	770	57	114
79	228	456	912	341	682	1364	1245	1007	531	1062
80	641	1282	1081	679	1358	1233	983	483	966	449
81	898	313	626	1252	1021	559	1118	753	23	46
82	92	184	368	736	1472	1461	1439	1395	1307	1131
83	779	75	150	300	600	1200	917	351	702	1404
84	1325	1167	851	219	438	876	269	538	1076	669
85	1338	1193	903	323	646	1292	1101	719	1438	1393
86	1303	1123	763	43	86	172	344	688	1376	1269
87	1055	627	1254	1025	567	1134	785	87	174	348
88	696	1392	1301	1119	755	27	54	108	216	432
89	864	245	490	980	477	954	425	850	217	434
90	868	253	506	1012	541	1082	681	1362	1241	999
91	515	1030	577	1154	825	167	334	668	1336	1189
92	895	307	614	1228	973	463	926	369	738	1476
93	1469	1455	1427	1371	1259	1035	587	1174	865	247
94	494	988	493	986	489	978	473	946	409	818
95	153	306	612	1224	965	447	894	305	610	1220
96	957	431	862	241	482	964	445	890	297	594
97	1188	893	303	606	1212	941	399	798	113	226
98	452	904	325	650	1300	1117	751	19	38	76
99	152	304	608	1216	949	415	830	177	354	708

P = 1483

INDICES

	0	1	2	3	4	5	6	7	8	9
100	66	223	717	1062	1018	575	153	797	1276	641
101	205	458	903	1241	1188	297	43	580	285	339
102	184	814	1231	594	10	873	391	50	1396	365
103	911	239	667	1374	68	935	214	308	225	568
104	471	560	719	1342	680	103	1064	1417	651	158
105	1020	148	220	638	577	870	1371	557	155	554
106	327	1097	799	1247	1178	330	1278	698	254	1162
107	643	1138	263	1100	207	411	848	524	460	432
108	1403	802	905	293	235	1413	1243	428	1354	1250
109	1190	1120	1425	1010	299	1358	1206	1181	45	549
110	1115	856	582	763	623	333	287	728	605	691
111	341	1254	739	1281	186	81	314	985	816	883
112	708	701	1233	861	1464	1147	596	1194	1270	257
113	12	829	96	478	875	138	18	1165	393	125
114	1305	1331	52	1124	38	646	1398	734	33	175
115	367	1223	1091	1141	913	587	1216	403	241	1429
116	112	266	669	1262	418	353	1376	841	1046	1103
117	70	497	1313	485	937	1014	180	210	216	250
118	231	1111	310	92	29	414	227	768	970	919
119	570	303	1157	851	473	348	772	777	562	757
120	835	527	721	1447	1053	1478	1344	1362	372	463
121	682	611	974	660	105	1002	993	435	1066	628
122	959	1390	1419	1210	953	1406	653	749	923	782
123	160	533	275	805	1022	1454	198	386	150	1185
124	1228	908	222	1061	574	796	640	457	1240	296
125	579	338	813	593	872	49	364	238	1373	934
126	307	567	559	1341	102	1416	157	147	637	869
127	556	553	1096	1246	329	697	1161	1137	1099	410
128	523	431	801	292	1412	427	1249	1119	1009	1357
129	1180	548	855	762	332	727	690	1253	1280	80
130	984	882	700	860	1146	1193	256	828	477	137
131	1164	124	1330	1123	645	733	174	1222	1140	586
132	402	1428	265	1261	352	840	1102	496	484	1013
133	209	249	1110	91	413	767	918	302	850	347
134	776	756	526	1446	1477	1361	462	610	659	1001
135	434	627	1389	1209	1405	748	781	532	804	1453
136	385	1184	907	1060	795	456	295	337	592	48
137	237	933	566	1340	1415	146	868	552	1245	696
138	1136	409	430	291	426	1118	1356	547	761	726
139	1252	79	881	859	1192	827	136	123	1122	732
140	1221	585	1427	1260	839	495	1012	248	90	766
141	301	346	755	1445	1360	609	1000	626	1208	747
142	531	1452	1183	1059	455	336	47	932	1339	145
143	551	695	408	290	1117	546	725	78	858	826
144	122	731	584	1259	494	247	765	345	1444	608
145	625	746	1451	1058	335	931	144	694	289	545
146	77	825	730	1258	246	344	607	745	1057	930
147	693	544	824	1257	343	744	929	543	1256	743
148	542	742	741							

POWER RESIDUES

	0	1	2	3	4	5	6	7	8	9
100	1416	1349	1215	947	411	822	161	322	644	1288
101	1093	703	1406	1329	1175	867	251	502	1004	525
102	1050	617	1234	985	487	974	465	930	377	754
103	25	50	100	200	400	800	117	234	468	936
104	389	778	73	146	292	584	1168	853	223	446
105	892	301	602	1204	925	367	734	1468	1453	1423
106	1363	1243	1003	523	1046	609	1218	953	423	846
107	209	418	836	189	378	756	29	58	116	232
108	464	928	373	746	9	18	36	72	144	288
109	576	1152	821	159	318	636	1272	1061	639	1278
110	1073	663	1326	1169	855	227	454	908	333	666
111	1332	1181	879	275	550	1100	717	1434	1385	1287
112	1091	699	1398	1313	1143	803	123	246	492	984
113	485	970	457	914	345	690	1380	1277	1071	659
114	1318	1153	823	163	326	652	1304	1125	767	51
115	102	204	408	816	149	298	596	1192	901	319
116	638	1276	1069	655	1310	1137	791	99	198	396
117	792	101	202	404	808	133	266	532	1064	645
118	1290	1097	711	1422	1361	1239	995	507	1014	545
119	1090	697	1394	1305	1127	771	59	118	236	472
120	944	405	810	137	274	548	1096	709	1418	1353
121	1223	963	443	886	289	578	1156	829	175	350
122	700	1400	1317	1151	819	155	310	620	1240	997
123	511	1022	561	1122	761	39	78	156	312	624
124	1248	1013	543	1086	689	1378	1273	1063	643	1286
125	1089	695	1390	1297	1111	739	1478	1473	1463	1443
126	1403	1323	1163	843	203	406	812	141	282	564
127	1128	773	63	126	252	504	1008	533	1066	649
128	1298	1113	743	3	6	12	24	48	96	192
129	384	768	53	106	212	424	848	213	426	852
130	221	442	884	285	570	1140	797	111	222	444
131	888	293	586	1172	861	239	478	956	429	858
132	233	466	932	381	762	41	82	164	328	656
133	1312	1141	799	115	230	460	920	357	714	1428
134	1373	1263	1043	603	1206	929	375	750	17	34
135	68	136	272	544	1088	693	1386	1289	1095	707
136	1414	1345	1207	931	379	758	33	66	132	264
137	528	1056	629	1258	1033	583	1166	849	215	430
138	860	237	474	948	413	826	169	338	676	1352
139	1221	959	435	870	257	514	1028	573	1146	809
140	135	270	540	1080	677	1354	1225	967	451	902
141	321	642	1284	1085	687	1374	1265	1047	611	1222
142	961	439	878	273	546	1092	701	1402	1321	1159
143	835	187	374	748	13	26	52	104	208	416
144	832	181	362	724	1448	1413	1343	1203	923	363
145	726	1452	1421	1359	1235	987	491	982	481	962
146	441	882	281	562	1124	765	47	94	188	376
147	752	21	42	84	168	336	672	1344	1205	927
148	371	742								

P = 1487

INDICES

	0	1	2	3	4	5	6	7	8	9
0		0	104	1476	208	1	94	1206	312	1466
1	105	876	198	201	1310	1477	416	278	84	449
2	209	1196	980	110	302	2	305	1456	1414	787
3	95	1080	520	866	382	1207	188	150	553	191
4	313	1431	1300	363	1084	1467	214	1244	406	926
5	106	268	409	805	74	877	32	439	891	939
6	199	551	1184	1186	624	202	970	1450	486	100
7	1311	498	292	504	254	1478	657	596	295	861
8	417	1446	49	1122	1404	279	467	777	1188	27
9	85	1407	318	1070	1348	450	510	1272	1030	856
10	210	1423	372	900	513	1197	909	1052	178	367
11	981	140	136	626	543	111	995	181	1043	1484
12	303	266	655	1421	1288	3	1290	1438	728	353
13	306	81	1074	169	68	1457	590	819	204	424
14	1415	1234	602	1077	396	788	608	916	358	1371
15	96	5	767	258	700	1081	399	1017	965	795
16	521	1316	64	972	153	867	1226	436	22	402
17	383	429	571	1331	881	1208	1292	929	131	1308
18	189	622	25	541	422	151	1174	1154	1452	1176
19	554	1119	614	127	1376	192	1134	1201	960	885
20	314	1440	41	507	476	1432	1004	90	617	1325
21	1301	1128	1013	488	1156	364	282	800	471	494
22	1085	479	244	534	240	1468	730	652	647	1275
23	215	586	1099	676	285	1245	1147	851	102	1454
24	407	594	370	1436	759	927	39	650	1392	1112
25	107	355	1394	986	56	269	832	783	457	1356
26	410	767	185	1313	1178	806	273	17	172	1344
27	75	330	694	1397	923	878	308	1114	528	1060
28	33	791	1338	1034	706	440	1181	1151	500	556
29	892	1262	712	236	1020	940	462	846	1475	311
30	200	83	109	1413	865	552	362	405	804	890
31	1185	485	503	294	1121	1187	1069	1029	899	177
32	625	1042	1420	727	168	203	1076	357	257	964
33	971	21	1330	130	540	1451	126	959	506	616
34	487	470	533	646	675	101	1435	1391	985	456
35	1312	171	1396	527	1033	499	235	1474	1412	803
36	293	898	726	256	129	505	645	984	526	1411
37	255	525	1278	1279	1258	1479	70	988	1280	579
38	658	1428	1223	1259	718	597	231	343	1480	1378
39	296	388	1238	71	1305	862	1064	1215	989	159
40	418	1459	58	1281	145	1447	611	1026	580	1163
41	50	809	1108	659	194	1123	721	414	1429	968
42	1405	993	1232	1224	1117	280	592	271	1260	1067
43	468	643	386	719	904	778	575	559	598	1136
44	1189	906	583	232	348	28	638	1361	344	682
45	86	821	834	1481	756	1408	751	262	1379	248
46	319	1266	690	297	1203	1071	780	1220	389	1170
47	1349	1007	1251	1239	955	451	206	785	72	859
48	511	351	698	1306	474	1273	54	1058	863	962
49	1031	577	143	1065	754	857	10	218	1216	115

POWER RESIDUES

	0	1	2	3	4	5	6	7	8	9
0	1	5	25	125	625	151	755	801	1031	694
1	496	993	504	1033	704	546	1243	267	1335	727
2	661	331	168	840	1226	182	910	89	445	738
3	716	606	56	280	1400	1052	799	1021	644	246
4	1230	202	1010	589	1458	1342	762	836	1206	82
5	410	563	1328	692	486	943	254	1270	402	523
6	1128	1179	1434	1222	162	810	1076	919	134	670
7	376	393	478	903	54	270	1350	802	1036	719
8	621	131	655	301	18	90	450	763	841	1231
9	207	1035	714	596	6	30	150	750	776	906
10	69	345	238	1190	2	10	50	250	1250	302
11	23	115	575	1388	992	499	1008	579	1408	1092
12	999	534	1183	1454	1322	662	336	193	965	364
13	333	178	890	1476	1432	1212	112	560	1313	617
14	111	555	1288	492	973	404	533	1178	1429	1197
15	37	185	925	164	820	1126	1169	1384	972	399
16	508	1053	804	1046	769	871	1381	957	324	133
17	665	351	268	1340	752	786	956	319	108	540
18	1213	117	585	1438	1242	262	1310	602	36	180
19	900	39	195	975	414	583	1428	1192	12	60
20	300	13	65	325	138	690	476	893	4	20
21	100	500	1013	604	46	230	1150	1289	497	998
22	529	1158	1329	697	511	1068	879	1421	1157	1324
23	672	386	443	728	666	356	293	1465	1377	937
24	224	1120	1139	1234	222	1110	1089	984	459	808
25	1066	869	1371	907	74	370	363	328	153	765
26	851	1281	457	798	1016	619	121	605	51	255
27	1275	427	648	266	1330	702	536	1193	17	85
28	425	638	216	1080	939	234	1170	1389	997	524
29	1133	1204	72	360	313	78	390	463	828	1166
30	1369	897	24	120	600	26	130	650	276	1380
31	952	299	8	40	200	1000	539	1208	92	460
32	813	1091	994	509	1058	829	1171	1394	1022	649
33	271	1355	827	1161	1344	772	886	1456	1332	712
34	586	1443	1267	387	448	753	791	981	444	733
35	691	481	918	129	645	251	1255	327	148	740
36	726	656	306	43	215	1075	914	109	545	1238
37	242	1210	102	510	1063	854	1296	532	1173	1404
38	1072	899	34	170	850	1276	432	673	391	468
39	853	1291	507	1048	779	921	144	720	626	156
40	780	926	169	845	1251	307	48	240	1200	52
41	260	1300	552	1273	417	598	16	80	400	513
42	1078	929	184	920	139	695	501	1018	629	171
43	855	1301	557	1298	542	1223	167	835	1201	57
44	285	1425	1177	1424	1172	1399	1047	774	896	19
45	95	475	888	1466	1382	962	349	258	1290	502
46	1023	654	296	1480	1452	1312	612	86	430	663
47	341	218	1090	989	484	933	204	1020	639	221
48	1105	1064	859	1321	657	311	68	340	213	1065
49	864	1346	782	936	219	1095	1014	609	71	355

P = 1487

INDICES

	0	1	2	3	4	5	6	7	8	9
50	211	426	459	990	12	1424	1090	392	160	323
51	373	224	936	419	887	901	561	634	1460	1321
52	514	667	871	59	289	1198	1417	1358	1282	220
53	910	919	377	146	121	1053	276	1298	1448	316
54	179	600	434	612	798	368	15	710	1027	531
55	982	1236	412	581	1218	141	632	432	1164	564
56	137	1144	895	51	1442	627	1138	1166	810	1095
57	544	740	1285	1109	1255	112	604	769	660	117
58	996	842	1366	195	816	182	340	933	1124	43
59	1044	1191	566	722	950	1485	93	875	415	1195
60	304	1079	187	1430	213	267	31	550	969	497
61	656	1445	466	1406	509	1422	908	139	994	265
62	1289	80	589	1233	607	4	398	1315	1225	428
63	1291	621	1173	1118	1133	1439	1003	1127	281	478
64	729	585	1146	593	38	354	831	766	272	329
65	307	790	1180	1261	461	82	361	484	1068	1041
66	1075	20	125	469	1434	170	234	897	644	524
67	69	1427	230	387	1063	1458	610	808	720	992
68	591	642	574	905	637	820	750	1265	779	1006
69	205	350	53	576	9	425	1089	223	560	666
70	1416	918	275	599	14	1235	631	1143	1137	739
71	603	841	339	1190	92	1078	30	1444	907	79
72	397	620	1002	584	830	789	360	19	233	1426
73	609	641	749	349	1088	917	630	840	29	619
74	359	640	629	639	1382	1372	1383	1102	1362	772
75	97	1373	174	345	1092	6	1384	1352	683	976
76	762	1103	46	87	1327	259	1363	1140	822	164
77	701	773	335	835	447	1082	98	1346	1482	394
78	400	1374	492	757	1342	1018	175	673	1409	1303
79	966	346	1168	752	1319	796	1093	948	263	36
80	522	7	77	1380	162	1317	1385	1334	249	1463
81	65	1353	715	320	1130	973	684	812	1267	1387
82	154	977	913	691	1212	868	763	332	298	325
83	1227	1104	825	1204	518	437	47	1050	1072	1015
84	23	88	1097	781	1336	403	1328	1472	1221	1024
85	384	260	696	390	375	430	1364	548	1171	482
86	572	1141	747	1350	490	1332	823	546	1008	251
87	882	165	679	1252	663	1209	702	1399	1240	226
88	1293	774	1010	956	687	930	336	1047	452	1158
89	132	836	742	207	1465	1309	448	301	786	381
90	190	1083	925	73	938	623	99	253	860	1403
91	26	1347	855	512	366	542	1483	1287	352	67
92	423	395	1370	699	794	152	401	880	1307	421
93	1175	1375	884	475	1324	1155	493	239	1274	284
94	1453	758	1111	55	1355	1177	1343	922	1059	705
95	555	1019	310	864	889	1120	176	167	963	539
96	615	674	455	1032	802	128	1410	1257	578	717
97	1377	1304	158	144	1162	193	967	1116	1066	903
98	1135	347	681	755	247	1202	1169	954	858	473
99	961	753	114	11	322	886	1320	288	219	120

POWER RESIDUES

	0	1	2	3	4	5	6	7	8	9
50	288	1440	1252	312	73	365	338	203	1015	614
51	96	480	913	104	520	1113	1104	1059	834	1196
52	32	160	800	1026	669	371	368	353	278	1390
53	1002	549	1258	342	223	1115	1114	1109	1084	959
54	334	183	915	114	570	1363	867	1361	857	1311
55	607	61	305	38	190	950	289	1445	1277	437
56	698	516	1093	1004	559	1308	592	1473	1417	1137
57	1224	172	860	1326	682	436	693	491	968	379
58	408	553	1278	442	723	641	231	1155	1314	622
59	136	680	426	643	241	1205	77	385	438	703
60	541	1218	142	710	576	1393	1017	624	146	730
61	676	406	543	1228	192	960	339	208	1040	739
62	721	631	181	905	64	320	113	565	1338	742
63	736	706	556	1293	517	1098	1029	684	446	743
64	741	731	681	431	668	366	343	228	1140	1239
65	247	1235	227	1135	1214	122	610	76	380	413
66	578	1403	1067	874	1396	1032	699	521	1118	1129
67	1184	1459	1347	787	961	344	233	1165	1364	872
68	1386	982	449	758	816	1106	1069	884	1446	1282
69	462	823	1141	1244	272	1360	852	1286	482	923
70	154	770	876	1406	1082	949	284	1420	1152	1299
71	547	1248	292	1460	1352	812	1086	969	384	433
72	678	416	593	1478	1442	1262	362	323	128	640
73	226	1130	1189	1484	1472	1412	1112	1099	1034	709
74	571	1368	892	1486	1482	1462	1362	862	1336	732
75	686	456	793	991	494	983	454	783	941	244
76	1220	152	760	826	1156	1319	647	261	1305	577
77	1398	1042	749	771	881	1431	1207	87	435	688
78	466	843	1241	257	1285	477	898	29	145	725
79	651	281	1405	1077	924	159	795	1001	544	1233
80	217	1085	964	359	308	53	265	1325	677	411
81	568	1353	817	1111	1094	1009	584	1433	1217	137
82	685	451	768	866	1356	832	1186	1469	1397	1037
83	724	646	256	1280	452	773	891	1481	1457	1337
84	737	711	581	1418	1142	1249	297	1485	1477	1437
85	1237	237	1185	1464	1372	912	99	495	988	479
86	908	79	395	488	953	304	33	165	825	1151
87	1294	522	1123	1154	1309	597	11	55	275	1375
88	927	174	870	1376	932	199	995	514	1083	954
89	309	58	290	1450	1302	562	1323	667	361	318
90	103	515	1088	979	434	683	441	718	616	106
91	530	1163	1354	822	1136	1219	147	735	701	531
92	1168	1379	947	274	1370	902	49	245	1225	177
93	885	1451	1307	587	1448	1292	512	1073	904	59
94	295	1475	1427	1187	1474	1422	1162	1349	797	1011
95	594	1483	1467	1387	987	474	883	1441	1257	337
96	198	990	489	958	329	158	790	976	419	608
97	66	330	163	815	1101	1044	759	821	1131	1194
98	22	110	550	1263	367	348	253	1265	377	398
99	503	1028	679	421	618	116	580	1413	1117	1124

P = 1487

INDICES

	0	1	2	3	4	5	6	7	8	9
100	315	797	530	1217	563	1441	1094	1254	116	815
101	42	949	1194	212	496	508	264	606	427	1132
102	477	37	328	460	1040	1433	523	1062	991	636
103	1005	8	665	13	738	91	78	829	1425	1087
104	618	1381	771	1091	975	1326	163	446	393	1341
105	1302	1318	35	161	1462	1129	1386	1211	324	517
106	1014	1335	1023	374	481	489	250	662	225	686
107	1157	1464	380	937	1402	365	66	793	420	1323
108	283	1354	704	888	538	801	716	1161	902	246
109	472	321	119	562	814	495	1131	1039	635	737
110	1086	974	1340	1461	516	480	685	1401	1322	537
111	245	813	736	515	536	535	1268	998	668	1269
112	241	1388	1248	872	999	1469	155	1036	60	669
113	731	978	1242	290	1270	653	914	569	1199	242
114	648	692	844	1418	1389	1276	1213	1230	1359	1249
115	216	869	708	1283	873	587	764	228	221	1000
116	1100	333	946	911	1470	677	299	1368	920	156
117	286	326	444	378	1037	1246	1228	442	147	61
118	1148	1105	1295	122	670	852	826	943	1054	732
119	103	1205	197	277	979	1455	519	149	1299	1243
120	408	438	1183	1449	291	595	48	776	317	1271
121	371	1051	135	180	654	1437	1073	818	601	915
122	760	1016	63	435	570	928	24	1153	613	1200
123	40	89	1012	799	243	651	1098	850	369	649
124	1393	782	184	16	693	1113	1337	1150	711	845
125	108	404	502	1028	1419	356	1329	958	532	1390
126	1395	1473	725	983	1277	987	1222	342	1237	1214
127	57	1025	1107	413	1231	270	385	558	582	1360
128	833	261	689	1219	1250	784	697	1057	142	217
129	458	391	935	633	870	1357	376	1297	433	709
130	411	431	894	1165	1284	768	1365	932	565	874
131	186	549	465	138	588	1314	1172	1126	1145	765
132	1179	483	124	896	229	807	573	1264	52	222
133	274	1142	338	1443	1001	18	748	839	628	1101
134	173	1351	45	1139	334	1345	491	672	1167	947
135	76	1333	714	811	912	331	824	1049	1096	1471
136	695	547	746	545	678	1398	1009	1046	741	300
137	924	252	854	1286	1369	879	883	238	1110	921
138	309	166	454	1256	157	1115	680	953	113	287
139	529	1253	1193	605	327	1061	664	828	770	445
140	34	1210	1022	661	379	792	703	1160	118	1038
141	1339	1400	735	997	1247	1035	1241	568	843	1229
142	707	227	945	1367	443	441	1294	942	196	148
143	1182	775	134	817	62	1152	1011	849	183	1149
144	501	957	724	341	1106	557	688	1056	934	1296
145	893	931	464	1125	123	1263	337	838	44	671
146	713	1048	745	1045	853	237	453	952	1192	827
147	1021	1159	734	567	944	941	133	848	723	1055
148	463	837	744	951	733	847	743			

POWER RESIDUES

	0	1	2	3	4	5	6	7	8	9
100	1159	1334	722	636	206	1030	689	471	868	1366
101	882	1436	1232	212	1060	839	1221	157	785	951
102	294	1470	1402	1062	849	1271	407	548	1253	317
103	98	490	963	354	283	1415	1127	1174	1409	1097
104	1024	659	321	118	590	1463	1367	887	1461	1357
105	837	1211	107	535	1188	1479	1447	1287	487	948
106	279	1395	1027	674	396	493	978	429	658	316
107	93	465	838	1216	132	660	326	143	715	601
108	31	155	775	901	44	220	1100	1039	734	696
109	506	1043	754	796	1006	569	1358	842	1236	232
110	1160	1339	747	761	831	1181	1444	1272	412	573
111	1378	942	249	1245	277	1385	977	424	633	191
112	955	314	83	415	588	1453	1317	637	211	1055
113	814	1096	1019	634	196	980	439	708	566	1343
114	767	861	1331	707	561	1318	642	236	1180	1439
115	1247	287	1435	1227	187	935	214	1070	889	1471
116	1407	1087	974	409	558	1303	567	1348	792	986
117	469	858	1316	632	186	930	189	945	264	1320
118	652	286	1430	1202	62	310	63	315	88	440
119	713	591	1468	1392	1012	599	21	105	525	1138
120	1229	197	985	464	833	1191	7	35	175	875
121	1401	1057	824	1146	1269	397	498	1003	554	1283
122	467	848	1266	382	423	628	166	830	1176	1419
123	1147	1274	422	623	141	705	551	1268	392	473
124	878	1416	1132	1199	47	235	1175	1414	1122	1149
125	1284	472	873	1391	1007	574	1383	967	374	383
126	428	653	291	1455	1327	687	461	818	1116	1119
127	1134	1209	97	485	938	229	1145	1264	372	373
128	378	403	528	1153	1304	572	1373	917	124	620
129	126	630	176	880	1426	1182	1449	1297	537	1198
130	42	210	1050	789	971	394	483	928	179	895
131	14	70	350	263	1315	627	161	805	1051	794
132	996	519	1108	1079	934	209	1045	764	846	1256
133	332	173	865	1351	807	1061	844	1246	282	1410
134	1102	1049	784	946	269	1345	777	911	94	470
135	863	1341	757	811	1081	944	259	1295	527	1148
136	1279	447	748	766	856	1306	582	1423	1167	1374
137	922	149	745	751	781	931	194	970	389	458
138	803	1041	744	746	756	806	1056	819	1121	1144
139	1259	347	248	1240	252	1260	352	273	1365	877
140	1411	1107	1074	909	84	420	613	91	455	788
141	966	369	358	303	28	140	700	526	1143	1254
142	322	123	615	101	505	1038	729	671	381	418
143	603	41	205	1025	664	346	243	1215	127	635
144	201	1005	564	1333	717	611	81	405	538	1203
145	67	335	188	940	239	1195	27	135	675	401
146	518	1103	1054	809	1071	894	9	45	225	1125
147	1164	1359	847	1261	357	298	3	15	75	375
148	388	453	778	916	119	595				

P = 1489

INDICES

	0	1	2	3	4	5	6	7	8	9
0		0	1222	190	956	740	1412	267	690	380
1	474	390	1146	633	1	930	424	675	114	454
2	208	457	124	39	880	1480	367	570	1223	353
3	664	130	158	580	409	1007	1336	1182	188	823
4	1430	41	191	905	1346	1120	1261	772	614	534
5	1214	865	101	261	304	1130	957	644	87	753
6	398	1344	1352	647	1380	1373	314	62	143	229
7	741	765	1070	889	916	182	1410	657	557	692
8	1164	760	1263	626	1413	1415	639	543	1080	205
9	854	900	995	320	506	1194	348	223	268	770
10	948	925	599	27	1323	1197	1483	379	38	1181
11	864	1372	691	319	378	779	1309	1013	487	942
12	132	780	1078	231	1086	732	381	1349	1114	1095
13	1107	968	48	721	1284	1310	1365	1212	1451	1040
14	475	962	499	1023	804	1093	623	724	650	1014
15	1404	1471	1144	1055	391	870	291	286	426	451
16	898	306	494	488	997	1320	360	1109	1147	1266
17	1149	834	373	1251	277	259	814	943	1427	698
18	588	95	634	46	729	434	54	1065	240	837
19	928	133	82	440	1445	75	2	1341	504	825
20	682	252	659	620	333	781	1249	419	1057	844
21	931	135	1217	955	113	157	1260	397	915	1079
22	598	1308	1106	803	425	372	53	681	112	111
23	513	847	1043	232	747	24	221	882	676	462
24	1354	237	514	950	812	1274	1453	1087	820	816
25	466	751	115	429	1083	117	848	337	829	1449
26	841	733	702	281	1270	1001	455	395	1018	808
27	1044	1288	1099	1090	946	382	1185	1327	774	510
28	209	1417	696	920	233	1384	757	308	538	1350
29	827	413	357	884	458	5	384	960	748	672
30	1138	1172	1205	1115	878	596	789	521	125	217
31	604	1062	25	670	20	1387	160	1096	185	743
32	632	569	40	1129	228	625	222	1371	731	1039
33	1054	1108	94	74	843	802	881	750	1000	509
34	883	520	568	801	107	969	985	713	11	108
35	1481	1203	548	445	677	17	1161	1132	432	49
36	322	908	1317	970	368	141	1268	245	463	421
37	168	528	1276	722	799	922	1462	986	571	1102
38	662	51	1355	1437	1304	1397	174	1285	1179	594
39	1297	714	1224	1158	1075	1432	238	1302	559	911
40	416	1311	1474	763	393	12	354	84	67	1256
41	515	1402	983	1020	153	1366	791	1230	578	109
42	665	607	1357	1152	951	667	689	123	1335	1213
43	1379	556	994	1482	131	1283	649	493	813	927
44	332	914	1042	1452	840	945	537	1204	159	1053
45	106	431	1275	173	415	152	1334	1041	1333	1245
46	247	549	581	14	777	1060	1454	146	481	329
47	1246	476	1443	1295	616	446	410	641	196	655
48	1088	327	1459	496	248	963	684	289	546	678
49	1008	978	1187	1028	821	22	554	1032	550	500

POWER RESIDUES

	0	1	2	3	4	5	6	7	8	9
0	1	14	196	1255	1191	295	1152	1238	953	1430
1	663	348	405	1203	463	526	1408	355	503	1086
2	314	1418	495	974	235	312	1390	103	1442	831
3	1211	575	605	1025	949	1374	1368	1284	108	23
4	322	41	574	591	829	1183	183	1073	132	359
5	559	381	867	226	186	1115	720	1146	1154	1266
6	1345	962	67	938	1220	701	880	408	1245	1051
7	1313	514	1240	981	333	195	1241	995	529	1450
8	943	1290	192	1199	407	1231	855	58	812	945
9	1318	584	731	1300	332	181	1045	1229	827	1155
10	1280	52	728	1258	1233	883	450	344	349	419
11	1399	229	228	214	18	252	550	255	592	843
12	1379	1438	775	427	22	308	1334	808	889	534
13	31	434	120	191	1185	211	1465	1153	1252	1149
14	1196	365	643	68	952	1416	467	582	703	908
15	800	777	455	414	1329	738	1398	215	32	448
16	316	1446	887	506	1128	902	716	1090	370	713
17	1048	1271	1415	453	386	937	1206	505	1114	706
18	950	1388	75	1050	1299	318	1474	1279	38	532
19	3	42	588	787	595	885	478	736	1370	1312
20	500	1044	1215	631	1389	89	1246	1065	20	280
21	942	1276	1485	1433	705	936	1192	309	1348	1004
22	655	236	326	97	1358	1144	1126	874	324	69
23	966	123	233	284	998	571	549	241	396	1077
24	188	1143	1112	678	558	367	671	460	484	820
25	1057	1397	201	1325	682	614	1151	1224	757	175
26	961	53	742	1454	999	585	745	7	98	1372
27	1340	892	576	619	1221	715	1076	174	947	1346
28	976	263	704	922	996	543	157	709	992	487
29	862	156	695	796	721	1160	1350	1032	1047	1257
30	1219	687	684	642	54	756	161	765	287	1040
31	1159	1336	836	1281	66	924	1024	935	1178	113
32	93	1302	360	573	577	633	1417	481	778	469
33	610	1095	440	204	1367	1270	1401	257	620	1235
34	911	842	1365	1242	1009	725	1216	645	96	1344
35	948	1360	1172	29	406	1217	659	292	1110	650
36	166	835	1267	1359	1158	1322	640	26	364	629
37	1361	1186	225	172	919	954	1444	859	114	107
38	9	126	275	872	296	1166	1434	719	1132	958
39	11	154	667	404	1189	267	760	217	60	840
40	1337	850	1477	1321	626	1319	598	927	1066	34
41	476	708	978	291	1096	454	400	1133	972	207
42	1409	369	699	852	16	224	158	723	1188	253
43	564	451	358	545	185	1101	524	1380	1452	971
44	193	1213	603	997	557	353	475	694	782	525
45	1394	159	737	1384	19	266	746	21	294	1138
46	1042	1187	239	368	685	656	250	522	1352	1060
47	1439	789	623	1277	10	140	471	638	1487	1461
48	1097	468	596	899	674	502	1072	118	163	793
49	679	572	563	437	162	779	483	806	861	142

P = 1489

INDICES

	0	1	2	3	4	5	6	7	8	9
50	200	1299	485	18	1337	177	163	1456	817	1486
51	1339	1156	582	1024	71	767	563	1162	1183	1441
52	575	726	467	974	436	449	15	805	1004	78
53	735	1133	189	674	129	1119	752	888	542	924
54	778	1094	1022	285	833	433	824	954	680	236
55	116	807	919	959	1061	624	508	444	244	50
56	1431	1255	1151	492	430	1059	654	1027	1455	725
57	1118	235	491	323	42	31	272	324	1084	630
58	561	893	147	651	91	265	618	909	192	584
59	1227	43	118	637	694	194	482	1015	406	1423
60	872	1318	906	442	939	32	849	1392	612	810
61	330	1405	523	1291	255	971	1347	1127	1439	273
62	338	609	796	472	1247	1472	404	1034	1242	369
63	1121	203	1382	325	830	601	1407	1167	477	1145
64	366	1429	303	142	1262	347	863	1085	1450	1143
65	359	587	1444	1056	1105	220	465	1269	773	356
66	788	631	842	10	1316	1461	1296	392	577	993
67	536	246	615	545	484	562	734	832	243	490
68	617	871	254	1241	302	464	535	301	1329	894
69	703	1389	719	1037	447	292	1233	716	1330	422
70	1215	65	937	148	282	214	179	1192	411	287
71	1239	1072	895	169	866	275	166	652	1271	387
72	56	294	642	427	1051	345	704	529	102	1140
73	1363	92	1002	1049	1467	1464	197	452	155	1400
74	1390	1277	262	1200	1010	266	456	1006	533	646
75	656	899	1196	941	720	723	305	258	836	619
76	396	846	1273	1448	1089	307	1171	1386	1038	800
77	1131	527	1396	910	1019	122	913	151	328	495
78	1031	1155	448	923	958	1026	892	193	809	471
79	1166	586	1460	489	1036	1191	293	1463	645	1447
80	150	585	1045	1279	1208	1046	497	998	127	1361
81	1234	987	88	1478	1306	1228	1289	1359	990	1280
82	249	1321	1136	552	717	572	754	98	1375	44
83	1100	29	525	1209	964	361	312	700	1331	1103
84	399	706	341	119	1091	518	886	1047	685	1110
85	401	1221	423	663	1345	86	1069	638	947	377
86	1113	498	290	1148	728	503	1216	52	1353	1082
87	1017	695	383	603	227	999	547	1267	661	1074
88	66	1356	648	105	776	195	1186	162	574	128
89	679	1150	271	1226	938	1438	1381	862	787	483
90	1328	936	165	1362	1009	835	1395	891	149	1305
91	1374	340	1068	1016	775	786	1067	1235	979	374
92	1469	711	283	1398	315	1174	1236	407	511	687
93	794	988	1188	1252	1368	317	215	175	63	860
94	980	1424	210	80	1177	89	1029	278	350	34
95	180	1286	144	8	375	873	1418	933	389	1479
96	822	260	61	759	1193	1180	230	1211	1470	1319
97	697	439	418	1307	23	815	280	1326	412	595
98	742	73	712	907	921	593	762	1229	555	944
99	1244	1294	288	1298	766	77	284	443	234	264

POWER RESIDUES

	0	1	2	3	4	5	6	7	8	9
50	499	1030	1019	865	198	1283	94	1316	556	339
51	279	928	1080	230	242	410	1273	1443	845	1407
52	341	307	1320	612	1123	832	1225	771	371	727
53	1244	1037	1117	748	49	686	670	446	288	1054
54	1355	1102	538	87	1218	673	488	876	352	461
55	498	1016	823	1099	496	988	431	78	1092	398
56	1105	580	675	516	1268	1373	1354	1088	342	321
57	27	378	825	1127	888	520	1324	668	418	1385
58	33	462	512	1212	589	801	791	651	180	1031
59	1033	1061	1453	985	389	979	305	1292	220	102
60	1428	635	1445	873	310	1362	1200	421	1427	621
61	1249	1107	608	1067	48	672	474	680	586	759
62	203	1353	1074	146	555	325	83	1162	1378	1424
63	579	661	320	13	182	1059	1425	593	857	86
64	1204	477	722	1174	57	798	749	63	882	436
65	148	583	717	1104	566	479	750	77	1078	202
66	1339	878	380	853	30	420	1413	425	1483	1405
67	313	1404	299	1208	533	17	238	354	489	890
68	548	227	200	1311	486	848	1449	929	1094	426
69	8	112	79	1106	594	871	282	970	179	1017
70	837	1295	262	690	726	1230	841	1351	1046	1243
71	1023	921	982	347	391	1007	697	824	1113	692
72	754	133	373	755	147	569	521	1338	864	184
73	1087	328	125	261	676	530	1464	1139	1056	1383
74	5	70	980	319	1488	1475	1293	234	298	1194
75	337	251	536	59	826	1141	1084	286	1026	963
76	81	1134	986	403	1175	71	994	515	1254	1177
77	99	1386	47	658	278	914	884	464	540	115
78	121	205	1381	1466	1167	1448	915	898	660	306
79	1306	416	1357	1130	930	1108	622	1263	1303	374
80	769	343	335	223	144	527	1422	551	269	788
81	609	1081	244	438	176	975	249	508	1156	1294
82	248	494	960	39	546	199	1297	290	1082	258
83	634	1431	677	544	171	905	758	189	1157	1308
84	444	260	662	334	209	1437	761	231	256	606
85	1039	1145	1140	1070	90	1260	1261	1275	1471	1237
86	939	1234	897	646	110	51	714	1062	1467	1181
87	155	681	600	955	1458	1055	1369	1298	304	1278
88	24	336	237	340	293	1124	846	1421	537	73
89	1022	907	786	581	689	712	1034	1075	160	751
90	91	1274	1457	1041	1173	43	602	983	361	587
91	773	399	1119	776	441	218	74	1036	1103	552
92	283	984	375	783	539	101	1414	439	190	1171
93	15	210	1451	957	1486	1447	901	702	894	604
94	1011	753	119	177	989	445	274	858	100	1400
95	243	424	1469	1209	547	213	4	56	784	553
96	297	1180	141	485	834	1253	1163	1392	131	345
97	363	615	1165	1420	523	1366	1256	1205	491	918
98	940	1248	1093	412	1301	346	377	811	931	1122
99	818	1029	1005	669	432	92	1288	164	807	875

P = 1489

INDICES

	0	1	2	3	4	5	6	7	8	9
100	1422	1290	1033	1428	219	992	1240	715	1071	344
101	1399	940	1385	1154	1190	1360	551	699	1220	502
102	1073	1225	890	710	316	33	758	1325	1293	991
103	501	589	297	590	896	1159	917	531	1175	850
104	309	903	460	1281	201	96	708	298	170	1076
105	183	69	1237	1393	539	875	738	250	1300	635
106	469	591	867	1433	1411	207	408	613	1351	1409
107	853	1322	486	47	622	897	276	239	658	1259
108	512	811	828	1098	756	1137	19	730	567	1160
109	167	1303	558	982	688	331	414	480	1458	553
110	1338	435	541	918	653	560	693	611	795	1406
111	358	1315	242	718	178	55	1466	532	1272	912
112	1165	1207	989	524	885	1112	226	573	164	1066
113	793	1176	388	417	761	1421	1189	1292	459	737
114	852	755	1457	241	225	851	57	1312	1264	139
115	1253	256	6	137	58	99	818	838	364	310
116	295	1475	627	966	1369	972	385	784	1313	1376
117	1487	929	352	904	643	764	1414	769	318	1348
118	961	869	1265	45	1340	134	371	461	428	394
119	1416	4	216	1128	749	1202	140	1101	1157	83
120	606	1282	1052	13	640	977	176	1440	673	953
121	1254	30	583	441	1126	202	346	355	544	300
122	64	274	1139	1199	257	526	1025	1446	1477	97
123	705	85	1081	104	861	339	1173	859	7	1210
124	72	76	343	709	530	68	206	1258	981	610
125	1206	1420	138	965	768	3	976	299	103	1257
126	855	856	1425	797	1116	1169	59	362	564	1342
127	335	171	1141	516	901	857	211	473	879	187
128	100	313	1163	505	37	1077	1364	1403	996	1426
129	81	1248	597	746	819	701	1184	826	877	184
130	93	984	321	798	1178	1473	790	1378	839	1332
131	1442	683	199	70	1003	1021	507	1117	90	405
132	522	403	365	1104	576	253	1232	1238	1050	154
133	1195	1170	1030	1035	126	1135	311	400	727	660
134	270	1394	1468	1367	349	60	279	1243	218	1219
135	296	707	468	621	566	540	1465	792	224	363
136	351	370	605	1125	1476	342	975	334	36	876
137	198	1231	269	565	35	1122	1063	1435	628	120
138	437	782	1123	739	453	579	771	1343	181	204
139	26	1012	967	1092	450	1250	1064	251	156	110
140	949	336	1287	1383	671	669	1370	519	16	420
141	1436	1301	1401	666	926	172	145	326	21	1485
142	973	887	806	1058	629	636	1391	608	600	1142
143	9	831	1388	213	386	1048	1005	845	121	470
144	1278	1358	28	517	376	602	161	935	785	686
145	79	932	438	592	263	1153	1324	902	874	1408
146	1097	479	1314	1111	736	136	783	868	1201	952
147	1198	858	1419	1168	186	745	1377	402	1134	1218
148	1124	1434	1011	668	1484	212	934	478	744	

POWER RESIDUES

	0	1	2	3	4	5	6	7	8	9
100	338	265	732	1314	528	1436	747	35	490	904
101	744	1482	1391	117	149	597	913	870	268	774
102	413	1315	542	143	513	1226	785	567	493	946
103	1332	780	497	1002	627	1333	794	693	768	329
104	139	457	442	232	270	802	805	847	1435	733
105	1328	724	1202	449	330	153	653	208	1423	565
106	465	554	311	1376	1396	187	1129	916	912	856
107	72	1008	711	1020	879	394	1049	1285	122	219
108	88	1232	869	254	578	647	124	247	480	764
109	273	844	1393	145	541	129	317	1460	1083	272
110	830	1197	379	839	1323	654	222	130	331	167
111	849	1463	1125	860	128	303	1264	1317	570	535
112	45	630	1375	1382	1480	1363	1214	617	1193	323
113	55	770	357	531	1478	1335	822	1085	300	1222
114	729	1272	1429	649	152	639	12	168	863	170
115	891	562	423	1455	1013	781	511	1198	393	1035
116	1089	356	517	1282	80	1120	790	637	1473	1265
117	1331	766	301	1236	925	1038	1131	944	1304	388
118	965	109	37	518	1296	276	886	492	932	1136
119	1014	795	707	964	95	1330	752	105	1470	1223
120	743	1468	1195	351	447	302	1250	1121	804	833
121	1239	967	137	429	50	700	866	212	1479	1349
122	1018	851	2	28	392	1021	893	590	815	987
123	417	1371	1326	696	810	917	926	1052	1327	710
124	1006	683	628	1347	990	459	470	624	1291	206
125	1395	173	933	1150	1210	561	409	1259	1247	1079
126	216	46	644	82	1148	1182	169	877	366	657
127	264	718	1118	762	245	452	372	741	1440	803
128	819	1043	1201	435	134	387	951	1402	271	816
129	1001	613	1137	1028	991	473	666	390	993	501
130	1058	1411	397	1091	384	909	814	973	221	116
131	135	401	1147	1168	1462	1111	664	362	601	969
132	165	821	1071	104	1456	1027	977	277	900	688
133	698	838	1309	458	456	428	36	504	1100	510
134	1184	197	1269	1387	61	854	44	616	1179	127
135	289	1068	62	868	240	382	881	422	1441	817
136	1015	809	903	730	1286	136	415	1343	934	1164
137	1406	327	111	65	910	828	1169	1476	1307	430
138	64	896	632	1403	285	1012	767	315	1432	691
139	740	1426	607	1053	1341	906	772	385	923	1010
140	739	1412	411	1287	150	611	1109	636	1459	1069
141	76	1064	6	84	1176	85	1190	281	956	1472
142	1251	1135	1000	599	941	1262	1289	178	1003	641
143	40	560	395	1063	1481	1377	1410	383	895	618
144	1207	519	1310	472	652	194	1227	799	763	259
145	648	138	443	246	466	568	507	1142	1098	482
146	792	665	376	797	735	1356	1116	734	1342	920
147	968	151	625	1305	402	1161	1364	1228	813	959
148	25	350	433	106	1484	1419	509	1170		

P = 1493

INDICES

	0	1	2	3	4	5	6	7	8	9
0		0	1	123	2	1459	124	26	3	246
1	1460	413	125	637	27	90	4	1199	247	398
2	1461	149	414	889	126	1426	638	369	28	943
3	91	586	5	536	1200	1485	248	1413	399	760
4	1462	205	150	132	415	213	890	408	127	52
5	1427	1322	639	964	370	380	29	521	944	1059
6	92	71	587	272	6	604	537	730	1201	1012
7	1486	598	249	1313	1414	57	400	439	761	1097
8	1463	492	206	1245	151	1166	133	1066	416	262
9	214	663	891	709	409	365	128	1055	53	659
10	1428	324	1323	549	640	116	965	1432	371	509
11	381	44	30	235	522	856	945	883	1060	1225
12	93	826	72	328	588	1393	273	461	7	255
13	605	972	538	424	731	336	1202	1106	1013	1327
14	1487	531	599	1050	250	910	1314	175	1415	901
15	58	1231	401	1445	440	553	762	471	1098	1087
16	1464	915	493	1138	207	503	1246	1214	152	1274
17	1167	644	134	1252	1067	1452	417	1182	263	814
18	215	956	664	194	892	1380	710	120	410	395
19	366	1482	129	1319	1056	727	54	1242	660	656
20	1429	853	325	969	1324	172	550	1135	641	811
21	117	724	966	721	1433	99	372	612	510	1436
22	382	344	45	1175	31	180	236	102	523	355
23	857	562	946	987	884	375	1061	1220	1226	189
24	94	1030	827	615	73	19	329	1035	589	1368
25	1394	513	274	1302	462	1289	8	1420	256	1439
26	606	1189	973	1042	539	931	425	385	732	702
27	337	300	1203	786	1107	347	1014	1150	1328	832
28	1488	1195	532	48	600	488	1051	231	251	906
29	911	1178	1315	807	176	1026	1416	782	902	34
30	59	158	1232	447	402	38	1446	183	441	672
31	554	620	763	282	472	239	1099	924	1088	1356
32	1465	63	916	105	494	571	1139	632	208	434
33	504	526	1247	167	1215	697	153	162	1275	358
34	1168	999	645	78	135	979	1253	860	1068	307
35	1453	1006	418	1236	1183	565	264	1348	815	1265
36	216	796	957	949	665	1280	195	678	893	451
37	1381	990	711	744	121	24	411	88	396	887
38	367	584	1483	758	130	406	1320	378	1057	270
39	728	596	55	1095	1243	1064	661	363	657	547
40	1430	42	854	1223	326	459	970	334	1325	1048
41	173	1229	551	1085	1136	1212	642	1450	812	192
42	118	1480	725	654	967	1133	722	97	1434	1173
43	100	560	373	187	613	1033	511	1287	1437	1040
44	383	298	345	830	46	229	1176	1024	32	445
45	181	618	237	1354	103	630	524	695	356	76
46	858	1004	563	1263	947	676	988	22	885	756
47	376	594	1062	545	1221	332	1227	1210	190	652
48	95	558	1031	1038	828	1022	616	628	74	1261
49	20	592	330	650	1036	626	590	624	1369	1371

POWER RESIDUES

	0	1	2	3	4	5	6	7	8	9
0	1	2	4	8	16	32	64	128	256	512
1	1024	555	1110	727	1454	1415	1337	1181	869	245
2	490	980	467	934	375	750	7	14	28	56
3	112	224	448	896	299	598	1196	899	305	610
4	1220	947	401	802	111	222	444	888	283	566
5	1132	771	49	98	196	392	784	75	150	300
6	600	1200	907	321	642	1284	1075	657	1314	1135
7	777	61	122	244	488	976	459	918	343	686
8	1372	1251	1009	525	1050	607	1214	935	377	754
9	15	30	60	120	240	480	960	427	854	215
10	430	860	227	454	908	323	646	1292	1091	689
11	1378	1263	1033	573	1146	799	105	210	420	840
12	187	374	748	3	6	12	24	48	96	192
13	384	768	43	86	172	344	688	1376	1259	1025
14	557	1114	735	1470	1447	1401	1309	1125	757	21
15	42	84	168	336	672	1344	1195	897	301	602
16	1204	915	337	674	1348	1203	913	333	666	1332
17	1171	849	205	410	820	147	294	588	1176	859
18	225	450	900	307	614	1228	963	433	866	239
19	478	956	419	838	183	366	732	1464	1435	1377
20	1261	1029	565	1130	767	41	82	164	328	656
21	1312	1131	769	45	90	180	360	720	1440	1387
22	1281	1069	645	1290	1087	681	1362	1231	969	445
23	890	287	574	1148	803	113	226	452	904	315
24	630	1260	1027	561	1122	751	9	18	36	72
25	144	288	576	1152	811	129	258	516	1032	571
26	1142	791	89	178	356	712	1424	1355	1217	941
27	389	778	63	126	252	504	1008	523	1046	599
28	1198	903	313	626	1252	1011	529	1058	623	1246
29	999	505	1010	527	1054	615	1230	967	441	882
30	271	542	1084	675	1350	1207	921	349	698	1396
31	1299	1105	717	1434	1375	1257	1021	549	1098	703
32	1406	1319	1145	797	101	202	404	808	123	246
33	492	984	475	950	407	814	135	270	540	1080
34	667	1334	1175	857	221	442	884	275	550	1100
35	707	1414	1335	1177	861	229	458	916	339	678
36	1356	1219	945	397	794	95	190	380	760	27
37	54	108	216	432	864	235	470	940	387	774
38	55	110	220	440	880	267	534	1068	643	1286
39	1079	665	1330	1167	841	189	378	756	19	38
40	76	152	304	608	1216	939	385	770	47	94
41	188	376	752	11	22	44	88	176	352	704
42	1408	1323	1153	813	133	266	532	1064	635	1270
43	1047	601	1202	911	329	658	1316	1139	785	77
44	154	308	616	1232	971	449	898	303	606	1212
45	931	369	738	1476	1459	1425	1357	1221	949	405
46	810	127	254	508	1016	539	1078	663	1326	1159
47	825	157	314	628	1256	1019	545	1090	687	1374
48	1255	1017	541	1082	671	1342	1191	889	285	570
49	1140	787	81	162	324	648	1296	1099	705	1410

P = 1493

INDICES

	0	1	2	3	4	5	6	7	8	9
50	1395	1337	514	1373	275	291	1303	1397	463	1077
51	1290	1339	9	767	1421	516	257	821	1440	1375
52	607	1363	1190	277	974	83	1043	293	540	286
53	932	1305	426	842	386	1399	733	937	703	465
54	338	482	301	1079	1204	476	787	1292	1108	317
55	348	1341	1015	1123	1151	11	1329	140	833	769
56	1489	243	1196	1423	533	202	49	518	601	1310
57	489	259	1052	113	232	823	252	1103	907	1442
58	912	1271	1179	1377	1316	850	808	609	177	984
59	1027	1365	1417	928	783	1192	903	779	35	279
60	60	431	159	976	1233	793	448	85	403	1092
61	39	1045	1447	1130	184	295	442	692	673	542
62	555	1258	621	288	764	1360	283	934	473	1120
63	240	1307	1100	847	925	428	1089	689	1357	844
64	1466	1469	64	388	917	222	106	1401	495	1472
65	572	735	1140	865	633	939	209	67	435	705
66	505	1389	527	467	1248	391	168	340	1216	1298
67	698	484	154	920	163	303	1276	580	359	1081
68	1169	225	1000	1206	646	1073	79	478	136	109
69	980	789	1254	685	861	1294	1069	1404	308	1110
70	1454	1408	1007	319	419	498	1237	350	1184	802
71	566	1343	265	1475	1349	1017	816	312	1266	1125
72	217	575	797	1153	958	877	950	13	666	738
73	1281	1331	196	1114	679	142	894	1143	452	835
74	1382	1158	991	771	712	868	745	1491	122	1458
75	25	245	412	636	89	1198	397	148	888	1425
76	368	942	585	535	1484	1412	759	204	131	212
77	407	51	1321	963	379	520	1058	70	271	603
78	729	1011	597	1312	56	438	1096	491	1244	1165
79	1065	261	662	708	364	1054	658	323	548	115
80	1431	508	43	234	855	882	1224	825	327	1392
81	460	254	971	423	335	1105	1326	530	1049	909
82	174	900	1230	1444	552	470	1086	914	1137	502
83	1213	1273	643	1251	1451	1181	813	955	193	1379
84	119	394	1481	1318	726	1241	655	852	968	171
85	1134	810	723	720	98	611	1435	343	1174	179
86	101	354	561	986	374	1219	188	1029	614	18
87	1034	1367	512	1301	1288	1419	1438	1188	1041	930
88	384	701	299	785	346	1149	831	1194	47	487
89	230	905	1177	806	1025	781	33	157	446	37
90	182	671	619	281	238	923	1355	62	104	570
91	631	433	525	160	696	161	357	998	77	978
92	859	306	1005	1235	564	1347	1264	795	948	1279
93	677	450	989	743	23	87	886	583	757	405
94	377	269	595	1094	1063	362	546	41	1222	458
95	333	1047	1228	1084	1211	1449	191	1479	653	1132
96	96	1172	559	186	1032	1286	1039	297	829	228
97	1023	444	617	1353	629	694	75	1003	1262	675
98	21	755	593	544	331	1209	651	557	1037	1021
99	627	1260	591	649	625	623	1370	1336	1372	290

POWER RESIDUES

	0	1	2	3	4	5	6	7	8	9
50	1327	1161	829	165	330	660	1320	1147	801	109
51	218	436	872	251	502	1004	515	1030	567	1134
52	775	57	114	228	456	912	331	662	1324	1155
53	817	141	282	564	1128	763	33	66	132	264
54	528	1056	619	1238	983	473	946	399	798	103
55	206	412	824	155	310	620	1240	987	481	962
56	431	862	231	462	924	355	710	1420	1347	1201
57	909	325	650	1300	1107	721	1442	1391	1289	1085
58	677	1354	1215	937	381	762	31	62	124	248
59	496	992	491	982	471	942	391	782	71	142
60	284	568	1136	779	65	130	260	520	1040	587
61	1174	855	217	434	868	243	486	972	451	902
62	311	622	1244	995	497	994	495	990	487	974
63	455	910	327	654	1308	1123	753	13	26	52
64	104	208	416	832	171	342	684	1368	1243	993
65	493	986	479	958	423	846	199	398	796	99
66	198	396	792	91	182	364	728	1456	1419	1345
67	1197	901	309	618	1236	979	465	930	367	734
68	1468	1443	1393	1293	1093	693	1386	1279	1065	637
69	1274	1055	617	1234	975	457	914	335	670	1340
70	1187	881	269	538	1076	659	1318	1143	793	93
71	186	372	744	1488	1483	1473	1453	1413	1333	1173
72	853	213	426	852	211	422	844	195	390	780
73	67	134	268	536	1072	651	1302	1111	729	1458
74	1423	1353	1213	933	373	746	1492	1491	1489	1485
75	1477	1461	1429	1365	1237	981	469	938	383	766
76	39	78	156	312	624	1248	1003	513	1026	559
77	1118	743	1486	1479	1465	1437	1381	1269	1045	597
78	1194	895	297	594	1188	883	273	546	1092	691
79	1382	1271	1049	605	1210	927	361	722	1444	1395
80	1297	1101	709	1418	1343	1193	893	293	586	1172
81	851	209	418	836	179	358	716	1432	1371	1249
82	1005	517	1034	575	1150	807	121	242	484	968
83	443	886	279	558	1116	739	1478	1463	1433	1373
84	1253	1013	533	1066	639	1278	1063	633	1266	1039
85	585	1170	847	201	402	804	115	230	460	920
86	347	694	1388	1283	1073	653	1306	1119	745	1490
87	1487	1481	1469	1445	1397	1301	1109	725	1450	1407
88	1321	1149	805	117	234	468	936	379	758	23
89	46	92	184	368	736	1472	1451	1409	1325	1157
90	821	149	298	596	1192	891	289	578	1156	819
91	145	290	580	1160	827	161	322	644	1288	1083
92	673	1346	1199	905	317	634	1268	1043	593	1186
93	879	265	530	1060	627	1254	1015	537	1074	655
94	1310	1127	761	29	58	116	232	464	928	363
95	726	1452	1411	1329	1165	837	181	362	724	1448
96	1403	1313	1133	773	53	106	212	424	848	203
97	406	812	131	262	524	1048	603	1206	919	345
98	690	1380	1267	1041	589	1178	863	233	466	932
99	371	742	1484	1475	1457	1421	1349	1205	917	341

P = 1493

INDICES

	0	1	2	3	4	5	6	7	8	9
100	1396	1076	1338	766	515	820	1374	1362	276	82
101	292	285	1304	841	1398	936	464	481	1078	475
102	1291	316	1340	1122	10	139	768	242	1422	201
103	517	1309	258	112	822	1102	1441	1270	1376	849
104	608	983	1364	927	1191	778	278	430	975	792
105	84	1091	1044	1129	294	691	541	1257	287	1359
106	933	1119	1306	846	427	688	843	1468	387	221
107	1400	1471	734	864	938	66	704	1388	466	390
108	339	1297	483	919	302	579	1080	224	1205	1072
109	477	108	788	684	1293	1403	1109	1407	318	497
110	349	801	1342	1474	1016	311	1124	574	1152	876
111	12	737	1330	1113	141	1142	834	1157	770	867
112	1490	1457	244	635	1197	147	1424	941	534	1411
113	203	211	50	962	519	69	602	1010	1311	437
114	490	1164	260	707	1053	322	114	507	233	881
115	824	1391	253	422	1104	529	908	899	1443	469
116	913	501	1272	1250	1180	954	1378	393	1317	1240
117	851	170	809	719	610	342	178	353	985	1218
118	1028	17	1366	1300	1418	1187	929	700	784	1148
119	1193	486	904	805	780	156	36	670	280	922
120	61	569	432	165	160	997	977	305	1234	1346
121	794	1278	449	742	86	582	404	268	1093	361
122	40	457	1046	1083	1448	1478	1131	1171	185	1285
123	296	227	443	1352	693	1002	674	754	543	1208
124	556	1020	1259	648	622	1335	289	1075	765	819
125	1361	81	284	840	935	480	474	315	1121	138
126	241	200	1308	111	1101	1269	848	982	926	777
127	429	791	1090	1128	690	1256	1358	1118	845	687
128	1467	220	1470	863	65	1387	389	1296	918	578
129	223	1071	107	683	1402	1406	496	800	1473	310
130	573	875	736	1112	1141	1156	866	1456	634	146
131	940	1410	210	961	68	1009	436	1163	706	321
132	506	880	1390	421	528	898	468	500	1249	953
133	392	1239	169	718	341	352	1217	16	1299	1186
134	699	1147	485	804	155	669	921	568	164	996
135	304	1345	1277	741	581	267	360	456	1082	1477
136	1170	1284	226	1351	1001	753	1207	1019	647	1334
137	1074	818	80	839	479	314	137	199	110	1268
138	981	776	790	1127	1255	1117	686	219	862	1386
139	1295	577	1070	682	1405	799	309	874	1111	1155
140	1455	145	1409	960	1008	1162	320	879	420	897
141	499	952	1238	717	351	15	1185	1146	803	668
142	567	995	1344	740	266	455	1476	1283	1350	752
143	1018	1333	817	838	313	198	1267	775	1126	1116
144	218	1385	576	681	798	873	1154	144	959	1161
145	878	896	951	716	14	1145	667	994	739	454
146	1282	751	1332	837	197	774	1115	1384	680	872
147	143	1160	895	715	1144	993	453	750	836	773
148	1383	871	1159	714	992	749	772	870	713	748
149	869	747	746							

POWER RESIDUES

	0	1	2	3	4	5	6	7	8	9
100	682	1364	1235	977	461	922	351	702	1404	1315
101	1137	781	69	138	276	552	1104	715	1430	1367
102	1241	989	485	970	447	894	295	590	1180	867
103	241	482	964	435	870	247	494	988	483	966
104	439	878	263	526	1052	611	1222	951	409	818
105	143	286	572	1144	795	97	194	388	776	59
106	118	236	472	944	395	790	87	174	348	696
107	1392	1291	1089	685	1370	1247	1001	509	1018	543
108	1086	679	1358	1223	953	413	826	159	318	636
109	1272	1051	609	1218	943	393	786	79	158	316
110	632	1264	1035	577	1154	815	137	274	548	1096
111	699	1398	1303	1113	733	1466	1439	1385	1277	1061
112	629	1258	1023	553	1106	719	1438	1383	1273	1053
113	613	1226	959	425	850	207	414	828	163	326
114	652	1304	1115	737	1474	1455	1417	1341	1189	885
115	277	554	1108	723	1446	1399	1305	1117	741	1482
116	1471	1449	1405	1317	1141	789	85	170	340	680
117	1360	1227	961	429	858	223	446	892	291	582
118	1164	835	177	354	708	1416	1339	1185	877	261
119	522	1044	595	1190	887	281	562	1124	755	17
120	34	68	136	272	544	1088	683	1366	1239	985
121	477	954	415	830	167	334	668	1336	1179	865
122	237	474	948	403	806	119	238	476	952	411
123	822	151	302	604	1208	923	353	706	1412	1331
124	1169	845	197	394	788	83	166	332	664	1328
125	1163	833	173	346	692	1384	1275	1057	621	1242
126	991	489	978	463	926	359	718	1436	1379	1265
127	1037	581	1162	831	169	338	676	1352	1211	929
128	365	730	1460	1427	1361	1229	965	437	874	255
129	510	1020	547	1094	695	1390	1287	1081	669	1338
130	1183	873	253	506	1012	531	1062	631	1262	1031
131	569	1138	783	73	146	292	584	1168	843	193
132	386	772	51	102	204	408	816	139	278	556
133	1112	731	1462	1431	1369	1245	997	501	1002	511
134	1022	551	1102	711	1422	1351	1209	925	357	714
135	1428	1363	1233	973	453	906	319	638	1276	1059
136	625	1250	1007	521	1042	591	1182	871	249	498
137	996	499	998	503	1006	519	1038	583	1166	839
138	185	370	740	1480	1467	1441	1389	1285	1077	661
139	1322	1151	809	125	250	500	1000	507	1014	535
140	1070	647	1294	1095	697	1394	1295	1097	701	1402
141	1311	1129	765	37	74	148	296	592	1184	875
142	257	514	1028	563	1126	759	25	50	100	200
143	400	800	107	214	428	856	219	438	876	259
144	518	1036	579	1158	823	153	306	612	1224	955
145	417	834	175	350	700	1400	1307	1121	749	5
146	10	20	40	80	160	320	640	1280	1067	641
147	1282	1071	649	1298	1103	713	1426	1359	1225	957
148	421	842	191	382	764	35	70	140	280	560
149	1120	747								

P = 1499

INDICES

	0	1	2	3	4	5	6	7	8	9
0		0	1	148	2	1448	149	665	3	296
1	1449	1021	150	1112	666	98	4	1371	297	859
2	1450	813	1022	1187	151	1398	1113	444	667	680
3	99	120	5	1169	1372	615	298	157	860	1260
4	1451	140	814	1032	1023	246	1188	1443	152	1330
5	1399	21	1114	180	445	971	668	1007	681	1000
6	100	1213	121	961	6	1062	1170	1125	1373	1335
7	616	1437	299	559	158	48	861	188	1261	640
8	1452	592	141	402	815	1321	1033	828	1024	793
9	247	279	1189	268	1444	809	153	176	1331	1317
10	1400	1404	22	1090	1115	763	181	83	446	1276
11	972	305	669	1234	1008	1137	682	1408	1001	538
12	101	544	1214	288	122	1348	962	1248	7	1180
13	1063	409	1171	26	1126	394	1374	480	1336	576
14	617	93	1438	635	300	630	560	1478	159	1094
15	49	1070	862	169	189	70	1262	1486	641	328
16	1453	354	593	458	142	1119	403	1204	816	726
17	1322	1155	1034	385	829	565	1025	1148	794	373
18	248	767	280	1361	1190	107	269	894	1445	1109
19	810	677	154	243	177	1210	1332	185	1318	265
20	1401	1273	1405	1345	23	90	1091	1483	1116	382
21	764	1106	182	87	84	982	447	785	1277	707
22	973	985	306	954	670	196	1235	1080	1009	450
23	1138	336	683	506	1409	1393	1002	788	539	164
24	102	780	545	740	1215	1280	289	473	123	550
25	1349	516	963	710	1249	1469	8	883	1181	822
26	1064	976	410	491	1172	130	27	941	1127	988
27	395	1099	1375	427	481	921	1337	309	577	416
28	618	745	94	116	1439	957	636	805	301	1244
29	631	324	561	673	1479	950	160	1465	1095	801
30	50	199	1071	54	863	1163	170	348	190	1238
31	71	718	1263	1220	1487	911	642	1083	329	203
32	1454	231	355	732	594	1012	459	1424	143	610
33	1120	1312	404	453	1205	1075	817	319	727	1382
34	1323	1141	1156	497	1035	1285	386	1052	830	339
35	566	58	1026	77	1149	1387	795	686	374	210
36	249	220	768	692	281	509	1362	867	1191	436
37	108	845	270	1412	895	1496	1446	294	1110	1369
38	811	1396	678	1167	155	138	244	1328	178	1005
39	1211	1060	1333	557	186	590	1319	791	266	174
40	1402	761	1274	1232	1406	542	1346	1178	24	478
41	91	628	1092	167	1484	352	1117	724	383	1146
42	765	105	1107	241	183	1271	88	380	85	783
43	983	194	448	504	786	778	1278	548	708	881
44	974	128	986	425	307	743	955	1242	671	1463
45	197	1161	1236	1218	1081	229	1010	608	451	317
46	1139	1283	337	75	684	218	507	434	1410	292
47	1394	136	1003	555	789	759	540	476	165	722
48	103	1269	781	502	546	126	741	1461	1216	606
49	1281	216	290	553	474	1267	124	604	551	602

POWER RESIDUES

	0	1	2	3	4	5	6	7	8	9
0	1	2	4	8	16	32	64	128	256	512
1	1024	549	1098	697	1394	1289	1079	659	1318	1137
2	775	51	102	204	408	816	133	266	532	1064
3	629	1258	1017	535	1070	641	1282	1065	631	1262
4	1025	551	1102	705	1410	1321	1143	787	75	150
5	300	600	1200	901	303	606	1212	925	351	702
6	1404	1309	1119	739	1478	1457	1415	1331	1163	827
7	155	310	620	1240	981	463	926	353	706	1412
8	1325	1151	803	107	214	428	856	213	426	852
9	205	410	820	141	282	564	1128	757	15	30
10	60	120	240	480	960	421	842	185	370	740
11	1480	1461	1423	1347	1195	891	283	566	1132	765
12	31	62	124	248	496	992	485	970	441	882
13	265	530	1060	621	1242	985	471	942	385	770
14	41	82	164	328	656	1312	1125	751	3	6
15	12	24	48	96	192	384	768	37	74	148
16	296	592	1184	869	239	478	956	413	826	153
17	306	612	1224	949	399	798	97	194	388	776
18	53	106	212	424	848	197	394	788	77	154
19	308	616	1232	965	431	862	225	450	900	301
20	602	1204	909	319	638	1276	1053	607	1214	929
21	359	718	1436	1373	1247	995	491	982	465	930
22	361	722	1444	1389	1279	1059	619	1238	977	455
23	910	321	642	1284	1069	639	1278	1057	615	1230
24	961	423	846	193	386	772	45	90	180	360
25	720	1440	1381	1263	1027	555	1110	721	1442	1385
26	1271	1043	587	1174	849	199	398	796	93	186
27	372	744	1488	1477	1455	1411	1323	1147	795	91
28	182	364	728	1456	1413	1327	1155	811	123	246
29	492	984	469	938	377	754	9	18	36	72
30	144	288	576	1152	805	111	222	444	888	277
31	554	1108	717	1434	1369	1239	979	459	918	337
32	674	1348	1197	895	291	582	1164	829	159	318
33	636	1272	1045	591	1182	865	231	462	924	349
34	698	1396	1293	1087	675	1350	1201	903	307	614
35	1228	957	415	830	161	322	644	1288	1077	655
36	1310	1121	743	1486	1473	1447	1395	1291	1083	667
37	1334	1169	839	179	358	716	1432	1365	1231	963
38	427	854	209	418	836	173	346	692	1384	1269
39	1039	579	1158	817	135	270	540	1080	661	1322
40	1145	791	83	166	332	664	1328	1157	815	131
41	262	524	1048	597	1194	889	279	558	1116	733
42	1466	1433	1367	1235	971	443	886	273	546	1092
43	685	1370	1241	983	467	934	369	738	1476	1453
44	1407	1315	1131	763	27	54	108	216	432	864
45	229	458	916	333	666	1332	1165	831	163	326
46	652	1304	1109	719	1438	1377	1255	1011	523	1046
47	593	1186	873	247	494	988	477	954	409	818
48	137	274	548	1096	693	1386	1273	1047	595	1190
49	881	263	526	1052	605	1210	921	343	686	1372

P = 1499

INDICES

	0	1	2	3	4	5	6	7	8	9
50	1350	1352	517	1301	964	1354	711	874	1250	519
51	1470	1224	9	1303	884	1040	1182	966	823	533
52	1065	1356	977	468	411	713	492	1491	1173	876
53	131	1296	28	1252	942	33	1128	521	989	853
54	396	1472	1100	915	1376	1226	428	1290	482	11
55	922	41	1338	1305	310	255	578	886	417	646
56	619	1042	746	662	95	1184	117	1257	1440	968
57	958	1434	637	825	806	1087	302	535	1245	391
58	632	1067	325	1201	562	1358	674	262	1480	979
59	951	333	161	470	1466	488	1096	413	802	947
60	51	715	200	1421	1072	494	55	207	864	1493
61	1164	1057	171	1175	349	238	191	878	1239	226
62	72	133	719	1458	1264	1298	1221	530	1488	30
63	912	38	643	1254	1084	1198	330	944	204	235
64	1455	35	232	835	356	1130	733	838	595	523
65	1013	933	460	991	1425	359	144	855	611	17
66	1121	398	1313	1133	405	1474	454	369	1206	1102
67	1076	736	818	917	320	344	728	1378	1383	841
68	1324	1228	1142	774	1157	430	498	598	1036	1292
69	1286	658	387	484	1053	526	831	13	340	654
70	567	924	59	1016	1027	43	78	571	1150	1340
71	1388	936	796	1307	687	585	375	312	211	463
72	250	257	221	928	769	580	693	994	282	888
73	510	905	1363	419	868	1428	1192	648	437	63
74	109	621	846	362	271	1044	1413	698	896	748
75	1497	147	1447	664	295	1020	1111	97	1370	858
76	812	1186	1397	443	679	119	1168	614	156	1259
77	139	1031	245	1442	1329	20	179	970	1006	999
78	1212	960	1061	1124	1334	1436	558	47	187	639
79	591	401	1320	827	792	278	267	808	175	1316
80	1403	1089	762	82	1275	304	1233	1136	1407	537
81	543	287	1347	1247	1179	408	25	393	479	575
82	92	634	629	1477	1093	1069	168	69	1485	327
83	353	457	1118	1203	725	1154	384	564	1147	372
84	766	1360	106	893	1108	676	242	1209	184	264
85	1272	1344	89	1482	381	1105	86	981	784	706
86	984	953	195	1079	449	335	505	1392	787	163
87	779	739	1279	472	549	515	709	1468	882	821
88	975	490	129	940	987	1098	426	920	308	415
89	744	115	956	804	1243	323	672	949	1464	800
90	198	53	1162	347	1237	717	1219	910	1082	202
91	230	731	1011	1423	609	1311	452	1074	318	1381
92	1140	496	1284	1051	338	57	76	1386	685	209
93	219	691	508	866	435	844	1411	1495	293	1368
94	1395	1166	137	1327	1004	1059	556	589	790	173
95	760	1231	541	1177	477	627	166	351	723	1145
96	104	240	1270	379	782	193	503	777	547	880
97	127	424	742	1241	1462	1160	1217	228	607	316
98	1282	74	217	433	291	135	554	758	475	721
99	1268	501	125	1460	605	215	552	1266	603	601

POWER RESIDUES

	0	1	2	3	4	5	6	7	8	9
50	1245	991	483	966	433	866	233	466	932	365
51	730	1460	1421	1343	1187	875	251	502	1004	509
52	1018	537	1074	649	1298	1097	695	1390	1281	1063
53	627	1254	1009	519	1038	577	1154	809	119	238
54	476	952	405	810	121	242	484	968	437	874
55	249	498	996	493	986	473	946	393	786	73
56	146	292	584	1168	837	175	350	700	1400	1301
57	1103	707	1414	1329	1159	819	139	278	556	1112
58	725	1450	1401	1303	1107	715	1430	1361	1223	947
59	395	790	81	162	324	648	1296	1093	687	1374
60	1249	999	499	998	497	994	489	978	457	914
61	329	658	1316	1133	767	35	70	140	280	560
62	1120	741	1482	1465	1431	1363	1227	955	411	822
63	145	290	580	1160	821	143	286	572	1144	789
64	79	158	316	632	1264	1029	559	1118	737	1474
65	1449	1399	1299	1099	699	1398	1297	1095	691	1382
66	1265	1031	563	1126	753	7	14	28	56	112
67	224	448	896	293	586	1172	845	191	382	764
68	29	58	116	232	464	928	357	714	1428	1357
69	1215	931	363	726	1452	1405	1311	1123	747	1494
70	1489	1479	1459	1419	1339	1179	859	219	438	876
71	253	506	1012	525	1050	601	1202	905	311	622
72	1244	989	479	958	417	834	169	338	676	1352
73	1205	911	323	646	1292	1085	671	1342	1185	871
74	243	486	972	445	890	281	562	1124	749	1498
75	1497	1495	1491	1483	1467	1435	1371	1243	987	475
76	950	401	802	105	210	420	840	181	362	724
77	1448	1397	1295	1091	683	1366	1233	967	435	870
78	241	482	964	429	858	217	434	868	237	474
79	948	397	794	89	178	356	712	1424	1349	1199
80	899	299	598	1196	893	287	574	1148	797	95
81	190	380	760	21	42	84	168	336	672	1344
82	1189	879	259	518	1036	573	1146	793	87	174
83	348	696	1392	1285	1071	643	1286	1073	647	1294
84	1089	679	1358	1217	935	371	742	1484	1469	1439
85	1379	1259	1019	539	1078	657	1314	1129	759	19
86	38	76	152	304	608	1216	933	367	734	1468
87	1437	1375	1251	1003	507	1014	529	1058	617	1234
88	969	439	878	257	514	1028	557	1114	729	1458
89	1417	1335	1171	843	187	374	748	1496	1493	1487
90	1475	1451	1403	1307	1115	731	1462	1425	1351	1203
91	907	315	630	1260	1021	543	1086	673	1346	1193
92	887	275	550	1100	701	1402	1305	1111	723	1446
93	1393	1287	1075	651	1302	1105	711	1422	1345	1191
94	883	267	534	1068	637	1274	1049	599	1198	897
95	295	590	1180	861	223	446	892	285	570	1140
96	781	63	126	252	504	1008	517	1034	569	1138
97	777	55	110	220	440	880	261	522	1044	589
98	1178	857	215	430	860	221	442	884	269	538
99	1076	653	1306	1113	727	1454	1409	1319	1139	779

P = 1499

INDICES

	0	1	2	3	4	5	6	7	8	9
100	1351	1300	1353	873	518	1223	1302	1039	965	532
101	1355	467	712	1490	875	1295	1251	32	520	852
102	1471	914	1225	1289	10	40	1304	254	885	645
103	1041	661	1183	1256	967	1433	824	1086	534	390
104	1066	1200	1357	261	978	332	469	487	412	946
105	714	1420	493	206	1492	1056	1174	237	877	225
106	132	1457	1297	529	29	37	1253	1197	943	234
107	34	834	1129	837	522	932	990	358	854	16
108	397	1132	1473	368	1101	735	916	343	1377	840
109	1227	773	429	597	1291	657	483	525	12	653
110	923	1015	42	570	1339	935	1306	584	311	462
111	256	927	579	993	887	904	418	1427	647	62
112	620	361	1043	697	747	146	663	1019	96	857
113	1185	442	118	613	1258	1030	1441	19	969	998
114	959	1123	1435	46	638	400	826	277	807	1315
115	1088	81	303	1135	536	286	1246	407	392	574
116	633	1476	1068	68	326	456	1202	1153	563	371
117	1359	892	675	1208	263	1343	1481	1104	980	705
118	952	1078	334	1391	162	738	471	514	1467	820
119	489	939	1097	919	414	114	803	322	948	799
120	52	346	716	909	201	730	1422	1310	1073	1380
121	495	1050	56	1385	208	690	865	843	1494	1367
122	1165	1326	1058	588	172	1230	1176	626	350	1144
123	239	378	192	776	879	423	1240	1159	227	315
124	73	432	134	757	720	500	1459	214	1265	600
125	1299	872	1222	1038	531	466	1489	1294	31	851
126	913	1288	39	253	644	660	1255	1432	1085	389
127	1199	260	331	486	945	1419	205	1055	236	224
128	1456	528	36	1196	233	833	836	931	357	15
129	1131	367	734	342	839	772	596	656	524	652
130	1014	569	934	583	461	926	992	903	1426	61
131	360	696	145	1018	856	441	612	1029	18	997
132	1122	45	399	276	1314	80	1134	285	406	573
133	1475	67	455	1152	370	891	1207	1342	1103	704
134	1077	1390	737	513	819	938	918	113	321	798
135	345	908	729	1309	1379	1049	1384	689	842	1366
136	1325	587	1229	625	1143	377	775	422	1158	314
137	431	756	499	213	599	871	1037	465	1293	850
138	1287	252	659	1431	388	259	485	1418	1054	223
139	527	1195	832	930	14	366	341	771	655	651
140	568	582	925	902	60	695	1017	440	1028	996
141	44	275	79	284	572	66	1151	890	1341	703
142	1389	512	937	112	797	907	1308	1048	688	1365
143	586	624	376	421	313	755	212	870	464	849
144	251	1430	258	1417	222	1194	929	365	770	650
145	581	901	694	439	995	274	283	65	889	702
146	511	111	906	1047	1364	623	420	754	869	848
147	1429	1416	1193	364	649	900	438	273	64	701
148	110	1046	622	753	847	1415	363	899	272	700
149	1045	752	1414	898	699	751	897	750	749	

POWER RESIDUES

	0	1	2	3	4	5	6	7	8	9
100	59	118	236	472	944	389	778	57	114	228
101	456	912	325	650	1300	1101	703	1406	1313	1127
102	755	11	22	44	88	176	352	704	1408	1317
103	1135	771	43	86	172	344	688	1376	1253	1007
104	515	1030	561	1122	745	1490	1481	1463	1427	1355
105	1211	923	347	694	1388	1277	1055	611	1222	945
106	391	782	65	130	260	520	1040	581	1162	825
107	151	302	604	1208	917	335	670	1340	1181	863
108	227	454	908	317	634	1268	1037	575	1150	801
109	103	206	412	824	149	298	596	1192	885	271
110	542	1084	669	1338	1177	855	211	422	844	189
111	378	756	13	26	52	104	208	416	832	165
112	330	660	1320	1141	783	67	134	268	536	1072
113	645	1290	1081	663	1326	1153	807	115	230	460
114	920	341	682	1364	1229	959	419	838	177	354
115	708	1416	1333	1167	835	171	342	684	1368	1237
116	975	451	902	305	610	1220	941	383	766	33
117	66	132	264	528	1056	613	1226	953	407	814
118	129	258	516	1032	565	1130	761	23	46	92
119	184	368	736	1472	1445	1391	1283	1067	635	1270
120	1041	583	1166	833	167	334	668	1336	1173	847
121	195	390	780	61	122	244	488	976	453	906
122	313	626	1252	1005	511	1022	545	1090	681	1362
123	1225	951	403	806	113	226	452	904	309	618
124	1236	973	447	894	289	578	1156	813	127	254
125	508	1016	533	1066	633	1266	1033	567	1134	769
126	39	78	156	312	624	1248	997	495	990	481
127	962	425	850	201	402	804	109	218	436	872
128	245	490	980	461	922	345	690	1380	1261	1023
129	547	1094	689	1378	1257	1015	531	1062	625	1250
130	1001	503	1006	513	1026	553	1106	713	1426	1353
131	1207	915	331	662	1324	1149	799	99	198	396
132	792	85	170	340	680	1360	1221	943	387	774
133	49	98	196	392	784	69	138	276	552	1104
134	709	1418	1337	1175	851	203	406	812	125	250
135	500	1000	501	1002	505	1010	521	1042	585	1170
136	841	183	366	732	1464	1429	1359	1219	939	379
137	758	17	34	68	136	272	544	1088	677	1354
138	1209	919	339	678	1356	1213	927	355	710	1420
139	1341	1183	867	235	470	940	381	762	25	50
140	100	200	400	800	101	202	404	808	117	234
141	468	936	373	746	1492	1485	1471	1443	1387	1275
142	1051	603	1206	913	327	654	1308	1117	735	1470
143	1441	1383	1267	1035	571	1142	785	71	142	284
144	568	1136	773	47	94	188	376	752	5	10
145	20	40	80	160	320	640	1280	1061	623	1246
146	993	487	974	449	898	297	594	1188	877	255
147	510	1020	541	1082	665	1330	1161	823	147	294
148	588	1176	853	207	414	828	157	314	628	1256
149	1013	527	1054	609	1218	937	375	750		

P = 1511

INDICES

	0	1	2	3	4	5	6	7	8	9
0		0	1342	740	1174	1124	572	1304	1006	1480
1	956	1	404	1248	1136	354	838	102	1312	1028
2	788	534	1343	731	236	738	1080	710	968	583
3	186	1418	670	741	1444	918	1144	43	860	478
4	620	529	366	409	1175	1094	563	1389	68	1098
5	570	842	912	497	542	1125	800	258	415	1161
6	18	398	1250	1274	502	862	573	965	1276	1471
7	750	1009	976	809	1385	1478	692	1305	310	683
8	452	1450	361	1055	198	1226	241	1323	1007	1240
9	926	1042	395	648	1221	642	1410	1201	930	1481
10	402	820	674	1090	744	148	329	867	374	728
11	957	783	632	1383	90	345	247	1218	993	1406
12	1360	2	230	1269	1082	352	1106	844	334	1149
13	694	1504	405	822	797	324	1108	418	1303	1311
14	582	619	841	1249	808	197	641	328	1217	333
15	1310	1309	524	72	1137	1032	142	205	515	1237
16	284	525	1282	450	193	355	887	281	30	986
17	1058	998	73	593	1155	532	839	391	1072	432
18	758	1023	874	1138	227	1167	480	103	1053	504
19	474	606	1242	1245	1033	92	762	1366	1313	444
20	234	195	652	377	506	143	922	701	576	1029
21	1490	895	161	239	699	23	206	1212	560	39
22	789	1350	615	776	464	708	1215	516	1432	601
23	177	535	79	56	1050	1003	825	1423	1238	1488
24	1192	1045	1344	680	62	712	1101	766	914	285
25	184	1307	938	732	676	456	166	846	981	1347
26	526	553	1336	393	237	111	654	470	629	518
27	156	1283	940	272	250	739	1135	737	1143	1388
28	414	1470	451	1041	673	1382	1081	323	640	204
29	29	431	473	194	160	775	1049	711	165	469
30	1142	203	1141	50	356	12	1414	622	969	320
31	864	51	1484	928	37	888	347	261	1069	584
32	116	97	357	1130	1114	476	282	1468	25	1183
33	187	1194	719	13	113	579	1372	31	818	613
34	890	1419	830	892	1415	1085	425	850	987	1436
35	364	448	671	1062	223	623	904	636	264	1059
36	590	546	855	742	706	423	970	1500	59	499
37	999	291	312	609	1445	1092	885	321	336	1460
38	306	74	438	870	1074	919	1077	379	865	1430
39	1434	833	594	734	1198	297	1145	131	276	52
40	66	984	27	1156	484	1064	209	44	338	688
41	1485	1158	754	955	533	669	408	541	861	691
42	1322	929	727	1359	1503	840	71	192	531	479
43	1365	575	38	176	1044	937	392	249	1381	1048
44	621	1068	1182	889	447	854	608	1073	296	208
45	540	530	1047	539	348	656	1264	597	433	812
46	9	349	367	245	1421	262	1398	972	882	759
47	835	945	657	410	1255	256	1070	467	1320	1400
48	1024	1291	877	1265	1176	815	512	585	1404	1190
49	544	875	933	685	598	1095	746	803	117	1151

POWER RESIDUES

	0	1	2	3	4	5	6	7	8	9
0	1	11	121	1331	1042	885	669	1315	866	460
1	527	1264	305	333	641	1007	500	967	60	660
2	1216	1288	569	215	854	328	586	402	1400	290
3	168	337	685	1491	1291	602	578	314	432	219
4	898	812	1377	37	407	1455	895	779	1014	577
5	303	311	399	1367	1438	708	233	1052	995	368
6	1026	709	244	1173	815	1410	400	1378	48	528
7	1275	426	153	172	381	1169	771	926	1120	232
8	1041	874	548	1495	1335	1086	1369	1460	950	1384
9	114	1254	195	634	930	1164	716	321	509	1066
10	1149	551	17	187	546	1473	1093	1446	796	1201
11	1123	265	1404	334	652	1128	320	498	945	1329
12	1020	643	1029	742	607	633	919	1043	896	790
13	1135	397	1345	1196	1068	1171	793	1168	760	805
14	1300	701	156	205	744	629	875	559	105	1155
15	617	743	618	754	739	574	270	1459	939	1263
16	294	212	821	1476	1126	298	256	1305	756	761
17	816	1421	521	1198	1090	1413	433	230	1019	632
18	908	922	1076	1259	250	1239	30	330	608	644
19	1040	863	427	164	293	201	700	145	84	924
20	1098	1501	1401	301	289	157	216	865	449	406
21	1444	774	959	1483	1203	1145	507	1044	907	911
22	955	1439	719	354	872	526	1253	184	513	1110
23	122	1342	1163	705	200	689	24	264	1393	213
24	832	86	946	1340	1141	463	560	116	1276	437
25	274	1503	1423	543	1440	730	475	692	57	627
26	853	317	465	582	358	916	1010	533	1330	1031
27	764	849	273	1492	1302	723	398	1356	1317	888
28	702	167	326	564	160	249	1228	1420	510	1077
29	1270	371	1059	1072	1215	1277	448	395	1323	954
30	1428	598	534	1341	1152	584	380	1158	650	1106
31	78	858	372	1070	1193	1035	808	1333	1064	1127
32	309	377	1125	287	135	1485	1225	1387	147	106
33	1166	738	563	149	128	1408	378	1136	408	1466
34	1016	599	545	1462	972	115	1265	316	454	461
35	538	1385	125	1375	15	165	304	322	520	1187
36	969	82	902	856	350	828	42	462	549	1506
37	1456	906	900	834	108	1188	980	203	722	387
38	1235	1497	1357	1328	1009	522	1209	1211	1233	1475
39	1115	177	436	263	1382	92	1012	555	61	671
40	1337	1108	100	1100	12	132	1452	862	416	43
41	473	670	1326	987	280	58	638	974	137	1507
42	1467	1027	720	365	993	346	784	1069	1182	914
43	988	291	179	458	505	1022	665	1271	382	1180
44	892	746	651	1117	199	678	1414	444	351	839
45	163	282	80	880	614	710	255	1294	635	941
46	1285	536	1363	1394	224	953	1417	477	714	299
47	267	1426	576	292	190	579	325	553	39	429
48	186	535	1352	1273	404	1422	532	1319	910	944
49	1318	899	823	1498	1368	1449	829	53	583	369

P = 1511

INDICES

	0	1	2	3	4	5	6	7	8	9
50	16	1021	1139	1357	770	434	564	216	508	98
51	288	603	1508	228	678	704	813	1390	1179	1333
52	358	172	385	1185	1168	1272	225	10	69	1462
53	1453	1131	486	267	302	481	461	1172	350	1099
54	1498	1402	1115	253	772	342	104	1464	82	368
55	571	101	967	477	569	397	975	1054	1220	147
56	246	843	1302	332	283	997	873	1244	505	22
57	1214	1422	913	1346	155	1469	472	49	36	475
58	1371	849	263	498	305	832	26	954	1502	936
59	607	596	881	1399	543	1020	1507	1184	301	341
60	974	1243	35	935	973	1126	1392	124	188	1117
61	1354	1127	1246	795	454	883	801	150	152	1195
62	696	1441	1393	1034	1316	1476	760	259	1379	145
63	720	1208	179	125	93	458	901	836	416	979
64	1458	14	1439	121	189	763	962	625	946	1162
65	308	442	114	1066	1300	1118	1367	779	1015	658
66	19	1427	1026	580	551	436	1355	1314	1455	6
67	411	399	1204	1278	1373	1448	650	1128	445	995
68	722	1256	1251	1120	662	32	724	1341	1247	235
69	917	562	257	1275	682	925	819	631	1268	796
70	196	141	280	1071	503	233	894	614	55	61
71	455	653	736	639	468	863	96	718	891	222
72	422	884	378	275	687	1321	574	1181	538	1420
73	255	511	802	507	1332	1452	1401	966	331	154
74	831	1506	123	151	144	1457	441	1025	1277	661
75	924	893	717	537	153	923	168	908	1292	1472
76	138	169	1416	522	270	1196	702	899	906	878
77	751	76	909	1086	211	646	697	577	1262	47
78	1266	1010	665	1293	426	1329	566	1442	1030	1133
79	129	1177	977	136	1473	851	108	1223	1394	1491
80	1408	1210	816	810	1369	139	988	1258	316	1035
81	896	951	41	513	1386	64	170	1437	520	1012
82	1317	162	990	492	586	1479	787	1417	365	496
83	501	1477	240	1200	373	1405	693	618	523	449
84	1154	1166	761	700	559	600	1191	1306	1335	271
85	672	774	1413	260	24	612	363	545	311	869
86	1197	1063	407	191	1380	207	8	944	876	684
87	769	703	224	1171	81	146	1213	848	880	934
88	453	1475	900	624	1014	5	721	561	279	638
89	686	1451	440	907	905	46	128	1209	40	491
90	372	599	362	943	879	637	371	218	180	790
91	488	219	1096	1056	429	752	265	1298	644	126
92	1351	1362	181	747	199	781	77	1060	1253	1018
93	94	616	1230	791	804	1227	714	910	591	158
94	667	459	777	1260	489	118	242	1038	1087	547
95	88	1001	902	465	299	220	1152	1324	1232	212
96	856	1326	1123	837	709	859	1097	17	1008	360
97	647	743	344	1105	417	1216	1236	1057	1022	1241
98	376	698	707	824	765	980	517	413	430	1140
99	927	1113	578	424	635	58	1459	1433	983	753

POWER RESIDUES

	0	1	2	3	4	5	6	7	8	9
50	1037	830	64	704	189	568	204	733	508	1055
51	1028	731	486	813	1388	158	227	986	269	1448
52	818	1443	763	838	152	161	260	1349	1240	41
53	451	428	175	414	21	231	1030	753	728	453
54	450	417	54	594	490	857	361	949	1373	1504
55	1434	664	1260	261	1360	1361	1372	1493	1313	844
56	218	887	691	46	506	1033	786	1091	1424	554
57	50	550	6	66	726	431	208	777	992	335
58	663	1249	140	29	319	487	824	1509	1489	1269
59	360	938	1252	173	392	1290	591	457	494	901
60	845	229	1008	511	1088	1391	191	590	446	373
61	1081	1314	855	339	707	222	931	1175	837	141
62	40	440	307	355	883	647	1073	1226	1398	268
63	1437	697	112	1232	1464	994	357	905	889	713
64	288	146	95	1045	918	1032	775	970	93	1023
65	676	1392	202	711	266	1415	455	472	659	1205
66	1167	749	684	1480	1170	782	1047	940	1274	415
67	32	352	850	284	102	1122	254	1283	514	1121
68	243	1162	694	79	869	493	890	724	409	1477
69	1137	419	76	836	130	1430	620	776	981	214
70	843	207	766	871	515	1132	364	982	225	964
71	27	297	245	1184	936	1230	1442	752	717	332
72	630	886	680	1436	686	1502	1412	422	109	1199
73	1101	23	253	1272	393	1301	712	277	25	275
74	3	33	363	971	104	1144	496	923	1087	1380
75	70	770	915	999	412	1510	1500	1390	180	469
76	626	842	196	645	1051	984	247	1206	1178	870
77	504	1011	544	1451	851	295	223	942	1296	657
78	1183	925	1109	111	1221	1343	1174	826	20	220
79	909	933	1197	1079	1292	613	699	134	1474	1104
80	56	616	732	497	934	1208	1200	1112	144	73
81	803	1278	459	516	1143	485	802	1267	338	696
82	101	1111	133	1463	983	236	1085	1358	1339	1130
83	342	740	585	391	1279	470	637	963	16	176
84	425	142	51	561	127	1397	257	1316	877	581
85	347	795	1190	1002	445	362	960	1494	1324	965
86	38	418	65	715	310	388	1246	107	1177	859
87	383	1191	1013	566	182	491	868	482	769	904
88	878	592	468	615	721	376	1114	166	315	443
89	340	718	343	751	706	211	810	1355	1306	767
90	882	636	952	1406	356	894	768	893	757	772
91	937	1241	52	572	248	1217	1299	690	35	385
92	1213	1255	206	755	750	695	90	990	313	421
93	98	1078	1281	492	879	603	589	435	252	1261
94	272	1481	1181	903	867	471	648	1084	1347	1218
95	1310	811	1366	1427	587	413	10	110	1210	1222
96	1354	1295	646	1062	1105	67	737	552	28	308
97	366	1004	467	604	600	556	72	792	1157	639
98	985	258	1327	998	401	1389	169	348	806	1311
99	822	1487	1247	118	1298	679	1425	565	171	370

P = 1511

INDICES

	0	1	2	3	4	5	6	7	8	9
100	1358	1043	853	1263	971	1319	1189	15	602	384
101	266	771	396	872	48	1501	340	1353	1440	178
102	120	1299	435	649	1340	1267	60	421	510	122
103	536	269	645	565	1222	315	1011	500	1165	1412
104	190	80	4	127	217	643	1017	666	1000	1122
105	1104	764	57	1188	1352	509	1411	1103	1294	292
106	1285	1295	963	1051	318	1363	99	1202	134	427
107	313	1376	293	626	1004	1147	182	289	931	793
108	1330	610	1234	1286	947	826	85	748	604	1482
109	174	567	1446	106	1296	1163	1424	1288	200	1509
110	403	730	1443	1093	799	964	309	1239	401	782
111	229	821	807	1031	886	390	1052	443	1489	1349
112	78	679	675	110	1134	322	164	319	115	1193
113	829	1061	705	1091	1076	130	337	690	1364	1067
114	1046	244	1254	814	745	215	1178	1461	1497	100
115	1301	1345	304	1019	1391	149	1378	978	307	1426
116	1203	1119	681	232	95	1180	330	660	137	75
117	664	135	1368	63	786	617	1334	868	768	1474
118	439	942	428	780	713	1037	1231	359	375	1112
119	852	871	1339	314	1016	1102	133	792	173	729
120	806	109	1075	214	1377	659	767	1111	805	386
121	958	387	1224	920	1466	294	20	915	949	1228
122	1186	784	959	1395	1078	326	627	1428	286	1206
123	715	1169	633	388	1492	380	1494	1005	1027	185
124	528	911	1273	1384	1225	1409	866	992	1148	581
125	1308	1281	592	226	91	921	1211	1431	1487	183
126	552	939	1040	159	11	346	1467	817	1435	589
127	290	437	733	483	668	70	248	295	811	834
128	1290	932	1356	677	1271	460	1463	1219	21	1370
129	595	34	794	1315	457	961	778	1454	994	916
130	140	735	274	1331	1456	167	898	1261	1132	1407
131	950	989	1199	558	611	7	847	278	490	487
132	1361	1229	1259	298	858	1235	412	982	383	119
133	268	3	1187	317	1146	84	1287	400	1348	828
134	243	303	231	785	1036	132	1110	948	1205	527
135	1280	1039	482	1270	960	897	277	382	827	1279
136	554	555	1088	462	1083	1396	952	53	494	86
137	1374	1337	556	548	1173	353	1079	42	67	1160
138	749	1449	394	1089	89	351	1107	327	514	985
139	757	605	651	238	463	1002	1100	845	628	1387
140	28	202	1483	1129	112	1084	903	1499	335	1429
141	65	1157	726	175	446	655	1397	466	1403	1150
142	287	171	485	252	568	996	471	953	300	1116
143	695	1207	1438	1065	550	1447	723	630	54	221
144	254	1505	716	521	210	1328	107	1257	519	495
145	1153	773	406	1170	1013	45	370	1297	1252	157
146	87	1325	343	823	634	1318	339	420	1164	1121
147	1284	1375	1233	105	798	389	163	689	1496	1425
148	663	941	1338	213	1465	325	1493	991	1486	588
149	1289	33	273	557	857	83	1109	381	493	1159

POWER RESIDUES

	0	1	2	3	4	5	6	7	8	9
100	1048	951	1395	235	1074	1237	8	88	968	71
101	781	1036	819	1454	884	658	1194	1046	929	1153
102	595	501	978	181	480	747	662	1238	19	209
103	788	1113	155	194	623	809	1344	1185	947	1351
104	1262	283	91	1001	434	241	1140	452	439	296
105	234	1063	1116	188	557	83	913	977	170	359
106	927	1131	353	861	405	1433	653	1139	441	318
107	476	703	178	447	384	1202	1134	386	1224	1376
108	26	286	124	1364	1405	345	773	948	1362	1383
109	103	1133	375	1103	45	495	912	966	49	539
110	1396	246	1195	1057	1050	973	126	1386	136	1496
111	1346	1207	1189	991	324	542	1429	609	655	1161
112	683	1469	1049	962	5	55	605	611	677	1403
113	323	531	1308	789	1124	276	14	154	183	502
114	989	302	300	278	36	396	1334	1075	1248	129
115	1419	499	956	1450	840	174	403	1411	411	1499
116	1379	59	649	1095	1468	1038	841	185	524	1231
117	1453	873	537	1374	4	44	484	791	1146	518
118	1165	727	442	329	597	523	1220	1332	1053	1006
119	489	846	240	1129	331	619	765	860	394	1312
120	833	97	1067	1160	672	1348	1229	1431	631	897
121	801	1256	217	876	570	226	975	148	117	1287
122	558	94	1034	797	1212	1244	85	935	1219	1321
123	932	1186	958	1472	1082	1325	976	159	238	1107
124	89	979	192	601	567	193	612	688	13	143
125	62	682	1458	928	1142	474	681	1447	807	1322
126	943	1307	778	1003	456	483	780	1025	698	123
127	1353	1284	525	1242	63	693	68	748	673	1359
128	1350	1251	162	271	1470	1060	1083	1336	1097	1490
129	1280	481	758	783	1058	1061	1094	1457	917	1021
130	654	1150	562	138	7	77	847	251	1250	151
131	150	139	18	198	667	1293	624	820	1465	1005
132	478	725	420	87	957	1461	961	1505	1445	785
133	1080	1303	734	519	1176	848	262	1371	1482	1192
134	1024	687	2	22	242	1151	573	259	1338	1119
135	221	920	1054	1017	610	666	1282	503	1000	423
136	120	1320	921	1065	1138	430	197	656	1172	804
137	1289	580	336	674	1370	1471	1071	1204	1156	628
138	864	438	285	113	1243	74	814	1399	279	47
139	517	1154	606	622	798	1223	1365	1416	466	593
140	479	736	541	1418	488	835	119	1309	800	1245
141	96	1056	1039	852	306	344	762	827	31	341
142	729	464	571	237	1096	1479	1159	661	1227	1409
143	389	1257	228	997	390	1268	349	817	1432	642
144	1018	621	787	1102	34	374	1092	1435	675	1381
145	81	891	735	530	1297	668	1304	745	640	996
146	379	1147	529	1286	547	1484	1214	1266	327	575
147	281	69	759	794	1179	881	625	831	75	825
148	9	99	1089	1402	312	410	1488	1258	239	1118
149	210	799	1234	1486	1236	1508	1478	1148	540	1407

P = 1511

INDICES

	0	1	2	3	4	5	6	7	8	9
150	756	201	725	251	549	1327	369	419	1495	587
151	755	0								

POWER RESIDUES

	0	1	2	3	4	5	6	7	8	9
150	367	1015	588	424	131	1441	741	596	512	1099
151										

P = 1523

INDICES

	0	1	2	3	4	5	6	7	8	9
0		0	1	186	2	161	187	1025	3	372
1	162	825	188	195	1026	347	4	491	373	782
2	163	1211	826	1432	189	322	196	558	1027	911
3	348	235	5	1011	492	1186	374	545	783	381
4	164	403	1212	1470	827	533	1433	16	190	528
5	323	677	197	115	559	986	1028	968	912	629
6	349	1201	236	1397	6	356	1012	463	493	96
7	1187	1077	375	473	546	508	784	328	382	805
8	165	744	404	1299	1213	652	1471	1097	828	432
9	534	1220	1434	421	17	943	191	907	529	1197
10	324	417	678	479	198	1372	116	57	560	682
11	987	731	1029	1125	969	71	913	567	630	1516
12	350	128	1202	589	237	483	1398	1334	7	134
13	357	340	1013	285	464	719	494	1462	97	884
14	1188	202	1078	1020	376	1072	474	714	547	88
15	509	794	785	863	329	396	383	1376	806	301
16	166	935	745	1417	405	1172	1300	552	1214	390
17	653	1154	1472	120	1098	1347	829	815	433	456
18	535	1266	1221	1387	1435	706	422	1316	18	61
19	944	158	192	1208	908	542	530	112	1198	93
20	325	649	418	414	679	564	480	282	199	85
21	1373	1169	117	1263	58	109	561	1260	683	659
22	988	686	732	1280	1030	694	1126	1509	970	662
23	72	514	914	1057	568	177	631	991	1517	1006
24	351	902	129	930	1203	689	590	977	238	1485
25	484	1065	1399	735	1335	838	8	595	135	48
26	358	1283	341	799	1014	276	286	618	465	1033
27	720	292	495	1406	1463	1147	98	697	885	607
28	1189	1230	203	1160	1079	1129	1021	1428	377	982
29	1073	1093	475	1512	715	790	548	1383	89	105
30	510	973	795	603	786	1362	864	27	330	665
31	397	1366	384	1051	1377	36	807	75	302	214
32	167	243	936	1273	746	517	1418	868	406	1041
33	1173	852	1301	917	553	624	1215	584	391	1311
34	654	1060	1155	31	1473	257	121	1478	1099	571
35	1348	753	830	1490	816	1238	434	180	457	334
36	536	42	1267	314	1222	634	1388	223	1436	775
37	707	1140	423	994	1317	669	19	1106	62	262
38	945	1520	159	370	193	489	1209	320	909	1009
39	543	401	531	526	113	966	1199	354	94	471
40	326	742	650	430	419	905	415	1370	680	1123
41	565	126	481	132	283	1460	200	1070	86	861
42	1374	933	1170	388	118	813	1264	704	59	1206
43	110	647	562	83	1261	1258	684	692	660	1055
44	989	900	687	1483	733	593	1281	274	1031	1404
45	695	1228	1127	980	1510	1381	971	1360	663	1049
46	73	241	515	1039	915	582	1058	255	569	1488
47	178	40	632	773	992	1104	1518	487	1007	524
48	352	740	903	1121	130	1068	931	811	1204	81
49	690	898	591	1402	978	1358	239	580	1486	771

POWER RESIDUES

	0	1	2	3	4	5	6	7	8	9
0	1	2	4	8	16	32	64	128	256	512
1	1024	525	1050	577	1154	785	47	94	188	376
2	752	1504	1485	1447	1371	1219	915	307	614	1228
3	933	343	686	1372	1221	919	315	630	1260	997
4	471	942	361	722	1444	1365	1207	891	259	518
5	1036	549	1098	673	1346	1169	815	107	214	428
6	856	189	378	756	1512	1501	1479	1435	1347	1171
7	819	115	230	460	920	317	634	1268	1013	503
8	1006	489	978	433	866	209	418	836	149	298
9	596	1192	861	199	398	796	69	138	276	552
10	1104	685	1370	1217	911	299	598	1196	869	215
11	430	860	197	394	788	53	106	212	424	848
12	173	346	692	1384	1245	967	411	822	121	242
13	484	968	413	826	129	258	516	1032	541	1082
14	641	1282	1041	559	1118	713	1426	1329	1135	747
15	1494	1465	1407	1291	1059	595	1190	857	191	382
16	764	5	10	20	40	80	160	320	640	1280
17	1037	551	1102	681	1362	1201	879	235	470	940
18	357	714	1428	1333	1143	763	3	6	12	24
19	48	96	192	384	768	13	26	52	104	208
20	416	832	141	282	564	1128	733	1466	1409	1295
21	1067	611	1222	921	319	638	1276	1029	535	1070
22	617	1234	945	367	734	1468	1413	1303	1083	643
23	1286	1049	575	1150	777	31	62	124	248	496
24	992	461	922	321	642	1284	1045	567	1134	745
25	1490	1457	1391	1259	995	467	934	345	690	1380
26	1237	951	379	758	1516	1509	1495	1467	1411	1299
27	1075	627	1254	985	447	894	265	530	1060	597
28	1194	865	207	414	828	133	266	532	1064	605
29	1210	897	271	542	1084	645	1290	1057	591	1182
30	841	159	318	636	1272	1021	519	1038	553	1106
31	689	1378	1233	943	363	726	1452	1381	1239	955
32	387	774	25	50	100	200	400	800	77	154
33	308	616	1232	941	359	718	1436	1349	1175	827
34	131	262	524	1048	573	1146	769	15	30	60
35	120	240	480	960	397	794	65	130	260	520
36	1040	557	1114	705	1410	1297	1071	619	1238	953
37	383	766	9	18	36	72	144	288	576	1152
38	781	39	78	156	312	624	1248	973	423	846
39	169	338	676	1352	1181	839	155	310	620	1240
40	957	391	782	41	82	164	328	656	1312	1101
41	679	1358	1193	863	203	406	812	101	202	404
42	808	93	186	372	744	1488	1453	1383	1243	963
43	403	806	89	178	356	712	1424	1325	1127	731
44	1462	1401	1279	1035	547	1094	665	1330	1137	751
45	1502	1481	1439	1355	1187	851	179	358	716	1432
46	1341	1159	795	67	134	268	536	1072	621	1242
47	961	399	798	73	146	292	584	1168	813	103
48	206	412	824	125	250	500	1000	477	954	385
49	770	17	34	68	136	272	544	1088	653	1306

P = 1523

INDICES

	0	1	2	3	4	5	6	7	8	9
50	485	738	1066	79	1400	578	736	576	1336	1338
51	839	1498	9	1340	596	640	136	841	49	306
52	359	1500	1284	1247	342	11	800	726	1015	1342
53	277	1001	287	598	619	218	466	642	1034	1353
54	721	138	293	1452	496	843	1407	444	1464	51
55	1148	171	99	308	698	892	886	361	608	143
56	1190	1502	1231	1114	204	1286	1161	247	1080	1249
57	1130	758	1022	344	1429	232	378	13	983	1394
58	1074	802	1094	940	476	728	1513	1331	716	1017
59	791	298	549	1344	1384	155	90	279	106	1277
60	511	1003	974	835	796	289	604	1425	787	600
61	1363	211	865	621	28	750	331	220	666	367
62	398	468	1367	1457	385	644	1052	271	1378	1036
63	37	521	808	1355	76	1495	303	723	215	1449
64	168	140	244	229	937	295	1274	1422	747	1454
65	518	1446	1419	498	869	501	407	845	1042	1324
66	1174	1409	853	872	1302	446	918	821	554	1466
67	625	504	1216	53	585	880	392	1150	1312	410
68	655	173	1061	614	1156	101	32	848	1474	310
69	258	962	122	700	1479	1045	1100	894	572	1243
70	1349	888	754	1327	831	363	1491	1442	817	610
71	1239	1177	435	145	181	1181	458	1192	335	1412
72	537	1504	43	1088	1268	1233	315	856	1223	1116
73	635	439	1389	206	224	875	1437	1288	776	1293
74	708	1163	1141	1305	424	249	995	149	1318	1082
75	670	449	20	1251	1107	955	63	1132	263	921
76	946	760	1521	185	160	1024	371	824	194	346
77	490	781	1210	1431	321	557	910	234	1010	1185
78	544	380	402	1469	532	15	527	676	114	985
79	967	628	1200	1396	355	462	95	1076	472	507
80	327	804	743	1298	651	1096	431	1219	420	942
81	906	1196	416	478	1371	56	681	730	1124	70
82	566	1515	127	588	482	1333	133	339	284	718
83	1461	883	201	1019	1071	713	87	793	862	395
84	1375	300	934	1416	1171	551	389	1153	119	1346
85	814	455	1265	1386	705	1315	60	157	1207	541
86	111	92	648	413	563	281	84	1168	1262	108
87	1259	658	685	1279	693	1508	661	513	1056	176
88	990	1005	901	929	688	976	1484	1064	734	837
89	594	47	1282	798	275	617	1032	291	1405	1146
90	696	606	1229	1159	1128	1427	981	1092	1511	789
91	1382	104	972	602	1361	26	664	1365	1050	35
92	74	213	242	1272	516	867	1040	851	916	623
93	583	1310	1059	30	256	1477	570	752	1489	1237
94	179	333	41	313	633	222	774	1139	993	668
95	1105	261	1519	369	488	319	1008	400	525	965
96	353	470	741	429	904	1369	1122	125	131	1459
97	1069	860	932	387	812	703	1205	646	82	1257
98	691	1054	899	1482	592	273	1403	1227	979	1380
99	1359	1048	240	1038	581	254	1487	39	772	1103

POWER RESIDUES

	0	1	2	3	4	5	6	7	8	9
50	1089	655	1310	1097	671	1342	1161	799	75	150
51	300	600	1200	877	231	462	924	325	650	1300
52	1077	631	1262	1001	479	958	393	786	49	98
53	196	392	784	45	90	180	360	720	1440	1357
54	1191	859	195	390	780	37	74	148	296	592
55	1184	845	167	334	668	1336	1149	775	27	54
56	108	216	432	864	205	410	820	117	234	468
57	936	349	698	1396	1269	1015	507	1014	505	1010
58	497	994	465	930	337	674	1348	1173	823	123
59	246	492	984	445	890	257	514	1028	533	1066
60	609	1218	913	303	606	1212	901	279	558	1116
61	709	1418	1313	1103	683	1366	1209	895	267	534
62	1068	613	1226	929	335	670	1340	1157	791	59
63	118	236	472	944	365	730	1460	1397	1271	1019
64	515	1030	537	1074	625	1250	977	431	862	201
65	402	804	85	170	340	680	1360	1197	871	219
66	438	876	229	458	916	309	618	1236	949	375
67	750	1500	1477	1431	1339	1155	787	51	102	204
68	408	816	109	218	436	872	221	442	884	245
69	490	980	437	874	225	450	900	277	554	1108
70	693	1386	1249	975	427	854	185	370	740	1480
71	1437	1351	1179	835	147	294	588	1176	829	135
72	270	540	1080	637	1274	1025	527	1054	585	1170
73	817	111	222	444	888	253	506	1012	501	1002
74	481	962	401	802	81	162	324	648	1296	1069
75	615	1230	937	351	702	1404	1285	1047	571	1142
76	761	1522	1521	1519	1515	1507	1491	1459	1395	1267
77	1011	499	998	473	946	369	738	1476	1429	1335
78	1147	771	19	38	76	152	304	608	1216	909
79	295	590	1180	837	151	302	604	1208	893	263
80	526	1052	581	1162	801	79	158	316	632	1264
81	1005	487	974	425	850	177	354	708	1416	1309
82	1095	667	1334	1145	767	11	22	44	88	176
83	352	704	1408	1293	1063	603	1206	889	255	510
84	1020	517	1034	545	1090	657	1314	1105	687	1374
85	1225	927	331	662	1324	1125	727	1454	1385	1247
86	971	419	838	153	306	612	1224	925	327	654
87	1308	1093	663	1326	1129	735	1470	1417	1311	1099
88	675	1350	1177	831	139	278	556	1112	701	1402
89	1281	1039	555	1110	697	1394	1265	1007	491	982
90	441	882	241	482	964	405	810	97	194	388
91	776	29	58	116	232	464	928	333	666	1332
92	1141	759	1518	1513	1503	1483	1443	1363	1203	883
93	243	486	972	421	842	161	322	644	1288	1053
94	583	1166	809	95	190	380	760	1520	1517	1511
95	1499	1475	1427	1331	1139	755	1510	1497	1471	1419
96	1315	1107	691	1382	1241	959	395	790	57	114
97	228	456	912	301	602	1204	885	247	494	988
98	453	906	289	578	1156	789	55	110	220	440
99	880	237	474	948	373	746	1492	1461	1399	1275

P = 1523

INDICES

	0	1	2	3	4	5	6	7	8	9
100	486	523	739	1120	1067	810	80	897	1401	1357
101	579	770	737	78	577	575	1337	1497	1339	639
102	840	305	1499	1246	10	725	1341	1000	597	217
103	641	1352	137	1451	842	443	50	170	307	891
104	360	142	1501	1113	1285	246	1248	757	343	231
105	12	1393	801	939	727	1330	1016	297	1343	154
106	278	1276	1002	834	288	1424	599	210	620	749
107	219	366	467	1456	643	270	1035	520	1354	1494
108	722	1448	139	228	294	1421	1453	1445	497	500
109	844	1323	1408	871	445	820	1465	503	52	879
110	1149	409	172	613	100	847	309	961	699	1044
111	893	1242	887	1326	362	1441	609	1176	144	1180
112	1191	1411	1503	1087	1232	855	1115	438	205	874
113	1287	1292	1162	1304	248	148	1081	448	1250	954
114	1131	920	759	184	1023	823	345	780	1430	556
115	233	1184	379	1468	14	675	984	627	1395	461
116	1075	506	803	1297	1095	1218	941	1195	477	55
117	729	69	1514	587	1332	338	717	882	1018	712
118	792	394	299	1415	550	1152	1345	454	1385	1314
119	156	540	91	412	280	1167	107	657	1278	1507
120	512	175	1004	928	975	1063	836	46	797	616
121	290	1145	605	1158	1426	1091	788	103	601	25
122	1364	34	212	1271	866	850	622	1309	29	1476
123	751	1236	332	312	221	1138	667	260	368	318
124	399	964	469	428	1368	124	1458	859	386	702
125	645	1256	1053	1481	272	1226	1379	1047	1037	253
126	38	1102	522	1119	809	896	1356	769	77	574
127	1496	638	304	1245	724	999	216	1351	1450	442
128	169	890	141	1112	245	756	230	1392	938	1329
129	296	153	1275	833	1423	209	748	365	1455	269
130	519	1493	1447	227	1420	1444	499	1322	870	819
131	502	878	408	612	846	960	1043	1241	1325	1440
132	1175	1179	1410	1086	854	437	873	1291	1303	147
133	447	953	919	183	822	779	555	1183	1467	674
134	626	460	505	1296	1217	1194	54	68	586	337
135	881	711	393	1414	1151	453	1313	539	411	1166
136	656	1506	174	927	1062	45	615	1144	1157	1090
137	102	24	33	1270	849	1308	1475	1235	311	1137
138	259	317	963	427	123	858	701	1255	1480	1225
139	1046	252	1101	1118	895	768	573	637	1244	998
140	1350	441	889	1111	755	1391	1328	152	832	208
141	364	268	1492	226	1443	1321	818	877	611	959
142	1240	1439	1178	1085	436	1290	146	952	182	778
143	1182	673	459	1295	1193	67	336	710	1413	452
144	538	1165	1505	926	44	1143	1089	23	1269	1307
145	1234	1136	316	426	857	1254	1224	251	1117	767
146	636	997	440	1110	1390	151	207	267	225	1320
147	876	958	1438	1084	1289	951	777	672	1294	66
148	709	451	1164	925	1142	22	1306	1135	425	1253
149	250	766	996	1109	150	266	1319	957	1083	950

POWER RESIDUES

	0	1	2	3	4	5	6	7	8	9
100	1027	531	1062	601	1202	881	239	478	956	389
101	778	33	66	132	264	528	1056	589	1178	833
102	143	286	572	1144	765	7	14	28	56	112
103	224	448	896	269	538	1076	629	1258	993	463
104	926	329	658	1316	1109	695	1390	1257	991	459
105	918	313	626	1252	981	439	878	233	466	932
106	341	682	1364	1205	887	251	502	1004	485	970
107	417	834	145	290	580	1160	797	71	142	284
108	568	1136	749	1498	1473	1423	1323	1123	723	1446
109	1369	1215	907	291	582	1164	805	87	174	348
110	696	1392	1261	999	475	950	377	754	1508	1493
111	1463	1403	1283	1043	563	1126	729	1458	1393	1263
112	1003	483	966	409	818	113	226	452	904	285
113	570	1140	757	1514	1505	1487	1451	1379	1235	947
114	371	742	1484	1445	1367	1211	899	275	550	1100
115	677	1354	1185	847	171	342	684	1368	1213	903
116	283	566	1132	741	1482	1441	1359	1195	867	211
117	422	844	165	330	660	1320	1117	711	1422	1321
118	1119	715	1430	1337	1151	779	35	70	140	280
119	560	1120	717	1434	1345	1167	811	99	198	396
120	792	61	122	244	488	976	429	858	193	386
121	772	21	42	84	168	336	672	1344	1165	807
122	91	182	364	728	1456	1389	1255	987	451	902
123	281	562	1124	725	1450	1377	1231	939	355	710
124	1420	1317	1111	699	1398	1273	1023	523	1046	569
125	1138	753	1506	1489	1455	1387	1251	979	435	870
126	217	434	868	213	426	852	181	362	724	1448
127	1373	1223	923	323	646	1292	1061	599	1198	873
128	223	446	892	261	522	1044	565	1130	737	1474
129	1425	1327	1131	739	1478	1433	1343	1163	803	83
130	166	332	664	1328	1133	743	1486	1449	1375	1227
131	931	339	678	1356	1189	855	187	374	748	1496
132	1469	1415	1307	1091	659	1318	1113	703	1406	1289
133	1055	587	1174	825	127	254	508	1016	509	1018
134	513	1026	529	1058	593	1186	849	175	350	700
135	1400	1277	1031	539	1078	633	1266	1009	495	990
136	457	914	305	610	1220	917	311	622	1244	965
137	407	814	105	210	420	840	157	314	628	1256
138	989	455	910	297	594	1188	853	183	366	732
139	1464	1405	1287	1051	579	1158	793	63	126	252
140	504	1008	493	986	449	898	273	546	1092	661
141	1322	1121	719	1438	1353	1183	843	163	326	652
142	1304	1085	647	1294	1065	607	1214	905	287	574
143	1148	773	23	46	92	184	368	736	1472	1421
144	1319	1115	707	1414	1305	1087	651	1302	1081	639
145	1278	1033	543	1086	649	1298	1073	623	1246	969
146	415	830	137	274	548	1096	669	1338	1153	783
147	43	86	172	344	688	1376	1229	935	347	694
148	1388	1253	983	443	886	249	498	996	469	938
149	353	706	1412	1301	1079	635	1270	1017	511	1022

P = 1523

INDICES

	0	1	2	3	4	5	6	7	8	9
150	671	65	450	924	21	1134	1252	765	1108	265
151	956	949	64	923	1133	764	264	948	922	763
152	947	762	761							

POWER RESIDUES

	0	1	2	3	4	5	6	7	8	9
150	521	1042	561	1122	721	1442	1361	1199	875	227
151	454	908	293	586	1172	821	119	238	476	952
152	381	762								

P = 1531

INDICES

	0	1	2	3	4	5	6	7	8	9
0		0	1	837	2	846	838	1026	3	144
1	847	1330	839	734	1027	153	4	1304	145	1245
2	848	333	1331	861	840	162	735	981	1028	890
3	154	1082	5	637	1305	342	146	527	1246	41
4	849	1265	334	1158	1332	990	862	211	841	522
5	163	611	736	1478	982	646	1029	552	891	102
6	155	1441	1083	1170	6	50	638	1516	1306	168
7	343	1281	147	1198	528	999	1247	826	42	1204
8	850	288	1266	1147	335	620	1159	197	1333	1136
9	991	230	863	389	212	561	842	329	523	1474
10	164	616	612	874	737	1179	1479	375	983	584
11	647	1364	1030	1114	553	177	892	878	103	800
12	156	1130	1442	572	1084	1008	1171	952	7	465
13	51	426	639	741	1517	297	1307	275	169	966
14	344	1048	1282	534	148	206	1199	1359	529	1183
15	1000	251	1248	1448	827	398	43	724	1205	785
16	851	357	289	627	1267	1483	1148	119	336	1468
17	621	1389	1160	591	198	1188	1334	939	1137	706
18	992	379	231	748	864	1373	390	1104	213	477
19	562	69	843	731	330	887	524	987	1475	1438
20	165	823	617	386	613	581	875	1005	738	1045
21	1180	721	1480	588	376	474	984	578	585	505
22	648	508	1365	658	1031	306	1115	1395	554	651
23	178	133	893	668	879	1057	104	511	801	256
24	157	547	1131	1125	1443	1368	573	449	1085	454
25	1009	89	1172	661	953	1457	8	492	466	23
26	52	1034	427	903	640	794	742	443	1518	309
27	298	1253	1308	1067	276	1492	170	1118	967	1226
28	345	1090	1049	811	1283	1398	535	761	149	1078
29	207	1166	1200	557	1360	948	530	781	1184	65
30	1001	654	252	1453	1249	757	1449	686	828	181
31	399	1524	44	459	725	486	1206	136	786	690
32	852	1212	358	1019	290	896	628	1421	1268	1237
33	1484	238	1149	671	120	832	337	1511	1469	421
34	622	882	1390	18	1161	1014	592	1297	199	1060
35	1189	185	1335	33	940	597	1138	107	707	1324
36	993	960	380	437	232	514	749	403	865	1409
37	1374	974	391	804	1105	315	214	94	478	916
38	563	259	70	1528	844	142	732	1302	331	160
39	888	635	525	1263	988	520	1476	550	1439	48
40	166	1196	824	286	618	1134	387	327	614	1177
41	582	1112	876	1128	1006	463	739	273	1046	204
42	1181	1446	722	355	1481	1466	589	937	377	1371
43	475	729	985	821	579	1043	586	576	506	304
44	649	666	509	545	1366	452	659	490	1032	792

POWER RESIDUES

	0	1	2	3	4	5	6	7	8	9
0	1	2	4	8	16	32	64	128	256	512
1	1024	517	1034	537	1074	617	1234	937	343	686
2	1372	1213	895	259	518	1036	541	1082	633	1266
3	1001	471	942	353	706	1412	1293	1055	579	1158
4	785	39	78	156	312	624	1248	965	399	798
5	65	130	260	520	1040	549	1098	665	1330	1129
6	727	1454	1377	1223	915	299	598	1196	861	191
7	382	764	1528	1525	1519	1507	1483	1435	1339	1147
8	763	1526	1521	1511	1491	1451	1371	1211	891	251
9	502	1004	477	954	377	754	1508	1485	1439	1347
10	1163	795	59	118	236	472	944	357	714	1428
11	1325	1119	707	1414	1297	1063	595	1190	849	167
12	334	668	1336	1141	751	1502	1473	1415	1299	1067
13	603	1206	881	231	462	924	317	634	1268	1005
14	479	958	385	770	9	18	36	72	144	288
15	576	1152	773	15	30	60	120	240	480	960
16	389	778	25	50	100	200	400	800	69	138
17	276	552	1104	677	1354	1177	823	115	230	460
18	920	309	618	1236	941	351	702	1404	1277	1023
19	515	1030	529	1058	585	1170	809	87	174	348
20	696	1392	1253	975	419	838	145	290	580	1160
21	789	47	94	188	376	752	1504	1477	1423	1315
22	1099	667	1334	1137	743	1486	1441	1351	1171	811
23	91	182	364	728	1456	1381	1231	931	331	662
24	1324	1117	703	1406	1281	1031	531	1062	593	1186
25	841	151	302	604	1208	885	239	478	956	381
26	762	1524	1517	1503	1475	1419	1307	1083	635	1270
27	1009	487	974	417	834	137	274	548	1096	661
28	1322	1113	695	1390	1249	967	403	806	81	162
29	324	648	1296	1061	591	1182	833	135	270	540
30	1080	629	1258	985	439	878	225	450	900	269
31	538	1076	621	1242	953	375	750	1500	1469	1407
32	1283	1035	539	1078	625	1250	969	407	814	97
33	194	388	776	21	42	84	168	336	672	1344
34	1157	783	35	70	140	280	560	1120	709	1418
35	1305	1079	627	1254	977	423	846	161	322	644
36	1288	1045	559	1118	705	1410	1289	1047	563	1126
37	721	1442	1353	1175	819	107	214	428	856	181
38	362	724	1448	1365	1199	867	203	406	812	93
39	186	372	744	1488	1445	1359	1187	843	155	310
40	620	1240	949	367	734	1468	1405	1279	1027	523
41	1046	561	1122	713	1426	1321	1111	691	1382	1233
42	935	339	678	1356	1181	831	131	262	524	1048
43	565	1130	729	1458	1385	1239	947	363	726	1452
44	1373	1215	899	267	534	1068	605	1210	889	247

P = 1531

INDICES

	0	1	2	3	4	5	6	7	8	9
45	307	1065	1116	1088	1396	1076	555	779	652	755
46	179	457	134	1210	894	1235	669	1509	880	1012
47	1058	31	105	958	512	1407	802	92	257	140
48	158	1261	548	1194	1132	1175	1126	271	1444	1464
49	1369	819	574	664	450	790	1086	777	455	1233
50	1010	956	90	1259	1173	1462	662	775	954	1460
51	1458	694	9	696	493	190	467	11	24	1428
52	53	698	1035	409	428	495	904	856	641	192
53	795	246	743	469	444	1221	1519	13	310	322
54	299	26	1254	1216	1309	1430	1068	1340	277	55
55	1493	605	171	700	1119	680	968	1037	1227	362
56	346	411	1091	368	1050	430	812	1314	1284	497
57	1399	924	536	906	762	1023	150	858	1079	38
58	208	643	1167	1278	1201	194	558	871	1361	797
59	949	294	531	248	782	116	1185	745	66	1435
60	1002	471	655	130	253	446	1454	900	1250	1223
61	758	945	1450	1521	687	1418	829	15	182	1321
62	400	312	1525	632	45	324	460	352	726	301
63	487	1073	1207	28	137	268	787	1256	691	1425
64	853	1218	1213	602	359	1311	1020	1275	291	1432
65	897	1415	629	1070	1422	1272	1269	1342	1238	1352
66	1485	279	239	1345	1150	57	672	221	121	1495
67	833	1241	338	607	1512	1143	1470	173	422	1355
68	623	702	883	717	1391	1121	19	1488	1162	682
69	1015	417	593	970	1298	282	200	1039	1061	1505
70	1190	1229	186	242	1336	364	34	112	941	348
71	598	1348	1139	413	108	1380	708	1093	1325	1153
72	994	370	961	1384	381	1052	438	60	233	432
73	515	932	750	814	404	675	866	1316	1410	712
74	1375	1286	975	224	392	499	805	1291	1106	1401
75	316	124	215	926	95	1097	479	538	917	1498
76	564	908	260	80	71	764	1529	836	845	1025
77	143	1329	733	152	1303	1244	332	860	161	980
78	889	1081	636	341	526	40	1264	1157	989	210
79	521	610	1477	645	551	101	1440	1169	49	1515
80	167	1280	1197	998	825	1203	287	1146	619	196
81	1135	229	388	560	328	1473	615	873	1178	374
82	583	1363	1113	176	877	799	1129	571	1007	951
83	464	425	740	296	274	965	1047	533	205	1358
84	1182	250	1447	397	723	784	356	626	1482	118
85	1467	1388	590	1187	938	705	378	747	1372	1103
86	476	68	730	886	986	1437	822	385	580	1004
87	1044	720	587	473	577	504	507	657	305	1394
88	650	132	667	1056	510	255	546	1124	1367	448
89	453	88	660	1456	491	22	1033	902	793	442
90	308	1252	1066	1491	1117	1225	1089	810	1397	760
91	1077	1165	556	947	780	64	653	1452	756	685
92	180	1523	458	485	135	689	1211	1018	895	1420
93	1236	237	670	831	1510	420	881	17	1013	1296
94	1059	184	32	596	106	1323	959	436	513	402
95	[illegible]	[illegible]	[illegible]	[illegible]	[illegible]	[illegible]	[illegible]	[illegible]	[illegible]	[illegible]

POWER RESIDUES

	0	1	2	3	4	5	6	7	8	9
45	494	988	445	890	249	498	996	461	922	313
46	626	1252	973	415	830	129	258	516	1032	533
47	1066	601	1202	873	215	430	860	189	378	756
48	1512	1493	1455	1379	1227	923	315	630	1260	989
49	447	894	257	514	1028	525	1050	569	1138	745
50	1490	1449	1367	1203	875	219	438	876	221	442
51	884	237	474	948	365	730	1460	1389	1247	963
52	395	790	49	98	196	392	784	37	74	148
53	296	592	1184	837	143	286	572	1144	757	1514
54	1497	1463	1395	1259	987	443	886	241	482	964
55	397	794	57	114	228	456	912	293	586	1172
56	813	95	190	380	760	1520	1509	1487	1443	1355
57	1179	827	123	246	492	984	437	874	217	434
58	868	205	410	820	109	218	436	872	213	426
59	852	173	346	692	1384	1237	943	355	710	1420
60	1309	1087	643	1286	1041	551	1102	673	1346	1161
61	791	51	102	204	408	816	101	202	404	808
62	85	170	340	680	1360	1189	847	163	326	652
63	1304	1077	623	1246	961	391	782	33	66	132
64	264	528	1056	581	1162	793	55	110	220	440
65	880	229	458	916	301	602	1204	877	223	446
66	892	253	506	1012	493	986	441	882	233	466
67	932	333	666	1332	1133	735	1470	1409	1287	1043
68	555	1110	689	1378	1225	919	307	614	1228	925
69	319	638	1276	1021	511	1022	513	1026	521	1042
70	553	1106	681	1362	1193	855	179	358	716	1432
71	1333	1135	739	1478	1425	1319	1107	683	1366	1201
72	871	211	422	844	157	314	628	1256	981	431
73	862	193	386	772	13	26	52	104	208	416
74	832	133	266	532	1064	597	1194	857	183	366
75	732	1464	1397	1263	995	459	918	305	610	1220
76	909	287	574	1148	765	1530	1529	1527	1523	1515
77	1499	1467	1403	1275	1019	507	1014	497	994	457
78	914	297	594	1188	845	159	318	636	1272	1013
79	495	990	449	898	265	530	1060	589	1178	825
80	119	238	476	952	373	746	1492	1453	1375	1219
81	907	283	566	1132	733	1466	1401	1271	1011	491
82	982	433	866	201	402	804	77	154	308	616
83	1232	933	335	670	1340	1149	767	3	6	12
84	24	48	96	192	384	768	5	10	20	40
85	80	160	320	640	1280	1029	527	1054	577	1154
86	777	23	46	92	184	368	736	1472	1413	1295
87	1059	587	1174	817	103	206	412	824	117	234
88	468	936	341	682	1364	1197	863	195	390	780
89	29	58	116	232	464	928	325	650	1300	1069
90	607	1214	897	263	526	1052	573	1146	761	1522
91	1513	1495	1459	1387	1243	955	379	758	1516	1501
92	1471	1411	1291	1051	571	1142	753	1506	1481	1431
93	1331	1131	731	1462	1393	1255	979	427	854	177
94	354	708	1416	1301	1071	611	1222	913	295	590
95	1180	829	127	254	508	1016	501	1002	473	946

P = 1531

INDICES

	0	1	2	3	4	5	6	7	8	9
96	159	634	1262	519	549	47	1195	285	1133	326
97	1176	1111	1127	462	272	203	1445	354	1465	936
98	1370	728	820	1042	575	303	665	544	451	489
99	791	1064	1087	1075	778	754	456	1209	1234	1508
100	1011	30	957	1406	91	139	1260	1193	1174	270
101	1463	818	663	789	776	1232	955	1258	1461	774
102	1459	693	695	189	10	1427	697	408	494	855
103	191	245	468	1220	12	321	25	1215	1429	1339
104	54	604	699	679	1036	361	410	367	429	1313
105	496	923	905	1022	857	37	642	1277	193	870
106	796	293	247	115	744	1434	470	129	445	899
107	1222	944	1520	1417	14	1320	311	631	323	351
108	300	1072	27	267	1255	1424	1217	601	1310	1274
109	1431	1414	1069	1271	1341	1351	278	1344	56	220
110	1494	1240	606	1142	172	1354	701	716	1120	1487
111	681	416	969	281	1038	1504	1228	241	363	111
112	347	1347	412	1379	1092	1152	369	1383	1051	59
113	431	931	813	674	1315	711	1285	223	498	1290
114	1400	123	925	1096	537	1497	907	79	763	835
115	1024	1328	151	1243	859	979	1080	340	39	1156
116	209	609	644	100	1168	1514	1279	997	1202	1145
117	195	228	559	1472	872	373	1362	175	798	570
118	950	424	295	964	532	1357	249	396	783	625
119	117	1387	1186	704	746	1102	67	885	1436	384
120	1003	719	472	503	656	1393	131	1055	254	1123
121	447	87	1455	21	901	441	1251	1490	1224	809
122	759	1164	946	63	1451	684	1522	484	688	1017
123	1419	236	830	419	16	1295	183	595	1322	435
124	401	972	313	914	1526	1300	633	518	46	284
125	325	1110	461	202	353	935	727	1041	302	543
126	488	1063	1074	753	1208	1507	29	1405	138	1192
127	269	817	788	1231	1257	773	692	188	1426	407
128	854	244	1219	320	1214	1338	603	678	360	366
129	1312	922	1021	36	1276	869	292	114	1433	128
130	898	943	1416	1319	630	350	1071	266	1423	600
131	1273	1413	1270	1350	1343	219	1239	1141	1353	715
132	1486	415	280	1503	240	110	1346	1378	1151	1382
133	58	930	673	710	222	1289	122	1095	1496	78
134	834	1327	1242	978	339	1155	608	99	1513	996
135	1144	227	1471	372	174	569	423	963	1356	395
136	624	1386	703	1101	884	383	718	502	1392	1054
137	1122	86	20	440	1489	808	1163	62	683	483
138	1016	235	418	1294	594	434	971	913	1299	517
139	283	1109	201	934	1040	542	1062	752	1506	1404
140	1191	816	1230	772	187	406	243	319	1337	677
141	365	921	35	868	113	127	942	1318	349	265
142	599	1412	1349	218	1140	714	414	1502	109	1377
143	1381	929	709	1288	1094	77	1326	977	1154	98
144	995	226	371	568	962	394	1385	1100	382	501
145	1053	85	439	807	61	482	234	1293	433	912

POWER RESIDUES

	0	1	2	3	4	5	6	7	8	9
96	361	722	1444	1357	1183	835	139	278	556	1112
97	693	1386	1241	951	371	742	1484	1437	1343	1155
98	779	27	54	108	216	432	864	197	394	788
99	45	90	180	360	720	1440	1349	1167	803	75
100	150	300	600	1200	869	207	414	828	125	250
101	500	1000	469	938	345	690	1380	1229	927	323
102	646	1292	1053	575	1150	769	7	14	28	56
103	112	224	448	896	261	522	1044	557	1114	697
104	1394	1257	983	435	870	209	418	836	141	282
105	564	1128	725	1450	1369	1207	883	235	470	940
106	349	698	1396	1261	991	451	902	273	546	1092
107	653	1306	1081	631	1262	993	455	910	289	578
108	1156	781	31	62	124	248	496	992	453	906
109	281	562	1124	717	1434	1337	1143	755	1510	1489
110	1447	1363	1195	859	187	374	748	1496	1461	1391
111	1251	971	411	822	113	226	452	904	277	554
112	1108	685	1370	1209	887	243	486	972	413	826
113	121	242	484	968	405	810	89	178	356	712
114	1424	1317	1103	675	1350	1169	807	83	166	332
115	664	1328	1125	719	1438	1345	1159	787	43	86
116	172	344	688	1376	1221	911	291	582	1164	797
117	63	126	252	504	1008	485	970	409	818	105
118	210	420	840	149	298	596	1192	853	175	350
119	700	1400	1269	1007	483	966	401	802	73	146
120	292	584	1168	805	79	158	316	632	1264	997
121	463	926	321	642	1284	1037	543	1086	641	1282
122	1033	535	1070	609	1218	905	279	558	1116	701
123	1402	1273	1015	499	998	465	930	329	658	1316
124	1101	671	1342	1153	775	19	38	76	152	304
125	608	1216	901	271	542	1084	637	1274	1017	503
126	1006	481	962	393	786	41	82	164	328	656
127	1312	1093	655	1310	1089	647	1294	1057	583	1166
128	801	71	142	284	568	1136	741	1482	1433	1335
129	1139	747	1494	1457	1383	1235	939	347	694	1388
130	1245	959	387	774	17	34	68	136	272	544
131	1088	645	1290	1049	567	1134	737	1474	1417	1303
132	1075	619	1238	945	359	718	1436	1341	1151	771
133	11	22	44	88	176	352	704	1408	1285	1039
134	547	1094	657	1314	1097	663	1326	1121	711	1422
135	1313	1095	659	1318	1105	679	1358	1185	839	147
136	294	588	1176	821	111	222	444	888	245	490
137	980	429	858	185	370	740	1480	1429	1327	1123
138	715	1430	1329	1127	723	1446	1361	1191	851	171
139	342	684	1368	1205	879	227	454	908	285	570
140	1140	749	1498	1465	1399	1267	1003	475	950	369
141	738	1476	1421	1311	1091	651	1302	1073	615	1230
142	929	327	654	1308	1085	639	1278	1025	519	1038
143	545	1090	649	1298	1065	599	1198	865	199	398
144	796	61	122	244	488	976	421	842	153	306
145	612	1224	917	303	606	1212	893	255	510	1020

P = 1531

INDICES

	0	1	2	3	4	5	6	7	8	9
146	516	1108	933	541	751	1403	815	771	405	318
147	676	920	867	126	1317	264	1411	217	713	1501
148	1376	928	1287	76	976	97	225	567	393	1099
149	500	84	806	481	1292	911	1107	540	1402	770
150	317	919	125	263	216	1500	927	75	96	566
151	1098	83	480	910	539	769	918	262	1499	74
152	565	82	909	768	261	73	81	767	72	766
153	765	0								

POWER RESIDUES

	0	1	2	3	4	5	6	7	8	9
146	509	1018	505	1010	489	978	425	850	169	338
147	676	1352	1173	815	99	198	396	792	53	106
148	212	424	848	165	330	660	1320	1109	687	1374
149	1217	903	275	550	1100	669	1338	1145	759	1518
150	1505	1479	1427	1323	1115	699	1398	1265	999	467
151	934	337	674	1348	1165	799	67	134	268	536
152	1072	613	1226	921	311	622	1244	957	383	766
153										

P = 1543

INDICES

	0	1	2	3	4	5	6	7	8	9
0		0	76	669	152	1	745	582	228	1338
1	77	705	821	878	658	670	304	234	1414	1331
2	153	1251	781	865	897	2	954	465	734	324
3	746	504	380	1374	310	583	1490	920	1407	5
4	229	805	1327	53	857	1339	941	396	973	1164
5	78	903	1030	1192	541	706	810	458	400	1155
6	822	641	580	378	456	879	1450	1524	386	1534
7	659	550	24	1139	996	671	1483	1287	81	767
8	305	1134	881	521	1403	235	129	993	933	1283
9	1415	1460	1017	1173	472	1332	1049	1034	1240	501
10	154	835	979	948	1106	1252	1268	1452	617	347
11	782	47	886	889	534	866	476	674	1231	816
12	898	1410	717	1474	656	3	454	1281	532	722
13	955	1045	1526	371	58	466	462	14	68	724
14	735	1065	626	41	100	325	1215	291	1072	344
15	747	526	17	30	1363	505	157	388	843	319
16	381	1447	1210	916	957	1375	597	1204	1479	214
17	311	1127	205	862	1069	584	1009	282	1359	590
18	1491	333	1536	1310	1093	921	1249	939	548	1047
19	1408	1213	1125	1314	1110	6	1316	1146	577	936
20	230	651	911	906	1055	806	1024	661	1182	494
21	1328	97	1344	1219	1528	54	693	1086	423	266
22	858	1112	123	832	962	1340	965	359	610	240
23	942	414	552	351	750	397	1307	1436	892	373
24	974	1060	1486	261	793	1165	8	667	732	1190
25	79	946	530	28	1357	904	608	26	798	1502
26	1031	120	1121	1380	60	1193	447	410	134	1347
27	542	1318	538	587	90	707	144	71	800	300
28	811	838	1141	1302	702	459	117	1387	176	468
29	401	161	1291	851	367	1156	1148	1170	420	201
30	823	635	602	1504	93	642	106	998	1439	75
31	581	820	233	780	464	379	919	1326	395	1029
32	457	579	1523	23	1286	880	992	1016	1033	978
33	1451	885	673	716	1280	1525	13	625	290	16
34	387	1209	1203	204	281	1535	938	1124	1145	910
35	660	1343	1085	122	358	551	1435	1485	666	529
36	25	1120	409	537	70	1140	1386	1290	1169	601
37	997	232	1325	1522	1015	672	624	1202	1123	1084
38	1484	408	1289	1324	1201	1288	1390	1391	1186	726
39	82	1099	1392	172	1222	768	653	1187	1012	1040

POWER RESIDUES

	0	1	2	3	4	5	6	7	8	9
0	1	5	25	125	625	39	195	975	246	1230
1	1521	1433	993	336	137	685	339	152	760	714
2	484	877	1299	323	72	360	257	1285	253	1265
3	153	765	739	609	1502	1338	518	1047	606	1487
4	1263	143	715	489	902	1424	948	111	555	1232
5	1531	1483	1243	43	215	1075	746	644	134	670
6	264	1320	428	597	1442	1038	561	1262	138	690
7	364	277	1385	753	679	309	2	10	50	250
8	1250	78	390	407	492	917	1499	1323	443	672
9	274	1370	678	304	1520	1428	968	211	1055	646
10	144	720	514	1027	506	987	306	1530	1478	1218
11	1461	1133	1036	551	1212	1431	983	286	1430	978
12	261	1305	353	222	1110	921	1519	1423	943	86
13	430	607	1492	1288	268	1340	528	1097	856	1194
14	1341	533	1122	981	276	1380	728	554	1227	1506
15	1358	618	4	20	100	500	957	156	780	814
16	984	291	1455	1103	886	1344	548	1197	1356	608
17	1497	1313	393	422	567	1292	288	1440	1028	511
18	1012	431	612	1517	1413	893	1379	723	529	1102
19	881	1319	423	572	1317	413	522	1067	706	444
20	677	299	1495	1303	343	172	860	1214	1441	1033
21	536	1137	1056	651	169	845	1139	1066	701	419
22	552	1217	1456	1108	911	1469	1173	1236	8	40
23	200	1000	371	312	17	85	425	582	1367	663
24	229	1145	1096	851	1169	1216	1451	1083	786	844
25	1134	1041	576	1337	513	1022	481	862	1224	1491
26	1283	243	1215	1446	1058	661	219	1095	846	1144
27	1091	826	1044	591	1412	888	1354	598	1447	1063
28	686	344	177	885	1339	523	1072	731	569	1302
29	338	147	735	589	1402	838	1104	891	1369	673
30	279	1395	803	929	16	80	400	457	742	624
31	34	170	850	1164	1191	1326	458	747	649	159
32	795	889	1359	623	29	145	725	539	1152	1131
33	1026	501	962	181	905	1439	1023	486	887	1349
34	573	1322	438	647	149	745	639	109	545	1182
35	1281	233	1165	1196	1351	583	1372	688	354	227
36	1135	1046	601	1462	1138	1061	676	294	1470	1178
37	1261	133	665	239	1195	1346	558	1247	63	315
38	32	160	800	914	1484	1248	68	340	157	785
39	839	1109	916	1494	1298	318	47	235	1175	1246

P = 1543

INDICES

	0	1	2	3	4	5	6	7	8	9
40	306	489	727	1382	987	1135	982	83	1131	1021
41	882	683	1100	195	737	522	1258	1393	570	219
42	1404	913	173	192	1420	236	1295	1223	62	710
43	130	181	769	895	1162	994	499	654	342	1067
44	934	960	1188	88	199	1284	908	1013	1038	1418
45	1416	1510	1041	1195	435	1461	686	307	316	699
46	1018	483	490	1465	628	1174	427	728	826	564
47	473	1057	1383	758	1512	1333	968	988	449	1370
48	1050	256	1136	574	20	1035	337	983	869	43
49	1241	761	84	558	743	502	808	1132	1266	1043
50	155	331	1022	412	606	836	104	883	1433	406
51	980	179	684	254	102	949	874	1101	36	1531
52	1107	1026	196	285	1197	1253	1456	738	136	188
53	1269	951	523	141	486	1453	210	1259	1423	327
54	618	1178	1394	1002	614	348	663	571	166	437
55	783	113	220	1349	147	48	876	1405	376	931
56	887	66	914	546	1217	890	1378	174	778	288
57	535	1184	193	340	1463	867	252	1421	544	441
58	477	1103	237	355	1367	675	927	1296	443	293
59	1232	273	1224	638	1246	817	496	63	277	688
60	899	362	711	1320	678	1411	38	131	169	33
61	718	1274	182	479	1074	1475	1515	770	151	1337
62	657	1330	896	323	309	4	856	1163	540	1154
63	455	1533	995	766	1402	1282	471	500	1105	346
64	533	815	655	721	57	723	99	343	1362	318
65	956	213	1068	589	1092	1046	1109	935	1054	493
66	1527	265	961	239	749	372	792	1189	1356	1501
67	59	1346	89	299	701	467	366	200	92	74
68	463	1028	1285	977	1279	15	280	909	357	528
69	69	600	1014	1083	1200	725	1221	1039	986	1020
70	736	218	1419	709	1161	1066	198	1417	434	698
71	627	563	1511	1369	19	42	742	1042	605	405
72	101	1530	1196	187	485	326	613	436	146	930
73	1216	287	1462	440	1366	292	1245	687	677	32
74	1073	1336	308	1153	1401	345	56	317	1091	492
75	748	1500	700	73	1278	527	1199	1019	1160	697
76	18	404	484	929	1365	31	1400	491	1277	696
77	1364	695	1466	593	1467	506	1262	629	802	594
78	158	1255	1175	789	1468	389	248	428	1298	507
79	844	1471	729	1519	1263	320	1088	827	1116	630
80	382	1079	565	302	803	1448	1458	474	1063	595
81	1211	691	1058	445	159	917	1207	1384	1097	1256
82	958	425	759	872	1176	1376	271	1513	813	790
83	598	740	1334	1398	1469	1205	646	969	295	390
84	1480	648	989	1507	249	215	268	450	1496	429
85	312	243	1371	840	1299	1128	138	1051	786	508
86	206	514	257	1234	845	863	971	1137	1238	1472
87	1070	860	575	830	730	585	418	21	1143	1520
88	1010	190	1036	756	1264	283	164	338	275	321
89	1360	297	984	185	1089	591	1114	870	1494	828

POWER RESIDUES

	0	1	2	3	4	5	6	7	8	9
40	58	290	1450	1078	761	719	509	1002	381	362
41	267	1335	503	972	231	1155	1146	1101	876	1294
42	298	1490	1278	218	1090	821	1019	466	787	849
43	1159	1166	1201	1376	708	454	727	549	1202	1381
44	733	579	1352	588	1397	813	979	266	1330	478
45	847	1149	1116	951	126	630	64	320	57	285
46	1425	953	136	680	314	27	135	675	289	1445
47	1053	636	94	470	807	949	116	580	1357	613
48	1522	1438	1018	461	762	724	534	1127	1006	401
49	462	767	749	659	209	1045	596	1437	1013	436
50	637	99	495	932	31	155	775	789	859	1209
51	1416	908	1454	1098	861	1219	1466	1158	1161	1176
52	1251	83	415	532	1117	956	151	755	689	359
53	252	1260	128	640	114	570	1307	363	272	1360
54	628	54	270	1350	578	1347	563	1272	188	940
55	71	355	232	1160	1171	1226	1501	1333	493	922
56	1524	1448	1068	711	469	802	924	1534	1498	1318
57	418	547	1192	1331	483	872	1274	198	990	321
58	62	310	7	35	175	875	1289	273	1365	653
59	179	895	1389	773	779	809	959	166	830	1064
60	691	369	302	1510	1378	718	504	977	256	1280
61	228	1140	1071	726	544	1177	1256	108	540	1157
62	1156	1151	1126	1001	376	337	142	710	464	777
63	799	909	1459	1123	986	301	1505	1353	593	1422
64	938	61	305	1525	1453	1093	836	1094	841	1119
65	966	201	1005	396	437	642	124	620	14	70
66	350	207	1035	546	1187	1306	358	247	1235	3
67	15	75	375	332	117	585	1382	738	604	1477
68	1213	1436	1008	411	512	1017	456	737	599	1452
69	1088	811	969	216	1080	771	769	759	709	459
70	752	674	284	1420	928	11	55	275	1375	703
71	429	602	1467	1163	1186	1301	333	122	610	1507
72	1363	643	129	645	139	695	389	402	467	792
73	874	1284	248	1240	28	140	700	414	527	1092
74	831	1069	716	494	927	6	30	150	750	664
75	234	1170	1221	1476	1208	1411	883	1329	473	822
76	1024	491	912	1474	1198	1361	633	79	395	432
77	617	1542	1538	1518	1418	918	1504	1348	568	1297
78	313	22	110	550	1207	1406	858	1204	1391	783
79	829	1059	666	244	1220	1471	1183	1286	258	1290
80	278	1390	778	804	934	41	205	1025	496	937
81	56	280	1400	828	1054	641	119	595	1432	988
82	311	12	60	300	1500	1328	468	797	899	1409
83	873	1279	223	1115	946	101	505	982	281	1405
84	853	1179	1266	158	790	864	1234	1541	1533	1493
85	1293	293	1465	1153	1136	1051	626	44	220	1100
86	871	1269	173	865	1239	23	115	575	1332	488
87	897	1399	823	1029	516	1037	556	1237	13	65
88	325	82	410	507	992	331	112	560	1257	113
89	565	1282	238	1190	1321	433	622	24	120	600

P = 1543

INDICES

	0	1	2	3	4	5	6	7	8	9
90	1492	1426	44	1304	1117	334	1271	1242	511	631
91	1537	224	762	1226	383	1311	392	85	775	1080
92	1094	125	559	1428	566	922	1541	744	704	303
93	1250	953	503	1489	804	940	902	809	640	1449
94	549	1482	1133	128	1459	1048	834	1267	46	475
95	1409	453	1044	461	1064	1214	525	156	1446	596
96	1126	1008	332	1248	1212	1315	650	1023	96	692
97	1111	964	413	1306	1059	7	945	607	119	446
98	1317	143	837	116	160	1147	634	105	819	918
99	578	991	884	12	1208	937	1342	1434	1119	1385
100	231	623	407	1389	1098	652	488	981	682	1257
101	912	1294	180	498	959	907	1509	685	482	426
102	1056	967	255	336	760	807	330	103	178	873
103	1025	1455	950	209	1177	662	112	875	65	1377
104	1183	251	1102	926	272	495	361	37	1273	1514
105	1329	855	1532	470	814	98	212	1108	264	791
106	1345	365	1027	279	599	1220	217	197	562	741
107	1529	612	286	1244	1335	55	1499	1198	403	1399
108	694	1261	1254	247	1470	1087	1078	1457	690	1206
109	424	270	739	645	647	267	242	137	513	970
110	859	417	189	163	296	1113	1425	1270	223	391
111	124	1540	952	901	1481	833	452	524	1007	649
112	963	944	142	633	990	1341	622	487	1293	1508
113	966	329	1454	111	250	360	854	211	364	216
114	611	1498	1260	1077	269	241	416	1424	1539	451
115	943	621	328	853	1497	415	620	619	517	430
116	553	518	1179	713	313	352	431	1395	1443	244
117	751	554	1003	226	1372	398	519	615	369	841
118	1308	1180	349	796	1300	1437	714	664	1322	1129
119	893	314	572	1431	139	374	353	167	764	1052
120	975	432	438	1158	787	1061	1396	784	754	509
121	1487	1444	114	680	207	262	245	221	109	515
122	794	752	1350	1228	258	1166	555	148	1150	1235
123	9	1004	49	1352	846	668	227	877	1413	864
124	733	1373	1406	52	972	1191	399	377	385	1138
125	80	520	932	1172	1239	947	616	888	1230	1473
126	531	370	67	40	1071	29	842	915	1478	861
127	1358	1309	547	1313	576	905	1181	1218	422	831
128	609	350	891	260	731	27	797	1379	133	586
129	799	1301	175	850	419	1503	1438	779	394	22
130	1032	715	289	203	1144	121	665	536	1168	1521
131	1122	1323	1185	171	1011	1381	1130	194	569	191
132	61	894	341	87	1037	1194	315	1464	825	757
133	448	573	868	557	1265	411	1432	253	35	284
134	135	140	1422	1001	165	1348	375	545	777	339
135	543	354	442	637	276	1319	168	478	150	322
136	539	765	1104	720	1361	588	1053	238	1355	298
137	91	976	356	1082	985	708	433	1368	604	186
138	145	439	676	1152	1090	72	1159	928	1276	592
139	801	788	1297	1518	1115	301	1062	444	1096	871

POWER RESIDUES

	0	1	2	3	4	5	6	7	8	9
90	1457	1113	936	51	255	1275	203	1015	446	687
91	349	202	1010	421	562	1267	163	815	989	316
92	37	185	925	1539	1523	1443	1043	586	1387	763
93	729	559	1252	88	440	657	199	995	346	187
94	935	46	230	1150	1121	976	251	1255	103	515
95	1032	531	1112	931	26	130	650	164	820	1014
96	441	662	224	1120	971	226	1130	1021	476	837
97	1099	866	1244	48	240	1200	1371	683	329	102
98	510	1007	406	487	892	1374	698	404	477	842
99	1124	991	326	87	435	632	74	370	307	1535
100	1503	1343	543	1172	1231	1526	1458	1118	961	176
101	880	1314	398	447	692	374	327	92	460	757
102	699	409	502	967	206	1030	521	1062	681	319
103	52	260	1300	328	97	485	882	1324	448	697
104	399	452	717	499	952	131	655	189	945	96
105	480	857	1199	1366	658	204	1020	471	812	974
106	241	1205	1396	808	954	141	705	439	652	174
107	870	1264	148	740	614	1527	1463	1143	1086	801
108	919	1509	1373	693	379	352	217	1085	796	894
109	1384	748	654	184	920	1514	1398	818	1004	391
110	412	517	1042	581	1362	638	104	520	1057	656
111	194	970	221	1105	896	1394	798	904	1434	998
112	361	262	1310	378	347	192	960	171	855	1189
113	1316	408	497	942	81	405	482	867	1249	73
114	365	282	1410	878	1304	348	197	985	296	1480
115	1228	1511	1383	743	629	59	295	1475	1203	1386
116	758	704	434	627	49	245	1225	1496	1308	368
117	297	1485	1253	93	465	782	824	1034	541	1162
118	1181	1276	208	1040	571	1312	388	397	442	667
119	249	1245	53	265	1325	453	722	524	1077	756
120	694	384	377	342	167	835	1089	816	994	341
121	162	810	964	191	955	146	730	564	1277	213
122	1065	696	394	427	592	1417	913	1479	1223	1486
123	1258	118	590	1407	863	1229	1516	1408	868	1254
124	98	490	907	1449	1073	736	594	1427	963	186
125	930	21	105	525	1082	781	819	1009	416	537
126	1142	1081	776	794	884	1334	498	947	106	530
127	1107	906	1444	1048	611	1512	1388	768	754	684
128	334	127	635	89	445	682	324	77	385	382
129	367	292	1460	1128	1011	426	587	1392	788	854
130	1184	1291	283	1415	903	1429	973	236	1180	1271
131	183	915	1489	1273	193	965	196	980	271	1355
132	603	1472	1188	1311	383	372	317	42	210	1050
133	621	19	95	475	832	1074	741	619	9	45
134	225	1125	996	351	212	1060	671	269	1345	553
135	1222	1481	1233	1536	1508	1368	668	254	1270	178
136	890	1364	648	154	770	764	734	584	1377	713
137	479	852	1174	1241	33	165	825	1039	566	1287
138	263	1315	403	472	817	999	366	287	1435	1003
139	386	387	392	417	542	1167	1206	1401	833	1079

P = 1543

INDICES

	0	1	2	3	4	5	6	7	8	9
140	812	1397	294	1506	1495	839	785	1233	1237	829
141	1142	755	274	184	1493	1303	510	1225	774	1427
142	703	1488	639	127	45	460	1445	1247	95	1305
143	118	115	818	11	1118	1388	681	497	481	335
144	177	208	64	925	1272	469	263	278	561	1243
145	402	246	689	644	512	162	222	900	1006	632
146	1292	110	363	1076	1538	852	516	712	1442	225
147	368	795	1321	1430	763	1157	753	679	108	1227
148	1149	1351	1412	51	384	1171	1229	39	1477	1312
149	421	259	132	849	393	202	1167	170	568	86
150	824	556	34	1000	776	636	149	719	1354	1081
151	603	1151	1275	1517	1095	1505	1236	183	773	126
152	94	10	480	924	560	643	1005	1075	1441	1429
153	107	50	1476	848	567	999	1353	1516	772	923
154	1440	847	771							

POWER RESIDUES

	0	1	2	3	4	5	6	7	8	9
140	766	744	634	84	420	557	1242	38	190	950
141	121	605	1482	1238	18	90	450	707	449	702
142	424	577	1342	538	1147	1106	901	1419	923	1529
143	1473	1193	1336	508	997	356	237	1185	1296	308
144	1540	1528	1468	1168	1211	1426	958	161	805	939
145	66	330	107	535	1132	1031	526	1087	806	944
146	91	455	732	574	1327	463	772	774	784	834
147	1084	791	869	1259	123	615	1532	1488	1268	168
148	840	1114	941	76	380	357	242	1210	1421	933
149	36	180	900	1414	898	1404	848	1154	1141	1076
150	751	669	259	1295	303	1515	1403	843	1129	1016
151	451	712	474	827	1049	616	1537	1513	1393	793
152	879	1309	373	322	67	335	132	660	214	1070
153	721	519	1052	631	69	345	182	910	1464	1148
154	1111	926								

P = 1549

INDICES

	0	1	2	3	4	5	6	7	8	9
0		0	1	798	2	1098	799	886	3	48
1	1099	384	800	33	887	348	4	1404	49	229
2	1100	136	385	490	801	648	34	846	888	557
3	349	899	5	1182	1405	436	50	961	230	831
4	1101	1366	137	724	386	1146	491	367	802	224
5	649	654	35	1017	847	1482	889	1027	558	1088
6	350	927	900	934	6	1131	1183	287	1406	1288
7	437	1196	51	642	962	1446	231	1270	832	1347
8	1102	96	1367	659	138	954	725	1355	387	968
9	1147	919	492	149	368	1327	803	794	225	432
10	650	283	655	428	36	1234	1018	541	848	377
11	1483	211	890	295	1028	40	559	81	1089	742
12	351	768	928	616	901	198	935	622	7	1522
13	1132	1238	1184	1115	288	396	1407	527	1289	1490
14	438	1165	1197	417	52	107	643	1022	963	763
15	1447	506	232	1452	1271	449	833	585	1348	267
16	1103	1376	97	545	1368	732	660	1217	139	66
17	955	277	726	1503	1356	1534	388	338	969	852
18	1148	1054	920	177	493	511	150	240	369	184
19	1328	907	804	321	795	381	226	843	433	721
20	651	1085	284	1443	656	916	429	538	37	613
21	1235	1487	1019	446	542	274	849	237	378	1440
22	1484	1437	212	1462	891	696	296	215	1029	1509
23	41	520	560	481	82	1465	1090	597	743	15
24	352	403	769	894	929	1322	617	262	902	1457
25	199	699	936	874	623	204	8	861	1523	299
26	1133	605	1239	1306	1185	567	1116	218	289	332
27	397	471	1408	169	528	1032	1290	1044	1491	947
28	439	1276	1166	1512	1198	577	418	704	53	1260
29	108	44	644	1362	1023	638	964	1230	764	523
30	1448	62	507	1081	233	477	1453	563	1272	1226
31	450	1249	834	454	586	484	1349	500	268	941
32	1104	1339	1377	85	98	681	546	1175	1369	1253
33	733	1468	661	1009	1218	1385	140	309	67	1093
34	956	1283	278	1110	727	838	1504	600	1357	676
35	1535	879	389	1299	339	746	970	1540	853	1067
36	1149	458	1055	18	921	192	178	868	494	1414
37	512	355	151	251	241	996	370	590	185	406
38	1329	1420	908	628	805	820	322	772	796	884
39	382	346	227	488	844	897	434	829	722	365
40	652	1480	1086	932	285	1194	1444	1345	657	1353
41	917	1325	430	426	539	209	38	740	614	620
42	1236	394	1488	415	1020	504	447	265	543	1215
43	275	1532	850	175	238	905	379	719	1441	536
44	1485	272	1438	1460	213	518	1463	13	892	260
45	697	202	297	1304	216	469	1030	945	1510	702
46	42	636	521	1079	561	1247	482	939	83	1173
47	1466	1383	1091	1108	598	877	744	1065	16	866
48	353	994	404	626	770	344	895	363	930	1343
49	1323	207	618	413	263	1530	903	534	1458	11

POWER RESIDUES

	0	1	2	3	4	5	6	7	8	9
0	1	2	4	8	16	32	64	128	256	512
1	1024	499	998	447	894	239	478	956	363	726
2	1452	1355	1161	773	1546	1543	1537	1525	1501	1453
3	1357	1165	781	13	26	52	104	208	416	832
4	115	230	460	920	291	582	1164	779	9	18
5	36	72	144	288	576	1152	755	1510	1471	1393
6	1237	925	301	602	1204	859	169	338	676	1352
7	1155	761	1522	1495	1441	1333	1117	685	1370	1191
8	833	117	234	468	936	323	646	1292	1035	521
9	1042	535	1070	591	1182	815	81	162	324	648
10	1296	1043	537	1074	599	1198	847	145	290	580
11	1160	771	1542	1535	1521	1493	1437	1325	1101	653
12	1306	1063	577	1154	759	1518	1487	1425	1301	1053
13	557	1114	679	1358	1167	785	21	42	84	168
14	336	672	1344	1139	729	1458	1367	1185	821	93
15	186	372	744	1488	1427	1305	1061	573	1146	743
16	1486	1423	1297	1045	541	1082	615	1230	911	273
17	546	1092	635	1270	991	433	866	183	366	732
18	1464	1379	1209	869	189	378	756	1512	1475	1401
19	1253	957	365	730	1460	1371	1193	837	125	250
20	500	1000	451	902	255	510	1020	491	982	415
21	830	111	222	444	888	227	454	908	267	534
22	1068	587	1174	799	49	98	196	392	784	19
23	38	76	152	304	608	1216	883	217	434	868
24	187	374	748	1496	1443	1337	1125	701	1402	1255
25	961	373	746	1492	1435	1321	1093	637	1274	999
26	449	898	247	494	988	427	854	159	318	636
27	1272	995	441	882	215	430	860	171	342	684
28	1368	1187	825	101	202	404	808	67	134	268
29	536	1072	595	1190	831	113	226	452	904	259
30	518	1036	523	1046	543	1086	623	1246	943	337
31	674	1348	1147	745	1490	1431	1313	1077	605	1210
32	871	193	386	772	1544	1539	1529	1509	1469	1389
33	1229	909	269	538	1076	603	1206	863	177	354
34	708	1416	1283	1017	485	970	391	782	15	30
35	60	120	240	480	960	371	742	1484	1419	1289
36	1029	509	1018	487	974	399	798	47	94	188
37	376	752	1504	1459	1369	1189	829	109	218	436
38	872	195	390	780	11	22	44	88	176	352
39	704	1408	1267	985	421	842	135	270	540	1080
40	611	1222	895	241	482	964	379	758	1516	1483
41	1417	1285	1021	493	986	423	846	143	286	572
42	1144	739	1478	1407	1265	981	413	826	103	206
43	412	824	99	198	396	792	35	70	140	280
44	560	1120	691	1382	1215	881	213	426	852	155
45	310	620	1240	931	313	626	1252	955	361	722
46	1444	1339	1129	709	1418	1287	1025	501	1002	455
47	910	271	542	1084	619	1238	927	305	610	1220
48	891	233	466	932	315	630	1260	971	393	786
49	23	46	92	184	368	736	1472	1395	1241	933

P = 1549

INDICES

	0	1	2	3	4	5	6	7	8	9
50	200	467	700	1077	937	1381	875	864	624	361
51	205	1528	9	1075	862	1526	1524	751	300	753
52	1134	89	606	302	1240	784	1307	755	1186	980
53	568	1136	1117	1399	219	91	290	102	333	608
54	398	164	472	304	1409	1475	170	1242	529	975
55	1033	786	1291	685	1045	1309	1492	130	948	757
56	440	1038	1277	1188	1167	1393	1513	982	1199	550
57	578	570	419	157	705	1138	54	122	1261	1119
58	109	1545	45	1401	645	1179	1363	221	1024	1128
59	639	93	965	791	1231	292	765	1519	524	104
60	1449	1373	63	335	508	318	1082	610	234	693
61	478	400	1454	858	564	166	1273	1257	1227	474
62	451	1336	1250	306	835	1296	455	1411	587	817
63	485	1477	1350	737	501	172	269	257	942	1244
64	1105	991	1340	531	1378	1072	86	977	99	1472
65	682	1035	547	119	1176	788	1370	690	1254	1293
66	734	988	1469	687	662	665	1010	1047	1219	712
67	1386	1311	141	668	310	1494	68	1154	1094	132
68	957	1013	1284	950	279	77	1111	759	728	1050
69	839	442	1505	1318	601	1040	1358	1222	677	1279
70	1536	247	880	1190	390	715	1300	1169	340	463
71	747	1395	971	1389	1541	1515	854	813	1068	984
72	1150	1314	459	1201	1056	1205	19	552	922	144
73	193	580	179	1432	869	572	495	671	1415	421
74	513	1060	356	159	152	313	252	707	242	1427
75	997	1140	371	1497	591	56	186	1209	407	124
76	1330	71	1421	1263	909	1002	629	1121	806	1157
77	821	111	323	23	773	1547	797	1097	885	47
78	383	32	347	1403	228	135	489	647	845	556
79	898	1181	435	960	830	1365	723	1145	366	223
80	653	1016	1481	1026	1087	926	933	1130	286	1287
81	1195	641	1445	1269	1346	95	658	953	1354	967
82	918	148	1326	793	431	282	427	1233	540	376
83	210	294	39	80	741	767	615	197	621	1521
84	1237	1114	395	526	1489	1164	416	106	1021	762
85	505	1451	448	584	266	1375	544	731	1216	65
86	276	1502	1533	337	851	1053	176	510	239	183
87	906	320	380	842	720	1084	1442	915	537	612
88	1486	445	273	236	1439	1436	1461	695	214	1508
89	519	480	1464	596	14	402	893	1321	261	1456
90	698	873	203	860	298	604	1305	566	217	331
91	470	168	1031	1043	946	1275	1511	576	703	1259
92	43	1361	637	1229	522	61	1080	476	562	1225
93	1248	453	483	499	940	1338	84	680	1174	1252
94	1467	1008	1384	308	1092	1282	1109	837	599	675
95	878	1298	745	1539	1066	457	17	191	867	1413
96	354	250	995	589	405	1419	627	819	771	883
97	345	487	896	828	364	1479	931	1193	1344	1352
98	1324	425	208	739	619	393	414	503	264	1214
99	1531	174	904	718	535	271	1459	517	12	259

POWER RESIDUES

	0	1	2	3	4	5	6	7	8	9
50	317	634	1268	987	425	850	151	302	604	1208
51	867	185	370	740	1480	1411	1273	997	445	890
52	231	462	924	299	598	1196	843	137	274	548
53	1096	643	1286	1023	497	994	439	878	207	414
54	828	107	214	428	856	163	326	652	1304	1059
55	569	1138	727	1454	1359	1169	789	29	58	116
56	232	464	928	307	614	1228	907	265	530	1060
57	571	1142	735	1470	1391	1233	917	285	570	1140
58	731	1462	1375	1201	853	157	314	628	1256	963
59	377	754	1508	1467	1385	1221	893	237	474	948
60	347	694	1388	1227	905	261	522	1044	539	1078
61	607	1214	879	209	418	836	123	246	492	984
62	419	838	127	254	508	1016	483	966	383	766
63	1532	1515	1481	1413	1277	1005	461	922	295	590
64	1180	811	73	146	292	584	1168	787	25	50
65	100	200	400	800	51	102	204	408	816	83
66	166	332	664	1328	1107	665	1330	1111	673	1346
67	1143	737	1474	1399	1249	949	349	698	1396	1243
68	937	325	650	1300	1051	553	1106	663	1326	1103
69	657	1314	1079	609	1218	887	225	450	900	251
70	502	1004	459	918	287	574	1148	747	1494	1439
71	1329	1109	669	1338	1127	705	1410	1271	993	437
72	874	199	398	796	43	86	172	344	688	1376
73	1203	857	165	330	660	1320	1091	633	1266	983
74	417	834	119	238	476	952	355	710	1420	1291
75	1033	517	1034	519	1038	527	1054	559	1118	687
76	1374	1199	849	149	298	596	1192	835	121	242
77	484	968	387	774	1548	1547	1545	1541	1533	1517
78	1485	1421	1293	1037	525	1050	551	1102	655	1310
79	1071	593	1186	823	97	194	388	776	3	6
80	12	24	48	96	192	384	768	1536	1523	1497
81	1445	1341	1133	717	1434	1319	1089	629	1258	967
82	385	770	1540	1531	1513	1477	1405	1261	973	397
83	794	39	78	156	312	624	1248	947	345	690
84	1380	1211	873	197	394	788	27	54	108	216
85	432	864	179	358	716	1432	1315	1081	613	1226
86	903	257	514	1028	507	1014	479	958	367	734
87	1468	1387	1225	901	253	506	1012	475	950	351
88	702	1404	1259	969	389	778	7	14	28	56
89	112	224	448	896	243	486	972	395	790	31
90	62	124	248	496	992	435	870	191	382	764
91	1528	1507	1465	1381	1213	877	205	410	820	91
92	182	364	728	1456	1363	1177	805	61	122	244
93	488	976	403	806	63	126	252	504	1008	467
94	934	319	638	1276	1003	457	914	279	558	1116
95	683	1366	1183	817	85	170	340	680	1360	1171
96	793	37	74	148	296	592	1184	819	89	178
97	356	712	1424	1299	1049	549	1098	647	1294	1039
98	529	1058	567	1134	719	1438	1327	1105	661	1322
99	1095	641	1282	1015	481	962	375	750	1500	1451

P = 1549

INDICES

	0	1	2	3	4	5	6	7	8	9
100	201	1303	468	944	701	635	1078	1246	938	1172
101	1382	1107	876	1064	865	993	625	343	362	1342
102	206	412	1529	533	10	466	1076	1380	863	360
103	1527	1074	1525	750	752	88	301	783	754	979
104	1135	1398	90	101	607	163	303	1474	1241	974
105	785	684	1308	129	756	1037	1187	1392	981	549
106	569	156	1137	121	1118	1544	1400	1178	220	1127
107	92	790	291	1518	103	1372	334	317	609	692
108	399	857	165	1256	473	1335	305	1295	1410	816
109	1476	736	171	256	1243	990	530	1071	976	1471
110	1034	118	787	689	1292	987	686	664	1046	711
111	1310	667	1493	1153	131	1012	949	76	758	1049
112	441	1317	1039	1221	1278	246	1189	714	1168	462
113	1394	1388	1514	812	983	1313	1200	1204	551	143
114	579	1431	571	670	420	1059	158	312	706	1426
115	1139	1496	55	1208	123	70	1262	1001	1120	1156
116	110	22	1546	1096	46	31	1402	134	646	555
117	1180	959	1364	1144	222	1015	1025	925	1129	1286
118	640	1268	94	952	966	147	792	281	1232	375
119	293	79	766	196	1520	1113	525	1163	105	761
120	1450	583	1374	730	64	1501	336	1052	509	182
121	319	841	1083	914	611	444	235	1435	694	1507
122	479	595	401	1320	1455	872	859	603	565	330
123	167	1042	1274	575	1258	1360	1228	60	475	1224
124	452	498	1337	679	1251	1007	307	1281	836	674
125	1297	1538	456	190	1412	249	588	1418	818	882
126	486	827	1478	1192	1351	424	738	392	502	1213
127	173	717	270	516	258	1302	943	634	1245	1171
128	1106	1063	992	342	1341	411	532	465	1379	359
129	1073	749	87	782	978	1397	100	162	1473	973
130	683	128	1036	1391	548	155	120	1543	1177	1126
131	789	1517	1371	316	691	856	1255	1334	1294	815
132	735	255	989	1070	1470	117	688	986	663	710
133	666	1152	1011	75	1048	1316	1220	245	713	461
134	1387	811	1312	1203	142	1430	669	1058	311	1425
135	1495	1207	69	1000	1155	21	1095	30	133	554
136	958	1143	1014	924	1285	1267	951	146	280	374
137	78	195	1112	1162	760	582	729	1500	1051	181
138	840	913	443	1434	1506	594	1319	871	602	329
139	1041	574	1359	59	1223	497	678	1006	1280	673
140	1537	189	248	1417	881	826	1191	423	391	1212
141	716	515	1301	633	1170	1062	341	410	464	358
142	748	781	1396	161	972	127	1390	154	1542	1125
143	1516	315	855	1333	814	254	1069	116	985	709
144	1151	74	1315	244	460	810	1202	1429	1057	1424
145	1206	999	20	29	553	1142	923	1266	145	373
146	194	1161	581	1499	180	912	1433	593	870	328
147	573	58	496	1005	672	188	1416	825	422	1211
148	514	632	1061	409	357	780	160	126	153	1124
149	314	1332	253	115	708	73	243	809	1428	1423

POWER RESIDUES

	0	1	2	3	4	5	6	7	8	9
100	1353	1157	765	1530	1511	1473	1397	1245	941	333
101	666	1332	1115	681	1362	1175	801	53	106	212
102	424	848	147	294	588	1176	803	57	114	228
103	456	912	275	550	1100	651	1302	1055	561	1122
104	695	1390	1231	913	277	554	1108	667	1334	1119
105	689	1378	1207	865	181	362	724	1448	1347	1145
106	741	1482	1415	1281	1013	477	954	359	718	1436
107	1323	1097	645	1290	1031	513	1026	503	1006	463
108	926	303	606	1212	875	201	402	804	59	118
109	236	472	944	339	678	1356	1163	777	5	10
110	20	40	80	160	320	640	1280	1011	473	946
111	343	686	1372	1195	841	133	266	532	1064	579
112	1158	767	1534	1519	1489	1429	1309	1069	589	1178
113	807	65	130	260	520	1040	531	1062	575	1150
114	751	1502	1455	1361	1173	797	45	90	180	360
115	720	1440	1331	1113	677	1354	1159	769	1538	1527
116	1505	1461	1373	1197	845	141	282	564	1128	707
117	1414	1279	1009	469	938	327	654	1308	1067	585
118	1170	791	33	66	132	264	528	1056	563	1126
119	703	1406	1263	977	405	810	71	142	284	568
120	1136	723	1446	1343	1137	725	1450	1351	1153	757
121	1514	1479	1409	1269	989	429	858	167	334	668
122	1336	1123	697	1394	1239	929	309	618	1236	923
123	297	594	1188	827	105	210	420	840	131	262
124	524	1048	547	1094	639	1278	1007	465	930	311
125	622	1244	939	329	658	1316	1083	617	1234	919
126	289	578	1156	763	1526	1503	1457	1365	1181	813
127	77	154	308	616	1232	915	281	562	1124	699
128	1398	1247	945	341	682	1364	1179	809	69	138
129	276	552	1104	659	1318	1087	625	1250	951	353
130	706	1412	1275	1001	453	906	263	526	1052	555
131	1110	671	1342	1135	721	1442	1335	1121	693	1386
132	1223	897	245	490	980	411	822	95	190	380
133	760	1520	1491	1433	1317	1085	621	1242	935	321
134	642	1284	1019	489	978	407	814	79	158	316
135	632	1264	979	409	818	87	174	348	696	1392
136	1235	921	293	586	1172	795	41	82	164	328
137	656	1312	1075	601	1202	855	161	322	644	1288
138	1027	505	1010	471	942	335	670	1340	1131	713
139	1426	1303	1057	565	1130	711	1422	1295	1041	533
140	1066	583	1166	783	17	34	68	136	272	544
141	1088	627	1254	959	369	738	1476	1403	1257	965
142	381	762	1524	1499	1449	1349	1149	749	1498	1447
143	1345	1141	733	1466	1383	1217	885	221	442	884
144	219	438	876	203	406	812	75	150	300	600
145	1200	851	153	306	612	1224	899	249	498	996
146	443	886	223	446	892	235	470	940	331	662
147	1324	1099	649	1298	1047	545	1090	631	1262	975
148	401	802	55	110	220	440	880	211	422	844
149	139	278	556	1112	675	1350	1151	753	1506	1463

P = 1549

INDICES

	0	1	2	3	4	5	6	7	8	9
150	998	28	1141	1265	372	1160	1498	911	592	327
151	57	1004	187	824	1210	631	408	779	125	1123
152	1331	114	72	808	1422	27	1264	1159	910	326
153	1003	823	630	778	1122	113	807	26	1158	325
154	822	777	112	25	324	776	24	775	774	

POWER RESIDUES

	0	1	2	3	4	5	6	7	8	9
150	1377	1205	861	173	346	692	1384	1219	889	229
151	458	916	283	566	1132	715	1430	1311	1073	597
152	1194	839	129	258	516	1032	515	1030	511	1022
153	495	990	431	862	175	350	700	1400	1251	953
154	357	714	1428	1307	1065	581	1162	775		

P = 1553

INDICES

	0	1	2	3	4	5	6	7	8	9
0		0	600	1	1200	489	601	1073	248	2
1	1089	1453	1201	335	121	490	848	1521	602	893
2	137	1074	501	284	249	978	935	3	721	1284
3	1090	751	1448	1454	569	10	1202	1430	1493	336
4	737	548	122	63	1101	491	884	1474	849	594
5	26	1522	1535	340	603	390	1321	894	332	734
6	138	519	1351	1075	496	824	502	141	1169	285
7	610	1053	250	1391	478	979	541	974	936	1418
8	1337	4	1148	908	722	458	663	1285	149	1544
9	1091	1408	1484	752	522	1382	1449	1480	1194	1455
10	626	227	570	534	583	11	940	1045	1203	658
11	990	1431	369	1163	1494	773	932	337	1334	1042
12	738	1354	1119	549	399	1467	123	859	1096	64
13	1424	1244	1102	414	741	492	217	207	885	1124
14	1210	1475	101	236	850	221	439	595	1078	762
15	27	1302	1141	1523	22	1240	1536	432	466	341
16	385	1357	604	1437	196	391	1508	800	1322	670
17	1058	895	1263	1198	333	499	749	735	592	330
18	139	539	456	520	532	367	1352	1422	1122	1076
19	430	1506	497	530	528	825	242	36	503	88
20	1226	142	827	805	1170	1037	1134	286	1183	794
21	611	244	1540	1054	93	552	251	272	1258	1392
22	38	304	479	727	969	980	211	129	542	505
23	1373	975	1532	1415	937	411	382	1419	90	1217
24	1338	1220	402	5	167	1083	1149	1228	999	909
25	515	97	723	185	1459	459	144	76	664	951
26	472	1286	292	377	150	829	1014	1545	1341	1470
27	1092	790	817	1409	807	879	1485	57	172	753
28	258	1365	523	1172	701	1383	836	69	1450	1490
29	821	1481	1039	436	1195	1223	126	1456	1362	619
30	627	1136	350	228	189	1008	571	889	622	535
31	288	111	584	712	1032	12	1066	959	941	1185
32	985	1046	405	862	1204	1313	485	659	796	995
33	991	81	556	1432	1400	630	370	613	1270	1164
34	106	652	1495	115	311	774	246	1519	933	8
35	1099	338	1349	1051	1335	1542	1192	1043	930	1465
36	739	234	1139	1355	1056	328	1120	34	1132	550
37	967	1413	400	95	470	1468	170	67	124	1006
38	1030	860	554	650	1097	1463	1130	65	1128	353
39	1425	253	842	1245	636	355	1103	362	688	415
40	274	322	742	1086	1427	493	1405	1331	218	1260
41	85	208	182	255	886	1397	231	1125	1394	901
42	1211	44	844	1476	588	947	102	40	693	237
43	1152	1247	851	682	872	222	306	1177	440	1157
44	638	596	904	192	1079	481	1327	763	17	357
45	28	449	811	1303	729	345	1142	1231	1105	1524
46	421	281	23	971	580	1241	463	364	1537	1214
47	1011	433	982	1516	467	319	690	342	265	155
48	386	213	268	1358	1002	417	605	707	767	1438
49	131	560	197	1253	276	392	47	574	1509	544

POWER RESIDUES

	0	1	2	3	4	5	6	7	8	9
0	1	3	9	27	81	243	729	634	349	1047
1	35	105	315	945	1282	740	667	448	1344	926
2	1225	569	154	462	1386	1052	50	150	450	1350
3	944	1279	731	640	367	1101	197	591	220	660
4	427	1281	737	658	421	1263	683	496	1488	1358
5	968	1351	947	1288	758	721	610	277	831	940
6	1267	695	532	43	129	387	1161	377	1131	287
7	861	1030	1537	1505	1409	1121	257	771	760	727
8	628	331	993	1426	1172	410	1230	584	199	597
9	238	714	589	214	642	373	1119	251	753	706
10	565	142	426	1278	728	631	340	1020	1507	1415
11	1139	311	933	1246	632	343	1029	1534	1496	1382
12	1040	14	42	126	378	1134	296	888	1111	227
13	681	490	1470	1304	806	865	1042	20	60	180
14	540	67	201	603	256	768	751	700	547	88
15	264	792	823	916	1195	479	1437	1205	509	1527
16	1475	1319	851	1000	1447	1235	599	244	732	643
17	376	1128	278	834	949	1294	776	775	772	763
18	736	655	412	1236	602	253	759	724	619	304
19	912	1183	443	1329	881	1090	164	492	1476	1322
20	860	1027	1528	1478	1328	878	1081	137	411	1233
21	593	226	678	481	1443	1223	563	136	408	1224
22	566	145	435	1305	809	874	1069	101	303	909
23	1174	416	1248	638	361	1083	143	429	1287	755
24	712	583	196	588	211	633	346	1038	8	24
25	72	216	648	391	1173	413	1239	611	280	840
26	967	1348	938	1261	677	478	1434	1196	482	1446
27	1232	590	217	651	400	1200	494	1482	1340	914
28	1189	461	1383	1043	23	69	207	621	310	930
29	1237	605	262	786	805	862	1033	1546	1532	1490
30	1364	986	1405	1109	221	663	436	1308	818	901
31	1150	344	1032	1543	1523	1463	1283	743	676	475
32	1425	1169	401	1203	503	1509	1421	1157	365	1095
33	179	537	58	174	522	13	39	117	351	1053
34	53	159	477	1431	1187	455	1365	989	1414	1136
35	302	906	1165	389	1167	395	1185	449	1347	935
36	1252	650	397	1191	467	1401	1097	185	555	112
37	336	1008	1471	1307	815	892	1123	263	789	814
38	889	1114	236	708	571	160	480	1440	1214	536
39	55	165	495	1485	1349	941	1270	704	559	124
40	372	1116	242	726	625	322	966	1345	929	1234
41	596	235	705	562	133	399	1197	485	1455	1259
42	671	460	1380	1034	1549	1541	1517	1445	1229	581
43	190	570	157	471	1413	1133	293	879	1084	146
44	438	1314	836	955	1312	830	937	1258	668	451
45	1353	953	1306	812	883	1096	182	546	85	255
46	765	742	673	466	1398	1088	158	474	1422	1160
47	374	1122	260	780	787	808	871	1060	74	222
48	666	445	1335	899	1144	326	978	1381	1037	5
49	15	45	135	405	1215	539	64	192	576	175

P = 1553

INDICES

	0	1	2	3	4	5	6	7	8	9
50	1115	801	697	324	1323	716	785	671	507	158
51	1059	912	744	896	676	1023	1264	1375	1551	1199
52	1072	1088	334	847	892	500	977	720	750	568
53	1429	736	62	883	593	1534	389	331	518	495
54	140	609	1390	540	1417	1147	457	148	1407	521
55	1479	625	533	939	657	368	772	1333	1353	398
56	858	1423	413	216	1123	100	220	1077	1301	21
57	431	384	1436	1507	669	1262	498	591	538	531
58	1421	429	529	241	87	826	1036	1182	243	92
59	271	37	726	210	504	1531	410	89	1219	166
60	1227	514	184	143	950	291	828	1340	789	806
61	56	257	1171	835	1489	1038	1222	1361	1135	188
62	888	287	711	1065	1184	404	1312	795	80	1399
63	612	105	114	245	7	1348	1541	929	233	1055
64	33	966	94	169	1005	553	1462	1127	252	635
65	361	273	1085	1404	1259	181	1396	1393	43	587
66	39	1151	681	305	1156	903	480	16	448	728
67	1230	420	970	462	1213	981	318	264	212	1001
68	706	130	1252	46	543	696	715	506	911	675
69	1374	1071	846	976	567	61	1533	517	608	1416
70	147	1478	938	771	397	412	99	1300	383	668
71	590	1420	240	1035	91	725	1530	1218	513	949
72	1339	55	834	1221	187	710	403	79	104	6
73	928	32	168	1461	634	1084	180	42	1150	1155
74	15	1229	461	317	1000	1251	695	910	1070	566
75	516	146	770	98	667	239	724	512	54	186
76	78	927	1460	179	1154	460	1250	1069	145	666
77	511	77	178	1249	665	177	176	952	953	1441
78	473	954	853	1287	1442	921	293	474	1236	378
79	955	684	151	854	962	830	1288	1500	1015	1443
80	874	1546	922	1292	1342	294	134	1471	475	224
81	1093	1237	453	791	379	374	818	956	308	1410
82	685	944	808	152	782	880	855	1179	1486	963
83	445	58	831	563	173	1289	442	754	1501	867
84	259	1016	644	1366	1444	1159	524	875	1188	1173
85	1547	162	702	923	640	1384	1293	757	837	1343
86	200	70	295	598	1451	135	1282	1491	1472	1319
87	822	476	906	1482	225	988	1040	1094	205	437
88	1238	194	1196	454	1504	1224	792	1256	127	380
89	1081	1457	375	815	1363	819	617	620	957	483
90	628	309	1049	1137	1411	1028	351	686	1329	229
91	945	870	190	809	279	1009	153	765	572	783
92	1021	890	881	1388	623	856	19	536	1180	408
93	289	1487	1063	112	964	359	585	446	262	713
94	59	395	1033	832	30	13	564	52	1067	174
95	919	960	1290	451	942	443	865	1186	755	1280
96	986	1502	813	1047	868	1019	406	260	50	863
97	1017	1305	1205	645	1307	1314	1367	1274	486	1445
98	731	660	1160	1207	797	525	301	996	876	347
99	992	1189	647	82	1174	577	557	1548	1144	1433

POWER RESIDUES

	0	1	2	3	4	5	6	7	8	9
50	525	22	66	198	594	229	687	508	1524	1466
51	1292	770	757	718	601	250	750	697	538	61
52	183	549	94	282	846	985	1402	1100	194	582
53	193	579	184	552	103	309	927	1228	578	181
54	543	76	228	684	499	1497	1385	1049	41	123
55	369	1107	215	645	382	1146	332	996	1435	1199
56	491	1473	1313	833	946	1285	749	694	529	34
57	102	306	918	1201	497	1491	1367	995	1432	1190
58	464	1392	1070	104	312	936	1255	659	424	1272
59	710	577	178	534	49	147	441	1323	863	1036
60	2	6	18	54	162	486	1458	1268	698	541
61	70	210	630	337	1011	1480	1334	896	1135	299
62	897	1138	308	924	1219	551	100	300	900	1147
63	335	1005	1462	1280	734	649	394	1182	440	1320
64	854	1009	1474	1316	842	973	1366	992	1423	1163
65	383	1149	341	1023	1516	1442	1220	554	109	327
66	981	1390	1064	86	258	774	769	754	709	574
67	169	507	1521	1457	1265	689	514	1542	1520	1454
68	1256	662	433	1299	791	820	907	1168	398	1194
69	476	1428	1178	428	1284	746	685	502	1506	1412
70	1130	284	852	1003	1456	1262	680	487	1461	1277
71	725	622	313	939	1264	686	505	1515	1439	1211
72	527	28	84	252	756	715	592	223	669	454
73	1362	980	1387	1055	59	177	531	40	120	360
74	1080	134	402	1206	512	1536	1502	1400	1094	176
75	528	31	93	279	837	958	1321	857	1018	1501
76	1397	1085	149	447	1341	917	1198	488	1464	1286
77	752	703	556	115	345	1035	1552	1550	1544	1526
78	1472	1310	824	919	1204	506	1518	1448	1238	608
79	271	813	886	1105	209	627	328	984	1399	1091
80	167	501	1503	1403	1103	203	609	274	822	913
81	1186	452	1356	962	1333	893	1126	272	816	895
82	1132	290	870	1057	65	195	585	202	606	265
83	795	832	943	1276	722	613	286	858	1021	1510
84	1424	1166	392	1176	422	1266	692	523	16	48
85	144	432	1296	782	793	826	925	1222	560	127
86	381	1143	323	969	1354	956	1315	839	964	1339
87	911	1180	434	1302	800	847	988	1411	1127	275
88	825	922	1213	533	46	138	414	1242	620	307
89	921	1210	524	19	57	171	513	1539	1511	1427
90	1175	419	1257	665	442	1326	872	1063	83	249
91	747	688	511	1533	1493	1373	1013	1486	1352	950
92	1297	785	802	853	1006	1465	1289	761	730	637
93	358	1074	116	348	1044	26	78	234	702	553
94	106	318	954	1309	821	910	1177	425	1275	719
95	604	259	777	778	781	790	817	898	1141	317
96	951	1300	794	829	934	1249	641	370	1110	224
97	672	463	1389	1061	77	231	693	526	25	75
98	225	675	472	1416	1142	320	960	1327	875	1072
99	110	330	990	1417	1145	329	987	1408	1118	248

P = 1553

INDICES

	0	1	2	3	4	5	6	7	8	9
100	163	1309	1401	703	1297	631	924	1233	371	641
101	1316	614	1385	916	1271	1294	1107	1165	758	1369
102	107	838	1512	653	1344	1526	1496	201	1276	116
103	71	1110	312	296	423	775	599	488	247	1452
104	120	1520	136	283	934	1283	1447	9	1492	547
105	1100	1473	25	339	1320	733	1350	823	1168	1052
106	477	973	1336	907	662	1543	1483	1381	1193	226
107	582	1044	989	1162	931	1041	1118	1466	1095	1243
108	740	206	1209	235	438	761	1140	1239	465	1356
109	195	799	1057	1197	748	329	455	366	1121	1505
110	527	35	1225	804	1133	793	1539	551	1257	303
111	968	128	1372	1414	381	1216	401	1082	998	96
112	1458	75	471	376	1013	1469	816	878	171	1364
113	700	68	820	435	125	618	349	1007	621	110
114	1031	958	984	861	484	994	555	629	1269	651
115	310	1518	1098	1050	1191	1464	1138	327	1131	1412
116	469	66	1029	649	1129	352	841	354	687	321
117	1426	1330	84	254	230	900	843	946	692	1246
118	871	1176	637	191	1326	356	810	344	1104	280
119	579	363	1010	1515	689	154	267	416	766	559
120	275	573	1114	323	784	157	743	1022	1550	1087
121	891	719	1428	882	388	494	1389	1146	1406	624
122	656	1332	857	215	219	20	1435	1261	537	428
123	86	1181	270	209	409	165	183	290	788	256
124	1488	1360	887	1064	1311	1398	113	1347	232	965
125	1004	1126	360	1403	1395	586	680	902	447	419
126	1212	263	705	45	714	674	845	60	607	1477
127	396	1299	589	1034	1529	948	833	709	103	31
128	633	41	14	316	694	565	769	238	53	926
129	1153	1068	510	1248	175	1440	852	920	1235	683
130	961	1499	873	1291	133	223	452	373	307	943
131	781	1178	444	562	441	866	643	1158	1187	161
132	639	756	199	597	1281	1318	905	987	204	193
133	1503	1255	1080	814	616	482	1048	1027	1328	869
134	278	764	1020	1387	18	407	1062	358	261	394
135	29	51	918	450	864	1279	812	1018	49	1304
136	1306	1273	730	1206	300	346	646	576	1143	1308
137	1296	1232	1315	915	1106	1368	1511	1525	1275	1109
138	422	487	119	282	1446	546	24	732	1167	972
139	661	1380	581	1161	1117	1242	1208	760	464	798
140	747	365	526	803	1538	302	1371	1215	997	74
141	1012	877	699	434	348	109	983	993	1268	1517
142	1190	326	468	648	840	320	83	899	691	1175
143	1325	343	578	1514	266	558	1113	156	1549	718
144	387	1145	655	214	1434	427	269	164	787	1359
145	1310	1346	1003	1402	679	418	704	673	606	1298
146	1528	708	632	315	768	925	509	1439	1234	1498
147	132	372	780	561	642	160	198	1317	203	1254
148	615	1026	277	1386	1061	393	917	1278	48	1272
149	299	575	1295	914	1510	1108	118	545	1166	1379

POWER RESIDUES

	0	1	2	3	4	5	6	7	8	9
100	744	679	484	1452	1250	644	379	1137	305	915
101	1192	470	1410	1124	266	798	841	970	1357	965
102	1342	920	1207	515	1545	1529	1481	1337	905	1162
103	380	1140	314	942	1273	713	586	205	615	292
104	876	1075	119	357	1071	107	321	963	1336	902
105	1153	353	1059	71	213	639	364	1092	170	510
106	1530	1484	1346	932	1243	623	316	948	1291	767
107	748	691	520	7	21	63	189	567	148	444
108	1332	890	1117	245	735	652	403	1209	521	10
109	30	90	270	810	877	1078	128	384	1152	350
110	1050	44	132	396	1188	458	1374	1016	1495	1379
111	1031	1540	1514	1436	1202	500	1500	1394	1076	122
112	366	1098	188	564	139	417	1251	647	388	1164
113	386	1158	368	1104	206	618	301	903	1156	362
114	1086	152	456	1368	998	1441	1217	545	82	246
115	738	661	430	1290	764	739	664	439	1317	845
116	982	1393	1073	113	339	1017	1498	1388	1058	68
117	204	612	283	849	994	1429	1181	437	1311	827
118	928	1231	587	208	624	319	957	1318	848	991
119	1420	1154	356	1068	98	294	882	1093	173	519
120	4	12	36	108	324	972	1363	983	1396	1082
121	140	420	1260	674	469	1407	1115	239	717	598
122	241	723	616	295	885	1102	200	600	247	741
123	670	457	1371	1007	1468	1298	788	811	880	1087
124	155	465	1395	1079	131	393	1179	431	1293	773
125	766	745	682	493	1479	1331	887	1108	218	654
126	409	1227	575	172	516	1548	1538	1508	1418	1148
127	338	1014	1489	1361	977	1378	1028	1531	1487	1355
128	959	1324	866	1045	29	87	261	783	796	835
129	952	1303	803	856	1015	1492	1370	1004	1459	1271
130	707	568	151	453	1359	971	1360	974	1369	1001
131	1450	1244	626	325	975	1372	1010	1477	1325	869
132	1054	56	168	504	1512	1430	1184	446	1338	908
133	1171	407	1221	557	118	354	1062	80	240	720
134	607	268	804	859	1024	1519	1451	1247	635	352
135	1056	62	186	558	121	363	1089	161	483	1449
136	1241	617	298	894	1129	281	843	976	1375	1019
137	1504	1406	1112	230	690	517	1551	1547	1535	1499
138	1391	1067	95	285	855	1012	1483	1343	923	1216
139	542	73	219	657	418	1254	656	415	1245	629
140	334	1002	1453	1253	653	406	1218	548	91	273
141	819	904	1159	371	1113	233	699	544	79	237
142	711	580	187	561	130	390	1170	404	1212	530
143	37	111	333	999	1444	1226	572	163	489	1467
144	1295	779	784	799	844	979	1384	1046	32	96
145	288	864	1039	11	33	99	297	891	1120	254
146	762	733	646	385	1155	359	1077	125	375	1125
147	269	807	868	1051	47	141	423	1269	701	550
148	97	291	873	1066	92	276	828	931	1240	614
149	289	867	1048	38	114	342	1026	1525	1469	1301

P = 1553

INDICES

	0	1	2	3	4	5	6	7	8	9
150	1116	759	746	802	1370	73	698	108	1267	325
151	839	898	1324	1513	1112	717	654	426	786	1345
152	678	672	1527	314	508	1497	779	159	202	1025
153	1060	1277	298	913	117	1378	745	72	1266	897
154	1111	425	677	313	778	1024	297	1377	1265	424
155	777	1376	776							

POWER RESIDUES

	0	1	2	3	4	5	6	7	8	9
150	797	838	961	1330	884	1099	191	573	166	498
151	1494	1376	1022	1513	1433	1193	473	1419	1151	347
152	1041	17	51	153	459	1377	1025	1522	1460	1274
153	716	595	232	696	535	52	156	468	1404	1106
154	212	636	355	1065	89	267	801	850	997	1438
155	1208	518								

P = 1559

INDICES

	0	1	2	3	4	5	6	7	8	9
0		0	406	1308	812	526	156	1072	1218	1058
1	932	1486	562	64	1478	276	66	205	1464	1
2	1338	822	334	1067	968	1052	470	808	326	1416
3	682	379	472	1236	611	40	312	77	407	1372
4	186	372	1228	395	740	26	1473	761	1374	586
5	1458	1513	876	1255	1214	454	732	1309	264	1361
6	1088	338	785	572	878	590	84	1176	1017	817
7	446	974	718	427	483	802	813	1000	220	1042
8	592	558	778	1463	76	731	801	1166	1146	489
9	432	1136	321	129	1167	527	222	227	992	986
10	306	1243	361	423	1282	1348	103	1197	62	537
11	860	1385	1138	1147	157	35	670	1122	209	1277
12	1494	1414	744	122	1191	20	978	257	1284	145
13	996	1060	490	1073	24	1334	1423	169	1223	1533
14	852	511	1380	1550	1124	384	833	336	889	664
15	1208	433	1219	1263	1406	905	626	554	1448	1005
16	998	581	964	42	1184	204	311	453	482	128
17	1137	1059	1207	127	14	566	1552	1111	895	1376
18	838	946	1542	88	727	603	535	133	15	322
19	933	1498	628	1395	633	340	1398	545	1392	18
20	712	926	91	930	767	898	829	567	130	1487
21	196	485	509	724	45	921	468	1451	943	177
22	1266	269	233	892	1544	552	1553	1168	563	1226
23	441	750	1076	1204	1528	1287	615	792	125	643
24	342	212	262	308	1150	1112	528	65	39	1213
25	426	320	1384	995	663	481	132	828	551	1149
26	1402	916	1466	1403	896	223	1479	239	430	298
27	182	1020	271	886	575	980	71	267	381	1437
28	1258	101	917	1377	228	277	398	1444	1530	410
29	790	1535	1239	1420	742	329	1295	736	1070	1131
30	56	1467	839	993	67	864	111	1221	254	173
31	1311	1065	1032	1188	960	1098	296	1502	1411	1344
32	1404	947	987	206	1370	1116	448	287	32	275
33	610	1254	717	1135	859	144	888	452	534	897
34	1543	307	1465	100	55	1343	533	1026	420	9
35	972	872	400	303	1517	1500	1301	1027	224	89
36	1244	2	1352	1164	390	953	494	1103	1133	1430
37	1009	769	941	1143	539	1328	421	1480	728	362
38	1339	7	346	775	1034	1526	243	1453	1039	1275
39	746	1272	246	810	951	10	240	604	424	823
40	1118	772	1332	443	497	1084	1336	5	1173	188
41	1304	1477	1235	875	973	431	536	1283	335	310
42	602	766	891	261	915	1257	1130	1410	451	1300
43	1327	950	874	873	299	134	1349	1068	583	1291
44	114	86	675	1470	639	1015	1298	414	392	1538
45	958	300	401	183	16	104	969	1044	74	1013
46	847	1023	1156	608	1482	655	52	919	376	690
47	135	304	1021	323	1198	1053	531	755	1049	215
48	748	141	618	331	668	753	714	463	1556	1350
49	1518	272	934	63	471	1512	445	488	61	256

POWER RESIDUES

	0	1	2	3	4	5	6	7	8	9
0	1	19	361	623	924	407	1497	381	1003	349
1	395	1269	726	1322	174	188	454	831	199	663
2	125	816	1473	1484	134	987	45	855	655	1532
3	1046	1166	328	1555	1483	115	626	981	1490	248
4	35	665	163	1538	1160	214	948	863	807	1302
5	1353	763	466	1059	1413	344	300	1023	729	1379
6	1257	498	108	493	13	247	16	304	1099	614
7	753	276	567	1419	458	907	84	37	703	885
8	1225	1449	1028	824	66	1254	441	584	183	359
9	585	202	720	1208	1126	1127	1146	1507	571	1495
10	343	281	662	106	455	850	560	1286	1049	1223
11	1411	306	1137	1336	440	565	1381	1295	1220	1354
12	782	827	123	778	751	238	1404	173	169	93
13	208	834	256	187	435	470	1135	1298	1277	878
14	1092	481	1344	592	335	129	892	1358	858	712
15	1056	1356	820	1549	1369	1067	6	114	607	620
16	867	883	1187	727	1341	535	811	1378	1238	137
17	1044	1128	1165	309	1194	860	750	219	1043	1109
18	804	1245	270	453	812	1397	40	760	409	1535
19	1103	690	638	1209	1145	1488	210	872	978	1433
20	724	1284	1011	501	165	17	323	1460	1237	118
21	683	505	241	1461	1256	479	1306	1429	648	1399
22	78	1482	96	265	358	566	1400	97	284	719
23	1189	765	504	222	1100	633	1114	899	1491	267
24	396	1288	1087	386	1098	595	392	1212	1202	1012
25	520	526	640	1247	308	1175	499	127	854	636
26	1171	423	242	1480	58	1102	671	277	586	221
27	1081	272	491	1534	1084	329	15	285	738	1550
28	1388	1428	629	1038	1014	558	1248	327	1536	1122
29	1051	1261	574	1552	1426	591	316	1327	269	434
30	451	774	675	353	471	1154	100	341	243	1499
31	419	166	36	684	524	602	525	621	886	1244
32	251	92	189	473	1192	822	28	532	754	295
33	928	483	1382	1314	22	418	147	1234	61	1159
34	195	587	240	1442	895	1415	382	1022	710	1018
35	634	1133	1260	555	1191	803	1226	1468	1389	1447
36	990	102	379	965	1186	708	980	1471	1446	971
37	1300	1315	41	779	770	599	468	1097	576	31
38	589	278	605	582	145	1196	898	1472	1465	1332
39	364	680	448	717	1151	43	817	1492	286	757
40	352	452	793	1036	976	1395	2	38	722	1246
41	289	814	1435	762	447	698	790	979	1452	1085
42	348	376	908	103	398	1326	250	73	1387	1409
43	268	415	90	151	1310	1505	533	773	656	1551
44	1407	230	1252	403	1421	496	70	1330	326	1517
45	761	428	337	167	55	1045	1147	1526	932	559
46	1267	688	600	487	1458	1199	955	996	216	986
47	26	494	32	608	639	1228	1506	552	1134	1279
48	916	255	168	74	1406	211	891	1339	497	89
49	132	949	882	1168	366	718	1170	404	1440	857

P = 1559

INDICES

	0	1	2	3	4	5	6	7	8	9
50	832	203	726	929	232	211	1401	1436	1069	1501
51	887	1499	538	809	1234	949	957	689	1555	1435
52	250	1062	1322	1182	314	316	251	584	1302	576
53	629	861	327	436	645	165	836	1126	704	514
54	588	1128	1426	696	677	1063	1292	1028	981	1396
55	1386	1417	477	556	673	353	787	1388	285	459
56	106	1441	507	1246	1323	115	225	72	634	1139
57	683	98	804	1248	292	561	378	1457	816	1145
58	1196	977	383	1183	87	90	268	341	1148	380
59	735	295	143	1516	1142	245	1476	1326	1537	375
60	462	1400	315	676	1245	382	1399	158	473	680
61	1270	825	517	1508	69	648	660	1489	579	1320
62	159	317	1471	3	1438	546	36	1237	1366	282
63	1504	1109	702	235	350	783	259	650	192	474
64	252	640	1353	1259	1393	671	612	596	218	1289
65	1522	1201	854	1368	693	28	438	1485	681	585
66	1016	1165	102	19	1123	41	1541	925	1265	642
67	550	266	1294	1097	858	302	940	1271	1303	1299
68	391	918	713	210	313	695	506	976	461	1319
69	191	1484	939	500	1432	501	826	577	415	954
70	1378	927	1278	78	806	1037	709	757	365	884
71	348	542	149	1446	1433	518	630	393	495	229
72	92	1495	408	1520	200	910	12	163	796	58
73	1359	600	900	502	1509	862	1539	1104	278	931
74	1415	1373	1175	800	1347	1190	1549	963	945	711
75	176	124	827	70	328	959	1134	399	768	745
76	187	450	413	51	752	231	1181	1425	1440	1195
77	374	578	649	437	301	1431	1445	899	123	373
78	1152	902	120	666	652	1080	1216	1428	1357	1153
79	416	661	646	402	1010	1531	830	1192	1229	966
80	1524	1547	1178	355	180	1107	849	48	903	955
81	1490	166	184	770	411	568	21	396	594	636
82	152	1057	325	760	83	730	1281	121	1379	580
83	837	17	942	791	131	979	741	1187	716	871
84	1008	1274	1172	1409	1297	654	667	928	1321	1127
85	105	1144	1536	1488	258	27	857	499	148	599
86	175	1194	1356	47	1280	653	1279	160	705	970
87	540	1240	197	1285	1474	1092	989	1492	139	1170
88	520	524	492	161	1081	79	318	515	1045	1329
89	1421	486	146	762	820	344	798	881	386	237
90	1364	1460	706	1217	807	1472	589	75	422	743
91	510	997	1375	1391	1450	614	480	574	1419	1031
92	1253	971	1429	1038	4	1129	1014	1481	330	725
93	1061	587	458	815	1325	659	782	692	1096	938
94	541	1358	710	1439	1427	848	729	1296	46	491
95	1459	1252	937	620	1161	466	1455	1094	621	1241
96	1154	758	547	697	1024	363	737	922	1074	1514
97	1159	369	1120	1047	869	866	404	1162	198	417
98	366	37	678	1157	1340	1071	469	25	877	1462
99	360	1413	851	1004	894	544	467	1286	662	885

POWER RESIDUES

	0	1	2	3	4	5	6	7	8	9
50	693	695	733	1455	1142	1431	686	562	1324	212
51	910	141	1120	1013	539	887	1263	612	715	1113
52	880	1130	1203	1031	881	1149	5	95	246	1556
53	1502	476	1249	346	338	186	416	109	512	374
54	870	940	711	1037	995	197	625	962	1129	1184
55	670	258	225	1157	157	1424	553	1153	81	1539
56	1179	575	12	228	1214	1240	175	207	815	1454
57	1123	1070	63	1197	917	274	529	697	771	618
58	829	161	1500	438	527	659	49	931	540	906
59	65	1235	80	1520	818	1511	647	1380	1276	859
60	731	1417	420	185	397	1307	1448	1009	463	1002
61	330	34	646	1361	915	236	1366	1010	482	1363
62	953	958	1053	1299	1296	1239	156	1405	192	530
63	716	1132	1241	194	568	1438	819	1530	1008	444
64	641	1266	669	239	1423	534	792	1017	615	772
65	637	1190	784	865	845	465	1040	1052	1280	935
66	616	791	998	254	149	1272	783	846	484	1401
67	116	645	1342	554	1172	442	603	544	982	1509
68	609	658	30	570	1476	1541	1217	1297	1258	517
69	469	1116	937	654	1513	685	543	963	1148	1545
70	1293	1182	632	1095	538	868	902	1548	1350	706
71	942	749	200	682	486	1439	838	332	72	1368
72	1048	1204	1050	1242	213	929	502	184	378	946
73	825	85	56	1064	1508	590	297	966	1205	1069
74	44	836	294	909	122	759	390	1174	480	1325
75	231	1271	764	485	1420	477	1268	707	961	1110
76	823	47	893	1377	1219	1335	421	204	758	371
77	813	1416	401	1383	1333	383	1041	1071	82	1558
78	1540	1198	936	635	1152	62	1178	556	1210	1164
79	290	833	237	1385	1371	1105	728	1360	896	1434
80	743	86	75	1425	572	1514	704	904	27	513
81	393	1231	4	76	1444	933	578	69	1311	1524
82	894	1396	21	399	1345	611	696	752	257	206
83	796	1093	500	146	1215	1259	536	830	180	302
84	1061	1451	1066	1546	1312	1543	1255	460	945	806
85	1283	992	140	1101	652	1475	1522	856	674	334
86	110	531	735	1493	305	1118	975	1376	1200	974
87	1357	839	351	433	432	413	52	988	64	1216
88	1278	897	1453	1104	709	999	273	510	336	148
89	1253	422	223	1119	994	178	264	339	205	777
90	732	1436	781	808	1321	155	1386	1390	1466	1351
91	725	1303	1372	1124	1089	424	261	282	681	467
92	1078	215	967	1224	1430	667	201	701	847	503
93	203	739	10	190	492	1553	1445	952	939	692
94	676	372	832	218	1024	748	181	321	1422	515
95	431	394	1250	365	699	809	1340	516	450	755
96	314	1289	1106	747	162	1519	799	1150	24	456
97	869	921	350	414	71	1349	687	581	126	835
98	275	548	1058	1394	1542	1236	99	322	1441	876
99	1054	1318	98	303	1080	253	130	911	160	1481

P = 1559

INDICES

	0	1	2	3	4	5	6	7	8	9
100	1238	1064	609	8	1132	1452	1335	1256	638	607
101	617	202	249	513	284	1456	1475	647	349	1367
102	1293	1483	347	57	944	1424	1215	1106	82	1408
103	1355	523	1363	1030	1095	1093	403	543	283	1029
104	656	776	1468	178	170	455	30	1317	720	108
105	722	290	657	622	990	1011	150	1505	982	53
106	1035	840	1267	1224	733	1250	842	155	1051	739
107	571	777	1242	1493	1532	1447	1110	1397	920	1527
108	994	270	1534	1310	274	419	1102	242	1083	914
109	1469	1155	140	831	1434	703	1387	377	244	68
110	234	853	265	190	883	795	962	1180	1079	179
111	759	1171	1193	519	236	1418	691	1454	865	893
112	512	1362	289	570	913	1078	94	95	171	548
113	521	1230	631	351	478	136	1040	112	1545	1381
114	1089	1114	504	1315	1210	194	96	456	698	525
115	967	394	784	557	305	1276	1222	553	1551	339
116	44	1203	1383	1019	789	172	31	1025	493	1525
117	496	260	674	1022	747	255	1554	1125	786	560
118	1141	1507	701	1200	549	1318	364	162	1548	230
119	651	354	324	1273	174	1169	385	573	781	465
120	868	1003	248	522	721	738	1082	1179	93	193
121	788	1199	247	1312	564	834	879	686	1086	764
122	118	1313	1231	109	923	80	356	1496	475	1389
123	1054	811	1066	1227	337	591	985	208	168	625
124	565	632	723	1075	319	181	409	253	286	532
125	952	1033	442	890	85	846	214	60	688	835
126	352	291	1515	516	1108	1521	641	460	756	11
127	1189	751	665	1177	1056	1007	598	138	880	479
128	658	1160	1046	850	201	1354	107	1050	241	961
129	1077	1209	1018	700	1002	117	624	687	137	623
130	370	1330	49	911	1260	1442	216	605	1099	1205
131	434	818	844	1307	333	371	1087	1041	991	1121
132	1422	904	13	1394	508	749	425	297	1529	1220
133	447	1342	389	774	1331	765	113	1012	1048	487
134	956	164	672	1247	142	824	1503	1288	1264	975
135	708	909	1346	50	119	1546	151	870	147	1491
136	797	613	1324	619	1119	1412	616	1407	719	154
137	1101	794	912	1314	1382	1506	867	763	167	59
138	597	116	332	773	1345	793	906	428	280	358
139	907	1261	1232	1090	983	405	821	185	1360	219
140	226	669	1333	1405	126	627	484	440	1212	429
141	1443	110	1115	54	1163	345	771	601	1290	73
142	754	444	948	644	555	803	294	1269	281	217
143	924	505	1036	199	799	412	901	1523	635	715
144	498	988	343	1449	814	936	368	359	606	81
145	1316	841	418	882	569	503	1202	1140	464	1085
146	207	213	1006	1001	1306	388	908	1100	357	1211
147	1268	367	387	22	1510	855	684	1557	1337	1371
148	263	999	221	34	23	1262	1206	1497	195	1225
149	38	238	397	863	1369	99	1351	6	1117	309

POWER RESIDUES

	0	1	2	3	4	5	6	7	8	9
100	77	1463	1294	1201	993	159	1462	1275	840	370
101	794	1055	1337	459	926	445	660	68	1292	1163
102	271	472	1173	461	964	1167	347	357	547	1039
103	1033	919	312	1251	384	1060	1432	705	923	388
104	1136	1317	79	1501	457	888	1282	973	1338	478
105	1287	1068	25	475	1230	1544	1274	821	9	171
106	131	930	521	545	1001	311	1232	23	437	508
107	298	985	7	133	968	1243	232	1290	1125	1108
108	785	884	1206	1088	405	1459	1218	1316	60	1140
109	1393	1523	875	1035	957	1034	938	673	315	1308
110	1467	1370	1086	367	737	1531	1027	805	1264	631
111	1076	177	245	1537	1141	1412	325	1498	400	1364
112	972	1319	117	664	144	1177	537	849	541	925
113	426	299	1004	368	756	333	91	170	112	569
114	1457	1180	594	373	851	579	88	113	588	259
115	244	1518	780	789	960	1091	462	983	1528	970
116	1281	954	977	1414	363	661	87	94	227	1195
117	879	1111	842	408	1516	742	67	1273	802	1207
118	1107	766	523	583	164	1557	1521	837	313	1270
119	745	124	797	1112	861	769	580	107	474	1211
120	1183	651	1456	1161	233	1309	1486	172	150	1291
121	1144	1469	1408	249	54	1026	786	903	8	152
122	1329	307	1156	138	1063	1489	229	1233	42	798
123	1131	1222	1392	1504	514	412	33	627	1000	292
124	871	959	1072	101	360	604	563	1343	573	1533
125	1065	1527	951	920	331	53	1007	425	280	643
126	1304	1391	1485	153	1348	668	220	1062	1470	1427
127	610	677	391	1193	841	389	1155	119	702	866
128	864	826	104	417	128	873	997	235	1347	649
129	1418	439	546	1020	672	296	947	844	446	679
130	429	356	528	678	410	1554	1464	1313	3	57
131	1083	310	1213	1221	1373	1143	1450	1047	1185	689
132	619	848	522	564	1362	934	597	430	375	889
133	1301	1334	402	1402	135	1006	406	1478	20	380
134	984	1547	1331	345	319	1384	1352	744	105	436
135	489	1496	362	642	1285	1030	862	788	941	730
136	1398	59	1121	1032	900	1510	628	1019	653	1494
137	324	1479	39	741	48	912	179	283	700	828
138	142	1139	1374	1162	252	111	550	1096	557	1229
139	1525	913	198	644	1323	193	549	1077	196	606
140	601	506	260	263	320	1403	154	1367	1029	843
141	427	318	1365	991	121	740	29	551	1115	918
142	293	890	1320	136	1025	767	542	944	787	922
143	369	775	694	714	1094	519	507	279	624	943
144	768	561	1305	1410	287	776	713	1075	158	1443
145	914	217	1005	387	1117	956	1015	577	50	950
146	901	1529	989	83	18	342	262	301	1042	1090
147	443	622	905	46	874	1016	596	411	14	266
148	377	927	464	1021	691	657	11	209	853	617
149	810	1359	877	1073	120	721	1227	1487	191	511

P = 1559

INDICES

	0	1	2	3	4	5	6	7	8	9
150	582	1043	530	1511	1233	435	476	97	734	679
151	1365	595	1540	694	805	1519	1174	449	1151	965
152	593	1186	856	1091	819	1390	457	1251	1158	1461
153	637	1105	29	1249	273	189	288	1113	43	559
154	780	685	984	845	1055	699	843	1341	707	153
155	279	439	293	935	1305	33	529	1185	779	

POWER RESIDUES

	0	1	2	3	4	5	6	7	8	9
150	355	509	317	1346	630	1057	1375	1181	613	734
151	1474	1503	495	51	969	1262	593	354	490	1515
152	723	1265	650	1437	800	1169	385	1079	234	1328
153	288	795	1074	139	1082	291	852	598	449	736
154	1512	666	182	340	224	1138	1355	801	1188	746
155	143	1158	176	226	1176	518	488	1477		

P = 1567

INDICES

	0	1	2	3	4	5	6	7	8	9
0		0	1054	1	542	157	1055	1280	30	2
1	1211	373	543	309	768	158	1084	1459	1056	1035
2	699	1281	1427	349	31	314	1363	3	256	1292
3	1212	874	572	374	947	1437	544	323	523	310
4	187	262	769	1274	915	159	1403	1493	1085	994
5	1368	1460	851	703	1057	530	1310	1036	780	1360
6	700	1238	362	1282	60	466	1428	231	435	350
7	925	1079	32	449	1377	315	11	87	1364	1176
8	1241	4	1316	176	257	50	762	1293	403	381
9	1213	23	891	875	981	1192	573	1423	482	375
10	856	1476	948	486	339	1438	191	365	545	277
11	18	324	798	956	524	506	268	311	848	1173
12	188	746	726	263	1416	471	770	1514	1114	1275
13	1520	1180	916	749	1285	160	1489	1110	1404	933
14	413	1494	567	682	1086	1449	1503	995	865	1225
15	1369	608	1065	1461	1141	1031	852	356	664	704
16	729	63	1058	71	804	531	1230	841	1311	618
17	1104	1037	250	426	781	28	1457	1361	1435	913
18	701	360	1077	1239	379	480	363	266	469	1283
19	680	1063	61	1102	911	467	1536	1538	1429	284
20	344	232	964	1006	436	419	1540	351	1393	1408
21	926	716	1245	1080	1419	1431	33	588	1331	450
22	1072	202	1378	558	286	316	444	147	12	830
23	1560	88	1322	346	1365	84	336	1177	661	477
24	1242	474	234	5	214	1151	1317	1344	904	177
25	1525	966	258	722	1002	51	602	42	763	37
26	1008	1294	668	884	404	860	237	382	773	438
27	1214	305	977	24	598	687	892	137	421	876
28	1467	118	982	125	55	1193	170	1542	574	1352
29	937	1424	991	8	483	1517	353	376	713	658
30	857	988	96	1477	553	1395	949	1198	629	487
31	519	1169	340	114	1410	1439	152	899	192	99
32	217	366	1117	928	546	623	1125	278	292	1207
33	19	246	718	325	329	388	799	691	106	957
34	592	1247	525	708	1304	507	1480	1154	269	1278
35	1082	312	945	1272	849	1236	923	1174	401	1421
36	189	504	1414	747	565	606	727	616	1433	264
37	1534	417	1417	556	1320	472	1523	35	771	135
38	168	1515	551	112	1115	244	590	1276	399	614
39	1521	242	1024	1181	1026	1333	917	739	1338	750
40	1398	1347	1286	1183	452	161	494	696	1490	1374
41	1473	1111	1028	1074	1405	333	881	934	896	1301
42	414	1335	204	1495	733	207	568	952	907	683
43	919	1380	1087	1555	76	1450	819	1384	1504	741
44	560	996	1256	1443	866	538	46	1226	1340	288
45	1370	635	1498	609	1201	180	1066	752	318	1462
46	1048	1161	1142	651	810	1032	1400	446	853	1511
47	1138	357	1390	81	665	1349	149	705	1531	736
48	730	632	1528	64	1288	14	1059	973	1268	72
49	639	197	805	1185	832	532	392	793	1231	141

POWER RESIDUES

	0	1	2	3	4	5	6	7	8	9
0	1	3	9	27	81	243	729	620	293	879
1	1070	76	228	684	485	1455	1231	559	110	330
2	990	1403	1075	91	273	819	890	1103	175	525
3	8	24	72	216	648	377	1131	259	777	764
4	725	608	257	771	746	671	446	1338	880	1073
5	85	255	765	728	617	284	852	989	1400	1066
6	64	192	576	161	483	1449	1213	505	1515	1411
7	1099	163	489	1467	1267	667	434	1302	772	749
8	680	473	1419	1123	235	705	548	77	231	693
9	512	1536	1474	1288	730	623	302	906	1151	319
10	957	1304	778	767	734	635	338	1014	1475	1291
11	739	650	383	1149	313	939	1250	616	281	843
12	962	1319	823	902	1139	283	849	980	1373	985
13	1388	1030	1523	1435	1171	379	1137	277	831	926
14	1211	499	1497	1357	937	1244	598	227	681	476
15	1428	1150	316	948	1277	697	524	5	15	45
16	135	405	1215	511	1533	1465	1261	649	380	1140
17	286	858	1007	1454	1228	550	83	249	747	674
18	455	1365	961	1316	814	875	1058	40	120	360
19	1080	106	318	954	1295	751	686	491	1473	1285
20	721	596	221	663	422	1266	664	425	1275	691
21	506	1518	1420	1126	244	732	629	320	960	1313
22	805	848	977	1364	958	1307	787	794	815	878
23	1067	67	201	603	242	726	611	266	798	827
24	914	1175	391	1173	385	1155	331	993	1412	1102
25	172	516	1548	1510	1396	1054	28	84	252	756
26	701	536	41	123	369	1107	187	561	116	348
27	1044	1565	1561	1549	1513	1405	1081	109	327	981
28	1376	994	1415	1111	199	597	224	672	449	1347
29	907	1154	328	984	1385	1021	1496	1354	928	1217
30	517	1551	1519	1423	1135	271	813	872	1049	13
31	39	117	351	1053	25	75	225	675	458	1374
32	988	1397	1057	37	111	333	999	1430	1156	334
33	1002	1439	1183	415	1245	601	236	708	557	104
34	312	936	1241	589	200	600	233	699	530	23
35	69	207	621	296	888	1097	157	471	1413	1105
36	181	543	62	186	558	107	321	963	1322	832
37	929	1220	526	11	33	99	297	891	1106	184
38	552	89	267	801	836	941	1256	634	335	1005
39	1448	1210	496	1488	1330	856	1001	1436	1174	388
40	1164	358	1074	88	264	792	809	860	1013	1472
41	1282	712	569	140	420	1260	646	371	1113	205
42	615	278	834	935	1238	580	173	519	1557	1537
43	1477	1297	757	704	545	68	204	612	269	807
44	854	995	1418	1120	226	678	467	1401	1069	73
45	219	657	404	1212	502	1506	1384	1018	1487	1327
46	847	974	1355	931	1226	544	65	195	585	188
47	564	125	375	1125	241	723	602	239	717	584
48	185	555	98	294	882	1079	103	309	927	1214
49	508	1524	1438	1180	406	1218	520	1560	1546	1504

P = 1567

INDICES

	0	1	2	3	4	5	6	7	8	9
50	1013	842	454	1562	1312	67	210	619	490	969
51	1105	163	90	1038	1096	643	251	300	1091	427
52	496	1324	782	1053	156	29	372	767	1458	698
53	348	1362	1291	571	1436	522	261	914	1492	1367
54	702	1309	1359	361	465	434	1078	1376	86	1240
55	175	761	380	890	1191	481	1475	338	364	17
56	955	267	1172	725	470	1113	1179	1284	1109	412
57	681	1502	1224	1064	1030	663	62	803	840	1103
58	425	1456	912	1076	479	468	1062	910	1537	343
59	1005	1539	1407	1244	1430	1330	201	285	146	1559
60	345	335	476	233	1150	903	965	1001	41	1007
61	883	236	437	976	686	420	117	54	1541	936
62	7	352	657	95	1394	628	1168	1409	898	216
63	927	1124	1206	717	387	105	1246	1303	1153	1081
64	1271	922	1420	1413	605	1432	416	1319	34	167
65	111	589	613	1023	1332	1337	1346	451	695	1472
66	1073	880	1300	203	206	906	1379	75	1383	559
67	1442	45	287	1497	179	317	1160	809	445	1137
68	80	148	735	1527	13	1267	196	831	792	1012
69	1561	209	968	89	642	1090	1323	155	766	347
70	570	260	1366	1358	433	85	760	1190	337	954
71	724	1178	411	1223	662	839	1455	478	909	1004
72	1243	200	1558	475	902	40	235	685	53	6
73	94	1167	215	1205	104	1152	921	604	1318	110
74	1022	1345	1471	1299	905	1382	44	178	808	79
75	1526	195	1011	967	1089	765	259	432	1189	723
76	1222	1454	1003	1557	39	52	1166	103	603	1021
77	1298	43	78	1010	764	1188	1453	38	102	1297
78	1009	1452	1296	1295	512	513	669	226	514	885
79	821	670	405	1547	227	861	826	515	238	1386
80	886	383	835	822	774	220	671	439	1506	406
81	1215	1042	1548	306	184	228	978	743	862	25
82	961	827	599	122	516	688	562	239	893	535
83	1387	138	369	887	422	998	384	877	789	836
84	1468	1018	823	119	1258	775	983	460	221	126
85	1261	672	56	1445	440	1194	395	1507	171	1120
86	407	1543	868	1216	575	583	1043	1353	1130	1549
87	938	540	307	1425	872	185	992	778	229	9
88	48	979	484	796	744	1518	931	863	354	1228
89	26	377	1100	962	714	1070	828	659	1342	600
90	858	596	123	989	986	517	97	290	689	1478
91	1234	563	554	549	240	1396	1372	894	950	817
92	536	1199	649	1388	630	637	139	488	298	370
93	520	463	888	1170	1500	423	341	144	999	115
94	626	385	1411	611	878	1440	1135	790	153	758
95	837	900	1203	1469	193	1220	1019	100	224	824
96	218	182	120	367	1016	1259	1118	1128	776	929
97	1068	984	547	647	461	624	756	222	1126	754
98	127	279	1251	1262	293	129	673	1208	320	57
99	20	845	1446	247	281	441	719	1464	1195	326

POWER RESIDUES

	0	1	2	3	4	5	6	7	8	9
50	1378	1000	1433	1165	361	1083	115	345	1035	1538
51	1480	1306	784	785	788	797	824	905	1148	310
52	930	1223	535	38	114	342	1026	1511	1399	1063
53	55	165	495	1485	1321	829	920	1193	445	1335
54	871	1046	4	12	36	108	324	972	1349	913
55	1172	382	1146	304	912	1169	373	1119	223	669
56	440	1320	826	911	1166	364	1092	142	426	1278
57	700	533	32	96	288	864	1025	1508	1390	1036
58	1541	1489	1333	865	1028	1517	1417	1117	217	651
59	386	1158	340	1020	1493	1345	901	1136	274	822
60	899	1130	256	768	737	644	365	1095	151	453
61	1359	943	1262	652	389	1167	367	1101	169	507
62	1521	1429	1153	325	975	1358	940	1253	625	308
63	924	1205	481	1443	1195	451	1353	925	1208	490
64	1470	1276	694	515	1545	1501	1369	973	1352	922
65	1199	463	1389	1033	1532	1462	1252	622	299	897
66	1124	238	714	575	158	474	1422	1132	262	786
67	791	806	851	986	1391	1039	1550	1516	1414	1108
68	190	570	143	429	1287	727	614	275	825	908
69	1157	337	1011	1466	1264	658	407	1221	529	20
70	60	180	540	53	159	477	1431	1159	343	1029
71	1520	1426	1144	298	894	1115	211	633	332	996
72	1421	1129	253	759	710	563	122	366	1098	160
73	480	1440	1186	424	1272	682	479	1437	1177	397
74	1191	439	1317	817	884	1085	121	363	1089	133
75	399	1197	457	1371	979	1370	976	1361	949	1280
76	706	551	86	258	774	755	698	527	14	42
77	126	378	1134	268	804	845	968	1337	877	1064
78	58	174	522	1566	1564	1558	1540	1486	1324	838
79	947	1274	688	497	1491	1339	883	1082	112	336
80	1008	1457	1237	577	164	492	1476	1294	748	677
81	464	1392	1042	1559	1543	1495	1351	919	1190	436
82	1308	790	803	842	959	1310	796	821	896	1121
83	229	687	494	1482	1312	802	839	950	1283	715
84	578	167	501	1503	1375	991	1406	1084	118	354
85	1062	52	156	468	1404	1078	100	300	900	1133
86	265	795	818	887	1094	148	444	1332	862	1019
87	1490	1336	874	1055	31	93	279	837	944	1265
88	661	416	1248	610	263	789	800	833	932	1229
89	553	92	276	828	917	1184	418	1254	628	317
90	951	1286	724	605	248	744	665	428	1284	718
91	587	194	582	179	537	44	132	396	1188	430
92	1290	736	641	356	1068	70	210	630	323	969
93	1340	886	1091	139	417	1251	619	290	870	1043
94	1562	1552	1522	1432	1162	352	1056	34	102	306
95	918	1187	427	1281	709	560	113	339	1017	1484
96	1318	820	893	1112	202	606	251	753	692	509
97	1527	1447	1207	487	1461	1249	613	272	816	881
98	1076	94	282	846	971	1346	904	1145	301	903
99	1142	292	876	1061	49	147	441	1323	835	938

P = 1567

INDICES

	0	1	2	3	4	5	6	7	8	9
100	501	396	330	1253	1508	389	1050	172	800	1147
101	1121	692	1264	408	107	1163	1544	958	457	869
102	593	295	1217	1248	1144	576	526	1485	584	709
103	131	1044	1305	653	1354	508	579	1131	1481	675
104	1550	1155	812	939	270	1565	541	1279	1210	308
105	1083	1034	1426	313	255	873	946	322	186	1273
106	1402	993	850	529	779	1237	59	230	924	448
107	10	1175	1315	49	402	22	980	1422	855	485
108	190	276	797	505	847	745	1415	1513	1519	748
109	1488	932	566	1448	864	607	1140	355	728	70
110	1229	617	249	27	1434	359	378	265	679	1101
111	1535	283	963	418	1392	715	1418	587	1071	557
112	443	829	1321	83	660	473	213	1343	1524	721
113	601	36	667	859	772	304	597	136	1466	124
114	169	1351	990	1516	712	987	552	1197	518	113
115	151	98	1116	622	291	245	328	690	591	707
116	1479	1277	944	1235	400	503	564	615	1533	555
117	1522	134	550	243	398	241	1025	738	1397	1182
118	493	1373	1027	332	895	1334	732	951	918	1554
119	818	740	1255	537	1339	634	1200	751	1047	650
120	1399	1510	1389	1348	1530	631	1287	972	638	1184
121	391	140	453	66	489	162	1095	299	495	1052
122	371	697	1290	521	1491	1308	464	1375	174	889
123	1474	16	1171	1112	1108	1501	1029	802	424	1075
124	1061	342	1406	1329	145	334	1149	1000	882	975
125	116	935	656	627	897	1123	386	1302	1270	1412
126	415	166	612	1336	694	879	205	74	1441	1496
127	1159	1136	734	1266	791	208	641	154	569	1357
128	759	953	410	838	908	199	901	684	93	1204
129	920	109	1470	1381	807	194	1088	431	1221	1556
130	1165	1020	77	1187	101	1451	511	225	820	1546
131	825	1385	834	219	1505	1041	183	742	960	121
132	561	534	368	997	788	1017	1257	459	1260	1444
133	394	1119	867	582	1129	539	871	777	47	795
134	930	1227	1099	1069	1341	595	985	289	1233	548
135	1371	816	648	636	297	462	1499	143	625	610
136	1134	757	1202	1219	223	181	1015	1127	1067	646
137	755	753	1250	128	319	844	280	1463	500	1252
138	1049	1146	1263	1162	456	294	1143	1484	130	652
139	578	674	811	1564	1209	1033	254	321	1401	528
140	58	447	1314	21	854	275	846	1512	1487	1447
141	1139	69	248	358	678	282	1391	586	442	82
142	212	720	666	303	1465	1350	711	1196	150	621
143	327	706	943	502	1532	133	397	737	492	331
144	731	1553	1254	633	1046	1509	1529	971	390	65
145	1094	1051	1289	1307	173	15	1107	801	1060	1328
146	1148	974	655	1122	1269	165	693	73	1158	1265
147	640	1356	409	198	92	108	806	430	1164	1186
148	510	1545	833	1040	959	533	787	458	393	581
149	870	794	1098	594	1232	815	296	142	1133	1218

POWER RESIDUES

	0	1	2	3	4	5	6	7	8	9
100	1247	607	254	762	719	590	203	609	260	780
101	773	752	689	500	1500	1366	964	1325	841	956
102	1301	769	740	653	392	1176	394	1182	412	1236
103	574	155	465	1395	1051	19	57	171	513	1539
104	1483	1315	811	866	1031	1526	1444	1198	460	1380
105	1006	1451	1219	523	2	6	18	54	162	486
106	1458	1240	586	191	573	152	456	1368	970	1343
107	895	1118	220	660	413	1239	583	182	546	71
108	213	639	350	1050	16	48	144	432	1296	754
109	695	518	1554	1528	1450	1216	514	1542	1492	1342
110	892	1109	193	579	170	510	1530	1456	1234	568
111	137	411	1233	565	128	384	1152	322	966	1331
112	859	1010	1463	1255	631	326	978	1367	967	1334
113	868	1037	1544	1498	1360	946	1271	679	470	1410
114	1096	154	462	1386	1024	1505	1381	1009	1460	1246
115	604	245	735	638	347	1041	1556	1534	1468	1270
116	676	461	1383	1015	1478	1300	766	731	626	311
117	933	1232	562	119	357	1071	79	237	711	566
118	131	393	1179	403	1209	493	1479	1303	775	758
119	707	554	95	285	855	998	1427	1147	307	921
120	1196	454	1362	952	1289	733	632	329	987	1394
121	1048	10	30	90	270	810	863	1022	1499	1363
122	955	1298	760	713	572	149	447	1341	889	1100
123	166	498	1494	1348	910	1163	355	1065	61	183
124	549	80	240	720	593	212	636	341	1023	1502
125	1372	982	1379	1003	1442	1192	442	1326	844	965
126	1328	850	983	1382	1012	1469	1273	685	488	1464
127	1258	640	353	1059	43	129	387	1161	349	1047
128	7	21	63	189	567	134	402	1206	484	1452
129	1222	532	29	87	261	783	782	779	770	743
130	662	419	1257	637	344	1032	1529	1453	1225	541
131	56	168	504	1512	1402	1072	82	246	738	647
132	374	1122	232	696	521	1563	1555	1531	1459	1243
133	595	218	654	395	1185	421	1263	655	398	1194
134	448	1344	898	1127	247	741	656	401	1203	475
135	1425	1141	289	867	1034	1535	1471	1279	703	542
136	59	177	531	26	78	234	702	539	50	150
137	450	1350	916	1181	409	1227	547	74	222	666
138	431	1293	745	668	437	1311	799	830	923	1202
139	472	1416	1114	208	624	305	915	1178	400	1200
140	466	1398	1060	46	138	414	1242	592	209	627
141	314	942	1259	643	362	1086	124	372	1116	214
142	642	359	1077	97	291	873	1052	22	66	198
143	594	215	645	368	1104	178	534	35	105	315
144	945	1268	670	443	1329	853	992	1409	1093	145
145	435	1305	781	776	761	716	581	176	528	17
146	51	153	459	1377	997	1424	1138	280	840	953
147	1292	742	659	410	1230	556	101	303	909	1160
148	346	1038	1547	1507	1387	1027	1514	1408	1090	136
149	408	1224	538	47	141	423	1269	673	452	1356

P = 1567

INDICES

	0	1	2	3	4	5	6	7	8	9
150	1014	645	1249	843	499	1145	455	1483	577	1563
151	253	527	1313	274	1486	68	677	585	211	302
152	710	620	942	132	491	1552	1045	970	1093	1306
153	1106	1327	654	164	1157	1355	91	429	509	1039
154	786	580	1097	814	1132	644	498	1482	252	273
155	676	301	941	1551	1092	1326	1156	428	785	813
156	497	272	940	1325	784	271	783			

POWER RESIDUES

	0	1	2	3	4	5	6	7	8	9
150	934	1235	571	146	438	1314	808	857	1004	1445
151	1201	469	1407	1087	127	381	1143	295	885	1088
152	130	390	1170	376	1128	250	750	683	482	1446
153	1204	478	1434	1168	370	1110	196	588	197	591
154	206	618	287	861	1016	1481	1309	793	812	869
155	1040	1553	1525	1441	1189	433	1299	763	722	599
156	230	690	503	1509	1393	1045				

P = 1571

INDICES

	0	1	2	3	4	5	6	7	8	9
0		0	1	1004	2	906	1005	892	3	438
1	907	1423	1006	295	893	340	4	605	439	1484
2	908	326	1424	1070	1007	242	296	1442	894	248
3	341	868	5	857	606	228	440	1063	1485	1299
4	909	1165	327	1415	1425	1344	1071	836	1008	214
5	243	39	297	1143	1443	759	895	918	249	1552
6	342	44	869	1330	6	1201	858	56	607	504
7	229	1369	441	374	1064	1246	1486	745	1300	1100
8	910	876	1166	1091	328	1511	1416	1252	1426	429
9	1345	1187	1072	302	837	820	1009	695	215	291
10	244	1340	40	741	298	1232	1144	266	1444	1236
11	760	497	896	530	919	406	250	733	1553	1497
12	343	1276	45	599	870	1148	1331	615	7	849
13	1202	564	859	806	57	778	608	938	505	1259
14	230	270	1370	148	442	1154	375	1218	1065	754
15	1247	1492	1487	1043	746	204	1301	1448	1101	577
16	911	392	877	645	1167	193	1092	954	329	590
17	1512	352	1417	1240	1253	1134	1427	986	430	471
18	1346	1381	1188	1048	1073	399	303	458	838	764
19	821	627	1010	654	696	635	216	903	292	323
20	245	1060	1341	1140	41	501	742	1508	299	1337
21	1233	730	1145	803	267	751	1445	190	1237	1378
22	761	900	498	800	897	680	531	1117	920	683
23	407	179	251	1020	734	172	1554	534	1498	718
24	344	928	1277	310	46	1120	600	209	871	525
25	1149	981	1332	923	616	945	8	28	850	385
26	1203	686	565	1457	860	479	807	1433	58	410
27	779	1324	609	621	939	95	506	182	1260	1306
28	231	971	271	1180	1371	254	149	487	443	1210
29	1155	129	376	1023	1219	888	1066	1295	755	1365
30	1248	737	1493	774	1488	950	1044	319	747	175
31	205	1453	1302	884	1449	666	1102	1557	578	101
32	912	1270	393	519	878	537	646	670	1168	158
33	194	992	1093	1501	955	962	330	13	591	1534
34	1513	721	353	1106	1418	1410	1241	261	1254	347
35	1135	167	1428	1360	987	705	431	931	472	1561
36	1347	1398	1382	710	1189	1280	1049	1524	1074	33
37	400	465	304	313	459	582	839	543	765	1542
38	822	49	628	512	1011	81	655	283	697	1123
39	636	105	217	1568	904	436	293	603	324	240
40	246	855	1061	1163	1342	212	1141	916	42	1199
41	502	372	743	874	1509	427	300	693	1338	1230
42	1234	528	731	1274	1146	847	804	936	268	1152
43	752	1041	1446	390	191	588	1238	984	1379	397
44	762	652	901	1058	499	1335	801	188	898	678
45	681	1018	532	926	1118	523	921	26	684	477
46	408	619	180	969	252	1208	1021	1293	735	948
47	173	882	1555	1268	535	156	1499	11	719	1408
48	345	1358	929	1396	1278	31	311	541	47	79
49	1121	1566	601	853	210	1197	872	691	526	845

POWER RESIDUES

	0	1	2	3	4	5	6	7	8	9
0	1	2	4	8	16	32	64	128	256	512
1	1024	477	954	337	674	1348	1125	679	1358	1145
2	719	1438	1305	1039	507	1014	457	914	257	514
3	1028	485	970	369	738	1476	1381	1191	811	51
4	102	204	408	816	61	122	244	488	976	381
5	762	1524	1477	1383	1195	819	67	134	268	536
6	1072	573	1146	721	1442	1313	1055	539	1078	585
7	1170	769	1538	1505	1439	1307	1043	515	1030	489
8	978	385	770	1540	1509	1447	1323	1075	579	1158
9	745	1490	1409	1247	923	275	550	1100	629	1258
10	945	319	638	1276	981	391	782	1564	1557	1543
11	1515	1459	1347	1123	675	1350	1129	687	1374	1177
12	783	1566	1561	1551	1531	1491	1411	1251	931	291
13	582	1164	757	1514	1457	1343	1115	659	1318	1065
14	559	1118	665	1330	1089	607	1214	857	143	286
15	572	1144	717	1434	1297	1023	475	950	329	658
16	1316	1061	551	1102	633	1266	961	351	702	1404
17	1237	903	235	470	940	309	618	1236	901	231
18	462	924	277	554	1108	645	1290	1009	447	894
19	217	434	868	165	330	660	1320	1069	567	1134
20	697	1394	1217	863	155	310	620	1240	909	247
21	494	988	405	810	49	98	196	392	784	1568
22	1565	1559	1547	1523	1475	1379	1187	803	35	70
23	140	280	560	1120	669	1338	1105	639	1278	985
24	399	798	25	50	100	200	400	800	29	58
25	116	232	464	928	285	570	1140	709	1418	1265
26	959	347	694	1388	1205	839	107	214	428	856
27	141	282	564	1128	685	1370	1169	767	1534	1497
28	1423	1275	979	387	774	1548	1525	1479	1387	1203
29	835	99	198	396	792	13	26	52	104	208
30	416	832	93	186	372	744	1488	1405	1239	907
31	243	486	972	373	746	1492	1413	1255	939	307
32	614	1228	885	199	398	796	21	42	84	168
33	336	672	1344	1117	663	1326	1081	591	1182	793
34	15	30	60	120	240	480	960	349	698	1396
35	1221	871	171	342	684	1368	1165	759	1518	1465
36	1359	1147	723	1446	1321	1071	571	1142	713	1426
37	1281	991	411	822	73	146	292	584	1168	765
38	1530	1489	1407	1243	915	259	518	1036	501	1002
39	433	866	161	322	644	1288	1005	439	878	185
40	370	740	1480	1389	1207	843	115	230	460	920
41	269	538	1076	581	1162	753	1506	1441	1311	1051
42	531	1062	553	1106	641	1282	993	415	830	89
43	178	356	712	1424	1277	983	395	790	9	18
44	36	72	144	288	576	1152	733	1466	1361	1151
45	731	1462	1353	1135	699	1398	1225	879	187	374
46	748	1496	1421	1271	971	371	742	1484	1397	1223
47	875	179	358	716	1432	1293	1015	459	918	265
48	530	1060	549	1098	625	1250	929	287	574	1148
49	725	1450	1329	1087	603	1206	841	111	222	444

P = 1571

INDICES

	0	1	2	3	4	5	6	7	8	9
50	1150	388	982	650	1333	676	924	24	617	1206
51	946	1266	9	1356	29	77	851	689	386	674
52	1204	1354	687	1352	566	568	1458	1473	861	570
53	480	420	808	1460	1434	1172	59	1475	411	67
54	780	863	1325	815	610	572	622	795	940	482
55	96	162	507	422	183	1403	1261	810	1307	140
56	232	1462	972	549	272	1436	1181	198	1372	1174
57	255	366	150	61	488	1312	444	1477	1211	88
58	1156	413	130	996	377	69	1024	1387	1220	782
59	889	337	1067	865	1296	833	756	1327	1366	1097
60	1249	817	738	494	1494	612	775	145	1489	574
61	951	1131	1045	624	320	1505	748	797	176	715
62	206	942	1454	1321	1303	484	885	771	1450	98
63	667	959	1103	164	1558	1521	579	509	102	237
64	913	424	1271	1038	394	185	520	966	879	1405
65	538	1194	647	1263	671	1470	1169	812	159	137
66	195	1309	993	334	1094	142	1502	1318	956	234
67	963	1467	331	1464	14	114	592	974	1535	17
68	1514	551	722	1285	354	274	1107	117	1419	1438
69	1411	1548	1242	1183	262	595	1255	200	348	454
70	1136	1374	168	977	1429	1176	1361	662	988	257
71	706	1538	432	368	932	1054	473	152	1562	20
72	1348	63	1399	362	1383	490	711	1517	1190	1314
73	1281	450	1050	446	1525	554	1075	1479	34	1086
74	401	1213	466	725	305	90	314	1529	460	1158
75	583	1288	840	415	544	828	766	132	1543	357
76	823	998	50	558	629	379	513	277	1012	71
77	82	1032	656	1026	284	1110	698	1389	1124	1079
78	637	1222	106	120	218	784	1569	1003	905	891
79	437	1422	294	339	604	1483	325	1069	241	1441
80	247	867	856	227	1062	1298	1164	1414	1343	835
81	213	38	1142	758	917	1551	43	1329	1200	55
82	503	1368	373	1245	744	1099	875	1090	1510	1251
83	428	1186	301	819	694	290	1339	740	1231	265
84	1235	496	529	405	732	1496	1275	598	1147	614
85	848	563	805	777	937	1258	269	147	1153	1217
86	753	1491	1042	203	1447	576	391	644	192	953
87	589	351	1239	1133	985	470	1380	1047	398	457
88	763	626	653	634	902	322	1059	1139	500	1507
89	1336	729	802	750	189	1377	899	799	679	1116
90	682	178	1019	171	533	717	927	309	1119	208
91	524	980	922	944	27	384	685	1456	478	1432
92	409	1323	620	94	181	1305	970	1179	253	486
93	1209	128	1022	887	1294	1364	736	773	949	318
94	174	1452	883	665	1556	100	1269	518	536	669
95	157	991	1500	961	12	1533	720	1105	1409	260
96	346	166	1359	704	930	1560	1397	709	1279	1523
97	32	464	312	581	542	1541	48	511	80	282
98	1122	104	1567	435	602	239	854	1162	211	915
99	1198	371	873	426	692	1229	527	1273	846	935

POWER RESIDUES

	0	1	2	3	4	5	6	7	8	9
50	888	205	410	820	69	138	276	552	1104	637
51	1274	977	383	766	1532	1493	1415	1259	947	323
52	646	1292	1013	455	910	249	498	996	421	842
53	113	226	452	904	237	474	948	325	650	1300
54	1029	487	974	377	754	1508	1445	1319	1067	563
55	1126	681	1362	1153	735	1470	1369	1167	763	1526
56	1481	1391	1211	851	131	262	524	1048	525	1050
57	529	1058	545	1090	609	1218	865	159	318	636
58	1272	973	375	750	1500	1429	1287	1003	435	870
59	169	338	676	1352	1133	695	1390	1209	847	123
60	246	492	984	397	794	17	34	68	136	272
61	544	1088	605	1210	849	127	254	508	1016	461
62	922	273	546	1092	613	1226	881	191	382	764
63	1528	1485	1399	1227	883	195	390	780	1560	1549
64	1527	1483	1395	1219	867	163	326	652	1304	1037
65	503	1006	441	882	193	386	772	1544	1517	1463
66	1355	1139	707	1414	1257	943	315	630	1260	949
67	327	654	1308	1045	519	1038	505	1010	449	898
68	225	450	900	229	458	916	261	522	1044	517
69	1034	497	994	417	834	97	194	388	776	1552
70	1533	1495	1419	1267	963	355	710	1420	1269	967
71	363	726	1452	1333	1095	619	1238	905	239	478
72	956	341	682	1364	1157	743	1486	1401	1231	891
73	211	422	844	117	234	468	936	301	602	1204
74	837	103	206	412	824	77	154	308	616	1232
75	893	215	430	860	149	298	596	1192	813	55
76	110	220	440	880	189	378	756	1512	1453	1335
77	1099	627	1254	937	303	606	1212	853	135	270
78	540	1080	589	1178	785	1570	1569	1567	1563	1555
79	1539	1507	1443	1315	1059	547	1094	617	1234	897
80	223	446	892	213	426	852	133	266	532	1064
81	557	1114	657	1314	1057	543	1086	601	1202	833
82	95	190	380	760	1520	1469	1367	1163	755	1510
83	1449	1327	1083	595	1190	809	47	94	188	376
84	752	1504	1437	1303	1035	499	998	425	850	129
85	258	516	1032	493	986	401	802	33	66	132
86	264	528	1056	541	1082	593	1186	801	31	62
87	124	248	496	992	413	826	81	162	324	648
88	1296	1021	471	942	313	626	1252	933	295	590
89	1180	789	7	14	28	56	112	224	448	896
90	221	442	884	197	394	788	5	10	20	40
91	80	160	320	640	1280	989	407	814	57	114
92	228	456	912	253	506	1012	453	906	241	482
93	964	357	714	1428	1285	999	427	854	137	274
94	548	1096	621	1242	913	255	510	1020	469	938
95	305	610	1220	869	167	334	668	1336	1101	631
96	1262	953	335	670	1340	1109	647	1294	1017	463
97	926	281	562	1124	677	1354	1137	703	1406	1241
98	911	251	502	1004	437	874	177	354	708	1416
99	1261	951	331	662	1324	1077	583	1166	761	1522

P = 1571

INDICES

	0	1	2	3	4	5	6	7	8	9
100	1151	1040	389	587	983	396	651	1057	1334	187
101	677	1017	925	522	25	476	618	968	1207	1292
102	947	881	1267	155	10	1407	1357	1395	30	540
103	78	1565	852	1196	690	844	387	649	675	23
104	1205	1265	1355	76	688	673	1353	1351	567	1472
105	569	419	1459	1171	1474	66	862	814	571	794
106	481	161	421	1402	809	139	1461	548	1435	197
107	1173	365	60	1311	1476	87	412	995	68	1386
108	781	336	864	832	1326	1096	816	493	611	144
109	573	1130	623	1504	796	714	941	1320	483	770
110	97	958	163	1520	508	236	423	1037	184	965
111	1404	1193	1262	1469	811	136	1308	333	141	1317
112	233	1466	1463	113	973	16	550	1284	273	116
113	1437	1547	1182	594	199	453	1373	976	1175	661
114	256	1537	367	1053	151	19	62	361	489	1516
115	1313	449	445	553	1478	1085	1212	724	89	1528
116	1157	1287	414	827	131	356	997	557	378	276
117	70	1031	1025	1109	1388	1078	1221	119	783	1002
118	890	1421	338	1482	1068	1440	866	226	1297	1413
119	834	37	757	1550	1328	54	1367	1244	1098	1089
120	1250	1185	818	289	739	264	495	404	1495	597
121	613	562	776	1257	146	1216	1490	202	575	643
122	952	350	1132	469	1046	456	625	633	321	1138
123	1506	728	749	1376	798	1115	177	170	716	308
124	207	979	943	383	1455	1431	1322	93	1304	1178
125	485	127	886	1363	772	317	1451	664	99	517
126	668	990	960	1532	1104	259	165	703	1559	708
127	1522	463	580	1540	510	281	103	434	238	1161
128	914	370	425	1228	1272	934	1039	586	395	1056
129	186	1016	521	475	967	1291	880	154	1406	1394
130	539	1564	1195	843	648	22	1264	75	672	1350
131	1471	418	1170	65	813	793	160	1401	138	547
132	196	364	1310	86	994	1385	335	831	1095	492
133	143	1129	1503	713	1319	769	957	1519	235	1036
134	964	1192	1468	135	332	1316	1465	112	15	1283
135	115	1546	593	452	975	660	1536	1052	18	360
136	1515	448	552	1084	723	1527	1286	826	355	556
137	275	1030	1108	1077	118	1001	1420	1481	1439	225
138	1412	36	1549	53	1243	1088	1184	288	263	403
139	596	561	1256	1215	201	642	349	468	455	632
140	1137	727	1375	1114	169	307	978	382	1430	92
141	1177	126	1362	316	663	516	989	1531	258	702
142	707	462	1539	280	433	1160	369	1227	933	585
143	1055	1015	474	1290	153	1393	1563	842	21	74
144	1349	417	64	792	1400	546	363	85	1384	830
145	491	1128	712	768	1518	1035	1191	134	1315	111
146	1282	1545	451	659	1051	359	447	1083	1526	825
147	555	1029	1076	1000	1480	224	35	52	1087	287
148	402	560	1214	641	467	631	726	1113	306	381
149	91	125	315	515	1530	701	461	279	1159	1226

POWER RESIDUES

	0	1	2	3	4	5	6	7	8	9
100	1473	1375	1179	787	3	6	12	24	48	96
101	192	384	768	1536	1501	1431	1291	1011	451	902
102	233	466	932	293	586	1172	773	1546	1521	1471
103	1371	1171	771	1542	1513	1455	1339	1107	643	1286
104	1001	431	862	153	306	612	1224	877	183	366
105	732	1464	1357	1143	715	1430	1289	1007	443	886
106	201	402	804	37	74	148	296	592	1184	797
107	23	46	92	184	368	736	1472	1373	1175	779
108	1558	1545	1519	1467	1363	1155	739	1478	1385	1199
109	827	83	166	332	664	1328	1085	599	1198	825
110	79	158	316	632	1264	957	343	686	1372	1173
111	775	1550	1529	1487	1403	1235	899	227	454	908
112	245	490	980	389	778	1556	1541	1511	1451	1331
113	1091	611	1222	873	175	350	700	1400	1229	887
114	203	406	812	53	106	212	424	848	125	250
115	500	1000	429	858	145	290	580	1160	749	1498
116	1425	1279	987	403	806	41	82	164	328	656
117	1312	1053	535	1070	569	1138	705	1410	1249	927
118	283	566	1132	693	1386	1201	831	91	182	364
119	728	1456	1341	1111	651	1302	1033	495	990	409
120	818	65	130	260	520	1040	509	1018	465	930
121	289	578	1156	741	1482	1393	1215	859	147	294
122	588	1176	781	1562	1553	1535	1499	1427	1283	995
123	419	838	105	210	420	840	109	218	436	872
124	173	346	692	1384	1197	823	75	150	300	600
125	1200	829	87	174	348	696	1392	1213	855	139
126	278	556	1112	653	1306	1041	511	1022	473	946
127	321	642	1284	997	423	846	121	242	484	968
128	365	730	1460	1349	1127	683	1366	1161	751	1502
129	1433	1295	1019	467	934	297	594	1188	805	39
130	78	156	312	624	1248	925	279	558	1116	661
131	1322	1073	575	1150	729	1458	1345	1119	667	1334
132	1097	623	1246	921	271	542	1084	597	1194	817
133	63	126	252	504	1008	445	890	209	418	836
134	101	202	404	808	45	90	180	360	720	1440
135	1309	1047	523	1046	521	1042	513	1026	481	962
136	353	706	1412	1253	935	299	598	1196	821	71
137	142	284	568	1136	701	1402	1233	895	219	438
138	876	181	362	724	1448	1325	1079	587	1174	777
139	1554	1537	1503	1435	1299	1027	483	966	361	722
140	1444	1317	1063	555	1110	649	1298	1025	479	958
141	345	690	1380	1189	807	43	86	172	344	688
142	1376	1181	791	11	22	44	88	176	352	704
143	1408	1245	919	267	534	1068	565	1130	689	1378
144	1185	799	27	54	108	216	432	864	157	314
145	628	1256	941	311	622	1244	917	263	526	1052
146	533	1066	561	1122	673	1346	1121	671	1342	1113
147	655	1310	1049	527	1054	537	1074	577	1154	737
148	1474	1377	1183	795	19	38	76	152	304	608
149	1216	861	151	302	604	1208	845	119	238	476

P = 1571

INDICES

	0	1	2	3	4	5	6	7	8	9
150	584	1014	1289	1392	841	73	416	791	545	84
151	829	1127	767	1034	133	110	1544	658	358	1082
152	824	1028	999	223	51	286	559	640	630	1112
153	380	124	514	700	278	1225	1013	1391	72	790
154	83	1126	1033	109	657	1081	1027	222	285	639
155	1111	123	699	1224	1390	789	1125	108	1080	221
156	638	122	1223	788	107	220	121	787	219	786
157	785	0								

POWER RESIDUES

	0	1	2	3	4	5	6	7	8	9
150	952	333	666	1332	1093	615	1230	889	207	414
151	828	85	170	340	680	1360	1149	727	1454	1337
152	1103	635	1270	969	367	734	1468	1365	1159	747
153	1494	1417	1263	955	339	678	1356	1141	711	1422
154	1273	975	379	758	1516	1461	1351	1131	691	1382
155	1193	815	59	118	236	472	944	317	634	1268
156	965	359	718	1436	1301	1031	491	982	393	786
157										

P = 1579

INDICES

	0	1	2	3	4	5	6	7	8	9
0		0	537	1	1074	1238	538	963	33	2
1	197	666	1075	1573	1500	1239	570	938	539	478
2	734	964	1203	16	34	898	532	3	459	244
3	198	1176	1107	667	1475	623	1076	186	1015	1574
4	1271	738	1501	889	162	1240	553	581	571	348
5	1435	939	1069	468	540	326	996	479	781	1497
6	735	431	135	965	66	1233	1204	210	434	17
7	1160	524	35	378	723	899	1552	51	533	844
8	230	4	1275	848	460	598	1426	245	699	1055
9	199	958	1090	1177	1118	138	1108	222	885	668
10	394	1194	1476	1025	28	624	1005	871	1077	1335
11	863	187	1533	79	1016	1254	1318	1575	456	323
12	1272	1332	968	739	672	558	1502	40	603	890
13	192	677	163	1441	747	1241	971	158	554	1558
14	119	582	1061	661	572	1482	915	349	1260	69
15	1436	609	511	940	588	836	1070	594	1381	469
16	767	979	541	742	234	327	1385	761	997	1568
17	1135	480	385	412	782	283	1236	1498	14	1105
18	736	1433	1495	432	49	1424	136	26	77	966
19	675	117	67	1379	759	1234	1422	757	1205	1540
20	931	211	153	1207	435	398	1562	18	565	1144
21	1161	1302	1542	525	1408	549	36	561	294	379
22	1400	933	724	365	492	900	616	812	1553	649
23	213	52	277	106	534	241	993	845	860	155
24	231	114	291	5	1505	8	1276	473	1209	849
25	1095	629	461	682	577	599	1140	437	1427	1149
26	729	246	1214	251	700	128	400	1056	1284	85
27	200	43	1508	959	695	1564	1091	310	517	1178
28	656	333	1119	1363	20	139	1198	123	1109	298
29	441	223	1452	567	886	1157	219	669	606	11
30	395	274	1146	1195	1048	91	1477	1291	1125	1026
31	1373	1163	29	1051	1131	625	340	878	1006	910
32	1304	872	1516	1416	1078	893	1279	1336	771	1544
33	864	314	344	188	1298	1448	1534	1345	527	80
34	94	264	1017	1311	922	1255	949	1410	1319	147
35	820	1576	195	476	457	184	551	324	64	376
36	1273	956	392	1333	454	38	969	1480	586	740
37	383	1431	673	1538	563	559	614	239	1503	680
38	1212	41	654	296	604	1289	338	891	1296	1309
39	193	954	381	678	1294	504	164	506	499	1442
40	1468	1402	748	1171	690	1242	166	852	972	983
41	935	159	521	882	555	508	1102	1559	103	726
42	120	1128	261	583	501	258	1062	1394	367	662
43	1086	408	573	1444	1098	1483	831	494	916	424
44	359	350	1470	305	1261	715	902	70	1029	1065
45	1437	1404	1153	610	1349	618	512	1353	1186	941
46	750	632	589	1463	814	837	643	802	1071	1173
47	778	595	1530	1555	1382	1376	1397	470	692	271
48	768	181	651	980	828	1460	542	1244	464	743
49	545	215	235	1182	1010	328	168	1487	1386	485

POWER RESIDUES

	0	1	2	3	4	5	6	7	8	9
0	1	3	9	27	81	243	729	608	245	735
1	626	299	897	1112	178	534	23	69	207	621
2	284	852	977	1352	898	1115	187	561	104	312
3	936	1229	529	8	24	72	216	648	365	1095
4	127	381	1143	271	813	860	1001	1424	1114	184
5	552	77	231	693	500	1500	1342	868	1025	1496
6	1330	832	917	1172	358	1074	64	192	576	149
7	447	1341	865	1016	1469	1249	589	188	564	113
8	339	1017	1472	1258	616	269	807	842	947	1262
9	628	305	915	1166	340	1020	1481	1285	697	512
10	1536	1450	1192	418	1254	604	233	699	518	1554
11	1504	1354	904	1133	241	723	590	191	573	140
12	420	1260	622	287	861	1004	1433	1141	265	795
13	806	839	938	1235	547	62	186	558	95	285
14	855	986	1379	979	1358	916	1169	349	1047	1562
15	1528	1426	1120	202	606	239	717	572	137	411
16	1233	541	44	132	396	1188	406	1218	496	1488
17	1306	760	701	524	1572	1558	1516	1390	1012	1457
18	1213	481	1443	1171	355	1065	37	111	333	999
19	1418	1096	130	390	1170	352	1056	10	30	90
20	270	810	851	974	1343	871	1034	1523	1411	1075
21	67	201	603	230	690	491	1473	1261	625	296
22	888	1085	97	291	873	1040	1541	1465	1237	553
23	80	240	720	581	164	492	1476	1270	652	377
24	1131	235	705	536	29	87	261	783	770	731
25	614	263	789	788	785	776	749	668	425	1275
26	667	422	1266	640	341	1023	1490	1312	778	755
27	686	479	1437	1153	301	903	1130	232	696	509
28	1527	1423	1111	175	525	1575	1567	1543	1471	1255
29	607	242	726	599	218	654	383	1149	289	867
30	1022	1487	1303	751	674	443	1329	829	908	1145
31	277	831	914	1163	331	993	1400	1042	1547	1483
32	1291	715	566	119	357	1071	55	165	495	1485
33	1297	733	620	281	843	950	1271	655	386	1158
34	316	948	1265	637	332	996	1409	1069	49	147
35	441	1323	811	854	983	1370	952	1277	673	440
36	1320	802	827	902	1127	223	669	428	1284	694
37	503	1509	1369	949	1268	646	359	1077	73	219
38	657	392	1176	370	1110	172	516	1548	1486	1300
39	742	647	362	1086	100	300	900	1121	205	615
40	266	798	815	866	1019	1478	1276	670	431	1293
41	721	584	173	519	1557	1513	1381	985	1376	970
42	1331	835	926	1199	439	1317	793	800	821	884
43	1073	61	183	549	68	204	612	257	771	734
44	623	290	870	1031	1514	1384	994	1403	1051	1574
45	1564	1534	1444	1174	364	1092	118	354	1062	28
46	84	252	756	689	488	1464	1234	544	53	159
47	477	1431	1135	247	741	644	353	1059	19	57
48	171	513	1539	1459	1219	499	1497	1333	841	944
49	1253	601	224	672	437	1311	775	746	659	398

P = 1579

INDICES

	0	1	2	3	4	5	6	7	8	9
50	54	762	1166	370	998	854	1219	1569	1114	279
51	1136	1341	99	481	974	685	386	1247	108	413
52	1266	1358	783	985	173	284	788	536	1237	32
53	665	1499	937	733	15	531	243	1106	622	1014
54	737	161	580	1434	467	995	1496	134	1232	433
55	523	722	50	229	847	1425	1054	1089	137	884
56	1193	27	870	862	78	1317	322	967	557	602
57	676	746	157	118	660	914	68	510	835	1380
58	978	233	760	1134	411	1235	1104	1494	1423	76
59	116	758	756	930	1206	1561	1143	1541	548	293
60	932	491	811	212	105	992	154	290	7	1208
61	628	576	436	728	250	399	84	1507	1563	516
62	332	19	122	440	566	218	10	1145	90	1124
63	1162	1130	877	1303	1415	1278	1543	343	1447	526
64	263	921	1409	819	475	550	375	391	37	585
65	1430	562	238	1211	295	337	1308	380	503	498
66	1401	689	851	934	881	1101	725	260	257	366
67	407	1097	493	358	304	901	1064	1152	617	1185
68	631	813	801	777	1554	1396	270	650	1459	463
69	214	1009	1486	53	369	1218	278	98	684	107
70	1357	172	535	664	732	242	1013	579	994	1231
71	721	846	1088	1192	861	321	601	156	913	834
72	232	410	1493	115	929	1142	292	810	991	6
73	575	249	1506	331	439	9	1123	876	1277	1446
74	920	474	390	1429	1210	1307	497	850	1100	256
75	1096	303	1151	630	776	269	462	1485	1217	683
76	171	731	578	720	1191	600	833	1492	1141	990
77	248	438	875	919	1428	496	255	1150	268	1216
78	730	1190	1491	247	918	254	1215	1490	253	252
79	1041	1042	701	426	1043	129	1036	702	401	1519
80	427	1057	361	1044	1285	639	130	86	1227	1037
81	201	352	703	44	1389	402	1509	1367	1520	960
82	1472	428	696	1251	1058	1565	1419	362	1092	307
83	1045	311	61	1286	518	421	640	1179	1263	131
84	657	488	87	334	798	1228	1120	717	1038	1364
85	795	202	21	1081	353	140	904	704	1199	1021
86	45	124	945	1390	1110	72	403	299	57	1510
87	442	205	1368	224	1031	1521	1453	1324	961	568
88	896	1473	887	1067	429	1158	842	697	220	1003
89	1252	670	1439	1059	607	765	1566	12	24	1420
90	396	1406	363	275	112	1093	1147	1282	308	1196
91	1155	1046	1049	1514	312	92	145	62	1478	612
92	1287	1292	1169	519	1126	1084	422	1027	1351	641
93	1374	826	1180	1164	1339	1264	30	620	132	1052
94	1315	658	1132	754	489	626	514	88	341	373
95	335	879	356	799	1007	1355	1229	911	808	1121
96	1305	774	718	873	1188	1039	1517	1225	1365	1417
97	419	796	1079	943	203	894	1001	22	1280	143
98	1082	1337	752	354	772	417	141	1545	1547	905
99	865	634	705	315	446	1200	345	1549	1022	189

POWER RESIDUES

	0	1	2	3	4	5	6	7	8	9
50	1194	424	1272	658	395	1185	397	1191	415	1245
51	577	152	456	1368	946	1259	619	278	834	923
52	1190	412	1236	550	71	213	639	338	1014	1463
53	1231	535	26	78	234	702	527	2	6	18
54	54	162	486	1458	1216	490	1470	1252	598	215
55	645	356	1068	46	138	414	1242	568	125	375
56	1125	217	651	374	1122	208	624	293	879	1058
57	16	48	144	432	1296	730	611	254	762	707
58	542	47	141	423	1269	649	368	1104	154	462
59	1386	1000	1421	1105	157	471	1413	1081	85	255
60	765	716	569	128	384	1152	298	894	1103	151
61	453	1359	919	1178	376	1128	226	678	455	1365
62	937	1232	538	35	105	315	945	1256	610	251
63	753	680	461	1383	991	1394	1024	1493	1321	805
64	836	929	1208	466	1398	1036	1529	1429	1129	229
65	687	482	1446	1180	382	1146	280	840	941	1244
66	574	143	429	1287	703	530	11	33	99	297
67	891	1094	124	372	1116	190	570	131	393	1179
68	379	1137	253	759	698	515	1545	1477	1273	661
69	404	1212	478	1434	1144	274	822	887	1082	88
70	264	792	797	812	857	992	1397	1033	1520	1402
71	1048	1565	1537	1453	1201	445	1335	847	962	1307
72	763	710	551	74	222	666	419	1257	613	260
73	780	761	704	533	20	60	180	540	41	123
74	369	1107	163	489	1467	1243	571	134	402	1206
75	460	1380	982	1367	943	1250	592	197	591	194
76	582	167	501	1503	1351	895	1106	160	480	1440
77	1162	328	984	1373	961	1304	754	683	470	1410
78	1072	58	174	522	1566	1540	1462	1228	526	1578
79	1576	1570	1552	1498	1336	850	971	1334	844	953
80	1280	682	467	1401	1045	1556	1510	1372	958	1295
81	727	602	227	681	464	1392	1018	1475	1267	643
82	350	1050	1571	1555	1507	1363	931	1214	484	1452
83	1198	436	1308	766	719	578	155	465	1395	1027
84	1502	1348	886	1079	79	237	711	554	83	249
85	747	662	407	1221	505	1515	1387	1003	1430	1132
86	238	714	563	110	330	990	1391	1015	1466	1240
87	562	107	321	963	1310	772	737	632	317	951
88	1274	664	413	1239	559	98	294	882	1067	43
89	129	387	1161	325	975	1346	880	1061	25	75
90	225	675	446	1338	856	989	1388	1006	1439	1159
91	319	957	1292	718	575	146	438	1314	784	773
92	740	641	344	1032	1517	1393	1021	1484	1294	724
93	593	200	600	221	663	410	1230	532	17	51
94	153	459	1377	973	1340	862	1007	1442	1168	346
95	1038	1535	1447	1183	391	1173	361	1083	91	273
96	819	878	1055	7	21	63	189	567	122	366
97	1098	136	408	1224	514	1542	1468	1246	580	161
98	483	1449	1189	409	1227	523	1569	1549	1489	1309
99	769	728	605	236	708	545	56	168	504	1512

P = 1579

INDICES

	0	1	2	3	4	5	6	7	8	9
100	591	46	1299	857	125	1449	907	946	1535	1465
101	1391	1346	178	1111	528	867	73	81	816	404
102	95	926	300	265	636	58	1018	839	1511	1312
103	1222	443	923	707	206	1256	645	1369	950	1526
104	225	1411	317	1032	1320	804	1522	148	710	1454
105	821	448	1325	1577	1073	962	196	1572	569	477
106	1202	897	458	1175	1474	185	1270	888	552	347
107	1068	325	780	430	65	209	1159	377	1551	843
108	1274	597	698	957	1117	221	393	1024	1004	1334
109	1532	1253	455	1331	671	39	191	1440	970	1557
110	1060	1481	1259	608	587	593	766	741	1384	1567
111	384	282	13	1432	48	25	674	1378	1421	1539
112	152	397	564	1301	1407	560	1399	364	615	648
113	276	240	859	113	1504	472	1094	681	1139	1148
114	1213	127	1283	42	694	309	655	1362	1197	297
115	1451	1156	605	273	1047	1290	1372	1050	339	909
116	1515	892	770	313	1297	1344	93	1310	948	146
117	194	183	63	955	453	1479	382	1537	613	679
118	653	1288	1295	953	1293	505	1467	1170	165	982
119	520	507	102	1127	500	1393	1085	1443	830	423
120	1469	714	1028	1403	1348	1352	749	1462	642	1172
121	1529	1375	691	180	827	1243	544	1181	167	484
122	1165	853	1113	1340	973	1246	1265	984	787	31
123	936	530	621	160	466	133	522	228	1053	883
124	869	1316	556	745	659	509	977	1133	1103	75
125	755	1560	547	490	104	289	627	727	83	515
126	121	217	89	1129	1414	342	262	818	374	584
127	237	336	502	688	880	259	406	357	1063	1184
128	800	1395	1458	1008	368	97	1356	663	1012	1230
129	1087	320	912	409	928	809	574	330	1122	1445
130	389	1306	1099	302	775	1484	170	719	832	989
131	874	495	267	1189	917	1489	1040	425	1035	1518
132	360	638	1226	351	1388	1366	1471	1250	1418	306
133	60	420	1262	487	797	716	794	1080	903	1020
134	944	71	56	204	1030	1323	895	1066	841	1002
135	1438	764	23	1405	111	1281	1154	1513	144	611
136	1168	1083	1350	825	1338	619	1314	753	513	372
137	355	1354	807	773	1187	1224	418	942	1000	142
138	751	416	1546	633	445	1548	590	856	906	1464
139	177	866	815	925	635	838	1221	706	644	1525
140	316	803	709	447	1072	1571	1201	1174	1269	346
141	779	208	1550	596	1116	1023	1531	1330	190	1556
142	1258	592	1383	281	47	1377	151	1300	1398	647
143	858	471	1138	126	693	1361	1450	272	1371	908
144	769	1343	947	182	452	1536	652	952	1466	981
145	101	1392	829	713	1347	1461	1528	179	543	483
146	1112	1245	786	529	465	227	868	744	976	74
147	546	288	82	216	1413	817	236	687	405	1183
148	1457	96	1011	319	927	329	388	301	169	988
149	266	1488	1034	637	1387	1249	59	486	793	1019

POWER RESIDUES

	0	1	2	3	4	5	6	7	8	9
100	1378	976	1349	889	1088	106	318	954	1283	691
101	494	1482	1288	706	539	38	114	342	1026	1499
102	1339	859	998	1415	1087	103	309	927	1202	448
103	1344	874	1043	1550	1492	1318	796	809	848	965
104	1316	790	791	794	803	830	911	1154	304	912
105	1157	313	939	1238	556	89	267	801	824	893
106	1100	142	426	1278	676	449	1347	883	1070	52
107	156	468	1404	1054	4	12	36	108	324	972
108	1337	853	980	1361	925	1196	430	1290	712	557
109	92	276	828	905	1136	250	750	671	434	1302
110	748	665	416	1248	586	179	537	32	96	288
111	864	1013	1460	1222	508	1524	1414	1084	94	282
112	846	959	1298	736	629	308	924	1193	421	1263
113	631	314	942	1247	583	170	510	1530	1432	1138
114	256	768	725	596	209	627	302	906	1139	259
115	777	752	677	452	1356	910	1151	295	885	1076
116	70	210	630	311	933	1220	502	1506	1360	922
117	1187	403	1209	469	1407	1063	31	93	279	837
118	932	1217	493	1479	1279	679	458	1374	964	1313
119	781	764	713	560	101	303	909	1148	286	858
120	995	1406	1060	22	66	198	594	203	609	248
121	744	653	380	1140	262	786	779	758	695	506
122	1518	1396	1030	1511	1375	967	1322	808	845	956
123	1289	709	548	65	195	585	176	528	5	15
124	45	135	405	1215	487	1461	1225	517	1551	1495
125	1327	823	890	1091	115	345	1035	1526	1420	1102
126	148	444	1332	838	935	1226	520	1560	1522	1408
127	1066	40	120	360	1080	82	246	738	635	326
128	978	1355	907	1142	268	804	833	920	1181	385
129	1155	307	921	1184	394	1182	388	1164	334	1002
130	1427	1123	211	633	320	960	1301	745	656	389
131	1167	343	1029	1508	1366	940	1241	565	116	348
132	1044	1553	1501	1345	877	1052	1577	1573	1561	1525
133	1417	1093	121	363	1089	109	327	981	1364	934
134	1223	511	1533	1441	1165	337	1011	1454	1204	454
135	1362	928	1205	457	1371	955	1286	700	521	1563
136	1531	1435	1147	283	849	968	1325	817	872	1037
137	1532	1438	1156	310	930	1211	475	1425	1117	193
138	579	158	474	1422	1108	166	498	1494	1324	814
139	863	1010	1451	1195	427	1281	685	476	1428	1126
140	220	660	401	1203	451	1353	901	1124	214	642
141	347	1041	1544	1474	1264	634	323	969	1328	826
142	899	1118	196	588	185	555	86	258	774	743
143	650	371	1113	181	543	50	150	450	1350	892
144	1097	133	399	1197	433	1299	739	638	335	1005
145	1436	1150	292	876	1049	1568	1546	1480	1282	688
146	485	1455	1207	463	1389	1009	1448	1186	400	1200
147	442	1326	820	881	1064	34	102	306	918	1175
148	367	1101	145	435	1305	757	692	497	1491	1315
149	787	782	767	722	587	182	546	59	177	531

P = 1579

INDICES

	0	1	2	3	4	5	6	7	8	9
150	55	1322	840	763	110	1512	1167	824	1313	371
151	806	1223	999	415	444	855	176	924	1220	1524
152	708	1570	1268	207	1115	1329	1257	280	150	646
153	1137	1360	1370	1342	451	951	100	712	1527	482
154	785	226	975	287	1412	686	1456	318	387	987
155	1033	1248	792	1321	109	823	805	414	175	1523
156	1267	1328	149	1359	450	711	784	286	1455	986
157	791	822	174	1327	449	285	790	1326	789	

POWER RESIDUES

	0	1	2	3	4	5	6	7	8	9
150	14	42	126	378	1134	244	732	617	272	816
151	869	1028	1505	1357	913	1160	322	966	1319	799
152	818	875	1046	1559	1519	1399	1039	1538	1456	1210
153	472	1416	1090	112	336	1008	1445	1177	373	1119
154	199	597	212	636	329	987	1382	988	1385	997
155	1412	1078	76	228	684	473	1419	1099	139	417
156	1251	595	206	618	275	825	896	1109	169	507
157	1521	1405	1057	13	39	117	351	1053		

P = 1583

INDICES

	0	1	2	3	4	5	6	7	8	9
0		0	346	602	692	1	948	623	1038	1204
1	347	576	1294	1568	969	603	1384	496	1550	1233
2	693	1225	922	836	58	2	332	224	1315	717
3	949	39	148	1178	842	624	314	1519	1579	588
4	1039	796	1571	1101	1268	1205	1182	1343	404	1246
5	348	1098	678	1256	570	577	79	253	1063	123
6	1295	270	385	245	494	1569	1524	1526	1188	1438
7	970	1094	660	1496	283	604	343	1199	934	700
8	1385	826	1142	506	335	497	1447	1319	32	1265
9	1551	609	1528	641	107	1234	750	1028	10	198
10	694	1376	1444	185	1024	1226	20	319	916	75
11	923	539	425	1404	599	837	1409	1190	469	1119
12	59	1152	616	1398	731	3	591	1202	840	121
13	333	73	288	274	290	225	1534	558	202	785
14	1316	363	1440	562	1006	718	260	266	629	1085
15	950	358	689	118	1545	40	1280	430	1046	276
16	149	1459	1172	996	1488	1179	852	972	681	1554
17	843	855	211	1501	83	625	378	725	29	111
18	315	1560	955	872	292	1520	987	1072	453	847
19	1580	330	1096	341	1374	589	356	376	544	166
20	1040	546	140	1340	208	797	531	458	1370	227
21	1572	188	366	114	665	1102	1262	662	421	516
22	1269	482	885	1090	771	1206	168	325	945	70
23	1183	219	173	1363	1536	1344	815	1302	1465	928
24	405	401	1498	1428	962	1247	162	1219	1077	1108
25	349	1042	937	1412	1548	1099	1186	639	467	560
26	679	339	419	1426	634	1257	620	285	636	673
27	571	153	298	1211	904	578	548	1334	1131	1243
28	80	819	709	1471	204	254	908	1419	1352	992
29	1064	48	606	1259	612	124	975	800	1431	822
30	1296	142	704	396	1035	271	464	1194	309	787
31	386	523	44	758	776	246	1392	345	622	1293
32	495	921	223	147	1518	1570	1342	677	252	384
33	1525	659	1198	1141	1318	1527	1027	1443	318	424
34	1189	615	1201	287	557	1439	265	688	429	1171
35	971	210	724	954	1071	1095	375	139	457	365
36	661	884	324	172	1301	1497	1218	936	638	418
37	284	297	1333	708	1418	605	799	703	1193	43
38	344	222	676	1197	1442	1200	687	723	138	323
39	935	1332	702	675	722	701	890	891	512	876
40	1386	533	892	25	486	827	104	513	554	564
41	1143	1160	877	746	804	507	134	1387	573	1531
42	336	684	534	965	712	498	460	893	1011	1164
43	1448	1253	26	393	1008	1320	767	487	862	809
44	33	868	828	155	1231	1266	1436	105	1117	1004
45	1552	1372	514	960	671	610	1291	555	416	720
46	1529	1229	565	1563	519	642	127	1144	300	567
47	108	1032	1161	95	66	1235	229	878	1274	449
48	751	1505	747	479	262	1029	192	805	1308	16
49	11	1112	508	1213	1565	199	1423	135	1454	54

POWER RESIDUES

	0	1	2	3	4	5	6	7	8	9
0	1	5	25	125	625	1542	1378	558	1207	1286
1	98	490	867	1169	1096	731	489	862	1144	971
2	106	530	1067	586	1347	403	432	577	1302	178
3	890	1284	88	440	617	1502	1178	1141	956	31
4	155	775	709	379	312	1560	1468	1008	291	1455
5	943	1549	1413	733	499	912	1394	638	24	120
6	600	1417	753	599	1412	728	474	787	769	679
7	229	1145	976	131	655	109	545	1142	961	56
8	280	1400	668	174	870	1184	1171	1106	781	739
9	529	1062	561	1222	1361	473	782	744	554	1187
10	1186	1181	1156	1031	406	447	652	94	470	767
11	669	179	895	1309	213	1065	576	1297	153	765
12	659	129	645	59	295	1475	1043	466	747	569
13	1262	1561	1473	1033	416	497	902	1344	388	357
14	202	1010	301	1505	1193	1216	1331	323	32	160
15	800	834	1004	271	1355	443	632	1577	1553	1433
16	833	999	246	1230	1401	673	199	995	226	1130
17	901	1339	363	232	1160	1051	506	947	1569	1513
18	1233	1416	748	574	1287	103	515	992	211	1055
19	526	1047	486	847	1069	596	1397	653	99	495
20	892	1294	138	690	284	1420	768	674	204	1020
21	351	172	860	1134	921	1439	863	1149	996	231
22	1155	1026	381	322	27	135	675	209	1045	476
23	797	819	929	1479	1063	566	1247	1486	1098	741
24	539	1112	811	889	1279	63	315	1575	1543	1383
25	583	1332	328	57	285	1425	793	799	829	979
26	146	730	484	837	1019	346	147	735	509	962
27	61	305	1525	1293	133	665	159	795	809	879
28	1229	1396	648	74	370	267	1335	343	132	660
29	134	670	184	920	1434	838	1024	371	272	1360
30	468	757	619	1512	1228	1391	623	1532	1328	308
31	1540	1368	508	957	36	180	900	1334	338	107
32	535	1092	711	389	362	227	1135	926	1464	988
33	191	955	26	130	650	84	420	517	1002	261
34	1305	193	965	76	380	317	2	10	50	250
35	1250	1501	1173	1116	831	989	196	980	151	755
36	609	1462	978	141	705	359	212	1060	551	1172
37	1111	806	864	1154	1021	356	197	985	176	880
38	1234	1421	773	699	329	62	310	1550	1418	758
39	624	1537	1353	433	582	1327	303	1515	1243	1466
40	998	241	1205	1276	48	240	1200	1251	1506	1198
41	1241	1456	948	1574	1538	1358	458	707	369	262
42	1310	218	1090	701	339	112	560	1217	1336	348
43	157	785	759	629	1562	1478	1058	541	1122	861
44	1139	946	1564	1488	1108	791	789	779	729	479
45	812	894	1304	188	940	1534	1338	358	207	1035
46	426	547	1152	1011	306	1530	1318	258	1290	118
47	590	1367	503	932	1494	1138	941	1539	1363	483
48	832	994	221	1105	776	714	404	437	602	1427
49	803	849	1079	646	64	320	17	85	425	542

P = 1583

INDICES

	0	1	2	3	4	5	6	7	8	9
50	695	1574	1388	472	1283	1377	176	574	312	268
51	1445	537	1532	1457	985	186	813	337	906	521
52	1025	882	685	1158	765	1227	190	535	980	90
53	21	1327	966	782	631	320	982	713	1019	240
54	917	437	499	580	644	76	1557	461	1250	1474
55	924	368	894	1323	98	540	1477	1012	7	1087
56	426	92	1165	1000	1055	1405	235	1449	550	129
57	600	1313	1254	932	183	838	116	27	1338	943
58	1410	1129	394	250	952	1191	23	1009	958	1272
59	470	978	1321	1336	1146	1120	195	768	1168	63
60	60	667	488	1148	1050	1153	742	863	1381	360
61	617	1329	810	584	1540	1399	655	34	1133	302
62	732	1060	869	306	390	4	1104	829	1122	433
63	592	1366	156	790	691	1203	968	1232	57	716
64	841	587	1267	1245	569	122	493	1437	282	699
65	334	1264	106	197	1023	74	598	1118	730	120
66	289	784	1005	1084	1544	275	1487	1553	82	110
67	291	846	1373	165	207	226	664	515	770	69
68	1535	927	961	1107	1547	559	633	672	903	1242
69	203	991	611	821	1034	786	775	1292	1517	383
70	1317	423	556	1170	1070	364	1300	417	1417	42
71	1441	322	721	875	485	563	803	1530	711	1163
72	1007	808	1230	1003	670	719	518	566	65	448
73	261	15	1564	53	1282	267	984	520	764	89
74	630	239	643	1473	97	1086	1054	128	182	942
75	951	1271	1145	62	1049	359	1539	301	389	432
76	690	715	568	698	1022	119	1543	109	206	68
77	1546	1241	1033	382	1069	41	484	1162	669	447
78	1281	88	96	941	1048	431	1021	67	1068	446
79	1047	445	1236	256	1237	277	858	230	1222	257
80	150	887	879	490	1238	1460	371	1275	832	278
81	1173	242	450	755	859	997	900	752	910	231
82	1489	1359	1506	1481	1223	1180	1092	748	1150	258
83	853	354	480	160	151	973	919	263	295	888
84	682	1434	1030	1421	880	1555	1311	193	1058	491
85	844	773	806	1052	1239	856	1357	1309	1510	1461
86	212	439	17	216	372	1502	739	12	1354	1276
87	84	1512	1113	650	833	626	1208	509	1155	279
88	379	1347	1214	526	1174	726	501	1566	1577	243
89	30	1402	200	994	451	112	1463	1424	1350	756
90	316	170	136	744	860	1561	1306	1455	1017	998
91	956	582	55	1082	901	873	762	696	1066	753
92	293	214	1575	1080	911	1521	327	1389	865	232
93	988	897	473	1125	1490	1073	646	1284	913	1360
94	454	476	1378	50	1507	848	441	177	412	1482
95	1581	947	575	1383	1224	331	38	313	795	1181
96	1097	78	269	1523	1093	342	825	1446	608	749
97	1375	19	538	1408	1151	590	72	1533	362	259
98	357	1279	1458	851	854	377	1559	986	329	355
99	545	530	187	1261	481	167	218	814	400	161

POWER RESIDUES

	0	1	2	3	4	5	6	7	8	9
50	1127	886	1264	1571	1523	1283	83	415	492	877
51	1219	1346	398	407	452	677	219	1095	726	464
52	737	519	1012	311	1555	1443	883	1249	1496	1148
53	991	206	1030	401	422	527	1052	511	972	111
54	555	1192	1211	1306	198	990	201	1005	276	1380
55	568	1257	1536	1348	408	457	702	344	137	685
56	259	1295	143	715	409	462	727	469	762	644
57	54	270	1350	418	507	952	11	55	275	1375
58	543	1132	911	1389	613	1482	1078	641	39	195
59	975	126	630	1567	1503	1183	1166	1081	656	114
60	570	1267	3	15	75	375	292	1460	968	91
61	455	692	294	1470	1018	341	122	610	1467	1003
62	266	1330	318	7	35	175	875	1209	1296	148
63	740	534	1087	686	264	1320	268	1340	368	257
64	1285	93	465	742	544	1137	936	1514	1238	1441
65	873	1199	1246	1481	1073	616	1497	1153	1016	331
66	72	360	217	1085	676	214	1070	601	1422	778
67	724	454	687	269	1345	393	382	327	52	260
68	1300	168	840	1034	421	522	1027	386	347	152
69	760	634	4	20	100	500	917	1419	763	649
70	79	395	392	377	302	1510	1218	1341	373	282
71	1410	718	424	537	1102	761	639	29	145	725
72	459	712	394	387	352	177	885	1259	1546	1398
73	658	124	620	1517	1253	1516	1248	1491	1123	866
74	1164	1071	606	1447	903	1349	413	482	827	969
75	96	480	817	919	1429	813	899	1329	313	1565
76	1493	1133	916	1414	738	524	1037	436	597	1402
77	678	224	1120	851	1089	696	314	1570	1518	1258
78	1541	1373	533	1082	661	139	695	309	1545	1393
79	633	1582	1578	1558	1458	958	41	205	1025	376
80	297	1485	1093	716	414	487	852	1094	721	439
81	612	1477	1053	516	997	236	1180	1151	1006	281
82	1405	693	299	1495	1143	966	81	405	442	627
83	1552	1428	808	874	1204	1271	23	115	575	1292
84	128	640	34	170	850	1084	671	189	945	1559
85	1463	983	166	830	984	171	855	1109	796	814
86	904	1354	438	607	1452	928	1474	1038	441	622
87	1527	1303	183	915	1409	713	399	412	477	802
88	844	1054	521	1022	361	222	1110	801	839	1029
89	396	397	402	427	552	1177	1136	931	1489	1113
90	816	914	1404	688	274	1370	518	1007	286	1430
91	818	924	1454	938	1524	1288	108	540	1117	836
92	1014	321	22	110	550	1167	1086	681	239	1195
93	1226	1381	573	1282	78	390	367	252	1260	1551
94	1423	783	749	579	1312	228	1140	951	6	30
95	150	750	584	1337	353	182	910	1384	588	1357
96	453	682	244	1220	1351	423	532	1077	636	14
97	70	350	167	835	1009	296	1480	1068	591	1372
98	528	1057	536	1097	736	514	987	186	930	1484
99	1088	691	289	1445	893	1299	163	815	909	1379

P = 1583

INDICES

	0	1	2	3	4	5	6	7	8	9
100	1041	1185	338	619	152	547	818	907	47	974
101	141	463	522	1391	920	1341	658	1026	614	264
102	209	374	883	1217	296	798	221	686	1331	889
103	532	103	1159	133	683	459	1252	766	867	1435
104	1371	1290	1228	126	1031	228	1504	191	1111	1422
105	1573	175	536	812	881	189	1326	981	436	1556
106	367	1476	91	234	1312	115	1128	22	977	194
107	666	741	1328	654	1059	1103	1365	967	586	492
108	1263	597	783	1486	845	663	926	632	990	774
109	422	1299	321	802	807	517	14	983	238	1053
110	1270	1538	714	1542	1240	483	87	1020	444	857
111	886	370	241	899	1358	1091	353	918	1433	1310
112	772	1356	438	738	1511	1207	1346	500	1401	1462
113	169	1305	581	761	213	326	896	645	475	440
114	946	37	77	824	18	71	1278	1558	529	217
115	1184	817	462	657	373	220	102	1251	1289	1503
116	174	1325	1475	1127	740	1364	596	925	1298	13
117	1537	86	369	352	1355	1345	1304	895	36	1277
118	816	101	1324	595	85	1303	100	99	1492	1513
119	1466	1493	541	144	1114	929	1514	1478	409	651
120	406	1467	1013	1135	834	402	1494	8	1396	627
121	1499	542	1088	1075	1209	1429	145	427	706	510
122	963	1115	93	1452	1156	1248	930	1166	304	280
123	163	1515	1001	180	380	1220	1479	1056	648	1348
124	1078	410	1406	398	1215	1109	652	236	736	527
125	350	407	1450	734	1175	1043	1468	551	779	727
126	938	1014	130	1286	502	1413	1136	601	1037	1567
127	1549	835	1314	1177	1578	1100	403	1255	1062	244
128	1187	1495	933	505	31	640	9	184	915	1403
129	468	1397	839	273	201	561	628	117	1045	995
130	680	1500	28	871	452	340	543	1339	1369	113
131	420	1089	944	1362	1464	1427	1076	1411	466	1425
132	635	1210	1130	1470	1351	1258	1430	395	308	757
133	621	146	251	1140	317	286	428	953	456	171
134	637	707	1192	1196	137	674	511	24	553	745
135	572	964	1010	392	861	154	1116	959	415	1562
136	299	94	1273	478	1307	1212	1453	471	311	1456
137	905	1157	979	781	1018	579	1249	1322	6	999
138	549	931	1337	249	957	1335	1167	1147	1380	583
139	1132	305	1121	789	56	1244	281	196	729	1083
140	81	164	769	1106	902	820	1516	1169	1416	874
141	710	1002	64	52	763	1472	181	61	388	697
142	205	381	668	940	1067	255	1221	489	831	754
143	909	1480	1149	159	294	1420	1057	1051	1509	215
144	1353	649	1154	525	1576	993	1349	743	1016	1081
145	1065	1079	864	1124	912	49	411	1382	794	1522
146	607	1407	361	850	328	1260	399	618	46	1390
147	613	1216	1330	132	866	125	1110	811	435	233
148	976	653	585	1485	989	801	237	1541	443	898
149	1432	737	1400	760	474	823	528	656	1288	1126

POWER RESIDUES

	0	1	2	3	4	5	6	7	8	9
100	563	1232	1411	723	449	662	144	720	434	587
101	1352	428	557	1202	1261	1556	1448	908	1374	538
102	1107	786	764	654	104	520	1017	336	97	485
103	842	1044	471	772	694	304	1520	1268	8	40
104	200	1000	251	1255	1526	1298	158	790	784	754
105	604	1437	853	1099	746	564	1237	1436	848	1074
106	621	1522	1278	58	290	1450	918	1424	788	774
107	704	354	187	935	1509	1213	1316	248	1240	1451
108	923	1449	913	1399	663	149	745	559	1212	1311
109	223	1115	826	964	71	355	192	960	51	255
110	1275	43	215	1075	626	1547	1403	683	249	1245
111	1476	1048	491	872	1194	1221	1356	448	657	119
112	595	1392	628	1557	1453	933	1499	1163	1066	581
113	1322	278	1390	618	1507	1203	1266	1581	1573	1533
114	1333	333	82	410	467	752	594	1387	603	1432
115	828	974	121	605	1442	878	1224	1371	523	1032
116	411	472	777	719	429	562	1227	1386	598	1407
117	703	349	162	810	884	1254	1521	1273	33	165
118	825	959	46	230	1150	1001	256	1280	68	340
119	117	585	1342	378	307	1535	1343	383	332	77
120	385	342	127	635	9	45	225	1125	876	1214
121	1321	273	1365	493	882	1244	1471	1023	366	247
122	1235	1426	798	824	954	21	105	525	1042	461
123	722	444	637	19	95	475	792	794	804	854
124	1104	771	689	279	1395	643	49	245	1225	1376
125	548	1157	1036	431	572	1277	53	265	1325	293
126	1465	993	216	1080	651	89	445	642	44	220
127	1100	751	589	1362	478	807	869	1179	1146	981
128	156	780	734	504	937	1519	1263	1566	1498	1158
129	1041	456	697	319	12	60	300	1500	1168	1091
130	706	364	237	1185	1176	1131	906	1364	488	857
131	1119	846	1064	571	1272	28	140	700	334	87
132	435	592	1377	553	1182	1161	1056	531	1072	611
133	1472	1028	391	372	277	1385	593	1382	578	1307
134	203	1015	326	47	235	1175	1126	881	1239	1446
135	898	1324	288	1440	868	1174	1121	856	1114	821
136	939	1529	1313	233	1165	1076	631	1572	1528	1308
137	208	1040	451	672	194	970	101	505	942	1544
138	1388	608	1457	953	16	80	400	417	502	927
139	1469	1013	316	1580	1568	1508	1208	1291	123	615
140	1492	1128	891	1289	113	565	1242	1461	973	116
141	580	1317	253	1265	1576	1548	1408	708	374	287
142	1435	843	1049	496	897	1319	263	1315	243	1215
143	1326	298	1490	1118	841	1039	446	647	69	345
144	142	710	384	337	102	510	967	86	430	567
145	1252	1511	1223	1366	498	907	1369	513	982	161
146	805	859	1129	896	1314	238	1190	1201	1256	1531
147	1323	283	1415	743	549	1162	1061	556	1197	1236
148	1431	823	949	1579	1563	1483	1083	666	164	820
149	934	1504	1188	1191	1206	1281	73	365	242	1210

P = 1583

INDICES

	0	1	2	3	4	5	6	7	8	9
150	1297	351	35	594	1491	143	408	1134	1395	1074
151	705	1451	303	179	647	397	735	733	778	1285
152	1036	1176	1061	504	914	272	1044	870	1368	1361
153	465	1469	307	1139	455	1195	552	391	414	477
154	310	780	5	248	1379	788	728	1105	1415	51
155	387	939	830	158	1508	524	1015	1123	793	849
156	45	131	434	1484	442	759	1287	593	1394	178
157	777	503	1367	1138	413	247	1414	157	792	1483
158	1393	1137	791							

POWER RESIDUES

	0	1	2	3	4	5	6	7	8	9
150	1301	173	865	1159	1046	481	822	944	1554	1438
151	858	1124	871	1189	1196	1231	1406	698	324	37
152	185	925	1459	963	66	330	67	335	92	460
153	717	419	512	977	136	680	234	1170	1101	756
154	614	1487	1103	766	664	154	770	684	254	1270
155	18	90	450	667	169	845	1059	546	1147	986
156	181	905	1359	463	732	494	887	1269	13	65
157	325	42	210	1050	501	922	1444	888	1274	38
158	190	950								

P = 1597

INDICES

	0	1	2	3	4	5	6	7	8	9
0		0	1089	504	582	975	1593	526	75	1008
1	468	1	1086	1375	19	1479	1164	340	501	782
2	1557	1030	1090	381	579	354	868	1512	1108	911
3	972	1118	657	505	1429	1501	1590	535	275	283
4	1050	806	523	260	583	387	1470	167	72	1052
5	1443	844	361	352	1005	976	601	1286	404	1464
6	465	1527	611	1534	150	754	1594	1018	922	885
7	994	1209	1083	1514	28	858	1364	527	1372	1177
8	543	420	299	1573	16	1315	1349	1415	76	474
9	1476	305	963	26	1256	161	1161	21	545	1009
10	936	1214	337	1276	1450	409	1441	192	498	392
11	469	1039	94	662	779	1356	1493	787	957	866
12	1554	2	1020	1310	104	1329	1027	1226	1239	764
13	247	66	1087	1308	511	891	415	677	378	123
14	487	671	702	1376	576	290	1007	1556	1117	522
15	351	149	857	1348	20	497	865	246	670	856
16	36	907	1509	37	1388	1480	1066	1046	1105	1154
17	808	194	842	840	908	880	1165	372	1563	607
18	969	1245	1394	435	456	1510	1115	341	749	442
19	1250	12	654	1075	1110	1258	38	157	502	102
20	429	1522	707	1437	1426	185	769	1389	943	783
21	1498	230	934	117	1281	1235	1587	48	1481	422
22	1558	119	532	266	1183	1362	155	347	272	1067
23	849	1031	986	903	280	1142	450	85	359	838
24	1047	950	1091	924	513	431	803	561	1193	481
25	822	1106	520	382	719	223	732	181	257	1061
26	1336	323	1155	1583	580	1327	801	978	4	343
27	384	914	1504	809	170	355	1467	757	1212	530
28	1576	477	164	1217	195	665	869	1332	69	680
29	1379	525	500	910	1049	843	610	1513	15	160
30	1440	786	1238	122	350	906	841	434	1109	184
31	1586	346	358	480	1335	913	163	909	349	912
32	1125	696	400	1122	1002	133	1126	896	881	693
33	973	1025	559	1543	539	397	598	697	647	1166
34	301	1119	1283	1578	335	264	333	999	401	142
35	373	1291	658	130	1461	588	1056	1370	100	1123
36	462	1564	738	506	887	893	1524	980	1545	218
37	1003	878	608	625	1430	237	242	690	1531	636
38	743	134	1101	970	147	1502	568	1268	603	1022
39	751	721	1127	570	1246	556	1591	1224	1191	216
40	1518	1540	1015	897	200	1395	930	536	919	1297
41	1274	1181	262	394	882	952	436	627	276	595
42	991	833	1319	1175	427	694	1206	457	774	284
43	728	644	1080	309	1137	794	974	1163	1511	274
44	1051	464	1208	298	25	1449	1355	1026	676	1116
45	855	807	1244	653	1436	1280	1361	449	560	256
46	342	1575	524	1237	479	1001	396	332	1369	1544
47	635	750	1539	261	1174	1136	1448	1360	331	330
48	540	314	443	1411	584	996	417	709	6	541
49	1520	398	296	1251	54	388	686	139	1570	1230

POWER RESIDUES

	0	1	2	3	4	5	6	7	8	9
0	1	11	121	1331	268	1351	488	577	1556	1146
1	1427	1324	191	504	753	298	84	924	582	14
2	154	97	1067	558	1347	444	93	1023	74	814
3	969	1077	668	960	978	1176	160	163	196	559
4	1358	565	1424	1291	1425	1302	1546	1036	217	790
5	705	1367	664	916	494	643	685	1147	1438	1445
6	1522	772	507	786	661	883	131	1441	1478	288
7	1571	1311	48	528	1017	8	88	968	1066	547
8	1226	710	1422	1269	1183	237	1010	1528	838	1233
9	787	672	1004	1462	112	1232	776	551	1270	1194
10	358	744	199	592	124	1364	631	553	1292	1436
11	1423	1280	1304	1568	1278	1282	1326	213	746	221
12	834	1189	303	139	1529	849	1354	521	940	758
13	353	689	1191	325	381	997	1385	862	1497	497
14	676	1048	349	645	707	1389	906	384	1030	151
15	64	704	1356	543	1182	226	889	197	570	1479
16	299	95	1045	316	282	1505	585	47	517	896
17	274	1417	1214	578	1567	1267	1161	1592	1542	992
18	1330	257	1230	754	309	205	658	850	1365	642
19	674	1026	107	1177	171	284	1527	827	1112	1053
20	404	1250	974	1132	1273	1227	721	1543	1003	1451
21	1588	1498	508	797	782	617	399	1195	369	865
22	1530	860	1475	255	1208	512	841	1266	1150	1471
23	211	724	1576	1366	653	795	760	375	931	659
24	861	1486	376	942	780	595	157	130	1430	1357
25	554	1303	1557	1157	1548	1058	459	258	1241	875
26	43	473	412	1338	345	601	223	856	1431	1368
27	675	1037	228	911	439	38	418	1404	1071	602
28	234	977	1165	39	429	1525	805	870	1585	1465
29	145	1595	1575	1355	532	1061	492	621	443	82
30	902	340	546	1215	589	91	1001	1429	1346	433
31	1569	1289	1403	1060	481	500	709	1411	1148	1449
32	1566	1256	1040	261	1274	1238	842	1277	1271	1205
33	479	478	467	346	612	344	590	102	1122	1163
34	17	187	460	269	1362	609	311	227	900	318
35	304	150	53	583	25	275	1428	1335	312	238
36	1021	52	572	1501	541	1160	1581	1421	1258	1062
37	503	742	177	350	656	828	1123	1174	138	1518
38	728	23	253	1186	270	1373	730	45	495	654
39	806	881	109	1199	413	1349	466	335	491	610
40	322	348	634	586	58	638	630	542	1171	105
41	1155	1526	816	991	1319	136	1496	486	555	1314
42	81	891	219	812	947	835	1200	424	1470	200
43	603	245	1098	899	307	183	416	1382	829	1134
44	1295	1469	189	482	511	830	1145	1416	1203	457
45	236	999	1407	1104	965	1033	184	427	1503	563
46	1402	1049	360	766	441	60	660	872	10	110
47	1210	534	1083	734	89	979	1187	281	1494	464
48	313	249	1142	1383	840	1255	1029	140	1540	970
49	1088	789	694	1246	930	648	740	155	108	1188

P = 1597

INDICES

	0	1	2	3	4	5	6	7	8	9
50	315	1550	599	370	13	593	1471	62	212	1288
51	1312	444	225	698	1270	655	1346	168	554	1344
52	829	127	1412	1402	648	1384	1076	1458	73	762
53	820	876	294	585	471	1167	1093	1111	1432	1053
54	1473	364	407	153	997	1367	302	79	1259	939
55	1444	97	960	107	250	418	705	1120	23	39
56	1069	845	1566	459	1253	41	710	946	1284	1561
57	158	989	362	516	825	735	1158	7	173	1579
58	872	503	18	353	1589	166	403	884	542	304
59	336	661	103	890	1006	245	1104	606	1249	1521
60	933	265	279	430	731	977	1211	679	1439	345
61	399	1542	334	587	1523	689	602	215	1273	832
62	1079	297	1435	1000	1447	708	1569	1287	828	875
63	406	106	1252	734	402	605	1438	831	405	621
64	618	622	189	55	1489	143	615	1427	495	1465
65	1222	552	619	234	389	1041	374	926	186	239
66	466	64	518	623	52	687	1036	1292	32	770
67	1486	1528	91	815	190	270	140	633	659	547
68	1390	851	612	740	776	56	1071	1571	1424	131
69	1353	944	1422	1535	492	1098	1490	1146	1231	1407
70	1462	967	784	1317	151	50	1219	144	954	316
71	81	589	549	1499	863	755	1189	1342	616	565
72	1551	206	1057	1454	231	1265	1595	1085	380	1428
73	386	600	1017	1371	473	935	1038	1019	1307	575
74	496	1065	371	748	101	1497	118	985	923	718
75	1326	1466	1331	14	183	1124	1024	1282	129	886
76	236	567	1223	918	594	727	463	1243	1236	1173
77	995	685	61	553	761	1472	96	1565	515	1588
78	244	1210	214	827	620	1221	63	90	739	491
79	49	1188	1084	1306	717	235	684	213	1305	507
80	1011	1482	1033	1515	508	286	390	847	1289	1537
81	888	861	423	1418	29	1012	412	1042	790	1313
82	767	894	674	1559	1351	859	1483	197	375	438
83	445	1261	1525	1392	120	425	1365	1034	88	927
84	484	226	326	981	812	533	668	528	1516	125
85	187	916	699	899	1546	1169	267	1294	1373	509
86	221	240	137	1271	573	219	1398	1184	630	1178
87	287	797	467	1029	656	259	1004	753	1363	1414
88	544	391	1553	65	701	1347	1387	879	1114	156
89	942	421	848	949	519	1582	169	664	609	433
90	348	692	300	1290	737	624	146	555	929	626
91	773	273	854	1574	1538	1410	53	592	1345	1457
92	1431	938	1068	988	17	889	730	688	1568	830
93	494	238	1485	850	1421	1316	862	1264	1037	984
94	128	1172	243	1187	1032	1417	1350	424	667	1293
95	629	1413	941	691	853	987	1420	1416	1419	1203
96	33	640	1403	1200	1532	454	904	1204	77	30
97	489	771	1506	649	202	637	1095	281	34	475
98	1013	1400	1487	725	1385	1132	744	1197	1143	641
99	1477	413	179	1529	1228	1077	1063	135	723	451

POWER RESIDUES

	0	1	2	3	4	5	6	7	8	9
50	292	18	198	581	3	33	363	799	804	859
51	1464	134	1474	244	1087	778	573	1512	662	894
52	252	1175	149	42	462	291	7	77	847	1332
53	279	1472	222	845	1310	37	407	1283	1337	334
54	480	489	588	80	880	98	1078	679	1081	712
55	1444	1511	651	773	518	907	395	1151	1482	332
56	458	247	1120	1141	1372	719	1521	761	386	1052
57	393	1129	1240	864	1519	739	144	1584	1454	24
58	264	1307	4	44	484	533	1072	613	355	711
59	1433	1390	917	505	764	419	1415	1192	336	502
60	731	56	616	388	1074	635	597	179	372	898
61	296	62	682	1114	1075	646	718	1510	640	652
62	784	639	641	663	905	373	909	417	1393	950
63	868	1563	1223	677	1059	470	379	975	1143	1394
64	961	989	1297	1491	431	1547	1047	338	524	973
65	1121	1152	1493	453	192	515	874	32	352	678
66	1070	591	113	1243	897	285	1538	948	846	1321
67	158	141	1551	1091	822	1057	448	137	1507	607
68	289	1582	1432	1379	796	771	496	665	927	615
69	377	953	901	329	425	1481	321	337	513	852
70	1387	884	142	1562	1212	556	1325	202	625	487
71	566	1435	1412	1159	1570	1300	1524	794	749	254
72	1197	391	1107	998	1396	983	1231	765	430	1536
73	926	604	256	1219	633	575	1534	904	362	788
74	683	1125	1196	380	986	1264	1128	1229	743	188
75	471	390	1096	877	65	715	1477	277	1450	1577
76	1377	774	529	1028	129	1419	1236	820	1035	206
77	669	971	1099	910	428	1514	684	1136	1317	114
78	1254	1018	19	209	702	1334	301	117	1287	1381
79	818	1013	1561	1201	435	1591	1531	871	1596	1586
80	1476	266	1329	246	1109	1020	41	451	170	273
81	1406	1093	844	1299	1513	673	1015	1583	1443	1500
82	530	1039	250	1153	1504	574	1523	783	628	520
83	929	637	619	421	1437	1434	1401	1038	239	1032
84	173	306	172	295	51	561	1380	807	892	230
85	933	681	1103	954	912	450	159	152	75	825
86	1090	811	936	714	1466	156	119	1309	26	286
87	1549	1069	580	1589	1509	629	531	1050	371	887
88	175	328	414	1360	587	69	759	364	810	925
89	593	135	1485	365	821	1046	327	403	1239	853
90	1398	1005	1473	233	966	1044	305	161	174	317
91	293	29	319	315	271	1384	851	1376	763	408
92	1294	1458	68	748	243	1076	657	839	1244	908
93	406	1272	1216	600	212	735	100	1100	921	549
94	1248	952	890	208	691	1213	567	1446	1533	893
95	241	1054	415	1371	708	1400	1027	118	1298	1502
96	552	1281	1315	92	1012	1550	1080	701	1323	180
97	383	1019	30	330	436	5	55	605	267	1340
98	367	843	1288	1392	939	747	232	955	923	571
99	1490	420	1426	1313	70	770	485	544	1193	347

P = 1597

INDICES

	0	1	2	3	4	5	6	7	8	9
100	1404	306	1043	208	92	901	1459	1134	1102	1340
101	86	1201	964	791	1151	816	1301	74	781	971
102	805	360	1533	27	1314	1160	191	956	763	486
103	148	1508	839	455	1257	768	47	271	837	821
104	322	1503	1216	1048	905	162	895	646	141	461
105	877	1100	569	199	951	1205	1162	675	255	634
106	313	295	369	1269	1383	1092	78	22	1560	871
107	660	278	586	1446	604	614	925	31	546	1352
108	966	548	1453	472	1496	1023	1242	514	490	1010
109	860	673	1391	811	1168	1397	752	1113	432	772
110	937	1484	1186	852	453	1094	1196	722	1339	804
111	1507	1215	198	1382	613	1241	1112	1338	1128	1129
112	562	650	338	376	1059	741	1548	1433	746	571
113	1130	1194	203	1277	439	1322	777	1140	1054	1358
114	1247	563	482	638	1451	446	9	57	318	1474
115	228	557	651	823	1096	410	1262	253	1072	713
116	365	176	1592	339	1107	282	1442	1526	1082	1572
117	1255	408	1492	1225	377	521	35	193	1393	1074
118	1425	1234	154	84	1192	1060	383	476	499	121
119	1334	132	597	998	99	217	742	720	1014	393
120	426	793	1354	448	1368	329	1519	1549	224	1401
121	470	1366	704	945	172	303	932	1541	1434	733
122	1488	1040	1035	632	1423	1406	80	205	1016	747
123	182	726	95	89	1304	1536	766	1260	325	898
124	572	258	1386	663	928	1456	493	1171	940	1199
125	201	1131	1062	1133	780	485	321	1099	368	1445
126	1495	1396	1195	1337	745	1357	227	175	1491	83
127	98	328	931	204	324	1198	1494	327	114	1147
128	111	961	115	537	1278	1156	1144	788	982	311
129	1232	43	108	1148	920	440	1584	642	958	813
130	715	1408	45	251	112	1298	1323	581	1478	867
131	534	71	1463	993	419	962	1275	778	1328	414
132	1555	669	1153	968	11	706	116	1182	1141	802
133	180	3	529	1378	785	357	1121	538	263	1055
134	979	1530	1021	1517	1180	1318	308	24	1279	395
135	1359	5	1229	1311	126	293	152	249	40	1157
136	883	1248	344	1078	105	188	233	51	269	1070
137	1145	953	564	385	1064	1330	917	760	1220	683
138	846	789	437	483	915	136	1028	700	1581	145
139	591	1567	983	628	639	1505	724	1227	900	1300
140	955	836	460	312	277	1452	810	452	1240	1547
141	1139	317	712	1254	1233	596	447	171	1405	765
142	1170	367	82	110	42	44	992	10	356	307
143	248	268	682	590	835	711	109	834	58	1468
144	1044	67	1295	818	550	59	947	1149	1320	319
145	758	209	1088	1374	578	1500	1469	1285	921	1176
146	1475	1213	93	1309	510	289	864	1045	1562	441
147	428	229	531	902	512	222	800	756	68	159
148	1585	695	558	1577	1460	892	241	1267	1190	1296
149	990	643	1207	652	478	1135	416	138	211	1343

POWER RESIDUES

	0	1	2	3	4	5	6	7	8	9
100	623	465	324	370	876	54	594	146	9	99
101	1089	800	815	980	1198	402	1228	732	67	737
102	122	1342	389	1085	756	331	447	126	1386	873
103	21	231	944	802	837	1222	666	938	736	111
104	1221	655	817	1002	1440	1467	167	240	1043	294
105	40	440	49	539	1138	1339	356	722	1554	1124
106	1185	259	1252	996	1374	741	166	229	922	560
107	1369	686	1158	1559	1179	193	526	995	1363	620
108	432	1558	1168	72	792	727	12	132	1452	2
109	22	242	1065	536	1105	976	1154	1515	695	1257
110	1051	382	1008	1506	596	168	251	1164	28	308
111	194	537	1116	1097	888	186	449	148	31	341
112	557	1336	323	359	755	320	326	392	1118	1119
113	1130	1251	985	1253	1007	1495	475	434	1580	1410
114	1137	1328	235	988	1286	1370	697	1279	1293	1447
115	1544	1014	1572	1322	169	262	1285	1359	576	1545
116	1025	96	1056	437	16	176	339	535	1094	855
117	1420	1247	941	769	474	423	1459	79	869	1574
118	1344	411	1327	224	867	1552	1102	943	791	716
119	1488	398	1184	248	1131	1262	1106	987	1275	1249
120	963	1011	1539	959	967	1055	426	1492	442	71
121	781	606	278	1461	101	1111	1042	283	1516	706
122	1378	785	650	762	397	1173	127	1397	994	1352
123	499	698	1290	1414	1181	215	768	463	302	128
124	1408	1115	1086	767	452	181	394	1140	1361	598
125	190	493	632	564	1413	1170	94	1034	195	548
126	1237	831	1156	1537	937	725	1587	1487	387	1063
127	514	863	1508	618	410	1316	103	1133	1284	1348
128	455	214	757	342	568	1457	57	627	509	808
129	903	351	667	949	857	1442	1489	409	1305	1579
130	1399	1016	1594	1564	1234	798	793	738	133	1463
131	123	1353	510	819	1024	85	935	703	1345	422
132	1448	1555	1135	1306	1590	1520	750	265	1318	125
133	1375	752	287	1560	1190	314	260	1263	1117	1108
134	1009	1517	717	1499	519	918	516	885	153	86
135	946	824	1079	690	1202	446	115	1265	1139	1350
136	477	456	225	878	76	836	1211	545	1204	468
137	357	733	78	858	1453	13	143	1573	1333	290
138	1593	1553	1113	1064	525	984	1242	866	164	207
139	680	1092	833	1178	182	405	1261	1095	866	1541
140	981	1209	523	962	1000	1418	1225	699	1301	1535
141	915	483	522	951	879	87	957	945	813	958
142	956	934	692	1224	688	1180	204	647	729	34
143	374	920	538	1127	1218	622	454	203	636	608
144	300	106	1166	50	550	1259	1073	624	476	445
145	104	1144	1405	1082	723	1565	1245	919	527	1006
146	1484	354	700	1312	59	649	751	276	1439	1456
147	46	506	775	540	1149	1460	90	990	1308	15
148	165	218	801	826	1101	932	670	982	1220	644
149	696	1268	1172	116	1276	1260	1084	745	210	713

P = 1597

INDICES

	0	1	2	3	4	5	6	7	8	9
150	819	363	959	458	824	165	1103	678	1272	874
151	617	551	517	814	775	1097	1218	1341	379	574
152	1325	566	60	826	716	285	411	196	87	124
153	220	796	1552	948	736	1409	729	1263	666	1202
154	488	1399	178	207	1150	1159	46	645	254	870
155	965	672	1185	1381	1058	1321	8	252	1081	1073
156	1333	792	703	631	1303	1455	320	174	113	310
157	714	70	1152	1377	1179	292	232	759	1580	1299
158	1138	366	681	817	577	288	799	1266	210	873
159	1324	795	177	1380	1302	291	798			

POWER RESIDUES

	0	1	2	3	4	5	6	7	8	9
150	1455	35	385	1041	272	1395	972	1110	1031	162
151	185	438	27	297	73	803	848	1343	400	1206
152	490	599	201	614	366	832	1167	61	671	993
153	1341	378	964	1022	63	693	1235	809	914	472
154	401	1217	611	333	469	368	854	1409	1126	1207
155	501	720	1532	882	120	1320	147	20	220	823
156	1068	569	1468	178	361	777	562	1391	928	626
157	498	687	1169	83	913	461	280	1483	343	579
158	1578	1388	895	263	1296	1480	310	216	779	584
159	36	396	1162	6	66	726				

P = 1601

INDICES

	0	1	2	3	4	5	6	7	8	9
0		0	52	1	104	1044	53	587	156	2
1	1096	633	105	225	639	1045	208	43	54	1152
2	1148	588	685	1519	157	488	277	3	691	776
3	1097	304	260	634	95	31	106	866	1204	226
4	1200	626	640	1030	737	1046	1571	706	209	1174
5	540	44	329	336	55	77	743	1153	828	953
6	1149	1568	356	589	312	1269	686	430	147	1520
7	83	341	158	359	918	489	1256	1220	278	240
8	1252	4	678	1405	692	1087	1082	777	789	1546
9	1098	812	23	305	758	596	261	166	1226	635
10	592	837	96	498	381	32	388	659	107	650
11	129	867	795	1313	1205	963	880	227	1005	630
12	1201	1266	20	627	408	1532	641	315	364	1031
13	1321	1471	738	139	482	1047	199	925	1572	325
14	135	707	393	858	210	220	411	1175	970	571
15	541	516	1308	45	1272	1348	330	8	292	337
16	1304	506	56	1280	730	78	1457	424	744	450
17	1139	1154	1134	1535	829	1075	841	954	1598	1094
18	1150	689	864	1569	75	310	357	676	810	590
19	648	1003	313	197	218	1270	1278	1132	687	646
20	644	431	889	1363	148	70	550	1521	433	185
21	84	621	440	342	711	474	159	891	702	360
22	181	268	919	1413	847	490	1365	318	1257	1065
23	1015	1221	932	510	279	150	1057	241	682	1171
24	1253	495	1318	5	72	618	679	1377	460	1406
25	1584	1343	693	552	367	1088	416	100	1083	1453
26	1373	778	1523	666	790	1380	191	1547	534	172
27	1099	435	251	813	977	1121	24	1515	377	306
28	187	1034	759	113	445	597	910	1213	262	86
29	272	167	463	1555	1227	397	1022	636	623	144
30	593	17	568	838	1360	1012	97	442	1324	499
31	1400	1327	382	1462	60	33	344	1564	389	1409
32	1356	660	558	1195	108	713	1332	651	782	1293
33	130	611	1509	868	476	1474	796	1248	502	1314
34	1191	937	1206	161	1186	964	1587	1038	881	766
35	1127	228	893	1286	1006	1385	50	631	1146	774
36	1202	704	741	1267	916	1403	21	835	127	628
37	362	923	409	1346	728	1533	862	1001	642	183
38	700	316	1055	616	365	664	249	1032	270	142
39	1322	1562	1330	1472	1184	1284	739	921	698	140
40	696	1497	483	529	941	1048	1415	1499	200	1527
41	122	926	602	1540	1573	849	485	326	237	385
42	136	1301	673	708	492	531	394	555	763	859
43	526	523	211	1367	943	221	754	1071	412	1244
44	233	1176	320	1050	971	990	1465	572	899	1166
45	542	1259	1417	517	370	256	1309	214	1117	46
46	1067	1501	1273	1239	984	1349	562	1443	331	1017
47	202	9	1109	63	293	40	734	338	1223	1529
48	1305	1091	547	507	1370	1210	57	934	124	1281
49	670	1163	731	819	1429	79	512	928	1458	1180

POWER RESIDUES

	0	1	2	3	4	5	6	7	8	9
0	1	3	9	27	81	243	729	586	157	471
1	1413	1037	1510	1328	782	745	634	301	903	1108
2	122	366	1098	92	276	828	883	1048	1543	1427
3	1079	35	105	315	945	1234	500	1500	1298	692
4	475	1425	1073	17	51	153	459	1377	929	1186
5	356	1068	2	6	18	54	162	486	1458	1172
6	314	942	1225	473	1419	1055	1564	1490	1268	602
7	205	615	244	732	595	184	552	55	165	495
8	1485	1253	557	70	210	630	289	867	1000	1399
9	995	1384	950	1249	545	34	102	306	918	1153
10	257	771	712	535	4	12	36	108	324	972
11	1315	743	628	283	849	946	1237	509	1527	1379
12	935	1204	410	1230	488	1464	1190	368	1104	110
13	330	990	1369	905	1114	140	420	1260	578	133
14	399	1197	389	1167	299	897	1090	68	204	612
15	235	705	514	1542	1424	1070	8	24	72	216
16	648	343	1029	1486	1256	566	97	291	873	1018
17	1453	1157	269	807	820	859	976	1327	779	736
18	607	220	660	379	1137	209	627	280	840	919
19	1156	266	798	793	778	733	598	193	579	136
20	408	1224	470	1410	1028	1483	1247	539	16	48
21	144	432	1296	686	457	1371	911	1132	194	582
22	145	435	1305	713	538	13	39	117	351	1053
23	1558	1472	1214	440	1320	758	673	418	1254	560
24	79	237	711	532	1596	1586	1556	1466	1196	386
25	1158	272	816	847	940	1219	455	1365	893	1078
26	32	96	288	864	991	1372	914	1141	221	663
27	388	1164	290	870	1009	1426	1076	26	78	234
28	702	505	1515	1343	827	880	1039	1516	1346	836
29	907	1120	158	474	1422	1064	1591	1571	1511	1331
30	791	772	715	544	31	93	279	837	910	1129
31	185	555	64	192	576	127	381	1143	227	681
32	442	1326	776	727	580	139	417	1251	551	52
33	156	468	1404	1010	1429	1085	53	159	477	1431
34	1091	71	213	639	316	948	1243	527	1581	1541
35	1421	1061	1582	1544	1430	1088	62	186	558	73
36	219	657	370	1110	128	384	1152	254	762	685
37	454	1362	884	1051	1552	1454	1160	278	834	901
38	1102	104	312	936	1207	419	1257	569	106	318
39	954	1261	581	142	426	1278	632	295	885	1054
40	1561	1481	1241	521	1563	1487	1259	575	124	372
41	1116	146	438	1314	740	619	256	768	703	508
42	1524	1370	908	1123	167	501	1503	1307	719	556
43	67	201	603	208	624	271	813	838	913	1138
44	212	636	307	921	1162	284	852	955	1264	590
45	169	507	1521	1361	881	1042	1525	1373	917	1150
46	248	744	631	292	876	1027	1480	1238	512	1536
47	1406	1016	1447	1139	215	645	334	1002	1405	1013
48	1438	1112	134	402	1206	416	1248	542	25	75
49	225	675	424	1272	614	241	723	568	103	309

P = 1601

INDICES

	0	1	2	3	4	5	6	7	8	9
50	36	425	1395	822	745	281	604	451	419	117
51	1140	946	468	1155	152	1542	1135	1339	1505	1536
52	1425	403	830	1059	1575	1076	718	347	842	1438
53	1432	955	243	851	1599	103	586	1095	224	207
54	1151	684	487	690	303	94	865	1199	1029	1570
55	1173	328	76	827	1567	311	429	82	358	1255
56	239	677	1086	788	811	757	165	591	497	387
57	649	794	962	1004	1265	407	314	1320	138	198
58	324	392	219	969	515	1271	7	1303	1279	1456
59	449	1133	1074	1597	688	74	675	647	196	1277
60	645	888	69	432	620	710	890	180	1412	1364
61	1064	931	149	681	494	71	1376	1583	551	415
62	1452	1522	1379	533	434	976	1514	186	112	909
63	85	462	396	622	16	1359	441	1399	1461	343
64	1408	557	712	781	610	475	1247	1190	160	1586
65	765	892	1384	1145	703	915	834	361	1345	861
66	182	1054	663	269	1561	1183	920	695	528	1414
67	1526	601	848	236	1300	491	554	525	1366	753
68	1243	319	989	898	1258	369	213	1066	1238	561
69	1016	1108	39	1222	1090	1369	933	669	818	511
70	1179	1394	280	418	945	151	1338	1424	1058	717
71	1437	242	102	223	683	302	1198	1172	826	428
72	1254	1085	756	496	793	1264	1319	323	968	6
73	1455	1073	73	195	887	619	179	1063	680	1375
74	414	1378	975	111	461	15	1398	1407	780	1246
75	1585	1383	914	1344	1053	1560	694	1525	235	553
76	752	988	368	1237	1107	1089	668	1178	417	1337
77	716	101	301	825	1084	792	322	1454	194	178
78	1374	974	14	779	1382	1052	1524	751	1236	667
79	1336	300	791	193	973	1381	750	1335	192	749
80	748	1548	1549	992	535	1550	581	173	993	1591
81	1100	536	1467	436	1551	724	252	582	1579	814
82	174	574	978	994	654	1122	1592	284	25	1101
83	901	1516	537	1217	378	1468	289	307	437	1168
84	188	1552	1353	1035	725	1494	760	253	544	114
85	583	785	446	1580	607	598	815	1261	911	175
86	578	1214	575	1480	263	979	1419	87	995	873
87	273	655	806	168	1123	519	464	1593	1296	1556
88	285	454	1228	26	372	398	1102	1483	1023	902
89	1042	637	1517	258	624	538	951	145	1218	1080
90	594	379	1311	18	1469	133	569	290	422	839
91	308	216	1361	438	266	1013	1169	458	98	189
92	1119	443	1553	566	1325	1354	1291	500	1036	48
93	1401	726	614	1328	1495	120	383	761	1069	1463
94	254	982	61	545	1161	34	115	1503	345	584
95	92	1565	786	960	390	447	1275	1410	1581	1512
96	1357	608	1143	661	599	1241	559	816	1422	1196
97	1262	885	109	912	986	714	176	1234	1333	579
98	722	652	1215	1351	783	576	871	1294	1481	949
99	131	264	564	612	980	90	1510	1420	1232	869

POWER RESIDUES

	0	1	2	3	4	5	6	7	8	9
50	927	1180	338	1014	1441	1121	161	483	1449	1145
51	233	699	496	1488	1262	584	151	453	1359	875
52	1024	1471	1211	431	1293	677	430	1290	668	403
53	1209	425	1275	623	268	804	811	832	895	1084
54	50	150	450	1350	848	943	1228	482	1446	1136
55	206	618	253	759	676	427	1281	641	322	966
56	1297	689	466	1398	992	1375	923	1168	302	906
57	1117	149	447	1341	821	862	985	1354	860	979
58	1336	806	817	850	949	1246	536	7	21	63
59	189	567	100	300	900	1099	95	285	855	964
60	1291	671	412	1236	506	1518	1352	854	961	1282
61	644	331	993	1378	932	1195	383	1149	245	735
62	604	211	633	298	894	1081	41	123	369	1107
63	119	357	1071	11	33	99	297	891	1072	14
64	42	126	378	1134	200	600	199	597	190	570
65	109	327	981	1342	824	871	1012	1435	1103	107
66	321	963	1288	662	385	1155	263	789	766	697
67	490	1470	1208	422	1266	596	187	561	82	246
68	738	613	238	714	541	22	66	198	594	181
69	543	28	84	252	756	667	400	1200	398	1194
70	380	1140	218	654	361	1083	47	141	423	1269
71	605	214	642	325	975	1324	770	709	526	1578
72	1532	1394	980	1339	815	844	931	1192	374	1122
73	164	492	1476	1226	476	1428	1082	44	132	396
74	1188	362	1086	56	168	504	1512	1334	800	799
75	796	787	760	679	436	1308	722	565	94	282
76	846	937	1210	428	1284	650	349	1047	1540	1418
77	1052	1555	1463	1187	359	1077	29	87	261	783
78	748	643	328	984	1351	851	952	1255	563	88
79	264	792	775	724	571	112	336	1008	1423	1067
80	1600	1598	1592	1574	1520	1358	872	1015	1444	1130
81	188	564	91	273	819	856	967	1300	698	493
82	1479	1235	503	1509	1325	773	718	553	58	174
83	522	1566	1496	1286	656	367	1101	101	303	909
84	1126	176	528	1584	1550	1448	1142	224	672	415
85	1245	533	1599	1595	1583	1547	1439	1115	143	429
86	1287	659	376	1128	182	546	37	111	333	999
87	1396	986	1357	869	1006	1417	1049	1546	1436	1106
88	116	348	1044	1531	1391	971	1312	734	601	202
89	606	217	651	352	1056	1567	1499	1295	683	448
90	1344	830	889	1066	1597	1589	1565	1493	1277	629
91	286	858	973	1318	752	655	364	1092	74	222
92	666	397	1191	371	1113	137	411	1233	497	1491
93	1271	611	232	696	487	1461	1181	341	1023	1468
94	1202	404	1212	434	1302	704	511	1533	1397	989
95	1366	896	1087	59	177	531	1593	1577	1529	1385
96	953	1258	572	115	345	1035	1504	1310	728	583
97	148	444	1332	794	781	742	625	274	822	865
98	994	1381	941	1222	464	1392	974	1321	761	682
99	445	1335	803	808	823	868	1003	1408	1022	1465

P = 1601

INDICES

	0	1	2	3	4	5	6	7	8	9
100	88	1445	477	996	1447	1475	874	1488	797	274
101	333	1249	656	479	503	807	471	1315	169	1019
102	1192	1124	998	938	520	1114	1207	465	204	162
103	1594	1449	1187	1297	1391	965	1557	11	1588	286
104	1477	1039	455	1158	882	1229	1111	767	27	876
105	1128	373	770	229	399	65	894	1103	1490	1287
106	1484	351	1007	1024	295	1386	903	799	51	1043
107	155	632	638	42	1147	1518	276	775	259	30
108	1203	625	736	705	539	335	742	952	355	1268
109	146	340	917	1219	1251	1404	1081	1545	22	595
110	1225	836	380	658	128	1312	879	629	19	1531
111	363	1470	481	924	134	857	410	570	1307	1347
112	291	505	729	423	1138	1534	840	1093	863	309
113	809	1002	217	1131	643	1362	549	184	439	473
114	701	267	846	317	1014	509	1056	1170	1317	617
115	459	1342	366	99	1372	665	190	171	250	1120
116	376	1033	444	1212	271	1554	1021	143	567	1011
117	1323	1326	59	1563	1355	1194	1331	1292	1508	1473
118	501	936	1185	1037	1126	1285	49	773	740	1402
119	126	922	727	1000	699	615	248	141	1329	1283
120	697	1496	940	1498	121	1539	484	384	672	530
121	762	522	942	1070	232	1049	1464	1165	1416	255
122	1116	1500	983	1442	201	62	733	1528	546	1209
123	123	1162	1428	927	35	821	603	116	467	1541
124	1504	402	1574	346	1431	850	585	206	486	93
125	1028	327	1566	81	238	787	164	386	961	406
126	137	391	514	1302	448	1596	674	1276	68	709
127	1411	930	493	1582	1451	532	1513	908	395	1358
128	1460	556	609	1189	764	1144	833	860	662	1182
129	527	600	1299	524	1242	897	212	560	38	1368
130	817	1393	944	1423	1436	222	1197	427	755	1263
131	967	1072	886	1062	413	110	1397	1245	913	1559
132	234	987	1106	1177	715	824	321	177	13	1051
133	1235	299	972	1334	747	991	580	1590	1466	723
134	1578	573	653	283	900	1216	288	1167	1352	1493
135	543	784	606	1260	577	1479	1418	872	805	518
136	1295	453	371	1482	1041	257	950	1079	1310	132
137	421	215	265	457	1118	565	1290	47	613	119
138	1068	981	1160	1502	91	959	1274	1511	1142	1240
139	1421	884	985	1233	721	1350	870	948	563	89
140	1231	1444	1446	1487	332	478	470	1018	997	1113
141	203	1448	1390	10	1476	1157	1110	875	769	64
142	1489	350	294	798	154	41	275	29	735	334
143	354	339	1250	1544	1224	657	878	1530	480	856
144	1306	504	1137	1092	808	1130	548	472	845	508
145	1316	1341	1371	170	375	1211	1020	1010	58	1193
146	1507	935	1125	772	125	999	247	1282	939	1538
147	671	521	231	1164	1115	1441	732	1208	1427	820
148	466	401	1430	205	1027	80	163	405	513	1595
149	67	929	1450	907	1459	1188	832	1181	1298	896

POWER RESIDUES

	0	1	2	3	4	5	6	7	8	9
100	1193	377	1131	191	573	118	354	1062	1585	1553
101	1457	1169	305	915	1144	230	690	469	1407	1019
102	1456	1166	296	888	1063	1588	1562	1484	1250	548
103	43	129	387	1161	281	843	928	1183	347	1041
104	1522	1364	890	1069	5	15	45	135	405	1215
105	443	1329	785	754	661	382	1146	236	708	523
106	1569	1505	1313	737	610	229	687	460	1380	938
107	1213	437	1311	731	592	175	525	1575	1523	1367
108	899	1096	86	258	774	721	562	85	255	765
109	694	481	1443	1127	179	537	10	30	90	270
110	810	829	886	1057	1570	1508	1322	764	691	472
111	1416	1046	1537	1409	1025	1474	1220	458	1374	920
112	1159	275	825	874	1021	1462	1184	350	1050	1549
113	1445	1133	197	591	172	516	1548	1442	1124	170
114	510	1530	1388	962	1285	653	358	1074	20	60
115	180	540	19	57	171	513	1539	1415	1043	1528
116	1382	944	1231	491	1473	1217	449	1347	839	916
117	1147	239	717	550	49	147	441	1323	767	700
118	499	1497	1289	665	394	1182	344	1032	1495	1283
119	647	340	1020	1459	1175	323	969	1306	716	547
120	40	120	360	1080	38	114	342	1026	1477	1229
121	485	1455	1163	287	861	982	1345	833	898	1093
122	77	231	693	478	1434	1100	98	294	882	1045
123	1534	1400	998	1393	977	1330	788	763	688	463
124	1389	965	1294	680	439	1317	749	646	337	1011
125	1432	1094	80	240	720	559	76	228	684	451
126	1353	857	970	1309	725	574	121	363	1089	65
127	195	585	154	462	1386	956	1267	599	196	588
128	163	489	1467	1199	395	1185	353	1059	1576	1526
129	1376	926	1177	329	987	1360	878	1033	1498	1292
130	674	421	1263	587	160	480	1440	1118	152	456
131	1368	902	1105	113	339	1017	1450	1148	242	726
132	577	130	390	1170	308	924	1171	311	933	1198
133	392	1176	326	978	1333	797	790	769	706	517
134	1551	1451	1151	251	753	658	373	1119	155	465
135	1395	983	1348	842	925	1174	320	960	1279	635
136	304	912	1135	203	609	226	678	433	1299	695
137	484	1452	1154	260	780	739	616	247	741	622
138	265	795	784	751	652	355	1065	1594	1580	1538
139	1412	1034	1501	1301	701	502	1506	1316	746	637
140	310	930	1189	365	1095	83	249	747	640	319
141	957	1270	608	223	669	406	1218	452	1356	866
142	997	1390	968	1303	707	520	1560	1478	1232	494
143	1482	1244	530	1590	1568	1502	1304	710	529	1587
144	1559	1475	1223	467	1401	1001	1402	1004	1411	1031
145	1492	1274	620	259	777	730	589	166	498	1494
146	1280	638	313	939	1216	446	1338	812	835	904
147	1111	131	393	1179	335	1005	1414	1040	1519	1355
148	863	988	1363	887	1060	1579	1535	1403	1007	1420
149	1058	1573	1517	1349	845	934	1201	401	1203	407

P = 1601

INDICES

	0	1	2	3	4	5	6	7	8	9
150	37	1392	1435	426	966	1061	1396	1558	1105	823
151	12	298	746	1589	1577	282	287	1492	605	1478
152	804	452	1040	1078	420	456	1289	118	1159	958
153	1141	883	720	947	1230	1486	469	1112	1389	1156
154	768	349	153	28	353	1543	877	855	1136	1129
155	844	1340	374	1009	1506	771	246	1537	230	1440
156	1426	400	1026	404	66	906	831	895	1434	1060
157	1104	297	1576	1491	803	1077	1288	957	719	1485
158	1388	348	352	854	843	1008	245	1439	1025	905
159	1433	296	802	956	1387	853	244	904	801	852
160	800	0								

POWER RESIDUES

	0	1	2	3	4	5	6	7	8	9
150	1221	461	1383	947	1240	518	1554	1460	1178	332
151	996	1387	959	1276	626	277	831	892	1075	23
152	69	207	621	262	786	757	670	409	1227	479
153	1437	1109	125	375	1125	173	519	1557	1469	1205
154	413	1239	515	1545	1433	1097	89	267	801	802
155	805	814	841	922	1165	293	879	1036	1507	1319
156	755	664	391	1173	317	951	1252	554	61	183
157	549	46	138	414	1242	524	1572	1514	1340	818
158	853	958	1273	617	250	750	649	346	1038	1513
159	1337	809	826	877	1030	1489	1265	593	178	534
160										

P = 1607

INDICES

	0	1	2	3	4	5	6	7	8	9
0		0	504	1352	1008	1	250	617	1512	1098
1	505	1131	754	1599	1121	1353	410	948	1602	563
2	1009	363	29	230	1258	2	497	844	19	425
3	251	606	914	877	1452	618	500	1436	1067	1345
4	1513	970	867	1383	533	1099	734	449	156	1234
5	506	694	1001	1500	1348	1132	523	309	929	1080
6	755	669	1110	109	1418	1600	1381	348	350	1582
7	1122	267	1004	774	334	1354	1571	142	243	638
8	411	590	1474	491	1371	949	281	171	1037	808
9	1603	610	1238	352	953	564	660	1525	132	623
10	1010	688	1198	560	1505	364	398	1560	246	272
11	30	1182	1027	1290	813	231	1433	1091	1584	1565
12	1259	656	1173	716	8	3	613	540	316	1129
13	498	667	279	1180	852	845	854	682	480	1521
14	20	195	771	1124	1508	426	1278	980	838	1389
15	252	217	469	440	646	607	747	128	1142	1246
16	915	847	1094	1331	372	878	995	1210	269	1592
17	1453	55	785	211	675	619	1541	826	1312	1516
18	501	537	1114	415	136	1437	856	473	1457	1461
19	1068	1535	1164	1006	423	1346	636	1503	1127	644
20	1514	94	1192	1042	96	971	1064	1328	403	88
21	868	684	902	13	458	1384	750	1223	776	520
22	534	941	80	920	1531	1100	188	182	1317	1194
23	735	1494	331	641	1595	450	482	384	463	764
24	157	1400	1160	336	71	1235	1220	556	512	237
25	507	1241	1117	1361	1044	695	820	547	27	447
26	1002	1523	1171	978	783	1501	78	554	1356	367
27	1349	313	1358	356	1186	1133	984	882	419	98
28	524	388	699	360	1275	310	22	1587	406	290
29	930	1271	176	1573	1484	1081	1342	369	287	223
30	756	394	721	434	973	670	944	200	1150	306
31	1111	197	1251	63	632	110	40	831	144	1556
32	1419	1306	1351	1511	1598	1601	229	18	876	1066
33	1382	155	1499	928	108	349	773	242	490	1036
34	351	131	559	245	1289	1583	715	315	1179	479
35	1123	837	439	1141	1330	268	210	1311	414	1456

POWER RESIDUES

	0	1	2	3	4	5	6	7	8	9
0	1	5	25	125	625	1518	1162	989	124	620
1	1493	1037	364	213	1065	504	913	1351	327	28
2	140	700	286	1430	722	396	373	258	1290	22
3	110	550	1143	894	1256	1459	867	1121	784	706
4	316	1580	1472	932	1446	802	796	766	616	1473
5	937	1471	927	1421	677	171	855	1061	484	813
6	851	1041	384	313	1565	1397	557	1178	1069	524
7	1013	244	1220	1279	1574	1442	782	696	266	1330
8	222	1110	729	431	548	1133	844	1006	209	1045
9	404	413	458	683	201	1005	204	1020	279	1395
10	547	1128	819	881	1191	1134	849	1031	334	63
11	315	1575	1447	807	821	891	1241	1384	492	853
12	1051	434	563	1208	1219	1274	1549	1317	157	785
13	711	341	98	490	843	1001	184	920	1386	502
14	903	1301	77	385	318	1590	1522	1182	1089	624
15	1513	1137	864	1106	709	331	48	240	1200	1179
16	1074	549	1138	869	1131	834	956	1566	1402	582
17	1303	87	435	568	1233	1344	292	1460	872	1146
18	909	1331	227	1135	854	1056	459	688	226	1130
19	829	931	1441	777	671	141	705	311	1555	1347
20	307	1535	1247	1414	642	1603	1587	1507	1107	714
21	356	173	865	1111	734	456	673	151	755	561
22	1198	1169	1024	299	1495	1047	414	463	708	326
23	23	115	575	1268	1519	1167	1014	249	1245	1404
24	592	1353	337	78	390	343	108	540	1093	644
25	6	30	150	750	536	1073	544	1113	744	506
26	923	1401	577	1278	1569	1417	657	71	355	168
27	840	986	109	545	1118	769	631	1548	1312	132
28	660	86	430	543	1108	719	381	298	1490	1022
29	289	1445	797	771	641	1598	1562	1382	482	803
30	801	791	741	491	848	1026	309	1545	1297	57
31	285	1425	697	271	1355	347	128	640	1593	1537
32	1257	1464	892	1246	1409	617	1478	962	1596	1552
33	1332	232	1160	979	74	370	243	1215	1254	1449
34	817	871	1141	884	1206	1209	1224	1299	67	335
35	68	340	93	465	718	376	273	1365	397	378

P = 1607

INDICES

	0	1	2	3	4	5	6	7	8	9
36	1005	1126	1041	402	12	775	919	1316	640	462
37	335	511	1360	26	977	1355	355	418	359	405
38	1572	286	433	1149	62	143	1510	875	927	489
39	244	1178	1140	413	401	639	25	358	1148	926
40	412	1147	598	599	90	591	1546	961	600	1023
41	1475	428	1568	91	226	492	907	1267	592	574
42	1372	740	1188	1547	1406	950	517	1286	962	870
43	282	83	1254	601	121	172	1280	793	1024	381
44	1038	726	1445	1476	584	809	1424	1135	429	453
45	1604	495	692	1569	686	611	215	1539	92	186
46	1239	982	392	227	835	353	1145	515	493	965
47	954	1480	986	908	888	565	967	992	1268	904
48	661	1429	298	593	58	1526	840	729	575	1077
49	133	303	118	1373	1060	624	1016	884	741	1087
50	1011	956	139	1189	15	689	259	1338	1548	1468
51	1199	1391	1324	1407	1051	561	531	1580	951	1563
52	1506	1590	421	518	69	365	1482	1554	1287	460
53	399	572	582	963	1058	1561	254	1262	871	759
54	247	664	817	283	256	273	860	100	84	161
55	31	988	1488	1255	1386	1183	923	66	602	1376
56	1028	219	892	122	1203	1291	864	1207	173	1264
57	814	652	526	1281	485	232	910	262	794	752
58	1434	1108	169	1025	680	1092	471	900	382	1169
59	1585	1249	240	1039	873	1566	791	390	727	1322
60	1260	890	898	1446	1225	657	938	712	1477	788
61	1174	442	1448	585	704	717	48	325	810	761
62	9	1074	701	1425	149	4	567	1440	1136	778
63	614	276	544	430	1335	541	648	1227	454	1365
64	317	294	204	1605	249	1130	409	362	496	605
65	499	969	733	693	522	668	1380	266	1570	589
66	280	609	659	687	397	1181	1432	655	612	666
67	853	194	1277	216	746	846	994	54	1540	536
68	855	1534	635	93	1063	683	749	940	187	1493
69	481	1399	1219	1240	819	1522	77	312	983	387
70	21	1270	1341	393	943	196	39	1305	228	154
71	772	130	714	836	209	1125	918	510	354	285
72	1509	1177	24	1146	1545	427	906	739	516	82
73	1279	725	1423	494	214	981	1144	1479	966	1428
74	839	302	1015	955	258	1390	530	1589	1481	571
75	253	663	859	987	922	218	863	651	909	1107
76	470	1248	790	889	937	441	47	1073	566	275
77	647	293	408	968	1379	608	1431	193	993	1533
78	748	1398	76	1269	38	129	917	1176	905	724
79	1143	301	529	662	862	1247	46	292	1430	1397
80	916	300	45	299	1102	848	1103	113	594	627
81	1095	849	444	59	1465	1332	1104	340	1527	102
82	373	114	932	841	466	879	595	1551	730	190
83	996	628	1411	576	165	1211	1096	1450	1078	1369
84	270	850	1244	134	86	1593	445	1273	304	106
85	1454	60	1021	119	184	56	1466	1056	1374	678

POWER RESIDUES

	0	1	2	3	4	5	6	7	8	9
36	283	1415	647	21	105	525	1018	269	1345	297
37	1485	997	164	820	886	1216	1259	1474	942	1496
38	1052	439	588	1333	237	1185	1104	699	281	1405
39	597	1378	462	703	301	1505	1097	664	106	530
40	1043	394	363	208	1040	379	288	1440	772	646
41	16	80	400	393	358	183	915	1361	377	278
42	1390	522	1003	194	970	29	145	725	411	448
43	633	1558	1362	382	303	1515	1147	914	1356	352
44	153	765	611	1448	812	846	1016	259	1295	47
45	235	1175	1054	449	638	1583	1487	1007	214	1070
46	529	1038	369	238	1190	1129	824	906	1316	152
47	760	586	1323	187	935	1461	877	1171	1034	349
48	138	690	236	1180	1079	574	1263	1494	1042	389
49	338	83	415	468	733	451	648	26	130	650
50	36	180	900	1286	2	10	50	250	1250	1429
51	717	371	248	1240	1379	467	728	426	523	1008
52	219	1095	654	56	280	1400	572	1253	1444	792
53	746	516	973	44	220	1100	679	181	905	1311
54	127	635	1568	1412	632	1553	1337	257	1285	1604
55	1592	1532	1232	1339	267	1335	247	1235	1354	342
56	103	515	968	19	95	475	768	626	1523	1187
57	1114	749	531	1048	419	488	833	951	1541	1277
58	1564	1392	532	1053	444	613	1458	862	1096	659
59	81	405	418	483	808	826	916	1366	402	403
60	408	433	558	1183	1094	649	31	155	775	661
61	91	455	668	126	630	1543	1287	7	35	175
62	875	1161	984	99	495	868	1126	809	831	941
63	1491	1027	314	1570	1422	682	196	980	79	395
64	368	233	1165	1004	199	995	154	770	636	1573
65	1437	757	571	1248	1419	667	121	605	1418	662
66	96	480	793	751	541	1098	669	131	655	61
67	305	1525	1197	1164	999	174	870	1136	859	1081
68	584	1313	137	685	211	1055	454	663	101	505
69	918	1376	452	653	51	255	1275	1554	1342	282
70	1410	622	1503	1087	614	1463	887	1221	1284	1599
71	1567	1407	607	1428	712	346	123	615	1468	912
72	1346	302	1510	1122	789	731	441	598	1383	487
73	828	926	1416	652	46	230	1150	929	1431	727
74	421	498	883	1201	1184	1099	674	156	780	686
75	216	1080	579	1288	12	60	300	1500	1072	539
76	1088	619	1488	1012	239	1195	1154	949	1531	1227
77	1314	142	710	336	73	365	218	1090	629	1538
78	1262	1489	1017	264	1320	172	860	1086	609	1438
79	762	596	1373	437	578	1283	1594	1542	1282	1589
80	1517	1157	964	1606	1602	1582	1482	982	89	445
81	618	1483	987	114	570	1243	1394	542	1103	694
82	256	1280	1579	1467	907	1321	177	885	1211	1234
83	1349	317	1585	1497	1057	464	713	351	148	740
84	486	823	901	1291	27	135	675	161	805	811
85	841	991	134	670	136	680	186	930	1436	752

P = 1607

INDICES

	0	1	2	3	4	5	6	7	8	9
86	786	1333	587	1061	152	212	1105	36	625	163
87	676	341	178	1017	1297	620	1528	476	885	1319
88	1542	103	1230	742	343	827	374	706	1088	1157
89	1313	115	322	1012	33	1517	933	1575	957	1031
90	502	842	999	140	1196	538	467	824	1190	180
91	1115	880	719	16	437	416	596	1284	690	990
92	137	1552	1486	260	896	1438	731	52	1339	737
93	857	191	43	1549	1019	474	997	50	1469	1415
94	1458	629	378	1200	1490	1462	1412	1083	1392	767
95	1069	577	1471	1325	1496	1536	166	1302	1408	1299
96	1165	1212	327	1052	802	1007	1097	1120	562	1257
97	424	1451	1344	532	1233	1347	1079	1417	1581	333
98	637	1370	807	952	622	1504	271	812	1564	7
99	1128	851	1520	1507	1388	645	1245	371	1591	674
100	1515	135	1460	422	643	95	87	457	519	1530
101	1193	1594	763	70	236	1043	446	782	366	1185
102	97	1274	289	1483	222	972	305	631	1555	1597
103	1065	107	1035	1288	478	1329	1455	11	461	976
104	404	61	488	400	925	89	1022	225	573	1405
105	869	120	380	583	452	685	185	834	964	887
106	903	57	1076	1059	1086	14	1467	1050	1562	68
107	459	1057	758	255	160	1385	1375	1202	1263	484
108	751	679	1168	872	1321	1224	787	703	760	148
109	777	1334	1364	248	604	521	588	396	665	745
110	535	1062	1492	818	386	942	153	208	284	1544
111	81	213	1427	257	570	921	1106	936	274	1378
112	1532	37	723	861	1396	1101	626	1464	101	465
113	189	164	1368	85	105	183	677	151	162	1296
114	1318	342	1156	32	1030	1195	179	436	989	895
115	736	1018	1414	1489	766	1495	1298	801	1256	1232
116	332	621	6	1387	673	642	1529	235	1184	221
117	1596	477	975	924	1404	451	886	1085	67	159
118	483	1320	147	603	744	385	1543	569	1377	1395
119	464	104	1295	1029	894	765	1231	672	220	1403
120	158	743	1394	893	1402	1401	344	1215	123	345
121	1161	828	1442	1204	1216	337	375	1047	1292	124
122	72	707	946	865	346	1236	1089	769	1208	1162
123	1221	1158	552	174	829	557	1314	1138	1265	1443
124	513	116	1578	815	1205	238	323	202	653	1217
125	508	1013	1071	527	338	1242	34	320	1282	376
126	1118	1518	780	486	1048	1362	934	1154	233	1293
127	1045	1576	1152	911	125	696	958	579	263	73
128	821	1032	798	795	708	548	503	616	753	947
129	28	843	913	1435	866	448	1000	308	1109	347
130	1003	141	1473	170	1237	1524	1197	1559	1026	1090
131	1172	539	278	681	770	979	468	127	1093	1209
132	784	825	1113	472	1163	1502	1191	1327	901	1222
133	79	181	330	383	1159	555	1116	546	1170	553
134	1357	881	698	1586	175	368	720	199	1250	830
135	1350	17	1498	241	558	314	438	1310	1040	1315

POWER RESIDUES

	0	1	2	3	4	5	6	7	8	9
86	546	1123	794	756	566	1223	1294	42	210	1050
87	429	538	1083	594	1363	387	328	33	165	825
88	911	1341	277	1385	497	878	1176	1059	474	763
89	601	1398	562	1203	1194	1149	924	1406	602	1403
90	587	1328	212	1060	479	788	726	416	473	758
91	576	1273	1544	1292	32	160	800	786	716	366
92	223	1115	754	556	1173	1044	399	388	333	58
93	290	1450	822	896	1266	1509	1117	764	606	1423
94	687	221	1105	704	306	1530	1222	1289	17	85
95	425	518	983	94	470	743	501	898	1276	1559
96	1367	407	428	533	1058	469	738	476	773	651
97	41	205	1025	304	1520	1172	1039	374	263	1315
98	147	735	461	698	276	1380	472	753	551	1148
99	919	1381	477	778	676	166	830	936	1466	902
100	1296	52	260	1300	72	360	193	965	4	20
101	100	500	893	1251	1434	742	496	873	1151	934
102	1456	852	1046	409	438	583	1308	112	560	1193
103	1144	899	1281	1584	1492	1032	339	88	440	593
104	1358	362	203	1015	254	1270	1529	1217	1264	1499
105	1067	514	963	1601	1577	1457	857	1071	534	1063
106	494	863	1101	684	206	1030	329	38	190	950
107	1536	1252	1439	767	621	1498	1062	489	838	976
108	59	295	1475	947	1521	1177	1064	499	888	1226
109	1309	117	585	1318	162	810	836	966	9	45
110	225	1125	804	806	816	866	1116	759	581	1298
111	62	310	1550	1322	182	910	1336	252	1260	1479
112	967	14	70	350	143	715	361	198	990	129
113	645	11	55	275	1375	447	628	1533	1237	1364
114	392	353	158	790	736	466	723	401	398	383
115	308	1540	1272	1539	1267	1514	1142	889	1231	1334
116	242	1210	1229	1324	192	960	1586	1502	1082	589
117	1338	262	1310	122	610	1443	787	721	391	348
118	133	665	111	555	1168	1019	274	1370	422	503
119	908	1326	202	1010	229	1145	904	1306	102	510
120	943	1501	1077	564	1213	1244	1399	567	1228	1319
121	167	835	961	1591	1527	1207	1214	1249	1424	692
122	246	1230	1329	217	1085	604	1413	637	1578	1462
123	882	1196	1159	974	49	245	1225	1304	92	460
124	693	251	1255	1454	842	996	159	795	761	591
125	1348	312	1560	1372	432	553	1158	969	24	120
126	600	1393	537	1078	569	1238	1369	417	478	783
127	701	291	1455	847	1021	284	1420	672	146	730
128	436	573	1258	1469	917	1371	427	528	1033	344
129	113	565	1218	1269	1524	1192	1139	874	1156	959
130	1581	1477	957	1571	1427	707	321	1605	1597	1557
131	1357	357	178	890	1236	1359	367	228	1140	879
132	1181	1084	599	1388	512	953	1551	1327	207	1035
133	354	163	815	861	1091	634	1563	1387	507	928
134	1426	702	296	1480	972	39	195	975	54	270
135	1350	322	3	15	75	375	268	1340	272	1360

P = 1607

INDICES

	0	1	2	3	4	5	6	7	8	9
136	1359	417	432	874	1139	357	597	960	1567	1266
137	1187	1285	1253	792	1444	1134	691	1538	391	514
138	985	991	297	728	117	883	138	1337	1323	1579
139	420	1553	581	1261	816	99	1487	65	891	1206
140	525	261	168	899	239	389	897	711	1447	324
141	700	1439	543	1226	203	361	732	265	658	654
142	1276	53	634	939	1218	311	1340	1304	713	509
143	23	738	1422	1478	1014	1588	858	650	789	1072
144	407	192	75	1175	528	291	44	112	443	339
145	931	1550	1410	1449	1243	1272	1020	1055	586	35
146	177	475	1229	705	321	1574	998	823	718	1283
147	1485	51	42	49	377	1082	1470	1301	326	1119
148	1343	1416	806	811	1519	370	1459	456	762	781
149	288	630	1034	10	487	224	379	833	1075	1049
150	757	1201	1167	702	1363	395	1491	207	1426	935
151	722	1463	1367	150	1155	435	1413	800	5	234
152	974	1084	146	568	1294	671	1393	1214	1441	1046
153	945	768	551	1137	1577	201	1070	319	779	1153
154	1151	578	797	615	912	307	1472	1558	277	126
155	1112	1326	329	545	697	198	1497	1309	431	959
156	1252	1537	296	1336	580	64	167	710	542	264
157	633	1303	1421	649	74	111	1409	1054	1228	822
158	41	1300	805	455	1033	832	1166	206	1366	799
159	145	1213	550	318	796	1557	328	1308	295	709
160	1420	1053	804	205	549	1307	803			

POWER RESIDUES

	0	1	2	3	4	5	6	7	8	9
136	372	253	1265	1504	1092	639	1588	1512	1132	839
137	981	84	420	493	858	1076	559	1188	1119	774
138	656	66	330	43	215	1075	554	1163	994	149
139	745	511	948	1526	1202	1189	1124	799	781	691
140	241	1205	1204	1199	1174	1049	424	513	958	1576
141	1452	832	946	1516	1152	939	1481	977	64	320
142	1600	1572	1432	732	446	623	1508	1112	739	481
143	798	776	666	116	580	1293	37	185	925	1411
144	627	1528	1212	1239	1374	442	603	1408	612	1453
145	837	971	34	170	850	1036	359	188	940	1486
146	1002	189	945	1511	1127	814	856	1066	509	938
147	1476	952	1546	1302	82	410	443	608	1433	737
148	471	748	526	1023	294	1470	922	1396	552	1153
149	944	1506	1102	689	231	1155	954	1556	1352	332
150	53	265	1325	197	985	104	520	993	144	720
151	386	323	8	40	200	1000	179	895	1261	1484
152	992	139	695	261	1305	97	485	818	876	1166
153	1009	224	1120	779	681	191	955	1561	1377	457
154	678	176	880	1186	1109	724	406	423	508	933
155	1451	827	921	1391	527	1028	319	1595	1547	1307
156	107	535	1068	519	988	119	595	1368	412	453
157	658	76	380	293	1465	897	1271	1534	1242	1389
158	517	978	69	345	118	590	1343	287	1435	747
159	521	998	169	845	1011	234	1170	1029	324	13
160	65	325	18	90	450	643				

P = 1609

INDICES

	0	1	2	3	4	5	6	7	8	9
0		0	1016	342	424	912	1358	1	1440	684
1	320	1096	766	1328	1017	1254	848	689	92	1365
2	1336	343	504	1287	174	216	736	1026	425	1421
3	662	198	256	1438	97	913	1108	1453	773	62
4	744	1062	1359	1051	1520	1596	695	195	1190	2
5	1232	1031	144	1507	434	400	1441	99	829	626
6	70	1355	1214	685	1272	632	846	630	1113	21
7	321	495	516	642	861	558	181	1097	1078	889
8	152	1368	470	1303	767	1601	459	155	928	713
9	1004	1329	103	540	1211	669	598	55	1018	172
10	640	761	439	822	1160	1255	915	1582	1450	1090
11	1416	187	849	813	1115	591	237	404	34	690
12	1086	584	763	1404	622	1128	93	31	680	1393
13	40	1491	254	1366	38	330	521	147	1037	1468
14	1337	537	1511	816	1532	725	50	344	269	1174
15	1574	656	1197	1373	505	1110	486	546	297	241
16	1168	1288	776	23	1486	742	711	1035	175	1048
17	1009	441	1475	264	1171	217	336	968	121	332
18	412	652	737	89	1119	757	1556	177	619	1027
19	77	732	6	1604	1071	974	426	802	1188	53
20	48	972	169	1422	1455	366	230	363	568	853
21	663	1057	323	837	990	355	858	199	498	984
22	824	409	1203	385	257	900	221	531	523	553
23	1607	1439	1253	503	1420	1107	1050	1231	98	1271
24	494	1077	1600	102	171	914	812	1085	30	37
25	536	268	1109	775	1047	335	88	76	801	1454
26	1056	497	899	1252	1270	811	774	1055	1054	1162
27	1346	939	1537	63	1163	1312	445	149	876	882
28	745	1347	1553	963	919	1011	224	1063	940	1378
29	133	397	1066	1424	1360	1538	1285	514	582	1007
30	982	1052	64	1103	605	659	781	753	1521	1164
31	518	326	1502	1412	1562	1597	1313	66	1257	909
32	576	316	696	446	184	1544	1039	1432	894	196
33	150	1391	119	529	443	1542	1191	877	456	1155
34	417	1294	1457	3	883	933	1280	789	579	1217
35	1233	746	1352	1182	376	1407	1137	1032	1348	644
36	1428	1122	60	926	145	1554	1105	917	527	138
37	165	1508	964	784	1193	1470	27	1141	435	920
38	1093	373	140	1477	1022	401	1012	127	479	279
39	382	368	1442	225	210	193	596	723	1069	100
40	1064	1292	380	1526	1185	672	830	941	863	602
41	1382	489	1246	627	1379	607	1584	202	261	206
42	71	134	465	879	1339	905	245	1356	398	1158
43	1371	167	266	980	1215	1067	1514	1044	392	1528
44	232	686	1425	1207	611	17	1401	1516	1273	1361
45	308	550	1237	998	1547	633	1539	560	1569	107
46	1015	683	847	1286	661	1452	1519	1030	828	631
47	515	888	458	539	639	1581	1114	583	679	329
48	1510	1173	485	22	1008	967	1118	731	1187	365
49	322	983	220	502	493	1084	1046	496	1053	1311

POWER RESIDUES

	0	1	2	3	4	5	6	7	8	9
0	1	7	49	343	792	717	192	1344	1363	1496
1	818	899	1466	608	1038	830	983	445	1506	888
2	1389	69	483	163	1141	1551	1203	376	1023	725
3	248	127	889	1396	118	826	955	249	134	938
4	130	910	1543	1147	1593	1497	825	948	200	1400
5	146	1022	718	199	1393	97	679	1535	1091	1201
6	362	925	39	273	302	505	317	610	1052	928
7	60	420	1331	1272	859	1186	257	190	1330	1265
8	810	843	1074	1082	1138	1530	1056	956	256	183
9	1281	922	18	126	882	1347	1384	34	238	57
10	399	1184	243	92	644	1290	985	459	1604	1574
11	1364	1503	867	1242	649	1325	1230	565	737	332
12	715	178	1246	677	1521	993	515	387	1100	1264
13	803	794	731	290	421	1338	1321	1202	369	974
14	382	1065	1019	697	52	364	939	137	959	277
15	330	701	80	560	702	87	609	1045	879	1326
16	1237	614	1080	1124	1432	370	981	431	1408	202
17	1414	244	99	693	24	168	1176	187	1309	1118
18	1390	76	532	506	324	659	1395	111	777	612
19	1066	1026	746	395	1156	47	329	694	31	217
20	1519	979	417	1310	1125	1439	419	1324	1223	516
21	394	1149	1607	1595	1511	923	25	175	1225	530
22	492	226	1582	1420	286	393	1142	1558	1252	719
23	206	1442	440	1471	643	1283	936	116	812	857
24	1172	159	1113	1355	1440	426	1373	1566	1308	1111
25	1341	1342	1349	1398	132	924	32	224	1568	1322
26	1209	418	1317	1174	173	1211	432	1415	251	148
27	1036	816	885	1368	1531	1063	1005	599	975	389
28	1114	1362	1489	769	556	674	1500	846	1095	1229
29	558	688	1598	1532	1070	1054	942	158	1106	1306
30	1097	1243	656	1374	1573	1357	1454	524	450	1541
31	1133	1495	811	850	1123	1425	321	638	1248	691
32	10	70	490	212	1484	734	311	568	758	479
33	135	945	179	1253	726	255	176	1232	579	835
34	1018	690	3	21	147	1029	767	542	576	814
35	871	1270	845	1088	1180	215	1505	881	1340	1335
36	1300	1055	949	207	1449	489	205	1435	391	1128
37	1460	566	744	381	1058	970	354	869	1256	747
38	402	1205	390	1121	1411	223	1561	1273	866	1235
39	600	982	438	1457	545	597	961	291	428	1387
40	55	385	1086	1166	117	819	906	1515	951	221
41	1547	1175	180	1260	775	598	968	340	771	570
42	772	577	821	920	4	28	196	1372	1559	1259
43	768	549	625	1157	54	378	1037	823	934	102
44	714	171	1197	334	729	276	323	652	1346	1377
45	1594	1504	874	1291	992	508	338	757	472	86
46	602	996	536	534	520	422	1345	1370	1545	1161
47	82	574	800	773	584	870	1263	796	745	388
48	1107	1313	1146	1586	1448	482	156	1092	1208	411
49	1268	831	990	494	240	71	497	261	218	1526

P = 1609

INDICES

	0	1	2	3	4	5	6	7	8	9
50	1552	1377	1284	1102	517	65	183	1390	455	932
51	1351	643	1104	783	1092	126	209	1291	862	606
52	464	1157	1513	1206	307	559	660	887	678	966
53	219	1310	182	782	463	886	462	674	570	1098
54	754	675	347	994	945	394	1079	1522	571	431
55	720	1178	1461	890	1165	1099	284	872	290	771
56	153	519	755	1418	961	117	371	1369	327	676
57	419	818	1240	1074	471	1503	348	421	786	338
58	1149	1304	1413	995	474	1316	832	855	768	1563
59	946	1144	693	667	1530	1602	1598	395	415	277
60	390	729	460	1314	1080	1496	511	1589	13	156
61	67	1523	189	1265	161	708	929	1258	572	1296
62	1534	705	1342	714	910	432	820	1195	970	534
63	1005	577	721	1399	1082	943	665	1330	317	1179
64	1592	1220	1332	234	104	697	1462	1385	1200	114
65	952	541	447	891	840	795	302	1326	1212	185
66	1166	851	799	751	1135	670	1545	1100	1459	727
67	950	843	599	1040	285	1242	1472	123	563	56
68	1433	873	702	1498	865	1059	1019	895	291	1227
69	341	319	688	173	197	772	1595	143	625	845
70	641	151	154	1210	760	1449	590	762	1392	520
71	815	1573	545	1485	440	120	756	5	52	229
72	836	823	530	1419	1076	29	334	898	1161	444
73	962	132	513	604	325	1256	1543	118	1154	1279
74	1181	1427	916	1192	372	478	192	379	601	1583
75	878	1370	1043	610	549	1568	1451	457	328	1117
76	501	1551	1389	1091	1156	677	885	346	430	283
77	1417	418	420	473	1143	414	1495	188	1295	819
78	1398	1591	1384	839	850	1458	1241	701	1226	1594
79	1209	814	4	1075	131	1153	477	1042	1116	884
80	472	1397	700	130	1396	592	934	1504	593	1276
81	80	312	238	1281	349	935	271	808	10	405
82	790	422	1505	437	654	46	35	580	787	594
83	15	491	992	691	1218	339	1277	1224	1222	613
84	1087	1234	1150	81	1481	352	287	585	747	1305
85	313	1132	1261	647	764	1353	1414	239	566	74
86	779	1405	1183	996	1282	1176	388	112	623	377
87	475	350	922	739	452	1129	1408	1317	936	158
88	1248	357	94	1138	833	272	615	1334	19	32
89	1033	856	809	1560	924	1244	681	1349	769	11
90	1324	588	1566	1394	645	1564	406	958	955	1445
91	41	1429	947	791	1576	1001	977	1492	1123	1145
92	423	1095	91	215	255	61	694	1506	69	629
93	860	1367	927	668	438	1089	236	1403	39	146
94	1531	655	296	741	1474	331	1555	1603	47	362
95	989	408	522	1106	1599	36	87	1251	1345	148
96	918	396	581	658	1501	908	1038	528	416	788
97	375	1121	526	1469	139	278	595	1525	1381	201
98	1338	166	391	16	1236	106	1518	538	1509	730
99	492	1376	454	125	1512	965	461	993	719	871

POWER RESIDUES

	0	1	2	3	4	5	6	7	8	9
50	1028	760	493	233	22	154	1078	1110	1334	1293
51	1006	606	1024	732	297	470	72	504	310	561
52	709	136	952	228	1596	1518	972	368	967	333
53	722	227	1589	1469	629	1185	250	141	987	473
54	93	651	1339	1328	1251	712	157	1099	1257	754
55	451	1548	1182	229	1603	1567	1315	1160	75	525
56	457	1590	1476	678	1528	1042	858	1179	208	1456
57	538	548	618	1108	1320	1195	320	631	1199	348
58	827	962	298	477	121	847	1102	1278	901	1480
59	706	115	805	808	829	976	396	1163	96	672
60	1486	748	409	1254	733	304	519	415	1296	1027
61	753	444	1499	839	1046	886	1375	1580	1406	188
62	1316	1167	124	868	1249	698	59	413	1282	929
63	67	469	65	455	1576	1378	1601	1553	1217	474
64	100	700	73	511	359	904	1501	853	1144	1572
65	1350	1405	181	1267	824	941	151	1057	963	305
66	526	464	30	210	1470	636	1234	593	933	95
67	665	1437	405	1226	537	541	569	765	528	478
68	128	896	1445	461	9	63	441	1478	692	17
69	119	833	1004	592	926	46	322	645	1297	1034
70	802	787	682	1556	1238	621	1129	1467	615	1087
71	1173	166	1162	89	623	1143	1565	1301	1062	998
72	550	632	1206	397	1170	145	1015	669	1465	601
73	989	487	191	1337	1314	1153	26	182	1274	873
74	1284	943	165	1155	40	280	351	848	1109	1327
75	1244	663	1423	307	540	562	716	185	1295	1020
76	704	101	707	122	854	1151	12	84	588	898
77	1459	559	695	38	266	253	162	1134	1502	860
78	1193	306	533	513	373	1002	578	828	969	347
79	820	913	1564	1294	1013	655	1367	1524	1014	662
80	1416	258	197	1379	1608	1602	1560	1266	817	892
81	1417	265	246	113	791	710	143	1001	571	779
82	626	1164	103	721	220	1540	1126	1446	468	58
83	406	1233	586	884	1361	1482	720	213	1491	783
84	654	1360	1475	671	1479	699	66	462	16	112
85	784	661	1409	209	1463	587	891	1410	216	1512
86	930	74	518	408	1247	684	1570	1336	1307	1104
87	1292	999	557	681	1549	1189	278	337	750	423
88	1352	1419	279	344	799	766	535	527	471	79
89	553	653	1353	1426	328	687	1591	1483	727	262
90	225	1575	1371	1552	1210	425	1366	1517	965	319
91	624	1150	5	35	245	106	742	367	960	284
92	379	1044	872	1277	894	1431	363	932	88	616
93	1094	1222	509	345	806	815	878	1319	1188	271
94	288	407	1240	635	1227	544	590	912	1557	1245
95	670	1472	650	1332	1279	908	1529	1049	907	1522
96	1000	564	730	283	372	995	529	485	177	1239
97	628	1178	201	1407	195	1365	1510	916	1585	1441
98	433	1422	300	491	219	1533	1077	1103	1285	950
99	214	1498	832	997	543	583	863	1214	453	1562

P = 1609

INDICES

	0	1	2	3	4	5	6	7	8	9
100	960	817	785	1315	692	276	510	1264	1533	1194
101	1081	1219	1199	794	798	726	1471	1497	340	142
102	759	1572	51	28	512	1278	191	609	500	345
103	1142	1590	1225	1152	699	1275	270	436	14	1223
104	1480	1131	565	1175	921	157	614	1559	1323	957
105	1575	1094	68	1088	295	361	86	657	374	1524
106	1235	1375	718	275	1198	141	190	1151	1479	1558
107	294	1374	1478	1266	82	1267	1586	986	506	1023
108	162	1482	83	1464	1363	1111	402	709	353	1268
109	1410	58	487	1013	930	288	1587	300	1447	547
110	128	1259	586	987	869	1321	298	480	573	748
111	507	249	1300	242	280	1297	1306	1024	179	1126
112	1169	383	1535	314	163	204	826	1289	369	706
113	1133	1483	1387	310	777	1443	1343	1262	84	1319
114	1435	24	226	715	648	1465	482	43	1487	211
115	911	765	1364	735	1437	743	194	433	1354	1112
116	557	469	712	597	821	1415	403	621	1490	1036
117	724	1196	240	710	263	411	176	1070	971	567
118	354	1202	552	1049	101	535	75	1269	938	875
119	1010	1065	1006	780	1411	575	1431	442	1293	578
120	1406	59	137	26	1476	381	722	1184	488	260
121	904	265	1527	1400	997	1014	1029	638	1172	1186
122	1083	1283	931	208	1205	218	673	944	1177	289
123	116	1239	337	831	666	389	1588	160	704	969
124	942	1331	113	301	750	949	122	864	318	624
125	1448	544	228	333	603	1180	378	548	1550	429
126	413	1383	1593	476	129	79	807	653	490	1221
127	351	1260	73	387	738	1247	1333	923	587	954
128	1000	90	628	235	740	988	1250	1500	1120	1380
129	105	453	870	509	793	758	608	698	1130	1322
130	360	717	1557	1585	1463	1409	299	868	248	178
131	203	1386	1318	481	734	556	620	262	1201	937
132	574	136	259	1028	207	115	159	749	543	1549
133	78	72	953	1249	508	359	867	733	135	542
134	358	250	251	1578	7	466	448	95	1301	252
135	650	1605	880	892	1139	243	1579	305	1072	1340
136	841	834	281	8	110	975	906	796	273	1298
137	467	902	427	246	303	616	1307	449	635	803
138	1357	1327	1335	1025	96	1061	1189	399	1213	20
139	180	1302	1003	54	1159	186	33	1127	253	1467
140	49	1372	1167	1034	1170	651	618	973	168	852
141	857	384	1606	1230	170	267	800	810	1536	881
142	223	1423	981	752	1561	315	893	1541	1456	1216
143	1136	925	164	1140	1021	367	1068	671	1245	205
144	244	979	231	1515	1546	682	827	1580	484	364
145	1045	1101	1350	1290	306	1309	569	393	1460	770
146	370	1073	1148	854	1529	728	12	707	1341	533
147	664	233	951	1325	1134	842	562	1058	687	844
148	589	1484	835	897	324	1426	600	1567	1388	282
149	1494	838	1208	1041	1395	311	9	45	991	612

POWER RESIDUES

	0	1	2	3	4	5	6	7	8	9
100	1280	915	1578	1392	90	630	1192	299	484	170
101	1190	285	386	1093	1215	460	2	14	98	686
102	1584	1434	384	1079	1117	1383	27	189	1323	1216
103	467	51	357	890	1403	167	1169	138	966	326
104	673	1493	797	752	437	1450	496	254	169	1183
105	236	43	301	498	268	267	260	211	1477	685
106	1577	1385	41	287	400	1191	292	435	1436	398
107	1177	194	1358	1461	573	793	724	241	78	546
108	604	1010	634	1220	495	247	120	840	1053	935
109	109	763	514	380	1051	921	11	77	539	555
110	667	1451	503	303	512	366	953	235	36	252
111	155	1085	1159	68	476	114	798	759	486	184
112	1288	971	361	918	1599	1539	1119	1397	125	875
113	1298	1041	851	1130	1474	664	1430	356	883	1354
114	1433	377	1030	774	591	919	1606	1588	1462	580
115	842	1067	1033	795	738	339	764	521	429	1394
116	104	728	269	274	309	554	660	1402	160	1120
117	1404	174	1218	481	149	1043	865	1228	551	639
118	1255	740	353	862	1207	404	1219	488	198	1386
119	48	336	743	374	1009	627	1171	152	1064	1012
120	648	1318	1181	222	1554	1224	523	443	1492	790
121	703	94	658	1388	62	434	1429	349	834	1011
122	641	1269	838	1039	837	1032	788	689	1605	1581
123	1413	237	50	350	841	1060	984	452	1555	1231
124	572	786	675	1507	895	1438	412	1275	880	1333
125	1286	957	263	232	15	105	735	318	617	1101
126	1271	852	1137	1523	1007	613	1073	1075	1089	1187
127	264	239	64	448	1527	1035	809	836	1025	739
128	346	813	864	1221	502	296	463	23	161	1127
129	1453	517	401	1198	341	778	619	1115	1369	1538
130	1112	1348	1391	83	581	849	1116	1376	1587	1455
131	531	499	275	316	603	1003	585	877	1312	1139
132	1537	1105	1299	1048	900	1473	657	1381	13	91
133	637	1241	642	1276	887	1382	20	140	980	424
134	1359	1468	622	1136	1516	958	270	281	358	897
135	1452	510	352	855	1158	61	427	1380	6	42
136	294	449	1534	1084	1152	19	133	931	81	567
137	751	430	1401	153	1071	1061	991	501	289	414
138	1289	978	410	1261	782	647	1311	1132	1488	762
139	507	331	708	129	903	1494	804	801	780	633
140	1213	446	1513	937	123	861	1200	355	876	1305
141	1090	1194	313	582	856	1165	110	770	563	723
142	234	29	203	1421	293	442	1485	741	360	911
143	1550	1196	327	680	1542	1140	1544	1154	33	231
144	8	56	392	1135	1509	909	1536	1098	1250	705
145	108	756	465	37	259	204	1428	342	785	668
146	1458	552	646	1304	1083	1145	1579	1399	139	973
147	375	1016	676	1514	944	172	1204	383	1072	1068
148	1040	844	1081	1131	1481	713	164	1148	1600	1546
149	1168	131	917	1592	1490	776	605	1017	683	1563

P = 1609

INDICES

	0	1	2	3	4	5	6	7	8	9
150	286	646	778	111	451	356	18	1243	1565	1444
151	976	214	859	1402	1473	407	1344	907	525	200
152	1517	124	959	1263	797	1571	499	1274	564	956
153	85	274	293	985	1362	57	1446	1320	1299	1125
154	825	309	1434	42	1436	468	1489	410	551	874
155	1430	25	903	637	1204	1238	703	948	227	428
156	806	386	999	1499	792	716	247	555	258	1548
157	866	1577	649	304	109	901	634	1060	1002	1466
158	617	1229	222	1540	1020	978	483	1308	1147	532
159	561	896	1493	44	450	213	524	1570	292	1124
160	1488	636	805	554	108	1228	1146	212	804	

POWER RESIDUES

	0	1	2	3	4	5	6	7	8	9
150	1287	964	312	575	807	822	927	53	371	988
151	480	142	994	522	436	1443	447	1520	986	466
152	44	308	547	611	1059	977	403	1212	439	1464
153	594	940	144	1008	620	1122	1418	272	295	456
154	1583	1427	335	736	325	666	1444	454	1569	1329
155	1258	761	500	282	365	946	186	1302	1069	1047
156	893	1424	314	589	905	1508	902	1487	755	458
157	1597	1525	1021	711	150	1050	914	1571	1343	1356
158	1447	475	107	749	416	1303	1076	1096	1236	607
159	1031	781	640	1262	789	696	45	315	596	954
160	242	85	595	947	193	1351	1412	230		

P = 1613

INDICES

	0	1	2	3	4	5	6	7	8	9
0		0	589	1	1178	335	590	1517	155	2
1	924	1367	1179	174	494	336	744	1072	591	794
2	1513	1518	344	1590	156	670	763	3	1083	1307
3	925	1066	1333	1368	49	240	1180	1015	1383	175
4	490	1125	495	135	933	337	567	1093	745	1422
5	1259	1073	1352	1471	592	90	60	795	284	704
6	1514	46	43	1519	310	509	345	985	638	1591
7	829	1535	157	367	1604	671	360	1272	764	661
8	1079	4	102	1192	1084	1407	724	1308	1522	1582
9	926	79	1156	1067	70	1129	1334	108	399	1369
10	236	869	50	1108	329	241	448	625	1181	8
11	679	1016	649	1378	1384	313	873	176	1293	977
12	491	1122	635	1126	632	1005	496	1209	899	136
13	1098	752	934	699	1574	338	1227	1499	568	523
14	1418	1094	512	1541	746	30	956	1423	581	1008
15	1260	990	949	1074	249	1401	1353	17	1250	1472
16	56	1495	593	148	691	91	169	1483	61	348
17	384	796	1313	864	285	575	499	705	559	1393
18	1515	742	668	47	133	1350	44	827	659	1520
19	106	446	311	630	697	510	988	54	346	557
20	825	986	1458	1212	639	1460	85	1592	918	549
21	830	516	1037	1536	1214	470	158	971	597	368
22	1268	1246	1605	641	1238	672	355	1057	361	213
23	902	1273	1462	686	765	1428	270	662	1566	1609
24	1080	87	99	5	1224	145	103	968	1221	1193
25	1594	841	1085	1345	186	1408	1488	139	725	920
26	75	1309	1341	456	1523	194	1288	1583	551	1022
27	927	1196	204	80	476	425	1157	832	1112	1068
28	395	1389	71	817	1101	1130	518	1030	1335	532
29	619	109	1545	1052	400	1039	1170	1370	1597	152
30	237	40	1579	870	1538	381	51	1235	838	1109
31	378	755	330	1216	606	242	227	1554	449	1062
32	645	626	472	254	1182	844	737	9	1280	998
33	680	160	758	1017	460	1320	650	1434	937	1379
34	973	821	1385	1327	290	314	1453	300	874	599
35	1164	177	1088	614	1294	258	1148	978	370	333
36	492	1588	1331	1123	1257	702	636	1270	722	1127
37	327	1376	633	750	1416	1006	1248	1481	497	1348
38	695	1210	1035	1244	900	1607	1219	137	1286	423
39	1099	1050	1577	753	643	996	935	298	1146	700
40	1414	1242	1575	1240	435	339	189	770	1228	412
41	437	1500	674	609	569	1527	1507	524	1138	341
42	1419	357	1105	1095	14	130	513	1563	191	1542
43	1059	1450	747	1411	1560	31	1186	772	957	363
44	245	1424	223	294	582	305	1230	1009	215	481
45	1261	880	944	991	34	414	950	904	802	1075
46	1491	95	250	431	439	1402	1275	230	1354	890
47	405	18	859	1502	1251	1464	543	1473	586	1304
48	57	1189	676	1496	688	443	594	142	201	149
49	734	611	692	767	1557	92	198	1440	170	66

POWER RESIDUES

	0	1	2	3	4	5	6	7	8	9
0	1	3	9	27	81	243	729	574	109	327
1	981	1330	764	679	424	1272	590	157	471	1413
2	1013	1426	1052	1543	1403	983	1336	782	733	586
3	145	435	1305	689	454	1362	860	967	1288	638
4	301	903	1096	62	186	558	61	183	549	34
5	102	306	918	1141	197	591	160	480	1440	1094
6	56	168	504	1512	1310	704	499	1497	1265	569
7	94	282	846	925	1162	260	780	727	568	91
8	273	819	844	919	1144	206	618	241	723	556
9	55	165	495	1485	1229	461	1383	923	1156	242
10	726	565	82	246	738	601	190	570	97	291
11	873	1006	1405	989	1354	836	895	1072	1603	1583
12	1523	1343	803	796	775	712	523	1569	1481	1217
13	425	1275	599	184	552	43	129	387	1161	257
14	771	700	487	1461	1157	245	735	592	163	489
15	1467	1175	299	897	1078	8	24	72	216	648
16	331	993	1366	872	1003	1396	962	1273	593	166
17	498	1494	1256	542	13	39	117	351	1053	1546
18	1412	1010	1417	1025	1462	1160	254	762	673	406
19	1218	428	1284	626	265	795	772	703	496	1488
20	1238	488	1464	1166	272	816	835	892	1063	1576
21	1502	1280	614	229	687	448	1344	806	805	802
22	793	766	685	442	1326	752	643	316	948	1231
23	467	1401	977	1318	728	571	100	300	900	1087
24	35	105	315	945	1222	440	1320	734	589	154
25	462	1386	932	1183	323	969	1294	656	355	1065
26	1582	1520	1334	776	715	532	1596	1562	1460	1154
27	236	708	511	1533	1373	893	1066	1585	1529	1361
28	857	958	1261	557	58	174	522	1566	1472	1190
29	344	1032	1483	1223	443	1329	761	670	397	1191
30	347	1041	1510	1304	686	445	1335	779	724	559
31	64	192	576	115	345	1035	1492	1250	524	1572
32	1490	1244	506	1518	1328	758	661	370	1110	104
33	312	936	1195	359	1077	5	15	45	135	405
34	1215	419	1257	545	22	66	198	594	169	507
35	1521	1337	785	742	613	226	678	421	1263	563
36	76	228	684	439	1317	725	562	73	219	657
37	358	1074	1609	1601	1577	1505	1289	641	310	930
38	1177	305	915	1132	170	510	1530	1364	866	985
39	1342	800	787	748	631	280	840	907	1108	98
40	294	882	1033	1486	1232	470	1410	1004	1399	971
41	1300	674	409	1227	455	1365	869	994	1369	881
42	1030	1477	1205	389	1167	275	825	862	973	1306
43	692	463	1389	941	1210	404	1212	410	1230	464
44	1392	950	1237	485	1455	1139	191	573	106	318
45	954	1249	521	1563	1463	1163	263	789	754	649
46	334	1002	1393	953	1246	512	1536	1382	920	1147
47	215	645	322	966	1285	629	274	822	853	946
48	1225	449	1347	815	832	883	1036	1495	1259	551
49	40	120	360	1080	14	42	126	378	1134	176

P = 1613

INDICES

	0	1	2	3	4	5	6	7	8	9
50	571	1484	1430	1134	62	1204	322	349	775	1529
51	385	272	465	797	728	1443	1314	848	1509	865
52	664	452	286	126	318	576	1045	526	500	1568
53	783	706	265	1299	560	960	1140	1394	1611	1177
54	1516	923	173	743	793	343	669	1082	1065	48
55	1014	489	134	566	1421	1351	89	283	45	309
56	984	828	366	359	660	101	1406	1521	78	69
57	107	235	1107	447	7	648	312	1292	1121	631
58	1208	1097	698	1226	522	511	29	580	989	248
59	16	55	147	168	347	1312	574	558	741	132
60	826	105	629	987	556	1457	1459	917	515	1213
61	970	1267	640	354	212	1461	1427	1565	86	1223
62	967	1593	1344	1487	919	1340	193	550	1195	475
63	831	394	816	517	531	1544	1038	1596	39	1537
64	1234	377	1215	226	1061	471	843	1279	159	459
65	1433	972	1326	1452	598	1087	257	369	1587	1256
66	1269	326	749	1247	1347	1034	1606	1285	1049	642
67	297	1413	1239	188	411	673	1526	1137	356	13
68	1562	1058	1410	1185	362	222	304	214	879	33
69	903	1490	430	1274	889	858	1463	585	1188	687
70	141	733	766	197	65	1429	1203	774	271	727
71	847	663	125	1044	1567	264	959	1610	922	792
72	1081	1013	565	88	308	365	100	77	234	6
73	1291	1207	1225	28	247	146	1311	740	104	555
74	916	969	353	1426	1222	1343	1339	1194	393	530
75	1595	1233	225	842	458	1325	1086	1586	325	1346
76	1284	296	187	1525	12	1409	221	878	1489	888
77	584	140	196	1202	726	124	263	921	1012	307
78	76	1290	27	1310	554	352	1342	392	1232	457
79	1585	1283	1524	220	887	195	123	1011	1289	553
80	391	1584	219	122	552	218	217	1023	1024	1358
81	928	1025	778	1197	1359	483	205	929	1001	81
82	1026	718	477	779	1263	426	1198	536	1158	1360
83	504	833	484	882	1113	206	115	1069	930	1532
84	396	1002	946	1390	82	683	72	1027	603	818
85	719	993	1102	478	540	1131	780	280	519	1264
86	36	1031	427	789	1336	1199	388	533	537	416
87	620	1159	163	110	1361	910	1546	505	952	1053
88	834	419	401	485	812	1040	883	906	1171	1114
89	894	1371	207	275	1598	116	804	153	1070	761
90	238	931	1469	41	1533	1077	1580	397	623	871
91	1003	1572	1539	947	1493	382	1391	657	52	83
92	468	1236	684	97	839	73	1020	1110	1028	1168
93	379	604	252	756	819	1162	331	720	1479	1217
94	994	433	607	1103	1448	243	479	800	228	541
95	441	1555	1132	463	450	781	1175	1063	281	1404
96	646	520	166	627	1265	965	473	37	1277	255
97	1032	409	1183	428	731	845	790	232	738	1337
98	1323	10	1200	25	1281	389	1356	999	534	113
99	681	538	787	161	417	892	759	621	655	1018

POWER RESIDUES

	0	1	2	3	4	5	6	7	8	9
50	528	1584	1526	1352	830	877	1018	1441	1097	65
51	195	585	142	426	1278	608	211	633	286	858
52	961	1270	584	139	417	1251	527	1581	1517	1325
53	749	634	289	867	988	1351	827	868	991	1360
54	854	949	1234	476	1428	1058	1561	1457	1145	209
55	627	268	804	799	784	739	604	199	597	178
56	534	1602	1580	1514	1316	722	553	46	138	414
57	1242	500	1500	1274	596	175	525	1575	1499	1271
58	587	148	444	1332	770	697	478	1434	1076	2
59	6	18	54	162	486	1458	1148	218	654	349
60	1047	1528	1358	848	931	1180	314	942	1213	413
61	1239	491	1473	1193	353	1059	1564	1466	1172	290
62	870	997	1378	908	1111	107	321	963	1276	602
63	193	579	124	372	1116	122	366	1098	68	204
64	612	223	669	394	1182	320	960	1267	575	112
65	336	1008	1411	1007	1408	998	1381	917	1138	188
66	564	79	237	711	520	1560	1454	1136	182	546
67	25	75	225	675	412	1236	482	1446	1112	110
68	330	990	1357	845	922	1153	233	699	484	1452
69	1130	164	492	1476	1202	380	1140	194	582	133
70	399	1197	365	1095	59	177	531	1593	1553	1433
71	1073	1606	1592	1550	1424	1046	1525	1349	821	850
72	937	1198	368	1104	86	258	774	709	514	1542
73	1400	974	1309	701	490	1470	1184	326	978	1321
74	737	598	181	543	16	48	144	432	1296	662
75	373	1119	131	393	1179	311	933	1186	332	996
76	1375	899	1084	26	78	234	702	493	1479	1211
77	407	1221	437	1311	707	508	1524	1346	812	823
78	856	955	1252	530	1590	1544	1406	992	1363	863
79	976	1315	719	544	19	57	171	513	1539	1391
80	947	1228	458	1374	896	1075	1612	1610	1604	1586
81	1532	1370	884	1039	1504	1286	632	283	849	934
82	1189	341	1023	1456	1142	200	600	187	561	70
83	210	630	277	831	880	1027	1468	1178	308	924
84	1159	251	753	646	325	975	1312	710	517	1551
85	1427	1055	1552	1430	1064	1579	1511	1307	695	472
86	1416	1022	1453	1133	173	519	1557	1445	1109	101
87	303	909	1114	116	348	1044	1519	1331	767	688
88	451	1353	833	886	1045	1522	1340	794	769	694
89	469	1407	995	1372	890	1057	1558	1448	1118	128
90	384	1152	230	690	457	1371	887	1048	1531	1367
91	875	1012	1423	1043	1516	1322	740	607	208	624
92	259	777	718	541	10	30	90	270	810	817
93	838	901	1090	44	132	396	1188	338	1014	1429
94	1061	1570	1484	1226	452	1356	842	913	1126	152
95	456	1368	878	1021	1450	1124	146	438	1314	716
96	535	1605	1589	1541	1397	965	1282	620	247	741
97	610	217	651	340	1020	1447	1115	119	357	1071
98	1600	1574	1496	1262	560	67	201	603	196	588
99	151	453	1359	851	940	1207	395	1185	329	987

P = 1613

INDICES

	0	1	2	3	4	5	6	7	8	9
100	1160	1446	461	164	407	1321	111	653	651	1362
101	181	1435	911	20	938	1547	1364	1380	506	1153
102	974	953	861	822	1054	183	1386	835	1317	1328
103	420	1504	291	402	1437	315	486	1118	1454	813
104	1253	301	1041	913	875	884	715	600	907	1466
105	1165	1172	22	178	1115	851	1089	895	545	615
106	1372	940	1295	208	854	259	276	1475	1149	1599
107	1549	979	117	710	371	805	588	334	154	1366
108	493	1071	1512	1589	762	1306	1332	239	1382	1124
109	932	1092	1258	1470	59	703	42	508	637	1534
110	1603	1271	1078	1191	723	1581	1155	1128	398	868
111	328	624	678	1377	872	976	634	1004	898	751
112	1573	1498	1417	1540	955	1007	948	1400	1249	1494
113	690	1482	383	863	498	1392	667	1349	658	445
114	696	53	824	1211	84	548	1036	469	596	1245
115	1237	1056	901	685	269	1608	98	144	1220	840
116	185	138	74	455	1287	1021	203	424	1111	1388
117	1100	1029	618	1051	1169	151	1578	380	837	754
118	605	1553	644	253	736	997	757	1319	936	820
119	289	299	1163	613	1147	332	1330	701	721	1375
120	1415	1480	694	1243	1218	422	1576	995	1145	1241
121	434	769	436	608	1506	340	1104	129	190	1449
122	1559	771	244	293	1229	480	943	413	801	94
123	438	229	404	1501	542	1303	675	442	200	610
124	1556	1439	570	1133	321	1528	464	1442	1508	451
125	317	525	782	1298	1139	1176	172	342	1064	488
126	1420	282	983	358	1405	68	1106	647	1120	1096
127	521	579	15	167	573	131	628	1456	514	1266
128	211	1564	966	1486	192	474	815	1543	38	376
129	1060	1278	1432	1451	256	1255	748	1033	1048	1412
130	410	1136	1561	1184	303	32	429	857	1187	732
131	64	773	846	1043	958	791	564	364	233	1206
132	246	739	915	1425	1338	529	224	1324	324	295
133	11	877	583	1201	262	306	26	351	1231	1282
134	886	1010	390	121	216	1357	777	482	1000	717
135	1262	535	503	881	114	1531	945	682	602	992
136	539	279	35	788	387	415	162	909	951	418
137	811	905	893	274	803	760	1468	1076	622	1571
138	1492	656	467	96	1019	1167	251	1161	1478	432
139	1447	799	440	462	1174	1403	165	964	1276	408
140	730	231	1322	24	1355	112	786	891	654	1445
141	406	652	180	19	1363	1152	860	182	1316	1503
142	1436	1117	1252	912	714	1465	21	850	544	939
143	853	1474	1548	709	587	1365	1511	1305	1381	1091
144	58	507	1602	1190	1154	867	677	975	897	1497
145	954	1399	689	862	666	444	823	547	595	1055
146	268	143	184	454	202	1387	617	150	836	1552
147	735	1318	288	612	1329	1374	693	421	1144	768
148	1505	128	1558	292	942	93	403	1302	199	1438
149	320	1441	316	1297	171	487	982	67	1119	578

POWER RESIDUES

	0	1	2	3	4	5	6	7	8	9
100	1348	818	841	910	1117	125	375	1125	149	447
101	1341	797	778	721	550	37	111	333	999	1384
102	926	1165	269	807	808	811	820	847	928	1171
103	287	861	970	1297	665	382	1146	212	636	295
104	885	1042	1513	1313	713	526	1578	1508	1298	668
105	391	1173	293	879	1024	1459	1151	227	681	430
106	1290	644	319	957	1258	548	31	93	279	837
107	898	1081	17	51	153	459	1377	905	1102	80
108	240	720	547	28	84	252	756	655	352	1056
109	1555	1439	1091	47	141	423	1269	581	130	390
110	1170	284	852	943	1216	422	1266	572	103	309
111	927	1168	278	834	889	1054	1549	1421	1037	1498
112	1268	578	121	363	1089	41	123	369	1107	95
113	285	855	952	1243	503	1509	1301	677	418	1254
114	536	1608	1598	1568	1478	1208	398	1194	356	1068
115	1591	1547	1415	1019	1444	1106	92	276	828	871
116	1000	1387	935	1192	350	1050	1537	1385	929	1174
117	296	888	1051	1540	1394	956	1255	539	4	12
118	36	108	324	972	1303	683	436	1308	698	481
119	1443	1103	83	249	747	628	271	813	826	865
120	982	1333	773	706	505	1515	1319	731	580	127
121	381	1143	203	609	214	642	313	939	1204	386
122	1158	248	744	619	244	732	583	136	408	1224
123	446	1338	788	751	640	307	921	1150	224	672
124	403	1209	401	1203	383	1149	221	663	376	1128
125	158	474	1422	1040	1507	1295	659	364	1092	50
126	150	450	1350	824	859	964	1279	611	220	660
127	367	1101	77	231	693	466	1398	968	1291	647
128	328	984	1339	791	760	667	388	1164	266	798
129	781	730	577	118	354	1062	1573	1493	1253	533
130	1599	1571	1487	1235	479	1437	1085	29	87	261
131	783	736	595	172	516	1548	1418	1028	1471	1187
132	335	1005	1402	980	1327	755	652	343	1029	1474
133	1196	362	1086	32	96	288	864	979	1324	746
134	625	262	786	745	622	253	759	664	379	1137
135	185	555	52	156	468	1404	986	1345	809	814
136	829	874	1009	1414	1016	1435	1079	11	33	99
137	297	891	1060	1567	1475	1199	371	1113	113	339
138	1017	1438	1088	38	114	342	1026	1465	1169	281
139	843	916	1135	179	537	1611	1607	1595	1559	1451
140	1127	155	465	1395	959	1264	566	85	255	765
141	682	433	1299	671	400	1200	374	1122	140	420
142	1260	554	49	147	441	1323	743	616	235	705
143	502	1506	1292	650	337	1011	1420	1034	1489	1241
144	497	1491	1247	515	1545	1409	1001	1390	944	1219
145	431	1293	653	346	1038	1501	1277	605	202	606
146	205	615	232	696	475	1425	1049	1534	1376	902
147	1093	53	159	477	1431	1067	1588	1538	1388	938
148	1201	377	1131	167	501	1503	1283	623	256	768
149	691	460	1380	914	1129	161	483	1449	1121	137

P = 1613

INDICES

	0	1	2	3	4	5	6	7	8	9
150	572	1455	210	1485	814	375	1431	1254	1047	1135
151	302	856	63	1042	563	1205	914	528	323	876
152	261	350	885	120	776	716	502	1530	601	278
153	386	908	810	273	1467	1570	466	1166	1477	798
154	1173	963	729	23	785	1444	179	1151	1315	1116
155	713	849	852	708	1510	1090	1601	866	896	1398
156	665	546	267	453	616	1551	287	1373	1143	127
157	941	1301	319	1296	981	577	209	374	1046	855
158	562	527	260	119	501	277	809	1569	1476	962
159	784	1150	712	707	1600	1397	266	1550	1142	1300
160	980	373	561	118	808	961	711	1396	1141	372
161	807	1395	806							

POWER RESIDUES

	0	1	2	3	4	5	6	7	8	9
150	411	1233	473	1419	1031	1480	1214	416	1248	518
151	1554	1436	1082	20	60	180	540	7	21	63
152	189	567	88	264	792	763	676	415	1245	509
153	1527	1355	839	904	1099	71	213	639	304	912
154	1123	143	429	1287	635	292	876	1015	1432	1070
155	1597	1565	1469	1181	317	951	1240	494	1482	1220
156	434	1302	680	427	1281	617	238	714	529	1587
157	1535	1379	911	1120	134	402	1206	392	1176	302
158	906	1105	89	267	801	790	757	658	361	1083
159	23	69	207	621	250	750	637	298	894	1069
160	1594	1556	1442	1100	74	222	666	385	1155	239
161	717	538								

P = 1619

INDICES

	0	1	2	3	4	5	6	7	8	9
0		0	1	754	2	218	755	1259	3	1508
1	219	774	756	101	1260	972	4	960	1509	1251
2	220	395	775	839	757	436	102	644	1261	574
3	973	347	5	1528	961	1477	1510	732	1252	855
4	221	174	396	1338	776	108	840	243	758	900
5	437	96	103	410	645	992	1262	387	575	267
6	974	617	348	1149	6	319	1529	826	962	1593
7	1478	421	1511	135	733	1190	1253	415	856	1444
8	222	1398	175	1572	397	1178	1339	1328	777	260
9	109	1360	841	1101	244	1469	759	13	901	664
10	438	1559	97	570	104	613	411	1097	646	650
11	993	1486	1263	281	388	1057	576	1609	268	601
12	975	1548	618	928	349	654	1150	1522	7	474
13	320	296	1530	892	827	862	963	1298	1594	144
14	1479	997	422	875	1512	792	136	36	734	1064
15	1191	1240	1254	850	416	565	857	1490	1445	1164
16	223	480	1399	555	176	128	1573	1495	398	202
17	1179	1141	1340	1267	1329	77	778	1021	261	922
18	110	329	1361	1371	842	950	1102	116	245	285
19	1470	548	760	378	14	1073	902	526	665	1450
20	439	1580	1560	215	98	392	571	729	105	407
21	614	1590	412	1175	1098	1556	647	1606	651	889
22	994	1061	1487	125	1264	326	282	523	389	1172
23	1058	1169	577	1115	1610	461	269	580	602	1004
24	976	1321	1549	534	619	1118	929	1352	350	708
25	655	335	1151	1613	1523	314	8	469	475	373
26	321	464	297	228	1531	628	893	1014	828	272
27	863	504	964	496	1299	1210	1595	583	145	237
28	1480	71	998	689	423	605	876	1433	1513	302
29	793	767	137	1007	37	485	735	1418	1065	940
30	1192	979	1241	695	1255	835	851	988	417	1324
31	566	597	858	1236	1491	1367	1446	1552	1165	1348
32	224	233	481	593	1400	537	556	1404	177	1502
33	129	1292	1574	622	1496	1044	399	1311	203	1035
34	1180	1121	1142	541	1341	193	1268	358	1330	932
35	78	745	779	1536	1022	639	262	1355	923	560
36	111	884	330	684	1362	353	1372	429	843	64
37	951	51	1103	711	117	1408	246	675	286	1377
38	1471	658	549	517	761	633	379	1228	15	338
39	1074	181	903	1050	527	44	666	1154	1451	28
40	440	161	1581	448	1561	1616	216	1506	99	958
41	393	434	572	1526	730	172	106	898	408	385
42	615	317	1591	133	413	1396	1176	258	1099	11
43	1557	611	648	279	1607	1546	652	472	890	1296
44	995	790	1062	848	1488	478	126	200	1265	1019
45	327	948	283	376	524	1578	390	405	1173	1604
46	1059	324	1170	1113	578	1319	1116	706	1611	467
47	462	626	270	494	581	69	603	300	1005	1416
48	977	833	1322	1234	1550	231	535	1500	620	1309
49	1119	191	930	1534	1353	882	351	62	709	673

POWER RESIDUES

	0	1	2	3	4	5	6	7	8	9
0	1	2	4	8	16	32	64	128	256	512
1	1024	429	858	97	194	388	776	1552	1485	1351
2	1083	547	1094	569	1138	657	1314	1009	399	798
3	1596	1573	1527	1435	1251	883	147	294	588	1176
4	733	1466	1313	1007	395	790	1580	1541	1463	1307
5	995	371	742	1484	1349	1079	539	1078	537	1074
6	529	1058	497	994	369	738	1476	1333	1047	475
7	950	281	562	1124	629	1258	897	175	350	700
8	1400	1181	743	1486	1353	1087	555	1110	601	1202
9	785	1570	1521	1423	1227	835	51	102	204	408
10	816	13	26	52	104	208	416	832	45	90
11	180	360	720	1440	1261	903	187	374	748	1496
12	1373	1127	635	1270	921	223	446	892	165	330
13	660	1320	1021	423	846	73	146	292	584	1168
14	717	1434	1249	879	139	278	556	1112	605	1210
15	801	1602	1585	1551	1483	1347	1075	531	1062	505
16	1010	401	802	1604	1589	1559	1499	1379	1139	659
17	1318	1017	415	830	41	82	164	328	656	1312
18	1005	391	782	1564	1509	1399	1179	739	1478	1337
19	1055	491	982	345	690	1380	1141	663	1326	1033
20	447	894	169	338	676	1352	1085	551	1102	585
21	1170	721	1442	1265	911	203	406	812	5	10
22	20	40	80	160	320	640	1280	941	263	526
23	1052	485	970	321	642	1284	949	279	558	1116
24	613	1226	833	47	94	188	376	752	1504	1389
25	1159	699	1398	1177	735	1470	1321	1023	427	854
26	89	178	356	712	1424	1229	839	59	118	236
27	472	944	269	538	1076	533	1066	513	1026	433
28	866	113	226	452	904	189	378	756	1512	1405
29	1191	763	1526	1433	1247	875	131	262	524	1048
30	477	954	289	578	1156	693	1386	1153	687	1374
31	1129	639	1278	937	255	510	1020	421	842	65
32	130	260	520	1040	461	922	225	450	900	181
33	362	724	1448	1277	935	251	502	1004	389	778
34	1556	1493	1367	1115	611	1222	825	31	62	124
35	248	496	992	365	730	1460	1301	983	347	694
36	1388	1157	695	1390	1161	703	1406	1193	767	1534
37	1449	1279	939	259	518	1036	453	906	193	386
38	772	1544	1469	1319	1019	419	838	57	114	228
39	456	912	205	410	820	21	42	84	168	336
40	672	1344	1069	519	1038	457	914	209	418	836
41	53	106	212	424	848	77	154	308	616	1232
42	845	71	142	284	568	1136	653	1306	993	367
43	734	1468	1317	1015	411	822	25	50	100	200
44	400	800	1600	1581	1543	1467	1315	1011	403	806
45	1612	1605	1591	1563	1507	1395	1171	723	1446	1273
46	927	235	470	940	261	522	1044	469	938	257
47	514	1028	437	874	129	258	516	1032	445	890
48	161	322	644	1288	957	295	590	1180	741	1482
49	1345	1071	523	1046	473	946	273	546	1092	565

P = 1619

INDICES

	0	1	2	3	4	5	6	7	8	9
50	656	631	336	1048	1152	159	1614	956	1524	896
51	315	1394	9	277	470	788	476	1017	374	403
52	322	1317	465	492	298	831	229	1307	1532	60
53	629	157	894	275	1015	1315	829	58	273	56
54	864	866	505	1083	969	868	497	21	1300	507
55	1211	207	1596	1085	584	86	146	967	238	1439
56	1481	870	72	724	999	499	690	1039	424	23
57	606	1108	877	1302	1434	1275	1514	509	303	1132
58	794	1213	768	1184	138	209	1008	1286	38	1598
59	486	1280	736	1087	1419	819	1066	586	941	1125
60	1193	88	980	716	1242	148	696	806	1256	969
61	836	344	852	240	989	1146	418	1441	1325	1466
62	567	1483	598	1519	859	872	1237	1161	1492	74
63	1368	545	1447	726	1553	122	1166	1001	1349	311
64	225	501	234	1430	482	692	594	1345	1401	1041
65	538	742	557	426	1405	514	178	25	1503	169
66	130	608	1293	197	1575	1110	623	1413	1497	879
67	1045	1391	400	1304	1312	1080	204	1436	1036	1272
68	1181	1277	1122	803	1143	1516	542	308	1342	511
69	194	1388	1269	305	359	362	1331	1134	933	251
70	79	796	746	365	780	1215	1537	1200	1023	770
71	640	1334	263	1186	1356	1093	924	140	561	1137
72	112	211	885	457	331	1010	685	936	1363	1288
73	354	680	1373	40	430	254	844	1600	65	187
74	952	488	52	82	1104	1282	712	1462	118	738
75	1409	799	247	1089	676	1458	287	1421	1378	749
76	1472	821	659	291	550	1068	518	368	762	588
77	634	1223	380	943	1229	783	16	1127	339	1425
78	1075	1195	182	1218	904	90	1051	916	528	982
79	45	1540	667	718	1155	1382	1452	1244	29	1203
80	441	150	162	909	1582	698	449	1026	1562	808
81	1617	753	217	1258	1507	773	100	971	959	1250
82	394	838	435	643	573	346	1527	1476	731	854
83	173	1337	107	242	899	95	409	991	386	266
84	616	1148	318	825	1592	420	134	1189	414	1443
85	1397	1571	1177	1327	259	1359	1100	1468	12	663
86	1558	569	612	1096	649	1485	280	1056	1608	600
87	1547	927	653	1521	473	295	891	861	1297	143
88	996	874	791	35	1063	1239	849	564	1489	1163
89	479	554	127	1494	201	1140	1266	76	1020	921
90	328	1370	949	115	284	547	377	1072	525	1449
91	1579	214	391	728	406	1589	1174	1555	1605	888
92	1060	124	325	522	1171	1168	1114	460	579	1003
93	1320	533	1117	1351	707	334	1612	313	468	372
94	463	227	627	1013	271	503	495	1209	582	236
95	70	688	604	1432	301	766	1006	484	1417	939
96	978	694	834	987	1323	596	1235	1366	1551	1347
97	232	592	536	1403	1501	1291	621	1043	1310	1034
98	1120	540	192	357	931	744	1535	638	1354	559
99	883	683	352	428	63	50	710	1407	674	1376

POWER RESIDUES

	0	1	2	3	4	5	6	7	8	9
50	1130	641	1282	945	271	542	1084	549	1098	577
51	1154	689	1378	1137	655	1310	1001	383	766	1532
52	1445	1271	923	227	454	908	197	394	788	1576
53	1533	1447	1275	931	243	486	972	325	650	1300
54	981	343	686	1372	1125	631	1262	905	191	382
55	764	1528	1437	1255	891	163	326	652	1304	989
56	359	718	1436	1253	887	155	310	620	1240	861
57	103	206	412	824	29	58	116	232	464	928
58	237	474	948	277	554	1108	597	1194	769	1538
59	1457	1295	971	323	646	1292	965	311	622	1244
60	869	119	238	476	952	285	570	1140	661	1322
61	1025	431	862	105	210	420	840	61	122	244
62	488	976	333	666	1332	1045	471	942	265	530
63	1060	501	1002	385	770	1540	1461	1303	987	355
64	710	1420	1221	823	27	54	108	216	432	864
65	109	218	436	872	125	250	500	1000	381	762
66	1524	1429	1239	859	99	198	396	792	1584	1549
67	1479	1339	1059	499	998	377	754	1508	1397	1175
68	731	1462	1305	991	363	726	1452	1285	951	283
69	566	1132	645	1290	961	303	606	1212	805	1610
70	1601	1583	1547	1475	1331	1043	467	934	249	498
71	996	373	746	1492	1365	1111	603	1206	793	1586
72	1553	1487	1355	1091	563	1126	633	1266	913	207
73	414	828	37	74	148	296	592	1184	749	1498
74	1377	1135	651	1302	985	351	702	1404	1189	759
75	1518	1417	1215	811	3	6	12	24	48	96
76	192	384	768	1536	1453	1287	955	291	582	1164
77	709	1418	1217	815	11	22	44	88	176	352
78	704	1408	1197	775	1550	1481	1343	1067	515	1030
79	441	882	145	290	580	1160	701	1402	1185	751
80	1502	1385	1151	683	1366	1113	607	1214	809	1618
81	1617	1615	1611	1603	1587	1555	1491	1363	1107	595
82	1190	761	1522	1425	1231	843	67	134	268	536
83	1072	525	1050	481	962	305	610	1220	821	23
84	46	92	184	368	736	1472	1325	1031	443	886
85	153	306	612	1224	829	39	78	156	312	624
86	1248	877	135	270	540	1080	541	1082	545	1090
87	561	1122	625	1250	881	143	286	572	1144	669
88	1338	1057	495	990	361	722	1444	1269	919	219
89	438	876	133	266	532	1064	509	1018	417	834
90	49	98	196	392	784	1568	1517	1415	1211	803
91	1606	1593	1567	1515	1411	1203	787	1574	1529	1439
92	1259	899	179	358	716	1432	1245	871	123	246
93	492	984	349	698	1396	1173	727	1454	1289	959
94	299	598	1196	773	1546	1473	1327	1035	451	902
95	185	370	740	1480	1341	1063	507	1014	409	818
96	17	34	68	136	272	544	1088	557	1114	609
97	1218	817	15	30	60	120	240	480	960	301
98	602	1204	789	1578	1537	1455	1291	963	307	614
99	1228	837	55	110	220	440	880	141	282	564

P = 1619

INDICES

	0	1	2	3	4	5	6	7	8	9
100	657	516	632	1227	337	180	1049	43	1153	27
101	160	447	1615	1505	957	433	1525	171	897	384
102	316	132	1395	257	10	610	278	1545	471	1295
103	789	847	477	199	1018	947	375	1577	404	1603
104	323	1112	1318	705	466	625	493	68	299	1415
105	832	1233	230	1499	1308	190	1533	881	61	672
106	630	1047	158	955	895	1393	276	787	1016	402
107	1316	491	830	1306	59	156	274	1314	57	55
108	865	1082	867	20	506	206	1084	85	966	1438
109	869	723	498	1038	22	1107	1301	1274	508	1131
110	1212	1183	208	1285	1597	1279	1086	818	585	1124
111	87	715	147	805	968	343	239	1145	1440	1465
112	1482	1518	871	1160	73	544	725	121	1000	310
113	500	1429	691	1344	1040	741	425	513	24	168
114	607	196	1109	1412	878	1390	1303	1079	1435	1271
115	1276	802	1515	307	510	1387	304	361	1133	250
116	795	364	1214	1199	769	1333	1185	1092	139	1136
117	210	456	1009	935	1287	679	39	253	1599	186
118	487	81	1281	1461	737	798	1088	1457	1420	748
119	820	290	1067	367	587	1222	942	782	1126	1424
120	1194	1217	89	915	981	1539	717	1381	1243	1202
121	149	908	697	1025	807	752	1257	772	970	1249
122	837	642	345	1475	853	1336	241	94	990	265
123	1147	824	419	1188	1442	1570	1326	1358	1467	662
124	568	1095	1484	1055	599	926	1520	294	860	142
125	873	34	1238	563	1162	553	1493	1139	75	920
126	1369	114	546	1071	1448	213	727	1588	1554	887
127	123	521	1167	459	1002	532	1350	333	312	371
128	226	1012	502	1208	235	687	1431	765	483	938
129	693	986	595	1365	1346	591	1402	1290	1042	1033
130	539	356	743	637	558	682	427	49	1406	1375
131	515	1226	179	42	26	446	1504	432	170	383
132	131	256	609	1544	1294	846	198	946	1576	1602
133	1111	704	624	67	1414	1232	1498	189	880	671
134	1046	954	1392	786	401	490	1305	155	1313	54
135	1081	19	205	84	1437	722	1037	1106	1273	1130
136	1182	1284	1278	817	1123	714	804	342	1144	1464
137	1517	1159	543	120	309	1428	1343	740	512	167
138	195	1411	1389	1078	1270	801	306	1386	360	249
139	363	1198	1332	1091	1135	455	934	678	252	185
140	80	1460	797	1456	747	289	366	1221	781	1423
141	1216	914	1538	1380	1201	907	1024	751	771	1248
142	641	1474	1335	93	264	823	1187	1569	1357	661
143	1094	1054	925	293	141	33	562	552	1138	919
144	113	1070	212	1587	886	520	458	531	332	370
145	1011	1207	686	764	937	985	1364	590	1289	1032
146	355	636	681	48	1374	1225	41	445	431	382
147	255	1543	845	945	1601	703	66	1231	188	670
148	953	785	489	154	53	18	83	721	1105	1129
149	1283	816	713	341	1463	1158	119	1427	739	166

POWER RESIDUES

	0	1	2	3	4	5	6	7	8	9
100	1128	637	1274	929	239	478	956	293	586	1172
101	725	1450	1281	943	267	534	1068	517	1034	449
102	898	177	354	708	1416	1213	807	1614	1609	1599
103	1579	1539	1459	1299	979	339	678	1356	1093	567
104	1134	649	1298	977	335	670	1340	1061	503	1006
105	393	786	1572	1525	1431	1243	867	115	230	460
106	920	221	442	884	149	298	596	1192	765	1530
107	1441	1263	907	195	390	780	1560	1501	1383	1147
108	675	1350	1081	543	1086	553	1106	593	1186	753
109	1506	1393	1167	715	1430	1241	863	107	214	428
110	856	93	186	372	744	1488	1357	1095	571	1142
111	665	1330	1041	463	926	233	466	932	245	490
112	980	341	682	1364	1109	599	1198	777	1554	1489
113	1359	1099	579	1158	697	1394	1169	719	1438	1257
114	895	171	342	684	1368	1117	615	1230	841	63
115	126	252	504	1008	397	794	1588	1557	1495	1371
116	1123	627	1254	889	159	318	636	1272	925	231
117	462	924	229	458	916	213	426	852	85	170
118	340	680	1360	1101	583	1166	713	1426	1233	847
119	75	150	300	600	1200	781	1562	1505	1391	1163
120	707	1414	1209	799	1598	1577	1535	1451	1283	947
121	275	550	1100	581	1162	705	1410	1201	783	1566
122	1513	1407	1195	771	1542	1465	1311	1003	387	774
123	1548	1477	1335	1051	483	966	313	626	1252	885
124	151	302	604	1208	797	1594	1569	1519	1419	1219
125	819	19	38	76	152	304	608	1216	813	7
126	14	28	56	112	224	448	896	173	346	692
127	1384	1149	679	1358	1097	575	1150	681	1362	1105
128	591	1182	745	1490	1361	1103	587	1174	729	1458
129	1297	975	331	662	1324	1029	439	878	137	274
130	548	1096	573	1146	673	1346	1073	527	1054	489
131	978	337	674	1348	1077	535	1070	521	1042	465
132	930	241	482	964	309	618	1236	853	87	174
133	348	696	1392	1165	711	1422	1225	831	43	86
134	172	344	688	1376	1133	647	1294	969	319	638
135	1276	933	247	494	988	357	714	1428	1237	855
136	91	182	364	728	1456	1293	967	315	630	1260
137	901	183	366	732	1464	1309	999	379	758	1516
138	1413	1207	795	1590	1561	1503	1387	1155	691	1382
139	1145	671	1342	1065	511	1022	425	850	81	162
140	324	648	1296	973	327	654	1308	997	375	750
141	1500	1381	1143	667	1334	1049	479	958	297	594
142	1188	757	1514	1409	1199	779	1558	1497	1375	1131
143	643	1286	953	287	574	1148	677	1354	1089	559
144	1118	617	1234	849	79	158	316	632	1264	909
145	199	398	796	1592	1565	1511	1403	1187	755	1510
146	1401	1183	747	1494	1369	1119	619	1238	857	95
147	190	380	760	1520	1421	1223	827	35	70	140
148	280	560	1120	621	1242	865	111	222	444	888
149	157	314	628	1256	893	167	334	668	1336	1053

P = 1619

INDICES

	0	1	2	3	4	5	6	7	8	9
150	1410	1077	800	1385	248	1197	1090	454	677	184
151	1459	1455	288	1220	1422	913	1379	906	750	1247
152	1473	92	822	1568	660	1053	292	32	551	918
153	1069	1586	519	530	369	1206	763	984	589	1031
154	635	47	1224	444	381	1542	944	702	1230	669
155	784	153	17	720	1128	815	340	1157	1426	165
156	1076	1384	1196	453	183	1454	1219	912	905	1246
157	91	1567	1052	31	917	1585	529	1205	983	1030
158	46	443	1541	701	668	152	719	814	1156	164
159	1383	452	1453	911	1245	1566	30	1584	1204	1029
160	442	700	151	813	163	451	910	1565	1583	1028
161	699	812	450	1564	1027	811	1563	810	809	

POWER RESIDUES

	0	1	2	3	4	5	6	7	8	9
150	487	974	329	658	1316	1013	407	814	9	18
151	36	72	144	288	576	1152	685	1370	1121	623
152	1246	873	127	254	508	1016	413	826	33	66
153	132	264	528	1056	493	986	353	706	1412	1205
154	791	1582	1545	1471	1323	1027	435	870	121	242
155	484	968	317	634	1268	917	215	430	860	101
156	202	404	808	1616	1613	1607	1595	1571	1523	1427
157	1235	851	83	166	332	664	1328	1037	455	910
158	201	402	804	1608	1597	1575	1531	1443	1267	915
159	211	422	844	69	138	276	552	1104	589	1178
160	737	1474	1329	1039	459	918	217	434	868	117
161	234	468	936	253	506	1012	405	810		

P = 1621

INDICES

	0	1	2	3	4	5	6	7	8	9
0		0	1	1548	2	1096	1549	1460	3	1476
1	1097	1204	1550	1574	1461	1024	4	1271	1477	1612
2	1098	1388	1205	1077	1551	572	1575	1404	1462	85
3	1025	710	5	1132	1272	936	1478	254	1613	1502
4	1099	513	1389	1581	1206	952	1078	615	1552	1300
5	573	1199	1576	495	1405	680	1463	1540	86	868
6	1026	171	711	1316	6	1050	1133	833	1273	1005
7	937	473	1479	629	255	500	1614	1044	1503	225
8	1100	1332	514	404	1390	747	1582	13	1207	945
9	953	1414	1079	638	616	1088	1553	191	1301	1060
10	574	282	1200	1400	1577	864	496	1410	1406	437
11	681	182	1464	851	1541	553	87	1430	869	1111
12	1027	788	172	441	712	48	1317	1071	7	1509
13	1051	560	1134	1452	834	880	1274	1147	1006	685
14	938	543	474	1158	1480	1181	630	1228	256	273
15	501	1515	1615	1127	1045	186	1504	912	226	423
16	1101	917	1333	379	515	608	405	203	1391	1528
17	748	1468	1583	960	14	412	1208	796	946	431
18	954	147	1415	99	1080	1350	639	855	617	1244
19	1089	1445	1554	231	192	978	1302	139	1061	892
20	575	761	283	1545	1201	1609	1401	933	1578	1196
21	865	830	497	401	1411	1057	1407	550	438	557
22	682	1225	183	376	1465	428	852	975	1542	827
23	554	972	88	1257	1431	91	870	153	1112	116
24	1028	1293	789	1260	173	776	442	1566	713	332
25	49	1434	1318	661	1072	675	8	1106	1510	94
26	1052	1561	561	842	1135	1591	1453	873	835	721
27	881	1167	1275	1342	1148	156	1007	584	686	566
28	939	1121	544	1115	475	1016	1159	353	1481	922
29	1182	119	631	1218	1229	344	257	988	274	1031
30	502	1421	1516	210	1616	1267	1128	1296	1046	1328
31	187	847	1505	1177	913	792	227	1192	424	1289
32	1102	1338	918	1263	1334	526	380	365	516	455
33	609	176	406	110	204	309	1392	530	1529	779
34	749	294	1469	1140	1584	481	961	445	15	1236
35	413	1358	1209	384	797	1569	947	1039	432	538
36	955	1604	148	716	1416	105	100	315	1081	369
37	1351	335	640	697	856	1596	618	39	1245	52
38	1090	999	1446	133	1555	520	232	1437	193	238
39	979	728	1303	488	140	1321	1062	320	893	1380
40	576	459	762	664	284	808	1546	1458	1202	1022
41	1610	1075	1402	708	934	1500	1579	613	1197	678
42	866	1314	831	471	498	223	402	11	1412	1086
43	1058	1398	1408	180	551	1109	439	1069	558	878
44	683	1156	1226	1513	184	421	377	201	1466	410
45	429	97	853	1443	976	890	1543	931	828	1055
46	555	374	973	970	89	114	1258	1564	1432	673
47	92	840	871	1165	154	564	1113	351	117	342
48	1029	208	1294	845	790	1287	1261	363	174	307
49	777	1138	443	1356	1567	536	714	313	333	1594

POWER RESIDUES

	0	1	2	3	4	5	6	7	8	9
0	1	2	4	8	16	32	64	128	256	512
1	1024	427	854	87	174	348	696	1392	1163	705
2	1410	1199	777	1554	1487	1353	1085	549	1098	575
3	1150	679	1358	1095	569	1138	655	1310	999	377
4	754	1508	1395	1169	717	1434	1247	873	125	250
5	500	1000	379	758	1516	1411	1201	781	1562	1503
6	1385	1149	677	1354	1087	553	1106	591	1182	743
7	1486	1351	1081	541	1082	543	1086	551	1102	583
8	1166	711	1422	1223	825	29	58	116	232	464
9	928	235	470	940	259	518	1036	451	902	183
10	366	732	1464	1307	993	365	730	1460	1299	977
11	333	666	1332	1043	465	930	239	478	956	291
12	582	1164	707	1414	1207	793	1586	1551	1481	1341
13	1061	501	1002	383	766	1532	1443	1265	909	197
14	394	788	1576	1531	1441	1261	901	181	362	724
15	1448	1275	929	237	474	948	275	550	1100	579
16	1158	695	1390	1159	697	1394	1167	713	1426	1231
17	841	61	122	244	488	976	331	662	1324	1027
18	433	866	111	222	444	888	155	310	620	1240
19	859	97	194	388	776	1552	1483	1345	1069	517
20	1034	447	894	167	334	668	1336	1051	481	962
21	303	606	1212	803	1606	1591	1561	1501	1381	1141
22	661	1322	1023	425	850	79	158	316	632	1264
23	907	193	386	772	1544	1467	1313	1005	389	778
24	1556	1491	1361	1101	581	1162	703	1406	1191	761
25	1522	1423	1225	829	37	74	148	296	592	1184
26	747	1494	1367	1113	605	1210	799	1598	1575	1529
27	1437	1253	885	149	298	596	1192	763	1526	1431
28	1241	861	101	202	404	808	1616	1611	1601	1581
29	1541	1461	1301	981	341	682	1364	1107	593	1186
30	751	1502	1383	1145	669	1338	1055	489	978	335
31	670	1340	1059	497	994	367	734	1468	1315	1009
32	397	794	1588	1555	1489	1357	1093	565	1130	639
33	1278	935	249	498	996	371	742	1484	1347	1073
34	525	1050	479	958	295	590	1180	739	1478	1335
35	1049	477	954	287	574	1148	675	1350	1079	537
36	1074	527	1054	487	974	327	654	1308	995	369
37	738	1476	1331	1041	461	922	223	446	892	163
38	326	652	1304	987	353	706	1412	1203	785	1570
39	1519	1417	1213	805	1610	1599	1577	1533	1445	1269
40	917	213	426	852	83	166	332	664	1328	1035
41	449	898	175	350	700	1400	1179	737	1474	1327
42	1033	445	890	159	318	636	1272	923	225	450
43	900	179	358	716	1432	1243	865	109	218	436
44	872	123	246	492	984	347	694	1388	1155	689
45	1378	1135	649	1298	975	329	658	1316	1011	401
46	802	1604	1587	1553	1485	1349	1077	533	1066	511
47	1022	423	846	71	142	284	568	1136	651	1302
48	983	345	690	1380	1139	657	1314	1007	393	786
49	1572	1523	1425	1229	837	53	106	212	424	848

P = 1621

INDICES

	0	1	2	3	4	5	6	7	8	9
50	50	131	1435	726	1319	1378	662	1456	1073	1498
51	676	469	9	1396	1107	876	1511	199	95	888
52	1053	968	1562	838	562	340	843	361	1136	534
53	1592	724	1454	467	874	886	836	359	722	884
54	882	73	1168	75	1276	1533	1343	1170	1149	27
55	157	77	1008	65	585	1278	687	645	567	1535
56	940	783	1122	1345	545	327	1116	1172	476	34
57	1017	1151	1160	1373	354	29	1482	753	923	159
58	1183	244	120	79	632	906	1219	1010	1230	702
59	345	67	258	298	989	587	275	820	1032	1280
60	503	1487	1422	689	1517	264	211	647	1617	1473
61	1268	569	1129	510	1297	1537	1047	626	1329	942
62	188	861	848	785	1506	1144	1178	1124	914	1525
63	793	1347	228	758	1193	547	425	1254	1290	329
64	1103	1588	1339	1118	919	985	1264	1174	1335	452
65	527	478	381	1601	366	36	517	485	456	1019
66	610	220	177	1153	407	928	111	1162	205	304
67	310	1375	1393	965	531	356	1530	62	780	31
68	750	903	295	1484	1470	623	1141	755	1585	449
69	482	925	962	900	446	161	16	164	1237	1185
70	414	1366	1359	246	1210	19	385	122	798	734
71	1570	81	948	167	1040	634	433	44	539	908
72	956	1240	1605	1221	149	657	717	1012	1417	1188
73	106	1232	101	995	316	704	1082	417	370	347
74	1352	1494	336	69	641	1369	698	260	857	1250
75	1597	300	619	1362	40	991	1246	599	53	589
76	1091	249	1000	277	1447	603	134	822	1556	1213
77	521	1034	233	1309	1438	1282	194	22	239	505
78	980	57	729	1489	1304	388	489	1424	141	770
79	1322	691	1063	125	321	1519	894	593	1381	266
80	577	801	460	213	763	393	665	649	285	737
81	809	1619	1547	1095	1459	1475	1203	1573	1023	1270
82	1611	1387	1076	571	1403	84	709	1131	935	253
83	1501	512	1580	951	614	1299	1198	494	679	1539
84	867	170	1315	1049	832	1004	472	628	499	1043
85	224	1331	403	746	12	944	1413	637	1087	190
86	1059	281	1399	863	1409	436	181	850	552	1429
87	1110	787	440	47	1070	1508	559	1451	879	1146
88	684	542	1157	1180	1227	272	1514	1126	185	911
89	422	916	378	607	202	1527	1467	959	411	795
90	430	146	98	1349	854	1243	1444	230	977	138
91	891	760	1544	1608	932	1195	829	400	1056	549
92	556	1224	375	427	974	826	971	1256	90	152
93	115	1292	1259	775	1565	331	1433	660	674	1105
94	93	1560	841	1590	872	720	1166	1341	155	583
95	565	1120	1114	1015	352	921	118	1217	343	987
96	1030	1420	209	1266	1295	1327	846	1176	791	1191
97	1288	1337	1262	525	364	454	175	109	308	529
98	778	293	1139	480	444	1235	1357	383	1568	1038
99	537	1603	715	104	314	368	334	696	1595	38

POWER RESIDUES

	0	1	2	3	4	5	6	7	8	9
50	75	150	300	600	1200	779	1558	1495	1369	1117
51	613	1226	831	41	82	164	328	656	1312	1003
52	385	770	1540	1459	1297	973	325	650	1300	979
53	337	674	1348	1075	529	1058	495	990	359	718
54	1436	1251	881	141	282	564	1128	635	1270	919
55	217	434	868	115	230	460	920	219	438	876
56	131	262	524	1048	475	950	279	558	1116	611
57	1222	823	25	50	100	200	400	800	1600	1579
58	1537	1453	1285	949	277	554	1108	595	1190	759
59	1518	1415	1209	797	1594	1567	1513	1405	1189	757
60	1514	1407	1193	765	1530	1439	1257	893	165	330
61	660	1320	1019	417	834	47	94	188	376	752
62	1504	1387	1153	685	1370	1119	617	1234	847	73
63	146	292	584	1168	715	1430	1239	857	93	186
64	372	744	1488	1355	1089	557	1114	607	1214	807
65	1614	1607	1593	1565	1509	1397	1173	725	1450	1279
66	937	253	506	1012	403	806	1612	1603	1585	1549
67	1477	1333	1045	469	938	255	510	1020	419	838
68	55	110	220	440	880	139	278	556	1112	603
69	1206	791	1582	1543	1465	1309	997	373	746	1492
70	1363	1105	589	1178	735	1470	1319	1017	413	826
71	31	62	124	248	496	992	363	726	1452	1283
72	945	269	538	1076	531	1062	503	1006	391	782
73	1564	1507	1393	1165	709	1418	1215	809	1618	1615
74	1609	1597	1573	1525	1429	1237	853	85	170	340
75	680	1360	1099	577	1154	687	1374	1127	633	1266
76	911	201	402	804	1608	1595	1569	1517	1413	1205
77	789	1578	1535	1449	1277	933	245	490	980	339
78	678	1356	1091	561	1122	623	1246	871	121	242
79	484	968	315	630	1260	899	177	354	708	1416
80	1211	801	1602	1583	1545	1469	1317	1013	405	810
81	1620	1619	1617	1613	1605	1589	1557	1493	1365	1109
82	597	1194	767	1534	1447	1273	925	229	458	916
83	211	422	844	67	134	268	536	1072	523	1046
84	471	942	263	526	1052	483	966	311	622	1244
85	867	113	226	452	904	187	374	748	1496	1371
86	1121	621	1242	863	105	210	420	840	59	118
87	236	472	944	267	534	1068	515	1030	439	878
88	135	270	540	1080	539	1078	535	1070	519	1038
89	455	910	199	398	796	1592	1563	1505	1389	1157
90	693	1386	1151	681	1362	1103	585	1170	719	1438
91	1255	889	157	314	628	1256	891	161	322	644
92	1288	955	289	578	1156	691	1382	1143	665	1330
93	1039	457	914	207	414	828	35	70	140	280
94	560	1120	619	1238	855	89	178	356	712	1424
95	1227	833	45	90	180	360	720	1440	1259	897
96	173	346	692	1384	1147	673	1346	1071	521	1042
97	463	926	231	462	924	227	454	908	195	390
98	780	1560	1499	1377	1133	645	1290	959	297	594
99	1188	755	1510	1399	1177	733	1466	1311	1001	381

P = 1621

INDICES

	0	1	2	3	4	5	6	7	8	9
100	51	998	132	519	1436	237	727	487	1320	319
101	1379	458	663	807	1457	1021	1074	707	1499	612
102	677	1313	470	222	10	1085	1397	179	1108	1068
103	877	1155	1512	420	200	409	96	1442	889	930
104	1054	373	969	113	1563	672	839	1164	563	350
105	341	207	844	1286	362	306	1137	1355	535	312
106	1593	130	725	1377	1455	1497	468	1395	875	198
107	887	967	837	339	360	533	723	466	885	358
108	883	72	74	1532	1169	26	76	64	1277	644
109	1534	782	1344	326	1171	33	1150	1372	28	752
110	158	243	78	905	1009	701	66	297	586	819
111	1279	1486	688	263	646	1472	568	509	1536	625
112	941	860	784	1143	1123	1524	1346	757	546	1253
113	328	1587	1117	984	1173	451	477	1600	35	484
114	1018	219	1152	927	1161	303	1374	964	355	61
115	30	902	1483	622	754	448	924	899	160	163
116	1184	1365	245	18	121	733	80	166	633	43
117	907	1239	1220	656	1011	1187	1231	994	703	416
118	346	1493	68	1368	259	1249	299	1361	990	598
119	588	248	276	602	821	1212	1033	1308	1281	21
120	504	56	1488	387	1423	769	690	124	1518	592
121	265	800	212	392	648	736	1618	1094	1474	1572
122	1269	1386	570	83	1130	252	511	950	1298	493
123	1538	169	1048	1003	627	1042	1330	745	943	636
124	189	280	862	435	849	1428	786	46	1507	1450
125	1145	541	1179	271	1125	910	915	606	1526	958
126	794	145	1348	1242	229	137	759	1607	1194	399
127	548	1223	426	825	1255	151	1291	774	330	659
128	1104	1559	1589	719	1340	582	1119	1014	920	1216
129	986	1419	1265	1326	1175	1190	1336	524	453	108
130	528	292	479	1234	382	1037	1602	103	367	695
131	37	997	518	236	486	318	457	806	1020	706
132	611	1312	221	1084	178	1067	1154	419	408	1441
133	929	372	112	671	1163	349	206	1285	305	1354
134	311	129	1376	1496	1394	197	966	338	532	465
135	357	71	1531	25	63	643	781	325	32	1371
136	751	242	904	700	296	818	1485	262	1471	508
137	624	859	1142	1523	756	1252	1586	983	450	1599
138	483	218	926	302	963	60	901	621	447	898
139	162	1364	17	732	165	42	1238	655	1186	993
140	415	1492	1367	1248	1360	597	247	601	1211	1307
141	20	55	386	768	123	591	799	391	735	1093
142	1571	1385	82	251	949	492	168	1002	1041	744
143	635	279	434	1427	45	1449	540	270	909	605
144	957	144	1241	136	1606	398	1222	824	150	773
145	658	1558	718	581	1013	1215	1418	1325	1189	523
146	107	291	1233	1036	102	694	996	235	317	805
147	705	1311	1083	1066	418	1440	371	670	348	1284
148	1353	128	1495	196	337	464	70	24	642	324
149	1370	241	699	817	261	507	858	1522	1251	982

POWER RESIDUES

	0	1	2	3	4	5	6	7	8	9
100	762	1524	1427	1233	845	69	138	276	552	1104
101	587	1174	727	1454	1287	953	285	570	1140	659
102	1318	1015	409	818	15	30	60	120	240	480
103	960	299	598	1196	771	1542	1463	1305	989	357
104	714	1428	1235	849	77	154	308	616	1232	843
105	65	130	260	520	1040	459	918	215	430	860
106	99	198	396	792	1584	1547	1473	1325	1029	437
107	874	127	254	508	1016	411	822	23	46	92
108	184	368	736	1472	1323	1025	429	858	95	190
109	380	760	1520	1419	1217	813	5	10	20	40
110	80	160	320	640	1280	939	257	514	1028	435
111	870	119	238	476	952	283	566	1132	643	1286
112	951	281	562	1124	627	1254	887	153	306	612
113	1224	827	33	66	132	264	528	1056	491	982
114	343	686	1372	1123	625	1250	879	137	274	548
115	1096	571	1142	663	1326	1031	441	882	143	286
116	572	1144	667	1334	1047	473	946	271	542	1084
117	547	1094	567	1134	647	1294	967	313	626	1252
118	883	145	290	580	1160	699	1398	1175	729	1458
119	1295	969	317	634	1268	915	209	418	836	51
120	102	204	408	816	11	22	44	88	176	352
121	704	1408	1195	769	1538	1455	1289	957	293	586
122	1172	723	1446	1271	921	221	442	884	147	294
123	588	1176	731	1462	1303	985	349	698	1396	1171
124	721	1442	1263	905	189	378	756	1512	1403	1185
125	749	1498	1375	1129	637	1274	927	233	466	932
126	243	486	972	323	646	1292	963	305	610	1220
127	819	17	34	68	136	272	544	1088	555	1110
128	599	1198	775	1550	1479	1337	1053	485	970	319
129	638	1276	931	241	482	964	307	614	1228	835
130	49	98	196	392	784	1568	1515	1409	1197	773
131	1546	1471	1321	1021	421	842	63	126	252	504
132	1008	395	790	1580	1539	1457	1293	965	309	618
133	1236	851	81	162	324	648	1296	971	321	642
134	1284	947	273	546	1092	563	1126	631	1262	903
135	185	370	740	1480	1339	1057	493	986	351	702
136	1404	1187	753	1506	1391	1161	701	1402	1183	745
137	1490	1359	1097	573	1146	671	1342	1063	505	1010
138	399	798	1596	1571	1521	1421	1221	821	21	42
139	84	168	336	672	1344	1067	513	1026	431	862
140	103	206	412	824	27	54	108	216	432	864
141	107	214	428	856	91	182	364	728	1456	1291
142	961	301	602	1204	787	1574	1527	1433	1245	869
143	117	234	468	936	251	502	1004	387	774	1548
144	1475	1329	1037	453	906	191	382	764	1528	1435
145	1249	877	133	266	532	1064	507	1014	407	814
146	7	14	28	56	112	224	448	896	171	342
147	684	1368	1115	609	1218	815	9	18	36	72
148	144	288	576	1152	683	1366	1111	601	1202	783
149	1566	1511	1401	1181	741	1482	1343	1065	509	1018

P = 1621

INDICES

	0	1	2	3	4	5	6	7	8	9
150	1598	217	301	59	620	897	1363	731	41	654
151	992	1491	1247	596	600	1306	54	767	590	390
152	1092	1384	250	491	1001	743	278	1426	1448	269
153	604	143	135	397	823	772	1557	580	1214	1324
154	522	290	1035	693	234	804	1310	1065	1439	669
155	1283	127	195	463	23	323	240	816	506	1521
156	981	216	58	896	730	653	1490	595	1305	766
157	389	1383	490	742	1425	268	142	396	771	579
158	1323	289	692	803	1064	668	126	462	322	815
159	1520	215	895	652	594	765	1382	741	267	395
160	578	288	802	667	461	814	214	651	764	740
161	394	287	666	813	650	739	286	812	738	811
162	810	0								

POWER RESIDUES

	0	1	2	3	4	5	6	7	8	9
150	415	830	39	78	156	312	624	1248	875	129
151	258	516	1032	443	886	151	302	604	1208	795
152	1590	1559	1497	1373	1125	629	1258	895	169	338
153	676	1352	1083	545	1090	559	1118	615	1230	839
154	57	114	228	456	912	203	406	812	3	6
155	12	24	48	96	192	384	768	1536	1451	1281
156	941	261	522	1044	467	934	247	494	988	355
157	710	1420	1219	817	13	26	52	104	208	416
158	832	43	86	172	344	688	1376	1131	641	1282
159	943	265	530	1060	499	998	375	750	1500	1379
160	1137	653	1306	991	361	722	1444	1267	913	205
161	410	820	19	38	76	152	304	608	1216	811
162										

P = 1627

INDICES

	0	1	2	3	4	5	6	7	8	9
0		0	771	1	1542	1347	772	454	687	2
1	492	396	1543	795	1225	1348	1458	743	773	266
2	1263	455	1167	610	688	1068	1566	3	370	1299
3	493	1450	603	397	1514	175	1544	1314	1037	796
4	408	387	1226	1043	312	1349	1381	598	1459	908
5	213	744	711	8	774	117	1141	267	444	698
6	1264	1260	595	456	1374	516	1168	391	659	611
7	946	162	689	101	459	1069	182	850	1567	148
8	1179	4	1158	760	371	464	188	1300	1083	1108
9	494	1249	526	1451	1369	1613	604	424	53	398
10	984	1377	1515	623	1482	176	779	632	1545	965
11	888	1315	286	937	1038	331	1215	797	1469	1197
12	409	792	405	388	1366	789	1227	1519	519	1044
13	1287	1013	313	720	1162	1350	1430	826	1382	470
14	91	599	933	1191	1460	1020	872	909	1230	1147
15	214	1118	953	745	1621	1171	712	588	919	9
16	324	1064	775	1135	303	118	1531	551	1142	1590
17	1235	268	959	131	445	1522	228	699	253	643
18	1265	769	394	1261	1297	1035	596	1139	514	457
19	758	524	1375	886	1195	517	824	870	1169	301
20	129	392	522	127	660	108	1394	612	627	662
21	947	573	1550	163	1403	764	690	278	110	102
22	33	1538	460	1527	1057	1070	82	1396	183	1047
23	1102	851	360	1088	1568	319	614	149	342	927
24	1180	810	1563	5	1176	629	1159	1061	511	761
25	1560	833	372	1006	664	465	1290	505	189	142
26	432	1301	158	949	1084	1355	1491	1109	307	836
27	495	41	575	1250	1597	1464	527	1029	1241	1452
28	862	1552	1370	1016	78	1614	336	841	605	1486
29	165	425	17	241	54	419	375	399	292	1405
30	985	1497	263	1378	98	981	1516	1618	766	624
31	316	155	1483	61	1359	177	64	692	780	69
32	1095	633	209	1009	1546	237	280	966	1074	1052
33	889	649	676	1316	1322	112	287	723	735	938
34	380	220	1039	1362	104	332	902	198	1216	122
35	667	798	999	35	1470	1509	1024	1198	1414	1421
36	410	532	1540	793	1165	1448	406	906	442	389
37	180	462	1367	621	284	790	1285	468	1228	586
38	1529	1520	1295	884	520	571	31	1045	340	1059
39	1288	1353	1595	1014	15	1495	314	67	1072	721
40	900	1507	1163	619	1293	1351	898	84	1431	86
41	879	827	539	1152	1383	481	1398	471	1433	992
42	92	351	1344	600	695	185	934	88	548	1192
43	1535	508	1461	260	1049	1021	881	876	873	1128
44	804	910	683	1104	1231	829	672	1148	202	48
45	215	783	853	1119	541	970	954	476	192	746
46	247	362	1622	1154	1131	1172	233	894	713	845
47	1090	589	1385	1439	920	1334	1113	10	72	1570
48	325	483	1581	1065	708	145	776	717	321	1136
49	1400	807	304	416	206	119	1282	616	1532	473

POWER RESIDUES

	0	1	2	3	4	5	6	7	8	9
0	1	3	9	27	81	243	729	560	53	159
1	477	1431	1039	1490	1216	394	1182	292	876	1001
2	1376	874	995	1358	820	833	872	989	1340	766
3	671	386	1158	220	660	353	1059	1550	1396	934
4	1175	271	813	812	809	800	773	692	449	1347
5	787	734	575	98	294	882	1019	1430	1036	1481
6	1189	313	939	1190	316	948	1217	397	1191	319
7	957	1244	478	1434	1048	1517	1297	637	284	852
8	929	1160	226	678	407	1221	409	1227	427	1281
9	589	140	420	1260	526	1578	1480	1186	304	912
10	1109	73	219	657	344	1032	1469	1153	205	615
11	218	654	335	1005	1388	910	1103	55	165	495
12	1485	1201	349	1047	1514	1288	610	203	609	200
13	600	173	519	1557	1417	997	1364	838	887	1034
14	1475	1171	259	777	704	485	1455	1111	79	237
15	711	506	1518	1300	646	311	933	1172	262	786
16	731	566	71	213	639	290	870	983	1322	712
17	509	1527	1327	727	554	35	105	315	945	1208
18	370	1110	76	228	684	425	1275	571	86	258
19	774	695	458	1374	868	977	1304	658	347	1041
20	1496	1234	448	1344	778	707	494	1482	1192	322
21	966	1271	559	50	150	450	1350	796	761	656
22	341	1023	1442	1072	1589	1513	1285	601	176	528
23	1584	1498	1240	466	1398	940	1193	325	975	1298
24	640	293	879	1010	1403	955	1238	460	1380	886
25	1031	1466	1144	178	534	1602	1552	1402	952	1229
26	433	1299	643	302	906	1091	19	57	171	513
27	1539	1363	835	878	1007	1394	928	1157	217	651
28	326	978	1307	667	374	1122	112	336	1008	1397
29	937	1184	298	894	1055	1538	1360	826	851	926
30	1151	199	597	164	492	1476	1174	268	804	785
31	728	557	44	132	396	1188	310	930	1163	235
32	705	488	1464	1138	160	480	1440	1066	1571	1459
33	1123	115	345	1035	1478	1180	286	858	947	1214
34	388	1164	238	714	515	1545	1381	889	1040	1493
35	1225	421	1263	535	1605	1561	1429	1033	1472	1162
36	232	696	461	1383	895	1058	1547	1387	907	1094
37	28	84	252	756	641	296	888	1037	1484	1198
38	340	1020	1433	1045	1508	1270	556	41	123	369
39	1107	67	201	603	182	546	11	33	99	297
40	891	1046	1511	1279	583	122	366	1098	40	120
41	360	1080	1613	1585	1501	1249	493	1479	1183	295
42	885	1028	1457	1117	97	291	873	992	1349	793
43	752	629	260	780	713	512	1536	1354	808	797
44	764	665	368	1104	58	174	522	1566	1444	1078
45	1607	1567	1447	1087	7	21	63	189	567	74
46	222	666	371	1113	85	255	765	668	377	1131
47	139	417	1251	499	1497	1237	457	1371	859	950
48	1223	415	1245	481	1443	1075	1598	1540	1366	844
49	905	1088	10	30	90	270	810	803	782	719

P = 1627

INDICES

	0	1	2	3	4	5	6	7	8	9
50	705	552	1604	655	1143	1098	151	1591	1435	170
51	1236	555	435	269	1276	344	960	994	913	132
52	1203	560	446	1256	929	1523	94	567	229	1220
53	500	700	636	1182	254	353	1078	644	1607	1304
54	1266	728	812	770	1346	686	395	1224	742	1262
55	609	1565	1298	602	174	1036	386	311	597	212
56	7	1140	697	594	515	658	161	458	849	1178
57	759	187	1107	525	1612	52	1376	1481	631	887
58	936	1214	1196	404	788	518	1012	1161	825	90
59	1190	871	1146	952	1170	918	1063	302	550	1234
60	130	227	642	393	1034	513	523	1194	869	128
61	126	1393	661	1549	763	109	1537	1056	1395	1101
62	1087	613	926	1562	628	510	832	663	504	431
63	948	1490	835	574	1463	1240	1551	77	840	164
64	240	374	1404	262	980	765	154	1358	691	1094
65	1008	279	1051	675	111	734	219	103	197	666
66	34	1023	1420	1539	1447	441	461	283	467	1528
67	883	30	1058	1594	1494	1071	1506	1292	83	878
68	1151	1397	991	1343	184	547	507	1048	875	803
69	1103	671	47	852	969	191	361	1130	893	1089
70	1438	1112	1569	1580	144	320	806	205	615	704
71	654	150	169	434	343	912	559	928	566	499
72	1181	1077	1303	811	685	741	1564	173	310	6
73	593	160	1177	1106	51	630	1213	787	1160	1189
74	951	1062	1233	641	512	868	1392	762	1055	1086
75	1561	831	430	834	1239	839	373	979	1357	1007
76	674	218	665	1419	440	466	29	1493	1291	1150
77	1342	506	802	46	190	892	1111	143	204	653
78	433	558	498	1302	740	309	159	50	786	950
79	640	1391	1085	429	838	1356	217	439	1492	1341
80	45	1110	652	497	308	785	1390	837	438	44
81	496	1389	43	42	855	856	576	1309	857	1251
82	24	577	1598	1121	1310	1465	297	858	528	679
83	1252	1030	543	25	1242	272	578	1453	137	1599
84	863	972	1122	1553	489	1311	1371	1246	1466	1017
85	956	298	79	1003	859	1615	1319	529	337	478
86	680	842	1279	1253	606	1478	1031	1487	194	544
87	166	1186	26	426	21	1243	18	748	273	242
88	1575	579	55	1325	1454	420	249	138	376	347
89	1600	400	1443	864	293	364	973	1406	819	1123
90	986	751	1554	1498	1624	490	264	368	1312	1379
91	115	1372	99	1156	1247	982	963	1467	1517	1428
92	1018	1619	1133	957	767	756	299	625	276	80
93	317	1174	1004	156	39	860	1484	290	1616	62
94	235	1320	1360	997	530	178	584	338	65	896
95	479	693	258	681	781	245	843	70	715	1280
96	1096	1274	1254	634	726	607	210	847	1479	1010
97	916	1032	1547	924	1488	238	1092	195	281	1504
98	545	967	1578	167	1075	591	1187	1053	977	27
99	890	738	427	650	1387	22	677	135	1244	1317

POWER RESIDUES

	0	1	2	3	4	5	6	7	8	9
50	530	1590	1516	1294	628	257	771	686	431	1293
51	625	248	744	605	188	564	65	195	585	128
52	384	1152	202	606	191	573	92	276	828	857
53	944	1205	361	1083	1622	1612	1582	1492	1222	412
54	1236	454	1362	832	869	980	1313	685	428	1284
55	598	167	501	1503	1255	511	1533	1345	781	716
56	521	1563	1435	1051	1526	1324	718	527	1581	1489
57	1213	385	1155	211	633	272	816	821	836	881
58	1016	1421	1009	1400	946	1211	379	1137	157	471
59	1413	985	1328	730	563	62	186	558	47	141
60	423	1269	553	32	96	288	864	965	1268	550
61	23	69	207	621	236	708	497	1491	1219	403
62	1209	373	1119	103	309	927	1154	208	624	245
63	735	578	107	321	963	1262	532	1596	1534	1348
64	790	743	602	179	537	1611	1579	1483	1195	331
65	993	1352	802	779	710	503	1509	1273	565	68
66	204	612	209	627	254	762	659	350	1050	1523
67	1315	691	446	1338	760	653	332	996	1361	829
68	860	953	1232	442	1326	724	545	8	24	72
69	216	648	317	951	1226	424	1272	562	59	177
70	531	1593	1525	1321	709	500	1500	1246	484	1452
71	1102	52	156	468	1404	958	1247	487	1461	1129
72	133	399	1197	337	1011	1406	964	1265	541	1623
73	1615	1591	1519	1303	655	338	1014	1415	991	1346
74	784	725	548	17	51	153	459	1377	877	1004
75	1385	901	1076	1601	1549	1393	925	1148	190	570
76	83	249	747	614	215	645	308	924	1145	181
77	543	2	6	18	54	162	486	1458	1120	106
78	318	954	1235	451	1353	805	788	737	584	125
79	375	1125	121	363	1089	13	39	117	351	1053
80	1532	1342	772	689	440	1320	706	491	1473	1165
81	241	723	542	1626	1624	1618	1600	1546	1384	898
82	1067	1574	1468	1150	196	588	137	411	1233	445
83	1335	751	626	251	753	632	269	807	794	755
84	638	287	861	956	1241	469	1407	967	1274	568
85	77	231	693	452	1356	814	815	818	827	854
86	935	1178	280	840	893	1052	1529	1333	745	608
87	197	591	146	438	1314	688	437	1311	679	410
88	1230	436	1308	670	383	1149	193	579	110	330
89	990	1343	775	698	467	1401	949	1220	406	1218
90	400	1200	346	1038	1487	1207	367	1101	49	147
91	441	1323	715	518	1554	1408	970	1283	595	158
92	474	1422	1012	1409	973	1292	622	239	717	524
93	1572	1462	1132	142	426	1278	580	113	339	1017
94	1424	1018	1427	1027	1454	1108	70	210	630	263
95	789	740	593	152	456	1368	850	923	1142	172
96	516	1548	1390	916	1121	109	327	981	1316	694
97	455	1365	841	896	1061	1556	1414	988	1337	757
98	644	305	915	1118	100	300	900	1073	1592	1522
99	1312	682	419	1257	517	1551	1399	943	1202	352

P = 1627

INDICES

	0	1	2	3	4	5	6	7	8	9
100	1476	19	1323	1441	749	113	1426	274	288	582
101	243	724	922	1576	736	1474	580	939	941	56
102	381	1336	1326	221	1206	1455	1040	943	421	1363
103	1115	250	105	357	139	333	58	377	903	12
104	348	199	1331	1601	1217	383	401	123	74	1444
105	668	563	865	799	1338	294	1000	1572	365	36
106	1271	974	1471	1328	1407	1510	327	820	1025	1410
107	1124	1199	223	987	1415	485	752	1422	449	1555
108	411	1208	1499	533	1583	1625	1541	453	491	794
109	1457	265	1166	1067	369	1449	1513	1313	407	1042
110	1380	907	710	116	443	1259	1373	390	945	100
111	181	147	1157	463	1082	1248	1368	423	983	622
112	778	964	285	330	1468	791	1365	1518	1286	719
113	1429	469	932	1019	1229	1117	1620	587	323	1134
114	1530	1589	958	1521	252	768	1296	1138	757	885
115	823	300	521	107	626	572	1402	277	32	1526
116	81	1046	359	318	341	809	1175	1060	1559	1005
117	1289	141	157	1354	306	40	1596	1028	861	1015
118	335	1485	16	418	291	1496	97	1617	315	60
119	63	68	208	236	1073	648	1321	722	379	1361
120	901	121	998	1508	1413	531	1164	905	179	620
121	1284	585	1294	570	339	1352	14	66	899	618
122	897	85	538	480	1432	350	694	87	1534	259
123	880	1127	682	828	201	782	540	475	246	1153
124	232	844	1384	1333	71	482	707	716	1399	415
125	1281	472	1603	1097	1434	554	1275	993	1202	1255
126	93	1219	635	352	1606	727	1345	1223	608	601
127	385	211	696	657	848	186	1611	1480	935	403
128	1011	89	1145	917	549	226	1033	1193	125	1548
129	1536	1100	925	509	503	1489	1462	76	239	261
130	153	1093	1050	733	196	1022	1446	282	882	1593
131	1505	877	990	546	874	670	968	1129	1437	1579
132	805	703	168	911	565	1076	684	172	592	1105
133	1212	1188	1232	867	1054	830	1238	978	673	1418
134	28	1149	801	891	203	557	739	49	639	428
135	216	1340	651	784	437	1388	854	1308	23	1120
136	296	678	542	271	136	971	488	1245	955	1002
137	1318	477	1278	1477	193	1185	20	747	1574	1324
138	248	346	1442	363	818	750	1623	367	114	1155
139	962	1427	1132	755	275	1173	38	289	234	996
140	583	895	257	244	714	1273	725	846	915	923
141	1091	1503	1577	590	976	737	1386	134	1475	1440
142	1425	581	921	1473	940	1335	1205	942	1114	356
143	57	11	1330	382	73	562	1337	1571	1270	1327
144	326	1409	222	484	448	1207	1582	452	1456	1066
145	1512	1041	709	1258	944	146	1081	422	777	329
146	1364	718	931	1116	322	1588	251	1137	822	106
147	1401	1525	358	808	1558	140	305	1027	334	417
148	96	59	207	647	378	120	1412	904	1283	569
149	13	617	537	349	1533	1126	200	474	231	1332

POWER RESIDUES

	0	1	2	3	4	5	6	7	8	9
100	1056	1541	1369	853	932	1169	253	759	650	323
101	969	1280	586	131	393	1179	283	849	920	1133
102	145	435	1305	661	356	1068	1577	1477	1177	277
103	831	866	971	1286	604	185	555	38	114	342
104	1026	1451	1099	43	129	387	1161	229	687	434
105	1302	652	329	987	1334	748	617	224	672	389
106	1167	247	741	596	161	483	1449	1093	25	75
107	225	675	398	1194	328	984	1325	721	536	1608
108	1570	1456	1114	88	264	792	749	620	233	699
109	470	1410	976	1301	649	320	960	1253	505	1515
110	1291	619	230	690	443	1329	733	572	89	267
111	801	776	701	476	1428	1030	1463	1135	151	453
112	1359	823	842	899	1070	1583	1495	1231	439	1317
113	697	464	1392	922	1139	163	489	1467	1147	187
114	561	56	168	504	1512	1282	592	149	447	1341
115	769	680	413	1239	463	1389	913	1112	82	246
116	738	587	134	402	1206	364	1092	22	66	198
117	594	155	465	1395	931	1166	244	732	569	80
118	240	720	533	1599	1543	1375	871	986	1331	739
119	590	143	429	1287	607	194	582	119	357	1071
120	1586	1504	1258	520	1560	1426	1024	1445	1081	1616
121	1594	1528	1330	736	581	116	348	1044	1505	1261
122	529	1587	1507	1267	547	14	42	126	378	1134
123	148	444	1332	742	599	170	510	1530	1336	754
124	635	278	834	875	998	1367	847	914	1115	91
125	273	819	830	863	962	1259	523	1569	1453	1105
126	61	183	549	20	60	180	540	1620	1606	1564
127	1438	1060	1553	1405	961	1256	514	1542	1372	862
128	959	1250	496	1488	1210	376	1128	130	390	1170
129	256	768	677	404	1212	382	1146	184	552	29
130	87	261	783	722	539	1617	1597	1537	1357	817
131	824	845	908	1097	37	111	333	999	1370	856
132	941	1196	334	1002	1379	883	1022	1439	1063	1562
133	1432	1042	1499	1243	475	1425	1021	1436	1054	1535
134	1351	799	770	683	422	1266	544	5	15	45
135	135	405	1215	391	1173	265	795	758	647	314
136	942	1199	343	1029	1460	1126	124	372	1116	94
137	282	846	911	1106	64	192	576	101	303	909
138	1100	46	138	414	1242	472	1416	994	1355	811
139	806	791	746	611	206	618	227	681	416	1248
140	490	1470	1156	214	642	299	897	1064	1565	1441
141	1069	1580	1486	1204	358	1074	1595	1531	1339	763
142	662	359	1077	1604	1558	1420	1006	1391	919	1130
143	136	408	1224	418	1254	508	1524	1318	700	473
144	1419	1003	1382	892	1049	1520	1306	664	365	1095
145	31	93	279	837	884	1025	1448	1090	16	48
146	144	432	1296	634	275	825	848	917	1124	118
147	354	1062	1559	1423	1015	1418	1000	1373	865	968
148	1277	577	104	312	936	1181	289	867	974	1295
149	631	266	798	767	674	395	1185	301	903	1082

P = 1627

INDICES

	0	1	2	3	4	5	6	7	8	9
150	706	414	1602	553	1201	1218	1605	1222	384	656
151	1610	402	1144	225	124	1099	502	75	152	732
152	1445	1592	989	669	1436	702	564	171	1211	866
153	1237	1417	800	556	638	1339	436	1307	295	270
154	487	1001	1277	1184	1573	345	817	366	961	754
155	37	995	256	1272	914	1502	975	133	1424	1472
156	1204	355	1329	561	1269	1408	447	451	1511	1257
157	1080	328	930	1587	821	1524	1557	1026	95	646
158	1411	568	536	1125	230	413	1200	1221	1609	224
159	501	731	988	701	1210	1416	637	1306	486	1183
160	816	753	255	1501	1423	354	1268	450	1079	1586
161	1556	645	535	412	1608	730	1209	1305	815	1500
162	1267	1585	534	729	814	1584	813			

POWER RESIDUES

	0	1	2	3	4	5	6	7	8	9
150	1619	1603	1555	1411	979	1310	676	401	1203	355
151	1065	1568	1450	1096	34	102	306	918	1127	127
152	381	1143	175	525	1575	1471	1159	223	669	380
153	1140	166	498	1494	1228	430	1290	616	221	663
154	362	1086	4	12	36	108	324	972	1289	613
155	212	636	281	843	902	1079	1610	1576	1474	1168
156	250	750	623	242	726	551	26	78	234	702
157	479	1437	1057	1544	1378	880	1013	1412	982	1319
158	703	482	1446	1084	1625	1621	1609	1573	1465	1141
159	169	507	1521	1309	673	392	1176	274	822	839
160	890	1043	1502	1252	502	1506	1264	538	1614	1588
161	1510	1276	574	95	285	855	938	1187	307	921
162	1136	154	462	1386	904	1085				

P = 1637

INDICES

	0	1	2	3	4	5	6	7	8	9
0		0	1	653	2	931	654	13	3	1306
1	932	1072	655	316	14	1584	4	1091	1307	1505
2	933	666	1073	196	656	226	317	323	15	1118
3	1585	726	5	89	1092	944	1308	1050	1506	969
4	934	1355	667	1601	1074	601	197	695	657	26
5	227	108	318	1564	324	367	16	522	1119	1569
6	1586	609	727	1319	6	1247	90	1280	1093	849
7	945	624	1309	471	1051	879	1507	1085	970	407
8	935	976	1356	899	668	386	1602	135	1075	455
9	602	329	198	1379	696	800	658	1200	27	742
10	228	1480	109	1068	319	1597	1565	875	325	871
11	368	67	17	1171	523	1127	1120	1622	1570	1104
12	1587	508	610	372	728	1157	1320	1334	7	618
13	1248	1410	91	1518	1281	1254	1094	994	850	71
14	946	1348	625	1388	1310	413	472	679	1052	565
15	880	1220	1508	761	1086	21	971	1166	408	581
16	936	209	977	1535	1357	1020	900	793	669	632
17	387	1175	1603	447	136	239	1076	586	456	1465
18	603	1151	330	1262	199	345	1380	527	697	336
19	801	50	659	558	1201	264	28	1424	743	1416
20	229	297	1481	1131	110	650	1069	1502	320	941
21	1598	105	1566	1277	876	896	326	739	872	1124
22	369	1407	68	676	18	1532	1172	1462	524	261
23	1128	102	1121	1459	1623	1626	1571	1060	1105	1295
24	1588	214	509	1629	611	957	373	185	729	1552
25	1158	1574	1321	1268	1335	1039	8	964	619	1063
26	1249	788	1411	97	92	859	1519	1108	1282	360
27	1255	1236	1095	982	995	1298	851	1208	72	396
28	947	1008	1349	1591	626	1453	1389	1368	1311	546
29	414	217	473	1490	680	864	1053	1395	566	512
30	881	1614	1221	497	1509	1540	762	1632	1087	85
31	22	1243	972	1196	1167	614	409	205	582	554
32	937	1528	210	960	978	542	1536	1524	1358	708
33	1021	376	901	720	794	575	670	1362	633	188
34	388	162	1176	39	1604	144	448	732	137	1030
35	240	639	1077	712	587	1555	457	121	1466	1113
36	604	1374	1152	1161	331	1402	1263	1448	200	1025
37	346	1577	1381	1229	528	174	698	1434	337	1324
38	802	351	51	777	660	380	559	1271	1202	156
39	265	1287	29	427	1425	1338	744	842	1417	535
40	230	905	298	1042	1482	271	1132	486	111	816
41	651	11	1070	1582	1503	194	321	724	942	967
42	1599	693	106	365	1567	1317	1278	622	877	405
43	897	133	327	798	740	1066	873	65	1125	1102
44	370	1332	1408	1252	69	1386	677	1218	19	579
45	1533	791	1173	237	1463	1260	525	48	262	1414
46	1129	1500	103	894	1122	674	1460	100	1624	1293
47	1627	183	1572	1037	1061	95	1106	1234	1296	394
48	1589	1366	215	862	510	495	1630	1241	612	552
49	958	1522	374	573	186	37	730	637	1553	1111

POWER RESIDUES

	0	1	2	3	4	5	6	7	8	9
0	1	2	4	8	16	32	64	128	256	512
1	1024	411	822	7	14	28	56	112	224	448
2	896	155	310	620	1240	843	49	98	196	392
3	784	1568	1499	1361	1085	533	1066	495	990	343
4	686	1372	1107	577	1154	671	1342	1047	457	914
5	191	382	764	1528	1419	1201	765	1530	1423	1209
6	781	1562	1487	1337	1037	437	874	111	222	444
7	888	139	278	556	1112	587	1174	711	1422	1207
8	777	1554	1471	1305	973	309	618	1236	835	33
9	66	132	264	528	1056	475	950	263	526	1052
10	467	934	231	462	924	211	422	844	51	102
11	204	408	816	1632	1627	1617	1597	1557	1477	1317
12	997	357	714	1428	1219	801	1602	1567	1497	1357
13	1077	517	1034	431	862	87	174	348	696	1392
14	1147	657	1314	991	345	690	1380	1123	609	1218
15	799	1598	1559	1481	1325	1013	389	778	1556	1475
16	1313	989	341	682	1364	1091	545	1090	543	1086
17	535	1070	503	1006	375	750	1500	1363	1089	541
18	1082	527	1054	471	942	247	494	988	339	678
19	1356	1075	513	1026	415	830	23	46	92	184
20	368	736	1472	1307	977	317	634	1268	899	161
21	322	644	1288	939	241	482	964	291	582	1164
22	691	1382	1127	617	1234	831	25	50	100	200
23	400	800	1600	1563	1489	1341	1045	453	906	175
24	350	700	1400	1163	689	1378	1119	601	1202	767
25	1534	1431	1225	813	1626	1615	1593	1549	1461	1285
26	933	229	458	916	195	390	780	1560	1483	1329
27	1021	405	810	1620	1603	1569	1501	1365	1093	549
28	1098	559	1118	599	1198	759	1518	1399	1161	685
29	1370	1103	569	1138	639	1278	919	201	402	804
30	1608	1579	1521	1405	1173	709	1418	1199	761	1522
31	1407	1177	717	1434	1231	825	13	26	52	104
32	208	416	832	27	54	108	216	432	864	91
33	182	364	728	1456	1275	913	189	378	756	1512
34	1387	1137	637	1274	911	185	370	740	1480	1323
35	1009	381	762	1524	1411	1185	733	1466	1295	953
36	269	538	1076	515	1030	423	846	55	110	220
37	440	880	123	246	492	984	331	662	1324	1011
38	385	770	1540	1443	1249	861	85	170	340	680
39	1360	1083	529	1058	479	958	279	558	1116	595
40	1190	743	1486	1335	1033	429	858	79	158	316
41	632	1264	891	145	290	580	1160	683	1366	1095
42	553	1106	575	1150	663	1326	1015	393	786	1572
43	1507	1377	1117	597	1194	751	1502	1367	1097	557
44	1114	591	1182	727	1454	1271	905	173	346	692
45	1384	1131	625	1250	863	89	178	356	712	1424
46	1211	785	1570	1503	1369	1101	565	1130	623	1246
47	855	73	146	292	584	1168	699	1398	1159	681
48	1362	1087	537	1074	511	1022	407	814	1628	1619
49	1601	1565	1493	1349	1061	485	970	303	606	1212

P = 1637

INDICES

	0	1	2	3	4	5	6	7	8	9
50	1159	1446	1575	172	1322	775	1269	1285	1336	533
51	1040	484	9	192	965	363	620	131	1064	1100
52	1250	1216	789	1258	1412	892	98	181	93	392
53	860	1239	1520	35	1109	170	1283	482	361	1098
54	1256	179	1237	168	1096	166	983	985	996	279
55	1299	987	852	420	1209	998	73	439	397	281
56	948	1180	1009	1301	1350	466	1592	989	627	292
57	1454	854	1390	703	1369	422	1312	43	547	1211
58	415	912	218	1000	474	917	1491	75	681	595
59	865	441	1054	1608	1396	399	567	433	513	283
60	882	247	1615	950	1222	1439	498	1182	1510	148
61	1541	1011	763	828	1633	1303	1088	223	86	1352
62	23	519	1244	468	973	452	1197	1594	1168	505
63	615	991	410	758	206	629	583	342	555	294
64	938	736	1529	1456	211	1549	961	856	979	1005
65	543	1392	1537	1193	1525	705	1359	141	709	1371
66	1022	1431	377	424	902	813	721	1314	795	1329
67	576	45	671	1034	1363	549	634	772	189	1213
68	389	479	163	417	1177	289	40	914	1605	244
69	145	220	449	755	733	1002	138	810	1031	476
70	241	807	640	919	1078	643	713	1493	588	305
71	1556	77	458	922	122	683	1467	312	1114	597
72	605	1081	1375	867	1153	1344	1162	443	332	646
73	1403	1056	1264	356	1449	1610	201	716	1026	1398
74	347	838	1578	401	1382	1496	1230	569	529	888
75	175	435	699	591	1435	515	338	1189	1325	285
76	803	308	352	884	52	56	778	249	661	1559
77	381	1617	560	1146	1272	952	1203	80	157	1224
78	266	60	1288	1441	30	461	428	500	1426	750
79	1339	1184	745	925	843	1512	1418	782	536	150
80	231	125	906	1543	299	1140	1043	1013	1483	686
81	272	765	1133	253	487	830	112	1470	817	1635
82	652	930	12	1305	1071	315	1583	1090	1504	665
83	195	225	322	1117	725	88	943	1049	968	1354
84	1600	600	694	25	107	1563	366	521	1568	608
85	1318	1246	1279	848	623	470	878	1084	406	975
86	898	385	134	454	328	1378	799	1199	741	1479
87	1067	1596	874	870	66	1170	1126	1621	1103	507
88	371	1156	1333	617	1409	1517	1253	993	70	1347
89	1387	412	678	564	1219	760	20	1165	580	208
90	1534	1019	792	631	1174	446	238	585	1464	1150
91	1261	344	526	335	49	557	263	1423	1415	296
92	1130	649	1501	940	104	1276	895	738	1123	1406
93	675	1531	1461	260	101	1458	1625	1059	1294	213
94	1628	956	184	1551	1573	1267	1038	963	1062	787
95	96	858	1107	359	1235	981	1297	1207	395	1007
96	1590	1452	1367	545	216	1489	863	1394	511	1613
97	496	1539	1631	84	1242	1195	613	204	553	1527
98	959	541	1523	707	375	719	574	1361	187	161
99	38	143	731	1029	638	711	1554	120	1112	1373

POWER RESIDUES

	0	1	2	3	4	5	6	7	8	9
50	787	1574	1511	1385	1133	629	1258	879	121	242
51	484	968	299	598	1196	755	1510	1383	1129	621
52	1242	847	57	114	228	456	912	187	374	748
53	1496	1355	1073	509	1018	399	798	1596	1555	1473
54	1309	981	325	650	1300	963	289	578	1156	675
55	1350	1063	489	978	319	638	1276	915	193	386
56	772	1544	1451	1265	893	149	298	596	1192	747
57	1494	1351	1065	493	986	335	670	1340	1043	449
58	898	159	318	636	1272	907	177	354	708	1416
59	1195	753	1506	1375	1113	589	1178	719	1438	1239
60	841	45	90	180	360	720	1440	1243	849	61
61	122	244	488	976	315	630	1260	883	129	258
62	516	1032	427	854	71	142	284	568	1136	635
63	1270	903	169	338	676	1352	1067	497	994	351
64	702	1404	1171	705	1410	1183	729	1458	1279	921
65	205	410	820	3	6	12	24	48	96	192
66	384	768	1536	1435	1233	829	21	42	84	168
67	336	672	1344	1051	465	930	223	446	892	147
68	294	588	1176	715	1430	1223	809	1618	1599	1561
69	1485	1333	1029	421	842	47	94	188	376	752
70	1504	1371	1105	573	1146	655	1310	983	329	658
71	1316	995	353	706	1412	1187	737	1474	1311	985
72	333	666	1332	1027	417	834	31	62	124	248
73	496	992	347	694	1388	1139	641	1282	927	217
74	434	868	99	198	396	792	1584	1531	1425	1213
75	789	1578	1519	1401	1165	693	1386	1135	633	1266
76	895	153	306	612	1224	811	1622	1607	1577	1517
77	1397	1157	677	1354	1071	505	1010	383	766	1532
78	1427	1217	797	1594	1551	1465	1293	949	261	522
79	1044	451	902	167	334	668	1336	1035	433	866
80	95	190	380	760	1520	1403	1169	701	1402	1167
81	697	1394	1151	665	1330	1023	409	818	1636	1635
82	1633	1629	1621	1605	1573	1509	1381	1125	613	1226
83	815	1630	1623	1609	1581	1525	1413	1189	741	1482
84	1327	1017	397	794	1588	1539	1441	1245	853	69
85	138	276	552	1104	571	1142	647	1294	951	265
86	530	1060	483	966	295	590	1180	723	1446	1255
87	873	109	218	436	872	107	214	428	856	75
88	150	300	600	1200	763	1526	1415	1193	749	1498
89	1359	1081	525	1050	463	926	215	430	860	83
90	166	332	664	1328	1019	401	802	1604	1571	1505
91	1373	1109	581	1162	687	1374	1111	585	1170	703
92	1406	1175	713	1426	1215	793	1586	1535	1433	1229
93	821	5	10	20	40	80	160	320	640	1280
94	923	209	418	836	35	70	140	280	560	1120
95	603	1206	775	1550	1463	1289	941	245	490	980
96	323	646	1292	947	257	514	1028	419	838	39
97	78	156	312	624	1248	859	81	162	324	648
98	1296	955	273	546	1092	547	1094	551	1102	567
99	1134	631	1262	887	137	274	548	1096	555	1110

P = 1637

INDICES

	0	1	2	3	4	5	6	7	8	9
100	1160	1401	1447	1024	1576	1228	173	1433	1323	350
101	776	379	1270	155	1286	426	1337	841	534	904
102	1041	270	485	815	10	1581	193	723	966	692
103	364	1316	621	404	132	797	1065	64	1101	1331
104	1251	1385	1217	578	790	236	1259	47	1413	1499
105	893	673	99	1292	182	1036	94	1233	393	1365
106	861	494	1240	551	1521	572	36	636	1110	1445
107	171	774	1284	532	483	191	362	130	1099	1215
108	1257	891	180	391	1238	34	169	481	1097	178
109	167	165	984	278	986	419	997	438	280	1179
110	1300	465	988	291	853	702	421	42	1210	911
111	999	916	74	594	440	1607	398	432	282	246
112	949	1438	1181	147	1010	827	1302	222	1351	518
113	467	451	1593	504	990	757	628	341	293	735
114	1455	1548	855	1004	1391	1192	704	140	1370	1430
115	423	812	1313	1328	44	1033	548	771	1212	478
116	416	288	913	243	219	754	1001	809	475	806
117	918	642	1492	304	76	921	682	311	596	1080
118	866	1343	442	645	1055	355	1609	715	1397	837
119	400	1495	568	887	434	590	514	1188	284	307
120	883	55	248	1558	1616	1145	951	79	1223	59
121	1440	460	499	749	1183	924	1511	781	149	124
122	1542	1139	1012	685	764	252	829	1469	1634	929
123	1304	314	1089	664	224	1116	87	1048	1353	599
124	24	1562	520	607	1245	847	469	1083	974	384
125	453	1377	1198	1478	1595	869	1169	1620	506	1155
126	616	1516	992	1346	411	563	759	1164	207	1018
127	630	445	584	1149	343	334	556	1422	295	648
128	939	1275	737	1405	1530	259	1457	1058	212	955
129	1550	1266	962	786	857	358	980	1206	1006	1451
130	544	1488	1393	1612	1538	83	1194	203	1526	540
131	706	718	1360	160	142	1028	710	119	1372	1400
132	1023	1227	1432	349	378	154	425	840	903	269
133	814	1580	722	691	1315	403	796	63	1330	1384
134	577	235	46	1498	672	1291	1035	1232	1364	493
135	550	571	635	1444	773	531	190	129	1214	890
136	390	33	480	177	164	277	418	437	1178	464
137	290	701	41	910	915	593	1606	431	245	1437
138	146	826	221	517	450	503	756	340	734	1547
139	1003	1191	139	1429	811	1327	1032	770	477	287
140	242	753	808	805	641	303	920	310	1079	1342
141	644	354	714	836	1494	886	589	1187	306	54
142	1557	1144	78	58	459	748	923	780	123	1138
143	684	251	1468	928	313	663	1115	1047	598	1561
144	606	846	1082	383	1376	1477	868	1619	1154	1515
145	1345	562	1163	1017	444	1148	333	1421	647	1274
146	1404	258	1057	954	1265	785	357	1205	1450	1487
147	1611	82	202	539	717	159	1027	118	1399	1226
148	348	153	839	268	1579	690	402	62	1383	234
149	1497	1290	1231	492	570	1443	530	128	889	32

POWER RESIDUES

	0	1	2	3	4	5	6	7	8	9
100	583	1166	695	1390	1143	649	1298	959	281	562
101	1124	611	1222	807	1614	1591	1545	1453	1269	901
102	165	330	660	1320	1003	369	738	1476	1315	993
103	349	698	1396	1155	673	1346	1055	473	946	255
104	510	1020	403	806	1612	1587	1537	1437	1237	837
105	37	74	148	296	592	1184	731	1462	1287	937
106	237	474	948	259	518	1036	435	870	103	206
107	412	824	11	22	44	88	176	352	704	1408
108	1179	721	1442	1247	857	77	154	308	616	1232
109	827	17	34	68	136	272	544	1088	539	1078
110	519	1038	439	878	119	238	476	952	267	534
111	1068	499	998	359	718	1436	1235	833	29	58
112	116	232	464	928	219	438	876	115	230	460
113	920	203	406	812	1624	1611	1585	1533	1429	1221
114	805	1610	1583	1529	1421	1205	773	1546	1455	1273
115	909	181	362	724	1448	1259	881	125	250	500
116	1000	363	726	1452	1267	897	157	314	628	1256
117	875	113	226	452	904	171	342	684	1368	1099
118	561	1122	607	1214	791	1582	1527	1417	1197	757
119	1514	1391	1145	653	1306	975	313	626	1252	867
120	97	194	388	776	1552	1467	1297	957	277	554
121	1108	579	1158	679	1358	1079	521	1042	447	894
122	151	302	604	1208	779	1558	1479	1321	1005	373
123	746	1492	1347	1057	477	954	271	542	1084	531
124	1062	487	974	311	622	1244	851	65	130	260
125	520	1040	443	886	135	270	540	1080	523	1046
126	455	910	183	366	732	1464	1291	945	253	506
127	1012	387	774	1548	1459	1281	925	213	426	852
128	67	134	268	536	1072	507	1014	391	782	1564
129	1491	1345	1053	469	938	239	478	956	275	550
130	1100	563	1126	615	1230	823	9	18	36	72
131	144	288	576	1152	667	1334	1031	425	850	63
132	126	252	504	1008	379	758	1516	1395	1153	669
133	1338	1039	441	882	127	254	508	1016	395	790
134	1580	1523	1409	1181	725	1450	1263	889	141	282
135	564	1128	619	1238	839	41	82	164	328	656
136	1312	987	337	674	1348	1059	481	962	287	574
137	1148	659	1318	999	361	722	1444	1251	865	93
138	186	372	744	1488	1339	1041	445	890	143	286
139	572	1144	651	1302	967	297	594	1188	739	1478
140	1319	1001	365	730	1460	1283	929	221	442	884
141	131	262	524	1048	459	918	199	398	796	1592
142	1547	1457	1277	917	197	394	788	1576	1515	1393
143	1149	661	1322	1007	377	754	1508	1379	1121	605
144	1210	783	1566	1495	1353	1069	501	1002	367	734
145	1468	1299	961	285	570	1140	643	1286	935	233
146	466	932	227	454	908	179	358	716	1432	1227
147	817	1634	1631	1625	1613	1589	1541	1445	1253	869
148	101	202	404	808	1616	1595	1553	1469	1301	965
149	293	586	1172	707	1414	1191	745	1490	1343	1049

P = 1637

INDICES

	0	1	2	3	4	5	6	7	8	9
150	176	276	436	463	700	909	592	430	1436	825
151	516	502	339	1546	1190	1428	1326	769	286	752
152	804	302	309	1341	353	835	885	1186	53	1143
153	57	747	779	1137	250	927	662	1046	1560	845
154	382	1476	1618	1514	561	1016	1147	1420	1273	257
155	953	784	1204	1486	81	538	158	117	1225	152
156	267	689	61	233	1289	491	1442	127	31	275
157	462	908	429	824	501	1545	1427	768	751	301
158	1340	834	1185	1142	746	1136	926	1045	844	1475
159	1513	1015	1419	256	783	1485	537	116	151	688
160	232	490	126	274	907	823	1544	767	300	833
161	1141	1135	1044	1474	1014	255	1484	115	687	489
162	273	822	766	832	1134	1473	254	114	488	821
163	831	1472	113	820	1471	819	818			

POWER RESIDUES

	0	1	2	3	4	5	6	7	8	9
150	461	922	207	414	828	19	38	76	152	304
151	608	1216	795	1590	1543	1449	1261	885	133	266
152	532	1064	491	982	327	654	1308	979	321	642
153	1284	931	225	450	900	163	326	652	1304	971
154	305	610	1220	803	1606	1575	1513	1389	1141	645
155	1290	943	249	498	996	355	710	1420	1203	769
156	1538	1439	1241	845	53	106	212	424	848	59
157	118	236	472	944	251	502	1004	371	742	1484
158	1331	1025	413	826	15	30	60	120	240	480
159	960	283	566	1132	627	1254	871	105	210	420
160	840	43	86	172	344	688	1376	1115	593	1186
161	735	1470	1303	969	301	602	1204	771	1542	1447
162	1257	877	117	234	468	936	235	470	940	243
163	486	972	307	614	1228	819				

P = 1657

INDICES

	0	1	2	3	4	5	6	7	8	9
0		0	342	1064	684	1533	1406	333	1026	472
1	219	1	92	1251	675	941	1368	1120	814	1570
2	561	1397	343	986	434	1410	1593	1536	1017	534
3	1283	898	54	1065	1462	210	1156	677	256	659
4	903	1045	83	1558	685	349	1328	710	776	666
5	96	528	279	605	222	1534	1359	978	876	1344
6	1625	1167	1240	805	396	1128	1407	1060	148	394
7	552	276	1498	1013	1019	818	598	334	1001	601
8	1245	944	1387	503	425	997	244	1598	1027	1548
9	691	1584	14	306	1052	1447	1118	734	1008	473
10	438	505	870	1588	621	1274	947	166	564	230
11	220	85	45	971	1320	863	1218	67	30	1453
12	311	2	1509	453	1582	1287	1147	983	738	966
13	1470	77	93	247	1402	1413	490	331	736	1565
14	894	118	618	1252	184	411	1355	74	1361	1641
15	1160	683	940	1592	676	775	1343	551	943	13
16	1587	1319	1286	489	73	942	845	1032	767	846
17	1339	386	586	794	284	87	1369	752	234	28
18	1033	1373	270	575	356	554	648	1121	1394	213
19	133	768	1460	773	1076	536	1350	746	815	930
20	780	468	847	867	1212	922	274	1458	963	1571
21	1616	1528	1289	1340	508	1435	906	1231	572	421
22	562	715	427	1613	387	226	1313	643	6	717
23	1205	1398	1560	432	409	587	372	9	139	1035
24	653	950	344	352	195	543	795	1165	268	1567
25	1629	105	1489	987	1325	405	1080	285	1308	1010
26	156	1006	419	23	435	482	589	956	88	980
27	99	320	832	992	673	1411	1078	127	251	1370
28	1236	784	460	1295	960	855	1594	1378	526	584
29	753	142	41	755	416	1221	47	1537	327	581
30	1502	235	1025	1569	1282	1044	278	804	1018	996
31	1117	165	29	965	893	682	1285	793	355	535
32	273	1230	5	1034	1628	1005	831	1294	415	1043
33	1284	1293	1187	1149	1374	937	1109	1140	1188	379
34	25	899	728	999	928	271	1136	1124	626	1150
35	429	1131	55	687	1094	153	576	861	370	859
36	1375	1484	59	1066	612	890	917	357	698	1517
37	896	938	990	1086	1463	695	80	129	555	262
38	475	391	1110	1431	146	211	1115	374	1418	649
39	878	450	36	1141	1088	478	1157	538	1272	1311
40	1122	749	810	493	1189	821	1209	678	1554	1541
41	1264	1395	616	21	144	380	1305	973	257	886
42	302	852	214	1182	1631	874	26	1500	850	660
43	121	376	1248	134	1573	1475	914	900	763	1445
44	904	1138	1057	179	769	1425	299	1049	729	881
45	568	1046	1655	91	985	1461	348	1358	1059	1000
46	1547	437	84	1508	246	183	774	844	751	1393
47	929	1615	714	1559	351	1324	481	1077	1377	326
48	995	272	1292	727	686	611	694	1114	537	1553
49	885	120	1137	1654	1507	350	610	609	253	1351

POWER RESIDUES

	0	1	2	3	4	5	6	7	8	9
0	1	11	121	1331	1385	322	228	851	1076	237
1	950	508	617	159	92	1012	1190	1491	1488	1455
2	1092	413	1229	263	1236	340	426	1372	179	312
3	118	1298	1022	1300	1044	1542	392	998	1036	1454
4	1081	292	1555	535	914	112	1232	296	1599	1019
5	1267	681	863	1208	32	352	558	1167	1238	362
6	668	720	1292	956	574	1343	1517	117	1287	901
7	1626	1316	1220	164	147	1617	1217	131	1441	938
8	376	822	757	42	462	111	1221	175	268	1291
9	945	453	12	132	1452	1059	50	550	1079	270
10	1313	1187	1458	1125	776	251	1104	545	1024	1322
11	1286	890	1505	1642	1492	1499	1576	766	141	1551
12	491	430	1416	663	665	687	929	277	1390	377
13	833	878	1373	190	433	1449	1026	1344	1528	238
14	961	629	291	1544	414	1240	384	910	68	748
15	1600	1030	1388	355	591	1530	260	1203	1634	1404
16	531	870	1285	879	1384	311	107	1177	1348	1572
17	722	1314	1198	1579	799	504	573	1332	1396	443
18	1559	579	1398	465	144	1584	854	1109	600	1629
19	1349	1583	843	988	926	244	1027	1355	1649	1569
20	689	951	519	738	1490	1477	1334	1418	685	907
21	35	385	921	189	422	1328	1352	1616	1206	10
22	110	1210	54	594	1563	623	225	818	713	1215
23	109	1199	1590	920	178	301	1654	1624	1294	978
24	816	691	973	761	86	946	464	133	1463	1180
25	1381	278	1401	498	507	606	38	418	1284	868
26	1263	637	379	855	1120	721	1303	1077	248	1071
27	182	345	481	320	206	609	71	781	306	52
28	572	1321	1275	769	174	257	1170	1271	725	1347
29	1561	601	1640	1470	1257	571	1310	1154	1095	446
30	1592	942	420	1306	1110	611	93	1023	1311	1165
31	1216	120	1320	1264	648	500	529	848	1043	1531
32	271	1324	1308	1132	853	1098	479	298	1621	1261
33	615	137	1507	7	77	847	1032	1410	597	1596
34	986	904	2	22	242	1005	1113	644	456	45
35	495	474	243	1016	1234	318	184	367	723	1325
36	1319	1253	527	826	801	526	815	680	852	1087
37	358	624	236	939	387	943	431	1427	784	339
38	415	1251	505	584	1453	1070	171	224	807	592
39	1541	381	877	1362	69	759	64	704	1116	677
40	819	724	1336	1440	927	255	1148	1029	1377	234
41	917	145	1595	975	783	328	294	1577	777	262
42	1225	219	752	1644	1514	84	924	222	785	350
43	536	925	233	906	24	264	1247	461	100	1100
44	501	540	969	717	1259	593	1552	502	551	1090
45	391	987	915	123	1353	1627	1327	1341	1495	1532
46	282	1445	982	860	1175	1326	1330	1374	201	554
47	1123	754	9	99	1089	380	866	1241	395	1031
48	1399	476	265	1258	582	1431	828	823	768	163
49	136	1496	1543	403	1119	710	1182	1403	520	749

P = 1657

INDICES

	0	1	2	3	4	5	6	7	8	9
50	315	440	447	1125	175	382	1329	254	11	1234
51	747	1346	1422	1450	627	1465	1650	711	1352	202
52	498	816	1348	791	761	1151	365	362	777	316
53	824	160	931	640	1298	43	430	1092	1322	667
54	441	1226	662	781	1174	107	1334	1132	1015	1639
55	97	448	1420	934	469	1618	593	1267	56	1153
56	1578	529	1126	646	802	848	1637	1277	1302	688
57	1197	295	280	176	64	740	868	1611	926	181
58	1095	836	484	606	383	1600	1097	1213	758	812
59	1563	154	389	445	223	1330	669	338	923	1486
60	188	291	577	1532	1367	1535	255	665	1624	275
61	1386	305	620	862	1146	330	1360	12	1338	1372
62	1459	866	507	225	371	1164	1307	979	1235	141
63	1024	964	1627	936	1135	860	697	261	877	748
64	615	1181	1572	1424	347	843	1376	1552	314	1345
65	1347	639	1173	1617	1636	1610	757	1485	1385	865
66	1626	1423	1635	123	1529	124	1491	1520	60	1021
67	1279	1168	1451	651	1482	1290	1530	399	721	1067
68	367	51	1241	628	1070	208	1341	125	1270	200
69	613	241	1478	806	1466	1442	968	509	1492	1496
70	771	891	1473	591	397	1651	1029	838	1436	1521
71	495	1073	918	228	1203	1129	712	443	1201	907
72	61	265	170	358	401	288	1408	1353	954	1416
73	1232	1022	1259	1254	699	1607	1040	1061	203	514
74	1238	573	1280	872	1332	1518	1428	975	149	499
75	1037	1261	422	1169	471	560	897	82	604	395
76	817	243	733	563	1452	1469	117	939	488	283
77	553	1349	1457	571	716	652	104	418	991	959
78	1220	277	792	414	378	428	1483	989	1430	1087
79	820	1304	1499	762	880	1546	1614	1291	1653	174
80	1464	364	1091	1014	1152	1196	835	388	1531	1145
81	1163	696	1551	1384	1020	366	240	1472	227	400
82	1606	1427	81	487	958	819	363	1550	486	1314
83	722	1191	1647	130	1315	909	599	778	1228	1055
84	644	1068	1194	192	556	723	1524	335	317	703
85	1216	7	368	324	186	263	1192	636	1002	825
86	463	786	718	52	1590	671	476	1648	259	602
87	161	655	1256	1206	1242	1620	1105	392	131	163
88	1246	932	1480	1544	1399	629	521	1381	1111	1316
89	111	945	641	624	1391	1561	1071	1645	1223	1432
90	910	69	1388	1299	341	1250	433	209	1327	977
91	147	600	690	504	44	452	1401	410	1342	1031
92	233	212	779	1527	426	431	194	404	588	126
93	525	580	1116	1229	1186	998	1093	889	79	373
94	1271	1540	301	375	1056	90	245	1323	693	608
95	10	201	823	1225	1419	645	63	1599	668	664
96	1337	140	614	638	1634	650	1069	1441	1028	442
97	953	513	1036	242	1456	413	879	1195	239	1549
98	1227	702	462	654	1479	623	340	451	193	888
99	692	663	952	701	951	807	595	798	37	557

POWER RESIDUES

	0	1	2	3	4	5	6	7	8	9
50	1611	1151	1062	83	913	101	1111	622	214	697
51	1039	1487	1444	971	739	1501	1598	1008	1146	1007
52	1135	886	1461	1158	1139	930	288	1511	51	561
53	1200	1601	1041	1509	29	319	195	488	397	1053
54	1641	1481	1378	245	1038	1476	1323	1297	1011	1179
55	1370	157	70	770	185	378	844	999	1047	1575
56	755	20	220	763	108	1188	1469	1246	450	1636
57	1426	773	218	741	1523	183	356	602	1651	1591
58	931	299	1632	1382	289	1522	172	235	928	266
59	1269	703	1105	556	1145	996	1014	1212	76	836
60	911	79	869	1274	758	53	583	1442	949	497
61	496	485	364	690	962	640	412	1218	142	1562
62	612	104	1144	985	893	1538	348	514	683	885
63	1450	1037	1465	1202	1623	1283	857	1142	963	651
64	533	892	1527	227	840	955	563	1222	186	389
65	965	673	775	240	983	871	1296	1000	1058	39
66	429	1405	542	991	959	607	49	539	958	596
67	1585	865	1230	274	1357	14	154	37	407	1163
68	1194	1535	315	151	4	44	484	353	569	1288
69	912	90	990	948	486	375	811	636	368	734
70	1446	993	981	849	1054	1652	1602	1052	1630	1360
71	47	517	716	1248	472	221	774	229	862	1197
72	1568	678	830	845	1010	1168	1249	483	342	448
73	1614	1184	1425	762	97	1067	138	1518	128	1408
74	575	1354	1638	1448	1015	1223	197	510	639	401
75	1097	468	177	290	1533	293	1566	656	588	1497
76	1554	524	793	438	1504	1631	1371	168	191	444
77	1570	700	1072	193	466	155	48	528	837	922
78	200	543	1002	1080	281	1434	861	1186	1447	1004
79	1102	523	782	317	173	246	1049	1597	997	1025
80	1333	1407	564	1233	307	63	693	995	1003	1091
81	402	1108	589	1508	18	198	521	760	75	825
82	790	405	1141	952	530	859	1164	1205	1656	1646
83	1536	326	272	1335	1429	806	581	1420	707	1149
84	1040	1498	1565	645	467	166	169	202	565	1244
85	428	1394	421	1317	1231	285	1478	1345	1539	359
86	635	357	613	115	1265	659	621	203	576	1365
87	102	1122	743	1545	425	1361	58	638	390	976
88	794	449	1625	1305	1099	490	419	1295	989	937
89	365	701	1083	314	140	1540	370	756	31	341
90	437	1493	1510	40	440	1526	216	719	1281	835
91	900	1615	1195	1546	436	1482	1389	366	712	1204
92	1645	1525	205	598	1607	1107	578	1387	344	470
93	199	532	881	1406	553	1112	633	335	371	767
94	152	15	165	158	81	891	1516	106	1166	1227
95	241	994	992	970	728	1380	267	1280	824	779
96	284	1467	1224	208	631	313	129	1419	696	1028
97	1366	113	1243	417	1273	747	1589	909	57	627
98	269	1302	1066	127	1397	454	23	253	1126	787
99	372	778	273	1346	1550	480	309	85	935	343

P = 1657

INDICES

	0	1	2	3	4	5	6	7	8	9
100	657	1585	782	808	789	345	1467	519	517	1142
101	724	548	15	1175	596	744	353	1443	1576	49
102	1089	1525	32	307	108	799	136	196	969	407
103	151	479	336	1199	1053	1335	38	631	544	510
104	840	532	1158	318	34	1448	1133	558	1103	796
105	1493	1083	707	539	704	1405	1119	1016	658	95
106	1166	1497	502	1051	1273	1217	982	735	1640	1586
107	385	269	772	1211	1434	1312	8	267	1009	98
108	783	40	1568	892	1004	1108	1123	369	1516	474
109	449	809	20	1630	1474	298	1357	750	325	884
110	439	1421	790	1297	106	592	1276	925	811	187
111	304	506	935	346	1609	1490	398	1269	1495	494
112	264	1258	871	470	1468	103	988	1652	1144	1605
113	1190	1193	323	1589	1619	520	1644	1326	1030	524
114	1539	822	637	1455	622	594	518	1575	406	839
115	1082	501	1210	1003	297	1275	1268	1143	523	1081
116	1437	1438	1178	679	826	309	948	57	725	1365
117	286	1522	1439	1514	1555	464	1100	167	1154	549
118	249	1309	496	1179	731	1542	787	101	565	1579
119	16	1602	1011	1074	680	912	1265	719	172	231
120	530	1176	633	157	919	827	218	1396	53	1557
121	221	1127	597	1597	1007	229	310	76	617	1591
122	72	86	647	745	962	420	1204	949	1488	22
123	672	854	46	803	354	1042	24	1130	58	1085
124	145	477	1208	972	849	1444	567	436	713	726
125	1506	381	1649	361	1321	1638	1577	294	483	444
126	1366	329	1306	260	313	864	1278	50	1477	590
127	1202	287	1039	974	603	282	1219	1303	1090	1383
128	957	908	1523	635	258	162	110	68	689	1526
129	1185	89	62	1440	238	887	656	547	31	1198
130	33	1404	981	266	1515	883	303	1257	322	1454
131	296	308	1099	100	171	1556	71	853	1207	360
132	312	281	109	546	321	359	465	456	215	1243
133	466	3	177	800	206	833	402	1101	1363	1183
134	1621	457	1510	65	137	857	993	289	168	190
135	1632	1106	216	454	741	197	1063	674	1409	1155
136	709	875	393	1244	1583	869	970	1581	1412	1354
137	550	766	27	132	467	1288	1612	408	542	1079
138	955	250	583	1501	164	4	1148	927	152	916
139	128	1417	1310	1263	851	1247	178	984	182	480
140	1113	252	1233	497	159	661	933	801	739	1096
141	337	1623	1371	1023	1180	1172	122	1481	207	967
142	837	1200	1415	1237	1260	732	570	377	1545	834
143	1471	485	1054	1215	785	1255	1543	1390	1249	1400
144	403	78	607	1336	512	461	700	788	743	135
145	630	1102	94	384	39	19	1296	1608	102	1643
146	1574	522	1364	248	1601	632	1596	961	1041	566
147	293	1476	1382	1184	1403	1098	545	205	856	1062
148	1580	541	915	1112	1622	1414	1214	511	18	1595
149	204	17	114	901	1317	458	491	759	841	115

POWER RESIDUES

	0	1	2	3	4	5	6	7	8	9
100	459	78	858	1153	1084	325	261	1214	98	1078
101	259	1192	1513	73	803	548	1057	28	308	74
102	814	669	731	1413	630	302	8	88	968	706
103	1138	919	167	180	323	239	972	750	1622	1272
104	736	1468	1235	329	305	41	451	1647	1547	447
105	1603	1063	94	1034	1432	839	944	442	1548	458
106	67	737	1479	1356	3	33	363	679	841	966
107	684	896	1571	711	1193	1524	194	477	276	1379
108	256	1159	1150	1051	1619	1239	373	789	394	1020
109	1278	802	537	936	354	580	1409	586	1475	1312
110	1176	1337	1451	1048	1586	876	1351	1605	1085	336
111	382	888	1483	1400	487	386	932	310	96	1056
112	17	187	400	1086	347	503	562	1211	65	715
113	1237	351	547	1046	1564	634	346	492	441	1537
114	337	393	1009	1157	1128	809	614	126	1386	333
115	349	525	804	559	1178	1359	36	396	1042	1520
116	150	1650	1580	810	625	247	1060	61	671	753
117	1655	1635	1415	652	544	1013	1201	1612	1162	1183
118	1414	641	423	1339	1473	1290	934	332	338	404
119	1130	831	856	1131	842	977	805	570	1299	1033
120	1421	718	1270	714	1226	230	873	1318	1242	406
121	1152	1073	204	587	1486	1433	850	1065	116	1276
122	780	295	1588	898	1593	953	541	980	838	933
123	321	217	730	1402	509	628	280	1423	740	1512
124	62	682	874	1329	1363	80	880	1395	432	1438
125	905	13	143	1573	733	1435	872	1307	1121	732
126	1424	751	1633	1393	410	1196	1557	557	1156	1117
127	688	940	398	1064	105	1155	1106	567	1266	670
128	742	1534	304	30	330	316	162	125	1375	212
129	675	797	482	331	327	283	1456	1103	534	903
130	1648	1558	568	1277	791	416	1262	626	258	1181
131	1392	399	1075	226	829	834	889	1494	1521	161
132	114	1254	538	947	475	254	1137	908	46	506
133	595	1574	744	1556	546	1035	1443	960	618	170
134	213	686	918	156	59	649	511	650	522	771
135	196	499	518	727	1369	146	1606	1096	457	56
136	616	148	1628	1338	1462	1169	1260	604	16	176
137	279	1412	619	181	334	360	646	478	287	1500
138	1587	887	1472	1279	813	658	610	82	902	1637
139	1437	894	1549	469	188	411	1207	21	231	884
140	1439	916	134	1474	1301	1055	6	66	726	1358
141	25	275	1368	135	1485	1422	729	1391	388	954
142	552	1101	512	661	643	445	1581	821	746	1578
143	788	383	899	1604	1074	215	708	1160	1161	1172
144	1293	967	695	1017	1245	439	1515	95	1045	1553
145	513	672	764	119	1309	1143	974	772	207	620
146	192	455	34	374	800	515	694	1006	1124	765
147	130	1430	817	702	1094	435	1471	1268	692	984
148	882	1417	674	786	361	657	599	1618	1228	252
149	1115	666	698	1050	1608	1118	699	1061	72	792

P = 1657

INDICES

	0	1	2	3	4	5	6	7	8	9
150	1379	515	1603	1504	764	112	1511	332	813	533
151	902	527	1239	1012	424	1446	946	66	737	1564
152	1159	1318	585	574	1075	921	905	642	138	1566
153	155	319	459	754	1281	681	830	1139	625	858
154	895	390	35	492	143	873	913	1048	1058	1392
155	994	119	446	1449	760	42	1333	1266	1301	180
156	1562	290	619	224	1134	842	756	1519	720	199
157	770	1072	169	1253	1331	559	116	417	1429	173
158	1162	1426	1646	191	185	670	1104	1380	1222	976
159	232	579	300	1224	1633	412	339	797	516	48
160	150	531	706	1050	1433	1107	1356	924	1494	1604
161	1538	500	1177	1513	730	911	217	75	1487	1084
162	1505	328	1038	634	237	882	70	455	1362	189
163	708	765	582	1262	158	1171	569	1389	742	1642
164	292	540	113	1503	423	920	829	1047	1300	198
165	1161	578	705	1512	236	1170	828			

POWER RESIDUES

	0	1	2	3	4	5	6	7	8	9
150	427	1383	300	1643	1503	1620	1250	494	463	122
151	1342	1506	1653	1613	1173	1304	1088	369	745	1567
152	667	709	1171	1282	846	1021	1289	923	211	664
153	676	808	603	5	55	605	27	297	1610	1140
154	941	409	1185	1436	883	1428	795	460	89	979
155	827	812	647	489	408	1174	1315	1209	43	473
156	232	895	1560	590	1519	139	1529	249	1082	303
157	19	209	642	434	1460	1147	1018	1256	560	1189
158	1480	1367	124	1364	91	1001	1069	160	103	1133
159	864	1219	153	26	286	1489	1466	1213	87	957
160	585	1464	1191	1502	1609	1129	820	735	1457	1114
161	655	577	1376	223	796	471	210	653	555	1134
162	875	1340	1484	1411	608	60	660	632	324	250
163	1093	424	1350	1594	964	662	654	566	1255	549
164	1068	149	1639	1459	1136	897	1582	832	867	1252
165	516	705	1127	798	493	452				

P = 1663

INDICES

	0	1	2	3	4	5	6	7	8	9
0		0	532	1	1064	271	533	1239	1596	2
1	803	1018	1065	1262	109	272	466	315	534	712
2	1335	1240	1550	472	1597	542	132	3	641	921
3	804	483	998	1019	847	1510	1066	259	1244	1263
4	205	1098	110	508	420	273	1004	1517	467	816
5	1074	316	664	21	535	1289	1173	713	1453	1208
6	1336	1294	1015	1241	1530	1533	1551	523	1379	473
7	380	1163	1598	1656	791	543	114	595	133	655
8	737	4	1630	1159	642	586	1040	922	952	1591
9	805	839	1536	484	387	983	999	625	1348	1020
10	1606	220	848	637	1196	1511	553	350	1067	1200
11	159	260	43	726	1245	743	323	1264	78	1554
12	206	374	164	1099	1547	813	111	634	400	509
13	403	605	421	289	1055	274	249	478	1005	868
14	912	1518	33	618	468	1192	526	817	1323	1410
15	1075	345	646	317	1127	754	665	512	1187	22
16	1269	49	536	1047	500	1290	29	436	1174	862
17	1118	714	1572	1382	1454	119	1484	1209	461	1493
18	1337	14	1371	1295	406	530	1016	1333	919	1242
19	1515	1171	1531	789	1157	1534	218	157	1552	398
20	476	524	752	498	1380	1369	1169	474	66	68
21	381	608	1085	1164	882	779	1599	60	70	1657
22	691	1577	792	440	575	544	1258	383	115	928
23	1275	596	855	590	134	126	610	656	424	1226
24	738	358	906	5	696	1087	1631	312	417	1160
25	1345	810	643	1490	1166	587	932	672	1041	1498
26	935	923	1137	884	953	292	821	1592	1587	1114
27	806	557	781	840	1010	1560	1537	298	1400	485
28	1444	1601	388	977	565	984	1150	675	1000	630
29	62	626	1058	450	1349	1479	193	1021	280	72
30	1607	85	877	221	1178	1565	849	960	1659	638
31	1286	1627	1197	246	1044	1512	57	693	554	277
32	139	351	581	1027	1068	142	1579	1201	1032	1094
33	160	494	561	261	968	794	44	1279	1394	727
34	1650	1501	1246	393	442	744	252	1327	324	1359
35	651	1265	354	577	79	1434	993	1555	363	150
36	207	1424	546	375	241	265	165	1301	938	1100
37	1062	1260	1548	481	203	814	1451	521	112	584
38	385	635	41	372	401	866	1321	510	27	117
39	404	787	750	606	689	926	422	310	930	290
40	1008	975	1056	83	1284	275	1030	1277	250	1432
41	239	479	39	785	1006	1430	598	869	600	198
42	913	176	1140	1519	1617	857	34	871	1414	619
43	1311	230	469	1071	592	1193	602	1184	527	1082
44	1223	818	447	136	1324	200	972	1411	1107	887
45	1076	454	128	346	915	1110	647	226	1460	318
46	145	612	1128	178	1387	755	1122	305	666	100
47	658	513	1142	1526	1188	1254	956	23	96	426
48	1270	1521	890	50	1438	896	537	1582	1228	1048
49	1619	683	501	1236	844	1291	949	740	30	859

POWER RESIDUES

	0	1	2	3	4	5	6	7	8	9
0	1	3	9	27	81	243	729	524	1572	1390
1	844	869	944	1169	181	543	1629	1561	1357	745
2	572	53	159	477	1431	967	1238	388	1164	166
3	498	1494	1156	142	426	1278	508	1524	1246	412
4	1236	382	1146	112	336	1008	1361	757	608	161
5	483	1449	1021	1400	874	959	1214	316	948	1181
6	217	651	290	870	947	1178	208	624	209	627
7	218	654	299	897	1028	1421	937	1148	118	354
8	1062	1523	1243	403	1209	301	903	1046	1475	1099
9	1634	1576	1402	880	977	1268	478	1434	976	1265
10	469	1407	895	1022	1403	883	986	1295	559	14
11	42	126	378	1134	76	228	684	389	1167	175
12	525	1575	1399	871	950	1187	235	705	452	1356
13	742	563	26	78	234	702	443	1329	661	320
14	960	1217	325	975	1262	460	1380	814	779	674
15	359	1077	1568	1378	808	761	620	197	591	110
16	330	990	1307	595	122	366	1098	1631	1567	1375
17	799	734	539	1617	1525	1249	421	1263	463	1389
18	841	860	917	1088	1601	1477	1105	1652	1630	1564
19	1366	772	653	296	888	1001	1340	694	419	1257
20	445	1335	679	374	1122	40	120	360	1080	1577
21	1405	889	1004	1349	721	500	1500	1174	196	588
22	101	303	909	1064	1529	1261	457	1371	787	698
23	431	1293	553	1659	1651	1627	1555	1339	691	410
24	1230	364	1092	1613	1513	1213	313	939	1154	136
25	408	1224	346	1038	1451	1027	1418	928	1121	87
26	111	333	999	1334	676	365	1095	1622	1540	1294
27	556	5	15	45	135	405	1215	319	957	1208
28	298	894	1019	1394	856	905	1052	1493	1153	133
29	399	1197	265	795	722	503	1509	1201	277	831
30	830	827	818	791	710	467	1401	877	968	1241
31	397	1191	247	741	560	17	51	153	459	1377
32	805	752	593	116	348	1044	1469	1081	1580	1414
33	916	1085	1592	1450	1024	1409	901	1040	1457	1045
34	1472	1090	1607	1495	1159	151	453	1359	751	590
35	107	321	963	1226	352	1056	1505	1189	241	723
36	506	1518	1228	358	1074	1559	1351	727	518	1554
37	1336	682	383	1149	121	363	1089	1604	1486	1132
38	70	210	630	227	681	380	1140	94	282	846
39	875	962	1223	343	1029	1424	946	1175	199	597
40	128	384	1152	130	390	1170	184	552	1656	1642
41	1600	1474	1096	1625	1549	1321	637	248	744	569
42	44	132	396	1188	238	714	479	1437	985	1292
43	550	1650	1624	1546	1312	610	167	501	1503	1183
44	223	669	344	1032	1433	973	1256	442	1326	652
45	293	879	974	1259	451	1353	733	536	1608	1498
46	1168	178	534	1602	1480	1114	16	48	144	432
47	1296	562	23	69	207	621	200	600	137	411
48	1233	373	1119	31	93	279	837	848	881	980
49	1277	505	1515	1219	331	993	1316	622	203	609

P = 1663

INDICES

	0	1	2	3	4	5	6	7	8	9
50	215	437	1342	295	1175	491	360	863	36	1079
51	1119	1233	1464	715	1204	908	1573	873	368	1383
52	1467	774	1455	1217	7	120	1416	798	1485	944
53	824	1210	1353	698	462	621	457	1494	1646	172
54	1338	1035	1089	15	1313	1471	1372	718	1542	1296
55	430	1633	407	232	830	531	270	1595	1017	108
56	314	1334	471	131	920	997	1509	1243	1097	419
57	1516	1073	20	1172	1207	1014	1532	1378	1162	790
58	594	736	1158	1039	1590	1535	982	1347	219	1195
59	349	158	725	322	1553	163	812	399	604	1054
60	477	911	617	525	1409	645	753	1186	48	499
61	435	1117	1381	1483	1492	1370	529	918	1170	1156
62	156	475	497	1168	67	1084	778	69	1576	574
63	382	1274	589	609	1225	905	1086	416	809	1165
64	671	934	883	820	1113	780	1559	1399	1600	564
65	674	61	449	192	71	876	1564	1658	1626	1043
66	692	138	1026	1578	1093	560	793	1393	1500	441
67	1326	650	576	992	149	545	264	937	1259	202
68	520	384	371	1320	116	749	925	929	974	1283
69	1276	238	784	597	197	1139	856	1413	229	591
70	1183	1222	135	971	886	127	1109	1459	611	1386
71	304	657	1525	955	425	889	895	1227	682	843
72	739	214	294	359	1078	1463	907	367	773	6
73	797	823	697	456	171	1088	1470	1541	1632	829
74	1594	313	130	1508	418	19	1013	1161	735	1589
75	1346	348	321	811	1053	616	644	47	1116	1491
76	917	155	1167	777	573	588	904	808	933	1112
77	1398	673	191	1563	1042	1025	559	1499	649	148
78	936	519	1319	924	1282	783	1138	228	1221	885
79	1458	303	954	894	842	293	1462	772	822	170
80	1540	1593	1507	1012	1588	320	615	1115	154	572
81	807	1397	1562	558	147	1318	782	1220	302	841
82	771	1539	1011	614	571	1561	1317	301	1538	570
83	300	299	1130	1131	1401	707	1132	486	730	1402
84	1445	180	708	1602	10	1133	389	1613	487	978
85	1389	731	566	1638	1403	985	284	1446	1151	757
86	181	676	762	709	1001	1653	1603	631	1124	11
87	63	123	1134	627	54	390	1059	307	1614	451
88	93	488	1350	105	979	1480	668	1390	194	211
89	732	1022	1504	567	281	102	1639	73	1419	1404
90	1608	336	986	86	660	285	878	1475	1447	222
91	1642	1152	1179	515	758	1566	330	182	850	1249
92	677	961	1144	763	1660	801	710	639	257	1002
93	1287	1528	1654	1628	837	1604	1198	76	632	247
94	1190	1125	1045	1570	12	1513	396	64	58	1256
95	124	694	1488	1135	555	1442	628	278	958	55
96	140	966	391	352	1422	1060	582	25	308	1028
97	1428	1615	1069	445	452	143	98	94	1580	947
98	489	1202	1215	1351	1033	428	106	1095	1376	980
99	161	1407	1481	495	1272	669	562	1624	1391	262

POWER RESIDUES

	0	1	2	3	4	5	6	7	8	9
50	164	492	1476	1102	1643	1603	1483	1123	43	129
51	387	1161	157	471	1413	913	1076	1565	1369	781
52	680	377	1131	67	201	603	146	438	1314	616
53	185	555	2	6	18	54	162	486	1458	1048
54	1481	1117	25	75	225	675	362	1086	1595	1459
55	1051	1490	1144	106	318	954	1199	271	813	776
56	665	332	996	1325	649	284	852	893	1016	1385
57	829	824	809	764	629	224	672	353	1059	1514
58	1216	322	966	1235	379	1137	85	255	765	632
59	233	699	434	1302	580	77	231	693	416	1248
60	418	1254	436	1308	598	131	393	1179	211	633
61	236	708	461	1383	823	806	755	602	143	429
62	1287	535	1605	1489	1141	97	291	873	956	1205
63	289	867	938	1151	127	381	1143	103	309	927
64	1118	28	84	252	756	605	152	456	1368	778
65	671	350	1050	1487	1135	79	237	711	470	1410
66	904	1049	1484	1126	52	156	468	1404	886	995
67	1322	640	257	771	650	287	861	920	1097	1628
68	1558	1348	718	491	1473	1093	1616	1522	1240	394
69	1182	220	660	317	951	1190	244	732	533	1599
70	1471	1087	1598	1468	1078	1571	1387	835	842	863
71	926	1115	19	57	171	513	1539	1291	547	1641
72	1597	1465	1069	1544	1306	592	113	339	1017	1388
73	838	851	890	1007	1358	748	581	80	240	720
74	497	1491	1147	115	345	1035	1442	1000	1337	685
75	392	1176	202	606	155	465	1395	859	914	1079
76	1574	1396	862	923	1106	1655	1639	1591	1447	1015
77	1382	820	797	728	521	1563	1363	763	626	215
78	645	272	816	785	692	413	1239	391	1173	193
79	579	74	222	666	335	1005	1352	730	527	1581
80	1417	925	1112	10	30	90	270	810	767	638
81	251	753	596	125	375	1125	49	147	441	1323
82	643	266	798	731	530	1590	1444	1006	1355	739
83	554	1662	1660	1654	1636	1582	1420	934	1139	91
84	273	819	794	719	494	1482	1120	34	102	306
85	918	1091	1610	1504	1186	232	696	425	1275	499
86	1497	1165	169	507	1521	1237	385	1155	139	417
87	1251	427	1281	517	1551	1327	655	302	906	1055
88	1502	1180	214	642	263	789	704	449	1347	715
89	482	1446	1012	1373	793	716	485	1455	1039	1454
90	1036	1445	1009	1364	766	635	242	726	515	1545
91	1309	601	140	420	1260	454	1362	760	617	188
92	564	29	87	261	783	686	395	1185	229	687
93	398	1194	256	768	641	260	780	677	368	1104
94	1649	1621	1537	1285	529	1587	1435	979	1274	496
95	1488	1138	88	264	792	713	476	1428	958	1211
96	307	921	1100	1637	1585	1429	961	1220	334	1002
97	1343	703	446	1338	688	401	1203	283	849	884
98	989	1304	586	95	285	855	902	1043	1466	1072
99	1553	1333	673	356	1068	1541	1297	565	32	96

P = 1663

INDICES

	0	1	2	3	4	5	6	7	8	9
100	747	195	969	1523	212	795	827	733	45	902
101	1023	1280	892	1505	1395	769	568	728	1611	282
102	1651	52	103	1502	334	1640	1247	255	74	394
103	1440	1420	443	1213	1405	745	900	1609	253	898
104	337	1328	1306	987	325	339	87	1360	539	661
105	652	550	286	1266	1330	879	355	1584	1476	578
106	1356	1448	80	1308	223	1435	1230	1643	994	722
107	1153	1556	989	1180	364	1050	516	151	704	759
108	208	327	1567	1425	1621	331	547	701	183	376
109	341	851	242	685	1250	266	412	678	166	89
110	962	1302	503	1145	939	186	764	1101	1362	1661
111	1063	1238	802	1261	465	711	1549	541	640	482
112	846	258	204	507	1003	815	663	1288	1452	1293
113	1529	522	379	1655	113	654	1629	585	951	838
114	386	624	1605	636	552	1199	42	742	77	373
115	1546	633	402	288	248	867	32	1191	1322	344
116	1126	511	1268	1046	28	861	1571	118	460	13
117	405	1332	1514	788	217	397	751	1368	65	607
118	881	59	690	439	1257	927	854	125	423	357
119	695	311	1344	1489	931	1497	1136	291	1586	556
120	1009	297	1443	976	1149	629	1057	1478	279	84
121	1177	959	1285	245	56	276	580	141	1031	493
122	967	1278	1649	392	251	1358	353	1433	362	1423
123	240	1300	1061	480	1450	583	40	865	26	786
124	688	309	1007	82	1029	1431	38	1429	599	175
125	1616	870	1310	1070	601	1081	446	199	1106	453
126	914	225	144	177	1121	99	1141	1253	95	1520
127	1437	1581	1618	1235	948	858	1341	490	35	1232
128	1203	872	1466	1216	1415	943	1352	620	1645	1034
129	1312	717	429	231	269	107	470	996	1096	1072
130	1206	1377	593	1038	981	1194	724	162	603	910
131	1408	1185	434	1482	528	1155	496	1083	1575	1273
132	1224	415	670	819	1558	563	448	875	1625	137
133	1092	1392	1325	991	263	201	370	748	973	237
134	196	1412	1182	970	1108	1385	1524	888	681	213
135	1077	366	796	455	1469	828	129	18	734	347
136	1052	46	916	776	903	1111	190	1024	648	518
137	1281	227	1457	893	1461	169	1506	319	153	1396
138	146	1219	770	613	1316	569	1129	706	729	179
139	9	1612	1388	1637	283	756	761	1652	1123	122
140	53	306	92	104	667	210	1503	101	1418	335
141	659	1474	1641	514	329	1248	1143	800	256	1527
142	836	75	1189	1569	395	1255	1487	1441	957	965
143	1421	24	1427	444	97	946	1214	427	1375	1406
144	1271	1623	746	1522	826	901	891	768	1610	51
145	333	254	1439	1212	899	897	1305	338	538	549
146	1329	1583	1355	1307	1229	721	988	1049	703	326
147	1620	700	340	684	411	88	502	185	1361	1237
148	464	540	845	506	662	1292	378	653	950	623
149	551	741	1545	287	31	343	1267	860	459	1331

POWER RESIDUES

	0	1	2	3	4	5	6	7	8	9
100	288	864	929	1124	46	138	414	1242	400	1200
101	274	822	803	746	575	62	186	558	11	33
102	99	297	891	1010	1367	775	662	323	969	1244
103	406	1218	328	984	1289	541	1623	1543	1303	583
104	86	258	774	659	314	942	1163	163	489	1467
105	1075	1562	1360	754	599	134	402	1206	292	876
106	965	1232	370	1110	4	12	36	108	324	972
107	1253	433	1299	571	50	150	450	1350	724	509
108	1527	1255	439	1317	625	212	636	245	735	542
109	1626	1552	1330	664	329	987	1298	568	41	123
110	369	1107	1658	1648	1618	1528	1258	448	1344	706
111	455	1365	769	644	269	807	758	611	170	510
112	1530	1264	466	1398	868	941	1160	154	462	1386
113	832	833	836	845	872	953	1196	262	786	695
114	422	1266	472	1416	922	1103	1646	1612	1510	1204
115	286	858	911	1070	1547	1315	619	194	582	83
116	249	747	578	71	213	639	254	762	623	206
117	618	191	573	56	168	504	1512	1210	304	912
118	1073	1556	1342	700	437	1311	607	158	474	1422
119	940	1157	145	435	1305	589	104	312	936	1145
120	109	327	981	1280	514	1542	1300	574	59	177
121	531	1593	1453	1033	1436	982	1283	523	1569	1381
122	817	788	701	440	1320	634	239	717	488	1464
123	1066	1535	1279	511	1533	1273	493	1479	1111	7
124	21	63	189	567	38	114	342	1026	1415	919
125	1094	1619	1531	1267	475	1425	949	1184	226	678
126	371	1113	13	39	117	351	1053	1496	1162	160
127	480	1440	994	1319	631	230	690	407	1221	337
128	1011	1370	784	689	404	1212	310	930	1127	55
129	165	495	1485	1129	61	183	549	1647	1615	1519
130	1231	367	1101	1640	1594	1456	1042	1463	1063	1526
131	1252	430	1290	544	1632	1570	1384	826	815	782
132	683	386	1158	148	444	1332	670	347	1041	1460
133	1054	1499	1171	187	561	20	60	180	540	1620
134	1534	1276	502	1506	1192	250	750	587	98	294
135	882	983	1286	532	1596	1462	1060	1517	1225	349
136	1047	1478	1108	1661	1657	1645	1609	1501	1177	205
137	615	182	546	1638	1588	1438	988	1301	577	68
138	204	612	173	519	1557	1345	709	464	1392	850
139	887	998	1331	667	338	1014	1379	811	770	647
140	278	834	839	854	899	1034	1439	991	1310	604
141	149	447	1341	697	428	1284	526	1578	1408	898
142	1031	1430	964	1229	361	1083	1586	1432	970	1247
143	415	1245	409	1227	355	1065	1532	1270	484	1452
144	1030	1427	955	1202	280	840	857	908	1061	1520
145	1234	376	1128	58	174	522	1566	1372	790	707
146	458	1374	796	725	512	1536	1282	520	1560	1354
147	736	545	1635	1579	1411	907	1058	1511	1207	295
148	885	992	1313	613	176	528	1584	1426	952	1193
149	253	759	614	179	537	1611	1507	1195	259	777

P = 1663

INDICES

	0	1	2	3	4	5	6	7	8	9
150	216	1367	880	438	853	356	1343	1496	1585	296
151	1148	1477	1176	244	579	492	1648	1357	361	1299
152	1449	864	687	81	37	174	1309	1080	1105	224
153	1120	1252	1436	1234	1340	1231	1465	942	1644	716
154	268	995	1205	1037	723	909	433	1154	1574	414
155	1557	874	1091	990	369	236	1181	1384	680	365
156	1468	17	1051	775	189	517	1456	168	152	1218
157	1315	705	8	1636	760	121	91	209	1417	1473
158	328	799	835	1568	1486	964	1426	945	1374	1622
159	825	767	332	1211	1304	548	1354	720	702	699
160	410	184	463	505	377	622	1544	342	458	1366
161	852	1495	1147	243	1647	1298	686	173	1104	1251
162	1339	941	267	1036	432	413	1090	235	679	16
163	188	167	1314	1635	90	1472	834	963	1373	766
164	1303	719	409	504	1543	1365	1146	1297	1103	940
165	431	234	187	1634	833	765	408	1364	1102	233
166	832	1363	831							

POWER RESIDUES

	0	1	2	3	4	5	6	7	8	9
150	668	341	1023	1406	892	1013	1376	802	743	566
151	35	105	315	945	1172	190	570	47	141	423
152	1269	481	1443	1003	1346	712	473	1419	931	1130
153	64	192	576	65	195	585	92	276	828	821
154	800	737	548	1644	1606	1492	1150	124	372	1116
155	22	66	198	594	119	357	1071	1550	1324	646
156	275	825	812	773	656	305	915	1082	1583	1423
157	943	1166	172	516	1548	1318	628	221	663	326
158	978	1271	487	1461	1057	1508	1198	268	804	749
159	584	89	267	801	740	557	8	24	72	216
160	648	281	843	866	935	1142	100	300	900	1037
161	1448	1018	1391	847	878	971	1250	424	1272	490
162	1470	1084	1589	1441	997	1328	658	311	933	1136
163	82	246	738	551	1653	1633	1573	1393	853	896
164	1025	1412	910	1067	1538	1288	538	1614	1516	1222
165	340	1020	1397	865	932	1133	73	219	657	308
166	924	1109								

P = 1667

INDICES

	0	1	2	3	4	5	6	7	8	9
0		0	1	1214	2	1457	1215	1031	3	762
1	1458	472	1216	374	1032	1005	4	436	763	982
2	1459	579	473	540	1217	1248	375	310	1033	1335
3	1006	720	5	20	437	822	764	281	983	1588
4	1460	1349	580	1536	474	553	541	484	1218	396
5	1249	1650	376	1330	311	263	1034	530	1336	805
6	1007	316	721	127	6	165	21	421	438	88
7	823	730	765	676	282	796	984	1503	1589	257
8	1461	1524	1350	405	581	227	1537	883	475	235
9	554	1405	542	268	485	773	1219	1160	397	1234
10	1250	813	1651	145	377	370	1331	549	312	1499
11	264	1495	1035	28	531	331	1337	1136	806	1467
12	1008	944	317	897	722	1039	128	463	7	1084
13	166	390	22	347	422	101	439	157	89	450
14	824	32	731	846	766	1126	677	1610	283	1394
15	797	1576	985	1198	1504	511	1590	535	258	878
16	1462	1571	1525	1322	1351	1477	406	1422	582	748
17	228	78	1538	335	884	613	476	353	236	1105
18	555	1054	1406	1530	543	72	269	908	486	1341
19	774	1280	1220	61	1161	1379	398	569	1235	1626
20	1251	1635	814	700	1652	1140	146	1302	378	1454
21	371	576	1332	278	550	1327	313	85	1500	224
22	265	810	1496	1133	1036	344	29	1391	532	1474
23	332	1051	1338	566	1137	275	807	1471	1468	184
24	1009	428	945	1072	318	187	898	1356	723	1619
25	1040	1189	129	1012	464	1441	8	657	1085	1312
26	167	431	391	1519	23	1121	348	1449	423	948
27	102	967	440	953	158	54	90	1075	451	1482
28	825	1433	33	1171	732	321	847	714	767	872
29	1127	708	678	190	1611	596	284	782	1395	914
30	798	901	1577	361	986	107	1199	1064	1505	1359
31	512	411	1591	1027	536	1584	259	726	879	141
32	1463	97	1572	1418	1526	1622	1323	1047	1352	1515
33	1478	592	407	1043	1423	212	583	972	749	1242
34	229	1192	79	1427	1539	1545	336	647	885	132
35	614	684	477	606	354	521	237	1015	1106	216
36	556	298	1055	492	1407	467	1531	791	544	445
37	73	695	270	1444	909	587	487	43	1342	741
38	775	11	1281	932	1221	1294	62	632	1162	660
39	1380	976	399	1604	570	48	1236	1088	1627	1561
40	1252	958	1636	1094	815	1315	701	753	1653	1551
41	1141	1371	147	170	1303	196	379	1664	1455	760
42	372	434	577	1246	1333	18	279	1347	551	394
43	1328	528	314	163	86	674	1501	1522	225	233
44	266	1158	811	368	1497	26	1134	942	1037	1082
45	345	155	30	1124	1392	1196	533	1569	1475	746
46	333	351	1052	70	1339	59	567	1633	1138	1452
47	276	83	808	342	1472	564	1469	426	185	1617
48	1010	655	429	1119	946	951	1073	1431	319	870
49	188	780	899	105	1357	1025	724	95	1620	1513

POWER RESIDUES

	0	1	2	3	4	5	6	7	8	9
0	1	2	4	8	16	32	64	128	256	512
1	1024	381	762	1524	1381	1095	523	1046	425	850
2	33	66	132	264	528	1056	445	890	113	226
3	452	904	141	282	564	1128	589	1178	689	1378
4	1089	511	1022	377	754	1508	1349	1031	395	790
5	1580	1493	1319	971	275	550	1100	533	1066	465
6	930	193	386	772	1544	1421	1175	683	1366	1065
7	463	926	185	370	740	1480	1293	919	171	342
8	684	1368	1069	471	942	217	434	868	69	138
9	276	552	1104	541	1082	497	994	321	642	1284
10	901	135	270	540	1080	493	986	305	610	1220
11	773	1546	1425	1183	699	1398	1129	591	1182	697
12	1394	1121	575	1150	633	1266	865	63	126	252
13	504	1008	349	698	1396	1125	583	1166	665	1330
14	993	319	638	1276	885	103	206	412	824	1648
15	1629	1591	1515	1363	1059	451	902	137	274	548
16	1096	525	1050	433	866	65	130	260	520	1040
17	413	826	1652	1637	1607	1547	1427	1187	707	1414
18	1161	655	1310	953	239	478	956	245	490	980
19	293	586	1172	677	1354	1041	415	830	1660	1653
20	1639	1611	1555	1443	1219	771	1542	1417	1167	667
21	1334	1001	335	670	1340	1013	359	718	1436	1205
22	743	1486	1305	943	219	438	876	85	170	340
23	680	1360	1053	439	878	89	178	356	712	1424
24	1181	695	1390	1113	559	1118	569	1138	609	1218
25	769	1538	1409	1151	635	1270	873	79	158	316
26	632	1264	861	55	110	220	440	880	93	186
27	372	744	1488	1309	951	235	470	940	213	426
28	852	37	74	148	296	592	1184	701	1402	1137
29	607	1214	761	1522	1377	1087	507	1014	361	722
30	1444	1221	775	1550	1433	1199	731	1462	1257	847
31	27	54	108	216	432	864	61	122	244	488
32	976	285	570	1140	613	1226	785	1570	1473	1279
33	891	115	230	460	920	173	346	692	1384	1101
34	535	1070	473	946	225	450	900	133	266	532
35	1064	461	922	177	354	708	1416	1165	663	1326
36	985	303	606	1212	757	1514	1361	1055	443	886
37	105	210	420	840	13	26	52	104	208	416
38	832	1664	1661	1655	1643	1619	1571	1475	1283	899
39	131	262	524	1048	429	858	49	98	196	392
40	784	1568	1469	1271	875	83	166	332	664	1328
41	989	311	622	1244	821	1642	1617	1567	1467	1267
42	867	67	134	268	536	1072	477	954	241	482
43	964	261	522	1044	421	842	17	34	68	136
44	272	544	1088	509	1018	369	738	1476	1285	903
45	139	278	556	1112	557	1114	561	1122	577	1154
46	641	1282	897	127	254	508	1016	365	730	1460
47	1253	839	11	22	44	88	176	352	704	1408
48	1149	631	1262	857	47	94	188	376	752	1504
49	1341	1015	363	726	1452	1237	807	1614	1561	1455

P = 1667

INDICES

	0	1	2	3	4	5	6	7	8	9
50	1041	970	1190	1543	130	604	1013	296	465	443
51	1442	41	9	1292	658	1602	1086	956	1313	1549
52	168	1662	432	16	392	161	1520	1156	24	1080
53	1122	1567	349	57	1450	340	424	653	949	868
54	103	93	968	602	441	1290	954	1660	159	1078
55	55	651	91	1288	1076	1286	452	454	1483	244
56	826	456	1434	925	34	1485	1172	889	733	246
57	322	993	848	828	715	122	768	458	873	1275
58	1128	1436	709	136	679	927	191	937	1612	36
59	597	117	285	1487	783	1258	1396	1174	915	618
60	799	891	902	1183	1578	735	362	290	987	248
61	108	858	1200	324	1065	688	1506	995	1360	1226
62	513	850	412	1266	1592	830	1028	1002	537	717
63	1585	481	260	124	727	254	880	770	142	1492
64	1464	460	98	843	1573	875	1419	610	1527	1277
65	1623	1299	1324	1130	1048	181	1353	1438	1516	964
66	1479	711	593	358	408	138	1044	209	1424	681
67	213	788	584	929	973	1558	750	193	1243	525
68	230	939	1193	67	80	1614	1428	1022	1540	38
69	1546	1153	337	599	648	241	886	119	133	114
70	615	287	685	1263	478	1489	607	178	355	785
71	522	1019	238	1260	1016	637	1107	1398	217	640
72	557	1176	299	1642	1056	917	493	1110	1408	620
73	468	306	1532	801	792	1401	545	893	446	507
74	74	904	696	220	271	1185	1445	1167	910	1580
75	588	643	488	737	44	1367	1343	364	742	560
76	776	292	12	864	1282	989	933	1179	1222	250
77	1295	205	63	110	633	302	1163	860	661	665
78	1381	1202	977	1645	400	326	1605	1100	571	1067
79	49	1059	1237	690	1089	669	1628	1508	1562	920
80	1253	997	959	1148	1637	1362	1095	496	816	1228
81	1316	1385	702	515	754	1113	1654	852	1552	501
82	1142	414	1372	1411	148	1268	171	1206	1304	1594
83	197	623	380	832	1665	1213	1456	1030	761	471
84	373	1004	435	981	578	539	1247	309	1334	719
85	19	821	280	1587	1348	1535	552	483	395	1649
86	1329	262	529	804	315	126	164	420	87	729
87	675	795	1502	256	1523	404	226	882	234	1404
88	267	772	1159	1233	812	144	369	548	1498	1494
89	27	330	1135	1466	943	896	1038	462	1083	389
90	346	100	156	449	31	845	1125	1609	1393	1575
91	1197	510	534	877	1570	1321	1476	1421	747	77
92	334	612	352	1104	1053	1529	71	907	1340	1279
93	60	1378	568	1625	1634	699	1139	1301	1453	575
94	277	1326	84	223	809	1132	343	1390	1473	1050
95	565	274	1470	183	427	1071	186	1355	1618	1188
96	1011	1440	656	1311	430	1518	1120	1448	947	966
97	952	53	1074	1481	1432	1170	320	713	871	707
98	189	595	781	913	900	360	106	1063	1358	410
99	1026	1583	725	140	96	1417	1621	1046	1514	591

POWER RESIDUES

	0	1	2	3	4	5	6	7	8	9
50	1243	819	1638	1609	1551	1435	1203	739	1478	1289
51	911	155	310	620	1240	813	1626	1585	1503	1339
52	1011	355	710	1420	1173	679	1358	1049	431	862
53	57	114	228	456	912	157	314	628	1256	845
54	23	46	92	184	368	736	1472	1277	887	107
55	214	428	856	45	90	180	360	720	1440	1213
56	759	1518	1369	1071	475	950	233	466	932	197
57	394	788	1576	1485	1303	939	211	422	844	21
58	42	84	168	336	672	1344	1021	375	750	1500
59	1333	999	331	662	1324	981	295	590	1180	693
60	1386	1105	543	1086	505	1010	353	706	1412	1157
61	647	1294	921	175	350	700	1400	1133	599	1198
62	729	1458	1249	831	1662	1657	1647	1627	1587	1507
63	1347	1027	387	774	1548	1429	1191	715	1430	1193
64	719	1438	1209	751	1502	1337	1007	347	694	1388
65	1109	551	1102	537	1074	481	962	257	514	1028
66	389	778	1556	1445	1223	779	1558	1449	1231	795
67	1590	1513	1359	1051	435	870	73	146	292	584
68	1168	669	1338	1009	351	702	1404	1141	615	1230
69	793	1586	1505	1343	1019	371	742	1484	1301	935
70	203	406	812	1624	1581	1495	1323	979	291	582
71	1164	661	1322	977	287	574	1148	629	1258	849
72	31	62	124	248	496	992	317	634	1268	869
73	71	142	284	568	1136	605	1210	753	1506	1345
74	1023	379	758	1516	1365	1063	459	918	169	338
75	676	1352	1037	407	814	1628	1589	1511	1355	1043
76	419	838	9	18	36	72	144	288	576	1152
77	637	1274	881	95	190	380	760	1520	1373	1079
78	491	982	297	594	1188	709	1418	1169	671	1342
79	1017	367	734	1468	1269	871	75	150	300	600
80	1200	733	1466	1265	863	59	118	236	472	944
81	221	442	884	101	202	404	808	1616	1565	1463
82	1259	851	35	70	140	280	560	1120	573	1146
83	625	1250	833	1666	1665	1663	1659	1651	1635	1603
84	1539	1411	1155	643	1286	905	143	286	572	1144
85	621	1242	817	1634	1601	1535	1403	1139	611	1222
86	777	1554	1441	1215	763	1526	1385	1103	539	1078
87	489	978	289	578	1156	645	1290	913	159	318
88	636	1272	877	87	174	348	696	1392	1117	567
89	1134	601	1202	737	1474	1281	895	123	246	492
90	984	301	602	1204	741	1482	1297	927	187	374
91	748	1496	1325	983	299	598	1196	725	1450	1233
92	799	1598	1529	1391	1115	563	1126	585	1170	673
93	1346	1025	383	766	1532	1397	1127	587	1174	681
94	1362	1057	447	894	121	242	484	968	269	538
95	1076	485	970	273	546	1092	517	1034	401	802
96	1604	1541	1415	1163	659	1318	969	271	542	1084
97	501	1002	337	674	1348	1029	391	782	1564	1461
98	1255	843	19	38	76	152	304	608	1216	765
99	1530	1393	1119	571	1142	617	1234	801	1602	1537

P = 1667

INDICES

	0	1	2	3	4	5	6	7	8	9
100	1042	211	971	1241	1191	1426	1544	646	131	683
101	605	520	1014	215	297	491	466	790	444	694
102	1443	586	42	740	10	931	1293	631	659	975
103	1603	47	1087	1560	957	1093	1314	752	1550	1370
104	169	195	1663	759	433	1245	17	1346	393	527
105	162	673	1521	232	1157	367	25	941	1081	154
106	1123	1195	1568	745	350	69	58	1632	1451	82
107	341	563	425	1616	654	1118	950	1430	869	779
108	104	1024	94	1512	969	1542	603	295	442	40
109	1291	1601	955	1548	1661	15	160	1155	1079	1566
110	56	339	652	867	92	601	1289	1659	1077	650
111	1287	1285	453	243	455	924	1484	888	245	992
112	827	121	457	1274	1435	135	926	936	35	116
113	1486	1257	1173	617	890	1182	734	289	247	857
114	323	687	994	1225	849	1265	829	1001	716	480
115	123	253	769	1491	459	842	874	609	1276	1298
116	1129	180	1437	963	710	357	137	208	680	787
117	928	1557	192	524	938	66	1613	1021	37	1152
118	598	240	118	113	286	1262	1488	177	784	1018
119	1259	636	1397	639	1175	1641	916	1109	619	305
120	800	1400	892	506	903	219	1184	1166	1579	642
121	736	1366	363	559	291	863	988	1178	249	204
122	109	301	859	664	1201	1644	325	1099	1066	1058
123	689	668	1507	919	996	1147	1361	495	1227	1384
124	514	1112	851	500	413	1410	1267	1205	1593	622
125	831	1212	1029	470	1003	980	538	308	718	820
126	1586	1534	482	1648	261	803	125	419	728	794
127	255	403	881	1403	771	1232	143	547	1493	329
128	1465	895	461	388	99	448	844	1608	1574	509
129	876	1320	1420	76	611	1103	1528	906	1278	1377
130	1624	698	1300	574	1325	222	1131	1389	1049	273
131	182	1070	1354	1187	1439	1310	1517	1447	965	52
132	1480	1169	712	706	594	912	359	1062	409	1582
133	139	1416	1045	590	210	1240	1425	645	682	519
134	214	490	789	693	585	739	930	630	974	46
135	1559	1092	751	1369	194	758	1244	1345	526	672
136	231	366	940	153	1194	744	68	1631	81	562
137	1615	1117	1429	778	1023	1511	1541	294	39	1600
138	1547	14	1154	1565	338	866	600	1658	649	1284
139	242	923	887	991	120	1273	134	935	115	1256
140	616	1181	288	856	686	1224	1264	1000	479	252
141	1490	841	608	1297	179	962	356	207	786	1556
142	523	65	1020	1151	239	112	1261	176	1017	635
143	638	1640	1108	304	1399	505	218	1165	641	1365
144	558	862	1177	203	300	663	1643	1098	1057	667
145	918	1146	494	1383	1111	499	1409	1204	621	1211
146	469	979	307	819	1533	1647	802	418	793	402
147	1402	1231	546	328	894	387	447	1607	508	1319
148	75	1102	905	1376	697	573	221	1388	272	1069
149	1186	1309	1446	51	1168	705	911	1061	1581	1415

POWER RESIDUES

	0	1	2	3	4	5	6	7	8	9
100	1407	1147	627	1254	841	15	30	60	120	240
101	480	960	253	506	1012	357	714	1428	1189	711
102	1422	1177	687	1374	1081	495	990	313	626	1252
103	837	7	14	28	56	112	224	448	896	125
104	250	500	1000	333	666	1332	997	327	654	1308
105	949	231	462	924	181	362	724	1448	1229	791
106	1582	1497	1327	987	307	614	1228	789	1578	1489
107	1311	955	243	486	972	277	554	1108	549	1098
108	529	1058	449	898	129	258	516	1032	397	794
109	1588	1509	1351	1035	403	806	1612	1557	1447	1227
110	787	1574	1481	1295	923	179	358	716	1432	1197
111	727	1454	1241	815	1630	1593	1519	1371	1075	483
112	966	265	530	1060	453	906	145	290	580	1160
113	653	1306	945	223	446	892	117	234	468	936
114	205	410	820	1640	1613	1559	1451	1235	803	1606
115	1545	1423	1179	691	1382	1097	527	1054	441	882
116	97	194	388	776	1552	1437	1207	747	1494	1321
117	975	283	566	1132	597	1194	721	1442	1217	767
118	1534	1401	1135	603	1206	745	1490	1313	959	251
119	502	1004	341	682	1364	1061	455	910	153	306
120	612	1224	781	1562	1457	1247	827	1654	1641	1615
121	1563	1459	1251	835	3	6	12	24	48	96
122	192	384	768	1536	1405	1143	619	1238	809	1618
123	1569	1471	1275	883	99	198	396	792	1584	1501
124	1335	1003	339	678	1356	1045	423	846	25	50
125	100	200	400	800	1600	1533	1399	1131	595	1190
126	713	1426	1185	703	1406	1145	623	1246	825	1650
127	1633	1599	1531	1395	1123	579	1158	649	1298	929
128	191	382	764	1528	1389	1111	555	1110	553	1106
129	545	1090	513	1026	385	770	1540	1413	1159	651
130	1302	937	207	414	828	1656	1645	1623	1579	1491
131	1315	963	259	518	1036	405	810	1620	1573	1479
132	1291	915	163	326	652	1304	941	215	430	860
133	53	106	212	424	848	29	58	116	232	464
134	928	189	378	756	1512	1357	1047	427	854	41
135	82	164	328	656	1312	957	247	494	988	309
136	618	1236	805	1610	1553	1439	1211	755	1510	1353
137	1039	411	822	1644	1621	1575	1483	1299	931	195
138	390	780	1560	1453	1239	811	1622	1577	1487	1307
139	947	227	454	908	149	298	596	1192	717	1434
140	1201	735	1470	1273	879	91	182	364	728	1456
141	1245	823	1646	1625	1583	1499	1331	995	323	646
142	1292	917	167	334	668	1336	1005	343	686	1372
143	1077	487	974	281	562	1124	581	1162	657	1314
144	961	255	510	1020	373	746	1492	1317	967	267
145	534	1068	469	938	209	418	836	5	10	20
146	40	80	160	320	640	1280	893	119	238	476
147	952	237	474	948	229	458	916	165	330	660
148	1320	973	279	558	1116	565	1130	593	1186	705
149	1410	1153	639	1278	889	111	222	444	888	109

P = 1667

INDICES

	0	1	2	3	4	5	6	7	8	9
150	589	1239	644	518	489	692	738	629	45	1091
151	1368	757	1344	671	365	152	743	1630	561	1116
152	777	1510	293	1599	13	1564	865	1657	1283	922
153	990	1272	934	1255	1180	855	1223	999	251	840
154	1296	961	206	1555	64	1150	111	175	634	1639
155	303	504	1164	1364	861	202	662	1097	666	1145
156	1382	498	1203	1210	978	818	1646	417	401	1230
157	327	386	1606	1318	1101	1375	572	1387	1068	1308
158	50	704	1060	1414	1238	517	691	628	1090	756
159	670	151	1629	1115	1509	1598	1563	1656	921	1271
160	1254	854	998	839	960	1554	1149	174	1638	503
161	1363	201	1096	1144	497	1209	817	416	1229	385
162	1317	1374	1386	1307	703	1413	516	627	755	150
163	1114	1597	1655	1270	853	838	1553	173	502	200
164	1143	1208	415	384	1373	1306	1412	626	149	1596
165	1269	837	172	199	1207	383	1305	625	1595	836
166	198	382	624	835	381	834	833			

POWER RESIDUES

	0	1	2	3	4	5	6	7	8	9
150	218	436	872	77	154	308	616	1232	797	1594
151	1521	1375	1083	499	998	329	658	1316	965	263
152	526	1052	437	874	81	162	324	648	1296	925
153	183	366	732	1464	1261	855	43	86	172	344
154	688	1376	1085	503	1006	345	690	1380	1093	519
155	1038	409	818	1636	1605	1543	1419	1171	675	1350
156	1033	399	798	1596	1525	1383	1099	531	1062	457
157	914	161	322	644	1288	909	151	302	604	1208
158	749	1498	1329	991	315	630	1260	853	39	78
159	156	312	624	1248	829	1658	1649	1631	1595	1523
160	1379	1091	515	1030	393	786	1572	1477	1287	907
161	147	294	588	1176	685	1370	1073	479	958	249
162	498	996	325	650	1300	933	199	398	796	1592
163	1517	1367	1067	467	934	201	402	804	1608	1549
164	1431	1195	723	1446	1225	783	1566	1465	1263	859
165	51	102	204	408	816	1632	1597	1527	1387	1107
166	547	1094	521	1042	417	834				

P = 1669

INDICES

	0	1	2	3	4	5	6	7	8	9
0		0	1	900	2	1586	901	509	3	132
1	1587	1331	902	745	510	818	4	715	133	1234
2	1588	1409	1332	1444	903	1504	746	1032	511	372
3	819	553	5	563	716	427	134	786	1235	1645
4	1589	1285	1410	26	1333	50	1445	1310	904	1018
5	1505	1615	747	1027	1033	1249	512	466	373	1038
6	820	1134	554	641	6	663	564	1065	717	676
7	428	1192	135	143	787	736	1236	172	1646	1012
8	1590	264	1286	1046	1411	633	27	1272	1334	98
9	51	1254	1446	1453	1311	1152	905	39	1019	1463
10	1506	189	1616	571	748	1327	1028	22	1034	732
11	1250	18	513	1596	467	1362	374	877	1039	1224
12	821	994	1135	517	555	1422	642	222	7	926
13	664	1639	565	75	1066	950	718	1436	677	1600
14	429	542	1193	408	136	290	144	250	788	322
15	737	1174	1237	847	173	471	1647	710	1013	259
16	1591	285	265	892	1287	481	1047	81	1412	1490
17	634	1366	28	1215	1273	345	1335	270	99	1075
18	52	623	1255	366	1447	704	1454	378	1312	1541
19	1153	1373	906	585	40	1563	1020	616	1464	1003
20	1507	297	190	881	1617	1203	572	1576	749	897
21	1328	1231	1029	424	23	1612	1035	1062	733	1043
22	1251	1460	19	1359	514	1636	1597	247	468	889
23	1363	1072	375	1560	878	1228	1040	244	1225	1161
24	822	1292	995	1164	1136	936	518	311	556	278
25	1423	825	643	1107	223	1533	8	155	927	1295
26	665	504	1640	1187	566	945	76	998	1067	1182
27	951	1627	719	486	1437	1167	678	442	1601	685
28	430	1482	543	1139	1194	384	409	126	137	1430
29	291	939	145	865	251	956	789	695	323	521
30	738	535	1175	1089	1238	1052	848	314	174	1471
31	472	1383	1648	1664	711	559	1014	659	260	35
32	1592	922	286	281	266	581	893	1632	1288	151
33	482	1426	1048	918	82	983	1413	86	1491	828
34	635	216	1367	1527	29	594	1216	646	1274	1318
35	346	109	1336	987	271	1110	100	456	1076	724
36	53	800	624	226	1256	61	367	1129	1448	1417
37	705	1536	1455	1102	379	654	1313	1117	1542	11
38	1154	1122	1374	600	907	90	586	158	41	760
39	1564	491	1021	871	617	930	1465	1096	1004	975
40	1508	1495	298	1298	191	182	882	449	1618	1395
41	1204	668	573	1547	1577	964	750	832	898	507
42	1329	816	1232	1442	1030	551	425	1643	24	1308
43	1613	1247	1036	639	1063	1190	734	1010	1044	1270
44	1252	1150	1461	569	20	16	1360	1222	515	220
45	1637	948	1598	406	248	1172	469	257	890	79
46	1364	343	1073	364	376	1371	1561	1001	879	1574
47	1229	1610	1041	1357	245	1070	1226	1159	1162	309
48	823	1531	1293	1185	996	1625	1165	683	1137	124
49	937	954	519	1087	312	1381	557	33	279	1630

POWER RESIDUES

	0	1	2	3	4	5	6	7	8	9
0	1	2	4	8	16	32	64	128	256	512
1	1024	379	758	1516	1363	1057	445	890	111	222
2	444	888	107	214	428	856	43	86	172	344
3	688	1376	1083	497	994	319	638	1276	883	97
4	194	388	776	1552	1435	1201	733	1466	1263	857
5	45	90	180	360	720	1440	1211	753	1506	1343
6	1017	365	730	1460	1251	833	1666	1663	1657	1645
7	1621	1573	1477	1285	901	133	266	532	1064	459
8	918	167	334	668	1336	1003	337	674	1348	1027
9	385	770	1540	1411	1153	637	1274	879	89	178
10	356	712	1424	1179	689	1378	1087	505	1010	351
11	702	1404	1139	609	1218	767	1534	1399	1129	589
12	1178	687	1374	1079	489	978	287	574	1148	627
13	1254	839	9	18	36	72	144	288	576	1152
14	635	1270	871	73	146	292	584	1168	667	1334
15	999	329	658	1316	963	257	514	1028	387	774
16	1548	1427	1185	701	1402	1135	601	1202	735	1470
17	1271	873	77	154	308	616	1232	795	1590	1511
18	1353	1037	405	810	1620	1571	1473	1277	885	101
19	202	404	808	1616	1563	1457	1245	821	1642	1615
20	1561	1453	1237	805	1610	1551	1433	1197	725	1450
21	1231	793	1586	1503	1337	1005	341	682	1364	1059
22	449	898	127	254	508	1016	363	726	1452	1235
23	801	1602	1535	1401	1133	597	1194	719	1438	1207
24	745	1490	1311	953	237	474	948	227	454	908
25	147	294	588	1176	683	1366	1063	457	914	159
26	318	636	1272	875	81	162	324	648	1296	923
27	177	354	708	1416	1163	657	1314	959	249	498
28	996	323	646	1292	915	161	322	644	1288	907
29	145	290	580	1160	651	1302	935	201	402	804
30	1608	1547	1425	1181	693	1386	1103	537	1074	479
31	958	247	494	988	307	614	1228	787	1574	1479
32	1289	909	149	298	596	1192	715	1430	1191	713
33	1426	1183	697	1394	1119	569	1138	607	1214	759
34	1518	1367	1065	461	922	175	350	700	1400	1131
35	593	1186	703	1406	1143	617	1234	799	1598	1527
36	1385	1101	533	1066	463	926	183	366	732	1464
37	1259	849	29	58	116	232	464	928	187	374
38	748	1496	1323	977	285	570	1140	611	1222	775
39	1550	1431	1193	717	1434	1199	729	1458	1247	825
40	1650	1631	1593	1517	1365	1061	453	906	143	286
41	572	1144	619	1238	807	1614	1559	1449	1229	789
42	1578	1487	1305	941	213	426	852	35	70	140
43	280	560	1120	571	1142	615	1230	791	1582	1495
44	1321	973	277	554	1108	547	1094	519	1038	407
45	814	1628	1587	1505	1341	1013	357	714	1428	1187
46	705	1410	1151	633	1266	863	57	114	228	456
47	912	155	310	620	1240	811	1622	1575	1481	1293
48	917	165	330	660	1320	971	273	546	1092	515
49	1030	391	782	1564	1459	1249	829	1658	1647	1625

P = 1669

INDICES

	0	1	2	3	4	5	6	7	8	9
50	1424	981	826	1525	644	107	1108	722	224	1127
51	1534	652	9	598	156	489	928	973	1296	447
52	666	962	505	1440	1641	1245	1188	1268	567	1220
53	946	1170	77	362	999	1608	1068	307	1183	681
54	952	1379	1628	1523	720	650	487	445	1438	1266
55	1168	1606	679	1521	443	1604	1602	769	686	771
56	431	1278	1483	688	544	1514	1140	773	1195	335
57	385	433	410	605	127	1280	138	1322	1431	1485
58	292	1555	940	690	146	795	866	546	252	119
59	957	1516	790	350	696	1142	324	235	522	775
60	739	166	536	1197	1176	912	1090	337	1239	113
61	1053	387	849	1402	315	435	175	355	1472	412
62	473	808	1384	607	1649	1340	1665	129	712	1501
63	560	1282	1015	463	660	140	261	95	36	1324
64	1593	991	923	1433	287	844	282	1487	267	701
65	582	294	894	1059	1633	1557	1289	275	152	942
66	483	1479	1427	692	1049	1661	919	148	83	591
67	984	797	1414	1114	87	868	1492	1392	829	548
68	636	1147	217	254	1368	1354	1528	121	30	104
69	595	959	1217	304	647	1518	1275	332	1319	792
70	347	163	110	352	1337	460	988	698	272	1658
71	1111	1144	101	329	457	326	1077	393	725	237
72	54	1080	801	524	625	208	227	777	1257	396
73	62	741	368	46	1130	168	1449	728	1418	538
74	706	1211	1537	1199	1456	240	1103	1178	380	531
75	655	914	1314	57	1118	1092	1543	1304	12	339
76	1155	1083	1123	1241	1375	765	601	115	908	804
77	91	1055	587	1350	159	389	42	527	761	851
78	1565	855	492	1404	1022	628	872	317	618	419
79	931	437	1466	211	1097	177	1005	1569	976	357
80	1509	230	1496	1474	299	203	1299	414	192	780
81	183	475	883	859	450	810	1619	1260	1396	1386
82	1205	197	669	609	574	399	1548	1651	1578	496
83	965	1342	751	65	833	1667	899	1585	508	131
84	1330	744	817	714	1233	1408	1443	1503	1031	371
85	552	562	426	785	1644	1284	25	49	1309	1017
86	1614	1026	1248	465	1037	1133	640	662	1064	675
87	1191	142	735	171	1011	263	1045	632	1271	97
88	1253	1452	1151	38	1462	188	570	1326	21	731
89	17	1595	1361	876	1223	993	516	1421	221	925
90	1638	74	949	1435	1599	541	407	289	249	321
91	1173	846	470	709	258	284	891	480	80	1489
92	1365	1214	344	269	1074	622	365	703	377	1540
93	1372	584	1562	615	1002	296	880	1202	1575	896
94	1230	423	1611	1061	1042	1459	1358	1635	246	888
95	1071	1559	1227	243	1160	1291	1163	935	310	277
96	824	1106	1532	154	1294	503	1186	944	997	1181
97	1626	485	1166	441	684	1481	1138	383	125	1429
98	938	864	955	694	520	534	1088	1051	313	1470
99	1382	1663	558	658	34	921	280	580	1631	150

POWER RESIDUES

	0	1	2	3	4	5	6	7	8	9
50	1581	1493	1317	965	261	522	1044	419	838	7
51	14	28	56	112	224	448	896	123	246	492
52	984	299	598	1196	723	1446	1223	777	1554	1439
53	1209	749	1498	1327	985	301	602	1204	739	1478
54	1287	905	141	282	564	1128	587	1174	679	1358
55	1047	425	850	31	62	124	248	496	992	315
56	630	1260	851	33	66	132	264	528	1056	443
57	886	103	206	412	824	1648	1627	1585	1501	1333
58	997	325	650	1300	931	193	386	772	1544	1419
59	1169	669	1338	1007	345	690	1380	1091	513	1026
60	383	766	1532	1395	1121	573	1146	623	1246	823
61	1646	1623	1577	1485	1301	933	197	394	788	1576
62	1483	1297	925	181	362	724	1448	1227	785	1570
63	1471	1273	877	85	170	340	680	1360	1051	433
64	866	63	126	252	504	1008	347	694	1388	1107
65	545	1090	511	1022	375	750	1500	1331	993	317
66	634	1268	867	65	130	260	520	1040	411	822
67	1644	1619	1569	1469	1269	869	69	138	276	552
68	1104	539	1078	487	974	279	558	1116	563	1126
69	583	1166	663	1326	983	297	594	1188	707	1414
70	1159	649	1298	927	185	370	740	1480	1291	913
71	157	314	628	1256	843	17	34	68	136	272
72	544	1088	507	1014	359	718	1436	1203	737	1474
73	1279	889	109	218	436	872	75	150	300	600
74	1200	731	1462	1255	841	13	26	52	104	208
75	416	832	1664	1659	1649	1629	1589	1509	1349	1029
76	389	778	1556	1443	1217	765	1530	1391	1113	557
77	1114	559	1118	567	1134	599	1198	727	1454	1239
78	809	1618	1567	1465	1261	853	37	74	148	296
79	592	1184	699	1398	1127	585	1170	671	1342	1015
80	361	722	1444	1219	769	1538	1407	1145	621	1242
81	815	1630	1591	1513	1357	1045	421	842	15	30
82	60	120	240	480	960	251	502	1004	339	678
83	1356	1043	417	834	1668	1667	1665	1661	1653	1637
84	1605	1541	1413	1157	645	1290	911	153	306	612
85	1224	779	1558	1447	1225	781	1562	1455	1241	813
86	1626	1583	1497	1325	981	293	586	1172	675	1350
87	1031	393	786	1572	1475	1281	893	117	234	468
88	936	203	406	812	1624	1579	1489	1309	949	229
89	458	916	163	326	652	1304	939	209	418	836
90	3	6	12	24	48	96	192	384	768	1536
91	1403	1137	605	1210	751	1502	1335	1001	333	666
92	1332	995	321	642	1284	899	129	258	516	1032
93	395	790	1580	1491	1313	957	245	490	980	291
94	582	1164	659	1318	967	265	530	1060	451	902
95	135	270	540	1080	491	982	295	590	1180	691
96	1382	1095	521	1042	415	830	1660	1651	1633	1597
97	1525	1381	1093	517	1034	399	798	1596	1523	1377
98	1085	501	1002	335	670	1340	1011	353	706	1412
99	1155	641	1282	895	121	242	484	968	267	534

P = 1669

INDICES

	0	1	2	3	4	5	6	7	8	9
100	1425	917	982	85	827	215	1526	593	645	1317
101	108	986	1109	455	723	799	225	60	1128	1416
102	1535	1101	653	1116	10	1121	599	89	157	759
103	490	870	929	1095	974	1494	1297	181	448	1394
104	667	1546	963	831	506	815	1441	550	1642	1307
105	1246	638	1189	1009	1269	1149	568	15	1221	219
106	947	405	1171	256	78	342	363	1370	1000	1573
107	1609	1356	1069	1158	308	1530	1184	1624	682	123
108	953	1086	1380	32	1629	980	1524	106	721	1126
109	651	597	488	972	446	961	1439	1244	1267	1219
110	1169	361	1607	306	680	1378	1522	649	444	1265
111	1605	1520	1603	768	770	1277	687	1513	772	334
112	432	604	1279	1321	1484	1554	689	794	545	118
113	1515	349	1141	234	774	165	1196	911	336	112
114	386	1401	434	354	411	807	606	1339	128	1500
115	1281	462	139	94	1323	990	1432	843	1486	700
116	293	1058	1556	274	941	1478	691	1660	147	590
117	796	1113	867	1391	547	1146	253	1353	120	103
118	958	303	1517	331	791	162	351	459	697	1657
119	1143	328	325	392	236	1079	523	207	776	395
120	740	45	167	727	537	1210	1198	239	1177	530
121	913	56	1091	1303	338	1082	1240	764	114	803
122	1054	1349	388	526	850	854	1403	627	316	418
123	436	210	176	1568	356	229	1473	202	413	779
124	474	858	809	1259	1385	196	608	398	1650	495
125	1341	64	1666	1584	130	743	713	1407	1502	370
126	561	784	1283	48	1016	1025	464	1132	661	674
127	141	170	262	631	96	1451	37	187	1325	730
128	1594	875	992	1420	924	73	1434	540	288	320
129	845	708	283	479	1488	1213	268	621	702	1539
130	583	614	295	1201	895	422	1060	1458	1634	887
131	1558	242	1290	934	276	1105	153	502	943	1180
132	484	440	1480	382	1428	863	693	533	1050	1469
133	1662	657	920	579	149	916	84	214	592	1316
134	985	454	798	59	1415	1100	1115	1120	88	758
135	869	1094	1493	180	1393	1545	830	814	549	1306
136	637	1008	1148	14	218	404	255	341	1369	1572
137	1355	1157	1529	1623	122	1085	31	979	105	1125
138	596	971	960	1243	1218	360	305	1377	648	1264
139	1519	767	1276	1512	333	603	1320	1553	793	117
140	348	233	164	910	111	1400	353	806	1338	1499
141	461	93	989	842	699	1057	273	1477	1659	589
142	1112	1390	1145	1352	102	302	330	161	458	1656
143	327	391	1078	206	394	44	726	1209	238	529
144	55	1302	1081	763	802	1348	525	853	626	417
145	209	1567	228	201	778	857	1258	195	397	494
146	63	1583	742	1406	369	783	47	1024	1131	673
147	169	630	1450	186	729	874	1419	72	539	319
148	707	478	1212	620	1538	613	1200	421	1457	886
149	241	933	1104	501	1179	439	381	862	532	1468

POWER RESIDUES

	0	1	2	3	4	5	6	7	8	9
100	1068	467	934	199	398	796	1592	1515	1361	1053
101	437	874	79	158	316	632	1264	859	49	98
102	196	392	784	1568	1467	1265	861	53	106	212
103	424	848	27	54	108	216	432	864	59	118
104	236	472	944	219	438	876	83	166	332	664
105	1328	987	305	610	1220	771	1542	1415	1161	653
106	1306	943	217	434	868	67	134	268	536	1072
107	475	950	231	462	924	179	358	716	1432	1195
108	721	1442	1215	761	1522	1375	1081	493	986	303
109	606	1212	755	1510	1351	1033	397	794	1588	1507
110	1345	1021	373	746	1492	1315	961	253	506	1012
111	355	710	1420	1171	673	1346	1023	377	754	1508
112	1347	1025	381	762	1524	1379	1089	509	1018	367
113	734	1468	1267	865	61	122	244	488	976	283
114	566	1132	595	1190	711	1422	1175	681	1362	1055
115	441	882	95	190	380	760	1520	1371	1073	477
116	954	239	478	956	243	486	972	275	550	1100
117	531	1062	455	910	151	302	604	1208	747	1494
118	1319	969	269	538	1076	483	966	263	526	1052
119	435	870	71	142	284	568	1136	603	1206	743
120	1486	1303	937	205	410	820	1640	1611	1553	1437
121	1205	741	1482	1295	921	173	346	692	1384	1099
122	529	1058	447	894	119	238	476	952	235	470
123	940	211	422	844	19	38	76	152	304	608
124	1216	763	1526	1383	1097	525	1050	431	862	55
125	110	220	440	880	91	182	364	728	1456	1243
126	817	1634	1599	1529	1389	1109	549	1098	527	1054
127	439	878	87	174	348	696	1392	1115	561	1122
128	575	1150	631	1262	855	41	82	164	328	656
129	1312	955	241	482	964	259	518	1036	403	806
130	1612	1555	1441	1213	757	1514	1359	1049	429	858
131	47	94	188	376	752	1504	1339	1009	349	698
132	1396	1123	577	1154	639	1278	887	105	210	420
133	840	11	22	44	88	176	352	704	1408	1147
134	625	1250	831	1662	1655	1641	1613	1557	1445	1221
135	773	1546	1423	1177	685	1370	1071	473	946	223
136	446	892	115	230	460	920	171	342	684	1368
137	1067	465	930	191	382	764	1528	1387	1105	541
138	1082	495	990	311	622	1244	819	1638	1607	1545
139	1421	1173	677	1354	1039	409	818	1636	1603	1537
140	1405	1141	613	1226	783	1566	1463	1257	845	21
141	42	84	168	336	672	1344	1019	369	738	1476
142	1283	897	125	250	500	1000	331	662	1324	979
143	289	578	1156	643	1286	903	137	274	548	1096
144	523	1046	423	846	23	46	92	184	368	736
145	1472	1275	881	93	186	372	744	1488	1307	945
146	221	442	884	99	198	396	792	1584	1499	1329
147	989	309	618	1236	803	1606	1543	1417	1165	661
148	1322	975	281	562	1124	579	1158	647	1294	919
149	169	338	676	1352	1035	401	802	1604	1539	1409

P = 1669

INDICES

	0	1	2	3	4	5	6	7	8	9
150	656	578	915	213	1315	453	58	1099	1119	757
151	1093	179	1544	813	1305	1007	13	403	340	1571
152	1156	1622	1084	978	1124	970	1242	359	1376	1263
153	766	1511	602	1552	116	232	909	1399	805	1498
154	92	841	1056	1476	588	1389	1351	301	160	1655
155	390	205	43	1208	528	1301	762	1347	852	416
156	1566	200	856	194	493	1582	1405	782	1023	672
157	629	185	873	71	318	477	619	612	420	885
158	932	500	438	861	1467	577	212	452	1098	756
159	178	812	1006	402	1570	1621	977	969	358	1262
160	1510	1551	231	1398	1497	840	1475	1388	300	1654
161	204	1207	1300	1346	415	199	193	1581	781	671
162	184	70	476	611	884	499	860	576	451	755
163	811	401	1620	968	1261	1550	1397	839	1387	1653
164	1206	1345	198	1580	670	69	610	498	575	754
165	400	967	1549	838	1652	1344	1579	68	497	753
166	966	837	1343	67	752	836	66	835	834	

POWER RESIDUES

	0	1	2	3	4	5	6	7	8	9
150	1149	629	1258	847	25	50	100	200	400	800
151	1600	1531	1393	1117	565	1130	591	1182	695	1390
152	1111	553	1106	543	1086	503	1006	343	686	1372
153	1075	481	962	255	510	1020	371	742	1484	1299
154	929	189	378	756	1512	1355	1041	413	826	1652
155	1635	1601	1533	1397	1125	581	1162	655	1310	951
156	233	466	932	195	390	780	1560	1451	1233	797
157	1594	1519	1369	1069	469	938	207	414	828	1656
158	1643	1617	1565	1461	1253	837	5	10	20	40
159	80	160	320	640	1280	891	113	226	452	904
160	139	278	556	1112	555	1110	551	1102	535	1070
161	471	942	215	430	860	51	102	204	408	816
162	1632	1595	1521	1373	1077	485	970	271	542	1084
163	499	998	327	654	1308	947	225	450	900	131
164	262	524	1048	427	854	39	78	156	312	624
165	1248	827	1654	1639	1609	1549	1429	1189	709	1418
166	1167	665	1330	991	313	626	1252	835		

P = 1693

INDICES

	0	1	2	3	4	5	6	7	8	9
0		0	1	1070	2	103	1071	1421	3	448
1	104	981	1072	60	1422	1173	4	1213	449	661
2	105	799	982	421	1073	206	61	1518	1423	913
3	1174	1680	5	359	1214	1524	450	26	662	1130
4	106	113	800	1412	983	551	422	396	1074	1150
5	207	591	62	1065	1519	1084	1424	39	914	1228
6	1175	1442	1681	177	6	163	360	1089	1215	1491
7	1525	1600	451	155	27	1276	663	710	1131	1261
8	107	896	114	1100	801	1316	1413	291	984	186
9	552	1481	423	1058	397	764	1075	616	1151	1429
10	208	1552	592	1393	63	902	1066	657	1520	587
11	1085	1096	1425	520	40	524	915	508	1229	942
12	1176	270	1443	1183	1682	309	178	1586	7	790
13	164	44	361	390	1090	1621	1216	924	1492	1672
14	1526	1466	1601	1041	452	1016	156	528	28	1384
15	1277	1562	664	1661	711	91	1132	233	1262	443
16	108	150	897	919	115	462	1101	1163	802	120
17	1317	1109	1414	1614	292	1627	985	606	187	512
18	553	404	1482	820	424	129	1059	502	398	1247
19	765	1305	1076	535	617	1233	1152	1351	1430	703
20	209	467	1553	642	593	216	1394	869	64	1642
21	903	946	1067	978	658	1515	1521	1409	588	1225
22	1086	1273	1097	1478	1426	654	521	1180	41	1669
23	525	88	916	1106	509	499	1230	639	943	1222
24	1177	496	271	274	1444	1253	1184	721	1683	478
25	310	277	179	1402	1587	694	8	1337	791	1447
26	165	1361	45	299	362	1168	391	1256	1091	1036
27	1622	864	1217	859	925	1187	1493	1455	1673	436
28	1527	1196	1467	724	1602	142	1042	1534	453	734
29	1017	1686	157	784	529	1331	29	807	1385	481
30	1278	1141	1563	930	665	1545	1662	313	712	771
31	92	543	1133	750	234	280	1263	571	444	202
32	109	35	151	182	898	266	920	1657	116	125
33	463	1405	1102	474	1164	1192	803	746	121	1590
34	1318	969	1110	879	1415	1594	1615	697	293	1651
35	1628	1578	986	348	607	11	188	320	513	489
36	554	1322	405	1340	1483	258	821	1498	425	561
37	130	794	1060	1311	503	1379	399	973	1248	1450
38	766	964	1306	994	1077	813	536	168	618	76
39	1234	1634	1153	1114	1352	1364	1431	54	704	1460
40	210	1030	468	48	1554	999	643	1007	594	883
41	217	302	1395	957	870	1203	65	1050	1643	365
42	904	1292	947	844	1068	1419	979	1171	659	419
43	1516	1678	1522	1128	1410	394	589	1082	1226	175
44	1087	1598	1274	1259	1098	289	1479	762	1427	1391
45	655	1094	522	940	1181	1584	42	1619	1670	1039
46	526	1560	89	441	917	1161	1107	1625	510	818
47	500	1303	1231	701	640	867	944	1513	1223	1476
48	1178	86	497	1220	272	719	275	692	1445	297
49	1254	862	1185	434	722	1532	1684	1329	479	928

POWER RESIDUES

	0	1	2	3	4	5	6	7	8	9
0	1	2	4	8	16	32	64	128	256	512
1	1024	355	710	1420	1147	601	1202	711	1422	1151
2	609	1218	743	1486	1279	865	37	74	148	296
3	592	1184	675	1350	1007	321	642	1284	875	57
4	114	228	456	912	131	262	524	1048	403	806
5	1612	1531	1369	1045	397	794	1588	1483	1273	853
6	13	26	52	104	208	416	832	1664	1635	1577
7	1461	1229	765	1530	1367	1041	389	778	1556	1419
8	1145	597	1194	695	1390	1087	481	962	231	462
9	924	155	310	620	1240	787	1574	1455	1217	741
10	1482	1271	849	5	10	20	40	80	160	320
11	640	1280	867	41	82	164	328	656	1312	931
12	169	338	676	1352	1011	329	658	1316	939	185
13	370	740	1480	1267	841	1682	1671	1649	1605	1517
14	1341	989	285	570	1140	587	1174	655	1310	927
15	161	322	644	1288	883	73	146	292	584	1168
16	643	1286	879	65	130	260	520	1040	387	774
17	1548	1403	1113	533	1066	439	878	63	126	252
18	504	1008	323	646	1292	891	89	178	356	712
19	1424	1155	617	1234	775	1550	1407	1121	549	1098
20	503	1006	319	638	1276	859	25	50	100	200
21	400	800	1600	1507	1321	949	205	410	820	1640
22	1587	1481	1269	845	1690	1687	1681	1669	1645	1597
23	1501	1309	925	157	314	628	1256	819	1638	1583
24	1473	1253	813	1626	1559	1425	1157	621	1242	791
25	1582	1471	1249	805	1610	1527	1361	1029	365	730
26	1460	1227	761	1522	1351	1009	325	650	1300	907
27	121	242	484	968	243	486	972	251	502	1004
28	315	630	1260	827	1654	1615	1537	1381	1069	445
29	890	87	174	348	696	1392	1091	489	978	263
30	526	1052	411	822	1644	1595	1497	1301	909	125
31	250	500	1000	307	614	1228	763	1526	1359	1025
32	357	714	1428	1163	633	1266	839	1678	1663	1633
33	1573	1453	1213	733	1466	1239	785	1570	1447	1201
34	709	1418	1143	593	1186	679	1358	1023	353	706
35	1412	1131	569	1138	583	1166	639	1278	863	33
36	66	132	264	528	1056	419	838	1676	1659	1625
37	1557	1421	1149	605	1210	727	1454	1215	737	1474
38	1255	817	1634	1575	1457	1221	749	1498	1303	913
39	133	266	532	1064	435	870	47	94	188	376
40	752	1504	1315	937	181	362	724	1448	1203	713
41	1426	1159	625	1250	807	1614	1535	1377	1061	429
42	858	23	46	92	184	368	736	1472	1251	809
43	1618	1543	1393	1093	493	986	279	558	1116	539
44	1078	463	926	159	318	636	1272	851	9	18
45	36	72	144	288	576	1152	611	1222	751	1502
46	1311	929	165	330	660	1320	947	201	402	804
47	1608	1523	1353	1013	333	666	1332	971	249	498
48	996	299	598	1196	699	1398	1103	513	1026	359
49	718	1436	1179	665	1330	967	241	482	964	235

P = 1693

INDICES

	0	1	2	3	4	5	6	7	8	9
50	311	541	278	200	180	1655	1403	1190	1588	877
51	695	1576	9	487	1338	1496	792	1377	1448	992
52	166	1632	1362	1458	46	1005	300	1201	363	842
53	1169	1676	392	173	1257	760	1092	1582	1037	439
54	1623	1301	865	1474	1218	690	860	1530	926	198
55	1188	1574	1494	990	1456	1199	1674	758	437	1472
56	1528	1572	1197	1470	1468	623	725	625	1603	352
57	143	727	1043	683	1535	627	454	1284	735	1605
58	1018	829	1687	354	158	611	785	145	530	649
59	1332	729	30	343	808	1045	1386	81	482	685
60	1279	15	1142	1537	1564	373	931	629	666	20
61	1546	456	1663	778	314	1286	713	192	772	737
62	93	247	544	1607	1134	412	751	1020	235	1239
63	281	831	1264	324	572	1689	445	1210	203	356
64	110	1147	36	160	152	893	183	613	899	517
65	267	787	921	1013	1658	147	117	603	126	532
66	464	1639	1406	651	1103	493	475	1334	1165	856
67	1193	731	804	1542	747	32	122	743	1591	345
68	1319	558	970	810	1111	1027	880	1047	1416	1125
69	1595	1388	1616	1158	698	83	294	1326	1652	484
70	1629	839	1579	687	987	1569	349	1281	608	340
71	12	17	189	409	321	1144	514	600	490	1539
72	555	1122	1323	1566	406	1119	1341	375	1484	1344
73	259	933	822	333	1499	631	426	378	562	668
74	131	99	795	22	1061	1487	1312	1548	504	386
75	1380	458	400	1347	974	1665	1249	1357	1451	780
76	767	262	965	316	1307	72	995	1288	1078	936
77	814	715	537	1373	169	194	619	825	77	774
78	1235	889	1635	739	1154	336	1115	95	1353	1369
79	1365	249	1432	1502	55	546	705	582	1461	1609
80	211	634	1031	1136	469	253	49	414	1555	429
81	1000	753	644	242	1008	1022	595	381	884	237
82	218	1436	303	1241	1396	565	958	283	871	677
83	1204	833	66	671	1051	1266	1644	1506	366	326
84	905	134	1293	574	948	223	845	1691	1069	102
85	1420	447	980	59	1172	1212	660	798	420	205
86	1517	912	1679	358	1523	25	1129	112	1411	550
87	395	1149	590	1064	1083	38	1227	1441	176	162
88	1088	1490	1599	154	1275	709	1260	895	1099	1315
89	290	185	1480	1057	763	615	1428	1551	1392	901
90	656	586	1095	519	523	507	941	269	1182	308
91	1585	789	43	389	1620	923	1671	1465	1040	1015
92	527	1383	1561	1660	90	232	442	149	918	461
93	1162	119	1108	1613	1626	605	511	403	819	128
94	501	1246	1304	534	1232	1350	702	466	641	215
95	868	1641	945	977	1514	1408	1224	1272	1477	653
96	1179	1668	87	1105	498	638	1221	495	273	1252
97	720	477	276	1401	693	1336	1446	1360	298	1167
98	1255	1035	863	858	1186	1454	435	1195	723	141
99	1533	733	1685	783	1330	806	480	1140	929	1544

POWER RESIDUES

	0	1	2	3	4	5	6	7	8	9
50	470	940	187	374	748	1496	1299	905	117	234
51	468	936	179	358	716	1432	1171	649	1298	903
52	113	226	452	904	115	230	460	920	147	294
53	588	1176	659	1318	943	193	386	772	1544	1395
54	1097	501	1002	311	622	1244	795	1590	1487	1281
55	869	45	90	180	360	720	1440	1187	681	1362
56	1031	369	738	1476	1259	825	1650	1607	1521	1349
57	1005	317	634	1268	843	1686	1679	1665	1637	1581
58	1469	1245	797	1594	1495	1297	901	109	218	436
59	872	51	102	204	408	816	1632	1571	1449	1205
60	717	1434	1175	657	1314	935	177	354	708	1416
61	1139	585	1170	647	1294	895	97	194	388	776
62	1552	1411	1129	565	1130	567	1134	575	1150	607
63	1214	735	1470	1247	801	1602	1511	1329	965	237
64	474	948	203	406	812	1624	1555	1417	1141	589
65	1178	663	1326	959	225	450	900	107	214	428
66	856	19	38	76	152	304	608	1216	739	1478
67	1263	833	1666	1639	1585	1477	1261	829	1658	1623
68	1553	1413	1133	573	1146	599	1198	703	1406	1119
69	545	1090	487	974	255	510	1020	347	694	1388
70	1083	473	946	199	398	796	1592	1491	1289	885
71	77	154	308	616	1232	771	1542	1391	1089	485
72	970	247	494	988	283	566	1132	571	1142	591
73	1182	671	1342	991	289	578	1156	619	1238	783
74	1566	1439	1185	677	1354	1015	337	674	1348	1003
75	313	626	1252	811	1622	1551	1409	1125	557	1114
76	535	1070	447	894	95	190	380	760	1520	1347
77	1001	309	618	1236	779	1558	1423	1153	613	1226
78	759	1518	1343	993	293	586	1172	651	1302	911
79	129	258	516	1032	371	742	1484	1275	857	21
80	42	84	168	336	672	1344	995	297	594	1188
81	683	1366	1039	385	770	1540	1387	1081	469	938
82	183	366	732	1464	1235	777	1554	1415	1137	581
83	1162	631	1262	831	1662	1631	1569	1445	1197	701
84	1402	1111	529	1058	423	846	1692	1691	1689	1685
85	1677	1661	1629	1565	1437	1181	669	1338	983	273
86	546	1092	491	982	271	542	1084	475	950	207
87	414	828	1656	1619	1545	1397	1101	509	1018	343
88	686	1372	1051	409	818	1636	1579	1465	1237	781
89	1562	1431	1169	645	1290	887	81	162	324	648
90	1296	899	105	210	420	840	1680	1667	1641	1589
91	1485	1277	861	29	58	116	232	464	928	163
92	326	652	1304	915	137	274	548	1096	499	998
93	303	606	1212	731	1462	1231	769	1538	1383	1073
94	453	906	119	238	476	952	211	422	844	1688
95	1683	1673	1653	1613	1533	1373	1053	413	826	1652
96	1611	1529	1365	1037	381	762	1524	1355	1017	341
97	682	1364	1035	377	754	1508	1323	953	213	426
98	852	11	22	44	88	176	352	704	1408	1123
99	553	1106	519	1038	383	766	1532	1371	1049	405

P = 1693

INDICES

	0	1	2	3	4	5	6	7	8	9
100	312	770	542	749	279	570	201	34	181	265
101	1656	124	1404	473	1191	745	1589	968	878	1593
102	696	1650	1577	347	10	319	488	1321	1339	257
103	1497	560	793	1310	1378	972	1449	963	993	812
104	167	75	1633	1113	1363	53	1459	1029	47	998
105	1006	882	301	956	1202	1049	364	1291	843	1418
106	1170	418	1677	1127	393	1081	174	1597	1258	288
107	761	1390	1093	939	1583	1618	1038	1559	440	1160
108	1624	817	1302	700	866	1512	1475	85	1219	718
109	691	296	861	433	1531	1328	927	540	199	1654
110	1189	876	1575	486	1495	1376	991	1631	1457	1004
111	1200	841	1675	172	759	1581	438	1300	1473	689
112	1529	197	1573	989	1198	757	1471	1571	1469	622
113	624	351	726	682	626	1283	1604	828	353	610
114	144	648	728	342	1044	80	684	14	1536	372
115	628	19	455	777	1285	191	736	246	1606	411
116	1019	1238	830	323	1688	1209	355	1146	159	892
117	612	516	786	1012	146	602	531	1638	650	492
118	1333	855	730	1541	31	742	344	557	809	1026
119	1046	1124	1387	1157	82	1325	483	838	686	1568
120	1280	339	16	408	1143	599	1538	1121	1565	1118
121	374	1343	932	332	630	377	667	98	21	1486
122	1547	385	457	1346	1664	1356	779	261	315	71
123	1287	935	714	1372	193	824	773	888	738	335
124	94	1368	248	1501	545	581	1608	633	1135	252
125	413	428	752	241	1021	380	236	1435	1240	564
126	282	676	832	670	1265	1505	325	133	573	222
127	1690	101	446	58	1211	797	204	911	357	24
128	111	549	1148	1063	37	1440	161	1489	153	708
129	894	1314	184	1056	614	1550	900	585	518	506
130	268	307	788	388	922	1464	1014	1382	1659	231
131	148	460	118	1612	604	402	127	1245	533	1349
132	465	214	1640	976	1407	1271	652	1667	1104	637
133	494	1251	476	1400	1335	1359	1166	1034	857	1453
134	1194	140	732	782	805	1139	1543	769	748	569
135	33	264	123	472	744	967	1592	1649	346	318
136	1320	256	559	1309	971	962	811	74	1112	52
137	1028	997	881	955	1048	1290	1417	417	1126	1080
138	1596	287	1389	938	1617	1558	1159	816	699	1511
139	84	717	295	432	1327	539	1653	875	485	1375
140	1630	1003	840	171	1580	1299	688	196	988	756
141	1570	621	350	681	1282	827	609	647	341	79
142	13	371	18	776	190	245	410	1237	322	1208
143	1145	891	515	1011	601	1637	491	854	1540	741
144	556	1025	1123	1156	1324	837	1567	338	407	598
145	1120	1117	1342	331	376	97	1485	384	1345	1355
146	260	70	934	1371	823	887	334	1367	1500	580
147	632	251	427	240	379	1434	563	675	669	1504
148	132	221	100	57	796	910	23	548	1062	1439
149	1488	707	1313	1055	1549	584	505	306	387	1463

POWER RESIDUES

	0	1	2	3	4	5	6	7	8	9
100	810	1620	1547	1401	1109	525	1050	407	814	1628
101	1563	1433	1173	653	1306	919	145	290	580	1160
102	627	1254	815	1630	1567	1441	1189	685	1370	1047
103	401	802	1604	1515	1337	981	269	538	1076	459
104	918	143	286	572	1144	595	1190	687	1374	1055
105	417	834	1668	1643	1593	1493	1293	893	93	186
106	372	744	1488	1283	873	53	106	212	424	848
107	3	6	12	24	48	96	192	384	768	1536
108	1379	1065	437	874	55	110	220	440	880	67
109	134	268	536	1072	451	902	111	222	444	888
110	83	166	332	664	1328	963	233	466	932	171
111	342	684	1368	1043	393	786	1572	1451	1209	725
112	1450	1207	721	1442	1191	689	1378	1063	433	866
113	39	78	156	312	624	1248	803	1606	1519	1345
114	997	301	602	1204	715	1430	1167	641	1282	871
115	49	98	196	392	784	1568	1443	1193	693	1386
116	1079	465	930	167	334	668	1336	979	265	530
117	1060	427	854	15	30	60	120	240	480	960
118	227	454	908	123	246	492	984	275	550	1100
119	507	1014	335	670	1340	987	281	562	1124	555
120	1110	527	1054	415	830	1660	1627	1561	1429	1165
121	637	1274	855	17	34	68	136	272	544	1088
122	483	966	239	478	956	219	438	876	59	118
123	236	472	944	195	390	780	1560	1427	1161	629
124	1258	823	1646	1599	1505	1317	941	189	378	756
125	1512	1331	969	245	490	980	267	534	1068	443
126	886	79	158	316	632	1264	835	1670	1647	1601
127	1509	1325	957	221	442	884	75	150	300	600
128	1200	707	1414	1135	577	1154	615	1230	767	1534
129	1375	1057	421	842	1684	1675	1657	1621	1549	1405
130	1117	541	1082	471	942	191	382	764	1528	1363
131	1033	373	746	1492	1291	889	85	170	340	680
132	1360	1027	361	722	1444	1195	697	1394	1095	497
133	994	295	590	1180	667	1334	975	257	514	1028
134	363	726	1452	1211	729	1458	1223	753	1506	1319
135	945	197	394	788	1576	1459	1225	757	1514	1335
136	977	261	522	1044	395	790	1580	1467	1241	789
137	1578	1463	1233	773	1546	1399	1105	517	1034	375
138	750	1500	1307	921	149	298	596	1192	691	1382
139	1071	449	898	103	206	412	824	1648	1603	1513
140	1333	973	253	506	1012	331	662	1324	955	217
141	434	868	43	86	172	344	688	1376	1059	425
142	850	7	14	28	56	112	224	448	896	99
143	198	396	792	1584	1475	1257	821	1642	1591	1489
144	1285	877	61	122	244	488	976	259	518	1036
145	379	758	1516	1339	985	277	554	1108	523	1046
146	399	798	1596	1499	1305	917	141	282	564	1128
147	563	1126	559	1118	543	1086	479	958	223	446
148	892	91	182	364	728	1456	1219	745	1490	1287
149	881	69	138	276	552	1104	515	1030	367	734

P = 1693

INDICES

	0	1	2	3	4	5	6	7	8	9
150	1381	230	459	1611	401	1244	1348	213	975	1270
151	1666	636	1250	1399	1358	1033	1452	139	781	1138
152	768	568	263	471	966	1648	317	255	1308	961
153	73	51	996	954	1289	416	1079	286	937	1557
154	815	1510	716	431	538	874	1374	1002	170	1298
155	195	755	620	680	826	646	78	370	775	244
156	1236	1207	890	1010	1636	853	740	1024	1155	836
157	337	597	1116	330	96	383	1354	69	1370	886
158	1366	579	250	239	1433	674	1503	220	56	909
159	547	1438	706	1054	583	305	1462	229	1610	1243
160	212	1269	635	1398	1032	138	1137	567	470	1647
161	254	960	50	953	415	285	1556	1509	430	873
162	1001	1297	754	679	645	369	243	1206	1009	852
163	1023	835	596	329	382	68	885	578	238	673
164	219	908	1437	1053	304	228	1242	1268	1397	137
165	566	1646	959	952	284	1508	872	1296	678	368
166	1205	851	834	328	67	577	672	907	1052	227
167	1267	136	1645	951	1507	1295	367	850	327	576
168	906	226	135	950	1294	849	575	225	949	848
169	224	847	846							

POWER RESIDUES

	0	1	2	3	4	5	6	7	8	9
150	1468	1243	793	1586	1479	1265	837	1674	1655	1617
151	1541	1389	1085	477	954	215	430	860	27	54
152	108	216	432	864	35	70	140	280	560	1120
153	547	1094	495	990	287	574	1148	603	1206	719
154	1438	1183	673	1346	999	305	610	1220	747	1494
155	1295	897	101	202	404	808	1616	1539	1385	1077
156	461	922	151	302	604	1208	723	1446	1199	705
157	1410	1127	561	1122	551	1102	511	1022	351	702
158	1404	1115	537	1074	455	910	127	254	508	1016
159	339	678	1356	1019	345	690	1380	1067	441	882
160	71	142	284	568	1136	579	1158	623	1246	799
161	1598	1503	1313	933	173	346	692	1384	1075	457
162	914	135	270	540	1080	467	934	175	350	700
163	1400	1107	521	1042	391	782	1564	1435	1177	661
164	1322	951	209	418	836	1672	1651	1609	1525	1357
165	1021	349	698	1396	1099	505	1010	327	654	1308
166	923	153	306	612	1224	755	1510	1327	961	229
167	458	916	139	278	556	1112	531	1062	431	862
168	31	62	124	248	496	992	291	582	1164	635
169	1270	847								

P = 1697

INDICES

	0	1	2	3	4	5	6	7	8	9
0		0	370	1	740	1559	371	735	1110	2
1	233	720	741	675	1105	1560	1480	1231	372	440
2	603	736	1090	52	1111	1422	1045	3	1475	171
3	234	527	154	721	1601	598	742	1137	810	676
4	973	316	1106	775	1460	1561	422	1665	1481	1470
5	96	1232	1415	694	373	583	149	441	541	934
6	604	941	897	737	524	538	1091	516	275	53
7	968	1320	1112	1168	1507	1423	1180	1455	1046	922
8	1343	4	686	1382	1476	1094	1145	172	134	779
9	235	1410	792	528	339	303	155	1098	144	722
10	466	1068	1602	838	89	599	1064	80	743	185
11	953	1138	519	1354	811	1611	911	677	1304	270
12	974	1440	1311	317	1267	1285	1107	595	894	776
13	908	1392	1461	1175	886	1562	645	801	423	278
14	1338	1666	1690	1395	1482	34	1538	1471	181	669
15	97	870	1550	1233	129	390	1416	1210	1292	695
16	17	787	374	1131	1056	584	56	618	150	1350
17	1464	442	1515	488	542	461	504	935	1149	295
18	605	1121	84	942	1162	1000	898	255	709	738
19	673	1088	525	971	1468	539	514	1178	1092	337
20	836	517	1438	906	276	179	1208	54	459	1160
21	969	1436	1434	1321	450	638	1113	1262	555	1169
22	1323	210	1508	758	889	1424	28	856	1181	452
23	285	1456	1281	1204	1047	1528	1674	923	640	1224
24	1344	346	114	5	1681	1333	687	1115	1637	1383
25	1655	1565	1477	772	965	1095	1264	867	1146	176
26	1278	173	66	747	135	557	1545	780	1256	163
27	236	101	1015	1411	1171	446	793	1075	648	529
28	12	1197	340	1325	364	304	69	1051	156	766
29	404	1099	212	570	145	797	551	723	1039	727
30	467	1510	1240	1069	224	804	1603	1359	499	839
31	760	979	90	750	1580	600	1662	1504	1065	891
32	387	81	1157	1671	744	401	1501	186	1426	704
33	954	395	426	1139	988	379	520	30	24	1355
34	138	1247	812	509	189	1612	858	947	912	1618
35	831	678	874	412	1305	1183	1519	271	665	281
36	975	880	1491	1441	454	1031	1312	560	1532	318
37	1370	1429	1268	287	625	1286	1079	846	1108	1229
38	1043	596	1458	692	895	1318	1341	777	142	78
39	909	1283	884	1393	1548	785	1462	293	707	1176
40	1206	636	887	1202	112	1563	1276	161	646	1049
41	549	802	1578	1669	424	1245	829	279	1530	844
42	1339	783	110	1667	108	957	1691	1676	820	1396
43	1008	959	1483	1554	1632	35	925	492	1539	194
44	1693	1472	580	683	182	642	1128	670	1259	1678
45	98	1036	398	871	1226	1273	1551	652	822	1234
46	655	731	130	1346	1651	391	1574	1398	1417	1251
47	202	1211	348	1495	1293	166	1010	696	1594	429
48	18	116	716	788	484	961	375	825	355	1132
49	7	40	1057	1402	1485	585	311	359	57	1683

POWER RESIDUES

	0	1	2	3	4	5	6	7	8	9
0	1	3	9	27	81	243	729	490	1470	1016
1	1351	659	280	840	823	772	619	160	480	1440
2	926	1081	1546	1244	338	1014	1345	641	226	678
3	337	1011	1336	614	145	435	1305	521	1563	1295
4	491	1473	1025	1378	740	523	1569	1313	545	1635
5	1511	1139	23	69	207	621	166	498	1494	1088
6	1567	1307	527	1581	1349	653	262	786	661	286
7	858	877	934	1105	1618	1460	986	1261	389	1167
8	107	321	963	1192	182	546	1638	1520	1166	104
9	312	936	1111	1636	1514	1148	50	150	450	1350
10	656	271	813	742	529	1587	1367	707	424	1272
11	422	1266	404	1212	242	726	481	1443	935	1108
12	1627	1487	1067	1504	1118	1657	1577	1337	617	154
13	462	1386	764	595	88	264	792	679	340	1020
14	1363	695	388	1164	98	294	882	949	1150	56
15	168	504	1512	1142	32	96	288	864	895	988
16	1267	407	1221	269	807	724	475	1425	881	946
17	1141	29	87	261	783	652	259	777	634	205
18	615	148	444	1332	602	109	327	981	1246	344
19	1032	1399	803	712	439	1317	557	1671	1619	1463
20	995	1288	470	1410	836	811	736	511	1533	1205
21	221	663	292	876	931	1096	1591	1379	743	532
22	1596	1394	788	667	304	912	1039	1420	866	901
23	1006	1321	569	10	30	90	270	810	733	502
24	1506	1124	1675	1631	1499	1103	1612	1442	932	1099
25	1600	1406	824	775	628	187	561	1683	1655	1571
26	1319	563	1689	1673	1625	1481	1049	1450	956	1171
27	119	357	1071	1516	1154	68	204	612	139	417
28	1251	359	1077	1534	1208	230	690	373	1119	1660
29	1586	1364	698	397	1191	179	537	1611	1439	923
30	1072	1519	1163	95	285	855	868	907	1024	1375
31	731	496	1488	1070	1513	1145	41	123	369	1107
32	1624	1478	1040	1423	875	928	1087	1564	1298	500
33	1500	1106	1621	1469	1013	1342	632	199	597	94
34	282	846	841	826	781	646	241	723	472	1416
35	854	865	898	997	1294	488	1464	998	1297	497
36	1491	1079	1540	1226	284	852	859	880	943	1132
37	2	6	18	54	162	486	1458	980	1243	335
38	1005	1318	560	1680	1646	1544	1238	320	960	1183
39	155	465	1395	791	676	331	993	1282	452	1356
40	674	325	975	1228	290	870	913	1042	1429	893
41	982	1249	353	1059	1480	1046	1441	929	1090	1573
42	1325	581	46	138	414	1242	332	996	1291	479
43	1437	917	1054	1465	1001	1306	524	1572	1322	572
44	19	57	171	513	1539	1223	275	825	778	637
45	214	642	229	687	364	1092	1579	1343	635	208
46	624	175	525	1575	1331	599	100	300	900	1003
47	1312	542	1626	1484	1058	1477	1037	1414	848	847
48	844	835	808	727	484	1452	962	1189	173	519
49	1557	1277	437	1311	539	1617	1457	977	1234	308

P = 1697

INDICES

	0	1	2	3	4	5	6	7	8	9
50	329	619	239	1556	151	931	1142	1351	1335	615
51	1465	207	1634	443	1237	701	1516	689	546	489
52	1648	37	543	45	436	462	1117	62	505	104
53	927	936	219	991	1150	1639	1626	296	533	494
54	606	658	471	1122	1385	48	85	996	1541	943
55	816	611	1163	1657	1445	1001	1018	196	899	1450
56	382	256	1567	261	710	1217	1695	739	734	232
57	674	1479	439	1089	1421	1474	526	1600	1136	972
58	774	421	1469	1414	582	540	940	523	515	967
59	1167	1179	921	685	1093	133	1409	338	1097	465
60	837	1063	184	518	1610	1303	1439	1266	594	907
61	1174	644	277	1689	33	180	869	128	1209	16
62	1130	55	1349	1514	460	1148	1120	1161	254	672
63	970	513	336	1437	178	458	1435	449	1261	1322
64	757	27	451	1280	1527	639	345	1680	1114	1654
65	771	1263	175	65	556	1255	100	1170	1074	11
66	1324	68	765	211	796	1038	1509	223	1358	759
67	749	1661	890	1156	400	1425	394	987	29	137
68	508	857	1617	873	1182	664	879	453	559	1369
69	286	1078	1228	1457	1317	141	1282	1547	292	1205
70	1201	1275	1048	1577	1244	1529	782	107	1675	1007
71	1553	924	193	579	641	1258	1035	1225	651	654
72	1345	1573	1250	347	165	1593	115	483	824	6
73	1401	310	1682	238	930	1334	206	1236	688	1647
74	44	1116	103	218	1638	532	657	1384	995	815
75	1656	1017	1449	1566	1216	733	1478	1420	1599	773
76	1413	939	966	920	132	1096	1062	1609	1265	1173
77	1688	868	15	1348	1147	253	512	177	448	756
78	1279	344	1653	174	1254	1073	67	795	222	748
79	1155	393	136	1616	663	558	1077	1316	1546	1200
80	1576	781	1006	192	1257	650	1572	164	482	1400
81	237	205	1646	102	531	994	1016	1215	1419	1412
82	919	1061	1172	14	252	447	343	1253	794	1154
83	1615	1076	1199	1005	649	481	204	530	1214	918
84	13	342	1153	1198	480	1213	341	479	478	1326
85	1327	1189	365	1328	350	305	1190	861	70	366
86	1378	1052	1329	1497	157	351	228	767	306	1642
87	405	1191	1295	1100	862	324	213	71	564	571
88	367	168	146	1379	950	798	1053	1085	552	1330
89	1012	724	1498	409	1040	158	1629	728	352	698
90	468	229	1406	1511	768	984	1241	307	1596	1070
91	1643	915	225	406	1022	805	1192	431	1604	1296
92	1025	1360	1101	299	500	863	20	840	325	417
93	761	214	248	980	72	118	91	565	1621	751
94	572	630	1581	368	718	601	169	808	1663	147
95	536	1505	1380	790	1066	951	268	892	799	1536
96	388	1054	486	82	1086	834	1158	553	854	1672
97	1331	963	745	1013	1195	402	725	497	1502	1499
98	377	187	410	1489	1427	1041	76	705	159	827
99	955	1630	681	396	729	200	427	353	357	1140

POWER RESIDUES

	0	1	2	3	4	5	6	7	8	9
50	924	1075	1528	1190	176	528	1584	1358	680	343
51	1029	1390	776	631	196	588	67	201	603	112
52	336	1008	1327	587	64	192	576	31	93	279
53	837	814	745	538	1614	1448	950	1153	65	195
54	585	58	174	522	1566	1304	518	1554	1268	410
55	1230	296	888	967	1204	218	654	265	795	688
56	367	1101	1606	1424	878	937	1114	1645	1541	1229
57	293	879	940	1123	1672	1622	1472	1022	1369	713
58	442	1326	584	55	165	495	1485	1061	1486	1064
59	1495	1091	1576	1334	608	127	381	1143	35	105
60	315	945	1138	20	60	180	540	1620	1466	1004
61	1315	551	1653	1565	1301	509	1527	1187	167	501
62	1503	1115	1648	1550	1256	374	1122	1669	1613	1445
63	941	1126	1681	1649	1553	1265	401	1203	215	645
64	238	714	445	1335	611	136	408	1224	278	834
65	805	718	457	1371	719	460	1380	746	541	1623
66	1475	1031	1396	794	685	358	1074	1525	1181	149
67	447	1341	629	190	570	13	39	117	351	1053
68	1462	992	1279	443	1329	593	82	246	738	517
69	1551	1259	383	1149	53	159	477	1431	899	1000
70	1303	515	1545	1241	329	987	1264	398	1194	188
71	564	1692	1682	1652	1562	1292	482	1446	944	1135
72	11	33	99	297	891	976	1231	299	897	994
73	1285	461	1383	755	568	7	21	63	189	567
74	4	12	36	108	324	972	1219	263	789	670
75	313	939	1120	1663	1595	1391	779	640	223	669
76	310	930	1093	1582	1352	662	289	867	904	1015
77	1348	650	253	759	580	43	129	387	1161	89
78	267	801	706	421	1263	395	1185	161	483	1449
79	953	1162	92	276	828	787	664	295	885	958
80	1177	137	411	1233	305	915	1048	1447	947	1144
81	38	114	342	1026	1381	749	550	1650	1556	1274
82	428	1284	458	1374	728	487	1461	989	1270	416
83	1248	350	1050	1453	965	1198	200	600	103	309
84	927	1084	1555	1271	419	1257	377	1131	1696	1694
85	1688	1670	1616	1454	968	1207	227	681	346	1038
86	1417	857	874	925	1078	1537	1217	257	771	616
87	151	453	1359	683	352	1056	1471	1019	1360	686
88	361	1083	1552	1262	392	1176	134	402	1206	224
89	672	319	957	1174	128	384	1152	62	186	558
90	1674	1628	1490	1076	1531	1199	203	609	130	390
91	1170	116	348	1044	1435	911	1036	1411	839	820
92	763	592	79	237	711	436	1308	530	1590	1376
93	734	505	1515	1151	59	177	531	1593	1385	761
94	586	61	183	549	1647	1547	1247	347	1041	1426
95	884	955	1168	110	330	990	1273	425	1275	431
96	1293	485	1455	971	1216	254	762	589	70	210
97	630	193	579	40	120	360	1080	1543	1235	311
98	933	1102	1609	1433	905	1018	1357	677	334	1002
99	1309	533	1599	1403	815	748	547	1641	1529	1193

P = 1697

INDICES

	0	1	2	3	4	5	6	7	8	9
100	699	434	989	469	609	380	230	1134	521	1407
101	1301	31	1512	334	25	769	9	1356	985	877
102	139	1242	577	1248	308	42	813	1597	1607	510
103	1071	661	190	1644	1059	1613	916	476	859	226
104	322	948	407	1404	913	1023	415	1619	806	266
105	832	1193	1487	679	432	1299	875	1605	474	413
106	1297	587	1306	1026	589	1184	1361	122	1520	1102
107	313	272	300	1308	666	501	903	282	864	361
108	976	21	1028	881	841	1125	1492	326	59	1442
109	418	591	455	762	1366	1032	215	1685	1313	249
110	1186	561	981	245	1533	73	331	319	119	1363
111	1371	92	1388	1430	566	621	1269	1622	124	288
112	752	1374	626	573	241	1287	631	1522	1080	1582
113	1587	847	369	1558	1109	719	1104	1230	602	51
114	1044	170	153	597	809	315	1459	1664	95	693
115	148	933	896	537	274	1319	1506	1454	1342	1381
116	1144	778	791	302	143	1067	88	79	952	1353
117	910	269	1310	1284	893	1391	885	800	1337	1394
118	1537	668	1549	389	1291	786	1055	617	1463	487
119	503	294	83	999	708	1087	1467	1177	835	905
120	1207	1159	1433	637	554	209	888	855	284	1203
121	1673	1223	113	1332	1636	1564	964	866	1277	746
122	1544	162	1014	445	647	1196	363	1050	403	569
123	550	726	1239	803	498	978	1579	1503	386	1670
124	1500	703	425	378	23	1246	188	946	830	411
125	1518	280	1490	1030	1531	1428	624	845	1042	691
126	1340	77	883	784	706	635	111	160	548	1668
127	828	843	109	956	819	958	1631	491	1692	682
128	1127	1677	397	1272	821	730	1650	1397	201	1494
129	1009	428	715	960	354	39	1484	358	328	1555
130	1141	614	1633	700	545	36	435	61	926	990
131	1625	493	470	47	1540	610	1444	195	381	260
132	1694	231	438	1473	1135	420	581	522	1166	684
133	1408	464	183	1302	593	643	32	127	1129	1513
134	1119	671	335	457	1260	26	1526	1679	770	64
135	99	10	764	1037	1357	1660	399	986	507	872
136	878	1368	1227	140	291	1274	1243	106	1552	578
137	1034	653	1249	1592	823	309	929	1235	43	217
138	656	814	1448	732	1598	938	131	1608	1687	1347
139	511	755	1652	1072	221	392	662	1315	1575	191
140	1571	1399	1645	993	1418	1060	251	1252	1614	1004
141	203	917	1152	1212	477	1188	349	860	1377	1496
142	227	1641	1294	323	563	167	949	1084	1011	408
143	1628	697	1405	983	1595	914	1021	430	1024	298
144	19	416	247	117	1620	629	717	807	535	789
145	267	1535	485	833	853	962	1194	496	376	1488
146	75	826	680	199	356	433	608	1133	1300	333
147	8	876	576	41	1606	660	1058	475	321	1403
148	414	265	1486	1298	473	586	588	121	312	1307
149	902	360	1027	1124	58	590	1365	1684	1185	244

POWER RESIDUES

	0	1	2	3	4	5	6	7	8	9
100	185	555	1665	1601	1409	833	802	709	430	1290
101	476	1428	890	973	1222	272	816	751	556	1668
102	1610	1436	914	1045	1438	920	1063	1492	1082	1549
103	1253	365	1095	1588	1370	716	451	1353	665	298
104	894	985	1258	380	1140	26	78	234	702	409
105	1227	287	861	886	961	1186	164	492	1476	1034
106	1405	821	766	601	106	318	954	1165	101	303
107	909	1030	1393	785	658	277	831	796	691	376
108	1128	1687	1667	1607	1427	887	964	1195	191	573
109	22	66	198	594	85	255	765	598	97	291
110	873	922	1069	1510	1136	14	42	126	378	1134
111	8	24	72	216	648	247	741	526	1578	1340
112	626	181	543	1629	1493	1085	1558	1280	446	1338
113	620	163	489	1467	1007	1324	578	37	111	333
114	999	1300	506	1518	1160	86	258	774	625	178
115	534	1602	1412	842	829	790	673	322	966	1201
116	209	627	184	552	1656	1574	1328	590	73	219
117	657	274	822	769	610	133	399	1197	197	591
118	76	228	684	355	1065	1498	1100	1603	1415	851
119	856	871	916	1051	1456	974	1225	281	843	832
120	799	700	403	1209	233	699	400	1200	206	618
121	157	471	1413	845	838	817	754	565	1695	1691
122	1679	1643	1535	1211	239	717	454	1362	692	379
123	1137	17	51	153	459	1377	737	514	1542	1232
124	302	906	1021	1366	704	415	1245	341	1023	1372
125	722	469	1407	827	784	655	268	804	715	448
126	1344	638	217	651	256	768	607	124	372	1116
127	1651	1559	1283	455	1365	701	406	1218	260	780
128	643	232	696	391	1173	125	375	1125	1678	1640
129	1526	1184	158	474	1422	872	919	1060	1483	1055
130	1468	1010	1333	605	118	354	1062	1489	1073	1522
131	1172	122	366	1098	1597	1397	797	694	385	1155
132	71	213	639	220	660	283	849	850	853	862
133	889	970	1213	245	735	508	1524	1178	140	420
134	1260	386	1158	80	240	720	463	1389	773	622
135	169	507	1521	1169	113	339	1017	1354	668	307
136	921	1066	1501	1109	1630	1496	1094	1585	1361	689
137	370	1110	1633	1505	1121	1666	1604	1418	860	883
138	952	1159	83	249	747	544	1632	1502	1112	1639
139	1523	1175	131	393	1179	143	429	1287	467	1401
140	809	730	493	1479	1043	1432	902	1009	1330	596
141	91	273	819	760	583	52	156	468	1404	818
142	757	574	25	75	225	675	328	984	1255	371
143	1113	1642	1532	1202	212	636	211	633	202	606
144	121	363	1089	1570	1316	554	1662	1592	1382	752
145	559	1677	1637	1517	1157	77	231	693	382	1146
146	44	132	396	1188	170	510	1530	1196	194	582
147	49	147	441	1323	575	28	84	252	756	571
148	16	48	144	432	1296	494	1482	1052	1459	983
149	1252	362	1086	1561	1289	473	1419	863	892	979

P = 1697

INDICES

	0	1	2	3	4	5	6	7	8	9
150	330	1362	1387	620	123	1373	240	1521	1586	1557
151	1103	50	152	314	94	932	273	1453	1143	301
152	87	1352	1309	1390	1336	667	1290	616	502	998
153	1466	904	1432	208	283	1222	1635	865	1543	444
154	362	568	1238	977	385	702	22	945	1517	1029
155	623	690	882	634	547	842	818	490	1126	1271
156	1649	1493	714	38	327	613	544	60	1624	46
157	1443	259	437	419	1165	463	592	126	1118	456
158	1525	63	763	1659	506	1367	290	105	1033	1591
159	928	216	1447	937	1686	754	220	1314	1570	992
160	250	1003	1151	1187	1376	1640	562	1083	1627	982
161	1020	297	246	628	534	1534	852	495	74	198
162	607	332	575	659	320	264	472	120	901	1123
163	1364	243	1386	1372	1585	49	93	1452	86	1389
164	1289	997	1431	1221	1542	567	384	944	622	633
165	817	1270	713	612	1623	258	1164	125	1524	1658
166	289	1590	1446	753	1569	1002	1375	1082	1019	627
167	851	197	574	263	900	242	1584	1451	1288	1220
168	383	632	712	257	1523	1589	1568	1081	850	262
169	1583	1219	711	1588	849	1218	848			

POWER RESIDUES

	0	1	2	3	4	5	6	7	8	9
150	1240	326	978	1237	317	951	1156	74	222	666
151	301	903	1012	1339	623	172	516	1548	1250	356
152	1068	1507	1127	1684	1658	1580	1346	644	235	705
153	418	1254	368	1104	1615	1451	959	1180	146	438
154	1314	548	1644	1538	1220	266	798	697	394	1182
155	152	456	1368	710	433	1299	503	1509	1133	5
156	15	45	135	405	1215	251	753	562	1686	1664
157	1598	1400	806	721	466	1398	800	703	412	1236
158	314	942	1129	1690	1676	1634	1508	1130	1693	1685
159	1661	1589	1373	725	478	1434	908	1027	1384	758
160	577	34	102	306	918	1057	1474	1028	1387	767
161	604	115	345	1035	1408	830	793	682	349	1047
162	1444	938	1117	1654	1568	1310	536	1608	1430	896
163	991	1276	434	1302	512	1536	1214	248	744	535
164	1605	1421	869	910	1033	1402	812	739	520	1560
165	1286	464	1392	782	649	250	750	553	1659	1583
166	1355	671	316	948	1147	47	141	423	1269	413
167	1239	323	969	1210	236	708	427	1281	449	1347
168	647	244	732	499	1497	1097	1594	1388	770	613
169	142	426	1278	440	1320	566				

P = 1699

INDICES

	0	1	2	3	4	5	6	7	8	9
0		0	747	1	1494	762	748	742	543	2
1	1509	61	1495	520	1489	763	1290	378	749	248
2	558	743	808	1440	544	1524	1267	3	538	1089
3	1510	1623	339	62	1125	1504	1496	1210	995	521
4	1305	1648	1490	1136	1555	764	489	95	1291	1484
5	573	379	316	511	750	823	1285	249	138	406
6	559	1162	672	744	1086	1282	809	1567	174	1441
7	553	218	545	1665	259	1525	44	803	1268	1411
8	354	4	697	812	539	1140	185	1090	604	1144
9	1511	1262	1236	1624	842	1010	340	1044	533	63
10	1320	371	1126	1636	1063	1505	1258	928	1497	1172
11	1570	1211	334	1580	996	504	885	522	1153	1120
12	1306	122	211	1649	1419	588	1491	1620	135	1137
13	331	974	1556	990	616	765	921	177	490	977
14	1300	96	965	581	1292	153	714	1485	1006	1347
15	574	85	791	380	1550	687	317	477	460	512
16	1101	484	751	781	1444	824	1559	429	1286	1040
17	189	250	932	114	139	568	1351	407	193	1451
18	560	1400	311	1163	285	274	673	439	1589	745
19	59	556	1087	993	93	1283	1280	257	810	1234
20	369	1568	1118	133	175	712	685	1442	112	309
21	554	367	307	219	1675	200	546	667	221	1666
22	619	898	260	597	1081	1526	629	1677	45	447
23	1251	804	1632	281	1269	857	202	1412	169	1374
24	355	1602	869	5	958	548	698	768	468	813
25	1335	1094	540	1501	669	1141	882	578	186	254
26	1078	1091	23	223	605	1273	39	1145	1363	1241
27	1512	68	1668	1263	924	1585	1237	1311	26	1625
28	349	621	843	101	14	1011	1328	692	341	756
29	900	1045	1461	1356	534	1168	55	64	396	262
30	1321	180	832	372	1538	226	1127	1531	599	1637
31	1434	1379	1064	703	1224	1506	1207	1083	1259	1150
32	150	929	1231	626	1498	346	1528	1173	493	837
33	1571	1642	608	1212	1176	631	335	1576	89	1581
34	936	1684	997	528	1679	505	861	734	886	1425
35	1315	523	400	47	1154	980	940	1121	500	1276
36	1307	496	449	123	1058	729	212	159	1032	1650
37	1021	1253	1420	797	1186	589	638	1609	1492	518
38	806	1621	1303	1482	136	1565	42	1138	840	1634
39	332	120	329	975	1004	475	1557	566	283	991
40	1116	365	617	445	167	766	880	1271	922	99
41	1459	178	1432	1148	491	1574	859	978	1056	795
42	1301	118	1114	97	1054	204	966	206	724	582
43	947	30	1293	266	1414	154	968	1688	715	453
44	1366	1486	1645	171	1007	208	1344	1348	130	1248
45	575	11	1376	86	726	326	792	1341	1194	381
46	300	357	1551	584	681	688	1028	1244	318	611
47	1604	478	949	1197	461	74	916	513	423	871
48	1102	32	651	485	1616	108	752	1017	7	782
49	1295	1477	1445	1467	1515	825	1215	960	1560	268

POWER RESIDUES

	0	1	2	3	4	5	6	7	8	9
0	1	3	9	27	81	243	729	488	1464	994
1	1283	451	1353	661	284	852	857	872	917	1052
2	1457	973	1220	262	786	659	278	834	803	710
3	431	1293	481	1443	931	1094	1583	1351	655	266
4	798	695	386	1158	76	228	684	353	1059	1478
5	1036	1409	829	788	665	296	888	965	1196	190
6	570	11	33	99	297	891	974	1223	271	813
7	740	521	1563	1291	475	1425	877	932	1097	1592
8	1378	736	509	1527	1183	151	453	1359	679	338
9	1014	1343	631	194	582	47	141	423	1269	409
10	1227	283	849	848	845	836	809	728	485	1455
11	967	1202	208	624	173	519	1557	1273	421	1263
12	391	1173	121	363	1089	1568	1306	520	1560	1282
13	448	1344	634	203	609	128	384	1152	58	174
14	522	1566	1300	502	1506	1120	1661	1585	1357	673
15	320	960	1181	145	435	1305	517	1551	1255	367
16	1101	1604	1414	844	833	800	701	404	1212	238
17	714	443	1329	589	68	204	612	137	411	1233
18	301	903	1010	1331	595	86	258	774	623	170
19	510	1530	1192	178	534	1602	1408	826	779	638
20	215	645	236	708	425	1275	427	1281	445	1335
21	607	122	366	1098	1595	1387	763	590	71	213
22	639	218	654	263	789	668	305	915	1046	1439
23	919	1058	1475	1027	1382	748	545	1635	1507	1123
24	1670	1612	1438	916	1049	1448	946	1139	19	57
25	171	513	1539	1219	259	777	632	197	591	74
26	222	666	299	897	992	1277	433	1299	499	1497
27	1093	1580	1342	628	185	555	1665	1597	1393	781
28	644	233	699	398	1194	184	552	1656	1570	1312
29	538	1614	1444	934	1103	1610	1432	898	995	1286
30	460	1380	742	527	1581	1345	637	212	636	209
31	627	182	546	1638	1516	1150	52	156	468	1404
32	814	743	530	1590	1372	718	455	1365	697	392
33	1176	130	390	1170	112	336	1008	1325	577	32
34	96	288	864	893	980	1241	325	975	1226	280
35	840	821	764	593	80	240	720	461	1383	751
36	554	1662	1588	1366	700	401	1203	211	633	200
37	600	101	303	909	1028	1385	757	572	17	51
38	153	459	1377	733	500	1500	1102	1607	1423	871
39	914	1043	1430	892	977	1232	298	894	983	1250
40	352	1056	1469	1009	1328	586	59	177	531	1593
41	1381	745	536	1608	1426	880	941	1124	1673	1621
42	1465	997	1292	478	1434	904	1013	1340	622	167
43	501	1503	1111	1634	1504	1114	1643	1531	1195	187
44	561	1683	1651	1555	1267	403	1209	229	687	362
45	1086	1559	1279	439	1317	553	1659	1579	1339	619
46	158	474	1422	868	905	1016	1349	649	248	744
47	533	1599	1399	799	698	395	1185	157	471	1413
48	841	824	773	620	161	483	1449	949	1148	46
49	138	414	1242	328	984	1253	361	1083	1550	1252

P = 1699

INDICES

	0	1	2	3	4	5	6	7	8	9
50	384	430	143	907	1287	1133	550	1041	1416	82
51	190	709	1629	251	1325	700	933	156	1001	115
52	127	71	140	1179	770	569	970	303	1352	1182
53	322	408	786	470	194	1690	412	1452	290	1545
54	561	892	815	1401	717	236	312	986	1671	1164
55	634	1337	286	455	360	275	773	1386	674	1656
56	1096	440	1368	659	1590	644	848	746	761	542
57	60	1488	377	557	1439	1266	1088	338	1503	994
58	1647	1554	94	572	510	1284	405	671	1281	173
59	217	258	802	353	811	184	1143	1235	1009	532
60	370	1062	927	1569	1579	884	1119	210	587	134
61	973	615	176	1299	580	713	1346	790	686	459
62	483	1443	428	188	113	1350	1450	310	273	1588
63	555	92	256	368	132	684	308	306	199	220
64	897	1080	1676	1250	280	201	1373	868	547	467
65	1093	668	577	1077	222	38	1240	1667	1584	25
66	620	13	691	899	1355	54	261	831	225	598
67	1378	1223	1082	149	625	1527	836	607	630	88
68	1683	1678	733	1314	46	939	1275	448	728	1031
69	1252	1185	1608	805	1481	41	1633	328	474	282
70	364	166	1270	1458	1147	858	794	1113	203	723
71	29	1413	1687	1365	170	1343	1247	1375	325	1193
72	356	680	1243	1603	1196	915	870	650	107	6
73	1476	1514	959	383	906	549	81	1628	699	1000
74	70	769	302	321	469	411	1544	814	235	1670
75	1336	359	1385	1095	658	847	541	376	1265	1502
76	1553	509	670	216	352	1142	531	926	883	586
77	614	579	789	482	187	1449	1587	255	683	198
78	1079	279	867	1092	1076	1239	24	690	53	224
79	1222	624	606	1682	1313	1274	1030	1607	40	473
80	165	1146	1112	28	1364	1246	1192	1242	914	106
81	1513	905	1627	69	320	1543	1669	1384	846	1264
82	508	351	925	613	481	1586	197	866	1238	52
83	623	1312	1606	164	27	1191	105	1626	1542	845
84	350	480	865	622	163	104	844	864	103	102
85	951	952	15	1693	953	1012	1471	16	1329	1199
86	1694	693	777	954	342	876	1013	757	463	1472
87	901	389	17	1046	737	1330	1462	76	1200	1357
88	415	1695	535	820	694	1169	918	778	56	664
89	955	65	393	343	397	515	877	263	297	1014
90	1322	889	758	181	425	464	833	1455	1473	373
91	1073	902	1539	873	390	227	243	18	1128	230
92	1047	1532	1104	738	600	1036	1331	1638	1428	1463
93	1435	34	77	1380	293	1201	1065	1519	1358	704
94	653	416	1225	1390	1696	1507	246	536	1208	487
95	821	1084	1663	695	1260	1318	1170	1151	1618	919
96	151	1548	779	930	1398	57	1232	110	665	627
97	855	956	1499	21	66	347	754	394	1529	1205
98	344	1174	526	398	494	1019	516	838	564	878
99	1572	1052	264	1643	9	298	609	421	1015	1213

POWER RESIDUES

	0	1	2	3	4	5	6	7	8	9
50	358	1074	1523	1171	115	345	1035	1406	820	761
51	584	53	159	477	1431	895	986	1259	379	1137
52	13	39	117	351	1053	1460	982	1247	343	1029
53	1388	766	599	98	294	882	947	1142	28	84
54	252	756	569	8	24	72	216	648	245	735
55	506	1518	1156	70	210	630	191	573	20	60
56	180	540	1620	1462	988	1265	397	1191	175	525
57	1575	1327	583	50	150	450	1350	652	257	771
58	614	143	429	1287	463	1389	769	608	125	375
59	1125	1676	1630	1492	1078	1535	1207	223	669	308
60	924	1073	1520	1162	88	264	792	677	332	996
61	1289	469	1407	823	770	611	134	402	1206	220
62	660	281	843	830	791	674	323	969	1208	226
63	678	335	1005	1316	550	1650	1552	1258	376	1128
64	1685	1657	1573	1321	565	1695	1687	1663	1591	1375
65	727	482	1446	940	1121	1664	1594	1384	754	563
66	1689	1669	1609	1429	889	968	1205	217	651	254
67	762	587	62	186	558	1674	1624	1474	1024	1373
68	721	464	1392	778	635	206	618	155	465	1395
69	787	662	287	861	884	953	1160	82	246	738
70	515	1545	1237	313	939	1118	1655	1567	1303	511
71	1533	1201	205	615	146	438	1314	544	1632	1498
72	1096	1589	1369	709	428	1284	454	1362	688	365
73	1095	1586	1360	682	347	1041	1424	874	923	1070
74	1511	1135	7	21	63	189	567	2	6	18
75	54	162	486	1458	976	1229	289	867	902	1007
76	1322	568	5	15	45	135	405	1215	247	741
77	524	1572	1318	556	1668	1606	1420	862	887	962
78	1187	163	489	1467	1003	1310	532	1596	1390	772
79	617	152	456	1368	706	419	1257	373	1119	1658
80	1576	1330	592	77	231	693	380	1140	22	66
81	198	594	83	249	747	542	1626	1480	1042	1427
82	883	950	1151	55	165	495	1485	1057	1472	1018
83	1355	667	302	906	1019	1358	676	329	987	1262
84	388	1164	94	282	846	839	818	755	566	1698
85	1696	1690	1672	1618	1456	970	1211	235	705	416
86	1248	346	1038	1415	847	842	827	782	647	242
87	726	479	1437	913	1040	1421	865	896	989	1268
88	406	1218	256	768	605	116	348	1044	1433	901
89	1004	1313	541	1623	1471	1015	1346	640	221	663
90	290	870	911	1034	1403	811	734	503	1509	1129
91	1688	1666	1600	1402	808	725	476	1428	886	959
92	1178	136	408	1224	274	822	767	602	107	321
93	963	1190	172	516	1548	1246	340	1020	1361	685
94	356	1068	1505	1117	1652	1558	1276	430	1290	472
95	1416	850	851	854	863	890	971	1214	244	732
96	497	1491	1075	1526	1180	142	426	1278	436	1308
97	526	1578	1336	610	131	393	1179	139	417	1251
98	355	1065	1496	1090	1571	1315	547	1641	1525	1177
99	133	399	1197	193	579	38	114	342	1026	1379

P = 1699

INDICES

	0	1	2	3	4	5	6	7	8	9
100	1131	1323	1177	784	890	632	1654	759	336	403
101	182	1577	1297	426	90	895	465	1582	829	834
102	937	1479	1456	1685	678	1474	998	233	374	529
103	1447	1074	1680	1110	903	506	50	1540	862	1469
104	874	735	818	391	887	1071	228	1426	1517	244
105	1316	1396	19	524	1050	1129	401	827	231	48
106	1069	1048	1155	1157	1533	981	1217	1105	941	1404
107	739	1122	1159	601	501	962	1037	1277	594	1332
108	1308	1535	1639	497	1562	1429	450	1025	1464	124
109	983	1436	1059	270	35	730	720	78	213	1219
110	1381	160	386	294	1033	1660	1202	1651	1107	1066
111	1022	432	1520	1254	435	1359	1421	943	705	798
112	145	654	1187	239	417	590	1406	1226	639	909
113	1391	1610	1595	1697	1493	741	1508	519	1289	247
114	807	1523	537	1622	1124	1209	1304	1135	488	1483
115	315	822	137	1161	1085	1566	552	1664	43	1410
116	696	1139	603	1261	841	1043	1319	1635	1257	1171
117	333	503	1152	121	1418	1619	330	989	920	976
118	964	152	1005	84	1549	476	1100	780	1558	1039
119	931	567	192	1399	284	438	58	992	1279	1233
120	1117	711	111	366	1674	666	618	596	628	446
121	1631	856	168	1601	957	767	1334	1500	881	253
122	22	1272	1362	67	923	1310	348	100	1327	755
123	1460	1167	395	179	1537	1530	1433	702	1206	1149
124	1230	345	492	1641	1175	1575	935	527	860	1424
125	399	979	499	495	1057	158	1020	796	637	517
126	1302	1564	839	119	1003	565	1115	444	879	98
127	1431	1573	1055	117	1053	205	946	265	967	452
128	1644	207	129	10	725	1340	299	583	1027	610
129	948	73	422	31	1615	1016	1294	1466	1214	267
130	142	1132	1415	708	1324	155	126	1178	969	1181
131	785	1689	289	891	716	985	633	454	772	1655
132	1367	643	760	1487	1438	337	1646	571	404	172
133	801	183	1008	1061	1578	209	972	1298	1345	458
134	427	1349	272	91	131	305	896	1249	1372	466
135	576	37	1583	12	1354	830	1377	148	835	87
136	732	938	727	1184	1480	327	363	1457	793	722
137	1686	1342	324	679	1195	649	1475	382	80	999
138	301	410	234	358	657	375	1552	215	530	585
139	788	1448	682	278	1075	689	1221	1681	1029	472
140	1111	1245	913	904	319	1383	507	612	196	51
141	1605	1190	1541	479	162	863	950	1692	1470	1198
142	776	875	462	388	736	75	414	819	917	663
143	392	514	296	888	424	1454	1072	872	242	229
144	1103	1035	1427	33	292	1518	652	1389	245	486
145	1662	1317	1617	1547	1397	109	854	20	753	1204
146	525	1018	563	1051	8	420	1130	783	1653	402
147	1296	894	828	1478	677	232	1446	1109	49	1468
148	817	1070	1516	1395	1049	826	1068	1156	1216	1403
149	1158	961	593	1534	1561	1024	982	269	719	1218

POWER RESIDUES

	0	1	2	3	4	5	6	7	8	9
100	739	518	1554	1264	394	1182	148	444	1332	598
101	95	285	855	866	899	998	1295	487	1461	985
102	1256	370	1110	1631	1495	1087	1562	1288	466	1398
103	796	689	368	1104	1613	1441	925	1076	1529	1189
104	169	507	1521	1165	97	291	873	920	1061	1484
105	1054	1463	991	1274	424	1272	418	1254	364	1092
106	1577	1333	601	104	312	936	1109	1628	1486	1060
107	1481	1045	1436	910	1031	1394	784	653	260	780
108	641	224	672	317	951	1154	64	192	576	29
109	87	261	783	650	251	753	560	1680	1642	1528
110	1186	160	480	1440	922	1067	1502	1108	1625	1477
111	1033	1400	802	707	422	1266	400	1200	202	606
112	119	357	1071	1514	1144	34	102	306	918	1055
113	1466	1000	1301	505	1515	1147	43	129	387	1161
114	85	255	765	596	89	267	801	704	413	1239
115	319	957	1172	118	354	1062	1487	1063	1490	1072
116	1517	1153	61	183	549	1647	1543	1231	295	885
117	956	1169	109	327	981	1244	334	1002	1307	523
118	1569	1309	529	1587	1363	691	374	1122	1667	1603
119	1411	835	806	719	458	1374	724	473	1419	859
120	878	935	1106	1619	1459	979	1238	316	948	1145
121	37	111	333	999	1298	496	1488	1066	1499	1099
122	1598	1396	790	671	314	942	1127	1682	1648	1546
123	1240	322	966	1199	199	597	92	276	828	785
124	656	269	807	722	467	1401	805	716	449	1347
125	643	230	690	371	1113	1640	1522	1168	106	318
126	954	1163	91	273	819	758	575	26	78	234
127	702	407	1221	265	795	686	359	1077	1532	1198
128	196	588	65	195	585	56	168	504	1512	1138
129	16	48	144	432	1296	490	1470	1012	1337	613
130	140	420	1260	382	1146	40	120	360	1080	1541
131	1225	277	831	794	683	350	1050	1451	955	1166
132	100	300	900	1001	1304	514	1542	1228	286	858
133	875	926	1079	1538	1216	250	750	551	1653	1561
134	1285	457	1371	715	446	1338	616	149	447	1341
135	625	176	528	1584	1354	664	293	879	938	1115
136	1646	1540	1222	268	804	713	440	1320	562	1686
137	1660	1582	1348	646	239	717	452	1356	670	311
138	933	1100	1601	1405	817	752	557	1671	1615	1447
139	943	1130	1691	1675	1627	1483	1051	1454	964	1193
140	181	543	1629	1489	1069	1508	1126	1679	1639	1519
141	1159	79	237	711	434	1302	508	1524	1174	124
142	372	1116	1649	1549	1249	349	1047	1442	928	1085
143	1556	1270	412	1236	310	930	1091	1574	1324	574
144	23	69	207	621	164	492	1476	1030	1391	775
145	626	179	537	1611	1435	907	1022	1367	703	410
146	1230	292	876	929	1088	1565	1297	493	1479	1039
147	1418	856	869	908	1025	1376	730	491	1473	1021
148	1364	694	383	1149	49	147	441	1323	571	14
149	42	126	378	1134	4	12	36	108	324	972

P = 1699

INDICES

	0	1	2	3	4	5	6	7	8	9
150	385	1659	1106	431	434	942	144	238	1405	908
151	1594	740	1288	1522	1123	1134	314	1160	551	1409
152	602	1042	1256	502	1417	988	963	83	1099	1038
153	191	437	1278	710	1673	595	1630	1600	1333	252
154	1361	1309	1326	1166	1536	701	1229	1640	934	1423
155	498	157	636	1563	1002	443	1430	116	945	451
156	128	1339	1026	72	1614	1465	141	707	125	1180
157	288	984	771	642	1437	570	800	1060	971	457
158	271	304	1371	36	1353	147	731	1183	362	721
159	323	648	79	409	656	214	787	277	1220	471
160	912	1382	195	1189	161	1691	775	387	413	662
161	295	1453	241	1034	291	1388	1661	1546	853	1203
162	562	419	1652	893	676	1108	816	1394	1067	1402
163	592	1023	718	1658	433	237	1593	1521	313	1408
164	1255	987	1098	436	1672	1599	1360	1165	1228	1422
165	635	442	944	1338	1613	706	287	641	799	456
166	1370	146	361	647	655	276	911	1188	774	661
167	240	1387	852	418	675	1393	591	1657	1592	1407
168	1097	1598	1227	441	1612	640	1369	646	910	660
169	851	1392	1591	1597	1611	645	850	1596	849	

POWER RESIDUES

	0	1	2	3	4	5	6	7	8	9
150	1217	253	759	578	35	105	315	945	1136	10
151	30	90	270	810	731	494	1482	1048	1445	937
152	1112	1637	1513	1141	25	75	225	675	326	978
153	1235	307	921	1064	1493	1081	1544	1234	304	912
154	1037	1412	838	815	746	539	1617	1453	961	1184
155	154	462	1386	760	581	44	132	396	1188	166
156	498	1494	1084	1553	1261	385	1155	67	201	603
157	110	330	990	1271	415	1245	337	1011	1334	604
158	113	339	1017	1352	658	275	825	776	629	188
159	564	1692	1678	1636	1510	1132	1697	1693	1681	1645
160	1537	1213	241	723	470	1410	832	797	692	377
161	1131	1694	1684	1654	1564	1294	484	1452	958	1175
162	127	381	1143	31	93	279	837	812	737	512
163	1536	1210	232	696	389	1167	103	309	927	1082
164	1547	1243	331	993	1280	442	1326	580	41	123
165	369	1107	1622	1468	1006	1319	559	1677	1633	1501
166	1105	1616	1450	952	1157	73	219	657	272	816
167	749	548	1644	1534	1204	214	642	227	681	344
168	1032	1397	793	680	341	1023	1370	712	437	1311
169	535	1605	1417	853	860	881	944	1133		

P = 1709

INDICES

	0	1	2	3	4	5	6	7	8	9
0		0	875	1	42	702	876	58	917	2
1	1577	1166	43	557	933	703	84	1118	877	129
2	744	59	333	387	918	1404	1432	3	100	1699
3	1578	736	959	1167	285	760	44	1358	1004	558
4	1619	1331	934	1255	1208	704	1262	220	85	116
5	571	1119	599	452	878	160	975	130	866	884
6	745	754	1611	60	126	1259	334	1443	1160	388
7	1635	638	919	337	525	1405	171	1224	1433	1366
8	786	4	498	226	101	112	422	1700	375	1602
9	1579	615	429	737	1095	831	960	481	991	1168
10	1446	1507	286	1524	1474	761	1327	1625	45	676
11	1035	1359	142	1084	1005	1089	33	559	51	1176
12	1620	624	1629	1332	778	398	935	1163	1001	1256
13	426	1173	1209	187	610	705	327	362	1263	434
14	802	221	1513	15	86	693	1212	117	1400	1323
15	572	1481	1046	1120	391	1438	600	1419	533	453
16	1661	445	879	643	1373	161	1101	1543	976	1114
17	987	131	1297	190	867	1462	1250	885	769	135
18	746	1638	1490	755	1304	352	1612	576	262	61
19	1706	1575	127	98	1356	1260	158	124	335	496
20	613	1444	674	49	1161	325	691	389	641	1295
21	1636	1704	494	639	792	249	920	794	1551	338
22	202	1675	526	488	1017	1406	251	708	172	415
23	256	1225	908	521	1434	922	926	1367	343	840
24	787	1129	1499	5	796	818	499	686	1653	227
25	1273	27	102	1553	330	113	168	1521	423	1416
26	1301	1701	340	1151	376	1154	1062	1603	1485	809
27	1580	204	1202	616	1237	862	430	198	1309	738
28	1677	365	1096	1144	680	832	890	1389	961	528
29	1568	482	379	948	992	1586	567	1169	490	944
30	1447	1313	648	1508	213	1456	287	1019	1266	1525
31	605	543	1475	238	586	762	1408	930	1328	1157
32	828	1626	1320	1247	46	253	1518	677	540	278
33	1036	1030	268	1360	710	437	143	1070	281	1085
34	154	194	1006	174	464	1090	1065	730	34	1050
35	629	560	417	273	52	1340	1644	1177	1010	1428
36	1621	258	805	625	657	1039	1630	233	471	1333
37	1227	510	779	1606	1451	399	1137	548	936	910
38	873	1164	742	1697	1002	218	973	1257	523	224
39	427	1505	1033	1174	999	360	1210	1436	1371	188
40	1488	1573	611	1293	1549	706	924	816	328	1149
41	1200	363	1566	942	1264	928	1516	435	462	271
42	803	508	871	222	1369	814	1514	812	1667	16
43	1124	661	87	345	1669	694	718	516	1213	178
44	1077	118	842	18	1401	596	1363	1324	184	1658
45	573	789	1126	1482	1583	1317	1047	1134	1290	1121
46	1131	663	392	1681	75	1439	1396	411	601	1501
47	89	1420	93	713	534	1533	1218	454	7	347
48	1662	207	296	446	666	1183	880	798	1671	644
49	1693	71	1374	1109	1561	162	820	696	1102	1347

POWER RESIDUES

	0	1	2	3	4	5	6	7	8	9
0	1	3	9	27	81	243	729	478	1434	884
1	943	1120	1651	1535	1187	143	429	1287	443	1329
2	569	1707	1703	1691	1655	1547	1223	251	753	550
3	1650	1532	1178	116	348	1044	1423	851	844	823
4	760	571	4	12	36	108	324	972	1207	203
5	609	118	354	1062	1477	1013	1330	572	7	21
6	63	189	567	1701	1685	1637	1493	1061	1474	1004
7	1303	491	1473	1001	1294	464	1392	758	565	1695
8	1667	1583	1331	575	16	48	144	432	1296	470
9	1410	812	727	472	1416	830	781	634	193	579
10	28	84	252	756	559	1677	1613	1421	845	826
11	769	598	85	255	765	586	49	147	441	1323
12	551	1653	1541	1205	197	591	64	192	576	19
13	57	171	513	1539	1199	179	537	1611	1415	827
14	772	607	112	336	1008	1315	527	1581	1325	557
15	1671	1595	1367	683	340	1020	1351	635	196	588
16	55	165	495	1485	1037	1402	788	655	256	768
17	595	76	228	684	343	1029	1378	716	439	1317
18	533	1599	1379	719	448	1344	614	133	399	1197
19	173	519	1557	1253	341	1023	1360	662	277	831
20	784	643	220	660	271	813	730	481	1443	911
21	1024	1363	671	304	912	1027	1372	698	385	1155
22	47	141	423	1269	389	1167	83	249	747	532
23	1596	1370	692	367	1101	1594	1364	674	313	939
24	1108	1615	1427	863	880	931	1084	1543	1211	215
25	645	226	678	325	975	1216	230	690	361	1083
26	1540	1202	188	564	1692	1658	1556	1250	332	996
27	1279	419	1257	353	1059	1468	986	1249	329	987
28	1252	338	1014	1333	581	34	102	306	918	1045
29	1426	860	871	904	1003	1300	482	1446	920	1051
30	1444	914	1033	1390	752	547	1641	1505	1097	1582
31	1328	566	1698	1676	1610	1412	818	745	526	1578
32	1316	530	1590	1352	638	205	615	136	408	1224
33	254	762	577	22	66	198	594	73	219	657
34	262	786	649	238	714	433	1299	479	1437	893
35	970	1201	185	555	1665	1577	1313	521	1563	1271
36	395	1185	137	411	1233	281	843	820	751	544
37	1632	1478	1016	1339	599	88	264	792	667	292
38	876	919	1048	1435	887	952	1147	23	69	207
39	621	154	462	1386	740	511	1533	1181	125	375
40	1125	1666	1580	1322	548	1644	1514	1124	1663	1571
41	1295	467	1401	785	646	229	687	352	1056	1459
42	959	1168	86	258	774	613	130	390	1170	92
43	276	828	775	616	139	417	1251	335	1005	1306
44	500	1500	1082	1537	1193	161	483	1449	929	1078
45	1525	1157	53	159	477	1431	875	916	1039	1408
46	806	709	418	1254	344	1032	1387	743	520	1560
47	1262	368	1104	1603	1391	755	556	1668	1586	1340
48	602	97	291	873	910	1021	1354	644	223	669
49	298	894	973	1210	212	636	199	597	82	246

P = 1709

INDICES

	0	1	2	3	4	5	6	7	8	9
50	440	1544	902	1466	977	501	720	1115	1205	635
51	988	395	1043	132	688	518	1298	1386	583	191
52	468	357	868	1655	1215	1463	318	146	1251	774
53	321	886	229	180	770	619	652	136	1684	1282
54	747	1275	1079	1639	369	1378	1491	305	404	756
55	29	120	1305	1424	1073	353	476	149	1613	104
56	844	577	1240	1597	263	78	311	62	1555	20
57	1707	41	57	1576	556	83	128	332	1403	99
58	735	284	1357	1618	1254	1261	115	598	159	865
59	753	125	1442	1634	336	170	1365	497	111	374
60	614	1094	480	1445	1523	1326	675	141	1088	50
61	623	777	1162	425	186	326	433	1512	692	1399
62	1480	390	1418	1660	642	1100	1113	1296	1461	768
63	1637	1303	575	1705	97	157	495	673	324	640
64	1703	791	793	201	487	250	414	907	921	342
65	1128	795	685	1272	1552	167	1415	339	1153	1484
66	203	1236	197	1676	1143	889	527	378	1585	489
67	1312	212	1018	604	237	1407	1156	1319	252	539
68	1029	709	1069	153	173	1064	1049	416	1339	1009
69	257	656	232	1226	1605	1136	909	741	217	522
70	1504	998	1435	1487	1292	923	1148	1565	927	461
71	507	1368	811	1123	344	717	177	841	595	183
72	788	1582	1133	1130	1680	1395	1500	92	1532	6
73	206	665	797	1692	1108	819	1346	901	500	1204
74	394	687	1385	467	1654	317	773	228	618	1683
75	1274	368	304	28	1423	475	103	1239	77	1554
76	40	555	331	734	1617	114	864	1441	169	110
77	1093	1522	140	622	424	432	1398	1417	1099	1460
78	1302	96	672	1702	200	413	341	684	166	1152
79	1235	1142	377	1311	603	1155	538	1068	1063	1338
80	655	1604	740	1503	1486	1147	460	810	716	594
81	1581	1679	91	205	1691	1345	1203	1384	316	617
82	367	1422	1238	39	733	863	109	139	431	1098
83	95	199	683	1234	1310	537	1337	739	1146	715
84	1678	1690	1383	366	38	108	1097	682	536	1145
85	1689	37	681	1688	1687	833	834	1535	891	835
86	291	1390	1536	243	962	892	1220	529	836	824
87	1569	292	1593	483	1391	456	380	1537	1053	949
88	244	1285	993	963	9	1587	893	384	568	1221
89	1471	1170	530	349	491	837	1059	945	825	727
90	1448	1570	1664	1314	293	632	649	1594	750	1509
91	484	209	214	1392	301	1457	457	1231	288	381
92	298	1020	1538	1195	1267	1054	848	1526	950	448
93	606	245	563	544	1286	1278	1476	994	668	239
94	964	1023	587	10	968	763	1588	1185	1409	894
95	700	931	385	957	1329	569	882	1158	1222	420
96	829	1472	1082	1627	1171	800	1321	531	1541	1248
97	350	1354	47	492	1673	254	838	1651	1519	1060
98	860	678	946	646	541	826	276	279	728	1642
99	1037	1449	1695	1031	1571	1198	269	1665	514	1361

POWER RESIDUES

	0	1	2	3	4	5	6	7	8	9
50	738	505	1515	1127	1672	1598	1376	710	421	1263
51	371	1113	1630	1472	998	1285	437	1311	515	1545
52	1217	233	699	388	1164	74	222	666	289	867
53	892	967	1192	158	474	1422	848	835	796	679
54	328	984	1243	311	933	1090	1561	1265	377	1131
55	1684	1634	1484	1034	1393	761	574	13	39	117
56	351	1053	1450	932	1087	1552	1238	296	888	955
57	1156	50	150	450	1350	632	187	561	1683	1631
58	1475	1007	1312	518	1554	1244	314	942	1117	1642
59	1508	1106	1609	1409	809	718	445	1335	587	52
60	156	468	1404	794	673	310	930	1081	1534	1184
61	134	402	1206	200	600	91	273	819	748	535
62	1605	1397	773	610	121	363	1089	1558	1256	350
63	1050	1441	905	1006	1309	509	1527	1163	71	213
64	639	208	624	163	489	1467	983	1240	302	906
65	1009	1318	536	1608	1406	800	691	364	1092	1567
66	1283	431	1293	461	1383	731	484	1452	938	1105
67	1606	1400	782	637	202	606	109	327	981	1234
68	284	852	847	832	787	652	247	741	514	1542
69	1208	206	618	145	435	1305	497	1491	1055	1456
70	950	1141	5	15	45	135	405	1215	227	681
71	334	1002	1297	473	1419	839	808	715	436	1308
72	506	1518	1136	1699	1679	1619	1439	899	988	1255
73	347	1041	1414	824	763	580	31	93	279	837
74	802	697	382	1146	20	60	180	540	1620	1442
75	908	1015	1336	590	61	183	549	1647	1523	1151
76	35	105	315	945	1126	1669	1589	1349	629	178
77	534	1602	1388	746	529	1587	1343	611	124	372
78	1116	1639	1499	1079	1528	1166	80	240	720	451
79	1353	641	214	642	217	651	244	732	487	1461
80	965	1186	140	420	1260	362	1086	1549	1229	269
81	807	712	427	1281	425	1275	407	1221	245	735
82	496	1488	1046	1429	869	898	985	1246	320	960
83	1171	95	285	855	856	859	868	895	976	1219
84	239	717	442	1326	560	1680	1622	1448	926	1069
85	1498	1076	1519	1139	1708	1706	1700	1682	1628	1466
86	980	1231	275	825	766	589	58	174	522	1566
87	1280	422	1266	380	1140	2	6	18	54	162
88	486	1458	956	1159	59	177	531	1593	1361	665
89	286	858	865	886	949	1138	1705	1697	1673	1601
90	1385	737	502	1506	1100	1591	1355	647	232	696
91	379	1137	1702	1688	1646	1520	1142	8	24	72
92	216	648	235	705	406	1218	236	708	415	1245
93	317	951	1144	14	42	126	378	1134	1693	1661
94	1565	1277	413	1239	299	897	982	1237	293	879
95	928	1075	1516	1130	1681	1625	1457	953	1150	32
96	96	288	864	883	940	1111	1624	1454	944	1123
97	1660	1562	1268	386	1158	56	168	504	1512	1118
98	1645	1517	1133	1690	1652	1538	1196	170	510	1530
99	1172	98	294	882	937	1102	1597	1373	701	394

P = 1709

INDICES

	0	1	2	3	4	5	6	7	8	9
100	1315	73	711	294	69	438	633	581	144	650
101	1376	1071	1595	55	282	751	372	1086	1510	1111
102	155	485	1270	195	210	1027	1007	215	1563	175
103	1393	1106	465	302	553	1091	1458	164	1066	458
104	1343	731	1232	1381	35	289	822	1051	382	1057
105	630	299	1193	561	1021	698	418	1539	1649	274
106	1196	67	53	1268	1104	1341	1055	1647	1645	849
107	1494	1178	1527	1349	1011	951	851	1429	449	783
108	1622	607	442	259	246	1496	806	564	1244	626
109	545	1546	658	1287	1180	1040	1279	308	1631	1477
110	904	234	995	1529	472	669	591	1334	240	1468
111	1228	965	1351	511	1024	1190	780	588	979	1607
112	11	1013	1452	969	407	400	764	503	1138	1589
113	953	549	1186	982	937	1410	722	911	895	853
114	874	701	916	1165	932	1117	743	386	1431	1698
115	958	759	1003	1330	1207	219	570	451	974	883
116	1610	1258	1159	637	524	1223	785	225	421	1601
117	428	830	990	1506	1473	1624	1034	1083	32	1175
118	1628	397	1000	1172	609	361	801	14	1211	1322
119	1045	1437	532	444	1372	1542	986	189	1249	134
120	1489	351	261	1574	1355	123	612	48	690	1294
121	493	248	1550	1674	1016	707	255	520	925	839
122	1498	817	1652	26	329	1520	1300	1150	1061	808
123	1201	861	1308	364	679	1388	1567	947	566	943
124	647	1455	1265	542	585	929	827	1246	1517	277
125	267	436	280	193	463	729	628	272	1643	1427
126	804	1038	470	509	1450	547	872	1696	972	223
127	1032	359	1370	1572	1548	815	1199	941	1515	270
128	870	813	1666	660	1668	515	1076	17	1362	1657
129	1125	1316	1289	662	74	410	88	712	1217	346
130	295	1182	1670	70	1560	695	439	1465	719	634
131	1042	517	582	356	1214	145	320	179	651	1281
132	1078	1377	403	119	1072	148	843	1596	310	19
133	56	82	1402	283	1253	597	752	1633	1364	373
134	479	1325	1087	776	185	1511	1479	1659	1112	767
135	574	156	323	790	486	906	1127	1271	1414	1483
136	196	888	1584	211	236	1318	1028	152	1048	1008
137	231	1135	216	997	1291	1564	506	1122	176	182
138	1132	1394	1531	664	1107	900	393	466	772	1682
139	303	474	76	554	1616	1440	1092	621	1397	1459
140	671	412	165	1141	602	1067	654	1502	459	593
141	90	1344	315	1421	732	138	94	1233	1336	714
142	1382	107	535	36	1686	1534	290	242	1219	823
143	1592	455	1052	1284	8	383	1470	348	1058	726
144	1663	631	749	208	300	1230	297	1194	847	447
145	562	1277	667	1022	967	1184	699	956	881	419
146	1081	799	1540	1353	1672	1650	859	645	275	1641
147	1694	1197	513	72	68	580	1375	54	371	1110
148	1269	1026	1562	1105	552	163	1342	1380	821	1056
149	1192	697	1648	66	1103	1646	1493	1348	850	782

POWER RESIDUES

	0	1	2	3	4	5	6	7	8	9
100	1182	128	384	1152	38	114	342	1026	1369	689
101	358	1074	1513	1121	1654	1544	1214	224	672	307
102	921	1054	1453	941	1114	1633	1481	1025	1366	680
103	331	993	1270	392	1176	110	330	990	1261	365
104	1095	1576	1310	512	1536	1190	152	456	1368	686
105	349	1047	1432	878	925	1066	1489	1049	1438	896
106	979	1228	266	798	685	346	1038	1405	797	682
107	337	1011	1324	554	1662	1568	1286	440	1320	542
108	1626	1460	962	1177	113	339	1017	1342	608	115
109	345	1035	1396	770	601	94	282	846	829	778
110	625	166	498	1494	1064	1483	1031	1384	734	493
111	1479	1019	1348	626	169	507	1521	1145	17	51
112	153	459	1377	713	430	1290	452	1356	650	241
113	723	460	1380	722	457	1371	695	376	1128	1675
114	1607	1403	791	664	283	849	838	805	706	409
115	1227	263	789	658	265	795	676	319	957	1162
116	68	204	612	127	381	1143	11	33	99	297
117	891	964	1183	131	393	1179	119	357	1071	1504
118	1094	1573	1301	485	1455	947	1132	1687	1643	1511
119	1115	1636	1490	1052	1447	923	1060	1471	995	1276
120	410	1230	272	816	739	508	1524	1154	44	132
121	396	1188	146	438	1314	524	1572	1298	476	1428
122	866	889	958	1165	77	231	693	370	1110	1621
123	1445	917	1042	1417	833	790	661	274	822	757
124	562	1686	1640	1502	1088	1555	1247	323	969	1198
125	176	528	1584	1334	584	43	129	387	1161	65
126	195	585	46	138	414	1242	308	924	1063	1480
127	1022	1357	653	250	750	541	1623	1451	935	1096
128	1579	1319	539	1617	1433	881	934	1093	1570	1292
129	458	1374	704	403	1209	209	627	172	516	1548
130	1226	260	780	631	184	552	1656	1550	1232	278
131	834	793	670	301	903	1000	1291	455	1365	677
132	322	966	1189	149	447	1341	605	106	318	954
133	1153	41	123	369	1107	1612	1418	836	799	688
134	355	1065	1486	1040	1411	815	736	499	1497	1073
135	1510	1112	1627	1463	971	1204	194	582	37	111
136	333	999	1288	446	1338	596	79	237	711	424
137	1272	398	1194	164	492	1476	1010	1321	545	1635
138	1487	1043	1420	842	817	742	517	1551	1235	287
139	861	874	913	1030	1381	725	466	1398	776	619
140	148	444	1332	578	25	75	225	675	316	948
141	1135	1696	1670	1592	1358	656	259	777	622	157
142	471	1413	821	754	553	1659	1559	1259	359	1077
143	1522	1148	26	78	234	702	397	1191	155	465
144	1395	767	592	67	201	603	100	300	900	991
145	1264	374	1122	1657	1553	1241	305	915	1036	1399
146	779	628	175	525	1575	1307	503	1509	1109	1618
147	1436	890	961	1174	104	312	936	1099	1588	1346
148	620	151	453	1359	659	268	804	703	400	1200
149	182	546	1638	1496	1070	1501	1085	1546	1220	242

P = 1709

INDICES

	0	1	2	3	4	5	6	7	8	9
150	441	1495	1243	1545	1179	307	903	1528	590	1467
151	1350	1189	978	1012	406	502	952	981	721	852
152	915	1116	1430	758	1206	450	1609	636	784	1600
153	989	1623	31	396	608	13	1044	443	985	133
154	260	122	689	247	1015	519	1497	25	1299	807
155	1307	1387	565	1454	584	1245	266	192	627	1426
156	469	546	971	358	1547	940	869	659	1075	1656
157	1288	409	1216	1181	1559	1464	1041	355	319	1280
158	402	147	309	81	1252	1632	478	775	1478	766
159	322	905	1413	887	235	151	230	996	505	181
160	1530	899	771	473	1615	620	670	1140	653	592
161	314	137	1335	106	1685	241	1591	1283	1469	725
162	748	1229	846	1276	966	955	1080	1352	858	1640
163	512	579	370	1025	551	1379	1191	65	1492	781
164	1242	306	589	1188	405	980	914	757	1608	1599
165	30	12	984	121	1014	24	1306	1453	265	1425
166	970	939	1074	408	1558	354	401	80	477	765
167	1412	150	504	898	1614	1139	313	105	1590	724
168	845	954	857	578	550	64	1241	1187	913	1598
169	983	23	264	938	1557	79	1411	897	312	723
170	856	63	912	22	1556	896	855	21	854	

POWER RESIDUES

	0	1	2	3	4	5	6	7	8	9
150	726	469	1407	803	700	391	1173	101	303	909
151	1018	1345	617	142	426	1278	416	1248	326	978
152	1225	257	771	604	103	309	927	1072	1507	1103
153	1600	1382	728	475	1425	857	862	877	922	1057
154	1462	968	1195	167	501	1503	1091	1564	1274	404
155	1212	218	654	253	759	568	1704	1694	1664	1574
156	1304	494	1482	1028	1375	707	412	1236	290	870
157	901	994	1273	401	1203	191	573	10	30	90
158	270	810	721	454	1362	668	295	885	946	1129
159	1678	1616	1430	872	907	1012	1327	563	1689	1649
160	1529	1169	89	267	801	694	373	1119	1648	1526
161	1160	62	186	558	1674	1604	1394	764	583	40
162	120	360	1080	1531	1175	107	321	963	1180	122
163	366	1098	1585	1337	593	70	210	630	181	543
164	1629	1469	989	1258	356	1068	1495	1067	1492	1058
165	1465	977	1222	248	744	523	1569	1289	449	1347
166	623	160	480	1440	902	997	1282	428	1284	434
167	1302	488	1464	974	1213	221	663	280	840	811
168	724	463	1389	749	538	1614	1424	854	853	850
169	841	814	733	490	1470	992	1267	383	1149	29
170	87	261	783	640	211	633	190	570		

P = 1721

INDICES

	0	1	2	3	4	5	6	7	8	9
0		0	1064	1	408	1684	1065	1227	1472	2
1	1028	1006	409	1129	571	1685	816	32	1066	836
2	372	1228	350	479	1473	1648	473	3	1635	463
3	1029	706	160	1007	1096	1191	410	153	180	1130
4	1436	1148	572	1144	1414	1686	1543	913	817	734
5	992	33	1537	628	1067	970	979	837	1527	1425
6	373	354	50	1229	1224	1093	351	755	440	480
7	535	1139	1474	953	1217	1649	1244	513	474	1402
8	780	4	492	842	1636	1716	488	464	758	1053
9	1030	636	887	707	257	800	161	582	78	1008
10	336	1236	1097	997	881	1192	1692	46	411	1383
11	314	154	323	1368	181	443	871	1131	769	1259
12	1437	292	1418	1149	1114	1612	573	266	568	1145
13	437	797	1415	343	99	1687	1504	964	1544	1079
14	1599	914	483	415	818	427	297	735	561	346
15	993	227	588	34	1577	670	1538	59	746	629
16	124	1706	1068	468	1556	971	186	1585	980	538
17	1060	838	1552	694	1528	1155	102	1426	397	1172
18	374	25	1700	355	231	117	51	1038	1321	1230
19	144	202	1225	814	1646	1094	1142	1535	352	533
20	1400	756	580	1690	441	1112	341	481	225	122
21	536	395	1036	1140	1110	1108	1475	213	727	954
22	1378	1161	1218	1477	1387	1650	712	1048	1245	402
23	1507	514	215	663	475	877	113	1403	603	450
24	781	729	1356	5	762	698	493	245	458	843
25	956	903	1637	1485	1330	1717	1632	967	489	1380
26	1501	465	141	210	759	592	1407	1054	1163	1561
27	1031	595	848	637	308	934	888	1220	423	708
28	943	986	258	274	1547	801	1479	655	162	64
29	1491	583	1361	808	79	1389	1625	1009	1410	1608
30	337	651	1291	1237	1652	318	1098	947	921	998
31	14	1082	882	714	1123	1193	90	680	1693	1469
32	1188	47	1050	868	412	1057	1532	1384	900	420
33	315	1247	1250	155	929	719	324	1306	1602	1369
34	404	1712	182	241	896	444	38	607	872	1509
35	499	1132	1166	1450	770	1103	1461	1260	516	1253
36	1438	1672	1089	293	1044	917	1419	217	1295	1150
37	1181	135	1115	854	382	1613	665	1592	574	1564
38	1208	267	1266	1682	569	477	158	1146	990	1423
39	438	511	486	798	879	1366	1416	795	1597	344
40	744	1583	100	115	1644	1688	1034	1159	1505	448
41	456	965	1405	932	1545	806	1289	1080	1186	418
42	1600	605	1459	915	380	1680	484	1581	454	416
43	452	1313	819	598	1277	428	71	1315	298	783
44	722	736	505	1345	562	1017	821	347	731	1241
45	994	434	56	228	392	600	589	1358	1466	35
46	851	741	1578	389	1279	671	7	327	1539	262
47	221	60	1177	430	747	764	1667	630	1514	686
48	125	1282	73	1707	700	546	1069	640	106	469
49	42	1317	1557	495	1309	972	1522	646	187	526

POWER RESIDUES

	0	1	2	3	4	5	6	7	8	9
0	1	3	9	27	81	243	729	466	1398	752
1	535	1605	1373	677	310	930	1069	1486	1016	1327
2	539	1617	1409	785	634	181	543	1629	1445	893
3	958	1153	17	51	153	459	1377	689	346	1038
4	1393	737	490	1470	968	1183	107	321	963	1168
5	62	186	558	1674	1580	1298	452	1356	626	157
6	471	1413	797	670	289	867	880	919	1036	1387
7	719	436	1308	482	1446	896	967	1180	98	294
8	882	925	1054	1441	881	922	1045	1414	800	679
9	316	948	1123	1648	1502	1064	1471	971	1192	134
10	402	1206	176	528	1584	1310	488	1464	950	1129
11	1666	1556	1226	236	708	403	1209	185	555	1665
12	1553	1217	209	627	160	480	1440	878	913	1018
13	1333	557	1671	1571	1271	371	1113	1618	1412	794
14	661	262	786	637	190	570	1710	1688	1622	1424
15	830	769	586	37	111	333	999	1276	386	1158
16	32	96	288	864	871	892	955	1144	1711	1691
17	1631	1451	911	1012	1315	503	1509	1085	1534	1160
18	38	114	342	1026	1357	629	166	498	1494	1040
19	1399	755	544	1632	1454	920	1039	1396	746	517
20	1551	1211	191	573	1719	1715	1703	1667	1559	1235
21	263	789	646	217	651	232	696	367	1101	1582
22	1304	470	1410	788	643	208	624	151	453	1359
23	635	184	552	1656	1526	1136	1687	1619	1415	803
24	688	343	1029	1366	656	247	741	502	1506	1076
25	1507	1079	1516	1106	1597	1349	605	94	282	846
26	817	730	469	1407	779	616	127	381	1143	1708
27	1682	1604	1370	668	283	849	826	757	550	1650
28	1508	1082	1525	1133	1678	1592	1334	560	1680	1598
29	1352	614	121	363	1089	1546	1196	146	438	1314
30	500	1500	1058	1453	917	1030	1369	665	274	822
31	745	514	1542	1184	110	330	990	1249	305	915
32	1024	1351	611	112	336	1008	1303	467	1401	761
33	562	1686	1616	1406	776	607	100	300	900	979
34	1216	206	618	133	399	1197	149	447	1341	581
35	22	66	198	594	61	183	549	1647	1499	1055
36	1444	890	949	1126	1657	1529	1145	1714	1700	1658
37	1532	1154	20	60	180	540	1620	1418	812	715
38	424	1272	374	1122	1645	1493	1037	1390	728	463
39	1389	725	454	1362	644	211	633	178	534	1602
40	1364	650	229	687	340	1020	1339	575	4	12
41	36	108	324	972	1195	143	429	1287	419	1257
42	329	987	1240	278	834	781	622	145	435	1305
43	473	1419	815	724	451	1353	617	130	390	1170
44	68	204	612	115	345	1035	1384	710	409	1227
45	239	717	430	1290	428	1284	410	1230	248	744
46	511	1533	1157	29	87	261	783	628	163	489
47	1467	959	1156	26	78	234	702	385	1155	23
48	69	207	621	142	426	1278	392	1176	86	258
49	774	601	82	246	738	493	1479	995	1264	350

P = 1721

INDICES

	0	1	2	3	4	5	6	7	8	9
50	300	1586	247	175	981	1200	829	539	674	785
51	1061	460	976	839	311	961	1553	199	724	695
52	845	1605	1529	1447	1205	1156	1274	738	103	958
53	1656	1427	751	557	398	10	507	1173	905	20
54	375	937	1659	26	192	1347	1701	1639	1372	356
55	278	1299	232	909	564	118	1487	131	52	553
56	287	1039	330	1019	1322	1332	1338	1231	891	1430
57	145	611	823	203	1719	407	1226	1027	1128	815
58	835	349	1647	1634	705	1095	152	1435	1143	1542
59	733	1536	969	1526	353	1223	754	534	952	1243
60	1401	491	1715	757	635	256	581	335	996	1691
61	1382	322	442	768	291	1113	265	436	342	1503
62	1078	482	426	560	226	1576	58	123	467	185
63	537	1551	1154	396	24	230	1037	143	813	1141
64	532	579	1111	224	394	1109	212	1377	1476	711
65	401	214	876	602	728	761	244	955	1484	1631
66	1379	140	591	1162	594	307	1219	942	273	1478
67	63	1360	1388	1409	650	1651	946	13	713	89
68	1468	1049	1056	899	1246	928	1305	403	240	37
69	1508	1165	1102	515	1671	1043	216	1180	853	664
70	1563	1265	476	989	510	878	794	743	114	1033
71	447	1404	805	1185	604	379	1580	451	597	70
72	782	504	1016	730	433	391	1357	850	388	6
73	261	1176	763	1513	1281	699	639	41	494	1521
74	525	246	1199	673	459	310	198	844	1446	1273
75	957	750	9	904	936	191	1638	277	908	1486
76	552	329	1331	890	610	1718	1026	834	1633	151
77	1541	968	1222	951	490	634	334	1381	767	264
78	1502	425	1575	466	1550	23	142	531	223	211
79	710	875	760	1483	139	593	941	62	1408	945
80	88	1055	927	239	1164	1670	1179	1562	988	793
81	1032	804	378	596	503	432	849	260	1512	638
82	1520	1198	309	1445	749	935	276	551	889	1025
83	150	1221	633	766	424	1549	530	709	1482	940
84	944	926	1669	987	803	502	259	1519	1444	275
85	1024	632	1548	1481	925	802	1518	1023	1480	1517
86	1516	656	657	620	163	658	1662	65	621	688
87	1492	164	1135	584	659	1119	1362	1663	127	809
88	66	84	80	622	1569	1390	689	1284	1626	1493
89	361	1010	165	29	1411	1136	75	1609	585	1169
90	338	660	1498	652	1120	1709	1292	1363	1456	1238
91	1664	172	1653	128	702	319	810	304	1099	67
92	195	948	85	548	922	81	1453	999	623	1620
93	15	1570	1071	1083	1391	1002	883	690	1326	715
94	1285	642	1124	1627	521	1194	1494	1350	91	362
95	108	681	1011	773	1694	166	858	1470	30	471
96	1189	1412	626	48	1137	778	1051	76	44	869
97	1610	97	413	586	1704	1058	1170	1319	1533	339
98	1106	1385	661	1354	901	1499	1559	421	653	1623
99	316	1121	866	1248	1710	497	1251	1293	1590	156

POWER RESIDUES

	0	1	2	3	4	5	6	7	8	9
50	1050	1429	845	814	721	442	1326	536	1608	1382
51	704	391	1173	77	231	693	358	1074	1501	1061
52	1462	944	1111	1612	1394	740	499	1497	1049	1426
53	836	787	640	199	597	70	210	630	169	507
54	1521	1121	1642	1484	1010	1309	485	1455	923	1048
55	1423	827	760	559	1677	1589	1325	533	1599	1355
56	623	148	444	1332	554	1662	1544	1190	128	384
57	1152	14	42	126	378	1134	1681	1601	1361	641
58	202	606	97	291	873	898	973	1198	152	456
59	1368	662	265	795	664	271	813	718	433	1299
60	455	1365	653	238	714	421	1263	347	1041	1402
61	764	571	1713	1697	1649	1505	1073	1498	1052	1435
62	863	868	883	928	1063	1468	962	1165	53	159
63	477	1431	851	832	775	604	91	273	819	736
64	487	1461	941	1102	1585	1313	497	1491	1031	1372
65	674	301	903	988	1243	287	861	862	865	874
66	901	982	1225	233	699	376	1128	1663	1547	1199
67	155	465	1395	743	508	1524	1130	1669	1565	1253
68	317	951	1132	1675	1583	1307	479	1437	869	886
69	937	1090	1549	1205	173	519	1557	1229	245	735
70	484	1452	914	1021	1342	584	31	93	279	837
71	790	649	226	678	313	939	1096	1567	1259	335
72	1005	1294	440	1320	518	1554	1220	218	654	241
73	723	448	1344	590	49	147	441	1323	527	1581
74	1301	461	1383	707	400	1200	158	474	1422	824
75	751	532	1596	1346	596	67	201	603	88	264
76	792	655	244	732	475	1425	833	778	613	118
77	354	1062	1465	953	1138	1693	1637	1469	965	1174
78	80	240	720	439	1317	509	1527	1139	1696	1646
79	1496	1046	1417	809	706	397	1191	131	393	1179
80	95	285	855	844	811	712	415	1245	293	879
81	916	1027	1360	638	193	579	16	48	144	432
82	1296	446	1338	572	1716	1706	1676	1586	1316	506
83	1518	1112	1615	1403	767	580	19	57	171	513
84	1539	1175	83	249	747	520	1560	1238	272	816
85	727	460	1380	698	373	1119	1636	1466	956	1147
86	1720	1718	1712	1694	1640	1478	992	1255	323	969
87	1186	116	348	1044	1411	791	652	235	705	394
88	1182	104	312	936	1087	1540	1178	92	276	828
89	763	568	1704	1670	1568	1262	344	1032	1375	683
90	328	984	1231	251	753	538	1614	1400	758	553
91	1659	1535	1163	47	141	423	1269	365	1095	1564
92	1250	308	924	1051	1432	854	841	802	685	334
93	1002	1285	413	1239	275	825	754	541	1623	1427
94	839	796	667	280	840	799	676	307	921	1042
95	1405	773	598	73	219	657	250	750	529	1587
96	1319	515	1545	1193	137	411	1233	257	771	592
97	55	165	495	1485	1013	1318	512	1536	1166	56
98	168	504	1512	1094	1561	1241	281	843	808	703
99	388	1164	50	150	450	1350	608	103	309	927

P = 1721

INDICES

	0	1	2	3	4	5	6	7	8	9
100	1364	1642	930	1457	1311	720	1239	1464	325	1665
101	544	1307	173	974	1603	1654	18	1370	129	1336
102	405	703	1524	1713	320	1076	183	811	1375	242
103	305	648	897	1100	1263	445	68	386	39	196
104	189	608	949	1573	873	86	791	1510	549	528
105	500	923	618	1133	82	359	1167	1454	302	1451
106	1000	519	771	624	95	1104	1621	1588	1462	16
107	1074	1261	1571	616	517	1072	249	1254	1084	251
108	1439	1392	281	1673	1003	177	1090	884	1256	294
109	691	1397	1045	1327	983	918	716	1086	1420	1286
110	1342	218	643	1202	1296	1125	253	1151	1628	1302
111	1182	522	831	136	1195	1441	1116	1495	1617	855
112	1351	541	383	92	1394	1614	363	1213	666	109
113	676	1593	682	283	575	1012	235	1565	774	787
114	1209	1695	1675	268	167	366	1267	859	1063	1683
115	1471	1005	570	31	371	478	472	462	159	1190
116	179	1147	1413	912	991	627	978	1424	49	1092
117	439	1138	1216	512	779	841	487	1052	886	799
118	77	1235	880	45	313	1367	870	1258	1417	1611
119	567	796	98	963	1598	414	296	345	587	669
120	745	1705	1555	1584	1059	693	101	1171	1699	116
121	1320	201	1645	1534	1399	1689	340	121	1035	1107
122	726	1160	1386	1047	1506	662	112	449	1355	697
123	457	902	1329	966	1500	209	1406	1560	847	933
124	422	985	1546	654	1490	807	1624	1607	1290	317
125	920	1081	1122	679	1187	867	1531	419	1249	718
126	1601	1711	895	606	498	1449	1460	1252	1088	916
127	1294	134	381	1591	1207	1681	157	1422	485	1365
128	1596	1582	1643	1158	455	931	1288	417	1458	1679
129	453	1312	1276	1314	721	1344	820	1240	55	599
130	1465	740	1278	326	220	429	1666	685	72	545
131	105	1316	1308	645	299	174	828	784	975	960
132	723	1604	1204	737	1655	556	506	19	1658	1346
133	1371	1298	563	130	286	1018	1337	1429	822	406
134	1127	348	704	1434	732	1525	753	1242	1714	255
135	995	321	290	435	1077	559	57	184	1153	229
136	812	578	393	1376	400	601	243	1630	590	306
137	272	1359	649	12	1467	898	1304	36	1101	1042
138	852	1264	509	742	446	1184	1579	69	1015	390
139	387	1175	1280	40	524	672	197	1272	8	190
140	907	328	609	833	1540	950	333	263	1574	22
141	222	874	138	61	87	238	1178	792	377	431
142	1511	1197	748	550	149	765	529	939	1668	501
143	1443	631	924	1022	1515	619	1661	687	1134	1118
144	126	83	1568	1283	360	28	74	1168	1497	1708
145	1455	171	701	303	194	547	1452	1619	1070	1001
146	1325	641	520	1349	107	772	857	470	625	777
147	43	96	1703	1318	1105	1353	1558	1622	865	496
148	1589	1641	1310	1463	543	973	17	1335	1523	1075
149	1374	647	1262	385	188	1572	790	527	617	358

POWER RESIDUES

	0	1	2	3	4	5	6	7	8	9
100	1060	1459	935	1084	1531	1151	11	33	99	297
101	891	952	1135	1684	1610	1388	722	445	1335	563
102	1689	1625	1433	857	850	829	766	577	10	30
103	90	270	810	709	406	1218	212	636	187	561
104	1683	1607	1379	695	364	1092	1555	1223	227	681
105	322	966	1177	89	267	801	682	325	975	1204
106	170	510	1530	1148	2	6	18	54	162	486
107	1458	932	1075	1504	1070	1489	1025	1354	620	139
108	417	1251	311	933	1078	1513	1097	1570	1268	362
109	1086	1537	1169	65	195	585	34	102	306	918
110	1033	1378	692	355	1065	1474	980	1219	215	645
111	214	642	205	615	124	372	1116	1627	1439	875
112	904	991	1252	314	942	1105	1594	1340	578	13
113	39	117	351	1053	1438	872	895	964	1171	71
114	213	639	196	588	43	129	387	1161	41	123
115	369	1107	1600	1358	632	175	525	1575	1283	407
116	1221	221	663	268	804	691	352	1056	1447	899
117	976	1207	179	537	1611	1391	731	472	1416	806
118	697	370	1110	1609	1385	713	418	1254	320	960
119	1159	35	105	315	945	1114	1621	1421	821	742
120	505	1515	1103	1588	1322	524	1572	1274	380	1140
121	1699	1655	1523	1127	1660	1538	1172	74	222	666
122	277	831	772	595	64	192	576	7	21	63
123	189	567	1701	1661	1541	1181	101	303	909	1006
124	1297	449	1347	599	76	228	684	331	993	1258
125	332	996	1267	359	1077	1510	1088	1543	1187	119
126	357	1071	1492	1034	1381	701	382	1146	1717	1709
127	1685	1613	1397	749	526	1578	1292	434	1302	464
128	1392	734	481	1443	887	940	1099	1576	1286	416
129	1248	302	906	997	1270	368	1104	1591	1331	551
130	1653	1517	1109	1606	1376	686	337	1011	1312	494
131	1482	1004	1291	431	1293	437	1311	491	1473	977
132	1210	188	564	1692	1634	1460	938	1093	1558	1232
133	254	762	565	1695	1643	1487	1019	1336	566	1698
134	1652	1514	1100	1579	1295	443	1329	545	1635	1463
135	947	1120	1639	1475	983	1228	242	726	457	1371
136	671	292	876	907	1000	1279	395	1185	113	339
137	1017	1330	548	1644	1490	1028	1363	647	220	660
138	259	777	610	109	327	981	1222	224	672	295
139	885	934	1081	1522	1124	1651	1511	1091	1552	1214
140	200	600	79	237	711	412	1236	266	798	673
141	298	894	961	1162	44	132	396	1188	122	366
142	1098	1573	1277	389	1167	59	177	531	1593	1337
143	569	1707	1679	1595	1343	587	40	120	360	1080
144	1519	1115	1624	1430	848	823	748	523	1569	1265
145	353	1059	1456	926	1057	1450	908	1003	1288	422
146	1266	356	1068	1483	1007	1300	458	1374	680	319
147	957	1150	8	24	72	216	648	223	669	286
148	858	853	838	793	658	253	759	556	1668	1562
149	1244	290	870	889	946	1117	1630	1448	902	985

P = 1721

INDICES

	0	1	2	3	4	5	6	7	8	9
150	301	518	94	1587	1073	615	248	250	280	176
151	1255	1396	982	1085	1341	1201	252	1301	830	1440
152	1616	540	1393	1212	675	282	234	786	1674	365
153	1062	1004	370	461	178	911	977	1091	1215	840
154	885	1234	312	1257	566	962	295	668	1554	692
155	1698	200	1398	120	725	1046	111	696	1328	208
156	846	984	1489	1606	919	678	1530	717	894	1448
157	1087	133	1206	1421	1595	1157	1287	1678	1275	1343
158	54	739	219	684	104	644	827	959	1203	555
159	1657	1297	285	1428	1126	1433	752	254	289	558
160	1152	577	399	1629	271	11	1303	1041	508	1183
161	1014	1174	523	1271	906	832	332	21	137	237
162	376	1196	148	938	1442	1021	1660	1117	1567	27
163	1496	170	193	1618	1324	1348	856	776	1702	1352
164	864	1640	542	1334	1373	384	789	357	93	614
165	279	1395	1340	1300	1615	1211	233	364	369	910
166	1214	1233	565	667	1697	119	110	207	1488	677
167	893	132	1594	1677	53	683	826	554	284	1432
168	288	576	270	1040	1013	1270	331	236	147	1020
169	1566	169	1323	775	863	1333	788	613	1339	1210
170	368	1232	1696	206	892	1676	825	1431	269	1269
171	146	168	862	612	367	205	824	1268	861	204
172	860	0								

POWER RESIDUES

	0	1	2	3	4	5	6	7	8	9
150	1234	260	780	619	136	408	1224	230	690	349
151	1047	1420	818	733	478	1434	860	859	856	847
152	820	739	496	1488	1022	1345	593	58	174	522
153	1566	1256	326	978	1213	197	591	52	156	468
154	1404	770	589	46	138	414	1242	284	852	835
155	784	631	172	516	1548	1202	164	492	1476	986
156	1237	269	807	700	379	1137	1690	1628	1442	884
157	931	1072	1495	1043	1408	782	625	154	462	1386
158	716	427	1281	401	1203	167	501	1503	1067	1480
159	998	1273	377	1131	1672	1574	1280	398	1194	140
160	420	1260	338	1014	1321	521	1563	1247	299	897
161	970	1189	125	375	1125	1654	1520	1118	1633	1457
162	929	1066	1477	989	1246	296	888	943	1108	1603
163	1367	659	256	768	583	28	84	252	756	547
164	1641	1481	1001	1282	404	1212	194	582	25	75
165	225	675	304	912	1015	1324	530	1590	1328	542
166	1626	1436	866	877	910	1009	1306	476	1428	842
167	805	694	361	1083	1528	1142	1705	1673	1577	1289
168	425	1275	383	1149	5	15	45	135	405	1215
169	203	609	106	318	954	1141	1702	1664	1550	1208
170	182	546	1638	1472	974	1201	161	483	1449	905
171	994	1261	341	1023	1348	602	85	255	765	574
172										

P = 1721

INDICES

	0	1	2	3	4	5	6	7	8	9
0		0	1064	1	408	1684	1065	1227	1472	2
1	1028	1006	409	1129	571	1685	816	32	1066	836
2	372	1228	350	479	1473	1648	473	3	1635	463
3	1029	706	160	1007	1096	1191	410	153	180	1130
4	1436	1148	572	1144	1414	1686	1543	913	817	734
5	992	33	1537	628	1067	970	979	837	1527	1425
6	373	354	50	1229	1224	1093	351	755	440	480
7	535	1139	1474	953	1217	1649	1244	513	474	1402
8	780	4	492	842	1636	1716	488	464	758	1053
9	1030	636	887	707	257	800	161	582	78	1008
10	336	1236	1097	997	881	1192	1692	46	411	1383
11	314	154	323	1368	181	443	871	1131	769	1259
12	1437	292	1418	1149	1114	1612	573	266	568	1145
13	437	797	1415	343	99	1687	1504	964	1544	1079
14	1599	914	483	415	818	427	297	735	561	346
15	993	227	588	34	1577	670	1538	59	746	629
16	124	1706	1068	468	1556	971	186	1585	980	538
17	1060	838	1552	694	1528	1155	102	1426	397	1172
18	374	25	1700	355	231	117	51	1038	1321	1230
19	144	202	1225	814	1646	1094	1142	1535	352	533
20	1400	756	580	1690	441	1112	341	481	225	122
21	536	395	1036	1140	1110	1108	1475	213	727	954
22	1378	1161	1218	1477	1387	1650	712	1048	1245	402
23	1507	514	215	663	475	877	113	1403	603	450
24	781	729	1356	5	762	698	493	245	458	843
25	956	903	1637	1485	1330	1717	1632	967	489	1380
26	1501	465	141	210	759	592	1407	1054	1163	1561
27	1031	595	848	637	308	934	888	1220	423	708
28	943	986	258	274	1547	801	1479	655	162	64
29	1491	583	1361	808	79	1389	1625	1009	1410	1608
30	337	651	1291	1237	1652	318	1098	947	921	998
31	14	1082	882	714	1123	1193	90	680	1693	1469
32	1188	47	1050	868	412	1057	1532	1384	900	420
33	315	1247	1250	155	929	719	324	1306	1602	1369
34	404	1712	182	241	896	444	38	607	872	1509
35	499	1132	1166	1450	770	1103	1461	1260	516	1253
36	1438	1672	1089	293	1044	917	1419	217	1295	1150
37	1181	135	1115	854	382	1613	665	1592	574	1564
38	1208	267	1266	1682	569	477	158	1146	990	1423
39	438	511	486	798	879	1366	1416	795	1597	344
40	744	1583	100	115	1644	1688	1034	1159	1505	448
41	456	965	1405	932	1545	806	1289	1080	1186	418
42	1600	605	1459	915	380	1680	484	1581	454	416
43	452	1313	819	598	1277	428	71	1315	298	783
44	722	736	505	1345	562	1017	821	347	731	1241
45	994	434	56	228	392	600	589	1358	1466	35
46	851	741	1578	389	1279	671	7	327	1539	262
47	221	60	1177	430	747	764	1667	630	1514	686
48	125	1282	73	1707	700	546	1069	640	106	469
49	42	1317	1557	495	1309	972	1522	646	187	526

POWER RESIDUES

	0	1	2	3	4	5	6	7	8	9
0	1	3	9	27	81	243	729	466	1398	752
1	535	1605	1373	677	310	930	1069	1486	1016	1327
2	539	1617	1409	785	634	181	543	1629	1445	893
3	958	1153	17	51	153	459	1377	689	346	1038
4	1393	737	490	1470	968	1183	107	321	963	1168
5	62	186	558	1674	1580	1298	452	1356	626	157
6	471	1413	797	670	289	867	880	919	1036	1387
7	719	436	1308	482	1446	896	967	1180	98	294
8	882	925	1054	1441	881	922	1045	1414	800	679
9	316	948	1123	1648	1502	1064	1471	971	1192	134
10	402	1206	176	528	1584	1310	488	1464	950	1129
11	1666	1556	1226	236	708	403	1209	185	555	1665
12	1553	1217	209	627	160	480	1440	878	913	1018
13	1333	557	1671	1571	1271	371	1113	1618	1412	794
14	661	262	786	637	190	570	1710	1688	1622	1424
15	830	769	586	37	111	333	999	1276	386	1158
16	32	96	288	864	871	892	955	1144	1711	1691
17	1631	1451	911	1012	1315	503	1509	1085	1534	1160
18	38	114	342	1026	1357	629	166	498	1494	1040
19	1399	755	544	1632	1454	920	1039	1396	746	517
20	1551	1211	191	573	1719	1715	1703	1667	1559	1235
21	263	789	646	217	651	232	696	367	1101	1582
22	1304	470	1410	788	643	208	624	151	453	1359
23	635	184	552	1656	1526	1136	1687	1619	1415	803
24	688	343	1029	1366	656	247	741	502	1506	1076
25	1507	1079	1516	1106	1597	1349	605	94	282	846
26	817	730	469	1407	779	616	127	381	1143	1708
27	1682	1604	1370	668	283	849	826	757	550	1650
28	1508	1082	1525	1133	1678	1592	1334	560	1680	1598
29	1352	614	121	363	1089	1546	1196	146	438	1314
30	500	1500	1058	1453	917	1030	1369	665	274	822
31	745	514	1542	1184	110	330	990	1249	305	915
32	1024	1351	611	112	336	1008	1303	467	1401	761
33	562	1686	1616	1406	776	607	100	300	900	979
34	1216	206	618	133	399	1197	149	447	1341	581
35	22	66	198	594	61	183	549	1647	1499	1055
36	1444	890	949	1126	1657	1529	1145	1714	1700	1658
37	1532	1154	20	60	180	540	1620	1418	812	715
38	424	1272	374	1122	1645	1493	1037	1390	728	463
39	1389	725	454	1362	644	211	633	178	534	1602
40	1364	650	229	687	340	1020	1339	575	4	12
41	36	108	324	972	1195	143	429	1287	419	1257
42	329	987	1240	278	834	781	622	145	435	1305
43	473	1419	815	724	451	1353	617	130	390	1170
44	68	204	612	115	345	1035	1384	710	409	1227
45	239	717	430	1290	428	1284	410	1230	248	744
46	511	1533	1157	29	87	261	783	628	163	489
47	1467	959	1156	26	78	234	702	385	1155	23
48	69	207	621	142	426	1278	392	1176	86	258
49	774	601	82	246	738	493	1479	995	1264	350

P = 1721

INDICES

	0	1	2	3	4	5	6	7	8	9
50	300	1586	247	175	981	1200	829	539	674	785
51	1061	460	976	839	311	961	1553	199	724	695
52	845	1605	1529	1447	1205	1156	1274	738	103	958
53	1656	1427	751	557	398	10	507	1173	905	20
54	375	937	1659	26	192	1347	1701	1639	1372	356
55	278	1299	232	909	564	118	1487	131	52	553
56	287	1039	330	1019	1322	1332	1338	1231	891	1430
57	145	611	823	203	1719	407	1226	1027	1128	815
58	835	349	1647	1634	705	1095	152	1435	1143	1542
59	733	1536	969	1526	353	1223	754	534	952	1243
60	1401	491	1715	757	635	256	581	335	996	1691
61	1382	322	442	768	291	1113	265	436	342	1503
62	1078	482	426	560	226	1576	58	123	467	185
63	537	1551	1154	396	24	230	1037	143	813	1141
64	532	579	1111	224	394	1109	212	1377	1476	711
65	401	214	876	602	728	761	244	955	1484	1631
66	1379	140	591	1162	594	307	1219	942	273	1478
67	63	1360	1388	1409	650	1651	946	13	713	89
68	1468	1049	1056	899	1246	928	1305	403	240	37
69	1508	1165	1102	515	1671	1043	216	1180	853	664
70	1563	1265	476	989	510	878	794	743	114	1033
71	447	1404	805	1185	604	379	1580	451	597	70
72	782	504	1016	730	433	391	1357	850	388	6
73	261	1176	763	1513	1281	699	639	41	494	1521
74	525	246	1199	673	459	310	198	844	1446	1273
75	957	750	9	904	936	191	1638	277	908	1486
76	552	329	1331	890	610	1718	1026	834	1633	151
77	1541	968	1222	951	490	634	334	1381	767	264
78	1502	425	1575	466	1550	23	142	531	223	211
79	710	875	760	1483	139	593	941	62	1408	945
80	88	1055	927	239	1164	1670	1179	1562	988	793
81	1032	804	378	596	503	432	849	260	1512	638
82	1520	1198	309	1445	749	935	276	551	889	1025
83	150	1221	633	766	424	1549	530	709	1482	940
84	944	926	1669	987	803	502	259	1519	1444	275
85	1024	632	1548	1481	925	802	1518	1023	1480	1517
86	1516	656	657	620	163	658	1662	65	621	688
87	1492	164	1135	584	659	1119	1362	1663	127	809
88	66	84	80	622	1569	1390	689	1284	1626	1493
89	361	1010	165	29	1411	1136	75	1609	585	1169
90	338	660	1498	652	1120	1709	1292	1363	1456	1238
91	1664	172	1653	128	702	319	810	304	1099	67
92	195	948	85	548	922	81	1453	999	623	1620
93	15	1570	1071	1083	1391	1002	883	690	1326	715
94	1285	642	1124	1627	521	1194	1494	1350	91	362
95	108	681	1011	773	1694	166	858	1470	30	471
96	1189	1412	626	48	1137	778	1051	76	44	869
97	1610	97	413	586	1704	1058	1170	1319	1533	339
98	1106	1385	661	1354	901	1499	1559	421	653	1623
99	316	1121	866	1248	1710	497	1251	1293	1590	156

POWER RESIDUES

	0	1	2	3	4	5	6	7	8	9
50	1050	1429	845	814	721	442	1326	536	1608	1382
51	704	391	1173	77	231	693	358	1074	1501	1061
52	1462	944	1111	1612	1394	740	499	1497	1049	1426
53	836	787	640	199	597	70	210	630	169	507
54	1521	1121	1642	1484	1010	1309	485	1455	923	1048
55	1423	827	760	559	1677	1589	1325	533	1599	1355
56	623	148	444	1332	554	1662	1544	1190	128	384
57	1152	14	42	126	378	1134	1681	1601	1361	641
58	202	606	97	291	873	898	973	1198	152	456
59	1368	662	265	795	664	271	813	718	433	1299
60	455	1365	653	238	714	421	1263	347	1041	1402
61	764	571	1713	1697	1649	1505	1073	1498	1052	1435
62	863	868	883	928	1063	1468	962	1165	53	159
63	477	1431	851	832	775	604	91	273	819	736
64	487	1461	941	1102	1585	1313	497	1491	1031	1372
65	674	301	903	988	1243	287	861	862	865	874
66	901	982	1225	233	699	376	1128	1663	1547	1199
67	155	465	1395	743	508	1524	1130	1669	1565	1253
68	317	951	1132	1675	1583	1307	479	1437	869	886
69	937	1090	1549	1205	173	519	1557	1229	245	735
70	484	1452	914	1021	1342	584	31	93	279	837
71	790	649	226	678	313	939	1096	1567	1259	335
72	1005	1294	440	1320	518	1554	1220	218	654	241
73	723	448	1344	590	49	147	441	1323	527	1581
74	1301	461	1383	707	400	1200	158	474	1422	824
75	751	532	1596	1346	596	67	201	603	88	264
76	792	655	244	732	475	1425	833	778	613	118
77	354	1062	1465	953	1138	1693	1637	1469	965	1174
78	80	240	720	439	1317	509	1527	1139	1696	1646
79	1496	1046	1417	809	706	397	1191	131	393	1179
80	95	285	855	844	811	712	415	1245	293	879
81	916	1027	1360	638	193	579	16	48	144	432
82	1296	446	1338	572	1716	1706	1676	1586	1316	506
83	1518	1112	1615	1403	767	580	19	57	171	513
84	1539	1175	83	249	747	520	1560	1238	272	816
85	727	460	1380	698	373	1119	1636	1466	956	1147
86	1720	1718	1712	1694	1640	1478	992	1255	323	969
87	1186	116	348	1044	1411	791	652	235	705	394
88	1182	104	312	936	1087	1540	1178	92	276	828
89	763	568	1704	1670	1568	1262	344	1032	1375	683
90	328	984	1231	251	753	538	1614	1400	758	553
91	1659	1535	1163	47	141	423	1269	365	1095	1564
92	1250	308	924	1051	1432	854	841	802	685	334
93	1002	1285	413	1239	275	825	754	541	1623	1427
94	839	796	667	280	840	799	676	307	921	1042
95	1405	773	598	73	219	657	250	750	529	1587
96	1319	515	1545	1193	137	411	1233	257	771	592
97	55	165	495	1485	1013	1318	512	1536	1166	56
98	168	504	1512	1094	1561	1241	281	843	808	703
99	388	1164	50	150	450	1350	608	103	309	927

P = 1721

INDICES

	0	1	2	3	4	5	6	7	8	9
100	1364	1642	930	1457	1311	720	1239	1464	325	1665
101	544	1307	173	974	1603	1654	18	1370	129	1336
102	405	703	1524	1713	320	1076	183	811	1375	242
103	305	648	897	1100	1263	445	68	386	39	196
104	189	608	949	1573	873	86	791	1510	549	528
105	500	923	618	1133	82	359	1167	1454	302	1451
106	1000	519	771	624	95	1104	1621	1588	1462	16
107	1074	1261	1571	616	517	1072	249	1254	1084	251
108	1439	1392	281	1673	1003	177	1090	884	1256	294
109	691	1397	1045	1327	983	918	716	1086	1420	1286
110	1342	218	643	1202	1296	1125	253	1151	1628	1302
111	1182	522	831	136	1195	1441	1116	1495	1617	855
112	1351	541	383	92	1394	1614	363	1213	666	109
113	676	1593	682	283	575	1012	235	1565	774	787
114	1209	1695	1675	268	167	366	1267	859	1063	1683
115	1471	1005	570	31	371	478	472	462	159	1190
116	179	1147	1413	912	991	627	978	1424	49	1092
117	439	1138	1216	512	779	841	487	1052	886	799
118	77	1235	880	45	313	1367	870	1258	1417	1611
119	567	796	98	963	1598	414	296	345	587	669
120	745	1705	1555	1584	1059	693	101	1171	1699	116
121	1320	201	1645	1534	1399	1689	340	121	1035	1107
122	726	1160	1386	1047	1506	662	112	449	1355	697
123	457	902	1329	966	1500	209	1406	1560	847	933
124	422	985	1546	654	1490	807	1624	1607	1290	317
125	920	1081	1122	679	1187	867	1531	419	1249	718
126	1601	1711	895	606	498	1449	1460	1252	1088	916
127	1294	134	381	1591	1207	1681	157	1422	485	1365
128	1596	1582	1643	1158	455	931	1288	417	1458	1679
129	453	1312	1276	1314	721	1344	820	1240	55	599
130	1465	740	1278	326	220	429	1666	685	72	545
131	105	1316	1308	645	299	174	828	784	975	960
132	723	1604	1204	737	1655	556	506	19	1658	1346
133	1371	1298	563	130	286	1018	1337	1429	822	406
134	1127	348	704	1434	732	1525	753	1242	1714	255
135	995	321	290	435	1077	559	57	184	1153	229
136	812	578	393	1376	400	601	243	1630	590	306
137	272	1359	649	12	1467	898	1304	36	1101	1042
138	852	1264	509	742	446	1184	1579	69	1015	390
139	387	1175	1280	40	524	672	197	1272	8	190
140	907	328	609	833	1540	950	333	263	1574	22
141	222	874	138	61	87	238	1178	792	377	431
142	1511	1197	748	550	149	765	529	939	1668	501
143	1443	631	924	1022	1515	619	1661	687	1134	1118
144	126	83	1568	1283	360	28	74	1168	1497	1708
145	1455	171	701	303	194	547	1452	1619	1070	1001
146	1325	641	520	1349	107	772	857	470	625	777
147	43	96	1703	1318	1105	1353	1558	1622	865	496
148	1589	1641	1310	1463	543	973	17	1335	1523	1075
149	1374	647	1262	385	188	1572	790	527	617	358

POWER RESIDUES

	0	1	2	3	4	5	6	7	8	9
100	1060	1459	935	1084	1531	1151	11	33	99	297
101	891	952	1135	1684	1610	1388	722	445	1335	563
102	1689	1625	1433	857	850	829	766	577	10	30
103	90	270	810	709	406	1218	212	636	187	561
104	1683	1607	1379	695	364	1092	1555	1223	227	681
105	322	966	1177	89	267	801	682	325	975	1204
106	170	510	1530	1148	2	6	18	54	162	486
107	1458	932	1075	1504	1070	1489	1025	1354	620	139
108	417	1251	311	933	1078	1513	1097	1570	1268	362
109	1086	1537	1169	65	195	585	34	102	306	918
110	1033	1378	692	355	1065	1474	980	1219	215	645
111	214	642	205	615	124	372	1116	1627	1439	875
112	904	991	1252	314	942	1105	1594	1340	578	13
113	39	117	351	1053	1438	872	895	964	1171	71
114	213	639	196	588	43	129	387	1161	41	123
115	369	1107	1600	1358	632	175	525	1575	1283	407
116	1221	221	663	268	804	691	352	1056	1447	899
117	976	1207	179	537	1611	1391	731	472	1416	806
118	697	370	1110	1609	1385	713	418	1254	320	960
119	1159	35	105	315	945	1114	1621	1421	821	742
120	505	1515	1103	1588	1322	524	1572	1274	380	1140
121	1699	1655	1523	1127	1660	1538	1172	74	222	666
122	277	831	772	595	64	192	576	7	21	63
123	189	567	1701	1661	1541	1181	101	303	909	1006
124	1297	449	1347	599	76	228	684	331	993	1258
125	332	996	1267	359	1077	1510	1088	1543	1187	119
126	357	1071	1492	1034	1381	701	382	1146	1717	1709
127	1685	1613	1397	749	526	1578	1292	434	1302	464
128	1392	734	481	1443	887	940	1099	1576	1286	416
129	1248	302	906	997	1270	368	1104	1591	1331	551
130	1653	1517	1109	1606	1376	686	337	1011	1312	494
131	1482	1004	1291	431	1293	437	1311	491	1473	977
132	1210	188	564	1692	1634	1460	938	1093	1558	1232
133	254	762	565	1695	1643	1487	1019	1336	566	1698
134	1652	1514	1100	1579	1295	443	1329	545	1635	1463
135	947	1120	1639	1475	983	1228	242	726	457	1371
136	671	292	876	907	1000	1279	395	1185	113	339
137	1017	1330	548	1644	1490	1028	1363	647	220	660
138	259	777	610	109	327	981	1222	224	672	295
139	885	934	1081	1522	1124	1651	1511	1091	1552	1214
140	200	600	79	237	711	412	1236	266	798	673
141	298	894	961	1162	44	132	396	1188	122	366
142	1098	1573	1277	389	1167	59	177	531	1593	1337
143	569	1707	1679	1595	1343	587	40	120	360	1080
144	1519	1115	1624	1430	848	823	748	523	1569	1265
145	353	1059	1456	926	1057	1450	908	1003	1288	422
146	1266	356	1068	1483	1007	1300	458	1374	680	319
147	957	1150	8	24	72	216	648	223	669	286
148	858	853	838	793	658	253	759	556	1668	1562
149	1244	290	870	889	946	1117	1630	1448	902	985

P = 1721

INDICES

	0	1	2	3	4	5	6	7	8	9
150	301	518	94	1587	1073	615	248	250	280	176
151	1255	1396	982	1085	1341	1201	252	1301	830	1440
152	1616	540	1393	1212	675	282	234	786	1674	365
153	1062	1004	370	461	178	911	977	1091	1215	840
154	885	1234	312	1257	566	962	295	668	1554	692
155	1698	200	1398	120	725	1046	111	696	1328	208
156	846	984	1489	1606	919	678	1530	717	894	1448
157	1087	133	1206	1421	1595	1157	1287	1678	1275	1343
158	54	739	219	684	104	644	827	959	1203	555
159	1657	1297	285	1428	1126	1433	752	254	289	558
160	1152	577	399	1629	271	11	1303	1041	508	1183
161	1014	1174	523	1271	906	832	332	21	137	237
162	376	1196	148	938	1442	1021	1660	1117	1567	27
163	1496	170	193	1618	1324	1348	856	776	1702	1352
164	864	1640	542	1334	1373	384	789	357	93	614
165	279	1395	1340	1300	1615	1211	233	364	369	910
166	1214	1233	565	667	1697	119	110	207	1488	677
167	893	132	1594	1677	53	683	826	554	284	1432
168	288	576	270	1040	1013	1270	331	236	147	1020
169	1566	169	1323	775	863	1333	788	613	1339	1210
170	368	1232	1696	206	892	1676	825	1431	269	1269
171	146	168	862	612	367	205	824	1268	861	204
172	860	0								

POWER RESIDUES

	0	1	2	3	4	5	6	7	8	9
150	1234	260	780	619	136	408	1224	230	690	349
151	1047	1420	818	733	478	1434	860	859	856	847
152	820	739	496	1488	1022	1345	593	58	174	522
153	1566	1256	326	978	1213	197	591	52	156	468
154	1404	770	589	46	138	414	1242	284	852	835
155	784	631	172	516	1548	1202	164	492	1476	986
156	1237	269	807	700	379	1137	1690	1628	1442	884
157	931	1072	1495	1043	1408	782	625	154	462	1386
158	716	427	1281	401	1203	167	501	1503	1067	1480
159	998	1273	377	1131	1672	1574	1280	398	1194	140
160	420	1260	338	1014	1321	521	1563	1247	299	897
161	970	1189	125	375	1125	1654	1520	1118	1633	1457
162	929	1066	1477	989	1246	296	888	943	1108	1603
163	1367	659	256	768	583	28	84	252	756	547
164	1641	1481	1001	1282	404	1212	194	582	25	75
165	225	675	304	912	1015	1324	530	1590	1328	542
166	1626	1436	866	877	910	1009	1306	476	1428	842
167	805	694	361	1083	1528	1142	1705	1673	1577	1289
168	425	1275	383	1149	5	15	45	135	405	1215
169	203	609	106	318	954	1141	1702	1664	1550	1208
170	182	546	1638	1472	974	1201	161	483	1449	905
171	994	1261	341	1023	1348	602	85	255	765	574
172										

P = 1723

INDICES

	0	1	2	3	4	5	6	7	8	9
0		0	207	1	414	1245	208	1227	621	2
1	1452	164	415	1509	1434	1246	828	839	209	916
2	1659	1228	371	1160	622	768	1716	3	1641	901
3	1453	1383	1035	165	1046	750	416	722	1123	1510
4	144	1148	1435	718	578	1247	1367	106	829	732
5	975	840	201	1551	210	1409	126	917	1108	375
6	1660	466	1590	1229	1242	1032	372	922	1253	1161
7	957	1155	623	279	929	769	1330	1391	1717	875
8	351	4	1355	431	1642	362	925	902	785	980
9	1454	1014	1574	1384	313	439	1036	951	939	166
10	1182	230	1047	802	408	751	36	197	417	400
11	1616	723	333	1256	1124	683	1315	1511	582	344
12	145	328	673	1149	75	291	1436	1697	1449	719
13	1239	1011	579	421	1129	1248	1460	1321	1368	133
14	1164	107	1362	1673	830	424	486	733	1136	617
15	976	565	1537	841	1598	906	202	250	1082	1552
16	558	665	211	793	1562	1410	638	960	127	1296
17	569	918	1132	1497	1109	273	992	376	1187	1192
18	1661	1172	1221	467	59	245	1591	1003	520	1230
19	646	1273	1243	1432	1158	1033	1146	973	373	1251
20	1389	923	437	406	1254	671	1009	1162	615	1080
21	958	990	243	1156	404	241	624	888	607	280
22	101	626	930	1567	540	770	1463	763	1331	1501
23	890	1392	1522	1208	1718	1351	789	876	551	609
24	352	50	535	5	880	255	1356	703	282	432
25	498	1541	1643	1324	182	363	1656	103	926	227
26	1446	903	1218	1077	786	1074	628	981	1336	1053
27	1455	1604	1667	1015	1528	932	1575	1119	340	1385
28	1371	1375	314	1421	1569	440	158	653	1037	1678
29	631	952	693	542	940	1620	1343	167	824	947
30	1183	223	772	231	22	1711	1048	136	83	803
31	1113	1465	409	698	457	752	1289	984	37	1065
32	765	198	872	33	418	555	1000	401	47	1333
33	1617	869	845	724	1167	445	334	739	1503	1257
34	776	1547	1125	237	1339	684	1704	892	1316	848
35	480	1512	1199	190	583	678	1394	345	1399	1100
36	146	110	1379	329	1428	1524	674	810	266	1150
37	452	1056	76	117	1210	292	727	688	1437	1609
38	853	1698	1480	1720	1450	914	1639	720	1365	1407
39	1240	277	1353	1012	1180	398	580	1695	1458	422
40	1596	791	1130	1170	644	1249	613	886	1461	1349
41	878	1322	1216	1602	1369	1676	822	134	1287	553
42	1165	235	1197	108	450	1607	1363	1693	611	1674
43	448	1308	831	1310	1095	425	814	354	487	1473
44	308	734	833	318	1137	503	52	618	747	1587
45	977	1312	1670	566	970	537	1538	337	1708	842
46	1097	1636	1599	305	7	907	1415	10	203	427
47	1558	251	996	882	1083	1684	758	1553	816	1018
48	559	509	257	666	742	474	212	356	1087	794
49	462	1358	1563	18	910	1411	489	660	639	601

POWER RESIDUES

	0	1	2	3	4	5	6	7	8	9
0	1	3	9	27	81	243	729	464	1392	730
1	467	1401	757	548	1644	1486	1012	1313	493	1479
2	991	1250	304	912	1013	1316	502	1506	1072	1493
3	1033	1376	682	323	969	1184	106	318	954	1139
4	1694	1636	1462	940	1097	1568	1258	328	984	1229
5	241	723	446	1338	568	1704	1666	1552	1210	184
6	552	1656	1522	1120	1637	1465	949	1124	1649	1501
7	1057	1448	898	971	1190	124	372	1116	1625	1429
8	841	800	677	308	924	1049	1424	826	755	542
9	1626	1432	850	827	758	551	1653	1513	1093	1556
10	1222	220	660	257	771	590	47	141	423	1269
11	361	1083	1526	1132	1673	1573	1273	373	1119	1634
12	1456	922	1043	1406	772	593	56	168	504	1512
13	1090	1547	1195	139	417	1251	307	921	1040	1397
14	745	512	1536	1162	40	120	360	1080	1517	1105
15	1592	1330	544	1632	1450	904	989	1244	286	858
16	851	830	767	578	11	33	99	297	891	950
17	1127	1658	1528	1138	1691	1627	1435	859	854	839
18	794	659	254	762	563	1689	1621	1417	805	692
19	353	1059	1454	916	1025	1352	610	107	321	963
20	1166	52	156	468	1404	766	575	2	6	18
21	54	162	486	1458	928	1061	1460	934	1079	1514
22	1096	1565	1249	301	903	986	1235	259	777	608
23	101	303	909	1004	1289	421	1263	343	1029	1364
24	646	215	645	212	636	185	555	1665	1549	1201
25	157	471	1413	793	656	245	735	482	1446	892
26	953	1136	1685	1609	1381	697	368	1104	1589	1321
27	517	1551	1207	175	525	1575	1279	391	1173	73
28	219	657	248	744	509	1527	1135	1682	1600	1354
29	616	125	375	1125	1652	1510	1084	1529	1141	1700
30	1654	1516	1102	1583	1303	463	1389	721	440	1320
31	514	1542	1180	94	282	846	815	722	443	1329
32	541	1623	1423	823	746	515	1545	1189	121	363
33	1089	1544	1186	112	336	1008	1301	457	1371	667
34	278	834	779	614	119	357	1071	1490	1024	1349
35	601	80	240	720	437	1311	487	1461	937	1088
36	1541	1177	85	255	765	572	1716	1702	1660	1534
37	1156	22	66	198	594	59	177	531	1593	1333
38	553	1659	1531	1147	1718	1708	1678	1588	1318	508
39	1524	1126	1655	1519	1111	1610	1384	706	395	1185
40	109	327	981	1220	214	642	203	609	104	312
41	936	1085	1532	1150	4	12	36	108	324	972
42	1193	133	399	1197	145	435	1305	469	1407	775
43	602	83	249	747	518	1554	1216	202	606	95
44	285	855	842	803	686	335	1005	1292	430	1290
45	424	1272	370	1110	1607	1375	679	314	942	1103
46	1586	1312	490	1470	964	1169	61	183	549	1647
47	1495	1039	1394	736	485	1455	919	1034	1379	691
48	350	1050	1427	835	782	623	146	438	1314	496
49	1488	1018	1331	547	1641	1477	985	1232	250	750

P = 1723

INDICES

	0	1	2	3	4	5	6	7	8	9
50	705	961	26	1264	128	1475	1531	1297	389	284
51	570	1506	141	919	310	325	1133	270	434	1498
52	1653	1418	1110	736	1425	274	1284	500	993	598
53	1281	377	835	935	1188	1442	1543	1193	1260	896
54	1662	320	89	1173	152	1645	1222	493	13	468
55	1139	95	60	380	1326	246	547	1061	1592	505
56	1578	1004	1582	184	521	779	1628	1231	54	1688
57	647	590	365	1274	860	206	1244	620	163	1433
58	838	1658	1159	1715	900	1034	749	1122	1147	577
59	105	974	1550	125	374	1589	1031	1252	1154	928
60	1390	350	430	924	979	1573	438	938	229	407
61	196	1615	1255	1314	343	672	290	1448	1010	1128
62	1320	1163	1672	485	616	1536	905	1081	664	1561
63	959	568	1496	991	1191	1220	244	519	1272	1157
64	972	1388	405	1008	1079	242	240	606	625	539
65	762	889	1207	788	608	534	254	281	1540	181
66	102	1445	1076	627	1052	1666	931	339	1374	1568
67	652	630	541	1342	946	771	1710	82	1464	456
68	983	764	32	999	1332	844	444	1502	1546	1338
69	891	479	189	1393	1099	1378	1523	265	1055	1209
70	687	852	1719	1638	1406	1352	397	1457	790	643
71	885	877	1601	821	552	1196	1606	610	1307	1094
72	353	307	317	51	1586	1669	536	1707	1635	6
73	9	1557	881	757	1017	256	473	1086	1357	909
74	659	704	1263	1530	283	140	324	433	1417	1424
75	499	1280	934	1542	895	88	1644	12	94	1325
76	1060	1577	183	1627	1687	364	205	162	1657	899
77	1121	104	124	1030	927	429	1572	228	1614	342
78	1447	1319	484	904	1560	1495	1219	1271	1387	1078
79	605	761	787	253	180	1075	1665	1373	629	945
80	81	982	998	443	1337	188	1377	1054	851	1405
81	1456	884	820	1605	1093	316	1668	1634	1556	1016
82	1085	658	1529	323	1423	933	87	93	1576	1686
83	161	1120	1029	1571	341	483	1494	1386	760	179
84	1372	80	442	1376	1404	819	315	1555	657	1422
85	92	160	1570	1493	178	441	818	656	159	177
86	655	654	1515	1516	1038	1020	1517	1679	1302	1039
87	632	709	1021	953	561	1518	694	1176	1680	543
88	515	1303	941	511	1040	1621	525	633	1344	1202
89	710	168	259	1022	825	715	954	948	72	562
90	1184	668	1519	224	155	695	773	807	1177	232
91	744	1681	23	595	544	1712	193	516	1049	476
92	1304	137	121	942	84	1490	512	804	214	1041
93	1114	1648	1622	1466	217	526	410	358	634	699
94	43	1345	458	586	1203	753	1089	711	1290	66
95	169	985	965	260	38	796	1023	1066	1225	826
96	766	1044	716	199	464	955	873	783	949	34
97	681	73	419	1360	563	556	1294	1185	1001	1144
98	669	402	1565	1520	48	496	225	1334	1117	156
99	1618	20	696	870	867	774	846	1397	808	725

POWER RESIDUES

	0	1	2	3	4	5	6	7	8	9
50	527	1581	1297	445	1335	559	1677	1585	1309	481
51	1443	883	926	1055	1442	880	917	1028	1361	637
52	188	564	1692	1630	1444	886	935	1082	1523	1123
53	1646	1492	1030	1367	655	242	726	455	1365	649
54	224	672	293	879	914	1019	1334	556	1668	1558
55	1228	238	714	419	1257	325	975	1202	160	480
56	1440	874	899	974	1199	151	453	1359	631	170
57	510	1530	1144	1709	1681	1597	1345	589	44	132
58	396	1188	118	354	1062	1463	943	1106	1595	1339
59	571	1713	1693	1633	1453	913	1016	1325	529	1587
60	1315	499	1497	1045	1412	790	647	218	654	239
61	717	428	1284	406	1218	208	624	149	447	1341
62	577	8	24	72	216	648	221	663	266	798
63	671	290	870	887	938	1091	1550	1204	166	498
64	1494	1036	1385	709	404	1212	190	570	1710	1684
65	1606	1372	670	287	861	860	857	848	821	740
66	497	1491	1027	1358	628	161	483	1449	901	980
67	1217	205	615	122	366	1098	1571	1267	355	1065
68	1472	970	1187	115	345	1035	1382	700	377	1131
69	1670	1564	1246	292	876	905	992	1253	313	939
70	1094	1559	1231	247	741	500	1500	1054	1439	871
71	890	947	1118	1631	1447	895	962	1163	43	129
72	387	1161	37	111	333	999	1274	376	1128	1661
73	1537	1165	49	147	441	1323	523	1569	1261	337
74	1011	1310	484	1452	910	1007	1298	448	1344	586
75	35	105	315	945	1112	1613	1393	733	476	1428
76	838	791	650	227	681	320	960	1157	25	75
77	225	675	302	906	995	1262	340	1020	1337	565
78	1695	1639	1471	967	1178	88	264	792	653	236
79	708	401	1203	163	489	1467	955	1142	1703	1663
80	1543	1183	103	309	927	1058	1451	907	998	1271
81	367	1101	1580	1294	436	1308	478	1434	856	845
82	812	713	416	1248	298	894	959	1154	16	48
83	144	432	1296	442	1326	532	1596	1342	580	17
84	51	153	459	1377	685	332	996	1265	349	1047
85	1418	808	701	380	1140	1697	1645	1489	1021	1340
86	574	1722	1720	1714	1696	1642	1480	994	1259	331
87	993	1256	322	966	1175	79	237	711	410	1230
88	244	732	473	1419	811	710	407	1221	217	651
89	230	690	347	1041	1400	754	539	1617	1405	769
90	584	29	87	261	783	626	155	465	1395	739
91	494	1482	1000	1277	385	1155	19	57	171	513
92	1539	1171	67	201	603	86	258	774	599	74
93	222	666	275	825	752	533	1599	1351	607	98
94	294	882	923	1046	1415	799	674	299	897	968
95	1181	97	291	873	896	965	1172	70	210	630
96	167	501	1503	1063	1466	952	1133	1676	1582	1300
97	454	1362	640	197	591	50	150	450	1350	604
98	89	267	801	680	317	951	1130	1667	1555	1219
99	211	633	176	528	1584	1306	472	1416	802	683

P = 1723

INDICES

	0	1	2	3	4	5	6	7	8	9
100	912	1178	1168	1214	233	446	1471	745	335	1413
101	1682	740	16	24	1504	1651	596	1258	491	545
102	777	858	1713	1548	348	194	1126	662	517	238
103	532	1050	1340	30	477	685	641	1305	1705	471
104	138	893	1625	122	1317	603	943	849	1632	85
105	481	1402	1491	1513	707	513	1200	70	805	191
106	1488	215	584	963	1042	679	1142	1115	1395	1469
107	1649	346	28	1623	1400	1486	1467	1101	1103	218
108	147	1266	527	111	296	411	1380	1105	359	330
109	130	635	1429	98	700	1525	220	44	675	1477
110	1346	811	302	459	267	149	587	1151	1533	1204
111	453	394	754	1057	1268	1090	77	1299	712	118
112	63	1291	1211	529	67	293	391	170	728	1235
113	986	689	113	966	1438	286	261	1610	173	39
114	854	298	797	1699	572	1024	1481	383	1067	1721
115	413	1226	1451	1508	827	915	370	767	1640	1382
116	1045	721	143	717	1366	731	200	1408	1107	465
117	1241	921	956	278	1329	874	1354	361	784	1013
118	312	950	1181	801	35	399	332	682	581	327
119	74	1696	1238	420	1459	132	1361	423	1135	564
120	1597	249	557	792	637	1295	1131	272	1186	1171
121	58	1002	645	1431	1145	1250	436	670	614	989
122	403	887	100	1566	1462	1500	1521	1350	550	49
123	879	702	497	1323	1655	226	1217	1073	1335	1603
124	1527	1118	1370	1420	157	1677	692	1619	823	222
125	21	135	1112	697	1288	1064	871	554	46	868
126	1166	738	775	236	1703	847	1198	677	1398	109
127	1427	809	451	116	726	1608	1479	913	1364	276
128	1179	1694	1595	1169	612	1348	1215	1675	1286	234
129	449	1692	447	1309	813	1472	832	502	746	1311
130	969	336	1096	304	1414	426	995	1683	815	508
131	741	355	461	17	488	600	25	1474	388	1505
132	309	269	1652	735	1283	597	834	1441	1259	319
133	151	492	1138	379	546	504	1581	778	53	589
134	859	619	837	1714	748	576	1549	1588	1153	349
135	978	937	195	1313	289	1127	1671	1535	663	567
136	1190	518	971	1007	239	538	1206	533	1539	1444
137	1051	338	651	1341	1709	455	31	843	1545	478
138	1098	264	686	1637	396	642	1600	1195	1306	306
139	1585	1706	8	756	472	908	1262	139	1416	1279
140	894	11	1059	1626	204	898	123	428	1613	1318
141	1559	1270	604	252	1664	944	997	187	850	883
142	1092	1633	1084	322	86	1685	1028	482	759	79
143	1403	1554	91	1492	817	176	1514	1019	1301	708
144	560	1175	514	510	524	1201	258	714	71	667
145	154	806	743	594	192	475	120	1489	213	1647
146	216	357	42	585	1088	65	964	795	1224	1043
147	463	782	680	1359	1293	1143	1564	495	1116	19
148	866	1396	911	1213	1470	1412	15	1650	490	857
149	347	661	531	29	640	470	1624	602	1631	1401

POWER RESIDUES

	0	1	2	3	4	5	6	7	8	9
100	326	978	1211	187	561	1683	1603	1363	643	206
101	618	131	393	1179	91	273	819	734	479	1437
102	865	872	893	956	1145	1712	1690	1624	1426	832
103	773	596	65	195	585	32	96	288	864	869
104	884	929	1064	1469	961	1160	34	102	306	918
105	1031	1370	664	269	807	698	371	1113	1616	1402
106	760	557	1671	1567	1255	319	957	1148	1721	1717
107	1705	1669	1561	1237	265	795	662	263	789	644
108	209	627	158	474	1422	820	737	488	1464	946
109	1115	1622	1420	814	719	434	1302	460	1380	694
110	359	1077	1508	1078	1511	1087	1538	1168	58	174
111	522	1566	1252	310	930	1067	1478	988	1241	277
112	831	770	587	38	114	342	1026	1355	619	134
113	402	1206	172	516	1548	1198	148	444	1332	550
114	1650	1504	1066	1475	979	1214	196	588	41	123
115	369	1107	1598	1348	598	71	213	639	194	582
116	23	69	207	621	140	420	1260	334	1002	1283
117	403	1209	181	543	1629	1441	877	908	1001	1280
118	394	1182	100	300	900	977	1208	178	534	1602
119	1360	634	179	537	1611	1387	715	422	1266	352
120	1056	1445	889	944	1109	1604	1366	652	233	699
121	374	1122	1643	1483	1003	1286	412	1236	262	786
122	635	182	546	1638	1468	958	1151	7	21	63
123	189	567	1701	1657	1525	1129	1664	1546	1192	130
124	390	1170	64	192	576	5	15	45	135	405
125	1215	199	597	68	204	612	113	339	1017	1328
126	538	1614	1396	742	503	1509	1081	1520	1114	1619
127	1411	787	638	191	573	1719	1711	1687	1615	1399
128	751	530	1590	1324	526	1578	1288	418	1254	316
129	948	1121	1640	1474	976	1205	169	507	1521	1117
130	1628	1438	868	881	920	1037	1388	718	431	1293
131	433	1299	451	1353	613	116	348	1044	1409	781
132	620	137	411	1233	253	759	554	1662	1540	1174
133	76	228	684	329	987	1238	268	804	689	344
134	1032	1373	673	296	888	941	1100	1577	1285	409
135	1227	235	705	392	1176	82	246	738	491	1473
136	973	1196	142	426	1278	388	1164	46	138	414
137	1242	280	840	797	668	281	843	806	695	362
138	1086	1535	1159	31	93	279	837	788	641	200
139	600	77	231	693	356	1068	1481	997	1268	358
140	1074	1499	1051	1430	844	809	704	389	1167	55
141	165	495	1485	1009	1304	466	1398	748	521	1563
142	1243	283	849	824	749	524	1572	1270	364	1092
143	1553	1213	193	579	14	42	126	378	1134	1679
144	1591	1327	535	1605	1369	661	260	780	617	128
145	384	1152	10	30	90	270	810	707	398	1194
146	136	408	1224	226	678	311	933	1076	1505	1069
147	1484	1006	1295	439	1317	505	1515	1099	1574	1276
148	382	1146	1715	1699	1651	1507	1075	1502	1060	1457
149	925	1052	1433	853	836	785	632	173	519	1557

P = 1723

INDICES

	0	1	2	3	4	5	6	7	8	9
150	706	69	1487	962	1141	1468	27	1485	1102	1265
151	295	1104	129	97	219	1476	301	148	1532	393
152	1267	1298	62	528	390	1234	112	285	172	297
153	571	382	412	1507	369	1381	142	730	1106	920
154	1328	360	311	800	331	326	1237	131	1134	248
155	636	271	57	1430	435	988	99	1499	549	701
156	1654	1072	1526	1419	691	221	1111	1063	45	737
157	1702	676	1426	115	1478	275	1594	1347	1285	1691
158	812	501	968	303	994	507	460	599	387	268
159	1282	1440	150	378	1580	588	836	575	1152	936
160	288	1534	1189	1006	1205	1443	650	454	1544	263
161	395	1194	1584	755	1261	1278	1058	897	1612	1269
162	1663	186	1091	321	1027	78	90	175	1300	1174
163	523	713	153	593	119	1646	41	64	1223	781
164	1292	494	865	1212	14	856	530	469	1630	68
165	1140	1484	294	96	300	392	61	1233	171	381
166	368	729	1327	799	1236	247	56	987	548	1071
167	690	1062	1701	114	1593	1690	967	506	386	1439
168	1579	574	287	1005	649	262	1583	1277	1611	185
169	1026	174	522	592	40	780	864	855	1629	1483
170	299	1232	367	798	55	1070	1700	1689	385	573
171	648	1276	1025	591	863	1482	366	1069	384	1275
172	862	1068	861							

POWER RESIDUES

	0	1	2	3	4	5	6	7	8	9
150	1225	229	687	338	1014	1319	511	1533	1153	13
151	39	117	351	1053	1436	862	863	866	875	902
152	983	1226	232	696	365	1095	1562	1240	274	822
153	743	506	1518	1108	1601	1357	625	152	456	1368
154	658	251	753	536	1608	1378	688	341	1023	1346
155	592	53	159	477	1431	847	818	731	470	1410
156	784	629	164	492	1476	982	1223	223	669	284
157	852	833	776	605	92	276	828	761	560	1680
158	1594	1336	562	1686	1612	1390	724	449	1347	595
159	62	186	558	1674	1576	1282	400	1200	154	462
160	1386	712	413	1239	271	813	716	425	1275	379
161	1137	1688	1618	1408	778	611	110	330	990	1247
162	295	885	932	1073	1496	1042	1403	763	566	1698
163	1648	1498	1048	1421	817	728	461	1383	703	386
164	1158	28	84	252	756	545	1635	1459	931	1070
165	1487	1015	1322	520	1560	1234	256	768	581	20
166	60	180	540	1620	1414	796	665	272	816	725
167	452	1356	622	143	429	1287	415	1245	289	867
168	878	911	1010	1307	475	1425	829	764	569	1707
169	1675	1579	1291	427	1281	397	1191	127	381	1143
170	1706	1672	1570	1264	346	1038	1391	727	458	1374
171	676	305	915	1022	1343	583	26	78	234	702
172	383	1149								

P = 1733

INDICES

	0	1	2	3	4	5	6	7	8	9
0		0	1	187	2	1433	188	1668	3	374
1	1434	855	189	594	1669	1620	4	772	375	338
2	1435	123	856	1280	190	1134	595	561	1670	46
3	1621	248	5	1042	773	1369	376	1565	339	781
4	1436	1597	124	24	857	75	1281	355	191	1604
5	1135	959	596	694	562	556	1671	525	47	1676
6	1622	330	249	310	6	295	1043	1511	774	1467
7	1370	722	377	148	1566	1321	340	791	782	577
8	1437	748	1598	1311	125	473	25	233	858	652
9	76	530	1282	435	356	39	192	219	1605	1229
10	1136	98	960	1335	597	1556	695	985	563	851
11	557	20	1672	1317	526	981	48	968	1677	708
12	1623	1710	331	52	250	835	311	138	7	211
13	296	161	1044	274	1512	262	775	1329	1468	972
14	1371	542	723	1449	378	1479	149	59	1567	367
15	1322	388	341	1146	792	1681	783	199	578	881
16	1438	1216	749	767	1599	743	1312	1474	126	1188
17	474	712	26	1351	234	1070	859	131	653	823
18	77	1089	531	517	1283	1266	436	1627	357	497
19	40	429	193	1360	220	482	1606	1062	1230	1405
20	1137	1698	99	1714	961	1298	1336	1654	598	1193
21	1557	938	696	909	986	1457	564	184	852	335
22	558	1366	21	956	1673	1508	1318	1308	527	1226
23	982	978	49	158	969	56	1678	764	709	820
24	1624	479	1711	935	332	1305	53	932	251	1498
25	836	254	312	403	139	660	8	1107	212	1501
26	297	420	162	627	1045	395	275	839	1513	1386
27	263	1663	776	717	1330	257	1469	1400	973	622
28	1372	1033	543	315	724	226	1450	1533	379	1544
29	1480	406	150	946	60	1377	1568	1416	368	142
30	1323	1692	389	285	342	31	1147	663	793	1522
31	1682	86	784	1291	200	11	579	1000	882	901
32	1439	1172	1217	1110	750	1728	768	1038	1600	291
33	744	215	1313	207	1475	1212	127	1356	1189	1504
34	475	1103	713	1540	27	1168	1352	300	235	488
35	1071	1155	860	304	132	423	654	895	824	548
36	78	676	1090	165	532	1581	518	1259	1284	239
37	1267	630	437	1343	1628	1022	358	640	498	1048
38	41	325	430	830	194	492	1361	398	221	995
39	483	320	1607	348	1063	278	1231	611	1406	461
40	1138	1075	1699	842	100	449	1715	688	962	1083
41	1299	1516	1337	1612	1655	1012	599	1159	1194	1389
42	1558	736	939	729	697	174	910	266	987	1636
43	1458	1238	565	864	185	1666	853	1618	336	1278
44	559	246	1367	779	22	353	957	554	1674	308
45	1509	720	1319	575	1309	231	528	37	1227	1333
46	983	18	979	706	50	136	159	260	970	1447
47	57	386	1679	879	765	1472	710	1068	821	515
48	1625	427	480	1403	1712	1652	936	1455	333	954
49	1306	976	54	818	933	930	252	658	1499	625

POWER RESIDUES

	0	1	2	3	4	5	6	7	8	9
0	1	2	4	8	16	32	64	128	256	512
1	1024	315	630	1260	787	1574	1415	1097	461	922
2	111	222	444	888	43	86	172	344	688	1376
3	1019	305	610	1220	707	1414	1095	457	914	95
4	190	380	760	1520	1307	881	29	58	116	232
5	464	928	123	246	492	984	235	470	940	147
6	294	588	1176	619	1238	743	1486	1239	745	1490
7	1247	761	1522	1311	889	45	90	180	360	720
8	1440	1147	561	1122	511	1022	311	622	1244	755
9	1510	1287	841	1682	1631	1529	1325	917	101	202
10	404	808	1616	1499	1265	797	1594	1455	1177	621
11	1242	751	1502	1271	809	1618	1503	1273	813	1626
12	1519	1305	877	21	42	84	168	336	672	1344
13	955	177	354	708	1416	1099	465	930	127	254
14	508	1016	299	598	1196	659	1318	903	73	146
15	292	584	1168	603	1206	679	1358	983	233	466
16	932	131	262	524	1048	363	726	1452	1171	609
17	1218	703	1406	1079	425	850	1700	1667	1601	1469
18	1205	677	1354	975	217	434	868	3	6	12
19	24	48	96	192	384	768	1536	1339	945	157
20	314	628	1256	779	1558	1383	1033	333	666	1332
21	931	129	258	516	1032	331	662	1324	915	97
22	194	388	776	1552	1371	1009	285	570	1140	547
23	1094	455	910	87	174	348	696	1392	1051	369
24	738	1476	1219	705	1410	1087	441	882	31	62
25	124	248	496	992	251	502	1004	275	550	1100
26	467	934	135	270	540	1080	427	854	1708	1683
27	1633	1533	1333	933	133	266	532	1064	395	790
28	1580	1427	1121	509	1018	303	606	1212	691	1382
29	1031	329	658	1316	899	65	130	260	520	1040
30	347	694	1388	1043	353	706	1412	1091	449	898
31	63	126	252	504	1008	283	566	1132	531	1062
32	391	782	1564	1395	1057	381	762	1524	1315	897
33	61	122	244	488	976	219	438	876	19	38
34	76	152	304	608	1216	699	1398	1063	393	786
35	1572	1411	1089	445	890	47	94	188	376	752
36	1504	1275	817	1634	1535	1337	941	149	298	596
37	1192	651	1302	871	9	18	36	72	144	288
38	576	1152	571	1142	551	1102	471	942	151	302
39	604	1208	683	1366	999	265	530	1060	387	774
40	1548	1363	993	253	506	1012	291	582	1164	595
41	1190	647	1294	855	1710	1687	1641	1549	1365	997
42	261	522	1044	355	710	1420	1107	481	962	191
43	382	764	1528	1323	913	93	186	372	744	1488
44	1243	753	1506	1279	825	1650	1567	1401	1069	405
45	810	1620	1507	1281	829	1658	1583	1433	1133	533
46	1066	399	798	1596	1459	1185	637	1274	815	1630
47	1527	1321	909	85	170	340	680	1360	987	241
48	482	964	195	390	780	1560	1387	1041	349	698
49	1396	1059	385	770	1540	1347	961	189	378	756

P = 1733

INDICES

	0	1	2	3	4	5	6	7	8	9
50	837	1661	255	620	313	1531	404	1375	140	283
51	661	84	9	899	1108	1036	213	1210	1502	1538
52	298	1153	421	546	163	1257	628	1020	1046	828
53	396	318	276	459	840	686	1514	1010	1387	727
54	264	1236	1664	1276	777	552	718	229	1331	704
55	258	384	1470	513	1401	1453	974	928	623	618
56	1373	82	1034	1536	544	1018	316	684	725	1274
57	227	382	1451	616	1534	682	380	680	1545	1547
58	1481	1247	407	1549	151	669	947	1483	61	586
59	1378	1249	1569	1094	1417	409	369	1592	143	1551
60	1324	1183	1693	153	390	1411	286	671	343	169
61	32	949	1148	508	664	1485	794	1490	1523	63
62	1683	109	87	588	785	536	1292	1380	201	605
63	12	1251	580	1125	1001	1571	883	466	902	1096
64	1440	1585	1173	1419	1218	1644	1111	411	751	799
65	1729	371	769	1131	1039	1594	1601	522	292	145
66	745	649	216	1553	1314	1707	208	1326	1476	1143
67	1213	1185	128	1263	1357	1695	1190	181	1505	155
68	476	1495	1104	392	714	1030	1541	1413	28	1288
69	1169	288	1353	1165	301	673	236	637	489	345
70	1072	1080	1156	171	861	243	305	34	133	876
71	424	951	655	1528	896	1150	825	1007	549	510
72	79	1271	677	666	1091	1180	166	1487	533	1122
73	1582	796	519	1704	1260	1492	1285	634	240	1525
74	1268	1119	631	65	438	68	1344	1685	1629	921
75	1023	111	359	441	641	89	499	1200	1049	590
76	42	71	326	787	431	847	831	538	195	1347
77	493	1294	1362	760	399	1382	222	1688	996	203
78	484	1577	321	607	1608	1632	349	14	1064	814
79	279	1253	1232	924	612	582	1407	105	462	1127
80	1139	1026	1076	1003	1700	917	843	1573	101	114
81	450	885	1716	118	689	468	963	362	1084	904
82	1300	1395	1517	1098	1338	444	1613	1442	1656	454
83	1013	1587	600	644	1160	1175	1195	809	1390	1421
84	1559	92	737	1220	940	889	730	1646	698	502
85	175	1113	911	1426	267	413	988	1203	1637	753
86	1459	1720	1239	801	566	1052	865	1731	186	1432
87	1667	373	854	593	1619	771	337	122	1279	1133
88	560	45	247	1041	1368	1564	780	1596	23	74
89	354	1603	958	693	555	524	1675	329	309	294
90	1510	1466	721	147	1320	790	576	747	1310	472
91	232	651	529	434	38	218	1228	97	1334	1555
92	984	850	19	1316	980	967	707	1709	51	834
93	137	210	160	273	261	1328	971	541	1448	1478
94	58	366	387	1145	1680	198	880	1215	766	742
95	1473	1187	711	1350	1069	130	822	1088	516	1265
96	1626	496	428	1359	481	1061	1404	1697	1713	1297
97	1653	1192	937	908	1456	183	334	1365	955	1507
98	1307	1225	977	157	55	763	819	478	934	1304
99	931	1497	253	402	659	1106	1500	419	626	394

POWER RESIDUES

	0	1	2	3	4	5	6	7	8	9
50	1512	1291	849	1698	1663	1593	1453	1173	613	1226
51	719	1438	1143	553	1106	479	958	183	366	732
52	1464	1195	657	1314	895	57	114	228	456	912
53	91	182	364	728	1456	1179	625	1250	767	1534
54	1335	937	141	282	564	1128	523	1046	359	718
55	1436	1139	545	1090	447	894	55	110	220	440
56	880	27	54	108	216	432	864	1728	1723	1713
57	1693	1653	1573	1413	1093	453	906	79	158	316
58	632	1264	795	1590	1447	1161	589	1178	623	1246
59	759	1518	1303	873	13	26	52	104	208	416
60	832	1664	1595	1457	1181	629	1258	783	1566	1399
61	1065	397	794	1588	1443	1153	573	1146	559	1118
62	503	1006	279	558	1116	499	998	263	526	1052
63	371	742	1484	1235	737	1474	1215	697	1394	1055
64	377	754	1508	1283	833	1666	1599	1465	1197	661
65	1322	911	89	178	356	712	1424	1115	497	994
66	255	510	1020	307	614	1228	723	1446	1159	585
67	1170	607	1214	695	1390	1047	361	722	1444	1155
68	577	1154	575	1150	567	1134	535	1070	407	814
69	1628	1523	1313	893	53	106	212	424	848	1696
70	1659	1585	1437	1141	549	1098	463	926	119	238
71	476	952	171	342	684	1368	1003	273	546	1092
72	451	902	71	142	284	568	1136	539	1078	423
73	846	1692	1651	1569	1405	1077	421	842	1684	1635
74	1537	1341	949	165	330	660	1320	907	81	162
75	324	648	1296	859	1718	1703	1673	1613	1493	1253
76	773	1546	1359	985	237	474	948	163	326	652
77	1304	875	17	34	68	136	272	544	1088	443
78	886	39	78	156	312	624	1248	763	1526	1319
79	905	77	154	308	616	1232	731	1462	1191	649
80	1298	863	1726	1719	1705	1677	1621	1509	1285	837
81	1674	1615	1497	1261	789	1578	1423	1113	493	986
82	239	478	956	179	358	716	1432	1131	529	1058
83	383	766	1532	1331	929	125	250	500	1000	267
84	534	1068	403	806	1612	1491	1249	765	1530	1327
85	921	109	218	436	872	11	22	44	88	176
86	352	704	1408	1083	433	866	1732	1731	1729	1725
87	1717	1701	1669	1605	1477	1221	709	1418	1103	473
88	946	159	318	636	1272	811	1622	1511	1289	845
89	1690	1647	1561	1389	1045	357	714	1428	1123	513
90	1026	319	638	1276	819	1638	1543	1353	973	213
91	426	852	1704	1675	1617	1501	1269	805	1610	1487
92	1241	749	1498	1263	793	1586	1439	1145	557	1114
93	495	990	247	494	988	243	486	972	211	422
94	844	1688	1643	1553	1373	1013	293	586	1172	611
95	1222	711	1422	1111	489	978	223	446	892	51
96	102	204	408	816	1632	1531	1329	925	117	234
97	468	936	139	278	556	1112	491	982	231	462
98	924	115	230	460	920	107	214	428	856	1712
99	1691	1649	1565	1397	1061	389	778	1556	1379	1025

P = 1733

INDICES

	0	1	2	3	4	5	6	7	8	9
100	838	1385	1662	716	256	1399	621	1032	314	225
101	1532	1543	405	945	1376	1415	141	1691	284	30
102	662	1521	85	1290	10	999	900	1171	1109	1727
103	1037	290	214	206	1211	1355	1503	1102	1539	1167
104	299	487	1154	303	422	894	547	675	164	1580
105	1258	238	629	1342	1021	639	1047	324	829	491
106	397	994	319	347	277	610	460	1074	841	448
107	687	1082	1515	1611	1011	1158	1388	735	728	173
108	265	1635	1237	863	1665	1617	1277	245	778	352
109	553	307	719	574	230	36	1332	17	705	135
110	259	1446	385	878	1471	1067	514	426	1402	1651
111	1454	953	975	817	929	657	624	1660	619	1530
112	1374	282	83	898	1035	1209	1537	1152	545	1256
113	1019	827	317	458	685	1009	726	1235	1275	551
114	228	703	383	512	1452	927	617	81	1535	1017
115	683	1273	381	615	681	679	1546	1246	1548	668
116	1482	585	1248	1093	408	1591	1550	1182	152	1410
117	670	168	948	507	1484	1489	62	108	587	535
118	1379	604	1250	1124	1570	465	1095	1584	1418	1643
119	410	798	370	1130	1593	521	144	648	1552	1706
120	1325	1142	1184	1262	1694	180	154	1494	391	1029
121	1412	1287	287	1164	672	636	344	1079	170	242
122	33	875	950	1527	1149	1006	509	1270	665	1179
123	1486	1121	795	1703	1491	633	1524	1118	64	67
124	1684	920	110	440	88	1199	589	70	786	846
125	537	1346	1293	759	1381	1687	202	1576	606	1631
126	13	813	1252	923	581	104	1126	1025	1002	916
127	1572	113	884	117	467	361	903	1394	1097	443
128	1441	453	1586	643	1174	808	1420	91	1219	888
129	1645	501	1112	1425	412	1202	752	1719	800	1051
130	1730	1431	372	592	770	121	1132	44	1040	1563
131	1595	73	1602	692	523	328	293	1465	146	789
132	746	471	650	433	217	96	1554	849	1315	966
133	1708	833	209	272	1327	540	1477	365	1144	197
134	1214	741	1186	1349	129	1087	1264	495	1358	1060
135	1696	1296	1191	907	182	1364	1506	1224	156	762
136	477	1303	1496	401	1105	418	393	1384	715	1398
137	1031	224	1542	944	1414	1690	29	1520	1289	998
138	1170	1726	289	205	1354	1101	1166	486	302	893
139	674	1579	237	1341	638	323	490	993	346	609
140	1073	447	1081	1610	1157	734	172	1634	862	1616
141	244	351	306	573	35	16	134	1445	877	1066
142	425	1650	952	816	656	1659	1529	281	897	1208
143	1151	1255	826	457	1008	1234	550	702	511	926
144	80	1016	1272	614	678	1245	667	584	1092	1590
145	1181	1409	167	506	1488	107	534	603	1123	464
146	1583	1642	797	1129	520	647	1705	1141	1261	179
147	1493	1028	1286	1163	635	1078	241	874	1526	1005
148	1269	1178	1120	1702	632	1117	66	919	439	1198
149	69	845	1345	758	1686	1575	1630	812	922	103

POWER RESIDUES

	0	1	2	3	4	5	6	7	8	9
100	317	634	1268	803	1606	1479	1225	717	1434	1135
101	537	1074	415	830	1660	1587	1441	1149	565	1130
102	527	1054	375	750	1500	1267	801	1602	1471	1209
103	685	1370	1007	281	562	1124	515	1030	327	654
104	1308	883	33	66	132	264	528	1056	379	758
105	1516	1299	865	1730	1727	1721	1709	1685	1637	1541
106	1349	965	197	394	788	1576	1419	1105	477	954
107	175	350	700	1400	1067	401	802	1604	1475	1217
108	701	1402	1071	409	818	1636	1539	1345	957	181
109	362	724	1448	1163	593	1186	639	1278	823	1646
110	1559	1385	1037	341	682	1364	995	257	514	1028
111	323	646	1292	851	1702	1671	1609	1485	1237	741
112	1482	1231	729	1458	1183	633	1266	799	1598	1463
113	1193	653	1306	879	25	50	100	200	400	800
114	1600	1467	1201	669	1338	943	153	306	612	1224
115	715	1430	1127	521	1042	351	702	1404	1075	417
116	834	1668	1603	1473	1213	693	1386	1039	345	690
117	1380	1027	321	642	1284	835	1670	1607	1481	1229
118	725	1450	1167	601	1202	671	1342	951	169	338
119	676	1352	971	209	418	836	1672	1611	1489	1245
120	757	1514	1295	857	1714	1695	1657	1581	1429	1125
121	517	1034	335	670	1340	947	161	322	644	1288
122	843	1686	1639	1545	1357	981	229	458	916	99
123	198	396	792	1584	1435	1137	541	1082	431	862
124	1724	1715	1697	1661	1589	1445	1157	581	1162	591
125	1182	631	1262	791	1582	1431	1129	525	1050	367
126	734	1468	1203	673	1346	959	185	370	740	1480
127	1227	721	1442	1151	569	1138	543	1086	439	878
128	23	46	92	184	368	736	1472	1211	689	1378
129	1023	313	626	1252	771	1542	1351	969	205	410
130	820	1640	1547	1361	989	245	490	980	227	454
131	908	83	166	332	664	1328	923	113	226	452
132	904	75	150	300	600	1200	667	1334	935	137
133	274	548	1096	459	918	103	206	412	824	1648
134	1563	1393	1053	373	746	1492	1251	769	1538	1343
135	953	173	346	692	1384	1035	337	674	1348	963
136	193	386	772	1544	1355	977	221	442	884	35
137	70	140	280	560	1120	507	1014	295	590	1180
138	627	1254	775	1550	1367	1001	269	538	1076	419
139	838	1676	1619	1505	1277	821	1642	1551	1369	1005
140	277	554	1108	483	966	199	398	796	1592	1451
141	1169	605	1210	687	1374	1015	297	594	1188	643
142	1286	839	1678	1623	1513	1293	853	1706	1679	1625
143	1517	1301	869	5	10	20	40	80	160	320
144	640	1280	827	1654	1575	1417	1101	469	938	143
145	286	572	1144	555	1110	487	974	215	430	860
146	1720	1707	1681	1629	1525	1317	901	69	138	276
147	552	1104	475	950	167	334	668	1336	939	145
148	290	580	1160	587	1174	615	1230	727	1454	1175
149	617	1234	735	1470	1207	681	1362	991	249	498

P = 1733

INDICES

	0	1	2	3	4	5	6	7	8	9
150	1024	915	112	116	360	1393	442	452	642	807
151	90	887	500	1424	1201	1718	1050	1430	591	120
152	43	1562	72	691	327	1464	788	470	432	95
153	848	965	832	271	539	364	196	740	1348	1086
154	494	1059	1295	906	1363	1223	761	1302	400	417
155	1383	1397	223	943	1689	1519	997	1725	204	1100
156	485	892	1578	1340	322	992	608	446	1609	733
157	1633	1615	350	572	15	1444	1065	1649	815	1658
158	280	1207	1254	456	1233	701	925	1015	613	1244
159	583	1589	1408	505	106	602	463	1641	1128	646
160	1140	178	1027	1162	1077	873	1004	1177	1701	1116
161	918	1197	844	757	1574	811	102	914	115	1392
162	451	806	886	1423	1717	1429	119	1561	690	1463
163	469	94	964	270	363	739	1085	1058	905	1222
164	1301	416	1396	942	1518	1724	1099	891	1339	991
165	445	732	1614	571	1443	1648	1657	1206	455	700
166	1014	1243	1588	504	601	1640	645	177	1161	872
167	1176	1115	1196	756	810	913	1391	805	1422	1428
168	1560	1462	93	269	738	1057	1221	415	941	1723
169	890	990	731	570	1647	1205	699	1242	503	1639
170	176	871	1114	755	912	804	1427	1461	268	1056
171	414	1722	989	569	1204	1241	1638	870	754	803
172	1460	1055	1721	568	1240	869	802	1054	567	868
173	1053	867	866							

POWER RESIDUES

	0	1	2	3	4	5	6	7	8	9
150	996	259	518	1036	339	678	1356	979	225	450
151	900	67	134	268	536	1072	411	822	1644	1555
152	1377	1021	309	618	1236	739	1478	1223	713	1426
153	1119	505	1010	287	574	1148	563	1126	519	1038
154	343	686	1372	1011	289	578	1156	579	1158	583
155	1166	599	1198	663	1326	919	105	210	420	840
156	1680	1627	1521	1309	885	37	74	148	296	592
157	1184	635	1270	807	1614	1495	1257	781	1562	1391
158	1049	365	730	1460	1187	641	1282	831	1662	1591
159	1449	1165	597	1194	655	1310	887	41	82	164
160	328	656	1312	891	49	98	196	392	784	1568
161	1403	1073	413	826	1652	1571	1409	1085	437	874
162	15	30	60	120	240	480	960	187	374	748
163	1496	1259	785	1570	1407	1081	429	858	1716	1699
164	1665	1597	1461	1189	645	1290	847	1694	1655	1577
165	1421	1109	485	970	207	414	828	1656	1579	1425
166	1117	501	1002	271	542	1084	435	870	7	14
167	28	56	112	224	448	896	59	118	236	472
168	944	155	310	620	1240	747	1494	1255	777	1554
169	1375	1017	301	602	1204	675	1350	967	201	402
170	804	1608	1483	1233	733	1466	1199	665	1330	927
171	121	242	484	968	203	406	812	1624	1515	1297
172	861	1722	1711	1689	1645	1557	1381	1029	325	650
173	1300	867								

P = 1741

INDICES

	0	1	2	3	4	5	6	7	8	9
0		0	1	158	2	928	159	1011	3	316
1	929	1216	160	1350	1012	1086	4	861	317	409
2	930	1169	1217	600	161	116	1351	474	1013	1522
3	1087	784	5	1374	862	199	318	37	410	1508
4	931	109	1170	1108	1218	1244	601	834	162	282
5	117	1019	1352	369	475	404	1014	567	1523	435
6	1088	1231	785	1327	6	538	1375	389	863	758
7	200	746	319	1055	38	274	411	487	1509	1551
8	932	632	110	572	1171	49	1109	1680	1219	578
9	1245	621	602	942	835	1337	163	611	283	1532
10	118	170	1020	68	1353	357	370	648	476	154
11	405	195	1015	385	568	1528	1524	1666	436	132
12	1089	692	1232	267	786	1044	1328	765	7	1266
13	539	1670	1376	1420	390	1402	864	1321	759	25
14	201	992	747	826	320	710	1056	440	39	674
15	275	586	412	1177	488	1712	1510	666	1552	527
16	933	1611	633	136	111	562	573	687	1172	960
17	50	725	1110	1157	1681	1127	1220	593	579	1093
18	1246	1569	622	1389	603	965	943	337	836	1485
19	1338	31	164	556	612	696	284	1429	1533	1541
20	119	547	171	793	1021	1037	69	916	1354	1625
21	358	1236	371	904	649	296	477	55	155	1213
22	406	471	196	1105	1016	432	386	271	569	618
23	1529	645	1525	264	1667	22	437	1709	133	722
24	1090	334	693	790	1233	1210	268	19	787	730
25	1045	733	1329	76	766	207	8	512	1267	1048
26	540	98	1671	847	1377	1297	1421	736	391	1476
27	1403	499	865	779	1322	1332	760	522	26	1100
28	202	1115	993	79	748	1495	827	1120	321	1722
29	711	769	1057	702	441	1363	40	1690	675	210
30	276	379	587	328	413	419	1178	11	489	226
31	1713	885	1511	1162	667	515	1553	1452	528	998
32	934	806	1612	1270	634	1466	137	312	112	105
33	563	1051	574	353	688	1317	1173	956	961	543
34	51	260	726	1293	1111	1686	1158	101	1682	814
35	1128	84	1221	973	594	1674	580	290	1094	1287
36	1247	818	1570	850	623	243	1390	1647	604	425
37	966	1380	944	1598	338	1202	837	1132	1486	1300
38	1339	923	32	753	165	1415	557	1424	613	93
39	697	1461	285	88	1430	739	1534	305	1542	1578
40	120	449	548	394	172	1560	794	1253	1022	1225
41	1038	1479	70	1446	917	1500	1355	183	1626	1406
42	359	1435	1237	1150	372	977	905	502	650	984
43	297	1729	478	1184	56	868	156	1009	1214	1084
44	407	598	472	782	197	1506	1106	832	1017	402
45	433	1325	387	744	272	1549	570	1678	619	1335
46	1530	66	646	193	1526	130	265	763	1668	1400
47	23	824	438	584	1710	525	134	685	723	1125
48	1091	1387	335	29	694	1539	791	914	1234	294
49	1211	1103	269	643	20	720	788	17	731	205

POWER RESIDUES

	0	1	2	3	4	5	6	7	8	9
0	1	2	4	8	16	32	64	128	256	512
1	1024	307	614	1228	715	1430	1119	497	994	247
2	494	988	235	470	940	139	278	556	1112	483
3	966	191	382	764	1528	1315	889	37	74	148
4	296	592	1184	627	1254	767	1534	1327	913	85
5	170	340	680	1360	979	217	434	868	1736	1731
6	1721	1701	1661	1581	1421	1101	461	922	103	206
7	412	824	1648	1555	1369	997	253	506	1012	283
8	566	1132	523	1046	351	702	1404	1067	393	786
9	1572	1403	1065	389	778	1556	1371	1001	261	522
10	1044	347	694	1388	1035	329	658	1316	891	41
11	82	164	328	656	1312	883	25	50	100	200
12	400	800	1600	1459	1177	613	1226	711	1422	1103
13	465	930	119	238	476	952	163	326	652	1304
14	867	1734	1727	1713	1685	1629	1517	1293	845	1690
15	1639	1537	1333	925	109	218	436	872	3	6
16	12	24	48	96	192	384	768	1536	1331	921
17	101	202	404	808	1616	1491	1241	741	1482	1223
18	705	1410	1079	417	834	1668	1595	1449	1157	573
19	1146	551	1102	463	926	111	222	444	888	35
20	70	140	280	560	1120	499	998	255	510	1020
21	299	598	1196	651	1302	863	1726	1711	1681	1621
22	1501	1261	781	1562	1383	1025	309	618	1236	731
23	1462	1183	625	1250	759	1518	1295	849	1698	1655
24	1569	1397	1053	365	730	1460	1179	617	1234	727
25	1454	1167	593	1186	631	1262	783	1566	1391	1041
26	341	682	1364	987	233	466	932	123	246	492
27	984	227	454	908	75	150	300	600	1200	659
28	1318	895	49	98	196	392	784	1568	1395	1049
29	357	714	1428	1115	489	978	215	430	860	1720
30	1699	1657	1573	1405	1069	397	794	1588	1435	1129
31	517	1034	327	654	1308	875	9	18	36	72
32	144	288	576	1152	563	1126	511	1022	303	606
33	1212	683	1366	991	241	482	964	187	374	748
34	1496	1251	761	1522	1303	865	1730	1719	1697	1653
35	1565	1389	1037	333	666	1332	923	105	210	420
36	840	1680	1619	1497	1253	765	1530	1319	897	53
37	106	212	424	848	1696	1651	1561	1381	1021	301
38	602	1204	667	1334	927	113	226	452	904	67
39	134	268	536	1072	403	806	1612	1483	1225	709
40	1418	1095	449	898	55	110	220	440	880	19
41	38	76	152	304	608	1216	691	1382	1023	305
42	610	1220	699	1398	1055	369	738	1476	1211	681
43	1362	983	225	450	900	59	118	236	472	944
44	147	294	588	1176	611	1222	703	1406	1071	401
45	802	1604	1467	1193	645	1290	839	1678	1615	1489
46	1237	733	1466	1191	641	1282	823	1646	1551	1361
47	981	221	442	884	27	54	108	216	432	864
48	1728	1715	1689	1637	1533	1325	909	77	154	308
49	616	1232	723	1446	1151	561	1122	503	1006	271

P = 1741

INDICES

	0	1	2	3	4	5	6	7	8	9
50	1046	845	734	497	1330	1098	77	1118	767	1361
51	208	326	9	883	513	996	1268	310	1049	1315
52	541	1291	99	82	1672	1285	848	1645	1378	1200
53	1298	751	1422	1459	737	1576	392	1251	1477	1498
54	1404	1148	500	1727	866	1082	780	830	1323	1547
55	1333	191	761	822	523	1123	27	912	1101	718
56	203	495	1116	324	994	1313	80	1643	749	1574
57	1496	1725	828	189	1121	716	322	1641	1723	714
58	712	1583	770	1585	1058	854	703	772	442	1193
59	1364	1587	41	252	1691	1060	676	1699	211	856
60	277	627	380	705	588	1620	329	774	414	951
61	420	444	1179	125	12	1195	490	247	227	1366
62	1714	1074	886	1589	1512	232	1163	43	668	898
63	516	254	1554	1394	1453	1693	529	1632	999	1062
64	935	464	807	678	1613	454	1271	1701	635	1651
65	1467	213	138	1737	313	858	113	1371	106	279
66	564	535	1052	629	575	608	354	382	689	1263
67	1318	707	1174	1608	957	590	962	553	544	1622
68	52	429	261	331	727	509	1294	776	1112	1719
69	1687	416	1159	803	102	953	1683	970	815	422
70	1129	1412	85	446	1222	180	974	1181	595	399
71	1675	127	581	1384	291	14	1095	880	1288	1197
72	1248	1079	819	492	1571	1638	851	249	624	948
73	244	229	1391	461	1648	1368	605	1605	426	1716
74	967	177	1381	1076	945	1602	1599	888	339	1659
75	1203	1591	838	891	1133	1514	1487	1140	1301	234
76	1340	342	924	1165	33	365	754	45	166	1662
77	1416	670	558	1565	1425	900	614	1206	94	518
78	698	222	1462	256	286	1594	89	1556	1431	1005
79	740	1396	1535	841	306	1455	1543	1309	1579	1695
80	121	894	450	531	549	799	395	1634	173	1136
81	1561	1001	795	657	1254	1064	1023	1517	1226	937
82	1039	661	1480	466	71	1490	1447	809	918	1441
83	1501	680	1356	1143	184	1615	1627	1258	1407	456
84	360	1304	1436	1273	1238	148	1151	1703	373	237
85	978	637	906	1068	503	1653	651	1343	985	1469
86	298	1278	1730	215	479	345	1185	140	57	1027
87	869	1739	157	927	1010	315	1215	1349	1085	860
88	408	1168	599	115	473	1521	783	1373	198	36
89	1507	108	1107	1243	833	281	1018	368	403	566
90	434	1230	1326	537	388	757	745	1054	273	486
91	1550	631	571	48	1679	577	620	941	1336	610
92	1531	169	67	356	647	153	194	384	1527	1665
93	131	691	266	1043	764	1265	1669	1419	1401	1320
94	24	991	825	709	439	673	585	1176	1711	665
95	526	1610	135	561	686	959	724	1156	1126	592
96	1092	1568	1388	964	336	1484	30	555	695	1428
97	1540	546	792	1036	915	1624	1235	903	295	54
98	1212	470	1104	431	270	617	644	263	21	1708
99	721	333	789	1209	18	729	732	75	206	511

POWER RESIDUES

	0	1	2	3	4	5	6	7	8	9
50	542	1084	427	854	1708	1675	1609	1477	1213	685
51	1370	999	257	514	1028	315	630	1260	779	1558
52	1375	1009	277	554	1108	475	950	159	318	636
53	1272	803	1606	1471	1201	661	1322	903	65	130
54	260	520	1040	339	678	1356	971	201	402	804
55	1608	1475	1209	677	1354	967	193	386	772	1544
56	1347	953	165	330	660	1320	899	57	114	228
57	456	912	83	166	332	664	1328	915	89	178
58	356	712	1424	1107	473	946	151	302	604	1208
59	675	1350	959	177	354	708	1416	1091	441	882
60	23	46	92	184	368	736	1472	1203	665	1330
61	919	97	194	388	776	1552	1363	985	229	458
62	916	91	182	364	728	1456	1171	601	1202	663
63	1326	911	81	162	324	648	1296	851	1702	1663
64	1585	1429	1117	493	986	231	462	924	107	214
65	428	856	1712	1683	1625	1509	1277	813	1626	1511
66	1281	821	1642	1543	1345	949	157	314	628	1256
67	771	1542	1343	945	149	298	596	1192	643	1286
68	831	1662	1583	1425	1109	477	954	167	334	668
69	1336	931	121	242	484	968	195	390	780	1560
70	1379	1017	293	586	1172	603	1206	671	1342	943
71	145	290	580	1160	579	1158	575	1150	559	1118
72	495	990	239	478	956	171	342	684	1368	995
73	249	498	996	251	502	1004	267	534	1068	395
74	790	1580	1419	1097	453	906	71	142	284	568
75	1136	531	1062	383	766	1532	1323	905	69	138
76	276	552	1104	467	934	127	254	508	1016	291
77	582	1164	587	1174	607	1214	687	1374	1007	273
78	546	1092	443	886	31	62	124	248	496	992
79	243	486	972	203	406	812	1624	1507	1273	805
80	1610	1479	1217	693	1386	1031	321	642	1284	827
81	1654	1567	1393	1045	349	698	1396	1051	361	722
82	1444	1147	553	1106	471	942	143	286	572	1144
83	547	1094	447	894	47	94	188	376	752	1504
84	1267	793	1586	1431	1121	501	1002	263	526	1052
85	363	726	1452	1163	585	1170	599	1198	655	1310
86	879	17	34	68	136	272	544	1088	435	870
87	1740	1739	1737	1733	1725	1709	1677	1613	1485	1229
88	717	1434	1127	513	1026	311	622	1244	747	1494
89	1247	753	1506	1271	801	1602	1463	1185	629	1258
90	775	1550	1359	977	213	426	852	1704	1667	1593
91	1445	1149	557	1114	487	974	207	414	828	1656
92	1571	1401	1061	381	762	1524	1307	873	5	10
93	20	40	80	160	320	640	1280	819	1638	1535
94	1329	917	93	186	372	744	1488	1235	729	1458
95	1175	609	1218	695	1390	1039	337	674	1348	955
96	169	338	676	1352	963	185	370	740	1480	1219
97	697	1394	1047	353	706	1412	1083	425	850	1700
98	1659	1577	1413	1085	429	858	1716	1691	1641	1541
99	1341	941	141	282	564	1128	515	1030	319	638

P = 1741

INDICES

	0	1	2	3	4	5	6	7	8	9
100	1047	97	846	1296	735	1475	498	778	1331	521
101	1099	1114	78	1494	1119	1721	768	701	1362	1689
102	209	378	327	418	10	225	884	1161	514	1451
103	997	805	1269	1465	311	104	1050	352	1316	955
104	542	259	1292	1685	100	813	83	972	1673	289
105	1286	817	849	242	1646	424	1379	1597	1201	1131
106	1299	922	752	1414	1423	92	1460	87	738	304
107	1577	448	393	1559	1252	1224	1478	1445	1499	182
108	1405	1434	1149	976	501	983	1728	1183	867	1008
109	1083	597	781	1505	831	401	1324	743	1548	1677
110	1334	65	192	129	762	1399	823	583	524	684
111	1124	1386	28	1538	913	293	1102	642	719	16
112	204	844	496	1097	1117	1360	325	882	995	309
113	1314	1290	81	1284	1644	1199	750	1458	1575	1250
114	1497	1147	1726	1081	829	1546	190	821	1122	911
115	717	494	323	1312	1642	1573	1724	188	715	1640
116	713	1582	1584	853	771	1192	1586	251	1059	1698
117	855	626	704	1619	773	950	443	124	1194	246
118	1365	1073	1588	231	42	897	253	1393	1692	1631
119	1061	463	677	453	1700	1650	212	1736	857	1370
120	278	534	628	607	381	1262	706	1607	589	552
121	1621	428	330	508	775	1718	415	802	952	969
122	421	1411	445	179	1180	398	126	1383	13	879
123	1196	1078	491	1637	248	947	228	460	1367	1604
124	1715	176	1075	1601	887	1658	1590	890	1513	1139
125	233	341	1164	364	44	1661	669	1564	899	1205
126	517	221	255	1593	1555	1004	1395	840	1454	1308
127	1694	893	530	798	1633	1135	1000	656	1063	1516
128	936	660	465	1489	808	1440	679	1142	1614	1257
129	455	1303	1272	147	1702	236	636	1067	1652	1342
130	1468	1277	214	344	139	1026	1738	926	314	1348
131	859	1167	114	1520	1372	35	107	1242	280	367
132	565	1229	536	756	1053	485	630	47	576	940
133	609	168	355	152	383	1664	690	1042	1264	1418
134	1319	990	708	672	1175	664	1609	560	958	1155
135	591	1567	963	1483	554	1427	545	1035	1623	902
136	53	469	430	616	262	1707	332	1208	728	74
137	510	96	1295	1474	777	520	1113	1493	1720	700
138	1688	377	417	224	1160	1450	804	1464	103	351
139	954	258	1684	812	971	288	816	241	423	1596
140	1130	921	1413	91	86	303	447	1558	1223	1444
141	181	1433	975	982	1182	1007	596	1504	400	742
142	1676	64	128	1398	582	683	1385	1537	292	641
143	15	843	1096	1359	881	308	1289	1283	1198	1457
144	1249	1146	1080	1545	820	910	493	1311	1572	187
145	1639	1581	852	1191	250	1697	625	1618	949	123
146	245	1072	230	896	1392	1630	462	452	1649	1735
147	1369	533	606	1261	1606	551	427	507	1717	801
148	968	1410	178	397	1382	878	1077	1636	946	459
149	1603	175	1600	1657	889	1138	340	363	1660	1563

POWER RESIDUES

	0	1	2	3	4	5	6	7	8	9
100	1276	811	1622	1503	1265	789	1578	1415	1089	437
101	874	7	14	28	56	112	224	448	896	51
102	102	204	408	816	1632	1523	1305	869	1738	1735
103	1729	1717	1693	1645	1549	1357	973	205	410	820
104	1640	1539	1337	933	125	250	500	1000	259	518
105	1036	331	662	1324	907	73	146	292	584	1168
106	595	1190	639	1278	815	1630	1519	1297	853	1706
107	1671	1601	1461	1181	621	1242	743	1486	1231	721
108	1442	1143	545	1090	439	878	15	30	60	120
109	240	480	960	179	358	716	1432	1123	505	1010
110	279	558	1116	491	982	223	446	892	43	86
111	172	344	688	1376	1011	281	562	1124	507	1014
112	287	574	1148	555	1110	479	958	175	350	700
113	1400	1059	377	754	1508	1275	809	1618	1495	1249
114	757	1514	1287	833	1666	1591	1441	1141	541	1082
115	423	846	1692	1643	1545	1349	957	173	346	692
116	1384	1027	313	626	1252	763	1526	1311	881	21
117	42	84	168	336	672	1344	947	153	306	612
118	1224	707	1414	1087	433	866	1732	1723	1705	1669
119	1597	1453	1165	589	1178	615	1230	719	1438	1135
120	529	1058	375	750	1500	1259	777	1554	1367	993
121	245	490	980	219	438	876	11	22	44	88
122	176	352	704	1408	1075	409	818	1636	1531	1321
123	901	61	122	244	488	976	211	422	844	1688
124	1635	1529	1317	893	45	90	180	360	720	1440
125	1139	537	1074	407	814	1628	1515	1289	837	1674
126	1607	1473	1205	669	1338	935	129	258	516	1032
127	323	646	1292	843	1686	1631	1521	1301	861	1722
128	1703	1665	1589	1437	1133	525	1050	359	718	1436
129	1131	521	1042	343	686	1372	1003	265	530	1060
130	379	758	1516	1291	841	1682	1623	1505	1269	797
131	1594	1447	1153	565	1130	519	1038	335	670	1340
132	939	137	274	548	1096	451	902	63	126	252
133	504	1008	275	550	1100	459	918	95	190	380
134	760	1520	1299	857	1714	1687	1633	1525	1309	877
135	13	26	52	104	208	416	832	1664	1587	1433
136	1125	509	1018	295	590	1180	619	1238	735	1470
137	1199	657	1314	887	33	66	132	264	528	1056
138	371	742	1484	1227	713	1426	1111	481	962	183
139	366	732	1464	1187	633	1266	791	1582	1423	1105
140	469	938	135	270	540	1080	419	838	1676	1611
141	1481	1221	701	1402	1063	385	770	1540	1339	937
142	133	266	532	1064	387	774	1548	1355	969	197
143	394	788	1576	1411	1081	421	842	1684	1627	1513
144	1285	829	1658	1575	1409	1077	413	826	1652	1563
145	1385	1029	317	634	1268	795	1590	1439	1137	533
146	1066	391	782	1564	1387	1033	325	650	1300	859
147	1718	1695	1649	1557	1373	1005	269	538	1076	411
148	822	1644	1547	1353	965	189	378	756	1512	1283
149	825	1650	1559	1377	1013	285	570	1140	539	1078

P = 1741

INDICES

	0	1	2	3	4	5	6	7	8	9
150	1204	220	1592	1003	839	1307	892	797	1134	655
151	1515	659	1488	1439	1141	1256	1302	146	235	1066
152	1341	1276	343	1025	925	1347	1166	1519	34	1241
153	366	1228	755	484	46	939	167	151	1663	1041
154	1417	989	671	663	559	1154	1566	1482	1426	1034
155	901	468	615	1706	1207	73	95	1473	519	1492
156	699	376	223	1449	1463	350	257	811	287	240
157	1595	920	90	302	1557	1443	1432	981	1006	1503
158	741	63	1397	682	1536	640	842	1358	307	1282
159	1456	1145	1544	909	1310	186	1580	1190	1696	1617
160	122	1071	895	1629	451	1734	532	1260	550	506
161	800	1409	396	877	1635	458	174	1656	1137	362
162	1562	219	1002	1306	796	654	658	1438	1255	145
163	1065	1275	1024	1346	1518	1240	1227	483	938	150
164	1040	988	662	1153	1481	1033	467	1705	72	1472
165	1491	375	1448	349	810	239	919	301	1442	980
166	1502	62	681	639	1357	1281	1144	908	185	1189
167	1616	1070	1628	1733	1259	505	1408	876	457	1655
168	361	218	1305	653	1437	144	1274	1345	1239	482
169	149	987	1152	1032	1704	1471	374	348	238	300
170	979	61	638	1280	907	1188	1069	1732	504	875
171	1654	217	652	143	1344	481	986	1031	1470	347
172	299	60	1279	1187	1731	874	216	142	480	1030
173	346	59	1186	873	141	1029	58	872	1028	871
174	870	0								

POWER RESIDUES

	0	1	2	3	4	5	6	7	8	9
150	415	830	1660	1579	1417	1093	445	890	39	78
151	156	312	624	1248	755	1510	1279	817	1634	1527
152	1313	885	29	58	116	232	464	928	115	230
153	460	920	99	198	396	792	1584	1427	1113	485
154	970	199	398	796	1592	1443	1145	549	1098	455
155	910	79	158	316	632	1264	787	1574	1407	1073
156	405	810	1620	1499	1257	773	1546	1351	961	181
157	362	724	1448	1155	569	1138	535	1070	399	798
158	1596	1451	1161	581	1162	583	1166	591	1182	623
159	1246	751	1502	1263	785	1570	1399	1057	373	746
160	1492	1243	745	1490	1239	737	1474	1207	673	1346
161	951	161	322	644	1288	835	1670	1599	1457	1173
162	605	1210	679	1358	975	209	418	836	1672	1603
163	1465	1189	637	1274	807	1614	1487	1233	725	1450
164	1159	577	1154	567	1134	527	1054	367	734	1468
165	1195	649	1298	855	1710	1679	1617	1493	1245	749
166	1498	1255	769	1538	1335	929	117	234	468	936
167	131	262	524	1048	355	710	1420	1099	457	914
168	87	174	348	696	1392	1043	345	690	1380	1019
169	297	594	1188	635	1270	799	1598	1455	1169	597
170	1194	647	1294	847	1694	1647	1553	1365	989	237
171	474	948	155	310	620	1240	739	1478	1215	689
172	1378	1015	289	578	1156	571	1142	543	1086	431
173	862	1724	1707	1673	1605	1469	1197	653	1306	871
174										

P = 1747

INDICES

	0	1	2	3	4	5	6	7	8	9
0		0	1	179	2	1703	180	307	3	358
1	1704	1293	181	1255	308	136	4	974	359	1416
2	1705	486	1294	328	182	1660	1256	537	309	1042
3	137	110	5	1472	975	264	360	859	1417	1434
4	1706	300	487	1450	1295	315	329	17	183	614
5	1661	1153	1257	275	538	1250	310	1595	1043	191
6	138	252	111	665	6	1212	1473	1320	976	507
7	265	395	361	1521	860	93	1418	1600	1435	1683
8	1707	716	301	389	488	931	1451	1221	1296	1513
9	316	1562	330	289	18	1373	184	514	615	1651
10	1662	36	1154	774	1258	443	276	1133	539	1048
11	1251	1038	311	248	1596	285	1044	1613	192	1281
12	139	840	253	479	112	1617	666	1548	7	1629
13	1213	913	1474	1723	1321	494	977	1466	508	629
14	266	196	396	802	362	999	1522	793	861	119
15	94	1031	1419	1332	1601	67	1436	1285	1684	454
16	1708	635	717	782	302	1429	390	769	489	764
17	932	28	1452	143	1222	221	1297	370	1514	1492
18	317	707	1563	431	331	816	290	521	19	844
19	1374	824	185	473	515	1391	616	898	1652	937
20	1663	1499	37	1349	1155	257	775	686	1259	963
21	444	1061	277	574	1134	1407	540	417	1049	1700
22	1252	483	1039	856	312	272	249	504	1597	928
23	286	33	1045	1610	1614	1720	193	116	1282	1426
24	140	704	841	895	254	571	480	925	113	568
25	1618	1397	667	1621	1549	1110	8	950	1630	1166
26	1214	1400	914	1457	1475	232	1724	1692	1322	670
27	495	1533	978	1741	1467	1207	509	1624	630	468
28	267	945	197	1307	397	1552	803	607	363	202
29	1000	693	1523	1113	794	148	862	84	120	1583
30	95	11	1032	215	1420	209	1333	1193	1602	953
31	68	1101	1437	733	1286	622	1685	1633	455	589
32	1709	1312	636	644	718	1169	783	1227	303	324
33	1430	1246	391	1217	770	1277	490	1027	765	427
34	933	1403	29	921	1453	464	144	1097	1223	917
35	222	46	1298	402	371	352	1515	1460	1493	226
36	318	1086	708	1019	1564	1478	432	1339	332	658
37	817	582	291	235	522	50	20	551	845	904
38	1375	1727	825	532	186	1557	474	62	516	1695
39	1392	1302	617	1092	899	1640	1653	1325	938	156
40	1664	1673	1500	1365	38	673	1350	406	1156	163
41	258	1645	776	498	687	346	1260	808	964	1266
42	445	1536	1062	375	278	888	575	559	1135	981
43	1408	1199	541	1007	418	1178	1050	1744	1701	356
44	1253	972	484	1658	1040	1470	857	298	313	612
45	273	1593	250	1210	505	1519	1598	714	929	1511
46	287	512	34	441	1046	246	1611	838	1615	1627
47	1721	1464	194	997	117	1330	1283	633	1427	762
48	141	368	705	814	842	471	896	1497	255	961
49	572	415	481	270	926	1608	114	702	569	566

POWER RESIDUES

	0	1	2	3	4	5	6	7	8	9
0	1	2	4	8	16	32	64	128	256	512
1	1024	301	602	1204	661	1322	897	47	94	188
2	376	752	1504	1261	775	1550	1353	959	171	342
3	684	1368	989	231	462	924	101	202	404	808
4	1616	1485	1223	699	1398	1049	351	702	1404	1061
5	375	750	1500	1253	759	1518	1289	831	1662	1577
6	1407	1067	387	774	1548	1349	951	155	310	620
7	1240	733	1466	1185	623	1246	745	1490	1233	719
8	1438	1129	511	1022	297	594	1188	629	1258	769
9	1538	1329	911	75	150	300	600	1200	653	1306
10	865	1730	1713	1679	1611	1475	1203	659	1318	889
11	31	62	124	248	496	992	237	474	948	149
12	298	596	1192	637	1274	801	1602	1457	1167	587
13	1174	601	1202	657	1314	881	15	30	60	120
14	240	480	960	173	346	692	1384	1021	295	590
15	1180	613	1226	705	1410	1073	399	798	1596	1445
16	1143	539	1078	409	818	1636	1525	1303	859	1718
17	1689	1631	1515	1283	819	1638	1529	1311	875	3
18	6	12	24	48	96	192	384	768	1536	1325
19	903	59	118	236	472	944	141	282	564	1128
20	509	1018	289	578	1156	565	1130	513	1026	305
21	610	1220	693	1386	1025	303	606	1212	677	1354
22	961	175	350	700	1400	1053	359	718	1436	1125
23	503	1006	265	530	1060	373	746	1492	1237	727
24	1454	1161	575	1150	553	1106	465	930	113	226
25	452	904	61	122	244	488	976	205	410	820
26	1640	1533	1319	891	35	70	140	280	560	1120
27	493	986	225	450	900	53	106	212	424	848
28	1696	1645	1543	1339	931	115	230	460	920	93
29	186	372	744	1488	1229	711	1422	1097	447	894
30	41	82	164	328	656	1312	877	7	14	28
31	56	112	224	448	896	45	90	180	360	720
32	1440	1133	519	1038	329	658	1316	885	23	46
33	92	184	368	736	1472	1197	647	1294	841	1682
34	1617	1487	1227	707	1414	1081	415	830	1660	1573
35	1399	1051	355	710	1420	1093	439	878	9	18
36	36	72	144	288	576	1152	557	1114	481	962
37	177	354	708	1416	1085	423	846	1692	1637	1527
38	1307	867	1734	1721	1695	1643	1539	1331	915	83
39	166	332	664	1328	909	71	142	284	568	1136
40	525	1050	353	706	1412	1077	407	814	1628	1509
41	1271	795	1590	1433	1119	491	982	217	434	868
42	1736	1725	1703	1659	1571	1395	1043	339	678	1356
43	965	183	366	732	1464	1181	615	1230	713	1426
44	1105	463	926	105	210	420	840	1680	1613	1479
45	1211	675	1350	953	159	318	636	1272	797	1594
46	1441	1135	523	1046	345	690	1380	1013	279	558
47	1116	485	970	193	386	772	1544	1341	935	123
48	246	492	984	221	442	884	21	42	84	168
49	336	672	1344	941	135	270	540	1080	413	826

P = 1747

INDICES

	0	1	2	3	4	5	6	7	8	9
50	1619	948	1398	230	668	1739	1622	943	1550	200
51	1111	82	9	207	951	731	1631	1310	1167	322
52	1215	1025	1401	462	915	400	1458	1084	1476	656
53	233	549	1725	1555	1693	1090	1323	1671	671	161
54	496	806	1534	886	979	1005	1742	970	1468	610
55	1208	712	510	244	1625	995	631	366	469	959
56	268	700	946	1737	198	205	1308	1023	398	654
57	1553	1669	804	1003	608	242	364	698	203	652
58	1001	696	694	1568	1524	1570	1114	129	795	1526
59	149	1077	863	1572	85	1238	121	1116	1584	1482
60	96	131	12	1678	1033	797	216	681	1421	1528
61	210	1272	1334	151	1194	436	1603	1079	954	1072
62	69	865	1102	74	1438	1574	734	1142	1287	87
63	623	1343	1686	1240	1634	1505	456	123	590	753
64	1710	1118	1313	1384	637	1586	645	336	719	1484
65	1170	596	784	98	1228	870	304	133	325	107
66	1431	14	1247	662	392	1680	1218	1370	771	1035
67	1278	1545	491	799	1028	451	766	218	428	821
68	934	683	1404	853	30	1423	922	1107	1454	1530
69	465	604	145	212	1098	586	1224	1274	918	43
70	223	1336	47	529	1299	153	403	343	372	1196
71	353	295	1516	438	1461	759	1494	1605	227	79
72	319	1081	1087	883	709	956	1020	239	1565	1074
73	1479	678	433	71	1340	750	333	867	659	1542
74	818	1104	583	526	292	76	236	747	523	1440
75	51	1443	21	1576	552	988	846	736	905	54
76	1376	1144	1728	1355	826	1289	533	1446	187	89
77	1558	1129	475	625	63	24	517	1345	1696	1716
78	1393	1688	1303	1579	618	1242	1093	1015	900	1636
79	1641	555	1654	1507	1326	411	939	458	157	991
80	1665	125	1674	1068	1501	592	1366	849	39	755
81	674	743	1351	1712	407	739	1157	1120	164	174
82	259	1315	1646	908	777	1386	499	1161	688	639
83	347	57	1261	1588	809	726	965	647	1267	1379
84	446	338	1537	1124	1063	721	376	1147	279	1486
85	889	1187	576	1172	560	1731	1136	598	982	168
86	1409	786	1200	1358	542	100	1008	381	419	1230
87	1179	829	1051	872	1745	178	1702	306	357	1292
88	1254	135	973	1415	485	327	1659	536	1041	109
89	1471	263	858	1433	299	1449	314	16	613	1152
90	274	1249	1594	190	251	664	1211	1319	506	394
91	1520	92	1599	1682	715	388	930	1220	1512	1561
92	288	1372	513	1650	35	773	442	1132	1047	1037
93	247	284	1612	1280	839	478	1616	1547	1628	912
94	1722	493	1465	628	195	801	998	792	118	1030
95	1331	66	1284	453	634	781	1428	768	763	27
96	142	220	369	1491	706	430	815	520	843	823
97	472	1390	897	936	1498	1348	256	685	962	1060
98	573	1406	416	1699	482	855	271	503	927	32
99	1609	1719	115	1425	703	894	570	924	567	1396

POWER RESIDUES

	0	1	2	3	4	5	6	7	8	9
50	1652	1557	1367	987	227	454	908	69	138	276
51	552	1104	461	922	97	194	388	776	1552	1357
52	967	187	374	748	1496	1245	743	1486	1225	703
53	1406	1065	383	766	1532	1317	887	27	54	108
54	216	432	864	1728	1709	1671	1595	1443	1139	531
55	1062	377	754	1508	1269	791	1582	1417	1087	427
56	854	1708	1669	1591	1435	1123	499	998	249	498
57	996	245	490	980	213	426	852	1704	1661	1575
58	1403	1059	371	742	1484	1221	695	1390	1033	319
59	638	1276	805	1610	1473	1199	651	1302	857	1714
60	1681	1615	1483	1219	691	1382	1017	287	574	1148
61	549	1098	449	898	49	98	196	392	784	1568
62	1389	1031	315	630	1260	773	1546	1345	943	139
63	278	556	1112	477	954	161	322	644	1288	829
64	1658	1569	1391	1035	323	646	1292	837	1674	1601
65	1455	1163	579	1158	569	1138	529	1058	369	738
66	1476	1205	663	1326	905	63	126	252	504	1008
67	269	538	1076	405	810	1620	1493	1239	731	1462
68	1177	607	1214	681	1362	977	207	414	828	1656
69	1565	1383	1019	291	582	1164	581	1162	577	1154
70	561	1122	497	994	241	482	964	181	362	724
71	1448	1149	551	1102	457	914	81	162	324	648
72	1296	845	1690	1633	1519	1291	835	1670	1593	1439
73	1131	515	1030	313	626	1252	757	1514	1281	815
74	1630	1513	1279	811	1622	1497	1247	747	1494	1241
75	735	1470	1193	639	1278	809	1618	1489	1231	715
76	1430	1113	479	958	169	338	676	1352	957	167
77	334	668	1336	925	103	206	412	824	1648	1549
78	1351	955	163	326	652	1304	861	1722	1697	1647
79	1547	1347	947	147	294	588	1176	605	1210	673
80	1346	945	143	286	572	1144	541	1082	417	834
81	1668	1589	1431	1115	483	966	185	370	740	1480
82	1213	679	1358	969	191	382	764	1528	1309	871
83	1742	1737	1727	1707	1667	1587	1427	1107	467	934
84	121	242	484	968	189	378	756	1512	1277	807
85	1614	1481	1215	683	1366	985	223	446	892	37
86	74	148	296	592	1184	621	1242	737	1474	1201
87	655	1310	873	1746	1745	1743	1739	1731	1715	1683
88	1619	1491	1235	723	1446	1145	543	1086	425	850
89	1700	1653	1559	1371	995	243	486	972	197	394
90	788	1576	1405	1063	379	758	1516	1285	823	1646
91	1545	1343	939	131	262	524	1048	349	698	1396
92	1045	343	686	1372	997	247	494	988	229	458
93	916	85	170	340	680	1360	973	199	398	796
94	1592	1437	1127	507	1014	281	562	1124	501	1002
95	257	514	1028	309	618	1236	725	1450	1153	559
96	1118	489	978	209	418	836	1672	1597	1447	1147
97	547	1094	441	882	17	34	68	136	272	544
98	1088	429	858	1716	1685	1623	1499	1251	755	1510
99	1273	799	1598	1449	1151	555	1110	473	946	145

P = 1747

INDICES

	0	1	2	3	4	5	6	7	8	9
100	1620	1109	949	1165	1399	1456	231	1691	669	1532
101	1740	1206	1623	467	944	1306	1551	606	201	692
102	1112	147	83	1582	10	214	208	1192	952	1100
103	732	621	1632	588	1311	643	1168	1226	323	1245
104	1216	1276	1026	426	1402	920	463	1096	916	45
105	401	351	1459	225	1085	1018	1477	1338	657	581
106	234	49	550	903	1726	531	1556	61	1694	1301
107	1091	1639	1324	155	1672	1364	672	405	162	1644
108	497	345	807	1265	1535	374	887	558	980	1198
109	1006	1177	1743	355	971	1657	1469	297	611	1592
110	1209	1518	713	1510	511	440	245	837	1626	1463
111	996	1329	632	761	367	813	470	1496	960	414
112	269	1607	701	565	947	229	1738	942	199	81
113	206	730	1309	321	1024	461	399	1083	655	548
114	1554	1089	1670	160	805	885	1004	969	609	711
115	243	994	365	958	699	1736	204	1022	653	1668
116	1002	241	697	651	695	1567	1569	128	1525	1076
117	1571	1237	1115	1481	130	1677	796	680	1527	1271
118	150	435	1078	1071	864	73	1573	1141	86	1342
119	1239	1504	122	752	1117	1383	1585	335	1483	595
120	97	869	132	106	13	661	1679	1369	1034	1544
121	798	450	217	820	682	852	1422	1106	1529	603
122	211	585	1273	42	1335	528	152	342	1195	294
123	437	758	1604	78	1080	882	955	238	1073	677
124	70	749	866	1541	1103	525	75	746	1439	1442
125	1575	987	735	53	1143	1354	1288	1445	88	1128
126	624	23	1344	1715	1687	1578	1241	1014	1635	554
127	1506	410	457	990	124	1067	591	848	754	742
128	1711	738	1119	173	1314	907	1385	1160	638	56
129	1587	725	646	1378	337	1123	720	1146	1485	1186
130	1171	1730	597	167	785	1357	99	380	1229	828
131	871	177	305	1291	134	1414	326	535	108	262
132	1432	1448	15	1151	1248	189	663	1318	393	91
133	1681	387	1219	1560	1371	1649	772	1131	1036	283
134	1279	477	1546	911	492	627	800	791	1029	65
135	452	780	767	26	219	1490	429	519	822	1389
136	935	1347	684	1059	1405	1698	854	502	31	1718
137	1424	893	923	1395	1108	1164	1455	1690	1531	1205
138	466	1305	605	691	146	1581	213	1191	1099	620
139	587	642	1225	1244	1275	425	919	1095	44	350
140	224	1017	1337	580	48	902	530	60	1300	1638
141	154	1363	404	1643	344	1264	373	557	1197	1176
142	354	1656	296	1591	1517	1509	439	836	1462	1328
143	760	812	1495	413	1606	564	228	941	80	729
144	320	460	1082	547	1088	159	884	968	710	993
145	957	1735	1021	1667	240	650	1566	127	1075	1236
146	1480	1676	679	1270	434	1070	72	1140	1341	1503
147	751	1382	334	594	868	105	660	1368	1543	449
148	819	851	1105	602	584	41	527	341	293	757
149	77	881	237	676	748	1540	524	745	1441	986

POWER RESIDUES

	0	1	2	3	4	5	6	7	8	9
100	290	580	1160	573	1146	545	1090	433	866	1732
101	1717	1687	1627	1507	1267	787	1574	1401	1055	363
102	726	1452	1157	567	1134	521	1042	337	674	1348
103	949	151	302	604	1208	669	1338	929	111	222
104	444	888	29	58	116	232	464	928	109	218
105	436	872	1744	1741	1735	1723	1699	1651	1555	1363
106	979	211	422	844	1688	1629	1511	1275	803	1606
107	1465	1183	619	1238	729	1458	1169	591	1182	617
108	1234	721	1442	1137	527	1054	361	722	1444	1141
109	535	1070	393	786	1572	1397	1047	347	694	1388
110	1029	311	622	1244	741	1482	1217	687	1374	1001
111	255	510	1020	293	586	1172	597	1194	641	1282
112	817	1634	1521	1295	843	1686	1625	1503	1259	771
113	1542	1337	927	107	214	428	856	1712	1677	1607
114	1467	1187	627	1254	761	1522	1297	847	1694	1641
115	1535	1323	899	51	102	204	408	816	1632	1517
116	1287	827	1654	1561	1375	1003	259	518	1036	325
117	650	1300	853	1706	1665	1583	1419	1091	435	870
118	1740	1733	1719	1691	1635	1523	1299	851	1702	1657
119	1567	1387	1027	307	614	1228	709	1418	1089	431
120	862	1724	1701	1655	1563	1379	1011	275	550	1100
121	453	906	65	130	260	520	1040	333	666	1332
122	917	87	174	348	696	1392	1037	327	654	1308
123	869	1738	1729	1711	1675	1603	1459	1171	595	1190
124	633	1266	785	1570	1393	1039	331	662	1324	901
125	55	110	220	440	880	13	26	52	104	208
126	416	832	1664	1581	1415	1083	419	838	1676	1605
127	1463	1179	611	1222	697	1394	1041	335	670	1340
128	933	119	238	476	952	157	314	628	1256	765
129	1530	1313	879	11	22	44	88	176	352	704
130	1408	1069	391	782	1564	1381	1015	283	566	1132
131	517	1034	321	642	1284	821	1642	1537	1327	907
132	67	134	268	536	1072	397	794	1588	1429	1111
133	475	950	153	306	612	1224	701	1402	1057	367
134	734	1468	1189	631	1262	777	1554	1361	975	203
135	406	812	1624	1501	1255	763	1526	1305	863	1726
136	1705	1663	1579	1411	1075	403	806	1612	1477	1207
137	667	1334	921	95	190	380	760	1520	1293	839
138	1678	1609	1471	1195	643	1286	825	1650	1553	1359
139	971	195	390	780	1560	1373	999	251	502	1004
140	261	522	1044	341	682	1364	981	215	430	860
141	1720	1693	1639	1531	1315	883	19	38	76	152
142	304	608	1216	685	1370	993	239	478	956	165
143	330	660	1320	893	39	78	156	312	624	1248
144	749	1498	1249	751	1502	1257	767	1534	1321	895
145	43	86	172	344	688	1376	1005	263	526	1052
146	357	714	1428	1109	471	942	137	274	548	1096
147	445	890	33	66	132	264	528	1056	365	730
148	1460	1173	599	1198	649	1298	849	1698	1649	1551
149	1355	963	179	358	716	1432	1117	487	974	201

P = 1747

INDICES

	0	1	2	3	4	5	6	7	8	9
150	52	1353	1444	1127	22	1714	1577	1013	553	409
151	989	1066	847	741	737	172	906	1159	55	724
152	1377	1122	1145	1185	1729	166	1356	379	827	176
153	1290	1413	534	261	1447	1150	188	1317	90	386
154	1559	1648	1130	282	476	910	626	790	64	779
155	25	1489	518	1388	1346	1058	1697	501	1717	892
156	1394	1163	1689	1204	1304	690	1580	1190	619	641
157	1243	424	1094	349	1016	579	901	59	1637	1362
158	1642	1263	556	1175	1655	1590	1508	835	1327	811
159	412	563	940	728	459	546	158	967	992	1734
160	1666	649	126	1235	1675	1269	1069	1139	1502	1381
161	593	104	1367	448	850	601	40	340	756	880
162	675	1539	744	985	1352	1126	1713	1012	408	1065
163	740	171	1158	723	1121	1184	165	378	175	1412
164	260	1149	1316	385	1647	281	909	789	778	1488
165	1387	1057	500	891	1162	1203	689	1189	640	423
166	348	578	58	1361	1262	1174	1589	834	810	562
167	727	545	966	1733	648	1234	1268	1138	1380	103
168	447	600	339	879	1538	984	1125	1011	1064	170
169	722	1183	377	1411	1148	384	280	788	1487	1056
170	890	1202	1188	422	577	1360	1173	833	561	544
171	1732	1233	1137	102	599	878	983	1010	169	1182
172	1410	383	787	1055	1201	421	1359	832	543	1232
173	101	877	1009	1181	382	1054	420	831	1231	876
174	1180	1053	830	875	1052	874	873			

POWER RESIDUES

	0	1	2	3	4	5	6	7	8	9
150	402	804	1608	1469	1191	635	1270	793	1586	1425
151	1103	459	918	89	178	356	712	1424	1101	455
152	910	73	146	292	584	1168	589	1178	609	1218
153	689	1378	1009	271	542	1084	421	842	1684	1621
154	1495	1243	739	1478	1209	671	1342	937	127	254
155	508	1016	285	570	1140	533	1066	385	770	1540
156	1333	919	91	182	364	728	1456	1165	583	1166
157	585	1170	593	1186	625	1250	753	1506	1265	783
158	1566	1385	1023	299	598	1196	645	1290	833	1666
159	1585	1423	1099	451	902	57	114	228	456	912
160	77	154	308	616	1232	717	1434	1121	495	990
161	233	466	932	117	234	468	936	125	250	500
162	1000	253	506	1012	277	554	1108	469	938	129
163	258	516	1032	317	634	1268	789	1578	1409	1071
164	395	790	1580	1413	1079	411	822	1644	1541	1335
165	923	99	198	396	792	1584	1421	1095	443	886
166	25	50	100	200	400	800	1600	1453	1159	571
167	1142	537	1074	401	802	1604	1461	1175	603	1206
168	665	1330	913	79	158	316	632	1264	781	1562
169	1377	1007	267	534	1068	389	778	1556	1365	983
170	219	438	876	5	10	20	40	80	160	320
171	640	1280	813	1626	1505	1263	779	1558	1369	991
172	235	470	940	133	266	532	1064	381	762	1524
173	1301	855	1710	1673	1599	1451	1155	563	1126	505
174	1010	273	546	1092	437	874				

P = 1753

INDICES

	0	1	2	3	4	5	6	7	8	9
0		0	1692	46	1632	327	1738	1	1572	92
1	267	1726	1678	1227	1693	373	1512	1078	32	1266
2	207	47	1666	57	1618	654	1167	138	1633	98
3	313	381	1452	20	1018	328	1724	251	1206	1273
4	147	1270	1739	749	1606	419	1749	566	1558	2
5	594	1124	1107	736	78	301	1573	1312	38	765
6	253	1414	321	93	1392	1554	1712	1435	958	103
7	268	1012	1664	1010	191	700	1146	1727	1213	1335
8	87	184	1210	1096	1679	1405	689	144	1546	1683
9	359	1228	1689	427	506	1593	1498	845	1694	66
10	534	1522	1064	1490	1047	374	676	634	18	1208
11	241	297	1513	541	1252	384	1730	1319	705	1079
12	193	1700	1354	1316	261	981	33	713	1332	795
13	1494	243	1652	1267	1375	465	898	406	43	603
14	208	612	952	1201	1604	425	950	48	131	402
15	640	839	1086	1170	1667	708	1153	317	1275	782
16	27	58	124	173	1150	347	1036	1705	1619	702
17	1345	1358	629	666	84	655	1486	811	1623	1736
18	299	1045	1168	1460	1629	578	367	1052	446	139
19	1533	50	1438	544	785	1600	1634	115	6	1114
20	474	1481	1462	99	1004	1597	1430	149	987	1240
21	314	858	616	1058	574	1076	1710	382	1148	1056

POWER RESIDUES

	0	1	2	3	4	5	6	7	8	9
0	1	7	49	343	648	1030	198	1386	937	1300
1	335	592	638	960	1461	1462	1469	1518	108	756
2	33	231	1617	801	348	683	1275	160	1120	828
3	537	253	18	126	882	915	1146	1010	58	406
4	1089	611	771	138	966	1503	3	21	147	1029
5	191	1337	594	652	1058	394	1005	23	161	1127
6	877	880	901	1048	324	515	99	693	1345	650
7	1044	296	319	480	1607	731	1611	759	54	378
8	893	992	1685	1277	174	1218	1514	80	560	414
9	1145	1003	9	63	441	1334	573	505	29	203
10	1421	1182	1262	69	483	1628	878	887	950	1391
11	972	1545	297	326	529	197	1379	888	957	1440
12	1315	440	1327	524	162	1134	926	1223	1549	325
13	522	148	1036	240	1680	1242	1682	1256	27	189
14	1323	496	1719	1515	87	609	757	40	280	207
15	1449	1378	881	908	1097	667	1163	1129	891	978
16	1587	591	631	911	1118	814	439	1320	475	1572
17	486	1649	1025	163	1141	975	1566	444	1355	720
18	1534	220	1540	262	81	567	463	1488	1651	1039
19	261	74	518	120	840	621	841	628	890	971
20	1538	248	1736	1634	920	1181	1255	20	140	980
21	1601	689	1317	454	1425	1210	1458	1441	1322	489

P = 1753

INDICES

	0	1	2	3	4	5	6	7	8	9
22	181	553	237	561	1453	746	481	273	1192	1515
23	324	21	1670	477	1259	893	645	1381	1019	962
24	133	835	1640	230	1294	329	1256	741	201	1142
25	921	1631	1725	31	653	1451	1272	1748	735	252
26	1434	190	183	1545	1592	1063	1207	1729	1315	1493
27	405	1603	838	1274	346	628	1735	366	543	473
28	148	573	552	1191	892	1639	1141	1271	1544	404
29	365	891	890	341	1740	1092	71	112	342	1284
30	580	750	779	1568	1026	1741	1110	1697	1607	1536
31	648	555	1093	995	257	420	1215	416	722	72
32	1719	680	1750	592	64	129	113	1254	1090	567
33	287	491	976	343	1645	10	1559	1507	642	587
34	1285	355	1298	3	569	430	606	581	24	369
35	595	1365	1426	1351	751	1339	1563	1125	1676	1412
36	239	780	985	1746	1108	1337	1400	883	1569	1362
37	518	737	307	1186	992	1027	386	1325	79	625
38	1473	759	1742	1549	1378	302	484	841	725	1111
39	1540	1135	1574	289	55	1662	1698	1343	1054	1313
40	414	1398	1421	1608	1402	511	39	225	944	563
41	1537	452	1370	766	89	1423	927	649	1180	971
42	254	1099	798	658	556	1732	998	1415	514	1247
43	1016	1094	1650	1043	322	471	1088	1323	996	166
44	121	94	493	1386	177	258	501	448	1393	869
45	686	1244	421	885	213	1555	1132	820	1455	1216
46	264	1348	1713	186	1610	754	417	504	1199	1436
47	833	363	585	723	1321	168	959	828	902	293
48	73	1478	775	104	1580	1172	170	1720	1234	219
49	269	978	1196	1176	681	393	141	1013	1082	350
50	861	1751	1571	372	1665	97	1723	748	593	1311
51	1391	1011	1212	1404	1688	65	675	540	192	712
52	1374	611	130	707	123	701	1485	1459	1532	114
53	1003	857	1147	745	1669	961	1255	30	1433	1728
54	345	572	1543	1091	778	1535	1214	591	286	1506
55	568	1364	1675	1336	306	624	483	288	413	224
56	88	1098	513	470	492	868	1131	185	832	827
57	1579	977	1081	96	1211	711	1484	744	344	590
58	305	1097	831	710	830	1646	281	1526	1680	1647
59	1032	161	11	1121	52	1406	282	1160	1224	1560
60	520	548	690	1527	719	275	1508	912	966	145
61	1681	41	1050	643	1637	1643	1547	1648	1476	1001
62	588	195	495	1684	1033	1308	935	1286	197	1329
63	360	162	1155	904	356	1040	662	1229	12	1104
64	1659	1299	620	1440	1690	1122	532	400	4	739
65	69	428	53	1384	1194	570	1030	1102	507	1407
66	227	278	431	599	916	1594	283	155	1585	607
67	1702	1388	1499	1161	1447	792	582	497	527	846
68	1225	319	295	25	1238	733	1695	1561	509	211
69	370	1673	546	67	521	930	1716	596	309	523
70	535	549	1305	1517	1366	939	1291	1523	691	946
71	1279	1427	1503	438	1065	1528	1616	1008	1352	1356

POWER RESIDUES

	0	1	2	3	4	5	6	7	8	9
22	1670	1172	1192	1332	559	407	1096	660	1114	786
23	243	1701	1389	958	1447	1364	783	222	1554	360
24	767	110	770	131	917	1160	1108	744	1702	1396
25	1007	37	259	60	420	1187	1297	314	445	1362
26	769	124	868	817	460	1467	1504	10	70	490
27	1677	1221	1535	227	1589	605	729	1597	661	1121
28	835	586	596	666	1156	1080	548	330	557	393
29	998	1727	1571	479	1600	682	1268	111	777	180
30	1260	55	385	942	1335	580	554	372	851	698
31	1380	895	1006	30	210	1470	1525	157	1099	681
32	1261	62	434	1285	230	1610	752	5	35	245
33	1715	1487	1644	990	1671	1179	1241	1675	1207	1437
34	1294	293	298	333	578	540	274	165	1155	1073
35	499	1740	1662	1116	800	341	634	932	1265	90
36	630	904	1069	471	1544	290	277	186	1302	349
37	690	1324	503	15	105	735	1639	955	1426	1217
38	1507	31	217	1519	115	805	376	879	894	999
39	1734	1620	822	495	1712	1466	1497	1714	1480	1595
40	647	1023	149	1043	289	270	137	959	1454	1413
41	1126	870	831	558	400	1047	317	466	1509	45
42	315	452	1411	1112	772	145	1015	93	651	1051
43	345	662	1128	884	929	1244	1696	1354	713	1485
44	1630	892	985	1636	934	1279	188	1316	447	1376
45	867	810	411	1124	856	733	1625	857	740	1674
46	1200	1388	951	1398	1021	135	945	1356	727	1583
47	563	435	1292	279	200	1400	1035	233	1631	899
48	1034	226	1582	556	386	949	1384	923	1202	1402
49	1049	331	564	442	1341	622	848	677	1233	1619
50	815	446	1369	818	467	1516	94	658	1100	688
51	1310	405	1082	562	428	1243	1689	1305	370	837
52	600	694	1352	699	1387	944	1349	678	1240	1668
53	1158	1094	646	1016	100	700	1394	993	1692	1326
54	517	113	791	278	193	1351	692	1338	601	701
55	1401	1042	282	221	1547	311	424	1215	1493	1686
56	1284	223	1561	409	1110	758	47	329	550	344
57	655	1079	541	281	214	1498	1721	1529	185	1295
58	300	347	676	1226	1570	472	1551	339	620	834
59	579	547	323	508	50	350	697	1373	846	663
60	1135	933	1272	139	973	1552	346	669	1177	1227
61	1577	521	141	987	1650	1032	212	1484	1623	843
62	642	988	1657	1081	555	379	900	1041	275	172
63	1204	1416	1147	1017	107	749	1737	1641	969	1524
64	150	1050	338	613	785	236	1652	1046	310	417
65	1166	1150	1038	254	25	175	1225	1563	423	1208
66	1444	1343	636	946	1363	776	173	1211	1465	1490
67	1665	1137	947	1370	825	516	106	742	1688	1298
68	321	494	1705	1417	1154	1066	450	1397	1014	86
69	602	708	1450	1385	930	1251	1745	1697	1361	762
70	75	525	169	1183	1269	118	826	523	155	1085
71	583	575	519	127	889	964	1489	1658	1088	604

P = 1753

INDICES

	0	1	2	3	4	5	6	7	8	9
72	179	1491	720	881	925	752	1686	468	1048	276
73	1277	75	1340	455	823	375	1509	1409	1302	1564
74	458	787	677	913	247	729	1126	1188	932	635
75	967	815	326	1677	1265	1166	19	146	565	77
76	1413	957	699	1209	1682	1497	1489	240	1318	260
77	242	42	424	1085	781	1035	665	298	1051	784
78	1480	986	1075	236	1514	644	229	920	1747	1591
79	1602	542	1638	889	1283	1109	994	1718	1253	1644
80	354	23	1338	984	1361	385	1548	1539	1342	1401
81	451	1179	1731	1649	165	500	884	263	503	1320
82	1477	1233	392	1570	1310	674	706	1002	29	777
83	1363	412	867	1080	589	280	1120	519	911	1636
84	194	196	1039	619	738	1029	598	1701	496	1237
85	1672	308	938	1502	1355	1685	454	457	1187	1264
86	956	1317	1034	1074	1590	993	983	450	262	1309
87	411	910	1028	937	1263	982	936	60	106	387
88	61	152	34	1287	433	1138	1326	107	117	714
89	198	158	441	80	388	311	1333	1330	809	479
90	626	62	1184	796	361	1372	825	1474	153	1614
91	1495	163	1072	1070	760	35	1395	244	1156	1465
92	204	1743	1288	487	1653	905	126	1582	1550	434
93	694	1268	357	601	444	1379	1139	8	1376	1041
94	773	855	303	1327	525	466	663	672	1261	485
95	108	462	899	1230	768	377	842	118	233	407
96	13	762	1418	726	715	871	44	1105	1520	638
97	1112	199	110	604	1660	175	1174	1541	159	1657
98	209	1300	918	1118	1136	442	1116	613	621	806
99	333	1575	81	537	953	1441	1022	895	290	389
100	801	1202	1691	91	1511	56	312	250	1605	1123
101	37	1553	1663	1334	688	426	533	633	1251	1699
102	1331	464	951	401	1152	172	1344	810	1628	49
103	5	1596	615	1055	480	476	132	740	652	189
104	1314	627	551	403	70	1567	647	415	63	490
105	641	429	1425	1411	1399	1185	1472	840	54	1397
106	943	1422	797	1246	1087	1385	685	819	1609	362
107	901	1171	1195	349	1722	1403	1373	1458	1668	571
108	285	623	512	826	1483	709	1031	1159	718	40
109	1475	1307	1154	1103	531	1383	226	154	1446	318
110	508	929	1304	945	1615	880	1276	1408	246	814
111	564	1496	423	783	228	888	353	1538	164	1232
112	28	279	1038	1236	453	1073	410	59	432	157
113	808	1371	1071	1464	125	600	772	671	767	761
114	1519	174	917	805	1021	90	36	632	1151	1595
115	651	1566	1424	1396	684	348	284	1158	530	928
116	245	887	1037	156	771	804	650	1157	770	1706
117	1586	1707	221	1181	1466	1220	1620	608	1587	335
118	972	205	101	703	1703	1708	1061	255	1744	1368
119	1346	1389	222	964	1100	1289	1164	1359	1500	1182
120	460	799	488	1444	630	1162	1467	338	659	1654
121	215	667	1448	1221	852	557	906	379	85	793

POWER RESIDUES

	0	1	2	3	4	5	6	7	8	9
72	722	1548	318	473	1558	388	963	1482	1609	745
73	1709	1445	1350	685	1289	258	53	371	844	649
74	1037	247	1729	1585	577	533	225	1575	507	43
75	301	354	725	1569	465	1502	1749	1725	1557	381
76	914	1139	961	1468	1511	59	413	1138	954	1419
77	1168	1164	1136	940	1321	482	1621	829	544	302
78	361	774	159	1113	779	194	1358	741	1681	1249
79	1731	1599	675	1219	1521	129	903	1062	422	1201
80	1395	1000	1741	1669	1165	1143	989	1664	1130	898
81	1027	177	1239	1661	1109	751	1751	1739	1655	1067
82	457	1446	1357	734	1632	906	1083	569	477	1586
83	584	582	568	470	1537	241	1687	1291	272	151
84	1057	387	956	1433	1266	97	679	1247	1717	1501
85	1742	1676	1214	1486	1637	941	1328	531	211	1477
86	1574	500	1747	1711	1459	1448	1371	832	565	449
87	1390	965	1496	1707	1431	1252	1752	1746	1704	1410
88	1105	723	1555	367	816	453	1418	1161	1115	793
89	292	291	284	235	1645	997	1720	1522	136	952
90	1405	1070	478	1593	633	925	1216	1500	1735	1627
91	871	838	607	743	1695	1347	664	1142	982	1615
92	787	250	1750	1732	1606	724	1562	416	1159	1101
93	695	1359	748	1730	1592	626	876	873	852	705
94	1429	1238	1654	1060	408	1103	709	1457	1434	1273
95	146	1022	142	994	1699	1375	860	761	68	476
96	1579	535	239	1673	1193	1339	608	750	1744	1690
97	1312	419	1180	1248	1724	1550	332	571	491	1684
98	1270	125	875	866	803	362	781	208	1456	1427
99	1224	1556	374	865	796	313	438	1313	426	1229
100	1591	619	827	530	204	1428	1231	1605	717	1513
101	73	511	71	497	1726	1564	430	1257	34	238
102	1666	1144	996	1713	1473	1546	304	375	872	845
103	656	1086	590	624	862	775	166	1162	1122	842
104	635	939	1314	433	1278	181	1267	104	728	1590
105	612	778	187	1309	398	1033	219	1533	213	1491
106	1672	1186	1290	265	102	714	1492	1679	1235	1633
107	913	1132	912	1125	863	782	215	1505	17	119
108	833	572	498	1733	1613	773	152	1064	436	1299
109	328	543	295	312	431	1264	83	581	561	421
110	1194	1346	657	1093	639	967	1510	52	364	795
111	306	389	970	1531	199	1393	986	1643	983	1622
112	836	593	645	1009	51	357	746	1716	1494	1693
113	1333	566	456	1439	1308	391	984	1629	885	936
114	1293	286	249	1743	1683	1263	76	532	218	1526
115	164	1148	1024	156	1092	632	918	1167	1157	1087
116	597	673	1205	1423	1196	1360	755	26	182	1274
117	153	1071	485	1642	976	1573	493	1698	1368	811
118	418	1173	1199	1381	902	1055	373	858	747	1723
119	1543	283	228	1596	654	1072	492	1691	1319	468
120	1523	143	1001	1748	1718	1508	38	266	109	763
121	82	574	512	78	546	316	459	1460	1455	1420

P = 1753

INDICES

	0	1	2	3	4	5	6	7	8	9
122	1621	271	1733	127	990	656	583	609	1577	999
123	1583	1006	1487	498	1588	1068	1416	1551	941	812
124	528	336	135	515	435	1469	1624	847	973	789
125	1248	695	875	1737	1226	206	137	1017	1269	1557
126	300	320	102	1145	1095	358	844	1046	296	704
127	980	1651	602	949	1169	26	1704	83	1044	445
128	1599	1461	1239	1709	560	323	1380	1293	1630	734
129	1062	837	472	1140	340	579	1696	256	679	1089
130	9	1297	368	1562	1745	517	1324	1377	1134	1053
131	510	1369	970	997	1042	120	447	212	1347	1198
132	167	774	218	140	371	1390	539	122	856	1432
133	1534	1674	223	1130	95	304	1525	51	547	965
134	1642	494	1328	661	1439	68	1101	915	1387	526
135	732	545	522	1290	437	178	467	822	786	931
136	1165	698	259	664	235	1601	1717	1360	1178	502
137	673	866	1635	597	1501	955	449	1262	151	116
138	310	1183	1613	1394	486	693	7	524	461	232
139	870	109	1656	1115	536	800	249	687	463	1627
140	475	550	489	1471	1245	900	1457	1482	1306	1445
141	879	422	1231	409	1463	1518	631	683	886	769
142	1219	100	1367	1163	1443	214	378	989	1005	940
143	1468	874	1556	843	948	1598	1292	339	1296	1133
144	119	217	1431	1524	660	731	821	234	865	150
145	692	1655	1626	1456	408	1218	988	947	216	864
146	1217	14	15	1241	1280	668	395	265	763	16
147	315	1428	1449	1024	1349	1419	1242	859	1504	1222
148	398	1714	727	1281	617	439	853	331	187	716
149	669	1059	1066	558	1128	1611	872	396	575	1529
150	907	849	755	45	266	1077	1617	380	1205	418
151	1106	764	1711	1009	86	143	505	1521	17	383
152	1353	794	897	1200	639	316	1149	1357	1622	577
153	1437	1113	1429	1057	180	272	1258	834	200	1450
154	182	1492	1734	1190	364	111	1025	554	721	128
155	975	586	605	1350	238	882	991	758	724	1661
156	1420	562	926	657	1015	1322	176	1243	1454	753
157	584	292	169	1175	860	747	1687	610	1531	960
158	1542	1505	482	469	1578	743	829	160	1223	274
159	1049	1000	934	903	1658	399	1193	277	1584	791
160	294	210	1715	1516	1278	1007	924	74	1301	728
161	325	76	1488	1084	1479	919	1282	22	1341	499
162	391	776	1119	618	1671	456	1589	909	105	1137
163	440	478	824	1069	203	1581	443	854	1260	376
164	1417	637	1173	1117	332	894	1510	1552	1250	171
165	614	188	646	1410	942	818	1721	622	717	1382
166	1303	813	352	1235	807	670	1020	1565	529	803
167	220	334	1060	963	459	337	851	270	1576	1067
168	134	788	136	1144	979	82	559	836	678	516
169	969	1197	538	1129	1641	914	436	697	1177	954
170	1612	231	248	1470	878	682	1442	873	1295	730
171	1625	863	394	1023	397	330	1127	848	1204	142

POWER RESIDUES

	0	1	2	3	4	5	6	7	8	9
122	1175	1213	1479	1588	598	680	1254	13	91	637
123	953	1412	1119	821	488	1663	1123	849	684	1282
124	209	1463	1476	1567	451	1404	1063	429	1250	1738
125	1648	1018	114	798	327	536	246	1722	1536	234
126	1638	948	1377	874	859	754	19	133	931	1258
127	41	287	256	39	273	158	1106	730	1604	710
128	1464	1483	1616	794	299	340	627	883	922	1195
129	1353	706	1436	1287	244	1708	1438	1301	342	641
130	981	1608	738	1660	1102	702	1408	1091	625	869
131	824	509	57	399	1040	268	123	861	768	117
132	819	474	1565	437	1306	377	886	943	1342	629
133	897	1020	128	896	1013	79	553	365	802	355
134	732	1618	808	397	1026	170	1190	1318	461	1474
135	1553	353	718	1520	122	854	719	1527	171	1197
136	1367	804	369	830	551	351	704	1422	1189	1311
137	412	1131	905	1076	520	134	938	1307	384	935
138	1286	237	1659	1095	653	1065	443	1348	671	1191
139	1325	510	64	448	1383	916	1153	1059	401	1054
140	366	809	404	1075	513	85	595	659	1107	737
141	1653	1053	359	760	61	427	1236	1640	962	1475
142	1560	402	1061	415	1152	1052	352	711	1471	1532
143	206	1442	1329	538	260	67	469	1530	192	1344
144	643	995	1706	1424	1203	1409	1098	674	1212	1472
145	1539	255	32	224	1568	458	1453	1406	1077	527
146	183	1281	202	1414	1133	919	1174	1206	1430	1245
147	1703	1403	1056	380	907	1090	618	820	481	1614
148	780	201	1407	1084	576	526	176	1232	1612	766
149	103	721	1541	269	130	910	1111	765	96	672
150	1198	1374	853	712	1478	1581	549	337	606	736
151	1646	1004	16	112	784	229	1603	703	1415	1140
152	968	1517	101	707	1443	1336	587	603	715	1499
153	1728	1578	528	190	1330	545	309	410	1117	807
154	390	977	1580	542	288	263	88	616	806	383
155	928	1237	1647	1011	65	455	1432	1259	48	336
156	599	687	1303	356	739	1667	1151	1045	303	368
157	823	502	8	56	392	991	1678	1228	1584	570
158	484	1635	927	1230	1598	668	1170	1178	1234	1626
159	864	789	264	95	665	1149	1031	205	1435	1280
160	195	1365	790	271	144	1008	44	308	403	1068
161	464	1495	1700	1382	909	1104	716	1506	24	168
162	1176	1220	1528	178	1246	1710	1452	1399	1028	184
163	1288	251	4	28	196	1372	839	614	792	285
164	242	1694	1340	615	799	334	585	589	617	813
165	432	1271	132	924	1209	1451	1392	979	1594	640
166	974	1559	395	1012	72	504	22	154	1078	534
167	232	1624	850	691	1331	552	358	753	12	84
168	588	610	764	89	623	855	726	1576	514	92
169	644	1002	2	14	98	686	1296	307	396	1019
170	121	847	670	1184	1276	167	1169	1171	1185	1283
171	216	1512	66	462	1481	1602	696	1366	797	320

P = 1753

INDICES

	0	1	2	3	4	5	6	7	8	9
172	896	576	1257	1189	974	757	1014	291	1530	742
173	933	790	923	1083	390	908	202	636	1249	817
174	351	802	850	1143	968	696	877	862	1203	756
175	922	816	876							

POWER RESIDUES

	0	1	2	3	4	5	6	7	8	9
172	487	1656	1074	506	36	252	11	77	539	267
173	116	812	425	1222	1542	276	179	1253	6	42
174	294	305	382	921	1188	1304	363	788	257	46
175	322	501								

P = 1759

INDICES

	0	1	2	3	4	5	6	7	8	9
0		0	484	1275	968	1344	1	671	1452	792
1	70	1510	485	194	1155	861	178	904	1276	1359
2	554	188	236	62	969	930	678	309	1639	409
3	1345	576	662	1027	1388	257	2	1209	85	1469
4	1038	1416	672	1310	720	378	546	224	1453	1342
5	1414	421	1162	1680	793	1096	365	876	893	165
6	71	1419	1060	1463	1146	1538	1511	1105	114	1337
7	741	1006	486	581	1693	447	569	423	195	831
8	1522	1584	142	869	1156	490	36	1684	1204	1392
9	862	865	1030	93	708	945	179	1555	68	544
10	140	647	905	1427	1646	1532	406	925	1277	1562
11	1580	726	849	1164	1360	1406	1377	986	649	1575
12	555	1262	145	933	1544	516	189	204	1630	827
13	264	1050	237	272	1589	1653	598	42	63	1259
14	1225	1499	1490	1704	970	1753	1065	859	419	1682
15	931	1195	1053	1696	907	162	679	31	1315	1197
16	248	733	310	1636	626	613	1353	443	1640	388
17	974	393	520	1218	410	1601	1688	1440	118	506
18	1346	351	1349	936	1514	795	577	656	1192	980
19	1429	1125	663	323	281	1055	552	363	1028	1628
20	624	622	1131	1080	1389	1002	153	854	372	1111
21	258	433	890	523	1409	896	3	1247	288	98
22	306	1098	1210	1236	1333	1722	1648	1182	86	887
23	132	1698	103	80	1470	1568	1133	348	301	244
24	1039	694	1746	1101	629	928	1417	1553	270	386
25	1000	692	673	1572	688	7	356	367	1311	122
26	748	1201	1534	1229	721	1266	756	909	315	873

POWER RESIDUES

	0	1	2	3	4	5	6	7	8	9
0	1	6	36	216	1296	740	922	255	1530	385
1	551	1547	487	1163	1701	1411	1430	1544	469	1055
2	1053	1041	969	537	1463	1742	1657	1147	1605	835
3	1492	157	942	375	491	1187	86	516	1337	986
4	639	316	137	822	1414	1448	1652	1117	1425	1514
5	289	1734	1609	859	1636	1021	849	1576	661	448
6	929	297	23	138	828	1450	1664	1189	98	588
7	10	60	360	401	647	364	425	791	1228	332
8	233	1398	1352	1076	1179	38	228	1368	1172	1755
9	1735	1615	895	93	558	1589	739	916	219	1314
10	848	1570	625	232	1392	1316	860	1642	1057	1065
11	1113	1401	1370	1184	68	408	689	616	178	1068
12	1131	1509	259	1554	529	1415	1454	1688	1333	962
13	495	1211	230	1380	1244	428	809	1336	980	603
14	100	600	82	492	1193	122	732	874	1726	1561
15	571	1667	1207	206	1236	380	521	1367	1166	1719
16	1519	319	155	930	303	59	354	365	431	827
17	1444	1628	973	561	1607	847	1564	589	16	96
18	576	1697	1387	1286	680	562	1613	883	21	126
19	756	1018	831	1468	13	78	468	1049	1017	825
20	1432	1556	541	1487	127	762	1054	1047	1005	753
21	1000	723	820	1402	1376	1220	284	1704	1429	1538
22	433	839	1516	301	47	282	1692	1357	1106	1359
23	1118	1431	1550	505	1271	590	22	132	792	1234
24	368	449	935	333	239	1434	1568	613	160	960
25	483	1139	1557	547	1523	343	299	35	210	1260
26	524	1385	1274	608	130	780	1162	1695	1375	1214

P = 1759

INDICES

	0	1	2	3	4	5	6	7	8	9
27	379	1150	1082	382	526	682	547	675	1743	1368
28	1709	1459	225	539	216	462	430	329	1454	50
29	479	1072	1549	878	1343	1509	903	61	408	256
30	1415	223	1679	164	1537	1005	422	868	1391	944
31	646	924	1163	1574	515	1049	41	1703	1681	161
32	732	442	1217	505	794	1124	362	1079	1110	895
33	1097	1181	79	243	927	691	366	1228	872	681
34	1458	328	877	255	1004	923	1702	504	894	690
35	327	503	414	415	166	592	602	1092	990	416
36	72	960	835	779	75	167	1420	983	240	450
37	1279	593	1061	820	1140	33	1676	603	1464	1012
38	155	1479	1609	1093	1147	9	807	344	765	991
39	1539	966	1036	567	847	417	1512	304	354	1547
40	1108	73	1106	770	1615	1170	1564	961	115	844
41	1486	1317	637	836	1338	455	856	776	1595	780
42	742	358	917	1016	1374	76	1007	332	135	1221
43	1380	168	487	220	1731	1270	772	1421	582	1186
44	790	376	1582	984	1694	978	1720	1199	59	241
45	448	1168	374	712	1666	451	570	369	1371	1213
46	616	1280	424	883	587	1437	564	594	196	18
47	294	1306	1617	1062	832	531	785	714	728	821
48	1523	1403	1178	250	472	1141	1585	12	1113	1153
49	1412	34	143	1313	279	130	754	1677	870	1138
50	1484	1718	1176	604	1157	233	298	1663	1172	1465
51	491	1252	840	1668	851	1013	37	1734	606	735
52	1232	156	1685	1033	260	1118	1713	1480	1205	124
53	1750	957	1240	1610	1393	511	799	23	1357	1094
54	863	202	1634	1626	1566	1148	866	253	1010	453
55	1166	10	1031	1502	1159	312	469	808	94	1504
56	435	173	185	345	709	750	1023	497	700	766
57	946	150	914	642	813	992	180	1243	534	1598
58	963	1540	1556	1432	275	572	1362	967	69	177
59	235	1638	1387	1037	545	1161	892	1145	740	568
60	141	1203	707	139	405	848	648	1543	263	597
61	1489	418	906	247	1352	519	117	1513	1428	551
62	1130	371	1408	305	1647	102	300	628	999	355
63	1533	314	525	1708	429	1548	407	1536	645	40
64	1216	1109	926	1457	1701	413	989	74	1278	1675
65	1608	764	846	1107	1563	636	1594	1373	1379	771
66	1581	58	1665	615	563	1616	727	471	1411	753
67	1175	1171	850	1231	1712	1239	1356	1565	1165	468
68	184	699	812	962	1361	1386	739	404	1488	116
69	1407	998	428	1215	988	845	1378	562	1174	1355
70	811	1487	987	810	898	1085	899	1318	650	723
71	1076	1623	1086	638	1576	1290	1474	1519	900	837
72	556	340	1444	211	1319	1339	1263	1400	559	618
73	651	456	146	1273	1467	445	724	857	934	96
74	5	1070	1077	777	1545	1268	1304	1661	1624	1596
75	517	762	402	209	1087	781	190	1323	1496	1089
76	639	743	205	475	335	1282	1577	359	1631	1493

POWER RESIDUES

	0	1	2	3	4	5	6	7	8	9
27	248	1488	133	798	1270	584	1745	1675	1255	494
28	1205	194	1164	1707	1447	1646	1081	1209	218	1308
29	812	1354	1088	1251	470	1061	1089	1257	506	1277
30	626	238	1428	1532	397	623	220	1320	884	27
31	162	972	555	1571	631	268	1608	853	1600	805
32	1312	836	1498	193	1158	1671	1231	350	341	287
33	1722	1537	427	803	1300	764	1066	1119	1437	1586
34	721	808	1330	944	387	563	1619	919	237	1422
35	1496	181	1086	1239	398	629	256	1536	421	767
36	1084	1227	326	197	1182	56	336	257	1542	457
37	983	621	208	1248	452	953	441	887	45	270
38	1620	925	273	1638	1033	921	249	1494	169	1014
39	807	1324	908	171	1026	879	1756	1741	1651	1111
40	1389	1298	752	994	687	604	106	636	298	29
41	174	1044	987	645	352	353	359	395	611	148
42	888	51	306	77	462	1013	801	1288	692	634
43	286	1716	1501	211	1266	560	1601	811	1348	1052
44	1035	933	321	167	1002	735	892	75	450	941
45	369	455	971	549	1535	415	731	868	1690	1345
46	1034	927	285	1710	1465	1754	1729	1579	679	556
47	1577	667	484	1145	1593	763	1060	1083	1221	290
48	1740	1645	1075	1173	2	12	72	432	833	1480
49	85	510	1301	770	1102	1335	974	567	1643	1063
50	1101	1329	938	351	347	323	179	1074	1167	1725
51	1555	535	1451	1670	1225	314	125	750	982	615
52	172	1032	915	213	1278	632	274	1644	1069	1137
53	1545	475	1091	1269	578	1709	1459	1718	1513	283
54	1698	1393	1322	896	99	594	46	276	1656	1141
55	1569	619	196	1176	20	120	720	802	1294	728
56	850	1582	697	664	466	1037	945	393	599	76
57	456	977	585	1751	1711	1471	31	186	1116	1419
58	1478	73	438	869	1696	1381	1250	464	1025	873
59	1720	1525	355	371	467	1043	981	609	136	816
60	1378	1232	356	377	503	1259	518	1349	1058	1071
61	1149	1617	907	165	990	663	460	1001	729	856
62	1618	913	201	1206	200	1200	164	984	627	244
63	1464	1748	1693	1363	1142	1575	655	412	713	760
64	1042	975	573	1679	1279	638	310	101	606	118
65	708	730	862	1654	1129	1497	187	1122	1455	1694
66	1369	1178	32	192	1152	1635	1015	813	1360	1124
67	1467	7	42	252	1512	277	1662	1177	26	156
68	936	339	275	1650	1105	1353	1082	1215	254	1524
69	349	335	251	1506	241	1446	1640	1045	993	681
70	568	1649	1099	1317	866	1678	1273	602	94	564
71	1625	955	453	959	477	1103	1341	1010	783	1180
72	44	264	1584	709	736	898	111	666	478	1109
73	1377	1226	320	161	966	519	1355	1094	1287	686
74	598	70	420	761	1048	1011	789	1216	260	1560
75	565	1631	991	669	496	1217	266	1596	781	1168
76	1731	1591	751	988	651	388	569	1655	1135	1533

P = 1759

INDICES

	0	1	2	3	4	5	6	7	8	9
77	493	1642	1291	918	828	1506	1249	1397	1475	1017
78	265	758	1450	718	1520	1375	1051	1190	1331	746
79	901	77	238	1613	788	783	838	1008	273	1128
80	1592	426	557	333	1590	319	1254	390	341	136
81	1654	437	290	667	1445	1222	599	911	1328	1657
82	212	1381	43	1559	1121	199	1320	169	64	1042
83	939	192	1340	488	1260	29	321	885	1264	221
84	1226	818	842	976	1401	1732	1500	175	100	56
85	560	1271	1491	317	816	1737	619	773	1705	53
86	106	1604	652	1422	971	804	704	1325	457	583
87	1754	1299	1256	589	147	1187	1066	1739	1670	395
88	1274	791	860	187	308	1026	1468	377	420	875
89	1462	1336	446	1583	1683	92	543	1531	725	985
90	932	826	1652	1498	858	1695	1196	612	392	1439
91	935	979	1054	621	853	522	97	1721	1697	347
92	1100	385	6	1200	908	381	1367	461	1071	60
93	163	943	1048	441	1078	242	680	922	502	1091
94	778	449	32	1478	343	566	1546	1169	1316	775
95	1015	1220	1269	375	1198	711	1212	1436	1305	713
96	249	1152	129	1717	1662	1667	734	1117	956	22
97	1625	452	311	172	496	641	1597	571	1637	1144
98	138	596	518	370	627	1707	39	412	763	1372
99	614	752	1238	698	403	1214	1354	1084	1622	1518
100	210	617	444	1069	1660	208	1088	1281	1641	1396
101	717	745	782	425	389	666	1656	198	191	884
102	975	55	1736	1603	1324	588	394	1025	1335	1530
103	1497	1438	521	384	460	440	1090	565	1219	1435
104	1716	21	640	595	411	697	1517	207	744	197
105	1602	1529	439	20	206	19	1689	108	608	1690
106	476	295	1441	499	1724	109	336	1307	119	528
107	995	609	1283	1618	507	482	83	1691	1578	1063
108	1347	286	686	477	360	833	352	1729	292	296
109	1632	532	1350	1606	737	1442	1494	786	937	702
110	1650	500	494	715	1515	684	228	1725	1643	729
111	796	399	953	110	1292	822	578	47	230	337
112	919	1524	657	1286	669	1308	829	1404	1193	654
113	1234	120	1507	1179	981	768	1184	529	1250	251
114	1430	549	634	996	1398	473	1126	27	1297	610
115	1476	1142	664	1527	1727	1284	1018	1586	324	1020
116	1447	1619	266	13	282	1424	158	508	759	1114
117	1056	948	88	483	1451	1154	553	677	661	84
118	719	1413	364	1059	113	1692	1521	35	1029	67
119	1645	1579	1376	144	1629	1588	1224	1064	1052	1314
120	625	973	1687	1348	1191	280	623	152	889	287
121	1332	131	1132	1745	269	687	747	755	1081	1742
122	215	478	902	1678	1390	514	731	361	78	871
123	1003	326	601	834	239	1139	154	806	1035	353
124	1614	1485	855	916	134	1730	789	1719	373	1370
125	586	293	784	1177	1112	278	1483	297	839	605
126	259	1749	798	1633	1009	1158	434	1022	913	533

POWER RESIDUES

	0	1	2	3	4	5	6	7	8	9
77	403	659	436	857	1624	949	417	743	940	363
78	419	755	1012	795	1252	476	1097	1305	794	1246
79	440	881	9	54	324	185	1110	1383	1262	536
80	1457	1706	1441	1610	865	1672	1237	386	557	1583
81	703	700	682	574	1685	1315	854	1606	841	1528
82	373	479	1115	1413	1442	1616	901	129	774	1126
83	1479	79	474	1085	1233	362	413	719	796	1258
84	512	1313	842	1534	409	695	652	394	605	112
85	672	514	1325	914	207	1242	416	737	904	147
86	882	15	90	540	1481	91	546	1517	307	83
87	498	1229	338	269	1614	889	57	342	293	1758
88	1753	1723	1543	463	1019	837	1504	229	1374	1208
89	212	1272	596	58	348	329	215	1290	704	706
90	718	790	1222	296	17	102	612	154	924	267
91	1602	817	1384	1268	572	1673	1243	422	773	1120
92	1443	1622	937	345	311	107	642	334	245	1470
93	25	150	900	123	738	910	183	1098	1311	830
94	1462	1736	1621	931	309	95	570	1661	1171	1749
95	1699	1399	1358	1112	1395	1334	968	531	1427	1526
96	361	407	683	580	1721	1531	391	587	4	24
97	144	864	1666	1201	170	1020	843	1540	445	911
98	189	1134	1527	367	443	899	117	702	694	646
99	358	389	575	1691	1351	1070	1143	1581	691	628
100	250	1500	205	1230	344	305	71	426	797	1264
101	548	1529	379	515	1331	950	423	779	1156	1659
102	1159	1677	1267	566	1637	1027	885	33	198	1188
103	92	552	1553	523	1379	1238	392	593	40	240
104	1440	1604	829	1456	1700	1405	1394	1328	932	315
105	131	786	1198	152	912	195	1170	1743	1663	1183
106	62	372	473	1079	1197	146	876	1738	1633	1003
107	741	928	291	1746	1681	1291	710	742	934	327
108	203	1218	272	1632	997	705	712	754	1006	759
109	1036	939	357	383	539	1475	55	330	221	1326
110	920	243	1458	1712	1477	67	402	653	400	641
111	328	209	1254	488	1169	1737	1627	967	525	1391
112	1310	824	1426	1520	325	191	1146	1599	799	1276
113	620	202	1212	236	1416	1460	1724	1549	499	1235
114	374	485	1151	1629	979	597	64	384	545	1511
115	271	1626	961	489	1175	14	84	504	1265	554
116	1565	595	52	312	113	678	550	1541	451	947
117	405	671	508	1289	698	670	502	1253	482	1133
118	1521	331	227	1362	1136	1539	439	875	1732	1597
119	787	1204	188	1128	1491	151	906	159	954	447
120	923	261	1566	601	88	528	1409	1418	1472	37
121	222	1332	956	459	995	693	640	322	173	1038
122	951	429	815	1372	1196	140	840	1522	337	263
123	1578	673	520	1361	1130	1503	223	1338	992	675
124	532	1433	1562	577	1703	1423	1502	217	1302	776
125	1138	1551	511	1307	806	1318	872	1714	1489	139
126	834	1486	121	726	838	1510	265	1590	745	952

P = 1759

INDICES

	0	1	2	3	4	5	6	7	8	9
127	274	234	891	706	262	1351	1129	299	524	644
128	1700	1607	1593	1664	1410	1711	183	738	427	1173
129	897	1075	1473	1443	558	1466	4	1303	401	1495
130	334	492	1248	1449	1330	787	1591	1253	289	1327
131	1120	938	320	841	99	815	105	703	1255	1669
132	307	1461	542	1651	391	852	1099	1366	1047	501
133	342	1014	1211	128	955	495	137	38	1237	1621
134	1659	716	1655	1735	1334	459	1715	1516	438	607
135	1723	994	82	685	291	736	1649	227	952	229
136	668	1233	1183	633	1296	1726	1446	157	87	660
137	112	1644	1223	1686	888	268	214	730	600	1034
138	133	585	1482	797	912	261	1699	182	1472	400
139	1329	1119	104	541	1046	954	1658	1714	81	951
140	1295	111	213	1481	1471	1045	1294	1293	1382	1206
141	1569	15	1383	823	44	125	1134	1756	1207	579
142	1560	1751	349	1245	1570	48	1122	958	302	218
143	16	231	200	1241	245	1673	1384	338	1321	1611
144	1040	802	824	920	170	1394	695	284	45	1525
145	65	512	1747	1301	126	658	1043	800	1102	536
146	1135	1287	940	24	630	464	1757	670	193	1358
147	929	575	1208	1309	1341	1095	1418	1104	580	830
148	489	864	1554	1426	1561	1405	1261	203	271	1258
149	1752	1194	30	1635	387	1600	350	655	322	1627
150	1001	432	1246	1235	886	1567	693	1552	1571	121
151	1265	1149	674	538	49	1508	222	867	1573	160
152	1123	1180	1227	254	689	591	959	982	819	1011
153	8	965	303	769	843	454	357	331	219	1185
154	977	1167	368	882	17	530	1402	11	1312	1137
155	232	1251	1733	1032	123	510	201	252	1501	1503
156	749	149	1242	1431	176	1160	1202	1542	246	550
157	101	313	1535	1456	1674	635	57	470	1230	467
158	1385	997	561	809	722	1289	339	1399	1272	95
159	1267	761	1322	474	1492	1505	757	1189	1612	1127
160	318	436	910	1558	1041	28	817	174	316	52
161	803	1298	1738	186	874	91	825	611	620	346
162	380	942	921	1477	774	710	1151	1116	171	1143
163	1706	751	1083	1068	1395	665	54	1024	383	1434
164	696	1528	107	498	527	481	285	1728	1605	701
165	683	398	46	1285	653	767	548	26	1526	1019
166	1423	947	676	1058	66	1587	972	151	1744	1741
167	513	325	805	915	1369	277	1748	1021	705	643
168	1710	1074	1302	1448	1326	814	1460	1365	127	1620
169	458	993	226	632	659	267	584	181	540	950
170	1044	14	1755	1244	217	1672	801	283	1300	535
171	463	574	1103	1425	1257	1599	431	1551	537	159
172	590	964	330	881	1136	509	148	1541	1455	466
173	1288	760	1188	1557	51	90	941	1115	1067	1433
174	480	397	25	1057	1740	276	1073	1364	631	949
175	1671	573	1550	880	465	89	396	1363	879	

POWER RESIDUES

	0	1	2	3	4	5	6	7	8	9
127	435	851	1588	733	880	3	18	108	648	370
128	461	1007	765	1072	1155	1653	1123	1461	1730	1585
129	715	772	1114	1407	1406	1400	1364	1148	1611	871
130	1708	1453	1682	1297	746	958	471	1067	1125	1473
131	43	258	1548	493	1199	158	948	411	707	724
132	826	1438	1592	757	1024	867	1684	1309	818	1390
133	1304	788	1210	224	1344	1028	891	69	414	725
134	832	1474	49	294	5	30	180	1080	1203	182
135	1092	1275	614	166	996	699	676	538	1469	19
136	114	684	586	1757	1747	1687	1327	926	279	1674
137	1249	458	989	657	424	785	1192	116	696	658
138	430	821	1408	1412	1436	1580	685	592	34	204
139	1224	308	89	534	1445	1634	1009	777	1144	1587
140	727	844	1546	481	1127	1485	115	690	622	214
141	1284	668	490	1181	50	300	41	246	1476	61
142	366	437	863	1660	1165	1713	1483	103	618	190
143	1140	1563	583	1739	1639	1039	957	465	1031	909
144	177	1062	1095	1293	722	814	1366	1160	1683	1303
145	782	1174	8	48	288	1728	1573	643	340	281
146	1686	1321	890	63	378	509	1295	734	886	39
147	234	1404	1388	1292	716	778	1150	1623	943	381
148	527	1403	1382	1256	500	1241	410	701	688	610
149	142	852	1594	769	1096	1299	758	1030	903	141
150	846	1558	553	1559	559	1595	775	1132	1515	295
151	11	66	396	617	184	1104	1347	1046	999	717
152	784	1186	80	480	1121	1449	1658	1153	1641	1051
153	1029	897	105	630	262	1572	637	304	65	390
154	581	1727	1567	607	124	744	946	399	635	292
155	1752	1717	1507	247	1482	97	582	1733	1603	823
156	1420	1484	109	654	406	677	544	1505	235	1410
157	1424	1508	253	1518	313	119	714	766	1078	1191
158	110	660	442	893	81	486	1157	1665	1195	134
159	804	1306	800	1282	656	418	749	976	579	1715
160	1495	175	1050	1023	861	1648	1093	1281	650	382
161	533	1439	1598	793	1240	404	665	472	1073	1161
162	1689	1339	998	711	748	970	543	1499	199	1194
163	128	768	1090	1263	542	1493	163	978	591	28
164	168	1008	771	1108	1371	1190	104	624	226	1356
165	1100	1323	902	135	810	1342	1016	819	1396	1340
166	1004	747	964	507	1283	662	454	965	513	1319
167	878	1750	1705	1435	1574	649	376	497	1223	302
168	53	318	149	894	87	522	1373	1202	176	1056
169	1059	1077	1185	74	444	905	153	918	231	1386
170	1280	644	346	317	143	858	1630	985	633	280
171	1680	1285	674	526	1397	1346	1040	963	501	1247
172	446	917	225	1350	1064	1107	1365	1154	1647	1087
173	1245	434	845	1552	517	1343	1022	855	1612	877
174	1744	1669	1219	278	1668	1213	242	1452	1676	1261
175	530	1421	1490	145	870	1702	1417	1466		

P = 1777

INDICES

	0	1	2	3	4	5	6	7	8	9
0		0	1176	1658	576	1	1058	1131	1752	1540
1	1177	1073	458	1714	531	1659	1152	738	940	853
2	577	1013	473	1518	1634	2	1114	1422	1707	283
3	1059	1330	552	955	138	1132	340	1630	253	1596
4	1753	1549	413	1646	1649	1541	918	1287	1034	486
5	1178	620	514	1640	822	1074	1107	735	1459	960
6	459	581	730	895	1728	1715	355	906	1314	1400
7	532	286	1516	1032	1030	1660	1429	428	996	235
8	1153	1304	949	13	1589	739	1046	165	1049	1081
9	941	1069	318	1212	687	854	434	1278	1662	837
10	578	609	20	1264	1690	1014	1040	1451	222	691
11	474	1512	507	178	135	1519	859	1478	360	93
12	1635	370	1757	1431	130	3	295	1245	1128	1528
13	1115	204	1531	208	306	1423	714	638	800	1121
14	1708	1169	1462	1011	916	284	432	368	430	615
15	1060	674	829	502	1604	1331	396	993	1411	1522
16	553	873	704	79	349	956	1189	1162	989	1652
17	139	617	446	998	1341	1133	449	842	481	537
18	341	1554	469	463	1494	1631	612	35	87	777
19	254	807	1610	1101	678	1597	1062	1700	237	767
20	1754	788	9	1414	1196	1550	664	1282	1090	150
21	414	217	440	168	851	1647	1398	685	91	914
22	1650	676	912	1155	1683	1542	1354	1620	1311	1098
23	919	310	259	189	878	1288	1536	117	1269	1447
24	1035	698	1546	1186	1157	487	831	791	1306	1671
25	1179	334	1471	815	645	621	528	1118	928	985
26	515	47	1380	597	931	1641	1384	963	1482	1685
27	823	504	114	951	38	1075	200	1349	521	1094
28	1108	899	569	65	862	736	411	904	316	1476
29	1460	1160	1608	683	1544	961	1606	719	15	1456
30	460	1001	74	491	229	582	1678	657	1004	1146
31	731	23	1572	1327	393	896	811	721	922	1356
32	1729	1333	273	1591	104	1716	1255	573	1525	642
33	356	868	589	1394	562	907	389	1205	1052	60
34	1315	627	17	1617	1622	1401	398	1300	741	1439
35	533	1360	1625	1345	242	287	1657	1751	1713	939
36	1517	1706	954	252	1645	1033	1639	1458	894	1313
37	1031	995	12	1048	1211	1661	1263	221	177	359
38	1430	1127	207	799	1010	429	501	1410	78	988
39	997	480	462	86	1100	236	1413	1089	167	90
40	1154	1310	188	1268	1185	1305	814	927	596	1481
41	950	520	64	315	682	14	490	1003	1326	921
42	1590	1524	1393	1051	1616	740	1344	1712	251	893
43	1047	176	798	77	85	166	1267	595	314	1325
44	1050	250	76	313	312	1082	555	497	1083	277
45	942	846	754	556	1020	1070	711	44	498	384
46	319	330	1486	1084	1435	1213	1365	493	278	261
47	688	875	936	943	1293	855	669	1404	847	545
48	435	1568	98	755	946	1279	586	41	557	1737
49	1663	1235	231	1021	191	838	706	1417	1071	338

POWER RESIDUES

	0	1	2	3	4	5	6	7	8	9
0	1	5	25	125	625	1348	1409	1714	1462	202
1	1010	1496	372	83	415	298	1490	342	1710	1442
2	102	510	773	311	1555	667	1558	682	1633	1057
3	1731	1547	627	1358	1459	187	935	1121	274	1370
4	1519	487	658	1513	457	508	763	261	1305	1194
5	639	1418	1759	1687	1327	1304	1189	614	1293	1134
6	339	1695	1367	1504	412	283	1415	1744	1612	952
7	1206	699	1718	1482	302	1510	442	433	388	163
8	815	521	828	586	1153	434	393	188	940	1146
9	399	218	1090	119	595	1198	659	1518	482	633
10	1388	1609	937	1131	324	1620	992	1406	1699	1387
11	1604	912	1006	1476	272	1360	1469	237	1185	594
12	1193	634	1393	1634	1062	1756	1672	1252	929	1091
13	124	620	1323	1284	1089	114	570	1073	34	170
14	850	696	1703	1407	1704	1412	1729	1537	577	1108
15	209	1045	1671	1247	904	966	1276	1049	1691	1347
16	1404	1689	1337	1354	1439	87	435	398	213	1065
17	1771	1747	1627	1027	1581	797	431	378	113	565
18	1048	1686	1322	1279	1064	1766	1722	1502	402	233
19	1165	494	693	1688	1332	1329	1314	1239	864	766
20	276	1380	1569	737	131	655	1498	382	133	665
21	1548	632	1383	1584	812	506	753	211	1055	1721
22	1497	377	108	540	923	1061	1751	1647	1127	304
23	1520	492	683	1638	1082	79	395	198	990	1396
24	1649	1137	354	1770	1742	1602	902	956	1226	799
25	441	428	363	38	190	950	1196	649	1468	232
26	1160	469	568	1063	1761	1697	1377	1554	662	1533
27	557	1008	1486	322	1610	942	1156	449	468	563
28	1038	1636	1072	29	145	725	71	355	1775	1767
29	1727	1527	527	858	736	126	630	1373	1534	562
30	1033	1611	947	1181	574	1093	134	670	1573	757
31	231	1155	444	443	438	413	288	1440	92	460
32	523	838	636	1403	1684	1312	1229	814	516	803
33	461	528	863	761	251	1255	944	1166	499	718
34	36	180	900	946	1176	549	968	1286	1099	164
35	820	546	953	1211	724	66	330	1650	1142	379
36	118	590	1173	534	893	911	1001	1451	147	735
37	121	605	1248	909	991	1401	1674	1262	979	1341
38	1374	1539	587	1158	459	518	813	511	778	336
39	1680	1292	1129	314	1570	742	156	780	346	1730
40	1542	602	1233	834	616	1303	1184	589	1168	509
41	768	286	1430	42	210	1050	1696	1372	1529	537
42	908	986	1376	1549	637	1408	1709	1437	77	385
43	148	740	146	730	96	480	623	1338	1359	1464
44	212	1060	1746	1622	1002	1456	172	860	746	176
45	880	846	676	1603	907	981	1351	1424	12	60
46	300	1500	392	183	915	1021	1551	647	1458	182
47	910	996	1426	22	110	550	973	1311	1224	789
48	391	178	890	896	926	1076	49	245	1225	794
49	416	303	1515	467	558	1013	1511	447	458	513

P = 1777

INDICES

	0	1	2	3	4	5	6	7	8	9
50	579	1044	1510	712	871	610	215	1534	45	409
51	21	387	1704	499	518	1265	328	584	385	880
52	1691	81	1223	320	780	1015	1773	292	331	1260
53	1041	724	784	1487	363	1452	882	419	1085	1559
54	223	834	1680	1436	1290	692	351	1720	1214	345
55	475	1136	1376	1366	749	1513	1697	270	494	1584
56	508	1693	299	279	1745	179	1241	659	262	1538
57	136	958	1587	689	304	1520	1492	148	876	983
58	860	1144	560	937	1008	1479	83	382	944	407
59	361	1582	1006	1294	119	94	1191	649	856	695
60	1636	1232	401	670	1250	371	1667	1767	1405	1296
61	1758	1225	1078	848	57	1432	404	1148	546	1271
62	131	1164	1199	436	972	4	727	32	1569	592
63	296	977	211	99	121	1246	322	424	756	50
64	1129	550	733	947	1449	1529	991	467	1280	257
65	1116	567	655	587	1749	205	925	796	42	96
66	1532	782	268	558	1765	209	794	25	1738	1037
67	307	1654	1565	1664	605	1424	452	763	1236	633
68	715	1502	27	232	1193	639	1017	980	1022	1578
69	801	1724	1574	192	700	1122	141	511	839	71
70	1709	1373	760	707	1025	1170	745	1740	1418	651
71	1463	1775	1057	1072	1151	1012	1113	1329	339	1548
72	917	619	1106	580	354	285	1428	1303	1045	1068
73	433	608	1039	1511	858	369	294	203	713	1168
74	431	673	395	872	1188	616	448	1553	611	806
75	1061	787	663	216	1397	675	1353	309	1535	697
76	830	333	527	46	1383	503	199	898	410	1159
77	1605	1000	1677	22	810	1332	1254	867	388	626
78	397	1359	1656	1705	1638	994	1262	1126	500	479
79	1412	1309	813	519	489	1523	1343	175	1266	249
80	554	845	710	329	1364	874	668	1567	585	1234
81	705	1043	214	386	327	80	1772	723	881	833
82	350	1135	1696	1692	1240	957	1491	1143	82	1581
83	1190	1231	1666	1224	403	1163	726	976	321	549
84	990	566	924	781	793	1653	451	1501	1016	1723
85	140	1372	744	1774	1112	618	1427	607	293	672
86	447	786	1352	332	198	999	1253	1358	1261	1308
87	1342	844	667	1042	1771	1134	1490	1230	725	565
88	450	1371	1426	785	1252	843	1489	1370	1488	600
89	482	601	1731	364	1673	538	483	1338	1453	1613
90	342	602	246	883	154	1555	1732	454	420	373
91	470	365	111	1086	1220	464	1674	1335	1560	1181
92	1495	539	1506	224	886	1632	484	1028	835	128
93	613	1339	765	1681	1669	36	1454	102	1437	1209
94	88	1614	275	1291	336	778	343	302	693	970
95	255	603	69	352	804	808	247	1238	1721	1769
96	1611	884	968	1215	1274	1102	155	1593	346	1473
97	679	1556	1762	476	1217	1598	1733	1442	1137	378
98	1063	455	635	1377	1407	1701	421	524	1367	1388
99	238	374	106	750	817	768	471	1285	1514	1276

POWER RESIDUES

	0	1	2	3	4	5	6	7	8	9
50	788	386	153	765	271	1355	1444	112	560	1023
51	1561	697	1708	1432	52	260	1300	1169	514	793
52	411	278	1390	1619	987	1381	1574	762	256	1280
53	1069	14	70	350	1750	1642	1102	179	895	921
54	1051	1701	1397	1654	1162	479	618	1313	1234	839
55	641	1428	32	160	800	446	453	488	663	1538
56	582	1133	334	1670	1242	879	841	651	1478	282
57	1410	1719	1487	327	1635	1067	4	20	100	500
58	723	61	305	1525	517	808	486	653	1488	332
59	1660	1192	629	1368	1509	437	408	263	1315	1244
60	889	891	901	951	1201	674	1593	857	731	101
61	505	748	186	930	1096	149	745	171	855	721
62	51	255	1275	1044	1666	1222	779	341	1705	1417
63	1754	1662	1202	679	1618	982	1356	1449	137	685
64	1648	1132	329	1645	1117	254	1270	1019	1541	597
65	1208	709	1768	1732	1552	652	1483	307	1535	567
66	1058	1736	1572	752	206	1030	1596	872	806	476
67	603	1238	859	741	151	755	221	1105	194	970
68	1296	1149	414	293	1465	217	1085	94	470	573
69	1088	109	545	948	1186	599	1218	759	241	1205
70	694	1693	1357	1454	162	810	496	703	1738	1582
71	802	456	503	738	136	680	1623	1007	1481	297
72	1485	317	1585	817	531	878	836	626	1353	1434
73	62	310	1550	642	1433	57	285	1425	17	85
74	425	348	1740	1592	852	706	1753	1657	1177	554
75	993	1411	1724	1512	452	483	638	1413	1734	1562
76	702	1733	1557	677	1608	932	1106	199	995	1421
77	1774	1762	1702	1402	1679	1287	1104	189	945	1171
78	524	843	661	1528	532	883	861	751	201	1005
79	1471	247	1235	844	666	1553	657	1508	432	383
80	138	690	1673	1257	954	1216	749	191	955	1221
81	774	316	1580	792	406	253	1265	994	1416	1749
82	1637	1077	54	270	1350	1419	1764	1712	1452	152
83	760	246	1230	819	541	928	1086	99	495	698
84	1713	1457	177	885	871	801	451	478	613	1288
85	1109	214	1070	19	95	475	598	1213	734	116
86	580	1123	284	1420	1769	1737	1577	777	331	1655
87	1167	504	743	161	805	471	578	1113	234	1170
88	519	818	536	903	961	1251	924	1066	1776	1772
89	1752	1652	1152	429	368	63	315	1575	767	281
90	1405	1694	1362	1479	287	1435	67	335	1675	1267
91	1004	1466	222	1110	219	1095	144	720	46	230
92	1150	419	318	1590	842	656	1503	407	258	1290
93	1119	264	1320	1269	1014	1516	472	583	1138	359
94	18	90	450	473	588	1163	484	643	1438	82
95	410	273	1365	1494	362	33	165	825	571	1078
96	59	295	1475	267	1335	1344	1389	1614	962	1256
97	949	1191	624	1343	1384	1589	837	631	1378	1559
98	687	1658	1182	579	1118	259	1295	1144	389	168
99	840	646	1453	157	785	371	78	390	173	865

P = 1777

INDICES

	0	1	2	3	4	5	6	7	8	9
100	1755	366	444	1698	910	789	112	717	271	1298
101	10	1087	1391	495	934	1415	1221	1718	1585	647
102	1197	465	1563	509	1104	1551	1675	173	1694	1499
103	665	1336	1504	300	1760	1283	1561	1319	280	1601
104	1091	1182	1257	1746	623	151	1496	1321	180	157
105	415	540	1173	1242	1468	218	1507	29	660	1227
106	441	225	124	263	184	169	887	575	1539	530
107	852	1633	282	137	1595	1648	485	821	959	1727
108	1399	1029	234	1588	1080	686	836	1689	690	134
109	92	129	1527	305	1120	915	614	1603	1521	348
110	1651	1340	536	1493	776	677	766	1195	149	850
111	913	1682	1097	877	1446	1156	1670	644	984	930
112	1684	37	1093	861	1475	1543	1455	228	1145	392
113	1355	103	641	561	59	1621	1438	241	938	1644
114	1312	1210	358	1009	987	1099	89	1184	1480	681
115	920	1615	892	84	1324	311	276	1019	383	1434
116	260	1292	544	945	1736	190	337	870	408	517
117	879	779	1259	362	1558	1289	344	748	1583	1744
118	1537	303	982	1007	406	118	694	1249	1295	56
119	1270	971	591	120	49	1448	256	1748	95	1764
120	1036	604	632	1192	1577	699	70	1024	650	1150
121	1547	353	1067	857	1167	1187	805	1396	696	1382
122	1158	809	625	1637	478	488	248	1363	1233	326
123	832	1239	1580	402	548	792	1722	1111	671	197
124	1307	1770	564	1251	599	1672	1612	153	372	1219
125	1180	885	127	1668	1208	335	969	803	1768	1273
126	1472	1216	377	1406	1387	816	1275	909	1297	933
127	646	1103	1498	1759	1600	622	156	1467	1226	183
128	529	1594	1726	1079	133	1119	347	775	849	1445
129	929	1474	391	58	1643	986	680	1323	1433	1735
130	516	1557	1743	405	55	48	1763	1576	1149	1166
131	1381	477	325	547	196	598	1218	1207	1272	1386
132	932	1599	182	132	1444	1642	1734	54	1165	195
133	1385	1443	194	1200	1201	964	1138	162	437	1202
134	1483	379	1054	973	965	1686	1064	159	5	1139
135	824	456	1628	728	163	505	636	702	33	438
136	115	1378	902	1570	1203	952	1408	62	593	1484
137	39	1702	417	297	380	1076	422	266	978	1055
138	201	525	1124	212	974	1350	1368	109	100	966
139	522	1389	1317	122	1687	1095	239	542	1247	1065
140	1109	375	773	323	160	900	107	143	425	6
141	570	751	145	757	1140	66	818	629	51	825
142	863	769	1175	1130	457	737	472	1421	551	1629
143	412	1286	513	734	729	905	1515	427	948	164
144	317	1277	19	1450	506	1477	1756	1244	1530	637
145	1461	367	828	992	703	1161	445	841	468	34
146	1609	1699	8	1281	439	684	911	1619	258	116
147	1545	790	1470	1117	1379	962	113	1348	568	903
148	1607	718	73	656	1571	720	272	572	588	1204
149	16	1299	1624	1750	953	1457	11	220	206	1409

POWER RESIDUES

	0	1	2	3	4	5	6	7	8	9
100	771	301	1505	417	308	1540	592	1183	584	1143
101	384	143	715	21	105	525	848	686	1653	1157
102	454	493	688	1663	1207	704	1743	1607	927	1081
103	74	370	73	365	48	240	1200	669	1568	732
104	106	530	873	811	501	728	86	430	373	88
105	440	423	338	1690	1342	1379	1564	712	6	30
106	150	750	196	980	1346	1399	1664	1212	729	91
107	455	498	713	11	55	275	1375	1544	612	1283
108	1084	89	445	448	463	538	913	1011	1501	397
109	208	1040	1646	1122	279	1395	1644	1112	229	1145
110	394	193	965	1271	1024	1566	722	56	280	1400
111	1669	1237	854	716	26	130	650	1473	257	1285
112	1094	139	695	1698	1382	1579	787	381	128	640
113	1423	7	35	175	875	821	551	978	1336	1349
114	1414	1739	1587	827	581	1128	309	1545	617	1308
115	1209	714	16	80	400	223	1115	244	1220	769
116	291	1455	167	835	621	1328	1309	1214	739	141
117	705	1748	1632	1052	1706	1422	2	10	50	250
118	1250	919	1041	1651	1147	404	243	1215	744	166
119	830	596	1203	684	1643	1107	204	1020	1546	622
120	1333	1334	1339	1364	1489	337	1685	1317	1254	939
121	1141	374	93	465	548	963	1261	974	1316	1249
122	914	1016	1526	522	833	611	1278	1059	1741	1597
123	877	831	601	1228	809	491	678	1613	957	1231
124	824	566	1053	1711	1447	127	635	1398	1659	1187
125	604	1243	884	866	776	326	1630	1042	1656	1172
126	529	868	786	376	103	515	798	436	403	238
127	1190	619	1318	1259	964	1266	999	1441	97	485
128	648	1463	207	1035	1621	997	1431	47	235	1175
129	544	943	1161	474	593	1188	609	1268	1009	1491
130	347	1735	1567	727	81	405	248	1240	869	791
131	401	228	1140	369	68	340	1700	1392	1629	1037
132	1631	1047	1681	1297	1154	439	418	313	1565	717
133	31	155	775	321	1605	917	1031	1601	897	931
134	1101	174	870	796	426	353	1765	1717	1477	277
135	1385	1594	862	756	226	1130	319	1595	867	781
136	351	1755	1667	1227	804	466	553	988	1386	1599
137	887	881	851	701	1728	1532	552	983	1361	1474
138	262	1310	1219	764	266	1330	1319	1264	989	1391
139	1624	1012	1506	422	333	1665	1217	754	216	1080
140	69	345	1725	1517	477	608	1263	984	1366	1499
141	387	158	790	396	203	1015	1521	497	708	1763
142	1707	1427	27	135	675	1598	882	856	726	76
143	380	123	615	1298	1159	464	543	938	1136	349
144	1745	1617	977	1331	1324	1289	1114	239	1195	644
145	1443	107	535	898	936	1126	299	1495	367	58
146	290	1450	142	710	1773	1757	1677	1277	1054	1716
147	1472	252	1260	969	1291	1124	289	1445	117	585
148	1148	409	268	1340	1369	1514	462	533	888	886
149	876	826	576	1103	184	920	1046	1676	1272	1029

P = 1777

INDICES

	0	1	2	3	4	5	6	7	8	9
150	461	1088	187	926	63	1002	1392	1711	797	594
151	75	496	753	43	1485	492	935	1403	97	40
152	230	1416	1509	1533	1703	583	1222	291	783	418
153	1679	1719	1375	269	298	658	1586	147	559	381
154	1005	648	400	1766	1077	1147	1198	31	210	423
155	732	466	654	795	267	24	1564	762	26	979
156	1573	510	759	1739	1056	1328	1105	1302	1038	202
157	394	1552	662	308	526	897	1676	866	1655	1125
158	812	174	709	1566	213	722	1695	1142	1665	975
159	923	1500	743	606	1351	1357	666	1229	1425	1369
160	1730	1337	245	453	110	1334	1505	1027	764	101
161	274	301	68	1237	967	1592	1761	1441	634	523
162	105	1284	443	716	1390	1717	1562	172	1503	1318
163	1256	1320	1172	28	123	574	281	820	233	1688
164	1526	1602	535	1194	1096	643	1092	227	640	240
165	357	1183	891	1018	543	869	1258	747	981	1248
166	590	1747	631	1023	1066	1395	624	1362	1579	1110
167	563	152	126	802	376	908	1497	1466	1725	774
168	390	1322	1742	1575	324	1206	181	53	193	161
169	1053	158	1627	701	901	61	416	265	1123	108
170	1316	541	772	142	144	628	1174	1420	512	426
171	18	1243	827	840	7	1618	1469	1347	72	571
172	1623	219	186	1710	752	1402	1508	290	1374	146
173	399	30	653	761	758	1301	661	865	708	1141
174	742	1228	244	1026	67	1440	442	171	1171	819
175	534	226	890	746	630	1361	125	1465	1741	52
176	1626	264	771	1419	826	1346	185	289	652	864
177	243	170	889	1464	770	288	888			

POWER RESIDUES

	0	1	2	3	4	5	6	7	8	9
150	1591	847	681	1628	1032	1606	922	1056	1726	1522
151	502	733	111	555	998	1436	72	360	23	115
152	575	1098	159	795	421	328	1640	1092	129	645
153	1448	132	660	1523	507	758	236	1180	569	1068
154	9	45	225	1125	294	1470	242	1210	719	41
155	205	1025	1571	747	181	905	971	1301	1174	539
156	918	1036	1626	1022	1556	672	1583	807	481	628
157	1363	1484	312	1560	692	1683	1307	1204	689	1668
158	1232	829	591	1178	559	1018	1536	572	1083	84
159	420	323	1615	967	1281	1074	39	195	975	1321
160	1274	1039	1641	1097	154	770	296	1480	292	1460
161	192	960	1246	899	941	1151	424	343	1715	1467
162	227	1135	344	1720	1492	352	1760	1692	1352	1429
163	37	185	925	1071	24	120	600	1223	784	366
164	53	265	1325	1294	1139	364	43	215	1075	44
165	220	1100	169	845	671	1578	782	356	3	15
166	75	375	98	490	673	1588	832	606	1253	934
167	1116	249	1245	894	916	1026	1576	772	306	1530
168	542	933	1111	224	1120	269	1345	1394	1639	1087
169	104	520	823	561	1028	1586	822	556	1003	1461
170	197	985	1371	1524	512	783	361	28	140	700
171	1723	1507	427	358	13	65	325	1625	1017	1531
172	547	958	1236	849	691	1678	1282	1079	64	320
173	1600	892	906	976	1326	1299	1164	489	668	1563
174	707	1758	1682	1302	1179	564	1043	1661	1197	654
175	1493	357	8	40	200	1000	1446	122	610	1273
176	1034	1616	972	1306	1199	664	1543	607	1258	959
177	1241	874	816	526	853	711				

P = 1783

INDICES

	0	1	2	3	4	5	6	7	8	9
0		0	848	813	1696	935	1661	188	762	1626
1	1	355	727	1183	1036	1748	1610	694	692	1025
2	849	1001	1203	1075	1575	88	249	657	102	237
3	814	663	676	1168	1542	1123	1540	438	91	214
4	1697	732	67	1008	269	779	141	722	641	376
5	936	1507	1097	1265	1505	1290	950	56	1085	1260
6	1662	1690	1511	32	1524	336	234	1374	608	106
7	189	1565	606	1761	1286	901	939	543	1062	467
8	763	1470	1580	1587	915	1629	74	1050	1117	855
9	1627	1371	989	1476	1570	178	1489	637	1224	199
10	2	431	573	873	163	154	331	846	571	1277
11	356	1251	16	260	904	228	151	1027	326	882
12	728	710	756	1545	577	1023	880	790	590	39
13	1184	471	1082	1213	440	1592	1456	556	954	392
14	1037	1535	631	1538	1454	1172	827	1189	352	208
15	1749	1292	5	538	1391	1598	128	1486	1315	296
16	1611	1263	536	1428	646	321	653	1150	1763	584
17	695	869	922	373	116	276	183	291	1703	187
18	693	656	437	721	55	1373	542	1049	636	845
19	1026	789	555	1188	1485	1149	290	1048	1047	918
20	850	405	1279	425	1421	1667	1721	919	1011	1380
21	1002	307	1179	596	1694	161	1419	851	343	792
22	1204	95	317	1020	864	1714	1108	406	1752	1396
23	1076	1356	999	708	93	1657	1174	1280	1730	1059
24	1576	410	1558	501	1604	1311	611	426	1425	618
25	89	952	1728	1430	1638	660	1438	1422	887	626
26	250	81	1319	897	148	418	279	1668	1288	1596
27	658	716	522	402	1404	443	20	1722	1240	507
28	103	1649	601	859	1479	991	604	920	520	1388
29	238	1450	1675	1100	255	413	1200	1012	1056	476
30	815	1196	358	1244	853	843	1386	1381	457	1686
31	664	1708	976	299	552	967	381	1003	1144	592
32	677	1659	329	1719	1384	1271	494	308	1494	910
33	1169	546	1501	282	216	527	829	1180	1432	1073
34	1543	1018	1717	564	1770	1041	1221	597	964	47
35	1124	58	1031	648	1139	718	769	1695	1035	1574
36	1541	268	1504	1523	1285	914	1569	162	903	576
37	439	1453	1390	645	115	54	1484	1420	1693	863
38	92	1603	1637	147	1403	1478	254	852	551	1383
39	215	1769	1138	1284	114	1402	113	344	1766	244
40	1698	1164	1253	64	345	623	1273	793	487	384
41	733	1369	787	1448	1767	740	77	1205	446	41
42	68	1176	1155	566	245	782	1444	96	760	569
43	1009	455	485	702	1699	203	1191	318	1640	1634
44	270	220	943	1332	1165	8	86	1021	1712	1269
45	780	1087	174	323	1254	524	818	865	462	1351
46	142	1776	422	192	65	629	1556	1715	941	1562
47	723	517	240	1363	346	1113	796	1109	125	1299
48	642	1621	1258	294	624	1572	1349	407	670	459
49	377	742	1459	931	1274	1134	491	1753	1466	682

POWER RESIDUES

	0	1	2	3	4	5	6	7	8	9
0	1	10	100	1000	1085	152	1520	936	445	884
1	1708	1033	1415	1669	643	1081	112	1120	502	1454
2	276	977	855	1418	1699	943	515	1584	1576	1496
3	696	1611	63	630	951	595	601	661	1261	129
4	1290	419	624	891	1778	1733	1283	349	1707	1023
5	1315	669	1341	929	375	184	57	570	351	1727
6	1223	1532	1056	1645	403	464	1074	42	420	634
7	991	995	1035	1435	86	860	1468	416	594	591
8	561	261	827	1138	682	1471	446	894	25	250
9	717	38	380	234	557	221	427	704	1691	863
10	1498	716	28	280	1017	1255	69	690	1551	1246
11	1762	1573	1466	396	394	374	174	1740	1353	1049
12	1575	1486	596	611	761	478	1214	1442	156	1560
13	1336	879	1658	533	1764	1593	1666	613	781	678
14	1431	46	460	1034	1425	1769	1643	383	264	857
15	1438	116	1160	902	105	1050	1585	1586	1596	1696
16	913	215	367	104	1040	1485	586	511	1544	1176
17	1062	1705	1003	1115	452	954	625	901	95	950
18	585	501	1444	176	1760	1553	1266	179	7	70
19	700	1651	463	1064	1725	1203	1332	839	1258	99
20	990	985	935	435	784	708	1731	1263	149	1490
21	636	1011	1195	1252	39	390	334	1557	1306	579
22	441	844	1308	599	641	1061	1695	903	115	1150
23	802	888	1748	1433	66	660	1251	29	290	1117
24	472	1154	842	1288	399	424	674	1391	1429	26
25	260	817	1038	1465	386	294	1157	872	1588	1616
26	113	1130	602	671	1361	1129	592	571	361	44
27	440	834	1208	1382	1339	909	175	1750	1453	266
28	877	1638	333	1547	1206	1362	1139	692	1571	1446
29	196	177	1770	1653	483	1264	159	1590	1636	313
30	1347	989	975	835	1218	1482	556	211	327	1487
31	606	711	1761	1563	1366	1179	1092	222	437	804
32	908	165	1650	453	964	725	118	1180	1102	322
33	1437	106	1060	1685	803	898	65	650	1151	812
34	988	965	735	218	397	404	474	1174	1042	1505
35	786	728	148	1480	536	11	110	1100	302	1237
36	1672	673	1381	1329	809	958	665	1301	529	1724
37	1193	1232	1622	173	1730	1253	49	490	1334	859
38	1458	316	1377	1289	409	524	1674	693	1581	1546
39	1196	1262	139	1390	1419	1709	1043	1515	886	1728
40	1233	1632	273	947	555	201	227	487	1304	559
41	241	627	921	295	1167	972	805	918	265	867
42	1538	1116	462	1054	1625	203	247	687	1521	946
43	545	101	1010	1185	1152	822	1088	182	37	370
44	134	1340	919	275	967	755	418	614	791	778
45	648	1131	612	771	578	431	744	308	1297	489
46	1324	759	458	1014	1225	1552	1256	79	790	768
47	548	131	1310	619	841	1278	299	1207	1372	1239
48	1692	873	1598	1716	1113	432	754	408	514	1574
49	1476	496	1394	1459	326	1477	506	1494	676	1411

P = 1783

INDICES

	0	1	2	3	4	5	6	7	8	9
50	937	181	18	1482	794	1366	496	1397	704	1516
51	1508	167	504	1682	488	26	1735	1077	1474	1186
52	1098	1282	929	1772	385	1089	1745	1357	996	368
53	1266	1104	1127	133	734	1781	354	1000	662	731
54	1506	1689	1564	1469	1370	430	1250	709	470	1534
55	1291	1262	868	655	788	404	306	94	1355	409
56	951	80	715	1648	1449	1195	1707	1658	545	1017
57	57	267	1452	1602	1768	1163	1368	1175	454	219
58	1086	1775	516	1620	741	180	166	1281	1103	1688
59	1261	79	266	1774	78	35	122	1731	1324	223
60	1663	36	262	1218	1206	1645	310	1060	1701	1238
61	1691	123	452	137	447	698	1305	1577	752	473
62	1512	1732	774	1043	42	176	1147	411	1400	1132
63	33	1325	1229	1120	69	1725	210	1559	1440	1409
64	1525	224	725	14	1177	974	785	502	450	1615
65	337	1664	1342	1152	1156	1406	560	1605	1758	672
66	235	37	1394	908	567	366	1130	1312	1064	51
67	1375	263	1677	361	246	745	498	612	139	825
68	609	1219	84	1248	783	1491	1412	427	836	666
69	107	1207	287	387	1445	1327	30	1426	895	1521
70	190	1646	906	1463	97	688	1496	619	205	957
71	1566	311	1617	1738	761	691	101	90	640	1084
72	607	1061	1116	1223	570	325	589	953	351	1314
73	1762	1702	635	1046	1010	342	1751	1729	1424	886
74	1287	1239	519	1055	456	1143	1493	1431	963	1034
75	902	1692	550	1765	486	445	759	1639	1711	461
76	940	124	669	1465	703	1473	995	661	469	1354
77	544	453	1102	1323	1700	751	1399	1439	449	1757
78	1063	138	835	894	204	639	350	1423	962	1710
79	468	448	961	1091	1192	1231	832	888	1092	1416
80	764	699	230	334	319	416	912	627	1193	364
81	1471	1306	339	1529	1641	581	1335	251	1232	1215
82	1581	1578	435	599	1635	1256	514	82	833	1066
83	1588	753	925	1070	271	303	1294	1320	889	197
84	916	474	242	680	221	1519	1414	898	1093	1672
85	1630	1513	510	586	944	22	1608	149	1417	379
86	75	1733	1303	99	1333	1308	1550	419	765	822
87	1051	775	257	481	1166	1211	706	280	700	131
88	1118	1044	1068	737	9	1226	398	1669	231	978
89	856	43	934	1747	87	1122	778	1289	335	900
90	1628	177	153	227	1022	1591	1171	1597	320	275
91	1372	1148	1666	160	1713	1656	1310	659	417	442
92	990	412	842	966	1270	526	1040	717	913	53
93	1477	1401	622	739	781	202	7	523	628	1112
94	1571	1133	1365	25	1088	1780	429	403	1194	1162
95	179	34	1644	697	175	1724	973	1405	365	744
96	1490	1326	687	690	324	341	1142	444	1472	750
97	638	1230	415	580	1255	302	1518	21	1307	1210
98	1225	1121	1590	1655	525	201	1779	1723	340	301
99	200	70	1339	1359	819	71	532	1241	1530	1095

POWER RESIDUES

	0	1	2	3	4	5	6	7	8	9
50	1629	243	647	1121	512	1554	1276	279	1007	1155
51	852	1388	1399	1509	826	1128	582	471	1144	742
52	288	1097	272	937	455	984	925	335	1567	1406
53	1579	1526	996	1045	1535	1086	162	1620	153	1530
54	1036	1445	186	77	770	568	331	1527	1006	1145
55	752	388	314	1357	1089	192	137	1370	1219	1492
56	656	1211	1412	1639	343	1647	423	664	1291	429
57	724	108	1080	102	1020	1285	369	124	1240	1702
58	973	815	1018	1265	169	1690	853	1398	1499	726
59	128	1280	319	1407	1589	1626	213	347	1687	823
60	1098	282	1037	1455	286	1077	72	720	68	680
61	1451	246	677	1421	1729	1243	1732	1273	249	707
62	1721	1163	932	405	484	1274	259	807	938	465
63	1084	142	1420	1719	1143	732	188	97	970	785
64	718	48	480	1234	1642	373	164	1640	353	1747
65	1423	1749	1443	166	1660	553	181	27	270	917
66	255	767	538	31	310	1317	689	1541	1146	762
67	488	1314	659	1241	1712	1073	32	320	1417	1689
68	843	1298	499	1424	1759	1543	1166	962	705	1701
69	963	715	18	180	17	170	1700	953	615	801
70	878	1648	433	764	508	1514	876	1628	233	547
71	121	1210	1402	1539	1126	562	271	927	355	1767
72	1623	183	47	470	1134	642	1071	12	120	1200
73	1302	539	41	410	534	1774	1693	883	1698	933
74	415	584	491	1344	959	675	1401	1529	1026	1345
75	969	775	618	831	1178	1082	122	1220	1502	756
76	428	714	8	80	800	868	1548	1216	1462	356
77	1777	1723	1183	1132	622	871	1578	1516	896	45
78	450	934	425	684	1491	646	1111	412	554	191
79	127	1270	219	407	504	1474	476	1194	1242	1722
80	1173	1032	1405	1569	1426	1779	1743	1383	1349	1009
81	1175	1052	1605	3	30	300	1217	1472	456	994
82	1025	1335	869	1558	1316	679	1441	146	1460	336
83	1577	1506	796	828	1148	782	688	1531	1046	1545
84	1186	1162	922	305	1267	189	107	1070	2	20
85	200	217	387	304	1257	89	890	1768	1633	283
86	1047	1555	1286	379	224	457	1004	1125	552	171
87	1710	1053	1615	103	1030	1385	1369	1209	1392	1439
88	126	1260	119	1190	1202	1322	739	258	797	838
89	1248	1782	1773	1683	783	698	1631	263	847	1338
90	899	75	750	368	114	1140	702	1671	663	1281
91	329	1507	806	928	365	84	840	1268	199	207
92	287	1087	172	1720	1153	832	1188	1182	1122	522
93	1654	493	1364	1159	892	5	50	500	1434	76
94	760	468	1114	442	854	1408	1599	1726	1213	1432
95	56	560	251	727	138	1380	1319	709	1741	1363
96	1149	792	788	748	348	1697	923	315	1367	1189
97	1192	1222	1522	956	645	1101	312	1337	889	1758
98	1533	1066	1745	1403	1549	1226	1562	1356	1079	92
99	920	285	1067	1755	1503	766	528	1714	1093	232

P = 1783

INDICES

	0	1	2	3	4	5	6	7	8	9
100	3	1726	1029	172	866	1340	548	508	1642	809
101	432	211	1344	1435	463	1360	1552	104	582	1594
102	574	1560	1015	49	1352	820	748	1650	1336	1377
103	874	1441	801	11	143	72	540	602	252	1347
104	164	1410	348	396	1777	533	838	860	1233	119
105	155	1526	811	871	423	1242	62	1480	1216	1461
106	332	225	170	1498	193	1531	981	992	1582	1652
107	847	726	1202	675	66	1096	1510	605	1579	988
108	572	15	755	1081	630	4	535	921	436	554
109	1278	1178	316	998	1557	1727	1318	521	600	1674
110	357	975	328	1500	1716	1030	1503	1389	1636	1137
111	1252	786	1154	484	942	173	421	239	1257	1458
112	17	503	928	1126	1563	867	714	1451	515	265
113	261	451	773	1228	724	1341	1393	1676	83	286
114	905	1616	1115	634	518	549	668	1101	834	960
115	229	338	434	924	241	509	1302	256	1067	933
116	152	1665	841	621	1364	1643	686	414	1589	1338
117	1028	1343	1014	800	347	810	169	1201	754	315
118	327	1153	927	772	1114	433	840	1013	926	969
119	883	1157	970	370	797	212	390	1057	1071	1632
120	729	1407	884	195	1110	1345	284	477	272	877
121	711	561	1158	948	126	1436	767	816	304	558
122	757	1606	971	60	1300	464	985	1197	1295	1679
123	1546	1759	371	400	643	1361	1600	359	1321	479
124	578	673	798	615	1622	1553	109	1245	890	1625
125	1024	236	213	375	1259	105	466	854	198	1276
126	881	38	391	207	295	583	186	844	917	1379
127	791	1395	1058	617	625	1595	506	1387	475	1685
128	591	909	1072	46	1573	575	862	1382	243	383
129	40	568	1633	1268	1350	1561	1298	458	681	1515
130	1185	367	730	1533	408	1016	218	1687	222	1237
131	472	1131	1408	1614	671	50	824	665	1520	956
132	1083	1313	885	1033	460	1353	1756	1709	1415	363
133	1214	1065	196	1671	378	821	130	977	899	274
134	441	52	1111	1161	743	749	1209	300	1094	808
135	1593	1376	1346	118	1460	1651	987	553	1673	1136
136	1457	264	285	959	932	1337	314	968	1631	876
137	557	1678	478	1624	1275	1378	1684	382	1514	1236
138	955	362	273	807	1135	875	1235	1004	511	1005
139	393	247	878	1106	492	1442	1743	1145	587	512
140	1038	746	712	983	1754	802	529	593	945	1006
141	1536	499	562	1330	1467	12	1053	678	23	394
142	632	613	1159	650	683	144	804	1660	1609	248
143	1539	140	949	233	938	73	1488	330	150	879
144	1455	826	127	652	182	541	289	1720	1418	1107
145	1173	610	1437	278	19	603	1199	1385	380	493
146	828	1220	768	1568	1483	253	112	1272	76	1443
147	1190	85	817	1555	795	1348	490	495	1734	1744
148	353	1249	305	1706	1367	165	121	309	1304	1146
149	209	784	559	1129	497	1411	29	1495	100	588

POWER RESIDUES

	0	1	2	3	4	5	6	7	8	9
100	537	21	210	317	1387	1389	1409	1609	43	430
101	734	208	297	1187	1172	1022	1305	569	341	1627
102	223	447	904	125	1250	19	190	117	1170	1002
103	1105	352	1737	1323	749	358	14	140	1400	1519
104	926	345	1667	623	881	1678	733	198	197	187
105	87	870	1568	1416	1679	743	298	1197	1272	239
106	607	721	78	780	668	1331	829	1158	882	1688
107	833	1198	1282	339	1607	23	230	517	1604	1776
108	1713	1083	132	1320	719	58	580	451	944	525
109	1684	793	798	848	1348	999	1075	52	520	1634
110	293	1147	772	588	531	1744	1393	1449	226	477
111	1204	1342	939	475	1184	1142	722	88	880	1668
112	633	981	895	35	350	1717	1123	532	1754	1493
113	666	1311	629	941	495	1384	1359	1109	392	354
114	1757	1523	966	745	318	1397	1489	626	911	195
115	167	1670	653	1181	1112	422	654	1191	1212	1422
116	1739	1343	949	575	401	444	874	1608	33	330
117	1517	906	145	1450	236	577	421	644	1091	212
118	337	1587	1606	13	130	1300	519	1624	193	147
119	1470	436	794	808	948	565	301	1227	1572	1456
120	296	1177	1072	22	220	417	604	691	1561	1346
121	979	875	1618	133	1330	819	1058	1665	603	681
122	1461	346	1677	723	98	980	885	1718	1133	632
123	971	795	818	1048	1565	1386	1379	1309	609	741
124	278	997	1055	1635	303	1247	1772	1673	683	1481
125	546	111	1110	402	454	974	825	1118	482	1254
126	59	590	551	161	1610	53	530	1734	1293	449
127	924	325	1467	406	494	1374	1259	109	1090	202
128	237	587	521	1644	393	364	74	740	268	897
129	55	550	151	1510	836	1228	1582	1556	1296	479
130	1224	1542	1156	862	1488	616	811	978	865	1518
131	916	245	667	1321	729	158	1580	1536	1096	262
132	837	1238	1682	773	598	631	961	695	1601	1746
133	1413	1649	443	864	1508	816	1028	1365	1169	992
134	1005	1135	652	1171	1012	1205	1352	1039	1475	486
135	1294	459	1024	1325	769	558	231	527	1704	993
136	1015	1235	1652	473	1164	942	505	1484	576	411
137	544	91	910	185	67	670	1351	1029	1375	1269
138	209	307	1287	389	324	1457	306	1277	289	1107
139	372	154	1540	1136	662	1271	229	507	1504	776
140	628	931	395	384	274	957	655	1201	1312	639
141	1041	1495	686	1511	846	1328	799	858	1448	216
142	377	204	257	787	738	248	697	1621	163	1630
143	253	747	338	1597	1706	1013	1215	1452	256	777
144	638	1031	1395	1469	426	694	1591	1646	413	564
145	291	1127	572	371	144	1440	136	1360	1119	492
146	1354	1059	1675	703	1681	763	498	1414	1659	543
147	81	810	968	765	518	1614	93	930	385	284
148	1057	1655	503	1464	376	194	157	1570	1436	96
149	960	685	1501	746	328	1497	706	1711	1063	1715

P = 1783

INDICES

	0	1	2	3	4	5	6	7	8	9
150	1750	1492	758	994	1398	349	831	911	1334	513
151	1293	1413	1607	1549	705	397	777	1170	1309	1039
152	6	428	972	1141	1517	1778	531	547	1551	747
153	539	837	61	980	1509	534	1317	1502	420	713
154	1392	667	1301	685	168	839	389	283	766	984
155	1599	108	465	185	505	861	1297	217	823	1755
156	129	1208	986	313	1683	1234	1742	528	1052	803
157	1487	288	1198	111	489	120	28	830	776	530
158	1316	388	1296	1741	27	156	157	1181	258	594
159	297	1446	1680	135	1736	1527	158	1433	482	946
160	1612	1328	1547	1584	1078	812	1182	1074	1167	1007
161	1264	31	1760	1586	1475	872	259	1544	1212	1537
162	537	1427	372	720	1187	424	595	1019	707	500
163	1429	896	401	858	1099	1243	298	1718	281	563
164	647	1522	644	146	1283	63	1447	565	701	1331
165	322	191	1362	293	930	1481	1681	1771	132	1468
166	654	1647	1601	1619	1773	1217	136	1042	1119	13
167	1151	907	360	1247	386	1462	1737	1222	1045	1054
168	1764	1464	1322	893	1090	333	1528	598	1069	679
169	585	98	480	736	1746	226	159	965	738	24
170	696	689	579	1654	1358	171	1434	48	10	395
171	870	1497	674	1080	997	1499	483	1125	1227	633
172	923	620	799	771	369	194	947	59	399	614
173	374	206	616	45	1267	1532	1613	1032	1670	1160
174	117	958	1623	806	1105	982	1329	649	232	651
175	277	1567	1554	1705	1128	993	1548	1140	979	684
176	184	312	110	1740	134	1583	1585	719	857	145
177	292	1618	1246	892	735	1653	1079	770	44	805
178	1704	1739	891							

POWER RESIDUES

	0	1	2	3	4	5	6	7	8	9
150	1103	332	1537	1106	362	54	540	51	510	1534
151	1076	62	620	851	1378	1299	509	1524	976	845
152	1318	699	1641	363	64	640	1051	1595	1686	813
153	998	1065	1735	1303	549	141	1410	1619	143	1430
154	36	360	34	340	1617	123	1230	1602	1756	1513
155	866	1528	1016	1245	1752	1473	466	1094	242	637
156	1021	1295	469	1124	542	71	710	1751	1463	366
157	94	940	485	1284	359	24	240	617	821	1078
158	82	820	1068	1765	1603	1766	1613	83	830	1168
159	982	905	135	1350	1019	1275	269	907	155	1550
160	1236	1662	573	381	244	657	1221	1512	856	1428
161	16	160	1600	1736	1313	649	1141	712	1771	1663
162	583	481	1244	1742	1373	1249	9	90	900	85
163	850	1368	1199	1292	439	824	1108	382	254	757
164	438	814	1008	1165	952	605	701	1661	563	281
165	1027	1355	1069	1775	1703	983	915	235	567	321
166	1427	6	60	600	651	1161	912	205	267	887
167	1738	1333	849	1358	1099	292	1137	672	1371	1229
168	1592	1656	513	1564	1376	1279	309	1307	589	541
169	61	610	751	378	214	357	4	40	400	434
170	774	608	731	178	1780	1753	1483	566	311	1327
171	789	758	448	914	225	467	1104	342	1637	323
172	1447	206	277	987	955	635	1001	1095	252	737
173	238	597	621	861	1478	516	1594	1676	713	1781
174	1763	1583	1566	1396	1479	526	1694	893	15	150
175	1500	736	228	497	1404	1559	1326	779	658	1231
176	1612	73	730	168	1680	753	398	414	574	391
177	344	1657	523	1664	593	581	461	1044	1525	986
178	945	535								

P = 1787

INDICES

	0	1	2	3	4	5	6	7	8	9
0		0	1	1268	2	1757	1269	1749	3	750
1	1758	1149	1270	695	1750	1239	4	1478	751	1283
2	1759	1231	1150	1571	1271	1728	696	232	1751	1047
3	1240	101	5	631	1479	1720	752	770	1284	177
4	1760	327	1232	51	1151	721	1572	1395	1272	1712
5	1729	960	697	1546	233	1120	1752	765	1048	1131
6	1241	597	102	713	6	666	632	918	1480	1053
7	1721	435	753	1342	771	1210	1285	1112	178	1455
8	1761	1500	328	813	1233	1449	52	529	1152	883
9	722	658	1573	1369	1396	1254	1273	469	1713	113
10	1730	1136	961	167	698	1202	1547	313	234	940
11	1121	252	1753	1227	766	1542	1049	1445	1132	1441
12	1242	512	598	1595	103	1699	714	1679	7	1319
13	667	1431	633	1246	919	203	1481	1467	1054	1064
14	1722	877	436	58	754	1018	1343	1194	772	516
15	1211	458	1286	442	1113	72	179	985	1456	1028
16	1762	1534	1501	120	329	602	814	580	1234	1390
17	1450	247	53	1686	530	1691	1153	613	884	1296
18	723	1599	659	79	1574	741	1370	841	1397	195
19	1255	1623	1274	86	470	148	1714	107	114	1038
20	1731	400	1137	1010	962	298	168	535	699	646
21	1203	1003	1548	1703	314	22	235	64	941	824
22	1122	387	253	372	1754	692	1228	1044	767	718
23	1543	594	1050	1109	1446	1366	1133	937	1442	1696
24	1243	874	513	982	599	1683	1596	192	104	295
25	1700	384	715	934	1680	931	8	1307	1320	733
26	668	11	1432	270	634	1517	1247	365	920	1310
27	204	1158	1482	140	1468	1091	1055	1323	1065	851
28	1723	760	878	507	437	736	59	290	755	1170
29	1019	1737	1344	671	1195	1102	773	1381	517	480
30	1212	14	459	618	1287	568	443	1637	1114	1435
31	73	186	180	1175	986	684	1457	273	1029	410
32	1763	1581	1535	975	1502	637	121	422	330	1358
33	603	1555	815	1520	581	889	1235	97	1391	709
34	1451	1250	248	1675	54	1024	1687	1619	531	368
35	1692	927	1154	286	614	406	885	923	1297	32
36	724	780	1600	1780	660	1313	80	1301	1575	1077
37	742	1509	1371	207	842	1181	1398	1742	196	263
38	1256	1161	1624	36	1275	1083	87	801	471	1485
39	149	1263	1715	913	108	1426	115	143	1039	728
40	1732	970	401	796	1138	1471	1011	133	963	1349
41	299	949	169	1094	536	784	700	546	647	1143
42	1204	1058	1004	359	1549	1420	1704	560	315	1326
43	23	1604	236	225	65	500	942	1068	825	992
44	1123	676	388	344	254	854	373	1784	1755	748
45	693	1476	1229	1726	1045	629	768	325	719	1710
46	1544	763	595	664	1051	1340	1110	1498	1447	881
47	1367	467	1134	1200	938	1225	1443	510	1697	1317
48	1244	1465	875	1016	514	440	983	1532	600	1388
49	1684	611	1597	739	193	84	105	398	296	644

POWER RESIDUES

	0	1	2	3	4	5	6	7	8	9
0	1	2	4	8	16	32	64	128	256	512
1	1024	261	522	1044	301	602	1204	621	1242	697
2	1394	1001	215	430	860	1720	1653	1519	1251	715
3	1430	1073	359	718	1436	1085	383	766	1532	1277
4	767	1534	1281	775	1550	1313	839	1678	1569	1351
5	915	43	86	172	344	688	1376	965	143	286
6	572	1144	501	1002	217	434	868	1736	1685	1583
7	1379	971	155	310	620	1240	693	1386	985	183
8	366	732	1464	1141	495	990	193	386	772	1544
9	1301	815	1630	1473	1159	531	1062	337	674	1348
10	909	31	62	124	248	496	992	197	394	788
11	1576	1365	943	99	198	396	792	1584	1381	975
12	163	326	652	1304	821	1642	1497	1207	627	1254
13	721	1442	1097	407	814	1628	1469	1151	515	1030
14	273	546	1092	397	794	1588	1389	991	195	390
15	780	1560	1333	879	1758	1729	1671	1555	1323	859
16	1718	1649	1511	1235	683	1366	945	103	206	412
17	824	1648	1509	1231	675	1350	913	39	78	156
18	312	624	1248	709	1418	1049	311	622	1244	701
19	1402	1017	247	494	988	189	378	756	1512	1237
20	687	1374	961	135	270	540	1080	373	746	1492
21	1197	607	1214	641	1282	777	1554	1321	855	1710
22	1633	1479	1171	555	1110	433	866	1732	1677	1567
23	1347	907	27	54	108	216	432	864	1728	1669
24	1551	1315	843	1686	1585	1383	979	171	342	684
25	1368	949	111	222	444	888	1776	1765	1743	1699
26	1611	1435	1083	379	758	1516	1245	703	1406	1025
27	263	526	1052	317	634	1268	749	1498	1209	631
28	1262	737	1474	1161	535	1070	353	706	1412	1037
29	287	574	1148	509	1018	249	498	996	205	410
30	820	1640	1493	1199	611	1222	657	1314	841	1682
31	1577	1367	947	107	214	428	856	1712	1637	1487
32	1187	587	1174	561	1122	457	914	41	82	164
33	328	656	1312	837	1674	1561	1335	883	1766	1745
34	1703	1619	1451	1115	443	886	1772	1757	1727	1667
35	1547	1307	827	1654	1521	1255	723	1446	1105	423
36	846	1692	1597	1407	1027	267	534	1068	349	698
37	1396	1005	223	446	892	1784	1781	1775	1763	1739
38	1691	1595	1403	1019	251	502	1004	221	442	884
39	1768	1749	1711	1635	1483	1179	571	1142	497	994
40	201	402	804	1608	1429	1071	355	710	1420	1053
41	319	638	1276	765	1530	1273	759	1518	1249	711
42	1422	1057	327	654	1308	829	1658	1529	1271	755
43	1510	1233	679	1358	929	71	142	284	568	1136
44	485	970	153	306	612	1224	661	1322	857	1714
45	1641	1495	1203	619	1238	689	1378	969	151	302
46	604	1208	629	1258	729	1458	1129	471	942	97
47	194	388	776	1552	1317	847	1694	1601	1415	1043
48	299	598	1196	605	1210	633	1266	745	1490	1193
49	599	1198	609	1218	649	1298	809	1618	1449	1111

P = 1787

INDICES

	0	1	2	3	4	5	6	7	8	9
50	1701	62	385	690	716	1107	935	872	1681	293
51	932	1305	9	1515	1308	138	1321	758	734	1168
52	669	1379	12	566	1433	1173	271	1579	635	1356
53	1518	95	1248	1022	366	284	921	778	1311	1075
54	205	1740	1159	1081	1483	911	141	968	1469	1347
55	1092	544	1056	1418	1324	223	1066	674	852	746
56	1724	323	761	1338	879	1198	508	1463	438	1386
57	737	396	60	1105	291	1513	756	1377	1171	1354
58	1020	776	1738	909	1345	1416	672	321	1196	1384
59	1103	1375	774	1414	1382	1412	518	520	481	490
60	1213	522	15	1668	460	483	619	211	1288	492
61	569	304	444	1215	1638	1566	1115	524	1436	453
62	74	17	187	846	181	1670	1176	128	987	462
63	685	279	1458	485	274	1650	1030	621	411	1185
64	1764	213	1582	954	1536	1290	976	1631	1503	494
65	638	1332	122	571	423	1402	331	306	1359	1773
66	604	446	1556	1655	816	1217	1521	832	582	1640
67	890	1746	1236	1568	98	174	1392	1117	710	432
68	1452	526	1251	164	249	1438	1676	200	55	455
69	1025	577	1688	76	1620	1035	532	19	369	591
70	1693	189	928	267	1155	848	287	1099	615	183
71	407	419	886	1672	924	29	1298	1178	33	1260
72	725	130	781	356	1601	989	1781	626	661	464
73	1314	1529	81	687	1302	1165	1576	281	1078	541
74	743	1460	1510	906	1372	487	208	1563	843	276
75	1182	1628	1399	1652	1743	429	197	1032	264	416
76	1257	623	1162	903	1625	413	37	40	1276	1187
77	1084	789	88	1766	802	43	472	215	1486	1610
78	150	1584	1264	1279	1716	956	914	809	109	1538
79	1427	1190	116	1292	144	999	1040	978	729	1087
80	1733	1633	971	705	402	1505	797	792	1139	496
81	1472	1494	1012	640	134	91	964	1334	1350	1408
82	300	124	950	1769	170	573	1095	352	537	425
83	785	805	701	1404	547	551	648	333	1144	46
84	1205	308	1059	242	1005	1361	360	475	1550	1775
85	1421	555	1705	606	561	218	316	448	1327	159
86	24	1558	1605	1489	237	1657	226	652	66	818
87	501	1613	943	1219	1069	1662	826	1523	993	153
88	1124	834	677	337	389	584	345	1587	255	1642
89	855	863	374	892	1785	1267	1756	1748	749	1148
90	694	1238	1477	1282	1230	1570	1727	231	1046	100
91	630	1719	769	176	326	50	720	1394	1711	959
92	1545	1119	764	1130	596	712	665	917	1052	434
93	1341	1209	1111	1454	1499	812	1448	528	882	657
94	1368	1253	468	112	1135	166	1201	312	939	251
95	1226	1541	1444	1440	511	1594	1698	1678	1318	1430
96	1245	202	1466	1063	876	57	1017	1193	515	457
97	441	71	984	1027	1533	119	601	579	1389	246
98	1685	1690	612	1295	1598	78	740	840	194	1622
99	85	147	106	1037	399	1009	297	534	645	1002

POWER RESIDUES

	0	1	2	3	4	5	6	7	8	9
50	435	870	1740	1693	1599	1411	1035	283	566	1132
51	477	954	121	242	484	968	149	298	596	1192
52	597	1194	601	1202	617	1234	681	1362	937	87
53	174	348	696	1392	997	207	414	828	1656	1525
54	1263	739	1478	1169	551	1102	417	834	1668	1549
55	1311	835	1670	1553	1319	851	1702	1617	1447	1107
56	427	854	1708	1629	1471	1155	523	1046	305	610
57	1220	653	1306	825	1650	1513	1239	691	1382	977
58	167	334	668	1336	885	1770	1753	1719	1651	1515
59	1243	699	1398	1009	231	462	924	61	122	244
60	488	976	165	330	660	1320	853	1706	1625	1463
61	1139	491	982	177	354	708	1416	1045	303	606
62	1212	637	1274	761	1522	1257	727	1454	1121	455
63	910	33	66	132	264	528	1056	325	650	1300
64	813	1626	1465	1143	499	998	209	418	836	1672
65	1557	1327	867	1734	1681	1575	1363	939	91	182
66	364	728	1456	1125	463	926	65	130	260	520
67	1040	293	586	1172	557	1114	441	882	1764	1741
68	1695	1603	1419	1051	315	630	1260	733	1466	1145
69	503	1006	225	450	900	13	26	52	104	208
70	416	832	1664	1541	1295	803	1606	1425	1063	339
71	678	1356	925	63	126	252	504	1008	229	458
72	916	45	90	180	360	720	1440	1093	399	798
73	1596	1405	1023	259	518	1036	285	570	1140	493
74	986	185	370	740	1480	1173	559	1118	449	898
75	9	18	36	72	144	288	576	1152	517	1034
76	281	562	1124	461	922	57	114	228	456	912
77	37	74	148	296	592	1184	581	1162	537	1074
78	361	722	1444	1101	415	830	1660	1533	1279	771
79	1542	1297	807	1614	1441	1095	403	806	1612	1437
80	1087	387	774	1548	1309	831	1662	1537	1287	787
81	1574	1361	935	83	166	332	664	1328	869	1738
82	1689	1591	1395	1003	219	438	876	1752	1717	1647
83	1507	1227	667	1334	881	1762	1737	1687	1587	1387
84	987	187	374	748	1496	1205	623	1246	705	1410
85	1033	279	558	1116	445	890	1780	1773	1759	1731
86	1675	1563	1339	891	1782	1777	1767	1747	1707	1627
87	1467	1147	507	1014	241	482	964	141	282	564
88	1128	469	938	89	178	356	712	1424	1061	335
89	670	1340	893	1786	1785	1783	1779	1771	1755	1723
90	1659	1531	1275	763	1526	1265	743	1486	1185	583
91	1166	545	1090	393	786	1572	1357	927	67	134
92	268	536	1072	357	714	1428	1069	351	702	1404
93	1021	255	510	1020	253	506	1012	237	474	948
94	109	218	436	872	1744	1701	1615	1443	1099	411
95	822	1644	1501	1215	643	1286	785	1570	1353	919
96	51	102	204	408	816	1632	1477	1167	547	1094
97	401	802	1604	1421	1055	323	646	1292	797	1594
98	1401	1015	243	486	972	157	314	628	1256	725
99	1450	1113	439	878	1756	1725	1663	1539	1291	795

P = 1787

INDICES

	0	1	2	3	4	5	6	7	8	9
100	1702	21	63	823	386	371	691	1043	717	593
101	1108	1365	936	1695	873	981	1682	191	294	383
102	933	930	1306	732	10	269	1516	364	1309	1157
103	139	1090	1322	850	759	506	735	289	1169	1736
104	670	1101	1380	479	13	617	567	1636	1434	185
105	1174	683	272	409	1580	974	636	421	1357	1554
106	1519	888	96	708	1249	1674	1023	1618	367	926
107	285	405	922	31	779	1779	1312	1300	1076	1508
108	206	1180	1741	262	1160	35	1082	800	1484	1262
109	912	1425	142	727	969	795	1470	132	1348	948
110	1093	783	545	1142	1057	358	1419	559	1325	1603
111	224	499	1067	991	675	343	853	1783	747	1475
112	1725	628	324	1709	762	663	1339	1497	880	466
113	1199	1224	509	1316	1464	1015	439	1531	1387	610
114	738	83	397	643	61	689	1106	871	292	1304
115	1514	137	757	1167	1378	565	1172	1578	1355	94
116	1021	283	777	1074	1739	1080	910	967	1346	543
117	1417	222	673	745	322	1337	1197	1462	1385	395
118	1104	1512	1376	1353	775	908	1415	320	1383	1374
119	1413	1411	519	489	521	1667	482	210	491	303
120	1214	1565	523	452	16	845	1669	127	461	278
121	484	1649	620	1184	212	953	1289	1630	493	1331
122	570	1401	305	1772	445	1654	1216	831	1639	1745
123	1567	173	1116	431	525	163	1437	199	454	576
124	75	1034	18	590	188	266	847	1098	182	418
125	1671	28	1177	1259	129	355	988	625	463	1528
126	686	1164	280	540	1459	905	486	1562	275	1627
127	1651	428	1031	415	622	902	412	39	1186	788
128	1765	42	214	1609	1583	1278	955	808	1537	1189
129	1291	998	977	1086	1632	704	1504	791	495	1493
130	639	90	1333	1407	123	1768	572	351	424	804
131	1403	550	332	45	307	241	1360	474	1774	554
132	605	217	447	158	1557	1488	1656	651	817	1612
133	1218	1661	1522	152	833	336	583	1586	1641	862
134	891	1266	1747	1147	1237	1281	1569	230	99	1718
135	175	49	1393	958	1118	1129	711	916	433	1208
136	1453	811	527	656	1252	111	165	311	250	1540
137	1439	1593	1677	1429	201	1062	56	1192	456	70
138	1026	118	578	245	1689	1294	77	839	1621	146
139	1036	1008	533	1001	20	822	370	1042	592	1364
140	1694	980	190	382	929	731	268	363	1156	1089
141	849	505	288	1735	1100	478	616	1635	184	682
142	408	973	420	1553	887	707	1673	1617	925	404
143	30	1778	1299	1507	1179	261	34	799	1261	1424
144	726	794	131	947	782	1141	357	558	1602	498
145	990	342	1782	1474	627	1708	662	1496	465	1223
146	1315	1014	1530	609	82	642	688	870	1303	136
147	1166	564	1577	93	282	1073	1079	966	542	221
148	744	1336	1461	394	1511	1352	907	319	1373	1410
149	488	1666	209	302	1564	451	844	126	277	1648

POWER RESIDUES

	0	1	2	3	4	5	6	7	8	9
100	1590	1393	999	211	422	844	1688	1589	1391	995
101	203	406	812	1624	1461	1135	483	966	145	290
102	580	1160	533	1066	345	690	1380	973	159	318
103	636	1272	757	1514	1241	695	1390	993	199	398
104	796	1592	1397	1007	227	454	908	29	58	116
105	232	464	928	69	138	276	552	1104	421	842
106	1684	1581	1375	963	139	278	556	1112	437	874
107	1748	1709	1631	1475	1163	539	1078	369	738	1476
108	1165	543	1086	385	770	1540	1293	799	1598	1409
109	1031	275	550	1100	413	826	1652	1517	1247	707
110	1414	1041	295	590	1180	573	1146	505	1010	233
111	466	932	77	154	308	616	1232	677	1354	921
112	55	110	220	440	880	1760	1733	1679	1571	1355
113	923	59	118	236	472	944	101	202	404	808
114	1616	1445	1103	419	838	1676	1565	1343	899	11
115	22	44	88	176	352	704	1408	1029	271	542
116	1084	381	762	1524	1261	735	1470	1153	519	1038
117	289	578	1156	525	1050	313	626	1252	717	1434
118	1081	375	750	1500	1213	639	1278	769	1538	1289
119	791	1582	1377	967	147	294	588	1176	565	1130
120	473	946	105	210	420	840	1680	1573	1359	931
121	75	150	300	600	1200	613	1226	665	1330	873
122	1746	1705	1623	1459	1131	475	950	113	226	452
123	904	21	42	84	168	336	672	1344	901	15
124	30	60	120	240	480	960	133	266	532	1064
125	341	682	1364	941	95	190	380	760	1520	1253
126	719	1438	1089	391	782	1564	1341	895	3	6
127	12	24	48	96	192	384	768	1536	1285	783
128	1566	1345	903	19	38	76	152	304	608	1216
129	645	1290	793	1586	1385	983	179	358	716	1432
130	1077	367	734	1468	1149	511	1022	257	514	1028
131	269	538	1076	365	730	1460	1133	479	958	129
132	258	516	1032	277	554	1108	429	858	1716	1645
133	1503	1219	651	1302	817	1634	1481	1175	563	1126
134	465	930	73	146	292	584	1168	549	1098	409
135	818	1636	1485	1183	579	1158	529	1058	329	658
136	1316	845	1690	1593	1399	1011	235	470	940	93
137	186	372	744	1488	1189	591	1182	577	1154	521
138	1042	297	594	1188	589	1178	569	1138	489	978
139	169	338	676	1352	917	47	94	188	376	752
140	1504	1221	655	1310	833	1666	1545	1303	819	1638
141	1489	1191	595	1190	593	1186	585	1170	553	1106
142	425	850	1700	1613	1439	1091	395	790	1580	1373
143	959	131	262	524	1048	309	618	1236	685	1370
144	953	119	238	476	952	117	234	468	936	85
145	170	340	680	1360	933	79	158	316	632	1264
146	741	1482	1177	567	1134	481	962	137	274	548
147	1096	405	810	1620	1453	1119	451	902	17	34
148	68	136	272	544	1088	389	778	1556	1325	863
149	1726	1665	1543	1299	811	1622	1457	1127	467	934

P = 1787

INDICES

	0	1	2	3	4	5	6	7	8	9
150	1183	952	1629	1330	1400	1771	1653	830	1744	172
151	430	162	198	575	1033	589	265	1097	417	27
152	1258	354	624	1527	1163	539	904	1561	1626	427
153	414	901	38	787	41	1608	1277	807	1188	997
154	1085	703	790	1492	89	1406	1767	350	803	549
155	44	240	473	553	216	157	1487	650	1611	1660
156	151	335	1585	861	1265	1146	1280	229	1717	48
157	957	1128	915	1207	810	655	110	310	1539	1592
158	1428	1061	1191	69	117	244	1293	838	145	1007
159	1000	821	1041	1363	979	381	730	362	1088	504
160	1734	477	1634	681	972	1552	706	1616	403	1777
161	1506	260	798	1423	793	946	1140	557	497	341
162	1473	1707	1495	1222	1013	608	641	869	135	563
163	92	1072	965	220	1335	393	1351	318	1409	1665
164	301	450	125	1647	951	1329	1770	829	171	161
165	574	588	1096	26	353	1526	538	1560	426	900
166	786	1607	806	996	702	1491	1405	349	548	239
167	552	156	649	1659	334	860	1145	228	47	1127
168	1206	654	309	1591	1060	68	243	837	1006	820
169	1362	380	361	503	476	680	1551	1615	1776	259
170	1422	945	556	340	1706	1221	607	868	562	1071
171	219	392	317	1664	449	1646	1328	828	160	587
172	25	1525	1559	899	1606	995	1490	348	238	155
173	1658	859	227	1126	653	1590	67	836	819	379
174	502	679	1614	258	944	339	1220	867	1070	391
175	1663	1645	827	586	1524	898	994	347	154	858
176	1125	1589	835	378	678	257	338	866	390	1644
177	585	897	346	857	1588	377	256	865	1643	896
178	856	376	864	895	375	894	893			

POWER RESIDUES

	0	1	2	3	4	5	6	7	8	9
150	81	162	324	648	1296	805	1610	1433	1079	371
151	742	1484	1181	575	1150	513	1026	265	530	1060
152	333	666	1332	877	1754	1721	1655	1523	1259	731
153	1462	1137	487	974	161	322	644	1288	789	1578
154	1369	951	115	230	460	920	53	106	212	424
155	848	1696	1605	1423	1059	331	662	1324	861	1722
156	1657	1527	1267	747	1494	1201	615	1230	673	1346
157	905	23	46	92	184	368	736	1472	1157	527
158	1054	321	642	1284	781	1562	1337	887	1774	1761
159	1735	1683	1579	1371	955	123	246	492	984	181
160	362	724	1448	1109	431	862	1724	1661	1535	1283
161	779	1558	1329	871	1742	1697	1607	1427	1067	347
162	694	1388	989	191	382	764	1528	1269	751	1502
163	1217	647	1294	801	1602	1417	1047	307	614	1228
164	669	1338	889	1778	1769	1751	1715	1643	1499	1211
165	635	1270	753	1506	1225	663	1326	865	1730	1673
166	1559	1331	875	1750	1713	1639	1491	1195	603	1206
167	625	1250	713	1426	1065	343	686	1372	957	127
168	254	508	1016	245	490	980	173	346	692	1384
169	981	175	350	700	1400	1013	239	478	956	125
170	250	500	1000	213	426	852	1704	1621	1455	1123
171	459	918	49	98	196	392	784	1568	1349	911
172	35	70	140	280	560	1120	453	906	25	50
173	100	200	400	800	1600	1413	1039	291	582	1164
174	541	1082	377	754	1508	1229	671	1342	897	7
175	14	28	56	112	224	448	896	5	10	20
176	40	80	160	320	640	1280	773	1546	1305	823
177	1646	1505	1223	659	1318	849	1698	1609	1431	1075
178	363	726	1452	1117	447	894				

P = 1789

INDICES

	0	1	2	3	4	5	6	7	8	9
0		0	651	1138	1302	1742	1	1294	165	488
1	605	561	652	1563	157	1092	816	1598	1139	431
2	1256	644	1212	178	1303	1696	426	1626	808	1088
3	1743	537	1467	1699	461	1248	2	503	1082	913
4	119	1017	1295	303	75	442	829	950	166	800
5	559	948	1077	1102	489	515	1459	1569	1739	1370
6	606	1062	1188	1782	330	1517	562	1418	1112	1316
7	111	1143	653	94	1154	1046	1733	67	1564	630
8	770	976	1668	1079	158	1552	954	438	726	126
9	1093	1069	1480	1675	1601	385	817	58	1451	1049
10	1210	1737	1599	378	1728	598	1753	145	1140	520
11	1166	1641	322	1403	432	132	602	263	233	1104
12	1257	1122	1713	367	51	1650	645	1298	981	1441
13	380	285	1213	1725	281	1580	1763	1284	179	1364
14	762	300	6	336	1304	1042	745	150	17	242
15	1697	1314	596	298	718	491	427	1521	1281	452
16	1421	1472	1627	741	531	1653	1730	1393	809	1338
17	415	919	1605	1659	1089	1202	1377	720	777	1183
18	1744	39	1720	412	343	457	538	371	464	1132
19	1036	517	1468	1483	709	867	314	1222	1700	163
20	73	768	600	594	462	971	1029	666	591	992
21	1249	678	616	493	796	257	3	43	1171	1232
22	29	1373	504	683	973	396	266	1461	1083	138
23	783	1205	1253	881	914	904	884	1768	1755	202
24	120	1199	1773	326	576	754	1018	206	702	429
25	513	1067	1296	739	161	902	1632	1099	304	9
26	1031	1576	936	1571	76	1056	588	1264	932	307
27	443	1634	626	419	147	469	830	403	227	1025
28	1413	1271	951	174	657	1523	987	523	167	1408
29	1693	1196	1396	1430	801	1324	668	399	893	1741
30	560	1597	177	1087	1247	1016	949	1101	1369	1516
31	1142	66	1078	125	384	1736	144	1402	1103	1649
32	284	1283	335	241	490	1471	1392	1658	1182	456
33	516	1221	593	991	256	1372	1460	880	201	753
34	1066	1098	1570	306	468	1270	522	1429	1740	1015
35	65	1401	240	455	1371	1097	1428	454	46	47
36	607	862	690	472	583	48	1063	875	994	1505
37	1108	608	1189	1779	1022	1000	1115	863	1783	11
38	1687	648	1168	691	331	21	346	791	1360	473
39	1518	1776	965	1423	85	584	563	360	814	1075
40	724	49	1419	312	1251	930	1245	1064	1113	1678
41	1622	634	1680	876	1317	1033	1242	714	1643	995
42	112	190	1329	1438	1267	1506	1144	568	1447	1474
43	908	1109	654	1161	694	392	34	609	95	1291
44	680	1288	236	1190	1155	80	1334	1380	1624	1780
45	1047	1578	917	664	324	1023	1734	1399	789	1436
46	1434	1001	68	480	116	1629	1532	1116	1565	924
47	1555	871	1535	864	631	339	618	1590	853	1784
48	771	278	62	822	636	12	977	938	1227	91
49	1405	1688	1669	898	857	1003	1353	649	1080	1152

POWER RESIDUES

	0	1	2	3	4	5	6	7	8	9
0	1	6	36	216	1296	620	142	852	1534	259
1	1554	379	485	1121	1359	998	621	148	888	1750
2	1555	385	521	1337	866	1618	763	1000	633	220
3	1320	764	1006	669	436	827	1384	1148	1521	181
4	1086	1149	1527	217	1302	656	358	359	365	401
5	617	124	744	886	1738	1483	1742	1507	97	582
6	1703	1273	482	1103	1251	350	311	77	462	983
7	531	1397	1226	200	1200	44	264	1584	559	1565
8	445	881	1708	1303	662	394	575	1661	1021	759
9	976	489	1145	1503	73	438	839	1456	1580	535
10	1421	1370	1064	1017	735	832	1414	1328	812	1294
11	608	70	420	731	808	1270	464	995	603	40
12	240	1440	1484	1748	1543	313	89	534	1415	1334
13	848	1510	115	690	562	1583	553	1529	229	1374
14	1088	1161	1599	649	316	107	642	274	1644	919
15	147	882	1714	1339	878	1690	1195	14	84	504
16	1235	254	1524	199	1194	8	48	288	1728	1423
17	1382	1136	1449	1538	283	1698	1243	302	23	138
18	828	1390	1184	1737	1477	1706	1291	590	1751	1561
19	421	737	844	1486	1760	1615	745	892	1774	1699
20	1249	338	239	1434	1448	1532	247	1482	1736	1471
21	1670	1075	1083	1131	1419	1358	992	585	1721	1381
22	1130	1413	1322	776	1078	1101	1239	278	1668	1063
23	1011	699	616	118	708	670	442	863	1600	655
24	352	323	149	894	1786	1771	1681	1141	1479	1718
25	1363	1022	765	1012	705	652	334	215	1290	584
26	1715	1345	914	117	702	634	226	1356	980	513
27	1289	578	1679	1129	1407	1286	560	1571	481	1097
28	1215	134	804	1246	320	131	786	1138	1461	1610
29	715	712	694	586	1727	1417	1346	920	153	918
30	141	846	1498	43	258	1548	343	269	1614	739
31	856	1558	403	629	196	1176	1689	1189	1767	1657
32	997	615	112	672	454	935	243	1458	1592	607
33	64	384	515	1301	650	322	143	858	1570	475
34	1061	999	627	184	1104	1257	386	527	1373	1082
35	1125	1383	1142	1485	1754	1579	529	1385	1154	1557
36	397	593	1769	1669	1069	1047	915	123	738	850
37	1522	187	1122	1365	1034	837	1444	1508	103	618
38	130	780	1102	1245	314	95	570	1631	841	1468
39	1652	967	435	821	1348	932	225	1350	944	297
40	1782	1747	1537	277	1662	1027	795	1192	1785	1765
41	1645	925	183	1098	1221	170	1020	753	940	273
42	1638	883	1720	1375	1094	1197	26	156	936	249
43	1494	19	114	684	526	1367	1046	909	87	522
44	1343	902	45	270	1620	775	1072	1065	1023	771
45	1048	921	159	954	357	353	329	185	1110	1293
46	602	34	204	1224	188	1128	1401	1250	344	275
47	1650	955	363	389	545	1481	1730	1435	1454	1568
48	463	989	567	1613	733	820	1342	896	9	54
49	324	155	930	213	1278	512	1283	542	1463	1622

P = 1789

INDICES

	0	1	2	3	4	5	6	7	8	9
50	1164	743	1718	1169	159	1691	1390	688	812	692
51	1553	1388	495	269	1750	332	955	1511	660	1009
52	1682	22	439	1573	1587	552	434	347	727	356
53	1707	70	1239	792	127	99	1583	533	958	1361
54	1094	1486	497	1177	1277	474	1070	1561	798	1550
55	1120	1519	1481	136	1054	1595	878	1777	1676	78
56	276	1509	134	966	1602	1357	825	482	1308	1424
57	386	1489	1638	1655	1174	86	818	1495	271	833
58	556	585	59	1663	259	217	293	564	1452	968
59	187	572	1319	361	1050	1058	1544	1301	604	815
60	1211	807	460	118	828	1076	1738	329	110	1732
61	1667	725	1600	1209	1752	321	232	50	379	1762
62	5	16	717	1420	1729	1604	776	342	1035	313
63	599	590	795	28	265	1252	1754	575	512	1631
64	935	931	146	1412	986	1395	892	1246	1141	143
65	334	1181	255	1065	521	239	45	582	1107	1114
66	1167	1359	84	723	1244	1679	1642	1266	907	33
67	235	1623	323	1433	1531	1534	852	635	1404	1352
68	1717	811	1749	1681	433	1238	957	1276	1119	877
69	133	1307	1173	555	292	1318	603	827	1666	231
70	716	1034	264	934	891	254	1106	1243	234	851
71	1748	1118	291	715	1105	290	697	1340	698	1644
72	1258	1672	1513	549	1341	996	1123	1615	1234	1464
73	699	113	1714	484	1526	104	1645	191	368	309
74	1759	1344	1259	1330	52	196	642	1567	1673	1439
75	1651	766	1766	417	1514	1268	646	712	662	89
76	550	1507	1299	26	31	252	1342	1145	982	1310
77	672	449	997	569	1442	445	223	1147	1124	1448
78	381	1704	639	926	1616	1475	286	500	736	921
79	1235	909	1214	837	1011	406	1465	1110	1726	760
80	1375	614	700	655	282	1426	963	1445	114	1162
81	1581	1636	108	984	1715	695	1764	734	541	1557
82	485	393	1285	579	543	1607	1527	35	180	528
83	1684	1541	105	610	1365	1347	506	375	1646	96
84	763	388	841	621	192	1292	301	628	130	1312
85	369	681	7	1322	1219	873	310	1289	337	1386
86	1559	1661	1760	237	1305	1613	24	758	1345	1191
87	1043	1193	685	546	1260	1156	746	1491	154	780
88	1331	81	151	421	887	674	53	1335	18	804
89	731	1537	197	1381	243	1137	487	1091	643	1625
90	1698	912	441	947	1568	1781	1315	1045	975	437
91	1674	1048	597	1640	262	366	1440	1579	299	149
92	297	451	1652	918	719	411	1131	866	767	665
93	492	1231	395	1204	1767	325	428	901	1575	1263
94	418	1024	1522	1195	398	1086	1515	1735	1282	1657
95	990	752	1269	1400	453	471	1504	999	647	790
96	1422	1074	929	633	713	1437	1473	391	1287	1379
97	663	1435	1628	870	1589	821	90	1002	742	687
98	268	1008	551	69	532	1176	1549	1594	1508	481
99	1654	832	216	571	1300	117	1731	320	15	341

POWER RESIDUES

	0	1	2	3	4	5	6	7	8	9
50	787	1144	1497	37	222	1332	836	1438	1472	1676
51	1111	1299	638	250	1500	55	330	191	1146	1509
52	109	654	346	287	1722	1387	1166	1629	829	1396
53	1220	164	984	537	1433	1442	1496	31	186	1116
54	1329	818	1330	824	1366	1040	873	1660	1015	723
55	760	982	525	1361	1010	693	580	1691	1201	50
56	300	11	66	396	587	1733	1453	1562	427	773
57	1060	993	591	1757	1597	637	244	1464	1628	823
58	1360	1004	657	364	395	581	1697	1237	266	1596
59	631	208	1248	332	203	1218	152	912	105	630
60	202	1212	116	696	598	10	60	360	371	437
61	833	1420	1364	1028	801	1228	212	1272	476	1067
62	1035	843	1480	1724	1399	1238	272	1632	847	1504
63	79	474	1055	963	411	677	484	1115	1323	782
64	1114	1317	746	898	21	126	756	958	381	497
65	1193	2	12	72	432	803	1240	284	1704	1279
66	518	1319	758	970	453	929	207	1242	296	1776
67	1711	1321	770	1042	885	1732	1447	1526	211	1266
68	440	851	1528	223	1338	872	1654	979	507	1253
69	362	383	509	1265	434	815	1312	716	718	730
70	802	1234	248	1488	1772	1687	1177	1695	1225	194
71	1164	1617	757	964	417	713	700	622	154	924
72	177	1062	1005	663	400	611	88	528	1379	1118
73	1341	890	1762	1627	817	1324	788	1150	1533	253
74	1518	163	978	501	1217	146	876	1678	1123	1371
75	1070	1053	951	339	245	1470	1664	1039	867	1624
76	799	1216	140	840	1462	1616	751	928	201	1206
77	80	480	1091	1179	1707	1297	626	178	1068	1041
78	879	1696	1231	230	1380	1124	1377	1106	1269	458
79	959	387	533	1409	1298	632	214	1284	548	1499
80	49	294	1764	1639	889	1756	1591	601	28	168
81	1008	681	508	1259	398	599	16	96	576	1667
82	1057	975	483	1109	1287	566	1607	697	604	46
83	276	1656	991	579	1685	1165	1623	793	1180	1713
84	1333	842	1474	1688	1183	1731	1441	1490	1784	1759
85	1609	709	676	478	1079	1107	1275	494	1175	1683
86	1153	1551	361	377	473	1049	927	195	1170	1653
87	973	471	1037	855	1552	367	413	689	556	1547
88	337	233	1398	1232	236	1416	1340	884	1726	1411
89	1310	704	646	298	1788	1783	1753	1573	493	1169
90	1647	937	255	1530	235	1410	1304	668	430	791
91	1168	1641	901	39	234	1404	1268	452	923	171
92	1026	789	1156	1569	469	1025	783	1120	1353	962
93	405	641	268	1608	703	640	262	1572	487	1133
94	1431	1430	1424	1388	1172	1665	1045	903	51	306
95	47	282	1692	1207	86	516	1307	686	538	1439
96	1478	1712	1327	806	1258	392	563	1589	589	1745
97	1525	205	1230	224	1344	908	81	486	1127	1395
98	1214	128	768	1030	813	1300	644	286	1716	1351
99	950	333	209	1254	368	419	725	772	1054	957

P = 1789

INDICES

	0	1	2	3	4	5	6	7	8	9
100	27	1630	1394	1180	581	722	32	1533	810	1275
101	554	230	253	1117	1339	548	1463	103	1343	1566
102	416	88	251	448	1146	925	920	405	613	1444
103	983	1556	1606	1540	374	620	1311	872	1660	757
104	545	779	673	1536	1090	946	436	365	450	865
105	1203	1262	1085	751	998	632	1378	820	1007	1593
106	570	340	721	229	102	447	1443	619	778	364
107	750	1592	446	1591	1184	211	1609	1185	224	854
108	1745	1128	349	212	1148	1785	40	1158	140	1610
109	1125	772	1721	1497	424	1186	1449	279	413	1027
110	1771	225	382	63	344	1327	787	855	1705	823
111	458	510	1529	1746	640	637	539	1217	729	1129
112	927	13	372	748	785	350	1617	978	465	273
113	220	213	1476	939	1133	1415	171	1149	287	1228
114	1037	247	352	1786	501	92	518	1040	37	41
115	737	1406	1469	860	358	1159	922	1689	1484	1493
116	1207	141	1236	1670	710	835	526	1611	910	899
117	868	1273	944	1126	1215	858	315	706	1619	773
118	838	1004	1223	844	182	1722	1012	1354	1701	317
119	1709	1498	407	650	164	156	1255	425	1466	1081
120	74	558	1458	1187	1111	1153	769	953	1479	1450
121	1727	1165	601	1712	980	280	761	744	595	1280
122	530	414	1376	1719	463	708	72	1028	615	1170
123	972	782	883	1772	701	160	1030	587	625	226
124	656	1692	667	176	1368	383	283	1391	592	200
125	467	64	1427	689	993	1021	1686	345	964	813
126	1250	1621	1241	1328	1446	693	679	1333	916	788
127	115	1554	617	61	1226	856	1163	1389	494	659
128	1586	1706	1582	496	797	1053	275	824	1637	270
129	258	186	1543	459	109	1751	4	775	794	511
130	985	333	44	83	906	1530	1716	956	1172	1665
131	890	1747	696	1512	1233	1525	1758	641	1765	661
132	30	671	222	638	735	1010	1374	962	107	540
133	542	1683	505	840	129	1218	1558	23	684	153
134	886	730	486	440	974	261	296	1130	394	1574
135	397	989	1503	928	1286	1588	267	1548	215	14
136	580	553	1462	250	612	373	544	435	1084	1006
137	101	749	1608	348	139	423	1770	786	1528	728
138	784	219	170	351	36	357	1206	525	943	1618
139	181	1708	1254	1457	1478	979	529	71	882	624
140	1367	466	1685	1240	915	1225	1585	274	1542	793
141	905	889	1757	221	106	128	885	295	1502	214
142	611	100	1769	169	942	1477	1366	1584	1756	1501
143	941	940	1348	534	203	477	1349	1134	507	959
144	121	846	535	1416	376	1362	1200	676	204	172
145	1647	1095	1774	566	478	1150	97	1487	327	1410
146	1350	288	764	498	577	1384	1135	1229	389	1178
147	755	209	508	1038	842	1278	1019	184	960	248
148	622	475	207	55	122	353	193	1071	703	1454
149	847	1787	1293	1562	430	1695	536	502	302	799

POWER RESIDUES

	0	1	2	3	4	5	6	7	8	9
100	375	461	977	495	1181	1719	1369	1058	981	519
101	1325	794	1186	1749	1549	349	305	41	246	1476
102	1700	1255	374	455	941	279	1674	1099	1227	206
103	1236	260	1560	415	701	628	190	1140	1473	1682
104	1147	1515	145	870	1642	907	75	450	911	99
105	594	1775	1705	1285	554	1535	265	1590	595	1781
106	1741	1501	61	366	407	653	340	251	1506	91
107	546	1487	1766	1651	961	399	605	52	312	83
108	498	1199	38	228	1368	1052	945	303	29	174
109	1044	897	15	90	540	1451	1550	355	341	257
110	1542	307	53	318	119	714	706	658	370	431
111	797	1204	68	408	659	376	467	1013	711	688
112	550	1511	121	726	778	1090	1173	1671	1081	1119
113	1347	926	189	1134	1437	1466	1640	895	3	18
114	108	648	310	71	426	767	1024	777	1084	1137
115	1455	1574	499	1205	74	444	875	1672	1087	1155
116	1563	433	809	1276	500	1211	110	660	382	503
117	1229	218	1308	692	574	1655	985	543	1469	1658
118	1003	651	328	179	1074	1077	1095	1203	62	372
119	443	869	1636	871	1648	943	291	1746	1531	241
120	1446	1520	175	1050	933	231	1386	1160	1593	613
121	100	600	22	132	792	1174	1677	1117	1335	854
122	1546	331	197	1182	1725	1405	1274	488	1139	1467
123	1646	931	219	1314	728	790	1162	1605	685	532
124	1403	1262	416	707	664	406	647	304	35	210
125	1260	404	635	232	1392	1196	20	120	720	742
126	874	1666	1051	939	267	1602	667	424	755	952
127	345	281	1686	1171	1659	1009	687	544	1475	1694
128	1219	158	948	321	137	822	1354	968	441	857
129	1564	439	845	1492	7	42	252	1512	127	762
130	994	597	4	24	144	864	1606	691	568	1619
131	769	1036	849	1516	151	906	69	414	695	592
132	1763	1633	853	1540	295	1770	1675	1105	1263	422
133	743	880	1702	1267	446	887	1744	1519	169	1014
134	717	724	766	1018	741	868	1630	835	1432	1436
135	1460	1604	679	496	1187	1755	1585	565	1601	661
136	388	539	1445	1514	139	834	1426	1400	1244	308
137	59	354	335	221	1326	800	1222	176	1056	969
138	447	893	1780	1735	1465	1634	859	1576	511	1277
139	506	1247	326	167	1002	645	292	1752	1567	457
140	953	351	317	113	678	490	1151	1539	289	1734
141	1459	1598	643	280	1680	1135	1443	1502	67	402
142	623	160	960	393	569	1625	805	1252	356	347
143	293	1758	1603	673	460	971	459	965	423	749
144	916	129	774	1066	1029	807	1264	428	779	1096
145	1209	98	588	1739	1489	1778	1723	1393	1202	56
146	336	227	1362	1016	729	796	1198	32	192	1152
147	1545	325	161	966	429	785	1132	1425	1394	1208
148	92	552	1523	193	1158	1581	541	1457	1586	571
149	1637	877	1684	1159	1587	577	1673	1093	1191	1779

P = 1789

INDICES

	0	1	2	3	4	5	6	7	8	9
150	514	1061	1417	93	629	1551	1068	57	377	519
151	131	1121	1297	1724	1363	1041	1313	1520	740	1337
152	1201	38	370	1482	162	970	677	42	682	137
153	903	1198	205	738	8	1055	1633	402	173	1407
154	1323	1596	1100	124	1648	1470	1220	879	305	1014
155	1096	861	874	1778	10	20	1775	359	311	1677
156	1032	189	567	1160	1290	79	1577	1398	479	923
157	338	277	937	897	1151	1690	1387	1510	1572	355
158	98	1485	1560	135	77	1356	1488	1494	1662	967
159	1057	806	328	1208	1761	1603	589	574	1411	142
160	238	1358	1265	1432	1351	1237	1306	826	933	850
161	289	1671	1614	483	308	195	765	711	25	1309
162	444	1703	499	836	759	1425	1635	733	578	527
163	1346	387	627	1321	1385	1612	1192	1490	420	803
164	1136	911	1044	1639	148	410	1230	900	1194	1656
165	470	1073	390	869	686	1175	831	319	1179	1274
166	547	87	404	1539	756	945	1261	819	228	363
167	210	1127	1157	1496	1026	1326	509	1216	747	272
168	1414	246	1039	859	1492	834	1272	705	843	316
169	155	557	952	1711	1279	707	781	586	175	199
170	1020	1620	1332	60	658	1052	185	774	82	1664
171	1524	670	961	839	152	260	988	1547	249	1005
172	422	218	524	1456	623	1224	888	294	168	1500
173	476	845	675	565	1409	1383	208	183	54	1453
174	1694	1060	56	1723	1336	969	1197	401	123	1013
175	19	188	1397	896	354	1355	805	573	1431	849
176	194	1702	732	1320	802	409	1072	318	1538	362
177	1325	245	704	1710	198	1051	669	1546	1455	1499
178	1382	1059	400	895	848	408	244	1545	894	

POWER RESIDUES

	0	1	2	3	4	5	6	7	8	9
150	1729	1429	1418	1352	956	369	425	761	988	561
151	1577	517	1313	722	754	946	309	65	390	551
152	1517	157	942	285	1710	1315	734	826	1378	1112
153	1305	674	466	1007	675	472	1043	891	1768	1663
154	1033	831	1408	1292	596	1787	1777	1717	1357	986
155	549	1505	85	510	1271	470	1031	819	1336	860
156	1582	547	1493	13	78	468	1019	747	904	57
157	342	263	1578	523	1349	938	261	1566	451	917
158	135	810	1282	536	1427	1406	1280	524	1355	974
159	477	1073	1071	1059	987	555	1541	301	17	102
160	612	94	564	1595	625	172	1032	825	1372	1076
161	1089	1167	1635	865	1612	727	784	1126	1389	1178
162	1701	1261	410	671	448	899	27	162	972	465
163	1001	639	256	1536	271	1626	811	1288	572	1643
164	913	111	666	418	719	736	838	1450	1544	319
165	125	750	922	165	990	573	1649	949	327	173
166	1038	861	1588	583	1709	1309	698	610	82	492
167	1163	1611	721	748	910	93	558	1559	409	665
168	412	683	520	1331	830	1402	1256	380	491	1157
169	1575	505	1241	290	1740	1495	25	150	900	33
170	198	1188	1761	1621	781	1108	1281	530	1391	1190
171	1773	1693	1213	122	732	814	1306	680	502	1223
172	182	1092	1185	1743	1513	133	798	1210	104	624
173	166	996	609	76	456	947	315	101	606	58
174	348	299	5	30	180	1080	1113	1311	710	682
175	514	1295	614	106	636	238	1428	1412	1316	740
176	862	1594	619	136	816	1318	752	934	237	1422
177	1376	1100	1233	242	1452	1556	391	557	1553	373
178	449	905	63	378	479	1085	1143	1491		

P = 1801

INDICES

	0	1	2	3	4	5	6	7	8	9
0		0	1584	532	1368	1142	316	92	1152	1064
1	926	1	100	211	1676	1674	936	70	848	1013
2	710	624	1585	465	1684	484	1795	1596	1460	639
3	1458	1009	720	533	1654	1234	632	1716	797	743
4	494	963	408	734	1369	406	249	1777	1468	184
5	268	602	1579	146	1380	1143	1244	1545	423	451
6	1242	981	793	1156	504	1353	317	1356	1438	997
7	1018	411	416	1200	1500	1016	581	93	527	471
8	278	328	747	699	192	1212	518	1171	1153	814
9	190	303	33	1541	1561	355	1252	1195	1768	1065
10	52	1022	386	1098	1363	1766	1730	778	1164	1509
11	927	448	1028	956	1329	1607	207	1275	235	162
12	1026	2	765	1495	577	1626	940	1489	288	1266
13	1137	657	101	1105	1140	938	1222	1399	781	105
14	802	509	195	212	200	1781	984	716	1284	1011
15	800	1701	365	1134	1677	351	311	599	255	678
16	62	557	112	251	531	1675	483	631	1776	422
17	996	277	302	385	955	576	937	983	598	1775
18	1774	138	87	1513	1617	1058	1325	71	1345	1688
19	139	583	1036	340	979	85	1552	1296	849	762
20	1636	88	806	731	170	305	882	1529	1147	1014
21	1550	704	1514	943	562	76	948	1101	1293	1732
22	711	281	232	1618	812	1548	740	522	1113	1657
23	1391	625	1791	4	1059	1119	19	1003	1746	1096
24	810	337	1586	860	549	1326	1279	1224	361	1231
25	1410	377	724	466	1273	1744	72	592	1050	8
26	921	1703	441	402	1685	1288	889	1346	924	655
27	722	1160	1006	835	1183	485	565	689	1689	273
28	586	391	293	1682	1779	887	1796	1055	1784	140
29	1565	1727	768	1318	500	1593	1068	1597	795	676
30	584	826	1485	1554	149	323	918	647	1461	1630
31	135	1037	95	1577	383	498	39	706	462	640
32	1646	1310	341	1083	1696	695	35	241	315	69
33	1459	742	267	980	415	698	1560	1765	206	1488
34	780	1010	61	276	86	339	169	75	739	1002
35	360	7	721	390	767	1553	382	694	1559	74
36	1558	226	1722	534	1671	542	1297	512	1401	227
37	842	238	1109	1162	1655	358	1129	850	1472	419
38	1723	221	367	187	820	1235	124	1798	763	858
39	1669	535	1336	1189	1080	1613	633	475	546	1637
40	1420	828	1672	1220	590	1470	515	1717	1754	1207
41	89	131	666	543	1313	41	931	637	798	1158
42	1334	807	488	1041	1298	554	727	1073	346	744
43	1660	1425	732	529	885	513	1077	1478	1516	1738
44	495	1248	65	171	16	156	1402	1543	596	674
45	1332	964	524	433	306	1445	897	228	1441	1666
46	1175	1166	409	1034	1575	883	1588	1788	843	1448
47	903	1131	1603	735	787	1497	1530	1210	880	239
48	594	127	121	1089	1370	537	644	1148	333	783
49	1110	683	1063	709	1008	407	145	503	1015	517

POWER RESIDUES

	0	1	2	3	4	5	6	7	8	9
0	1	11	121	1331	233	762	1178	351	259	1048
1	722	738	914	1049	733	859	444	1282	1495	236
2	795	1541	742	958	1533	654	1791	1691	591	1098
3	1272	1385	827	92	1012	326	1785	1625	1666	316
4	1675	415	963	1588	1259	1242	1055	799	1585	1226
5	879	664	100	1100	1294	1627	1688	558	735	881
6	686	342	160	1760	1350	442	1260	1253	1176	329
7	17	187	256	1015	359	347	215	564	801	1607
8	1468	1740	1130	1624	1655	195	344	182	201	410
9	908	983	7	77	847	312	1631	1732	1042	656
10	12	132	1452	1564	995	139	1529	610	1307	1770
11	1460	1652	162	1782	1592	1303	1726	976	1731	1031
12	535	482	1700	690	386	644	1681	481	1689	569
13	856	411	919	1104	1338	310	1609	1490	181	190
14	289	1378	750	1046	700	496	53	583	1010	304
15	1543	764	1200	593	1120	1514	445	1293	1616	1567
16	1028	502	119	1309	1792	1702	712	628	1505	346
17	204	443	1271	1374	706	562	779	1365	607	1274
18	1407	1069	953	1478	49	539	526	383	611	1318
19	90	990	84	924	1159	142	1562	973	1698	668
20	144	1584	1215	758	1134	1668	338	116	1276	1429
21	1311	13	143	1573	1094	1228	901	906	961	1566
22	1017	381	589	1076	1030	524	361	369	457	1425
23	1267	1330	222	641	1648	118	1298	1671	371	479
24	1667	327	1796	1746	1196	549	636	1593	1314	46
25	506	163	1793	1713	833	158	1738	1108	1382	794
26	1530	621	1428	1300	1693	613	1340	332	50	550
27	647	1714	844	279	1268	1341	343	171	80	880
28	675	221	630	1527	588	1065	909	994	128	1408
29	1080	1074	1008	282	1301	1704	734	870	565	812
30	1728	998	172	91	1001	205	454	1392	904	939
31	1324	156	1716	866	521	328	6	66	726	782
32	1398	970	1665	305	1554	885	730	826	81	891
33	796	1552	863	488	1766	1416	1168	241	850	345
34	193	322	1741	1141	1745	1185	428	1106	1360	552
35	669	155	1705	745	991	95	1045	689	375	523
36	350	248	927	1192	505	152	1672	382	600	1197
37	560	757	1123	1547	808	1684	514	251	960	1555
38	896	851	356	314	1653	173	102	1122	1536	687
39	353	281	1290	1583	1204	637	1604	1435	1377	739
40	925	1170	263	1092	1206	659	45	495	42	462
41	1480	71	781	1387	849	334	72	792	1508	379
42	567	834	169	58	638	1615	1556	907	972	1687
43	547	614	1351	453	1381	783	1409	1091	1195	538
44	515	262	1081	1085	1129	1613	1534	665	111	1221
45	824	59	649	1736	1086	1140	1734	1064	898	873
46	598	1175	318	1697	657	23	253	982	1797	1757
47	1317	79	869	554	691	397	765	1211	714	650
48	1747	1207	670	166	25	275	1224	857	422	1040
49	634	1571	1072	986	40	440	1238	1011	315	1664

P = 1801

INDICES

	0	1	2	3	4	5	6	7	8	9
50	1194	1163	161	1136	508	364	250	954	1057	1551
51	1528	1292	1656	809	376	440	834	1778	1592	917
52	705	314	1487	359	225	1108	186	1079	1469	930
53	1072	1515	673	1174	1130	120	708	507	439	185
54	506	966	944	670	790	851	619	430	967	245
55	269	1652	349	563	473	1590	1473	1505	57	945
56	370	603	175	1396	77	298	1466	420	1563	129
57	671	1521	1580	1115	839	949	1568	1386	1724	872
58	1349	791	1511	147	552	617	1102	862	284	222
59	1377	28	852	153	1381	1304	579	1294	460	1736
60	368	1052	610	620	1269	1144	1338	178	1733	1263
61	107	188	702	265	431	837	1245	1536	1414	712
62	1719	261	821	906	1679	968	1361	1546	167	1786
63	282	1301	1623	1236	490	831	246	395	424	1475
64	1430	233	1094	1556	125	608	867	270	1480	452
65	479	1633	1619	1523	25	1799	99	464	1653	405
66	1243	1355	526	813	51	447	764	1104	199	350
67	482	982	1344	761	1549	280	1790	859	1272	1287
68	564	1054	794	1629	1645	741	60	389	1670	357
69	123	474	1753	1157	1659	1247	523	1033	786	536
70	144	953	1591	929	505	1651	174	1114	551	1303
71	1337	1535	166	1474	478	1354	1343	1628	1658	1650
72	1342	1190	10	869	1506	1123	318	1191	1455	1392
73	326	804	1081	14	296	58	1185	1357	11	399
74	626	1756	22	1614	893	353	946	1763	1439	870
75	142	1792	913	909	634	1043	1256	371	203	998
76	1507	1389	5	1601	151	476	1771	662	604	1518
77	1019	1124	1708	1060	1582	1493	547	540	642	176
78	1453	412	319	435	1120	1741	973	1638	864	934
79	1397	1048	417	1192	259	20	330	845	1421	47
80	1204	78	612	1201	1456	1699	1004	1187	374	829
81	1254	1091	299	1692	1501	1393	1538	1747	991	1367
82	1673	1794	1715	1467	450	1017	327	32	1097	1328
83	1625	1221	715	254	421	1773	582	805	942	811
84	1118	1278	591	923	272	1564	825	94	1082	414
85	338	381	511	1471	857	1419	130	487	528	15
86	1444	1587	1209	332	516	1527	313	672	669	472
87	297	1567	861	459	1262	1718	1300	1093	1522	50
88	279	59	1032	550	1649	325	1755	912	1600	1581
89	1740	329	1186	990	1327	1117	380	1208	458	1648
90	1116	216	748	1358	308	1280	217	427	90	286
91	1229	840	681	700	12	855	1225	749	1450	132
92	959	1179	950	622	193	400	818	362	1359	1761
93	667	1197	1372	1569	1572	1213	627	1416	1232	309
94	687	544	915	1428	1387	1030	519	1757	571	1411
95	1281	1238	1314	182	994	1725	664	1172	23	1491
96	378	218	1711	42	1705	1482	873	1321	1154	1615
97	321	725	428	197	932	1227	117	1350	567	815
98	894	773	467	91	847	638	493	601	792	1199
99	191	354	1729	1274	287	104	799	556	301	1512

POWER RESIDUES

	0	1	2	3	4	5	6	7	8	9
50	294	1433	1355	497	64	704	540	537	504	141
51	1551	852	367	435	1183	406	864	499	86	946
52	1401	1003	227	696	452	1370	662	78	858	433
53	1161	164	3	33	363	391	699	485	1733	1053
54	777	1343	365	413	941	1346	398	776	1332	244
55	883	708	584	1021	425	1073	997	161	1771	1471
56	1773	1493	214	553	680	276	1235	978	1753	1273
57	1396	948	1423	1245	1088	1162	175	124	1364	596
58	1153	76	836	191	300	1499	280	1279	1462	1674
59	404	842	257	1026	480	1678	448	1326	178	157
60	1727	987	51	561	768	1244	1077	1041	645	1692
61	602	1219	802	1618	1589	1270	1363	585	1032	546
62	603	1230	923	1148	21	231	740	936	1291	1594
63	1325	167	36	396	754	1090	1184	417	985	29
64	319	1708	778	1354	486	1744	1174	307	1576	1127
65	1591	1292	1605	1446	1498	269	1158	131	1441	1443
66	1465	1707	767	1233	956	1511	412	930	1225	868
67	543	570	867	532	449	1337	299	1488	159	1749
68	1229	912	1027	491	1799	1779	1559	940	1335	277
69	1246	1099	1283	1506	357	325	1774	1504	335	83
70	913	1038	612	1329	211	520	317	1686	536	493
71	20	220	619	1406	1058	832	147	1617	1578	1149
72	32	352	270	1169	252	971	1676	426	1084	1118
73	1492	203	432	1150	43	473	1601	1402	1014	348
74	226	685	331	39	429	1117	1481	82	902	917
75	1082	1096	1250	1143	1767	1427	1289	1572	1083	1107
76	1371	673	199	388	666	122	1342	354	292	1411
77	1113	1437	1399	981	1786	1636	1787	1647	107	1177
78	340	138	1518	489	1777	1537	698	474	1612	1523
79	544	581	988	62	682	298	1477	38	418	996
80	150	1650	140	1540	731	837	202	421	1029	513
81	240	839	224	663	89	979	1764	1394	926	1181
82	384	622	1439	1421	1223	846	301	1510	401	809
83	1695	635	1582	1193	516	273	1202	615	1362	574
84	911	1016	370	468	1546	797	1563	984	18	198
85	377	545	592	1109	1393	915	1060	854	389	677
86	243	872	587	1054	788	1464	1696	646	1703	723
87	749	1035	579	966	1621	1622	1633	1754	1284	1517
88	478	1656	206	465	1513	434	1172	285	1334	266
89	1125	1569	1050	744	980	1775	1515	456	1414	1146
90	1800	1790	1680	470	1568	1039	623	1450	1542	753
91	1079	1063	887	752	1068	942	1357	519	306	1565
92	1006	260	1059	843	268	1147	10	110	1210	703
93	529	416	974	1709	789	1475	16	176	135	1485
94	126	1386	838	213	542	559	746	1002	216	575
95	922	1137	1701	701	507	174	113	1243	1066	920
96	1115	1459	1641	41	451	1359	541	548	625	1472
97	1784	1614	1545	786	1442	1454	1586	1237	1000	194
98	333	61	671	177	146	1606	1457	1619	1600	1391
99	893	818	1794	1724	954	1489	170	69	759	1145

P = 1801

INDICES

	0	1	2	3	4	5	6	7	8	9
100	978	304	947	521	1745	1230	920	1159	292	1317
101	148	497	34	1764	738	73	841	220	1335	1219
102	1312	553	1076	1542	1440	1447	593	682	160	808
103	224	119	618	1504	1562	871	1376	1051	701	905
104	489	607	98	1103	1271	356	143	1534	9	13
105	892	1042	1770	539	863	46	1253	1793	714	922
106	856	1526	1299	911	457	285	958	1196	914	181
107	1704	1226	492	555	291	1218	223	606	1769	910
108	290	442	750	758	728	443	454	1378	574	1066
109	635	437	403	1451	214	1074	751	1405	29	691
110	53	1044	1436	1686	133	1423	347	759	257	853
111	1374	1023	1257	770	1289	960	1641	745	729	1694
112	154	1464	387	372	1759	890	1180	649	1661	444
113	82	1382	1250	1099	204	1664	1347	951	1713	1426
114	455	343	1305	753	1364	999	899	925	623	719
115	733	1379	1352	580	1170	1767	1508	1025	656	194
116	1133	530	575	1324	1295	1146	1731	1390	336	723
117	401	1182	886	1067	646	461	68	779	6	1721
118	1161	819	1612	514	636	345	1737	1331	1165	1602
119	1088	1007	363	833	1078	438	244	369	1520	1510
120	152	1268	836	1360	394	1479	404	481	1053	1752
121	928	477	1122	1184	1762	202	1517	1452	1047	611
122	1691	449	1772	824	486	668	49	1739	215	680
123	621	1571	1029	663	1320	566	1198	977	496	1075
124	1503	1270	45	957	605	573	690	1373	1463	1249
125	752	1169	1145	67	1330	1519	1751	1690	1570	44
126	66	1406	1085	1339	1407	1608	1020	230	274	1573
127	615	172	30	569	179	1086	208	1125	1259	587
128	1214	1605	17	692	878	1734	1340	1276	1709	756
129	392	628	651	157	54	1150	1264	1408	236	1061
130	263	294	1417	115	1403	1045	1307	108	1609	163
131	1583	210	1683	1233	248	1544	1437	470	189	1021
132	1027	1494	1139	1780	310	630	597	1687	1635	703
133	231	3	548	1743	888	688	1783	675	134	1309
134	266	275	766	541	1128	1797	545	1206	1333	1424
135	64	432	1574	1496	643	502	1056	916	1071	965
136	348	1395	838	616	578	177	1413	1785	1429	1632
137	525	760	1644	1246	173	1627	1454	398	141	1388
138	1707	434	258	1698	1537	31	941	413	1443	1566
139	1031	989	307	854	817	1415	570	1490	320	772
140	1728	520	737	1446	1375	1533	713	180	289	436
141	1435	769	1758	1663	898	1024	335	1720	1087	1267
142	1121	823	1319	572	1750	229	1258	755	262	209
143	1138	1742	1127	501	1412	397	1442	771	1434	822
144	1126	658	974	659	1594	1282	653	1667	1290	1621
145	907	1260	102	1639	975	1069	1239	986	1176	961
146	110	1680	588	1106	865	660	1598	1315	80	1167
147	1642	559	969	1215	1141	935	1595	796	183	1241
148	410	746	1540	1362	1606	939	1398	1283	677	995
149	137	1035	730	561	1547	18	1223	1049	654	585

POWER RESIDUES

	0	1	2	3	4	5	6	7	8	9
100	1789	1669	349	237	806	1662	272	1191	494	31
101	341	149	1639	19	209	498	75	825	70	770
102	1266	1319	101	1111	1415	1157	120	1320	112	1232
103	945	1390	882	697	463	1491	192	311	1620	1611
104	1512	423	1051	755	1101	1305	1748	1218	791	1497
105	258	1037	601	1208	681	287	1356	508	185	234
106	773	1299	1682	492	9	99	1089	1173	296	1455
107	1597	1358	530	427	1095	1239	1022	436	1194	527
108	394	732	848	323	1752	1262	1275	1418	1190	483
109	1711	811	1717	877	642	1659	239	828	103	1133
110	1657	217	586	1043	667	133	1463	1685	525	372
111	490	1788	1658	228	707	573	900	895	840	235
112	784	1420	1212	725	771	1277	1440	1432	1344	376
113	534	471	1579	1160	153	1683	503	130	1430	1322
114	134	1474	5	55	605	1252	1165	208	487	1755
115	1295	1638	8	88	968	1643	63	693	419	1007
116	271	1180	373	501	108	1188	461	1469	1751	1251
117	1154	87	957	1522	533	460	1458	1630	1721	921
118	1126	1580	1171	274	1213	736	892	807	1673	393
119	721	727	793	1519	500	97	1067	931	1236	989
120	73	803	1629	1710	800	1596	1347	409	897	862
121	477	1645	85	935	1280	1473	1795	1735	1075	1019
122	403	831	136	1496	247	916	1071	975	1720	910
123	1005	249	938	1313	35	385	633	1560	951	1456
124	1608	1479	60	660	56	616	1373	695	441	1249
125	1132	1646	96	1056	810	1706	756	1112	1426	1278
126	1451	1553	874	609	1296	1649	129	1419	1201	604
127	1241	1044	678	254	993	117	1287	1550	841	246
128	905	950	1445	1487	148	1628	1699	679	265	1114
129	1448	1520	511	218	597	1164	197	366	424	1062
130	876	631	1538	709	595	1142	1756	1306	1759	1339
131	321	1730	1020	414	952	1467	1729	1009	293	1422
132	1234	967	1632	1743	1163	186	245	894	829	114
133	1254	1187	450	1348	420	1018	392	710	606	1263
134	1286	1539	720	716	672	188	267	1136	1690	580
135	977	1742	1152	65	715	661	67	737	903	928
136	1203	626	1483	104	1144	1778	1548	819	4	44
137	484	1722	932	1247	1110	1404	1036	590	1087	1151
138	54	594	1131	1635	1776	1526	577	944	1379	761
139	1167	230	729	815	1761	1361	563	790	1486	137
140	1507	368	446	1304	1737	1097	1261	1264	1297	1660
141	250	949	1434	1366	618	1395	937	1302	1715	855
142	400	798	1574	1105	1349	431	1139	1723	943	1368
143	640	1637	1798	1768	1438	1410	1102	1316	68	748
144	1024	458	1436	1388	860	455	1403	1025	469	1557
145	918	1093	1217	780	1376	728	804	1640	30	330
146	28	308	1587	1248	1121	1525	566	823	48	528
147	405	853	378	556	713	639	1626	1677	437	1205
148	648	1725	965	1610	1501	302	1521	522	339	127
149	1397	959	1544	775	1321	123	1353	475	1623	1644

P = 1801

INDICES

	0	1	2	3	4	5	6	7	8	9
150	1726	1484	1576	1695	697	168	693	1400	418	1668
151	827	665	1040	884	155	896	1787	879	782	1193
152	1291	1486	1173	789	1589	1465	1385	283	1735	106
153	260	1622	1555	24	446	1789	388	785	1302	1341
154	803	21	908	150	1492	972	844	373	1366	1624
155	1277	510	331	1261	324	379	426	1449	1760	686
156	1237	1710	196	846	103	919	219	159	904	891
157	1525	491	757	213	1422	1640	648	1712	718	1132
158	1181	1611	832	393	201	48	976	1462	43	614
159	1604	650	114	247	629	1782	1205	1070	1631	1706
160	988	736	1662	1749	396	652	985	79	1240	136
161	1483	1039	788	445	971	425	158	717	613	987
162	1038	874	875	1498	83	37	1476	55	1285	1202
163	1177	96	1322	876	1531	1383	775	1431	1151	1012
164	1457	962	1578	1155	1499	1211	1251	777	234	1265
165	801	1700	111	384	1616	84	881	1100	1112	1095
166	1409	1702	1005	1681	499	322	38	240	205	1001
167	1557	237	366	1188	589	40	726	1477	595	1665
168	902	126	1062	1135	375	1107	707	429	56	128
169	1348	27	609	264	1678	830	866	463	198	1286
170	122	952	165	868	295	352	1255	661	641	933
171	1203	1090	1714	253	271	1418	312	1092	1599	1647
172	1228	1178	1371	1427	993	1481	116	600	300	1316
173	1311	118	97	538	456	1217	453	1404	256	1693
174	81	342	1351	1323	645	344	243	480	1046	679
175	1502	1168	1084	568	877	1149	1306	469	1634	1308
176	63	1394	1643	1697	816	1532	334	754	1433	1620
177	109	558	1539	560	696	895	1384	784	1365	685
178	1524	1610	113	1748	970	36	774	776	1111	1000
179	901	26	164	252	992	1216	242	468	1432	684
180	900	0								

POWER RESIDUES

	0	1	2	3	4	5	6	7	8	9
150	74	814	1750	1240	1033	557	724	760	1156	109
151	1199	582	999	183	212	531	438	1216	769	1255
152	1198	571	878	653	1780	1570	1061	865	510	207
153	476	1634	1765	1405	1047	711	617	1384	816	1772
154	1482	93	1023	447	1315	57	627	1494	225	674
155	210	509	196	355	303	1532	643	1670	360	358
156	336	94	1034	568	845	290	1389	871	576	933
157	1258	1231	934	1269	1352	464	1502	313	1642	52
158	572	889	774	1310	2	22	242	861	466	1524
159	555	702	518	295	1444	1476	27	297	1466	1718
160	888	763	1189	472	1590	1281	1484	115	1265	1308
161	1781	1581	1182	395	743	969	1654	184	223	652
162	1769	1449	1531	632	1549	830	125	1375	717	683
163	309	1598	1369	651	1758	1328	200	399	787	1453
164	1575	1116	1470	1762	1372	684	320	1719	899	884
165	719	705	551	658	34	374	512	229	718	694
166	430	1128	1602	1413	1135	1679	459	1447	1509	390
167	688	364	402	820	15	165	14	154	1694	624
168	1461	1663	283	1312	24	264	1103	1327	189	278
169	1257	1220	813	1739	1119	1503	324	1763	1383	805
170	1651	151	1661	261	1070	964	1599	1380	772	1288
171	1561	962	1577	1138	1712	822	37	407	875	620
172	1417	1179	362	380	578	955	1500	291	1400	992
173	106	1166	219	608	1285	1528	599	1186	439	1227
174	890	785	1431	1333	255	1004	238	817	1783	1603
175	1424	1256	1209	692	408	886	741	947	1412	1124
176	1558	929	1214	747	1013	337	105	1155	98	1078
177	1052	766	1222	835	180	179	168	47	517	284
178	1323	145	1595	1336	288	1367	629	1516	467	1535
179	676	232	751	1057	821	26	286	1345	387	655
180										

P = 1811

INDICES

	0	1	2	3	4	5	6	7	8	9
0		0	525	1286	1050	466	1	1450	1575	762
1	991	554	526	1416	165	1752	290	1454	1287	1125
2	1516	926	1079	942	1051	932	131	238	690	1698
3	467	98	815	30	169	106	2	1245	1650	892
4	231	751	1451	1730	1604	1228	1467	187	1576	1090
5	1457	930	656	1498	763	1020	1215	601	413	1189
6	992	658	623	402	1340	72	555	1192	694	418
7	631	1785	527	1043	1770	408	365	194	1417	869
8	756	1524	1276	673	166	110	445	1174	319	1297
9	1753	1056	182	1384	712	1591	291	1500	1615	1316
10	172	163	1455	443	1181	1392	213	121	1288	1807
11	1545	721	1740	91	1126	1408	938	368	1714	1094
12	1517	1108	1183	227	1148	1398	927	770	55	1206
13	597	777	1080	765	1717	704	1219	1766	943	539
14	1156	1473	500	160	1052	354	1568	566	485	1321
15	933	1284	890	406	719	564	132	517	1394	974
16	1281	582	239	1638	1801	496	1198	1387	691	1022
17	635	77	970	1438	1699	572	844	665	12	840
18	468	1724	1581	134	707	1711	99	198	1237	1688
19	306	325	816	103	215	1358	330	1793	31	1659
20	697	668	688	1338	170	1217	968	1704	1706	1679
21	107	1367	738	1261	646	386	3	1548	522	519
22	260	1060	1246	1378	455	1694	616	701	1651	1161
23	123	1480	1463	1733	893	653	429	345	1619	398
24	232	603	1633	1000	1708	1556	752	731	1673	149
25	113	218	1452	1496	1295	1396	580	1791	1731	885
26	1122	650	1302	827	1605	154	1290	773	432	887
27	1229	805	1744	532	481	1486	1468	415	1064	860
28	1681	492	188	995	1025	1067	685	391	1577	1098
29	879	976	283	592	1091	1655	1010	792	36	548
30	1458	1370	1809	1449	1415	1124	931	97	1244	1729
31	1089	1019	657	1191	1042	868	109	1055	1499	442
32	1806	1407	1107	769	764	538	353	1283	516	1637
33	1021	571	1723	197	102	1658	1216	1366	1547	1377
34	1160	652	602	730	1495	884	153	804	414	994
35	1097	1654	1369	96	1190	441	537	570	1365	729
36	993	440	439	584	296	1509	659	585	1232	1513
37	426	1138	624	297	723	874	1762	1304	403	1510
38	831	246	850	715	1341	660	628	682	740	1251
39	73	586	855	253	508	1335	556	1233	374	241
40	1222	1559	1193	1514	1213	180	53	1799	695	427
41	1742	1242	1493	829	419	1139	421	15	394	559
42	632	625	82	949	1263	576	1786	298	1171	1446
43	911	1029	528	724	263	1640	1047	257	1044	875
44	785	42	1585	747	1771	1763	93	797	980	1607
45	409	1305	1141	760	1226	1522	366	404	1686	1692
46	648	790	195	1511	178	40	448	1361	1418	832
47	1178	1803	954	474	870	247	334	450	923	342
48	757	851	1128	58	348	156	1525	716	423	1114
49	271	1166	1277	1342	1256	1782	388	1425	674	661

POWER RESIDUES

	0	1	2	3	4	5	6	7	8	9
0	1	6	36	216	1296	532	1381	1042	819	1292
1	508	1237	178	1068	975	417	691	524	1333	754
2	902	1790	1685	1055	897	1760	1505	1786	1661	911
3	33	198	1188	1695	1115	1257	298	1788	1673	983
4	465	979	441	835	1388	1084	1071	993	525	1339
5	790	1118	1275	406	625	128	768	986	483	1087
6	1089	1101	1173	1605	575	1639	779	1052	879	1652
7	857	1520	65	390	529	1363	934	171	1026	723
8	716	674	422	721	704	602	1801	1751	1451	1462
9	1528	113	678	446	865	1568	353	307	31	186
10	1116	1263	334	193	1158	1515	35	210	1260	316
11	85	510	1249	250	1500	1756	1481	1642	797	1160
12	1527	107	642	230	1380	1036	783	1076	1023	705
13	608	26	156	936	183	1098	1155	1497	1738	1373
14	994	531	1375	1006	603	1807	1787	1667	947	249
15	1494	1720	1265	346	265	1590	485	1099	1161	1533
16	143	858	1526	101	606	14	84	504	1213	34
17	204	1224	100	600	1789	1679	1019	681	464	973
18	405	619	92	552	1501	1762	1517	47	282	1692
19	1097	1149	1461	1522	77	462	961	333	187	1122
20	1299	550	1489	1690	1085	1077	1029	741	824	1322
21	688	506	1225	106	636	194	1164	1551	251	1506
22	1792	1697	1127	1329	730	758	926	123	738	806
23	1214	40	240	1440	1396	1132	1359	910	27	162
24	972	399	583	1687	1067	969	381	475	1039	801
25	1184	1671	971	393	547	1471	1582	437	811	1244
26	220	1320	676	434	793	1136	1383	1054	891	1724
27	1289	490	1129	1341	802	1190	1707	1187	1689	1079
28	1041	813	1256	292	1752	1457	1498	1744	1409	1210
29	16	96	576	1645	815	1268	364	373	427	751
30	884	1682	1037	789	1112	1239	190	1140	1407	1198
31	1755	1475	1606	581	1675	995	537	1411	1222	88
32	528	1357	898	1766	1541	191	1146	1443	1414	1240
33	196	1176	1623	683	476	1045	837	1400	1156	1503
34	1774	1589	479	1063	945	237	1422	1288	484	1093
35	1125	1317	658	326	145	870	1598	533	1387	1078
36	1035	777	1040	807	1220	76	456	925	117	702
37	590	1729	1319	670	398	577	1651	851	1484	1660
38	905	1808	1793	1703	1163	1545	215	1290	496	1165
39	1557	287	1722	1277	418	697	560	1549	239	1434
40	1360	916	63	378	457	931	153	918	75	450
41	889	1712	1217	58	348	277	1662	917	69	414
42	673	416	685	488	1117	1269	370	409	643	236
43	1416	1252	268	1608	593	1747	1427	1318	664	362
44	361	355	319	103	618	86	516	1285	466	985
45	477	1051	873	1616	641	224	1344	820	1298	544
46	1453	1474	1600	545	1459	1510	5	30	180	1080
47	1047	849	1472	1588	473	1027	729	752	890	1718
48	1253	274	1644	809	1232	148	888	1706	1181	1653
49	863	1556	281	1686	1061	933	165	990	507	1231

P = 1811

INDICES

	0	1	2	3	4	5	6	7	8	9
50	638	863	743	1428	167	629	211	498	10	644
51	111	683	1105	1363	506	909	446	741	1410	914
52	1647	1292	1175	1252	17	48	1352	1552	320	74
53	679	141	5	357	1298	587	957	316	1412	1644
54	1754	856	1330	1200	459	463	1057	254	1006	1420
55	201	1013	183	509	940	1187	1589	775	1385	1336
56	396	1484	1017	802	713	557	1520	1164	1550	800
57	1592	1234	1210	1611	916	64	292	375	1623	1389
58	1404	313	1501	242	808	834	1117	1076	1616	1223
59	370	1269	1535	434	1317	1560	561	1135	1073	1594
60	173	1194	85	144	524	1574	164	1515	130	814
61	1649	1603	1456	1214	622	693	1769	755	444	181
62	1614	1180	1544	937	1182	54	1716	1155	1567	889
63	1393	1800	634	843	1580	1236	214	696	967	737
64	521	454	122	428	1632	1672	1294	1121	1289	1743
65	1063	1024	878	1009	1808	1243	1041	1805	352	1722
66	1546	1494	1096	536	438	1231	722	830	627	854
67	373	1212	1741	420	81	1170	262	784	92	1140
68	1685	177	1177	333	1127	422	1255	637	210	1104
69	1409	16	678	956	1329	1005	939	395	1519	1209
70	1622	807	369	560	84	129	621	1613	1715	633
71	966	1631	1062	1040	1095	626	80	1684	1254	677
72	1518	83	965	79	964	820	1109	950	821	476
73	224	1374	1184	1264	1110	1032	1757	1746	228	577
74	951	207	1663	918	1149	1787	822	1435	1248	1571
75	1399	299	477	1504	19	1750	928	1172	225	972
76	1356	1478	771	1447	1375	872	1240	795	56	912
77	1185	1267	1153	534	1207	1030	1265	361	1776	66
78	598	529	1111	126	1380	983	778	725	1033	303
79	50	1541	1081	264	1758	1440	899	118	766	1641
80	1747	249	274	1597	1718	1048	229	363	1738	483
81	705	258	578	281	514	294	1220	1045	952	8
82	457	1402	1767	876	208	962	1354	897	944	786
83	1664	1701	946	734	540	43	919	336	1084	1145
84	1157	1586	1150	1778	607	1488	1474	748	1788	471
85	1101	377	501	1772	823	543	1696	70	161	1764
86	1436	1677	1554	490	1053	94	1249	574	788	1423
87	355	798	1572	452	782	1038	1569	981	1400	68
88	1310	1470	567	1608	300	1131	1272	1625	486	410
89	478	268	618	1312	1322	1306	1505	24	322	1796
90	934	1142	20	846	1666	380	1285	761	1751	925
91	237	29	891	1227	929	600	401	417	407	1523
92	1173	1383	1315	1391	720	367	226	1205	703	1472
93	565	405	973	495	76	664	133	1687	1357	667
94	1703	1260	518	1693	1479	344	999	148	1395	649
95	772	531	859	1066	975	791	1448	1728	867	1406
96	1282	196	1376	883	1653	569	583	1512	873	245
97	681	252	240	179	1241	14	948	1445	1639	41
98	796	759	1691	39	1802	449	57	1113	1781	862
99	497	1362	913	47	140	315	1199	1419	1186	1483

POWER RESIDUES

	0	1	2	3	4	5	6	7	8	9
50	142	852	1490	1696	1121	1293	514	1273	394	553
51	1507	1798	1733	1343	814	1262	328	157	942	219
52	1314	640	218	1308	604	2	12	72	432	781
53	1064	951	273	1638	773	1016	663	356	325	139
54	834	1382	1048	855	1508	1804	1769	1559	299	1794
55	1709	1199	1761	1511	11	66	396	565	1579	419
56	703	596	1765	1535	155	930	147	882	1670	965
57	357	331	175	1050	867	1580	425	739	812	1250
58	256	1536	161	966	363	367	391	535	1399	1150
59	1467	1558	293	1758	1493	1714	1229	130	780	1058
60	915	57	342	241	1446	1432	1348	844	1442	1408
61	1204	1791	1691	1091	1113	1245	226	1356	892	1730
62	1325	706	614	62	372	421	715	668	386	505
63	1219	70	420	709	632	170	1020	687	500	1189
64	1701	1151	1473	1594	509	1243	214	1284	460	949
65	261	1566	341	235	1410	1216	52	312	61	366
66	385	499	1183	1665	935	177	1062	939	201	1206
67	1803	1763	1523	83	498	1177	1629	719	692	530
68	1369	970	387	511	1255	286	1716	1241	202	1212
69	28	168	1008	615	68	408	637	200	1200	1767
70	1547	227	1362	928	135	810	1238	184	1104	1191
71	1713	1223	94	564	1573	383	487	1111	1233	154
72	924	111	666	374	433	787	1100	1167	1569	359
73	343	247	1482	1648	833	1376	1012	639	212	1272
74	388	517	1291	502	1201	1773	1583	443	847	1460
75	1516	41	246	1476	1612	617	80	480	1069	981
76	453	907	9	54	324	133	798	1166	1563	323
77	127	762	950	267	1602	557	1531	131	786	1094
78	1131	1353	874	1622	677	440	829	1352	868	1586
79	461	955	297	1782	1637	767	980	447	871	1604
80	569	1603	563	1567	347	271	1626	701	584	1693
81	1103	1185	1677	1007	609	32	192	1152	1479	1630
82	725	728	746	854	1502	1768	1553	263	1578	413
83	667	380	469	1003	585	1699	1139	1401	1162	1539
84	179	1074	1011	633	176	1056	903	1796	1721	1271
85	382	481	1075	1017	669	392	541	1435	1366	952
86	279	1674	989	501	1195	1737	1367	958	315	79
87	474	1033	765	968	375	439	823	1316	652	290
88	1740	1385	1066	963	345	259	1554	269	1614	629
89	152	912	39	234	1404	1180	1647	827	1340	796
90	1154	1491	1702	1157	1509	1810	1805	1775	1595	515
91	1279	430	769	992	519	1303	574	1633	743	836
92	1394	1120	1287	478	1057	909	21	126	756	914
93	51	306	25	150	900	1778	1613	623	116	696
94	554	1513	23	138	828	1346	832	1370	976	423
95	727	740	818	1286	472	1021	693	536	1405	1186
96	1683	1043	825	1328	724	722	710	638	206	1236
97	172	1032	759	932	159	954	291	1746	1421	1282
98	448	877	1640	785	1088	1095	1137	1389	1090	1107
99	1209	10	60	360	349	283	1698	1133	1365	946

P = 1811

INDICES

	0	1	2	3	4	5	6	7	8	9
100	1163	1610	1388	833	1268	1134	143	813	692	1179
101	1154	842	736	1671	1023	1804	535	853	1169	176
102	636	955	1208	128	1630	1683	78	475	1031	206
103	1434	1503	971	871	1266	360	125	302	1439	248
104	362	280	7	961	1700	335	1777	470	542	1676
105	573	451	67	1130	267	23	845	924	599	1382
106	1204	494	666	343	530	1727	882	244	13	758
107	1112	46	1482	1133	841	852	127	205	359	279
108	469	1129	1381	1726	45	204	1725	59	984	60
109	988	613	1582	349	779	985	1531	190	135	157
110	726	61	1538	810	708	1526	1034	989	1465	1274
111	1712	717	304	614	1300	34	100	424	51	1583
112	921	504	199	1115	1542	350	1327	222	1238	272
113	1082	780	235	997	1689	1167	265	986	1325	836
114	307	1278	1759	1532	1735	1627	326	1343	1441	191
115	589	641	817	1257	900	136	338	903	104	1783
116	119	158	838	384	216	389	767	727	1333	1027
117	1359	1426	1642	62	1601	1119	331	675	1748	1539
118	895	488	1794	662	250	811	959	277	32	639
119	275	709	1086	1349	1660	864	1598	1527	309	551
120	698	744	1719	1035	610	1069	669	1429	1049	990
121	289	1078	689	168	230	1466	655	412	1339	630
122	364	1275	318	711	171	212	1739	1713	1147	596
123	1218	499	484	718	1280	1197	969	11	706	305
124	329	687	1705	645	259	615	1462	1618	1707	112
125	579	1301	431	480	1680	684	282	35	1414	1088
126	108	1106	515	101	1159	152	1368	1364	295	425
127	1761	849	739	507	1221	52	1492	393	1262	910
128	1046	1584	979	1225	647	447	953	922	347	270
129	387	742	9	505	1646	1351	4	1411	458	200
130	1588	1016	1549	915	1403	1116	1534	1072	523	1648
131	1768	1543	1566	1579	520	1293	877	351	437	372
132	261	1176	209	1328	1621	620	1061	1253	963	223
133	1756	1662	1247	18	1355	1239	1152	1775	1379	49
134	898	273	1737	513	456	1353	945	1083	606	1100
135	1695	1553	787	781	1309	1271	617	321	1665	236
136	400	1314	702	75	1702	998	858	866	1652	680
137	947	1690	1780	139	1162	142	735	1168	1629	1433
138	124	6	541	266	1203	881	1481	358	44	987
139	1530	1537	1464	1299	920	1326	234	1324	1734	588
140	337	837	1332	1600	894	958	1085	308	609	288
141	654	317	1146	1279	328	1461	430	1413	1158	1760
142	1491	978	346	1645	1587	1533	1565	436	1620	1755
143	1151	1736	605	1308	399	857	1779	1628	1202	1529
144	233	1331	608	327	1490	1564	604	1201	1489	1344
145	1345	88	1634	460	1475	1442	1346	285	1001	464
146	749	192	89	1319	1709	1058	1789	590	1635	1507
147	1557	255	472	642	461	311	753	1007	1102	818
148	1476	116	732	1421	378	1258	1443	1669	1674	202
149	502	901	1347	594	150	1014	1773	137	286	1562

POWER RESIDUES

	0	1	2	3	4	5	6	7	8	9
100	243	1458	1504	1780	1625	695	548	1477	1618	653
101	296	1776	1601	551	1495	1726	1301	562	1561	311
102	55	330	169	1014	651	284	1704	1169	1581	431
103	775	1028	735	788	1106	1203	1785	1655	875	1628
104	713	656	314	73	438	817	1280	436	805	1208
105	4	24	144	864	1562	317	91	546	1465	1546
106	221	1326	712	650	278	1668	953	285	1710	1205
107	1797	1727	1307	598	1777	1607	587	1711	1211	22
108	132	792	1130	1347	838	1406	1192	1719	1259	310
109	49	294	1764	1529	119	714	662	350	289	1734
110	1349	850	1478	1624	689	512	1261	322	121	726
111	734	782	1070	987	489	1123	1305	586	1705	1175
112	1617	647	260	1560	305	19	114	684	482	1081
113	1053	885	1688	1073	1005	597	1771	1571	371	415
114	679	452	901	1784	1649	839	1412	1228	124	744
115	842	1430	1336	772	1010	627	140	840	1418	1264
116	340	229	1374	1000	567	1591	491	1135	1377	1018
117	675	428	757	920	87	522	1321	682	470	1009
118	621	104	624	122	732	770	998	555	1519	59
119	354	313	67	402	601	1795	1715	1235	166	996
120	543	1447	1438	1384	1060	927	129	774	1022	699
121	572	1621	671	404	613	56	336	205	1230	136
122	816	1274	400	589	1723	1283	454	913	45	270
123	1620	665	368	397	571	1615	635	188	1128	1335
124	766	974	411	655	308	37	222	1332	748	866
125	1574	389	523	1327	718	686	494	1153	1485	1666
126	941	213	1278	424	733	776	1034	771	1004	591
127	1735	1355	886	1694	1109	1221	82	492	1141	1413
128	1234	160	960	327	151	906	3	18	108	648
129	266	1596	521	1315	646	254	1524	89	534	1393
130	1114	1251	262	1572	377	451	895	1748	1433	1354
131	880	1658	893	1736	1361	922	99	594	1753	1463
132	1534	149	894	1742	1397	1138	1395	1126	1323	694
133	542	1441	1402	1168	1575	395	559	1543	203	1218
134	64	384	493	1147	1449	1450	1456	1492	1708	1193
135	1725	1295	526	1345	826	1334	760	938	195	1170
136	1587	467	991	513	1267	358	337	211	1266	352
137	301	1806	1781	1631	731	764	962	339	223	1338
138	784	1082	1059	921	93	558	1537	167	1002	579
139	1663	923	105	630	158	948	255	1530	125	750
140	878	1646	821	1304	580	1669	959	321	115	690
141	518	1297	538	1417	1258	304	13	78	468	997
142	549	1483	1654	869	1592	497	1171	1593	503	1207
143	1809	1799	1739	1379	1030	747	860	1538	173	1038
144	795	1148	1455	1486	1672	977	429	763	956	303
145	7	42	252	1512	17	102	612	50	300	1800
146	1745	1415	1246	232	1392	1108	1215	46	276	1656
147	881	1664	929	141	846	1454	1480	1636	761	944
148	231	1386	1072	999	561	1555	275	1650	845	1448
149	1444	1420	1276	412	661	344	253	1518	53	318

P = 1811

INDICES

	0	1	2	3	4	5	6	7	8	9
150	114	184	824	339	1002	26	219	510	544	904
151	465	553	1453	941	1697	105	750	186	1497	1188
152	71	1784	193	672	1296	1590	162	120	90	1093
153	1397	776	1765	159	1320	563	581	1386	1437	839
154	1710	324	1792	1337	1678	385	1059	700	1732	397
155	1555	217	1790	826	886	1485	491	390	591	547
156	1123	1018	1054	768	1636	1657	651	803	95	728
157	1508	1137	1303	714	1250	1334	1558	1798	828	558
158	575	1028	256	746	1606	1521	789	1360	473	341
159	155	1165	1424	1427	643	908	1291	1551	356	1643
160	462	1012	774	801	799	63	312	1075	433	1593
161	1573	1602	754	936	888	1235	453	1120	1008	1721
162	1230	1211	783	332	1103	1004	806	1612	1039	676
163	819	1373	1745	917	1570	1749	1477	794	533	65
164	982	1540	117	1596	482	293	1401	896	733	1144
165	1487	376	69	489	1422	1037	1469	1624	1311	1795
166	379	28	416	1390	1471	663	1259	147	1065	1405
167	568	251	1444	38	861	314	1609	812	1670	175
168	1682	1502	301	960	1675	22	493	243	1132	278
169	203	612	189	809	1273	33	503	221	996	835
170	1626	640	902	383	1026	1118	487	276	1348	550
171	1068	1077	411	710	595	1196	686	1617	479	1087
172	151	848	392	1224	269	1350	1015	1071	1578	371
173	619	1661	1774	512	1099	1270	1313	865	138	1432
174	880	1536	1323	1599	287	1460	977	435	1307	1528
175	1563	87	284	1318	1506	310	115	1668	593	1561
176	25	552	185	671	1092	562	323	699	825	546
177	1656	1136	1797	745	340	907	1011	1074	935	1720
178	1003	1372	793	1595	1143	1036	27	146	37	174
179	21	611	220	382	549	1195	847	1070	511	1431
180	1459	86	1667	670	545	906	1371	145	381	1430
181	905	0								

POWER RESIDUES

	0	1	2	3	4	5	6	7	8	9
150	97	582	1681	1031	753	896	1754	1469	1570	365
151	379	463	967	369	403	607	20	120	720	698
152	566	1585	455	919	81	486	1105	1197	1749	1439
153	1390	1096	1143	1425	1306	592	1741	1391	1102	1179
154	1641	791	1124	1311	622	110	660	338	217	1302
155	568	1597	527	1351	862	1550	245	1470	1576	401
156	595	1759	1499	1750	1445	1426	1312	628	146	876
157	1634	749	872	1610	605	8	48	288	1728	1313
158	634	182	1092	1119	1281	442	841	1424	1300	556
159	1525	95	570	1609	599	1783	1643	803	1196	1743
160	1403	1174	1611	611	44	264	1584	449	883	1676
161	1001	573	1627	707	620	98	588	1717	1247	238
162	1428	1324	700	578	1657	887	1700	1145	1437	1378
163	1024	711	644	242	1452	1468	1564	329	163	978
164	435	799	1172	1599	539	1423	1294	520	1309	610
165	38	228	1368	964	351	295	1770	1565	335	199
166	1194	1731	1331	742	830	1358	904	1802	1757	1487
167	1678	1013	645	248	1488	1684	1049	861	1544	209
168	1254	280	1680	1025	717	680	458	937	189	1134
169	1371	982	459	943	225	1350	856	1514	29	174
170	1044	831	1364	940	207	1242	208	1248	244	1464
171	1540	185	1110	1227	118	708	626	134	804	1202
172	1779	1619	659	332	181	1086	1083	1065	957	309
173	43	258	1548	233	1398	1144	1431	1342	808	1226
174	112	672	410	649	272	1632	737	800	1178	1635
175	755	908	15	90	540	1429	1330	736	794	1142
176	1419	1270	376	445	859	1532	137	822	1310	616
177	74	444	853	1496	1732	1337	778	1046	843	1436
178	1372	988	495	1159	1521	71	426	745	848	1466
179	1552	257	1542	197	1182	1659	899	1772	1577	407
180	631	164	984	471	1015	657	320	109	654	302
181										

P = 1823

INDICES

	0	1	2	3	4	5	6	7	8	9
0		0	1132	1670	442	1	980	906	1574	1518
1	1133	1318	290	1232	216	1671	884	1246	828	1780
2	443	754	628	361	1422	2	542	1366	1348	1662
3	981	1763	194	1166	556	907	138	232	1090	1080
4	1575	931	64	271	1760	1519	1493	53	732	1812
5	1134	1094	1674	1109	676	1319	658	1628	972	1039
6	291	1747	1073	602	1326	1233	476	1583	1688	209
7	217	1641	1270	1130	1364	1672	400	402	390	1530
8	885	1214	241	1042	1196	1247	1403	1510	1070	739
9	829	316	803	1611	1185	1781	42	485	1122	1014
10	444	84	404	935	984	755	419	107	1808	1557
11	629	80	1790	1698	938	362	282	928	349	330
12	1423	814	1057	779	383	3	1734	392	636	119
13	543	1102	1608	864	893	1367	998	1565	1341	563
14	1349	1723	951	728	580	1663	440	1660	674	1528
15	982	117	1532	942	1534	1764	1522	1457	840	957
16	195	1267	524	574	1373	1167	352	720	506	642
17	557	1476	713	1389	820	908	380	887	49	944
18	139	1010	1448	1595	113	233	921	742	495	450
19	1091	377	1174	796	1617	1081	432	527	324	1409
20	1576	1431	1216	746	1536	932	245	57	294	1276
21	65	704	1551	1489	1239	272	1118	847	867	978
22	1761	656	1212	417	1100	1520	1008	243	248	1766
23	1494	250	1414	1179	238	54	1481	1378	1462	987
24	733	1003	124	1062	367	1813	89	1190	1515	890
25	1135	481	1044	1679	1524	1095	1768	1427	1251	1138
26	1675	1358	412	1744	918	1110	174	587	203	1207
27	677	458	308	164	875	1320	651	1198	1695	1459
28	659	1496	1033	1756	261	1629	38	15	1712	670
29	973	333	1572	1164	970	1040	1806	862	838	1593
30	292	1177	1249	1754	842	1748	252	800	844	783
31	1074	1113	832	339	767	603	150	550	267	1158
32	1327	1777	577	1204	1656	1234	1706	1405	683	959
33	477	1416	1484	1750	30	1584	1638	429	1774	1546
34	1689	1259	786	896	23	210	699	158	130	1300
35	218	776	1512	60	197	1642	1181	178	254	436
36	1271	1738	320	662	758	1131	905	289	1245	627
37	1365	193	231	63	52	1673	1627	1072	1582	1269
38	401	240	1509	802	484	403	106	1789	927	1056
39	391	1607	1564	950	1659	1531	1456	523	719	712
40	886	1447	741	1173	526	1215	56	1550	846	1211
41	242	1413	1377	123	1189	1043	1426	411	586	307
42	1197	1032	14	1571	861	1248	799	831	549	576
43	1404	1483	428	785	157	1511	177	319	288	230
44	1071	1508	1788	1563	522	740	1549	1376	410	13
45	830	427	318	1787	1375	317	1380	1381	1076	790
46	804	312	1382	1220	724	1612	489	1077	1370	667
47	1186	1305	791	1589	688	1782	772	805	297	1169
48	43	1464	313	1115	1256	486	372	1383	1499	422
49	1123	1281	1221	1086	500	1015	825	725	200	947

POWER RESIDUES

	0	1	2	3	4	5	6	7	8	9
0	1	5	25	125	625	1302	1041	1559	503	692
1	1637	893	819	449	422	287	1435	1706	1238	721
2	1782	1618	798	344	1720	1308	1071	1709	1253	796
3	334	1670	1058	1644	928	994	1324	1151	286	1430
4	1681	1113	96	480	577	1062	1664	1028	1494	178
5	890	804	374	47	235	1175	406	207	1035	1529
6	353	1765	1533	373	42	210	1050	1604	728	1817
7	1793	1673	1073	1719	1303	1046	1584	628	1317	1116
8	111	555	952	1114	101	505	702	1687	1143	246
9	1230	681	1582	618	1267	866	684	1597	693	1642
10	918	944	1074	1724	1328	1171	386	107	535	852
11	614	1247	766	184	920	954	1124	151	755	129
12	645	1402	1541	413	242	1210	581	1082	1764	1528
13	348	1740	1408	1571	563	992	1314	1101	36	180
14	900	854	624	1297	1016	1434	1701	1213	596	1157
15	316	1580	608	1217	616	1257	816	434	347	1735
16	1383	1446	1761	1513	273	1365	1356	1311	1086	1784
17	1628	848	594	1147	266	1330	1181	436	357	1785
18	1633	873	719	1772	1568	548	917	939	1049	1599
19	703	1692	1168	371	32	160	800	354	1770	1558
20	498	667	1512	268	1340	1231	686	1607	743	69
21	345	1725	1333	1196	511	732	14	70	350	1750
22	1458	1821	1813	1773	1573	573	1042	1564	528	817
23	439	372	37	185	925	979	1249	776	234	1170
24	381	82	410	227	1135	206	1030	1504	228	1140
25	231	1155	306	1530	358	1790	1658	998	1344	1251
26	786	284	1420	1631	863	669	1522	318	1590	658
27	1467	43	215	1075	1729	1353	1296	1011	1409	1576
28	588	1117	116	580	1077	1739	1403	1546	438	367
29	12	60	300	1500	208	1040	1554	478	567	1012
30	1414	1601	713	1742	1418	1621	813	419	272	1360
31	1331	1186	461	482	587	1112	91	455	452	437
32	362	1810	1758	1498	198	990	1304	1051	1609	753
33	119	595	1152	291	1455	1806	1738	1398	1521	313
34	1565	533	842	564	997	1339	1226	661	1482	118
35	590	1127	166	830	504	697	1662	1018	1444	1751
36	1463	23	115	575	1052	1614	778	244	1220	631
37	1332	1191	486	607	1212	591	1132	191	955	1129
38	176	880	754	124	620	1277	916	934	1024	1474
39	78	390	127	635	1352	1291	986	1284	951	1109
40	76	380	77	385	102	510	727	1812	1768	1548
41	448	417	262	1310	1081	1759	1503	223	1115	106
42	530	827	489	622	1287	966	1184	451	432	337
43	1685	1133	196	980	1254	801	359	1795	1683	1123
44	146	730	4	20	100	500	677	1562	518	767
45	189	945	1079	1749	1453	1796	1688	1148	271	1355
46	1306	1061	1659	1003	1369	1376	1411	1586	638	1367
47	1366	1361	1336	1211	586	1107	66	330	1650	958
48	1144	251	1255	806	384	97	485	602	1187	466
49	507	712	1737	1393	1496	188	940	1054	1624	828

P = 1823

INDICES

	0	1	2	3	4	5	6	7	8	9
50	445	568	1613	8	354	85	989	490	834	1047
51	405	214	1078	1324	737	936	561	1371	448	1237
52	985	916	668	765	1544	756	1054	1187	228	722
53	420	735	1306	341	1719	108	1335	792	517	1308
54	1809	817	1590	858	1440	1558	1296	689	185	1443
55	630	1620	1783	614	508	81	1005	773	769	1503
56	1791	590	806	134	343	1699	1066	298	1393	1345
57	939	1692	1170	225	1147	363	1022	44	1802	644
58	283	126	1465	605	882	929	474	314	280	1721
59	350	375	1116	1001	172	331	148	1257	903	1605
60	1424	1506	487	1279	559	815	1064	373	152	594
61	1058	1285	1384	1036	110	780	154	1500	93	708
62	384	1727	423	1645	142	4	1471	1124	77	1478
63	1735	369	1282	552	1682	393	1399	1222	468	1337
64	637	596	1087	571	1709	120	514	501	966	535
65	544	695	1016	1150	715	1103	1815	826	269	1686
66	1609	347	726	504	794	865	1060	201	1162	265
67	894	1243	948	584	1561	1368	1084	446	856	1391
68	999	91	569	1160	96	1566	206	1614	1155	519
69	1342	1287	9	98	1290	564	1262	355	610	1027
70	1350	811	86	190	822	1724	1192	990	1329	994
71	952	1226	491	302	1310	729	1386	835	1568	182
72	581	19	1048	851	1452	1664	1794	406	68	910
73	441	1517	215	1779	1421	1661	555	1079	1759	1811
74	675	1038	1325	208	1363	1529	1195	738	1184	1013
75	983	1556	937	329	382	118	892	562	579	1527
76	1533	956	1372	641	819	943	112	449	1616	1408
77	1535	1275	1238	977	1099	1765	237	986	366	889
78	1523	1137	917	1206	874	1458	260	669	969	1592
79	841	782	766	1157	1655	958	29	1545	22	1299
80	196	435	757	626	51	1268	483	1055	1658	711
81	525	1210	1188	306	860	575	156	229	521	12
82	1374	789	723	666	687	1168	1255	421	499	946
83	353	1046	736	1236	1543	721	1718	1307	1439	1442
84	507	1502	342	1344	1146	643	881	1720	171	1604
85	558	593	109	707	141	1477	1681	1336	1708	534
86	714	1685	793	264	1560	1390	95	518	1289	1026
87	821	993	1309	181	1451	909	1420	1810	1362	1012
88	381	1526	818	1407	1098	888	873	1591	1654	1298
89	50	710	859	11	686	945	1542	1441	1145	1603
90	140	533	1559	1025	1450	1011	1097	1297	685	1602
91	1449	1601	690	538	691	1596	386	186	100	539
92	114	648	1444	1051	692	234	530	631	34	1597
93	922	1770	1621	961	387	743	680	1784	1799	187
94	496	1729	615	1292	101	451	899	509	1820	540
95	1092	398	82	1732	115	378	1429	1006	479	649
96	1175	1704	774	1625	1445	797	425	770	566	1052
97	1618	1020	1504	1469	693	1082	809	1792	1554	235
98	433	1253	591	1418	531	528	396	807	1632	632
99	325	1647	135	1264	35	1410	1332	344	257	1598

POWER RESIDUES

	0	1	2	3	4	5	6	7	8	9
50	494	647	1412	1591	663	1492	168	840	554	947
51	1089	1799	1703	1223	646	1407	1566	538	867	689
52	1622	818	444	397	162	810	404	197	985	1279
53	926	984	1274	901	859	649	1422	1641	913	919
54	949	1099	26	130	650	1427	1666	1038	1544	428
55	317	1585	633	1342	1241	736	34	170	850	604
56	1197	516	757	139	695	1652	968	1194	501	682
57	1587	643	1392	1491	163	815	429	322	1610	758
58	144	720	1777	1593	673	1542	418	267	1335	1206
59	561	982	1264	851	609	1222	641	1382	1441	1736
60	1388	1471	63	315	1575	583	1092	1814	1778	1598
61	698	1667	1043	1569	553	942	1064	1674	1078	1744
62	1428	1671	1063	1669	1053	1619	803	369	22	110
63	550	927	989	1299	1026	1484	128	640	1377	1416
64	1611	763	169	845	579	1072	1714	1278	921	959
65	1149	276	1380	1431	1686	1138	221	1105	56	280
66	1400	1531	363	1815	1783	1623	823	469	522	787
67	289	1445	1756	1488	148	740	54	270	1350	1281
68	936	1034	1524	328	1640	908	894	824	474	547
69	912	914	924	974	1224	651	1432	1691	1163	346
70	1730	1358	1321	1136	211	1055	1629	853	619	1272
71	891	809	399	172	860	654	1447	1766	1538	398
72	167	835	529	822	464	497	662	1487	143	715
73	1752	1468	48	240	1200	531	832	514	747	89
74	445	402	187	935	1029	1499	203	1015	1429	1676
75	1088	1794	1678	1098	21	105	525	802	364	1820
76	1808	1748	1448	1771	1563	523	792	314	1570	558
77	967	1189	476	557	962	1164	351	1755	1483	123
78	615	1252	791	309	1545	433	342	1710	1258	821
79	459	472	537	862	664	1497	193	965	1179	426
80	307	1535	383	92	460	477	562	987	1289	976
81	1234	701	1682	1118	121	605	1202	541	882	764
82	174	870	704	1697	1193	496	657	1462	18	90
83	450	427	312	1560	508	717	1762	1518	298	1490
84	158	790	304	1520	308	1540	408	217	1085	1779
85	1603	723	1792	1668	1048	1594	678	1567	543	892
86	814	424	297	1485	133	665	1502	218	1090	1804
87	1728	1348	1271	886	784	274	1370	1381	1436	1711
88	1263	846	584	1097	16	80	400	177	885	779
89	249	1245	756	134	670	1527	343	1715	1283	946
90	1084	1774	1578	598	1167	366	7	35	175	875
91	729	1822	1818	1798	1698	1198	521	782	264	1320
92	1131	186	930	1004	1374	1401	1536	388	117	585
93	1102	41	205	1025	1479	103	515	752	114	570
94	1027	1489	153	765	179	895	829	499	672	1537
95	393	142	710	1727	1343	1246	761	159	795	329
96	1645	933	1019	1449	1776	1588	648	1417	1616	788
97	294	1470	58	290	1450	1781	1613	773	219	1095
98	6	30	150	750	104	520	777	239	1195	506
99	707	1712	1268	871	709	1722	1318	1121	136	680

P = 1823

INDICES

	0	1	2	3	4	5	6	7	8	9
100	1577	1634	1700	463	923	1432	1140	1067	1486	1771
101	1217	277	299	1436	1622	747	144	1394	357	962
102	1537	1668	1346	1107	388	933	634	940	47	744
103	246	1677	1693	1752	681	58	1580	1171	547	1785
104	295	6	226	612	1800	1277	75	1148	854	188
105	66	327	364	624	497	705	1360	1023	32	1730
106	1552	461	45	622	616	1490	1473	1803	1029	1293
107	1240	26	645	72	102	273	1649	284	618	452
108	1119	414	127	1586	900	848	168	1466	750	510
109	868	1126	606	1352	1821	979	1317	883	753	541
110	1762	137	930	1492	1093	657	1746	475	1640	399
111	1213	1402	315	41	83	418	79	281	813	1733
112	1101	997	1722	439	116	1521	1266	351	1475	379
113	1009	920	376	431	1430	244	703	1117	655	1007
114	249	1480	1002	88	480	1767	1357	173	457	650
115	1495	37	332	1805	1176	251	1112	149	1776	1705
116	1415	1637	1258	698	775	1180	1737	904	192	1626
117	239	105	1606	1455	1446	55	1412	1425	1031	798
118	1482	176	1507	1548	426	1379	311	488	1304	771
119	1463	371	1280	824	567	988	213	560	915	1053
120	734	1334	816	1295	1619	1004	589	1065	1691	1021
121	125	473	374	147	1505	1063	1284	153	1726	1470
122	368	1398	595	513	694	1814	346	1059	1242	1083
123	90	205	1286	1261	810	1191	1225	1385	18	1793
124	1516	554	1037	1194	1555	891	955	111	1274	236
125	1136	259	781	28	434	482	1209	155	788	1254
126	1045	1717	1501	880	592	1680	1684	94	992	1419
127	1525	872	709	1541	532	1096	1600	385	647	529
128	1769	679	1728	898	397	1428	1703	424	1019	808
129	1252	395	1646	1331	1633	1139	276	143	1667	633
130	1676	1579	5	74	326	1359	460	1472	25	1648
131	413	167	1125	1316	136	1745	1401	78	996	1265
132	919	702	1479	1356	36	1111	1636	1736	104	1411
133	175	310	370	212	1333	588	472	1283	1397	345
134	204	1224	553	954	258	1208	1716	1683	871	1599
135	678	1702	394	275	1578	459	166	1400	701	1635
136	309	471	1223	1715	1701	165	470	469	1228	464
137	876	1229	1338	1741	924	1321	465	638	1651	1433
138	652	877	597	160	1141	1199	1230	1088	600	1068
139	1696	1339	572	493	1487	1460	1742	1710	337	1772
140	660	925	121	286	1218	1497	1322	515	132	278
141	1034	466	502	1153	300	1757	639	967	304	1437
142	262	1652	536	1797	1623	1630	1434	545	620	748
143	39	653	696	1302	145	16	878	1017	1314	1395
144	1713	598	1151	1312	358	671	161	716	762	963
145	974	1142	1104	454	1538	334	1200	1816	220	1669
146	1573	1231	827	360	1347	1165	1089	270	731	1108
147	971	601	1687	1129	389	1041	1069	1610	1121	934
148	1807	1697	348	778	635	863	1340	727	673	941
149	839	573	505	1388	48	1594	494	795	323	745

POWER RESIDUES

	0	1	2	3	4	5	6	7	8	9
100	1577	593	1142	241	1205	556	957	1139	226	1130
101	181	905	879	749	99	495	652	1437	1716	1288
102	971	1209	576	1057	1639	903	869	699	1672	1068
103	1694	1178	421	282	1410	1581	613	1242	741	59
104	295	1475	83	415	252	1260	831	509	722	1787
105	1643	923	969	1199	526	807	389	122	610	1227
106	666	1507	243	1215	606	1207	566	1007	1389	1476
107	88	440	377	62	310	1550	458	467	512	737
108	39	195	975	1229	676	1557	493	642	1387	1466
109	38	190	950	1104	51	255	1275	906	884	774
110	224	1120	131	655	1452	1791	1663	1023	1469	53
111	265	1325	1156	311	1555	483	592	1137	216	1080
112	1754	1478	98	490	627	1312	1091	1809	1753	1473
113	73	365	2	10	50	250	1250	781	259	1295
114	1006	1384	1451	1786	1638	898	844	574	1047	1589
115	653	1442	1741	1413	1596	688	1617	793	319	1595
116	683	1592	668	1517	293	1465	33	165	825	479
117	572	1037	1539	403	192	960	1154	301	1505	233
118	1165	356	1780	1608	748	94	470	527	812	414
119	247	1235	706	1707	1243	746	84	420	277	1385
120	1456	1811	1763	1523	323	1615	783	269	1345	1256
121	811	409	222	1110	81	405	202	1010	1404	1551
122	463	492	637	1362	1341	1236	711	1732	1368	1371
123	1386	1461	13	65	325	1625	833	519	772	214
124	1070	1704	1228	671	1532	368	17	85	425	302
125	1510	258	1290	981	1259	826	484	597	1162	341
126	1705	1233	696	1657	993	1319	1126	161	805	379
127	72	360	1800	1708	1248	771	209	1045	1579	603
128	1192	491	632	1337	1216	611	1232	691	1632	868
129	694	1647	943	1069	1699	1203	546	907	889	799
130	349	1745	1433	1696	1188	471	532	837	539	872
131	714	1747	1443	1746	1438	1721	1313	1096	11	55
132	275	1375	1406	1561	513	742	64	320	1600	708
133	1717	1293	996	1334	1201	536	857	639	1372	1391
134	1486	138	690	1627	843	569	1022	1464	28	140
135	700	1677	1093	1819	1803	1723	1323	1146	261	1305
136	1056	1634	878	744	74	370	27	135	675	1552
137	468	517	762	164	820	454	447	412	237	1185
138	456	457	462	487	612	1237	716	1757	1493	173
139	865	679	1572	568	1017	1439	1726	1338	1221	636
140	1357	1316	1111	86	430	327	1635	883	769	199
141	995	1329	1176	411	232	1160	331	1655	983	1269
142	876	734	24	120	600	1177	416	257	1285	956
143	1134	201	1005	1379	1426	1661	1013	1419	1626	838
144	544	897	839	549	922	964	1174	401	182	910
145	904	874	724	1797	1693	1173	396	157	785	279
146	1395	1506	238	1190	481	582	1087	1789	1653	973
147	1219	626	1307	1066	1684	1128	171	855	629	1322
148	1141	236	1180	431	332	1660	1008	1394	1501	213
149	1065	1679	1103	46	230	1150	281	1405	1556	488

P = 1823

INDICES

	0	1	2	3	4	5	6	7	8	9
150	293	1488	866	416	247	1178	1461	1061	1514	1678
151	1250	1743	202	163	1694	1755	1711	1163	837	1753
152	843	338	266	1203	682	1749	1773	895	129	59
153	253	661	1244	62	1581	801	926	949	718	1172
154	845	122	585	1570	548	784	287	1562	409	1786
155	1075	1219	1369	1588	296	1114	1498	1085	199	7
156	833	1323	447	764	227	340	516	857	184	613
157	768	133	1392	224	1801	604	279	1000	902	1278
158	151	1035	92	1644	76	551	467	570	965	1149
159	268	503	1161	583	855	1159	1154	97	609	189
160	1328	301	1567	850	67	1778	1758	207	1183	328
161	578	640	1615	976	365	1205	968	1156	21	625
162	1657	305	520	665	498	1235	1438	1343	170	706
163	1707	263	1288	180	1361	1406	1653	10	1144	1024
164	684	537	99	1050	33	960	1798	1291	1819	1731
165	478	1624	565	1468	1553	1417	1631	1263	256	462
166	1485	1435	356	1106	46	1751	546	611	853	623
167	31	621	1028	71	617	1585	749	1351	752	1491
168	1639	40	812	438	1474	430	654	87	456	1804
169	1775	697	191	1454	1030	1547	1303	823	914	1294
170	1690	146	1725	512	1241	1260	17	1193	1273	27
171	787	879	991	1540	646	897	1018	1330	1666	73
172	24	1315	995	1355	103	211	1396	953	870	274
173	700	1714	1227	1740	1650	159	599	492	336	285
174	131	1152	303	1796	619	1301	1313	1311	761	453
175	219	359	730	1128	1120	777	672	1387	322	415
176	1513	162	836	1202	128	61	717	1569	408	1587
177	198	763	183	223	901	1643	964	582	608	849
178	1182	975	20	664	169	179	1143	1049	1818	1467
179	255	1105	852	70	751	437	455	1453	913	511
180	1272	1539	1665	1354	869	1739	335	1795	760	1127
181	321	1201	407	222	607	663	1817	69	912	1353
182	759	221	911							

POWER RESIDUES

	0	1	2	3	4	5	6	7	8	9
150	617	1262	841	559	972	1214	601	1182	441	382
151	87	435	352	1760	1508	248	1240	731	9	45
152	225	1125	156	780	254	1270	881	759	149	745
153	79	395	152	760	154	770	204	1020	1454	1801
154	1713	1273	896	834	524	797	339	1695	1183	446
155	407	212	1060	1654	978	1244	751	109	545	902
156	864	674	1547	443	392	137	685	1602	718	1767
157	1543	423	292	1460	8	40	200	1000	1354	1301
158	1036	1534	378	67	335	1675	1083	1769	1553	473
159	542	887	789	299	1495	183	915	929	999	1349
160	1276	911	909	899	849	599	1172	391	132	660
161	1477	93	465	502	687	1612	768	194	970	1204
162	551	932	1014	1424	1651	963	1169	376	57	285
163	1425	1656	988	1294	1001	1359	1326	1161	336	1680
164	1108	71	355	1775	1583	623	1292	991	1309	1076
165	1734	1378	1421	1636	888	794	324	1620	808	394
166	147	735	29	145	725	1802	1718	1298	1021	1459
167	3	15	75	375	52	260	1300	1031	1509	253
168	1265	856	634	1347	1266	861	659	1472	68	340
169	1700	1208	571	1032	1514	278	1390	1481	113	565
170	1002	1364	1351	1286	961	1159	326	1630	858	644
171	1397	1516	288	1440	1731	1363	1346	1261	836	534
172	847	589	1122	141	705	1702	1218	621	1282	941
173	1059	1649	953	1119	126	630	1327	1166	361	1805
174	1733	1373	1396	1511	263	1315	1106	61	305	1525
175	333	1665	1033	1519	303	1515	283	1415	1606	738
176	44	220	1100	31	155	775	229	1145	256	1280
177	931	1009	1399	1526	338	1690	1158	321	1605	733
178	19	95	475	552	937	1039	1549	453	442	387
179	112	560	977	1239	726	1807	1743	1423	1646	938
180	1044	1574	578	1067	1689	1153	296	1480	108	540
181	877	739	49	245	1225	656	1457	1816	1788	1648
182	948	1094								

P = 1831

INDICES

	0	1	2	3	4	5	6	7	8	9
0		0	1368	1	906	504	1369	1699	444	2
1	42	1111	907	747	1237	505	1812	1425	1370	1263
2	1410	1700	649	1346	445	1008	285	3	775	120
3	43	539	1350	1112	963	373	908	717	801	748
4	948	731	1238	685	187	506	884	620	1813	1568
5	546	1426	1653	72	1371	1615	313	1264	1488	1744
6	1411	872	77	1701	888	1251	650	1561	501	1347
7	1741	220	446	1276	255	1009	339	980	286	806
8	486	4	269	770	776	99	223	121	1555	931
9	44	616	422	540	158	1767	1351	1474	1106	1113
10	84	292	964	1806	1191	374	1440	397	909	1054
11	1153	718	1681	449	802	20	1026	749	1282	1294
12	949	392	410	732	1445	1512	1239	1580	426	686
13	789	594	188	1132	1099	507	39	714	885	613
14	1279	621	1588	28	1814	624	814	1569	1623	693
15	547	1271	1707	1427	518	1043	1654	995	344	73
16	24	1215	1372	605	1637	1616	308	258	314	1494
17	1467	1265	1591	1165	1489	877	1093	1745	469	1604
18	1412	743	154	873	1790	1221	78	706	1526	1702
19	1305	764	889	1071	1012	1252	644	571	651	31
20	1452	1562	1660	1819	502	1235	1344	1348	729	544
21	1742	499	978	221	1765	1189	447	408	592	1277
22	691	342	256	1091	1219	1010	1817	976	340	1386
23	1388	981	564	668	287	1124	820	807	832	1390
24	487	1030	1760	5	1778	242	270	180	983	771
25	1050	1301	777	627	1118	100	1794	566	224	586
26	327	122	132	173	1556	576	670	932	637	1784
27	45	781	1407	617	252	289	423	1040	151	541
28	817	170	159	678	1126	1768	1396	600	1352	1020
29	162	1475	352	822	1107	418	1161	1114	231	263
30	85	554	809	293	1245	1376	965	1572	56	1807
31	581	834	1192	1081	533	375	1712	681	1441	1231
32	1392	398	753	858	910	1755	143	1055	1175	489
33	1154	1504	1676	719	1626	235	1682	1225	1032	450
34	1005	1650	803	1437	1129	21	703	1762	1027	634
35	415	750	631	1061	1283	724	7	1295	1142	1319
36	950	696	281	393	1522	1780	411	402	1328	733
37	759	1771	1446	459	244	1513	1064	867	1240	384
38	843	1581	302	272	427	1484	609	687	550	298
39	790	941	182	595	109	1310	189	14	1399	1133
40	990	985	1100	1286	1198	508	1357	1828	40	1261
41	773	715	882	1613	886	1274	267	614	82	1052
42	1280	1578	37	622	516	603	1589	741	1303	29
43	727	406	1815	1122	1776	625	130	779	815	1018
44	229	1570	1710	1753	1624	1435	629	694	757	382
45	548	12	1355	1272	514	1120	1708	10	924	1428
46	926	1671	519	794	102	1044	206	1641	1655	1430
47	662	996	358	1796	345	441	370	74	928	1023
48	25	1464	568	1216	1298	148	1373	1673	1316	606
49	1610	226	1638	1545	1548	1617	521	89	309	710

POWER RESIDUES

	0	1	2	3	4	5	6	7	8	9
0	1	3	9	27	81	243	729	356	1068	1373
1	457	1371	451	1353	397	1191	1742	1564	1030	1259
2	115	345	1035	1274	160	480	1440	658	143	429
3	1287	199	597	1791	1711	1471	751	422	1266	136
4	408	1224	10	30	90	270	810	599	1797	1729
5	1525	913	908	893	848	713	308	924	941	992
6	1145	1604	1150	1619	1195	1754	1600	1138	1583	1087
7	1430	628	53	159	477	1431	631	62	186	558
8	1674	1360	418	1254	100	300	900	869	776	497
9	1491	811	602	1806	1756	1606	1156	1637	1249	85
10	255	765	464	1392	514	1542	964	1061	1352	394
11	1182	1715	1483	787	530	1590	1108	1493	817	620
12	29	87	261	783	518	1554	1000	1169	1676	1366
13	436	1308	262	786	527	1581	1081	1412	574	1722
14	1504	850	719	326	978	1103	1478	772	485	1455
15	703	278	834	671	182	546	1638	1252	94	282
16	846	707	290	870	779	506	1518	892	845	704
17	281	843	698	263	789	536	1608	1162	1655	1303
18	247	741	392	1176	1697	1429	625	44	132	396
19	1188	1733	1537	949	1016	1217	1820	1798	1732	1534
20	940	989	1136	1577	1069	1376	466	1398	532	1596
21	1126	1547	979	1106	1487	799	566	1698	1432	634
22	71	213	639	86	258	774	491	1473	757	440
23	1320	298	894	851	722	335	1005	1184	1721	1501
24	841	692	245	735	374	1122	1535	943	998	1163
25	1658	1312	274	822	635	74	222	666	167	501
26	1503	847	710	299	897	860	749	416	1248	82
27	246	738	383	1149	1616	1186	1727	1519	895	854
28	731	362	1086	1427	619	26	78	234	702	275
29	825	644	101	303	909	896	857	740	389	1167
30	1670	1348	382	1146	1607	1159	1646	1276	166	498
31	1494	820	629	56	168	504	1512	874	791	542
32	1626	1216	1817	1789	1705	1453	697	260	780	509
33	1527	919	926	947	1010	1199	1766	1636	1246	76
34	228	684	221	663	158	474	1422	604	1812	1774
35	1660	1318	292	876	797	560	1680	1378	472	1416
36	586	1758	1612	1174	1691	1411	571	1713	1477	769
37	476	1428	622	35	105	315	945	1004	1181	1712
38	1474	760	449	1347	379	1137	1580	1078	1403	547
39	1641	1261	121	363	1089	1436	646	107	321	963
40	1058	1343	367	1101	1472	754	431	1293	217	651
41	122	366	1098	1463	727	350	1050	1319	295	885
42	824	641	92	276	828	653	128	384	1152	1625
43	1213	1808	1762	1624	1210	1799	1735	1543	967	1070
44	1379	475	1425	613	8	24	72	216	648	113
45	339	1017	1220	1829	1825	1813	1777	1669	1345	373
46	1119	1526	916	917	920	929	956	1037	1280	178
47	534	1602	1144	1601	1141	1592	1114	1511	871	782
48	515	1545	973	1088	1433	637	80	240	720	329
49	987	1130	1559	1015	1214	1811	1771	1651	1291	211

P = 1831

INDICES

	0	1	2	3	4	5	6	7	8	9
50	588	259	839	1667	315	796	165	1495	656	329
51	1468	1145	1332	1266	104	480	1592	1731	124	1166
52	1695	1551	1490	1046	1500	878	1541	134	1094	862
53	114	1746	208	1478	470	901	175	1605	1322	849
54	1413	1643	319	744	945	1558	155	389	1620	874
55	1657	1383	1791	675	578	1222	1519	938	79	1432
56	355	707	1538	672	1527	953	216	1703	664	529
57	1306	366	934	765	138	524	890	998	558	1072
58	1530	639	1013	1183	1720	1253	360	825	645	1802
59	1786	572	699	737	652	1798	1599	32	1631	47
60	1453	1689	92	1563	347	896	1661	956	783	1820
61	914	1367	503	443	1110	1236	1424	1409	1345	284
62	119	1349	372	800	730	186	619	545	71	312
63	1743	76	1250	500	219	254	979	485	769	222
64	930	421	1766	1105	291	1190	396	1152	448	1025
65	1293	409	1511	425	593	1098	713	1278	27	813
66	692	1706	1042	343	1214	1636	257	1466	1164	1092
67	1603	153	1220	1525	763	1011	570	1451	1818	1343
68	543	977	1188	591	341	1218	975	1387	667	819
69	1389	1759	241	982	1300	1117	565	326	172	669
70	1783	1406	288	150	169	1125	599	161	821	1160
71	262	808	1375	55	833	532	680	1391	857	142
72	488	1675	234	1031	1649	1128	1761	414	1060	6
73	1318	280	1779	1327	1770	243	866	842	271	608
74	297	181	1309	1398	984	1197	1827	772	1612	266
75	1051	36	602	1302	405	1775	778	228	1752	628
76	381	1354	1119	923	1670	101	1640	661	1795	369
77	1022	567	147	1315	225	1547	88	587	1666	164
78	328	1331	479	123	1550	1499	133	113	1477	174
79	848	318	1557	1619	1382	577	937	354	671	215
80	528	933	523	557	638	1719	824	1785	736	1598
81	46	91	895	782	1366	1109	1408	118	799	618
82	311	1249	253	768	420	290	1151	1292	424	712
83	812	1041	1635	1163	152	762	1450	542	590	974
84	818	240	1116	171	1405	168	160	261	54	679
85	141	233	1127	1059	279	1769	841	296	1397	1826
86	265	601	1774	1751	1353	1669	660	1021	1314	87
87	163	478	1498	1476	317	1381	353	527	556	823
88	1597	894	1108	798	1248	419	1291	811	1162	1449
89	973	1115	167	53	232	278	295	264	1750	659
90	86	1497	1380	555	893	1247	810	972	52	294
91	658	1379	1246	51	1378	1377	462	463	966	331
92	464	1573	1209	967	57	1725	332	1808	1470	465
93	582	1001	1574	835	1179	1210	1193	1147	968	1082
94	200	58	534	247	1726	376	1334	333	1713	193
95	1809	682	1738	1471	1442	1268	466	1232	561	583
96	1393	1078	1002	399	106	1575	754	438	836	859
97	1516	1180	911	482	1211	1756	854	1194	144	212
98	1148	1056	1594	969	1176	1075	1083	490	1086	201
99	1155	1733	59	1505	1457	535	1677	1067	248	720

POWER RESIDUES

	0	1	2	3	4	5	6	7	8	9
50	633	68	204	612	5	15	45	135	405	1215
51	1814	1780	1678	1372	454	1362	424	1272	154	462
52	1386	496	1488	802	575	1725	1513	877	800	569
53	1707	1459	715	314	942	995	1154	1631	1231	31
54	93	279	837	680	209	627	50	150	450	1350
55	388	1164	1661	1321	301	903	878	803	578	1734
56	1540	958	1043	1298	232	696	257	771	482	1446
57	676	197	591	1773	1657	1309	265	795	554	1662
58	1324	310	930	959	1046	1307	259	777	500	1500
59	838	683	218	654	131	393	1179	1706	1456	706
60	287	861	752	425	1275	163	489	1467	739	386
61	1158	1643	1267	139	417	1251	91	273	819	626
62	47	141	423	1269	145	435	1305	253	759	446
63	1338	352	1056	1337	349	1047	1310	268	804	581
64	1743	1567	1039	1286	196	588	1764	1630	1228	22
65	66	198	594	1782	1684	1390	508	1524	910	899
66	866	767	470	1410	568	1704	1450	688	233	699
67	266	798	563	1689	1405	553	1659	1315	283	849
68	716	317	951	1022	1235	43	129	387	1161	1652
69	1294	220	660	149	447	1341	361	1083	1418	592
70	1776	1666	1336	346	1038	1283	187	561	1683	1387
71	499	1497	829	656	137	411	1233	37	111	333
72	999	1166	1667	1339	355	1065	1364	430	1290	208
73	624	41	123	369	1107	1490	808	593	1779	1675
74	1363	427	1281	181	543	1629	1225	13	39	117
75	351	1053	1328	322	966	1067	1370	448	1344	370
76	1110	1499	835	674	191	573	1719	1495	823	638
77	83	249	747	410	1230	28	84	252	756	437
78	1311	271	813	608	1824	1810	1768	1642	1264	130
79	390	1170	1679	1375	463	1389	505	1515	883	818
80	623	38	114	342	1026	1247	79	237	711	302
81	906	887	830	659	146	438	1314	280	840	689
82	236	708	293	879	806	587	1761	1621	1201	1772
83	1654	1300	238	714	311	933	968	1073	1388	502
84	1506	856	737	380	1140	1589	1105	1484	790	539
85	1617	1189	1736	1546	976	1097	1460	718	323	969
86	1076	1397	529	1587	1099	1466	736	377	1131	1562
87	1024	1241	61	183	549	1647	1279	175	525	1575
88	1063	1358	412	1236	46	138	414	1242	64	192
89	576	1728	1522	904	881	812	605	1815	1783	1687
90	1399	535	1605	1153	1628	1222	4	12	36	108
91	324	972	1085	1424	610	1830	1828	1822	1804	1750
92	1588	1102	1475	763	458	1374	460	1380	478	1434
93	640	89	267	801	572	1716	1486	796	557	1671
94	1351	391	1173	1688	1402	544	1632	1234	40	120
95	360	1080	1409	565	1695	1423	607	1821	1801	1741
96	1561	1021	1232	34	102	306	918	923	938	983
97	1118	1523	907	890	839	686	227	681	212	636
98	77	231	693	248	744	401	1203	1778	1672	1354
99	400	1200	1769	1645	1273	157	471	1413	577	1731

P = 1831

INDICES

	0	1	2	3	4	5	6	7	8	9
100	126	1727	1627	1339	377	236	1205	1335	1683	1168
101	334	1226	1533	1714	1033	493	194	451	1697	1810
102	1006	961	683	1651	870	1739	804	1553	1472	1438
103	18	1443	1130	1586	1269	22	1492	467	704	642
104	1233	1763	1089	562	1028	1048	584	635	1038	1394
105	416	1243	1079	751	1502	1003	632	1140	400	1062
106	1482	107	1284	880	1576	725	1016	755	8	204
107	439	1296	1543	837	1143	1693	860	1320	387	1517
108	951	136	1181	697	1687	912	282	69	483	394
109	1096	1212	1523	1186	1757	1781	1158	855	412	864
110	1195	403	921	145	1329	846	213	734	116	1149
111	760	1403	1057	1772	476	1595	1447	1748	970	460
112	1723	1177	245	1736	1076	1514	210	1084	1065	1203
113	491	868	1584	1087	1241	1480	202	385	67	1156
114	844	474	1734	1582	472	60	303	1256	1506	273
115	62	1458	428	903	536	1485	96	1678	610	305
116	1068	688	177	249	551	1172	721	299	1258	127
117	791	1607	1728	942	363	1628	183	1508	1340	596
118	1324	378	110	1363	237	1311	275	1206	190	851
119	1336	15	1137	1684	1400	64	1169	1134	1415	335
120	991	828	1227	986	1460	1534	1101	1645	1715	1287
121	434	1034	1199	430	494	509	321	195	1358	1418
122	452	1829	905	1698	41	746	1811	1262	648	1007
123	774	538	962	716	947	684	883	1567	1652	1614
124	1487	871	887	1560	1740	1275	338	805	268	98
125	1554	615	157	1473	83	1805	1439	1053	1680	19
126	1281	391	1444	1579	788	1131	38	612	1587	623
127	1622	1270	517	994	23	604	307	1493	1590	876
128	468	742	1789	705	1304	1070	643	30	1659	1234
129	728	498	1764	407	690	1090	1816	1385	563	1123
130	831	1029	1777	179	1049	626	1793	585	131	575
131	636	780	251	1039	816	677	1395	1019	351	417
132	230	553	1244	1571	580	1080	1711	1230	752	1754
133	1174	1503	1625	1224	1004	1436	702	633	630	723
134	1141	695	1521	401	758	458	1063	383	301	1483
135	549	940	108	13	989	1285	1356	1260	881	1273
136	81	1577	515	740	726	1121	129	1017	1709	1434
137	756	11	513	9	925	793	205	1429	357	440
138	927	1463	1297	1672	1609	1544	520	709	838	795
139	655	1144	103	1730	1694	1045	1540	861	207	900
140	1321	1642	944	388	1656	674	1518	1431	1537	952
141	663	365	137	997	1529	1182	359	1801	698	1797
142	1630	1688	346	955	913	442	1423	283	371	185
143	70	75	218	484	929	1104	395	1024	1510	1097
144	26	1705	1213	1465	1602	1524	569	1342	1187	1217
145	666	1758	1299	325	1782	149	598	1159	1374	531
146	856	1674	1648	413	1317	1326	865	607	1308	1196
147	1611	35	404	227	380	922	1639	368	146	1546
148	1665	1330	1549	112	847	1618	936	214	522	1718
149	735	90	1365	117	310	767	1150	711	1634	761

POWER RESIDUES

	0	1	2	3	4	5	6	7	8	9
100	1531	931	962	1055	1334	340	1020	1229	25	75
101	225	675	194	582	1746	1576	1066	1367	439	1317
102	289	867	770	479	1437	649	116	348	1044	1301
103	241	723	338	1014	1211	1802	1744	1570	1048	1313
104	277	831	662	155	465	1395	523	1569	1045	1304
105	250	750	419	1257	109	327	981	1112	1505	853
106	728	353	1059	1346	376	1128	1553	997	1160	1649
107	1285	193	579	1737	1549	985	1124	1541	961	1052
108	1325	313	939	986	1127	1550	988	1133	1568	1042
109	1295	223	669	176	528	1584	1090	1439	655	134
110	402	1206	1787	1699	1435	643	98	294	882	815
111	614	11	33	99	297	891	842	695	254	762
112	455	1365	433	1299	235	705	284	852	725	344
113	1032	1265	133	399	1197	1760	1618	1192	1745	1573
114	1057	1340	358	1074	1391	511	1533	937	980	1109
115	1496	826	647	110	330	990	1139	1586	1096	1457
116	709	296	888	833	668	173	519	1557	1009	1196
117	1757	1609	1165	1664	1330	328	984	1121	1532	934
118	971	1082	1415	583	1749	1585	1093	1448	682	215
119	645	104	312	936	977	1100	1469	745	404	1212
120	1805	1753	1597	1129	1556	1006	1187	1730	1528	922
121	935	974	1091	1442	664	161	483	1449	685	224
122	672	185	555	1665	1333	337	1011	1202	1775	1663
123	1327	319	957	1040	1289	205	615	14	42	126
124	378	1134	1571	1051	1322	304	912	905	884	821
125	632	65	195	585	1755	1603	1147	1610	1168	1673
126	1357	409	1227	19	57	171	513	1539	955	1034
127	1271	151	453	1359	415	1245	73	219	657	140
128	420	1260	118	354	1062	1355	403	1209	1796	1726
129	1516	886	827	650	119	357	1071	1382	484	1452
130	694	251	753	428	1284	190	570	1710	1468	742
131	395	1185	1724	1510	868	773	488	1464	730	359
132	1077	1400	538	1614	1180	1709	1465	733	368	1104
133	1481	781	512	1536	946	1007	1190	1739	1555	1003
134	1178	1703	1447	679	206	618	23	69	207	621
135	32	96	288	864	761	452	1356	406	1218	1823
136	1807	1759	1615	1183	1718	1492	814	611	2	6
137	18	54	162	486	1458	712	305	915	914	911
138	902	875	794	551	1653	1297	229	687	230	690
139	239	717	320	960	1049	1316	286	858	743	398
140	1194	1751	1591	1111	1502	844	701	272	816	617
141	20	60	180	540	1620	1198	1763	1627	1219	1826
142	1816	1786	1696	1426	616	17	51	153	459	1377
143	469	1407	559	1677	1369	445	1335	343	1029	1256
144	106	318	954	1031	1262	124	372	1116	1517	889
145	836	677	200	600	1800	1738	1552	994	1151	1622
146	1204	1781	1681	1381	481	1443	667	170	510	1530
147	928	953	1028	1253	97	291	873	788	533	1599
148	1135	1574	1060	1349	385	1155	1634	1240	58	174
149	522	1566	1036	1277	169	507	1521	901	872	785

P = 1831

INDICES

	0	1	2	3	4	5	6	7	8	9
150	589	239	1404	260	140	1058	840	1825	1773	1668
151	1313	477	316	526	1596	797	1290	1448	166	277
152	1749	1496	892	971	657	50	461	330	1208	1724
153	1469	1000	1178	1146	199	246	1333	192	1737	1267
154	560	1077	105	437	1515	481	853	211	1593	1074
155	1085	1732	1456	1066	125	1338	1204	1167	1532	492
156	1696	960	869	1552	17	1585	1491	641	1088	1047
157	1037	1242	1501	1139	1481	879	1015	203	1542	1692
158	386	135	1686	68	1095	1185	1157	863	920	845
159	115	1402	475	1747	1722	1735	209	1202	1583	1479
160	66	473	471	1255	61	902	95	304	176	1171
161	1257	1606	362	1507	1323	1362	274	850	1136	63
162	1414	827	1459	1644	433	429	320	1417	904	745
163	647	537	946	1566	1486	1559	337	97	156	1804
164	1679	390	787	611	1621	993	306	875	1788	1069
165	1658	497	689	1384	830	178	1792	574	250	676
166	350	552	579	1229	1173	1223	701	722	1520	457
167	300	939	988	1259	80	739	128	1433	512	792
168	356	1462	1608	708	654	1729	1539	899	943	673
169	1536	364	1528	1800	1629	954	1422	184	217	1103
170	1509	1704	1601	1341	665	324	597	530	1647	1325
171	1307	34	379	367	1664	111	935	1717	1364	766
172	1633	238	139	1824	1312	525	1289	276	891	49
173	1207	999	198	191	559	436	852	1073	1455	1337
174	1531	959	16	640	1036	1138	1014	1691	1685	1184
175	919	1401	1721	1201	65	1254	94	1170	361	1361
176	1135	826	432	1416	646	1565	336	1803	786	992
177	1787	496	829	573	349	1228	700	456	987	738
178	511	1461	653	898	1535	1799	1421	1102	1600	323
179	1646	33	1663	1716	1632	1823	1288	48	197	435
180	1454	958	1035	1690	918	1200	93	1360	431	1564
181	785	495	348	455	510	897	1420	322	1662	1822
182	196	957	917	1359	784	454	1419	1821	916	453
183	915	0								

POWER RESIDUES

	0	1	2	3	4	5	6	7	8	9
150	524	1572	1054	1331	331	993	1148	1613	1177	1700
151	1438	652	125	375	1125	1544	970	1079	1406	556
152	1668	1342	364	1092	1445	673	188	564	1692	1414
153	580	1740	1558	1012	1205	1784	1690	1408	562	1686
154	1396	526	1578	1072	1385	493	1479	775	494	1482
155	784	521	1563	1027	1250	88	264	792	545	1635
156	1243	67	201	603	1809	1765	1633	1237	49	147
157	441	1323	307	921	932	965	1064	1361	421	1263
158	127	381	1143	1598	1132	1565	1033	1268	142	426
159	1278	172	516	1548	982	1115	1514	880	809	596
160	1788	1702	1444	670	179	537	1611	1171	1682	1384
161	490	1470	748	413	1239	55	165	495	1485	793
162	548	1644	1270	148	444	1332	334	1002	1175	1694
163	1420	598	1794	1720	1498	832	665	164	492	1476
164	766	467	1401	541	1623	1207	1790	1708	1462	724
165	341	1023	1238	52	156	468	1404	550	1650	1288
166	202	606	1818	1792	1714	1480	778	503	1509	865
167	764	461	1383	487	1461	721	332	996	1157	1640
168	1258	112	336	1008	1193	1748	1582	1084	1421	601
169	1803	1747	1579	1075	1394	520	1560	1018	1223	7
170	21	63	189	567	1701	1441	661	152	456	1368
171	442	1326	316	948	1013	1208	1793	1717	1489	805
172	584	1752	1594	1120	1529	925	944	1001	1172	1685
173	1393	517	1551	991	1142	1595	1123	1538	952	1025
174	1244	70	210	630	59	177	531	1593	1117	1520
175	898	863	758	443	1329	325	975	1094	1451	691
176	242	726	347	1041	1292	214	642	95	285	855
177	734	371	1113	1508	862	755	434	1302	244	732
178	365	1095	1454	700	269	807	590	1770	1648	1282
179	184	552	1656	1306	256	768	473	1419	595	1785
180	1693	1417	589	1767	1639	1255	103	309	927	950
181	1019	1226	16	48	144	432	1296	226	678	203
182	609	1827	1819	1795	1723	1507	859	746	407	1221
183										

P = 1847

INDICES

	0	1	2	3	4	5	6	7	8	9
0		0	170	524	340	1	694	188	510	1048
1	171	624	864	120	358	525	680	1481	1218	1825
2	341	712	794	430	1034	2	290	1572	528	28
3	695	1101	850	1148	1651	189	1388	352	149	644
4	511	44	882	85	964	1049	600	637	1204	376
5	172	159	460	321	1742	625	698	503	198	1040
6	865	1709	1271	1236	1020	121	1318	1346	1821	954
7	359	633	1558	1715	522	526	319	812	814	1188
8	681	250	214	841	1052	1482	255	552	1134	82
9	1219	308	770	1625	807	1826	1374	1284	546	1672
10	342	1579	329	816	630	713	491	1816	66	1059
11	795	876	868	887	673	431	368	1168	1210	1669
12	1035	1248	33	568	1441	3	1406	1519	1190	609
13	291	685	1488	167	1516	1573	145	275	1124	1314
14	529	1161	803	744	1728	29	39	900	692	1099
15	696	248	489	683	982	1102	984	1334	1358	845
16	851	618	420	195	384	1149	1011	470	1222	240
17	1652	1027	425	74	722	190	1304	1564	252	1255
18	1389	1104	478	387	940	353	1795	259	977	1760
19	150	1065	1544	670	1454	645	716	397	1842	573
20	512	24	1749	216	499	45	986	1478	800	603
21	883	1258	661	1157	140	86	236	1289	1229	393
22	965	1601	1046	1649	1038	1050	1057	1514	843	938
23	601	1336	538	971	1338	638	1380	1712	1839	1457
24	1205	1586	1418	774	203	377	738	99	1611	1365
25	173	108	1576	1054	1689	160	1360	93	779	540
26	461	1076	855	1429	1658	322	337	606	1686	1200
27	1743	1830	315	832	445	626	1294	582	1484	303
28	699	847	1331	1328	973	504	914	232	52	1116
29	199	1808	209	311	1070	1041	862	350	1269	550
30	866	273	418	257	659	1710	853	230	1152	1340
31	1272	1131	1154	407	1504	1237	1528	1777	1015	652
32	1021	494	788	1460	590	122	365	1583	554	825
33	1319	620	1181	1400	640	1347	1392	1342	410	1411
34	1822	1725	1197	564	595	955	244	1790	892	1251
35	360	1692	1474	1136	1734	634	422	347	1425	1382
36	1559	1804	1274	1772	648	1716	557	1786	1110	1092
37	523	509	119	1217	429	527	1147	148	84	1203
38	320	197	1235	1820	1714	813	840	1133	1624	545
39	815	65	886	1209	567	1189	166	1123	743	691
40	682	1357	194	1221	73	251	386	976	669	1841
41	215	799	1156	1228	1648	842	970	1838	773	1610
42	1053	778	1428	1685	831	1483	1327	51	310	1268
43	256	1151	406	1014	1459	553	1399	409	563	891
44	1135	1424	1771	1109	1216	83	1819	1623	1208	742
45	1220	668	1227	772	1684	309	1013	562	1108	1207
46	771	1107	1506	1507	708	1626	1141	372	1508	1534
47	808	12	1550	709	36	1827	163	1369	1627	614
48	1375	472	1756	1142	1588	1285	944	1239	373	719
49	547	828	908	1509	269	1673	1781	821	1535	759

POWER RESIDUES

	0	1	2	3	4	5	6	7	8	9
0	1	5	25	125	625	1278	849	551	908	846
1	536	833	471	508	693	1618	702	1663	927	941
2	1011	1361	1264	779	201	1005	1331	1114	29	145
3	725	1778	1502	122	610	1203	474	523	768	146
4	730	1803	1627	747	41	205	1025	1431	1614	682
5	1563	427	288	1440	1659	907	841	511	708	1693
6	1077	1691	1067	1641	817	391	108	540	853	571
7	1008	1346	1189	404	173	865	631	1308	999	1301
8	964	1126	89	445	378	43	215	1075	1681	1017
9	1391	1414	1529	257	1285	884	726	1783	1527	247
10	1235	634	1323	1074	1676	992	1266	789	251	1255
11	734	1823	1727	1247	694	1623	727	1788	1552	372
12	13	65	325	1625	737	1838	1802	1622	722	1763
13	1427	1594	582	1063	1621	717	1738	1302	969	1151
14	214	1070	1656	892	766	136	680	1553	377	38
15	190	950	1056	1586	542	863	621	1258	749	51
16	255	1275	834	476	533	818	396	133	665	1478
17	2	10	50	250	1250	709	1698	1102	1816	1692
18	1072	1666	942	1016	1386	1389	1404	1479	7	35
19	175	875	681	1558	402	163	815	381	58	290
20	1450	1709	1157	244	1220	559	948	1046	1536	292
21	1460	1759	1407	1494	82	410	203	1015	1381	1364
22	1279	854	576	1033	1471	1814	1682	1022	1416	1539
23	307	1535	287	1435	1634	782	216	1080	1706	1142
24	169	845	531	808	346	1730	1262	769	151	755
25	81	405	178	890	756	86	430	303	1515	187
26	935	981	1211	514	723	1768	1452	1719	1207	494
27	623	1268	799	301	1505	137	685	1578	502	663
28	1468	1799	1607	647	1388	1399	1454	1729	1257	744
29	26	130	650	1403	1474	1829	1757	1397	1444	1679
30	1007	1341	1164	279	1395	1434	1629	757	91	455
31	428	293	1465	1784	1532	272	1360	1259	754	76
32	380	53	265	1325	1084	1726	1242	669	1498	102
33	510	703	1668	952	1066	1636	792	266	1330	1109
34	4	20	100	500	653	1418	1549	357	1785	1537
35	297	1485	37	185	925	931	961	1111	14	70
36	350	1750	1362	1269	804	326	1630	762	116	580
37	1053	1571	467	488	593	1118	49	245	1225	584
38	1073	1671	967	1141	164	820	406	183	915	881
39	711	1708	1152	219	1095	1781	1517	197	985	1231
40	614	1223	574	1023	1421	1564	432	313	1565	437
41	338	1690	1062	1616	692	1613	677	1538	302	1510
42	162	810	356	1780	1512	172	860	606	1183	374
43	23	115	575	1028	1446	1689	1057	1591	567	988
44	1246	689	1598	602	1163	274	1370	1309	1004	1326
45	1089	1751	1367	1294	929	951	1061	1611	667	1488
46	52	260	1300	959	1101	1811	1667	947	1041	1511
47	167	835	481	558	943	1021	1411	1514	182	910
48	856	586	1083	1721	1217	544	873	671	1508	152
49	760	106	530	803	321	1605	637	1338	1149	[illegible]04

P = 1847

INDICES

	0	1	2	3	4	5	6	7	8	9
50	343	994	278	809	1746	1580	1224	764	13	1420
51	330	57	1530	1551	263	817	949	1261	710	598
52	631	1372	1246	37	1025	714	1599	736	1828	860
53	492	242	507	164	776	1817	10	1779	1370	1000
54	67	1437	154	1628	485	1060	1002	1385	615	911
55	796	7	1464	1376	752	877	1654	1703	473	205
56	869	783	1017	1757	1501	888	1498	438	1143	928
57	674	69	1084	1589	402	432	222	767	1286	1194
58	369	1029	132	945	379	1169	481	654	1240	1080
59	1211	921	1032	374	520	1670	1439	1097	720	571
60	1036	1363	443	548	588	1249	427	689	829	740
61	34	757	1023	909	400	569	1322	1662	1510	1493
62	1442	156	1301	270	1324	4	577	1127	1674	1833
63	1407	76	1698	1782	101	1520	1185	496	822	1681
64	1191	1641	664	1536	958	610	1630	283	760	1664
65	292	1813	535	344	1753	686	724	917	995	1613
66	1489	1467	790	279	1351	168	1570	458	810	327
67	1517	487	1562	1747	1512	1574	580	416	1581	1472
68	146	192	49	1225	1367	276	734	1462	765	441
69	1125	533	414	14	114	1315	1062	1525	1421	1495
70	530	836	16	331	1644	1162	1306	1767	58	175
71	804	390	592	1531	517	745	1595	135	1552	748
72	1729	1004	128	264	1444	30	96	116	818	1298
73	40	1566	727	950	110	901	1280	124	1262	1845
74	693	623	679	711	289	1100	1387	43	599	158
75	697	1708	1317	632	318	249	254	307	1373	1578
76	490	875	367	1247	1405	684	144	1160	38	247
77	983	617	1010	1026	1303	1103	1794	1064	715	23
78	985	1257	235	1600	1056	1335	1379	1585	737	107
79	1359	1075	336	1829	1293	846	913	1807	861	272
80	852	1130	1527	493	364	619	1391	1724	243	1691
81	421	1803	556	508	1146	196	839	64	165	1356
82	385	798	969	777	1326	1150	1398	1423	1818	667
83	1012	1106	1140	11	162	471	943	827	1780	993
84	1223	56	948	1371	1598	241	9	1436	1001	6
85	1653	782	1497	68	221	1028	480	920	1438	1362
86	426	756	1321	155	576	75	1184	1640	1629	1812
87	723	1466	1569	486	579	191	733	532	1061	835
88	1305	389	1594	1003	95	1565	1279	622	1386	1707
89	253	874	143	616	1793	1256	1378	1074	912	1129
90	1390	1802	838	797	1397	1105	942	55	8	781
91	479	755	1183	1465	732	388	1278	873	1377	1801
92	941	754	1277	753	1676	354	1677	18	878	454
93	1796	355	1311	1655	542	260	1678	1402	1704	931
94	978	19	182	474	1720	1761	879	467	206	1835
95	151	455	333	870	1539	1066	1797	1176	784	463
96	1545	356	642	1018	80	671	1312	382	1758	138
97	1455	1656	1114	1502	1409	646	543	1646	889	706
98	717	261	998	1499	1078	398	1679	1349	439	515
99	1843	1403	105	1144	991	574	1705	730	929	78

POWER RESIDUES

	0	1	2	3	4	5	6	7	8	9
50	1020	1406	1489	57	285	1425	1584	532	813	371
51	8	40	200	1000	1306	989	1251	714	1723	1227
52	594	1123	74	370	3	15	75	375	28	140
53	700	1653	877	691	1608	652	1413	1524	232	1160
54	259	1295	934	976	1186	389	98	490	603	1168
55	299	1495	87	435	328	1640	812	366	1830	1762
56	1422	1569	457	438	343	1715	1187	394	123	615
57	1228	599	1148	199	995	1281	864	626	1283	874
58	676	1533	277	1385	1384	1379	1354	1229	604	1173
59	324	1620	712	1713	1177	344	1720	1212	519	748
60	46	230	1150	209	1045	1531	267	1335	1134	129
61	645	1378	1349	1204	479	548	893	771	161	805
62	331	1655	887	741	11	55	275	1375	1334	1129
63	104	520	753	71	355	1775	1487	47	235	1175
64	334	1670	962	1116	39	195	975	1181	364	1820
65	1712	1172	319	1595	587	1088	1746	1342	1169	304
66	1520	212	1060	1606	642	1363	1274	829	451	408
67	193	965	1131	114	570	1003	1321	1064	1626	742
68	16	80	400	153	765	131	655	1428	1599	607
69	1188	399	148	740	6	30	150	750	56	280
70	1400	1459	1754	1382	1369	1304	979	1201	464	473
71	518	743	21	105	525	778	196	980	1206	489
72	598	1143	174	870	656	1433	1624	732	1813	1677
73	997	1291	914	876	686	1583	527	788	246	1230
74	609	1198	449	398	143	715	1728	1252	719	1748
75	1352	1219	554	923	921	911	861	611	1208	499
76	648	1393	1424	1579	507	688	1593	577	1038	1496
77	92	460	453	418	243	1215	534	823	421	258
78	1290	909	851	561	958	1096	1786	1542	322	1610
79	662	1463	1774	1482	22	110	550	903	821	411
80	208	1040	1506	142	710	1703	1127	94	470	503
81	668	1493	77	385	78	390	103	515	728	1793
82	1577	497	638	1343	1174	329	1645	837	491	608
83	1193	424	273	1365	1284	879	701	1658	902	816
84	386	83	415	228	1140	159	795	281	1405	1484
85	32	160	800	306	1530	262	1310	1009	1351	1214
86	529	798	296	1480	12	60	300	1500	112	560
87	953	1071	1661	917	891	761	111	555	928	946
88	1036	1486	42	210	1050	1556	392	113	565	978
89	1196	439	348	1740	1312	1019	1401	1464	1779	1507
90	147	735	1828	1752	1372	1319	1054	1576	492	613
91	1218	549	898	796	286	1430	1609	657	1438	1649
92	857	591	1108	1846	1842	1822	1722	1222	569	998
93	1296	939	1001	1311	1014	1376	1339	1154	229	1145
94	184	920	906	836	486	583	1068	1646	842	516
95	733	1818	1702	1122	69	345	1725	1237	644	1373
96	1324	1079	1701	1117	44	220	1100	1806	1642	822
97	416	233	1165	284	1420	1559	407	188	940	1006
98	1336	1139	154	770	156	780	206	1030	1456	1739
99	1307	994	1276	839	501	658	1443	1674	982	1216

P = 1847

INDICES

	0	1	2	3	4	5	6	7	8	9
100	513	932	1164	675	448	25	979	300	70	857
101	1750	20	1394	1085	934	217	183	89	1590	895
102	500	475	227	403	1700	46	1721	1308	433	1088
103	987	1762	1119	223	1431	1479	880	1344	768	1166
104	801	468	1542	1287	1416	604	207	1775	1195	1784
105	884	1836	1769	370	906	1259	152	436	1030	1660
106	662	456	412	133	677	1158	334	62	946	1638
107	141	871	180	380	103	87	1540	60	1170	961
108	237	1067	1607	482	324	1290	1798	1413	655	450
109	1230	1177	1172	1241	1555	394	785	1620	1081	1522
110	966	464	177	1212	1634	1602	1546	1616	922	339
111	1047	357	1824	1033	27	1650	643	963	375	1741
112	1039	1019	953	521	1187	1051	81	806	1671	629
113	1058	672	1668	1440	608	1515	1313	1727	1098	981
114	844	383	239	721	1254	939	1759	1453	572	498
115	602	139	392	1037	937	1337	1456	202	1364	1688
116	539	1657	1199	444	302	972	1115	1069	549	658
117	1339	1503	651	589	824	639	1410	594	1250	1733
118	1381	647	1091	428	1202	1713	544	566	690	72
119	1840	1647	1609	830	1267	1458	890	1215	741	1683
120	1206	707	1533	35	613	1587	718	268	758	1745
121	1419	262	597	1024	859	775	999	484	910	751
122	204	1500	927	401	1193	378	1079	519	570	587
123	739	399	1492	1323	1832	100	1680	957	1663	1752
124	1612	1350	326	1511	1471	1366	440	113	1494	1643
125	174	516	747	1443	1297	109	1844	288	157	317
126	1577	1404	246	1302	22	1055	106	1292	271	363
127	1690	1145	1355	1325	666	161	992	1597	5	220
128	1361	575	1811	578	834	94	1706	1792	1128	1396
129	780	731	1800	1675	453	541	930	1719	1834	1538
130	462	79	137	1408	705	1077	514	990	77	447
131	856	933	894	1699	1087	1430	1165	1415	1783	905
132	1659	676	1637	102	960	323	449	1554	1521	1633
133	338	26	1740	1186	628	607	980	1253	497	936
134	1687	301	657	823	1732	1201	71	1266	1682	612
135	1744	858	750	1192	586	1831	1751	1470	1642	1296
136	316	21	362	665	219	833	1395	452	1537	704
137	446	1086	904	959	1632	627	935	1731	611	585
138	1295	218	703	1631	584	583	184	1694	284	185
139	1485	90	1232	761	1695	304	1591	297	1665	285
140	700	896	1006	293	186	848	501	212	1814	1486
141	1332	476	1476	536	91	1329	228	1179	345	1233
142	974	404	560	1754	762	505	1701	130	687	1696
143	915	47	1765	725	305	233	1722	1138	918	1592
144	53	1309	1174	996	298	1117	434	1605	1614	1666
145	200	1089	266	1490	286	1809	988	1738	1468	701
146	210	1763	1736	791	897	312	1120	1243	280	1007
147	1071	224	1450	1352	294	1042	1432	1446	169	187
148	863	1480	793	1571	849	351	881	636	459	502
149	1270	1345	1557	811	213	551	769	1283	328	1815

POWER RESIDUES

	0	1	2	3	4	5	6	7	8	9
100	539	848	546	883	721	1758	1402	1469	1804	1632
101	772	166	830	456	433	318	1590	562	963	1121
102	64	320	1600	612	1213	524	773	171	855	581
103	1058	1596	592	1113	24	120	600	1153	224	1120
104	59	295	1475	1834	1782	1522	222	1110	9	45
105	225	1125	84	420	253	1265	784	226	1130	109
106	545	878	696	1633	777	191	955	1081	1711	1167
107	294	1470	1809	1657	897	791	261	1305	984	1226
108	589	1098	1796	1592	572	1013	1371	1314	1029	1451
109	1714	1182	369	1845	1837	1797	1597	597	1138	149
110	745	31	155	775	181	905	831	461	458	443
111	368	1840	1812	1672	972	1166	289	1445	1684	1032
112	1466	1789	1557	397	138	690	1603	627	1288	899
113	801	311	1555	387	88	440	353	1765	1437	1644
114	832	466	483	568	993	1271	814	376	33	165
115	825	431	308	1540	312	1560	412	213	1065	1631
116	767	141	705	1678	1002	1316	1039	1501	117	585
117	1078	1696	1092	1766	1442	1669	957	1091	1761	1417
118	1544	332	1660	912	866	636	1333	1124	79	395
119	128	640	1353	1224	579	1048	1546	342	1710	1162
120	269	1345	1184	379	48	240	1200	459	448	393
121	118	590	1103	1821	1717	1197	444	373	18	90
122	450	403	168	840	506	683	1568	452	413	218
123	1090	1756	1392	1419	1554	382	63	315	1575	487
124	588	1093	1771	1467	1794	1582	522	763	121	605
125	1178	349	1745	1337	1144	179	895	781	211	1055
126	1581	517	738	1843	1827	1747	1347	1194	429	298
127	1490	62	310	1550	362	1810	1662	922	916	886
128	736	1833	1777	1497	97	485	578	1043	1521	217
129	1085	1731	1267	794	276	1380	1359	1254	729	1798
130	1602	622	1263	774	176	880	706	1683	1027	1441
131	1664	932	966	1136	139	695	1628	752	66	330
132	1650	862	616	1233	624	1273	824	426	283	1415
133	1534	282	1410	1509	157	785	231	1155	234	1170
134	309	1545	337	1685	1037	1491	67	335	1675	987
135	1241	664	1473	1824	1732	1272	819	401	158	790
136	256	1280	859	601	1158	249	1245	684	1573	477
137	538	843	521	758	96	480	553	918	896	786
138	236	1180	359	1795	1587	547	888	746	36	180
139	900	806	336	1680	1012	1366	1289	904	826	436
140	333	1665	937	991	1261	764	126	630	1303	974
141	1176	339	1695	1087	1741	1317	1044	1526	242	1210
142	509	698	1643	827	441	358	1790	1562	422	263
143	1315	1034	1476	1839	1807	1647	847	541	858	596
144	1133	124	620	1253	724	1773	1477	1844	1832	1772
145	1472	1819	1707	1147	194	970	1156	239	1195	434
146	323	1615	687	1588	552	913	871	661	1458	1749
147	1357	1244	679	1548	352	1760	1412	1519	207	1035
148	1481	17	85	425	278	1390	1409	1504	132	660
149	1453	1724	1232	619	1248	699	1648	852	566	983

P = 1847

INDICES

	0	1	2	3	4	5	6	7	8	9
150	867	1167	32	1518	1487	274	802	899	488	1333
151	419	469	424	1563	477	258	1543	396	1748	1477
152	660	1288	1045	1513	537	1711	1417	98	1575	92
153	854	605	314	581	1330	231	208	349	417	229
154	1153	1776	787	1582	1180	1341	1196	1789	1473	346
155	1273	1785	118	147	1234	1132	885	1122	193	975
156	1155	1837	1427	50	405	408	1770	1622	1226	561
157	1505	371	1549	1368	1755	1238	907	820	277	763
158	1529	1260	1245	735	506	1778	153	1384	1463	1702
159	1016	437	1083	766	131	653	1031	1096	442	688
160	1022	1661	1300	1126	1697	495	663	282	534	916
161	789	457	1561	415	48	1461	413	1524	15	1766
162	591	134	127	115	726	123	678	42	1316	306
163	366	1159	1009	1063	234	1584	335	1806	1526	1723
164	555	63	968	1422	1139	826	947	1435	1496	919
165	1320	1639	1568	531	1593	621	142	1073	837	54
166	1182	872	1276	17	1310	1401	181	466	332	1175
167	641	381	1113	1645	997	1348	104	729	1163	299
168	1393	88	226	1307	1118	1343	1541	1774	1768	435
169	411	61	179	59	1606	1412	1171	1619	176	1615
170	1823	962	952	805	1667	1726	238	1452	391	201
171	1198	1068	650	593	1090	565	1608	1214	1532	267
172	596	483	926	518	1491	956	325	112	746	287
173	245	1291	1354	1596	1810	1791	1799	1718	136	989
174	893	1414	1636	1553	1739	1252	656	1265	749	1469
175	361	451	903	1730	702	1693	1231	296	1005	211
176	1475	1178	559	129	1764	1137	1173	1604	265	1737
177	1735	1242	1449	1445	792	635	1556	1282	31	898
178	423	395	1044	97	313	348	786	1788	117	1121
179	1426	1621	1548	819	1244	1383	1082	1095	1299	281
180	1560	1523	126	41	1008	1805	967	1434	1567	1072
181	1275	465	1112	728	225	1773	178	1618	951	1451
182	649	1213	925	111	1353	1717	1635	1264	902	295
183	558	1603	1448	1281	1043	1787	1547	1094	125	1433
184	1111	1617	924	1263	1447	1093	923			

POWER RESIDUES

	0	1	2	3	4	5	6	7	8	9
150	1221	564	973	1171	314	1570	462	463	468	493
151	618	1243	674	1523	227	1135	134	670	1503	127
152	635	1328	1099	1801	1617	697	1638	802	316	1580
153	512	713	1718	1202	469	498	643	1368	1299	954
154	1076	1686	1042	1516	192	960	1106	1836	1792	1572
155	472	513	718	1743	1327	1094	1776	1492	72	360
156	1800	1612	672	1513	177	885	731	1808	1652	872
157	666	1483	27	135	675	1528	252	1260	759	101
158	505	678	1543	327	1635	787	241	1205	484	573
159	1018	1396	1439	1654	882	716	1733	1277	844	526
160	783	221	1105	1831	1767	1447	1694	1082	1716	1192
161	419	248	1240	659	1448	1699	1107	1841	1817	1697
162	1097	1791	1567	447	388	93	465	478	543	868
163	646	1383	1374	1329	1104	1826	1742	1322	1069	1651
164	867	641	1358	1249	704	1673	977	1191	414	223
165	1115	34	170	850	556	933	971	1161	264	1320
166	1059	1601	617	1238	649	1398	1449	1704	1132	119
167	595	1128	99	495	628	1293	924	926	936	986
168	1236	639	1348	1199	454	423	268	1340	1159	254
169	1270	809	351	1755	1387	1394	1429	1604	632	1313
170	1024	1426	1589	557	938	996	1286	889	751	61
171	305	1525	237	1185	384	73	365	1825	1737	1297
172	944	1026	1436	1639	807	341	1705	1137	144	720
173	1753	1377	1344	1179	354	1770	1462	1769	1457	1744
174	1332	1119	54	270	1350	1209	504	673	1518	202
175	1010	1356	1239	654	1423	1574	482	563	968	1146
176	189	945	1031	1461	1764	1432	1619	707	1688	1052
177	1566	442	363	1815	1687	1047	1541	317	1585	537
178	838	496	633	1318	1049	1551	367	1835	1787	1547
179	347	1735	1287	894	776	186	930	956	1086	1736
180	1292	919	901	811	361	1805	1637	797	291	1455
181	1734	1282	869	651	1408	1499	107	535	828	446
182	383	68	340	1700	1112	19	95	475	528	793
183	271	1355	1234	629	1298	949	1051	1561	417	238
184	1190	409	198	990	1256	739				

P = 1861

INDICES

	0	1	2	3	4	5	6	7	8	9
0		0	1	546	2	1080	547	1145	3	1092
1	1081	421	548	1185	1146	1626	4	1450	1093	1429
2	1082	1691	422	1537	549	300	1186	1638	1147	144
3	1627	1162	5	967	1451	365	1094	1050	1430	1731
4	1083	622	1692	739	423	312	1538	346	550	430
5	301	136	1187	1112	1639	1501	1148	115	145	1633
6	1628	465	1163	377	6	405	968	479	1452	223
7	366	1370	1095	1724	1051	846	1431	1566	1732	1676
8	1084	324	623	873	1693	670	740	690	424	172
9	313	470	1539	1708	347	649	551	594	431	1513
10	302	576	137	982	1188	911	1113	1172	1640	1343
11	1502	1596	1149	178	116	757	146	417	1634	735
12	1629	842	466	1168	1164	1380	378	657	7	1285
13	406	1422	969	714	480	858	1453	829	224	1384
14	367	892	1371	1606	1096	1224	1725	976	1052	246
15	847	812	1432	682	1567	382	1733	989	1677	1658
16	1085	822	325	101	624	187	874	1058	1694	510
17	671	661	741	1271	691	1445	425	319	173	1219
18	314	1845	471	1011	1540	270	1709	11	348	923
19	650	1209	552	1002	595	951	432	262	1514	204
20	303	1025	577	1289	138	1702	983	769	1189	1850
21	912	338	1114	56	1173	1819	1641	447	1344	410
22	1503	775	1597	633	1150	1392	179	1239	117	1071
23	758	252	147	543	418	1426	1635	362	736	133
24	1630	476	843	870	467	1510	1169	754	1165	1419
25	1381	973	379	98	658	1216	8	948	1286	335
26	407	1236	1423	867	970	332	715	718	481	1137
27	859	1809	1454	1016	830	721	225	587	1385	394
28	368	1828	893	484	1372	1195	1607	1767	1097	1040
29	1225	1140	1726	1365	977	853	1053	199	247	862
30	848	24	813	1122	1433	1545	683	1812	1568	1528
31	383	533	1734	903	990	1457	1678	75	1659	565
32	1086	1718	823	1019	326	1485	102	29	625	1491
33	188	833	875	282	1059	1559	1695	275	511	724
34	672	1583	662	1575	742	1303	1272	228	692	1856
35	1446	963	426	401	320	590	174	1281	1220	818
36	315	998	1846	1388	472	944	1012	1036	1541	1714
37	271	397	1710	782	12	66	349	1329	924	371
38	651	1203	1210	559	553	786	1003	1831	596	613
39	952	1127	433	108	263	896	1515	84	205	1260
40	304	16	1026	487	578	1404	1290	1471	139	460
41	1703	1375	984	918	770	93	1190	70	1851	1198
42	913	1247	339	1438	1115	1750	57	1610	1174	292
43	1820	1757	1642	353	448	1770	1345	1106	411	1839
44	1504	1522	776	1100	1598	1252	634	792	1151	1333
45	1393	1043	180	1358	1240	1550	118	35	1072	1228
46	759	518	253	160	148	928	544	1143	419	1624
47	1427	1535	1636	1160	363	1729	737	344	134	1499
48	1631	375	477	1368	844	1674	871	688	468	647
49	1511	980	1170	1594	755	733	1166	655	1420	856

POWER RESIDUES

	0	1	2	3	4	5	6	7	8	9
0	1	2	4	8	16	32	64	128	256	512
1	1024	187	374	748	1496	1131	401	802	1604	1347
2	833	1666	1471	1081	301	602	1204	547	1094	327
3	654	1308	755	1510	1159	457	914	1828	1795	1729
4	1597	1333	805	1610	1359	857	1714	1567	1273	685
5	1370	879	1758	1655	1449	1037	213	426	852	1704
6	1547	1233	605	1210	559	1118	375	750	1500	1139
7	417	834	1668	1475	1089	317	634	1268	675	1350
8	839	1678	1495	1129	397	794	1588	1315	769	1538
9	1215	569	1138	415	830	1660	1459	1057	253	506
10	1012	163	326	652	1304	747	1494	1127	393	786
11	1572	1283	705	1410	959	57	114	228	456	912
12	1824	1787	1713	1565	1269	677	1354	847	1694	1527
13	1193	525	1050	239	478	956	51	102	204	408
14	816	1632	1403	945	29	58	116	232	464	928
15	1856	1851	1841	1821	1781	1701	1541	1221	581	1162
16	463	926	1852	1843	1825	1789	1717	1573	1285	709
17	1418	975	89	178	356	712	1424	987	113	226
18	452	904	1808	1755	1649	1437	1013	165	330	660
19	1320	779	1558	1255	649	1298	735	1470	1079	297
20	594	1188	515	1030	199	398	796	1592	1323	785
21	1570	1279	697	1394	927	1854	1847	1833	1805	1749
22	1637	1413	965	69	138	276	552	1104	347	694
23	1388	915	1830	1799	1737	1613	1365	869	1738	1615
24	1369	877	1754	1647	1433	1005	149	298	596	1192
25	523	1046	231	462	924	1848	1835	1809	1757	1653
26	1445	1029	197	394	788	1576	1291	721	1442	1023
27	185	370	740	1480	1099	337	674	1348	835	1670
28	1479	1097	333	666	1332	803	1606	1351	841	1682
29	1503	1145	429	858	1716	1571	1281	701	1402	943
30	25	50	100	200	400	800	1600	1339	817	1634
31	1407	953	45	90	180	360	720	1440	1019	177
32	354	708	1416	971	81	162	324	648	1296	731
33	1462	1063	265	530	1060	259	518	1036	211	422
34	844	1688	1515	1169	477	954	47	94	188	376
35	752	1504	1147	433	866	1732	1603	1345	829	1658
36	1455	1049	237	474	948	35	70	140	280	560
37	1120	379	758	1516	1171	481	962	63	126	252
38	504	1008	155	310	620	1240	619	1238	615	1230
39	599	1198	535	1070	279	558	1116	371	742	1484
40	1107	353	706	1412	963	65	130	260	520	1040
41	219	438	876	1752	1643	1425	989	117	234	468
42	936	11	22	44	88	176	352	704	1408	955
43	49	98	196	392	784	1568	1275	689	1378	895
44	1790	1719	1577	1293	725	1450	1039	217	434	868
45	1736	1611	1361	861	1722	1583	1305	749	1498	1135
46	409	818	1636	1411	961	61	122	244	488	976
47	91	182	364	728	1456	1051	241	482	964	67
48	134	268	536	1072	283	566	1132	403	806	1612
49	1363	865	1730	1599	1337	813	1626	1391	921	1842

P = 1861

INDICES

	0	1	2	3	4	5	6	7	8	9
50	1382	1604	974	810	380	1656	99	1056	659	1443
51	1217	1009	9	1207	949	202	1287	767	336	1817
52	408	631	1237	250	1424	131	868	752	971	1214
53	333	865	716	1807	719	392	482	1765	1138	851
54	860	1120	1810	531	1455	563	1017	27	831	1557
55	722	1573	226	961	588	816	1386	1034	395	64
56	369	557	1829	1125	894	1258	485	1469	1373	91
57	1196	1436	1608	1755	1768	1837	1098	790	1041	1548
58	1226	158	1141	1533	1727	1497	1366	686	978	731
59	854	808	1054	1007	200	1815	248	750	863	390
60	849	529	25	1571	814	62	1123	1467	1434	1835
61	1546	1531	684	806	1813	388	1569	1465	1529	386
62	384	1315	534	1317	1735	600	904	536	991	640
63	1458	1319	1679	884	76	1737	1660	1615	566	602
64	1087	617	1719	906	824	505	1020	538	327	194
65	1486	993	103	1745	30	642	626	956	1492	1460
66	189	1780	834	1321	876	1794	283	1681	1060	1179
67	1560	886	1696	1131	276	78	512	125	725	1739
68	673	1785	1584	1662	663	49	1576	1617	743	437
69	1304	568	1273	798	229	604	693	212	1857	1089
70	1447	297	964	619	427	112	402	1721	321	169
71	591	908	175	839	1282	826	1221	679	819	507
72	316	267	999	1022	1847	444	1389	540	473	1416
73	945	329	1013	1825	1037	196	1542	900	1715	1488
74	272	1300	398	995	1711	1326	783	105	13	457
75	67	1747	350	1519	1330	32	925	1157	372	644
76	652	1653	1204	628	1211	1762	560	958	554	88
77	787	1494	1004	526	1832	1462	597	881	614	191
78	953	1791	1128	1782	434	209	109	836	264	1413
79	897	1323	1516	1650	85	878	206	1647	1261	1796
80	305	1264	17	285	1027	42	488	1683	579	1799
81	1405	1062	1291	495	1472	1181	140	308	461	1562
82	1704	1339	1376	888	985	1267	919	1698	771	358
83	94	1133	1191	20	71	278	1852	940	1199	80
84	914	288	1248	514	340	1590	1439	127	1116	1030
85	1751	727	58	1311	1611	1741	1175	45	293	675
86	1821	453	1758	1787	1643	491	354	1586	449	237
87	1771	1664	1346	1686	1107	665	412	241	1840	51
88	1505	582	1523	1578	777	1399	1101	1619	1599	1802
89	1253	745	635	1775	793	439	1152	1408	1334	1306
90	1394	702	1044	570	181	1065	1359	1275	1241	1668
91	1551	800	119	1294	36	231	1073	707	1229	606
92	760	498	519	695	254	1350	161	214	149	1475
93	929	1859	545	1079	1144	1091	420	1184	1625	1449
94	1428	1690	1536	299	1637	143	1161	966	364	1049
95	1730	621	738	311	345	429	135	1111	1500	114
96	1632	464	376	404	478	222	1369	1723	845	1565
97	1675	323	872	669	689	171	469	1707	648	593
98	1512	575	981	910	1171	1342	1595	177	756	416
99	734	841	1167	1379	656	1284	1421	713	857	828

POWER RESIDUES

	0	1	2	3	4	5	6	7	8	9
50	1823	1785	1709	1557	1253	645	1290	719	1438	1015
51	169	338	676	1352	843	1686	1511	1161	461	922
52	1844	1827	1793	1725	1589	1317	773	1546	1231	601
53	1202	543	1086	311	622	1244	627	1254	647	1294
54	727	1454	1047	233	466	932	3	6	12	24
55	48	96	192	384	768	1536	1211	561	1122	383
56	766	1532	1203	545	1090	319	638	1276	691	1382
57	903	1806	1751	1641	1421	981	101	202	404	808
58	1616	1371	881	1762	1663	1465	1069	277	554	1108
59	355	710	1420	979	97	194	388	776	1552	1243
60	625	1250	639	1278	695	1390	919	1838	1815	1769
61	1677	1493	1125	389	778	1556	1251	641	1282	703
62	1406	951	41	82	164	328	656	1312	763	1526
63	1191	521	1042	223	446	892	1784	1707	1553	1245
64	629	1258	655	1310	759	1518	1175	489	978	95
65	190	380	760	1520	1179	497	994	127	254	508
66	1016	171	342	684	1368	875	1750	1639	1417	973
67	85	170	340	680	1360	859	1718	1575	1289	717
68	1434	1007	153	306	612	1224	587	1174	487	974
69	87	174	348	696	1392	923	1846	1831	1801	1741
70	1621	1381	901	1802	1743	1625	1389	917	1834	1807
71	1753	1645	1429	997	133	266	532	1064	267	534
72	1068	275	550	1100	339	678	1356	851	1702	1543
73	1225	589	1178	495	990	119	238	476	952	43
74	86	172	344	688	1376	891	1782	1703	1545	1229
75	597	1194	527	1054	247	494	988	115	230	460
76	920	1840	1819	1777	1693	1525	1189	517	1034	207
77	414	828	1656	1451	1041	221	442	884	1768	1675
78	1489	1117	373	746	1492	1123	385	770	1540	1219
79	577	1154	447	894	1788	1715	1569	1277	693	1386
80	911	1822	1783	1705	1549	1237	613	1226	591	1182
81	503	1006	151	302	604	1208	555	1110	359	718
82	1436	1011	161	322	644	1288	715	1430	999	137
83	274	548	1096	331	662	1324	787	1574	1287	713
84	1426	991	121	242	484	968	75	150	300	600
85	1200	539	1078	295	590	1180	499	998	135	270
86	540	1080	299	598	1196	531	1062	263	526	1052
87	243	486	972	83	166	332	664	1328	795	1590
88	1319	777	1554	1247	633	1266	671	1342	823	1646
89	1431	1001	141	282	564	1128	395	790	1580	1299
90	737	1474	1087	313	626	1252	643	1286	711	1422
91	983	105	210	420	840	1680	1499	1137	413	826
92	1652	1443	1025	189	378	756	1512	1163	465	930
93	1860	1859	1857	1853	1845	1829	1797	1733	1605	1349
94	837	1674	1487	1113	365	730	1460	1059	257	514
95	1028	195	390	780	1560	1259	657	1314	767	1534
96	1207	553	1106	351	702	1404	947	33	66	132
97	264	528	1056	251	502	1004	147	294	588	1176
98	491	982	103	206	412	824	1648	1435	1009	157
99	314	628	1256	651	1302	743	1486	1111	361	722

P = 1861

INDICES

	0	1	2	3	4	5	6	7	8	9
100	1383	891	1605	1223	975	245	811	681	381	988
101	1657	821	100	186	1057	509	660	1270	1444	318
102	1218	1844	1010	269	10	922	1208	1001	950	261
103	203	1024	1288	1701	768	1849	337	55	1818	446
104	409	774	632	1391	1238	1070	251	542	1425	361
105	132	475	869	1509	753	1418	972	97	1215	947
106	334	1235	866	331	717	1136	1808	1015	720	586
107	393	1827	483	1194	1766	1039	1139	1364	852	198
108	861	23	1121	1544	1811	1527	532	902	1456	74
109	564	1717	1018	1484	28	1490	832	281	1558	274
110	723	1582	1574	1302	227	1855	962	400	589	1280
111	817	997	1387	943	1035	1713	396	781	65	1328
112	370	1202	558	785	1830	612	1126	107	895	83
113	1259	15	486	1403	1470	459	1374	917	92	69
114	1197	1246	1437	1749	1609	291	1756	352	1769	1105
115	1838	1521	1099	1251	791	1332	1042	1357	1549	34
116	1227	517	159	927	1142	1623	1534	1159	1728	343
117	1498	374	1367	1673	687	646	979	1593	732	654
118	855	1603	809	1655	1055	1442	1008	1206	201	766
119	1816	630	249	130	751	1213	864	1806	391	1764
120	850	1119	530	562	26	1556	1572	960	815	1033
121	63	556	1124	1257	1468	90	1435	1754	1836	789
122	1547	157	1532	1496	685	730	807	1006	1814	749
123	389	528	1570	61	1466	1834	1530	805	387	1464
124	385	1314	1316	599	535	639	1318	883	1736	1614
125	601	616	905	504	537	193	992	1744	641	955
126	1459	1779	1320	1793	1680	1178	885	1130	77	124
127	1738	1784	1661	48	1616	436	567	797	603	211
128	1088	296	618	111	1720	168	907	838	825	678
129	506	266	1021	443	539	1415	328	1824	195	899
130	1487	1299	994	1325	104	456	1746	1518	31	1156
131	643	1652	627	1761	957	87	1493	525	1461	880
132	190	1790	1781	208	835	1412	1322	1649	877	1646
133	1795	1263	284	41	1682	1798	1061	494	1180	307
134	1561	1338	887	1266	1697	357	1132	19	277	939
135	79	287	513	1589	126	1029	726	1310	1740	44
136	674	452	1786	490	1585	236	1663	1685	664	240
137	50	581	1577	1398	1618	1801	744	1774	438	1407
138	1305	701	569	1064	1274	1667	799	1293	230	706
139	605	497	694	1349	213	1474	1858	1078	1090	1183
140	1448	1689	298	142	965	1048	620	310	428	1110
141	113	463	403	221	1722	1564	322	668	170	1706
142	592	574	909	1341	176	415	840	1378	1283	712
143	827	890	1222	244	680	987	820	185	508	1269
144	317	1843	268	921	1000	260	1023	1700	1848	54
145	445	773	1390	1069	541	360	474	1508	1417	96
146	946	1234	330	1135	1014	585	1826	1193	1038	1363
147	197	22	1543	1526	901	73	1716	1483	1489	280
148	273	1581	1301	1854	399	1279	996	942	1712	780
149	1327	1201	784	611	106	82	14	1402	458	916

POWER RESIDUES

	0	1	2	3	4	5	6	7	8	9
100	1444	1027	193	386	772	1544	1227	593	1186	511
101	1022	183	366	732	1464	1067	273	546	1092	323
102	646	1292	723	1446	1031	201	402	804	1608	1355
103	849	1698	1535	1209	557	1114	367	734	1468	1075
104	289	578	1156	451	902	1804	1747	1633	1405	949
105	37	74	148	296	592	1184	507	1014	167	334
106	668	1336	811	1622	1383	905	1810	1759	1657	1453
107	1045	229	458	916	1832	1803	1745	1629	1397	933
108	5	10	20	40	80	160	320	640	1280	699
109	1398	935	9	18	36	72	144	288	576	1152
110	443	886	1772	1683	1505	1149	437	874	1748	1635
111	1409	957	53	106	212	424	848	1696	1531	1201
112	541	1082	303	606	1212	563	1126	391	782	1564
113	1267	673	1346	831	1662	1463	1065	269	538	1076
114	291	582	1164	467	934	7	14	28	56	112
115	224	448	896	1792	1723	1585	1309	757	1514	1167
116	473	946	31	62	124	248	496	992	123	246
117	492	984	107	214	428	856	1712	1563	1265	669
118	1338	815	1630	1399	937	13	26	52	104	208
119	416	832	1664	1467	1073	285	570	1140	419	838
120	1676	1491	1121	381	762	1524	1187	513	1026	191
121	382	764	1528	1195	529	1058	255	510	1020	179
122	358	716	1432	1003	145	290	580	1160	459	918
123	1836	1811	1761	1661	1461	1061	261	522	1044	227
124	454	908	1816	1771	1681	1501	1141	421	842	1684
125	1507	1153	445	890	1780	1699	1537	1213	565	1130
126	399	798	1596	1331	801	1602	1343	825	1650	1439
127	1017	173	346	692	1384	907	1814	1767	1673	1485
128	1109	357	714	1428	995	129	258	516	1032	203
129	406	812	1624	1387	913	1826	1791	1721	1581	1301
130	741	1482	1103	345	690	1380	899	1798	1735	1609
131	1357	853	1706	1551	1241	621	1242	623	1246	631
132	1262	663	1326	791	1582	1303	745	1490	1119	377
133	754	1508	1155	449	898	1796	1731	1601	1341	821
134	1642	1423	985	109	218	436	872	1744	1627	1393
135	925	1850	1839	1817	1773	1685	1509	1157	453	906
136	1812	1763	1665	1469	1077	293	586	1172	483	966
137	71	142	284	568	1136	411	822	1644	1427	993
138	125	250	500	1000	139	278	556	1112	363	726
139	1452	1043	225	450	900	1800	1739	1617	1373	885
140	1770	1679	1497	1133	405	810	1620	1379	897	1794
141	1727	1593	1325	789	1578	1295	729	1458	1055	249
142	498	996	131	262	524	1048	235	470	940	19
143	38	76	152	304	608	1216	571	1142	423	846
144	1692	1523	1185	509	1018	175	350	700	1400	939
145	17	34	68	136	272	544	1088	315	630	1260
146	659	1318	775	1550	1239	617	1234	607	1214	567
147	1134	407	814	1628	1395	929	1858	1855	1849	1837
148	1813	1765	1669	1477	1093	325	650	1300	739	1478
149	1095	329	658	1316	771	1542	1223	585	1170	479

P = 1861

INDICES

	0	1	2	3	4	5	6	7	8	9
150	68	1245	1748	290	351	1104	1520	1250	1331	1356
151	33	516	926	1622	1158	342	373	1672	645	1592
152	653	1602	1654	1441	1205	765	629	129	1212	1805
153	1763	1118	561	1555	959	1032	555	1256	89	1753
154	788	156	1495	729	1005	748	527	60	1833	804
155	1463	1313	598	638	882	1613	615	503	192	1743
156	954	1778	1792	1177	1129	123	1783	47	435	796
157	210	295	110	167	837	677	265	442	1414	1823
158	898	1298	1324	455	1517	1155	1651	1760	86	524
159	879	1789	207	1411	1648	1645	1262	40	1797	493
160	306	1337	1265	356	18	938	286	1588	1028	1309
161	43	451	489	235	1684	239	580	1397	1800	1773
162	1406	700	1063	1666	1292	705	496	1348	1473	1077
163	1182	1688	141	1047	309	1109	462	220	1563	667
164	1705	573	1340	414	1377	711	889	243	986	184
165	1268	1842	920	259	1699	53	772	1068	359	1507
166	95	1233	1134	584	1192	1362	21	1525	72	1482
167	279	1580	1853	1278	941	779	1200	610	81	1401
168	915	1244	289	1103	1249	1355	515	1621	341	1671
169	1591	1601	1440	764	128	1804	1117	1554	1031	1255
170	1752	155	728	747	59	803	1312	637	1612	502
171	1742	1777	1176	122	46	795	294	166	676	441
172	1822	1297	454	1154	1759	523	1788	1410	1644	39
173	492	1336	355	937	1587	1308	450	234	238	1396
174	1772	699	1665	704	1347	1076	1687	1046	1108	219
175	666	572	413	710	242	183	1841	258	52	1067
176	1506	1232	583	1361	1524	1481	1579	1277	778	609
177	1400	1243	1102	1354	1620	1670	1600	763	1803	1553
178	1254	154	746	802	636	501	1776	121	794	165
179	440	1296	1153	522	1409	38	1335	936	1307	233
180	1395	698	703	1075	1045	218	571	709	182	257
181	1066	1231	1360	1480	1276	608	1242	1353	1669	762
182	1552	153	801	500	120	164	1295	521	37	935
183	232	697	1074	217	708	256	1230	1479	607	1352
184	761	152	499	163	520	934	696	216	255	1478
185	1351	151	162	933	215	1477	150	932	1476	931
186	930	0								

POWER RESIDUES

	0	1	2	3	4	5	6	7	8	9
150	958	55	110	220	440	880	1760	1659	1457	1053
151	245	490	980	99	198	396	792	1584	1307	753
152	1506	1151	441	882	1764	1667	1473	1085	309	618
153	1236	611	1222	583	1166	471	942	23	46	92
154	184	368	736	1472	1083	305	610	1220	579	1158
155	455	910	1820	1779	1697	1533	1205	549	1098	335
156	670	1340	819	1638	1415	969	77	154	308	616
157	1232	603	1206	551	1102	343	686	1372	883	1766
158	1671	1481	1101	341	682	1364	867	1734	1607	1353
159	845	1690	1519	1177	493	986	111	222	444	888
160	1776	1691	1521	1181	501	1002	143	286	572	1144
161	427	854	1708	1555	1249	637	1274	687	1374	887
162	1774	1687	1513	1165	469	938	15	30	60	120
163	240	480	960	59	118	236	472	944	27	54
164	108	216	432	864	1728	1595	1329	797	1594	1327
165	793	1586	1311	761	1522	1183	505	1010	159	318
166	636	1272	683	1366	871	1742	1623	1385	909	1818
167	1775	1689	1517	1173	485	970	79	158	316	632
168	1264	667	1334	807	1614	1367	873	1746	1631	1401
169	941	21	42	84	168	336	672	1344	827	1654
170	1447	1033	205	410	820	1640	1419	977	93	186
171	372	744	1488	1115	369	738	1476	1091	321	642
172	1284	707	1414	967	73	146	292	584	1168	475
173	950	39	78	156	312	624	1248	635	1270	679
174	1358	855	1710	1559	1257	653	1306	751	1502	1143
175	425	850	1700	1539	1217	573	1146	431	862	1724
176	1587	1313	765	1530	1199	537	1074	287	574	1148
177	435	870	1740	1619	1377	893	1786	1711	1561	1261
178	661	1322	783	1566	1271	681	1362	863	1726	1591
179	1321	781	1562	1263	665	1330	799	1598	1335	809
180	1618	1375	889	1778	1695	1529	1197	533	1066	271
181	542	1084	307	614	1228	595	1190	519	1038	215
182	430	860	1720	1579	1297	733	1466	1071	281	562
183	1124	387	774	1548	1235	609	1218	575	1150	439
184	878	1756	1651	1441	1021	181	362	724	1448	1035
185	209	418	836	1672	1483	1105	349	698	1396	931
186										

P = 1867

INDICES

	0	1	2	3	4	5	6	7	8	9
0		0	1	387	2	837	388	1120	3	774
1	838	818	389	59	1121	1224	4	597	775	1395
2	839	1507	819	1253	390	1674	60	1161	1122	1745
3	1225	827	5	1205	598	91	776	1721	1396	446
4	840	141	1508	854	820	1611	1254	1085	391	374
5	1675	984	61	1231	1162	1655	1123	1782	1746	1502
6	1226	1429	828	28	6	896	1206	1518	599	1640
7	92	514	777	767	1722	195	1397	72	447	1355
8	841	1548	142	255	1509	1434	855	266	821	360
9	1612	1179	1255	1214	1086	366	392	1794	375	1592
10	1676	532	985	217	62	478	1232	727	1163	1457
11	1656	242	1124	565	1783	224	1747	833	1503	1717
12	1227	1636	1430	528	829	645	29	172	7	1241
13	897	1017	1207	649	1519	132	600	1729	1641	234
14	93	1472	515	877	778	716	768	761	1723	33
15	196	333	1398	1371	73	1664	448	208	1356	1618
16	842	507	1549	1837	143	176	256	1340	1510	118
17	1435	303	856	1824	267	928	822	23	361	167
18	1613	11	1180	1816	1256	692	1215	1415	1087	415
19	367	16	393	1056	1795	1283	376	1245	1593	1556
20	1677	39	533	999	986	978	218	161	63	347
21	479	1097	1233	901	728	1691	1164	81	1458	1154
22	1657	656	243	1185	1125	582	566	48	1784	1021
23	225	459	1748	1317	834	56	1504	1742	1718	1608
24	1228	1426	1637	69	1431	1211	529	1454	830	642
25	646	1469	30	205	173	1821	8	412	1242	975
26	898	653	1018	1739	1208	202	650	747	1520	750
27	133	105	601	1566	1730	626	1642	1523	235	1601
28	94	556	1473	663	516	753	878	1261	779	1194
29	717	315	769	136	762	473	1724	113	34	1312
30	197	108	334	919	1399	400	1372	353	74	604
31	1665	545	449	430	209	865	1357	1569	1619	697
32	843	1114	508	126	1550	1733	1838	1844	144	339
33	177	1329	257	629	1341	489	1511	1276	119	952
34	1436	1645	304	1494	857	611	1825	1303	268	1526
35	929	1220	823	1081	24	1351	362	238	168	873
36	1614	924	12	157	1181	1604	1817	101	1257	915
37	693	485	1216	97	1416	1032	1088	1804	416	285
38	368	559	17	1420	394	909	1057	1628	1796	1476
39	1284	1850	377	1404	1246	326	1594	666	1557	1036
40	1678	804	40	886	534	519	1000	673	987	1390
41	979	250	219	756	162	1092	64	621	348	947
42	480	881	1098	1859	1234	405	902	683	729	1264
43	1692	1808	1165	1063	82	1103	1459	782	1155	1173
44	1658	1148	657	1297	244	1197	1186	420	1126	1445
45	583	959	567	720	49	150	1785	1377	1022	1758
46	226	318	460	289	1749	185	1318	1864	835	772
47	57	595	1505	1672	1743	1203	1719	139	1609	372
48	1229	1780	1427	894	1638	765	70	1546	1432	358
49	1212	1792	530	476	1455	563	831	1634	643	1239

POWER RESIDUES

	0	1	2	3	4	5	6	7	8	9
0	1	2	4	8	16	32	64	128	256	512
1	1024	181	362	724	1448	1029	191	382	764	1528
2	1189	511	1022	177	354	708	1416	965	63	126
3	252	504	1008	149	298	596	1192	517	1034	201
4	402	804	1608	1349	831	1662	1457	1047	227	454
5	908	1816	1765	1663	1459	1051	235	470	940	13
6	26	52	104	208	416	832	1664	1461	1055	243
7	486	972	77	154	308	616	1232	597	1194	521
8	1042	217	434	868	1736	1605	1343	819	1638	1409
9	951	35	70	140	280	560	1120	373	746	1492
10	1117	367	734	1468	1069	271	542	1084	301	602
11	1204	541	1082	297	594	1188	509	1018	169	338
12	676	1352	837	1674	1481	1095	323	646	1292	717
13	1434	1001	135	270	540	1080	293	586	1172	477
14	954	41	82	164	328	656	1312	757	1514	1161
15	455	910	1820	1773	1679	1491	1115	363	726	1452
16	1037	207	414	828	1656	1445	1023	179	358	716
17	1432	997	127	254	508	1016	165	330	660	1320
18	773	1546	1225	583	1166	465	930	1860	1853	1839
19	1811	1755	1643	1419	971	75	150	300	600	1200
20	533	1066	265	530	1060	253	506	1012	157	314
21	628	1256	645	1290	713	1426	985	103	206	412
22	824	1648	1429	991	115	230	460	920	1840	1813
23	1759	1651	1435	1003	139	278	556	1112	357	714
24	1428	989	111	222	444	888	1776	1685	1503	1139
25	411	822	1644	1421	975	83	166	332	664	1328
26	789	1578	1289	711	1422	977	87	174	348	696
27	1392	917	1834	1801	1735	1603	1339	811	1622	1377
28	887	1774	1681	1495	1123	379	758	1516	1165	463
29	926	1852	1837	1807	1747	1627	1387	907	1814	1761
30	1655	1443	1019	171	342	684	1368	869	1738	1609
31	1351	835	1670	1473	1079	291	582	1164	461	922
32	1844	1821	1775	1683	1499	1131	395	790	1580	1293
33	719	1438	1009	151	302	604	1208	549	1098	329
34	658	1316	765	1530	1193	519	1038	209	418	836
35	1672	1477	1087	307	614	1228	589	1178	489	978
36	89	178	356	712	1424	981	95	190	380	760
37	1520	1173	479	958	49	98	196	392	784	1568
38	1269	671	1342	817	1634	1401	935	3	6	12
39	24	48	96	192	384	768	1536	1205	543	1086
40	305	610	1220	573	1146	425	850	1700	1533	1199
41	531	1062	257	514	1028	189	378	756	1512	1157
42	447	894	1788	1709	1551	1235	603	1206	545	1090
43	313	626	1252	637	1274	681	1362	857	1714	1561
44	1255	643	1286	705	1410	953	39	78	156	312
45	624	1248	629	1258	649	1298	729	1458	1049	231
46	462	924	1848	1829	1791	1715	1563	1259	651	1302
47	737	1474	1081	295	590	1180	493	986	105	210
48	420	840	1680	1493	1119	371	742	1484	1101	335
49	670	1340	813	1626	1385	903	1806	1745	1623	1379

P = 1867

INDICES

	0	1	2	3	4	5	6	7	8	9
50	647	1727	1470	714	31	1369	206	505	174	116
51	1822	21	9	690	413	1054	1243	37	976	345
52	899	79	654	580	1019	1315	1740	1424	1209	640
53	203	410	651	200	748	1564	1521	554	751	1192
54	134	111	106	398	602	428	1567	1112	1731	337
55	627	1274	1643	609	1524	1079	236	922	1602	913
56	95	1802	557	907	1474	1402	664	802	517	1388
57	754	619	879	403	1262	1061	780	1146	1195	1443
58	718	1375	316	183	770	1670	137	1778	763	356
59	474	1632	1725	1367	114	688	35	77	1313	638
60	198	552	109	426	335	607	920	1800	1400	1386
61	401	1144	1373	1668	354	1365	75	550	605	1384
62	1666	548	546	1480	450	1482	431	734	210	452
63	866	1539	1358	1484	1570	1009	1620	433	698	1288
64	844	736	1115	441	509	212	127	1335	1551	454
65	1734	468	1839	868	1845	1854	145	1541	340	1269
66	178	1360	1330	1043	258	1486	630	1132	1342	1572
67	490	381	1512	1011	1277	969	120	1622	953	1048
68	1437	435	1646	793	305	700	1495	1408	858	1290
69	612	1697	1826	846	1304	1071	269	738	1527	1704
70	930	1117	1221	1250	824	443	1082	1652	25	511
71	1352	263	363	214	239	1714	169	129	874	330
72	1615	1337	925	1813	13	1553	158	1688	1182	456
73	1605	1451	1818	1736	102	1598	1258	470	916	542
74	694	1841	486	1491	1217	870	98	1029	1417	1847
75	1033	670	1089	1856	1805	1170	417	147	286	592
76	369	1543	560	711	18	342	1421	1561	395	1271
77	910	799	1058	180	1629	635	1797	1362	1477	1536
78	1285	1332	1851	1040	378	1045	1405	1068	1247	260
79	327	1685	1595	1488	667	589	1558	632	1037	1682
80	1679	1134	805	1585	41	1344	887	1137	535	1574
81	520	277	1001	492	674	808	988	383	1391	87
82	980	1514	251	1588	220	1013	757	1833	163	1279
83	1093	44	65	971	622	311	349	122	948	1347
84	481	1624	882	943	1099	955	1860	890	1235	1050
85	406	1108	903	1439	684	1140	730	437	1265	965
86	1693	1648	1809	538	1166	795	1064	1581	83	307
87	1104	1577	1460	702	783	1765	1156	1497	1174	523
88	1659	1410	1149	1464	658	860	1298	280	245	1292
89	1198	500	1187	614	421	1004	1127	1699	1446	706
90	584	1828	960	495	568	848	721	297	50	1306
91	151	677	1786	1073	1378	787	1023	271	1759	811
92	227	740	319	573	461	1529	290	991	1750	1706
93	186	1769	1319	932	1865	386	836	1119	773	817
94	58	1223	596	1394	1506	1252	1673	1160	1744	826
95	1204	90	1720	445	140	853	1610	1084	373	983
96	1230	1654	1781	1501	1428	27	895	1517	1639	513
97	766	194	71	1354	1547	254	1433	265	359	1178
98	1213	365	1793	1591	531	216	477	726	1456	241
99	564	223	832	1716	1635	527	644	171	1240	1016

POWER RESIDUES

	0	1	2	3	4	5	6	7	8	9
50	891	1782	1697	1527	1187	507	1014	161	322	644
51	1288	709	1418	969	71	142	284	568	1136	405
52	810	1620	1373	879	1758	1649	1431	995	123	246
53	492	984	101	202	404	808	1616	1365	863	1726
54	1585	1303	739	1478	1089	311	622	1244	621	1242
55	617	1234	601	1202	537	1074	281	562	1124	381
56	762	1524	1181	495	990	113	226	452	904	1808
57	1749	1631	1395	923	1846	1825	1783	1699	1531	1195
58	523	1046	225	450	900	1800	1733	1599	1331	795
59	1590	1313	759	1518	1169	471	942	17	34	68
60	136	272	544	1088	309	618	1236	605	1210	553
61	1106	345	690	1380	893	1786	1705	1543	1219	571
62	1142	417	834	1668	1469	1071	275	550	1100	333
63	666	1332	797	1594	1321	775	1550	1233	599	1198
64	529	1058	249	498	996	125	250	500	1000	133
65	266	532	1064	261	522	1044	221	442	884	1768
66	1669	1471	1075	283	566	1132	397	794	1588	1309
67	751	1502	1137	407	814	1628	1389	911	1822	1777
68	1687	1507	1147	427	854	1708	1549	1231	595	1190
69	513	1026	185	370	740	1480	1093	319	638	1276
70	685	1370	873	1746	1625	1383	899	1798	1729	1591
71	1315	763	1526	1185	503	1006	145	290	580	1160
72	453	906	1812	1757	1647	1427	987	107	214	428
73	856	1712	1557	1247	627	1254	641	1282	697	1394
74	921	1842	1817	1767	1667	1467	1067	267	534	1068
75	269	538	1076	285	570	1140	413	826	1652	1437
76	1007	147	294	588	1176	485	970	73	146	292
77	584	1168	469	938	9	18	36	72	144	288
78	576	1152	437	874	1748	1629	1391	915	1830	1793
79	1719	1571	1275	683	1366	865	1730	1593	1319	771
80	1542	1217	567	1134	401	802	1604	1341	815	1630
81	1393	919	1838	1809	1751	1635	1403	939	11	22
82	44	88	176	352	704	1408	949	31	62	124
83	248	496	992	117	234	468	936	5	10	20
84	40	80	160	320	640	1280	693	1386	905	1810
85	1753	1639	1411	955	43	86	172	344	688	1376
86	885	1770	1673	1479	1091	315	630	1260	653	1306
87	745	1490	1113	359	718	1436	1005	143	286	572
88	1144	421	842	1684	1501	1135	403	806	1612	1357
89	847	1694	1521	1175	483	966	65	130	260	520
90	1040	213	426	852	1704	1541	1215	563	1126	385
91	770	1540	1213	559	1118	369	738	1476	1085	303
92	606	1212	557	1114	361	722	1444	1021	175	350
93	700	1400	933	1866	1865	1863	1859	1851	1835	1803
94	1739	1611	1355	843	1686	1505	1143	419	838	1676
95	1485	1103	339	678	1356	845	1690	1513	1159	451
96	902	1804	1741	1615	1363	859	1718	1569	1271	675
97	1350	833	1666	1465	1063	259	518	1036	205	410
98	820	1640	1413	959	51	102	204	408	816	1632
99	1397	927	1854	1841	1815	1763	1659	1451	1035	203

P = 1867

INDICES

	0	1	2	3	4	5	6	7	8	9
100	648	131	1728	233	1471	876	715	760	32	332
101	1370	1663	207	1617	506	1836	175	1339	117	302
102	1823	927	22	166	10	1815	691	1414	414	15
103	1055	1282	1244	1555	38	998	977	160	346	1096
104	900	1690	80	1153	655	1184	581	47	1020	458
105	1316	55	1741	1607	1425	68	1210	1453	641	1468
106	204	1820	411	974	652	1738	201	746	749	104
107	1565	625	1522	1600	555	662	752	1260	1193	314
108	135	472	112	1311	107	918	399	352	603	544
109	429	864	1568	696	1113	125	1732	1843	338	1328
110	628	488	1275	951	1644	1493	610	1302	1525	1219
111	1080	1350	237	872	923	156	1603	100	914	484
112	96	1031	1803	284	558	1419	908	1627	1475	1849
113	1403	325	665	1035	803	885	518	672	1389	249
114	755	1091	620	946	880	1858	404	682	1263	1807
115	1062	1102	781	1172	1147	1296	1196	419	1444	958
116	719	149	1376	1757	317	288	184	1863	771	594
117	1671	1202	138	371	1779	893	764	1545	357	1791
118	475	562	1633	1238	1726	713	1368	504	115	20
119	689	1053	36	344	78	579	1314	1423	639	409
120	199	1563	553	1191	110	397	427	1111	336	1273
121	608	1078	921	912	1801	906	1401	801	1387	618
122	402	1060	1145	1442	1374	182	1669	1777	355	1631
123	1366	687	76	637	551	425	606	1799	1385	1143
124	1667	1364	549	1383	547	1479	1481	733	451	1538
125	1483	1008	432	1287	735	440	211	1334	453	467
126	867	1853	1540	1268	1359	1042	1485	1131	1571	380
127	1010	968	1621	1047	434	792	699	1407	1289	1696
128	845	1070	737	1703	1116	1249	442	1651	510	262
129	213	1713	128	329	1336	1812	1552	1687	455	1450
130	1735	1597	469	541	1840	1490	869	1028	1846	669
131	1855	1169	146	591	1542	710	341	1560	1270	798
132	179	634	1361	1535	1331	1039	1044	1067	259	1684
133	1487	588	631	1681	1133	1584	1343	1136	1573	276
134	491	807	382	86	1513	1587	1012	1832	1278	43
135	970	310	121	1346	1623	942	954	889	1049	1107
136	1438	1139	436	964	1647	537	794	1580	306	1576
137	701	1764	1496	522	1409	1463	859	279	1291	499
138	613	1003	1698	705	1827	494	847	296	1305	676
139	1072	786	270	810	739	572	1528	990	1705	1768
140	931	385	1118	816	1222	1393	1251	1159	825	89
141	444	852	1083	982	1653	1500	26	1516	512	193
142	1353	253	264	1177	364	1590	215	725	240	222
143	1715	526	170	1015	130	232	875	759	331	1662
144	1616	1835	1338	301	926	165	1814	1413	14	1281
145	1554	997	159	1095	1689	1152	1183	46	457	54
146	1606	67	1452	1467	1819	973	1737	745	103	624
147	1599	661	1259	313	471	1310	917	351	543	863
148	695	124	1842	1327	487	950	1492	1301	1218	1349
149	871	155	99	483	1030	283	1418	1626	1848	324

POWER RESIDUES

	0	1	2	3	4	5	6	7	8	9
100	406	812	1624	1381	895	1790	1713	1559	1251	635
101	1270	673	1346	825	1650	1433	999	131	262	524
102	1048	229	458	916	1832	1797	1727	1587	1307	747
103	1494	1121	375	750	1500	1133	399	798	1596	1325
104	783	1566	1265	663	1326	785	1570	1273	679	1358
105	849	1698	1529	1191	515	1030	193	386	772	1544
106	1221	575	1150	433	866	1732	1597	1327	787	1574
107	1281	695	1390	913	1826	1785	1703	1539	1211	555
108	1110	353	706	1412	957	47	94	188	376	752
109	1504	1141	415	830	1660	1453	1039	211	422	844
110	1688	1509	1151	435	870	1740	1613	1359	851	1702
111	1537	1207	547	1094	321	642	1284	701	1402	937
112	7	14	28	56	112	224	448	896	1792	1717
113	1567	1267	667	1334	801	1602	1337	807	1614	1361
114	855	1710	1553	1239	611	1222	577	1154	441	882
115	1764	1661	1455	1043	219	438	876	1752	1637	1407
116	947	27	54	108	216	432	864	1728	1589	1311
117	755	1510	1153	439	878	1756	1645	1423	979	91
118	182	364	728	1456	1045	223	446	892	1784	1701
119	1535	1203	539	1078	289	578	1156	445	890	1780
120	1693	1519	1171	475	950	33	66	132	264	528
121	1056	245	490	980	93	186	372	744	1488	1109
122	351	702	1404	941	15	30	60	120	240	480
123	960	53	106	212	424	848	1696	1525	1183	499
124	998	129	258	516	1032	197	394	788	1576	1285
125	703	1406	945	23	46	92	184	368	736	1472
126	1077	287	574	1148	429	858	1716	1565	1263	659
127	1318	769	1538	1209	551	1102	337	674	1348	829
128	1658	1449	1031	195	390	780	1560	1253	639	1278
129	689	1378	889	1778	1689	1511	1155	443	886	1772
130	1677	1487	1107	347	694	1388	909	1818	1769	1671
131	1475	1083	299	598	1196	525	1050	233	466	932
132	1864	1861	1855	1843	1819	1771	1675	1483	1099	331
133	662	1324	781	1562	1257	647	1294	721	1442	1017
134	167	334	668	1336	805	1610	1353	839	1678	1489
135	1111	355	710	1420	973	79	158	316	632	1264
136	661	1322	777	1554	1241	615	1230	593	1186	505
137	1010	153	306	612	1224	581	1162	457	914	1828
138	1789	1711	1555	1243	619	1238	609	1218	569	1138
139	409	818	1636	1405	943	19	38	76	152	304
140	608	1216	565	1130	393	786	1572	1277	687	1374
141	881	1762	1657	1447	1027	187	374	748	1496	1125
142	383	766	1532	1197	527	1054	241	482	964	61
143	122	244	488	976	85	170	340	680	1360	853
144	1706	1545	1223	579	1158	449	898	1796	1725	1583
145	1299	731	1462	1057	247	494	988	109	218	436
146	872	1744	1621	1375	883	1766	1665	1463	1059	251
147	502	1004	141	282	564	1128	389	778	1556	1245
148	623	1246	625	1250	633	1266	665	1330	793	1586
149	1305	743	1486	1105	343	686	1372	877	1754	1641

P = 1867

INDICES

	0	1	2	3	4	5	6	7	8	9
150	1034	884	671	248	1090	945	1857	681	1806	1101
151	1171	1295	418	957	148	1756	287	1862	593	1201
152	370	892	1544	1790	561	1237	712	503	19	1052
153	343	578	1422	408	1562	1190	396	1110	1272	1077
154	911	905	800	617	1059	1441	181	1776	1630	686
155	636	424	1798	1142	1363	1382	1478	732	1537	1007
156	1286	439	1333	466	1852	1267	1041	1130	379	967
157	1046	791	1406	1695	1069	1702	1248	1650	261	1712
158	328	1811	1686	1449	1596	540	1489	1027	668	1168
159	590	709	1559	797	633	1534	1038	1066	1683	587
160	1680	1583	1135	275	806	85	1586	1831	42	309
161	1345	941	888	1106	1138	963	536	1579	1575	1763
162	521	1462	278	498	1002	704	493	295	675	785
163	809	571	989	1767	384	815	1392	1158	88	851
164	981	1499	1515	192	252	1176	1589	724	221	525
165	1014	231	758	1661	1834	300	164	1412	1280	996
166	1094	1151	45	53	66	1466	972	744	623	660
167	312	1309	350	862	123	1326	949	1300	1348	154
168	482	282	1625	323	883	247	944	680	1100	1294
169	956	1755	1861	1200	891	1789	1236	502	1051	577
170	407	1189	1109	1076	904	616	1440	1775	685	423
171	1141	1381	731	1006	438	465	1266	1129	966	790
172	1694	1701	1649	1711	1810	1448	539	1026	1167	708
173	796	1533	1065	586	1582	274	84	1830	308	940
174	1105	962	1578	1762	1461	497	703	294	784	570
175	1766	814	1157	850	1498	191	1175	723	524	230
176	1660	299	1411	995	1150	52	1465	743	659	1308
177	861	1325	1299	153	281	322	246	679	1293	1754
178	1199	1788	501	576	1188	1075	615	1774	422	1380
179	1005	464	1128	789	1700	1710	1447	1025	707	1532
180	585	273	1829	939	961	1761	496	293	569	813
181	849	190	722	229	298	994	51	742	1307	1324
182	152	321	678	1753	1787	575	1074	1773	1379	463
183	788	1709	1024	1531	272	938	1760	292	812	189
184	228	993	741	1323	320	1752	574	1772	462	1708
185	1530	937	291	188	992	1322	1751	1771	1707	936
186	187	1321	1770	935	1320	934	933			

POWER RESIDUES

	0	1	2	3	4	5	6	7	8	9
150	1415	963	59	118	236	472	944	21	42	84
151	168	336	672	1344	821	1642	1417	967	67	134
152	268	536	1072	277	554	1108	349	698	1396	925
153	1850	1833	1799	1731	1595	1323	779	1558	1249	631
154	1262	657	1314	761	1522	1177	487	974	81	162
155	324	648	1296	725	1450	1033	199	398	796	1592
156	1317	767	1534	1201	535	1070	273	546	1092	317
157	634	1268	669	1338	809	1618	1369	871	1742	1617
158	1367	867	1734	1601	1335	803	1606	1345	823	1646
159	1425	983	99	198	396	792	1584	1301	735	1470
160	1073	279	558	1116	365	730	1460	1053	239	478
161	956	45	90	180	360	720	1440	1013	159	318
162	636	1272	677	1354	841	1682	1497	1127	387	774
163	1548	1229	591	1182	497	994	121	242	484	968
164	69	138	276	552	1104	341	682	1364	861	1722
165	1577	1287	707	1414	961	55	110	220	440	880
166	1760	1653	1439	1011	155	310	620	1240	613	1226
167	585	1170	473	946	25	50	100	200	400	800
168	1600	1333	799	1598	1329	791	1582	1297	727	1454
169	1041	215	430	860	1720	1573	1279	691	1382	897
170	1794	1721	1575	1283	699	1398	929	1858	1849	1831
171	1795	1723	1579	1291	715	1430	993	119	238	476
172	952	37	74	148	296	592	1184	501	1002	137
173	274	548	1096	325	650	1300	733	1466	1065	263
174	526	1052	237	474	948	29	58	116	232	464
175	928	1856	1845	1823	1779	1691	1515	1163	459	918
176	1836	1805	1743	1619	1371	875	1750	1633	1399	931
177	1862	1857	1847	1827	1787	1707	1547	1227	587	1174
178	481	962	57	114	228	456	912	1824	1781	1695
179	1523	1179	491	982	97	194	388	776	1552	1237
180	607	1214	561	1122	377	754	1508	1149	431	862
181	1724	1581	1295	723	1446	1025	183	366	732	1464
182	1061	255	510	1020	173	346	692	1384	901	1802
183	1737	1607	1347	827	1654	1441	1015	163	326	652
184	1304	741	1482	1097	327	654	1308	749	1498	1129
185	391	782	1564	1261	655	1310	753	1506	1145	423
186	846	1692	1517	1167	467	934				

P = 1871

INDICES

	0	1	2	3	4	5	6	7	8	9
0		0	1216	1430	562	718	776	655	1778	990
1	64	1545	122	1626	1	278	1124	1196	336	1269
2	1280	215	891	733	1338	1436	972	550	1217	1397
3	1494	1640	470	1105	542	1373	1552	368	615	1186
4	626	199	1431	1848	237	1708	79	364	684	1310
5	782	756	318	686	1766	393	563	829	743	726
6	840	1510	986	1645	1686	474	451	1371	1758	293
7	719	1399	898	1448	1584	996	1831	330	532	98
8	1842	110	1415	1752	777	44	1194	957	1453	66
9	1054	411	1295	1200	1580	117	30	883	656	665
10	128	1285	102	1795	1534	933	32	57	1112	75
11	1609	1798	1779	1456	175	1451	89	746	72	1851
12	186	1220	856	1629	332	284	991	264	1032	1408
13	1690	1302	1667	54	717	1268	1104	363	1509	995
14	65	1794	745	1301	244	245	794	870	930	695
15	342	1539	1177	316	1546	488	1748	1504	1314	246
16	1188	1388	1326	1792	761	1823	1098	1802	123	1382
17	1260	389	540	795	303	221	799	286	1282	981
18	400	511	1627	1070	641	1086	546	871	926	1205
19	1333	1122	1246	662	229	34	2	601	11	1787
20	1344	931	631	182	1318	917	1141	1723	880	944
21	279	227	1248	959	1273	696	458	425	1291	1008
22	955	952	1144	114	1125	556	802	1420	1391	343
23	797	1760	1305	1682	92	1082	1288	1528	1197	291
24	1402	921	566	1540	202	158	975	1025	1548	1312
25	1500	455	337	408	1480	1474	378	1178	754	1023
26	1036	517	648	1774	1013	1404	1270	1496	63	1337
27	614	317	450	1841	1579	1111	855	1103	341	760
28	1281	1245	1140	954	91	1547	647	854	1460	522
29	1461	443	140	1615	216	1444	276	225	41	489
30	1558	633	885	845	523	358	1532	1556	892	1355
31	1704	877	1094	1749	850	493	660	864	1462	1072
32	534	1487	734	595	672	1192	1138	1505	107	1019
33	1169	675	444	1358	1148	219	1339	763	728	1016
34	606	1315	1605	95	1756	1011	141	1321	1519	1208
35	1437	306	145	249	1502	247	628	1411	327	178
36	1616	668	1727	780	973	296	416	1769	1857	1189
37	432	1341	1762	993	217	1714	272	1153	551	620
38	679	1694	468	1389	592	1048	8	968	1445	866
39	1250	59	1218	862	1817	816	1227	1327	1133	1484
40	690	1869	277	1396	1847	828	1398	43	664	1455
41	263	1793	487	1381	1069	600	226	555	290	407
42	1495	1244	1443	1354	594	762	305	295	619	861
43	42	1243	1674	1368	1641	1675	637	132	354	1824
44	301	430	298	1038	490	784	1330	255	471	1369
45	1772	1744	148	1099	766	1129	737	351	1559	1746
46	143	923	1106	1642	651	48	1028	1803	1308	156
47	428	1064	634	1523	874	835	543	1676	1507	1146
48	748	124	267	948	1782	1601	886	1638	1418	1352
49	1374	638	321	723	371	1383	894	184	658	1592

POWER RESIDUES

	0	1	2	3	4	5	6	7	8	9
0	1	14	196	873	996	847	632	1364	386	1662
1	816	198	901	1388	722	753	1187	1650	648	1588
2	1651	662	1784	653	1658	760	1285	1151	1146	1076
3	96	1344	106	1484	195	859	800	1845	1507	517
4	1625	298	430	407	85	1190	1692	1236	465	897
5	1332	1809	1003	945	133	1862	1745	107	1498	391
6	1732	1796	821	268	10	140	89	1246	605	986
7	707	543	118	1652	676	109	1526	783	1607	46
8	644	1532	867	912	1542	1007	1001	917	1612	116
9	1624	284	234	1405	960	343	1060	1743	79	1106
10	516	1611	102	1428	1282	1109	558	328	850	674
11	81	1134	908	1486	223	1251	675	95	1330	1781
12	611	1070	12	168	481	1121	726	809	100	1400
13	890	1234	437	505	1457	1688	1180	1552	1147	1090
14	292	346	1102	460	827	352	1186	1636	452	715
15	655	1686	1152	1160	1272	969	469	953	245	1559
16	1245	591	790	1705	1418	1142	1020	1183	1594	1735
17	1838	1409	1016	1127	810	114	1596	1763	359	1284
18	1137	950	203	971	497	1345	120	1680	1068	1855
19	1647	606	1000	903	1416	1114	628	1308	1473	41
20	574	552	244	1545	1049	1589	1665	858	786	1649
21	634	1392	778	1537	937	21	294	374	1494	335
22	948	175	579	622	1224	297	416	211	1083	194
23	845	604	972	511	1541	993	805	44	616	1140
24	992	791	1719	1614	144	145	159	355	1228	353
25	1200	1832	1325	1711	1502	447	645	1546	1063	1785
26	667	1854	1633	410	127	1778	569	482	1135	922
27	1682	1096	376	1522	727	823	296	402	15	210
28	1069	1869	1843	1479	125	1750	177	607	1014	1099
29	418	239	1475	69	966	427	365	1368	442	575
30	566	440	547	174	565	426	351	1172	1440	1450
31	1590	1679	1054	1659	774	1481	153	271	52	728
32	837	492	1275	1011	1057	1701	1362	358	1270	941
33	77	1078	124	1736	1852	1605	18	252	1657	746
34	1089	278	150	229	1335	1851	1591	1693	1250	661
35	1770	457	785	1635	438	519	1653	690	305	528
36	1779	583	678	137	47	658	1728	1740	37	518
37	1639	494	1303	1403	932	1822	1185	1622	256	1713
38	1530	839	520	1667	886	1178	1524	755	1215	171
39	523	1709	1474	55	770	1425	1240	521	1681	1082
40	180	649	1602	1847	1535	909	1500	419	253	1671
41	942	91	1274	997	861	828	366	1382	638	1448
42	1562	1287	1179	1538	951	217	1167	1370	470	967
43	441	561	370	1438	1422	1198	1804	933	1836	1381
44	624	1252	689	291	332	906	1458	1702	1376	554
45	272	66	924	1710	1488	251	1643	550	216	1153
46	1174	1468	1842	1465	1800	877	1052	1631	382	1606
47	32	448	659	1742	65	910	1514	615	1126	796
48	1789	723	767	1383	652	1644	564	412	155	299
49	444	603	958	315	668	1868	1829	1283	1123	754

P = 1871

INDICES

	0	1	2	3	4	5	6	7	8	9
50	846	1362	1671	1232	1553	133	1624	942	826	1261
51	820	233	1594	1819	524	643	100	39	369	355
52	382	397	1733	390	1864	1651	1120	966	359	1466
53	750	1716	616	1825	842	775	1279	541	683	985
54	1830	1053	1533	71	1666	793	1187	302	925	630
55	457	796	201	753	449	646	1557	849	106	1604
56	627	431	591	1132	486	304	300	765	1307	266
57	893	819	1863	682	200	299	806	1440	1738	222
58	807	537	1659	361	1356	1464	961	1114	1432	1039
59	790	161	1492	800	1441	699	1257	1347	1705	1089
60	904	1263	1849	491	231	68	191	287	1739	1612
61	1574	120	878	1845	902	477	238	785	701	1376
62	1050	1283	223	721	440	1002	1095	504	196	1564
63	1709	1331	6	1657	210	982	808	1066	418	519
64	1750	758	833	1183	80	256	1811	1159	18	401
65	538	1855	484	23	851	150	1323	568	365	472
66	515	349	21	512	1660	772	704	260	494	1544
67	1435	1185	685	1370	109	116	74	1628	362	1538
68	1822	980	661	1722	951	1081	1311	1773	1102	442
69	357	1071	1357	1320	667	1713	865	1395	554	1242
70	783	1745	1522	1637	1361	642	1465	70	848	818
71	1463	1088	1844	503	757	149	1543	1721	1394	1087
72	962	580	14	481	1073	963	126	274	319	1100
73	1512	1174	1632	547	1115	1588	1203	1046	535	581
74	1648	585	687	767	1108	1413	339	872	1433	712
75	1060	908	1488	15	499	387	1767	1130	1836	1838
76	25	927	1040	730	1684	1034	735	482	1808	1077
77	394	738	1224	911	314	1206	791	583	212	1468
78	596	1074	1275	77	564	352	208	1814	1163	1334
79	162	241	573	1266	673	964	479	822	830	1560
80	36	1056	1215	1123	1493	236	742	897	1193	127
81	174	1031	744	1747	1259	640	10	1247	801	1401
82	1479	62	1139	275	1703	671	727	144	415	678
83	1816	663	1442	636	1771	650	1506	320	1623	381
84	841	924	590	805	789	230	700	5	1810	514
85	108	1101	1521	1542	1511	1107	1835	1223	207	35
86	1258	414	589	1834	1020	1513	714	82	987	1643
87	1021	1127	1853	3	1348	939	1570	465	1170	1175
88	1517	1664	1646	652	1514	1004	384	602	1706	919
89	130	1655	676	1633	1471	1699	1687	49	715	1167
90	1118	12	1090	193	1364	1229	445	548	112	405
91	475	1029	83	1427	1567	1788	905	87	1092	824
92	1359	1116	269	1155	452	1804	988	915	1867	1345
93	1264	709	374	437	1149	1589	654	214	1372	1309
94	1644	329	410	932	1850	53	869	1387	220	1204
95	181	424	1759	157	1022	1840	853	632	492	1018
96	94	1410	1340	1047	1483	1380	294	429	1128	155
97	947	183	232	1650	984	752	764	536	698	1611
98	720	1065	1854	771	1537	1319	69	579	1587	711
99	729	582	240	235	1400	635	4	413	938	918

POWER RESIDUES

	0	1	2	3	4	5	6	7	8	9
50	1201	1846	1521	713	627	1294	1277	1039	1449	1576
51	1483	181	663	1798	849	660	1756	261	1783	639
52	1462	1758	289	304	514	1583	1581	1553	1161	1286
53	1165	1342	78	1092	320	738	977	581	650	1616
54	172	537	34	476	1051	1617	186	733	907	1472
55	27	378	1550	1119	698	417	225	1279	1067	1841
56	1451	1604	4	56	784	1621	242	1517	657	1714
57	1544	1035	1393	792	1733	1810	1017	1141	1006	987
58	721	739	991	777	1523	741	1019	1169	1398	862
59	842	562	384	1634	424	323	780	1565	1329	1767
60	415	197	887	1192	1720	1628	340	1018	1155	1202
61	1860	1717	1586	1623	270	38	532	1835	1367	428
62	379	1564	1315	1571	1413	1072	40	560	356	1242
63	549	202	957	301	472	995	833	436	491	1261
64	815	184	705	515	1597	1777	555	286	262	1797
65	835	464	883	1136	936	7	98	1372	498	1359
66	316	682	193	831	408	99	1386	694	361	1312
67	1529	825	324	794	1761	331	892	1262	829	380
68	1578	1511	573	538	48	672	53	742	1033	1365
69	400	1858	1689	1194	1748	149	215	1139	978	595
70	846	618	1168	1384	666	1840	1437	1408	1002	931
71	1808	989	749	1131	866	898	1346	134	5	70
72	980	623	1238	493	1289	1207	59	826	338	990
73	763	1327	1739	23	322	766	1369	456	771	1439
74	1436	1394	806	58	812	142	117	1638	480	1107
75	530	1807	975	553	258	1741	51	714	641	1490
76	279	164	425	337	976	567	454	743	1047	1561
77	1273	983	665	1826	1241	535	6	84	1176	1496
78	363	1340	50	700	445	617	1154	1188	1664	844
79	590	776	1509	545	146	173	551	230	1349	176
80	593	818	226	1293	1263	843	576	580	636	1420
81	1170	1412	1058	1715	1558	1231	395	1788	709	571
82	510	1527	797	1803	919	1640	508	1499	405	57
83	798	1817	1115	642	1504	475	1037	1421	1184	1608
84	60	840	534	1863	1759	303	500	1387	708	557
85	314	654	1672	956	287	276	122	1708	1460	1730
86	1768	429	393	1760	317	696	389	1704	1404	946
87	147	187	747	1103	474	1023	1225	311	612	1084
88	208	1041	1477	97	1358	302	486	1191	1706	1432
89	1338	22	308	570	496	1331	1795	807	72	1008
90	1015	1113	614	1112	600	916	1598	1791	751	1159
91	1258	773	1467	1828	1269	927	1752	205	999	889
92	1220	241	1503	461	841	548	188	761	1299	1347
93	148	201	943	105	1470	1870	1857	1675	998	875
94	1024	1239	507	1485	209	1055	1673	970	483	1149
95	1118	684	221	1223	283	220	1209	87	1218	213
96	1111	586	720	725	795	1775	527	1765	387	1676
97	1012	1071	26	364	1354	246	1573	1441	1464	1786
98	681	179	635	1406	974	539	62	868	926	1738
99	9	126	1764	373	1480	139	75	1050	1603	1861

P = 1871

INDICES

	0	1	2	3	4	5	6	7	8	9
100	192	86	708	52	1017	1649	578	85	899	1524
101	1349	323	970	1142	288	900	172	576	607	586
102	166	1043	1449	875	940	1635	1165	1724	1740	1525
103	1859	1776	1316	688	1255	571	1585	836	1571	507
104	1598	881	1613	1350	1079	1662	1606	768	1210	204
105	997	544	466	1736	312	945	1575	324	812	1679
106	96	1109	1062	258	1832	1677	1171	558	188	280
107	121	971	625	1765	1757	1414	29	1608	331	1508
108	1176	1097	399	228	879	1143	1287	1499	1012	340
109	139	1531	533	1147	1518	1726	271	1249	1846	289
110	1673	1329	142	873	1417	1670	99	749	1665	105
111	1862	960	903	901	195	832	1322	1434	950	553
112	1843	125	1647	498	1807	1274	478	173	1702	1622
113	1520	713	1516	1470	111	268	653	180	1482	697
114	239	577	165	1254	1209	1061	28	138	1416	949
115	1515	27	152	459	786	608	1084	1692	1438	909
116	153	528	1753	1783	1005	530	1577	426	702	587
117	810	1718	307	1489	460	1800	778	1602	385	422
118	136	1292	1377	167	838	376	146	16	787	1596
119	45	887	603	1297	693	1009	1051	1044	435	1620
120	250	500	609	1429	1195	1639	1707	725	1447	956
121	1284	1450	1407	1300	1503	388	1085	1786	958	1419
122	920	1473	1336	953	224	876	1191	1015	248	1768
123	1693	815	1454	1353	131	1743	47	1145	722	941
124	396	774	629	1131	1439	160	67	1375	1656	1158
125	348	115	441	1636	1720	1173	1412	1837	910	1813
126	1055	639	677	804	1222	1126	1003	1166	1426	914
127	328	1839	154	770	412	322	1634	506	1735	557
128	1096	1725	104	497	179	26	529	421	1296	724
129	1472	1742	1157	803	505	1741	1234	1135	1617	928
130	1754	1828	1201	372	1700	1235	1239	1421	197	1526
131	1366	1562	669	1041	1784	622	1581	1384	1688	1136
132	1731	1392	1565	1860	1237	252	1728	731	1006	598
133	118	895	50	1618	1476	344	1710	1777	890	1551
134	781	1685	531	1294	31	185	716	929	1325	798
135	1332	1317	1290	1304	974	1035	1578	1459	884	659
136	1168	1755	326	1761	7	689	1068	618	297	736
137	427	1781	657	1593	1119	1829	448	1306	1658	1256
138	1573	439	417	483	703	1821	666	847	13	1202
139	1059	1683	211	572	741	1478	1770	1809	588	1569
140	129	1363	1091	373	868	93	983	1586	707	171
141	1858	1078	811	624	1286	1672	194	1701	164	1083
142	809	837	434	1406	1190	395	1719	1425	103	1233
143	1365	1236	889	1289	1067	1572	740	706	433	739
144	308	977	1796	1554	1230	1240	1697	1529	419	508
145	309	560	1342	1225	1490	1161	1535	134	446	1422
146	858	1198	520	1599	978	463	1763	912	461	1212
147	934	1625	549	198	392	292	1751	882	1797	283
148	994	315	1801	510	33	943	113	1527	454	1403
149	759	1614	1555	1486	218	1207	779	1152	58	827

POWER RESIDUES

	0	1	2	3	4	5	6	7	8	9
100	1731	1782	625	1266	885	1164	1328	1753	219	1195
101	1762	345	1088	264	1825	1227	339	1004	959	329
102	864	870	954	259	1755	247	1587	1637	466	911
103	1528	811	128	1792	765	1355	260	1769	443	589
104	762	1313	1543	1021	1197	1790	737	963	385	1648
105	620	1196	1776	541	90	1260	801	1859	1703	1390
106	750	1145	1062	1771	471	981	637	1434	1366	414
107	183	691	319	724	781	1579	1525	769	1411	1044
108	1519	685	235	1419	1156	1216	185	719	711	599
109	902	1402	918	1626	312	626	1280	1081	166	453
110	729	851	688	277	136	33	462	855	744	1061
111	1757	275	108	1512	587	734	921	1668	900	1374
112	526	1751	191	803	16	224	1265	871	968	455
113	757	1243	563	398	1830	1297	1319	1627	326	822
114	282	206	1013	1085	222	1237	479	1093	334	934
115	1850	1577	1497	377	1536	923	1696	1292	1249	647
116	1574	1455	1660	788	1677	1026	1267	899	1360	330
117	878	1066	1827	1255	731	879	1080	152	257	1727
118	1726	1712	1516	643	1518	671	39	546	160	369
119	1424	1226	325	808	86	1204	17	238	1461	1744
120	93	1302	1389	736	949	189	775	1495	349	1144
121	1048	1575	1469	1856	1661	802	2	28	392	1746
122	121	1694	1264	857	772	1453	1632	396	1802	905
123	1444	1506	503	1429	1296	1305	1431	1324	1697	1306
124	1445	1520	699	431	421	281	192	817	212	1097
125	390	1718	1600	1819	1143	1034	1379	596	860	814
126	170	509	1513	601	930	1794	793	1747	135	19
127	266	1853	1619	214	1125	782	1593	1721	1642	536
128	20	280	178	621	1210	101	1414	1086	236	1433
129	1352	218	1181	1566	1343	92	1288	1193	1734	1824
130	1213	143	131	1834	1353	232	1377	568	468	939
131	49	686	249	1615	158	341	1032	1351	204	985
132	693	347	1116	656	1700	1348	162	397	1816	1101
133	446	631	1350	190	789	1691	1222	269	24	336
134	962	371	1452	1618	200	929	1780	597	874	1010
135	1043	1505	489	1233	423	309	584	692	333	920
136	1654	704	501	1401	904	1430	1310	1501	433	449
137	673	67	938	35	490	1247	619	1182	1580	1539
138	965	413	169	495	1317	1599	1805	947	161	383
139	1620	228	1321	1655	718	697	403	29	406	71
140	994	819	240	1489	265	1839	1423	1212	129	1806
141	961	357	1256	745	1075	82	1148	1104	488	1219
142	227	1307	1459	1716	1572	1427	1268	913	1556	1203
143	3	42	588	748	1117	670	25	350	1158	1244
144	577	594	832	422	295	388	1690	1208	73	1022
145	1211	115	1610	88	1232	409	113	1582	1567	1357
146	288	290	318	710	585	706	529	1793	779	1551
147	1133	894	1290	1221	255	1699	1334	1837	1395	820
148	254	1685	1138	964	399	1844	1493	321	752	1173
149	1454	1646	592	804	30	420	267	1867	1815	1087

P = 1871

INDICES

	0	1	2	3	4	5	6	7	8	9
150	406	1367	254	922	834	1351	1231	38	1715	792
151	1603	681	1113	1262	476	1563	1182	567	1184	1080
152	1241	502	273	584	386	1076	76	821	1030	670
153	380	1541	81	1663	1698	404	1154	213	423	1379
154	1610	234	84	1042	570	203	257	1607	1530	1669
155	552	1469	137	527	1799	1595	1428	1785	814	159
156	1812	769	420	1827	621	597	1293	1458	1780	1820
157	1568	623	1424	976	1160	1211	509	1151	680	1075
158	1378	526	1457	525	1789	1582	612	1026	19	205
159	310	346	1695	1276	168	1790	176	644	906	1385
160	1252	1549	402	998	561	335	469	78	839	1583
161	1452	101	88	1689	243	1313	539	545	1343	1272
162	1390	565	377	613	90	40	1093	1137	605	1501
163	1856	467	1226	262	593	353	147	1027	747	370
164	825	1732	1278	456	485	1737	1491	190	1049	209
165	17	20	73	356	1360	1393	1631	338	24	313
166	1162	1214	9	1815	788	206	1852	383	1117	1566
167	1866	409	852	946	1536	937	969	1164	1597	311
168	187	398	270	1861	1806	1481	151	1576	135	692
169	1446	1335	46	347	1221	1734	1156	1238	1730	1475
170	1324	325	447	1058	867	163	888	1696	857	391
171	453	253	1181	379	569	813	1423	611	1251	242
172	604	1277	1630	1865	1805	1729	1180	1179	366	1680
173	859	1000	60	574	1298	169	333	1652	989	732
174	367	755	473	97	1199	56	1219	1267	694	1791
175	285	1121	916	1007	1681	1024	516	1110	521	844
176	863	674	1010	177	992	967	1868	599	860	1037
177	350	1063	1600	1591	1818	965	1052	545	265	360
178	1346	119	1001	518	22	259	979	1712	817	480
179	1045	907	1033	1467	1265	896	61	649	513	1833
180	464	1654	1228	823	436	1386	1409	751	710	51
181	575	1775	1661	1678	1764	1498	1328	831	1621	1253
182	1691	1717	375	1619	1299	1014	773	1172	913	496
183	1134	1561	251	1550	1303	617	438	1477	170	1405
184	705	559	462	282	1485	37	501	403	1668	1826
185	1150	345	334	1271	261	189	1213	936	691	1057
186	610	999	55	843	1590	1711	1653	1497	495	281
187	935	0								

POWER RESIDUES

	0	1	2	3	4	5	6	7	8	9
150	250	1629	354	1214	157	327	836	478	1079	138
151	61	854	730	865	884	1150	1132	880	1094	348
152	1130	852	702	473	1009	1029	1309	1487	237	1447
153	1548	1091	306	542	104	1456	1674	984	679	151
154	243	1531	853	716	669	11	154	285	248	1601
155	1833	1339	36	504	1443	1492	307	556	300	458
156	799	1831	1311	1515	629	1322	1669	914	1570	1399
157	876	1038	1435	1380	610	1056	1687	1166	1356	274
158	94	1316	1585	1609	74	1036	1407	988	735	935
159	1864	1773	499	1373	512	1555	1189	1678	1040	1463
160	1772	485	1177	1510	559	342	1046	1547	1077	110
161	1540	979	609	1042	1491	293	360	1298	1333	1823
162	1199	1818	1129	838	506	1471	13	182	677	123
163	1722	1656	732	893	1276	1025	1253	703	487	1205
164	31	434	463	869	940	63	882	1122	740	1005
165	973	525	1737	1866	1801	891	1248	633	1378	582
166	664	1812	1045	1533	881	1108	544	132	1848	1549
167	1105	502	1415	1100	432	435	477	1065	1813	1059
168	1729	1754	233	1391	764	1341	64	896	1318	1613
169	130	1820	1157	1230	381	1592	1707	1446	1534	895
170	1304	1417	1128	824	310	598	888	1206	45	630
171	1336	1865	1787	695	375	1508	531	1821	1171	1426
172	1254	717	683	207	1027	1281	1095	362	1326	1725
173	1698	1320	1641	522	1695	1278	1053	1645	578	608
174	1028	1295	1291	1235	451	701	459	813	156	313
175	640	1476	83	1162	1300	1361	344	1074	68	952
176	231	1363	372	1466	1814	1073	54	756	1229	367
177	1396	834	450	687	263	1811	1031	1337	8	112
178	1568	1371	484	1163	1314	1557	1217	199	915	1584
179	1595	1749	163	411	141	103	1442	1478	111	1554
180	1175	1482	167	467	925	1724	1684	1124	768	1397
181	848	646	1560	1259	787	1663	830	394	1774	513
182	1569	1385	680	165	439	533	1849	1563	1301	1375
183	540	76	1064	1799	863	856	758	1257	759	1271
184	955	273	80	1120	712	613	1098	404	43	602
185	944	119	1666	872	982	651	1630	368	1410	1030
186	1323	1683	1110	572	524	1723	1670	928	1766	401
187										

P = 1873

INDICES

	0	1	2	3	4	5	6	7	8	9
0		0	922	862	1844	951	1784	752	894	1724
1	1	330	834	1140	1674	1813	1816	1467	774	712
2	923	1614	1252	1233	1756	30	190	714	724	615
3	863	291	866	1192	517	1703	1696	1217	1634	130
4	1845	857	664	410	302	803	283	779	806	1504
5	952	457	1112	7	1636	1281	1646	1574	1537	947
6	1785	483	1213	604	1788	219	242	138	1439	223
7	753	1460	746	1712	267	892	684	1082	1052	1349
8	895	1576	1779	463	1586	546	1332	1477	1224	1166
9	1725	20	1205	1153	1701	1663	1728	1087	554	182
10	2	1443	1379	874	162	693	929	1105	686	392
11	331	207	696	1211	624	312	587	992	1869	347
12	835	660	1405	1719	263	981	1526	925	838	1272
13	1141	1264	1164	1464	1060	1665	489	1001	1145	38
14	1675	1641	510	1470	1668	1566	762	494	1189	648
15	1814	585	1606	1319	132	1242	102	1368	399	869
16	1817	113	626	1501	829	271	1385	430	636	408
17	1468	564	382	533	527	782	274	1809	216	1398
18	775	1539	942	1345	255	296	203	1797	751	1466
19	713	1216	778	1573	137	1081	1476	1086	1104	991
20	924	1000	493	1367	429	1808	1796	1085	1084	1042
21	1615	338	1851	450	155	1361	1608	1043	1314	702
22	1253	735	1129	1208	1618	1754	261	1616	1546	899
23	1234	72	1509	1766	42	1730	919	339	1269	1108
24	1757	387	1582	566	455	583	769	1852	1185	1325
25	31	771	576	1563	1847	1408	1760	451	322	97
26	191	467	314	1050	214	958	514	156	110	1121
27	715	1004	1411	882	51	360	195	1362	960	143
28	725	949	691	1806	1432	653	520	1609	718	1062
29	616	77	1684	1336	1416	26	239	1044	1570	501
30	864	1162	1507	433	656	1434	369	1315	1054	1736
31	292	1776	1024	1039	418	1555	1321	703	1791	945
32	867	95	1035	307	1548	1170	551	1254	1751	1531
33	1193	1299	435	1069	1352	1089	1558	736	1330	201
34	518	621	1486	384	1304	1174	1455	1130	1449	823
35	1704	1854	1196	671	859	539	1138	1209	448	1037
36	1697	1424	589	1522	1864	791	395	1619	1177	709
37	1218	759	1125	879	847	1843	1673	1755	516	301
38	1635	1787	266	1585	1700	161	623	262	1059	1667
39	131	828	526	254	136	428	154	1617	41	454
40	1846	213	50	1431	1415	655	417	1547	1351	1303
41	858	1863	846	1699	135	1414	134	900	92	178
42	665	558	1260	631	901	1497	1372	1235	1077	460
43	411	1612	658	733	93	556	364	73	1624	84
44	303	1356	1657	535	179	245	258	1510	668	174
45	804	1187	1183	1447	666	971	596	1767	1821	309
46	284	1579	994	706	559	232	816	43	964	890
47	780	358	1841	740	1261	742	319	1731	158	438
48	807	485	1309	975	632	166	1488	920	1377	491
49	1505	48	1691	210	902	1133	235	340	375	1747

POWER RESIDUES

	0	1	2	3	4	5	6	7	8	9
0	1	10	100	1000	635	731	1691	53	530	1554
1	556	1814	1283	1592	936	1868	1823	1373	619	571
2	91	910	1608	1096	1595	966	295	1077	1405	939
3	25	250	627	651	891	1418	1069	1325	139	1390
4	789	398	234	467	924	1748	623	611	491	1164
5	402	274	867	1178	542	1674	1756	703	1411	999
6	625	631	691	1291	1672	1736	503	1284	1602	1036
7	995	585	231	437	624	621	591	291	1037	1005
8	685	1231	1072	1355	439	644	821	718	1561	626
9	641	791	418	434	594	321	1337	259	717	1551
10	526	1514	156	1560	616	541	1664	1656	1576	776
11	268	807	578	161	1610	1116	1795	1093	1565	666
12	1041	1045	1085	1485	1739	533	1584	856	1068	1315
13	39	390	154	1540	416	414	394	194	67	670
14	1081	1445	1339	279	917	1678	1796	1103	1665	1666
15	1676	1776	903	1538	396	214	267	797	478	1034
16	975	385	104	1040	1035	985	485	1104	1675	1766
17	803	538	1634	1356	449	744	1821	1353	419	444
18	694	1321	99	990	535	1604	1056	1195	712	1501
19	26	260	727	1651	1526	276	887	1378	669	1071
20	1345	339	1517	186	1860	1743	573	111	1110	1735
21	493	1184	602	401	264	767	178	1780	943	65
22	650	881	1318	69	690	1281	1572	736	1741	553
23	1784	983	465	904	1548	496	1214	902	1528	296
24	1087	1505	66	660	981	445	704	1421	1099	1625
25	1266	1422	1109	1725	393	184	1840	1543	446	714
26	1521	226	387	124	1240	1162	382	74	740	1781
27	953	165	1650	1516	176	1760	743	1811	1253	1292
28	1682	1836	1503	46	460	854	1048	1115	1785	993
29	565	31	310	1227	1032	955	185	1850	1643	1446
30	1349	379	44	440	654	921	1718	323	1357	459
31	844	948	115	1150	262	747	1851	1653	1546	476
32	1014	775	258	707	1451	1399	879	1298	1742	563
33	11	110	1100	1635	1366	549	1744	583	211	237
34	497	1224	1002	655	931	1818	1323	119	1190	662
35	1001	645	831	818	688	1261	1372	609	471	964
36	275	877	1278	1542	436	614	521	1464	1529	306
37	1187	632	701	1391	799	498	1234	1102	1655	1566
38	676	1141	172	1720	343	1557	586	241	537	1624
39	1256	1322	109	1090	1535	366	1787	1013	765	158
40	1580	816	668	1061	1245	1212	882	1328	169	1690
41	43	430	554	1794	1083	1465	1539	406	314	1267
42	1432	1209	852	1028	915	1658	1596	976	395	204
43	167	1670	1716	303	1157	332	1447	1359	479	1044
44	1075	1385	739	1771	853	1038	1015	785	358	1707
45	213	257	697	1351	399	244	567	51	510	1354
46	429	544	1694	83	830	808	588	261	737	1751
47	653	911	1618	1196	722	1601	1026	895	1458	1469
48	1579	806	568	61	610	481	1064	1275	1512	136
49	1360	489	1144	202	147	1470	1589	906	1568	696

P = 1873

INDICES

	0	1	2	3	4	5	6	7	8	9
50	953	1292	1693	66	1498	522	613	1270	897	1529
51	458	592	810	1426	1373	1825	1244	1109	1019	1395
52	1113	366	1389	730	1236	1644	100	1758	1136	594
53	8	799	1436	125	1078	184	1032	388	171	1834
54	1637	105	54	529	461	1343	1804	1583	973	335
55	1282	1327	1117	229	412	1158	10	567	1065	1550
56	1647	787	1871	329	1613	290	856	456	482	1459
57	1575	19	1442	206	659	1263	1640	584	112	563
58	1538	1215	999	337	734	71	386	770	466	1003
59	948	76	1161	1775	94	1298	620	1853	1423	758
60	1786	827	212	1862	557	1611	1355	1186	1578	357
61	484	47	1291	591	365	798	104	1326	786	18
62	1214	75	826	46	74	60	89	32	1340	812
63	605	61	371	1200	1625	4	841	772	1867	1312
64	1789	90	1017	784	85	351	1229	577	598	1277
65	220	33	1473	470	304	343	801	1564	581	1172
66	243	1341	349	1597	1357	543	119	1848	402	198
67	139	813	608	1772	1658	744	380	1409	1123	1839
68	1440	606	1543	1284	536	80	1306	1761	354	1147
69	224	62	505	934	180	989	499	452	1745	756
70	754	372	904	57	246	720	1593	323	1781	985
71	1461	1201	188	1524	259	549	1370	98	87	570
72	747	1626	474	1249	1511	645	572	192	914	1428
73	1713	5	1317	1561	669	1445	227	468	1631	442
74	268	842	1681	276	175	1599	1801	315	1769	1857
75	893	773	723	1633	805	1536	1438	1051	1223	553
76	685	1868	837	1144	1188	398	635	215	750	1103
77	1083	1313	1545	1268	1184	321	109	959	717	1569
78	1053	1790	1750	1329	1448	447	1176	515	1058	40
79	1350	91	1076	1623	667	1820	963	157	1376	374
80	896	1018	1135	170	972	1064	481	111	465	1422
81	1577	785	1339	1866	597	580	401	1122	353	1744
82	1780	86	913	1630	1768	1222	749	716	1057	1375
83	464	352	1056	1099	1822	1381	1014	1005	1100	1095
84	1587	1230	1480	1811	310	1359	1553	1412	1823	796
85	547	578	422	444	285	1515	127	883	1382	1256
86	1333	599	662	508	1580	1484	1655	52	1015	1679
87	1478	1278	1286	939	995	1733	674	361	1006	326
88	1225	221	406	1119	707	888	1457	196	1101	1677
89	1167	34	1180	1491	560	477	1590	1363	1096	906
90	1726	1474	237	152	233	618	497	961	1588	1295
91	21	471	1518	793	817	424	871	144	1231	1717
92	1206	305	629	728	44	1247	1628	726	1481	1827
93	1154	344	1738	766	965	876	14	950	1812	29
94	1702	802	1280	218	891	545	1662	692	311	980
95	1664	1565	1241	270	781	295	1080	1807	1360	1753
96	1729	582	1407	957	359	652	25	1433	1554	1169
97	1088	1173	538	790	1842	160	427	654	1413	1496
98	555	244	970	231	741	165	1132	521	1824	1643
99	183	1342	1157	289	1262	70	1297	1610	797	59

POWER RESIDUES

	0	1	2	3	4	5	6	7	8	9
50	1341	299	1117	1805	1193	692	1301	1772	863	1138
51	142	1420	1089	1525	266	787	378	34	340	1527
52	286	987	505	1304	1802	1163	392	174	1740	543
53	1684	1856	1703	173	1730	443	684	1221	972	355
54	1677	1786	1003	665	1031	945	85	850	1008	715
55	1531	326	1387	759	98	980	435	604	421	464
56	894	1448	1369	579	171	1710	243	557	1824	1383
57	719	1571	726	1641	1426	1149	252	647	851	1018
58	815	658	961	245	577	151	1510	116	1160	362
59	1747	613	511	1364	529	1544	456	814	648	861
60	1118	1815	1293	1692	63	630	681	1191	672	1101
61	1645	1466	1549	506	1314	29	290	1027	905	1558
62	596	341	1537	386	114	1140	162	1620	1216	922
63	1728	423	484	1094	1575	766	168	1680	1816	1303
64	1792	1063	1265	1412	1009	725	1631	1326	149	1490
65	1789	1033	965	285	977	405	304	1167	432	574
66	121	1210	862	1128	42	420	454	794	448	734
67	1721	353	1657	1586	876	1268	1442	1309	1852	1663
68	1646	1476	1649	1506	76	760	108	1080	1435	1239
69	1152	282	947	105	1050	1135	112	1120	1835	1493
70	1819	1333	219	317	1297	1732	463	884	1348	369
71	1817	1313	19	190	27	270	827	778	288	1007
72	705	1431	1199	752	28	280	927	1778	923	1738
73	523	1484	1729	433	584	221	337	1497	1859	1733
74	473	984	475	1004	675	1131	72	720	1581	826
75	768	188	7	70	700	1381	699	1371	599	371
76	1837	1513	146	1460	1489	1779	933	1838	1523	246
77	587	251	637	751	18	180	1800	1143	192	47
78	470	954	175	1750	643	811	618	561	1864	1783
79	973	365	1777	913	1638	1396	849	998	615	531
80	1564	656	941	45	450	754	48	480	1054	1175
81	512	1374	629	671	1091	1545	466	914	1648	1496
82	1849	1633	1346	349	1617	1186	622	601	391	164
83	1640	1416	1049	1125	12	120	1200	762	128	1280
84	1562	636	741	1791	1053	1165	412	374	1867	1813
85	1273	1492	1809	1233	1092	1555	566	41	410	354
86	1667	1686	3	30	300	1127	32	320	1327	159
87	1590	916	1668	1696	103	1030	935	1858	1723	373
88	1857	1713	273	857	1078	1415	1039	1025	885	1358
89	469	944	75	750	8	80	800	508	1334	229
90	417	424	494	1194	702	1401	899	1498	1869	1833
91	1473	1619	1206	822	728	1661	1626	1276	1522	236
92	487	1124	2	20	200	127	1270	1462	1509	106
93	1060	1235	1112	1755	693	1311	1872	1863	1773	873
94	1238	1142	182	1820	1343	319	1317	59	590	281
95	937	5	50	500	1254	1302	1782	963	265	777
96	278	907	1578	796	468	934	1848	1623	1246	1222
97	982	455	804	548	1734	483	1084	1475	1639	1406
98	949	125	1250	1262	1382	709	1471	1599	1006	695
99	1331	199	117	1170	462	874	1248	1242	1182	582

P = 1873

INDICES

	0	1	2	3	4	5	6	7	8	9
100	3	350	342	542	743	79	988	719	548	644
101	1444	1598	1535	397	320	446	1819	1063	579	1221
102	1380	1358	1514	1483	1732	887	476	617	423	1246
103	875	544	294	651	159	164	69	78	445	886
104	163	120	1288	1400	439	121	1652	1685	286	832
105	694	1849	1022	844	808	1289	186	1337	1516	1533
106	930	403	1721	641	486	1401	1047	1417	128	36
107	1106	199	82	1832	1310	440	1093	27	884	1603
108	687	140	1027	414	976	122	1451	240	1383	512
109	393	814	854	117	633	1653	23	1045	1257	248
110	332	609	377	147	167	1686	1151	1571	1334	252
111	208	1773	932	1621	1489	287	115	502	600	1741
112	697	1659	1709	1829	921	833	1251	865	663	1111
113	1212	745	1778	1204	1378	695	1404	1163	509	1605
114	625	381	941	777	492	1850	1128	1508	1581	575
115	313	1410	690	1683	1506	1023	1034	434	1485	1195
116	588	1124	265	525	49	845	1259	657	1656	1182
117	993	1840	1308	1690	1692	809	1388	1435	53	1116
118	1870	1441	998	1160	211	1290	825	370	1016	1472
119	348	607	1542	504	903	187	473	1316	1680	722
120	836	1544	1749	1075	1134	1338	912	1055	1479	421
121	661	1285	405	1179	236	1517	628	1737	1279	1240
122	1406	537	969	1156	341	1534	1513	293	1287	1021
123	1720	81	1026	853	376	931	1708	1777	940	689
124	264	1307	997	1541	1748	404	968	1025	996	1010
125	982	1762	1011	278	954	1722	390	1040	1734	1301
126	1527	355	983	1420	1293	642	250	419	675	1493
127	926	1148	1763	850	1694	487	917	1556	362	1030
128	839	225	1012	12	67	1402	1706	1322	1007	1670
129	1273	63	279	602	1499	1048	1520	704	327	1595
130	1142	506	955	639	523	1418	1392	1792	1226	677
131	1265	935	1723	711	614	129	1503	946	222	1348
132	1165	181	391	346	1271	37	647	868	407	1397
133	1465	990	1041	701	898	1107	1324	96	1120	142
134	1061	500	1735	944	1530	200	822	1036	708	300
135	1666	453	1302	177	459	83	173	308	889	437
136	490	1746	1528	1394	593	1833	334	1549	1458	562
137	1002	757	356	17	811	1311	1276	1171	197	1838
138	1146	755	984	569	1427	441	1856	552	1102	1568
139	39	373	1421	1743	1374	1094	795	1255	1678	325
140	1676	905	1294	1716	1826	28	979	1752	1168	1495
141	1642	58	643	1220	1245	885	831	1532	35	1602
142	511	247	251	1740	1110	1604	574	1194	1181	1115
143	1471	721	420	1239	1020	688	1009	1300	1492	1029
144	1669	1594	676	1347	1396	141	299	436	561	1837
145	1567	324	1494	1601	1114	1028	1836	1070	478	1071
146	763	1782	927	1794	367	415	611	1353	1591	479
147	495	986	1149	910	1390	977	681	1090	1364	1072
148	1190	1462	1764	1067	731	123	1198	1559	1097	764
149	649	1202	851	699	1237	1452	819	737	907	1783

POWER RESIDUES

	0	1	2	3	4	5	6	7	8	9
100	201	137	1370	589	271	837	878	1288	1642	1436
101	1249	1252	1282	1582	836	868	1188	642	801	518
102	1434	1229	1052	1155	312	1247	1232	1082	1455	1439
103	1279	1552	536	1614	1156	322	1347	359	1717	313
104	1257	1332	209	217	297	1097	1605	1066	1295	1712
105	263	757	78	780	308	1207	832	828	788	388
106	134	1340	289	1017	805	558	1834	1483	1719	333
107	1457	1459	1479	1679	1806	1203	792	428	534	1594
108	956	195	77	770	208	207	197	97	970	335
109	1477	1659	1606	1076	1395	839	898	1488	1769	833
110	838	888	1388	769	198	107	1070	1335	239	517
111	1424	1129	52	520	1454	1429	1179	552	1774	883
112	1338	269	817	678	1161	372	1847	1613	1146	222
113	347	1597	986	495	1204	802	528	1534	356	1687
114	13	130	1300	1762	763	138	1380	689	1271	1472
115	1609	1106	1695	93	930	1808	1223	992	555	1804
116	1183	592	301	1137	132	1320	89	890	1408	969
117	325	1377	659	971	345	1577	786	368	1807	1213
118	892	1428	1169	452	774	248	607	451	764	148
119	1480	1689	33	330	1427	1159	352	1647	1486	1749
120	633	711	1491	1799	1133	92	920	1708	223	357
121	1697	113	1130	62	620	581	191	37	370	1827
122	1413	1019	825	758	88	880	1308	1842	1563	646
123	841	918	1688	23	230	427	524	1494	1829	1433
124	1219	952	155	1550	516	1414	1029	925	1758	723
125	1611	1126	22	220	327	1397	859	1098	1615	1166
126	422	474	994	575	131	1310	1862	1763	773	238
127	507	1324	129	1290	1662	1636	1376	649	871	1218
128	942	55	550	1754	683	1211	872	1228	1042	1055
129	1185	612	501	1264	1402	909	1598	996	595	331
130	1437	1259	1352	409	344	1567	686	1241	1172	482
131	1074	1375	639	771	218	307	1197	732	1701	153
132	1530	316	1287	1632	1336	249	617	551	1764	783
133	338	1507	86	860	1108	1715	293	1057	1205	812
134	628	661	991	545	1704	183	1830	1443	1319	79
135	790	408	334	1467	1559	606	441	664	1021	845
136	958	215	277	897	1478	1669	1706	203	157	1570
137	716	1541	426	514	1394	829	798	488	1134	102
138	1020	835	858	1088	1515	166	1660	1616	1176	522
139	1474	1629	1306	1822	1363	519	1444	1329	179	1790
140	1043	1065	1285	1612	1136	122	1220	962	255	677
141	1151	272	847	978	415	404	294	1067	1305	1812
142	1263	1392	809	598	361	1737	513	1384	729	1671
143	1726	403	284	967	305	1177	532	1574	756	68
144	680	1181	572	101	1010	735	1731	453	784	348
145	1607	1086	1495	1839	1533	346	1587	886	1368	569
146	71	710	1481	1699	133	1330	189	17	170	1700
147	143	1430	1189	652	901	1518	196	87	870	1208
148	842	928	1788	1023	865	1158	342	1547	486	1114
149	1775	893	1438	1269	1452	1409	979	425	504	1294

P = 1873

INDICES

	0	1	2	3	4	5	6	7	8	9
150	1815	189	1695	282	1645	241	683	1331	1727	928
151	586	1525	488	761	101	1384	273	202	1475	1795
152	1607	260	918	768	1759	513	194	519	238	368
153	1320	550	1557	1454	1137	394	1672	622	153	416
154	133	1371	363	257	595	815	318	1487	234	612
155	1243	99	1031	1803	9	855	1639	385	619	1354
156	103	88	840	1228	800	118	379	1305	498	1592
157	1369	571	226	1800	1437	634	108	1175	962	480
158	400	748	1013	1552	126	1654	673	1456	1589	496
159	870	1627	13	1661	1079	24	426	1131	1296	987
160	1818	475	68	1651	185	1046	1092	1450	22	1150
161	114	1250	1403	1127	1033	1258	1387	824	472	911
162	627	1512	1707	967	389	249	916	1705	1519	1391
163	1502	646	1323	821	172	333	1275	1855	794	978
164	830	573	1008	298	1835	610	680	1197	818	682
165	272	193	1671	317	1638	378	107	672	425	1091
166	1386	915	1274	679	106	148	149	860	872	1365
167	431	1429	64	1860	55	168	150	540	145	1073
168	637	1714	280	1649	530	1687	861	1139	1232	1191
169	409	6	603	1711	462	1152	873	1210	1718	1463
170	1469	1318	1500	532	1344	1572	1366	449	1207	1765
171	565	1562	1049	881	1805	1335	432	1038	306	1068
172	383	670	1521	878	1584	253	1430	1698	630	732
173	534	1446	705	739	974	209	65	1425	729	124
174	528	228	328	205	336	1774	1861	590	45	1199
175	783	469	1596	1771	1283	933	56	1523	1248	1560
176	275	1632	1143	1267	1328	1622	169	1865	1629	1098
177	1810	443	507	938	1118	1490	151	792	727	765
178	217	269	956	789	230	288	541	396	1482	650
179	1399	843	640	1831	413	116	146	1620	1828	1203
180	776	1682	524	1689	1159	503	1074	1178	1155	852
181	1540	277	1419	849	11	601	638	710	345	700
182	943	176	1393	16	568	1742	1715	1219	1739	1238
183	1346	1600	1793	909	1066	698	281	760	767	1453
184	256	1802	1227	1799	1551	1660	1650	1126	966	820
185	297	316	678	1859	1648	1710	531	880	877	738
186	204	1770	1266	937	788	1830	1688	848	15	908
187	1798	1858	936							

POWER RESIDUES

	0	1	2	3	4	5	6	7	8	9
150	1702	163	1630	1316	49	490	1154	302	1147	232
151	447	724	1621	1226	1022	855	1058	1215	912	1628
152	1296	1722	363	1757	713	1511	126	1260	1362	509
153	1344	329	1417	1059	1225	1012	755	58	580	181
154	1810	1243	1192	682	1201	772	228	407	324	1367
155	559	1844	1583	846	968	315	1277	1532	336	1487
156	1759	733	1711	253	657	951	145	1450	1389	779
157	298	1107	1705	193	57	570	81	810	608	461
158	864	1148	242	547	1724	383	84	840	908	1588
159	896	1468	1569	706	1441	1299	1752	663	1011	745
160	1831	1453	1419	1079	1425	1139	152	1520	216	287
161	997	605	431	564	21	210	227	397	224	367
162	1797	1113	1765	793	438	634	721	1591	926	1768
163	823	738	1761	753	38	380	54	540	1654	1556
164	576	141	1410	989	525	1504	56	560	1854	1683
165	1846	1603	1046	1095	1585	866	1168	442	674	1121
166	1845	1593	946	95	950	135	1350	389	144	1440
167	1289	1652	1536	376	14	140	1400	889	1398	869
168	1198	742	1801	1153	292	1047	1105	1685	1866	1803
169	1173	492	1174	502	1274	1502	36	360	1727	413
170	384	94	940	35	350	1627	1286	1622	1236	1122
171	1855	1693	73	730	1681	1826	1403	919	1698	123
172	1230	1062	1255	1312	9	90	900	1508	96	960
173	235	477	1024	875	1258	1342	309	1217	932	1828
174	1423	1119	1825	1393	819	698	1361	499	1244	1202
175	782	328	1407	959	225	377	24	240	527	1524
176	256	687	1251	1272	1482	1709	233	457	824	748
177	1861	1753	673	1111	1745	593	311	1237	1132	82
178	820	708	1461	1499	6	60	600	381	64	640
179	781	318	1307	1832	1463	1519	206	187	1870	1843
180	1573	746	1841	1553	546	1714	283	957	205	177
181	1770	843	938	15	150	1500	16	160	1600	1016
182	795	458	834	848	988	515	1404	929	1798	1123
183	1865	1793	1073	1365	539	1644	1456	1449	1379	679
184	1171	472	974	375	4	40	400	254	667	1051
185	1145	212	247	597	351	1637	1386	749	1871	1853
186	1673	1746	603	411	364	1767	813	638	761	118
187	1180	562								

P = 1877

INDICES

	0	1	2	3	4	5	6	7	8	9
0		0	1	791	2	37	792	730	3	1582
1	38	1867	793	1265	731	828	4	1639	1583	305
2	39	1521	1868	381	794	74	1266	497	732	577
3	829	1747	5	782	1640	767	1584	1360	306	180
4	40	1200	1522	835	1869	1619	382	751	795	1460
5	75	554	1267	163	498	28	733	1096	578	1862
6	830	860	1748	436	6	1302	783	206	1641	1172
7	768	1419	1585	255	1361	865	307	721	181	1387
8	41	1288	1201	1500	1523	1676	836	1368	1870	1296
9	1620	119	383	662	752	342	796	397	1461	1573
10	76	1217	555	1612	1268	1558	164	1753	499	93
11	29	275	734	230	1097	418	579	971	1863	493
12	831	1858	861	115	1749	111	437	1780	7	1626
13	1303	1042	784	1035	207	534	1642	469	1173	441
14	769	1542	1420	1256	1586	614	256	375	1362	1441
15	866	1447	308	1345	722	1784	182	1813	1388	954
16	42	1111	1289	594	1202	819	1501	987	1524	654
17	1677	11	837	1275	1369	804	1871	777	1297	392
18	1621	1106	120	1651	384	1397	663	1630	753	1227
19	343	744	797	125	398	217	1462	624	1574	192
20	77	997	1218	1307	556	1237	1613	87	1269	296
21	1559	286	165	334	1754	872	500	601	94	1046
22	30	1028	276	1597	735	1656	231	1795	1098	678
23	419	1512	580	324	972	788	1864	302	494	764
24	832	551	1859	203	862	1497	116	1570	1750	415
25	112	1039	438	372	1781	591	8	389	1627	214
26	1304	283	1043	1792	785	200	1036	211	208	62
27	535	1185	1643	910	470	65	1174	1018	442	1453
28	770	890	1543	538	1421	1133	1257	54	1587	1402
29	615	1188	257	639	376	23	1363	488	1442	1646
30	867	1565	1448	132	309	897	1346	913	723	527
31	1785	137	183	1084	1814	473	1389	1158	955	568
32	43	668	1112	68	1290	1339	595	884	1203	1481
33	820	1177	1502	1066	988	243	1525	1698	655	1021
34	1678	1738	12	314	838	1209	1276	445	1370	1685
35	805	1762	1872	1635	778	1456	1298	1284	393	226
36	1622	610	1107	773	121	292	1652	547	385	906
37	1398	893	664	1694	1631	902	754	1842	1228	1546
38	344	695	745	269	798	758	126	541	399	1604
39	218	144	1463	1833	625	1424	1575	462	193	1826
40	78	1846	998	1136	1219	1325	1308	1351	557	1487
41	1238	1260	1614	716	88	1537	1270	1232	297	57
42	1560	1061	287	457	166	1713	335	1590	1755	171
43	873	405	501	1550	602	1405	95	686	1047	918
44	31	1166	1029	618	277	1333	1598	356	736	348
45	1657	1191	232	362	1796	156	1099	520	679	260
46	420	1718	1513	1010	581	699	325	642	973	936
47	789	728	1865	826	303	379	495	1745	765	178
48	833	749	552	26	1860	434	204	1417	863	1385
49	1498	1366	117	340	1571	1610	1751	273	416	491

POWER RESIDUES

	0	1	2	3	4	5	6	7	8	9
0	1	2	4	8	16	32	64	128	256	512
1	1024	171	342	684	1368	859	1718	1559	1241	605
2	1210	543	1086	295	590	1180	483	966	55	110
3	220	440	880	1760	1643	1409	941	5	10	20
4	40	80	160	320	640	1280	683	1366	855	1710
5	1543	1209	541	1082	287	574	1148	419	838	1676
6	1475	1073	269	538	1076	275	550	1100	323	646
7	1292	707	1414	951	25	50	100	200	400	800
8	1600	1323	769	1538	1199	521	1042	207	414	828
9	1656	1435	993	109	218	436	872	1744	1611	1345
10	813	1626	1375	873	1746	1615	1353	829	1658	1439
11	1001	125	250	500	1000	123	246	492	984	91
12	182	364	728	1456	1035	193	386	772	1544	1211
13	545	1090	303	606	1212	547	1094	311	622	1244
14	611	1222	567	1134	391	782	1564	1251	625	1250
15	623	1246	615	1230	583	1166	455	910	1820	1763
16	1649	1421	965	53	106	212	424	848	1696	1515
17	1153	429	858	1716	1555	1233	589	1178	479	958
18	39	78	156	312	624	1248	619	1238	599	1198
19	519	1038	199	398	796	1592	1307	737	1474	1071
20	265	530	1060	243	486	972	67	134	268	536
21	1072	267	534	1068	259	518	1036	195	390	780
22	1560	1243	609	1218	559	1118	359	718	1436	995
23	113	226	452	904	1808	1739	1601	1325	773	1546
24	1215	553	1106	335	670	1340	803	1606	1335	793
25	1586	1295	713	1426	975	73	146	292	584	1168
26	459	918	1836	1795	1713	1549	1221	565	1130	383
27	766	1532	1187	497	994	111	222	444	888	1776
28	1675	1473	1069	261	522	1044	211	422	844	1688
29	1499	1121	365	730	1460	1043	209	418	836	1672
30	1467	1057	237	474	948	19	38	76	152	304
31	608	1216	555	1110	343	686	1372	867	1734	1591
32	1305	733	1466	1055	233	466	932	1864	1851	1825
33	1773	1669	1461	1045	213	426	852	1704	1531	1185
34	493	986	95	190	380	760	1520	1163	449	898
35	1796	1715	1553	1229	581	1162	447	894	1788	1699
36	1521	1165	453	906	1812	1747	1617	1357	837	1674
37	1471	1065	253	506	1012	147	294	588	1176	475
38	950	23	46	92	184	368	736	1472	1067	257
39	514	1028	179	358	716	1432	987	97	194	388
40	776	1552	1227	577	1154	431	862	1724	1571	1265
41	653	1306	735	1470	1063	249	498	996	115	230
42	460	920	1840	1803	1729	1581	1285	693	1386	895
43	1790	1703	1529	1181	485	970	63	126	252	504
44	1008	139	278	556	1112	347	694	1388	899	1798
45	1719	1561	1245	613	1226	575	1150	423	846	1692
46	1507	1137	397	794	1588	1299	721	1442	1007	137
47	274	548	1096	315	630	1260	643	1286	695	1390
48	903	1806	1735	1593	1309	741	1482	1087	297	594
49	1188	499	998	119	238	476	952	27	54	108

P = 1877

INDICES

	0	1	2	3	4	5	6	7	8	9
50	113	1778	1040	532	439	1254	373	1445	1782	952
51	592	985	9	802	390	1649	1628	742	215	190
52	1305	85	284	870	1044	1595	1793	1510	786	762
53	201	1568	1037	589	212	1790	209	1183	63	1451
54	536	52	1186	21	1644	130	911	135	471	566
55	66	882	1175	241	1019	312	443	1760	1454	224
56	771	545	891	900	1544	267	539	142	1422	1824
57	1134	1349	1258	1535	55	455	1588	403	1403	916
58	616	354	1189	154	258	1008	640	726	377	176
59	24	1415	1364	1608	489	530	1443	983	1647	188
60	868	1508	1566	1788	1449	19	133	880	310	222
61	898	140	1347	453	914	152	724	1413	528	186
62	1786	878	138	150	184	148	1085	1087	1815	1123
63	474	1089	1390	1077	1159	1817	956	849	569	1125
64	44	1467	669	476	1113	1663	69	1091	1291	1853
65	1340	1392	596	410	885	1079	1204	1837	1482	1161
66	821	1249	1178	1819	1503	1072	1067	958	989	512
67	244	851	1526	629	1699	571	656	1807	1022	1127
68	1679	710	1739	46	13	506	315	1469	839	1428
69	1210	671	1277	427	446	478	1371	963	1686	1115
70	806	1316	1763	1665	1873	1579	1636	71	779	1197
71	1457	1093	1299	252	1285	1293	394	1555	227	1855
72	1623	466	611	1342	1108	651	774	1394	122	994
73	293	598	1653	321	548	412	386	197	907	887
74	1399	485	894	1081	665	1478	1695	1206	1632	607
75	903	1839	755	1830	1843	1484	1229	1710	1547	1163
76	345	517	696	823	746	1382	270	1251	799	82
77	759	1180	127	238	542	1821	400	1005	1605	1505
78	219	1410	145	1074	1464	1850	1834	1069	626	707
79	1425	960	1576	249	463	991	194	1475	1827	514
80	79	1002	1847	246	999	1148	1137	853	1220	1151
81	1326	1528	1309	100	1352	631	558	1140	1488	1701
82	1239	1725	1261	573	1615	856	717	658	89	107
83	1538	1809	1271	1223	1233	1024	298	368	58	1129
84	1561	1154	1062	1681	288	691	458	712	167	1329
85	1714	1741	336	948	1591	48	1756	1531	172	15
86	874	845	406	508	502	1312	1551	317	603	1378
87	1406	1471	96	103	687	841	1048	1052	919	1430
88	32	1355	1167	1212	1030	814	619	673	278	634
89	1334	1279	1599	1056	357	429	737	561	349	448
90	1658	1802	1192	480	233	1143	363	1373	1797	923
91	157	965	1100	1491	521	1688	680	1772	261	1117
92	421	1704	1719	808	1514	1434	1011	1318	582	1242
93	700	1765	326	928	643	1667	974	1728	937	1875
94	790	36	729	1581	1866	1264	827	1638	304	1520
95	380	73	496	576	1746	781	766	1359	179	1199
96	834	1618	750	1459	553	162	27	1095	1861	859
97	435	1301	205	1171	1418	254	864	720	1386	1287
98	1499	1675	1367	1295	118	661	341	396	1572	1216
99	1611	1557	1752	92	274	229	417	970	492	1857

POWER RESIDUES

	0	1	2	3	4	5	6	7	8	9
50	216	432	864	1728	1579	1281	685	1370	863	1726
51	1575	1273	669	1338	799	1598	1319	761	1522	1167
52	457	914	1828	1779	1681	1485	1093	309	618	1236
53	595	1190	503	1006	135	270	540	1080	283	566
54	1132	387	774	1548	1219	561	1122	367	734	1468
55	1059	241	482	964	51	102	204	408	816	1632
56	1387	897	1794	1711	1545	1213	549	1098	319	638
57	1276	675	1350	823	1646	1415	953	29	58	116
58	232	464	928	1856	1835	1793	1709	1541	1205	533
59	1066	255	510	1020	163	326	652	1304	731	1462
60	1047	217	434	868	1736	1595	1313	749	1498	1119
61	361	722	1444	1011	145	290	580	1160	443	886
62	1772	1667	1457	1037	197	394	788	1576	1275	673
63	1346	815	1630	1383	889	1778	1679	1481	1085	293
64	586	1172	467	934	1868	1859	1841	1805	1733	1589
65	1301	725	1450	1023	169	338	676	1352	827	1654
66	1431	985	93	186	372	744	1488	1099	321	642
67	1284	691	1382	887	1774	1671	1465	1053	229	458
68	916	1832	1787	1697	1517	1157	437	874	1748	1619
69	1361	845	1690	1503	1129	381	762	1524	1171	465
70	930	1860	1843	1809	1741	1605	1333	789	1578	1279
71	681	1362	847	1694	1511	1145	413	826	1652	1427
72	977	77	154	308	616	1232	587	1174	471	942
73	7	14	28	56	112	224	448	896	1792	1707
74	1537	1197	517	1034	191	382	764	1528	1179	481
75	962	47	94	188	376	752	1504	1131	385	770
76	1540	1203	529	1058	239	478	956	35	70	140
77	280	560	1120	363	726	1452	1027	177	354	708
78	1416	955	33	66	132	264	528	1056	235	470
79	940	3	6	12	24	48	96	192	384	768
80	1536	1195	513	1026	175	350	700	1400	923	1846
81	1815	1753	1629	1381	885	1770	1663	1449	1021	165
82	330	660	1320	763	1526	1175	473	946	15	30
83	60	120	240	480	960	43	86	172	344	688
84	1376	875	1750	1623	1369	861	1722	1567	1257	637
85	1274	671	1342	807	1614	1351	825	1650	1423	969
86	61	122	244	488	976	75	150	300	600	1200
87	523	1046	215	430	860	1720	1563	1249	621	1242
88	607	1214	551	1102	327	654	1308	739	1478	1079
89	281	562	1124	371	742	1484	1091	305	610	1220
90	563	1126	375	750	1500	1123	369	738	1476	1075
91	273	546	1092	307	614	1228	579	1158	439	878
92	1756	1635	1393	909	1818	1759	1641	1405	933	1866
93	1855	1833	1789	1701	1525	1173	469	938	1876	1875
94	1873	1869	1861	1845	1813	1749	1621	1365	853	1706
95	1535	1193	509	1018	159	318	636	1272	667	1334
96	791	1582	1287	697	1394	911	1822	1767	1657	1437
97	997	117	234	468	936	1872	1867	1857	1837	1797
98	1717	1557	1237	597	1194	511	1022	167	334	668
99	1336	795	1590	1303	729	1458	1039	201	402	804

P = 1877

INDICES

	0	1	2	3	4	5	6	7	8	9
100	114	110	1779	1625	1041	1034	533	468	440	1541
101	1255	613	374	1440	1446	1344	1783	1812	953	1110
102	593	818	986	653	10	1274	803	776	391	1105
103	1650	1396	1629	1226	743	124	216	623	191	996
104	1306	1236	86	295	285	333	871	600	1045	1027
105	1596	1655	1794	677	1511	323	787	301	763	550
106	202	1496	1569	414	1038	371	590	388	213	282
107	1791	199	210	61	1184	909	64	1017	1452	889
108	537	1132	53	1401	1187	638	22	487	1645	1564
109	131	896	912	526	136	1083	472	1157	567	667
110	67	1338	883	1480	1176	1065	242	1697	1020	1737
111	313	1208	444	1684	1761	1634	1455	1283	225	609
112	772	291	546	905	892	1693	901	1841	1545	694
113	268	757	540	1603	143	1832	1423	461	1825	1845
114	1135	1324	1350	1486	1259	715	1536	1231	56	1060
115	456	1712	1589	170	404	1549	1404	685	917	1165
116	617	1332	355	347	1190	361	155	519	259	1717
117	1009	698	641	935	727	825	378	1744	177	748
118	25	433	1416	1384	1365	339	1609	272	490	1777
119	531	1253	1444	951	984	801	1648	741	189	84
120	869	1594	1509	761	1567	588	1789	1182	1450	51
121	20	129	134	565	881	240	311	1759	223	544
122	899	266	141	1823	1348	1534	454	402	915	353
123	153	1007	725	175	1414	1607	529	982	187	1507
124	1787	18	879	221	139	452	151	1412	185	877
125	149	147	1086	1122	1088	1076	1816	848	1124	1466
126	475	1662	1090	1852	1391	409	1078	1836	1160	1248
127	1818	1071	957	511	850	628	570	1806	1126	709
128	45	505	1468	1427	670	426	477	962	1114	1315
129	1664	1578	70	1196	1092	251	1292	1554	1854	465
130	1341	650	1393	993	597	320	411	196	886	484
131	1080	1477	1205	606	1838	1829	1483	1709	1162	516
132	822	1381	1250	81	1179	237	1820	1004	1504	1409
133	1073	1849	1068	706	959	248	990	1474	513	1001
134	245	1147	852	1150	1527	99	630	1139	1700	1724
135	572	855	657	106	1808	1222	1023	367	1128	1153
136	1680	690	711	1328	1740	947	47	1530	14	844
137	507	1311	316	1377	1470	102	840	1051	1429	1354
138	1211	813	672	633	1278	1055	428	560	447	1801
139	479	1142	1372	922	964	1490	1687	1771	1116	1703
140	807	1433	1317	1241	1764	927	1666	1727	1874	35
141	1580	1263	1637	1519	72	575	780	1358	1198	1617
142	1458	161	1094	858	1300	1170	253	719	1286	1674
143	1294	660	395	1215	1556	91	228	969	1856	109
144	1624	1033	467	1540	612	1439	1343	1811	1109	817
145	652	1273	775	1104	1395	1225	123	622	995	1235
146	294	332	599	1026	1654	676	322	300	549	1495
147	413	370	387	281	198	60	908	1016	888	1131
148	1400	637	486	1563	895	525	1082	1156	666	1337
149	1479	1064	1696	1736	1207	1683	1633	1282	608	290

POWER RESIDUES

	0	1	2	3	4	5	6	7	8	9
100	1608	1339	801	1602	1327	777	1554	1231	585	1170
101	463	926	1852	1827	1777	1677	1477	1077	277	554
102	1108	339	678	1356	835	1670	1463	1049	221	442
103	884	1768	1659	1441	1005	133	266	532	1064	251
104	502	1004	131	262	524	1048	219	438	876	1752
105	1627	1377	877	1754	1631	1385	893	1786	1695	1513
106	1149	421	842	1684	1491	1105	333	666	1332	787
107	1574	1271	665	1330	783	1566	1255	633	1266	655
108	1310	743	1486	1095	313	626	1252	627	1254	631
109	1262	647	1294	711	1422	967	57	114	228	456
110	912	1824	1771	1665	1453	1029	181	362	724	1448
111	1019	161	322	644	1288	699	1398	919	1838	1799
112	1721	1565	1253	629	1258	639	1278	679	1358	839
113	1678	1479	1081	285	570	1140	403	806	1612	1347
114	817	1634	1391	905	1810	1743	1609	1341	805	1610
115	1343	809	1618	1359	841	1682	1487	1097	317	634
116	1268	659	1318	759	1518	1159	441	882	1764	1651
117	1425	973	69	138	276	552	1104	331	662	1324
118	771	1542	1207	537	1074	271	542	1084	291	582
119	1164	451	902	1804	1731	1585	1293	709	1418	959
120	41	82	164	328	656	1312	747	1494	1111	345
121	690	1380	883	1766	1655	1433	989	101	202	404
122	808	1616	1355	833	1666	1455	1033	189	378	756
123	1512	1147	417	834	1668	1459	1041	205	410	820
124	1640	1403	929	1858	1839	1801	1725	1573	1269	661
125	1322	767	1534	1191	505	1010	143	286	572	1144
126	411	822	1644	1411	945	13	26	52	104	208
127	416	832	1664	1451	1025	173	346	692	1384	891
128	1782	1687	1497	1117	357	714	1428	979	81	162
129	324	648	1296	715	1430	983	89	178	356	712
130	1424	971	65	130	260	520	1040	203	406	812
131	1624	1371	865	1730	1583	1289	701	1402	927	1854
132	1831	1785	1693	1509	1141	405	810	1620	1363	849
133	1698	1519	1161	445	890	1780	1683	1489	1101	325
134	650	1300	723	1446	1015	153	306	612	1224	571
135	1142	407	814	1628	1379	881	1762	1647	1417	957
136	37	74	148	296	592	1184	491	982	87	174
137	348	696	1392	907	1814	1751	1625	1373	869	1738
138	1599	1321	765	1530	1183	489	978	79	158	316
139	632	1264	651	1302	727	1454	1031	185	370	740
140	1480	1083	289	578	1156	435	870	1740	1603	1329
141	781	1562	1247	617	1234	591	1182	487	974	71
142	142	284	568	1136	395	790	1580	1283	689	1378
143	879	1758	1639	1401	925	1850	1823	1769	1661	1445
144	1013	149	298	596	1192	507	1014	151	302	604
145	1208	539	1078	279	558	1116	355	710	1420	963
146	49	98	196	392	784	1568	1259	641	1282	687
147	1374	871	1742	1607	1337	797	1594	1311	745	1490
148	1103	329	658	1316	755	1510	1143	409	818	1636
149	1395	913	1826	1775	1673	1469	1061	245	490	980

P = 1877

INDICES

	0	1	2	3	4	5	6	7	8	9
150	904	1692	1840	693	756	1602	1831	460	1844	1323
151	1485	714	1230	1059	1711	169	1548	684	1164	1331
152	346	360	518	1716	697	934	824	1743	747	432
153	1383	338	271	1776	1252	950	800	740	83	1593
154	760	587	1181	50	128	564	239	1758	543	265
155	1822	1533	401	352	1006	174	1606	981	1506	17
156	220	451	1411	876	146	1121	1075	847	1465	1661
157	1851	408	1835	1247	1070	510	627	1805	708	504
158	1426	425	961	1314	1577	1195	250	1553	464	649
159	992	319	195	483	1476	605	1828	1708	515	1380
160	80	236	1003	1408	1848	705	247	1473	1000	1146
161	1149	98	1138	1723	854	105	1221	366	1152	689
162	1327	946	1529	843	1310	1376	101	1050	1353	812
163	632	1054	559	1800	1141	921	1489	1770	1702	1432
164	1240	926	1726	34	1262	1518	574	1357	1616	160
165	857	1169	718	1673	659	1214	90	968	108	1032
166	1539	1438	1810	816	1272	1103	1224	621	1234	331
167	1025	675	299	1494	369	280	59	1015	1130	636
168	1562	524	1155	1336	1063	1735	1682	1281	289	1691
169	692	1601	459	1322	713	1058	168	683	1330	359
170	1715	933	1742	431	337	1775	949	739	1592	586
171	49	563	1757	264	1532	351	173	980	16	450
172	875	1120	846	1660	407	1246	509	1804	503	424
173	1313	1194	1552	648	318	482	604	1707	1379	235
174	1407	704	1472	1145	97	1722	104	365	688	945
175	842	1375	1049	811	1053	1799	920	1769	1431	925
176	33	1517	1356	159	1168	1672	1213	967	1031	1437
177	815	1102	620	330	674	1493	279	1014	635	523
178	1335	1734	1280	1690	1600	1321	1057	682	358	932
179	430	1774	738	585	562	263	350	979	449	1119
180	1659	1245	1803	423	1193	647	481	1706	234	703
181	1144	1721	364	944	1374	810	1798	1768	924	1516
182	158	1671	966	1436	1101	329	1492	1013	522	1733
183	1689	1320	681	931	1773	584	262	978	1118	1244
184	422	646	1705	702	1720	943	809	1767	1515	1670
185	1435	328	1012	1732	1319	930	583	977	1243	645
186	701	942	1766	1669	327	1731	929	976	644	941
187	1668	1730	975	940	1729	939	938			

POWER RESIDUES

	0	1	2	3	4	5	6	7	8	9
150	83	166	332	664	1328	779	1558	1239	601	1202
151	527	1054	231	462	924	1848	1819	1761	1645	1413
152	949	21	42	84	168	336	672	1344	811	1622
153	1367	857	1714	1551	1225	573	1146	415	830	1660
154	1443	1009	141	282	564	1128	379	758	1516	1155
155	433	866	1732	1587	1297	717	1434	991	105	210
156	420	840	1680	1483	1089	301	602	1204	531	1062
157	247	494	988	99	198	396	792	1584	1291	705
158	1410	943	9	18	36	72	144	288	576	1152
159	427	854	1708	1539	1201	525	1050	223	446	892
160	1784	1691	1505	1133	389	778	1556	1235	593	1186
161	495	990	103	206	412	824	1648	1419	961	45
162	90	180	360	720	1440	1003	129	258	516	1032
163	187	374	748	1496	1115	353	706	1412	947	17
164	34	68	136	272	544	1088	299	598	1196	515
165	1030	183	366	732	1464	1051	225	450	900	1800
166	1723	1569	1261	645	1290	703	1406	935	1870	1863
167	1849	1821	1765	1653	1429	981	85	170	340	680
168	1360	843	1686	1495	1113	349	698	1396	915	1830
169	1783	1689	1501	1125	373	746	1492	1107	337	674
170	1348	819	1638	1399	921	1842	1807	1737	1597	1317
171	757	1514	1151	425	850	1700	1523	1169	461	922
172	1844	1811	1745	1613	1349	821	1642	1407	937	1874
173	1871	1865	1853	1829	1781	1685	1493	1109	341	682
174	1364	851	1702	1527	1177	477	954	31	62	124
175	248	496	992	107	214	428	856	1712	1547	1217
176	557	1114	351	702	1404	931	1862	1847	1817	1757
177	1637	1397	917	1834	1791	1705	1533	1189	501	1002
178	127	254	508	1016	155	310	620	1240	603	1206
179	535	1070	263	526	1052	227	454	908	1816	1755
180	1633	1389	901	1802	1727	1577	1277	677	1354	831
181	1662	1447	1017	157	314	628	1256	635	1270	663
182	1326	775	1550	1223	569	1138	399	798	1596	1315
183	753	1506	1135	393	786	1572	1267	657	1314	751
184	1502	1127	377	754	1508	1139	401	802	1604	1331
185	785	1570	1263	649	1298	719	1438	999	121	242
186	484	968	59	118	236	472	944	11	22	44
187	88	176	352	704	1408	939				

P = 1879

INDICES

	0	1	2	3	4	5	6	7	8	9
0		0	712	1167	1424	1238	1	1586	258	456
1	72	1403	713	1099	420	527	970	1798	1168	731
2	784	875	237	997	1425	598	1811	1623	1132	1420
3	1239	1597	1682	692	632	946	2	1049	1443	388
4	1496	1755	1587	150	949	1694	1709	382	259	1294
5	1310	1087	645	1418	457	763	1844	20	254	652
6	73	994	431	164	516	459	1404	974	1344	286
7	1658	1698	714	798	1761	1765	277	1111	1100	373
8	330	912	589	242	421	1158	862	709	1661	136
9	528	807	543	886	1094	91	971	210	128	1859
10	144	765	1799	369	1357	235	252	1092	1169	952
11	1475	338	678	1667	732	357	966	1555	1364	1506
12	785	928	1706	1044	1143	1836	876	1284	1228	1317
13	1171	335	238	439	1686	983	178	1846	998	554
14	492	1549	532	624	1426	780	1510	583	595	1033
15	599	1200	989	376	1823	957	1812	525	1085	707
16	1042	705	1624	398	1301	52	954	1123	1133	320
17	1870	1187	1574	22	1421	306	495	1819	848	1003
18	1240	1153	1519	283	1255	409	1598	1323	1806	1331
19	803	1525	1683	1015	922	1626	840	735	693	266
20	856	263	1477	1128	633	1115	1081	1453	191	256
21	947	328	964	987	1804	1388	3	1305	1664	87
22	309	1019	1050	772	1390	1054	501	845	1444	1063
23	1069	400	1678	1208	389	1620	198	1540	340	434
24	1497	1036	1640	201	540	654	1756	1830	1855	1409
25	670	1059	1588	522	118	447	62	1561	151	757
26	5	1876	1047	796	950	778	1151	1303	520	1716
27	1695	1460	890	96	680	123	1710	365	1266	175
28	1204	75	383	213	1244	1258	1336	1463	260	1718
29	1492	1377	344	1866	1295	12	1307	1148	1745	218
30	1311	1736	34	54	1701	354	1088	109	657	1536
31	1669	159	646	938	1237	1402	1797	996	1419	945
32	1754	381	1417	651	458	1697	1110	241	135	90
33	764	1091	1666	1505	1835	334	1845	623	1032	956
34	704	1122	21	1002	408	1524	734	1127	255	1387
35	1018	844	1207	433	653	1058	1560	795	1715	122
36	74	1462	1865	217	353	158	995	650	89	333
37	1121	1126	432	121	157	1125	640	641	165	1610
38	1515	573	359	642	517	471	1727	606	1634	166
39	460	917	1552	1502	1447	1611	1405	892	978	1606
40	1568	1516	975	818	311	272	1840	574	1345	1594
41	1827	1135	1793	360	287	1480	903	1721	968	643
42	1659	1141	1040	838	1676	518	1699	702	638	1791
43	222	472	715	98	139	69	498	1728	799	559
44	1021	1750	1731	607	1762	1374	1484	322	224	1635
45	1766	1280	1213	489	1557	167	278	602	1775	1543
46	1781	461	1112	1138	512	246	42	918	1101	682
47	454	1692	910	1553	374	1329	1052	1874	1146	1503
48	331	270	1748	1872	474	1448	913	740	1252	1565
49	1366	1612	590	1340	664	1219	689	1406	243	131

POWER RESIDUES

	0	1	2	3	4	5	6	7	8	9
0	1	6	36	216	1296	260	1560	1844	1669	619
1	1835	1615	295	1770	1225	1713	883	1540	1724	949
2	57	342	173	1038	591	1667	607	1763	1183	1461
3	1250	1863	1783	1303	302	1812	1477	1346	560	1481
4	1370	704	466	917	1744	1069	777	904	1666	601
5	1727	967	165	990	303	1818	1513	1562	1856	1741
6	1051	669	256	1536	1700	805	1072	795	1012	435
7	731	628	10	60	360	281	1686	721	568	1529
8	1658	553	1439	1118	1071	789	976	219	1314	368
9	329	95	570	1541	1730	985	273	1638	433	719
10	556	1457	1226	1719	919	1756	1141	1209	1617	307
11	1842	1657	547	1403	902	1654	529	1295	254	1524
12	1628	373	359	275	1650	505	1151	1269	98	588
13	1649	499	1115	1053	681	328	89	534	1325	434
14	725	592	1673	643	100	600	1721	931	1828	1573
15	43	258	1548	1772	1237	1785	1315	374	365	311
16	1866	1801	1411	950	63	378	389	455	851	1348
17	572	1553	1802	1417	986	279	1674	649	136	816
18	1138	1191	1509	1538	1712	877	1504	1508	1532	1676
19	661	208	1248	1851	1711	871	1468	1292	236	1416
20	980	243	1458	1232	1755	1135	1173	1401	890	1582
21	97	582	1613	283	1698	793	1000	363	299	1794
22	1369	698	430	701	448	809	1096	939	1876	1861
23	1771	1231	1749	1099	957	105	630	22	132	792
24	994	327	83	498	1109	1017	465	911	1708	853
25	1360	644	106	636	58	348	209	1254	8	48
26	288	1728	973	201	1206	1599	199	1194	1527	1646
27	481	1007	405	551	1427	1046	639	76	456	857
28	1384	788	970	183	1098	951	69	414	605	1751
29	1111	1029	537	1343	542	1373	722	574	1565	1874
30	1849	1699	799	1036	579	1595	175	1050	663	220
31	1320	404	545	1391	830	1222	1695	775	892	1594
32	169	1014	447	803	1060	723	580	1601	211	1266
33	80	480	1001	369	335	131	786	958	111	666
34	238	1428	1052	675	292	1752	1117	1065	753	760
35	802	1054	687	364	305	1830	1585	115	690	382
36	413	599	1715	895	1612	277	1662	577	1583	103
37	618	1829	1579	79	474	965	153	918	1750	1105
38	993	321	47	282	1692	757	784	946	39	234
39	1404	908	1690	745	712	514	1205	1593	163	978
40	231	1386	800	1042	615	1811	1471	1310	344	185
41	1110	1023	501	1127	1125	1113	1041	609	1775	1255
42	14	84	504	1145	1233	1761	1171	1389	818	1150
43	1263	62	372	353	239	1434	1088	891	1588	133
44	798	1030	543	1379	758	790	982	255	1530	1664
45	589	1655	535	1331	470	941	9	54	324	65
46	390	461	887	1564	1868	1813	1483	1382	776	898
47	1630	385	431	707	484	1025	513	1199	1557	1826
48	1561	1850	1705	835	1252	1875	1855	1735	1015	453
49	839	1276	140	840	1282	176	1056	699	436	737

P = 1879

INDICES

	0	1	2	3	4	5	6	7	8	9
50	1382	412	1771	893	422	125	1234	1487	830	979
51	1159	506	774	476	395	1607	863	1785	1469	1189
52	717	1569	710	1441	1759	1473	1508	1517	1662	116
53	1490	1108	1863	976	137	452	1232	292	550	819
54	529	1712	294	442	1602	312	808	112	1392	1450
55	835	273	544	81	1077	1576	100	1841	887	1249
56	38	612	787	575	1095	1027	925	620	78	1346
57	92	726	170	814	297	1595	972	367	552	304
58	326	1828	211	943	1056	915	700	1136	129	450
59	724	24	141	1794	1860	866	579	1433	930	361
60	145	49	570	1430	746	288	766	26	535	417
61	1066	1481	1800	1268	821	404	1369	904	370	9
62	503	742	871	1722	1358	1196	1650	1423	71	969
63	236	1131	631	1495	1708	644	253	515	1657	276
64	588	1660	1093	143	251	677	1363	1142	1170	177
65	531	594	1822	1041	953	1573	847	1254	802	839
66	1476	190	1803	308	500	1677	339	539	669	61
67	1046	519	679	1203	1335	343	1744	1700	1668	1796
68	1416	134	1834	703	733	1206	1714	352	1120	639
69	358	1633	1446	1567	1839	1792	967	1675	221	497
70	1730	223	1556	1780	41	909	1145	473	1365	688
71	1770	829	394	716	1507	1862	549	1601	834	99
72	786	77	296	325	699	140	929	745	1065	1368
73	870	70	1707	587	1362	1821	801	499	1045	1743
74	1833	1119	1838	1729	1144	393	833	698	869	800
75	1837	868	1352	348	1353	560	877	385	444	1689
76	349	1022	1285	660	1071	1614	1354	1751	1229	1349
77	1183	850	561	1732	1318	317	468	46	878	608
78	1172	1223	1629	1165	386	1763	336	581	281	85
79	445	1375	239	215	1604	67	1690	1485	440	302
80	402	592	350	323	1687	65	1530	1005	1023	225
81	984	1788	674	749	1286	1636	179	881	428	1263
82	661	1767	1847	1435	627	1290	1072	1281	999	1246
83	314	1532	1615	1214	555	483	1680	1342	1355	490
84	493	962	1853	1242	1752	1558	1550	636	510	1380
85	1230	168	533	249	1414	547	1350	279	625	932
86	934	752	1184	603	1427	1260	810	1007	851	1776
87	781	195	1210	666	562	1544	1511	185	1271	1155
88	1733	1782	584	16	565	1179	1319	462	596	992
89	208	437	318	1113	1034	363	936	1385	469	1139
90	600	1338	114	1025	47	513	1201	686	391	1221
91	879	247	990	1645	1314	1521	609	43	377	104
92	615	1276	1173	919	1824	1647	1850	825	1224	1102
93	958	147	754	1326	1630	683	1813	1465	1394	227
94	1166	455	526	874	1622	691	387	1693	1086	19
95	163	285	1764	911	708	885	1858	234	337	1554
96	1043	1316	982	1548	582	375	706	51	1186	1818
97	282	1330	1625	262	1452	986	86	1053	399	1539
98	200	1408	446	1875	1302	95	174	1257	1376	1147
99	53	1535	1401	380	240	1504	955	1523	843	794

POWER RESIDUES

	0	1	2	3	4	5	6	7	8	9
50	664	226	1356	620	1841	1651	511	1187	1485	1394
51	848	1330	464	905	1672	637	64	384	425	671
52	268	1608	253	1518	1592	157	942	15	90	540
53	1361	650	142	852	1354	608	1769	1219	1677	667
54	244	1464	1268	92	552	1433	1082	855	1372	716
55	538	1349	578	1589	139	834	1246	1839	1639	439
56	755	772	874	1486	1400	884	1546	1760	1165	1353
57	602	1733	1003	381	407	563	1499	1478	1352	596
58	1697	787	964	147	882	1534	1688	733	640	82
59	492	1073	801	1048	651	148	888	1570	25	150
60	900	1642	457	863	1420	1004	387	443	779	916
61	1738	1033	561	1487	1406	920	1762	1177	1425	1034
62	567	1523	1622	337	143	858	1390	824	1186	1479
63	1358	632	34	204	1224	1707	847	1324	428	689
64	376	377	383	419	635	52	312	1872	1837	1627
65	367	323	59	354	245	1470	1304	308	1848	1693
66	763	820	1162	1335	494	1085	873	1480	1364	668
67	250	1500	1484	1388	812	1114	1047	645	112	672
68	274	1644	469	935	1852	1717	907	1684	709	496
69	1097	945	33	198	1188	1491	1430	1064	747	724
70	586	1637	427	683	340	161	966	159	954	87
71	522	1253	2	12	72	432	713	520	1241	1809
72	1459	1238	1791	1351	590	1661	571	1547	1766	1201
73	1569	19	114	684	346	197	1182	1455	1214	1647
74	487	1043	621	1847	1687	727	604	1745	1075	813
75	1120	1083	861	1408	932	1834	1609	259	1554	1808
76	1453	1202	1575	55	330	101	606	1757	1147	1245
77	1833	1603	223	1338	512	1193	1521	1610	265	1590
78	145	870	1462	1256	20	120	720	562	1493	1442
79	1136	1179	1437	1106	999	357	263	1578	73	438
80	749	736	658	190	1140	1203	1581	91	546	1397
81	866	1438	1112	1035	573	1559	1838	1633	403	539
82	1355	614	1805	1435	1094	927	1804	1429	1058	711
83	508	1169	1377	746	718	550	1421	1010	423	659
84	196	1176	1419	998	351	227	1362	656	178	1068
85	771	868	1450	1184	1467	1286	200	1200	1563	1862
86	1777	1267	86	516	1217	1665	595	1691	751	748
87	730	622	1853	1723	943	21	126	756	778	910
88	1702	817	1144	1227	1725	955	93	558	1469	1298
89	272	1632	397	503	1139	1197	1545	1754	1129	1137
90	1185	1473	1322	416	617	1823	1543	1742	1057	705
91	472	953	81	486	1037	585	1631	391	467	923
92	1780	1285	194	1164	1347	566	1517	1586	121	726
93	598	1709	859	1396	860	1402	896	1618	313	1878
94	1873	1843	1663	583	1619	319	35	210	1260	44
95	264	1584	109	654	166	996	339	155	930	1822
96	1537	1706	841	1288	212	1272	116	696	418	629
97	16	96	576	1577	67	402	533	1319	398	509
98	1175	1413	962	135	810	1102	975	213	1278	152
99	912	1714	889	1576	61	366	317	23	138	828

P = 1879

INDICES

	0	1	2	3	4	5	6	7	8	9
100	216	332	1124	572	605	1501	1605	271	1134	1720
101	837	1790	68	1749	321	488	1542	245	1691	1873
102	1871	1564	1218	411	1486	475	1188	1472	1107	291
103	441	1449	1575	611	619	813	303	914	23	1432
104	1429	416	403	741	1422	1494	275	676	593	1253
105	307	60	342	133	351	1566	496	908	828	1600
106	324	1367	1820	1118	697	347	1688	1613	849	45
107	1164	84	66	591	1004	748	1262	1289	1531	1341
108	1241	1379	546	751	1006	665	1154	1178	436	1384
109	1024	1220	1520	1275	824	1325	226	690	284	233
110	1547	1817	985	1407	1256	379	793	1500	1789	244
111	410	290	812	415	675	132	1599	346	83	1288
112	750	1383	1324	1816	1499	414	1287	413	1807	898
113	1739	1808	1637	1772	1332	205	790	899	180	894
114	804	106	1438	1740	882	423	1526	768	1009	1809
115	429	126	1684	1868	1079	1638	1264	1235	1016	1725
116	1038	1773	662	1488	923	568	1655	1333	1768	831
117	1627	426	1412	206	1848	980	841	617	1162	791
118	1436	1160	736	28	853	900	628	507	694	1297
119	1578	181	1291	775	267	1672	1642	895	1073	477
120	857	729	761	805	1282	396	264	1618	1458	107
121	1000	1608	1478	1278	738	1439	1247	864	1129	537
122	1778	1741	315	1786	634	14	102	883	1533	1470
123	1116	231	203	424	1616	1190	1082	154	721	1527
124	1215	718	1454	1192	1583	769	556	1570	192	1175
125	30	1010	484	711	257	419	783	1810	1681	1442
126	948	1309	1843	430	1343	1760	329	861	542	127
127	1356	1474	965	1705	1227	1685	491	1509	988	1084
128	1300	1869	494	1518	1805	921	855	1080	963	1663
129	1389	1068	197	1639	1854	117	4	1150	889	1265
130	1243	1491	1306	33	656	1236	1753	1109	1665	1031
131	407	1017	1559	1864	88	156	1514	1726	1551	977
132	310	1826	902	1039	637	138	1020	1483	1212	1774
133	511	453	1051	1747	1251	663	1381	1233	773	1468
134	1758	1489	1231	293	1391	1076	37	924	169	551
135	1055	723	578	569	534	820	502	1649	630	1656
136	250	530	846	1802	668	1334	1415	1713	1445	220
137	40	1769	548	295	1064	1361	1832	832	1351	443
138	1070	1182	467	1628	280	1603	401	1529	673	427
139	626	313	1679	1852	509	1413	933	809	1209	1270
140	564	207	935	113	390	1313	614	1849	753	1393
141	1621	162	1857	981	1185	1451	199	173	1400	842
142	604	836	1541	1217	1106	618	1428	274	341	827
143	696	1163	1261	545	435	823	1546	792	811	82
144	1498	1738	789	1437	1008	1078	1037	1654	1411	1161
145	852	1577	1641	760	1457	737	1777	101	202	720
146	1582	29	782	1842	541	1226	1299	854	196	888
147	655	406	1513	901	1211	1250	1757	36	577	629
148	667	39	1831	466	672	508	563	613	1856	1399
149	1105	695	1545	788	1410	1456	1581	1298	1512	576

POWER RESIDUES

	0	1	2	3	4	5	6	7	8	9
100	1210	1623	343	179	1074	807	1084	867	1444	1148
101	1251	1869	1819	1519	1598	193	1158	1311	350	221
102	1326	440	761	808	1090	903	1660	565	1511	1550
103	1784	1309	338	149	894	1606	241	1446	1160	1323
104	422	653	160	960	123	738	670	262	1572	37
105	222	1332	476	977	225	1350	584	1625	355	251
106	1506	1520	1604	229	1374	728	610	1781	1291	230
107	1380	764	826	1198	1551	1790	1345	554	1445	1154
108	1287	206	1236	1779	1279	158	948	51	306	1836
109	1621	331	107	642	94	564	1505	1514	1568	13
110	78	468	929	1816	1501	1490	1424	1028	531	1307
111	326	77	462	893	1600	205	1230	1743	1063	741
112	688	370	341	167	1002	375	371	347	203	1218
113	1671	631	28	168	1008	411	587	1643	463	899
114	1636	421	647	124	744	706	478	989	297	1782
115	1297	266	1596	181	1086	879	1516	1580	85	510
116	1181	1449	1178	1431	1070	783	940	3	18	108
117	648	130	780	922	1774	1249	1857	1747	1087	885
118	1552	1796	1381	770	862	1414	968	171	1026	519
119	1235	1773	1243	1821	1531	1670	625	1871	1831	1591
120	151	906	1678	673	280	1680	685	352	233	1398
121	872	1474	1328	452	833	1240	1803	1423	1022	495
122	1091	909	1696	781	928	1810	1465	1274	128	768
123	850	1342	536	1337	506	1157	1305	314	5	30
124	180	1080	843	1300	284	1704	829	1216	1659	559
125	1475	1334	488	1049	657	184	1104	987	285	1710
126	865	1432	1076	819	1156	1299	278	1668	613	1799
127	1399	878	1510	1544	1748	1093	921	1768	1213	1641
128	451	827	1204	1587	127	762	814	1126	1119	1077
129	825	1192	1515	1574	49	294	1764	1189	1497	1466
130	1280	164	984	267	1602	217	1302	296	1776	1261
131	50	300	1800	1405	914	1726	961	129	774	886
132	1558	1832	1597	187	1122	1095	933	1840	1645	475
133	971	189	1134	1167	1365	674	286	1716	901	1648
134	493	1079	837	1264	68	408	569	1535	1694	769
135	856	1378	752	754	766	838	1270	104	624	1865
136	1795	1375	734	646	118	708	490	1061	729	616
137	1817	1507	1526	1640	445	791	988	291	1746	1081
138	849	1336	500	1121	1089	897	1624	349	215	1290
139	224	1344	548	1409	938	1870	1825	1555	1814	1489
140	1418	992	315	11	66	396	497	1103	981	249
141	1494	1448	1172	1395	854	1366	680	322	53	318
142	29	174	1044	627	4	24	144	864	1426	1040
143	603	1739	1039	597	1703	823	1180	1443	1142	1215
144	1653	523	1259	38	228	1368	692	394	485	1031
145	549	1415	974	207	1242	1815	1495	1454	1208	1611
146	271	1626	361	287	1722	937	1864	1789	1339	518
147	1229	1737	1027	525	1271	110	660	202	1212	1635
148	415	611	1787	1327	446	797	1024	507	1163	1341
149	530	1301	290	1740	1045	633	40	240	1440	1124

P = 1879

INDICES

	0	1	2	3	4	5	6	7	8	9
150	671	1104	1580	1579	186	1096	1060	1371	187	182
151	1272	1028	1589	56	1097	1292	1156	926	523	1013
152	1061	776	1734	621	119	1592	1372	268	1783	79
153	448	1194	188	1673	585	1347	63	960	183	1643
154	17	93	1562	906	1273	896	566	727	152	1703
155	1029	1074	1180	171	758	1397	1590	478	1320	815
156	6	480	57	858	463	298	1877	1585	1098	730
157	597	1596	1048	149	1293	762	993	973	797	372
158	1157	806	209	368	951	356	927	1283	438	553
159	779	1199	524	397	319	305	1152	1322	1014	265
160	1114	327	1304	771	1062	1619	1035	1829	521	756
161	777	1459	364	212	1717	11	1735	108	937	944
162	1696	1090	622	1001	1386	1057	1461	649	120	1609
163	470	916	891	817	1593	1479	1140	701	97	558
164	1373	1279	601	1137	681	1328	269	739	1339	130
165	124	505	1784	1440	115	451	1711	111	80	1248
166	1026	725	366	942	449	865	48	25	1267	8
167	1195	1130	514	142	176	1572	189	538	1202	1795
168	1205	1632	1674	1779	687	1861	76	744	586	1742
169	392	867	384	659	1348	316	1222	580	214	301
170	64	1787	880	1434	1245	482	961	635	248	931
171	1259	194	184	15	991	362	1337	685	1644	103
172	1646	146	1464	873	18	884	1315	50	261	1538
173	94	1534	1522	571	1719	487	1563	1471	610	1431
174	1493	59	907	1117	44	747	1378	1177	1274	232
175	378	289	345	1815	897	204	105	767	1867	1724
176	567	425	616	27	1296	1671	728	1617	1277	536
177	13	230	153	1191	1174	418	1308	860	1704	1083
178	920	1067	1149	32	1030	155	1825	1482	1746	1467
179	1075	722	1648	1801	219	1360	1181	1528	1851	1269
180	1312	161	172	1216	826	822	1737	1653	759	719
181	1225	405	35	465	1398	1455	1103	1370	55	1012
182	1591	1193	959	905	1702	1396	479	1584	148	371
183	355	1198	1321	770	755	10	1089	648	816	557
184	1327	504	110	941	7	1571	1631	743	658	300
185	481	193	684	872	1537	486	58	1176	1814	1723
186	1670	229	859	31	1466	1359	160	1652	464	1011
187	1395	1197	647	940	299	485	228	1651	939	

POWER RESIDUES

	0	1	2	3	4	5	6	7	8	9
150	1107	1005	393	479	995	333	119	714	526	1277
151	146	876	1498	1472	1316	380	401	527	1283	182
152	1092	915	1732	997	345	191	1146	1239	1797	1387
153	806	1078	831	1228	1731	991	309	1854	1729	979
154	237	1422	1016	459	875	1492	1436	1100	963	141
155	846	1318	392	473	959	117	702	454	845	1312
156	356	257	1542	1736	1021	489	1055	693	400	521
157	1247	1845	1675	655	172	1032	555	1451	1190	1503
158	1502	1496	1460	1244	1827	1567	7	42	252	1512
159	1556	1820	1525	1634	409	575	1571	31	186	1116
160	1059	717	544	1385	794	1006	399	515	1211	1629
161	379	395	491	1067	765	832	1234	1767	1207	1605
162	235	1410	944	27	162	972	195	1170	1383	782
163	934	1846	1681	691	388	449	815	1132	1155	1293
164	242	1452	1196	1539	1718	913	1720	925	1792	1357
165	626	1877	1867	1807	1447	1166	1359	638	70	420
166	641	88	528	1289	218	1308	332	113	678	310
167	1860	1765	1195	1533	1682	697	424	665	232	1392
168	836	1258	32	192	1152	1275	134	804	1066	759
169	796	1018	471	947	45	270	1620	325	71	426
170	677	304	1824	1549	1778	1273	122	732	634	46
171	276	1656	541	1367	686	358	269	1614	289	1734
172	1009	417	623	1859	1759	1159	1317	386	437	743
173	700	442	773	880	1522	1616	301	1806	1441	1130
174	1143	1221	1689	739	676	298	1788	1333	482	1013
175	441	767	844	1306	320	41	246	1476	1340	524
176	1265	74	444	785	952	75	450	821	1168	1371
177	710	502	1133	1161	1329	458	869	1456	1220	1683
178	703	460	881	1528	1652	517	1223	1701	811	1108
179	1011	429	695	412	593	1679	679	316	17	102
180	612	1793	1363	662	214	1284	188	1128	1131	1149
181	1257	26	156	936	1858	1753	1123	1101	969	177
182	1062	735	652	154	924	1786	1321	410	581	1607
183	247	1482	1376	740	682	334	125	750	742	694
184	406	557	1463	1262	56	336	137	822	1174	1407
185	926	1798	1393	842	1294	248	1488	1412	956	99
186	594	1685	715	532	1313	362	293	1758	1153	1281
187	170	1020	483	1019	477	983	261	1566		

P = 1889

INDICES

	0	1	2	3	4	5	6	7	8	9
0		0	1684	1	1480	188	1685	13	1276	2
1	1872	1093	1481	862	1697	189	1072	992	1686	1125
2	1668	14	889	1598	1277	376	658	3	1493	1374
3	1873	649	868	1094	788	201	1482	1635	921	863
4	1464	1439	1698	1204	685	190	1394	1370	1073	26
5	172	993	454	1531	1687	1281	1289	1126	1170	76
6	1669	1035	445	15	664	1050	890	313	584	1599
7	1885	1490	1278	1232	1431	377	717	1106	659	624
8	1260	4	1235	70	1494	1180	1000	1375	481	710
9	1874	875	1190	650	1166	1313	869	1213	1710	1095
10	1856	748	789	1347	250	202	1327	1837	1483	1434
11	1077	1636	1085	1764	922	1786	966	864	1760	1005
12	1465	298	831	1440	241	564	1699	883	460	1205
13	846	528	686	1138	109	191	380	1565	1395	1317
14	1681	1371	1286	67	1074	1562	1028	27	1227	211
15	173	569	513	994	902	837	455	1539	420	1532
16	1056	1611	1688	720	1031	1282	1754	305	1290	1724
17	976	1127	796	604	1171	389	277	77	506	167
18	1670	1584	671	1036	986	1823	446	197	962	16
19	1109	30	665	1455	1009	1051	1506	20	891	764
20	1652	314	544	1387	585	1627	1143	1600	46	330
21	1886	1870	1123	1491	1633	1392	1279	662	1230	1233
22	873	1854	1432	1758	881	378	1560	900	718	794
23	1582	1107	762	44	660	1558	1556	625	801	322
24	1261	1475	94	5	627	214	1236	99	37	71
25	360	1617	1495	803	679	1181	256	917	1001	1648
26	642	1376	324	116	482	1719	934	711	1793	728
27	1875	1263	176	876	1361	1469	1191	159	1113	651
28	1477	646	1167	1177	1082	1314	1751	1452	870	96
29	1358	1214	824	1675	1711	264	1023	1096	7	572
30	1857	1217	365	749	309	1223	790	629	698	1348
31	633	857	251	352	1335	203	216	1065	1328	579
32	852	1838	1407	229	1484	1238	516	1435	827	1383
33	1078	1416	1550	1637	101	501	1086	1341	1520	1765
34	772	1742	923	39	592	1787	400	1658	967	1830
35	185	865	73	997	1761	1678	302	1006	1851	34
36	1466	362	1380	299	467	1420	832	555	782	1441
37	1619	1544	242	145	1881	565	758	348	1700	1497
38	905	884	1714	470	461	1294	1251	1206	805	1101
39	847	702	1302	529	1704	812	687	681	560	1139
40	1448	778	110	1511	340	192	1183	840	381	267
41	1423	1566	939	89	1396	258	1730	1318	126	955
42	1682	1091	1666	1372	919	1368	1287	1048	1429	68
43	1188	746	1075	1003	458	1563	1026	835	1029	602
44	669	28	1650	328	1228	898	1554	212	677	114
45	174	644	1356	570	696	1063	514	499	590	995
46	1378	1542	903	1099	558	838	1728	1366	456	326
47	1354	1540	1352	409	421	1501	597	1533	118	411
48	1057	609	1271	1612	1778	1401	1689	484	423	721
49	10	785	1032	478	1783	1283	1721	1503	1755	357

POWER RESIDUES

	0	1	2	3	4	5	6	7	8	9
0	1	3	9	27	81	243	729	298	894	793
1	490	1470	632	7	21	63	189	567	1701	1325
2	197	591	1773	1541	845	646	49	147	441	1323
3	191	573	1719	1379	359	1077	1342	248	744	343
4	1029	1198	1705	1337	233	699	208	624	1872	1838
5	1736	1430	512	1536	830	601	1803	1631	1115	1456
6	590	1770	1532	818	565	1695	1307	143	429	1287
7	83	249	747	352	1056	1279	59	177	531	1593
8	1001	1114	1453	581	1743	1451	575	1725	1397	413
9	1239	1828	1706	1340	242	726	289	867	712	247
10	741	334	1002	1117	1462	608	1824	1694	1304	134
11	402	1206	1729	1409	449	1347	263	789	478	1434
12	524	1572	938	925	886	769	418	1254	1873	1841
13	1745	1457	593	1779	1559	899	808	535	1605	1037
14	1222	1777	1553	881	754	373	1119	1468	626	1878
15	1856	1790	1592	998	1105	1426	500	1500	722	277
16	831	604	1812	1658	1196	1699	1319	179	537	1611
17	1055	1276	50	150	450	1350	272	816	559	1677
18	1253	1870	1832	1718	1376	350	1050	1261	5	15
19	45	135	405	1215	1756	1490	692	187	561	1683
20	1271	35	105	315	945	946	949	958	985	1066
21	1309	149	447	1341	245	735	316	948	955	976
22	1039	1228	1795	1607	1043	1240	1831	1715	1367	323
23	969	1018	1165	1606	1040	1231	1804	1634	1124	1483
24	671	124	372	1116	1459	599	1797	1613	1061	1294
25	104	312	936	919	868	715	256	768	415	1245
26	1846	1760	1502	728	295	885	766	409	1227	1792
27	1598	1016	1159	1588	986	1069	1318	176	528	1584
28	974	1033	1210	1741	1445	557	1671	1235	1816	1670
29	1232	1807	1643	1151	1564	914	853	670	121	363
30	1089	1378	356	1068	1315	167	501	1503	731	304
31	912	847	652	67	201	603	1809	1649	1169	1618
32	1076	1339	239	717	262	786	469	1407	443	1329
33	209	627	1881	1865	1817	1673	1241	1834	1724	1394
34	404	1212	1747	1463	611	1833	1721	1385	377	1131
35	1504	734	313	939	928	895	796	499	1497	713
36	250	750	361	1083	1360	302	906	829	598	1794
37	1604	1034	1213	1750	1472	638	25	75	225	675
38	136	408	1224	1783	1571	935	916	859	688	175
39	525	1575	947	952	967	1012	1147	1552	878	745
40	346	1038	1225	1786	1580	962	997	1102	1417	473
41	1419	479	1437	533	1599	1019	1168	1615	1067	1312
42	158	474	1422	488	1464	614	1842	1748	1466	620
43	1860	1802	1628	1106	1429	509	1527	803	520	1560
44	902	817	562	1686	1280	62	186	558	1674	1244
45	1843	1751	1475	647	52	156	468	1404	434	1302
46	128	384	1152	1567	923	880	751	364	1092	1387
47	383	1149	1558	896	799	508	1524	794	493	1479
48	659	88	264	792	487	1461	605	1815	1667	1223
49	1780	1562	908	835	616	1848	1766	1520	782	457

P = 1889

INDICES

	0	1	2	3	4	5	6	7	8	9
50	156	306	1413	1848	1291	936	599	1725	475	435
51	977	1245	52	1128	713	1535	797	575	1444	605
52	438	1459	1172	1795	120	390	1800	1641	278	1308
53	1515	78	730	413	507	137	1589	168	524	1119
54	1671	1877	1059	1585	1860	1622	672	980	1157	1037
55	1265	611	987	637	1843	1824	909	285	447	178
56	1273	198	442	707	963	64	973	17	878	1614
57	1110	1220	1547	31	1248	86	666	1363	1780	1456
58	1154	83	1010	736	620	1052	1471	1403	1507	1774
59	60	21	819	132	892	1193	1691	765	368	245
60	1653	55	1013	315	161	486	545	1527	105	1388
61	1019	344	586	1115	425	1628	494	1864	1144	1811
62	429	1601	653	723	47	752	148	331	1131	739
63	1887	1479	12	1871	861	1071	1124	888	375	1492
64	648	787	1634	1463	1203	1393	25	453	1280	1169
65	1034	663	312	1884	1231	716	623	1234	1179	480
66	874	1165	1212	1855	1346	1326	1433	1084	1785	1759
67	297	240	882	845	1137	379	1316	1285	1561	1226
68	568	901	1538	1055	719	1753	1723	795	388	505
69	1583	985	196	1108	1454	1505	763	543	1626	45
70	1869	1632	661	872	1757	1559	793	761	1557	800
71	1474	626	98	359	802	255	1647	323	1718	1792
72	1262	1360	158	1476	1176	1750	95	823	263	6
73	1216	308	628	632	351	215	578	1406	1237	826
74	1415	100	1340	771	38	399	1829	72	1677	1850
75	361	466	554	1618	144	757	1496	1713	1293	804
76	701	1703	680	1447	1510	1182	266	938	257	125
77	1090	918	1047	1187	1002	1025	601	1649	897	676
78	643	695	498	1377	1098	1727	325	1351	1500	117
79	608	1777	483	9	477	1720	356	1412	935	474
80	1244	712	574	437	1794	1799	1307	729	136	523
81	1876	1859	979	1264	636	908	177	441	63	877
82	1219	1247	1362	1153	735	1470	1773	818	1192	367
83	54	160	1526	1018	1114	493	1810	652	751	1130
84	1478	860	887	647	1462	24	1168	311	715	1178
85	1164	1345	1083	296	844	1315	1225	1537	1752	387
86	984	1453	542	1868	871	792	799	97	254	1717
87	1359	1175	822	1215	631	577	825	1339	398	1676
88	465	143	1712	700	1446	265	124	1046	1024	896
89	694	1097	1350	607	8	355	473	573	1798	135
90	1858	635	440	1218	1152	1772	366	1525	492	750
91	859	1461	310	1163	295	1224	386	541	791	253
92	1174	630	1338	464	699	123	895	1349	354	1797
93	634	1151	1524	858	1162	385	252	1337	122	353
94	1150	1161	1336	1149	1148	204	205	392	217	206
95	1297	1066	393	1196	1329	218	1802	580	207	1578
96	853	1298	405	1839	1067	1643	1408	394	1574	230
97	1197	1735	1485	1330	280	1239	219	1254	517	1803
98	1694	1436	581	1310	828	208	274	1384	1579	914
99	1079	854	1517	1417	1299	952	1551	406	153	1638

POWER RESIDUES

	0	1	2	3	4	5	6	7	8	9
50	1371	335	1005	1126	1489	689	178	534	1602	1028
51	1195	1696	1310	152	456	1368	326	978	1045	1246
52	1849	1769	1529	809	538	1614	1064	1303	131	393
53	1179	1648	1166	1609	1049	1258	1885	1877	1853	1781
54	1565	917	862	697	202	606	1818	1676	1250	1861
55	1805	1637	1133	1510	752	367	1101	1414	464	1392
56	398	1194	1693	1301	125	375	1125	1486	680	151
57	453	1359	299	897	802	517	1551	875	736	319
58	957	982	1057	1282	68	204	612	1836	1730	1412
59	458	1374	344	1032	1207	1732	1418	476	1428	506
60	1518	776	439	1317	173	519	1557	893	790	481
61	1443	551	1653	1181	1654	1184	1663	1211	1744	1454
62	584	1752	1478	656	79	237	711	244	732	307
63	921	874	733	310	930	901	814	553	1659	1199
64	1708	1346	260	780	451	1353	281	843	640	31
65	93	279	837	622	1866	1820	1682	1268	26	78
66	234	702	217	651	64	192	576	1728	1406	440
67	1320	182	546	1638	1136	1519	779	448	1344	254
68	762	397	1191	1684	1274	44	132	396	1188	1675
69	1247	1852	1778	1556	890	781	454	1362	308	924
70	883	760	391	1173	1630	1112	1447	563	1689	1289
71	89	267	801	514	1542	848	655	76	228	684
72	163	489	1467	623	1869	1829	1709	1349	269	807
73	532	1596	1010	1141	1534	824	583	1749	1469	629
74	1887	1883	1871	1835	1727	1403	431	1293	101	303
75	909	838	625	1875	1847	1763	1511	755	376	1128
76	1495	707	232	696	199	597	1791	1595	1007	1132
77	1507	743	340	1020	1171	1624	1094	1393	401	1203
78	1720	1382	368	1104	1423	491	1473	641	34	102
79	306	918	865	706	229	687	172	516	1548	866
80	709	238	714	253	759	388	1164	1603	1031	1204
81	1723	1391	395	1185	1666	1220	1771	1535	827	592
82	1776	1550	872	727	292	876	739	328	984	1063
83	1300	122	366	1098	1405	437	1311	155	465	1395
84	407	1221	1774	1544	854	673	130	390	1170	1621
85	1085	1366	320	960	991	1084	1363	311	933	910
86	841	634	13	39	117	351	1053	1270	32	96
87	288	864	703	220	660	91	273	819	568	1704
88	1334	224	672	127	381	1143	1540	842	637	22
89	66	198	594	1782	1568	926	889	778	445	1335
90	227	681	154	462	1386	380	1140	1531	815	556
91	1668	1226	1789	1589	989	1078	1345	257	771	424
92	1272	38	114	342	1026	1189	1678	1256	1879	1859
93	1799	1619	1079	1348	266	798	505	1515	767	412
94	1236	1819	1679	1259	1888	1886	1880	1862	1808	1646
95	1160	1591	995	1096	1399	419	1257	1882	1868	1826
96	1700	1322	188	564	1692	1298	116	348	1044	1243
97	1840	1742	1448	566	1698	1316	170	510	1530	812
98	547	1641	1145	1546	860	691	184	552	1656	1190
99	1681	1265	17	51	153	459	1377	353	1059	1288

P = 1889

INDICES

	0	1	2	3	4	5	6	7	8	9
100	1840	80	102	1068	1209	502	1644	768	1087	1409
101	732	1342	395	1769	1521	1575	271	1766	231	415
102	773	1198	1041	1743	1736	1815	924	1486	509	40
103	1331	808	593	281	371	1788	1240	139	401	220
104	234	1659	1255	224	968	518	1591	1831	1804	534
105	186	1695	1596	866	1437	170	74	582	1104	998
106	1311	248	1762	829	526	1679	209	418	303	275
107	1821	1007	1385	1121	1852	1580	320	35	915	932
108	1467	1080	1673	363	855	850	1381	1518	1656	300
109	1418	1879	468	1300	776	1421	953	1427	833	1552
110	1061	556	407	1269	783	154	433	1442	1639	1587
111	1620	1841	705	1545	81	58	243	103	1862	146
112	1069	1201	1882	1210	238	566	503	1624	759	1645
113	1748	349	769	552	1701	1088	674	1498	1410	1305
114	906	733	1016	885	1343	982	1715	396	1044	471
115	1770	293	462	1522	1159	1295	1576	1572	1252	272
116	950	1207	1767	1039	806	232	532	1102	416	318
117	848	774	1267	703	1199	1746	1303	1042	1570	530
118	1744	613	1705	1737	615	813	1816	1605	688	925
119	989	682	1487	1707	561	510	164	1140	41	639
120	1449	1332	1739	779	809	1663	111	594	1845	1512
121	282	617	341	372	1323	193	1789	1826	1184	1241
122	815	841	140	489	382	402	911	268	221	1818
123	1424	235	290	1567	1660	287	940	1256	1607	90
124	225	336	1397	969	449	259	519	690	1731	1592
125	548	1319	1832	180	127	1805	927	956	535	943
126	1683	187	1275	1092	1696	991	1667	1597	657	1373
127	867	200	920	1438	684	1369	171	1530	1288	75
128	444	1049	583	1489	1430	1105	1259	69	999	709
129	1189	1312	1709	747	249	1836	1076	1763	965	1004
130	830	563	459	527	108	1564	1680	66	1027	210
131	512	836	419	1610	1030	304	975	603	276	166
132	670	1822	961	29	1008	19	1651	1386	1142	329
133	1122	1391	1229	1853	880	899	1581	43	1555	321
134	93	213	36	1616	678	916	641	115	933	727
135	175	1468	1112	645	1081	1451	1357	1674	1022	571
136	364	1222	697	856	1334	1064	851	228	515	1382
137	1549	500	1519	1741	591	1657	184	996	301	33
138	1379	1419	781	1543	1880	347	904	469	1250	1100
139	1301	811	559	777	339	839	1422	88	1729	954
140	1665	1367	1428	745	457	834	668	327	1553	113
141	1355	1062	589	1541	557	1365	1353	408	596	410
142	1270	1400	422	784	1782	1502	155	1847	598	434
143	51	1534	1443	1458	119	1640	1514	412	1588	1118
144	1058	1621	1156	610	1842	284	1272	706	972	1613
145	1546	85	1779	82	619	1402	59	131	1690	244
146	1012	485	104	343	424	1863	428	722	147	738
147	11	1070	374	786	1202	452	1033	1883	622	479
148	1211	1325	1784	239	1136	1284	567	1054	1722	504
149	195	1504	1625	1631	1756	760	1473	358	1646	1791

POWER RESIDUES

	0	1	2	3	4	5	6	7	8	9
100	86	258	774	433	1299	119	357	1071	1324	194
101	582	1746	1460	602	1806	1640	1142	1537	833	610
102	1830	1712	1358	296	888	775	436	1308	146	438
103	1314	164	492	1476	650	61	183	549	1647	1163
104	1600	1022	1177	1642	1148	1555	887	772	427	1281
105	65	195	585	1755	1487	683	160	480	1440	542
106	1626	1100	1411	455	1365	317	951	964	1003	1120
107	1471	635	16	48	144	432	1296	110	330	990
108	1081	1354	284	852	667	112	336	1008	1135	1516
109	770	421	1263	11	33	99	297	891	784	463
110	1389	389	1167	1612	1058	1285	77	231	693	190
111	570	1710	1352	278	834	613	1839	1739	1439	539
112	1617	1073	1330	212	636	19	57	171	513	1539
113	839	628	1884	1874	1844	1754	1484	674	133	399
114	1197	1702	1328	206	618	1854	1784	1574	944	943
115	940	931	904	823	580	1740	1442	548	1644	1154
116	1573	941	934	913	850	661	94	282	846	649
117	58	174	522	1566	920	871	724	283	849	658
118	85	255	765	406	1218	1765	1517	773	430	1290
119	92	276	828	595	1785	1577	953	970	1021	1174
120	1633	1121	1474	644	43	129	387	1161	1594	1004
121	1123	1480	662	97	291	873	730	301	903	820
122	571	1713	1361	305	915	856	679	148	444	1332
123	218	654	73	219	657	82	246	738	325	975
124	1036	1219	1768	1526	800	511	1533	821	574	1722
125	1388	386	1158	1585	977	1042	1237	1822	1688	1286
126	80	240	720	271	813	550	1650	1172	1627	1103
127	1420	482	1446	560	1680	1262	8	24	72	216
128	648	55	165	495	1485	677	142	426	1278	56
129	168	504	1512	758	385	1155	1576	950	961	994
130	1093	1390	392	1176	1639	1139	1528	806	529	1587
131	983	1060	1291	95	285	855	676	139	417	1251
132	1864	1814	1664	1214	1753	1481	665	106	318	954
133	973	1030	1201	1714	1364	314	942	937	922	877
134	742	337	1011	1144	1543	851	664	103	309	927
135	892	787	472	1416	470	1410	452	1356	290	870
136	721	274	822	577	1731	1415	467	1401	425	1275
137	47	141	423	1269	29	87	261	783	460	1380
138	362	1086	1369	329	987	1072	1327	203	609	1827
139	1703	1331	215	645	46	138	414	1242	1837	1733
140	1421	485	1455	587	1761	1505	737	322	966	1009
141	1138	1525	797	502	1506	740	331	993	1090	1381
142	365	1095	1396	410	1230	1801	1625	1097	1402	428
143	1284	74	222	666	109	327	981	1054	1273	41
144	123	369	1107	1432	518	1554	884	763	400	1200
145	1711	1355	287	861	694	193	579	1737	1433	521
146	1563	911	844	643	40	120	360	1080	1351	275
147	825	586	1758	1496	710	241	723	280	840	631
148	4	12	36	108	324	972	1027	1192	1687	1283
149	71	213	639	28	84	252	756	379	1137	1522

P = 1889

INDICES

	0	1	2	3	4	5	6	7	8	9
150	157	1749	262	307	350	1405	1414	770	1828	1849
151	553	756	1292	1702	1509	937	1089	1186	600	675
152	497	1726	1499	1776	476	1411	1243	436	1306	522
153	978	907	62	1246	734	817	53	1017	1809	1129
154	886	23	714	1344	843	1536	983	1867	798	1716
155	821	576	397	142	1445	1045	693	606	472	134
156	439	1771	491	1460	294	540	1173	463	894	1796
157	1523	384	121	1160	1147	391	1296	1195	1801	1577
158	404	1642	1573	1734	279	1253	1693	1309	273	913
159	1516	951	152	79	1208	767	731	1768	270	414
160	1040	1814	508	807	370	138	233	223	1590	533
161	1595	169	1103	247	525	417	1820	1120	319	931
162	1672	849	1655	1878	775	1426	1060	1268	432	1586
163	704	57	1861	1200	237	1623	1747	551	673	1304
164	1015	981	1043	292	1158	1571	949	1038	531	317
165	1266	1745	1569	612	614	1604	988	1706	163	638
166	1738	1662	1844	616	1322	1825	814	488	910	1817
167	289	286	1606	335	448	689	547	179	926	942
168	1274	990	656	199	683	1529	443	1488	1258	708
169	1708	1835	964	562	107	65	511	1609	974	165
170	960	18	1141	1390	879	42	92	1615	640	726
171	1111	1450	1021	1221	1333	227	1548	1740	183	32
172	780	346	1249	810	338	87	1664	744	667	112
173	588	1364	595	1399	1781	1846	50	1457	1513	1117
174	1155	283	971	84	618	130	1011	342	427	737
175	373	451	621	1324	1135	1053	194	1630	1472	1790
176	261	1404	1827	755	1508	1185	496	1775	1242	521
177	61	816	1808	22	842	1866	820	141	692	133
178	490	539	893	383	1146	1194	403	1733	1692	912
179	151	766	269	1813	369	222	1594	246	1819	930
180	1654	1425	431	56	236	550	1014	291	948	316
181	1568	1603	162	1661	1321	487	288	334	546	941
182	655	1528	1257	1834	106	1608	959	1389	91	725
183	1020	226	182	345	337	743	587	1398	49	1116
184	970	129	426	450	1134	1629	260	754	495	520
185	1807	1865	691	538	1145	1732	150	1812	1593	929
186	430	549	947	1602	1320	333	654	1833	958	724
187	181	742	48	128	1133	753	1806	537	149	928
188	946	332	957	741	1132	536	945	740	944	

POWER RESIDUES

	0	1	2	3	4	5	6	7	8	9
150	788	475	1425	497	1491	695	196	588	1764	1514
151	764	403	1209	1738	1436	530	1590	992	1087	1372
152	338	1014	1153	1570	932	907	832	607	1821	1685
153	1277	53	159	477	1431	515	1545	857	682	157
154	471	1413	461	1383	371	1113	1450	572	1716	1370
155	332	996	1099	1408	446	1338	236	708	235	705
156	226	678	145	435	1305	137	411	1233	1810	1652
157	1178	1645	1157	1582	968	1015	1156	1579	959	988
158	1075	1336	230	690	181	543	1629	1109	1438	536
159	1608	1046	1249	1858	1796	1610	1052	1267	23	69
160	207	621	1863	1811	1655	1187	1672	1238	1825	1697
161	1313	161	483	1449	569	1707	1343	251	753	370
162	1110	1441	545	1635	1127	1492	698	205	615	1845
163	1757	1493	701	214	642	37	111	333	999	1108
164	1435	527	1581	965	1006	1129	1498	716	259	777
165	442	1326	200	600	1800	1622	1088	1375	347	1041
166	1234	1813	1661	1205	1726	1400	422	1266	20	60
167	180	540	1620	1082	1357	293	879	748	355	1065
168	1306	140	420	1260	2	6	18	54	162	486
169	1458	596	1788	1586	980	1051	1264	14	42	126
170	378	1134	1513	761	394	1182	1657	1193	1690	1292
171	98	294	882	757	382	1146	1549	869	718	265
172	795	496	1488	686	169	507	1521	785	466	1398
173	416	1248	1855	1787	1583	971	1024	1183	1660	1202
174	1717	1373	341	1023	1180	1651	1175	1636	1130	1501
175	725	286	858	685	166	498	1494	704	223	669
176	118	354	1062	1297	113	339	1017	1162	1597	1013
177	1150	1561	905	826	589	1767	1523	791	484	1452
178	578	1734	1424	494	1482	668	115	345	1035	1216
179	1759	1499	719	268	804	523	1569	929	898	805
180	526	1578	956	979	1048	1255	1876	1850	1772	1538
181	836	619	1857	1793	1601	1025	1186	1669	1229	1798
182	1616	1070	1321	185	555	1665	1217	1762	1508	746
183	349	1047	1252	1867	1823	1691	1295	107	321	963
184	1000	1111	1444	554	1662	1208	1735	1427	503	1509
185	749	358	1074	1333	221	663	100	300	900	811
186	544	1632	1118	1465	617	1851	1775	1547	863	700
187	211	633	10	30	90	270	810	541	1623	1091
188	1384	374	1122	1477	653	70	210	630		

P = 1901

INDICES

	0	1	2	3	4	5	6	7	8	9
0		0	1	979	2	1254	980	466	3	58
1	1255	1808	981	1244	467	333	4	509	59	340
2	1256	1445	1809	1175	982	608	1245	1037	468	356
3	334	722	5	887	510	1720	60	1829	341	323
4	1257	107	1446	1098	1810	1312	1176	1138	983	932
5	609	1488	1246	406	1038	1162	469	1319	357	289
6	335	1483	723	524	6	598	888	1090	511	254
7	1721	867	61	684	1830	1587	342	374	324	1222
8	1258	116	108	728	1447	1763	1099	1335	1811	1410
9	1313	1710	1177	1701	1139	1594	984	967	933	1866
10	610	1619	1489	129	1247	799	407	549	1039	1424
11	1163	908	470	747	1320	529	358	1302	290	975
12	336	1716	1484	1086	724	1862	525	1569	7	177
13	599	1573	889	806	1091	391	512	42	255	845
14	1722	217	868	1152	62	1610	685	11	1831	716
15	1588	1379	343	567	375	76	325	478	1223	1385
16	1259	1641	117	181	109	241	729	1048	1448	588
17	1764	398	1100	93	1336	1074	1812	1268	1411	603
18	1314	1405	1711	562	1178	1183	1702	417	1140	1503
19	1595	703	985	1001	968	1577	934	899	1867	155
20	611	169	1620	822	1490	1361	130	1233	1248	248
21	800	893	408	1846	550	452	1040	1188	1425	1663
22	1164	1753	909	349	471	666	748	810	1321	1201
23	530	1353	359	876	1303	492	291	301	976	1805
24	337	1034	1717	1095	1485	286	1087	1584	725	1707
25	1863	546	526	1083	1570	842	8	73	178	395
26	600	414	1574	819	890	1660	807	489	1092	543
27	392	486	513	789	43	516	256	1775	846	780
28	1723	422	218	792	869	673	1153	573	63	1018
29	1611	46	686	1122	12	1543	1832	945	717	519
30	1589	1564	1380	698	344	837	568	259	376	1108
31	77	1690	326	1145	479	1778	1224	920	1386	264
32	1260	1528	1642	849	118	1852	182	503	110	1604
33	242	783	730	1887	1049	444	1449	736	589	1726
34	1765	630	399	1398	1101	1508	94	425	1337	21
35	1075	381	1813	208	1269	221	1412	54	604	103
36	1315	680	1406	795	1712	38	563	584	1179	165
37	1184	872	1703	1656	418	941	1141	1600	1504	676
38	1596	648	704	1113	986	1628	1002	1156	969	556
39	1578	1684	935	652	900	576	1868	193	156	1785
40	612	1893	170	66	1621	1370	823	1737	1491	708
41	1362	1021	131	755	1234	82	1249	1824	249	1614
42	801	236	894	1196	409	1117	1847	49	551	231
43	453	316	1041	1536	1189	689	1426	1515	1664	658
44	1165	990	1754	1125	910	764	350	1695	472	1747
45	667	15	749	458	811	1064	1322	1632	1202	1546
46	531	367	1354	1880	360	1055	877	1835	1304	1556
47	493	1457	292	1006	302	948	977	464	1806	331
48	338	1173	1035	720	1718	321	1096	1136	1486	1160
49	287	522	1088	865	1585	1220	726	1333	1708	1592

POWER RESIDUES

	0	1	2	3	4	5	6	7	8	9
0	1	2	4	8	16	32	64	128	256	512
1	1024	147	294	588	1176	451	902	1804	1707	1513
2	1125	349	698	1396	891	1782	1663	1425	949	1898
3	1895	1889	1877	1853	1805	1709	1517	1133	365	730
4	1460	1019	137	274	548	1096	291	582	1164	427
5	854	1708	1515	1129	357	714	1428	955	9	18
6	36	72	144	288	576	1152	403	806	1612	1323
7	745	1490	1079	257	514	1028	155	310	620	1240
8	579	1158	415	830	1660	1419	937	1874	1847	1793
9	1685	1469	1037	173	346	692	1384	867	1734	1567
10	1233	565	1130	359	718	1436	971	41	82	164
11	328	656	1312	723	1446	991	81	162	324	648
12	1296	691	1382	863	1726	1551	1201	501	1002	103
13	206	412	824	1648	1395	889	1778	1655	1409	917
14	1834	1767	1633	1365	829	1658	1415	929	1858	1815
15	1729	1557	1213	525	1050	199	398	796	1592	1283
16	665	1330	759	1518	1135	369	738	1476	1051	201
17	402	804	1608	1315	729	1458	1015	129	258	516
18	1032	163	326	652	1304	707	1414	927	1854	1807
19	1713	1525	1149	397	794	1588	1275	649	1298	695
20	1390	879	1758	1615	1329	757	1514	1127	353	706
21	1412	923	1846	1791	1681	1461	1021	141	282	564
22	1128	355	710	1420	939	1878	1855	1809	1717	1533
23	1165	429	858	1716	1531	1161	421	842	1684	1467
24	1033	165	330	660	1320	739	1478	1055	209	418
25	836	1672	1443	985	69	138	276	552	1104	307
26	614	1228	555	1110	319	638	1276	651	1302	703
27	1406	911	1822	1743	1585	1269	637	1274	647	1294
28	687	1374	847	1694	1487	1073	245	490	980	59
29	118	236	472	944	1888	1875	1849	1797	1693	1485
30	1069	237	474	948	1896	1891	1881	1861	1821	1741
31	1581	1261	621	1242	583	1166	431	862	1724	1547
32	1193	485	970	39	78	156	312	624	1248	595
33	1190	479	958	15	30	60	120	240	480	960
34	19	38	76	152	304	608	1216	531	1062	223
35	446	892	1784	1667	1433	965	29	58	116	232
36	464	928	1856	1811	1721	1541	1181	461	922	1844
37	1787	1673	1445	989	77	154	308	616	1232	563
38	1126	351	702	1404	907	1814	1727	1553	1205	509
39	1018	135	270	540	1080	259	518	1036	171	342
40	684	1368	835	1670	1439	977	53	106	212	424
41	848	1696	1491	1081	261	522	1044	187	374	748
42	1496	1091	281	562	1124	347	694	1388	875	1750
43	1599	1297	693	1386	871	1742	1583	1265	629	1258
44	615	1230	559	1118	335	670	1340	779	1558	1215
45	529	1058	215	430	860	1720	1539	1177	453	906
46	1812	1723	1545	1189	477	954	7	14	28	56
47	112	224	448	896	1792	1683	1465	1029	157	314
48	628	1256	611	1222	543	1086	271	542	1084	267
49	534	1068	235	470	940	1880	1859	1817	1733	1565

P = 1901

INDICES

	0	1	2	3	4	5	6	7	8	9
50	1864	127	547	906	527	973	1084	1567	1571	389
51	843	1150	9	1377	74	1383	179	1046	396	1072
52	601	560	415	701	1575	153	820	1231	891	450
53	1661	347	808	1351	490	1803	1093	1582	544	840
54	393	817	487	484	514	778	790	571	44	1541
55	517	696	257	1688	1776	262	847	501	781	442
56	1724	1396	423	379	219	101	793	582	870	939
57	674	1111	1154	1682	574	1783	64	1735	1019	80
58	1612	1194	47	314	687	656	1123	1693	13	1062
59	1544	1878	1833	1455	946	329	718	1134	520	1218
60	1590	904	1565	1148	1381	1070	699	1229	345	1801
61	838	482	569	694	260	440	377	580	1109	1781
62	78	312	1691	1876	327	1216	1146	1227	480	438
63	1779	1874	1225	1872	921	923	1387	276	265	925
64	1261	830	1529	1389	1643	1431	850	278	119	197
65	1853	267	183	1278	504	927	111	742	1605	1263
66	243	1029	784	832	731	160	1888	1531	1050	1328
67	445	1391	1450	1211	737	1645	590	1520	1727	1433
68	1766	1789	631	852	400	1296	1399	280	1102	1650
69	1509	121	95	432	426	199	1338	616	22	1855
70	1076	641	382	269	1814	1471	209	185	1270	1669
71	222	1280	1413	1897	55	506	605	884	104	929
72	1316	595	681	113	1407	964	796	744	1713	174
73	39	1607	564	1638	585	1265	1180	998	166	245
74	1185	663	873	1031	1704	70	1657	786	419	1015
75	942	834	1142	1525	1601	733	1505	205	677	162
76	1597	1625	649	1890	705	1821	1114	1533	987	1744
77	1629	1052	1003	1170	1157	1330	970	1374	557	447
78	1579	775	1685	1393	936	1732	653	1452	901	1798
79	577	1213	1869	827	194	739	157	1208	1786	1647
80	613	1468	1894	592	171	995	67	1522	1622	1741
81	1371	1729	824	1465	1738	1435	1492	1438	709	1768
82	1363	1344	1022	1791	132	1495	756	633	1235	144
83	83	854	1250	1441	1825	402	250	1759	1615	1298
84	802	712	237	1401	895	1842	1197	282	410	1771
85	1118	1104	1848	626	50	1652	552	1366	232	1511
86	454	1552	317	123	1042	1347	1537	97	1190	1130
87	690	434	1427	1025	1516	428	1665	960	659	201
88	1166	1794	991	1340	1755	622	1126	618	911	135
89	765	24	351	1478	1696	1857	473	1498	1748	1078
90	668	915	16	643	750	759	459	384	812	1677
91	1065	271	1323	636	1633	1816	1203	139	1547	1473
92	532	1238	368	211	1355	537	1881	187	361	147
93	1056	1272	878	769	1836	1671	1305	86	1557	224
94	494	1289	1458	1282	293	857	1007	1415	303	28
95	949	1899	978	1253	465	57	1807	1243	332	508
96	339	1444	1174	607	1036	355	721	886	1719	1828
97	322	106	1097	1311	1137	931	1487	405	1161	1318
98	288	1482	523	597	1089	253	866	683	1586	373
99	1221	115	727	1762	1334	1409	1709	1700	1593	966

POWER RESIDUES

	0	1	2	3	4	5	6	7	8	9
50	1229	557	1114	327	654	1308	715	1430	959	17
51	34	68	136	272	544	1088	275	550	1100	299
52	598	1196	491	982	63	126	252	504	1008	115
53	230	460	920	1840	1779	1657	1413	925	1850	1799
54	1697	1493	1085	269	538	1076	251	502	1004	107
55	214	428	856	1712	1523	1145	389	778	1556	1211
56	521	1042	183	366	732	1464	1027	153	306	612
57	1224	547	1094	287	574	1148	395	790	1580	1259
58	617	1234	567	1134	367	734	1468	1035	169	338
59	676	1352	803	1606	1311	721	1442	983	65	130
60	260	520	1040	179	358	716	1432	963	25	50
61	100	200	400	800	1600	1299	697	1394	887	1774
62	1647	1393	885	1770	1639	1377	853	1706	1511	1121
63	341	682	1364	827	1654	1407	913	1826	1751	1601
64	1301	701	1402	903	1806	1711	1521	1141	381	762
65	1524	1147	393	786	1572	1243	585	1170	439	878
66	1756	1611	1321	741	1482	1063	225	450	900	1800
67	1699	1497	1093	285	570	1140	379	758	1516	1131
68	361	722	1444	987	73	146	292	584	1168	435
69	870	1740	1579	1257	613	1226	551	1102	303	606
70	1212	523	1046	191	382	764	1528	1155	409	818
71	1636	1371	841	1682	1463	1025	149	298	596	1192
72	483	966	31	62	124	248	496	992	83	166
73	332	664	1328	755	1510	1119	337	674	1348	795
74	1590	1279	657	1314	727	1454	1007	113	226	452
75	904	1808	1715	1529	1157	413	826	1652	1403	905
76	1810	1719	1537	1173	445	890	1780	1659	1417	933
77	1866	1831	1761	1621	1341	781	1562	1223	545	1090
78	279	558	1116	331	662	1324	747	1494	1087	273
79	546	1092	283	566	1132	363	726	1452	1003	105
80	210	420	840	1680	1459	1017	133	266	532	1064
81	227	454	908	1816	1731	1561	1221	541	1082	263
82	526	1052	203	406	812	1624	1347	793	1586	1271
83	641	1282	663	1326	751	1502	1103	305	610	1220
84	539	1078	255	510	1020	139	278	556	1112	323
85	646	1292	683	1366	831	1662	1423	945	1890	1879
86	1857	1813	1725	1549	1197	493	986	71	142	284
87	568	1136	371	742	1484	1067	233	466	932	1864
88	1827	1753	1605	1309	717	1434	967	33	66	132
89	264	528	1056	211	422	844	1688	1475	1049	197
90	394	788	1576	1251	601	1202	503	1006	111	222
91	444	888	1776	1651	1401	901	1802	1703	1505	1109
92	317	634	1268	635	1270	639	1278	655	1310	719
93	1438	975	49	98	196	392	784	1568	1235	569
94	1138	375	750	1500	1099	297	594	1188	475	950
95	1900	1899	1897	1893	1885	1869	1837	1773	1645	1389
96	877	1754	1607	1313	725	1450	999	97	194	388
97	776	1552	1203	505	1010	119	238	476	952	3
98	6	12	24	48	96	192	384	768	1536	1171
99	441	882	1764	1627	1353	805	1610	1319	737	1474

P = 1901

INDICES

	0	1	2	3	4	5	6	7	8	9
100	1865	1618	128	798	548	1423	907	746	528	1301
101	974	1715	1085	1861	1568	176	1572	805	390	41
102	844	216	1151	1609	10	715	1378	566	75	477
103	1384	1640	180	240	1047	587	397	92	1073	1267
104	602	1404	561	1182	416	1502	702	1000	1576	898
105	154	168	821	1360	1232	247	892	1845	451	1187
106	1662	1752	348	665	809	1200	1352	875	491	300
107	1804	1033	1094	285	1583	1706	545	1082	841	72
108	394	413	818	1659	488	542	485	788	515	1774
109	779	421	791	672	572	1017	45	1121	1542	944
110	518	1563	697	836	258	1107	1689	1144	1777	919
111	263	1527	848	1851	502	1603	782	1886	443	735
112	1725	629	1397	1507	424	20	380	207	220	53
113	102	679	794	37	583	164	871	1655	940	1599
114	675	647	1112	1627	1155	555	1683	651	575	192
115	1784	1892	65	1369	1736	707	1020	754	81	1823
116	1613	235	1195	1116	48	230	315	1535	688	1514
117	657	989	1124	763	1694	1746	14	457	1063	1631
118	1545	366	1879	1054	1834	1555	1456	1005	947	463
119	330	1172	719	320	1135	1159	521	864	1219	1332
120	1591	126	905	972	1566	388	1149	1376	1382	1045
121	1071	559	700	152	1230	449	346	1350	1802	1581
122	839	816	483	777	570	1540	695	1687	261	500
123	441	1395	378	100	581	938	1110	1681	1782	1734
124	79	1193	313	655	1692	1061	1877	1454	328	1133
125	1217	903	1147	1069	1228	1800	481	693	439	579
126	1780	311	1875	1215	1226	437	1873	1871	922	275
127	924	829	1388	1430	277	196	266	1277	926	741
128	1262	1028	831	159	1530	1327	1390	1210	1644	1519
129	1432	1788	851	1295	279	1649	120	431	198	615
130	1854	640	268	1470	184	1668	1279	1896	505	883
131	928	594	112	963	743	173	1606	1637	1264	997
132	244	662	1030	69	785	1014	833	1524	732	204
133	161	1624	1889	1820	1532	1743	1051	1169	1329	1373
134	446	774	1392	1731	1451	1797	1212	826	738	1207
135	1646	1467	591	994	1521	1740	1728	1464	1434	1437
136	1767	1343	1790	1494	632	143	853	1440	401	1758
137	1297	711	1400	1841	281	1770	1103	625	1651	1365
138	1510	1551	122	1346	96	1129	433	1024	427	959
139	200	1793	1339	621	617	134	23	1477	1856	1497
140	1077	914	642	758	383	1676	270	635	1815	138
141	1472	1237	210	536	186	146	1271	768	1670	85
142	223	1288	1281	856	1414	27	1898	1252	56	1242
143	507	1443	606	354	885	1827	105	1310	930	404
144	1317	1481	596	252	682	372	114	1761	1408	1699
145	965	1617	797	1422	745	1300	1714	1860	175	804
146	40	215	1608	714	565	476	1639	239	586	91
147	1266	1403	1181	1501	999	897	167	1359	246	1844
148	1186	1751	664	1199	874	299	1032	284	1705	1081
149	71	412	1658	541	787	1773	420	671	1016	1120

POWER RESIDUES

	0	1	2	3	4	5	6	7	8	9
100	1047	193	386	772	1544	1187	473	946	1892	1883
101	1865	1829	1757	1613	1325	749	1498	1095	289	578
102	1156	411	822	1644	1387	873	1746	1591	1281	661
103	1322	743	1486	1071	241	482	964	27	54	108
104	216	432	864	1728	1555	1209	517	1034	167	334
105	668	1336	771	1542	1183	465	930	1860	1819	1737
106	1573	1245	589	1178	455	910	1820	1739	1577	1253
107	605	1210	519	1038	175	350	700	1400	899	1798
108	1695	1489	1077	253	506	1012	123	246	492	984
109	67	134	268	536	1072	243	486	972	43	86
110	172	344	688	1376	851	1702	1503	1105	309	618
111	1236	571	1142	383	766	1532	1163	425	850	1700
112	1499	1097	293	586	1172	443	886	1772	1643	1385
113	869	1738	1575	1249	597	1194	487	974	47	94
114	188	376	752	1504	1107	313	626	1252	603	1206
115	511	1022	143	286	572	1144	387	774	1548	1195
116	489	978	55	110	220	440	880	1760	1619	1337
117	773	1546	1191	481	962	23	46	92	184	368
118	736	1472	1043	185	370	740	1480	1059	217	434
119	868	1736	1571	1241	581	1162	423	846	1692	1483
120	1065	229	458	916	1832	1763	1625	1349	797	1594
121	1287	673	1346	791	1582	1263	625	1250	599	1198
122	495	990	79	158	316	632	1264	627	1254	607
123	1214	527	1054	207	414	828	1656	1411	921	1842
124	1783	1665	1429	957	13	26	52	104	208	416
125	832	1664	1427	953	5	10	20	40	80	160
126	320	640	1280	659	1318	735	1470	1039	177	354
127	708	1416	931	1862	1823	1745	1589	1277	653	1306
128	711	1422	943	1886	1871	1841	1781	1661	1421	941
129	1882	1863	1825	1749	1597	1293	685	1370	839	1678
130	1455	1009	117	234	468	936	1872	1843	1785	1669
131	1437	973	45	90	180	360	720	1440	979	57
132	114	228	456	912	1824	1747	1593	1285	669	1338
133	775	1550	1199	497	994	87	174	348	696	1392
134	883	1766	1631	1361	821	1642	1383	865	1730	1559
135	1217	533	1066	231	462	924	1848	1795	1689	1477
136	1053	205	410	820	1640	1379	857	1714	1527	1153
137	405	810	1620	1339	777	1554	1207	513	1026	151
138	302	604	1208	515	1030	159	318	636	1272	643
139	1286	671	1342	783	1566	1231	561	1122	343	686
140	1372	843	1686	1471	1041	181	362	724	1448	995
141	89	178	356	712	1424	947	1894	1887	1873	1845
142	1789	1677	1453	1005	109	218	436	872	1744	1587
143	1273	645	1290	679	1358	815	1630	1359	817	1634
144	1367	833	1666	1431	961	21	42	84	168	336
145	672	1344	787	1574	1247	593	1186	471	942	1884
146	1867	1833	1765	1629	1357	813	1626	1351	801	1602
147	1303	705	1410	919	1838	1775	1649	1397	893	1786
148	1671	1441	981	61	122	244	488	976	51	102
149	204	408	816	1632	1363	825	1650	1399	897	1794

P = 1901

INDICES

	0	1	2	3	4	5	6	7	8	9
150	943	1562	835	1106	1143	918	1526	1850	1602	1885
151	734	628	1506	19	206	52	678	36	163	1654
152	1598	646	1626	554	650	191	1891	1368	706	753
153	1822	234	1115	229	1534	1513	988	762	1745	456
154	1630	365	1053	1554	1004	462	1171	319	1158	863
155	1331	125	971	387	1375	1044	558	151	448	1349
156	1580	815	776	1539	1686	499	1394	99	937	1680
157	1733	1192	654	1060	1453	1132	902	1068	1799	692
158	578	310	1214	436	1870	274	828	1429	195	1276
159	740	1027	158	1326	1209	1518	1787	1294	1648	430
160	614	639	1469	1667	1895	882	593	962	172	1636
161	996	661	68	1013	1523	203	1623	1819	1742	1168
162	1372	773	1730	1796	825	1206	1466	993	1739	1463
163	1436	1342	1493	142	1439	1757	710	1840	1769	624
164	1364	1550	1345	1128	1023	958	1792	620	133	1476
165	1496	913	757	1675	634	137	1236	535	145	767
166	84	1287	855	26	1251	1241	1442	353	1826	1309
167	403	1480	251	371	1760	1698	1616	1421	1299	1859
168	803	214	713	475	238	90	1402	1500	896	1358
169	1843	1750	1198	298	283	1080	411	540	1772	670
170	1119	1561	1105	917	1849	1884	627	18	51	35
171	1653	645	553	190	1367	752	233	228	1512	761
172	455	364	1553	461	318	862	124	386	1043	150
173	1348	814	1538	498	98	1679	1191	1059	1131	1067
174	691	309	435	273	1428	1275	1026	1325	1517	1293
175	429	638	1666	881	961	1635	660	1012	202	1818
176	1167	772	1795	1205	992	1462	1341	141	1756	1839
177	623	1549	1127	957	619	1475	912	1674	136	534
178	766	1286	25	1240	352	1308	1479	370	1697	1420
179	1858	213	474	89	1499	1357	1749	297	1079	539
180	669	1560	916	1883	17	34	644	189	751	227
181	760	363	460	861	385	149	813	497	1678	1058
182	1066	308	272	1274	1324	1292	637	880	1634	1011
183	1817	771	1204	1461	140	1838	1548	956	1474	1673
184	533	1285	1239	1307	369	1419	212	88	1356	296
185	538	1559	1882	33	188	226	362	860	148	496
186	1057	307	1273	1291	879	1010	770	1460	1837	955
187	1672	1284	1306	1418	87	295	1558	32	225	859
188	495	306	1290	1009	1459	954	1283	1417	294	31
189	858	305	1008	953	1416	30	304	952	29	951
190	950	0								

POWER RESIDUES

	0	1	2	3	4	5	6	7	8	9
150	1687	1473	1045	189	378	756	1512	1123	345	690
151	1380	859	1718	1535	1169	437	874	1748	1595	1289
152	677	1354	807	1614	1327	753	1506	1111	321	642
153	1284	667	1334	767	1534	1167	433	866	1732	1563
154	1225	549	1098	295	590	1180	459	918	1836	1771
155	1641	1381	861	1722	1543	1185	469	938	1876	1851
156	1801	1701	1501	1101	301	602	1204	507	1014	127
157	254	508	1016	131	262	524	1048	195	390	780
158	1560	1219	537	1074	247	494	988	75	150	300
159	600	1200	499	998	95	190	380	760	1520	1139
160	377	754	1508	1115	329	658	1316	731	1462	1023
161	145	290	580	1160	419	838	1676	1451	1001	101
162	202	404	808	1616	1331	761	1522	1143	385	770
163	1540	1179	457	914	1828	1755	1609	1317	733	1466
164	1031	161	322	644	1288	675	1350	799	1598	1295
165	689	1378	855	1710	1519	1137	373	746	1492	1083
166	265	530	1060	219	438	876	1752	1603	1305	709
167	1418	935	1870	1839	1777	1653	1405	909	1818	1735
168	1569	1237	573	1146	391	782	1564	1227	553	1106
169	311	622	1244	587	1174	447	894	1788	1675	1449
170	997	93	186	372	744	1488	1075	249	498	996
171	91	182	364	728	1456	1011	121	242	484	968
172	35	70	140	280	560	1120	339	678	1356	811
173	1622	1343	785	1570	1239	577	1154	407	814	1628
174	1355	809	1618	1335	769	1538	1175	449	898	1796
175	1691	1481	1061	221	442	884	1768	1635	1369	837
176	1674	1447	993	85	170	340	680	1360	819	1638
177	1375	849	1698	1495	1089	277	554	1108	315	630
178	1260	619	1238	575	1150	399	798	1596	1291	681
179	1362	823	1646	1391	881	1762	1623	1345	789	1578
180	1255	609	1218	535	1070	239	478	956	11	22
181	44	88	176	352	704	1408	915	1830	1759	1617
182	1333	765	1530	1159	417	834	1668	1435	969	37
183	74	148	296	592	1184	467	934	1868	1835	1769
184	1637	1373	845	1690	1479	1057	213	426	852	1704
185	1507	1113	325	650	1300	699	1398	895	1790	1679
186	1457	1013	125	250	500	1000	99	198	396	792
187	1584	1267	633	1266	631	1262	623	1246	591	1182
188	463	926	1852	1803	1705	1509	1117	333	666	1332
189	763	1526	1151	401	802	1604	1307	713	1426	951
190										

P = 1907

INDICES

	0	1	2	3	4	5	6	7	8	9
0		0	1	396	2	617	397	246	3	792
1	618	1219	398	1020	247	1013	4	1099	793	1869
2	619	642	1220	590	399	1234	1021	1188	248	536
3	1014	1459	5	1615	1100	863	794	77	1870	1416
4	620	1004	643	745	1221	1409	591	1521	400	492
5	1235	1495	1022	1112	1189	1836	249	359	537	911
6	1015	1404	1460	1038	6	1637	1616	258	1101	986
7	864	1336	795	724	78	1630	1871	1465	1417	1773
8	621	1584	1005	1317	644	1716	746	932	1222	275
9	1410	1266	592	1855	1522	580	401	996	493	105
10	1236	435	1496	1272	1023	1259	1113	1076	1190	1043
11	1837	473	250	1054	360	1207	538	1812	912	1345
12	1016	532	1405	1400	1461	1851	1039	1847	7	1141
13	1638	1430	1617	209	259	1805	1102	972	987	1169
14	865	11	1337	333	796	1153	725	888	79	1900
15	1631	1135	1872	1891	1466	170	1418	1145	1774	1508
16	622	836	1585	94	1006	326	1318	598	645	134
17	1717	755	747	1642	933	1480	1223	1307	276	241
18	1411	1331	1267	1800	593	694	1856	412	1523	1434
19	581	1684	402	1878	997	127	494	420	106	699
20	1237	654	436	782	1497	1621	1273	1382	1024	1182
21	1260	164	1114	1732	1077	1362	1191	1705	1044	1120
22	1838	213	474	444	251	120	1055	310	361	674
23	1208	1861	539	1695	1813	232	913	263	1346	614
24	1017	639	533	74	1406	1109	1401	983	1462	1713
25	1852	432	1040	1809	1848	206	8	1897	1142	323
26	1639	1328	1431	417	1618	1729	210	671	260	1106
27	1806	1325	1103	1662	973	547	988	1665	1170	345
28	866	769	12	1738	1338	976	334	1250	797	292
29	1154	1392	726	550	889	1528	80	501	1901	1610
30	1632	991	1136	831	1873	115	1892	287	1467	1668
31	171	1560	1419	1092	1146	1655	1775	1173	1509	1755
32	623	1472	837	1062	1586	348	95	1439	1007	1767
33	327	1376	1319	869	599	875	646	810	135	1450
34	1718	772	756	738	748	1603	1643	1083	934	15
35	1481	302	1224	1673	1308	47	277	1741	242	586
36	1412	1832	1332	928	1268	1341	1801	1131	594	1796
37	695	1358	1857	979	413	341	1524	1556	1435	734
38	582	337	1685	1292	403	176	1879	1537	998	1253
39	128	1689	495	1826	421	484	107	800	700	605
40	1238	1782	655	573	437	295	783	1296	1498	370
41	1622	1368	1274	1157	1383	28	1025	1565	1183	906
42	1261	1395	165	407	1115	427	1733	1650	1078	729
43	1363	845	1192	525	1706	1549	1045	553	1121	180
44	1839	1284	214	850	475	892	445	390	252	1424
45	121	317	1056	1531	311	1883	362	818	675	381
46	1209	83	1862	881	540	566	1696	461	1814	504
47	233	1541	914	58	264	1197	1347	1904	615	790
48	1018	1097	640	1232	534	1613	75	1002	1407	490
49	1110	357	1402	1635	984	722	1463	1582	1714	273

POWER RESIDUES

	0	1	2	3	4	5	6	7	8	9
0	1	2	4	8	16	32	64	128	256	512
1	1024	141	282	564	1128	349	698	1396	885	1770
2	1633	1359	811	1622	1337	767	1534	1161	415	830
3	1660	1413	919	1838	1769	1631	1355	803	1606	1305
4	703	1406	905	1810	1713	1519	1131	355	710	1420
5	933	1866	1825	1743	1579	1251	595	1190	473	946
6	1892	1877	1847	1787	1667	1427	947	1894	1881	1855
7	1803	1699	1491	1075	243	486	972	37	74	148
8	296	592	1184	461	922	1844	1781	1655	1403	899
9	1798	1689	1471	1035	163	326	652	1304	701	1402
10	897	1794	1681	1455	1003	99	198	396	792	1584
11	1261	615	1230	553	1106	305	610	1220	533	1066
12	225	450	900	1800	1693	1479	1051	195	390	780
13	1560	1213	519	1038	169	338	676	1352	797	1594
14	1281	655	1310	713	1426	945	1890	1873	1839	1771
15	1635	1363	819	1638	1369	831	1662	1417	927	1854
16	1801	1695	1483	1059	211	422	844	1688	1469	1031
17	155	310	620	1240	573	1146	385	770	1540	1173
18	439	878	1756	1605	1303	699	1398	889	1778	1649
19	1391	875	1750	1593	1279	651	1302	697	1394	881
20	1762	1617	1327	747	1494	1081	255	510	1020	133
21	266	532	1064	221	442	884	1768	1629	1351	795
22	1590	1273	639	1278	649	1298	689	1378	849	1698
23	1489	1071	235	470	940	1880	1853	1799	1691	1475
24	1043	179	358	716	1432	957	7	14	28	56
25	112	224	448	896	1792	1677	1447	987	67	134
26	268	536	1072	237	474	948	1896	1885	1863	1819
27	1731	1555	1203	499	998	89	178	356	712	1424
28	941	1882	1857	1807	1707	1507	1107	307	614	1228
29	549	1098	289	578	1156	405	810	1620	1333	759
30	1518	1129	351	702	1404	901	1802	1697	1487	1067
31	227	454	908	1816	1725	1543	1179	451	902	1804
32	1701	1495	1083	259	518	1036	165	330	660	1320
33	733	1466	1025	143	286	572	1144	381	762	1524
34	1141	375	750	1500	1093	279	558	1116	325	650
35	1300	693	1386	865	1730	1553	1199	491	982	57
36	114	228	456	912	1824	1741	1575	1243	579	1158
37	409	818	1636	1365	823	1646	1385	863	1726	1545
38	1183	459	918	1836	1765	1623	1339	771	1542	1177
39	447	894	1788	1669	1431	955	3	6	12	24
40	48	96	192	384	768	1536	1165	423	846	1692
41	1477	1047	187	374	748	1496	1085	263	526	1052
42	197	394	788	1576	1245	583	1166	425	850	1700
43	1493	1079	251	502	1004	101	202	404	808	1616
44	1325	743	1486	1065	223	446	892	1784	1661	1415
45	923	1846	1785	1663	1419	931	1862	1817	1727	1547
46	1187	467	934	1868	1829	1751	1595	1283	659	1318
47	729	1458	1009	111	222	444	888	1776	1645	1383
48	859	1718	1529	1151	395	790	1580	1253	599	1198
49	489	978	49	98	196	392	784	1568	1229	551

P = 1907

INDICES

	0	1	2	3	4	5	6	7	8	9
50	1853	994	433	1257	1041	1052	1810	530	1849	1139
51	207	970	9	1151	1898	1889	1143	834	324	132
52	1640	1305	1329	692	1432	1876	418	652	1619	1180
53	1730	1703	211	118	672	1693	261	637	1107	1711
54	1807	1895	1326	1727	1104	1660	1663	767	974	290
55	548	499	989	113	1666	1090	1171	1470	346	1765
56	867	808	770	1601	13	1671	1739	1830	1339	1794
57	977	1554	335	174	1251	1824	798	1780	293	368
58	1155	1563	1393	425	727	523	551	1282	890	1422
59	1529	816	81	564	502	56	1902	1095	1611	488
60	1633	1580	992	1050	1137	1149	832	1303	1874	1178
61	116	635	1893	1658	288	111	1468	806	1669	1792
62	172	1778	1561	521	1420	562	1093	1578	1147	1176
63	1656	804	1776	560	1174	558	1510	1512	1756	222
64	624	1514	1473	824	838	1758	1063	704	1587	224
65	349	195	96	626	1440	141	1008	1516	1768	468
66	328	1475	1377	609	1320	826	870	1126	600	840
67	876	717	647	1760	811	516	136	1065	1451	1242
68	1719	706	773	941	757	1589	739	1070	749	226
69	1604	922	1644	351	1084	1786	935	197	16	185
70	1482	98	303	40	1225	628	1674	681	1309	1442
71	48	659	278	143	1742	950	243	1010	587	1456
72	1413	1518	1833	1035	1333	1770	929	577	1269	470
73	1342	1844	1802	330	1132	1505	595	1477	1797	1681
74	696	1379	1359	441	1858	611	980	203	414	1322
75	342	1247	1525	828	1557	1752	1436	872	735	299
76	583	1128	338	1289	1686	602	1293	25	404	842
77	177	387	1880	878	1538	787	999	719	1254	967
78	129	649	1690	1724	496	1762	1827	1821	422	813
79	485	1300	108	518	801	219	701	138	606	714
80	1239	1067	1783	37	656	1453	574	1502	438	1244
81	296	22	784	1721	1297	711	1499	708	371	152
82	1623	775	1369	374	1275	943	1158	855	1384	759
83	29	155	1026	1591	1566	1215	1184	741	907	1626
84	1262	1072	1396	1165	166	751	408	778	1116	228
85	428	667	1734	1606	1651	1372	1079	924	730	480
86	1364	1646	846	377	1193	353	526	688	1707	1086
87	1550	1278	1046	1788	554	191	1122	937	181	946
88	1840	199	1285	963	215	18	851	1161	476	187
89	893	897	446	1484	391	858	253	100	1425	89
90	122	305	318	1387	1057	42	1532	901	312	1227
91	1884	762	363	630	819	511	676	1676	382	32
92	1210	683	84	450	1863	1311	882	158	541	1444
93	567	455	1697	50	462	1029	1815	661	505	1488
94	234	280	1542	1594	915	145	59	66	265	1744
95	1198	1569	1348	952	1905	395	616	245	791	1218
96	1019	1012	1098	1868	641	589	1233	1187	535	1458
97	1614	862	76	1415	1003	744	1408	1520	491	1494
98	1111	1835	358	910	1403	1037	1636	257	985	1335
99	723	1629	1464	1772	1583	1316	1715	931	274	1265

POWER RESIDUES

	0	1	2	3	4	5	6	7	8	9
50	1102	297	594	1188	469	938	1876	1845	1783	1659
51	1411	915	1830	1753	1599	1291	675	1350	793	1586
52	1265	623	1246	585	1170	433	866	1732	1557	1207
53	507	1014	121	242	484	968	29	58	116	232
54	464	928	1856	1805	1703	1499	1091	275	550	1100
55	293	586	1172	437	874	1748	1589	1271	635	1270
56	633	1266	625	1250	593	1186	465	930	1860	1813
57	1719	1531	1155	403	806	1612	1317	727	1454	1001
58	95	190	380	760	1520	1133	359	718	1436	965
59	23	46	92	184	368	736	1472	1037	167	334
60	668	1336	765	1530	1153	399	798	1596	1285	663
61	1326	745	1490	1073	239	478	956	5	10	20
62	40	80	160	320	640	1280	653	1306	705	1410
63	913	1826	1745	1583	1259	611	1222	537	1074	241
64	482	964	21	42	84	168	336	672	1344	781
65	1562	1217	527	1054	201	402	804	1608	1309	711
66	1422	937	1874	1841	1775	1643	1379	851	1702	1497
67	1087	267	534	1068	229	458	916	1832	1757	1607
68	1307	707	1414	921	1842	1777	1647	1387	867	1734
69	1561	1215	523	1046	185	370	740	1480	1053	199
70	398	796	1592	1277	647	1294	681	1362	817	1634
71	1361	815	1630	1353	799	1598	1289	671	1342	777
72	1554	1201	495	990	73	146	292	584	1168	429
73	858	1716	1525	1143	379	758	1516	1125	343	686
74	1372	837	1674	1441	975	43	86	172	344	688
75	1376	845	1690	1473	1039	171	342	684	1368	829
76	1658	1409	911	1822	1737	1567	1227	547	1094	281
77	562	1124	341	682	1364	821	1642	1377	847	1694
78	1481	1055	203	406	812	1624	1341	775	1550	1193
79	479	958	9	18	36	72	144	288	576	1152
80	397	794	1588	1269	631	1262	617	1234	561	1122
81	337	674	1348	789	1578	1249	591	1182	457	914
82	1828	1749	1591	1275	643	1286	665	1330	753	1506
83	1105	303	606	1212	517	1034	161	322	644	1288
84	669	1338	769	1538	1169	431	862	1724	1541	1175
85	443	886	1772	1637	1367	827	1654	1401	895	1790
86	1673	1439	971	35	70	140	280	560	1120	333
87	666	1332	757	1514	1121	335	670	1340	773	1546
88	1185	463	926	1852	1797	1687	1467	1027	147	294
89	588	1176	445	890	1780	1653	1399	891	1782	1657
90	1407	907	1814	1721	1535	1163	419	838	1676	1445
91	983	59	118	236	472	944	1888	1869	1831	1755
92	1603	1299	691	1382	857	1714	1521	1135	363	726
93	1452	997	87	174	348	696	1392	877	1754	1601
94	1295	683	1366	825	1650	1393	879	1758	1609	1311
95	715	1430	953	1906	1905	1903	1899	1891	1875	1843
96	1779	1651	1395	883	1766	1625	1343	779	1558	1209
97	511	1022	137	274	548	1096	285	570	1140	373
98	746	1492	1077	247	494	988	69	138	276	552
99	1104	301	602	1204	501	1002	97	194	388	776

P = 1907

INDICES

	0	1	2	3	4	5	6	7	8	9
100	1854	579	995	104	434	1271	1258	1075	1042	472
101	1053	1206	1811	1344	531	1399	1850	1846	1140	1429
102	208	1804	971	1168	10	332	1152	887	1899	1134
103	1890	169	1144	1507	835	93	325	597	133	754
104	1641	1479	1306	240	1330	1799	693	411	1433	1683
105	1877	126	419	698	653	781	1620	1381	1181	163
106	1731	1361	1704	1119	212	443	119	309	673	1860
107	1694	231	262	613	638	73	1108	982	1712	431
108	1808	205	1896	322	1327	416	1728	670	1105	1324
109	1661	546	1664	344	768	1737	975	1249	291	1391
110	549	1527	500	1609	990	830	114	286	1667	1559
111	1091	1654	1172	1754	1471	1061	347	1438	1766	1375
112	868	874	809	1449	771	737	1602	1082	14	301
113	1672	46	1740	585	1831	927	1340	1130	1795	1357
114	978	340	1555	733	336	1291	175	1536	1252	1688
115	1825	483	799	604	1781	572	294	1295	369	1367
116	1156	27	1564	905	1394	406	426	1649	728	844
117	524	1548	552	179	1283	849	891	389	1423	316
118	1530	1882	817	380	82	880	565	460	503	1540
119	57	1196	1903	789	1096	1231	1612	1001	489	356
120	1634	721	1581	272	993	1256	1051	529	1138	969
121	1150	1888	833	131	1304	691	1875	651	1179	1702
122	117	1692	636	1710	1894	1726	1659	766	289	498
123	112	1089	1469	1764	807	1600	1670	1829	1793	1553
124	173	1823	1779	367	1562	424	522	1281	1421	815
125	563	55	1094	487	1579	1049	1148	1302	1177	634
126	1657	110	805	1791	1777	520	561	1577	1175	803
127	559	557	1511	221	1513	823	1757	703	223	194
128	625	140	1515	467	1474	608	825	1125	839	716
129	1759	515	1064	1241	705	940	1588	1069	225	921
130	350	1785	196	184	97	39	627	680	1441	658
131	142	949	1009	1455	1517	1034	1769	576	469	1843
132	329	1504	1476	1680	1378	440	610	202	1321	1246
133	827	1751	871	298	1127	1288	601	24	841	386
134	877	786	718	966	648	1723	1761	1820	812	1299
135	517	218	137	713	1066	36	1452	1501	1243	21
136	1720	710	707	151	774	373	942	854	758	154
137	1590	1214	740	1625	1071	1164	750	777	227	666
138	1605	1371	923	479	1645	376	352	687	1085	1277
139	1787	190	936	945	198	962	17	1160	186	896
140	1483	857	99	88	304	1386	41	900	1226	761
141	629	510	1675	31	682	449	1310	157	1443	454
142	49	1028	660	1487	279	1593	144	65	1743	1568
143	951	394	244	1217	1011	1867	588	1186	1457	861
144	1414	743	1519	1493	1834	909	1036	256	1334	1628
145	1771	1315	930	1264	578	103	1270	1074	471	1205
146	1343	1398	1845	1428	1803	1167	331	886	1133	168
147	1506	92	596	753	1478	239	1798	410	1682	125
148	697	780	1380	162	1360	1118	442	308	1859	230
149	612	72	981	430	204	321	415	669	1323	545

POWER RESIDUES

	0	1	2	3	4	5	6	7	8	9
100	1552	1197	487	974	41	82	164	328	656	1312
101	717	1434	961	15	30	60	120	240	480	960
102	13	26	52	104	208	416	832	1664	1421	935
103	1870	1833	1759	1611	1315	723	1446	985	63	126
104	252	504	1008	109	218	436	872	1744	1581	1255
105	603	1206	505	1010	113	226	452	904	1808	1709
106	1511	1115	323	646	1292	677	1354	801	1602	1297
107	687	1374	841	1682	1457	1007	107	214	428	856
108	1712	1517	1127	347	694	1388	869	1738	1569	1231
109	555	1110	313	626	1252	597	1194	481	962	17
110	34	68	136	272	544	1088	269	538	1076	245
111	490	980	53	106	212	424	848	1696	1485	1063
112	219	438	876	1752	1597	1287	667	1334	761	1522
113	1137	367	734	1468	1029	151	302	604	1208	509
114	1018	129	258	516	1032	157	314	628	1256	605
115	1210	513	1026	145	290	580	1160	413	826	1652
116	1397	887	1774	1641	1375	843	1686	1465	1023	139
117	278	556	1112	317	634	1268	629	1258	609	1218
118	529	1058	209	418	836	1672	1437	967	27	54
119	108	216	432	864	1728	1549	1191	475	950	1900
120	1893	1879	1851	1795	1683	1459	1011	115	230	460
121	920	1840	1773	1639	1371	835	1670	1433	959	11
122	22	44	88	176	352	704	1408	909	1818	1729
123	1551	1195	483	966	25	50	100	200	400	800
124	1600	1293	679	1358	809	1618	1329	751	1502	1097
125	287	574	1148	389	778	1556	1205	503	1006	105
126	210	420	840	1680	1453	999	91	182	364	728
127	1456	1005	103	206	412	824	1648	1389	871	1742
128	1577	1247	587	1174	441	882	1764	1621	1335	763
129	1526	1145	383	766	1532	1157	407	814	1628	1349
130	791	1582	1257	607	1214	521	1042	177	354	708
131	1416	925	1850	1793	1679	1451	995	83	166	332
132	664	1328	749	1498	1089	271	542	1084	261	522
133	1044	181	362	724	1448	989	71	142	284	568
134	1136	365	730	1460	1013	119	238	476	952	1904
135	1901	1895	1883	1859	1811	1715	1523	1139	371	742
136	1484	1061	215	430	860	1720	1533	1159	411	822
137	1644	1381	855	1710	1513	1119	331	662	1324	741
138	1482	1057	207	414	828	1656	1405	903	1806	1705
139	1503	1099	291	582	1164	421	842	1684	1461	1015
140	123	246	492	984	61	122	244	488	976	45
141	90	180	360	720	1440	973	39	78	156	312
142	624	1248	589	1178	449	898	1796	1685	1463	1019
143	131	262	524	1048	189	378	756	1512	1117	327
144	654	1308	709	1418	929	1858	1809	1711	1515	1123
145	339	678	1356	805	1610	1313	719	1438	969	31
146	62	124	248	496	992	77	154	308	616	1232
147	557	1114	321	642	1284	661	1322	737	1474	1041
148	175	350	700	1400	893	1786	1665	1423	939	1878
149	1849	1791	1675	1443	979	51	102	204	408	816

P = 1907

INDICES

	0	1	2	3	4	5	6	7	8	9
150	343	1736	1248	1390	1526	1608	829	285	1558	1653
151	1753	1060	1437	1374	873	1448	736	1081	300	45
152	584	926	1129	1356	339	732	1290	1535	1687	482
153	603	571	1294	1366	26	904	405	1648	843	1547
154	178	848	388	315	1881	379	879	459	1539	1195
155	788	1230	1000	355	720	271	1255	528	968	1887
156	130	690	650	1701	1691	1709	1725	765	497	1088
157	1763	1599	1828	1552	1822	366	423	1280	814	54
158	486	1048	1301	633	109	1790	519	1576	802	556
159	220	822	702	193	139	466	607	1124	715	514
160	1240	939	1068	920	1784	183	38	679	657	948
161	1454	1033	575	1842	1503	1679	439	201	1245	1750
162	297	1287	23	385	785	965	1722	1819	1298	217
163	712	35	1500	20	709	150	372	853	153	1213
164	1624	1163	776	665	1370	478	375	686	1276	189
165	944	961	1159	895	856	87	1385	899	760	509
166	30	448	156	453	1027	1486	1592	64	1567	393
167	1216	1866	1185	860	742	1492	908	255	1627	1314
168	1263	102	1073	1204	1397	1427	1166	885	167	91
169	752	238	409	124	779	161	1117	307	229	71
170	429	320	668	544	1735	1389	1607	284	1652	1059
171	1373	1447	1080	44	925	1355	731	1534	481	570
172	1365	903	1647	1546	847	314	378	458	1194	1229
173	354	270	527	1886	689	1700	1708	764	1087	1598
174	1551	365	1279	53	1047	632	1789	1575	555	821
175	192	465	1123	513	938	919	182	678	947	1032
176	1841	1678	200	1749	1286	384	964	1818	216	34
177	19	149	852	1212	1162	664	477	685	188	960
178	894	86	898	508	447	452	1485	63	392	1865
179	859	1491	254	1313	101	1203	1426	884	90	237
180	123	160	306	70	319	543	1388	283	1058	1446
181	43	1354	1533	569	902	1545	313	457	1228	269
182	1885	1699	763	1597	364	52	631	1574	820	464
183	512	918	677	1031	1677	1748	383	1817	33	148
184	1211	663	684	959	85	507	451	62	1864	1490
185	1312	1202	883	236	159	69	542	282	1445	1353
186	568	1544	456	268	1698	1596	51	1573	463	917
187	1030	1747	1816	147	662	958	506	61	1489	1201
188	235	68	281	1352	1543	267	1595	1572	916	1746
189	146	957	60	1200	67	1351	266	1571	1745	956
190	1199	1350	1570	955	1349	954	953			

POWER RESIDUES

	0	1	2	3	4	5	6	7	8	9
150	1632	1357	807	1614	1321	735	1470	1033	159	318
151	636	1272	637	1274	641	1282	657	1314	721	1442
152	977	47	94	188	376	752	1504	1101	295	590
153	1180	453	906	1812	1717	1527	1147	387	774	1548
154	1189	471	942	1884	1861	1815	1723	1539	1171	435
155	870	1740	1573	1239	571	1142	377	754	1508	1109
156	311	622	1244	581	1162	417	834	1668	1429	951
157	1902	1897	1887	1867	1827	1747	1587	1267	627	1254
158	601	1202	497	994	81	162	324	648	1296	685
159	1370	833	1666	1425	943	1886	1865	1823	1739	1571
160	1235	563	1126	345	690	1380	853	1706	1505	1103
161	299	598	1196	485	970	33	66	132	264	528
162	1056	205	410	820	1640	1373	839	1678	1449	991
163	75	150	300	600	1200	493	986	65	130	260
164	520	1040	173	346	692	1384	861	1722	1537	1167
165	427	854	1708	1509	1111	315	630	1260	613	1226
166	545	1090	273	546	1092	277	554	1108	309	618
167	1236	565	1130	353	706	1412	917	1834	1761	1615
168	1323	739	1478	1049	191	382	764	1528	1149	391
169	782	1564	1221	535	1070	233	466	932	1864	1821
170	1735	1563	1219	531	1062	217	434	868	1736	1565
171	1223	539	1078	249	498	996	85	170	340	680
172	1360	813	1626	1345	783	1566	1225	543	1086	265
173	530	1060	213	426	852	1704	1501	1095	283	566
174	1132	357	714	1428	949	1898	1889	1871	1835	1763
175	1619	1331	755	1510	1113	319	638	1276	645	1290
176	673	1346	785	1570	1233	559	1118	329	658	1316
177	725	1450	993	79	158	316	632	1264	621	1242
178	577	1154	401	802	1604	1301	695	1390	873	1746
179	1585	1263	619	1238	569	1138	369	738	1476	1045
180	183	366	732	1464	1021	135	270	540	1080	253
181	506	1012	117	234	468	936	1872	1837	1767	1627
182	1347	787	1574	1241	575	1150	393	786	1572	1237
183	567	1134	361	722	1444	981	55	110	220	440
184	880	1760	1613	1319	731	1462	1017	127	254	508
185	1016	125	250	500	1000	93	186	372	744	1488
186	1069	231	462	924	1848	1789	1671	1435	963	19
187	38	76	152	304	608	1216	525	1050	193	386
188	772	1544	1181	455	910	1820	1733	1559	1211	515
189	1030	153	306	612	1224	541	1082	257	514	1028
190	149	298	596	1192	477	954				

P = 1913

INDICES

	0	1	2	3	4	5	6	7	8	9
0		0	272	1	544	1077	273	1070	816	2
1	1349	1145	545	999	1342	1078	1088	712	274	1169
2	1621	1071	1417	1466	817	242	1271	3	1614	494
3	1350	821	1360	1146	984	235	546	1514	1441	1000
4	1893	1133	1343	338	1689	1079	1738	209	1089	228
5	514	713	1543	1487	275	310	1886	1170	766	1750
6	1622	1552	1093	1072	1632	164	1418	856	1256	1467
7	507	541	818	763	1786	243	1713	303	1272	851
8	253	4	1405	34	1615	1789	610	495	49	1574
9	1351	157	98	822	481	334	1361	294	500	1147
10	786	1016	985	520	1815	236	1759	725	547	1866
11	582	1515	246	104	1442	631	1038	1001	110	1782
12	1894	378	1824	1134	1365	1319	1344	694	1904	339
13	436	465	1690	327	1128	1080	1528	1647	1739	1716
14	779	210	813	232	1090	1571	1035	229	146	1730
15	515	1427	73	714	575	1898	1544	905	1123	1488
16	525	624	276	1705	1677	311	306	1524	1887	86
17	149	1171	882	1160	767	1312	321	1751	1846	741
18	1623	127	429	1553	370	679	1094	1857	753	1073
19	606	1520	1633	1275	566	165	772	1733	1419	866
20	1058	857	1288	1564	1257	298	792	1468	175	402
21	508	384	119	542	997	1415	819	1891	226	764
22	854	1711	1787	479	518	244	376	434	1714	144
23	903	304	1310	368	1273	1286	382	852	142	140
24	254	262	650	5	184	1305	1406	256	1637	35
25	1591	1430	1616	699	966	1790	264	1328	611	672
26	708	496	737	704	50	652	599	1575	1400	1236
27	1352	974	1800	158	7	1387	99	201	76	823
28	1051	1117	482	186	1085	335	504	291	1362	1424
29	1843	295	1307	669	501	915	418	1148	90	553
30	787	1408	1699	1017	345	717	986	1224	847	521
31	258	892	1816	918	1177	237	1395	1828	1760	1639
32	797	726	896	1881	548	1241	65	1867	37	1279
33	583	490	578	1516	1796	21	247	1593	358	105
34	421	54	1443	1298	1154	632	1432	1725	1039	1766
35	1584	1002	593	25	111	1618	206	1783	1013	1901
36	1895	426	399	379	701	1840	1825	1151	642	1135
37	951	645	1366	968	217	1320	1025	1493	1345	153
38	878	695	1792	1107	1905	1380	1547	340	838	283
39	437	266	1044	466	93	16	1691	1653	1138	328
40	1330	933	1129	1820	1560	1081	1836	747	1529	613
41	570	1648	1064	908	1740	1111	447	1717	674	1264
42	780	556	656	211	391	954	814	710	1269	233
43	1687	1485	1091	539	251	1572	498	723	1036	1317
44	1126	230	71	622	147	739	751	1731	790	1413
45	516	366	648	1428	706	1234	74	289	416	715
46	1175	1879	576	52	1582	1899	640	1491	1545	14
47	1558	906	654	1483	1124	1411	414	1489	412	1369
48	526	601	534	625	922	1371	277	1603	456	1706
49	1577	169	1678	1206	528	312	1909	1611	307	1402

POWER RESIDUES

	0	1	2	3	4	5	6	7	8	9
0	1	3	9	27	81	243	729	274	822	553
1	1659	1151	1540	794	469	1407	395	1185	1642	1100
2	1387	335	1005	1102	1393	353	1059	1264	1879	1811
3	1607	995	1072	1303	83	249	747	328	984	1039
4	1204	1699	1271	1900	1874	1796	1562	860	667	88
5	264	792	463	1389	341	1023	1156	1555	839	604
6	1812	1610	1004	1099	1384	326	978	1021	1150	1537
7	785	442	1326	152	456	1368	278	834	589	1767
8	1475	599	1797	1565	869	694	169	507	1521	737
9	298	894	769	394	1182	1633	1073	1306	92	276
10	828	571	1713	1313	113	339	1017	1138	1501	677
11	118	354	1062	1273	1906	1892	1850	1724	1346	212
12	636	1908	1898	1868	1778	1508	698	181	543	1629
13	1061	1270	1897	1865	1769	1481	617	1851	1727	1355
14	239	717	238	714	229	687	148	444	1332	170
15	510	1530	764	379	1137	1498	668	91	273	819
16	544	1632	1070	1297	65	195	585	1755	1439	491
17	1473	593	1779	1511	707	208	624	1872	1790	1544
18	806	505	1515	719	244	732	283	849	634	1902
19	1880	1814	1616	1022	1153	1546	812	523	1569	881
20	730	277	831	580	1740	1394	356	1068	1291	47
21	141	423	1269	1894	1856	1742	1400	374	1122	1453
22	533	1599	971	1000	1087	1348	218	654	49	147
23	441	1323	143	429	1287	35	105	315	945	922
24	853	646	25	75	225	675	112	336	1008	1111
25	1420	434	1302	80	240	720	247	741	310	930
26	877	718	241	723	256	768	391	1173	1606	992
27	1063	1276	2	6	18	54	162	486	1458	548
28	1644	1106	1405	389	1167	1588	938	901	790	457
29	1371	287	861	670	97	291	873	706	205	615
30	1845	1709	1301	77	231	693	166	498	1494	656
31	55	165	495	1485	629	1887	1835	1679	1211	1720
32	1334	176	528	1584	926	865	682	133	399	1197
33	1678	1208	1711	1307	95	285	855	652	43	129
34	387	1161	1570	884	739	304	912	823	556	1668
35	1178	1621	1037	1198	1681	1217	1738	1388	338	1014
36	1129	1474	596	1788	1538	788	451	1353	233	699
37	184	552	1656	1142	1513	713	226	678	121	363
38	1089	1354	236	708	211	633	1899	1871	1787	1535
39	779	424	1272	1903	1883	1823	1643	1103	1396	362
40	1086	1345	209	627	1881	1817	1625	1049	1234	1789
41	1541	797	478	1434	476	1428	458	1374	296	888
42	751	340	1020	1147	1528	758	361	1083	1336	182
43	546	1638	1088	1351	227	681	130	390	1170	1597
44	965	982	1033	1186	1645	1109	1414	416	1248	1831
45	1667	1175	1612	1010	1117	1438	488	1464	566	1698
46	1268	1891	1847	1715	1319	131	393	1179	1624	1046
47	1225	1762	1460	554	1662	1160	1567	875	712	223
48	669	94	282	846	625	1875	1799	1571	887	748
49	331	993	1066	1285	29	87	261	783	436	1308

P = 1913

INDICES

	0	1	2	3	4	5	6	7	8	9
50	1863	1525	1702	603	1888	181	971	87	1238	590
51	150	1833	536	1172	1600	1597	883	1354	944	1161
52	980	627	768	197	1009	1313	976	1533	322	1020
53	924	1752	871	220	1847	1802	1672	742	1508	1373
54	1624	886	1246	128	160	1031	430	843	279	1554
55	1659	1663	371	9	473	680	348	1605	1095	1337
56	1323	1858	1389	1473	754	1181	458	1074	1357	1747
57	607	101	776	1521	563	1708	1634	1384	1696	1276
58	203	1104	567	720	1579	166	941	1028	773	78
59	1187	1734	690	171	1420	947	362	867	825	81
60	1059	1537	1680	858	59	1455	1289	1053	617	1565
61	989	1208	1258	829	1496	299	1119	136	793	929
62	530	1469	1164	732	176	484	1190	403	1449	314
63	509	664	1667	385	188	1771	120	1227	1911	543
64	1069	1348	998	1087	1168	1416	241	1613	820	983
65	1513	1892	337	1737	227	1542	309	765	1551	1631
66	855	506	762	1712	850	1404	1788	48	156	480
67	293	785	519	1758	1865	245	630	109	377	1364
68	693	435	326	1527	1715	812	1570	145	1426	574
69	904	524	1704	305	85	881	1311	1845	126	369
70	1856	605	1274	771	865	1287	297	174	383	996
71	1890	853	478	375	143	1309	1285	141	261	183
72	255	1590	698	263	671	736	651	1399	973	6
73	200	1050	185	503	1423	1306	914	89	1407	344
74	1223	257	917	1394	1638	895	1240	36	489	1795
75	1592	420	1297	1431	1765	592	1617	1012	425	700
76	1150	950	967	1024	152	1791	1379	837	265	92
77	1652	1329	1819	1835	612	1063	1110	673	555	390
78	709	1686	538	497	1316	70	738	789	365	705
79	288	1174	51	639	13	653	1410	411	600	921
80	1602	1576	1205	1908	1401	1701	180	1237	1832	1599
81	1353	979	196	975	1019	870	1801	1507	885	159
82	842	1658	8	347	1336	1388	1180	1356	100	562
83	1383	202	719	940	77	689	946	824	1536	58
84	1052	988	828	1118	928	1163	483	1448	663	187
85	1226	1068	1086	240	982	336	1541	1550	505	849
86	47	292	1757	629	1363	325	811	1425	523	84
87	1844	1855	770	296	995	477	1308	260	1589	670
88	1398	199	502	913	343	916	894	488	419	1764
89	1011	1149	1023	1378	91	1818	1062	554	1685	1315
90	788	287	638	1409	920	1204	1700	1831	978	1018
91	1506	841	346	1179	561	718	688	1535	987	927
92	1447	1225	239	1540	848	1756	324	522	1854	994
93	259	1397	912	893	1763	1022	1817	1684	286	919
94	1830	1505	1178	687	926	238	1755	1853	1396	1762
95	1683	1829	686	1754	1761	685	684	1640	1641	805
96	798	1642	873	727	806	440	897	799	1194	1882
97	1643	222	549	874	1875	1242	728	861	66	807
98	1849	1868	441	1215	38	898	1478	1280	800	1804
99	584	1195	269	491	1883	31	579	1644	1674	1517

POWER RESIDUES

	0	1	2	3	4	5	6	7	8	9
50	98	294	882	733	286	858	661	70	210	630
51	1890	1844	1706	1292	50	150	450	1350	224	672
52	103	309	927	868	691	160	480	1440	494	1482
53	620	1860	1754	1436	482	1446	512	1536	782	433
54	1299	71	213	639	4	12	36	108	324	972
55	1003	1096	1375	299	897	778	421	1263	1876	1802
56	1580	914	829	574	1722	1340	194	582	1746	1412
57	410	1230	1777	1505	689	154	462	1386	332	996
58	1075	1312	110	330	990	1057	1258	1861	1757	1445
59	509	1527	755	352	1056	1255	1852	1730	1364	266
60	798	481	1443	503	1509	701	190	570	1710	1304
61	86	258	774	409	1227	1768	1478	608	1824	1646
62	1112	1423	443	1329	161	483	1449	521	1563	863
63	676	115	345	1035	1192	1663	1163	1576	902	793
64	466	1398	368	1104	1399	371	1113	1426	452	1356
65	242	726	265	795	472	1416	422	1266	1885	1829
66	1661	1157	1558	848	631	1893	1853	1733	1373	293
67	879	724	259	777	418	1254	1849	1721	1337	185
68	555	1665	1169	1594	956	955	952	943	916	835
69	592	1776	1502	680	127	381	1143	1516	722	253
70	759	364	1092	1363	263	789	454	1362	260	780
71	427	1281	17	51	153	459	1377	305	915	832
72	583	1749	1421	437	1311	107	321	963	976	1015
73	1132	1483	623	1869	1781	1517	725	262	786	445
74	1335	179	537	1611	1007	1108	1411	407	1221	1750
75	1424	446	1338	188	564	1692	1250	1837	1685	1229
76	1774	1496	662	73	219	657	58	174	522	1566
77	872	703	196	588	1764	1466	572	1716	1322	140
78	420	1260	1867	1775	1499	671	100	300	900	787
79	448	1344	206	618	1854	1736	1382	320	960	967
80	988	1051	1240	1807	1595	959	964	979	1024	1159
81	1564	866	685	142	426	1278	8	24	72	216
82	648	31	93	279	837	598	1794	1556	842	613
83	1839	1691	1247	1828	1658	1148	1531	767	388	1164
84	1579	911	820	547	1641	1097	1378	308	924	859
85	664	79	237	711	220	660	67	201	603	1809
86	1601	977	1018	1141	1510	704	199	597	1791	1547
87	815	532	1596	962	973	1006	1105	1402	380	1140
88	1507	695	172	516	1548	818	541	1623	1043	1216
89	1735	1379	311	933	886	745	322	966	985	1042
90	1213	1726	1352	230	690	157	471	1413	413	1239
91	1804	1586	932	883	736	295	885	742	313	939
92	904	799	484	1452	530	1590	944	919	844	619
93	1857	1745	1409	401	1203	1696	1262	1873	1793	1553
94	833	586	1758	1448	518	1554	836	595	1785	1529
95	761	370	1110	1417	425	1275	1912	1910	1904	1886
96	1832	1670	1184	1639	1091	1360	254	762	373	1119
97	1444	506	1518	728	271	813	526	1578	908	811
98	520	1560	854	649	34	102	306	918	841	610
99	1830	1664	1166	1585	929	874	709	214	642	13

P = 1913

INDICES

	0	1	2	3	4	5	6	7	8	9
100	223	1302	1797	550	62	22	875	744	248	1876
101	453	1594	1243	1744	359	729	1510	106	862	1047
102	422	67	193	55	808	1375	1444	1850	1872	1299
103	1869	1458	1155	442	1626	633	1216	352	1433	39
104	1252	1726	899	888	1040	1479	469	1767	1281	407
105	1585	801	1248	1003	1805	1461	594	585	1292	26
106	1196	130	112	270	1143	1619	492	1439	207	1884
107	162	1784	32	96	1014	580	1780	1902	1645	1033
108	1896	1675	1158	427	1518	1056	400	224	432	380
109	1303	964	702	1798	1115	1841	551	845	1826	63
110	19	1152	23	397	643	876	281	1136	745	445
111	952	249	620	646	1877	1556	1367	454	1609	969
112	1595	1007	218	1244	1661	1321	1745	1694	1026	360
113	1453	1494	730	1665	1346	1511	1629	154	107	1568
114	879	863	373	696	1048	1221	1793	423	835	1108
115	68	11	1906	194	1656	1381	56	661	1548	809
116	475	341	1376	636	839	1445	992	284	1851	682
117	438	1873	1213	267	1300	451	1045	1870	350	467
118	1459	1141	94	1156	962	17	443	1607	1692	1627
119	1219	1654	634	1211	1139	1217	1097	329	353	1099
120	1331	1434	1809	934	40	1339	1130	1253	331	1821
121	1727	318	1561	900	1325	1082	889	355	1837	1041
122	1261	748	1480	1860	1530	470	1101	614	1768	759
123	571	1282	1391	1649	408	1333	1065	1586	1201	909
124	802	1475	1741	1249	1436	1112	1004	832	448	1806
125	756	1718	1462	1811	675	595	1721	1265	586	1183
126	781	1293	936	557	27	1776	657	1197	460	212
127	131	42	392	113	1499	955	271	1076	815	1144
128	1341	711	1620	1465	1270	493	1359	234	1440	1132
129	1688	208	513	1486	1885	1749	1092	163	1255	540
130	1785	302	252	33	609	1573	97	333	499	1015
131	1814	724	581	103	1037	1781	1823	1318	1903	464
132	1127	1646	778	231	1034	1729	72	1897	1122	623
133	1676	1523	148	1159	320	740	428	678	752	1519
134	565	1732	1057	1563	791	401	118	1414	225	1710
135	517	433	902	367	381	139	649	1304	1636	1429
136	965	1327	707	703	598	1235	1799	1386	75	1116
137	1084	290	1842	668	417	552	1698	716	846	891
138	1176	1827	796	1880	64	1278	577	20	357	53
139	1153	1724	1583	24	205	1900	398	1839	641	644
140	216	1492	877	1106	1546	282	1043	15	1137	932
141	1559	746	569	907	446	1263	655	953	1268	1484
142	250	722	1125	621	750	1412	647	1233	415	1878
143	1581	1490	1557	1482	413	1368	533	1370	455	168
144	527	1610	1862	602	970	589	535	1596	943	626
145	1008	1532	923	219	1671	1372	1245	1030	278	1662
146	472	1604	1322	1472	457	1746	775	1707	1695	1103
147	1578	1027	1186	170	361	80	1679	1454	616	1207
148	1495	135	529	731	1189	313	1666	1770	1910	1347
149	1167	1612	1512	1736	308	1630	761	1403	155	784

POWER RESIDUES

	0	1	2	3	4	5	6	7	8	9
100	39	117	351	1053	1246	1825	1649	1121	1450	524
101	1572	890	757	358	1074	1309	101	303	909	814
102	529	1587	935	892	763	376	1128	1471	587	1761
103	1457	545	1635	1079	1324	146	438	1314	116	348
104	1044	1219	1744	1406	392	1176	1615	1019	1144	1519
105	731	280	840	607	1821	1637	1085	1342	200	600
106	1800	1574	896	775	412	1236	1795	1559	851	640
107	7	21	63	189	567	1701	1277	5	15	45
108	135	405	1215	1732	1370	284	852	643	16	48
109	144	432	1296	62	186	558	1674	1196	1675	1199
110	1684	1226	1765	1469	581	1743	1403	383	1149	1534
111	776	415	1245	1822	1640	1094	1369	281	843	616
112	1848	1718	1328	158	474	1422	440	1320	134	402
113	1206	1705	1289	41	123	369	1107	1408	398	1194
114	1669	1181	1630	1064	1279	11	33	99	297	891
115	760	367	1101	1390	344	1032	1183	1636	1082	1333
116	173	519	1557	845	622	1866	1772	1490	644	19
117	57	171	513	1539	791	460	1380	314	942	913
118	826	565	1695	1259	1864	1766	1472	590	1770	1484
119	626	1878	1808	1598	968	991	1060	1267	1888	1838
120	1688	1238	1801	1577	905	802	493	1479	611	1833
121	1673	1193	1666	1172	1603	983	1036	1195	1672	1190
122	1657	1145	1522	740	307	921	850	637	1911	1907
123	1895	1859	1751	1427	455	1365	269	807	508	1524
124	746	325	975	1012	1123	1456	542	1626	1052	1243
125	1816	1622	1040	1207	1708	1298	68	204	612	1836
126	1682	1220	1747	1415	419	1257	1858	1748	1418	428
127	1284	26	78	234	702	193	579	1737	1385	329
128	987	1048	1231	1780	1514	716	235	705	202	606
129	1818	1628	1058	1261	1870	1784	1526	752	343	1029
130	1174	1609	1001	1090	1357	245	735	292	876	715
131	232	696	175	525	1575	899	784	439	1317	125
132	375	1125	1462	560	1680	1214	1729	1361	257	771
133	400	1200	1687	1235	1792	1550	824	559	1677	1205
134	1702	1280	14	42	126	378	1134	1489	641	10
135	30	90	270	810	517	1551	827	568	1704	1286
136	32	96	288	864	679	124	372	1116	1435	479
137	1437	485	1455	539	1617	1025	1162	1573	893	766
138	385	1155	1552	830	577	1731	1367	275	825	562
139	1686	1232	1783	1523	743	316	948	931	880	727
140	268	804	499	1497	665	82	246	738	301	903
141	796	475	1425	449	1347	215	645	22	66	198
142	594	1782	1520	734	289	867	688	151	453	1359
143	251	753	346	1038	1201	1690	1244	1819	1631	1067
144	1288	38	114	342	1026	1165	1582	920	847	628
145	1884	1826	1652	1130	1477	605	1815	1619	1031	1180
146	1627	1055	1252	1843	1703	1283	23	69	207	621
147	1863	1763	1463	563	1689	1241	1810	1604	986	1045
148	1222	1753	1433	473	1419	431	1293	53	159	477
149	1431	467	1401	377	1131	1480	614	1842	1700	1274

P = 1913

INDICES

	0	1	2	3	4	5	6	7	8	9
150	1864	108	692	1526	1569	573	1703	880	125	604
151	864	173	1889	374	1284	182	697	735	972	1049
152	1422	88	1222	1393	1239	1794	1296	591	424	949
153	151	836	1651	1834	1109	389	537	69	364	1173
154	12	410	1601	1907	179	1598	195	869	884	1657
155	1335	1355	1382	939	945	57	827	1162	662	1067
156	981	1549	46	628	810	83	769	476	1588	198
157	342	487	1010	1377	1061	1314	637	1203	977	840
158	560	1534	1446	1539	323	993	911	1021	285	1504
159	925	1852	1682	1753	683	804	872	439	1193	221
160	1874	860	1848	1214	1477	1803	268	30	1673	1301
161	61	743	452	1743	1509	1046	192	1374	1871	1457
162	1625	351	1251	887	468	406	1247	1460	1291	129
163	1142	1438	161	95	1779	1032	1157	1055	431	963
164	1114	844	18	396	280	444	619	1555	1608	1006
165	1660	1693	1452	1664	1628	1567	372	1220	834	10
166	1655	660	474	635	991	681	1212	450	349	1140
167	961	1606	1218	1210	1096	1098	1808	1338	330	317
168	1324	354	1260	1859	1100	758	1390	1332	1200	1474
169	1435	831	755	1810	1720	1182	935	1775	459	41
170	1498	1075	1340	1464	1358	1131	512	1748	1254	301
171	608	332	1813	102	1822	463	777	1728	1121	1522
172	319	677	564	1562	117	1709	901	138	1635	1326
173	597	1385	1083	667	1697	890	795	1277	356	1723
174	204	1838	215	1105	1042	931	568	1262	1267	721
175	749	1232	1580	1481	532	167	1861	588	942	1531
176	1670	1029	471	1471	774	1102	1185	79	615	134
177	1188	1769	1166	1735	760	783	691	572	124	172
178	1283	734	1421	1392	1295	948	1650	388	363	409
179	178	868	1334	938	826	1066	45	82	1587	486
180	1060	1202	559	1538	910	1503	1681	803	1192	859
181	1476	29	60	1742	191	1456	1250	405	1290	1437
182	1778	1054	1113	395	618	1005	1451	1566	833	659
183	990	449	960	1209	1807	316	1259	757	1199	830
184	1719	1774	1497	1463	511	300	1812	462	1120	676
185	116	137	596	666	794	1722	214	930	1266	1231
186	531	587	1669	1470	1184	133	1165	782	123	733
187	1294	387	177	937	44	485	558	1502	1191	28
188	190	404	1777	394	1450	658	959	315	1198	1773
189	510	461	115	665	213	1230	1668	132	122	386
190	43	1501	189	393	958	1772	114	1229	121	1500
191	957	1228	956							

POWER RESIDUES

	0	1	2	3	4	5	6	7	8	9
150	1909	1901	1877	1805	1589	941	910	817	538	1614
151	1016	1135	1492	650	37	111	333	999	1084	1339
152	191	573	1719	1331	167	501	1503	683	136	408
153	1224	1759	1451	527	1581	917	838	601	1803	1583
154	923	856	655	52	156	468	1404	386	1158	1561
155	857	658	61	183	549	1647	1115	1432	470	1410
156	404	1212	1723	1343	203	609	1827	1655	1139	1504
157	686	145	435	1305	89	267	801	490	1470	584
158	1752	1430	464	1392	350	1050	1237	1798	1568	878
159	721	250	750	337	1011	1120	1447	515	1545	809
160	514	1542	800	487	1461	557	1671	1187	1648	1118
161	1441	497	1491	647	28	84	252	756	355	1065
162	1282	20	60	180	540	1620	1034	1189	1654	1136
163	1495	659	64	192	576	1728	1358	248	744	319
164	957	958	961	970	997	1078	1321	137	411	1233
165	1786	1532	770	397	1191	1660	1154	1549	821	550
166	1650	1124	1459	551	1653	1133	1486	632	1896	1862
167	1760	1454	536	1608	998	1081	1330	164	492	1476
168	602	1806	1592	950	937	898	781	430	1290	44
169	132	396	1188	1651	1127	1468	578	1734	1376	302
170	906	805	502	1506	692	163	489	1467	575	1725
171	1349	221	663	76	228	684	139	417	1251	1840
172	1694	1256	1855	1739	1391	347	1041	1210	1717	1325
173	149	447	1341	197	591	1773	1493	653	46	138
174	414	1242	1813	1613	1013	1126	1465	569	1707	1295
175	59	177	531	1593	953	946	925	862	673	106
176	318	954	949	934	889	754	349	1047	1228	1771
177	1487	635	1905	1889	1841	1697	1265	1882	1820	1634
178	1076	1315	119	357	1071	1300	74	222	666	85
179	255	765	382	1146	1525	749	334	1002	1093	1366
180	272	816	535	1605	989	1054	1249	1834	1676	1202
181	1693	1253	1846	1712	1310	104	312	936	895	772
182	403	1209	1714	1316	122	366	1098	1381	317	951
183	940	907	808	511	1533	773	406	1218	1741	1397
184	365	1095	1372	290	870	697	178	534	1602	980
185	1027	1168	1591	947	928	871	700	187	561	1683
186	1223	1756	1442	500	1500	674	109	327	981	1030
187	1177	1618	1028	1171	1600	974	1009	1114	1429	461
188	1383	323	969	994	1069	1294	56	168	504	1512
189	710	217	651	40	120	360	1080	1327	155	465
190	1395	359	1077	1318	128	384	1152	1543	803	496
191	1488	638								

P = 1931

INDICES

	0	1	2	3	4	5	6	7	8	9
0		0	1	1104	2	1634	1105	882	3	278
1	1635	1780	1106	1663	883	808	4	1461	279	246
2	1636	56	1781	1872	1107	1338	1664	1382	884	1471
3	809	621	5	954	1462	586	280	182	247	837
4	1637	1004	57	20	1782	1912	1873	1893	1108	1764
5	1339	635	1665	627	1383	1484	885	1350	1472	980
6	810	51	622	1160	6	1367	955	1565	1463	1046
7	587	466	281	255	183	512	248	732	838	444
8	1638	556	1005	874	58	1165	21	645	1783	1531
9	1913	615	1874	1725	1894	1880	1109	572	1765	128
10	1340	1825	636	1418	1666	1690	628	390	1384	342
11	1485	1286	886	1139	1351	1576	1473	11	981	413
12	811	1630	52	178	623	1042	1161	1821	7	1124
13	1368	654	956	1128	1566	1086	1464	1745	1047	1855
14	588	1067	467	1513	282	1175	256	938	184	1372
15	513	272	249	1739	733	325	839	1752	445	1731
16	1639	824	557	232	1006	658	875	1079	59	1396
17	1166	524	22	69	646	290	1784	154	1532	397
18	1914	960	616	1155	1875	1816	1726	1311	1895	334
19	1881	1316	1110	1260	573	541	1766	1132	129	1275
20	1341	739	1826	423	637	708	1419	220	1667	96
21	1691	692	629	1570	391	1654	1385	1503	343	1359
22	1486	1194	1287	1900	887	1616	1140	608	1352	1090
23	1577	1836	1474	597	12	1597	982	1548	414	1208
24	812	136	1631	1660	53	1468	179	1909	624	48
25	1043	729	1162	1722	1822	339	8	1039	1125	1064
26	1369	1749	655	66	957	331	1129	705	1567	1191
27	1087	1545	1465	1719	1746	1188	1048	1051	1856	899
28	589	1328	1068	457	468	1054	1514	1886	283	992
29	1176	1676	257	1859	939	684	185	1232	1373	1605
30	514	902	273	999	250	1685	1740	1391	734	592
31	326	1227	840	487	1753	864	446	1331	1732	1321
32	1640	1494	825	1707	558	1071	233	1446	1007	845
33	659	379	876	460	1080	1269	60	1440	1397	313
34	1167	471	525	716	23	750	70	1097	647	1057
35	291	1115	1785	206	155	170	1533	1517	398	795
36	1915	492	961	804	617	1889	1156	440	1876	1282
37	1817	1509	1727	286	1312	216	1896	1204	335	1541
38	1882	995	1317	1265	1111	436	1261	298	574	1179
39	542	1403	1767	1758	1133	148	130	1679	1276	302
40	1342	479	740	354	1827	260	424	32	638	1647
41	709	919	1420	1862	221	578	1668	1029	97	1302
42	1692	942	693	241	630	869	1571	933	392	687
43	1655	1183	1386	308	1504	349	344	188	1360	1253
44	1487	112	1195	764	1288	1235	1901	546	888	119
45	1617	854	1141	1376	609	319	1353	451	1091	913
46	1578	1608	1837	1407	1475	1429	598	193	13	517
47	1598	926	983	1800	1549	1584	415	905	1209	1771
48	813	1845	137	1928	1632	276	1661	1459	54	1336
49	1469	952	180	1002	1910	1762	625	1348	49	1365

POWER RESIDUES

	0	1	2	3	4	5	6	7	8	9
0	1	2	4	8	16	32	64	128	256	512
1	1024	117	234	468	936	1872	1813	1695	1459	987
2	43	86	172	344	688	1376	821	1642	1353	775
3	1550	1169	407	814	1628	1325	719	1438	945	1890
4	1849	1767	1603	1275	619	1238	545	1090	249	498
5	996	61	122	244	488	976	21	42	84	168
6	336	672	1344	757	1514	1097	263	526	1052	173
7	346	692	1384	837	1674	1417	903	1806	1681	1431
8	931	1862	1793	1655	1379	827	1654	1377	823	1646
9	1361	791	1582	1233	535	1070	209	418	836	1672
10	1413	895	1790	1649	1367	803	1606	1281	631	1262
11	593	1186	441	882	1764	1597	1263	595	1190	449
12	898	1796	1661	1391	851	1702	1473	1015	99	198
13	396	792	1584	1237	543	1086	241	482	964	1928
14	1925	1919	1907	1883	1835	1739	1547	1163	395	790
15	1580	1229	527	1054	177	354	708	1416	901	1802
16	1673	1415	899	1798	1665	1399	867	1734	1537	1143
17	355	710	1420	909	1818	1705	1479	1027	123	246
18	492	984	37	74	148	296	592	1184	437	874
19	1748	1565	1199	467	934	1868	1805	1679	1427	923
20	1846	1761	1591	1251	571	1142	353	706	1412	893
21	1786	1641	1351	771	1542	1153	375	750	1500	1069
22	207	414	828	1656	1381	831	1662	1393	855	1710
23	1489	1047	163	326	652	1304	677	1354	777	1554
24	1177	423	846	1692	1453	975	19	38	76	152
25	304	608	1216	501	1002	73	146	292	584	1168
26	405	810	1620	1309	687	1374	817	1634	1337	743
27	1486	1041	151	302	604	1208	485	970	9	18
28	36	72	144	288	576	1152	373	746	1492	1053
29	175	350	700	1400	869	1738	1545	1159	387	774
30	1548	1165	399	798	1596	1261	591	1182	433	866
31	1732	1533	1135	339	678	1356	781	1562	1193	455
32	910	1820	1709	1487	1043	155	310	620	1240	549
33	1098	265	530	1060	189	378	756	1512	1093	255
34	510	1020	109	218	436	872	1744	1557	1183	435
35	870	1740	1549	1167	403	806	1612	1293	655	1310
36	689	1378	825	1650	1369	807	1614	1297	663	1326
37	721	1442	953	1906	1881	1831	1731	1531	1131	331
38	662	1324	717	1434	937	1874	1817	1703	1475	1019
39	107	214	428	856	1712	1493	1055	179	358	716
40	1432	933	1866	1801	1671	1411	891	1782	1633	1335
41	739	1478	1025	119	238	476	952	1904	1877	1823
42	1715	1499	1067	203	406	812	1624	1317	703	1406
43	881	1762	1593	1255	579	1158	385	770	1540	1149
44	367	734	1468	1005	79	158	316	632	1264	597
45	1194	457	914	1828	1725	1519	1107	283	566	1132
46	333	666	1332	733	1466	1001	71	142	284	568
47	1136	341	682	1364	797	1594	1257	583	1166	401
48	802	1604	1277	623	1246	561	1122	313	626	1252
49	573	1146	361	722	1444	957	1914	1897	1863	1795

P = 1931

INDICES

	0	1	2	3	4	5	6	7	8	9
50	1044	253	730	554	1163	1529	1723	570	1823	1688
51	340	1137	9	1628	1040	1122	1126	1743	1065	1173
52	1370	1737	1750	822	656	1394	67	152	958	1814
53	332	1258	1130	737	706	94	1568	1501	1192	1614
54	1088	595	1546	134	1466	46	1720	1037	1747	329
55	1189	1717	1049	1326	1052	990	1857	1230	900	1683
56	590	485	1329	1492	1069	843	458	1438	469	748
57	1055	204	1515	490	1887	1280	284	1202	993	434
58	1177	1756	1677	477	258	1645	1860	1027	940	867
59	685	306	186	110	1233	117	1374	449	1606	1427
60	515	1798	903	1843	274	1334	1000	1346	251	1527
61	1686	1626	1741	1735	1392	1812	735	1499	593	44
62	327	1324	1228	483	841	746	488	1200	1754	1643
63	865	108	447	1796	1332	1525	1733	1497	1322	744
64	1641	1794	1495	1792	826	828	1708	531	559	830
65	1072	677	234	1710	1447	358	1008	533	846	769
66	660	561	380	368	877	832	461	1413	1081	1074
67	1270	1831	61	679	1441	790	1398	236	314	1454
68	1168	1712	472	1807	526	1449	717	264	24	360
69	751	1293	71	1010	1098	1559	648	535	1058	1701
70	292	848	1116	428	1786	771	207	777	156	662
71	171	722	1534	563	1518	1217	399	382	796	36
72	1916	370	493	1240	962	879	805	1869	618	834
73	1890	1481	1157	463	441	642	1877	1415	1283	410
74	1818	1083	1510	269	1728	1076	287	1152	1313	1272
75	217	1651	1897	1833	1205	1906	336	63	1542	896
76	1883	681	996	1224	1318	1443	1266	713	1112	792
77	437	213	1262	1400	299	29	575	238	1180	1250
78	543	316	1404	923	1768	1456	1759	551	1134	1170
79	149	91	131	1714	1680	1435	1277	474	303	1424
80	1343	1809	480	105	741	528	355	365	1828	1451
81	261	1556	425	719	33	1866	639	266	1648	893
82	710	26	920	88	1421	362	1863	85	222	753
83	579	225	1669	1295	1030	783	98	73	1303	756
84	1693	1012	943	502	694	1100	242	582	631	1561
85	870	124	1572	650	934	228	393	537	688	604
86	1656	1060	1184	1672	1387	1703	309	166	1505	294
87	350	1298	345	850	189	1924	1361	1118	1254	1033
88	1488	430	113	1622	1196	1788	765	786	1289	773
89	1236	406	1902	209	547	101	889	779	120	162
90	1618	158	855	76	1142	664	1377	975	610	173
91	320	1306	1354	724	452	859	1092	1536	914	759
92	1579	565	1609	199	1838	1520	1408	1696	1476	1219
93	1430	80	599	401	194	1015	14	384	518	1591
94	1599	798	927	946	984	38	1801	1146	1550	1918
95	1585	505	416	372	906	1020	1210	495	1772	697
96	814	1242	1846	668	138	964	1929	1103	1633	881
97	277	1779	1662	807	1460	245	55	1871	1337	1381
98	1470	620	953	585	181	836	1003	19	1911	1892
99	1763	634	626	1483	1349	979	50	1159	1366	1564

POWER RESIDUES

	0	1	2	3	4	5	6	7	8	9
50	1659	1387	843	1686	1441	951	1902	1873	1815	1699
51	1467	1003	75	150	300	600	1200	469	938	1876
52	1821	1711	1491	1051	171	342	684	1368	805	1610
53	1289	647	1294	657	1314	697	1394	857	1714	1497
54	1063	195	390	780	1560	1189	447	894	1788	1645
55	1359	787	1574	1217	503	1006	81	162	324	648
56	1296	661	1322	713	1426	921	1842	1753	1575	1219
57	507	1014	97	194	388	776	1552	1173	415	830
58	1660	1389	847	1694	1457	983	35	70	140	280
59	560	1120	309	618	1236	541	1082	233	466	932
60	1864	1797	1663	1395	859	1718	1505	1079	227	454
61	908	1816	1701	1471	1011	91	182	364	728	1456
62	981	31	62	124	248	496	992	53	106	212
63	424	848	1696	1461	991	51	102	204	408	816
64	1632	1333	735	1470	1009	87	174	348	696	1392
65	853	1706	1481	1031	131	262	524	1048	165	330
66	660	1320	709	1418	905	1810	1689	1447	963	1926
67	1921	1911	1891	1851	1771	1611	1291	651	1302	673
68	1346	761	1522	1113	295	590	1180	429	858	1716
69	1501	1071	211	422	844	1688	1445	959	1918	1905
70	1879	1827	1723	1515	1099	267	534	1068	205	410
71	820	1640	1349	767	1534	1137	343	686	1372	813
72	1626	1321	711	1422	913	1826	1721	1511	1091	251
73	502	1004	77	154	308	616	1232	533	1066	201
74	402	804	1608	1285	639	1278	625	1250	569	1138
75	345	690	1380	829	1658	1385	839	1678	1425	919
76	1838	1745	1559	1187	443	886	1772	1613	1295	659
77	1318	705	1410	889	1778	1625	1319	707	1414	897
78	1794	1657	1383	835	1670	1409	887	1774	1617	1303
79	675	1350	769	1538	1145	359	718	1436	941	1882
80	1833	1735	1539	1147	363	726	1452	973	15	30
81	60	120	240	480	960	1920	1909	1887	1843	1755
82	1579	1227	523	1046	161	322	644	1288	645	1290
83	649	1298	665	1330	729	1458	985	39	78	156
84	312	624	1248	565	1130	329	658	1316	701	1402
85	873	1746	1561	1191	451	902	1804	1677	1423	915
86	1830	1729	1527	1123	315	630	1260	589	1178	425
87	850	1700	1469	1007	83	166	332	664	1328	725
88	1450	969	7	14	28	56	112	224	448	896
89	1792	1653	1375	819	1638	1345	759	1518	1105	279
90	558	1116	301	602	1204	477	954	1908	1885	1839
91	1747	1563	1195	459	918	1836	1741	1551	1171	411
92	822	1644	1357	783	1566	1201	471	942	1884	1837
93	1743	1555	1179	427	854	1708	1485	1039	147	294
94	588	1176	421	842	1684	1437	943	1886	1841	1751
95	1571	1211	491	982	33	66	132	264	528	1056
96	181	362	724	1448	965	1930	1929	1927	1923	1915
97	1899	1867	1803	1675	1419	907	1814	1697	1463	995
98	59	118	236	472	944	1888	1845	1759	1587	1243
99	555	1110	289	578	1156	381	762	1524	1117	303

P = 1931

INDICES

	0	1	2	3	4	5	6	7	8	9
100	1045	465	254	511	731	443	555	873	1164	644
101	1530	614	1724	1879	571	127	1824	1417	1689	389
102	341	1285	1138	1575	10	412	1629	177	1041	1820
103	1123	653	1127	1085	1744	1854	1066	1512	1174	937
104	1371	271	1738	324	1751	1730	823	231	657	1078
105	1395	523	68	289	153	396	959	1154	1815	1310
106	333	1315	1259	540	1131	1274	738	422	707	219
107	95	691	1569	1653	1502	1358	1193	1899	1615	607
108	1089	1835	596	1596	1547	1207	135	1659	1467	1908
109	47	728	1721	338	1038	1063	1748	65	330	704
110	1190	1544	1718	1187	1050	898	1327	456	1053	1885
111	991	1675	1858	683	1231	1604	901	998	1684	1390
112	591	1226	486	863	1330	1320	1493	1706	1070	1445
113	844	378	459	1268	1439	312	470	715	749	1096
114	1056	1114	205	169	1516	794	491	803	1888	439
115	1281	1508	285	215	1203	1540	994	1264	435	297
116	1178	1402	1757	147	1678	301	478	353	259	31
117	1646	918	1861	577	1028	1301	941	240	868	932
118	686	1182	307	348	187	1252	111	763	1234	545
119	118	853	1375	318	450	912	1607	1406	1428	192
120	516	925	1799	1583	904	1770	1844	1927	275	1458
121	1335	951	1001	1761	1347	1364	252	553	1528	569
122	1687	1136	1627	1121	1742	1172	1736	821	1393	151
123	1813	1257	736	93	1500	1613	594	133	45	1036
124	328	1716	1325	989	1229	1682	484	1491	842	1437
125	747	203	489	1279	1201	433	1755	476	1644	1026
126	866	305	109	116	448	1426	1797	1842	1333	1345
127	1526	1625	1734	1811	1498	43	1323	482	745	1199
128	1642	107	1795	1524	1496	743	1793	1791	827	530
129	829	676	1709	357	532	768	560	367	831	1412
130	1073	1830	678	789	235	1453	1711	1806	1448	263
131	359	1292	1009	1558	534	1700	847	427	770	776
132	661	721	562	1216	381	35	369	1239	878	1868
133	833	1480	462	641	1414	409	1082	268	1075	1151
134	1271	1650	1832	1905	62	895	680	1223	1442	712
135	791	212	1399	28	237	1249	315	922	1455	550
136	1169	90	1713	1434	473	1423	1808	104	527	364
137	1450	1555	718	1865	265	892	25	87	361	84
138	752	224	1294	782	72	755	1011	501	1099	581
139	1560	123	649	227	536	603	1059	1671	1702	165
140	293	1297	849	1923	1117	1032	429	1621	1787	785
141	772	405	208	100	778	161	157	75	663	974
142	172	1305	723	858	1535	758	564	198	1519	1695
143	1218	79	400	1014	383	1590	797	945	37	1145
144	1917	504	371	1019	494	696	1241	667	963	1102
145	880	1778	806	244	1870	1380	619	584	835	18
146	1891	633	1482	978	1158	1563	464	510	442	872
147	643	613	1878	126	1416	388	1284	1574	411	176
148	1819	652	1084	1853	1511	936	270	323	1729	230
149	1077	522	288	395	1153	1309	1314	539	1273	421

POWER RESIDUES

	0	1	2	3	4	5	6	7	8	9
100	606	1212	493	986	41	82	164	328	656	1312
101	693	1386	841	1682	1433	935	1870	1809	1687	1443
102	955	1910	1889	1847	1763	1595	1259	587	1174	417
103	834	1668	1405	879	1758	1585	1239	547	1094	257
104	514	1028	125	250	500	1000	69	138	276	552
105	1104	277	554	1108	285	570	1140	349	698	1396
106	861	1722	1513	1095	259	518	1036	141	282	564
107	1128	325	650	1300	669	1338	745	1490	1049	167
108	334	668	1336	741	1482	1033	135	270	540	1080
109	229	458	916	1832	1733	1535	1139	347	694	1388
110	845	1690	1449	967	3	6	12	24	48	96
111	192	384	768	1536	1141	351	702	1404	877	1754
112	1577	1223	515	1030	129	258	516	1032	133	266
113	532	1064	197	394	788	1576	1221	511	1022	113
114	226	452	904	1808	1685	1439	947	1894	1857	1783
115	1635	1339	747	1494	1057	183	366	732	1464	997
116	63	126	252	504	1008	85	170	340	680	1360
117	789	1578	1225	519	1038	145	290	580	1160	389
118	778	1556	1181	431	862	1724	1517	1103	275	550
119	1100	269	538	1076	221	442	884	1768	1605	1279
120	627	1254	577	1154	377	754	1508	1085	239	478
121	956	1912	1893	1855	1779	1627	1323	715	1430	929
122	1858	1785	1639	1347	763	1526	1121	311	622	1244
123	557	1114	297	594	1188	445	890	1780	1629	1327
124	723	1446	961	1922	1913	1895	1859	1787	1643	1355
125	779	1558	1185	439	878	1756	1581	1231	531	1062
126	193	386	772	1544	1157	383	766	1532	1133	335
127	670	1340	749	1498	1065	199	398	796	1592	1253
128	575	1150	369	738	1476	1021	111	222	444	888
129	1776	1621	1311	691	1382	833	1666	1401	871	1742
130	1553	1175	419	838	1676	1421	911	1822	1713	1495
131	1059	187	374	748	1496	1061	191	382	764	1528
132	1125	319	638	1276	621	1242	553	1106	281	562
133	1124	317	634	1268	605	1210	489	978	25	50
134	100	200	400	800	1600	1269	607	1214	497	994
135	57	114	228	456	912	1824	1717	1503	1075	219
136	438	876	1752	1573	1215	499	998	65	130	260
137	520	1040	149	298	596	1192	453	906	1812	1693
138	1455	979	27	54	108	216	432	864	1728	1525
139	1119	307	614	1228	525	1050	169	338	676	1352
140	773	1546	1161	391	782	1564	1197	463	926	1852
141	1773	1615	1299	667	1334	737	1474	1017	103	206
142	412	824	1648	1365	799	1598	1265	599	1198	465
143	930	1860	1789	1647	1363	795	1590	1249	567	1134
144	337	674	1348	765	1530	1129	327	654	1308	685
145	1370	809	1618	1305	679	1358	785	1570	1209	487
146	974	17	34	68	136	272	544	1088	245	490
147	980	29	58	116	232	464	928	1856	1781	1631
148	1331	731	1462	993	55	110	220	440	880	1760
149	1589	1247	563	1126	321	642	1284	637	1274	617

P = 1931

INDICES

	0	1	2	3	4	5	6	7	8	9
150	218	690	1652	1357	1898	606	1834	1595	1206	1658
151	1907	727	337	1062	64	703	1543	1186	897	455
152	1884	1674	682	1603	997	1389	1225	862	1319	1705
153	1444	377	1267	311	714	1095	1113	168	793	802
154	438	1507	214	1539	1263	296	1401	146	300	352
155	30	917	576	1300	239	931	1181	347	1251	762
156	544	852	317	911	1405	191	924	1582	1769	1926
157	1457	950	1760	1363	552	568	1135	1120	1171	820
158	150	1256	92	1612	132	1035	1715	988	1681	1490
159	1436	202	1278	432	475	1025	304	115	1425	1841
160	1344	1624	1810	42	481	1198	106	1523	742	1790
161	529	675	356	767	366	1411	1829	788	1452	1805
162	262	1291	1557	1699	426	775	720	1215	34	1238
163	1867	1479	640	408	267	1150	1649	1904	894	1222
164	711	211	27	1248	921	549	89	1433	1422	103
165	363	1554	1864	891	86	83	223	781	754	500
166	580	122	226	602	1670	164	1296	1922	1031	1620
167	784	404	99	160	74	973	1304	857	757	197
168	1694	78	1013	1589	944	1144	503	1018	695	666
169	1101	1777	243	1379	583	17	632	977	1562	509
170	871	612	125	387	1573	175	651	1852	935	322
171	229	521	394	1308	538	420	689	1356	605	1594
172	1657	726	1061	702	1185	454	1673	1602	1388	861
173	1704	376	310	1094	167	801	1506	1538	295	145
174	351	916	1299	930	346	761	851	910	190	1581
175	1925	949	1362	567	1119	819	1255	1611	1034	987
176	1489	201	431	1024	114	1840	1623	41	1197	1522
177	1789	674	766	1410	787	1804	1290	1698	774	1214
178	1237	1478	407	1149	1903	1221	210	1247	548	1432
179	102	1553	890	82	780	499	121	601	163	1921
180	1619	403	159	972	856	196	77	1588	1143	1017
181	665	1776	1378	16	976	508	611	386	174	1851
182	321	520	1307	419	1355	1593	725	701	453	1601
183	860	375	1093	800	1537	144	915	929	760	909
184	1580	948	566	818	1610	986	200	1023	1839	40
185	1521	673	1409	1803	1697	1213	1477	1148	1220	1246
186	1431	1552	81	498	600	1920	402	971	195	1587
187	1016	1775	15	507	385	1850	519	418	1592	700
188	1600	374	799	143	928	908	947	817	985	1022
189	39	672	1802	1212	1147	1245	1551	497	1919	970
190	1586	1774	506	1849	417	699	373	142	907	816
191	1021	671	1211	1244	496	969	1773	1848	698	141
192	815	670	1243	968	1847	140	669	967	139	966
193	965	0								

POWER RESIDUES

	0	1	2	3	4	5	6	7	8	9
150	1234	537	1074	217	434	868	1736	1541	1151	371
151	742	1484	1037	143	286	572	1144	357	714	1428
152	925	1850	1769	1607	1283	635	1270	609	1218	505
153	1010	89	178	356	712	1424	917	1834	1737	1543
154	1155	379	758	1516	1101	271	542	1084	237	474
155	948	1896	1861	1791	1651	1371	811	1622	1313	695
156	1390	849	1698	1465	999	67	134	268	536	1072
157	213	426	852	1704	1477	1023	115	230	460	920
158	1840	1749	1567	1203	475	950	1900	1869	1807	1683
159	1435	939	1878	1825	1719	1507	1083	235	470	940
160	1880	1829	1727	1523	1115	299	598	1196	461	922
161	1844	1757	1583	1235	539	1078	225	450	900	1800
162	1669	1407	883	1766	1601	1271	611	1222	513	1026
163	121	242	484	968	5	10	20	40	80	160
164	320	640	1280	629	1258	585	1170	409	818	1636
165	1341	751	1502	1073	215	430	860	1720	1509	1087
166	243	486	972	13	26	52	104	208	416	832
167	1664	1397	863	1726	1521	1111	291	582	1164	397
168	794	1588	1245	559	1118	305	610	1220	509	1018
169	105	210	420	840	1680	1429	927	1854	1777	1623
170	1315	699	1398	865	1730	1529	1127	323	646	1292
171	653	1306	681	1362	793	1586	1241	551	1102	273
172	546	1092	253	506	1012	93	186	372	744	1488
173	1045	159	318	636	1272	613	1226	521	1042	153
174	306	612	1224	517	1034	137	274	548	1096	261
175	522	1044	157	314	628	1256	581	1162	393	786
176	1572	1213	495	990	49	98	196	392	784	1568
177	1205	479	958	1916	1901	1871	1811	1691	1451	971
178	11	22	44	88	176	352	704	1408	885	1770
179	1609	1287	643	1286	641	1282	633	1266	601	1202
180	473	946	1892	1853	1775	1619	1307	683	1366	801
181	1602	1273	615	1230	529	1058	185	370	740	1480
182	1029	127	254	508	1016	101	202	404	808	1616
183	1301	671	1342	753	1506	1081	231	462	924	1848
184	1765	1599	1267	603	1206	481	962	1924	1917	1903
185	1875	1819	1707	1483	1035	139	278	556	1112	293
186	586	1172	413	826	1652	1373	815	1630	1329	727
187	1454	977	23	46	92	184	368	736	1472	1013
188	95	190	380	760	1520	1109	287	574	1148	365
189	730	1460	989	47	94	188	376	752	1504	1077
190	223	446	892	1784	1637	1343	755	1510	1089	247
191	494	988	45	90	180	360	720	1440	949	1898
192	1865	1799	1667	1403	875	1750	1569	1207	483	966
193										

P = 1933

INDICES

	0	1	2	3	4	5	6	7	8	9
0		0	1563	1698	1194	1	1329	202	825	1464
1	1564	1587	960	82	1765	1699	456	1413	1095	1123
2	1195	1900	1218	1736	591	2	1645	1230	1396	1105
3	1330	1461	87	1353	1044	203	726	1154	754	1780
4	826	1913	1531	98	849	1465	1367	382	222	404
5	1565	1179	1276	242	861	1588	1027	889	736	412
6	961	1036	1092	1666	1650	83	984	459	675	1502
7	1766	192	357	1456	785	1700	385	1789	1411	1529
8	457	996	1544	1753	1162	1414	1661	871	480	716
9	1096	284	998	1227	13	1124	1785	939	35	1119
10	1196	1608	810	1400	907	1901	1805	73	492	10
11	1219	920	658	513	520	1737	367	1546	43	1615
12	592	1242	667	1679	723	3	1297	663	1281	1796
13	1646	320	615	1325	90	1231	306	900	1133	249
14	1397	148	1755	1669	1920	1106	1087	170	416	1112
15	1331	1248	16	945	1420	1462	1042	410	1160	8
16	88	6	627	776	1175	1354	1384	1164	793	164
17	1045	655	1292	709	502	204	111	178	347	1071
18	727	1081	1847	802	629	1155	858	1068	1576	1432
19	755	1138	1416	1100	570	1781	1598	1522	750	1257
20	827	225	1239	1307	441	1914	1031	1268	538	778
21	1532	546	1436	1890	1636	99	123	1663	1573	1222
22	850	1495	551	1253	289	1466	144	1687	151	1749
23	1368	1555	1930	1643	1177	383	1606	1295	1246	109
24	223	142	873	762	298	405	1310	1205	354	1519
25	1566	875	928	1391	294	1180	912	854	1427	1356
26	1277	637	1883	1762	246	243	956	482	1653	397
27	862	1490	1869	50	531	1589	764	1127	1812	993
28	1028	842	1711	20	1386	890	1300	183	1551	894
29	737	705	718	1773	1733	413	47	885	743	1818
30	962	300	879	1374	1579	1037	576	1853	1051	1166
31	1093	96	673	1225	41	1667	791	1098	1571	760
32	1651	1771	1569	604	258	84	407	1708	806	584
33	985	845	1015	686	795	460	424	1319	1727	279
34	676	1116	286	606	923	1503	340	1715	133	609
35	1767	1312	1674	1758	1741	193	1910	1381	702	166
36	358	314	712	1008	1478	1457	433	1000	260	1445
37	786	444	489	1640	699	1701	1207	1187	1063	1719
38	386	429	769	128	1047	1790	731	1562	201	959
39	1412	1217	1229	86	1153	1530	381	1275	888	1091
40	458	356	1788	1543	870	997	938	809	72	657
41	1545	666	662	614	899	1754	169	15	409	626
42	1163	1291	177	1846	1067	1415	1521	1238	1267	1435
43	1662	550	1686	1929	1294	872	1204	927	853	1882
44	481	1868	1126	1710	182	717	884	878	1852	672
45	1097	1568	1707	1014	1318	285	1714	1673	1380	711
46	999	488	1186	768	1561	1228	1274	1787	808	661
47	14	176	1237	1685	926	1125	877	1706	1672	1185
48	1786	1236	1705	1704	504	940	393	505	1861	542
49	36	267	941	586	836	1120	1917	394	1150	472

POWER RESIDUES

	0	1	2	3	4	5	6	7	8	9
0	1	5	25	125	625	1192	161	805	159	795
1	109	545	792	94	470	417	152	760	1867	1603
2	283	1415	1276	581	972	994	1104	1654	538	757
3	1852	1528	1841	1473	1566	98	490	517	652	1327
4	836	314	1570	118	590	1017	1219	296	1480	1601
5	273	1365	1026	1264	521	672	1427	1336	881	539
6	762	1877	1653	533	732	1727	903	649	1312	761
7	1872	1628	408	107	535	742	1777	1153	1899	1763
8	1083	1549	13	65	325	1625	393	32	160	800
9	134	670	1417	1286	631	1222	311	1555	43	215
10	1075	1509	1746	998	1124	1754	1038	1324	821	239
11	1195	176	880	534	737	1752	1028	1274	571	922
12	744	1787	1203	216	1080	1534	1871	1623	383	1915
13	1843	1483	1616	348	1740	968	974	1004	1154	1904
14	1788	1208	241	1205	226	1130	1784	1188	141	705
15	1592	228	1140	1834	1438	1391	1156	1914	1838	1458
16	1491	1656	548	807	169	845	359	1795	1243	416
17	147	735	1742	978	1024	1254	471	422	177	885
18	559	862	444	287	1435	1376	1081	1539	1896	1748
19	1008	1174	71	355	1775	1143	1849	1513	1766	1098
20	1624	388	7	35	175	875	509	612	1127	1769
21	1113	1699	763	1882	1678	658	1357	986	1064	1454
22	1471	1556	48	240	1200	201	1005	1159	1929	1913
23	1833	1433	1366	1031	1289	646	1297	686	1497	1686
24	698	1557	53	265	1325	826	264	1320	801	139
25	695	1542	1911	1823	1383	1116	1714	838	324	1620
26	368	1840	1468	1541	1906	1798	1258	491	522	677
27	1452	1461	1506	1731	923	749	1812	1328	841	339
28	1695	743	1782	1178	91	455	342	1710	818	224
29	1120	1734	938	824	254	1270	551	822	244	1220
30	301	1505	1726	898	624	1187	136	680	1467	1536
31	1881	1673	633	1232	361	1805	1293	666	1397	1186
32	131	655	1342	911	689	1512	1761	1073	1499	1696
33	748	1807	1303	716	1647	503	582	977	1019	1229
34	346	1730	918	724	1687	703	1582	178	890	584
35	987	1069	1479	1596	248	1240	401	72	360	1800
36	1268	541	772	1927	1903	1783	1183	116	580	967
37	969	979	1029	1279	596	1047	1369	1046	1364	1021
38	1239	396	47	235	1175	76	380	1900	1768	1108
39	1674	638	1257	486	497	552	827	269	1345	926
40	764	1887	1703	783	49	245	1225	326	1630	418
41	157	785	59	295	1475	1576	148	740	1767	1103
42	1649	513	632	1227	336	1680	668	1407	1236	381
43	1905	1793	1233	366	1830	1418	1291	656	1347	936
44	814	204	1020	1234	371	1855	1543	1916	1848	1508
45	1741	973	999	1129	1779	1163	16	80	400	67
46	335	1675	643	1282	611	1122	1744	988	1074	1504
47	1721	873	499	562	877	519	662	1377	1086	1564
48	88	440	267	1335	876	514	637	1252	461	372
49	1860	1568	108	540	767	1902	1778	1158	1924	1888

P = 1933

INDICES

	0	1	2	3	4	5	6	7	8	9
50	1197	930	506	335	559	1609	1022	1862	1857	206
51	811	1658	543	421	485	1401	1058	37	987	475
52	908	54	268	746	1514	1902	1393	942	1809	1540
53	1806	1876	587	63	113	74	1284	837	28	59
54	493	361	1121	847	1500	11	1613	1918	162	568
55	1220	296	395	1731	758	921	1443	1151	624	180
56	659	834	473	1498	1342	514	1583	1198	1017	1344
57	521	118	931	904	1746	1738	1182	507	525	866
58	368	23	336	1829	349	1547	1404	560	1364	652
59	44	1288	1610	688	516	1616	374	1023	1449	1506
60	593	914	1863	1923	510	1243	1005	1858	1210	1073
61	668	464	207	1213	1484	1680	682	812	797	1585
62	724	1034	1659	918	304	4	856	544	1604	635
63	1298	94	422	312	729	664	1202	486	391	1656
64	1282	832	1402	462	1200	1797	235	1059	1821	67
65	1647	1429	38	1879	1339	321	437	988	215	1083
66	616	1799	476	1261	646	1326	317	909	426	1019
67	91	691	55	1895	950	1232	1358	269	1842	1141
68	307	1453	747	601	1849	901	237	1515	554	324
69	1134	1631	1903	1321	1346	250	1696	1394	240	1409
70	1398	1279	943	345	1305	149	1389	1810	1372	804
71	1756	1061	1541	1265	1012	1670	333	1807	1729	523
72	1921	1602	1877	1840	343	1107	639	588	1109	528
73	1088	1511	64	1190	631	171	1823	114	1076	1620
74	417	971	75	281	120	1113	1271	1285	330	275
75	1332	1885	838	641	818	1249	694	29	1350	1157
76	17	69	60	212	400	946	1691	494	678	933
77	1421	620	362	965	1193	1463	1764	1122	590	1104
78	1043	1779	848	403	860	411	1649	1501	784	1528
79	1161	715	12	1118	906	9	519	1614	722	1795
80	89	248	1919	1111	1419	7	1174	163	501	1070
81	628	1431	569	1256	440	777	1635	1221	288	1748
82	1176	108	297	1518	293	1355	245	396	530	992
83	1385	893	1732	1817	1578	1165	40	759	257	583
84	794	278	922	608	1740	165	1477	1444	698	1718
85	1046	958	1152	1090	869	656	898	625	1066	1434
86	1293	1881	181	671	1317	710	1560	660	925	1184
87	503	541	835	471	558	205	484	474	1513	1539
88	112	58	1499	567	757	179	1341	1343	1745	865
89	348	651	515	1505	509	1072	1483	1584	303	634
90	728	1655	1199	66	1338	1082	645	1018	949	1140
91	1848	323	1345	1408	1304	803	1011	522	342	527
92	630	1619	119	274	817	1156	399	932	1192	1103
93	859	1527	905	1794	1418	1069	439	1747	292	991
94	1577	582	1739	1717	868	1433	1316	1183	557	1538
95	756	864	508	633	1337	1139	1303	526	816	1102
96	1417	990	867	1537	1336	1101	1335	369	135	370
97	571	1833	24	451	136	1782	1492	337	173	371
98	1599	1474	1830	1722	572	1523	217	350	467	1834
99	751	773	1548	611	25	1258	781	1405	103	452

POWER RESIDUES

	0	1	2	3	4	5	6	7	8	9
50	1708	808	174	870	484	487	502	577	952	894
51	604	1087	1569	113	565	892	594	1037	1319	796
52	114	570	917	719	1662	578	957	919	729	1712
53	828	274	1370	1051	1389	1146	1864	1588	208	1040
54	1334	871	489	512	627	1202	211	1055	1409	1246
55	431	222	1110	1684	688	1507	1736	948	874	504
56	587	1002	1144	1854	1538	1891	1723	883	549	812
57	194	970	984	1054	1404	1221	306	1530	1851	1523
58	1816	1348	941	839	329	1645	493	532	727	1702
59	778	24	120	600	1067	1469	1546	1931	1923	1883
60	1683	683	1482	1611	323	1615	343	1715	843	349
61	1745	993	1099	1629	413	132	660	1367	1036	1314
62	771	1922	1878	1658	558	857	419	162	810	184
63	920	734	1737	953	899	629	1212	261	1305	726
64	1697	753	1832	1428	1341	906	664	1387	1136	1814
65	1338	891	589	1012	1194	171	855	409	112	560
66	867	469	412	127	635	1242	411	122	610	1117
67	1719	863	449	312	1560	68	340	1700	768	1907
68	1803	1283	616	1147	1869	1613	333	1665	593	1032
69	1294	671	1422	1311	756	1847	1503	1716	848	374
70	1870	1618	358	1790	1218	291	1455	1476	1581	173
71	865	459	362	1810	1318	791	89	445	292	1460
72	1501	1706	798	124	620	1167	36	180	900	634
73	1237	386	1930	1918	1858	1558	58	290	1450	1451
74	1456	1481	1606	298	1490	1651	523	682	1477	1586
75	198	990	1084	1554	38	190	950	884	554	837
76	319	1595	243	1215	276	1380	1101	1639	463	382
77	1910	1818	1358	991	1089	1579	163	815	209	1045
78	1359	996	1114	1704	788	74	370	1850	1518	1791
79	1223	316	1580	168	840	334	1670	618	1157	1919
80	1863	1583	183	915	709	1612	328	1640	468	407
81	102	510	617	1152	1894	1738	958	924	754	1837
82	1453	1466	1531	1856	1548	8	40	200	1000	1134
83	1804	1288	641	1272	561	872	494	537	752	1827
84	1403	1216	281	1405	1226	331	1655	543	782	44
85	220	1100	1634	438	257	1285	626	1197	186	930
86	784	54	270	1350	951	889	579	962	944	854
87	404	87	435	242	1210	251	1255	476	447	302
88	1510	1751	1023	1249	446	297	1485	1626	398	57
89	285	1425	1326	831	289	1445	1426	1331	856	414
90	137	685	1492	1661	573	932	794	104	520	667
91	1402	1211	256	1280	601	1072	1494	1671	623	1182
92	111	555	842	344	1720	868	474	437	252	1260
93	501	572	927	769	1912	1828	1408	1241	406	97
94	485	492	527	702	1577	153	765	1892	1728	908
95	674	1437	1386	1131	1789	1213	266	1330	851	389
96	12	60	300	1500	1701	773	1932	1928	1908	1808
97	1308	741	1772	1128	1774	1138	1824	1388	1141	1839
98	1463	1516	1781	1173	66	330	1650	518	657	1352
99	961	939	829	279	1395	1176	81	405	92	460

P = 1933

INDICES

	0	1	2	3	4	5	6	7	8	9
100	828	1871	561	1825	137	226	1898	1365	190	1783
101	1240	1085	653	1596	1493	1308	1488	45	1769	338
102	442	379	1289	882	174	1915	52	1611	116	372
103	1032	233	689	1694	1600	1269	618	517	106	1475
104	539	1481	1617	1314	1831	779	377	375	1145	1723
105	1533	533	1024	1078	573	547	1440	1450	1171	1524
106	1437	1801	1507	1469	218	1891	1626	594	1676	351
107	1637	1147	915	327	468	100	1591	1864	1622	1835
108	124	186	1924	80	752	1664	478	511	1131	774
109	1574	1888	1244	1760	1549	1223	1725	1006	199	612
110	851	766	1859	419	26	1496	1362	1211	389	1259
111	552	1263	1074	210	782	1254	255	669	1743	1406
112	290	1535	465	1594	104	1467	1129	208	973	453
113	145	953	1214	1055	829	1688	648	1485	975	1872
114	152	978	1681	195	562	1750	535	683	1377	1826
115	1369	1814	813	77	138	1556	156	798	497	227
116	1931	1328	1586	455	1899	1644	1460	725	1912	1366
117	1178	1026	1035	983	191	384	995	1660	283	1784
118	1607	1804	919	366	1241	1296	319	305	147	1086
119	1247	1041	5	1383	654	110	1080	857	1137	1597
120	224	1030	545	122	1494	143	1554	1605	141	1309
121	874	911	636	955	1489	763	841	1299	704	46
122	299	575	95	790	1770	406	844	423	1115	339
123	1311	1909	313	432	443	1206	428	730	1216	380
124	355	937	665	168	1290	1520	549	1203	1867	883
125	1567	1713	487	1273	175	876	1235	392	266	1916
126	929	1021	1657	1057	53	1392	1875	1283	360	1612
127	295	1442	833	1582	117	1181	22	1403	1287	373
128	913	1004	463	681	1033	855	93	1201	831	234
129	1428	436	1798	316	690	1357	1452	236	1630	1695
130	1278	1388	1060	332	1601	638	1510	1822	970	1270
131	1884	693	68	1690	619	1763	1778	1648	714	518
132	247	1173	1430	1634	107	244	892	39	277	1476
133	957	897	1880	1559	540	483	57	1340	650	1482
134	1654	644	322	1010	1618	398	1526	438	581	1315
135	863	1302	989	1334	1832	1491	1473	216	772	780
136	1870	1897	1084	1487	378	51	232	617	1480	376
137	532	1439	1800	1625	1146	1590	185	477	1887	1724
138	765	1361	1262	254	1534	1128	952	647	977	534
139	1813	155	1327	1459	1025	994	1803	318	1040	1079
140	1029	1553	910	840	574	843	1908	427	936	548
141	1712	1234	1020	1874	1441	21	1003	92	435	1451
142	1387	1509	692	1777	1172	891	896	56	643	1525
143	1301	1472	1896	231	1438	184	1360	951	154	1802
144	1552	1907	1233	1002	1508	895	1471	1359	1906	1470
145	738	739	270	820	219	706	740	1843	159	1892
146	719	271	1142	980	1627	1774	821	308	262	595
147	1734	220	1454	33	1677	414	707	748	1251	352
148	48	741	602	131	1638	886	1844	1850	1683	1148
149	744	160	902	1447	916	1819	1893	238	1838	328

POWER RESIDUES

	0	1	2	3	4	5	6	7	8	9
100	367	1835	1443	1416	1281	606	1097	1619	363	1815
101	1343	916	714	1637	453	332	1660	568	907	669
102	1412	1261	506	597	1052	1394	1171	56	280	1400
103	1201	206	1030	1284	621	1172	61	305	1525	1826
104	1398	1191	156	780	34	170	850	384	1920	1868
105	1608	308	1540	1901	1773	1133	1799	1263	516	647
106	1302	711	1622	378	1890	1718	858	424	187	935
107	809	179	895	609	1112	1694	738	1757	1053	1399
108	1196	181	905	659	1362	1011	1189	146	730	1717
109	853	399	62	310	1550	18	90	450	317	1585
110	193	965	959	929	779	29	145	725	1692	728
111	1707	803	149	745	1792	1228	341	1705	793	99
112	495	542	777	19	95	475	442	277	1385	1126
113	1764	1088	1574	138	690	1517	1786	1198	191	955
114	909	679	1462	1511	1756	1048	1374	1071	1489	1646
115	498	557	852	394	37	185	925	759	1862	1578
116	158	790	84	420	167	835	309	1545	1926	1898
117	1758	1058	1424	1321	806	164	820	234	1170	51
118	255	1275	576	947	869	479	462	377	1885	1693
119	733	1732	928	774	4	20	100	500	567	902
120	644	1287	636	1247	436	247	1235	376	1880	1668
121	608	1107	1669	613	1132	1794	1238	391	22	110
122	550	817	219	1095	1609	313	1565	93	465	392
123	27	135	675	1442	1411	1256	481	472	427	202
124	1010	1184	121	605	1092	1594	238	1190	151	755
125	1842	1478	1591	223	1115	1709	813	199	995	1109
126	1679	663	1382	1111	1689	713	1632	428	207	1035
127	1309	746	1797	1253	466	397	52	260	1300	701
128	1572	128	640	1267	536	747	1802	1278	591	1022
129	1244	421	172	860	434	237	1185	126	630	1217
130	286	1430	1351	956	914	704	1587	203	1015	1209
131	246	1230	351	1755	1043	1349	946	864	454	337
132	1685	693	1532	1861	1573	133	665	1392	1161	6
133	30	150	750	1817	1353	966	964	954	904	654
134	1337	886	564	887	569	912	694	1537	1886	1698
135	758	1857	1553	33	165	825	259	1295	676	1447
136	1436	1381	1106	1664	588	1007	1169	46	230	1150
137	1884	1688	708	1607	303	1515	1776	1148	1874	1638
138	458	357	1785	1193	166	830	284	1420	1301	706
139	1597	253	1265	526	697	1552	28	140	700	1567
140	103	515	642	1277	586	997	1119	1729	913	699
141	1562	78	390	17	85	425	192	960	934	804
142	154	770	1917	1853	1533	1866	1598	258	1290	651
143	1322	811	189	945	859	429	212	1060	1434	1371
144	1056	1414	1271	556	847	369	1845	1493	1666	598
145	1057	1419	1296	681	1472	1561	73	365	1825	1393
146	1166	31	155	775	9	45	225	1125	1759	1063
147	1449	1446	1431	1356	981	1039	1329	846	364	1820
148	1368	1041	1339	896	614	1137	1819	1363	1016	1214
149	271	1355	976	1014	1204	221	1105	1659	563	882

P = 1933

INDICES

	0	1	2	3	4	5	6	7	8	9
150	963	720	1516	696	469	301	272	555	449	101
151	880	1143	325	197	1592	1375	981	1135	788	1865
152	1580	1628	1632	579	1623	1038	1775	1904	31	1836
153	577	822	1322	1424	125	1854	309	1347	564	187
154	1052	263	251	446	1925	1167	596	1697	824	81
155	1094	1735	1395	1352	753	97	221	241	735	1665
156	674	1455	1410	1752	479	1226	34	1399	491	512
157	42	1678	1280	1324	1132	1668	415	944	1159	775
158	792	708	346	801	1575	1099	749	1306	537	1889
159	1572	1252	150	1642	1245	761	353	1390	1426	1761
160	1652	49	1811	19	1550	1772	742	1373	1050	1224
161	1570	603	805	685	1726	605	132	1757	701	1007
162	259	1639	1062	127	200	85	887	1542	71	613
163	408	1845	1266	1928	852	1709	1851	1013	1379	767
164	807	1684	1671	1703	1860	585	1149	334	1856	420
165	986	745	1808	62	27	846	161	1730	623	1497
166	1016	903	524	1828	1363	687	1448	1922	1209	1212
167	796	917	1603	311	390	461	1820	1878	214	1260
168	425	1894	1841	600	553	1320	239	344	1371	1264
169	1728	1839	1108	1189	1075	280	329	640	1349	211
170	677	964	589	402	783	1117	721	1110	500	1255
171	287	1517	529	1816	256	607	697	1089	1065	670
172	924	470	1512	566	1744	1504	302	65	948	1407
173	341	273	1191	1793	291	1716	556	632	815	1536
174	134	450	172	1721	466	610	102	1824	189	1595
175	1768	881	115	1693	105	1313	1144	1077	1170	1468
176	1675	326	1621	79	1130	1759	198	418	388	209
177	1742	1593	972	1054	974	194	1376	76	496	454
178	1911	982	282	365	146	1382	1136	121	140	954
179	703	789	1114	431	1215	167	1866	1272	265	1056
180	359	1581	1286	680	830	315	1629	331	969	1689
181	713	1633	276	1558	649	1009	580	1333	771	1486
182	1479	1624	1886	253	976	1458	1039	839	935	1873
183	434	1776	642	230	153	1001	1905	819	158	979
184	261	32	1250	130	1682	1446	1837	695	448	196
185	787	578	30	1423	563	445	823	1351	734	1751
186	490	1323	1158	800	536	1641	1425	18	1049	684
187	700	126	70	1927	1378	1702	1855	61	622	1827
188	1208	310	213	599	1370	1188	1348	401	499	1815
189	1064	565	947	1792	814	1720	188	1692	1169	78
190	387	1053	495	364	139	430	264	679	968	1557
191	770	252	934	229	157	129	447	1422	733	799
192	1048	1926	621	598	498	1791	1168	363	967	228
193	732	597	966							

POWER RESIDUES

	0	1	2	3	4	5	6	7	8	9
150	544	787	69	345	1725	893	599	1062	1444	1421
151	1306	731	1722	878	524	687	1502	1711	823	249
152	1245	426	197	985	1059	1429	1346	931	789	79
153	395	42	210	1050	1384	1121	1739	963	949	879
154	529	712	1627	403	82	410	117	585	992	1094
155	1604	288	1440	1401	1206	231	1155	1909	1813	1333
156	866	464	387	2	10	50	250	1250	451	322
157	1610	318	1590	218	1090	1584	188	940	834	304
158	1520	1801	1273	566	897	619	1162	11	55	275
159	1375	1076	1514	1771	1123	1749	1013	1199	196	980
160	1034	1304	721	1672	628	1207	236	1180	101	505
161	592	1027	1269	546	797	119	595	1042	1344	921
162	739	1762	1078	1524	1821	1373	1066	1464	1521	1806
163	1298	691	1522	1811	1323	816	214	1070	1484	1621
164	373	1865	1593	233	1165	26	130	650	1317	786
165	64	320	1600	268	1340	901	639	1262	511	622
166	1177	86	430	217	1085	1559	63	315	1575	143
167	715	1642	478	457	352	1760	1068	1474	1571	123
168	615	1142	1844	1488	1641	473	432	227	1135	1809
169	1313	766	1897	1753	1033	1299	696	1547	3	15
170	75	375	1875	1643	483	482	477	452	327	1635
171	443	282	1410	1251	456	347	1735	943	849	379
172	1895	1743	983	1049	1379	1096	1614	338	1690	718
173	1657	553	832	294	1470	1551	23	115	575	942
174	844	354	1770	1118	1724	888	574	937	819	229
175	1145	1859	1563	83	415	142	710	1617	353	1765
176	1093	1599	263	1315	776	14	70	350	1750	1018
177	1224	321	1605	293	1465	1526	1831	1423	1316	781
178	39	195	975	1009	1179	96	480	467	402	77
179	385	1925	1893	1733	933	799	129	645	1292	661
180	1372	1061	1439	1396	1181	106	530	717	1652	528
181	707	1602	278	1390	1151	1889	1713	833	299	1495
182	1676	648	1307	736	1747	1003	1149	1879	1663	583
183	982	1044	1354	971	989	1079	1529	1846	1498	1691
184	723	1682	678	1457	1486	1631	423	182	910	684
185	1487	1636	448	307	1535	1876	1648	508	607	1102
186	1644	488	507	602	1077	1519	1796	1248	441	272
187	1360	1001	1139	1829	1413	1266	531	722	1677	653
188	1332	861	439	262	1310	751	1822	1378	1091	1589
189	213	1065	1459	1496	1681	673	1432	1361	1006	1164
190	21	105	525	692	1527	1836	1448	1441	1406	1231
191	356	1780	1168	41	205	1025	1259	496	547	802
192	144	720	1667	603	1082	1544	1921	1873	1633	433
193	232	1160								

P = 1949

INDICES

	0	1	2	3	4	5	6	7	8	9
0		0	1	691	2	536	692	19	3	1382
1	537	577	693	184	20	1227	4	921	1383	1886
2	538	710	578	1183	694	1072	185	125	21	260
3	1228	549	5	1268	922	555	1384	1860	1887	875
4	539	1191	711	1024	579	1918	1184	361	695	38
5	1073	1612	186	781	126	1113	22	629	261	1655
6	1229	686	550	1401	6	720	1269	1406	923	1874
7	556	854	1385	453	1861	1763	1888	596	876	1061
8	540	816	1192	330	712	1457	1025	951	580	804
9	1919	203	1185	1240	362	474	696	1818	39	11
10	1074	316	1613	65	187	1246	782	774	127	749
11	1114	603	23	74	630	1719	262	1566	1656	940
12	1230	1154	687	1882	551	1608	1402	326	7	1715
13	721	725	1270	1905	1407	661	924	1503	1875	1645
14	557	1052	855	761	1386	796	454	729	1862	1483
15	1764	1784	1889	355	597	1085	877	1001	1062	1472
16	541	1202	817	1274	1193	1804	331	420	713	368
17	1458	1320	1026	1581	952	1091	581	398	805	1909
18	1920	134	204	1377	1186	448	1241	1498	363	144
19	475	1312	697	375	1819	1411	40	173	12	654
20	1075	149	317	279	1614	1727	66	617	188	515
21	1247	665	783	1545	775	1560	128	568	750	1144
22	1115	1105	604	827	24	506	75	928	631	589
23	1720	1287	263	480	1567	897	1657	1752	941	883
24	1231	1681	1155	1507	688	574	1883	122	552	1021
25	1609	1652	1403	1760	327	200	8	771	1716	1879
26	722	1642	726	1082	1271	1317	1906	1495	1408	276
27	662	1141	925	894	1504	1649	1876	1492	1646	1931
28	558	1364	1053	1934	856	1165	762	1210	1387	1842
29	797	561	455	1594	730	243	1863	702	1484	1367
30	1765	1043	1785	1007	1890	1222	356	1056	598	756
31	1086	612	878	1136	1002	1937	1063	643	1473	837
32	542	1465	1203	859	818	1256	1275	1440	1194	380
33	1805	1168	332	1294	421	1942	714	1709	369	765
34	1459	1126	1321	57	1027	462	1582	1213	953	104
35	1092	309	582	1624	399	1390	806	1631	1910	1035
36	1921	1824	135	1845	205	989	1378	1068	1187	625
37	449	800	1242	1150	1499	351	364	444	145	564
38	476	1017	1313	1360	698	1132	376	458	1820	440
39	1412	156	41	1416	174	1597	13	848	655	648
40	1076	1434	150	733	318	1352	280	489	1615	160
41	1728	246	67	1674	618	866	189	388	516	1866
42	1248	341	666	1743	784	45	1546	705	776	1452
43	1561	1478	129	1540	569	1487	751	1121	1145	1347
44	1116	1420	1106	1370	605	1340	828	226	25	1327
45	507	1768	76	527	929	739	632	178	590	1046
46	1721	270	1288	842	264	1776	481	1788	1568	1425
47	898	1692	1658	1601	1753	1010	942	215	884	292
48	1232	96	1682	1893	1156	406	1508	972	689	17
49	575	1225	1884	1181	123	547	553	873	1022	359

POWER RESIDUES

	0	1	2	3	4	5	6	7	8	9
0	1	2	4	8	16	32	64	128	256	512
1	1024	99	198	396	792	1584	1219	489	978	7
2	14	28	56	112	224	448	896	1792	1635	1321
3	693	1386	823	1646	1343	737	1474	999	49	98
4	196	392	784	1568	1187	425	850	1700	1451	953
5	1906	1863	1777	1605	1261	573	1146	343	686	1372
6	795	1590	1231	513	1026	103	206	412	824	1648
7	1347	745	1490	1031	113	226	452	904	1808	1667
8	1385	821	1642	1335	721	1442	935	1870	1791	1633
9	1317	685	1370	791	1582	1215	481	962	1924	1899
10	1849	1749	1549	1149	349	698	1396	843	1686	1423
11	897	1794	1639	1329	709	1418	887	1774	1599	1249
12	549	1098	247	494	988	27	54	108	216	432
13	864	1728	1507	1065	181	362	724	1448	947	1894
14	1839	1729	1509	1069	189	378	756	1512	1075	201
15	402	804	1608	1267	585	1170	391	782	1564	1179
16	409	818	1636	1323	697	1394	839	1678	1407	865
17	1730	1511	1073	197	394	788	1576	1203	457	914
18	1828	1707	1465	981	13	26	52	104	208	416
19	832	1664	1379	809	1618	1287	625	1250	551	1102
20	255	510	1020	91	182	364	728	1456	963	1926
21	1903	1857	1765	1581	1213	477	954	1908	1867	1785
22	1621	1293	637	1274	599	1198	447	894	1788	1627
23	1305	661	1322	695	1390	831	1662	1375	801	1602
24	1255	561	1122	295	590	1180	411	822	1644	1339
25	729	1458	967	1934	1919	1889	1829	1709	1469	989
26	29	58	116	232	464	928	1856	1763	1577	1205
27	461	922	1844	1739	1529	1109	269	538	1076	203
28	406	812	1624	1299	649	1298	647	1294	639	1278
29	607	1214	479	958	1916	1883	1817	1685	1421	893
30	1786	1623	1297	645	1290	631	1262	575	1150	351
31	702	1404	859	1718	1487	1025	101	202	404	808
32	1616	1283	617	1234	519	1038	127	254	508	1016
33	83	166	332	664	1328	707	1414	879	1758	1567
34	1185	421	842	1684	1419	889	1778	1607	1265	581
35	1162	375	750	1500	1051	153	306	612	1224	499
36	998	47	94	188	376	752	1504	1059	169	338
37	676	1352	755	1510	1071	193	386	772	1544	1139
38	329	658	1316	683	1366	783	1566	1183	417	834
39	1668	1387	825	1650	1351	753	1506	1063	177	354
40	708	1416	883	1766	1583	1217	485	970	1940	1931
41	1913	1877	1805	1661	1373	797	1594	1239	529	1058
42	167	334	668	1336	723	1446	943	1886	1823	1697
43	1445	941	1882	1815	1681	1413	877	1754	1559	1169
44	389	778	1556	1163	377	754	1508	1067	185	370
45	740	1480	1011	73	146	292	584	1168	387	774
46	1548	1147	345	690	1380	811	1622	1295	641	1282
47	615	1230	511	1022	95	190	380	760	1520	1091
48	233	466	932	1864	1779	1609	1269	589	1178	407
49	814	1628	1307	665	1330	711	1422	895	1790	16[illegible]

P = 1949

INDICES

	0	1	2	3	4	5	6	7	8	9
50	1610	1111	1653	1399	1404	852	1761	1059	328	949
51	201	472	9	63	772	601	1717	938	1880	324
52	723	659	1643	759	727	1782	1083	1470	1272	418
53	1318	1089	1907	1375	1496	1310	1409	652	277	615
54	663	1558	1142	825	926	1285	895	881	1505	120
55	1650	198	1877	1080	1493	1139	1647	1929	1932	1208
56	559	241	1365	1005	1054	610	1935	835	857	1438
57	1166	1940	763	55	1211	307	1388	1033	1843	1066
58	798	349	562	1358	456	154	1595	646	731	487
59	244	864	1864	1741	703	1476	1485	1345	1368	224
60	1766	737	1044	840	1786	1690	1008	290	1891	970
61	1223	545	357	1397	1057	470	599	322	757	1468
62	1087	1308	613	823	879	196	1137	1206	1003	833
63	1938	305	1064	1356	644	862	1474	222	838	288
64	543	468	1466	821	1204	303	860	286	819	284
65	1257	1259	1276	1794	1441	1261	1195	1835	381	1278
66	1806	231	1169	1796	333	493	1295	1443	422	1518
67	1943	1263	715	1813	1710	1197	370	501	766	1837
68	1460	1619	1127	383	1322	91	58	1280	1028	965
69	463	1808	1583	30	1214	233	954	164	105	1171
70	1093	1854	310	1798	583	1588	1625	335	400	114
71	1391	495	807	1732	1632	1297	1911	1574	1036	1445
72	1922	84	1825	424	136	1332	1846	1520	206	250
73	990	1945	1379	918	1069	1265	1188	35	626	717
74	450	813	801	1815	1243	71	1151	1712	1500	793
75	352	1199	365	395	445	372	146	512	565	503
76	477	1678	1018	768	1314	891	1361	1839	699	1219
77	1133	1462	377	1706	459	1621	1821	622	441	1129
78	1413	1431	157	385	42	1537	1417	1324	175	1773
79	1598	93	14	870	849	60	656	415	649	1282
80	1077	238	1435	1030	151	1738	734	967	319	193
81	1353	465	281	1832	490	1810	1616	962	161	1585
82	1729	81	247	32	68	392	1675	1216	619	1534
83	867	235	190	959	389	956	517	674	1867	166
84	1249	520	342	107	667	904	1744	1173	785	677
85	46	1095	1547	532	706	1856	777	1870	1453	312
86	1562	1901	1479	1800	130	169	1541	585	570	1638
87	1488	1590	752	1252	1122	1627	1146	436	1348	337
88	1117	523	1421	402	1107	934	1371	116	606	345
89	1341	1393	829	299	227	497	26	110	1328	809
90	508	1702	1769	1734	77	670	528	1634	930	1698
91	740	1299	633	907	179	1913	591	744	1047	1576
92	1722	1747	271	1038	1289	984	843	1447	265	1176
93	1777	1924	482	1303	1789	86	1569	788	1426	1827
94	899	431	1693	426	1659	680	1602	138	1754	637
95	1011	1334	943	49	216	1848	885	1528	293	1522
96	1233	1098	97	208	1683	911	1894	252	1157	1550
97	407	992	1509	1664	973	1947	690	535	18	1381
98	576	183	1226	920	1885	709	1182	1071	124	259
99	548	1267	554	1859	874	1190	1023	1917	360	37

POWER RESIDUES

	0	1	2	3	4	5	6	7	8	9
50	1313	677	1354	759	1518	1087	225	450	900	1800
51	1651	1353	757	1514	1079	209	418	836	1672	1395
52	841	1682	1415	881	1762	1575	1201	453	906	1812
53	1675	1401	853	1706	1463	977	5	10	20	40
54	80	160	320	640	1280	611	1222	495	990	31
55	62	124	248	496	992	35	70	140	280	560
56	1120	291	582	1164	379	758	1516	1083	217	434
57	868	1736	1523	1097	245	490	980	11	22	44
58	88	176	352	704	1408	867	1734	1519	1089	229
59	458	916	1832	1715	1481	1013	77	154	308	616
60	1232	515	1030	111	222	444	888	1776	1603	1257
61	565	1130	311	622	1244	539	1078	207	414	828
62	1656	1363	777	1554	1159	369	738	1476	1003	57
63	114	228	456	912	1824	1699	1449	949	1898	1847
64	1745	1541	1133	317	634	1268	587	1174	399	798
65	1596	1243	537	1074	199	398	796	1592	1235	521
66	1042	135	270	540	1080	211	422	844	1688	1427
67	905	1810	1671	1393	837	1674	1399	849	1698	1447
68	945	1890	1831	1713	1477	1005	61	122	244	488
69	976	3	6	12	24	48	96	192	384	768
70	1536	1123	297	594	1188	427	854	1708	1467	985
71	21	42	84	168	336	672	1344	739	1478	1007
72	65	130	260	520	1040	131	262	524	1048	147
73	294	588	1176	403	806	1612	1275	601	1202	455
74	910	1820	1691	1433	917	1834	1719	1489	1029	109
75	218	436	872	1744	1539	1129	309	618	1236	523
76	1046	143	286	572	1144	339	678	1356	763	1526
77	1103	257	514	1028	107	214	428	856	1712	1475
78	1001	53	106	212	424	848	1696	1443	937	1874
79	1799	1649	1349	749	1498	1047	145	290	580	1160
80	371	742	1484	1019	89	178	356	712	1424	899
81	1798	1647	1345	741	1482	1015	81	162	324	648
82	1296	643	1286	623	1246	543	1086	223	446	892
83	1784	1619	1289	629	1258	567	1134	319	638	1276
84	603	1206	463	926	1852	1755	1561	1173	397	794
85	1588	1227	505	1010	71	142	284	568	1136	323
86	646	1292	635	1270	591	1182	415	830	1660	1371
87	793	1586	1223	497	994	39	78	156	312	624
88	1248	547	1094	239	478	956	1912	1875	1801	1653
89	1357	765	1530	1111	273	546	1092	235	470	940
90	1880	1811	1673	1397	845	1690	1431	913	1826	1703
91	1457	965	1930	1911	1873	1797	1645	1341	733	1466
92	983	17	34	68	136	272	544	1088	227	454
93	908	1816	1683	1417	885	1770	1591	1233	517	1034
94	119	238	476	952	1904	1859	1769	1589	1229	509
95	1018	87	174	348	696	1392	835	1670	1391	833
96	1666	1383	817	1634	1319	689	1378	807	1614	1279
97	609	1218	487	974	1948	1947	1945	1941	1933	1917
98	1885	1821	1693	1437	925	1850	1751	1553	1157	365
99	730	1460	971	1942	1935	1921	1893	1837	1725	1501

P = 1949

INDICES

	0	1	2	3	4	5	6	7	8	9
100	1611	780	1112	628	1654	685	1400	719	1405	1873
101	853	452	1762	595	1060	815	329	1456	950	803
102	202	1239	473	1817	10	315	64	1245	773	748
103	602	73	1718	1565	939	1153	1881	1607	325	1714
104	724	1904	660	1502	1644	1051	760	795	728	1482
105	1783	354	1084	1000	1471	1201	1273	1803	419	367
106	1319	1580	1090	397	1908	133	1376	447	1497	143
107	1311	374	1410	172	653	148	278	1726	616	514
108	664	1544	1559	567	1143	1104	826	505	927	588
109	1286	479	896	1751	882	1680	1506	573	121	1020
110	1651	1759	199	770	1878	1641	1081	1316	1494	275
111	1140	893	1648	1491	1930	1363	1933	1164	1209	1841
112	560	1593	242	701	1366	1042	1006	1221	1055	755
113	611	1135	1936	642	836	1464	858	1255	1439	379
114	1167	1293	1941	1708	764	1125	56	461	1212	103
115	308	1623	1389	1630	1034	1823	1844	988	1067	624
116	799	1149	350	443	563	1016	1359	1131	457	439
117	155	1415	1596	847	647	1433	732	1351	488	159
118	245	1673	865	387	1865	340	1742	44	704	1451
119	1477	1539	1486	1120	1346	1419	1369	1339	225	1326
120	1767	526	738	177	1045	269	841	1775	1787	1424
121	1691	1600	1009	214	291	95	1892	405	971	16
122	1224	1180	546	872	358	1110	1398	851	1058	948
123	471	62	600	937	323	658	758	1781	1469	417
124	1088	1374	1309	651	614	1557	824	1284	880	119
125	197	1079	1138	1928	1207	240	1004	609	834	1437
126	1939	54	306	1032	1065	348	1357	153	645	486
127	863	1740	1475	1344	223	736	839	1689	289	969
128	544	1396	469	321	1467	1307	822	195	1205	832
129	304	1355	861	221	287	467	820	302	285	283
130	1258	1793	1260	1834	1277	230	1795	492	1442	1517
131	1262	1812	1196	500	1836	1618	382	90	1279	964
132	1807	29	232	163	1170	1853	1797	1587	334	113
133	494	1731	1296	1573	1444	83	423	1331	1519	249
134	1944	917	1264	34	716	812	1814	70	1711	792
135	1198	394	371	511	502	1677	767	890	1838	1218
136	1461	1705	1620	621	1128	1430	384	1536	1323	1772
137	92	869	59	414	1281	237	1029	1737	966	192
138	464	1831	1809	961	1584	80	31	391	1215	1533
139	234	958	955	673	165	519	106	903	1172	676
140	1094	531	1855	1869	311	1900	1799	168	584	1637
141	1589	1251	1626	435	336	522	401	933	115	344
142	1392	298	496	109	808	1701	1733	669	1633	1697
143	1298	906	1912	743	1575	1746	1037	983	1446	1175
144	1923	1302	85	787	1826	430	425	679	137	636
145	1333	48	1847	1527	1521	1097	207	910	251	1549
146	991	1663	1946	534	1380	182	919	708	1070	258
147	1266	1858	1189	1916	36	779	627	684	718	1872
148	451	594	814	1455	802	1238	1816	314	1244	747
149	72	1564	1152	1606	1713	1903	1501	1050	794	1481

POWER RESIDUES

	0	1	2	3	4	5	6	7	8	9
100	1053	157	314	628	1256	563	1126	303	606	1212
101	475	950	1900	1851	1753	1557	1165	381	762	1524
102	1099	249	498	996	43	86	172	344	688	1376
103	803	1606	1263	577	1154	359	718	1436	923	1846
104	1743	1537	1125	301	602	1204	459	918	1836	1723
105	1497	1045	141	282	564	1128	307	614	1228	507
106	1014	79	158	316	632	1264	579	1158	367	734
107	1468	987	25	50	100	200	400	800	1600	1251
108	553	1106	263	526	1052	155	310	620	1240	531
109	1062	175	350	700	1400	851	1702	1455	961	1922
110	1895	1841	1733	1517	1085	221	442	884	1768	1587
111	1225	501	1002	55	110	220	440	880	1760	1571
112	1193	437	874	1748	1547	1145	341	682	1364	779
113	1558	1167	385	770	1540	1131	313	626	1252	555
114	1110	271	542	1084	219	438	876	1752	1555	1161
115	373	746	1492	1035	121	242	484	968	1936	1923
116	1897	1845	1741	1533	1117	285	570	1140	331	662
117	1324	699	1398	847	1694	1439	929	1858	1767	1585
118	1221	493	986	23	46	92	184	368	736	1472
119	995	41	82	164	328	656	1312	675	1350	751
120	1502	1055	161	322	644	1288	627	1254	559	1118
121	287	574	1148	347	694	1388	827	1654	1359	769
122	1538	1127	305	610	1220	491	982	15	30	60
123	120	240	480	960	1920	1891	1833	1717	1485	1021
124	93	186	372	744	1488	1027	105	210	420	840
125	1680	1411	873	1746	1543	1137	325	650	1300	651
126	1302	655	1310	671	1342	735	1470	991	33	66
127	132	264	528	1056	163	326	652	1304	659	1318
128	687	1374	799	1598	1247	545	1090	231	462	924
129	1848	1747	1545	1141	333	666	1332	715	1430	911
130	1822	1695	1441	933	1866	1783	1617	1285	621	1242
131	535	1070	191	382	764	1528	1107	265	530	1060
132	171	342	684	1368	787	1574	1199	449	898	1796
133	1643	1337	725	1450	951	1902	1855	1761	1573	1197
134	445	890	1780	1611	1273	597	1194	439	878	1756
135	1563	1177	405	810	1620	1291	633	1266	583	1166
136	383	766	1532	1115	281	562	1124	299	598	1196
137	443	886	1772	1595	1241	533	1066	183	366	732
138	1464	979	9	18	36	72	144	288	576	1152
139	355	710	1420	891	1782	1615	1281	613	1226	503
140	1006	63	126	252	504	1008	67	134	268	536
141	1072	195	390	780	1560	1171	393	786	1572	1195
142	441	882	1764	1579	1209	469	938	1876	1803	1657
143	1365	781	1562	1175	401	802	1604	1259	569	1138
144	327	654	1308	667	1334	719	1438	927	1854	1759
145	1569	1189	429	858	1716	1483	1017	85	170	340
146	680	1360	771	1542	1135	321	642	1284	619	1238
147	527	1054	159	318	636	1272	595	1190	431	862
148	1724	1499	1049	149	298	596	1192	435	870	1740
149	1531	1113	277	554	1108	267	534	1068	187	374

P = 1949

INDICES

	0	1	2	3	4	5	6	7	8	9
150	353	999	1200	1802	366	1579	396	132	446	142
151	373	171	147	1725	513	1543	566	1103	504	587
152	478	1750	1679	572	1019	1758	769	1640	1315	274
153	892	1490	1362	1163	1840	1592	700	1041	1220	754
154	1134	641	1463	1254	378	1292	1707	1124	460	102
155	1622	1629	1822	987	623	1148	442	1015	1130	438
156	1414	846	1432	1350	158	1672	386	339	43	1450
157	1538	1119	1418	1338	1325	525	176	268	1774	1423
158	1599	213	94	404	15	1179	871	1109	850	947
159	61	936	657	1780	416	1373	650	1556	1283	118
160	1078	1927	239	608	1436	53	1031	347	152	485
161	1739	1343	735	1688	968	1395	320	1306	194	831
162	1354	220	466	301	282	1792	1833	229	491	1516
163	1811	499	1617	89	963	28	162	1852	1586	112
164	1730	1572	82	1330	248	916	33	811	69	791
165	393	510	1676	889	1217	1704	620	1429	1535	1771
166	868	413	236	1736	191	1830	960	79	390	1532
167	957	672	518	902	675	530	1868	1899	167	1636
168	1250	434	521	932	343	297	108	1700	668	1696
169	905	742	1745	982	1174	1301	786	429	678	635
170	47	1526	1096	909	1548	1662	533	181	707	257
171	1857	1915	778	683	1871	593	1454	1237	313	746
172	1563	1605	1902	1049	1480	998	1801	1578	131	141
173	170	1724	1542	1102	586	1749	571	1757	1639	273
174	1489	1162	1591	1040	753	640	1253	1291	1123	101
175	1628	986	1147	1014	437	845	1349	1671	338	1449
176	1118	1337	524	267	1422	212	403	1178	1108	946
177	935	1779	1372	1555	117	1926	607	52	346	484
178	1342	1687	1394	1305	830	219	300	1791	228	1515
179	498	88	27	1851	111	1571	1329	915	810	790
180	509	888	1703	1428	1770	412	1735	1829	78	1531
181	671	901	529	1898	1635	433	931	296	1699	1695
182	741	981	1300	428	634	1525	908	1661	180	256
183	1914	682	592	1236	745	1604	1048	997	1577	140
184	1723	1101	1748	1756	272	1161	1039	639	1290	100
185	985	1013	844	1670	1448	1336	266	211	1177	945
186	1778	1554	1925	51	483	1686	1304	218	1790	1514
187	87	1850	1570	914	789	887	1427	411	1828	1530
188	900	1897	432	295	1694	980	427	1524	1660	255
189	681	1235	1603	996	139	1100	1755	1160	638	99
190	1012	1669	1335	210	944	1553	50	1685	217	1513
191	1849	913	886	410	1529	1896	294	979	1523	254
192	1234	995	1099	1159	98	1668	209	1552	1684	1512
193	912	409	1895	978	253	994	1158	1667	1551	1511
194	408	977	993	1666	1510	976	1665	975	974	

POWER RESIDUES

	0	1	2	3	4	5	6	7	8	9
150	748	1496	1043	137	274	548	1096	243	486	972
151	1944	1939	1929	1909	1869	1789	1629	1309	669	1338
152	727	1454	959	1918	1887	1825	1701	1453	957	1914
153	1879	1809	1669	1389	829	1658	1367	785	1570	1191
154	433	866	1732	1515	1081	213	426	852	1704	1459
155	969	1938	1927	1905	1861	1773	1597	1245	541	1082
156	215	430	860	1720	1491	1033	117	234	468	936
157	1872	1795	1641	1333	717	1434	919	1838	1727	1505
158	1061	173	346	692	1384	819	1638	1327	705	1410
159	871	1742	1535	1121	293	586	1172	395	790	1580
160	1211	473	946	1892	1835	1721	1493	1037	125	250
161	500	1000	51	102	204	408	816	1632	1315	681
162	1362	775	1550	1151	353	706	1412	875	1750	1551
163	1153	357	714	1428	907	1814	1679	1409	869	1738
164	1527	1105	261	522	1044	139	278	556	1112	275
165	550	1100	251	502	1004	59	118	236	472	944
166	1888	1827	1705	1461	973	1946	1943	1937	1925	1901
167	1853	1757	1565	1181	413	826	1652	1355	761	1522
168	1095	241	482	964	1928	1907	1865	1781	1613	1277
169	605	1210	471	942	1884	1819	1689	1429	909	1818
170	1687	1425	901	1802	1655	1361	773	1546	1143	337
171	674	1348	747	1494	1039	129	258	516	1032	115
172	230	460	920	1840	1731	1513	1077	205	410	820
173	1640	1331	713	1426	903	1806	1663	1377	805	1610
174	1271	593	1186	423	846	1692	1435	921	1842	1735
175	1521	1093	237	474	948	1896	1843	1737	1525	1101
176	253	506	1012	75	150	300	600	1200	451	902
177	1804	1659	1369	789	1578	1207	465	930	1860	1771
178	1593	1237	525	1050	151	302	604	1208	467	934
179	1868	1787	1625	1301	653	1306	663	1326	703	1406
180	863	1726	1503	1057	165	330	660	1320	691	1382
181	815	1630	1311	673	1346	743	1486	1023	97	194
182	388	776	1552	1155	361	722	1444	939	1878	1807
183	1665	1381	813	1626	1303	657	1314	679	1358	767
184	1534	1119	289	578	1156	363	726	1452	955	1910
185	1871	1793	1637	1325	701	1402	855	1710	1471	993
186	37	74	148	296	592	1184	419	838	1676	1403
187	857	1714	1479	1009	69	138	276	552	1104	259
188	518	1036	123	246	492	984	19	38	76	152
189	304	608	1216	483	966	1932	1915	1881	1813	1677
190	1405	861	1722	1495	1041	133	266	532	1064	179
191	358	716	1432	915	1830	1711	1473	997	45	90
192	180	360	720	1440	931	1862	1775	1601	1253	557
193	1114	279	558	1116	283	566	1132	315	630	1260
194	571	1142	335	670	1340	731	1462	975		

P = 1951

INDICES

	0	1	2	3	4	5	6	7	8	9
0		0	604	1	1208	406	605	842	1812	2
1	1010	1433	1209	1508	1446	407	466	486	606	1392
2	1614	843	87	316	1813	812	162	3	100	1099
3	1011	1710	1070	1434	1090	1248	1210	212	46	1509
4	268	19	1447	1033	691	408	920	819	467	1684
5	1416	487	766	798	607	1839	704	1393	1703	749
6	1615	880	364	844	1674	1914	88	1688	1694	317
7	1852	112	1814	1611	816	813	650	325	163	1001
8	872	4	623	156	101	892	1637	1100	1295	755
9	1012	400	1524	1711	1423	1798	1071	794	338	1435
10	70	653	1091	1163	1370	1249	1402	1181	1211	827
11	493	213	1308	1500	47	722	357	1510	1353	1328
12	269	916	1484	20	968	1218	1448	1488	328	1034
13	568	1039	692	284	342	409	348	963	921	1885
14	506	820	716	991	468	1505	265	1685	1420	913
15	1417	1651	1254	488	929	166	767	1454	1605	799
16	1476	1158	608	1147	1227	1840	760	1539	705	1066
17	1496	1394	291	9	1704	1654	1899	750	1359	1123
18	1616	785	1004	881	178	618	365	1919	77	845
19	452	1934	1675	808	1398	1915	942	382	89	499
20	674	1689	1257	1941	1695	425	1767	318	24	875
21	1853	1739	56	113	1785	1439	1815	602	1431	1612
22	1097	44	817	702	1912	814	154	1522	651	491
23	1326	326	961	263	164	1225	7	1002	1932	672
24	873	1429	1520	5	138	140	624	950	1572	157
25	1822	1531	102	1749	142	893	932	1387	1638	1054
26	1172	1101	1643	626	1296	1204	888	756	946	1827
27	1013	740	952	401	1567	295	1525	1342	539	1712
28	1110	1574	1424	169	1320	1799	1595	861	1072	972
29	159	795	869	1178	339	1155	74	1436	1517	1824
30	71	1875	305	654	1858	1286	1092	1197	1533	1164
31	770	1262	1371	31	108	1250	259	104	1403	582
32	130	1182	1762	1878	1212	370	1751	828	1831	1661
33	494	643	1364	214	193	144	1309	1457	1670	1501
34	150	1193	48	576	895	723	613	434	358	386
35	308	1511	553	934	1354	518	13	1329	1727	1336
36	270	834	1389	917	1608	67	1485	926	782	21
37	1222	1640	969	256	573	1219	681	657	1449	1273
38	1056	1489	588	1779	329	731	1412	1035	52	1174
39	569	802	1546	1040	986	1407	693	684	1103	285
40	1278	201	343	1268	1861	410	595	1645	349	1017
41	1029	964	421	1591	922	562	628	1886	1479	62
42	507	523	393	821	660	1298	717	1722	439	992
43	93	1289	469	1379	1206	1506	85	1708	266	1682
44	1701	1686	648	890	1421	1161	1306	914	566	1883
45	1418	1452	758	1652	176	806	1255	1737	1095	489
46	1930	948	930	1202	1565	167	867	1873	768	580
47	1829	1455	611	516	1606	254	586	800	1276	1015
48	1477	1720	83	1159	174	1200	609	1718	742	1148
49	744	300	1228	1585	1554	1841	226	954	761	1150

POWER RESIDUES

	0	1	2	3	4	5	6	7	8	9
0	1	3	9	27	81	243	729	236	708	173
1	519	1557	769	356	1068	1253	1808	1522	664	41
2	123	369	1107	1370	208	624	1872	1714	1240	1769
3	1405	313	939	866	647	1941	1921	1861	1681	1141
4	1472	514	1542	724	221	663	38	114	342	1026
5	1127	1430	388	1164	1541	721	212	636	1908	1822
6	1564	790	419	1257	1820	1558	772	365	1095	1334
7	100	300	900	749	296	888	713	188	564	1692
8	1174	1571	811	482	1446	436	1308	22	66	198
9	594	1782	1444	430	1290	1919	1855	1663	1087	1310
10	28	84	252	756	317	951	902	755	314	942
11	875	674	71	213	639	1917	1849	1645	1033	1148
12	1493	577	1731	1291	1922	1864	1690	1168	1553	757
13	320	960	929	836	557	1671	1111	1382	244	732
14	245	735	254	762	335	1005	1064	1241	1772	1414
15	340	1020	1109	1376	226	678	83	249	747	290
16	870	659	26	78	234	702	155	465	1395	283
17	849	596	1788	1462	484	1452	454	1362	184	552
18	1656	1066	1247	1790	1468	502	1506	616	1848	1642
19	1024	1121	1412	334	1002	1055	1214	1691	1171	1562
20	784	401	1203	1658	1072	1265	1844	1630	988	1013
21	1088	1313	37	111	333	999	1046	1187	1610	928
22	833	548	1644	1030	1139	1466	496	1488	562	1686
23	1156	1517	649	1947	1939	1915	1843	1627	979	986
24	1007	1070	1259	1826	1576	826	527	1581	841	572
25	1716	1246	1787	1459	475	1425	373	1119	1406	316
26	948	893	728	233	699	146	438	1314	40	120
27	360	1080	1289	1916	1846	1636	1006	1067	1250	1799
28	1495	583	1749	1345	133	399	1197	1640	1018	1103
29	1358	172	516	1548	742	275	825	524	1572	814
30	491	1473	517	1551	751	302	906	767	350	1050
31	1199	1646	1036	1157	1520	658	23	69	207	621
32	1863	1687	1159	1526	676	77	231	693	128	384
33	1152	1505	613	1839	1615	943	878	683	98	294
34	882	695	134	402	1206	1667	1099	1346	136	408
35	1224	1721	1261	1832	1594	880	689	116	348	1044
36	1181	1592	874	671	62	186	558	1674	1120	1409
37	325	975	974	971	962	935	854	611	1833	1597
38	889	716	197	591	1773	1417	349	1047	1190	1619
39	955	914	791	422	1266	1847	1639	1015	1094	1331
40	91	273	819	506	1518	652	5	15	45	135
41	405	1215	1694	1180	1589	865	644	1932	1894	1780
42	1438	412	1236	1757	1369	205	615	1845	1633	997
43	1040	1169	1556	766	347	1041	1172	1565	793	428
44	1284	1901	1801	1501	601	1803	1507	619	1857	1669
45	1105	1364	190	570	1710	1228	1733	1297	1940	1918
46	1852	1654	1060	1229	1736	1306	16	48	144	432
47	1296	1937	1909	1825	1573	817	500	1500	598	1794
48	1480	538	1614	940	869	656	17	51	153	459
49	1377	229	687	110	330	990	1019	1106	1367	199

P = 1951

INDICES

	0	1	2	3	4	5	6	7	8	9
50	476	1540	185	1622	706	1059	403	1067	746	1634
51	1497	503	1536	1395	41	1569	292	302	1658	10
52	1776	1026	1705	1562	297	1655	1230	246	1900	632
53	1808	751	1492	1527	1360	1587	1550	1124	481	1167
54	1617	855	1344	786	1556	1233	1005	1744	221	882
55	899	541	179	1843	1946	619	1143	134	366	591
56	1714	1920	228	667	78	1906	773	846	1924	1112
57	453	956	249	1935	1465	1128	1676	121	1576	809
58	763	998	1399	281	1473	1916	1782	1426	943	1152
59	1759	383	678	1265	90	1734	171	500	478	1903
60	675	444	529	1690	909	1322	1258	1542	512	1942
61	1890	377	1696	332	1801	426	187	1044	1768	447
62	1374	319	1866	1597	25	1624	635	876	712	698
63	1854	727	863	1740	708	1894	57	1242	1186	114
64	734	1074	1786	1061	416	1440	532	34	1816	232
65	974	603	405	1811	1432	1445	485	1613	315	161
66	1098	1069	1247	45	18	690	818	1415	797	703
67	748	363	1913	1693	111	815	324	871	155	1636
68	754	1523	1797	337	652	1369	1180	492	1499	356
69	1327	1483	1217	327	1038	341	962	505	990	264
70	912	1253	165	1604	1157	1226	1538	1495	8	1898
71	1122	1003	617	76	1933	1397	381	673	1940	1766
72	874	55	1438	1430	43	1911	1521	1325	262	6
73	671	1519	139	1571	1530	141	1386	1171	625	887
74	1826	951	294	538	1573	1319	860	158	1177	73
75	1823	304	1285	1532	1261	107	103	129	1877	1750
76	1660	1363	143	1669	1192	894	433	307	933	12
77	1335	1388	66	781	1639	572	656	1055	1778	1411
78	1173	1545	1406	1102	200	1860	1644	1028	1590	627
79	61	392	1297	438	1288	1205	1707	1700	889	1305
80	1882	757	805	1094	947	1564	1872	1828	515	585
81	1014	82	1199	741	299	1553	953	475	1621	402
82	1633	1535	1568	1657	1025	296	245	1807	1526	1549
83	1166	1343	1232	220	540	1945	133	1713	666	772
84	1111	248	1127	1575	997	1472	1425	1758	1264	170
85	1902	528	1321	511	376	1800	1043	1373	1596	634
86	697	862	1893	1185	1073	415	33	973	1810	484
87	160	1246	689	796	362	110	870	753	336	1179
88	355	1216	340	989	1252	1156	1494	1121	75	380
89	1765	1437	1910	261	1518	1529	1170	1825	537	859
90	72	1284	106	1876	1362	1191	306	1334	780	655
91	1410	1405	1859	1589	391	1287	1699	1881	1093	1871
92	584	1198	1552	1620	1534	1024	1806	1165	219	132
93	771	1126	1471	1263	527	375	1372	696	1184	32
94	483	688	109	335	1215	1251	1120	1764	260	1169
95	858	105	1190	779	1404	390	1880	583	1619	1805
96	131	1470	374	1183	687	1214	1763	857	778	1879
97	1804	373	1213	777	372	371	1346	1347	1752	238
98	1348	829	904	1753	1832	788	239	1662	208	1349
99	495	1106	830	644	1558	905	1365	429	1754	215

POWER RESIDUES

	0	1	2	3	4	5	6	7	8	9
50	597	1791	1471	511	1533	697	140	420	1260	1829
51	1585	853	608	1824	1570	808	473	1419	355	1065
52	1244	1781	1441	421	1263	1838	1612	934	851	602
53	1806	1516	646	1938	1912	1834	1600	898	743	278
54	834	551	1653	1057	1220	1709	1225	1724	1270	1859
55	1675	1123	1418	352	1056	1217	1700	1198	1643	1027
56	1130	1439	415	1245	1784	1450	448	1344	130	390
57	1170	1559	775	374	1122	1415	343	1029	1136	1457
58	469	1407	319	957	920	809	476	1428	382	1146
59	1487	559	1677	1129	1436	406	1218	1703	1207	1670
60	1108	1373	217	651	2	6	18	54	162	486
61	1458	472	1416	346	1038	1163	1538	712	185	555
62	1665	1093	1328	82	246	738	263	789	416	1248
63	1793	1477	529	1587	859	626	1878	1732	1294	1931
64	1891	1771	1411	331	993	1028	1133	1448	442	1326
65	76	228	684	101	303	909	776	377	1131	1442
66	424	1272	1865	1693	1177	1580	838	563	1689	1165
67	1544	730	239	717	200	600	1800	1498	592	1776
68	1426	376	1128	1433	397	1191	1622	964	941	872
69	665	44	132	396	1188	1613	937	860	629	1887
70	1759	1375	223	669	56	168	504	1512	634	1902
71	1804	1510	628	1884	1750	1348	142	426	1278	1883
72	1747	1339	115	345	1035	1154	1511	631	1893	1777
73	1429	385	1155	1514	640	1920	1858	1672	1114	1391
74	271	813	488	1464	490	1470	508	1524	670	59
75	177	531	1593	877	680	89	267	801	452	1356
76	166	498	1494	580	1740	1318	52	156	468	1404
77	310	930	839	566	1698	1192	1625	973	968	953
78	908	773	368	1104	1361	181	543	1629	985	1004
79	1061	1232	1745	1333	97	291	873	668	53	159
80	477	1431	391	1173	1568	802	455	1365	193	579
81	1737	1309	25	75	225	675	74	222	666	47
82	141	423	1269	1856	1666	1096	1337	109	327	981
83	992	1025	1124	1421	361	1083	1298	1943	1927	1879
84	1735	1303	7	21	63	189	567	1701	1201	1652
85	1054	1211	1682	1144	1481	541	1623	967	950	899
86	746	287	861	632	1896	1786	1456	466	1398	292
87	876	677	80	240	720	209	627	1881	1741	1321
88	61	183	549	1647	1039	1166	1547	739	266	798
89	443	1329	85	255	765	344	1032	1145	1484	550
90	1650	1048	1193	1628	982	995	1034	1151	1502	604
91	1812	1534	700	149	447	1341	121	363	1089	1316
92	46	138	414	1242	1775	1423	367	1101	1352	154
93	462	1386	256	768	353	1059	1226	1727	1279	1886
94	1756	1366	196	588	1764	1390	268	804	461	1383
95	247	741	272	816	497	1491	571	1713	1237	1760
96	1378	232	696	137	411	1233	1748	1342	124	372
97	1116	1397	289	867	650	1950	1948	1942	1924	1870
98	1708	1222	1715	1243	1778	1432	394	1182	1595	883
99	698	143	429	1287	1910	1828	1582	844	581	1743

P = 1951

INDICES

	0	1	2	3	4	5	6	7	8	9
100	1080	1833	194	1235	789	145	276	240	1310	1084
101	1663	1458	1007	209	1671	397	1350	1502	288	496
102	151	1746	1107	1194	190	831	49	559	645	577
103	223	1559	896	118	906	724	312	1366	614	884
104	430	435	1630	1755	359	1281	216	387	901	1081
105	309	1047	1834	1512	850	195	554	543	1236	935
106	462	790	1355	1050	146	519	181	277	14	1315
107	241	1330	204	1311	1728	1845	1085	1337	1771	1664
108	271	1135	1459	835	1948	1008	1390	98	210	918
109	1837	1672	1609	621	398	68	825	1351	1486	346
110	1503	927	1145	289	783	450	497	22	600	152
111	1223	136	1747	1641	738	1108	970	1515	1195	257
112	368	191	574	551	832	1220	1271	50	682	593
113	560	658	1377	646	1450	1928	578	1274	1716	224
114	1057	39	1560	1490	853	897	589	1922	119	1780
115	1732	907	330	1864	725	732	230	313	1413	322
116	1367	1036	1602	615	53	669	885	1175	127	431
117	570	198	436	803	80	1631	1547	664	1756	1041
118	413	360	987	1908	1282	1408	1869	217	694	1118
119	388	685	775	902	1104	1078	1082	286	557	310
120	1279	848	1048	202	1133	1835	344	598	1513	1269
121	1926	851	1862	1600	196	411	1116	555	596	1114
122	544	1646	981	1237	350	546	936	1018	455	463
123	1030	1849	791	965	1648	1356	422	958	1051	1592
124	28	147	923	983	520	563	251	182	629	1140
125	278	1887	1239	15	1480	1937	1316	63	1302	242
126	508	352	1331	524	1467	205	394	1627	1312	822
127	548	1729	661	1130	1846	1299	1790	1086	718	938
128	1338	1723	1678	1772	440	1793	1665	993	1020	272
129	94	123	1136	1290	638	1460	470	457	836	1380
130	1578	1949	1207	841	1009	1507	465	1391	86	811
131	99	1709	1089	211	267	1032	919	1683	765	1838
132	1702	879	1673	1687	1851	1610	649	1000	622	891
133	1294	399	1422	793	69	1162	1401	826	1307	721
134	1352	915	967	1487	567	283	347	1884	715	1504
135	1419	1650	928	1453	1475	1146	759	1065	290	1653
136	1358	784	177	1918	451	807	941	498	1256	424
137	23	1738	1784	601	1096	701	153	490	960	1224
138	1931	1428	137	949	1821	1748	931	1053	1642	1203
139	945	739	1566	1341	1109	168	1594	971	868	1154
140	1516	1874	1857	1196	769	30	258	581	1761	369
141	1830	642	192	1456	149	575	612	385	552	517
142	1726	833	1607	925	1221	255	680	1272	587	730
143	51	801	985	683	1277	1267	594	1016	420	561
144	1478	522	659	1721	92	1378	84	1681	647	1160
145	565	1451	175	1736	1929	1201	866	579	610	253
146	1275	1719	173	1717	743	1584	225	1149	184	1058
147	745	502	40	301	1775	1561	1229	631	1491	1586
148	480	854	1555	1743	898	1842	1142	590	227	1905
149	1923	955	1464	120	762	280	1781	1151	677	1733

POWER RESIDUES

	0	1	2	3	4	5	6	7	8	9
100	1327	79	237	711	182	546	1638	1012	1085	1304
101	10	30	90	270	810	479	1437	409	1227	1730
102	1288	1913	1837	1609	925	824	521	1563	787	410
103	1230	1739	1315	43	129	387	1161	1532	694	131
104	393	1179	1586	856	617	1851	1651	1051	1202	1655
105	1063	1238	1763	1387	259	777	380	1140	1469	505
106	1515	643	1929	1885	1753	1357	169	507	1521	661
107	32	96	288	864	641	1923	1867	1699	1195	1634
108	1000	1049	1196	1637	1009	1076	1277	1880	1738	1312
109	34	102	306	918	803	458	1374	220	660	29
110	87	261	783	398	1194	1631	991	1022	1115	1394
111	280	840	569	1707	1219	1706	1216	1697	1189	1616
112	946	887	710	179	537	1611	931	842	575	1725
113	1273	1868	1702	1204	1661	1081	1292	1925	1873	1717
114	1249	1796	1486	556	1668	1102	1355	163	489	1467
115	499	1497	589	1767	1399	295	885	704	161	483
116	1449	445	1335	103	309	927	830	539	1617	949
117	896	737	260	780	389	1167	1550	748	293	879
118	686	107	321	963	938	863	638	1914	1840	1618
119	952	905	764	341	1023	1118	1403	307	921	812
120	485	1455	463	1389	265	795	434	1302	4	12
121	36	108	324	972	965	944	881	692	125	375
122	1125	1424	370	1110	1379	235	705	164	492	1476
123	526	1578	832	545	1635	1003	1058	1223	1718	1252
124	1805	1513	637	1911	1831	1591	871	662	35	105
125	315	945	884	701	152	456	1368	202	606	1818
126	1552	754	311	933	848	593	1779	1435	403	1209
127	1676	1126	1427	379	1137	1460	478	1434	400	1200
128	1649	1045	1184	1601	901	752	305	915	794	431
129	1293	1928	1882	1744	1330	88	264	792	425	1275
130	1874	1720	1258	1823	1567	799	446	1338	112	336
131	1008	1073	1268	1853	1657	1069	1256	1817	1549	745
132	284	852	605	1815	1543	727	230	690	119	357
133	1071	1262	1835	1603	907	770	359	1077	1280	1889
134	1765	1393	277	831	542	1626	976	977	980	989
135	1016	1097	1340	118	354	1062	1235	1754	1360	178
136	534	1602	904	761	332	996	1037	1160	1529	685
137	104	312	936	857	620	1860	1678	1132	1445	433
138	1299	1946	1936	1906	1816	1546	736	257	771	362
139	1086	1307	19	57	171	513	1539	715	194	582
140	1746	1336	106	318	954	911	782	395	1185	1604
141	910	779	386	1158	1523	667	50	150	450	1350
142	148	444	1332	94	282	846	587	1761	1381	241
143	723	218	654	11	33	99	297	891	722	215
144	645	1935	1903	1807	1519	655	14	42	126	378
145	1134	1451	451	1353	157	471	1413	337	1011	1082
146	1295	1934	1900	1798	1492	574	1722	1264	1841	1621
147	961	932	845	584	1752	1354	160	480	1440	418
148	1254	1811	1531	691	122	366	1098	1343	127	381
149	1143	1478	532	1596	886	707	170	510	1530	688

P = 1951

INDICES

	0	1	2	3	4	5	6	7	8	9
150	477	443	908	1541	1889	331	186	446	1865	1623
151	711	726	707	1241	733	1060	531	231	404	1444
152	314	1068	17	1414	747	1692	323	1635	1796	1368
153	1498	1482	1037	504	911	1603	1537	1897	616	1396
154	1939	54	42	1324	670	1570	1385	886	293	1318
155	1176	303	1260	128	1659	1668	432	11	65	571
156	1777	1544	199	1027	60	437	1706	1304	804	1563
157	514	81	298	474	1632	1656	244	1548	1231	1944
158	665	247	996	1757	1901	510	1042	633	1892	414
159	1809	1245	361	752	354	988	1493	379	1909	1528
160	536	1283	1361	1333	1409	1588	1698	1870	1551	1023
161	218	1125	526	695	482	334	1119	1168	1189	389
162	1618	1469	686	856	1803	776	1345	237	903	787
163	207	1105	1557	428	1079	1234	275	1083	1006	396
164	287	1745	189	558	222	117	311	883	1629	1280
165	900	1046	849	542	461	1049	180	1314	203	1844
166	1770	1134	1947	97	1836	620	824	345	1144	449
167	599	135	737	1514	367	550	1270	592	1376	1927
168	1715	38	852	1921	1731	1863	229	321	1601	668
169	126	197	79	663	412	1907	1868	1117	774	1077
170	556	847	1132	597	1925	1599	1115	1113	980	545
171	454	1848	1647	957	27	982	250	1139	1238	1936
172	1301	351	1466	1626	547	1129	1789	937	1677	1792
173	1019	122	637	456	1577	840	464	810	1088	1031
174	764	878	1850	999	1293	792	1400	720	966	282
175	714	1649	1474	1064	1357	1917	940	423	1783	700
176	959	1427	1820	1052	944	1340	1593	1153	1856	29
177	1760	641	148	384	1725	924	679	729	984	1266
178	419	521	91	1680	564	1735	865	252	172	1583
179	183	501	1774	630	479	1742	1141	1904	1463	279
180	676	442	1888	445	710	1240	530	1443	16	1691
181	1795	1481	910	1896	1938	1323	1384	1317	1259	1667
182	64	1543	59	1303	513	473	243	1943	995	509
183	1891	1244	353	378	535	1332	1697	1022	525	333
184	1188	1468	1802	236	206	427	274	395	188	116
185	1628	1045	460	1313	1769	96	823	448	736	549
186	1375	37	1730	320	125	662	1867	1076	1131	1598
187	979	1847	26	1138	1300	1625	1788	1791	636	839
188	1087	877	1292	719	713	1063	939	699	1819	1339
189	1855	640	1724	728	418	1679	864	1582	1773	1741
190	1462	441	709	1442	1794	1895	1383	1666	58	472
191	994	1243	534	1021	1187	235	273	115	459	95
192	735	36	124	1075	978	1137	1787	838	1291	1062
193	1818	639	417	1581	1461	1441	1382	471	533	234
194	458	35	977	837	1817	1580	1381	233	976	1579
195	975	0								

POWER RESIDUES

	0	1	2	3	4	5	6	7	8	9
150	113	339	1017	1100	1349	145	435	1305	13	39
151	117	351	1053	1208	1673	1117	1400	298	894	731
152	242	726	227	681	92	276	828	533	1599	895
153	734	251	753	308	924	821	512	1536	706	167
154	501	1503	607	1821	1561	781	392	1176	1577	829
155	536	1608	922	815	494	1482	544	1632	994	1031
156	1142	1475	523	1569	805	464	1392	274	822	515
157	1545	733	248	744	281	843	578	1734	1300	1949
158	1945	1933	1897	1789	1465	493	1479	535	1605	913
159	788	413	1239	1766	1396	286	858	623	1869	1705
160	1213	1688	1162	1535	703	158	474	1422	364	1092
161	1325	73	219	657	20	60	180	540	1620	958
162	923	818	503	1509	625	1875	1723	1267	1850	1648
163	1042	1175	1574	820	509	1527	679	86	258	774
164	371	1113	1388	262	786	407	1221	1712	1234	1751
165	1351	151	453	1359	175	525	1575	823	518	1554
166	760	329	987	1010	1079	1286	1907	1819	1555	763
167	338	1014	1091	1322	64	192	576	1728	1282	1895
168	1783	1447	439	1317	49	147	441	1323	67	201
169	603	1809	1525	673	68	204	612	1836	1606	916
170	797	440	1320	58	174	522	1566	796	437	1311
171	31	93	279	837	560	1680	1138	1463	487	1461
172	481	1443	427	1281	1892	1774	1420	358	1074	1271
173	1862	1684	1150	1499	595	1785	1453	457	1371	211
174	633	1899	1795	1483	547	1641	1021	1112	1385	253
175	759	326	978	983	998	1043	1178	1583	847	590
176	1770	1408	322	966	947	890	719	206	618	1854
177	1660	1078	1283	1898	1792	1474	520	1560	778	383
178	1149	1496	586	1758	1372	214	642	1926	1876	1726
179	1276	1877	1729	1285	1904	1810	1528	682	95	285
180	855	614	1842	1624	970	959	926	827	530	1590
181	868	653	8	24	72	216	648	1944	1930	1888
182	1762	1384	250	750	299	897	740	269	807	470
183	1410	328	984	1001	1052	1205	1664	1090	1319	55
184	165	495	1485	553	1659	1075	1274	1871	1711	1231
185	1742	1324	70	210	630	1890	1768	1402	304	912
186	785	404	1212	1685	1153	1508	622	1866	1696	1186
187	1607	919	806	467	1401	301	903	758	323	969
188	956	917	800	449	1347	139	417	1251	1802	1504
189	610	1830	1588	862	635	1905	1813	1537	709	176
190	528	1584	850	599	1797	1489	565	1695	1183	1598
191	892	725	224	672	65	195	585	1755	1363	187
192	561	1683	1147	1490	568	1704	1210	1679	1135	1454
193	460	1380	238	714	191	573	1719	1255	1814	1540
194	718	203	609	1827	1579	835	554	1662	1084	1301
195										

P = 1973

INDICES

	0	1	2	3	4	5	6	7	8	9
0		0	1	881	2	1537	882	63	3	1762
1	1538	706	883	680	64	446	4	1506	1763	198
2	1539	944	707	1678	884	1102	681	671	65	1450
3	447	700	5	1587	1507	1600	1764	430	199	1561
4	1540	1638	945	1830	708	1327	1679	1027	885	126
5	1103	415	682	1439	672	271	66	1079	1451	80
6	448	1925	701	1825	6	245	1588	1955	1508	587
7	1601	381	1765	316	431	11	200	769	1562	871
8	1541	1552	1639	1286	946	1071	1831	359	709	725
9	1328	743	1680	1581	1028	1735	886	1034	127	496
10	1104	1460	416	792	683	509	1440	250	673	1901
11	272	1311	67	162	1080	1243	1452	470	81	1569
12	449	1412	1926	547	702	667	1826	76	7	739
13	246	543	1589	261	1956	236	1509	1193	588	1593
14	1602	1908	382	1386	1766	1015	317	1007	432	98
15	12	1844	201	1296	770	265	1563	828	872	348
16	1542	1741	1553	1609	1640	1152	1287	1789	947	1360
17	1072	1960	1832	1881	360	1165	710	961	726	282
18	1329	1057	744	834	1681	1967	1582	240	1029	734
19	1736	1273	887	1278	1035	1126	128	329	497	1940
20	1105	864	1461	1513	417	1203	793	1468	684	904
21	510	1627	1441	1262	251	1395	674	763	1902	1197
22	273	214	1312	1717	68	892	163	1811	1081	919
23	1244	1650	1453	912	471	592	82	1752	1570	936
24	450	338	1413	461	1927	1663	548	878	703	195
25	668	1597	1827	412	77	1952	8	1283	740	493
26	247	1240	544	540	1590	1004	262	1606	1957	279
27	237	1123	1510	1624	1194	1808	589	458	1594	490
28	1603	1805	1909	1912	383	644	1387	1701	1767	1040
29	1016	1915	318	1499	1008	1617	433	1377	99	386
30	13	1893	1845	369	202	1490	1297	647	771	1673
31	266	354	1564	1839	829	1390	873	485	349	184
32	1543	1131	1742	1704	1554	1782	1610	810	1641	1090
33	1153	1770	1288	220	1790	1520	948	1216	1361	1043
34	1073	1406	1961	189	1833	152	1882	1019	361	530
35	1166	1351	711	133	962	1918	727	478	283	175
36	1330	396	1058	321	745	1853	835	37	1682	1428
37	1968	1502	1583	122	241	1548	1030	158	735	1011
38	1737	957	1274	900	888	334	1279	1620	1036	1486
39	1127	1212	129	1424	330	436	498	1318	1941	1142
40	1106	440	865	1380	1462	1117	1514	1136	418	228
41	1204	102	794	143	1469	851	685	502	905	389
42	511	52	1628	817	1442	636	1263	16	252	295
43	1396	1179	675	1322	764	1896	1903	1876	1198	1747
44	274	1888	215	1848	1313	290	1718	979	69	1945
45	893	372	164	753	1812	308	1082	27	920	205
46	1245	1723	1651	424	1454	1146	913	1493	472	46
47	593	1709	83	564	1753	1300	1571	1229	937	91
48	451	1110	339	650	1414	599	462	114	1928	518
49	1664	774	549	984	879	61	704	444	196	1676

POWER RESIDUES

	0	1	2	3	4	5	6	7	8	9
0	1	2	4	8	16	32	64	128	256	512
1	1024	75	150	300	600	1200	427	854	1708	1443
2	913	1826	1679	1385	797	1594	1215	457	914	1828
3	1683	1393	813	1626	1279	585	1170	367	734	1468
4	963	1926	1879	1785	1597	1221	469	938	1876	1779
5	1585	1197	421	842	1684	1395	817	1634	1295	617
6	1234	495	990	7	14	28	56	112	224	448
7	896	1792	1611	1249	525	1050	127	254	508	1016
8	59	118	236	472	944	1888	1803	1633	1293	613
9	1226	479	958	1916	1859	1745	1517	1061	149	298
10	596	1192	411	822	1644	1315	657	1314	655	1310
11	647	1294	615	1230	487	974	1948	1923	1873	1773
12	1573	1173	373	746	1492	1011	49	98	196	392
13	784	1568	1163	353	706	1412	851	1702	1431	889
14	1778	1583	1193	413	826	1652	1331	689	1378	783
15	1566	1159	345	690	1380	787	1574	1175	377	754
16	1508	1043	113	226	452	904	1808	1643	1313	653
17	1306	639	1278	583	1166	359	718	1436	899	1798
18	1623	1273	573	1146	319	638	1276	579	1158	343
19	686	1372	771	1542	1111	249	498	996	19	38
20	76	152	304	608	1216	459	918	1836	1699	1425
21	877	1754	1535	1097	221	442	884	1768	1563	1153
22	333	666	1332	691	1382	791	1582	1191	409	818
23	1636	1299	625	1250	527	1054	135	270	540	1080
24	187	374	748	1496	1019	65	130	260	520	1040
25	107	214	428	856	1712	1451	929	1858	1743	1513
26	1053	133	266	532	1064	155	310	620	1240	507
27	1014	55	110	220	440	880	1760	1547	1121	269
28	538	1076	179	358	716	1432	891	1782	1591	1209
29	445	890	1780	1587	1201	429	858	1716	1459	945
30	1890	1807	1641	1309	645	1290	607	1214	455	910
31	1820	1667	1361	749	1498	1023	73	146	292	584
32	1168	363	726	1452	931	1862	1751	1529	1085	197
33	394	788	1576	1179	385	770	1540	1107	241	482
34	964	1928	1883	1793	1613	1253	533	1066	159	318
35	636	1272	571	1142	311	622	1244	515	1030	87
36	174	348	696	1392	811	1622	1271	569	1138	303
37	606	1212	451	902	1804	1635	1297	621	1242	511
38	1022	71	142	284	568	1136	299	598	1196	419
39	838	1676	1379	785	1570	1167	361	722	1444	915
40	1830	1687	1401	829	1658	1343	713	1426	879	1758
41	1543	1113	253	506	1012	51	102	204	408	816
42	1632	1291	609	1218	463	926	1852	1731	1489	1005
43	37	74	148	296	592	1184	395	790	1580	1187
44	401	802	1604	1235	497	994	15	30	60	120
45	240	480	960	1920	1867	1761	1549	1125	277	554
46	1108	243	486	972	1944	1915	1857	1741	1509	1045
47	117	234	468	936	1872	1771	1569	1165	357	714
48	1428	883	1766	1559	1145	317	634	1268	563	1126
49	279	558	1116	259	518	1036	99	198	396	792

P = 1973

INDICES

	0	1	2	3	4	5	6	7	8	9
50	669	698	1598	1559	1828	1025	413	269	78	1823
51	1953	379	9	869	1284	357	741	1733	494	790
52	248	1309	1241	1567	545	74	541	234	1591	1384
53	1005	1842	263	346	1607	1787	1958	1163	280	832
54	238	1271	1124	1938	1511	1466	1625	1393	1195	1715
55	1809	1648	590	934	459	876	1595	1950	491	538
56	1604	1121	1806	488	1910	1699	1913	1615	384	367
57	645	352	1388	182	1702	808	1768	1518	1041	187
58	1017	1349	1916	173	319	35	1500	1546	1009	898
59	1618	1210	434	1140	1378	1134	100	849	387	815
60	14	1177	1894	1745	1846	977	370	306	203	422
61	1491	1707	1298	89	648	112	772	59	1674	1557
62	267	377	355	788	1565	232	1840	1785	830	1936
63	1391	1646	874	536	486	1613	350	806	185	171
64	1544	1208	1132	813	1743	304	1705	110	1555	786
65	1783	1644	1611	169	811	108	1642	106	1091	1093
66	1154	657	1771	1095	1289	1798	221	1156	1791	626
67	1521	659	949	798	1217	1773	1362	570	1044	1097
68	1074	720	1407	1291	1962	758	190	1800	1834	147
69	153	223	1883	559	1020	1158	362	1172	531	1793
70	1167	1337	1352	628	712	1473	134	1523	963	1861
71	1919	661	728	406	479	951	284	1817	176	800
72	1331	855	397	1219	1059	580	322	1775	746	1342
73	1854	1364	836	1254	38	572	1683	689	1429	1046
74	1969	1759	1503	1099	1584	1635	123	1076	242	313
75	1549	722	1031	506	159	1409	736	1190	1012	1293
76	1738	1357	958	1964	1275	861	901	760	889	909
77	335	192	1280	1001	1621	1802	1037	1374	1487	1836
78	1128	1087	1213	149	130	393	1425	155	331	1421
79	437	225	499	633	1319	1885	1942	24	1143	561
80	1107	515	441	1022	866	1306	1381	1160	1463	931
81	1118	364	1515	32	1137	1174	419	56	229	533
82	1205	783	103	1795	795	717	144	1169	1470	403
83	852	1339	686	1632	503	1354	906	1371	390	630
84	512	928	53	714	1629	925	818	1475	1443	821
85	637	136	1264	619	17	1525	253	1478	296	965
86	1397	610	1180	1863	676	1446	1323	1921	765	1577
87	1897	663	1904	824	1877	730	1199	210	1748	408
88	275	640	1889	481	216	526	1849	953	1314	139
89	291	286	1719	1225	980	1819	70	1267	1946	178
90	894	973	373	802	165	622	754	1333	1813	1250
91	309	857	1083	20	28	399	921	606	206	1221
92	1246	1528	1724	1061	1652	1532	425	582	1455	256
93	1147	324	914	1235	1494	1777	473	1481	47	748
94	594	1728	1710	1344	84	299	565	1856	1754	996
95	1301	1366	1572	968	1230	838	938	1065	92	1256
96	452	1400	1111	40	340	843	651	574	1415	613
97	600	1685	463	1656	115	691	1929	1183	519	1431
98	1665	1691	775	1048	550	1866	985	1971	880	1536
99	62	1761	705	679	445	1505	197	943	1677	1101

POWER RESIDUES

	0	1	2	3	4	5	6	7	8	9
50	1584	1195	417	834	1668	1363	753	1506	1039	105
51	210	420	840	1680	1387	801	1602	1231	489	978
52	1956	1939	1905	1837	1701	1429	885	1770	1567	1161
53	349	698	1396	819	1638	1303	633	1266	559	1118
54	263	526	1052	131	262	524	1048	123	246	492
55	984	1968	1963	1953	1933	1893	1813	1653	1333	693
56	1386	799	1598	1223	473	946	1892	1811	1649	1325
57	677	1354	735	1470	967	1934	1895	1817	1661	1349
58	725	1450	927	1854	1735	1497	1021	69	138	276
59	552	1104	235	470	940	1880	1787	1601	1229	485
60	970	1940	1907	1841	1709	1445	917	1834	1695	1417
61	861	1722	1471	969	1938	1903	1833	1693	1413	853
62	1706	1439	905	1810	1647	1321	669	1338	703	1406
63	839	1678	1383	793	1586	1199	425	850	1700	1427
64	881	1762	1551	1129	285	570	1140	307	614	1228
65	483	966	1932	1891	1809	1645	1317	661	1322	671
66	1342	711	1422	871	1742	1511	1049	125	250	500
67	1000	27	54	108	216	432	864	1728	1483	993
68	13	26	52	104	208	416	832	1664	1355	737
69	1474	975	1950	1927	1881	1789	1605	1237	501	1002
70	31	62	124	248	496	992	11	22	44	88
71	176	352	704	1408	843	1686	1399	825	1650	1327
72	681	1362	751	1502	1031	89	178	356	712	1424
73	875	1750	1527	1081	189	378	756	1512	1051	129
74	258	516	1032	91	182	364	728	1456	939	1878
75	1783	1593	1213	453	906	1812	1651	1329	685	1370
76	767	1534	1095	217	434	868	1736	1499	1025	77
77	154	308	616	1232	491	982	1964	1955	1937	1901
78	1829	1685	1397	821	1642	1311	649	1298	623	1246
79	519	1038	103	206	412	824	1648	1323	673	1346
80	719	1438	903	1806	1639	1305	637	1274	575	1150
81	327	654	1308	643	1286	599	1198	423	846	1692
82	1411	849	1698	1423	873	1746	1519	1065	157	314
83	628	1256	539	1078	183	366	732	1464	955	1910
84	1847	1721	1469	965	1930	1887	1801	1629	1285	597
85	1194	415	830	1660	1347	721	1442	911	1822	1671
86	1369	765	1530	1087	201	402	804	1608	1243	513
87	1026	79	158	316	632	1264	555	1110	247	494
88	988	3	6	12	24	48	96	192	384	768
89	1536	1099	225	450	900	1800	1627	1281	589	1178
90	383	766	1532	1091	209	418	836	1672	1371	769
91	1538	1103	233	466	932	1864	1755	1537	1101	229
92	458	916	1832	1691	1409	845	1690	1407	841	1682
93	1391	809	1618	1263	553	1106	239	478	956	1912
94	1851	1729	1485	997	21	42	84	168	336	672
95	1344	715	1430	887	1774	1575	1177	381	762	1524
96	1075	177	354	708	1416	859	1718	1463	953	1906
97	1839	1705	1437	901	1802	1631	1289	605	1210	447
98	894	1788	1603	1233	493	986	1972	1971	1969	1965
99	1957	1941	1909	1845	1717	1461	949	1898	1823	1673

P = 1973

INDICES

	0	1	2	3	4	5	6	7	8	9
100	670	1449	699	1586	1599	429	1560	1637	1829	1326
101	1026	125	414	1438	270	1078	79	1924	1824	244
102	1954	586	380	315	10	768	870	1551	1285	1070
103	358	724	742	1580	1734	1033	495	1459	791	508
104	249	1900	1310	161	1242	469	1568	1411	546	666
105	75	738	542	260	235	1192	1592	1907	1385	1014
106	1006	97	1843	1295	264	827	347	1740	1608	1151
107	1788	1359	1959	1880	1164	960	281	1056	833	1966
108	239	733	1272	1277	1125	328	1939	863	1512	1202
109	1467	903	1626	1261	1394	762	1196	213	1716	891
110	1810	918	1649	911	591	1751	935	337	460	1662
111	877	194	1596	411	1951	1282	492	1239	539	1003
112	1605	278	1122	1623	1807	457	489	1804	1911	643
113	1700	1039	1914	1498	1616	1376	385	1892	368	1489
114	646	1672	353	1838	1389	484	183	1130	1703	1781
115	809	1089	1769	219	1519	1215	1042	1405	188	151
116	1018	529	1350	132	1917	477	174	395	320	1852
117	36	1427	1501	121	1547	157	1010	956	899	333
118	1619	1485	1211	1423	435	1317	1141	439	1379	1116
119	1135	227	101	142	850	501	388	51	816	635
120	15	294	1178	1321	1895	1875	1746	1887	1847	289
121	978	1944	371	752	307	26	204	1722	423	1145
122	1492	45	1708	563	1299	1228	90	1109	649	598
123	113	517	773	983	60	443	1675	697	1558	1024
124	268	1822	378	868	356	1732	789	1308	1566	73
125	233	1383	1841	345	1786	1162	831	1270	1937	1465
126	1392	1714	1647	933	875	1949	537	1120	487	1698
127	1614	366	351	181	807	1517	186	1348	172	34
128	1545	897	1209	1139	1133	848	814	1176	1744	976
129	305	421	1706	88	111	58	1556	376	787	231
130	1784	1935	1645	535	1612	805	170	1207	812	303
131	109	785	1643	168	107	105	1092	656	1094	1797
132	1155	625	658	797	1772	569	1096	719	1290	757
133	1799	146	222	558	1157	1171	1792	1336	627	1472
134	1522	1860	660	405	950	1816	799	854	1218	579
135	1774	1341	1363	1253	571	688	1045	1758	1098	1634
136	1075	312	721	505	1408	1189	1292	1356	1963	860
137	759	908	191	1000	1801	1373	1835	1086	148	392
138	154	1420	224	632	1884	23	560	514	1021	1305
139	1159	930	363	31	1173	55	532	782	1794	716
140	1168	402	1338	1631	1353	1370	629	927	713	924
141	1474	820	135	618	1524	1477	964	609	1862	1445
142	1920	1576	662	823	729	209	407	639	480	525
143	952	138	285	1224	1818	1266	177	972	801	621
144	1332	1249	856	19	398	605	1220	1527	1060	1531
145	581	255	323	1234	1776	1480	747	1727	1343	298
146	1855	995	1365	967	837	1064	1255	1399	39	842
147	573	612	1684	1655	690	1182	1430	1690	1047	1865
148	1970	1535	1760	678	1504	942	1100	1448	1585	428
149	1636	1325	124	1437	1077	1923	243	585	314	767

POWER RESIDUES

	0	1	2	3	4	5	6	7	8	9
100	1373	773	1546	1119	265	530	1060	147	294	588
101	1176	379	758	1516	1059	145	290	580	1160	347
102	694	1388	803	1606	1239	505	1010	47	94	188
103	376	752	1504	1035	97	194	388	776	1552	1131
104	289	578	1156	339	678	1356	739	1478	983	1966
105	1959	1945	1917	1861	1749	1525	1077	181	362	724
106	1448	923	1846	1719	1465	957	1914	1855	1737	1501
107	1029	85	170	340	680	1360	747	1494	1015	57
108	114	228	456	912	1824	1675	1377	781	1562	1151
109	329	658	1316	659	1318	663	1326	679	1358	743
110	1486	999	25	50	100	200	400	800	1600	1227
111	481	962	1924	1875	1777	1581	1189	405	810	1620
112	1267	561	1122	271	542	1084	195	390	780	1560
113	1147	321	642	1284	595	1190	407	814	1628	1283
114	593	1186	399	798	1596	1219	465	930	1860	1747
115	1521	1069	165	330	660	1320	667	1334	695	1390
116	807	1614	1255	537	1074	175	350	700	1400	827
117	1654	1335	697	1394	815	1630	1287	601	1202	431
118	862	1724	1475	977	1954	1935	1897	1821	1669	1365
119	757	1514	1055	137	274	548	1096	219	438	876
120	1752	1531	1089	205	410	820	1640	1307	641	1282
121	591	1182	391	782	1564	1155	337	674	1348	723
122	1446	919	1838	1703	1433	893	1786	1599	1225	477
123	954	1908	1843	1713	1453	933	1866	1759	1545	1117
124	261	522	1044	115	230	460	920	1840	1707	1441
125	909	1818	1663	1353	733	1466	959	1918	1863	1753
126	1533	1093	213	426	852	1704	1435	897	1794	1615
127	1257	541	1082	191	382	764	1528	1083	193	386
128	772	1544	1115	257	514	1028	83	166	332	664
129	1328	683	1366	759	1518	1063	153	306	612	1224
130	475	950	1900	1827	1681	1389	805	1610	1247	521
131	1042	111	222	444	888	1776	1579	1185	397	794
132	1588	1203	433	866	1732	1491	1009	45	90	180
133	360	720	1440	907	1814	1655	1337	701	1402	831
134	1662	1351	729	1458	943	1886	1799	1625	1277	581
135	1162	351	702	1404	835	1670	1367	761	1522	1071
136	169	338	676	1352	731	1462	951	1902	1831	1689
137	1405	837	1674	1375	777	1554	1135	297	594	1188
138	403	806	1612	1251	529	1058	143	286	572	1144
139	315	630	1260	547	1094	215	430	860	1720	1467
140	961	1922	1871	1769	1565	1157	341	682	1364	755
141	1510	1047	121	242	484	968	1936	1899	1825	1677
142	1381	789	1578	1183	393	786	1572	1171	369	738
143	1476	979	1958	1943	1913	1853	1733	1493	1013	53
144	106	212	424	848	1696	1419	865	1730	1487	1001
145	29	58	116	232	464	928	1856	1739	1505	1037
146	101	202	404	808	1616	1259	545	1090	207	414
147	828	1656	1339	705	1410	847	1694	1415	857	1714
148	1455	937	1874	1775	1577	1181	389	778	1556	1139
149	305	610	1220	467	934	1868	1763	1553	1133	293

P = 1973

INDICES

	0	1	2	3	4	5	6	7	8	9
150	1550	1069	723	1579	1032	1458	507	1899	160	468
151	1410	665	737	259	1191	1906	1013	96	1294	826
152	1739	1150	1358	1879	959	1055	1965	732	1276	327
153	862	1201	902	1260	761	212	890	917	910	1750
154	336	1661	193	410	1281	1238	1002	277	1622	456
155	1803	642	1038	1497	1375	1891	1488	1671	1837	483
156	1129	1780	1088	218	1214	1404	150	528	131	476
157	394	1851	1426	120	156	955	332	1484	1422	1316
158	438	1115	226	141	500	50	634	293	1320	1874
159	1886	288	1943	751	25	1721	1144	44	562	1227
160	1108	597	516	982	442	696	1023	1821	867	1731
161	1307	72	1382	344	1161	1269	1464	1713	932	1948
162	1119	1697	365	180	1516	1347	33	896	1138	847
163	1175	975	420	87	57	375	230	1934	534	804
164	1206	302	784	167	104	655	1796	624	796	568
165	718	756	145	557	1170	1335	1471	1859	404	1815
166	853	578	1340	1252	687	1757	1633	311	504	1188
167	1355	859	907	999	1372	1085	391	1419	631	22
168	513	1304	929	30	54	781	715	401	1630	1369
169	926	923	819	617	1476	608	1444	1575	822	208
170	638	524	137	1223	1265	971	620	1248	18	604
171	1526	1530	254	1233	1479	1726	297	994	966	1063
172	1398	841	611	1654	1181	1689	1864	1534	677	941
173	1447	427	1324	1436	1922	584	766	1068	1578	1457
174	1898	467	664	258	1905	95	825	1149	1878	1054
175	731	326	1200	1259	211	916	1749	1660	409	1237
176	276	455	641	1496	1890	1670	482	1779	217	1403
177	527	475	1850	119	954	1483	1315	1114	140	49
178	292	1873	287	750	1720	43	1226	596	981	695
179	1820	1730	71	343	1268	1712	1947	1696	179	1346
180	895	846	974	86	374	1933	803	301	166	654
181	623	567	755	556	1334	1858	1814	577	1251	1756
182	310	1187	858	998	1084	1418	21	1303	29	780
183	400	1368	922	616	607	1574	207	523	1222	970
184	1247	603	1529	1232	1725	993	1062	840	1653	1688
185	1533	940	426	1435	583	1067	1456	466	257	94
186	1148	1053	325	1258	915	1659	1236	454	1495	1669
187	1778	1402	474	118	1482	1113	48	1872	749	42
188	595	694	1729	342	1711	1695	1345	845	85	1932
189	300	653	566	555	1857	576	1755	1186	997	1417
190	1302	779	1367	615	1573	522	969	602	1231	992
191	839	1687	939	1434	1066	465	93	1052	1257	1658
192	453	1668	1401	117	1112	1871	41	693	341	1694
193	844	1931	652	554	575	1185	1416	778	614	521
194	601	991	1686	1433	464	1051	1657	1667	116	1870
195	692	1693	1930	553	1184	777	520	990	1432	1050
196	1666	1869	1692	552	776	989	1049	1868	551	988
197	1867	987	986							

POWER RESIDUES

	0	1	2	3	4	5	6	7	8	9
150	586	1172	371	742	1484	995	17	34	68	136
151	272	544	1088	203	406	812	1624	1275	577	1154
152	335	670	1340	707	1414	855	1710	1447	921	1842
153	1711	1449	925	1850	1727	1481	989	5	10	20
154	40	80	160	320	640	1280	587	1174	375	750
155	1500	1027	81	162	324	648	1296	619	1238	503
156	1006	39	78	156	312	624	1248	523	1046	119
157	238	476	952	1904	1835	1697	1421	869	1738	1503
158	1033	93	186	372	744	1488	1003	33	66	132
159	264	528	1056	139	278	556	1112	251	502	1004
160	35	70	140	280	560	1120	267	534	1068	163
161	326	652	1304	635	1270	567	1134	295	590	1180
162	387	774	1548	1123	273	546	1092	211	422	844
163	1688	1403	833	1666	1359	745	1490	1007	41	82
164	164	328	656	1312	651	1302	631	1262	551	1102
165	231	462	924	1848	1723	1473	973	1946	1919	1865
166	1757	1541	1109	245	490	980	1960	1947	1921	1869
167	1765	1557	1141	309	618	1236	499	998	23	46
168	92	184	368	736	1472	971	1942	1911	1849	1725
169	1477	981	1962	1951	1929	1885	1797	1621	1269	565
170	1130	287	574	1148	323	646	1292	611	1222	471
171	942	1884	1795	1617	1261	549	1098	223	446	892
172	1784	1595	1217	461	922	1844	1715	1457	941	1882
173	1791	1609	1245	517	1034	95	190	380	760	1520
174	1067	161	322	644	1288	603	1206	439	878	1756
175	1539	1105	237	474	948	1896	1819	1665	1357	741
176	1482	991	9	18	36	72	144	288	576	1152
177	331	662	1324	675	1350	727	1454	935	1870	1767
178	1561	1149	325	650	1300	627	1254	535	1070	167
179	334	668	1336	699	1398	823	1646	1319	665	1330
180	687	1374	775	1550	1127	281	562	1124	275	550
181	1100	227	454	908	1816	1659	1345	717	1434	895
182	1790	1607	1241	509	1018	63	126	252	504	1008
183	43	86	172	344	688	1376	779	1558	1143	313
184	626	1252	531	1062	151	302	604	1208	443	886
185	1772	1571	1169	365	730	1460	947	1894	1815	1657
186	1341	709	1418	863	1726	1479	985	1970	1967	1961
187	1949	1925	1877	1781	1589	1205	437	874	1748	1523
188	1073	173	346	692	1384	795	1590	1207	441	882
189	1764	1555	1137	301	602	1204	435	870	1740	1507
190	1041	109	218	436	872	1744	1515	1057	141	282
191	564	1128	283	566	1132	291	582	1164	355	710
192	1420	867	1734	1495	1017	61	122	244	488	976
193	1952	1931	1889	1805	1637	1301	629	1258	543	1086
194	199	398	796	1592	1211	449	898	1796	1619	1265
195	557	1114	255	510	1020	67	134	268	536	1072
196	171	342	684	1368	763	1526	1079	185	370	740
197	1480	987								

P = 1979

INDICES

	0	1	2	3	4	5	6	7	8	9
0		0	1	1176	2	1022	1177	1894	3	374
1	1023	580	1178	316	1895	220	4	333	375	1846
2	1024	1092	581	813	1179	66	317	1550	1896	570
3	221	1016	5	1756	334	938	376	295	1847	1492
4	1025	389	1093	175	582	1396	814	918	1180	1810
5	67	1509	318	1069	1551	1602	1897	1044	571	1216
6	222	556	1017	290	6	1338	1757	795	335	11
7	939	456	377	1420	296	1242	1848	496	1493	925
8	1026	748	390	1115	1094	1355	176	1746	583	1500
9	1397	232	815	214	919	890	1181	1457	1811	954
10	68	1343	1510	1702	319	136	1070	1683	1552	947
11	1603	1471	1898	1227	1045	1835	572	690	1217	249
12	223	1160	557	1565	1018	1088	291	1065	7	1351
13	1339	686	1758	1762	796	594	336	1628	12	850
14	940	116	457	896	378	1592	1421	1008	297	1766
15	1243	677	1849	707	497	60	1494	701	926	267
16	1027	729	749	624	391	800	1116	866	1095	632
17	1356	242	177	279	1747	1960	584	414	1501	1432
18	1398	598	233	1732	816	1317	215	913	920	1466
19	891	1955	1182	1776	1458	536	1812	340	955	1535
20	69	1971	1344	486	1511	1411	1703	1187	320	448
21	137	1641	1071	1632	1684	1197	1553	932	948	618
22	1604	649	1472	1522	1899	440	1228	1610	1046	16
23	1836	1672	573	843	691	1940	1218	123	250	1781
24	224	517	1161	1924	558	854	1566	184	1019	313
25	1089	567	292	1393	1066	553	8	493	1352	211
26	1340	944	687	1085	1759	113	1763	698	797	276
27	595	1463	337	1408	1629	646	13	120	851	1390
28	941	273	117	85	458	88	897	305	379	666
29	1593	655	1422	461	1009	260	298	152	1767	1129
30	1244	91	678	541	1850	1578	708	1440	498	900
31	61	1039	1495	1155	702	1312	927	308	268	1150
32	1028	881	730	201	750	382	625	145	392	834
33	801	717	1117	669	867	1817	1096	976	633	425
34	1357	1596	243	1726	178	1033	280	525	1748	658
35	1961	1866	585	1651	415	1478	1502	1425	1433	783
36	1399	1714	599	358	234	464	1733	345	817	763
37	1318	985	216	1012	914	286	921	886	1467	1061
38	892	263	1956	1951	1183	1518	1777	549	1459	301
39	537	1146	1813	1862	341	1947	956	155	1536	960
40	70	1273	1972	1332	1345	1770	487	875	1512	735
41	1412	826	1704	1132	1188	159	321	48	449	1528
42	138	1247	1642	1292	1072	399	1633	472	1685	94
43	1198	1540	1554	1171	933	790	949	681	619	531
44	1605	206	650	196	1473	544	1523	964	1900	741
45	441	969	1229	1853	1611	1254	1047	1664	17	1883
46	1837	1581	1673	74	574	1236	844	480	692	711
47	1941	1877	1219	755	124	1912	251	1443	1782	1277
48	225	611	518	1905	1162	501	1925	25	559	1800
49	855	1207	1567	903	185	1976	1020	372	314	331

POWER RESIDUES

	0	1	2	3	4	5	6	7	8	9
0	1	2	4	8	16	32	64	128	256	512
1	1024	69	138	276	552	1104	229	458	916	1832
2	1685	1391	803	1606	1233	487	974	1948	1917	1855
3	1731	1483	987	1974	1969	1959	1939	1899	1819	1659
4	1339	699	1398	817	1634	1289	599	1198	417	834
5	1668	1357	735	1470	961	1922	1865	1751	1523	1067
6	155	310	620	1240	501	1002	25	50	100	200
7	400	800	1600	1221	463	926	1852	1725	1471	963
8	1926	1873	1767	1555	1131	283	566	1132	285	570
9	1140	301	602	1204	429	858	1716	1453	927	1854
10	1729	1479	979	1958	1937	1895	1811	1643	1307	635
11	1270	561	1122	265	530	1060	141	282	564	1128
12	277	554	1108	237	474	948	1896	1813	1647	1315
13	651	1302	625	1250	521	1042	105	210	420	840
14	1680	1381	783	1566	1153	327	654	1308	637	1274
15	569	1138	297	594	1188	397	794	1588	1197	415
16	830	1660	1341	703	1406	833	1666	1353	727	1454
17	929	1858	1737	1495	1011	43	86	172	344	688
18	1376	773	1546	1113	247	494	988	1976	1973	1967
19	1955	1931	1883	1787	1595	1211	443	886	1772	1565
20	1151	323	646	1292	605	1210	441	882	1764	1549
21	1119	259	518	1036	93	186	372	744	1488	997
22	15	30	60	120	240	480	960	1920	1861	1743
23	1507	1035	91	182	364	728	1456	933	1866	1753
24	1527	1075	171	342	684	1368	757	1514	1049	119
25	238	476	952	1904	1829	1679	1379	779	1558	1137
26	295	590	1180	381	762	1524	1069	159	318	636
27	1272	565	1130	281	562	1124	269	538	1076	173
28	346	692	1384	789	1578	1177	375	750	1500	1021
29	63	126	252	504	1008	37	74	148	296	592
30	1184	389	778	1556	1133	287	574	1148	317	634
31	1268	557	1114	249	498	996	13	26	52	104
32	208	416	832	1664	1349	719	1438	897	1794	1609
33	1239	499	998	17	34	68	136	272	544	1088
34	197	394	788	1576	1173	367	734	1468	957	1914
35	1849	1719	1459	939	1878	1777	1575	1171	363	726
36	1452	925	1850	1721	1463	947	1894	1809	1639	1299
37	619	1238	497	994	9	18	36	72	144	288
38	576	1152	325	650	1300	621	1242	505	1010	41
39	82	164	328	656	1312	645	1290	601	1202	425
40	850	1700	1421	863	1726	1473	967	1934	1889	1799
41	1619	1259	539	1078	177	354	708	1416	853	1706
42	1433	887	1774	1569	1159	339	678	1356	733	1466
43	953	1906	1833	1687	1395	811	1622	1265	551	1102
44	225	450	900	1800	1621	1263	547	1094	209	418
45	836	1672	1365	751	1502	1025	71	142	284	568
46	1136	293	586	1172	365	730	1460	941	1882	1785
47	1591	1203	427	854	1708	1437	895	1790	1601	1223
48	467	934	1868	1757	1535	1091	203	406	812	1624
49	1269	559	1118	257	514	1028	77	154	308	616

P = 1979

INDICES

	0	1	2	3	4	5	6	7	8	9
50	1090	64	568	1754	293	387	1394	1808	1067	1042
51	554	1336	9	1418	494	746	1353	1498	212	1455
52	1341	134	945	1225	688	1158	1086	1349	1760	1626
53	114	1590	1764	705	699	727	798	630	277	412
54	596	1315	1464	1774	338	1969	1409	446	1630	930
55	647	438	14	841	121	515	852	311	1391	491
56	942	111	274	1406	118	271	86	664	459	150
57	89	1576	898	1153	306	879	380	832	667	974
58	1594	1031	656	1649	1423	1712	462	761	1010	884
59	261	1516	299	1860	153	1271	1768	733	1130	46
60	1245	397	92	1169	679	204	542	739	1851	1662
61	1579	1234	709	753	1441	609	499	1798	901	370
62	62	385	1040	1416	1496	132	1156	1624	703	628
63	1313	1967	928	839	309	109	269	148	1151	830
64	1029	1710	882	1858	731	395	202	1660	751	1796
65	383	130	626	837	146	1708	393	1794	835	1792
66	802	804	718	1825	1118	806	670	1383	868	720
67	1818	1136	1097	1827	977	1616	634	1120	426	1373
68	1358	808	1597	1741	244	672	1727	1192	179	1385
69	1034	1721	281	870	526	1872	1749	722	659	41
70	1962	1820	1867	163	586	1138	1652	1259	416	1099
71	1479	1299	1503	1829	1426	1918	1434	979	784	325
72	1400	1618	1715	1693	600	636	359	168	235	1122
73	465	508	1734	428	346	52	818	1375	764	1052
74	1319	1360	986	1891	217	810	1013	1489	915	1599
75	287	453	922	1743	887	1699	1468	246	1062	591
76	893	674	264	863	1957	1729	1952	1532	1184	1194
77	1519	1669	1778	181	550	1082	1460	1387	302	257
78	538	1036	1147	142	1814	1723	1863	780	342	283
79	1948	1143	957	872	156	1289	1537	528	961	1251
80	71	1874	1274	22	1973	1751	1333	1452	1346	724
81	1771	435	488	661	876	1646	1513	43	736	606
82	1413	1964	827	1657	1705	1822	1133	1370	1189	1869
83	160	1296	322	165	49	1888	450	588	1529	1079
84	139	1140	1248	1449	1643	1654	1293	1076	1073	1261
85	400	1108	1634	418	473	1264	1686	1101	95	1932
86	1199	1481	1541	403	1555	1301	1172	1842	934	1505
87	791	1111	950	1831	682	1004	620	1428	532	1637
88	1606	1920	207	642	651	1436	197	421	1474	981
89	545	1328	1524	786	965	476	1901	327	742	1586
90	442	1402	970	1267	1230	1620	1854	1788	1612	1717
91	1255	1689	1048	1695	1665	776	18	602	1884	1104
92	1838	638	1582	772	1674	361	75	98	575	170
93	1237	1678	845	237	481	1935	693	1124	712	353
94	1942	467	1878	1202	1220	510	756	365	125	1736
95	1913	1484	252	430	1444	999	1783	348	1278	1544
96	226	54	612	79	519	820	1906	406	1163	1377
97	502	1283	1926	766	26	1558	560	1054	1801	102
98	856	1321	1208	1304	1568	1362	904	32	186	988
99	1977	1175	1021	1893	373	579	315	219	332	1845

POWER RESIDUES

	0	1	2	3	4	5	6	7	8	9
50	1232	485	970	1940	1901	1823	1667	1355	731	1462
51	945	1890	1801	1623	1267	555	1110	241	482	964
52	1928	1877	1775	1571	1163	347	694	1388	797	1594
53	1209	439	878	1756	1533	1087	195	390	780	1560
54	1141	303	606	1212	445	890	1780	1581	1183	387
55	774	1548	1117	255	510	1020	61	122	244	488
56	976	1952	1925	1871	1763	1547	1115	251	502	1004
57	29	58	116	232	464	928	1856	1733	1487	995
58	11	22	44	88	176	352	704	1408	837	1674
59	1369	759	1518	1057	135	270	540	1080	181	362
60	724	1448	917	1834	1689	1399	819	1638	1297	615
61	1230	481	962	1924	1869	1759	1539	1099	219	438
62	876	1752	1525	1071	163	326	652	1304	629	1258
63	537	1074	169	338	676	1352	725	1450	921	1842
64	1705	1431	883	1766	1553	1127	275	550	1100	221
65	442	884	1768	1557	1135	291	582	1164	349	698
66	1396	813	1626	1273	567	1134	289	578	1156	333
67	666	1332	685	1370	761	1522	1065	151	302	604
68	1208	437	874	1748	1517	1055	131	262	524	1048
69	117	234	468	936	1872	1765	1551	1123	267	534
70	1068	157	314	628	1256	533	1066	153	306	612
71	1224	469	938	1876	1773	1567	1155	331	662	1324
72	669	1338	697	1394	809	1618	1257	535	1070	161
73	322	644	1288	597	1194	409	818	1636	1293	607
74	1214	449	898	1796	1613	1247	515	1030	81	162
75	324	648	1296	613	1226	473	946	1892	1805	1631
76	1283	587	1174	369	738	1476	973	1946	1913	1847
77	1715	1451	923	1846	1713	1447	915	1830	1681	1383
78	787	1574	1169	359	718	1436	893	1786	1593	1207
79	435	870	1740	1501	1023	67	134	268	536	1072
80	165	330	660	1320	661	1322	665	1330	681	1362
81	745	1490	1001	23	46	92	184	368	736	1472
82	965	1930	1881	1783	1587	1195	411	822	1644	1309
83	639	1278	577	1154	329	658	1316	653	1306	633
84	1266	553	1106	233	466	932	1864	1749	1519	1059
85	139	278	556	1112	245	490	980	1960	1941	1903
86	1827	1675	1371	763	1526	1073	167	334	668	1336
87	693	1386	793	1586	1193	407	814	1628	1277	575
88	1150	321	642	1284	589	1178	377	754	1508	1037
89	95	190	380	760	1520	1061	143	286	572	1144
90	309	618	1236	493	986	1972	1965	1951	1923	1867
91	1755	1531	1083	187	374	748	1496	1013	47	94
92	188	376	752	1504	1029	79	158	316	632	1264
93	549	1098	217	434	868	1736	1493	1007	35	70
94	140	280	560	1120	261	522	1044	109	218	436
95	872	1744	1509	1039	99	198	396	792	1584	1189
96	399	798	1596	1213	447	894	1788	1597	1215	451
97	902	1804	1629	1279	579	1158	337	674	1348	717
98	1434	889	1778	1577	1175	371	742	1484	989	1978
99	1977	1975	1971	1963	1947	1915	1851	1723	1467	955

P = 1979

INDICES

	0	1	2	3	4	5	6	7	8	9
100	1091	812	65	1549	569	1015	1755	937	294	1491
101	388	174	1395	917	1809	1508	1068	1601	1043	1215
102	555	289	1337	794	10	455	1419	1241	495	924
103	747	1114	1354	1745	1499	231	213	889	1456	953
104	1342	1701	135	1682	946	1470	1226	1834	689	248
105	1159	1564	1087	1064	1350	685	1761	593	1627	849
106	115	895	1591	1007	1765	676	706	59	700	266
107	728	623	799	865	631	241	278	1959	413	1431
108	597	1731	1316	912	1465	1954	1775	535	339	1534
109	1970	485	1410	1186	447	1640	1631	1196	931	617
110	648	1521	439	1609	15	1671	842	1939	122	1780
111	516	1923	853	183	312	566	1392	552	492	210
112	943	1084	112	697	275	1462	1407	645	119	1389
113	272	84	87	304	665	654	460	259	151	1128
114	90	540	1577	1439	899	1038	1154	1311	307	1149
115	880	200	381	144	833	716	668	1816	975	424
116	1595	1725	1032	524	657	1865	1650	1477	1424	782
117	1713	357	463	344	762	984	1011	285	885	1060
118	262	1950	1517	548	300	1145	1861	1946	154	959
119	1272	1331	1769	874	734	825	1131	158	47	1527
120	1246	1291	398	471	93	1539	1170	789	680	530
121	205	195	543	963	740	968	1852	1253	1663	1882
122	1580	73	1235	479	710	1876	754	1911	1442	1276
123	610	1904	500	24	1799	1206	902	1975	371	330
124	63	1753	386	1807	1041	1335	1417	745	1497	1454
125	133	1224	1157	1348	1625	1589	704	726	629	411
126	1314	1773	1968	445	929	437	840	514	310	490
127	110	1405	270	663	149	1575	1152	878	831	973
128	1030	1648	1711	760	883	1515	1859	1270	732	45
129	396	1168	203	738	1661	1233	752	608	1797	369
130	384	1415	131	1623	627	1966	838	108	147	829
131	1709	1857	394	1659	1795	129	836	1707	1793	1791
132	803	1824	805	1382	719	1135	1826	1615	1119	1372
133	807	1740	671	1191	1384	1720	869	1871	721	40
134	1819	162	1137	1258	1098	1298	1828	1917	978	324
135	1617	1692	635	167	1121	507	427	51	1374	1051
136	1359	1890	809	1488	1598	452	1742	1698	245	590
137	673	862	1728	1531	1193	1668	180	1081	1386	256
138	1035	141	1722	779	282	1142	871	1288	527	1250
139	1873	21	1750	1451	723	434	660	1645	42	605
140	1963	1656	1821	1369	1868	1295	164	1887	587	1078
141	1139	1448	1653	1075	1260	1107	417	1263	1100	1931
142	1480	402	1300	1841	1504	1110	1830	1003	1427	1636
143	1919	641	1435	420	980	1327	785	475	326	1585
144	1401	1266	1619	1787	1716	1688	1694	775	601	1103
145	637	771	360	97	169	1677	236	1934	1123	352
146	466	1201	509	364	1735	1483	429	998	347	1543
147	53	78	819	405	1376	1282	765	1557	1053	101
148	1320	1303	1361	31	987	1174	1892	578	218	1844
149	811	1548	1014	936	1490	173	916	1507	1600	1214

POWER RESIDUES

	0	1	2	3	4	5	6	7	8	9
100	1910	1841	1703	1427	875	1750	1521	1063	147	294
101	588	1176	373	746	1492	1005	31	62	124	248
102	496	992	5	10	20	40	80	160	320	640
103	1280	581	1162	345	690	1380	781	1562	1145	311
104	622	1244	509	1018	57	114	228	456	912	1824
105	1669	1359	739	1478	977	1954	1929	1879	1779	1579
106	1179	379	758	1516	1053	127	254	508	1016	53
107	106	212	424	848	1696	1413	847	1694	1409	839
108	1678	1377	775	1550	1121	263	526	1052	125	250
109	500	1000	21	42	84	168	336	672	1344	709
110	1418	857	1714	1449	919	1838	1697	1415	851	1702
111	1425	871	1742	1505	1031	83	166	332	664	1328
112	677	1354	729	1458	937	1874	1769	1559	1139	299
113	598	1196	413	826	1652	1325	671	1342	705	1410
114	841	1682	1385	791	1582	1185	391	782	1564	1149
115	319	638	1276	573	1146	313	626	1252	525	1050
116	121	242	484	968	1936	1893	1807	1635	1291	603
117	1206	433	866	1732	1485	991	3	6	12	24
118	48	96	192	384	768	1536	1093	207	414	828
119	1656	1333	687	1374	769	1538	1097	215	430	860
120	1720	1461	943	1886	1793	1607	1235	491	982	1964
121	1949	1919	1859	1739	1499	1019	59	118	236	472
122	944	1888	1797	1615	1251	523	1046	113	226	452
123	904	1808	1637	1295	611	1222	465	930	1860	1741
124	1503	1027	75	150	300	600	1200	421	842	1684
125	1389	799	1598	1217	455	910	1820	1661	1343	707
126	1414	849	1698	1417	855	1710	1441	903	1806	1633
127	1287	595	1190	401	802	1604	1229	479	958	1916
128	1853	1727	1475	971	1942	1905	1831	1683	1387	795
129	1590	1201	423	846	1692	1405	831	1662	1345	711
130	1422	865	1730	1481	983	1966	1953	1927	1875	1771
131	1563	1147	315	630	1260	541	1082	185	370	740
132	1480	981	1962	1945	1911	1843	1707	1435	891	1782
133	1585	1191	403	806	1612	1245	511	1022	65	130
134	260	520	1040	101	202	404	808	1616	1253	527
135	1054	129	258	516	1032	85	170	340	680	1360
136	741	1482	985	1970	1961	1943	1907	1835	1691	1403
137	827	1654	1329	679	1358	737	1474	969	1938	1897
138	1815	1651	1323	667	1334	689	1378	777	1554	1129
139	279	558	1116	253	506	1012	45	90	180	360
140	720	1440	901	1802	1625	1271	563	1126	273	546
141	1092	205	410	820	1640	1301	623	1246	513	1026
142	73	146	292	584	1168	357	714	1428	877	1754
143	1529	1079	179	358	716	1432	885	1770	1561	1143
144	307	614	1228	477	954	1908	1837	1695	1411	843
145	1686	1393	807	1614	1249	519	1038	97	194	388
146	776	1552	1125	271	542	1084	189	378	756	1512
147	1045	111	222	444	888	1776	1573	1167	355	710
148	1420	861	1722	1465	951	1902	1825	1671	1363	747
149	1494	1009	39	78	156	312	624	1248	517	1034

P = 1979

INDICES

	0	1	2	3	4	5	6	7	8	9
150	288	793	454	1240	923	1113	1744	230	888	952
151	1700	1681	1469	1833	247	1563	1063	684	592	848
152	894	1006	675	58	265	622	864	240	1958	1430
153	1730	911	1953	534	1533	484	1185	1639	1195	616
154	1520	1608	1670	1938	1779	1922	182	565	551	209
155	1083	696	1461	644	1388	83	303	653	258	1127
156	539	1438	1037	1310	1148	199	143	715	1815	423
157	1724	523	1864	1476	781	356	343	983	284	1059
158	1949	547	1144	1945	958	1330	873	824	157	1526
159	1290	470	1538	788	529	194	962	967	1252	1881
160	72	478	1875	1910	1275	1903	23	1205	1974	329
161	1752	1806	1334	744	1453	1223	1347	1588	725	410
162	1772	444	436	513	489	1404	662	1574	877	972
163	1647	759	1514	1269	44	1167	737	1232	607	368
164	1414	1622	1965	107	828	1856	1658	128	1706	1790
165	1823	1381	1134	1614	1371	1739	1190	1719	1870	39
166	161	1257	1297	1916	323	1691	166	506	50	1050
167	1889	1487	451	1697	589	861	1530	1667	1080	255
168	140	778	1141	1287	1249	20	1450	433	1644	604
169	1655	1368	1294	1886	1077	1447	1074	1106	1262	1930
170	401	1840	1109	1002	1635	640	419	1326	474	1584
171	1265	1786	1687	774	1102	770	96	1676	1933	351
172	1200	363	1482	997	1542	77	404	1281	1556	100
173	1302	30	1173	577	1843	1547	935	172	1506	1213
174	792	1239	1112	229	951	1680	1832	1562	683	847
175	1005	57	621	239	1429	910	533	483	1638	615
176	1607	1937	1921	564	208	695	643	82	652	1126
177	1437	1309	198	714	422	522	1475	355	982	1058
178	546	1944	1329	823	1525	469	787	193	966	1880
179	477	1909	1902	1204	328	1805	743	1222	1587	409
180	443	512	1403	1573	971	758	1268	1166	1231	367
181	1621	106	1855	127	1789	1380	1613	1738	1718	38
182	1256	1915	1690	505	1049	1486	1696	860	1666	254
183	777	1286	19	432	603	1367	1885	1446	1105	1929
184	1839	1001	639	1325	1583	1785	773	769	1675	350
185	362	996	76	1280	99	29	576	1546	171	1212
186	1238	228	1679	1561	846	56	238	909	482	614
187	1936	563	694	81	1125	1308	713	521	354	1057
188	1943	822	468	192	1879	1908	1203	1804	1221	408
189	511	1572	757	1165	366	105	126	1379	1737	37
190	1914	504	1485	859	253	1285	431	1366	1445	1928
191	1000	1324	1784	768	349	995	1279	28	1545	1211
192	227	1560	55	908	613	562	80	1307	520	1056
193	821	191	1907	1803	407	1571	1164	104	1378	36
194	503	858	1284	1365	1927	1323	767	994	27	1210
195	1559	907	561	1306	1055	190	1802	1570	103	35
196	857	1364	1322	993	1209	906	1305	189	1569	34
197	1363	992	905	188	33	991	187	990	989	

POWER RESIDUES

	0	1	2	3	4	5	6	7	8	9
150	89	178	356	712	1424	869	1738	1497	1015	51
151	102	204	408	816	1632	1285	591	1182	385	770
152	1540	1101	223	446	892	1784	1589	1199	419	838
153	1676	1373	767	1534	1089	199	398	796	1592	1205
154	431	862	1724	1469	959	1918	1857	1735	1491	1003
155	27	54	108	216	432	864	1728	1477	975	1950
156	1921	1863	1747	1515	1051	123	246	492	984	1968
157	1957	1935	1891	1803	1627	1275	571	1142	305	610
158	1220	461	922	1844	1709	1439	899	1798	1617	1255
159	531	1062	145	290	580	1160	341	682	1364	749
160	1498	1017	55	110	220	440	880	1760	1541	1103
161	227	454	908	1816	1653	1327	675	1350	721	1442
162	905	1810	1641	1303	627	1254	529	1058	137	274
163	548	1096	213	426	852	1704	1429	879	1758	1537
164	1095	211	422	844	1688	1397	815	1630	1281	583
165	1166	353	706	1412	845	1690	1401	823	1646	1313
166	647	1294	609	1218	457	914	1828	1677	1375	771
167	1542	1105	231	462	924	1848	1717	1455	931	1862
168	1745	1511	1043	107	214	428	856	1712	1445	911
169	1822	1665	1351	723	1446	913	1826	1673	1367	755
170	1510	1041	103	206	412	824	1648	1317	655	1310
171	641	1282	585	1170	361	722	1444	909	1818	1657
172	1335	691	1382	785	1570	1161	343	686	1372	765
173	1530	1081	183	366	732	1464	949	1898	1817	1655
174	1331	683	1366	753	1506	1033	87	174	348	696
175	1392	805	1610	1241	503	1006	33	66	132	264
176	528	1056	133	266	532	1064	149	298	596	1192
177	405	810	1620	1261	543	1086	193	386	772	1544
178	1109	239	478	956	1912	1845	1711	1443	907	1814
179	1649	1319	659	1318	657	1314	649	1298	617	1234
180	489	978	1956	1933	1887	1795	1611	1243	507	1014
181	49	98	196	392	784	1568	1157	335	670	1340
182	701	1402	825	1650	1321	663	1326	673	1346	713
183	1426	873	1746	1513	1047	115	230	460	920	1840
184	1701	1423	867	1734	1489	999	19	38	76	152
185	304	608	1216	453	906	1812	1645	1311	643	1286
186	593	1186	393	786	1572	1165	351	702	1404	829
187	1658	1337	695	1390	801	1602	1225	471	942	1884
188	1789	1599	1219	459	918	1836	1693	1407	835	1670
189	1361	743	1486	993	7	14	28	56	112	224
190	448	896	1792	1605	1231	483	966	1932	1885	1791
191	1603	1227	475	950	1900	1821	1663	1347	715	1430
192	881	1762	1545	1111	243	486	972	1944	1909	1839
193	1699	1419	859	1718	1457	935	1870	1761	1543	1107
194	235	470	940	1880	1781	1583	1187	395	790	1580
195	1181	383	766	1532	1085	191	382	764	1528	1077
196	175	350	700	1400	821	1642	1305	631	1262	545
197	1090	201	402	804	1608	1237	495	990		

P = 1987

INDICES

	0	1	2	3	4	5	6	7	8	9
0		0	1	1075	2	1775	1076	1220	3	164
1	1776	272	1077	1357	1221	864	4	466	165	1891
2	1777	309	273	743	1078	1564	1358	1239	1222	1389
3	865	76	5	1347	467	1009	166	1018	1892	446
4	1778	1805	310	413	274	1939	744	54	1079	454
5	1565	1541	1359	1333	1240	61	1223	980	1390	1424
6	866	11	77	1384	6	1146	1348	1864	468	1818
7	1010	764	167	1744	1019	653	1893	1492	447	506
8	1779	328	1806	697	311	255	414	478	275	123
9	1940	591	745	1151	55	1680	1080	1256	455	436
10	1566	1556	1542	1953	1360	98	1334	839	1241	406
11	62	107	1224	1875	981	532	1391	1521	1425	1686
12	867	544	12	894	78	1353	1385	1935	7	1488
13	1147	402	1349	1125	1865	1028	469	1590	1819	1577
14	1011	1129	765	1629	168	1178	1745	1529	1020	1201
15	654	714	1894	630	1493	1851	448	1869	507	422
16	1780	1963	329	1978	1807	1136	698	1375	312	728
17	256	69	415	1032	479	798	276	513	124	886
18	1941	1716	592	1086	746	807	1152	738	56	473
19	1681	709	1081	197	1257	235	456	1669	437	1285
20	1567	953	1557	623	1543	1594	1954	907	1361	177
21	99	1104	1335	1839	840	202	1242	1296	407	833
22	63	1823	108	1613	1225	1728	1876	1059	982	855
23	533	581	1392	1884	1522	1829	1426	1581	1687	1643
24	868	428	545	1403	13	243	895	1262	79	1772
25	1354	306	1386	1015	1936	1330	8	1815	1489	252
26	1148	1553	403	1518	1350	1122	1126	1198	1866	1133
27	1029	1713	470	1666	1591	1836	1820	852	1578	240
28	1012	1550	1130	849	766	769	1630	1039	169	932
29	1179	345	1746	772	1530	1213	1021	1511	1202	114
30	655	1633	715	645	1895	1786	631	1095	1494	1042
31	1852	461	449	323	1870	1173	508	172	423	1661
32	1781	1914	1964	371	330	935	1979	1481	1808	1274
33	1137	1903	699	1182	1376	1653	313	1919	729	964
34	257	348	70	1674	416	1607	1033	604	480	1749
35	799	610	277	1312	514	553	125	775	887	299
36	1942	1796	1717	1619	593	1533	1087	1112	747	1969
37	808	567	1153	1216	739	442	57	760	474	1949
38	1682	1024	710	1371	1082	1281	198	577	1258	1514
39	236	1209	457	1477	1670	295	438	1205	1286	214
40	1568	376	954	1433	1558	117	624	1290	1544	1601
41	1595	679	1955	658	908	486	1362	666	178	1452
42	100	1636	1105	218	1336	44	1840	1231	841	718
43	203	523	1243	335	1297	267	408	648	834	1572
44	64	618	1824	1193	109	1898	1614	290	1226	1700
45	1729	91	1877	1789	1060	380	983	1413	856	1705
46	534	634	582	33	1393	940	1885	691	1523	1098
47	1830	958	1427	685	1582	1469	1688	1497	1644	1755
48	869	389	429	1052	546	1045	1404	1437	14	1067
49	244	1734	896	1855	1263	225	80	1984	1773	162

POWER RESIDUES

	0	1	2	3	4	5	6	7	8	9
0	1	2	4	8	16	32	64	128	256	512
1	1024	61	122	244	488	976	1952	1917	1847	1707
2	1427	867	1734	1481	975	1950	1913	1839	1691	1395
3	803	1606	1225	463	926	1852	1717	1447	907	1814
4	1641	1295	603	1206	425	850	1700	1413	839	1678
5	1369	751	1502	1017	47	94	188	376	752	1504
6	1021	55	110	220	440	880	1760	1533	1079	171
7	342	684	1368	749	1498	1009	31	62	124	248
8	496	992	1984	1981	1975	1963	1939	1891	1795	1603
9	1219	451	902	1804	1621	1255	523	1046	105	210
10	420	840	1680	1373	759	1518	1049	111	222	444
11	888	1776	1565	1143	299	598	1196	405	810	1620
12	1253	519	1038	89	178	356	712	1424	861	1722
13	1457	927	1854	1721	1455	923	1846	1705	1423	859
14	1718	1449	911	1822	1657	1327	667	1334	681	1362
15	737	1474	961	1922	1857	1727	1467	947	1894	1801
16	1615	1243	499	998	9	18	36	72	144	288
17	576	1152	317	634	1268	549	1098	209	418	836
18	1672	1357	727	1454	921	1842	1697	1407	827	1654
19	1321	655	1310	633	1266	545	1090	193	386	772
20	1544	1101	215	430	860	1720	1453	919	1838	1689
21	1391	795	1590	1193	399	798	1596	1205	423	846
22	1692	1397	807	1614	1241	495	990	1980	1973	1959
23	1931	1875	1763	1539	1091	195	390	780	1560	1133
24	279	558	1116	245	490	980	1960	1933	1879	1771
25	1555	1123	259	518	1036	85	170	340	680	1360
26	733	1466	945	1890	1793	1599	1211	435	870	1740
27	1493	999	11	22	44	88	176	352	704	1408
28	829	1658	1329	671	1342	697	1394	801	1602	1217
29	447	894	1788	1589	1191	395	790	1580	1173	359
30	718	1436	885	1770	1553	1119	251	502	1004	21
31	42	84	168	336	672	1344	701	1402	817	1634
32	1281	575	1150	313	626	1252	517	1034	81	162
33	324	648	1296	605	1210	433	866	1732	1477	967
34	1934	1881	1775	1563	1139	291	582	1164	341	682
35	1364	741	1482	977	1954	1921	1855	1723	1459	931
36	1862	1737	1487	987	1974	1961	1935	1883	1779	1571
37	1155	323	646	1292	597	1194	401	802	1604	1221
38	455	910	1820	1653	1319	651	1302	617	1234	481
39	962	1924	1861	1735	1483	979	1958	1929	1871	1755
40	1523	1059	131	262	524	1048	109	218	436	872
41	1744	1501	1015	43	86	172	344	688	1376	765
42	1530	1073	159	318	636	1272	557	1114	241	482
43	964	1928	1869	1751	1515	1043	99	198	396	792
44	1584	1181	375	750	1500	1013	39	78	156	312
45	624	1248	509	1018	49	98	196	392	784	1568
46	1149	311	622	1244	501	1002	17	34	68	136
47	272	544	1088	189	378	756	1512	1037	87	174
48	348	696	1392	797	1594	1201	415	830	1660	1333
49	679	1358	729	1458	929	1858	1729	1471	955	1910

P = 1987

INDICES

	0	1	2	3	4	5	6	7	8	9
50	1355	464	307	1562	1387	1345	1016	1803	1937	452
51	1331	978	9	1144	1816	1742	1490	326	253	121
52	1149	1254	1554	96	404	1873	1519	542	1351	1486
53	1123	1588	1127	1176	1199	628	1867	1961	1134	726
54	1030	511	1714	805	471	195	1667	951	1592	175
55	1837	1294	1821	1726	853	1882	1579	426	241	1770
56	1013	1813	1551	1120	1131	1664	850	1548	767	930
57	770	1509	1631	1784	1040	321	170	1912	933	1272
58	1180	1917	346	1605	1747	1310	773	1794	1531	1967
59	1214	758	1022	1279	1512	1475	1203	374	115	1599
60	656	664	1634	42	716	333	646	616	1896	1698
61	1787	1411	632	938	1096	683	1495	387	1043	1065
62	1853	1982	462	1343	450	1142	324	1252	1871	1484
63	1174	1959	509	193	173	1724	424	1811	1662	928
64	1782	1910	1915	1308	1965	1277	372	662	331	1696
65	936	385	1980	1140	1482	191	1809	1908	1275	1694
66	1138	1906	1904	912	700	914	1183	146	1377	702
67	1654	283	314	916	1920	817	730	1185	965	490
68	258	148	349	988	71	1379	1675	1930	417	704
69	1608	1325	1034	1656	605	1366	481	285	1750	973
70	800	316	611	923	278	918	1313	790	515	1922
71	554	670	126	819	776	1418	888	732	300	1167
72	1943	1187	1797	1503	1718	967	1620	182	594	492
73	1534	879	1088	260	1113	1318	748	150	1970	1444
74	809	351	568	1456	1154	990	1217	861	740	73
75	443	51	58	1381	761	503	475	1677	1950	104
76	1683	1932	1025	1626	711	419	1372	795	1083	706
77	1282	904	199	1610	578	1640	1259	1327	1515	1710
78	237	1036	1210	642	458	1658	1478	1650	1671	607
79	296	1109	439	1368	1206	211	1287	483	215	520
80	1569	287	377	30	955	1752	1434	222	1559	975
81	118	539	625	802	1291	1767	1545	318	1602	755
82	1596	613	680	1340	1956	925	659	188	909	280
83	487	1927	1363	920	667	1164	179	1315	1453	48
84	101	792	1637	639	1106	517	219	1764	1337	1924
85	45	1761	1841	556	1232	1844	842	672	719	139
86	204	128	524	559	1244	821	336	21	1298	778
87	268	1235	409	1420	649	587	835	890	1573	1847
88	65	734	619	829	1825	302	1194	845	110	1169
89	1899	600	1615	1945	291	675	1227	1189	1701	1465
90	1730	1799	92	722	1878	1505	1790	38	1061	1720
91	381	142	984	969	1414	875	857	1622	1706	207
92	535	184	635	135	583	596	34	131	1394	494
93	941	359	1886	1536	692	527	1524	881	1099	1398
94	1831	1090	959	562	1428	262	686	157	1583	1115
95	1470	1247	1689	1320	1498	498	1645	750	1756	824
96	870	152	390	1003	430	1972	1053	339	547	1446
97	1046	945	1405	811	1438	24	15	353	1068	395
98	245	570	1735	1301	897	1458	1856	363	1264	1156
99	226	781	81	992	1985	1074	1774	1219	163	271

POWER RESIDUES

	0	1	2	3	4	5	6	7	8	9
50	1833	1679	1371	755	1510	1033	79	158	316	632
51	1264	541	1082	177	354	708	1416	845	1690	1393
52	799	1598	1209	431	862	1724	1461	935	1870	1753
53	1519	1051	115	230	460	920	1840	1693	1399	811
54	1622	1257	527	1054	121	242	484	968	1936	1885
55	1783	1579	1171	355	710	1420	853	1706	1425	863
56	1726	1465	943	1886	1785	1583	1179	371	742	1484
57	981	1962	1937	1887	1787	1587	1187	387	774	1548
58	1109	231	462	924	1848	1709	1431	875	1750	1513
59	1039	91	182	364	728	1456	925	1850	1713	1439
60	891	1782	1577	1167	347	694	1388	789	1578	1169
61	351	702	1404	821	1642	1297	607	1214	441	882
62	1764	1541	1095	203	406	812	1624	1261	535	1070
63	153	306	612	1224	461	922	1844	1701	1415	843
64	1686	1385	783	1566	1145	303	606	1212	437	874
65	1748	1509	1031	75	150	300	600	1200	413	826
66	1652	1317	647	1294	601	1202	417	834	1668	1349
67	711	1422	857	1714	1441	895	1790	1593	1199	411
68	822	1644	1301	615	1230	473	946	1892	1797	1607
69	1227	467	934	1868	1749	1511	1035	83	166	332
70	664	1328	669	1338	689	1378	769	1538	1089	191
71	382	764	1528	1069	151	302	604	1208	429	858
72	1716	1445	903	1806	1625	1263	539	1078	169	338
73	676	1352	717	1434	881	1762	1537	1087	187	374
74	748	1496	1005	23	46	92	184	368	736	1472
75	957	1914	1841	1695	1403	819	1638	1289	591	1182
76	377	754	1508	1029	71	142	284	568	1136	285
77	570	1140	293	586	1172	357	714	1428	869	1738
78	1489	991	1982	1977	1967	1947	1907	1827	1667	1347
79	707	1414	841	1682	1377	767	1534	1081	175	350
80	700	1400	813	1626	1265	543	1086	185	370	740
81	1480	973	1946	1905	1823	1659	1331	675	1350	713
82	1426	865	1730	1473	959	1918	1849	1711	1435	883
83	1766	1545	1103	219	438	876	1752	1517	1047	107
84	214	428	856	1712	1437	887	1774	1561	1135	283
85	566	1132	277	554	1108	229	458	916	1832	1677
86	1367	747	1494	1001	15	30	60	120	240	480
87	960	1920	1853	1719	1451	915	1830	1673	1359	731
88	1462	937	1874	1761	1535	1083	179	358	716	1432
89	877	1754	1521	1055	123	246	492	984	1968	1949
90	1911	1835	1683	1379	771	1542	1097	207	414	828
91	1656	1325	663	1326	665	1330	673	1346	705	1410
92	833	1666	1345	703	1406	825	1650	1313	639	1278
93	569	1138	289	578	1156	325	650	1300	613	1226
94	465	930	1860	1733	1479	971	1942	1897	1807	1627
95	1267	547	1094	201	402	804	1608	1229	471	942
96	1884	1781	1575	1163	339	678	1356	725	1450	913
97	1826	1665	1343	699	1398	809	1618	1249	511	1022
98	57	114	228	456	912	1824	1661	1335	683	1366
99	745	1490	993	1986	1985	1983	1979	1971	1955	1923

P = 1987

INDICES

	0	1	2	3	4	5	6	7	8	9
100	1356	863	465	1890	308	742	1563	1238	1388	75
101	1346	1008	1017	445	1804	412	1938	53	453	1540
102	1332	60	979	1423	10	1383	1145	1863	1817	763
103	1743	652	1491	505	327	696	254	477	122	590
104	1150	1679	1255	435	1555	1952	97	838	405	106
105	1874	531	1520	1685	543	893	1352	1934	1487	401
106	1124	1027	1589	1576	1128	1628	1177	1528	1200	713
107	629	1850	1868	421	1962	1977	1135	1374	727	68
108	1031	797	512	885	1715	1085	806	737	472	708
109	196	234	1668	1284	952	622	1593	906	176	1103
110	1838	201	1295	832	1822	1612	1727	1058	854	580
111	1883	1828	1580	1642	427	1402	242	1261	1771	305
112	1014	1329	1814	251	1552	1517	1121	1197	1132	1712
113	1665	1835	851	239	1549	848	768	1038	931	344
114	771	1212	1510	113	1632	644	1785	1094	1041	460
115	322	1172	171	1660	1913	370	934	1480	1273	1902
116	1181	1652	1918	963	347	1673	1606	603	1748	609
117	1311	552	774	298	1795	1618	1532	1111	1968	566
118	1215	441	759	1948	1023	1370	1280	576	1513	1208
119	1476	294	1204	213	375	1432	116	1289	1600	678
120	657	485	665	1451	1635	217	43	1230	717	522
121	334	266	647	1571	617	1192	1897	289	1699	90
122	1788	379	1412	1704	633	32	939	690	1097	957
123	684	1468	1496	1754	388	1051	1044	1436	1066	1733
124	1854	224	1983	161	463	1561	1344	1802	451	977
125	1143	1741	325	120	1253	95	1872	541	1485	1587
126	1175	627	1960	725	510	804	194	950	174	1293
127	1725	1881	425	1769	1812	1119	1663	1547	929	1508
128	1783	320	1911	1271	1916	1604	1309	1793	1966	757
129	1278	1474	373	1598	663	41	332	615	1697	1410
130	937	682	386	1064	1981	1342	1141	1251	1483	1958
131	192	1723	1810	927	1909	1307	1276	661	1695	384
132	1139	190	1907	1693	1905	911	913	145	701	282
133	915	816	1184	489	147	987	1378	1929	703	1324
134	1655	1365	284	972	315	922	917	789	1921	669
135	818	1417	731	1166	1186	1502	966	181	491	878
136	259	1317	149	1443	350	1455	989	860	72	50
137	1380	502	1676	103	1931	1625	418	794	705	903
138	1609	1639	1326	1709	1035	641	1657	1649	606	1108
139	1367	210	482	519	286	29	1751	221	974	538
140	801	1766	317	754	612	1339	924	187	279	1926
141	919	1163	1314	47	791	638	516	1763	1923	1760
142	555	1843	671	138	127	558	820	20	777	1234
143	1419	586	889	1846	733	828	301	844	1168	599
144	1944	674	1188	1464	1798	721	1504	37	1719	141
145	968	874	1621	206	183	134	595	130	493	358
146	1535	526	880	1397	1089	561	261	156	1114	1246
147	1319	497	749	823	151	1002	1971	338	1445	944
148	810	23	352	394	569	1300	1457	362	1155	780
149	991	1073	1218	270	862	1889	741	1237	74	1007

POWER RESIDUES

	0	1	2	3	4	5	6	7	8	9
100	1859	1731	1475	963	1926	1865	1743	1499	1011	35
101	70	140	280	560	1120	253	506	1012	37	74
102	148	296	592	1184	381	762	1524	1061	135	270
103	540	1080	173	346	692	1384	781	1562	1137	287
104	574	1148	309	618	1236	485	970	1940	1893	1799
105	1611	1235	483	966	1932	1877	1767	1547	1107	227
106	454	908	1816	1645	1303	619	1238	489	978	1956
107	1925	1863	1739	1491	995	3	6	12	24	48
108	96	192	384	768	1536	1085	183	366	732	1464
109	941	1882	1777	1567	1147	307	614	1228	469	938
110	1876	1765	1543	1099	211	422	844	1688	1389	791
111	1582	1177	367	734	1468	949	1898	1809	1631	1275
112	563	1126	265	530	1060	133	266	532	1064	141
113	282	564	1128	269	538	1076	165	330	660	1320
114	653	1306	625	1250	513	1026	65	130	260	520
115	1040	93	186	372	744	1488	989	1978	1969	1951
116	1915	1843	1699	1411	835	1670	1353	719	1438	889
117	1778	1569	1151	315	630	1260	533	1066	145	290
118	580	1160	333	666	1332	677	1354	721	1442	897
119	1794	1601	1215	443	886	1772	1557	1127	267	534
120	1068	149	298	596	1192	397	794	1588	1189	391
121	782	1564	1141	295	590	1180	373	746	1492	997
122	7	14	28	56	112	224	448	896	1792	1597
123	1207	427	854	1708	1429	871	1742	1497	1007	27
124	54	108	216	432	864	1728	1469	951	1902	1817
125	1647	1307	627	1254	521	1042	97	194	388	776
126	1552	1117	247	494	988	1976	1965	1943	1899	1811
127	1635	1283	579	1158	329	658	1316	645	1290	593
128	1186	385	770	1540	1093	199	398	796	1592	1197
129	407	814	1628	1269	551	1102	217	434	868	1736
130	1485	983	1966	1945	1903	1819	1651	1315	643	1286
131	585	1170	353	706	1412	837	1674	1361	735	1470
132	953	1906	1825	1663	1339	691	1382	777	1554	1121
133	255	510	1020	53	106	212	424	848	1696	1405
134	823	1646	1305	623	1246	505	1010	33	66	132
135	264	528	1056	125	250	500	1000	13	26	52
136	104	208	416	832	1664	1341	695	1390	793	1586
137	1185	383	766	1532	1077	167	334	668	1336	685
138	1370	753	1506	1025	63	126	252	504	1008	29
139	58	116	232	464	928	1856	1725	1463	939	1878
140	1769	1551	1115	243	486	972	1944	1901	1815	1643
141	1299	611	1222	457	914	1828	1669	1351	715	1430
142	873	1746	1505	1023	59	118	236	472	944	1888
143	1789	1591	1195	403	806	1612	1237	487	974	1948
144	1909	1831	1675	1363	739	1478	969	1938	1889	1791
145	1595	1203	419	838	1676	1365	743	1486	985	1970
146	1953	1919	1851	1715	1443	899	1798	1609	1231	475
147	950	1900	1813	1639	1291	595	1190	393	786	1572
148	1157	327	654	1308	629	1258	529	1058	129	258
149	516	1032	77	154	308	616	1232	477	954	1908

P = 1987

INDICES

	0	1	2	3	4	5	6	7	8	9
150	444	411	52	1539	59	1422	1382	1862	762	651
151	504	695	476	589	1678	434	1951	837	105	530
152	1684	892	1933	400	1026	1575	1627	1527	712	1849
153	420	1976	1373	67	796	884	1084	736	707	233
154	1283	621	905	1102	200	831	1611	1057	579	1827
155	1641	1401	1260	304	1328	250	1516	1196	1711	1834
156	238	847	1037	343	1211	112	643	1093	459	1171
157	1659	369	1479	1901	1651	962	1672	602	608	551
158	297	1617	1110	565	440	1947	1369	575	1207	293
159	212	1431	1288	677	484	1450	216	1229	521	265
160	1570	1191	288	89	378	1703	31	689	956	1467
161	1753	1050	1435	1732	223	160	1560	1801	976	1740
162	119	94	540	1586	626	724	803	949	1292	1880
163	1768	1118	1546	1507	319	1270	1603	1792	756	1473
164	1597	40	614	1409	681	1063	1341	1250	1957	1722
165	926	1306	660	383	189	1692	910	144	281	815
166	488	986	1928	1323	1364	971	921	788	668	1416
167	1165	1501	180	877	1316	1442	1454	859	49	501
168	102	1624	793	902	1638	1708	640	1648	1107	209
169	518	28	220	537	1765	753	1338	186	1925	1162
170	46	637	1762	1759	1842	137	557	19	1233	585
171	1845	827	843	598	673	1463	720	36	140	873
172	205	133	129	357	525	1396	560	155	1245	496
173	822	1001	337	943	22	393	1299	361	779	1072
174	269	1888	1236	1006	410	1538	1421	1861	650	694
175	588	433	836	529	891	399	1574	1526	1848	1975
176	66	883	735	232	620	1101	830	1056	1826	1400
177	303	249	1195	1833	846	342	111	1092	1170	368
178	1900	961	601	550	1616	564	1946	574	292	1430
179	676	1449	1228	264	1190	88	1702	688	1466	1049
180	1731	159	1800	1739	93	1585	723	948	1879	1117
181	1506	1269	1791	1472	39	1408	1062	1249	1721	1305
182	382	1691	143	814	985	1322	970	787	1415	1500
183	876	1441	858	500	1623	901	1707	1647	208	27
184	536	752	185	1161	636	1758	136	18	584	826
185	597	1462	35	872	132	356	1395	154	495	1000
186	942	392	360	1071	1887	1005	1537	1860	693	432
187	528	398	1525	1974	882	231	1100	1055	1399	248
188	1832	341	1091	367	960	549	563	573	1429	1448
189	263	87	687	1048	158	1738	1584	947	1116	1268
190	1471	1407	1248	1304	1690	813	1321	786	1499	1440
191	499	900	1646	26	751	1160	1757	17	825	1461
192	871	355	153	999	391	1070	1004	1859	431	397
193	1973	230	1054	247	340	366	548	572	1447	86
194	1047	1737	946	1267	1406	1303	812	785	1439	899
195	25	1159	16	1460	354	998	1069	1858	396	229
196	246	365	571	85	1736	1266	1302	784	898	1158
197	1459	997	1857	228	364	84	1265	783	1157	996
198	227	83	782	995	82	994	993			

POWER RESIDUES

	0	1	2	3	4	5	6	7	8	9
150	1829	1671	1355	723	1446	905	1810	1633	1279	571
151	1142	297	594	1188	389	778	1556	1125	263	526
152	1052	117	234	468	936	1872	1757	1527	1067	147
153	294	588	1176	365	730	1460	933	1866	1745	1503
154	1019	51	102	204	408	816	1632	1277	567	1134
155	281	562	1124	261	522	1044	101	202	404	808
156	1616	1245	503	1006	25	50	100	200	400	800
157	1600	1213	439	878	1756	1525	1063	139	278	556
158	1112	237	474	948	1896	1805	1623	1259	531	1062
159	137	274	548	1096	205	410	820	1640	1293	599
160	1198	409	818	1636	1285	583	1166	345	690	1380
161	773	1546	1105	223	446	892	1784	1581	1175	363
162	726	1452	917	1834	1681	1375	763	1526	1065	143
163	286	572	1144	301	602	1204	421	842	1684	1381
164	775	1550	1113	239	478	956	1912	1837	1687	1387
165	787	1574	1161	335	670	1340	693	1386	785	1570
166	1153	319	638	1276	565	1130	273	546	1092	197
167	394	788	1576	1165	343	686	1372	757	1514	1041
168	95	190	380	760	1520	1053	119	238	476	952
169	1904	1821	1655	1323	659	1318	649	1298	609	1218
170	449	898	1796	1605	1223	459	918	1836	1685	1383
171	779	1558	1129	271	542	1084	181	362	724	1448
172	909	1818	1649	1311	635	1270	553	1106	225	450
173	900	1800	1613	1239	491	982	1964	1941	1895	1803
174	1619	1251	515	1030	73	146	292	584	1168	349
175	698	1396	805	1610	1233	479	958	1916	1845	1703
176	1419	851	1702	1417	847	1694	1401	815	1630	1273
177	559	1118	249	498	996	5	10	20	40	80
178	160	320	640	1280	573	1146	305	610	1220	453
179	906	1812	1637	1287	587	1174	361	722	1444	901
180	1802	1617	1247	507	1014	41	82	164	328	656
181	1312	637	1274	561	1122	257	514	1028	69	138
182	276	552	1104	221	442	884	1768	1549	1111	235
183	470	940	1880	1773	1559	1131	275	550	1100	213
184	426	852	1704	1421	855	1710	1433	879	1758	1529
185	1071	155	310	620	1240	493	986	1972	1957	1927
186	1867	1747	1507	1027	67	134	268	536	1072	157
187	314	628	1256	525	1050	113	226	452	904	1808
188	1629	1271	555	1110	233	466	932	1864	1741	1495
189	1003	19	38	76	152	304	608	1216	445	890
190	1780	1573	1159	331	662	1324	661	1322	657	1314
191	641	1282	577	1154	321	642	1284	581	1162	337
192	674	1348	709	1418	849	1698	1409	831	1662	1337
193	687	1374	761	1522	1057	127	254	508	1016	45
194	90	180	360	720	1440	893	1786	1585	1183	379
195	758	1516	1045	103	206	412	824	1648	1309	631
196	1262	537	1074	161	322	644	1288	589	1178	369
197	738	1476	965	1930	1873	1759	1531	1075	163	326
198	652	1304	621	1242	497	994				

P = 1993

INDICES

	0	1	2	3	4	5	6	7	8	9
0		0	1202	1004	412	1	214	827	1614	16
1	1203	1269	1416	702	37	1005	824	690	1218	1362
2	413	1831	479	877	626	2	1904	1020	1239	1725
3	215	1768	34	281	1892	828	428	1763	572	1706
4	1615	1162	1041	1914	1681	17	87	1317	1828	1654
5	1204	1694	1114	1259	230	1270	449	374	935	802
6	1417	132	978	843	1236	703	1483	475	1102	1881
7	38	1750	1630	455	973	1006	1774	104	916	220
8	825	32	372	370	251	691	1124	737	891	1345
9	1219	1529	1289	780	527	1363	1038	1842	864	1285
10	414	607	904	62	324	1832	469	253	1432	1546
11	480	775	1651	1936	1576	878	145	718	12	1517
12	627	546	1334	174	188	3	53	882	446	926
13	1905	1230	693	197	1677	1021	312	1965	1091	284
14	1240	329	960	1971	840	1726	1657	666	183	743
15	216	509	984	706	1306	1769	126	1126	1422	271
16	35	1704	1234	1343	1574	282	1572	1845	1453	1404
17	1893	1378	334	946	1939	829	101	1806	555	353
18	429	929	739	1136	499	1764	1982	1959	1729	1847
19	573	163	248	636	1052	1707	74	670	495	797
20	1616	1479	1809	560	114	1163	1264	893	1526	639
21	1042	1507	1671	762	1455	1915	642	603	756	1459
22	1682	1392	1977	21	861	18	1146	1188	786	1086
23	88	1108	1347	308	1920	1318	1214	1224	727	1406
24	1829	85	1748	1036	544	1655	1376	72	1390	1374
25	1205	1383	1255	154	92	1695	1648	1221	136	598
26	1115	1741	440	1153	1895	1260	1399	357	887	649
27	231	1207	1514	541	1175	1271	301	399	1486	1784
28	450	81	1531	1585	170	375	1181	1989	50	1380
29	936	854	867	108	1868	803	1385	297	1945	1579
30	1418	749	1711	1611	194	133	1908	1291	516	1066
31	979	1664	1328	1660	336	844	632	319	1473	1002
32	1237	1257	914	60	444	704	553	558	784	152
33	1484	1609	782	1779	1055	476	663	1511	614	948
34	1103	1045	588	489	1536	1882	156	1131	1149	393
35	39	1722	1303	1781	1016	1751	1757	529	1555	1490
36	1631	732	139	1550	1941	456	346	425	1701	1178
37	974	94	1192	1441	1169	1007	939	435	1057	1859
38	1775	1886	1365	1911	1450	105	1838	1930	262	831
39	917	1567	1276	242	1872	221	1697	617	7	1201
40	826	1415	689	478	1019	33	1762	1040	1316	1113
41	373	977	474	1629	103	371	736	1288	1841	903
42	252	1650	717	1333	881	692	1964	959	665	983
43	1125	1233	1844	333	1805	738	1958	247	669	1808
44	892	1670	602	1976	1187	1346	1223	1747	71	1254
45	1220	439	356	1513	398	1530	1988	866	296	1710
46	1290	1327	318	913	557	781	1510	587	1130	1302
47	528	138	424	1191	434	1364	1929	1275	616	688
48	1039	473	1287	716	958	1843	246	601	1746	355
49	865	317	586	423	1274	1286	600	585	584	592

POWER RESIDUES

	0	1	2	3	4	5	6	7	8	9
0	1	5	25	125	625	1132	1674	398	1990	1978
1	1918	1618	118	590	957	799	9	45	225	1125
2	1639	223	1115	1589	1966	1858	1318	611	1062	1324
3	641	1212	81	405	32	160	800	14	70	350
4	1750	778	1897	1513	1586	1951	1783	943	729	1652
5	288	1440	1221	126	630	1157	1799	1023	1129	1659
6	323	1615	103	515	582	917	599	1002	1024	1134
7	1684	448	247	1235	196	980	914	584	927	649
8	1252	281	1405	1046	1244	241	1205	46	230	1150
9	1764	848	254	1270	371	1855	1303	536	687	1442
10	1231	176	880	414	77	385	1925	1653	293	1465
11	1346	751	1762	838	204	1020	1114	1584	1941	1733
12	693	1472	1381	926	644	1227	156	780	1907	1563
13	1836	1208	61	305	1525	1646	258	1290	471	362
14	1810	1078	1404	1041	1219	116	580	907	549	752
15	1767	863	329	1645	253	1265	346	1730	678	1397
16	1006	1044	1234	191	955	789	1952	1788	968	854
17	284	1420	1121	1619	123	615	1082	1424	1141	1719
18	623	1122	1624	148	740	1707	563	822	124	620
19	1107	1549	1766	858	304	1520	1621	133	665	1332
20	681	1412	1081	1419	1116	1594	1991	1983	1943	1743
21	743	1722	638	1197	6	30	150	750	1757	813
22	79	395	1975	1903	1543	1736	708	1547	1756	808
23	54	270	1350	771	1862	1338	711	1562	1831	1183
24	1929	1673	393	1965	1853	1293	486	437	192	960
25	814	84	420	107	535	682	1417	1106	1544	1741
26	733	1672	388	1940	1728	668	1347	756	1787	963
27	829	159	795	1982	1938	1718	618	1097	1499	1516
28	1601	33	165	825	139	695	1482	1431	1176	1894
29	1498	1511	1576	1901	1533	1686	458	297	1485	1446
30	1251	276	1380	921	619	1102	1524	1641	233	1165
31	1839	1223	136	680	1407	1056	1294	491	462	317
32	1585	1946	1758	818	104	520	607	1042	1224	141
33	705	1532	1681	433	172	860	314	1570	1871	1383
34	936	694	1477	1406	1051	1269	366	1830	1178	1904
35	1548	1761	833	179	895	489	452	267	1335	696
36	1487	1456	1301	526	637	1192	1974	1898	1518	1611
37	83	415	82	410	57	285	1425	1146	1744	748
38	1747	763	1822	1138	1704	548	747	1742	738	1697
39	513	572	867	349	1745	753	1772	888	454	277
40	1385	946	744	1727	663	1322	631	1162	1824	1148
41	1754	798	4	20	100	500	507	542	717	1592
42	1981	1933	1693	493	472	367	1835	1203	36	180
43	900	514	577	892	474	377	1885	1453	1286	451
44	262	1310	571	862	324	1620	128	640	1207	56
45	280	1400	1021	1119	1609	73	365	1825	1153	1779
46	923	629	1152	1774	898	504	527	642	1217	106
47	530	657	1292	481	412	67	335	1675	403	22
48	110	550	757	1792	988	954	784	1927	1663	343
49	1715	603	1022	1124	1634	198	990	964	834	184

P = 1993

INDICES

	0	1	2	3	4	5	6	7	8	9
50	415	857	593	950	465	608	1356	416	1294	1502
51	905	1282	858	390	431	63	1338	594	1800	1950
52	325	1117	951	873	1642	1833	363	466	1105	1754
53	470	818	609	1864	1559	254	97	1357	1851	931
54	1433	966	417	1933	724	1547	1743	1295	385	148
55	481	1095	1503	1047	1601	776	696	906	994	624
56	1652	971	1283	186	741	1937	795	859	1372	1173
57	1577	442	391	1167	1199	879	1252	432	590	1640
58	146	1197	64	536	77	719	1310	1339	1078	1138
59	13	1674	595	1447	1499	1518	1155	1801	789	66
60	628	565	1951	491	921	547	821	326	1396	1564
61	1335	27	1118	1298	501	175	1718	952	276	304
62	189	1897	874	180	538	4	870	1643	1538	461
63	54	406	1834	519	1521	883	683	364	212	1766
64	447	30	467	1228	124	927	1262	1106	1646	79
65	1906	1607	1755	1884	1760	1231	1986	471	1354	816
66	694	1195	819	404	1984	198	989	610	265	1025
67	1678	1401	1865	900	721	1022	1816	1560	158	677
68	313	200	255	1437	1790	1966	1691	98	746	1961
69	1092	1813	1358	120	341	285	359	1852	1595	1312
70	1241	1468	932	1133	513	330	991	1434	226	673
71	961	236	967	653	1731	1972	765	418	700	570
72	841	889	1934	1089	1341	1727	760	725	1151	48
73	1658	612	1548	260	1627	667	911	1744	388	1849
74	184	1076	1296	210	402	744	651	386	379	1080
75	217	111	149	395	1637	510	267	482	1069	1158
76	985	1924	1096	381	575	707	1121	1504	660	1324
77	1307	233	1048	1541	1140	1770	1464	1602	41	532
78	127	1027	777	753	486	1127	1444	697	1082	165
79	1423	771	907	834	1819	272	1209	995	411	15
80	36	1361	625	1724	1891	1705	1680	1653	229	801
81	1235	1880	972	219	250	1344	526	1284	323	1545
82	1575	1516	187	925	1676	283	839	742	1305	270
83	1573	1403	1938	352	498	1846	1051	796	113	638
84	1454	1458	860	1085	1919	1405	543	1373	91	597
85	1894	648	1174	1783	169	1379	1867	1578	193	1065
86	335	1001	443	151	1054	947	1535	392	1015	1489
87	1940	1177	1168	1858	1449	830	1871	1200	1018	1112
88	102	902	880	982	1804	1807	1186	1253	397	1709
89	556	1301	433	687	957	354	1273	591	464	1501
90	430	1949	1641	1753	1558	930	723	147	1600	623
91	740	1172	1198	1639	76	1137	1498	65	920	1563
92	500	303	537	460	1520	1765	123	78	1759	815
93	1983	1024	720	676	1789	1960	340	1311	512	672
94	1730	569	1340	47	1626	1848	401	1079	1636	1157
95	574	1323	1139	531	485	164	1818	14	1890	800
96	249	1544	1675	269	497	637	1918	596	168	1064
97	1053	1488	1448	1111	1803	1708	956	1500	1557	622
98	75	1562	1519	814	1788	671	1625	1156	484	799
99	496	1063	1802	621	1787	798	1786	790	1794	791

POWER RESIDUES

	0	1	2	3	4	5	6	7	8	9
50	920	614	1077	1399	1016	1094	1484	1441	1226	151
51	755	1782	938	704	1527	1656	308	1540	1721	633
52	1172	1874	1398	1011	1069	1359	816	94	470	357
53	1785	953	779	1902	1538	1711	583	922	624	1127
54	1649	273	1365	846	244	1220	121	605	1032	1174
55	1884	1448	1261	326	1630	178	890	464	327	1635
56	203	1015	1089	1459	1316	601	1012	1074	1384	941
57	719	1602	38	190	950	764	1827	1163	1829	1173
58	1879	1423	1136	1694	498	497	492	467	342	1710
59	578	897	499	502	517	592	967	849	259	1295
60	496	487	442	217	1085	1439	1216	101	505	532
61	667	1342	731	1662	338	1690	478	397	1985	1953
62	1793	993	979	909	559	802	24	120	600	1007
63	1049	1259	316	1580	1921	1633	193	965	839	209
64	1045	1239	216	1080	1414	1091	1469	1366	851	269
65	1345	746	1737	713	1572	1881	1433	1186	1944	1748
66	768	1847	1263	336	1680	428	147	735	1682	438
67	197	985	939	709	1552	1781	933	679	1402	1031
68	1169	1859	1323	636	1187	1949	1773	893	479	402
69	17	85	425	132	660	1307	556	787	1942	1738
70	718	1597	13	65	325	1625	153	765	1832	1188
71	1954	1798	1018	1104	1534	1691	483	422	117	585
72	932	674	1377	906	544	727	1642	238	1190	1964
73	1848	1268	361	1805	1053	1279	416	87	435	182
74	910	564	827	149	745	1732	688	1447	1256	301
75	1505	1546	1751	783	1922	1638	218	1090	1464	1341
76	726	1637	213	1065	1339	716	1587	1956	1808	1068
77	1354	791	1962	1838	1218	111	555	782	1917	1613
78	93	465	332	1660	328	1640	228	1140	1714	598
79	997	999	1009	1059	1309	566	837	199	995	989
80	959	809	59	295	1475	1396	1001	1019	1109	1559
81	1816	1108	1554	1791	983	929	659	1302	531	662
82	1317	606	1037	1199	16	80	400	7	35	175
83	875	389	1945	1753	793	1972	1888	1468	1361	826
84	144	720	1607	63	315	1575	1896	1508	1561	1826
85	1158	1804	1048	1254	291	1455	1296	501	512	567
86	842	224	1120	1614	98	490	457	292	1460	1321
87	626	1137	1699	523	622	1117	1599	23	115	575
88	882	424	127	635	1182	1924	1648	268	1340	721
89	1612	88	440	207	1035	1189	1959	1823	1143	1729
90	673	1372	881	419	102	510	557	792	1967	1863
91	1343	736	1687	463	322	1610	78	390	1950	1778
92	918	604	1027	1149	1759	823	129	645	1232	181
93	905	539	702	1517	1606	58	290	1450	1271	376
94	1880	1428	1161	1819	1123	1629	173	865	339	1695
95	503	522	617	1092	1474	1391	976	894	484	427
96	142	710	1557	1806	1058	1304	541	712	1567	1856
97	1308	561	812	74	370	1850	1278	411	62	310
98	1550	1771	883	429	152	760	1807	1063	1329	666
99	1337	706	1537	1706	558	797	1992	1988	1968	1868

P = 1993

INDICES

	0	1	2	3	4	5	6	7	8	9
100	1617	806	67	1492	1795	1480	160	629	1667	792
101	1810	523	566	1071	1618	561	504	1952	712	807
102	115	452	492	57	68	1164	1592	922	1633	1493
103	1265	679	548	1245	1796	894	1010	822	1160	1481
104	1527	143	327	1570	161	640	83	1397	852	630
105	1043	344	1565	734	1668	1508	315	1336	964	793
106	1672	1716	28	987	1811	763	1074	1119	769	524
107	1456	1533	1299	1496	567	1916	1061	502	141	1072
108	643	202	176	1736	1619	604	1143	1719	1926	562
109	757	645	953	1426	505	1460	1587	277	1350	1953
110	1683	1429	305	1552	713	1393	257	190	811	808
111	1978	1876	1898	1098	116	22	204	875	1826	453
112	862	172	181	944	493	19	1388	539	1943	58
113	1147	1439	5	1331	69	1189	582	871	383	1165
114	787	178	1644	898	1593	1087	377	1539	409	923
115	89	1856	462	458	1634	1109	1792	55	850	1494
116	1348	942	407	577	1266	309	1738	1835	1279	680
117	1921	1183	520	579	549	1319	288	1522	348	1246
118	1215	1968	884	239	1797	1225	657	684	709	895
119	728	1621	365	1032	1011	1407	1991	213	1268	823
120	1830	1903	1767	427	1161	86	1693	448	131	1482
121	1749	1773	31	1123	1528	1037	606	468	774	144
122	545	52	1229	311	328	1656	508	125	1703	1571
123	1377	100	928	1981	162	73	1478	1263	1506	641
124	1391	1145	1107	1213	84	1375	1382	1647	1740	1398
125	1206	300	80	1180	853	1384	748	1907	1663	631
126	1256	552	1608	662	1044	155	1721	1756	731	345
127	93	938	1885	1837	1566	1696	1414	1761	976	735
128	1649	1963	1232	1957	1669	1222	438	1987	1326	1509
129	137	1928	472	245	316	599	856	1355	1281	1337
130	1116	362	817	96	965	1742	1094	695	970	794
131	441	1251	1196	1309	1673	1154	564	820	26	1717
132	1896	869	405	682	29	1261	1606	1985	1194	988
133	1400	1815	199	1690	1812	358	1467	990	235	764
134	888	759	611	910	1075	650	110	266	1923	1120
135	232	1463	1026	1443	770	1208	1360	1679	1879	525
136	1515	838	1402	1050	1457	542	647	1866	1000	1534
137	1176	1870	901	1185	1300	1272	1948	722	1171	1497
138	302	122	1023	339	568	400	1322	1817	1543	1917
139	1487	955	1561	1624	1062	1785	805	159	522	503
140	451	1591	678	1009	142	82	343	314	1715	1073
141	1532	1060	201	1142	644	1586	1428	256	1875	203
142	171	1387	1438	581	177	376	1855	1791	941	1737
143	1182	287	1967	656	1620	1990	1902	1692	1772	605
144	51	507	99	1477	1144	1381	299	747	551	1720
145	937	1413	1962	437	1927	855	361	1093	1250	563
146	868	1605	1814	1466	758	109	1462	1359	837	646
147	1869	1947	121	1321	954	804	1590	342	1059	1427
148	1386	1854	286	1901	506	298	1412	360	1604	1461
149	1946	1589	1853	1411	1588	1580	1581	1596	290	278

POWER RESIDUES

	0	1	2	3	4	5	6	7	8	9
100	1368	861	319	1595	3	15	75	375	1875	1403
101	1036	1194	1984	1948	1768	868	354	1770	878	404
102	27	135	675	1382	931	669	1352	781	1912	1588
103	1961	1833	1193	1979	1923	1643	243	1215	96	480
104	407	42	210	1050	1264	341	1705	553	772	1867
105	1363	836	194	970	864	334	1670	378	1890	1478
106	1411	1076	1394	991	969	859	309	1545	1746	758
107	1797	1013	1079	1409	1066	1344	741	1712	588	947
108	749	1752	788	1947	1763	843	229	1145	1739	723
109	1622	138	690	1457	1306	551	762	1817	1113	1579
110	1916	1608	68	340	1700	528	647	1242	231	1155
111	1789	973	879	409	52	260	1300	521	612	1067
112	1349	766	1837	1213	86	430	157	785	1932	1688
113	468	347	1735	703	1522	1631	183	915	589	952
114	774	1877	1413	1086	1444	1241	226	1130	1664	348
115	1740	728	1647	263	1315	596	987	949	759	1802
116	1038	1204	41	205	1025	1139	1709	573	872	374
117	1870	1378	911	569	852	274	1370	871	369	1845
118	1253	286	1430	1171	1869	1373	886	444	227	1135
119	1689	473	372	1860	1328	661	1312	581	912	574
120	877	399	2	10	50	250	1250	271	1355	796
121	1987	1963	1843	1243	236	1180	1914	1598	18	90
122	450	257	1285	446	237	1185	1939	1723	643	1222
123	131	655	1282	431	162	810	64	320	1600	28
124	140	700	1507	1556	1801	1033	1179	1909	1573	1886
125	1458	1311	576	887	449	252	1260	321	1605	53
126	265	1325	646	1237	206	1030	1164	1834	1198	11
127	55	275	1375	896	494	477	392	1960	1828	1168
128	1854	1298	511	562	817	99	495	482	417	92
129	460	307	1535	1696	508	547	742	1717	613	1072
130	1374	891	469	352	1760	828	154	770	1857	1313
131	586	937	699	1502	1531	1676	408	47	235	1175
132	1889	1473	1386	951	769	1852	1288	461	312	1560
133	1821	1133	1679	423	122	610	1057	1299	516	587
134	942	724	1627	163	815	89	445	232	1160	1814
135	1098	1504	1541	1726	658	1297	506	537	692	1467
136	1356	801	19	95	475	382	1910	1578	1911	1583
137	1936	1708	568	847	249	1245	246	1230	171	855
138	289	1445	1246	251	1255	296	1480	1421	1126	1644
139	248	1240	221	1105	1539	1716	608	1047	1249	266
140	1330	671	1362	831	169	845	239	1195	1989	1973
141	1893	1493	1486	1451	1276	401	12	60	300	1500
142	1521	1626	158	790	1957	1813	1093	1479	1416	1101
143	1519	1616	108	540	707	1542	1731	683	1422	1131
144	1669	373	1865	1353	786	1937	1713	593	972	874
145	384	1920	1628	168	840	214	1070	1364	841	219
146	1095	1489	1466	1351	776	1887	1463	1336	701	1512
147	1581	1926	1658	318	1590	1971	1883	1443	1236	201
148	1005	1039	1209	66	330	1650	278	1390	971	869
149	359	1795	1003	1029	1159	1809	1073	1379	916	594

P = 1993

INDICES

	0	1	2	3	4	5	6	7	8	9
150	1419	1582	1313	1861	1351	750	1597	1242	847	1954
151	1712	291	1469	43	1684	1612	279	933	368	1430
152	195	1420	1134	1524	306	134	1583	514	1777	1553
153	1909	1314	331	294	714	1292	1862	992	534	1394
154	517	1352	1435	224	258	1067	751	227	350	191
155	980	1598	674	1888	812	1665	1243	962	1734	809
156	1329	848	237	129	1979	1661	1955	968	1688	1877
157	337	1713	654	1248	1899	845	292	1732	1367	1099
158	633	1470	1973	1369	117	320	44	766	1029	23
159	1474	1685	419	1822	205	1003	1613	701	1217	876
160	1238	280	571	1913	1827	1258	934	842	1101	454
161	915	369	890	779	863	61	1431	1935	11	173
162	445	196	1090	1970	182	705	1421	1342	1452	945
163	554	1135	1728	635	494	559	1525	761	755	20
164	785	307	726	1035	1389	153	135	1152	886	540
165	1485	1584	49	107	1944	1610	515	1659	1472	59
166	783	1778	613	488	1148	1780	1554	1549	1700	1440
167	1056	1910	261	241	6	477	1315	1628	1840	1332
168	664	332	668	1975	70	1512	295	912	1129	1190
169	615	715	1745	422	583	949	1293	389	1799	872
170	1104	1863	1850	1932	384	1046	993	185	1371	1166
171	589	535	1077	1446	788	490	1395	1297	275	179
172	1537	518	211	1227	1645	1883	1353	403	264	899
173	157	1436	745	119	1594	1132	225	652	699	1088
174	1150	259	387	209	378	394	1068	380	659	1540
175	40	752	1081	833	410	1723	228	218	322	924
176	1304	351	112	1084	90	1782	192	150	1014	1857
177	1017	981	396	686	463	1752	1599	1638	919	459
178	1758	675	511	46	1635	530	1889	268	167	1110
179	1556	813	483	620	1793	1491	1666	1070	711	56
180	1632	1244	1159	1569	851	733	963	986	768	1495
181	140	1735	1925	1425	1349	1551	810	1097	1825	943
182	1942	1330	382	897	408	457	849	576	1278	578
183	347	238	708	1031	1267	426	130	1122	773	310
184	1702	1980	1505	1212	1739	1179	1662	661	730	1836
185	975	1956	1325	244	1280	95	969	1308	25	681
186	1193	1689	234	909	1922	1442	1878	1049	999	1184
187	1170	338	1542	1623	521	1008	1714	1141	1874	580
188	940	655	1771	1476	550	436	1249	1465	836	1320
189	1058	1900	1603	1410	289	1860	846	42	367	1523
190	1776	293	533	223	349	1887	1733	128	1687	1247
191	1366	1368	1028	1821	1216	1912	1100	778	10	1969
192	1451	634	754	1034	885	106	1471	487	1699	240
193	1839	1974	1128	421	1798	1931	1370	1445	274	1226
194	263	118	698	208	658	832	321	1083	1013	685
195	918	45	166	619	710	1568	767	1424	1824	896
196	1277	1030	772	1211	729	243	24	908	998	1622
197	1873	1475	835	1409	366	222	1686	1820	9	1033
198	1698	420	273	207	1012	618	1823	1210	997	1408
199	8	206	996							

POWER RESIDUES

	0	1	2	3	4	5	6	7	8	9
150	977	899	509	552	767	1842	1238	211	1055	1289
151	466	337	1685	453	272	1360	821	119	595	982
152	924	634	1177	1899	1523	1636	208	1040	1214	91
153	455	282	1410	1071	1369	866	344	1720	628	1147
154	1749	773	1872	1388	961	819	109	545	732	1667
155	363	1815	1103	1529	1666	358	1790	978	904	534
156	677	1392	981	919	609	1052	1274	391	1955	1803
157	1043	1229	166	830	164	820	114	570	857	299
158	1495	1496	1501	1526	1651	283	1415	1096	1494	1491
159	1476	1401	1026	1144	1734	698	1497	1506	1551	1776
160	908	554	777	1892	1488	1461	1326	651	1262	331
161	1655	303	1515	1596	8	40	200	1000	1014	1084
162	1434	1191	1969	1873	1393	986	944	734	1677	413
163	72	360	1800	1028	1154	1784	948	754	1777	913
164	579	902	524	627	1142	1724	648	1247	256	1280
165	421	112	560	807	49	245	1225	146	730	1657
166	313	1565	1846	1258	311	1555	1796	1008	1054	1284
167	441	212	1060	1314	591	962	824	134	670	1357
168	806	44	220	1100	1514	1591	1976	1908	1568	1861
169	1333	686	1437	1206	51	255	1275	396	1980	1928
170	1668	368	1840	1228	161	805	39	195	975	889
171	459	302	1510	1571	1876	1408	1061	1319	616	1087
172	1449	1266	351	1755	803	29	145	725	1632	188
173	940	714	1577	1906	1558	1811	1083	1429	1166	1844
174	1248	261	1305	546	737	1692	488	447	242	1210
175	71	355	1775	903	529	652	1267	356	1780	928
176	654	1277	406	37	185	925	639	1202	31	155
177	775	1882	1438	1211	76	380	1900	1528	1661	333
178	1665	353	1765	853	279	1395	996	994	984	934
179	684	1427	1156	1794	998	1004	1034	1184	1934	1698
180	518	597	992	974	884	434	177	885	439	202
181	1010	1064	1334	691	1462	1331	676	1387	956	794
182	1977	1913	1593	1986	1958	1818	1118	1604	48	240
183	1200	21	105	525	632	1167	1849	1273	386	1930
184	1678	418	97	485	432	167	835	189	945	739
185	1702	538	697	1492	1481	1426	1151	1769	873	379
186	1895	1503	1536	1701	533	672	1367	856	294	1470
187	1371	876	394	1970	1878	1418	1111	1569	1866	1358
188	811	69	345	1725	653	1272	381	1905	1553	1786
189	958	804	34	170	850	264	1320	621	1112	1574
190	1891	1483	1436	1201	26	130	650	1257	306	1530
191	1671	383	1915	1603	43	215	1075	1389	966	844
192	234	1170	1864	1348	761	1812	1088	1454	1291	476
193	387	1935	1703	543	722	1617	113	565	832	174
194	870	364	1820	1128	1654	298	1490	1471	1376	901
195	519	602	1017	1099	1509	1566	1851	1283	436	187
196	935	689	1452	1281	426	137	685	1432	1181	1919
197	1623	143	715	1582	1931	1683	443	222	1110	1564
198	1841	1233	186	930	664	1327	656	1287	456	287
199	1435	1196								

P = 1997

INDICES

	0	1	2	3	4	5	6	7	8	9
0		0	1	447	2	813	448	1416	3	894
1	814	849	449	543	1417	1260	4	1560	895	319
2	815	1863	850	489	450	1626	544	1341	1418	1062
3	1261	1535	5	1296	1561	233	896	654	320	990
4	816	1609	1864	827	851	1707	490	1619	451	836
5	1627	11	545	1240	1342	1662	1419	766	1063	1329
6	1262	704	1536	314	6	1356	1297	1278	1562	936
7	234	474	897	201	655	77	321	269	991	222
8	817	1788	1610	1361	1865	377	828	1509	852	1138
9	1708	1959	491	1982	1620	1132	452	949	837	1743
10	1628	1670	12	1495	546	680	1241	577	1343	336
11	1663	1101	1420	1755	767	1302	1064	1437	1330	980
12	1263	1698	705	60	1537	443	315	229	7	1274
13	1357	1739	1298	1735	1279	158	1563	1799	937	1588
14	235	70	475	1392	898	1875	202	1283	656	1717
15	78	20	322	458	270	352	992	308	223	1687
16	818	1905	1789	162	1611	113	1362	967	1866	1086
17	378	1213	829	1769	1510	1046	853	1776	1139	1567
18	1709	597	1960	1151	492	1467	1983	413	1621	761
19	1133	1693	453	1462	950	1803	838	1525	1744	1600
20	1629	1725	1671	482	13	426	1496	1383	547	1168
21	681	941	1242	921	578	1640	1344	955	337	648
22	1664	107	1102	1916	1421	524	1756	1592	768	1108
23	1303	716	1065	734	1438	436	1331	669	981	1372
24	1264	1931	1699	239	706	1649	61	862	1538	1808
25	444	846	316	1338	230	824	8	1326	1275	74
26	1358	1956	1740	574	1299	57	1736	1585	1280	349
27	159	1210	1564	410	1800	479	938	645	1589	433
28	236	843	71	1582	476	1579	1393	1029	899	1124
29	1876	1396	203	1922	1284	146	657	194	1718	1032
30	79	247	21	121	323	1517	459	902	271	1942
31	353	293	993	1530	309	1127	224	1682	1688	1911
32	819	1024	1906	1879	1790	173	163	783	1612	1039
33	114	1399	1363	1548	968	95	1867	1178	1087	206
34	379	388	1214	256	830	1749	1770	1925	1511	501
35	1047	1884	854	1250	1777	1287	1140	1427	1568	1856
36	1710	638	598	149	1961	1014	1152	1974	493	507
37	1468	660	1984	1483	414	890	1622	1605	762	197
38	1134	676	1694	1795	454	1082	1463	1721	951	730
39	1804	53	839	190	1526	1035	1745	634	1601	186
40	1630	1186	1726	82	1672	605	483	1503	14	1634
41	427	250	1497	749	1384	178	548	39	1169	24
42	682	530	942	517	1243	1190	922	124	579	1839
43	1641	1406	1345	1053	956	326	338	808	649	931
44	1665	1730	108	1520	1103	1951	1917	168	1422	725
45	525	462	1757	467	1593	776	769	86	1109	905
46	1304	1454	717	875	1066	799	735	274	1439	698
47	437	755	1332	1676	670	1945	982	138	1373	788
48	1265	1197	1932	356	1700	1762	240	1832	707	609
49	1650	296	62	626	863	560	1539	1890	1809	996

POWER RESIDUES

	0	1	2	3	4	5	6	7	8	9
0	1	2	4	8	16	32	64	128	256	512
1	1024	51	102	204	408	816	1632	1267	537	1074
2	151	302	604	1208	419	838	1676	1355	713	1426
3	855	1710	1423	849	1698	1399	801	1602	1207	417
4	834	1668	1339	681	1362	727	1454	911	1822	1647
5	1297	597	1194	391	782	1564	1131	265	530	1060
6	123	246	492	984	1968	1939	1881	1765	1533	1069
7	141	282	564	1128	259	518	1036	75	150	300
8	600	1200	403	806	1612	1227	457	914	1828	1659
9	1321	645	1290	583	1166	335	670	1340	683	1366
10	735	1470	943	1886	1775	1553	1109	221	442	884
11	1768	1539	1081	165	330	660	1320	643	1286	575
12	1150	303	606	1212	427	854	1708	1419	841	1682
13	1367	737	1474	951	1902	1807	1617	1237	477	954
14	1908	1819	1641	1285	573	1146	295	590	1180	363
15	726	1452	907	1814	1631	1265	533	1066	135	270
16	540	1080	163	326	652	1304	611	1222	447	894
17	1788	1579	1161	325	650	1300	603	1206	415	830
18	1660	1323	649	1298	599	1198	399	798	1596	1195
19	393	786	1572	1147	297	594	1188	379	758	1516
20	1035	73	146	292	584	1168	339	678	1356	715
21	1430	863	1726	1455	913	1826	1655	1313	629	1258
22	519	1038	79	158	316	632	1264	531	1062	127
23	254	508	1016	35	70	140	280	560	1120	243
24	486	972	1944	1891	1785	1573	1149	301	602	1204
25	411	822	1644	1291	585	1170	343	686	1372	747
26	1494	991	1982	1967	1937	1877	1757	1517	1037	77
27	154	308	616	1232	467	934	1868	1739	1481	965
28	1930	1863	1729	1461	925	1850	1703	1409	821	1642
29	1287	577	1154	311	622	1244	491	982	1964	1931
30	1865	1733	1469	941	1882	1767	1537	1077	157	314
31	628	1256	515	1030	63	126	252	504	1008	19
32	38	76	152	304	608	1216	435	870	1740	1483
33	969	1938	1879	1761	1525	1053	109	218	436	872
34	1744	1491	985	1970	1943	1889	1781	1565	1133	269
35	538	1076	155	310	620	1240	483	966	1932	1867
36	1737	1477	957	1914	1831	1665	1333	669	1338	679
37	1358	719	1438	879	1758	1519	1041	85	170	340
38	680	1360	723	1446	895	1790	1583	1169	341	682
39	1364	731	1462	927	1854	1711	1425	853	1706	1415
40	833	1666	1335	673	1346	695	1390	783	1566	1135
41	273	546	1092	187	374	748	1496	995	1990	1983
42	1969	1941	1885	1773	1549	1101	205	410	820	1640
43	1283	569	1138	279	558	1116	235	470	940	1880
44	1763	1529	1061	125	250	500	1000	3	6	12
45	24	48	96	192	384	768	1536	1075	153	306
46	612	1224	451	902	1804	1611	1225	453	906	1812
47	1627	1257	517	1034	71	142	284	568	1136	275
48	550	1100	203	406	812	1624	1251	505	1010	23
49	46	92	184	368	736	1472	947	1894	1791	1585

P = 1997

INDICES

	0	1	2	3	4	5	6	7	8	9
50	445	1414	847	1258	317	487	1339	1533	231	988
51	825	1617	9	1660	1327	312	1276	472	75	220
52	1359	1507	1957	1130	1741	1493	575	1099	1300	978
53	58	227	1737	156	1586	1390	1281	18	350	1685
54	160	965	1211	1044	1565	1149	411	1691	1801	1598
55	480	1381	939	1638	646	1914	1590	714	434	1370
56	237	860	844	822	72	572	1583	1208	477	431
57	1580	1027	1394	144	1030	119	900	291	1125	1909
58	1877	781	1397	93	204	254	1923	1882	1285	1854
59	147	1972	658	888	195	1793	1719	51	1033	184
60	80	1501	248	176	22	515	122	1404	324	929
61	1518	166	460	774	903	873	272	753	1943	786
62	354	1830	294	558	994	1256	1531	1615	310	218
63	1128	1097	225	1388	1683	1042	1689	1379	1912	1368
64	820	1206	1025	117	1907	91	1880	1970	1791	182
65	174	1402	164	871	784	556	1613	1095	1040	1366
66	115	1968	1400	554	1364	552	1549	1551	969	367
67	96	1553	1868	403	1179	971	1088	1114	207	369
68	380	43	389	98	1215	616	257	1555	831	1783
69	1750	1870	1771	1163	1926	405	1512	1173	502	1181
70	1048	794	1885	973	855	883	1251	1090	1778	910
71	1288	1116	1141	28	1428	209	1569	1819	1857	371
72	1711	915	639	382	599	692	150	45	1962	686
73	1015	391	1153	1224	1975	100	494	131	508	1217
74	1469	1309	661	618	1985	534	1484	259	415	1993
75	891	1557	1623	1293	1606	833	763	1353	198	1785
76	1135	946	677	1752	1695	1271	1796	1872	455	1902
77	1083	1773	1464	1459	1722	1165	952	521	731	1928
78	1805	1323	54	407	840	1121	191	1514	1527	1021
79	1036	1175	1746	1247	635	504	1602	1079	187	1183
80	1631	36	1187	1050	1727	722	83	796	1673	1194
81	606	1887	484	1657	1504	975	15	1146	1635	857
82	428	288	251	885	1498	926	750	1253	1385	1203
83	179	1092	549	400	40	1780	1170	880	25	912
84	683	128	531	1290	943	1899	518	1118	1244	33
85	1191	1143	923	397	125	30	580	583	1840	1430
86	1642	1476	1407	211	1346	586	1054	1571	957	1071
87	327	1821	339	1843	809	1859	650	1236	932	373
88	1666	1433	1731	1713	109	593	1521	917	1104	1645
89	1952	641	1918	1938	169	384	1423	1479	726	601
90	526	804	463	694	1758	1410	468	152	1594	568
91	777	47	770	214	87	1964	1110	1159	906	688
92	1305	1349	1455	1017	718	284	876	393	1067	589
93	800	1155	736	740	275	1226	1440	1057	699	1977
94	438	303	756	102	1333	1574	1677	496	671	744
95	1946	133	983	960	139	510	1374	362	789	1219
96	1266	1074	1198	1471	1933	279	357	1311	1701	330
97	1763	663	241	1008	1833	620	708	1824	610	1987
98	1651	1230	297	536	63	342	627	1486	864	1316
99	561	261	1540	1846	1891	417	1810	1444	997	1995

POWER RESIDUES

	0	1	2	3	4	5	6	7	8	9
50	1173	349	698	1396	795	1590	1183	369	738	1476
51	955	1910	1823	1649	1301	605	1210	423	846	1692
52	1387	777	1554	1111	225	450	900	1800	1603	1209
53	421	842	1684	1371	745	1490	983	1966	1935	1873
54	1749	1501	1005	13	26	52	104	208	416	832
55	1664	1331	665	1330	663	1326	655	1310	623	1246
56	495	990	1980	1963	1929	1861	1725	1453	909	1818
57	1639	1281	565	1130	263	526	1052	107	214	428
58	856	1712	1427	857	1714	1431	865	1730	1463	929
59	1858	1719	1441	885	1770	1543	1089	181	362	724
60	1448	899	1798	1599	1201	405	810	1620	1243	489
61	978	1956	1915	1833	1669	1341	685	1370	743	1486
62	975	1950	1903	1809	1621	1245	493	986	1972	1947
63	1897	1797	1597	1197	397	794	1588	1179	361	722
64	1444	891	1782	1567	1137	277	554	1108	219	438
65	876	1752	1507	1017	37	74	148	296	592	1184
66	371	742	1484	971	1942	1887	1777	1557	1117	237
67	474	948	1896	1795	1593	1189	381	762	1524	1051
68	105	210	420	840	1680	1363	729	1458	919	1838
69	1679	1361	725	1450	903	1806	1615	1233	469	938
70	1876	1755	1513	1029	61	122	244	488	976	1952
71	1907	1817	1637	1277	557	1114	231	462	924	1848
72	1699	1401	805	1610	1223	449	898	1796	1595	1193
73	389	778	1556	1115	233	466	932	1864	1731	1465
74	933	1866	1735	1473	949	1898	1799	1601	1205	413
75	826	1652	1307	617	1234	471	942	1884	1771	1545
76	1093	189	378	756	1512	1027	57	114	228	456
77	912	1824	1651	1305	613	1226	455	910	1820	1643
78	1289	581	1162	327	654	1308	619	1238	479	958
79	1916	1835	1673	1349	701	1402	807	1614	1231	465
80	930	1860	1723	1449	901	1802	1607	1217	437	874
81	1748	1499	1001	5	10	20	40	80	160	320
82	640	1280	563	1126	255	510	1020	43	86	172
83	344	688	1376	755	1510	1023	49	98	196	392
84	784	1568	1139	281	562	1124	251	502	1004	11
85	22	44	88	176	352	704	1408	819	1638	1279
86	561	1122	247	494	988	1976	1955	1913	1829	1661
87	1325	653	1306	615	1230	463	926	1852	1707	1417
88	837	1674	1351	705	1410	823	1646	1295	593	1186
89	375	750	1500	1003	9	18	36	72	144	288
90	576	1152	307	614	1228	459	918	1836	1675	1353
91	709	1418	839	1678	1359	721	1442	887	1774	1551
92	1105	213	426	852	1704	1411	825	1650	1303	609
93	1218	439	878	1756	1515	1033	69	138	276	552
94	1104	211	422	844	1688	1379	761	1522	1047	97
95	194	388	776	1552	1107	217	434	868	1736	1475
96	953	1906	1815	1633	1269	541	1082	167	334	668
97	1336	675	1350	703	1406	815	1630	1263	529	1058
98	119	238	476	952	1904	1811	1625	1253	509	1018
99	39	78	156	312	624	1248	499	998	1996	1995

P = 1997

INDICES

	0	1	2	3	4	5	6	7	8	9
100	446	812	1415	893	848	542	1259	1559	318	1862
101	488	1625	1340	1061	1534	1295	232	653	989	1608
102	826	1706	1618	835	10	1239	1661	765	1328	703
103	313	1355	1277	935	473	200	76	268	221	1787
104	1360	376	1508	1137	1958	1981	1131	948	1742	1669
105	1494	679	576	335	1100	1754	1301	1436	979	1697
106	59	442	228	1273	1738	1734	157	1798	1587	69
107	1391	1874	1282	1716	19	457	351	307	1686	1904
108	161	112	966	1085	1212	1768	1045	1775	1566	596
109	1150	1466	412	760	1692	1461	1802	1524	1599	1724
110	481	425	1382	1167	940	920	1639	954	647	106
111	1915	523	1591	1107	715	733	435	668	1371	1930
112	238	1648	861	1807	845	1337	823	1325	73	1955
113	573	56	1584	348	1209	409	478	644	432	842
114	1581	1578	1028	1123	1395	1921	145	193	1031	246
115	120	1516	901	1941	292	1529	1126	1681	1910	1023
116	1878	172	782	1038	1398	1547	94	1177	205	387
117	255	1748	1924	500	1883	1249	1286	1426	1855	637
118	148	1013	1973	506	659	1482	889	1604	196	675
119	1794	1081	1720	729	52	189	1034	633	185	1185
120	81	604	1502	1633	249	748	177	38	23	529
121	516	1189	123	1838	1405	1052	325	807	930	1729
122	1519	1950	167	724	461	466	775	85	904	1453
123	874	798	273	697	754	1675	1944	137	787	1196
124	355	1761	1831	608	295	625	559	1889	995	1413
125	1257	486	1532	987	1616	1659	311	471	219	1506
126	1129	1492	1098	977	226	155	1389	17	1684	964
127	1043	1148	1690	1597	1380	1637	1913	713	1369	859
128	821	571	1207	430	1026	143	118	290	1908	780
129	92	253	1881	1853	1971	887	1792	50	183	1500
130	175	514	1403	928	165	773	872	752	785	1829
131	557	1255	1614	217	1096	1387	1041	1378	1367	1205
132	116	90	1969	181	1401	870	555	1094	1365	1967
133	553	551	1550	366	1552	402	970	1113	368	42
134	97	615	1554	1782	1869	1162	404	1172	1180	793
135	972	882	1089	909	1115	27	208	1818	370	914
136	381	691	44	685	390	1223	99	130	1216	1308
137	617	533	258	1992	1556	1292	832	1352	1784	945
138	1751	1270	1871	1901	1772	1458	1164	520	1927	1322
139	406	1120	1513	1020	1174	1246	503	1078	1182	35
140	1049	721	795	1193	1886	1656	974	1145	856	287
141	884	925	1252	1202	1091	399	1779	879	911	127
142	1289	1898	1117	32	1142	396	29	582	1429	1475
143	210	585	1570	1070	1820	1842	1858	1235	372	1432
144	1712	592	916	1644	640	1937	383	1478	600	803
145	693	1409	151	567	46	213	1963	1158	687	1348
146	1016	283	392	588	1154	739	1225	1056	1976	302
147	101	1573	495	743	132	959	509	361	1218	1073
148	1470	278	1310	329	662	1007	619	1823	1986	1229
149	535	341	1485	1315	260	1845	416	1443	1994	811

POWER RESIDUES

	0	1	2	3	4	5	6	7	8	9
100	1993	1989	1981	1965	1933	1869	1741	1485	973	1946
101	1895	1793	1589	1181	365	730	1460	923	1846	1695
102	1393	789	1578	1159	321	642	1284	571	1142	287
103	574	1148	299	598	1196	395	790	1580	1163	329
104	658	1316	635	1270	543	1086	175	350	700	1400
105	803	1606	1215	433	866	1732	1467	937	1874	1751
106	1505	1013	29	58	116	232	464	928	1856	1715
107	1433	869	1738	1479	961	1922	1847	1697	1397	797
108	1594	1191	385	770	1540	1083	169	338	676	1352
109	707	1414	831	1662	1327	657	1314	631	1262	527
110	1054	111	222	444	888	1776	1555	1113	229	458
111	916	1832	1667	1337	677	1354	711	1422	847	1694
112	1391	785	1570	1143	289	578	1156	315	630	1260
113	523	1046	95	190	380	760	1520	1043	89	178
114	356	712	1424	851	1702	1407	817	1634	1271	545
115	1090	183	366	732	1464	931	1862	1727	1457	917
116	1834	1671	1345	693	1386	775	1550	1103	209	418
117	836	1672	1347	697	1394	791	1582	1167	337	674
118	1348	699	1398	799	1598	1199	401	802	1604	1211
119	425	850	1700	1403	809	1618	1239	481	962	1924
120	1851	1705	1413	829	1658	1319	641	1282	567	1134
121	271	542	1084	171	342	684	1368	739	1478	959
122	1918	1839	1681	1365	733	1466	935	1870	1743	1489
123	981	1962	1927	1857	1717	1437	877	1754	1511	1025
124	53	106	212	424	848	1696	1395	793	1586	1175
125	353	706	1412	827	1654	1311	625	1250	503	1006
126	15	30	60	120	240	480	960	1920	1843	1689
127	1381	765	1530	1063	129	258	516	1032	67	134
128	268	536	1072	147	294	588	1176	355	710	1420
129	843	1686	1375	753	1506	1015	33	66	132	264
130	528	1056	115	230	460	920	1840	1683	1369	741
131	1482	967	1934	1871	1745	1493	989	1978	1959	1921
132	1845	1693	1389	781	1562	1127	257	514	1028	59
133	118	236	472	944	1888	1779	1561	1125	253	506
134	1012	27	54	108	216	432	864	1728	1459	921
135	1842	1687	1377	757	1514	1031	65	130	260	520
136	1040	83	166	332	664	1328	659	1318	639	1278
137	559	1118	239	478	956	1912	1827	1657	1317	637
138	1274	551	1102	207	414	828	1656	1315	633	1266
139	535	1070	143	286	572	1144	291	582	1164	331
140	662	1324	651	1302	607	1214	431	862	1724	1451
141	905	1810	1623	1249	501	1002	7	14	28	56
142	112	224	448	896	1792	1587	1177	357	714	1428
143	859	1718	1439	881	1762	1527	1057	117	234	468
144	936	1872	1747	1497	997	1994	1991	1985	1973	1949
145	1901	1805	1613	1229	461	922	1844	1691	1385	773
146	1546	1095	193	386	772	1544	1091	185	370	740
147	1480	963	1926	1855	1713	1429	861	1722	1447	897
148	1794	1591	1185	373	746	1492	987	1974	1951	1905
149	1813	1629	1261	525	1050	103	206	412	824	1648

P = 1997

INDICES

	0	1	2	3	4	5	6	7	8	9
150	892	541	1558	1861	1624	1060	1294	652	1607	1705
151	834	1238	764	702	1354	934	199	267	1786	375
152	1136	1980	947	1668	678	334	1753	1435	1696	441
153	1272	1733	1797	68	1873	1715	456	306	1903	111
154	1084	1767	1774	595	1465	759	1460	1523	1723	424
155	1166	919	953	105	522	1106	732	667	1929	1647
156	1806	1336	1324	1954	55	347	408	643	841	1577
157	1122	1920	192	245	1515	1940	1528	1680	1022	171
158	1037	1546	1176	386	1747	499	1248	1425	636	1012
159	505	1481	1603	674	1080	728	188	632	1184	603
160	1632	747	37	528	1188	1837	1051	806	1728	1949
161	723	465	84	1452	797	696	1674	136	1195	1760
162	607	624	1888	1412	485	986	1658	470	1505	1491
163	976	154	16	963	1147	1596	1636	712	858	570
164	429	142	289	779	252	1852	886	49	1499	513
165	927	772	751	1828	1254	216	1386	1377	1204	89
166	180	869	1093	1966	550	365	401	1112	41	614
167	1781	1161	1171	792	881	908	26	1817	913	690
168	684	1222	129	1307	532	1991	1291	1351	944	1269
169	1900	1457	519	1321	1119	1019	1245	1077	34	720
170	1192	1655	1144	286	924	1201	398	878	126	1897
171	31	395	581	1474	584	1069	1841	1234	1431	591
172	1643	1936	1477	802	1408	566	212	1157	1347	282
173	587	738	1055	301	1572	742	958	360	1072	277
174	328	1006	1822	1228	340	1314	1844	1442	810	540
175	1860	1059	651	1704	1237	701	933	266	374	1979
176	1667	333	1434	440	1732	67	1714	305	110	1766
177	594	758	1522	423	918	104	1105	666	1646	1335
178	1953	346	642	1576	1919	244	1939	1679	170	1545
179	385	498	1424	1011	1480	673	727	631	602	746
180	527	1836	805	1948	464	1451	695	135	1759	623
181	1411	985	469	1490	153	962	1595	711	569	141
182	778	1851	48	512	771	1827	215	1376	88	868
183	1965	364	1111	613	1160	791	907	1816	689	1221
184	1306	1990	1350	1268	1456	1320	1018	1076	719	1654
185	285	1200	877	1896	394	1473	1068	1233	590	1935
186	801	565	1156	281	737	300	741	359	276	1005
187	1227	1313	1441	539	1058	1703	700	265	1978	332
188	439	66	304	1765	757	422	103	665	1334	345
189	1575	243	1678	1544	497	1010	672	630	745	1835
190	1947	1450	134	622	984	1489	961	710	140	1850
191	511	1826	1375	867	363	612	790	1815	1220	1989
192	1267	1319	1075	1653	1199	1895	1472	1232	1934	564
193	280	299	358	1004	1312	538	1702	264	331	65
194	1764	421	664	344	242	1543	1009	629	1834	1449
195	621	1488	709	1849	1825	866	611	1814	1988	1318
196	1652	1894	1231	563	298	1003	537	263	64	420
197	343	1542	628	1448	1487	1848	865	1813	1317	1893
198	562	1002	262	419	1541	1447	1847	1812	1892	1001
199	418	1446	1811	1000	1445	999	998			

POWER RESIDUES

	0	1	2	3	4	5	6	7	8	9
150	1299	601	1202	407	814	1628	1259	521	1042	87
151	174	348	696	1392	787	1574	1151	305	610	1220
152	443	886	1772	1547	1097	197	394	788	1576	1155
153	313	626	1252	507	1014	31	62	124	248	496
154	992	1984	1971	1945	1893	1789	1581	1165	333	666
155	1332	667	1334	671	1342	687	1374	751	1502	1007
156	17	34	68	136	272	544	1088	179	358	716
157	1432	867	1734	1471	945	1890	1783	1569	1141	285
158	570	1140	283	566	1132	267	534	1068	139	278
159	556	1112	227	454	908	1816	1635	1273	549	1098
160	199	398	796	1592	1187	377	754	1508	1019	41
161	82	164	328	656	1312	627	1254	511	1022	47
162	94	188	376	752	1504	1011	25	50	100	200
163	400	800	1600	1203	409	818	1636	1275	553	1106
164	215	430	860	1720	1443	889	1778	1559	1121	245
165	490	980	1960	1923	1849	1701	1405	813	1626	1255
166	513	1026	55	110	220	440	880	1760	1523	1049
167	101	202	404	808	1616	1235	473	946	1892	1787
168	1577	1157	317	634	1268	539	1078	159	318	636
169	1272	547	1094	191	382	764	1528	1059	121	242
170	484	968	1936	1875	1753	1509	1021	45	90	180
171	360	720	1440	883	1766	1535	1073	149	298	596
172	1192	387	774	1548	1099	201	402	804	1608	1219
173	441	882	1764	1531	1065	133	266	532	1064	131
174	262	524	1048	99	198	396	792	1584	1171	345
175	690	1380	763	1526	1055	113	226	452	904	1808
176	1619	1241	485	970	1940	1883	1769	1541	1085	173
177	346	692	1384	771	1542	1087	177	354	708	1416
178	835	1670	1343	689	1378	759	1518	1039	81	162
179	324	648	1296	595	1190	383	766	1532	1067	137
180	274	548	1096	195	390	780	1560	1123	249	498
181	996	1992	1987	1977	1957	1917	1837	1677	1357	717
182	1434	871	1742	1487	977	1954	1911	1825	1653	1309
183	621	1242	487	974	1948	1899	1801	1605	1213	429
184	858	1716	1435	873	1746	1495	993	1986	1975	1953
185	1909	1821	1645	1293	589	1178	359	718	1436	875
186	1750	1503	1009	21	42	84	168	336	672	1344
187	691	1382	767	1534	1071	145	290	580	1160	323
188	646	1292	587	1174	351	702	1404	811	1622	1247
189	497	994	1988	1979	1961	1925	1853	1709	1421	845
190	1690	1383	769	1538	1079	161	322	644	1288	579
191	1158	319	638	1276	555	1110	223	446	892	1784
192	1571	1145	293	586	1172	347	694	1388	779	1558
193	1119	241	482	964	1928	1859	1721	1445	893	1786
194	1575	1153	309	618	1236	475	950	1900	1803	1609
195	1221	445	890	1780	1563	1129	261	522	1044	91
196	182	364	728	1456	915	1830	1663	1329	661	1322
197	647	1294	591	1182	367	734	1468	939	1878	1759
198	1521	1045	93	186	372	744	1488	979	1958	1919
199	1841	1685	1373	749	1498	999				

P = 1999

INDICES

	0	1	2	3	4	5	6	7	8	9
0		0	510	1	1020	652	511	807	1530	2
1	1162	1882	1021	798	1317	653	42	1361	512	559
2	1672	808	394	1888	1531	1304	1308	3	1827	619
3	1163	590	552	1883	1871	1459	1022	486	1069	799
4	184	1546	1318	1407	904	654	400	985	43	1614
5	1814	1362	1818	1582	513	536	339	560	1129	934
6	1673	1432	1100	809	1062	1450	395	719	383	1889
7	1969	1054	1532	825	996	1305	1579	691	1309	1226
8	694	4	58	275	1828	15	1917	620	1414	153
9	1164	1605	910	591	1495	1211	553	261	126	1884
10	326	1134	1872	1758	330	1460	94	1312	1023	973
11	1046	487	849	947	1070	542	1639	800	1444	170
12	185	1766	1942	1547	1610	1956	1319	1841	1572	1408
13	1960	219	905	1366	1229	655	893	1684	401	1264
14	481	986	1564	682	44	1271	1335	1615	1506	1301
15	1815	1223	91	1363	1201	1242	1819	520	1736	1583
16	1204	697	514	1385	568	537	785	1629	340	1596
17	525	561	429	1668	1130	113	1924	935	663	280
18	1674	647	117	1433	1420	1138	1101	1245	7	810
19	1721	1988	1063	1726	771	1451	636	456	396	1837
20	836	720	1644	1426	384	200	270	1890	840	443
21	1970	1323	604	1055	1822	61	1533	1397	1483	826
22	1556	161	997	1528	1359	1306	1457	902	1580	1098
23	1052	692	151	124	1310	1637	1954	1227	680	89
24	695	523	278	5	454	268	59	1357	122	276
25	468	470	1829	1772	353	16	84	1028	1918	1293
26	472	621	729	1928	1415	236	1876	154	1739	1831
27	1165	66	1403	1606	196	1188	911	1865	1774	592
28	991	744	1496	704	76	1212	1192	355	554	724
29	1781	262	1845	1011	127	1586	18	1885	1811	688
30	327	216	1733	1135	601	86	1873	1008	1711	1759
31	1752	1854	331	256	1030	1461	248	749	95	503
32	1714	1313	1207	1920	1024	104	1895	974	1078	1792
33	1047	1286	1295	488	141	1371	850	1377	108	948
34	1035	474	1071	423	939	543	180	1762	1640	700
35	623	801	436	1657	1445	1706	1173	171	790	731
36	186	1118	1157	1767	627	1477	1943	915	1930	1548
37	1648	391	1611	1576	1755	1957	517	1417	1320	677
38	233	1842	500	177	1573	1343	238	1409	1281	860
39	1961	1251	1146	220	966	1878	906	1664	349	1367
40	1346	1857	1230	1388	156	656	1936	370	894	1746
41	710	1685	780	1741	402	927	1350	1265	953	1899
42	482	1440	1833	987	1114	667	1565	241	334	683
43	571	1167	45	133	1907	1272	1993	449	1336	1982
44	68	1616	671	881	1507	805	40	1302	1869	1405
45	1816	1430	1967	1224	1412	259	92	540	1608	1364
46	1562	1221	1202	1594	661	1243	634	198	1820	1526
47	149	521	466	1291	1737	1863	1190	1584	599	254
48	1205	1284	1033	698	788	913	515	1341	964	1386
49	778	1438	569	1980	1867	538	632	1861	786	1978

POWER RESIDUES

	0	1	2	3	4	5	6	7	8	9
0	1	3	9	27	81	243	729	188	564	1692
1	1078	1235	1706	1120	1361	85	255	765	296	888
2	665	1995	1987	1963	1891	1675	1027	1082	1247	1742
3	1228	1685	1057	1172	1517	553	1659	979	938	815
4	446	1338	16	48	144	432	1296	1889	1669	1009
5	1028	1085	1256	1769	1309	1928	1786	1360	82	246
6	738	215	645	1935	1807	1423	271	813	440	1320
7	1961	1885	1657	973	920	761	284	852	557	1671
8	1015	1046	1139	1418	256	768	305	915	746	239
9	717	152	456	1368	106	318	954	863	590	1770
10	1312	1937	1813	1441	325	975	926	779	338	1014
11	1043	1130	1391	175	525	1575	727	182	546	1638
12	916	749	248	744	233	699	98	294	882	647
13	1941	1825	1477	433	1299	1898	1696	1090	1271	1814
14	1444	334	1002	1007	1022	1067	1202	1607	823	470
15	1410	232	696	89	267	801	404	1212	1637	913
16	740	221	663	1989	1969	1909	1729	1189	1568	706
17	119	357	1071	1214	1643	931	794	383	1149	1448
18	346	1038	1115	1346	40	120	360	1080	1241	1724
19	1174	1523	571	1713	1141	1424	274	822	467	1401
20	205	615	1845	1537	613	1839	1519	559	1677	1033
21	1100	1301	1904	1714	1144	1433	301	903	710	131
22	393	1179	1538	616	1848	1546	640	1920	1762	1288
23	1865	1597	793	380	1140	1421	265	795	386	1158
24	1475	427	1281	1844	1534	604	1812	1438	316	948
25	845	536	1608	826	479	1437	313	939	818	455
26	1365	97	291	873	620	1860	1582	748	245	735
27	206	618	1854	1564	694	83	249	747	242	726
28	179	537	1611	835	506	1518	556	1668	1006	1019
29	1058	1175	1526	580	1740	1222	1667	1003	1010	1031
30	1094	1283	1850	1552	658	1974	1924	1774	1324	1973
31	1921	1765	1297	1892	1678	1036	1109	1328	1985	1957
32	1873	1621	865	596	1788	1366	100	300	900	701
33	104	312	936	809	428	1284	1853	1561	685	56
34	168	504	1512	538	1614	844	533	1599	799	398
35	1194	1583	751	254	762	287	861	584	1752	1258
36	1775	1327	1982	1948	1846	1540	622	1866	1600	802
37	407	1221	1664	994	983	950	851	554	1662	988
38	965	896	689	68	204	612	1836	1510	532	1596
39	790	371	1113	1340	22	66	198	594	1782	1348
40	46	138	414	1242	1727	1183	1550	652	1956	1870
41	1612	838	515	1545	637	1911	1735	1207	1622	868
42	605	1815	1447	343	1029	1088	1265	1796	1390	172
43	516	1548	646	1938	1816	1450	352	1056	1169	1508
44	526	1578	736	209	627	1881	1645	937	812	437
45	1311	1934	1804	1414	244	732	197	591	1773	1321
46	1964	1894	1684	1054	1163	1490	472	1416	250	750
47	251	753	260	780	341	1023	1070	1211	1634	904
48	713	140	420	1260	1781	1345	37	111	333	999
49	998	995	986	959	878	635	1905	1717	1153	1460

P = 1999

INDICES

	0	1	2	3	4	5	6	7	8	9
50	978	1630	980	1776	341	1786	284	1597	863	1464
51	526	1632	594	562	1538	412	430	869	1803	1669
52	982	993	1131	1569	1239	114	440	1951	1925	1778
53	746	936	388	346	664	1964	251	281	343	1498
54	1675	1515	576	648	1913	1625	118	1788	706	1434
55	1698	1178	1421	35	377	1139	286	78	1102	207
56	1501	1246	1254	752	8	1599	1214	811	586	845
57	1722	192	1702	1989	865	1194	1064	739	1234	1727
58	293	1082	772	1466	357	1452	1521	1678	637	1149
59	98	457	528	556	397	822	323	1838	1198	644
60	837	1634	726	721	245	420	1645	1661	1111	1427
61	596	1783	385	204	1518	201	223	506	271	564
62	264	1891	366	960	841	610	766	444	1540	1847
63	1971	1092	758	1324	1259	495	605	414	1013	1056
64	226	579	1823	969	1717	62	432	129	1534	818
65	614	1398	407	1182	1484	871	1588	827	304	1392
66	1557	1040	1796	162	1805	20	998	509	651	1529
67	1881	1316	1360	1671	1887	1307	618	551	1458	1068
68	1545	903	984	1813	1581	338	933	1099	1449	382
69	1053	995	690	693	274	1916	152	909	1210	125
70	1133	329	1311	1045	946	1638	169	1941	1955	1571
71	218	1228	1683	480	681	1334	1300	90	1241	1735
72	696	567	1628	524	1667	1923	279	116	1137	6
73	1987	770	455	835	1425	269	442	603	60	1482
74	160	1358	901	1051	123	1953	88	277	267	121
75	469	352	1027	471	1927	1875	1830	1402	1187	1773
76	743	75	354	1780	1010	17	687	1732	85	1710
77	1853	1029	748	1713	1919	1894	1791	1294	1370	107
78	473	938	1761	622	1656	1172	730	1156	1476	1929
79	390	1754	1416	232	176	237	859	1145	1877	348
80	1856	155	369	709	1740	1349	1898	1832	666	333
81	1166	1906	448	67	880	39	1404	1966	258	1607
82	1220	660	197	148	1290	1189	253	1032	912	963
83	1437	1866	1860	977	1775	283	1463	593	411	1802
84	992	1238	1950	745	345	250	1497	575	1624	705
85	1177	376	77	1500	751	1213	844	1701	1193	1233
86	1081	356	1677	97	555	322	643	725	419	1110
87	1782	1517	505	263	959	765	1846	757	494	1012
88	578	1716	128	613	1181	1587	1391	1795	19	650
89	1315	1886	550	1544	1812	932	381	689	1915	1209
90	328	945	1940	217	479	1299	1734	1627	1922	1136
91	769	1424	602	159	1050	87	120	1026	1874	1186
92	74	1009	1731	1852	1712	1790	106	1760	1171	1475
93	1753	175	1144	1855	708	1897	332	447	38	257
94	659	1289	1031	1436	976	1462	1801	1949	249	1623
95	375	750	1700	1080	96	642	1109	504	764	493
96	1715	1180	1794	1314	1543	380	1208	1939	1298	1921
97	1423	1049	1025	73	1851	105	1474	1143	1896	37
98	1288	975	1948	374	1079	1108	492	1793	379	1297
99	1048	1850	1142	1287	373	491	1296	1141	490	489

POWER RESIDUES

	0	1	2	3	4	5	6	7	8	9
50	382	1146	1439	319	957	872	617	1851	1555	667
51	2	6	18	54	162	486	1458	376	1128	1385
52	157	471	1413	241	723	170	510	1530	592	1776
53	1330	1991	1975	1927	1783	1351	55	165	495	1485
54	457	1371	115	345	1035	1106	1319	1958	1876	1630
55	892	677	32	96	288	864	593	1779	1339	19
56	57	171	513	1539	619	1857	1573	721	164	492
57	1476	430	1290	1871	1615	847	542	1626	880	641
58	1923	1771	1315	1946	1840	1522	568	1704	1114	1343
59	31	93	279	837	512	1536	610	1830	1492	478
60	1434	304	912	737	212	636	1908	1726	1180	1541
61	625	1875	1627	883	650	1950	1852	1558	676	29
62	87	261	783	350	1050	1151	1454	364	1092	1277
63	1832	1498	496	1488	466	1398	196	588	1764	1294
64	1883	1651	955	866	599	1797	1393	181	543	1629
65	889	668	5	15	45	135	405	1215	1646	940
66	821	464	1392	178	534	1602	808	425	1275	1826
67	1480	442	1326	1979	1939	1819	1459	379	1137	1412
68	238	714	143	429	1287	1862	1588	766	299	897
69	692	77	231	693	80	240	720	161	483	1449
70	349	1047	1142	1427	283	849	548	1644	934	803
71	410	1230	1691	1075	1226	1679	1039	1118	1355	67
72	201	603	1809	1429	289	867	602	1806	1420	262
73	786	359	1077	1232	1697	1093	1280	1841	1525	577
74	1731	1195	1586	760	281	843	530	1590	772	317
75	951	854	563	1689	1069	1208	1625	877	632	1896
76	1690	1072	1217	1652	958	875	626	1878	1636	910
77	731	194	582	1746	1240	1721	1165	1496	490	1470
78	412	1236	1709	1129	1388	166	498	1494	484	1452
79	358	1074	1223	1670	1012	1037	1112	1337	13	39
80	117	351	1053	1160	1481	445	1335	7	21	63
81	189	567	1701	1105	1316	1949	1849	1549	649	1947
82	1843	1531	595	1785	1357	73	219	657	1971	1915
83	1747	1243	1730	1192	1577	733	200	600	1800	1402
84	208	624	1872	1618	856	569	1707	1123	1370	112
85	336	1008	1025	1076	1229	1688	1066	1199	1598	796
86	389	1167	1502	508	1524	574	1722	1168	1505	517
87	1551	655	1965	1897	1693	1081	1244	1733	1201	1604
88	814	443	1329	1988	1966	1900	1702	1108	1325	1976
89	1930	1792	1378	136	408	1224	1673	1021	1064	1193
90	1580	742	227	681	44	132	396	1188	1565	697
91	92	276	828	485	1455	367	1101	1304	1913	1741
92	1225	1676	1030	1091	1274	1823	1471	415	1245	1736
93	1210	1631	895	686	59	177	531	1593	781	344
94	1032	1097	1292	1877	1633	901	704	113	339	1017
95	1052	1157	1472	418	1254	1763	1291	1874	1624	874
96	623	1869	1609	829	488	1464	394	1182	1547	643
97	1929	1789	1369	109	327	981	944	833	500	1500
98	502	1506	520	1560	682	47	141	423	1269	1808
99	1426	280	840	521	1563	691	74	222	666	1998

P = 1999

INDICES

	0	1	2	3	4	5	6	7	8	9
100	1488	1489	142	297	1490	1372	288	143	851	49
101	298	1378	794	1491	109	80	1373	949	1974	289
102	1036	897	144	475	1104	852	1072	26	50	424
103	922	299	940	209	1379	544	315	795	181	716
104	1492	1763	1503	110	1641	1095	81	701	1749	1374
105	624	1248	950	802	463	1975	437	32	290	1658
106	1256	1037	1446	1331	898	1707	856	145	1174	754
107	476	172	761	1105	791	713	853	732	10	1073
108	187	875	27	1119	1086	51	1158	1601	425	1768
109	137	923	628	735	300	1478	1216	941	1944	1327
110	210	916	1688	1380	1931	813	545	1549	887	316
111	1649	1018	796	392	588	182	1612	1127	717	1577
112	13	1493	1756	847	1764	1958	1262	1504	518	783
113	111	1418	1724	1642	1321	1554	1096	678	1355	82
114	234	194	702	1843	214	1750	501	1076	1375	178
115	1704	625	1574	498	1249	1344	1744	951	239	1991
116	803	1410	1592	464	1282	776	1976	861	867	438
117	1962	1911	33	1252	190	291	1147	1196	1659	221
118	608	1257	967	405	1038	1879	1066	1447	907	167
119	1332	1665	833	899	350	741	1708	1368	1154	857
120	1347	878	146	1858	1236	1175	1231	417	755	1389
121	930	477	157	1729	173	657	1621	762	1937	1472
122	1106	371	295	792	895	920	714	1747	30	854
123	711	1084	733	1686	1016	11	781	1353	1074	1742
124	774	188	403	831	876	928	1470	28	1351	1468
125	1120	1266	1276	1087	954	1122	52	1900	359	1159
126	483	1059	1602	1441	1268	426	1834	1454	1769	988
127	1005	138	1115	1278	924	668	1523	629	1566	1695
128	736	242	1089	301	335	1680	1479	684	229	1217
129	572	956	942	1168	639	1945	46	312	1328	134
130	1124	211	1908	1151	917	1273	1692	1689	1994	54
131	1381	450	100	1932	1337	582	814	1983	1902	546
132	69	459	1550	1617	308	888	672	361	317	882
133	530	1650	1508	1997	1019	806	1161	797	41	558
134	393	1303	1826	589	1870	485	183	1406	399	1613
135	1817	535	1128	1431	1061	718	1968	824	1578	1225
136	57	14	1413	1604	1494	260	325	1757	93	972
137	848	541	1443	1765	1609	1840	1959	1365	892	1263
138	1563	1270	1505	1222	1200	519	1203	1384	784	1595
139	428	112	662	646	1419	1244	1720	1725	635	1836
140	1643	199	839	1322	1821	1396	1555	1527	1456	1097
141	150	1636	679	522	453	1356	467	1771	83	1292
142	728	235	1738	65	195	1864	990	703	1191	723
143	1844	1585	1810	215	600	1007	1751	255	247	502
144	1206	103	1077	1285	140	1376	1034	422	179	699
145	435	1705	789	1117	626	914	1647	1575	516	676
146	499	1342	1280	1250	965	1663	1345	1387	1935	1745
147	779	926	952	1439	1113	240	570	132	1992	1981
148	670	804	1868	1429	1411	539	1561	1593	633	1525
149	465	1862	598	1283	787	1340	777	1979	631	1977

POWER RESIDUES

	0	1	2	3	4	5	6	7	8	9
100	1996	1990	1972	1918	1756	1270	1811	1435	307	921
101	764	293	879	638	1914	1744	1234	1703	1111	1334
102	4	12	36	108	324	972	917	752	257	771
103	314	942	827	482	1446	340	1020	1061	1184	1553
104	661	1983	1951	1855	1567	703	110	330	990	971
105	914	743	230	690	71	213	639	1917	1753	1261
106	1784	1354	64	192	576	1728	1186	1559	679	38
107	114	342	1026	1079	1238	1715	1147	1442	328	984
108	953	860	581	1743	1231	1694	1084	1253	1760	1282
109	1847	1543	631	1893	1681	1045	1136	1409	229	687
110	62	186	558	1674	1024	1073	1220	1661	985	956
111	869	608	1824	1474	424	1272	1817	1453	361	1083
112	1250	1751	1255	1766	1300	1901	1705	1117	1352	58
113	174	522	1566	700	101	303	909	728	185	555
114	1665	997	992	977	932	797	392	1176	1529	589
115	1767	1303	1910	1732	1198	1595	787	362	1086	1259
116	1778	1336	10	30	90	270	810	431	1293	1880
117	1642	928	785	356	1068	1205	1616	850	551	1653
118	961	884	653	1959	1879	1639	919	758	275	825
119	476	1428	286	858	575	1725	1177	1532	598	1794
120	1384	154	462	1386	160	480	1440	322	966	899
121	698	95	285	855	566	1698	1096	1289	1868	1606
122	820	461	1383	151	453	1359	79	237	711	134
123	402	1206	1619	859	578	1734	1204	1613	841	524
124	1572	718	155	465	1395	187	561	1683	1051	1154
125	1463	391	1173	1520	562	1686	1060	1181	1544	634
126	1902	1708	1126	1379	139	417	1251	1754	1264	1793
127	1381	145	435	1305	1916	1750	1252	1757	1273	1820
128	1462	388	1164	1493	481	1443	331	993	980	941
129	824	473	1419	259	777	332	996	989	968	905
130	716	149	447	1341	25	75	225	675	26	78
131	234	702	107	321	963	890	671	14	42	126
132	378	1134	1403	211	633	1899	1699	1099	1298	1895
133	1687	1063	1190	1571	715	146	438	1314	1943	1831
134	1495	487	1461	385	1155	1466	400	1200	1601	805
135	416	1248	1745	1237	1712	1138	1415	247	741	224
136	672	17	51	153	459	1377	133	399	1197	1592
137	778	335	1005	1016	1049	1148	1445	337	1011	1034
138	1103	1310	1931	1795	1387	163	489	1467	403	1209
139	1628	886	659	1977	1933	1801	1405	217	651	1953
140	1861	1585	757	272	816	449	1347	43	129	387
141	1161	1484	454	1362	88	264	792	377	1131	1394
142	184	552	1656	970	911	734	203	609	1827	1483
143	451	1353	61	183	549	1647	943	830	491	1473
144	421	1263	1790	1372	118	354	1062	1187	1562	688
145	65	195	585	1755	1267	1802	1408	226	678	35
146	105	315	945	836	509	1527	583	1749	1249	1748
147	1246	1739	1219	1658	976	929	788	365	1095	1286
148	1859	1579	739	218	654	1962	1888	1666	1000	1001
149	1004	1013	1040	1121	1364	94	282	846	539	1617

P = 1999

INDICES

	0	1	2	3	4	5	6	7	8	9
150	979	1785	862	1631	1537	868	981	1568	439	1777
151	387	1963	342	1514	1912	1787	1697	34	285	206
152	1253	1598	585	191	864	738	292	1465	1520	1148
153	527	821	1197	1633	244	1660	595	203	222	563
154	365	609	1539	1091	1258	413	225	968	431	817
155	406	870	303	1039	1804	508	1880	1670	617	1067
156	983	337	1448	994	273	908	1132	1044	168	1570
157	1682	1333	1240	566	1666	115	1986	834	441	1481
158	900	1952	266	351	1926	1401	742	1779	686	1709
159	747	1893	1369	937	1655	1155	389	231	858	347
160	368	1348	665	1905	879	1965	1219	147	252	962
161	1859	282	410	1237	344	574	1176	1499	843	1232
162	1676	321	418	1516	958	756	577	612	1390	649
163	549	931	1914	944	478	1626	768	158	119	1185
164	1730	1789	1170	174	707	446	658	1435	1800	1622
165	1699	641	763	1179	1542	1938	1422	72	1473	36
166	1947	1107	378	1849	372	1140	1487	296	287	48
167	793	79	1973	896	1103	25	921	208	314	715
168	1502	1094	1748	1247	462	31	1255	1330	855	753
169	760	712	9	874	1085	1600	136	734	1215	1326
170	1687	812	886	1017	587	1126	12	846	1261	782
171	1723	1553	1354	193	213	1075	1703	497	1743	1990
172	1591	775	866	1910	189	1195	607	404	1065	166
173	832	740	1153	877	1235	416	929	1728	1620	1471
174	294	919	29	1083	1015	1352	773	830	1469	1467
175	1275	1121	358	1058	1267	1453	1004	1277	1522	1694
176	1088	1679	228	955	638	311	1123	1150	1691	53
177	99	581	1901	458	307	360	529	1996	1160	557
178	1825	484	398	534	1060	823	56	1603	324	971
179	1442	1839	891	1269	1199	1383	427	645	1719	1835
180	838	1395	1455	1635	452	1770	727	64	989	722
181	1809	1006	246	102	139	421	434	1116	1646	675
182	1279	1662	1934	925	1112	131	669	1428	1560	1524
183	597	1339	630	1784	1536	1567	386	1513	1696	205
184	584	737	1519	820	243	202	364	1090	224	816
185	302	507	616	336	272	1043	1681	565	1985	1480
186	265	1400	685	1892	1654	230	367	1904	1218	961
187	409	573	842	320	957	611	548	943	767	1184
188	1169	445	1799	640	1541	71	1946	1848	1486	47
189	1972	24	313	1093	461	1329	759	873	135	1325
190	885	1125	1260	1552	212	496	1590	1909	606	165
191	1152	415	1619	918	1014	829	1274	1057	1003	1693
192	227	310	1690	580	306	1995	1824	533	55	970
193	890	1382	1718	1394	451	63	1808	101	433	674
194	1933	130	1559	1338	1535	1512	583	819	363	815
195	615	1042	1984	1399	1653	1903	408	319	547	1183
196	1798	70	1485	23	460	872	884	1551	1589	164
197	1618	828	1002	309	305	532	889	1393	1807	673
198	1558	1511	362	1041	1652	318	1797	22	883	163
199	1001	531	1806	1510	1651	21	1000	1509	999	

POWER RESIDUES

	0	1	2	3	4	5	6	7	8	9
150	853	560	1680	1042	1127	1382	148	444	1332	1997
151	1993	1981	1945	1837	1513	541	1623	871	614	1842
152	1528	586	1758	1276	1829	1489	469	1407	223	669
153	8	24	72	216	648	1944	1834	1504	514	1542
154	628	1884	1654	964	893	680	41	123	369	1107
155	1322	1967	1903	1711	1135	1406	220	660	1980	1942
156	1828	1486	460	1380	142	426	1278	1835	1507	523
157	1569	709	128	384	1152	1457	373	1119	1358	76
158	228	684	53	159	477	1431	295	885	656	1968
159	1906	1720	1162	1487	463	1389	169	507	1521	565
160	1695	1087	1262	1787	1363	91	273	819	458	1374
161	124	372	1116	1349	49	147	441	1323	1970	1912
162	1738	1216	1649	949	848	545	1635	907	722	167
163	501	1503	511	1533	601	1803	1411	235	705	116
164	348	1044	1133	1400	202	606	1818	1456	370	1110
165	1331	1994	1984	1954	1864	1594	784	353	1059	1178
166	1535	607	1821	1465	397	1191	1574	724	173	519
167	1557	673	20	60	180	540	1620	862	587	1761
168	1285	1856	1570	712	137	411	1233	1700	1102	1307
169	1922	1768	1306	1919	1759	1279	1838	1516	550	1650
170	952	857	572	1716	1150	1451	355	1065	1196	1589
171	769	308	924	773	320	960	881	644	1932	1798
172	1396	190	570	1710	1132	1397	193	579	1737	1213
173	1640	922	767	302	906	719	158	474	1422	268
174	804	413	1239	1718	1156	1469	409	1227	1682	1048
175	1145	1436	310	930	791	374	1122	1367	103	309
176	927	782	347	1041	1124	1373	121	363	1089	1268
177	1805	1417	253	759	278	834	503	1509	529	1587
178	763	290	870	611	1833	1501	505	1515	547	1641
179	925	776	329	987	962	887	662	1986	1960	1882
180	1648	946	839	518	1554	664	1992	1978	1936	1810
181	1432	298	894	683	50	150	450	1350	52	156
182	468	1404	214	642	1926	1780	1342	28	84	252
183	756	269	807	422	1266	1799	1399	199	597	1791
184	1375	127	381	1143	1430	292	876	629	1887	1663
185	991	974	923	770	311	933	800	401	1203	1610
186	832	497	1491	475	1425	277	831	494	1482	448
187	1344	34	102	306	918	755	266	798	395	1185
188	1556	670	11	33	99	297	891	674	23	69
189	207	621	1863	1591	775	326	978	935	806	419
190	1257	1772	1318	1955	1867	1603	811	434	1302	1907
191	1723	1171	1514	544	1632	898	695	86	258	774
192	323	969	908	725	176	528	1584	754	263	789
193	368	1104	1313	1940	1822	1468	406	1218	1655	967
194	902	707	122	366	1098	1295	1886	1660	982	947
195	842	527	1581	745	236	708	125	375	1125	1376
196	130	390	1170	1511	535	1605	817	452	1356	70
197	210	630	1890	1672	1018	1055	1166	1499	499	1497
198	493	1479	439	1317	1952	1858	1576	730	191	573
199	1719	1159	1478	436	1308	1925	1777	1333		

P = 9

INDICES

	0	1	2	3	4	5	6	7	8	9
0		0	1		2	5		4	3	

POWER RESIDUES

	0	1	2	3	4	5	6	7	8	9
0	1	2	4	8	7	5				

P = 25

INDICES

	0	1	2	3	4	5	6	7	8	9
0		0	1	7	2		8	5	3	14
1		16	9	19	6		4	13	15	18
2		12	17	11	10					

POWER RESIDUES

	0	1	2	3	4	5	6	7	8	9
0	1	2	4	8	16	7	14	3	6	12
1	24	23	21	17	9	18	11	22	19	13
2										

P = 27

INDICES

	0	1	2	3	4	5	6	7	8	9
0		0	1		2	5		16	3	
1	6	13		8	17		4	15		12
2	7	0	14	11		10	9			

POWER RESIDUES

	0	1	2	3	4	5	6	7	8	9
0	1	2	4	8	16	5	10	20	13	26
1	25	23	19	11	22	17	7	14		
2										

P = 49

INDICES

	0	1	2	3	4	5	6	7	8	9
0		0	26	1	10	29	27		36	2
1	13	40	11	33		30	20	25	28	35
2	39	0	24	38	37	16	17	3		18
3	14	7	4	41	9		12	32	19	34
4	23	15		6	8	31	22	5	21	

POWER RESIDUES

	0	1	2	3	4	5	6	7	8	9
0	1	3	9	27	32	47	43	31	44	34
1	4	12	36	10	30	41	25	26	29	38
2	16	48	46	40	22	17	2	6	18	5
3	15	45	37	13	39	19	8	24	23	20
4	11	33								

P = 81

INDICES

	0	1	2	3	4	5	6	7	8	9
0		0	1		2	23		16	3	
1	24	13		8	17		4	33		48
2	25	0	14	11		46	9		18	37
3		20	5		34	39		42	49	
4	26	53		22	15		12	7		32
5	47	0	10	45		36	19		38	41
6		52	21		6	31		44	35	
7	40	51		30	43		50	29		28
8	27	0								

POWER RESIDUES

	0	1	2	3	4	5	6	7	8	9
0	1	2	4	8	16	32	64	47	13	26
1	52	23	46	11	22	44	7	14	28	56
2	31	62	43	5	10	20	40	80	79	77
3	73	65	49	17	34	68	55	29	58	35
4	70	59	37	74	67	53	25	50	19	38
5	76	71	61	41						
6										
7										
8										

P = 121

INDICES

	0	1	2	3	4	5	6	7	8	9
0		0	1	88	2	74	89	7	3	66
1	75	0	90	101	8	52	4	49	67	83
2	76	95		70	91	38	102	44	9	17
3	53	86	5		50	81	68	42	84	79
4	77	23	96	25		30	71	98	92	14
5	39	27	103	106	45		10	61	18	32
6	54	109	87	73	6	65		100	51	48
7	82	94	69	37	43	16	85		80	41
8	78	22	24	29	97	13	26	105		60
9	31	108	72	64	99	47	93	36	15	
10	40	21	28	12	104	59	107	63	46	35
11		20	11	58	62	34	19	57	33	56
12	55	0								

POWER RESIDUES

	0	1	2	3	4	5	6	7	8	9
0	1	2	4	8	16	32	64	7	14	28
1	56	112	103	85	49	98	75	29	58	116
2	111	101	81	41	82	43	86	51	102	83
3	45	90	59	118	115	109	97	73	25	50
4	100	79	37	74	27	54	108	95	69	17
5	34	68	15	30	60	120	119	117	113	105
6	89	57	114	107	93	65	9	18	36	72
7	23	46	92	63	5	10	20	40	80	39
8	78	35	70	19	38	76	31	62	3	6
9	12	24	48	96	71	21	42	84	47	94
10	67	13	26	52	104	87	53	106	91	61
11										
12										

P = 125

INDICES

	0	1	2	3	4	5	6	7	8	9
0		0	1	7	2		8	85	3	14
1		76	9	39	86		4	73	15	18
2		92	77	31	10		40	21	87	62
3		48	5	83	74		16	29	19	46
4	0000	44	93	95	78		32	97	11	70
5		80	41	67	22		88	25	63	34
6		56	49	99	6		84	13	75	38
7		72	17	91	30		20	61	47	82
8		28	45	43	94		96	69	79	66
9	0000	24	33	55	98		12	37	71	90
10		60	81	27	42		68	65	23	54
11		36	89	59	26		64	53	35	58
12		52	57	51	50					

POWER RESIDUES

	0	1	2	3	4	5	6	7	8	9
0	1	2	4	8	16	32	64	3	6	12
1	24	48	96	67	9	18	36	72	19	38
2	76	27	54	108	91	57	114	103	81	37
3	74	23	46	92	59	118	111	97	69	13
4	26	52	104	83	41	82	39	78	31	62
5	124	123	121	117	109	93	61	122	119	113
6	101	77	29	58	116	107	89	53	106	87
7	49	98	71	17	34	68	11	22	44	88
8	51	102	79	33	66	7	14	28	56	112
9	99	73	21	42	84	43	86	47	94	63
10										
11										
12										

P = 169

INDICES

	0	1	2	3	4	5	6	7	8	9
0		0	1	124	2	9	125	107	3	92
1	10	103	126		108	133	4	146	93	65
2	11	75	104	130	127	18		60	109	40
3	134	21	5	71	147	116	94	151	66	
4	12	85	76	122	105	101	131	63	128	58
5	19	114		120	61	112	110	33	41	35
6	135	140	22	43	6		72	37	148	98
7	117	137	95	51	152	142	67	54		24
8	13	28	86	45	77	155	123	8	106	91
9	102	0	132	145	64	74	129	17	59	39
10	20	70	115	150		84	121	100	62	57
11	113	119	111	32	34	139	42		36	97
12	136	50	141	53	23	27	44	154	7	90
13		144	73	16	38	69	149	83	99	56
14	118	31	138		96	49	52	26	153	89
15	143	15	68	82	55	30		48	25	88
16	14	81	29	47	87	80	46	79	78	

POWER RESIDUES

	0	1	2	3	4	5	6	7	8	9
0	1	2	4	8	16	32	64	128	87	5
1	10	20	40	80	160	151	133	97	25	50
2	100	31	62	124	79	158	147	125	81	162
3	155	141	113	57	114	59	118	67	134	99
4	29	58	116	63	126	83	166	163	157	145
5	121	73	146	123	77	154	139	109	49	98
6	27	54	108	47	94	19	38	76	152	135
7	101	33	66	132	95	21	42	84	168	167
8	165	161	153	137	105	41	82	164	159	149
9	129	89	9	18	36	72	144	119	69	138
10	107	45	90	11	22	44	88	7	14	28
11	56	112	55	110	51	102	35	70	140	111
12	53	106	43	86	3	6	12	24	48	96
13	23	46	92	15	30	60	120	71	142	115
14	61	122	75	150	131	93	17	34	68	136
15	103	37	74	148	127	85				
16										

P = 243

INDICES

	0	1	2	3	4	5	6	7	8	9
0		0	1		2	23		70	3	
1	24	121		8	71		4	33		156
2	25	0	122	65		46	9		72	37
3		20	5		34	93		96	157	
4	26	53		130	123		66	61		140
5	47	0	10	99		144	73		38	149
6		160	21		6	31		44	35	
7	94	51		138	97		158	29		136
8	27	0	54	109		56	131		124	111
9	0000	78	67		62	17		58	141	
10	48	133		14	11		100	117		126
11	145	0	74	113		88	39		150	103
12		80	161		22	69		120	7	
13	32	155		64	45		36	19		92
14	95	0	52	129		60	139		98	143
15		148	159		30	43		50	137	
16	28	135		108	55		110	77		16
17	57	0	132	13		116	125		112	87
18		102	79		68	119		154	63	
19	18	91		128	59		142	147		42
20	49	0	134	107		76	15		12	115
21		86	101		118	153		90	127	
22	146	41		106	75		114	85		152
23	89	0	40	105		84	151		104	83
24		82	81							

POWER RESIDUES

	0	1	2	3	4	5	6	7	8	9
0	1	2	4	8	16	32	64	128	13	26
1	52	104	208	173	103	206	169	95	190	137
2	31	62	124	5	10	20	40	80	160	77
3	154	65	130	17	34	68	136	29	58	116
4	232	221	199	155	67	134	25	50	100	200
5	157	71	142	41	82	164	85	170	97	194
6	145	47	94	188	133	23	46	92	184	125
7	7	14	28	56	112	224	205	167	91	182
8	121	242	241	239	235	227	211	179	115	230
9	217	191	139	35	70	140	37	74	148	53
10	106	212	181	119	238	233	223	203	163	83
11	166	89	178	113	226	209	175	107	214	185
12	127	11	22	44	88	176	109	218	193	143
13	43	86	172	101	202	161	79	158	73	146
14	49	98	196	149	55	110	220	197	151	59
15	118	236	229	215	187	131	19	38	76	152
16	61	122								
17										
18										
19	0000									
20										
21										
22										
23										
24										

P = 289

INDICES	0	1	2	3	4	5	6	7	8	9
0		0	190	1	108	229	191	155	26	2
1	147	23	109	196	73	230	216		192	14
2	65	156	213	223	27	186	114	3	263	125
3	148	9	134	24		112	110	129	204	197
4	255	171	74	226	131	231	141	100	217	38
5	104	0	32	206	193	252	181	15	43	234
6	66	259	199	157	52	153	214	184		224
7	30	257	28	165	47	187	122	178	115	167
8	173	4	89	118	264		144	126	49	76
9	149	79	59	10	18	243	135	189	228	25
10	22	72		64	222	113	124	133	111	203
11	170	130	99	103	205	180	233	198	152	
12	256	46	177	172	117	143	75	58	242	227
13	71	221	132	169	102	232		176	142	241
14	220	101	175	219	218	82	83	39	237	84
15	105	6	40		96	238	33	268	85	207
16	91	106	194	211	7	253	36	41	182	120
17		16	62	97	44	69	239	235	266	34
18	67	247	269	260	249	86	200		208	158
19	161	92	53	271	107	154	146	195	215	13
20	212	185	262	8		128	254	225	140	37
21	31	251	42	258	51	183	29	164	121	166
22	88	0	48	78	17	188	21	63	123	202
23	98	179	151	45	116	57	70	168		240
24	174	81	236	5	95	267	90	210	35	119
25	61	68	265	246	248		160	270	145	12
26	261	127	139	250	50	163	87	77	20	201
27	150	56		80	94	209	60	245	159	11
28	138	162	19	55	93	244	137	54	136	

POWER RESIDUES	0	1	2	3	4	5	6	7	8	9
0	1	3	9	27	81	243	151	164	203	31
1	93	279	259	199	19	57	171	224	94	282
2	268	226	100	11	33	99	8	24	72	216
3	70	210	52	156	179	248	166	209	49	147
4	152	167	212	58	174	233	121	74	222	88
5	264	214	64	192	287	283	271	235	127	92
6	276	250	172	227	103	20	60	180	251	175
7	236	130	101	14	42	126	89	267	223	91
8	273	241	145	146	149	158	185	266	220	82
9	246	160	191	284	274	244	154	173	230	112
10	47	141	134	113	50	150	161	194	4	12
11	36	108	35	105	26	78	234	124	83	249
12	169	218	76	228	106	29	87	261	205	37
13	111	44	132	107	32	96	288	286	280	262
14	208	46	138	125	86	258	196	10	30	90
15	270	232	118	65	195	7	21	63	189	278
16	256	190	281	265	217	73	219	79	237	133
17	110	41	123	80	240	142	137	122	77	231
18	115	56	168	215	67	201	25	75	225	97
19	2	6	18	54	162	197	13	39	117	62
20	186	269	229	109	38	114	53	159	188	275
21	247	163	200	22	66	198	16	48	144	143
22	140	131	104	23	69	207	43	129	98	5
23	15	45	135	116	59	177	242	148	155	176
24	239	139	128	95	285	277	253	181	254	184
25	263	211	55	165	206	40	120	71	213	61
26	183	260	202	28	84	252	178	245	157	182
27	257	193								
28										

P = 343

INDICES

	0	1	2	3	4	5	6	7	8	9
0		0	194	1	94	29	195		288	2
1	223	208	95	285		30	188	25	196	245
2	123	0	108	164	289	58	185	3		228
3	224	133	88	209	219		96	74	145	286
4	23	183		6	8	31	64	215	189	
5	252	26	85	10	197	237		246	128	13
6	124	263	33		282	20	109	112	119	165
7		66	290	79	268	59	45		186	56
8	217	4	83	261		54	200	229	202	191
9	225	0	258	134	115	274	89	231		210
10	152	169	220	71	279		204	254	97	40
11	137	75		240	146	193	28	287	207	
12	24	122	163	184	227	87		144	182	7
13	214	251	9		12	32	19	118	65	267
14	0000	216	260	199	190	257	273		168	278
15	253	136	239	27		162	86	181	250	11
16	117	0	198	272	277	238	161	249		276
17	248	247	100	101	129		102	14	91	130
18	125	51		264	158	103	34	233	15	
19	174	92	283	106	131	21		126	110	43
20	52	113	69		120	212	265	166	179	159
21		156	104	67	154	35	291		234	80
22	37	16	269	171		60	140	175	46	293
23	93	0	222	284	187	244	107	57		132
24	218	73	22	5	63		84	236	127	262
25	281	111		78	44	55	82	53	201	
26	114	230	151	70	203	39		192	206	121
27	226	143	213		18	266	259	256	167	135
28		180	116	271	160	275	99		90	50
29	157	232	173	105		42	68	211	178	155
30	153	0	36	170	139	292	221	243		72
31	62	235	280	77	81		150	38	205	142
32	17	255		270	98	49	172	41	177	
33	138	242	61	76	149	141		48	176	241
34	148	47	147							

POWER RESIDUES

	0	1	2	3	4	5	6	7	8	9
0	1	3	9	27	81	243	43	129	44	132
1	53	159	134	59	177	188	221	320	274	136
2	65	195	242	40	120	17	51	153	116	5
3	15	45	135	62	186	215	302	220	317	265
4	109	327	295	199	254	76	228	341	337	325
5	289	181	200	257	85	255	79	237	25	75
6	225	332	310	244	46	138	71	213	296	202
7	263	103	309	241	37	111	333	313	253	73
8	219	314	256	82	246	52	156	125	32	96
9	288	178	191	230	4	12	36	108	324	286
10	172	173	176	185	212	293	193	236	22	66
11	198	251	67	201	260	94	282	160	137	68
12	204	269	121	20	60	180	197	248	58	174
13	179	194	239	31	93	279	151	110	330	304
14	226	335	319	271	127	38	114	342	340	334
15	316	262	100	300	214	299	211	290	184	209
16	284	166	155	122	23	69	207	278	148	101
17	303	223	326	292	190	227	338	328	298	208
18	281	157	128	41	123	26	78	234	16	48
19	144	89	267	115	2	6	18	54	162	143
20	86	258	88	264	106	318	268	118	11	33
21	99	297	205	272	130	47	141	80	240	34
22	102	306	232	10	30	90	270	124	29	87
23	261	97	291	187	218	311	247	55	165	152
24	113	339	331	307	235	19	57	171	170	167
25	158	131	50	150	107	321	277	145	92	276
26	142	83	249	61	183	206	275	139	74	222
27	323	283	163	146	95	285	169	164	149	104
28	312	250	64	192	233	13	39	117	8	24
29	72	216	305	229						
30										
31										
32										
33										
34										

P = 361

INDICES

	0	1	2	3	4	5	6	7	8	9
0		0	1	139	2	232	140	150	3	278
1	233	102	141	329	151	29	4	226	279	
2	234	289	103	146	142	122	330	75	152	17
3	30	303	5	241	227	40	280	45		126
4	235	67	290	52	104	168	147	26	143	300
5	123	23	331	83	76	334	153		18	181
6	31	92	304	86	6	219	242	269	228	285
7	41	79	281	112	46	261		252	127	337
8	236	214	68	186	291	116	53	156	105	59
9	169	137	148	100	27		144	73	301	38
10	124	50	24	21	332	179	84	267	77	259
11	335	184	154	135		36	19	265	182	34
12	32	204	93	206	305	12	87	95	7	191
13	220	208	243		270	307	229	326	286	14
14	42	165	80	89	282	249	113	97	47	256
15	262	9		162	253	193	128	196	338	222
16	237	296	215	210	69	131	187	245	292	316
17	117	0	54	199	157	272	106	320	60	309
18	170	341	138	231	149	277	101	328	28	225
19	0000	288	145	121	74	16	302	240	39	44
20	125	66	51	167	25	299	22	82	333	
21	180	91	85	218	268	284	78	111	260	251
22	336	213	185	115	155	58	136	99		72
23	37	49	20	178	266	258	183	134	35	264
24	33	203	205	11	94	190	207		306	325
25	13	164	88	248	96	255	8	161	192	195
26	221	295	209	130	244	315		198	271	319
27	308	340	230	276	327	224	287	120	15	239
28	43	65	166	298	81		90	217	283	110
29	250	212	114	57	98	71	48	177	257	133
30	263	202	10	189		324	163	247	254	160
31	194	294	129	314	197	318	339	275	223	119
32	238	64	297		216	109	211	56	70	176
33	132	201	188	323	246	159	293	313	317	274
34	118	63		108	55	175	200	322	158	312
35	273	62	107	174	321	311	61	173	310	172
36	171	0								

POWER RESIDUES

	0	1	2	3	4	5	6	7	8	9
0	1	2	4	8	16	32	64	128	256	151
1	302	243	125	250	139	278	195	29	58	116
2	232	103	206	51	102	204	47	94	188	15
3	30	60	120	240	119	238	115	230	99	198
4	35	70	140	280	199	37	74	148	296	231
5	101	202	43	86	172	344	327	293	225	89
6	178	356	351	341	321	281	201	41	82	164
7	328	295	229	97	194	27	54	108	216	71
8	142	284	207	53	106	212	63	126	252	143
9	286	211	61	122	244	127	254	147	294	227
10	93	186	11	22	44	88	176	352	343	325
11	289	217	73	146	292	223	85	170	340	319
12	277	193	25	50	100	200	39	78	156	312
13	263	165	330	299	237	113	226	91	182	3
14	6	12	24	48	96	192	23	46	92	184
15	7	14	28	56	112	224	87	174	348	335
16	309	257	153	306	251	141	282	203	45	90
17	180	360	359	357	353	345	329	297	233	105
18	210	59	118	236	111	222	83	166	332	303
19	245	129	258	155	310	259	157	314	267	173
20	346	331	301	241	121	242	123	246	131	262
21	163	326	291	221	81	162	324	287	213	65
22	130	260	159	318	275	189	17	34	68	136
23	272	183	5	10	20	40	80	160	320	279
24	197	33	66	132	264	167	334	307	253	145
25	290	219	77	154	308	255	149	298	235	109
26	218	75	150	300	239	117	234	107	214	67
27	134	268	175	350	339	317	273	185	9	18
28	36	72	144	288	215	69	138	276	191	21
29	42	84	168	336	311	261	161	322	283	205
30	49	98	196	31	62	124	248	135	270	179
31	358	355	349	337	313	265	169	338	315	269
32	177	354	347	333	305	249	137	274	187	13
33	26	52	104	208	55	110	220	79	158	316
34	271	181								
35										
36										

P = 529

INDICES

	0	1	2	3	4	5	6	7	8	9
0		0	200	16	400	1	216	129	94	32
1	201	449	416	190	329	17	294	29	232	499
2	401	145	143		110	2	390	48	23	150
3	217	424	494	465	229	130	432	373	193	206
4	95	210	345	27	343	33		220	310	258
5	202	45	84	305	248	450	223	9	350	168
6	417	369	118	161	188	191	159	35	429	
7	330	112	126	356	67	18	393	72	406	487
8	295	64	410	461	39	30	227	166	37	291
9	233	319		440	420	500	4	89	458	481
10	402	362	245	75	284	146	505	215	448	293
11	144	389	423	431	209		44	222	368	158
12	111	392	63	226	318	3	361	504	388	43
13	391	360	359	122	235	49	123	99		154
14	24	236	312	133	326	151	50	274	267	141
15	218	124	87	61	272	425	100	81	181	321
16	495	0	264	332	104	466	155	260	239	380
17	230	25	427	438	366	131	237	184	491	78
18	433	313	13	385		374	134	478	114	177
19	194	327	204	186	289	207	152	102	175	413
20	96	51	56	279	445	211	275		484	442
21	346	268	199	128	415	28	142	47	493	372
22	344	219	83	8	117	34	125	71	409	165
23		88	244	214	422	221	62	503	358	98
24	311	273	86	80	263	259	426	183	12	477
25	203	101	55		198	46	82	70	243	502
26	85	182	54	69	53	306	322	307	435	338
27	249	496	323	335	299	451		308	354	456
28	224	265	436	173	6	10	333	339	20	58
29	351	105	250	315	474	169	467	497	341	
30	418	156	324	378	287	370	261	336	472	91
31	119	240	300	395	281	162	381	452	15	93
32	189	231		22	464	192	26	309	304	349
33	160	428	355	405	460	36	439	457	74	447
34	430	367	225	387	121		132	266	60	180
35	331	238	437	490	384	113	185	174	278	483
36	127	492	7	408	213	357	79	11		242
37	68	434	334	353	172	19	314	340	377	471
38	394	14	21	303	404	73	386	59	489	277
39	407	0	352	376	302	488	375	106	107	138
40	296	135	251	108	256	65	479	316	139	364
41	411	115	475	297		462	178	170	136	397
42	40	195	468	252	399	31	328	498	109	149
43	228	205	342	257	247	167	187		66	486
44	38	290	419	480	283	292	208	157	317	42
45	234	153	325	140	271	320	103	379	365	77
46		176	288	412	444	441	414	371	116	164
47	421	97	262	476	197	501	52	337	298	455
48	5	57	473		286	90	280	92	463	348
49	459	446	120	179	383	482	212	241	171	470

POWER RESIDUES

	0	1	2	3	4	5	6	7	8	9
0	1	5	25	125	96	480	284	362	223	57
1	285	367	248	182	381	318	3	15	75	375
2	288	382	323	28	140	171	326	43	215	17
3	85	425	9	45	225	67	335	88	440	84
4	420	513	449	129	116	51	255	217	27	135
5	146	201	476	264	262	252	202	481	289	387
6	348	153	236	122	81	405	438	74	370	263
7	257	227	77	385	338	103	515	459	179	366
8	243	157	256	222	52	260	242	152	231	97
9	485	309	487	319	8	40	200	471	239	137
10	156	251	197	456	164	291	397	398	403	428
11	24	120	71	355	188	411	468	224	62	310
12	492	344	133	136	151	226	72	360	213	7
13	35	175	346	143	186	401	418	503	399	408
14	453	149	216	22	110	21	105	525	509	429
15	29	145	196	451	139	166	301	447	119	66
16	330	63	315	517	469	229	87	435	59	295
17	417	498	374	283	357	198	461	189	416	493
18	349	158	261	247	177	356	193	436	64	320
19	13	65	325	38	190	421	518	474	254	212
20	2	10	50	250	192	431	39	195	446	114
21	41	205	496	364	233	107	6	30	150	221
22	47	235	117	56	280	342	123	86	430	34
23	170	321	18	90	450	134	141	176	351	168
24	311	497	369	258	232	102	510	434	54	270
25	292	402	423	528	524	504	404	433	49	245
26	167	306	472	244	162	281	347	148	211	526
27	514	454	154	241	147	206	501	389	358	203
28	486	314	512	444	104	520	484	304	462	194
29	441	89	445	109	16	80	400	413	478	274
30	312	502	394	383	328	53	265	267	277	327
31	48	240	142	181	376	293	407	448	124	91
32	455	159	266	272	302	452	144	191	426	14
33	70	350	163	286	372	273	307	477	269	287
34	377	298	432	44	220	42	210	521	489	329
35	58	290	392	373	278	332	73	365	238	132
36	131	126	101	505	409	458	174	341	118	61
37	305	467	219	37	185	396	393	378	303	457
38	169	316	522	494	354	183	386	343	128	111
39	26	130	121	76	380	313	507	419	508	424
40	4	20	100	500	384	333	78	390	363	228
41	82	410	463	199	466	214	12	60	300	442
42	94	470	234	112	31	155	246	172	331	68
43	340	113	36	180	371	268	282	352	173	336
44	93	465	209	516	464	204	491	339	108	11
45	55	275	317	527	519	479	279	337	98	490
46	334	83	415	488	324	33	165	296	422	523
47	499	379	308	482	294	412	473	249	187	406
48	443	99	495	359	208	511	439	79	395	388
49	353	178	361	218	32	160	271	297	427	19

P = 529

INDICES

	0	1	2	3	4	5	6	7	8	9
50	403	276	301	137	255	363		396	398	148
51	246	485	282	41	270	76	443	163	196	454
52	285	347	382	469	254	147	269	453	253	

POWER RESIDUES

	0	1	2	3	4	5	6	7	8	9
50	95	475	259	237	127	106				
51										
52										

P = 625

INDICES

	0	1	2	3	4	5	6	7	8	9
0		0	1	107	2		108	485	3	214
1		476	109	139	486		4	173	215	418
2		92	477	431	110		140	321	487	162
3		48	5	83	174		216	329	419	246
4	0000	44	93	195	478		432	97	111	470
5		280	141	367	322		488	25	163	134
6		456	49	199	6		84	13	175	38
7		272	217	291	330		420	461	247	482
8		428	45	243	94		196	269	479	266
9	0000	124	433	155	98		112	337	471	190
10		60	281	127	142		368	65	323	54
11		436	489	259	26		164	353	135	158
12		452	457	151	50		200	101	7	302
13		308	85	403	14		176	209	39	286
14	0000	204	273	115	218		292	77	331	410
15		340	421	387	462		248	105	483	474
16		416	429	319	46		244	193	95	278
17		132	197	11	270		480	241	267	122
18		188	125	63	434		156	149	99	306
19	0000	284	113	75	338		472	317	191	130
20		120	61	147	282		128	145	143	394
21		396	369	379	66		324	33	55	398
22		312	437	371	490		260	381	27	442
23		68	165	223	354		136	89	159	326
24	0000	364	453	35	458		152	57	51	350
25		400	201	407	102		8	185	303	314
26		376	309	439	86		404	373	15	18
27		492	177	231	210		40	21	287	262
28		448	205	383	274		116	29	219	346
29	0000	444	293	495	78		332	297	411	70
30		180	341	167	422		388	225	463	234
31		356	249	499	106		484	213	475	138
32		172	417	91	430		320	161	47	82
33		328	245	43	194		96	469	279	366
34	0000	24	133	455	198		12	37	271	290
35		460	481	427	242		268	265	123	154
36		336	189	59	126		64	53	435	258
37		352	157	451	150		100	301	307	402
38		208	285	203	114		76	409	339	386
39	0000	104	473	415	318		192	277	131	10
40		240	121	187	62		148	305	283	74
41		316	129	119	146		144	393	395	378
42		32	397	311	370		380	441	67	222
43		88	325	363	34		56	349	399	406
44	0000	184	313	375	438		372	17	491	230
45		20	261	447	382		28	345	443	494
46		296	69	179	166		224	233	355	498
47		212	137	171	90		160	81	327	42
48		468	365	23	454		36	289	459	426
49	0000	264	153	335	58		52	257	351	450

POWER RESIDUES

	0	1	2	3	4	5	6	7	8	9
0	1	2	4	8	16	32	64	128	256	512
1	399	173	346	67	134	268	536	447	269	538
2	451	277	554	483	341	57	114	228	456	287
3	574	523	421	217	434	243	486	347	69	138
4	276	552	479	333	41	82	164	328	31	62
5	124	248	496	367	109	218	436	247	494	363
6	101	202	404	183	366	107	214	428	231	462
7	299	598	571	517	409	193	386	147	294	588
8	551	477	329	33	66	132	264	528	431	237
9	474	323	21	42	84	168	336	47	94	188
10	376	127	254	508	391	157	314	3	6	12
11	24	48	96	192	384	143	286	572	519	413
12	201	402	179	358	91	182	364	103	206	412
13	199	398	171	342	59	118	236	472	319	13
14	26	52	104	208	416	207	414	203	406	187
15	374	123	246	492	359	93	186	372	119	238
16	476	327	29	58	116	232	464	303	606	587
17	549	473	321	17	34	68	136	272	544	463
18	301	602	579	533	441	257	514	403	181	362
19	99	198	396	167	334	43	86	172	344	63
20	126	252	504	383	141	282	564	503	381	137
21	274	548	471	317	9	18	36	72	144	288
22	576	527	429	233	466	307	614	603	581	537
23	449	273	546	467	309	618	611	597	569	513
24	401	177	354	83	166	332	39	78	156	312
25	624	623	621	617	609	593	561	497	369	113
26	226	452	279	558	491	357	89	178	356	87
27	174	348	71	142	284	568	511	397	169	338
28	51	102	204	408	191	382	139	278	556	487
29	349	73	146	292	584	543	461	297	594	563
30	501	377	129	258	516	407	189	378	131	262
31	524	423	221	442	259	518	411	197	394	163
32	326	27	54	108	216	432	239	478	331	37
33	74	148	296	592	559	493	361	97	194	388
34	151	302	604	583	541	457	289	578	531	437
35	249	498	371	117	234	468	311	622	619	613
36	601	577	529	433	241	482	339	53	106	212
37	424	223	446	267	534	443	261	522	419	213
38	426	227	454	283	566	507	389	153	306	612
39	599	573	521	417	209	418	211	422	219	438
40	251	502	379	133	266	532	439	253	506	387
41	149	298	596	567	509	393	161	322	19	38
42	76	152	304	608	591	557	489	353	81	162
43	324	23	46	92	184	368	111	222	444	263
44	526	427	229	458	291	582	539	453	281	562
45	499	373	121	242	484	343	61	122	244	488
46	351	77	154	308	616	607	589	553	481	337
47	49	98	196	392	159	318	11	22	44	88
48	176	352	79	158	316	7	14	28	56	112
49	224	448	271	542	459	293	586	547	469	313

INDICES P = 625 POWER RESIDUES

	0	1	2	3	4	5	6	7	8	9
50		300	401	207	202		408	385	103	414
51		276	9	239	186		304	73	315	118
52		392	377	31	310		440	221	87	362
53		348	405	183	374		16	229	19	446
54	0000	344	493	295	178		232	497	211	170
55		80	41	467	22		288	425	263	334
56		256	449	299	206		384	413	275	238
57		72	117	391	30		220	361	347	182
58		228	445	343	294		496	169	79	466
59	0000	424	333	255	298		412	237	71	390
60		360	181	227	342		168	465	423	254
61		236	389	359	226		464	253	235	358
62		252	357	251	250					

	0	1	2	3	4	5	6	7	8	9
50										
51										
52										
53										
54	0000									
55										
56										
57										
58										
59	0000									
60										
61										
62										

P = 729

INDICES

	0	1	2	3	4	5	6	7	8	9
0		0	1		2	23		394	3	
1	24	283		332	395		4	33		318
2	25	0	284	389		46	333		396	199
3		344	5		34	417		258	319	
4	26	215		454	285		390	385		302
5	47	0	334	423		306	397		200	473
6		160	345		6	355		206	35	
7	418	51		462	259		320	191		136
8	27	0	216	109		56	455		286	273
9	0000	240	391		386	341		382	303	
10	48	133		338	335		424	117		126
11	307	0	398	437		412	201		474	427
12		80	161		346	69		120	7	
13	356	479		226	207		36	19		254
14	419	0	52	129		222	463		260	467
15		310	321		192	367		374	137	
16	28	297		432	217		110	401		178
17	57	0	456	13		440	287		274	87
18		264	241		392	281		316	387	
19	342	415		452	383		304	471		204
20	49	0	134	107		238	339		336	115
21		410	425		118	477		252	127	
22	308	365		430	399		438	85		314
23	413	0	202	105		408	475		428	83
24	0000	406	81		162	325		164	347	
25	70	327		186	121		8	233		166
26	357	0	480	349		446	227		208	171
27		72	37		20	329		196	255	
28	420	157		188	53		130	123		66
29	223	0	464	371		10	261		468	235
30		362	311		322	183		168	193	
31	368	359		94	375		138	97		482
32	29	0	298	351		378	433		218	293
33		448	111		402	229		62	179	
34	58	141		210	457		14	173		100
35	441	0	288	145		74	275		88	39
36		150	265		242	485		22	393	
37	282	331		32	317		388	45		198
38	343	0	416	257		214	453		384	301
39	0000	422	305		472	159		354	205	
40	50	461		190	135		108	55		272
41	239	0	340	381		132	337		116	125
42		436	411		426	79		68	119	
43	478	225		18	253		128	221		466
44	309	0	366	373		296	431		400	177
45		12	439		86	263		280	315	
46	414	451		470	203		106	237		114
47	409	0	476	251		364	429		84	313
48		104	407		82	405		324	163	
49	326	185		232	165		348	445		170

POWER RESIDUES

	0	1	2	3	4	5	6	7	8	9
0	1	2	4	8	16	32	64	128	256	512
1	295	590	451	173	346	692	655	581	433	137
2	274	548	367	5	10	20	40	80	160	320
3	640	551	373	17	34	68	136	272	544	359
4	718	707	685	641	553	377	25	50	100	200
5	400	71	142	284	568	407	85	170	340	680
6	631	533	337	674	619	509	289	578	427	125
7	250	500	271	542	355	710	691	653	577	425
8	121	242	484	239	478	227	454	179	358	716
9	703	677	625	521	313	626	523	317	634	539
10	349	698	667	605	481	233	466	203	406	83
11	166	332	664	599	469	209	418	107	214	428
12	127	254	508	287	574	419	109	218	436	143
13	286	572	415	101	202	404	79	158	316	632
14	535	341	682	635	541	353	706	683	637	545
15	361	722	715	701	673	617	505	281	562	395
16	61	122	244	488	247	494	259	518	307	614
17	499	269	538	347	694	659	589	449	169	338
18	676	623	517	305	610	491	253	506	283	566
19	403	77	154	308	616	503	277	554	379	29
20	58	116	232	464	199	398	67	134	268	536
21	343	686	643	557	385	41	82	164	328	656
22	583	437	145	290	580	431	133	266	532	335
23	670	611	493	257	514	299	598	467	205	410
24	91	182	364	728	727	725	721	713	697	665
25	601	473	217	434	139	278	556	383	37	74
26	148	296	592	455	181	362	724	719	709	689
27	649	569	409	89	178	356	712	695	661	593
28	457	185	370	11	22	44	88	176	352	704
29	679	629	529	329	658	587	445	161	322	644
30	559	389	49	98	196	392	55	110	220	440
31	151	302	604	479	229	458	187	374	19	38
32	76	152	304	608	487	245	490	251	502	275
33	550	371	13	26	52	104	208	416	103	206
34	412	95	190	380	31	62	124	248	496	263
35	526	323	646	563	397	65	130	260	520	311
36	622	515	301	602	475	221	442	155	310	620
37	511	293	586	443	157	314	628	527	325	650
38	571	413	97	194	388	47	94	188	376	23
39	46	92	184	368	7	14	28	56	112	224
40	448	167	334	668	607	485	241	482	235	470
41	211	422	115	230	460	191	382	35	70	140
42	280	560	391	53	106	212	424	119	238	476
43	223	446	163	326	652	575	421	113	226	452
44	175	350	700	671	613	497	265	530	331	662
45	595	461	193	386	43	86	172	344	688	647
46	565	401	73	146	292	584	439	149	298	596
47	463	197	394	59	118	236	472	215	430	131
48	262	524	319	638	547	365				
49	0000									

P = 729

INDICES

	0	1	2	3	4	5	6	7	8	9
50	71	0	328	195		156	187		122	65
51		370	9		234	361		182	167	
52	358	93		96	481		350	377		292
53	447	0	228	61		140	209		172	99
54	0000	144	73		38	149		484	21	
55	330	31		44	197		256	213		300
56	421	0	158	353		460	189		54	271
57		380	131		124	435		78	67	
58	224	17		220	465		372	295		176
59	11	0	262	279		450	469		236	113
60		250	363		312	103		404	323	
61	184	231		444	169		194	155		64
62	369	0	360	181		92	95		376	291
63		60	139		98	143		148	483	
64	30	43		212	299		352	459		270
65	379	0	434	77		16	219		294	175
66		278	449		112	249		102	403	
67	230	443		154	63		180	91		290
68	59	0	142	147		42	211		458	269
69	0000	76	15		174	277		248	101	
70	442	153		90	289		146	41		268
71	75	0	276	247		152	89		40	267
72		246	151		266	245		244	243	

POWER RESIDUES

	0	1	2	3	4	5	6	7	8	9
50										
51										
52										
53										
54	0000									
55										
56										
57										
58										
59	0000									
60										
61										
62										
63										
64	0000									
65										
66										
67										
68										
69	0000									
70										
71										
72										

P = 841

INDICES

	0	1	2	3	4	5	6	7	8	9
0		0	1	537	2	302	538	376	3	262
1	303	81	539	662	377	27	4	469	263	625
2	304	101	82	804	540	604	663	799	378	
3	28	421	5	618	470	678	264	311	626	387
4	305	203	102	321	83	564	805	39	541	752
5	605	194	664	372	800	383	379	350		56
6	29	285	422	638	6	152	619	178	471	529
7	679	354	265	139	312	329	627	457	388	297
8	306	524	204	184	103	771	322		84	449
9	565	226	806	146	40	115	542	555	753	343
10	606	209	195	60	665	403	373	24	801	418
11	384	36	380	635	351	294		112	57	33
12	30	162	286	740	423	94	639	165	7	46
13	153	251	620	189	179	289	472	493	530	244
14	680	576	355	743	266		140	477	313	646
15	330	426	628	731	458	723	389	483	298	97
16	307	368	525	767	205	108	185	642	104	512
17	772	75	323	238		168	85	593	450	498
18	566	516	227	10	807	613	147	550	41	363
19	116	49	543	121	556	689	754	776	344	156
20	607	715	210		196	505	61	254	666	706
21	404	535	374	79	25	623	802	797	419	676
22	385	319	37	192	381	54	636	176	352	327
23	295	182		224	113	341	58	22	34	292
24	31	738	163	249	287	242	741	475	424	721
25	95	765	640	73	166	496	8	548	47	687
26	154	0	252	533	621	674	190	174	180	339
27	290	247	473	763	494	685	531	172	245	683
28	681	276	577	278	356	652	744	579	267	126
29	0000	280	141	89	478	358	314	68	647	654
30	331	697	427	746	629	587	732	581	459	597
31	724	269	390	216	484	128	299	659	98	
32	308	561	369	282	526	454	768	143	206	415
33	109	91	186	573	643	480	105	235	513	360
34	773	502	76	316	324	19	239	70		336
35	169	649	86	694	594	656	451	570	499	333
36	567	438	517	699	228	441	11	429	808	465
37	614	748	148	520	551	631	42		364	589
38	117	702	50	734	544	759	122	583	557	231
39	690	461	755	788	777	599	345	444	157	726
40	608	792	716	271	211	14		392	197	397
41	506	218	62	432	255	486	667	781	707	130
42	405	811	536	301	375	261	80	661	26	468
43	624	100	803	603	798		420	617	677	310
44	386	202	320	563	38	751	193	371	382	349
45	55	284	637	151	177	528	353	138	328	456
46	296	523	183	770		448	225	145	114	554
47	342	208	59	402	23	417	35	634	293	111
48	32	161	739	93	164	45	250	188	288	492
49	243	575	742		476	645	425	730	722	482

POWER RESIDUES

	0	1	2	3	4	5	6	7	8	9
0	1	2	4	8	16	32	64	128	256	512
1	183	366	732	623	405	810	779	717	593	345
2	690	539	237	474	107	214	428	15	30	60
3	120	240	480	119	238	476	111	222	444	47
4	94	188	376	752	663	485	129	258	516	191
5	382	764	687	533	225	450	59	118	236	472
6	103	206	412	824	807	773	705	569	297	594
7	347	694	547	253	506	171	342	684	527	213
8	426	11	22	44	88	176	352	704	567	293
9	586	331	662	483	125	250	500	159	318	636
10	431	21	42	84	168	336	672	503	165	330
11	660	479	117	234	468	95	190	380	760	679
12	517	193	386	772	703	565	289	578	315	630
13	419	838	835	829	817	793	745	649	457	73
14	146	292	584	327	654	467	93	186	372	744
15	647	453	65	130	260	520	199	398	796	751
16	661	481	121	242	484	127	254	508	175	350
17	700	559	277	554	267	534	227	454	67	134
18	268	536	231	462	83	166	332	664	487	133
19	266	532	223	446	51	102	204	408	816	791
20	741	641	441	41	82	164	328	656	471	101
21	202	404	808	775	709	577	313	626	411	822
22	803	765	689	537	233	466	91	182	364	728
23	615	389	778	715	589	337	674	507	173	346
24	692	543	245	490	139	278	556	271	542	243
25	486	131	262	524	207	414	828	815	789	737
26	633	425	9	18	36	72	144	288	576	311
27	622	403	806	771	701	561	281	562	283	566
28	291	582	323	646	451	61	122	244	488	135
29	270	540	239	478	115	230	460	79	158	316
30	632	423	5	10	20	40	80	160	320	640
31	439	37	74	148	296	592	343	686	531	221
32	442	43	86	172	344	688	535	229	458	75
33	150	300	600	359	718	595	349	698	555	269
34	538	235	470	99	198	396	792	743	645	449
35	57	114	228	456	71	142	284	568	295	590
36	339	678	515	189	378	756	671	501	161	322
37	644	447	53	106	212	424	7	14	28	56
38	112	224	448	55	110	220	440	39	78	156
39	312	624	407	814	787	733	625	409	818	795
40	749	657	473	105	210	420	840	839	837	833
41	825	809	777	713	585	329	658	475	109	218
42	436	31	62	124	248	496	151	302	604	367
43	734	627	413	826	811	781	721	601	361	722
44	603	365	730	619	397	794	747	653	465	89
45	178	356	712	583	325	650	459	77	154	308
46	616	391	782	723	605	369	738	635	429	17
47	34	68	136	272	544	247	494	147	294	588
48	335	670	499	157	314	628	415	830	819	797
49	753	665	489	137	274	548	255	510	179	358

P = 841

INDICES

	0	1	2	3	4	5	6	7	8	9
50	96	367	766	107	641	511	74	237	167	592
51	497	515	9	612	549	362	48	120	688	775
52	155	714		504	253	705	534	78	622	796
53	675	318	191	53	175	326	181	223	340	21
54	291	737	248	241	474	720	764	72	495	547
55	686	0	532	673	173	338	246	762	684	171
56	682	275	277	651	578	125	279	88	357	67
57	653	696	745	586	580	596	268	215	127	658
58		560	281	453	142	414	90	572	479	234
59	359	501	315	18	69	335	648	693	655	569
60	332	437	698	440	428	464	747	519	630	
61	588	701	733	758	582	230	460	787	598	443
62	725	791	270	13	391	396	217	431	485	780
63	129	810	300	260	660	467	99	602		616
64	309	201	562	750	370	348	283	150	527	137
65	455	522	769	447	144	553	207	401	416	633
66	110	160	92	44	187	491	574		644	729
67	481	366	106	510	236	591	514	611	361	119
68	774	713	503	704	77	795	317	52	325	222
69	20	736	240	719	71	546		672	337	761
70	170	274	650	124	87	66	695	585	595	214
71	657	559	452	413	571	233	500	17	334	692
72	568	436	439	463	518		700	757	229	786
73	442	790	12	395	430	779	809	259	466	601
74	615	200	749	347	149	136	521	446	552	400
75	632	159	43	490		728	365	509	590	610
76	118	712	703	794	51	221	735	718	545	671
77	760	273	123	65	584	213	558	412	232	16
78	691	435	462		756	785	789	394	778	258
79	600	199	346	135	445	399	158	489	727	508
80	609	711	793	220	717	670	272	64	212	411
81	15	434		784	393	257	198	134	398	488
82	507	710	219	669	63	410	433	783	256	133
83	487	709	668	409	782	132	708	408	131	407
84	406	0								

POWER RESIDUES

	0	1	2	3	4	5	6	7	8	9
50	716	591	341	682	523	205	410	820	799	757
51	673	505	169	338	676	511	181	362	724	607
52	373	746	651	461	81	162	324	648	455	69
53	138	276	552	263	526	211	422	3	6	12
54	24	48	96	192	384	768	695	549	257	514
55	187	374	748	655	469	97	194	388	776	711
56	581	321	642	443	45	90	180	360	720	599
57	357	714	587	333	666	491	141	282	564	287
58	574	307	614	387	774	707	573	305	610	379
59	758	675	509	177	354	708	575	309	618	395
60	790	739	637	433	25	50	100	200	400	800
61	759	677	513	185	370	740	639	437	33	66
62	132	264	528	215	430	19	38	76	152	304
63	608	375	750	659	477	113	226	452	63	126
64	252	504	167	334	668	495	149	298	596	351
65	702	563	285	570	299	598	355	710	579	317
66	634	427	13	26	52	104	208	416	832	823
67	805	769	697	553	265	530	219	438	35	70
68	140	280	560	279	558	275	550	259	518	195
69	390	780	719	597	353	706	571	301	602	363
70	726	611	381	762	683	525	209	418	836	831
71	821	801	761	681	521	201	402	804	767	693
72	545	249	498	155	310	620	399	798	755	669
73	497	153	306	612	383	766	691	541	241	482
74	123	246	492	143	286	572	303	606	371	742
75	643	445	49	98	196	392	784	727	613	385
76	770	699	557	273	546	251	502	163	326	652
77	463	85	170	340	680	519	197	394	788	735
78	629	417	834	827	813	785	729	617	393	786
79	731	621	401	802	763	685	529	217	434	27
80	54	108	216	432	23	46	92	184	368	736
81	631	421								
82										
83										
84										

P = 961

INDICES

	0	1	2	3	4	5	6	7	8	9
0		0	624	1	318	440	625	658	12	2
1	134	323	319	401	352	441	636	727	626	214
2	758	659	17	87	13	880	95	3	46	459
3	135	0	330	324	421	168	320	835	838	402
4	452	74	353	889	641	442	711	366	637	386
5	574	728	719	497	627	763	670	215	153	556
6	759	735		660	24	841	18	200	115	88
7	792	902	14	383	529	881	532	51	96	547
8	146	4	698	779	47	237	583	460	335	303
9	136	129	405		60	654	331	798	80	325
10	268	252	422	884	413	169	191	622	321	756
11	457	836	364	668	839	527	777	403	250	455
12	453	646	429	75		390	354	751	648	890
13	535	448	642	872	824	443	739	431	712	591
14	486	367	596	724	638	899	77	387	223	40
15	575	603	226	729	675		720	54	241	498
16	770	745	628	102	392	764	473	379	671	802
17	861	216	277	356	154	608	29	557	927	43
18	760	695	753	736	99	345		120	684	661
19	348	650	25	808	492	842	704	503	19	911
20	892	201	876	187	116	514	578	89	107	537
21	793	550	815	903	316	399	15		450	384
22	151	198	530	235	58	882	362	644	533	589
23	221	52	471	606	97	806	874	548	149	587
24	147	613	340	5	123	826	699	615		780
25	84	571	48	410	445	238	342	812	584	563
26	229	461	142	741	336	7	566	304	518	209
27	137	687	433	130	125	273	406	69	285	
28	180	714	61	828	290	655	418	732	332	524
29	593	799	701	232	81	66	847	326	664	488
30	269	617	297	253	850	245	423	916	369	885
31		510	414	481	678	170	865	598	192	782
32	464	623	439	11	322	351	726	757	86	94
33	458	329	167	837	73	640	365	573	496	669
34	555	0	840	114	901	528	50	145	778	582
35	302	404	653	79	251	412	621	456	667	776
36	454	428	389	647	447	823	430	485	723	76
37	39	225		240	744	391	378	860	355	28
38	42	752	344	683	649	491	502	891	186	577
39	536	814	398	449	197	57	643	220	605	873
40	586	339	825		570	444	811	228	740	565
41	208	432	272	284	713	289	731	592	231	846
42	487	296	244	368	509	677	597	463	10	725
43	93	166	639	495		900	144	301	78	620
44	775	388	822	722	224	743	859	41	682	501
45	576	397	56	604	338	569	227	207	283	730
46	845	243	676	9	165		300	774	721	858
47	500	55	568	282	242	164	773	499	281	772
48	771	306	307	746	34	308	629	707	747	103
49	520	35	393	256	309	765		630	474	211

POWER RESIDUES

	0	1	2	3	4	5	6	7	8	9
0	1	3	9	27	81	243	729	265	795	463
1	428	323	8	24	72	216	648	22	66	198
2	594	821	541	662	64	192	576	767	379	176
3	528	623	908	802	484	491	512	575	764	370
4	149	447	380	179	537	650	28	84	252	756
5	346	77	231	693	157	471	452	395	224	672
6	94	282	846	616	887	739	295	885	733	277
7	831	571	752	334	41	123	369	146	438	353
8	98	294	882	724	250	750	328	23	69	207
9	621	902	784	430	329	26	78	234	702	184
10	552	695	163	489	506	557	710	208	624	911
11	811	511	572	755	343	68	204	612	875	703
12	187	561	722	244	732	274	822	544	671	91
13	273	819	535	644	10	30	90	270	810	508
14	563	728	262	786	436	347	80	240	720	238
15	714	220	660	58	174	522	605	854	640	959
16	955	943	907	799	475	464	431	332	35	105
17	315	945	913	817	529	626	917	829	565	734
18	280	840	598	833	577	770	388	203	609	866
19	676	106	318	954	940	898	772	394	221	663
20	67	201	603	848	622	905	793	457	410	269
21	807	499	536	647	19	57	171	513	578	773
22	397	230	690	148	444	371	152	456	407	260
23	780	418	293	879	715	223	669	85	255	765
24	373	158	474	461	422	305	915	823	547	680
25	118	354	101	303	909	805	493	518	593	818
26	532	635	944	910	808	502	545	674	100	300
27	900	778	412	275	825	553	698	172	516	587
28	800	478	473	458	413	278	834	580	779	415
29	284	852	634	941	901	781	421	302	906	796
30	466	437	350	89	267	801	481	482	485	494
31	521	602	845	613	878	712	214	642	4	12
32	36	108	324	11	33	99	297	891	751	331
33	32	96	288	864	670	88	264	792	454	401
34	242	726	256	768	382	185	555	704	190	570
35	749	325	14	42	126	378	173	519	596	827
36	559	716	226	678	112	336	47	141	423	308
37	924	850	628	923	847	619	896	766	376	167
38	501	542	665	73	219	657	49	147	441	362
39	125	375	164	492	515	584	791	451	392	215
40	645	13	39	117	351	92	276	828	562	725
41	253	759	355	104	312	936	886	736	286	858
42	652	34	102	306	918	832	574	761	361	122
43	366	137	411	272	816	526	617	890	748	322
44	5	15	45	135	405	254	762	364	131	393
45	218	654	40	120	360	119	357	110	330	29
46	87	261	783	427	320	960	958	952	934	880
47	718	232	696	166	498	533	638	953	937	889
48	745	313	939	895	763	367	140	420	299	897
49	769	385	194	582	785	433	338	53	159	477

INDICES — P = 961

	0	1	2	3	4	5	6	7	8	9
50	708	380	265	748	672	692	104	803	139	521
51	862	111	36	217	506	394	278	689	257	357
52	853	310	155	543	766	609	435		30	174
53	631	558	260	475	928	132	212	44	833	709
54	761	22	381	696	127	266	754	248	749	737
55	897	673	100	275	693	346	909	105		360
56	804	121	408	140	685	178	522	662	914	863
57	349	71	112	651	426	37	26	184	218	809
58	287	507	493	820	395	843	856	279	705	
59	690	504	541	258	20	895	358	912	182	854
60	893	919	311	202	921	156	877	716	544	188
61	869	767	117	313	610	515	63	436	579	375
62		90	204	31	108	830	175	538	372	632
63	794	923	559	551	292	261	816	787	476	904
64	158	929	317	657	133	400	635	213	16	879
65	45	0	420	834	451	888	710	385	718	762
66	152	734	23	199	791	382	531	546	697	236
67	334	128	59	797	267	883	190	755	363	526
68	249	645		750	534	871	738	590	595	898
69	222	602	674	53	769	101	472	801	276	607
70	926	694	98	119	347	807	703	910	875	513
71	106	549	315		150	234	361	588	470	805
72	148	612	122	614	83	409	341	562	141	6
73	517	686	124	68	179	827	417	523	700	65
74	663	616	849	915		480	864	781	438	350
75	85	328	72	572	554	113	49	581	652	411
76	666	427	446	484	38	239	377	27	343	490
77	185	813	196	219	585		810	564	271	288
78	230	295	508	462	92	494	143	619	821	742
79	681	396	337	206	844	8	299	857	567	163
80	280	305	33	706	519	255		210	264	691
81	138	110	505	688	852	542	434	173	259	131
82	832	21	126	247	896	274	908	359	407	177
83	913	70	425	183	286	819	855		540	894
84	181	918	920	715	868	312	62	374	203	829
85	371	922	291	786	157	656	634	878	419	887
86	717	733	790	545	333	796	189	525		870
87	594	601	768	800	925	118	702	512	314	233
88	469	611	82	561	516	67	416	64	848	479
89	437	327	553	580	665	483	376	489	195	
90	270	294	91	618	680	205	298	162	32	254
91	263	109	851	172	831	246	907	176	424	818
92	539	917	867	373	370	785	633	886	789	795
93		600	924	511	468	560	415	478	552	482
94	194	293	679	161	262	171	906	817	866	784
95	788	599	467	477	193	160	905	783	466	159
96	465	0								

POWER RESIDUES

	0	1	2	3	4	5	6	7	8	9
50	470	449	386	197	591	812	514	581	782	424
51	311	933	877	709	205	615	884	730	268	804
52	490	509	566	737	289	867	679	115	345	74
53	222	666	76	228	684	130	390	209	627	920
54	838	592	815	523	608	863	667	79	237	711
55	211	633	938	892	754	340	59	177	531	632
56	935	883	727	259	777	409	266	798	472	455
57	404	251	753	337	50	150	450	389	206	618
58	893	757	349	86	258	774	400	239	717	229
59	687	139	417	290	870	688	142	426	317	951
60	931	871	691	151	453	398	233	699	175	525
61	614	881	721	241	723	247	741	301	903	787
62	439	356	107	321	2	6	18	54	162	486
63	497	530	629	926	856	646	16	48	144	432
64	335	44	132	396	227	681	121	363	128	384
65	191	573	758	352	95	285	855	643	7	21
66	63	189	567	740	298	894	760	358	113	339
67	56	168	504	551	692	154	462	425	314	942
68	904	790	448	383	188	564	731	271	813	517
69	590	809	505	554	701	181	543	668	82	246
70	738	292	876	706	196	588	803	487	500	539
71	656	46	138	414	281	843	607	860	658	52
72	156	468	443	368	143	429	326	17	51	153
73	459	416	287	861	661	61	183	549	686	136
74	408	263	789	445	374	161	483	488	503	548
75	683	127	381	182	546	677	109	327	20	60
76	180	540	659	55	165	495	524	611	872	694
77	160	480	479	476	467	440	359	116	348	83
78	249	747	319	957	949	925	853	637	950	928
79	862	664	70	210	630	929	865	673	97	291
80	873	697	169	507	560	719	235	705	193	579
81	776	406	257	771	391	212	636	947	919	835
82	583	788	442	365	134	402	245	735	283	849
83	625	914	820	538	653	37	111	333	38	114
84	342	65	195	585	794	460	419	296	888	742
85	304	912	814	520	599	836	586	797	469	446
86	377	170	510	569	746	316	948	922	844	610
87	869	685	133	399	236	708	202	606	857	649
88	25	75	225	675	103	309	927	859	655	43
89	129	387	200	600	839	595	824	550	689	145
90	435	344	71	213	639	956	946	916	826	556
91	707	199	597	830	568	743	307	921	841	601
92	842	604	851	631	932	874	700	178	534	641
93										
94	0000									
95										
96										

P = 1331

INDICES

	0	1	2	3	4	5	6	7	8	9
0		0	1	638	2	184	639	557	3	66
1	185	0	640	1201	558	822	4	159	67	1073
2	186	1195		290	641	368	1202	704	559	347
3	823	966	5		160	741	68	1142	1074	629
4	187	463	1196	245		250	291	868	642	1114
5	369	797	1203	876	705		560	501	348	912
6	824	989	967	623	6	175		1090	161	928
7	742	204	69	697	1143	1006	1075		630	481
8	188	132	464	29	1197	343	246	985		390
9	251	548	292	394	869	47	643	146	1115	
10	370	681	798	12	1204	169	877	833	706	255
11		570	561	938	502	474	349	57	913	716
12	825	0	990	1101	968	552	624	199	7	883
13	176	405		420	1091	888	162	444	929	727
14	743	296	205		70	531	698	542	1144	119
15	1007	493	1076	225		1150	631	398	482	304
16	189	847	133	96	465		30	181	1198	1192
17	344	1139	247	873	986	925		340	391	678
18	252	54	549	417	293	116	395		870	51
19	48	82	644	839	147	813	1116	85		410
20	371	518	682	904	799	647	13	356	1205	
21	170	141	878	842	834	429	707	313	256	125
22		150	571	1128	562	434	939	327	503	816
23	475	0	350	451	58	1052	914	1119	717	583
24	826	1045		770	991	88	1102	1064	969	667
25	553	286	625		200	981	8	712	884	489
26	177	413	406	425		1060	421	1028	1092	374
27	889	457	163	1186	445		930	521	728	1032
28	744	959	297	1013	206	685		1020	71	318
29	532	784	699	907	543	1096	1145		120	281
30	1008	802	494	109	1077	1173	226	615		650
31	1151	378	632	1084	399	807	483	16	305	
32	190	261	848	22	134	359	97	893	466	215
33		1160	31	1208	182	64	1199	157	1193	366
34	345	0	1140	461	248	1112	874	499	987	173
35	926	695		130	341	388	392	144	679	167
36	253	936	55		550	881	418	442	294	529
37	117	223	396	845		1190	871	338	52	114
38	49	837	83	516	645		840	311	148	432
39	814	449	1117	1043	86	665		710	411	1058
40	372	1184	519	957	683	316	905		800	1171
41	648	1082	14	259	357	213	1206	155		1110
42	171	128	142	934	879	527	843	336	835	
43	430	1041	708	1182	314	1169	257	153	126	525
44	0000	1180	151	1178	572	574	1129	757	563	576
45	435	0	940	1131	328	732	504	759	817	863
46	476	565		920	351	578	452	104	59	437
47	1053	1036	915		1120	231	718	942	584	239
48	827	1133	1046	275		330	771	748	992	734
49	89	777	1103	506	1065		970	761	668	602

POWER RESIDUES

	0	1	2	3	4	5	6	7	8	9
0	1	2	4	8	16	32	64	128	256	512
1	1024	717	103	206	412	824	317	634	1268	1205
2	1079	827	323	646	1292	1253	1175	1019	707	83
3	166	332	664	1328	1325	1319	1307	1283	1235	1139
4	947	563	1126	921	511	1022	713	95	190	380
5	760	189	378	756	181	362	724	117	234	468
6	936	541	1082	833	335	670	9	18	36	72
7	144	288	576	1152	973	615	1230	1129	927	523
8	1046	761	191	382	764	197	394	788	245	490
9	980	629	1258	1185	1039	747	163	326	652	1304
10	1277	1223	1115	899	467	934	537	1074	817	303
11	606	1212	1093	855	379	758	185	370	740	149
12	298	596	1192	1053	775	219	438	876	421	842
13	353	706	81	162	324	648	1296	1261	1191	1051
14	771	211	422	844	357	714	97	194	388	776
15	221	442	884	437	874	417	834	337	674	17
16	34	68	136	272	544	1088	845	359	718	105
17	210	420	840	349	698	65	130	260	520	1040
18	749	167	334	668	5	10	20	40	80	160
19	320	640	1280	1229	1127	923	515	1030	729	127
20	254	508	1016	701	71	142	284	568	1136	941
21	551	1102	873	415	830	329	658	1316	1301	1271
22	1211	1091	851	371	742	153	306	612	1224	1117
23	903	475	950	569	1138	945	559	1118	905	479
24	958	585	1170	1009	687	43	86	172	344	688
25	45	90	180	360	720	109	218	436	872	413
26	826	321	642	1284	1237	1143	955	579	1158	985
27	639	1278	1225	1119	907	483	966	601	1202	1073
28	815	299	598	1196	1061	791	251	502	1004	677
29	23	46	92	184	368	736	141	282	564	1128
30	925	519	1038	745	159	318	636	1272	1213	1095
31	859	387	774	217	434	868	405	810	289	578
32	1156	981	631	1262	1193	1055	779	227	454	908
33	485	970	609	1218	1105	879	427	854	377	754
34	177	354	708	85	170	340	680	29	58	116
35	232	464	928	525	1050	769	207	414	828	325
36	650	1300	1269	1207	1083	835	339	678	25	50
37	100	200	400	800	269	538	1076	821	311	622
38	1244	1157	983	635	1270	1209	1087	843	355	710
39	89	178	356	712	93	186	372	744	157	314
40	628	1256	1181	1031	731	131	262	524	1048	765
41	199	398	796	261	522	1044	757	183	366	732
42	133	266	532	1064	797	263	526	1052	773	215
43	430	860	389	778	225	450	900	469	938	545
44	1090	849	367	734	137	274	548	1096	861	391
45	782	233	466	932	533	1066	801	271	542	1084
46	837	343	686	41	82	164	328	656	1312	1293
47	1255	1179	1027	723	115	230	460	920	509	1018
48	705	79	158	316	632	1264	1197	1063	795	259
49	518	1036	741	151	302	604	1208	1085	839	347

P = 1331

INDICES

	0	1	2	3	4	5	6	7	8	9
50	554	819	287	963	626	865		620	201	478
51	982	44	9	567	713	196	885		490	301
52	178	922	414	79	407	353	426	1125		580
53	1061	978	422	454	1029	1017	1093	106	375	
54	890	61	458	692	164	439	1187	513	446	1055
55		210	931	1038	522	754	729	917	1033	236
56	745	0	960	41	298	1122	1014	689	207	233
57	686	655		720	1021	658	72	944	319	267
58	533	586	785		700	241	908	1002	544	829
59	1097	723	1146	1135		900	121	1048	282	1024
60	1009	277	803	1156	495		110	661	1078	332
61	1174	859	227	773	616	75		750	651	998
62	1152	994	379	947	633	736	1085		400	91
63	808	322	484	779	17	383	306	1105		270
64	191	508	262	854	849	1067	23	536	135	
65	360	951	98	972	894	589	467	763	216	595
66		670	1161	788	32	604	1209	637	183	556
67	65	0	1200	821	158	1072	1194	289	367	703
68	346	965		740	1141	628	462	244	249	867
69	1113	796	875		500	911	988	622	174	1089
70	927	203	696	1005		480	131	28	342	984
71	389	547	393	46	145		680	11	168	832
72	254	569	937	473	56	715		1100	551	198
73	882	404	419	887	443	726	295		530	541
74	118	492	224	1149	397	303	846	95		180
75	1191	1138	872	924	339	677	53	416	115	
76	50	81	838	812	84	409	517	903	646	355
77		140	841	428	312	124	149	1127	433	326
78	815	0	450	1051	1118	582	1044	769	87	1063
79	666	285		980	711	488	412	424	1059	1027
80	373	456	1185		520	1031	958	1012	684	1019
81	317	783	906	1095		280	801	108	1172	614
82	649	377	1083	806	15		260	21	358	892
83	214	1159	1207	63	156	365		460	1111	498
84	172	694	129	387	143	166	935		880	441
85	528	222	844	1189	337	113	836	515		310
86	431	448	1042	664	709	1057	1183	956	315	
87	1170	1081	258	212	154	1109	127	933	526	335
88		1040	1181	1168	152	524	1179	1177	573	756
89	575	0	1130	731	758	862	564	919	577	103
90	436	1035		230	941	238	1132	274	329	747
91	733	776	505		760	601	818	962	864	619
92	477	43	566	195		300	921	78	352	1124
93	579	977	453	1016	105		60	691	438	512
94	1054	209	1037	753	916	235		40	1121	688
95	232	654	719	657	943	266	585		240	1001
96	828	722	1134	899	1047	1023	276	1155		660
97	331	858	772	74	749	997	993	946	735	
98	90	321	778	382	1104	269	507	853	1066	535
99	0000	950	971	588	762	594	669	787	603	636

POWER RESIDUES

	0	1	2	3	4	5	6	7	8	9
50	694	57	114	228	456	912	493	986	641	1282
51	1233	1135	939	547	1094	857	383	766	201	402
52	804	277	554	1108	885	439	878	425	850	369
53	738	145	290	580	1160	989	647	1294	1257	1183
54	1035	739	147	294	588	1176	1021	711	91	182
55	364	728	125	250	500	1000	669	7	14	28
56	56	112	224	448	896	461	922	513	1026	721
57	111	222	444	888	445	890	449	898	465	930
58	529	1058	785	239	478	956	581	1162	993	655
59	1310	1289	1247	1163	995	659	1318	1305	1279	1227
60	1123	915	499	998	665	1330	1329	1327	1323	1315
61	1299	1267	1203	1075	819	307	614	1228	1125	919
62	507	1014	697	63	126	252	504	1008	685	39
63	78	156	312	624	1248	1165	999	667	3	6
64	12	24	48	96	192	384	768	205	410	820
65	309	618	1236	1141	951	571	1142	953	575	1150
66	969	607	1214	1097	863	395	790	249	498	996
67	661	1322	1313	1295	1259	1187	1043	755	179	358
68	716	101	202	404	808	285	570	1140	949	567
69	1134	937	543	1086	841	351	702	73	146	292
70	584	1168	1005	679	27	54	108	216	432	864
71	397	794	257	514	1028	725	119	238	476	952
72	573	1146	961	591	1182	1033	735	139	278	556
73	1112	893	455	910	489	978	625	1250	1169	1007
74	683	35	70	140	280	560	1120	909	487	974
75	617	1234	1137	943	555	1110	889	447	894	457
76	914	497	994	657	1314	1297	1263	1195	1059	787
77	243	486	972	613	1226	1121	911	491	982	633
78	1266	1201	1071	811	291	582	1164	997	663	1326
79	1321	1311	1291	1251	1171	1011	691	51	102	204
80	408	816	301	602	1204	1077	823	315	630	1260
81	1189	1047	763	195	390	780	229	458	916	501
82	1002	673	15	30	60	120	240	480	960	589
83	1178	1025	719	107	214	428	856	381	762	193
84	386	772	213	426	852	373	746	161	322	644
85	1288	1245	1159	987	643	1286	1241	1151	971	611
86	1222	1113	895	459	918	505	1010	689	47	94
87	188	376	752	173	346	692	53	106	212	424
88	848	365	730	129	258	516	1032	733	135	270
89	540	1080	829	327	654	1308	1285	1239	1147	963
90	595	1190	1049	767	203	406	812	293	586	1172
91	1013	695	59	118	236	472	944	557	1114	897
92	463	926	521	1042	753	175	350	700	69	138
93	276	552	1104	877	423	846	361	722	113	226
94	452	904	477	954	577	1154	977	623	1246	1161
95	991	651	1302	1273	1215	1099	867	403	806	281
96	562	1124	917	503	1006	681	31	62	124	248
97	496	992	653	1306	1281	1231	1131	931	531	1062
98	793	255	510	1020	709	87	174	348	696	61
99	122	244	488	976	621	1242	1153	975	619	1238

P = 1331

INDICES

	0	1	2	3	4	5	6	7	8	9
100	555	0	820	1071	288	702	964	739	627	243
101	866	795		910	621	1088	202	1004	479	27
102	983	546	45		10	831	568	472	714	1099
103	197	403	886	725		540	491	1148	302	94
104	179	1137	923	676	415		80	811	408	902
105	354	139	427	123	1126	325		1050	581	768
106	1062	284	979	487	423	1026	455		1030	1011
107	1018	782	1094	279	107	613	376	805		20
108	891	1158	62	364	459	497	693	386	165	
109	440	221	1188	112	514	309	447	663	1056	955
110		1080	211	1108	932	334	1039	1167	523	1176
111	755	0	730	861	918	102	1034	229	237	273
112	746	775		600	961	618	42	194	299	77
113	1123	976	1015		690	511	208	752	234	39
114	687	653	656	265		1000	721	898	1022	1154
115	659	857	73	996	945		320	381	268	852
116	534	949	587	593	786	635		1070	701	738
117	242	794	909	1087	1003	26	545		830	471
118	1098	402	724	539	1147	93	1136	675		810
119	901	138	122	324	1049	767	283	486	1025	
120	1010	781	278	612	804	19	1157	363	496	385
121		220	111	308	662	954	1079	1107	333	1166
122	1175	0	860	101	228	272	774	599	617	193
123	76	975		510	751	38	652	264	999	897
124	1153	856	995		380	851	948	592	634	1069
125	737	793	1086	25		470	401	538	92	674
126	809	137	323	766	485		780	611	18	362
127	384	219	307	953	1106	1165		100	271	598
128	192	974	509	37	263	896	855		850	591
129	1068	792	24	469	537	673	136	765		610
130	361	218	952	1164	99	597	973	36	895	
131	590	791	468	672	764	609	217	1163	596	35
132		790	671	608	1162	34	789	607	33	606
133	605	0								

POWER RESIDUES

	0	1	2	3	4	5	6	7	8	9
100	1145	959	587	1174	1017	703	75	150	300	600
101	1200	1069	807	283	566	1132	933	535	1070	809
102	287	574	1148	965	599	1198	1065	799	267	534
103	1068	805	279	558	1116	901	471	942	553	1106
104	881	431	862	393	786	241	482	964	597	1194
105	1057	783	235	470	940	549	1098	865	399	798
106	265	530	1060	789	247	494	988	645	1290	1249
107	1167	1003	675	19	38	76	152	304	608	1216
108	1101	871	411	822	313	626	1252	1173	1015	699
109	67	134	268	536	1072	813	295	590	1180	1029
110	727	123	246	492	984	637	1274	1217	1103	875
111	419	838	345	690	49	98	196	392	784	237
112	474	948	565	1130	929	527	1054	777	223	446
113	892	453	906	481	962	593	1186	1041	751	171
114	342	684	37	74	148	296	592	1184	1037	743
115	155	310	620	1240	1149	967	603	1206	1081	831
116	331	662	1324	1317	1303	1275	1219	1107	883	435
117	870	409	818	305	610	1220	1109	887	443	886
118	441	882	433	866	401	802	273	546	1092	853
119	375	750	169	338	676	21	42	84	168	336
120	672	13	26	52	104	208	416	832	333	666
121										
122										
123										
124										
125										
126										
127										
128										
129										
130										
131										
132										
133										

P = 1369

INDICES

	0	1	2	3	4	5	6	7	8	9
0		0	1	314	2	1211	315	104	3	628
1	1212	678	316	371	105	193	4	79	629	35
2	1213	418	679	483	317	1090	372	942	106	165
3	194	1197	5	992	80	1315	630		36	685
4	1214	1010	419	99	680	507	484	816	318	208
5	1091	393	373	256	943	557	107	349	166	499
6	195	929	1198	732	6	250	993	950	81	797
7	1316	512	631	594		72	37	782	686	959
8	1215	1256	1011	340	420	1290	100	479	681	553
9	508	475	485	179	817	1246	319	1239	209	1306
10	1092	402	394	489	374	297	257	308	944	1279
11	558	0	108	721	350	362	167	999	500	183
12	196	24	930	1324	1199	969	733	760	7	413
13	251	1285	994	139	951	821	82	120	798	538
14	1317	1130	513	1049	632	44	595	522		144
15	73	1250	38	707	783	1076	687	52	960	570
16	1216	587	1257	913	1012	871	341	323	421	742
17	1291	663	101	190	480	1194	682	813	554	729
18	509	956	476	1243	486		180	757	818	1046
19	1247	567	320	1191	1240	564	210	1108	1307	213
20	1093	1264	403	269	395	889	490	1111	375	713
21	298	840	258	826	309	1310	945	1301	1280	908
22	559	450		216	109	386	722	455	351	896
23	363	1096	168	1182	1000	695	501	1273	184	1267
24	197	467	25	238	931	87	1325	406	1200	654
25	970	1137	734	1161	761	272	8	1207	414	
26	252	793	1286	398	995	135	140	867	952	1104
27	822	892	83	789	121	436	799	125	539	493
28	1318	751	1131	605	514	228	1050	1114	633	158
29	45	221	596	440	523	378		288	145	854
30	74	203	1251	716	39	808	708	462	784	803
31	1077	301	688	331	53	611	961	1066	571	843
32	1217	622	588	114	1258	129	914	261	1013	920
33	872	1171	342		324	829	422	1082	743	1035
34	1292	543	664	312	102	676	191	33	481	940
35	1195	1313	683	97	814	391	555	497	730	948
36	510	70	957	338	477	473	1244	1304	487	306
37		360	181	1322	758	1283	819	536	1047	520
38	1248	1074	568	911	321	661	1192	727	1241	755
39	565	562	211	267	1109	838	1308	906	214	453
40	1094	693	1265	236	404	1135	270		396	865
41	890	434	491	603	1112	219	376	852	714	460
42	299	609	841	112	259	1169	827	1033	310	31
43	1311	389	946	336	1302	358	1281	518	909	725
44	560	836	451	234		432	217	458	110	1031
45	387	356	723	232	456	354	352	1019	897	1021
46	364	1123	1097	899	169	58	1183	1023	1001	1054
47	696	366	502	777	1274	1125	185	884	1268	1099
48	198	0	468	901	26	1118	239	171	932	1227
49	88	60	1326	244	407	1185	1201	616	655	1025

POWER RESIDUES

	0	1	2	3	4	5	6	7	8	9
0	1	2	4	8	16	32	64	128	256	512
1	1024	679	1358	1347	1325	1281	1193	1017	665	1330
2	1291	1213	1057	745	121	242	484	968	567	1134
3	899	429	858	347	694	19	38	76	152	304
4	608	1216	1063	757	145	290	580	1160	951	533
5	1066	763	157	314	628	1256	1143	917	465	930
6	491	982	595	1190	1011	653	1306	1243	1117	865
7	361	722	75	150	300	600	1200	1031	693	17
8	34	68	136	272	544	1088	807	245	490	980
9	591	1182	995	621	1242	1115	861	353	706	43
10	86	172	344	688	7	14	28	56	112	224
11	448	896	423	846	323	646	1292	1215	1061	753
12	137	274	548	1096	823	277	554	1108	847	325
13	650	1300	1231	1093	817	265	530	1060	751	133
14	266	532	1064	759	149	298	596	1192	1015	661
15	1322	1275	1181	993	617	1234	1099	829	289	578
16	1156	943	517	1034	699	29	58	116	232	464
17	928	487	974	579	1158	947	525	1050	731	93
18	186	372	744	119	238	476	952	535	1070	771
19	173	346	692	15	30	60	120	240	480	960
20	551	1102	835	301	602	1204	1039	709	49	98
21	196	392	784	199	398	796	223	446	892	415
22	830	291	582	1164	959	549	1098	827	285	570
23	1140	911	453	906	443	886	403	806	243	486
24	972	575	1150	931	493	986	603	1206	1043	717
25	65	130	260	520	1040	711	53	106	212	424
26	848	327	654	1308	1247	1125	881	393	786	203
27	406	812	255	510	1020	671	1342	1315	1261	1153
28	937	505	1010	651	1302	1235	1101	833	297	594
29	1188	1007	645	1290	1211	1053	737	105	210	420
30	840	311	622	1244	1119	869	369	738	107	214
31	428	856	343	686	3	6	12	24	48	96
32	192	384	768	167	334	668	1336	1303	1237	1105
33	841	313	626	1252	1135	901	433	866	363	726
34	83	166	332	664	1328	1287	1205	1041	713	57
35	114	228	456	912	455	910	451	902	435	870
36	371	742	115	230	460	920	471	942	515	1030
37	691	13	26	52	104	208	416	832	295	590
38	1180	991	613	1226	1083	797	225	450	900	431
39	862	355	710	51	102	204	408	816	263	526
40	1052	735	101	202	404	808	247	494	988	607
41	1214	1059	749	129	258	516	1032	695	21	42
42	84	168	336	672	1344	1319	1269	1169	969	569
43	1138	907	445	890	411	822	275	550	1100	831
44	293	586	1172	975	581	1162	955	541	1082	795
45	221	442	884	399	798	227	454	908	447	894
46	419	838	307	614	1228	1087	805	241	482	964
47	559	1118	867	365	730	91	182	364	728	87
48	174	348	696	23	46	92	184	368	736	103
49	206	412	824	279	558	1116	863	357	714	59

P = 1369

INDICES

	0	1	2	3	4	5	6	7	8	9
50	971	637	1138	1003	735	281	1162	1056	762	646
51	273	698	9	977	1208	368	415	162		504
52	253	926	794	779	1287	176	399	1276	996	966
53	136	1127	141	49	868	187	953	1043	1105	886
54	823	447	893	1270	84	1158	790	1101	122	225
55	437	200	800	1063	126		540	937	494	470
56	1319	1071	752	903	1132	600	606	28	515	429
57	229	1120	1051	881	1115	241	634	643	159	173
58	46	444	222	934	597	878	441	1229	524	1232
59	379	90		576	289	62	146	527	855	1328
60	75	988	204	246	1252	1235	717	409	40	583
61	809	1187	709	382	463	1203	785	154	804	618
62	1078	93	302	657	689	848	332	1027	54	
63	612	973	962	1154	1067	639	572	579	844	1140
64	1218	1144	623	1005	589	292	115	737	1259	1177
65	130	283	915	65	262	1164	1014	1222	921	1058
66	873	149	1172	764	343	18		648	325	530
67	830	275	423	1148	1083	700	744	858	1036	11
68	1293	769	544	979	665	1331	313	1210	103	627
69	677	370	192	78	34	417	482	1089	941	164
70	1196	991	1314		684	1009	98	506	815	207
71	392	255	556	348	498	928	731	249	949	796
72	511	593	71	781	958	1255	339	1289	478	552
73	474	178	1245	1238	1305	401	488	296	307	1278
74	0000	720	361	998	182	23	1323	968	759	412
75	1284	138	820	119	537	1129	1048	43	521	143
76	1249	706	1075	51	569	586	912	870	322	741
77	662	189	1193	812	728	955	1242		756	1045
78	566	1190	563	1107	212	1263	268	888	1110	712
79	839	825	1309	1300	907	449	215	385	454	895
80	1095	1181	694	1272	1266	466	237	86	405	653
81	1136	1160	271	1206		792	397	134	866	1103
82	891	788	435	124	492	750	604	227	1113	157
83	220	439	377	287	853	202	715	807	461	802
84	300	330	610	1065	842	621	113	128	260	919
85	1170	0	828	1081	1034	542	311	675	32	939
86	1312	96	390	496	947	69	337	472	1303	305
87	359	1321	1282	535	519	1073	910	660	726	754
88	561	266	837	905	452	692	235	1134		864
89	433	602	218	851	459	608	111	1168	1032	30
90	388	335	357	517	724	835	233	431	457	1030
91	355	231	353	1018	1020	1122	898	57	1022	1053
92	365	776	1124	883	1098		900	1117	170	1226
93	59	243	1184	615	1024	636	1002	280	1055	645
94	697	976	367	161	503	925	778	175	1275	965
95	1126	48	186	1042	885	446	1269	1157	1100	224
96	199	1062		936	469	1070	902	599	27	428
97	1119	880	240	642	172	443	933	877	1228	1231
98	89	575	61	526	1327	987	245	1234	408	582
99	1186	381	1202	153	617	92	656	847	1026	

POWER RESIDUES

	0	1	2	3	4	5	6	7	8	9
50	118	236	472	944	519	1038	707	45	90	180
51	360	720	71	142	284	568	1136	903	437	874
52	379	758	147	294	588	1176	983	597	1194	1019
53	669	1338	1307	1245	1121	873	377	754	139	278
54	556	1112	855	341	682	1364	1359	1349	1329	1289
55	1209	1049	729	89	178	356	712	55	110	220
56	440	880	391	782	195	390	780	191	382	764
57	159	318	636	1272	1175	981	593	1186	1003	637
58	1274	1179	989	609	1218	1067	765	161	322	644
59	1288	1207	1045	721	73	146	292	584	1168	967
60	565	1130	891	413	826	283	566	1132	895	421
61	842	315	630	1260	1151	933	497	994	619	1238
62	1107	845	321	642	1284	1199	1029	689	9	18
63	36	72	144	288	576	1152	935	501	1002	635
64	1270	1171	973	577	1154	939	509	1018	667	1334
65	1299	1229	1089	809	249	498	996	623	1246	1123
66	877	385	770	171	342	684	1368	1367	1365	1361
67	1353	1337	1305	1241	1113	857	345	690	11	22
68	44	88	176	352	704	39	78	156	312	624
69	1248	1127	885	401	802	235	470	940	511	1022
70	675	1350	1331	1293	1217	1065	761	153	306	612
71	1224	1079	789	209	418	836	303	606	1212	1055
72	741	113	226	452	904	439	878	387	774	179
73	358	716	63	126	252	504	1008	647	1294	1219
74	1069	769	169	338	676	1352	1335	1301	1233	1097
75	825	281	562	1124	879	389	778	187	374	748
76	127	254	508	1016	663	1326	1283	1197	1025	681
77	1362	1355	1341	1313	1257	1145	921	473	946	523
78	1046	723	77	154	308	616	1232	1095	821	273
79	546	1092	815	261	522	1044	719	69	138	276
80	552	1104	839	309	618	1236	1103	837	305	610
81	1220	1071	773	177	354	708	47	94	188	376
82	752	135	270	540	1080	791	213	426	852	335
83	670	1340	1311	1253	1137	905	441	882	395	790
84	211	422	844	319	638	1276	1183	997	625	1250
85	1131	893	417	834	299	598	1196	1023	677	1354
86	1339	1309	1249	1129	889	409	818	267	534	1068
87	767	165	330	660	1320	1271	1173	977	585	1170
88	971	573	1146	923	477	954	539	1078	787	205
89	410	820	271	542	1084	799	229	458	916	463
90	926	483	966	563	1126	883	397	794	219	438
91	876	383	766	163	326	652	1304	1239	1109	849
92	329	658	1316	1263	1157	945	521	1042	715	61
93	122	244	488	976	583	1166	963	557	1114	859
94	349	698	27	54	108	216	432	864	359	718
95	67	134	268	536	1072	775	181	362	724	79
96	158	316	632	1264	1159	949	529	1058	747	125
97	250	500	1000	631	1262	1155	941	513	1026	683
98	1366	1363	1357	1345	1321	1273	1177	985	601	1202
99	1035	701	33	66	132	264	528	1056	743	117

P = 1369

INDICES

	0	1	2	3	4	5	6	7	8	9
100	972	1153	638	578	1139	1143	1004	291	736	1176
101	282	64	1163	1221	1057	148	763	17	647	529
102	274	1147	699	857	10	768	978	1330	1209	626
103	369	77	416	1088	163	990		1008	505	206
104	254	347	927	248	795	592	780	1254	1288	551
105	177	1237	400	295	1277	719	997	22	967	411
106	137	118	1128	42	142	705	50	585	869	740
107	188	811	954		1044	1189	1106	1262	887	711
108	824	1299	448	384	894	1180	1271	465	85	652
109	1159	1205	791	133	1102	787	123	749	226	156
110	438	286	201	806	801	329	1064	620	127	918
111		1080	541	674	938	95	495	68	471	304
112	1320	534	1072	659	753	265	904	691	1133	863
113	601	850	607	1167	29	334	516	834	430	1029
114	230	1017	1121	56	1052	775	882		1116	1225
115	242	614	635	279	644	975	160	924	174	964
116	47	1041	445	1156	223	1061	935	1069	598	427
117	879	641	442	876	1230	574	525	986	1233	581
118	380	152	91	846		1152	577	1142	290	1175
119	63	1220	147	16	528	1146	856	767	1329	625
120	76	1087	989	1007	205	346	247	591	1253	550
121	1236	294	718	21	410	117	41	704	584	739
122	810	0	1188	1261	710	1298	383	1179	464	651
123	1204	132	786	748	155	285	805	328	619	917
124	1079	673	94	67	303	533	658	264	690	862
125	849	1166	333	833	1028	1016	55	774		1224
126	613	278	974	923	963	1040	1155	1060	1068	426
127	640	875	573	985	580	151	845	1151	1141	1174
128	1219	15	1145	766	624	1086	1006	345	590	549
129	293	20	116	703	738		1260	1297	1178	650
130	131	747	284	327	916	672	66	532	263	861
131	1165	832	1015	773	1223	277	922	1039	1059	425
132	874	984	150	1150	1173	14	765	1085	344	548
133	19	702		1296	649	746	326	671	531	860
134	831	772	276	1038	424	983	1149	13	1084	547
135	701	1295	745	670	859	771	1037	982	12	546
136	1294	669	770	981	545	668	980	667	666	

POWER RESIDUES

	0	1	2	3	4	5	6	7	8	9
100	234	468	936	503	1006	643	1286	1203	1037	705
101	41	82	164	328	656	1312	1255	1141	913	457
102	914	459	918	467	934	499	998	627	1254	1139
103	909	449	898	427	854	339	678	1356	1343	1317
104	1265	1161	953	537	1074	779	189	378	756	143
105	286	572	1144	919	469	938	507	1014	659	1318
106	1267	1165	961	553	1106	843	317	634	1268	1167
107	965	561	1122	875	381	762	155	310	620	1240
108	1111	853	337	674	1348	1327	1285	1201	1033	697
109	25	50	100	200	400	800	231	462	924	479
110	958	547	1094	819	269	538	1076	783	197	394
111	788	207	414	828	287	574	1148	927	485	970
112	571	1142	915	461	922	475	950	531	1062	755
113	141	282	564	1128	887	405	810	251	502	1004
114	639	1278	1187	1005	641	1282	1195	1021	673	1346
115	1323	1277	1185	1001	633	1266	1163	957	545	1090
116	811	253	506	1012	655	1310	1251	1133	897	425
117	850	331	662	1324	1279	1189	1009	649	1298	1227
118	1085	801	233	466	932	495	990	611	1222	1075
119	781	193	386	772	175	350	700	31	62	124
120	248	496	992	615	1230	1091	813	257	514	1028
121	687	5	10	20	40	80	160	320	640	1280
122	1191	1013	657	1314	1259	1149	929	489	978	587
123	1174	979	589	1178	987	605	1210	1051	733	97
124	194	388	776	183	366	732	95	190	380	760
125	151	302	604	1208	1047	725	81	162	324	648
126	1296	1223	1077	785	201	402	804	239	478	956
127	543	1086	803	237	474	948	527	1054	739	109
128	218	436	872	375	750	131	262	524	1048	727
129	85	170	340	680	1360	1351	1333	1297	1225	1081
130	793	217	434	868	367	734	99	198	396	792
131	215	430	860	351	702	35	70	140	280	560
132	1120	871	373	746	123	246	492	984	599	1198
133	1027	685								
134	0000									
135										
136										

P = 1681

INDICES

	0	1	2	3	4	5	6	7	8	9
0		0	1306	335	972	1262	1	559	638	670
1	928	643	1307	1511	225	1597	304	1633	336	209
2	594	894	309	396	973	884	1177	1005	1531	167
3	1263	708	1610	978	1299	181	2	832	1515	206
4	260	0	560	1586	1615	292	62	641	639	1118
5	550	328	843	1627	671	265	1197	544	1473	1096
6	929	1114	374	1229	1276	1133	644	1577	965	731
7	1487	1063	1308	90	498	1219	1181	1202	1512	235
8	1566	1340		1120	226	1255	1252	502	1281	719
9	1598	430	1368	1043	307	1471	305	797	784	1313
10	216	9	1634	1494	509	516	1293	404	337	925
11	1571	1167	863	268	210	18	1139	541	762	552
12	595	1286	780		40	506	895	572	942	281
13	799	438	310	768	1243	627	631	345	397	1024
14	1153	976	729	514	974	1429	1396	1453	164	737
15	885	771	847	663	868	330	1178	1059	1541	322
16	1232	955	1006	220		600	786	535	1532	1382
17	921	879	918	190	168	1443	947	1431	385	1637
18	1264	993	96	1449	1034	454	709	636	1613	1564
19	1137	845	1611	527	463	1468	450	698	979	901
20	1522	272	1315	726	1300		1160	1066	175	852
21	182	1561	959	1398	70	1208	3	1267	591	425
22	1237	1504	833	856	529	1554	1574	1629	1516	133
23	1324	1537	805	811	207	263	428	570	218	899
24	261	1082	952	35	446	740		80	1346	1455
25	172	622	561	1039	238	1590	608	203	1587	1391
26	465	837	104	673	1616	1249	434	1054	909	756
27	293	1084	297	765	11	1527	63	1028	690	1378
28	819	1261	642	1632	395	166	180		640	1626
29	1095	1132	1062	1201	1119	718	1470	8	403	267
30	551	505	437	344	513	736	329	954	534	189
31	1636	453	844	697	725	851	1207	1503	1628	810
32	898	739	621	202	672	755	1526	1260		1200
33	266	735	452	1502	201	1199	1198	1350	1048	603
34	587	1351	545	37	584	353	1496	1049	1474	14
35	1109	876	613	604	1097	685	51	887	1303	588
36	930	418	659	1621	1402	1352	1115	1246	700	
37	120	546	375	1412	302	841	1279	38	1230	448
38	803	907	511	585	1277	824	193	616	129	354
39	1134	389	116	773	364	1497	645	891	567	1103
40	1188	1050	1578	579	981	962	392	1475	966	140
41		680	826	15	732	742	1481	1359	518	1110
42	1488	1003	1227	1311	625	877	1064	33	1376	849
43	874	614	1309	996	933	124	257	605	91	247
44	903	148	1170	1098	499	341	522	1072	195	686
45	1220	0	1240	1106	1295	52	1182	481	1439	998
46	990	888	1203	1547	471	665	477	1304	1513	496
47	1569	1394	94	589	236	1093	1524	657	565	931
48	1567	703	748	1290	618	419	1341	82	112	555
49	406	660		160	1386	935	1012	1622	1121	1519

POWER RESIDUES

	0	1	2	3	4	5	6	7	8	9
0	1	6	36	216	1296	1052	1269	890	297	101
1	606	274	1644	1459	349	413	797	1420	115	690
2	778	1306	1112	1629	1369	1490	535	1529	769	1252
3	788	1366	1472	427	881	243	1458	343	377	581
4	124	744	1102	1569	1009	1011	1023	1095	1527	757
5	1180	356	455	1049	1251	782	1330	1256	812	1510
6	655	568	46	276	1656	1531	781	1324	1220	596
7	214	1284	980	837	1660	1555	925	507	1361	1442
8	247	1482	487	1241	722	970	777	1300	1076	1413
9	73	438	947	639	472	1151	182	1092	1509	649
10	532	1511	661	604	262	1572	1027	1119	1671	1621
11	1321	1202	488	1247	758	1186	392	671	664	622
12	370	539	1553	913	435	929	531	1505	625	388
13	647	520	1439	229	1374	1520	715	928	525	1469
14	409	773	1276	932	549	1613	1273	914	441	965
15	747	1120	1677	1657	1537	817	1540	835	1648	1483
16	493	1277	938	585	148	888	285	29	174	1044
17	1221	602	250	1500	595	208	1248	764	1222	608
18	286	35	210	1260	836	1654	1519	709	892	309
19	173	1038	1185	386	635	448	1007	999	951	663
20	616	334	323	257	1542	847	39	234	1404	19
21	114	684	742	1090	1497	577	100	600	238	1428
22	163	978	825	1588	1123	14	84	504	1343	1334
23	1280	956	693	796	1414	79	474	1163	254	1524
24	739	1072	1389	1610	1255	806	1474	439	953	675
25	688	766	1234	680	718	946	633	436	935	567
26	40	240	1440	235	1410	55	330	299	113	678
27	706	874	201	1206	512	1391	1622	1327	1238	704
28	862	129	774	1282	968	765	1228	644	502	1331
29	1262	848	45	270	1620	1315	1166	272	1632	1387
30	1598	1183	374	563	16	96	576	94	564	22
31	132	792	1390	1616	1291	1022	1089	1491	541	1565
32	985	867	159	954	681	724	982	849	51	306
33	155	930	537	1541	841	3	18	108	648	526
34	1475	445	989	891	303	137	822	1570	1015	1047
35	1239	710	898	345	389	653	556	1655	1525	745
36	1108	1605	1225	626	394	683	736	1054	1281	962
37	729	1012	1029	1131	62	372	551	1625	1345	1346
38	1352	1388	1604	1219	590	178	1068	1365	1466	391
39	665	628	406	755	1168	284	23	138	828	1606
40	1231	662	610	298	107	642	490	1259	830	1618
41	1303	1094	1521	721	964	741	1084	1461	361	485
42	1229	650	538	1547	877	219	1314	1160	236	1416
43	91	546	1595	1165	266	1596	1171	302	131	786
44	1354	1400	1676	1651	1501	601	244	1464	379	593
45	196	1176	332	311	185	1110	1617	1297	1058	1305
46	1106	1593	1153	194	1164	260	1560	955	687	760
47	1198	464	1103	1575	1045	1227	638	466	1115	1647
48	1477	457	1061	1323	1214	560	1679	1669	1609	1249
49	770	1258	824	1582	1087	1479	469	1133	74	444

P = 1681

INDICES

	0	1	2	3	4	5	6	7	8	9
50	1478	870	288	1403	227	1271	705	77	1544	1353
51	1256	649	274	1214	1509	1116	1253	1284	1057	525
52	131	1247	503	1348	1410	138	339	701	1282	792
53	915	126	100		720	26	575	332	422	121
54	1599	318	750	1328	1603	547	431	745	1317	144
55	1193	376	1369	794	694	789	356	1413	1044	1457
56	485	971	927	303	308	1530	1298	259	61	842
57	1472	1275	1486	1180		1280	306	215	1292	862
58	761	39	798	630	728	163	867	1231	785	917
59	384	1033	1136	449	1314	174	69	1236	1573	804
60	217	445	171	607	103	908	10	818	179	1061
61	402	512	1635	1206	620		200	586	1495	612
62	1302	1401	119	1278	510	128	363	1187	391	825
63	517	624	873	256	1169	194	1294	989	476	93
64	564	617	405	1011	287	1543	1508	130	338	99
65	421	1602	1192	355	926	60		760	866	1135
66	1572	102	401	199	118	390	1168	563	1507	1191
67	865	117	864	713	1016	249	714	774	269	1356
68	253	324	1017	365	211	1607	1343	468	250	1498
69	19	1421	1162	232	715	646	1140		1320	1146
70	775	892	542	1041	279	598	270	568	763	187
71	351	905	1357	1104	553	136	969	1234	254	1189
72	596	413	84	1417	325	1051	1287	1143	1068	370
73	1018	1579	781	722	912	1075	366	580		240
74	1426	415	212	982	41	359	1078	150	1608	963
75	507	1151	945	957	1344	393	896	49	114	1374
76	469	1476	573	1484	177	285	251	967	943	28
77	490	538	1499	141	282	1592	1435	86	20	
78	800	66	55	1172	1422	681	439	1558	30	1008
79	1163	827	311	985	557	1584	233	16	769	634
80	854	1389	716	733	1244	577	245	1091	647	743
81	628	610	58	1419	1141	1482	632	155	1446	1100
82		1360	346	1335	492	222	1321	519	398	1550
83	408	1363	1147	1111	1025	157	184	73	776	1489
84	1154	334	669	1596	893	1004	977	205	291	327
85	543	1228	730	1218	1339	501	1042	1312	515	1166
86	540	0	280	626	975	1452	662	321	599	878
87	1430	1448	1563	1467	271	1065	1397	424	1553	1536
88	569	34	1454	1589	836	1053	764	1377	165	1131
89	7	343	188	850	738	1259	1501	602	352	875
90	886	1620		840	906	615	772	1102	961	679
91	1358	1310	848	123	147	1071	1105	997	664	1393
92	656	1289	554	934	869	76	1213	524	137	125
93	331	1327	143	788	970	258	1179	861	162	1032
94	1235	606	1060		1400	1186	255	92	1542	1601
95	759	198	1190	248	323	467	231	1145	597	904
96	1233	1416	369	1074	414	149	956	1373	284	537
97	85	1171	1007	1583	1388	1090	1418	1099	221	1362
98	72	1595	326	500		320	1466	1535	1052	342
99	601	839	678	1070	1288	523	787	1031	1185	197

POWER RESIDUES

	0	1	2	3	4	5	6	7	8	9
50	983	855	87	522	1451	301	125	750	1138	104
51	624	382	611	304	143	858	105	630	418	827
52	1600	1195	446	995	927	519	1433	193	1158	224
53	1344	1340	1316	1172	308	167	1002	969	771	1264
54	860	117	702	850	57	342	371	545	1589	1129
55	50	300	119	714	922	489	1253	794	1402	7
56	42	252	1512	667	640	478	1187	398	707	880
57	237	1422	127	762	1210	536	1535	805	1468	403
58	737	1060	1317	1178	344	383	617	340	359	473
59	1157	218	1308	1124	20	120	720	958	705	868
60	165	990	897	339	353	437	941	603	256	1536
61	811	1504	619	352	431	905	387	641	484	1223
62	614	322	251	1506	631	424	863	135	810	1498
63	583	136	816	1534	799	1432	187	1122	8	48
64	288	47	282	11	66	396	695	808	1486	511
65	1385	1586	1111	1623	1333	1274	920	477	1181	362
66	491	1265	866	153	918	465	1109	1611	1261	842
67	9	54	324	263	1578	1063	1335	1286	992	909
68	411	785	1348	1364	1460	355	449	1013	1035	1167
69	278	1668	1603	1213	554	1643	1453	313	197	1182
70	368	527	1481	481	1205	506	1355	1406	31	186
71	1116	1653	1513	673	676	694	802	1450	295	89
72	534	1523	733	1036	1173	314	203	1218	584	142
73	852	69	414	803	1456	331	305	149	894	321
74	245	1470	415	809	1492	547	1601	1201	482	1211
75	542	1571	1021	1083	1455	325	269	1614	1279	950
76	657	580	118	708	886	273	1638	1423	133	798
77	1426	151	906	393	677	700	838	1666	1591	1141
78	122	732	1030	1137	98	588	166	996	933	555
79	1649	1489	529	1493	553	1637	1417	97	582	130
80	780	1318	1184	380	599	232	1392	1628	1363	1454
81	319	233	1398	1664	1579	1069	1371	1502	607	280
82	1680	1675	1645	1465	385	629	412	791	1384	1580
83	1075	1407	37	222	1332	1268	884	261	1566	991
84	903	375	569	52	312	191	1146	152	912	429
85	893	315	209	1254	800	1438	223	1338	1304	1100
86	1557	937	579	112	672	670	658	586	154	924
87	501	1325	1226	632	430	899	351	425	869	171
88	1026	1113	1635	1405	25	150	900	357	461	1085
89	1467	397	701	844	21	126	756	1174	320	239
90	1434	199	1194	440	959	711	904	381	605	268
91	1608	1243	734	1042	1209	530	1499	589	172	1032
92	1149	170	1020	1077	1419	109	654	562	10	60
93	360	479	1193	434	923	495	1289	1010	1017	1059
94	1311	1142	128	768	1246	752	1150	176	1056	1293
95	1034	1161	242	1452	307	161	966	753	1156	212
96	1272	908	405	749	1132	68	408	767	1240	716
97	934	561	4	24	144	864	141	846	33	198
98	1188	404	743	1096	1533	793	1396	1652	1507	637
99	460	1079	1431	181	1086	1473	433	917	459	1073

P = 1681

INDICES

	0	1	2	3	4	5	6	7	8	9
100	1144	1073	536	1089	1594	1534	1069	196	1533	44
101	937	45	371	687	1383	348	1210	938	1019	1221
102	922	752	315	46	1580		880	106	1175	372
103	782	1241	919	1158	950	688	723	1107	191	1225
104	1437	1384	913	1296	169	474	1014	349	1076	53
105	1444	1337	5	1211	367	1183	948	1330	458	939
106	581	482	1432	675	1406	1020		1440	386	815
107	1332	1222	241	999	1638	830	88	923	1427	991
108	1265	1037	1624	753	416	889	994	494	1269	316
109	213	1204	97	1605	411	47	983	1548	1450	1618
110	859	1581	42	472	1035	1126	460		360	666
111	455	652	22	881	1079	478	710	1128	1123	107
112	151	1305	637	224	593	1176	1609	1514	1614	549
113	1196	373	964	497	1565	1251	1367	783	508	1570
114	1138	779	941	1242	1152	1395	846	1540		920
115	946	95	1612	462	1521	1159	958	590	528	1323
116	427	951	1345	237	464	433	296	689	394	1094
117	1469	436	533	724	897	1525	451	1047	583	1108
118	50	658	699	301	802	192	115	566	980	
119	1480	1226	1375	932	902	521	1239	1438	470	1568
120	1523	747	111	1385	1477	704	273	1056	1409	914
121	574	749	1316	693	484	1297	1485	1291	727	383
122	68	170	178	619	1301	362	872	475	286	420
123		400	1506	1015	252	1342	1161	1319	278	350
124	968	83	1067	911	1425	1077	944	113	176	489
125	1434	54	29	556	853	244	57	1445	491	407
126	183	668	290	1338	539	661	1562	1552	835	6
127	1500	0	960	146	655	1212	142	161	1399	758
128	230	368	283	1387	71	1465	677	1184	1593	936
129	1209	314	1174	949	1436	1013	4	457	1405	1331
130	87	1623	1268	410	858	459	21	1122	592	1195
131	1366	940		1520	426	295	532	582	801	1479
132	1238	110	1408	483	67	871	1505	277	1424	1433
133	56	289	834	654	229	676	1173	1404	857	1365
134	531	1407	1423	228	530	378	379	1021	682	1272
135	1555	1086	380		440	706	1575	1492	1022	1441
136	1559	78	1630	808	683	387	31	1545	1517	24
137	1273	816	1009	1354	134	1149	1556	1333	1164	1257
138	1325	1371	1087	1223	828	650	1538	299	381	242
139	312	275	806	1460		1000	986	1215	812	1462
140	441	1639	558	1510	208	883	707	831	1585	1117
141	264	1113	1576	89	234	1254	429	796	1493	924
142	17	1285	571	767	1023	1428	770	1058	219	1381
143	1442	992	635	526	900		1560	1266	855	132
144	262	1081	79	1038	1390	1248	1083	1027	1631	1625
145	717	504	953	696	809	754	734	1349	36	13
146	684	417	1245	1411	447	823	388	890	578	139
147	741	1002	32	995	246	340		480	1546	495
148	1092	702	81	159	1518	1270	648	1283	1347	791
149	25	317	744	793	1456	1529	1274	214	629	916

POWER RESIDUES

	0	1	2	3	4	5	6	7	8	9
100	1395	1646	1471	421	845	27	162	972	789	1372
101	1508	643	496	1295	1046	1233	674	682	730	1018
102	1065	1347	1358	1424	139	834	1642	1447	277	1662
103	1567	997	939	591	184	1104	1581	1081	1443	253
104	1518	703	856	93	558	1667	1597	1177	338	347
105	401	725	988	885	267	1602	1207	518	1427	157
106	942	609	292	71	426	875	207	1242	728	1006
107	993	915	447	1001	963	735	1048	1245	746	1114
108	1641	1441	241	1446	271	1626	1351	1382	1568	1003
109	975	807	1480	475	1169	290	59	354	443	977
110	819	1552	907	399	713	916	453	1037	1179	350
111	419	833	1636	1411	61	366	515	1409	49	294
112	83	498	1307	1118	1665	1585	1105	1587	1117	1659
113	1549	889	291	65	390	659	592	190	1140	116
114	696	814	1522	727	1000	957	699	832	1630	1375
115	1526	751	1144	140	840	1678	1663	1573	1033	1155
116	206	1236	692	790	1378	1544	859	111	666	634
117	442	971	783	1336	1292	1028	1125	26	156	936
118	573	76	456	1055	1287	998	945	627	400	719
119	952	669	652	550	1619	1309	1130	56	336	335
120	329	293	77	462	1091	1503	613	316	215	1290
121	1016	1053	1275	926	513	1397	1658	1543	853	75
122	450	1019	1071	1383	1574	1039	1191	422	851	63
123	378	587	160	960	717	940	597	220	1320	1196
124	452	1031	1143	134	804	1462	367	521	1445	265
125	1590	1135	86	516	1415	85	510	1379	1550	895
126	327	281	5	30	180	1080	1437	217	1302	1088
127	1485	505	1349	1370	1496	571	64	384	623	376
128	575	88	528	1487	517	1421	121	726	994	921
129	483	1217	578	106	636	454	1043	1215	566	34
130	204	1224	620	358	467	1121	2	12	72	432
131	911	423	857	99	594	202	1212	548	1607	1237
132	698	826	1594	1159	230	1380	1556	931	543	1577
133	1057	1299	1070	1377	1538	823	1576	1051	1263	854
134	81	486	1235	686	754	1162	248	1488	523	1457
135	337	341	365	509	1373	1514	679	712	910	417
136	821	1564	979	831	1624	1339	1310	1136	92	552
137	1631	1381	1562	967	759	1192	428	887	279	1674
138	1639	1429	169	1014	1041	1203	494	1283	974	801
139	1444	259	1554	919	471	1145	146	876	213	1278
140	944	621	364	503	1337	1298	1064	1341	1322	1208
141	524	1463	373	557	1661	1561	961	723	976	813
142	1516	691	784	1342	1328	1244	740	1078	1425	145
143	870	177	1062	1329	1250	776	1294	1040	1197	458
144	1067	1359	1430	175	1050	1257	818	1546	871	183
145	1098	1545	865	147	882	249	1494	559	1673	1633
146	1393	1634	1399	1670	1615	1285	986	873	195	1170
147	296	95	570	58	348	407	761	1204	500	1319
148	1190	416	815	1528	763	1216	572	70	420	839
149	1672	1627	1357	1418	103	618	346	395	689	772

P = 1681

INDICES

	0	1	2	3	4	5	6	7	8	9
150	173	444	817	1205	611	127	623	988	1010	98
151	59	101	562	712	1355	1606	1420		1040	186
152	135	412	1142	721	239	358	1150	48	1483	27
153	1591	65	1557	984	633	576	609	154	1334	1549
154	156	333	204	1217	1165	1451	1447	423	1588	1130
155	1258	1619	1101	122	1392	75	1326	860		1600
156	466	1415	1372	1582	1361	319	838	1030	1088	43
157	347	751	105	1157	1224	473	1336	1329	674	814
158	829	1036	493	1604	1617	1125	651	1127	223	548
159	1250	778	1539	461	1322	432	435	1046	300	
160	520	746	1055	692	382	361	399	1318	910	488
161	243	667	1551	145	757	1464	313	456	409	1194
162	294	109	276	653	1364	377	1085	1491	807	23
163	1148	1370	298	1459	1461	882	1112	795	766	1380
164	0000	1080	1026	695	12	822	1001	479	158	790
165	1528	443	987	711	185	357	64	153	1216	1129
166	74	1414	1029	1156	813	1124	777	1045	691	487
167	1463	108	1490	1458	1379	821	442	152	1155	486
168	820									

POWER RESIDUES

	0	1	2	3	4	5	6	7	8	9
150	1270	896	333	317	221	1326	1232	668	646	514
151	1403	13	78	468	1127	38	228	1368	1484	499
152	1313	1154	200	1200	476	1175	326	275	1650	1495
153	565	28	168	1008	1005	987	879	231	1386	1592
154	1147	158	948	645	508	1367	1478	463	1097	1539
155	829	1612	1267	878	225	1350	1376	1532	787	1360
156	1436	211	1266	872	189	1134	80	480	1199	470
157	1139	110	660	598	226	1356	1412	67	402	731
158	1024	1101	1563	973	795	1408	43	258	1548	883
159	255	1530	775	1288	1004	981	843	15	90	540
160	1559	949	651	544	1583	1093	1515	685	748	1126
161	32	192	1152	188	1128	44	264	1584	1099	1551
162	901	363	497	1301	1082	1449	289	53	318	227
163	1362	1448	283	17	102	612	310	179	1074	1401
164										
165										
166										
167										
168										

P = 1849

INDICES

	0	1	2	3	4	5	6	7	8	9
0		0	1539	1	1272	193	1540	245	1005	2
1	1732	1458	1273	1040	1784	194	738	668	1541	817
2	1465	246	1191	1780	1006	386	773	3	1517	41
3	1733	1798	471	1459	401	438	1274	1687	550	1041
4	1198	174	1785		924	195	1513	600	739	490
5	119	669	506	1102	1542	1651	1250	818	1580	570
6	1466	1793	1531	247	204	1233	1192	292	134	1781
7	171	131	1007	1523	1420	387	283	1703	774	1400
8	931	4	1713	1492	1518	861		42	657	1219
9	1734	1285	1246	1799	333	1010	472	1626	223	1460
10	1658	1160	402	458	239	439	835	162	1275	604
11	1384	1688	983	339	551	167	1313	1042	303	913
12	1199	1110	1526	175	1264	579	1786	1056	1743	
13	966	1119	925	1062	25	196	1673	1803	1514	1648
14	1710	601	1670	692	740	234	1256	491	1153	1423
15	120	1317	16	670	1436	185	507	971	1133	1103
16	664	219	1543	695	1446	1652	1225	718	1251	274
17	594	819		84	1581	631	390	571	952	1547
18	1467	212	1018	1794	979	74	1532	320	66	248
19	743	61	205	78	1359	1234	1762	1184	1193	675
20	1391	293	893	286	135	367	191	1782	1778	469
21	172	117	568	132	1701		1008	237	337	1524
22	1117	1708	1421	1131	716	388	72	1357	284	566
23	1706	1704	1046	995	775	793	36	1401	646	1048
24	932	395	843	5	1259	683	1714	51	997	1493
25	312	98	1519	1432	789	862	1476	777		126
26	699	43	852	1663	658	1295	795	1220	1564	156
27	1735	494	1406	1286	1536	38	1247	1489	1381	1800
28	1443	58	334	680	1403	1011	425	419	473	1336
29	1773	1627	989	648	224	763	886	1461	1156	1014
30	1659	0	1050	1161	1555	180	403	1414	1169	459
31	1724	934	240	307	704	440	866	1368	836	1499
32	397	163	1758	1485	1276	1426	428	605	1179	845
33	1385	263	958	1689	451	485	984	350	7	340
34	327	1450	552	735		168	1623	1261	1314	949
35	364	1043	123	422	304	324	685	914	1280	446
36	1200	1634	1751	1111	751	1716	1527	688	712	176
37	1613	1347	1265	545	53	580	1605	1081	1787	1320
38	476	1057	1600	999	1744	90	1617		1092	279
39	967	642	1495	1120	917	1593	926	1480	408	1063
40	1124	314	26	1032	626	197	19	1339	1674	1569
41	100	1804	1730	815	1515	1685	1511	1649	202	1521
42	1711	1283	1656	602	301	1054	1671	232	1434	693
43		210	741	673	1776	235	70	791	1257	1430
44	850	492	1441	1334	1154	1412	864	1424	449	733
45	121	1632	1611	1318	1090	1478	17	1683	299	671
46	1439	1630	1437	535	779	186	728	1351	508	537
47	526	972	1575		1134	1203	379	1104	781	826
48	665	921	128	220	576	13	1544	188	992	696
49	416	701	1447	709	1590	1653	730	376	1226	1025

POWER RESIDUES

	0	1	2	3	4	5	6	7	8	9
0	1	3	9	27	81	243	729	338	1014	1193
1	1730	1492	778	485	1455	667	152	456	1368	406
2	1218	1805	1717	1453	661	134	402	1206	1769	1609
3	1129	1538	916	899	848	695	236	708	275	825
4	626	29	87	261	783	500	1500	802	557	1671
5	1315	247	741	374	1122	1517	853	710	281	843
6	680	191	573	1719	1459	679	188	564	1692	1378
7	436	1308	226	678	185	555	1665	1297	193	579
8	1737	1513	841	674	173	519	1557	973	1070	1361
9	385	1155	1616	1150	1601	1105	1466	700	251	753
10	410	1230	1841	1825	1777	1633	1201	1754	1564	994
11	1133	1550	952	1007	1172	1667	1303	211	633	50
12	150	450	1350	352	1056	1319	259	777	482	1446
13	640	71	213	639	68	204	612	1836	1810	1732
14	1498	796	539	1617	1153	1610	1132	1547	943	980
15	1091	1424	574	1722	1468	706	269	807	572	1716
16	1450	652	107	321	963	1040	1271	115	345	1035
17	1256	70	210	630	41	123	369	1107	1472	718
18	305	915	896	839	668	155	465	1395	487	1461
19	685	206	618	5	15	45	135	405	1215	1796
20	1690	1372	418	1254	64	192	576	1728	1486	760
21	431	1293	181	543	1629	1189	1718	1456	670	161
22	483	1449	649	98	294	882	797	542	1626	1180
23	1691	1375	427	1281	145	435	1305	217	651	104
24	312	936	959	1028	1235	7	21	63	189	567
25	1701	1405	517	1551	955	1016	1199	1748	1546	940
26	971	1064	1343	331	993	1130	1541	925	926	929
27	938	965	1046	1289	169	507	1521	865	746	389
28	1167	1652	1258	76	228	684	203	609	1827	1783
29	1651	1255	67	201	603	1809	1729	1489	769	458
30	1374	424	1272	118	354	1062	1337	313	939	968
31	1055	1316	250	750	401	1203	1760	1582	1048	1295
32	187	561	1683	1351	355	1065	1346	340	1020	1211
33	1784	1654	1264	94	282	846	689	218	654	113
34	339	1017	1202	1757	1573	1021	1214	1793	1681	1345
35	337	1011	1184	1703	1411	535	1605	1117	1502	808
36	575	1725	1477	733	350	1050	1301	205	615	1845
37	1837	1813	1741	1525	877	782	497	1491	775	476
38	1428	586	1758	1576	1030	1241	25	75	225	675
39	176	528	1584	1054	1313	241	723	320	960	1031
40	1244	34	102	306	918	905	866	749	398	1194
41	1733	1501	805	566	1698	1396	490	1470	712	287
42	861	734	353	1059	1328	286	858	725	326	978
43	1085	1406	520	1560	982	1097	1442	628	35	105
44	315	945	986	1109	1478	736	359	1077	1382	448
45	1344	334	1002	1157	1622	1168	1655	1267	103	309
46	927	932	947	992	1127	1532	898	845	686	209
47	627	32	96	288	864	743	380	1140	1571	1015
48	1196	1739	1519	859	728	335	1005	1166	1649	1249
49	49	147	441	1323	271	813	590	1770	1612	1138

P = 1849

INDICES

	0	1	2	3	4	5	6	7	8	9
50	45	719	1637	1229	1252	1353	1165	275	522	854
51	595	1768	1209	820	510	651		252	1665	85
52	432	1327	1582	539	585	632	1396	660	391	1754
53	1028	572	528	1214	953	355	1297	1548	1695	142
54	1468	974	227	213	1139	797	1019	874	1269	1795
55	1577	858	980	1645	1222	75	1114	48	1533	
56	1176	321	1597	1566	67	532	413	249	1136	766
57	744	769	158	62	152	360	206	1205	1069	79
58	1506	1737	1360	754	722	1235	381	1559	1763	809
59	496	1185	619	1073	1194	1106	889	676	747	1408
60	1392	609		294	783	1303	894	613	1288	287
61	1719	1640	136	828	1147	368	902	1538	192	1004
62	1457	1783	667	1464	1779	772	40	470	437	549
63	173	923	599	118	1101	1249	569	1530	1232	133
64	130	1419	1702	930	1491		1218	1245	1009	222
65	1159	238	161	1383	338	1312	912	1525	578	1742
66	1118	24	1802	1709	691	1255	1422	15	184	1132
67	218	1445	717	593	83	389	1546	1017	73	65
68	60	1358	1183	1390	285	190	468	567		336
69	1707	715	1356	1705	994	35	1047	842	682	996
70	97	788	776	698	1662	794	155	1405	37	1380
71	57	1402	418	1772	647	885	1013	1049	179	1168
72	933	703	1367	396	1484	427	844	957	484	6
73	1449	0	1260	363	421	684	445	1750	1715	711
74	1346	52	1080	475	998	1616	278	1494	1592	407
75	313	625	1338	99	814	1510	1520	1655	1053	1433
76	209	1775	790	849	1333	863	732	1610	1477	298
77	1629	778	1350	525		378	825	127	12	991
78	700	1589	375	44	1228	1164	853	1208	650	1664
79	1326	584	659	1027	1213	1296	141	226	796	1268
80	857	1221	47	1175	1565	412	765	157	359	1068
81	1736	721	1558	495	1072	888	1407		1302	1287
82	1639	1146	1537	1456	1463	39	548	598	1248	1231
83	1418	1490	1244	1158	1382	911	1741	1801	1254	183
84	1444	82	1016	59	1389	467	335	1355	34	681
85	787	1661	1404	56	1771	1012	1167	1366	426	483
86		420	1749	1345	474	277	406	1337	1509	1052
87	1774	1332	1609	1628	524	824	990	374	1163	649
88	583	1212	225	856	1174	764	1067	1557	887	1301
89	1145	1462	597	1417	1157	1740	182	1015	466	33
90	1660	1770	1365		1344	405	1051	1608	823	1162
91	1211	1173	1556	1144	1416	181	32	1364	404	822
92	1172	1415	1363	1171	1170	267	268	460	512	269
93	1725	1307	461	935	1084	513	241	653	270	308
94	259	1726	705	148	1308	441		462	867	757
95	936	1369	112	1085	837	254	514	1500	559	242
96	398	1790	654	164	1667	271	1759	1128	309	1486
97	1552	260	1277	87	1727	1427	725	706	429	871
98	149	606	434	1309	1180	1377	442	846	1323	
99	1386	1329	463	264	109	868	959	501	758	1690

POWER RESIDUES

	0	1	2	3	4	5	6	7	8	9
50	1565	997	1142	1577	1033	1250	52	156	468	1404
51	514	1542	928	935	956	1019	1208	1775	1627	1183
52	1700	1402	508	1524	874	773	470	1410	532	1596
53	1090	1421	565	1695	1387	463	1389	469	1407	523
54	1569	1009	1178	1685	1357	373	1119	1508	826	629
55	38	114	342	1026	1229	1838	1816	1750	1552	958
56	1025	1226	1829	1789	1669	1309	229	687	212	636
57	59	177	531	1593	1081	1394	484	1452	658	125
58	375	1125	1526	880	791	524	1572	1018	1205	1766
59	1600	1102	1457	673	170	510	1530	892	827	632
60	47	141	423	1269	109	327	981	1094	1433	601
61	1803	1711	1435	607	1821	1765	1597	1093	1430	592
62	1776	1630	1192	1727	1483	751	404	1212	1787	1663
63	1291	175	525	1575	1027	1232	1847	1843	1831	1795
64	1687	1363	391	1173	1670	1312	238	714	293	879
65	788	515	1545	937	962	1037	1262	88	264	792
66	527	1581	1045	1286	160	480	1440	622	17	51
67	153	459	1377	433	1299	199	597	1791	1675	1327
68	283	849	698	245	735	356	1068	1355	367	1101
69	1454	664	143	429	1287	163	489	1467	703	260
70	780	491	1473	721	314	942	977	1082	1397	493
71	1479	739	368	1104	1463	691	224	672	167	501
72	1503	811	584	1752	1558	976	1079	1388	466	1398
73	496	1488	766	449	1347	343	1029	1238	16	48
74	144	432	1296	190	570	1710	1432	598	1794	1684
75	1354	364	1092	1427	583	1749	1549	949	998	1145
76	1586	1060	1331	295	885	806	569	1707	1423	571
77	1713	1441	625	26	78	234	702	257	771	464
78	1392	478	1434	604	1812	1738	1516	850	701	254
79	762	437	1311	235	705	266	798	545	1635	1207
80	1772	1618	1156	1619	1159	1628	1186	1709	1429	589
81	1767	1603	1111	1484	754	413	1239	19	57	171
82	513	1539	919	908	875	776	479	1437	613	1839
83	1819	1759	1579	1039	1268	106	318	954	1013	1190
84	1721	1465	697	242	726	329	987	1112	1487	763
85	440	1320	262	786	509	1527	883	800	551	1653
86	1261	85	255	765	446	1338	316	948	995	1136
87	1559	979	1088	1415	547	1641	1225	1826	1780	1642
88	1228	1835	1807	1723	1471	715	296	888	815	596
89	1788	1666	1300	202	606	1818	1756	1570	1012	1187
90	1712	1438	616	1848	1846	1840	1822	1768	1606	1120
91	1511	835	656	119	357	1071	1364	394	1182	1697
92	1393	481	1443	631	44	132	396	1188	1715	1447
93	643	80	240	720	311	933	950	1001	1154	1613
94	1141	1574	1024	1223	1820	1762	1588	1066	1349	349
95	1047	1292	178	534	1602	1108	1475	727	332	996
96	1139	1568	1006	1169	1658	1276	130	390	1170	1661
97	1285	157	471	1413	541	1623	1171	1664	1294	184
98	552	1656	1270	112	336	1008	1175	1676	1330	292
99	876	779	488	1464	694	233	699	248	744	383

P = 1849

INDICES

	0	1	2	3	4	5	6	7	8	9
100	1584	937	452	1238	1370	486	962	113	985	541
101	1086	351	898	838	8	479	255	341	587	515
102	328	345	1501	1451	942	560	553	634	243	736
103	384	399		504	1791	169	1398	655	1624	833
104	165	1262	1060	1668	1315	662	272	950	318	1760
105	365	1699	1129	1044	393	310	124	1562	1487	423
106	761	1553	305	1756	261	325	947	1278	686	1603
107	88	915	1030	1728	1281		1428	447	1681	726
108	1201	574	707	1635	1766	430	1752	1693	872	1112
109	530	150	752	617	607	1717	1002	435	1528	1216
110	1310	689	591	1181	713	95	1378	177	955	443
111	1614	812	847	1348	1587	1324	1266	357		546
112	909	1387	54	1747	1330	581	1299	464	1606	30
113	265	1082	146	110	1788	1550	869	1321	499	960
114	477	940	502	1058	1697	759	1601	1679	1691	1000
115	93	1585	1745	144	938	91	802	453	1618	804
116	1239	0	1470	1371	1093	1188	487	280	455	963
117	968	976	114	643	1292	986	1496	1620	542	1121
118	229	1087	918	519	352	1594	806	899	927	215
119	839	1481	622	9	409	1241	480	1064	1141	256
120	1125	106	342	315		588	27	799	516	1033
121	1036	329	627	1472	346	198	1021	1502	20	1076
122	1452	1340	1373	943	1675	876	561	1570	880	554
123	101	1095	635	1805	1271	244	1731	1039	737	816
124	1190	385	1516	1797	400	1686	1197		1512	489
125	505	1650	1579	1792	203	291	170	1522	282	1399
126	1712	860	656	1284	332	1625	1657	457	834	603
127	982	166	302	1109	1263	1055	965	1061	1672	1647
128	1669	233	1152	1316	1435	970	663	694	1224	273
129	0000	630	951	211	978	319	742	77	1761	674
130	892	366	1777	116	1700	236	1116	1130	71	565
131	1045	792	645	394	1258	50	311	1431	1475	125
132	851	1294	1563	493	1535	1488	1442	679	424	1335
133	988	762	1155		1554	1413	1723	306	865	1498
134	1757	1425	1178	262	450	349	326	734	1622	948
135	122	323	1279	1633	750	687	1612	544	1604	1319
136	1599	89	1091	641	916	1479	1123	1031	18	1568
137	1729	1684	201	1282	300	231		672	69	1429
138	1440	1411	448	1631	1089	1682	1438	534	727	536
139	1574	1202	780	920	575	187	415	708	729	1024
140	1636	1352	521	1767	509	251	431	538	1395	1753
141	527	354	1694	973	1138	873	1576	1644	1113	
142	1596	531	1135	768	151	1204	1505	753	380	808
143	618	1105	746	608	782	612	1718	827	901	1003
144	666	771	436	922	1100	1529	129	929	1217	221
145	160	1311	577	23	690	14	217	592	1545	64
146	1182	189		714	993	841	96	697	154	1379
147	417	884	178	702	1483	956	1448	362	444	710
148	1079	1615	1591	624	813	1654	208	848	731	297
149	1349	377	11	1588	1227	1207	1325	1026	140	1267

POWER RESIDUES

	0	1	2	3	4	5	6	7	8	9
100	1149	1598	1096	1439	619	8	24	72	216	648
101	95	285	855	716	299	897	842	677	182	546
102	1638	1216	1799	1699	1399	499	1497	793	530	1590
103	1072	1367	403	1209	1778	1636	1210	1781	1645	1237
104	13	39	117	351	1053	1310	232	696	239	717
105	302	906	869	758	425	1275	127	381	1143	1580
106	1042	1277	133	399	1197	1742	1528	886	809	578
107	1734	1504	814	593	1779	1639	1219	1808	1726	1480
108	742	377	1131	1544	934	953	1010	1181	1694	1384
109	454	1362	388	1164	1643	1231	1844	1834	1804	1714
110	1444	634	53	159	477	1431	595	1785	1657	1273
111	121	363	1089	1418	556	1668	1306	220	660	131
112	393	1179	1688	1366	400	1200	1751	1555	967	1052
113	1307	223	669	158	474	1422	568	1704	1414	544
114	1632	1198	1745	1537	913	890	821	614	1842	1828
115	1786	1660	1282	148	444	1332	298	894	833	650
116	101	303	909	878	785	506	1518	856	719	308
117	924	923	920	911	884	803	560	1680	1342	328
118	984	1103	1460	682	197	591	1773	1621	1165	1646
119	1240	22	66	198	594	1782	1648	1246	40	120
120	360	1080	1391	475	1425	577	1731	1495	787	512
121	1536	910	881	794	533	1599	1099	1448	646	89
122	267	801	554	1662	1288	166	498	1494	784	503
123	1509	829	638	65	195	585	1755	1567	1003	1160
124	1631	1195	1736	1510	832	647	92	276	828	635
125	56	168	504	1512	838	665	146	438	1314	244
126	732	347	1041	1274	124	372	1116	1499	799	548
127	1644	1234	4	12	36	108	324	972	1067	1352
128	358	1074	1373	421	1263	91	273	819	608	1824
129	1774	1624	1174	1673	1321	265	795	536	1608	1126
130	1529	889	818	605	1815	1747	1543	931	944	983
131	1100	1451	655	116	348	1044	1283	151	453	1359
132	379	1137	1562	988	1115	1496	790	521	1563	991
133	1124	1523	871	764	443	1329	289	867	752	407
134	1221	1814	1744	1534	904	863	740	371	1113	1490
135	772	467	1401	505	1515	847	692	227	681	194
136	582	1746	1540	922	917	902	857	722	317	951
137	1004	1163	1640	1222	1817	1753	1561	985	1106	1469
138	709	278	834	653	110	330	990	1121	1514	844
139	683	200	600	1800	1702	1408	526	1578	1036	1259
140	79	237	711	284	852	707	272	816	599	1797
141	1693	1381	445	1335	307	921	914	893	830	641
142	74	222	666	149	447	1341	325	975	1076	1379
143	439	1317	253	759	428	1284	154	462	1386	460
144	1380	442	1326	280	840	671	164	492	1476	730
145	341	1023	1220	1811	1735	1507	823	620	11	33
146	99	297	891	824	623	20	60	180	540	1620
147	1162	1637	1213	1790	1672	1318	256	768	455	1365
148	397	1191	1724	1474	724	323	969	1058	1325	277
149	831	644	83	249	747	392	1176	1679	1339	319

P = 1849

INDICES

	0	1	2	3	4	5	6	7	8	9
150	46	411	358	720	1071		1638	1455	547	1230
151	1243	910	1253	81	1388	1354	786	55	1166	482
152	1748	276	1508	1331	523	373	582	855	1066	1300
153	596	1739	465	1769	1343	1607	1210	1143	31	821
154	1362	266	511	1306	1083	652	258	147		756
155	111	253	558	1789	1666	1127	1551	86	724	870
156	433	1376	1322	1328	108	500	1583	1237	961	540
157	897	478	586	344	941	633	383	503	1397	832
158	1059	661	317	1698	392	1561	760	1755	946	1602
159	1029	0	1680	573	1765	1692	529	616	1001	1215
160	590	94	954	811	1586	356	908	1746	1298	29
161	145	1549	498	939	1696	1678	92	143	801	803
162	1469	1187	454	975	1291	1619	228	518	805	214
163	621	1240	1140	105		798	1035	1471	1020	1075
164	1372	875	879	1094	1270	1038	1189	1796	1196	488
165	1578	290	281	859	331	456	981	1108	964	1646
166	1151	969	1223	629	977	76	891	115	1115	564
167	644	49	1474	1293	1534	678	987		1722	1497
168	1177	348	1621	322	749	543	1598	640	1122	1567
169	200	230	68	1410	1088	533	1573	919	414	1023
170	520	250	1394	353	1137	1643	1595	767	1504	807
171	745	611	900	770	1099	928	159	22	216	63
172		840	153	883	1482	361	1078	623	207	296
173	10	1206	139	410	1070	1454	1242	80	785	481
174	1507	372	1065	1738	1342	1142	1361	1305	257	755
175	557	1126	723	1375	107	1236	896	343	382	831
176	316	1560	945		1764	615	589	810	907	28
177	497	1677	800	1186	1290	517	620	104	1034	1074
178	878	1037	1195	289	330	1107	1150	628	890	563
179	1473	677	1721	347	748	639	199	1409	1572	1022
180	1393	1642	1503	610	1098	21		882	1077	295
181	138	1453	784	371	1341	1304	556	1374	895	830
182	944	614	906	1676	1289	103	877	288	1149	562
183	1720	638	1571	1641	1097	881	137	370	555	829
184	905	102	1148	637	1096	369	904	636	903	

POWER RESIDUES

	0	1	2	3	4	5	6	7	8	9
150	957	1022	1217	1802	1708	1426	580	1740	1522	868
151	755	416	1248	46	138	414	1242	28	84	252
152	756	419	1257	73	219	657	122	366	1098	1445
153	637	62	186	558	1674	1324	274	822	617	2
154	6	18	54	162	486	1458	676	179	537	1611
155	1135	1556	970	1061	1334	304	912	887	812	587
156	1761	1585	1057	1322	268	804	563	1689	1369	409
157	1227	1832	1798	1696	1390	472	1416	550	1650	1252
158	58	174	522	1566	1000	1151	1604	1114	1493	781
159	494	1482	748	395	1185	1706	1420	562	1686	1360
160	382	1146	1589	1069	1358	376	1128	1535	907	872
161	767	452	1356	370	1110	1481	745	386	1158	1625
162	1177	1682	1348	346	1038	1265	97	291	873	770
163	461	1383	451	1353	361	1083	1400	502	1506	820
164	611	1833	1801	1705	1417	553	1659	1279	139	417
165	1251	55	165	495	1485	757	422	1266	100	300
166	900	851	704	263	789	518	1554	964	1043	1280
167	142	426	1278	136	408	1224	1823	1771	1615	1147
168	1592	1078	1385	457	1371	415	1245	37	111	333
169	999	1148	1595	1087	1412	538	1614	1144	1583	1051
170	1304	214	642	77	231	693	230	690	221	663
171	140	420	1260	82	246	738	365	1095	1436	610
172	1830	1792	1678	1336	310	930	941	974	1073	1370
173	412	1236	10	30	90	270	810	581	1743	1531
174	895	836	659	128	384	1152	1607	1123	1520	862
175	737	362	1086	1409	529	1587	1063	1340	322	966
176	1049	1298	196	588	1764	1594	1084	1403	511	1533
177	901	854	713	290	870	761	434	1302	208	624
178	23	69	207	621	14	42	126	378	1134	1553
179	961	1034	1253	61	183	549	1647	1243	31	93
180	279	837	662	137	411	1233				
181										
182										
183										
184